S0-BRH-949

INTERNATIONAL HANDBOOK OF UNIVERSITIES

AND OTHER INSTITUTIONS OF HIGHER EDUCATION

TWELFTH EDITION

IAU - THE INTERNATIONAL ASSOCIATION OF UNIVERSITIES

The origins of IAU go back to the League of Nations. The Association was formally established after World War II, at the initiative of Unesco. Representatives of 150 universities took part in its founding Conference at Nice in 1950.
The membership of IAU is composed of individual university institutions in over 120 countries, and of other major associations of universities (Associate Members). In addition, IAU co-operates with a vast network of other international and national organizations concerned with higher education and is thus in a very real sense representative of the world higher education community.

Objectives

The Association's constitution sets out its main objectives. These are to give expression to the 'obligation of universities as social institutions to promote, through teaching and research, the principles of freedom and justice, of human dignity and solidarity, and to develop material and moral aid on an international level', by providing 'a centre of co-operation at the international level among the universities and similar institutions of higher education of all countries, as well as among organizations in the field of higher education generally.'

Organization

– **The General Conference of Member Institutions** meets every five years, determines general policy and elects the President and the Administrative Board.

– **The Administrative Board** (see p. 1387), made up of twenty outstanding university leaders and scholars from all parts of the world, gives effect to the decisions of the General Conference and supervises the activities of the International Universities Bureau. The Board meets yearly.

– **The President** is elected by the General Conference and chairs the Board.

– **The International Universities Bureau (IUB)**, with headquarters at Unesco House in Paris, is the permanent Secretariat of the Association and its major instrument of action. The Director of the Bureau also acts as Secretary-General of IAU.

ACTIVITIES

IAU and its International Universities Bureau propose a variety of activities and services to its Member Institutions and the international community of higher education - teachers and researchers, administrators and students, policy- and decision-makers.

Information

Under a formal agreement with Unesco, IAU operates, at its International Universities Bureau, the joint IAU/Unesco Information Centre on Higher Education. The Centre holds some 40,000 volumes and a large collection of unpublished materials. It receives about 300 specialized periodicals and maintains an up-to-date collection of some 4,000 calendars, catalogues and yearbooks of major higher education institutions, as well as international and national directories and guides to higher education. With three computerized databases on higher education - one institutional, a second bibliographical and a third devoted to research on higher education - it provides ready access to reliable and up-to-date information. The three databases interlink with other national and international information centres and data networks. IAU is thus in a key position to facilitate, through the use of modern information and communication technologies, worldwide access to academic expertise through the development of an international *Clearing-house for Academic Resource Information Networks*.

Studies, Research and Meetings

In keeping with its worldwide responsibilities, the studies and research programme of IAU focuses on issues which are either common to institutions and systems across the world or on comparative analyses of situations in which differences may be particularly helpful in understanding current developments in higher education. Conferences, symposia, colloquia, seminars, round tables and workshops allow for such topics to be discussed on the international forum which IAU provides to the representatives of higher education.

Academic Mobility and Co-operation

IAU is dedicated to the development of co-operation and exchange between higher education institutions on a worldwide basis. Special attention is being paid to three major aspects : co-operation between institutions in developed countries, between developed and developing countries, and finally between developing countries.
IAU acts as the coordinating agency of TRACE - the computerized *Trans Regional Academic Mobility and Credential Evaluation Information Network*. TRACE is a co-operative venture involving national and international academic bodies. Its purpose is to improve the quality of, and ready access to standardized comparable data on higher education systems, institutions, qualifications and credentials.
In terms of practical support to academic mobility, IAU sponsors the *International Student Identity Card* which is issued conjointly by the International Student Travel Confederation and the International Union of Students. In addition, to further facilitate academic exchange, an *International Academic Card* and an *International Currency Clearing System* for university co-operation are under development.
Furthermore, IAU is establishing, together with other partners, a computerized *Information and Clearing-house System* for the exchange of publications, material and scholars among university institutions worldwide.
As a contribution to efforts of bridging the technology gap, IAU has developed the *University-based Critical Mass System for Information Technology* (USIT).

Publications

A list of IAU publications is given on pages 1388 to 1389.

Headquarters

Unesco House, 1, rue Miollis, 75732 Paris Cedex 15, France
Telephone : (33-1) 45 68 25 45 Telefax : (33-1) 47 34 76 05 Telex : 250615 IUB F Cables : UNIVASOC

INTERNATIONAL HANDBOOK OF UNIVERSITIES

AND OTHER INSTITUTIONS OF HIGHER EDUCATION

TWELFTH EDITION

FOR
THE INTERNATIONAL ASSOCIATION OF UNIVERSITIES
1 RUE MIOLLIS, 75732 PARIS CEDEX 15

Prepared by the International Universities Bureau

Director: FRANZ EBERHARD

Edited by: ANN C.M. TAYLOR

Published every two years.

Twelfth Edition 1991
Published in the United States and Canada by
STOCKTON PRESS
15 East 26th Street, New York
N.Y. 10010, USA

Library of Congress Cataloging-in-Publication Data

International handbook of universities and other institutions of higher education – 2nd ed. (1962)-- Paris: International Association of Universities, c1962-
v.; 25-29 cm.
Biennial
Continues: International handbook of universities
ISSN 0074-6215 = International handbook of universities and other institutions of higher education.
1. Universities and colleges – Directories. I. International Association of Universities.

L900.158 378-dc19 86-640857
AACR 2 MARC-S
8604

Library of Congress
ISBN 1-56159-005-3

Published in the United Kingdom by
MACMILLAN PUBLISHERS LTD
(Journals Division) 1991
Distributed by Globe Book Services Ltd
Brunel Road, Houndmills
Basingstoke, Hants RG21 2XS, England

British Library of Cataloguing in Publication Data.

International handbook of universities and other institutions of higher education, —
12th ed. 1991.
1. Universities and colleges — Directories
I. Eberhard, F II. Taylor, Ann C M III.
International Association of Universities
378′.0025

ISBN 0-333-43643-1
ISSN 0074-6215

IAU ISBN 92-9002-154-3

Printed in Great Britain

CONTENTS

*The *Commonwealth Universities Yearbook* contains information about university institutions in :

AUSTRALIA
BANGLADESH
BOTSWANA
BRITAIN
BRUNEI
DARUSSALAM
CANADA
GHANA
GUYANA
HONG KONG
INDIA
KENYA
LESOTHO
MALAWI
MALAYSIA
MALTA
MAURITIUS
NEW ZEALAND
NIGERIA
PAKISTAN
PAPUA NEW GUINEA
SIERRA LEONE
SINGAPORE
SOUTH PACIFIC
SRI LANKA
SWAZILAND
TANZANIA
UGANDA
WEST INDIES
ZAMBIA
ZIMBABWE

*******American Universities and Colleges* contains information about university institutions in :

UNITED STATES OF AMERICA

The designations employed in this volume and the presentation of the material do not imply any expression of opinion on the part of the International Association of Universities concerning the legal status of any country, or of its authorities, or concerning the delimitations of the frontiers of any country or territory.

COMPANION VOLUMES :

* COMMONWEALTH UNIVERSITIES YEARBOOK. Editor, Eileen A. Archer.
ISBN 0 85143 126 7
(Association of Commonwealth Universities, John Foster House, 36 Gordon Square, London ZC1H 0PF).

** AMERICAN UNIVERSITIES AND COLLEGES. Thirteenth Edition, 1987. ISBN 0 89925 179.
(Walter de Gruyter, Inc. for American Council on Education, 1 Dupont Circle, Suite 801, Washington, D.C. 20036).

PREFACE

THIS, the Twelfth Edition of the *International Handbook of Universities,* is the first one that has been produced entirely from a computerized database developed at the IAU/Unesco Information Centre on Higher Education of the International Universities Bureau, thus providing for a further improvement of this standard reference work, both as to the quantity and the quality of new data.

The *International Handbook of Universities* was first published by the International Association of Universities in 1959 in response to the growing demand for authoritative information about universities and other institutions of higher education throughout the world. Two other reference works*, providing detailed information in the English language about universities and colleges in the Commonwealth and in the United States of America, also edited by academic bodies, were already well established and the *Handbook* was conceived as a companion volume to them, extending the information they contain to cover all other parts of the world.

The continuing development of higher education in all parts of the world makes it necessary to re-edit the *Handbook* at regular intervals. The Twelfth Edition covers one hundred and sixteen countries and territories. New institutions, established since the compilation of the previous edition, are included for the first time and in a number of country chapters the individual entries have been extensively revised to take account of important changes in the organization and structure of higher education. This applies in particular to Central and East European institutions. Such changes are reflected as far as they have been communicated to IAU before 30 September 1990.

The compilation of the *Handbook* involves work on documents in many languages, covering a wide range of continuously evolving systems of higher education. The work on this Edition, co-ordinated by Ann Taylor, was marked by the intricacies of adopting the new, computer-supported approach. The team involved took up the challenge and, with the essential support provided by colleagues from Unesco, successfully fought the odds in implementing the change. Every effort has been made to ensure that the entries are as comprehensive as possible and that the information is presented accurately. Comments and corrections which will help to improve the next edition of the *Handbook* will be most welcome. Together with new technology, this will allow, in the future, to provide the reader with still more complete, reliable and up-to-date information.

The International Bureau of Universities is indebted to those many universities and institutions of higher education which have provided updated material for this Edition. Where information was not received in time for inclusion, the entries contained in the Eleventh Edition have been retained.

Franz Eberhard

---

* COMMONWEALTH UNIVERSITIES YEARBOOK and AMERICAN UNIVERSITIES AND COLLEGES (see p. vi)

GUIDE TO THE ENTRIES

THERE are entries for more than eight thousand universities and other institutions of higher education in one hundred and sixteen countries and territories. The information presented relates, as far as possible, to the academic year 1989-90.

COUNTRY CHAPTERS

The country entries are presented country by country, and for those with a large number of institutions they appear as a rule in two main groups :

(i) Universities, including Technical Universities, where relevant ;
(ii) Other Institutions of Higher Education.

Where it appeared helpful, subdivisions have been introduced to identify institutions, such as those concerned with technical or professional education or with teacher training. It should be noted, however, that *independent* schools of theology are not covered.

This classification has been adopted for the practical convenience of those consulting the *Handbook,* and in no way constitutes an attempt at 'evaluation'. It is hoped that it will be particularly useful in the case of countries in which many fields of professional and technological education are covered not, or not only, by universities, but by specialized schools and institutes.

The terms 'university' and 'institution of higher education', as is well known, carry varying connotations in different countries and the selection of institutions for description in the *Handbook* has, therefore, been based principally on the practices of the relevant national academic and educational bodies. The inclusion of an institution, in consequence, does not imply any comment by the International Association of Universities. Similarly, the designations employed for countries and territories do not imply any expression of opinion with regard to their status or the delimitations of their frontiers.

INSTITUTIONAL ENTRIES

The individual entries identify the institutions by name and postal address and give basic information about them.

The lists of faculties and departments, institutes, schools and colleges, etc. are intended primarily as a general guide to the academic structure of the institutions of which they form a part, and their various titles are therefore given in English.

These are followed by brief descriptions of the history and structure of the institutions and, where the information has been provided, by notes on any special arrangements for co-operation with university institutions in other countries.

Admission requirements are normally for those courses leading to a first degree or similar qualification. Requirements for admission to certain short diploma or less formal courses may be less stringent ; those for admission to studies leading to higher degrees and specialized diplomas more exacting.

The names of degrees, diplomas and professional qualifications are generally given in the language of the country concerned. The duration of studies, indicated in years or semesters, is normally the minimum period required. Translations into English of fields of study are included where they are likely to be helpful, but basic terms and titles such as *Kandidaat, Licence, Promovaný,* etc., which do not correspond directly to those used in English-speaking institutions, have not been translated. Translations have not been included for words and phrases which do not differ substantially from the English. A reference volume*, compiled by the International Association of Universities for Unesco, contains glossaries of such terms and titles, together with brief descriptions of the conditions for the award of the corresponding degrees and diplomas.

The tables which indicate the composition of academic staffs show this in descending order of rank, and the respective titles are given in the language of the country concerned. In a few cases, however, institutions have themselves employed English or French terminology, and this has been retained. It will be noted that some have used a more restrictive definition of academic staff in compiling these tables than in indicating the size of the staff of their different faculties, departments and schools. The figures given under the latter headings (and also in the entries where no table is given) are for full-time staff, with those for part-time staff in parentheses.

A number reference to each institution will be found in the Index under its official title and, where relevant, also under the English translation provided for it.

Membership to the International Association of Universities is indicated by an asterisk (*) preceding the name of the institution.

---

* *World Guide to Higher Education : A Comparative Study of Systems, Degrees and Qualifications.* Third Edition, 1991. The Unesco Press, Unesco, 7 place de Fontenoy, 75700 Paris, France.

ABBREVIATIONS

As the *Handbook* is intended for international use, abbreviations have been employed as little as possible. They are :

A.	–	–	–	Academy
C.	–	–	–	College
Ce.	–	–	–	Centre
D.	–	–	–	Department/Division
F.	–	–	–	Faculty
I.	–	–	–	Institute
L.	–	–	–	Laboratory
P.	–	–	–	Programme
S.	–	–	–	School
Sec.	–	–	–	Section
Sem.	–	–	–	Seminar
U.	–	–	–	University
Ut.	–	–	–	Unit
c.	–	–	–	*circa*
sem	–	–	–	semester(s)
vols	–	–	–	volumes
yr(s)	–	–	–	year(s)

Degree and Diploma Abbreviations

Apart from the almost universal use of the style Dr., the use of letters of contractions to signify particular academic or professional qualifications is customary in some countries, but not in others. Abbreviations of this nature are listed, where relevant, in the information given about the degrees and diplomas awarded by the different institutions.

AFGHANISTAN

Universities

1 ***POHANTOON-E-KABUL**

Kabul University
Aliabad, Kabul
Telephone: 40341-3
President: Tahair Enayat (1990-)
Administrative Pro-Rector: Naim Ashrafi

F. of Agriculture (including Forestry and Animal Husbandry)
Dean: Seddiq Zarabi; *staff* 62
F. of Education
Dean: Ghulam Dastagir Hazrati; *staff* 25
F. of Economics
Dean: Nazir Ahmad Shahidy; *staff* 37
F. of Fine Arts
Dean: Naim Farhaan; *staff* 30
F. of Geosciences
Dean: A. Qureischie; *staff* 27 (1)
F. of Law and Political Science
Dean: Wadir Sofi; *staff* 30 (2)
F. of Literature and Languages
Dean: A. Quayume Qawim; *staff* 124
F. of Pharmacy
Dean: Rahim Khoshdil; *staff* 26
F. of Natural Sciences
Dean: Nissar Ahmed Nissar; *staff* 26
F. of Natural Sciences
Dean: Ehsan Arghandewal; *staff* 67
F. of Social Sciences
Dean: Ghulam Hazrat Nabipoor; *staff* 15
F. of Journalism
Dean: Kazim Ahang; *staff* 14
F. of Veterinary Medicine
Dean: Aminuddin Amin; *staff* 30
F. of Engineering (including Architecture)
Dean: A. Karoukhi; *staff* 30

Founded 1932 as a faculty of medicine. Became university by State Decree 1945. Co-educational since 1958. Faculty of Medicine detached 1979. A State institution under the jurisdiction of the Ministry of Higher and Vocational Education. Residential facilities for academic staff and students.

Arrangements in co-operation with: University of Sofia; Tashkent State University; Tajik State University; Humboldt University; Delhi University; University of Warsaw; Masaryk University, Brno.

Academic Year: March to January (March-July; September-January).

Admission Requirements: Secondary school certificate (baccalaureate) or equivalent.

Fees: None.

Languages of Instruction: Dari and Pashtu.

Degrees and Diplomas: Bachelor of–Arts, B.A.; Science, B.Sc., 4 yrs; Master of Science, M.S., 2 ½-3 further yrs. Doctor of–Philosophy, Ph.D.; Veterinary Medicine, D.V.M., 5 yrs.

Libraries: Central Library, 200,000 vols; libraries of the faculties, total, *c.* 38,060.

Special Facilities (Museums, etc.): Museums: Historical; Fine Arts.

Publications: Journals of: Science (every 2 months); Social Sciences and Humanities (quarterly).

Press or Publishing House: Publications Department.

Academic Staff, 1990-91:

Rank	Full-time
Pohand (Full Professors)	37
Pohandwal (Associate Professors)	44
Pohandoi (Junior Associate Professors)	57
Pohanmal (Assistant Professors)	84
Pohanyar (Lecturers)	189
Pohyalai (Instructors)	81
Total	492

Student Enrolment, 1990-91:

	Men	Women	Total
Of the country	5364	4003	9367
Of other countries	35	15	50
Total	5399	4018	9417

2 **UNIVERSITY OF NENGARHAR**

Jalalabad

F. of Medicine
F. of Agriculture
F. of Engineering
F. of Education

Founded 1963. A State institution responsible to the Ministry of Higher Education.

3 **UNIVERSITY OF ISLAMIC STUDIES**

Kabul

Founded 1988.

Other Institutions

4 **KABUL POLYTECHNIC**

Kabul

F. of Construction Engineering
F. of Geology
F. of Electromechanical Engineering

Founded 1967. A State institution responsible to the Ministry of Higher Education.

5 **HIGHER AGRICULTURAL TRAINING INSTITUTE**

Kabul

Veterinary Medicine
Forestry
Cooperative Studies

Founded 1971, acquired present status and title 1975. A State institution responsible to the Ministry of Higher Education.

6 **COMMUNICATIONS TRAINING CENTRE**

Kabul

Communications

Founded 1964. A State institution responsible to the Ministry of Communications.

7 **INSTITUTE OF FINANCE AND MANAGEMENT**

Kabul

Finance and Management

Founded 1971. A State institution responsible to the Ministry of Higher Education.

8 **JUNIOR INSTITUTE FOR MEDICAL EDUCATION**
Kabul

Medicine
Founded 1979. A State institution responsible to the Ministry of Public Health.

9 **HIGHER TECHNICAL SCHOOL**
Balkh

Engineering
Founded 1971. A State institution responsible to the Ministry of Higher Education.

10 **HIGHER TECHNICAL SCHOOL**
Kabul

Engineering
Founded 1974. A State institution responsible to the Ministry of Higher Education.

11 **INSTITUTE OF PEDAGOGY**
Darull Aman Watt, Kabul

D. of Chemistry and Biology
D. of Mathematics
D. of Physics
D. of Dari
D. of Pashtu
D. of English
D. of Social Studies
D. of Library Science
Founded 1983. A State institution responsible to the Ministry of Education.

12 **BALKH HIGHER TEACHERS' TRAINING COLLEGE**
Balkh

Teacher Training
Founded 1970. A State institution responsible to the Ministry of Higher Education.

13 **FARYAB HIGHER TEACHERS' TRAINING COLLEGE**
Maimana City Faryab Province

Teacher Training
Founded 1978. A State institution responsible to the Ministry of Higher Education.

14 **HELMAND HIGHER TEACHERS' TRAINING COLLEGE**
Lashkeragh City, Helmand

Teacher Training
Founded 1978. A State institution responsible to the Ministry of Higher Education.

15 **HERAT HIGHER TEACHERS' TRAINING COLLEGE**
Herat City, Herat Province

Teacher Training
Founded 1972. A State institution responsible to the Ministry of Higher Education.

16 **KANDAHAR HIGHER TEACHERS' TRAINING COLLEGE**
Kandahar City, Kandahar Province

Teacher Training
Founded 1965. A State institution responsible to the Ministry of Higher Education.

17 **KUNDOZ HIGHER TEACHERS' TRAINING COLLEGE**
Kundoz

Teacher Training
Founded 1970. A State institution responsible to the Ministry of Higher Education.

18 **NENGARHAR HIGHER TEACHERS' TRAINING INSTITUTE**
Jalal Abad City, Nengarhar Province

Teacher Training
Founded 1970. A State institution responsible to the Ministry of Higher Education.

19 **PAKTIA HIGHER TEACHERS' TRAINING INSTITUTE**
Gerdiz City, Paktia Province

Teacher Training
Founded 1970. A State institution responsible to the Ministry of Higher Education.

20 **PARWAN HIGHER TEACHERS' TRAINING INSTITUTE**
Parwan

Teacher Training
A State institution responsible to the Ministry of Higher Education.

21 **ROSHAN HIGHER TEACHERS' TRAINING COLLEGE**
Kabul

Teacher Training
Founded 1965. A State institution responsible to the Ministry of Higher Education.

22 **SAMANGAN HIGHER TEACHERS' TRAINING INSTITUTE**
Aiback City, Samangan Province

Teacher Training
Founded 1978. A State institution responsible to the Ministry of Higher Education.

23 **SYED JAMALUDDIN HIGHER TEACHERS' TRAINING COLLEGE**
Shier Shah Meena, Kabul

Teacher Training
Founded 1941. A State institution responsible to the Ministry of Higher Education.

24 **TAKHAR HIGHER TEACHERS' TRAINING INSTITUTE**
Kundoz City, Kundoz Province

Teacher Training
A State institution responsible to the Ministry of Higher Education.

25 **INSTITUTE OF PHYSICAL EDUCATION AND SPORT**
Kabul

Physical Education
Founded 1975. A State institution responsible to the Ministry of Higher Education.

26 **ABU HANEEFA MADRASA**
Institute of Religious Studies
Parwan Meena, Kabul

Arabic and Religious Studies
Founded 1964. A State institution responsible to the Ministry of Education.

27 **ABU MOSLEM DARUL ULOOM**
Institute of Religious Studies
Maimana City, Faryab Province

Arabic and Religious Studies
Founded 1936. A State institution responsible to the Ministry of Education.

28 **ARABIC DARUL ULOOM**
Andarabi Street, Kabul

Arabic and Religious Studies
Founded 1919. A State institution responsible to the Ministry of Education.

29 **DARUL ULOOM ASADEA**
Institute of Religious Studies
Mazar-i-Shareef, Balkh Province

Arabic and Religious Studies

Founded 1936. A State institution responsible to the Ministry of Education.

30 **FAKHRUL MADARES MADRASA**

Institute of Religious Studies

Herat

Arabic and Religious Studies

Founded 1933. A State institution responsible to the Ministry of Education.

31 **JAME MADRASA**

Institute of Religious Studies

Herat City

Arabic and Religious Studies

Founded 1923. A State institution responsible to the Ministry of Education.

32 **MOHAMMADIA MADRASA**

Institute of Religious Studies

Kandahar City

Arabic and Religious Studies

Founded 1971. A State institution responsible to the Ministry of Education.

33 **NAJMUL MADRASA**

Institute of Religious Studies

Jalal Abad City, Nengarhar Province

Arabic and Religious Studies

Founded 1931. A State institution responsible to the Ministry of Education.

34 **RUHANI DARUL ULOOM**

Institute of Religious Studies

Gerdiz City, Paktia Province

Arabic and Religious Studies

Founded 1972. A State institution responsible to the Ministry of Education.

35 **TAKHARISTAN MADRASA**

Institute of Religious Studies

Kundoz City

Arabic and Religious Studies

Founded 1939. A State institution responsible to the Ministry of Education.

ALBANIA

Universities

36 **UNIVERSITETI I TIRANËS**
Tirana University
Prof. Petit Radovicka, Tirana
Telex: 060400/2211+
Telephone: 82-58

F. of Mechanical and Electrical Engineering
F. of Construction Engineering (including Architecture)
F. of Geology and Mining
F. of Natural Sciences (including Mathematics and Pharmacy)
F. of Medicine
F. of Economics (including Accountancy)
F. of Political Science and Law
F. of History and Philology
Folklore I.

Branches in: Bérat, Durrës, Elbasan, Korça, Shkodër and Vlorë.

Founded 1957 incorporating former institutes of engineering, medicine, economics, law, and science. A State institution under the jurisdiction of the Ministry of Education and Culture. Governing body: the University Council. Residential facilities for students.

Academic Year: September to June (September-December; January-May).

Admission Requirements: Secondary school certificate.

Fees: None.

Language of Instruction: Albanian.

Degrees and Diplomas: Bachelor in various fields, 4 yrs. Candidate of Sciences. Doktor.

Libraries: Central Libraries, *c.* 351,600 vols; also faculty libraries.

Special Facilities (Museums, etc.): Museum of Natural Sciences.

Publications: Studi albanica; Studime historike; Studime filologjike; Buletini i shkencave te Natyres; Buletini i shkencave mjeksore.

Academic Staff: c. 930.

Student Enrolment: c. 9400

Other Institutions

37 **INSTITUTI I LARTË BÜJQËSOR**
Higher Institute of Agriculture
Kamëz, Tiranë
Telephone: 28201
Rector: Haxhi Aliko (1988-)
Assistant-Rector: Fatmir Musta

F. of Agriculture
Dean: Andrea Shundi; *staff* 75 (5)
F. of Veterinary Science
Dean: Vasil Tola; *staff* 62 (16)
F. of Forestry
Dean: Mihallaq Kotro; *staff* 56 (1)
F. of Agricultural Economics
Dean: Palok Kolnika; *staff* 92 (33)

Branches in: Durrës, Lushnje and Vlorë.

Founded 1951. A State institution under the jurisdiction of the Ministry of Education. Residential facilities for 3200 students.

Arrangements for co-operation with Cukurova University

Academic Year: September to June (September-December; January-June).

Admission Requirements: Secondary school certificate (Diplloma e Pjekurisë).

Fees: None.

Language of Instruction: Albanian.

Degrees and Diplomas: Diplomas, 4-4 ½ yrs. Candidate of Sciences, 3-5 yrs. Docent, a further 3 yrs. Doktor, a further 5 yrs. Teaching qualifications.

Library: Central Library, 140,200 vols.

Special Facilities (Museums, etc.): Museums of: Anatomy; Fauna. Campus is dendrological park.

Publications: Buletini i Shkencave Bujqësore; faculty publications.

Academic Staff, 1989-90:

Rank	Full-time	Part-time
Profesorë	3	–
Doktorë	4	–
Docentë	23	–
Kandidat Shkence	86	1
Pedagogë	48	54
Asistentë pedagogë	121	–
Total	285	55

Student Enrolment, 1989-90:

	Men	Women	Total
Of the country	1965	2335	4300*

*Also 1005 external students.

38 **INSTITUTI I LARTË BÜJQËSOR**
Institute of Agriculture
Korcë

Agriculture

Founded 1971. A State institution under the jurisdiction of the Ministry of Education and Culture.

39 **INSTITUTI I LARTË I ARTEVE**
Institute of Fine Arts
Tiranë

F. of Figurative Art
F. of Drama
F. of Music
F. of Choreography

Founded 1966. A State institution under the jurisdiction of the Ministry of Education and Culture.

Student Enrolment: c. 800 (Also *c.* 500 external students).

40 **INSTITUTI I LARTË I KULTURËS FIZIKE 'VOJO KUSHI'**
Institute of Physical Education
Tiranë
Cables: Instituti Fizkulturës
Telephone: 48-14

Physical Education

Founded 1958 as school, acquired present status 1960. A State institution under the jurisdiction of the Ministry of Education and Culture. The institute has a section providing secondary level education. Residential facilities for students.

Academic Year: September to June (September-December; January-June).

Admission Requirements: Secondary school certificate and competitive entrance examination.

Fees: None.

Language of Instruction: Albanian.

Degrees and Diplomas: Teaching qualifications, 3 yrs (4 yrs for students by correspondence).

Publication: Problèmes d'éducation physique.

Academic Staff: c. 50.

Student Enrolment: c. 300.

41 **INSTITUTI I LARTË PEDAGOGJIK 'ALEKSANDËR XHUVANI'**
Rruga 'Kozma Neska', Elbasan
Telephone: (545) 2872
Rector: Agron Tago
Secretary: Bardha Barci

Teacher Training (Philology and Literature, Biochemistry, and Mathematics and Physics)

Founded 1971.

Academic Year: September to June (September-January; February-June).

Admission Requirements: Secondary school certificate.

Fees: None.

Language of Instruction: Albanian.

Degrees and Diplomas: Diplomë, 4 yrs. Certifikatë, postgraduate qualification.

Library: 100,000 vols (including 25,000 in foreign languages).

Special Facilities (Museums, etc.): Museums of: Biology and Botany.

Publication: Vjetari (annually).

Academic Staff, 1989-90: 19 (2).

Student Enrolment, 1989-90:

	Men	Women	Total
Of the country	380	580	960*

*Also 1470 external students.

42 **INSTITUTI I LARTË PEDAGOGJIK**

Gjirokastra

Teacher Training (Mathematics and Physics, History and Geography, and Biochemistry)

Founded 1971. A State institution under the jurisdiction of the Ministry of Education and Culture.

43 **INSTITUTI I LARTË PEDAGOGJIK**

Teacher Training Institute

Shkodra

Telephone: 571

Teacher Training (Philology and Literature, Mathematics and Physics,) Biochemistry, History and Geography

Founded 1957, acquired present status 1970. A State institution under the jurisdiction of the Ministry of Education and Culture. Residential facilities for academic staff and students.

Academic Year: September to June (September-January; February-June).

Admission Requirements: Secondary school certificate.

Fees: None.

Language of Instruction: Albanian.

Degrees and Diplomas: Mësues i shkollës televjeçare (teaching qualification), 3 yrs.

Library: Institute Library, *c.* 64,000 vols.

Publication: Buletin Shkencor.

Academic Staff: c. 70.

Student Enrolment: c. 700 (Also *c.* 2000 external students and *c.* 350 evening students).

ALGERIA

Universities

44 ***UNIVERSITÉ D'ALGER**
University of Algiers
2, rue Didouche Mourad, Alger
Telex: 66529 UNIAL DZ
Telephone: 64-69-70
Recteur: Slimane Chikh

I. of Medical Sciences
I. of Arabic Language and Literature
I. of Law and Administration
I. of Economics
I. of Social Sciences and Psychology
I. of Foreign Languages
I. of Library Science and Documentation
I. of Political Science
I. of Education
I. of Speech Therapy
I. of Archaeology
I. of History
I. of Philosophy
I. of Translation and Interpretation

Founded 1859 as a school of medicine and pharmacy, followed in 1879 by schools of law, science, and letters. Formally established as university 1909. Residential facilities for students.

Academic Year: October to June (October-December; January-April; April-June).

Admission Requirements: Secondary school certificate (baccalauréat) or recognized equivalent or entrance examination.

Languages of Instruction: Arabic and French.

Degrees and Diplomas: Certificat de Capacité en Droit, law, 2 yrs. Licence in–Law; Economics; Science; Letters and Human Sciences, 4 yrs. Magister, 2 yrs after Licence; Diplôme (professional qualification) in–Midwifery, 3 yrs; Dentistry, 4 yrs; Pharmacy, 5 yrs; Medicine, 6 yrs. Doctorates by thesis.

Special Facilities (Museums, etc.): Musée du Bardo; Musée national des Beaux-Arts; Musée Savorgnan de Brazza; Musée Stéphane Csell; Musée Franchet d'Esperey.

Publications: Bulletin d'Information Historique; Revue Africaine; Majalatou Koulyat el Adab; Errihla el Maghribia; Revue Lybica; Sciences Médicales de Constantine.

Academic Staff: c. 1530.

Student Enrolment: c. 17,086.

45 ***UNIVERSITÉ DES SCIENCES ET DE LA TECHNOLOGIE HOUARI BOUMEDIÈNE**
B.P.139, El Alia, Bab Ezzouar, Alger
Telex: 643433
Telephone: 75-12-85
Recteur: Salah Djebaili (1989-)
Secrétaire général: Layachi Fennouh

I. of Natural Sciences
Director: Mounira Bensalem; *staff* 2
I. of Chemistry
Director: Said Djadoun; *staff* 3
I. of Physics
Director: Amar Benchaala; *staff* 3
I. of Mathematics (including Data Processing)
Director: Amar El-Kolli; *staff* 3
I. of Earth Sciences
Director: Dalila Ait-Kaci; *staff* 3
I. of Electronics
Director: Abdelhamid Adane; *staff* 3
I. of Cremical Engineering
Director: Khedidja Alia; *staff* 3
I. of Mechanical Engineering
Director: Said Seghour; *staff* 3
I. of Computer Sciences
Director: Abdelkader Khelladi; *staff* 3
I. of Civil Engineering
Director: Ali Chaker; *staff* 3
I. of Higher Technical Studies
Director: Achour Soualmia; *staff* 3

Founded 1974. Responsible to the Ministry of Education and Scientific Research. Governing body: the Conseil.

Academic Year: September to July (September-January; February-June).

Admission Requirements: Secondary school certificate (baccalauréat).

Fees: None.

Languages of Instruction: Arabic and French.

Degrees and Diplomas: Diplôme d'études supérieures (D.E.S.), 4 yrs. Magister, 2 yrs after D.E.S. Diplôme d'Ingénieur (in various fields), 5 yrs. Doctorat d'Etat.

Libraries: Central Library; libraries of the institutes.

Special Facilities (Museums, etc.): Earth Sciences Museum; Biological Garden.

Academic Staff, 1990:

Rank	Full-time
Professeurs	99
Maîtres de conférences	51
Chargés de cours	264
Maîtres-assistants titulaires et stagiaires	764
Adjoints d'Enseignement	70
Total	1248

Student Enrolment: c. 13,000.

46 **UNIVERSITÉ D'ANNABA**
Route El-Hadjar, Annaba
Telex: 81847 UARTO DZ
Telephone: 83-34-29/30
Recteur: Mokhtar Sellami

I. of Computer Sciences
Director: M. Siyahia; *staff* 33
I. of Mines and Metallurgy
Director: M. Berkani; *staff* 112
I. of Civil Engineering
Director: M. Habita; *staff* 58 (1)
I. of Electrotechnology
Director: M. Djeghaba; *staff* 77
I. of Natural Sciences
Director: M. Ouartsi; *staff* 107
I. of Economics
Director: M. Madi; *staff* 46
I. of Foreign Languages (English and French)
Director: Mme Kadi; *staff* 39 (22)
I. of Arabic Language and Literature
Director: M. Ailane; *staff* 39
I. of Social Sciences
Director: M. Amir; *staff* 83
I. of Law
Director: m. Baali; *staff* 56
I. of Exact Sciences
Director: M. Kahoul; *staff* 228

Founded 1971 as Institute of Mining and Metallurgy, acquired present status and title 1975. Responsible to theMinistry of Higher Education and Scientific Research. Residential facilities for academic staff and students.

Arrangements for co-operation with: University of Glasgow; Institut national des Sciences appliquées, Lyon; Université de Nice.

Academic Year: September to July (September-January; March-July).

Admission Requirements: Secondary school certificate (baccalauréat) or foreign equivalent.

Fees (Dinars): 78 per annum.

Languages of Instruction: Arabic and French.

Degrees and Diplomas: Licence, 4 yrs. Diplôme de Technicien supérieur, 2.5 yrs. Diplôme d'études supérieures (D.E.S.), 4 yrs. Diplôme d'Ingénieur (in various fields), 5 yrs. Magister, a further 3 yrs.

Libraries: Central Library, 18,500 vols; libraries of the Institutes.

Academic Staff, 1986-87:

Rank	Full-time	Part-time
Professeurs	19	–
Maîtres de conférences	152	–
Chargés de cours	5	–
Maîtres-Assistants	266	–
Assistants	493	23
Total	935	23

Student Enrolment, 1986-87:

	Men	Women	Total
Of the country	7727	3847	11,574
Of other countries	156	36	192
Total	7883	3883	11,766

47 **UNIVERSITÉ DE CONSTANTINE**

University of Constantine

Ain-El-Bey, Constantine

Telex: 92436 UNCZL DZ

Telephone: 69-73-85

Recteur: Ali Benslitane

I. of Biological Sciences
I. of Economics
I. of Medical Sciences
I. of Physical Education and Sport
I. of Arabic Language and Literature
I. of Construction Engineering
I. of Foreign Languages
I. of Social Sciences
I. of Education and Psychology
I. of Law and Administrative Sciences
I. of Earth Sciences
I. of Architecture and Town Planning
I. of Exact Sciences
I. of History
I. of Veterinary Medicine
I. of Food Technology
I. of Physics
I. of Chemistry

Founded 1961 as Centre universitaire attached to the University of Algiers, acquired present status 1969. Governing body: the Conseil universitaire, composed of the deans and representatives of the academic staff and students. Responsible to the Ministry of Higher Education and Scientific Research. Residential facilities for academic students and students.

Arrangement for co-operation with universities in France and Arab countries.

Academic Year: September to June (September-January; February-June).

Admission Requirements: Secondary school certificate (baccalauréat) or entrance examination.

Languages of Instruction: Arabic and French.

Degrees and Diplomas: Licence, 3–24 yrs. Doctorat in Medicine, 6 yrs.

Academic Staff: c. 1000.

Student Enrolment: c. 12,000.

48 **UNIVERSITÉ D'ORAN**

University of Oran

Rue du Colonel Lofti, Es Senia, Oran

Recteur: Murad Taleb

I. of Economics
I. of Medical Sciences
I. of Arabic Language and Literature
I. of Foreign Languages
I. of Social Sciences
I. of Mathematics
I. of Physics
I. of Chemistry
I. of Earth Sciences
I. of Biological Sciences
I. of Exact Sciences
I. of History
I. of Demography
I. of Law and Administrative Sciences

Founded 1961 as Centre universitaire d'Oran attached to the Uni-versity of Algiers. Acquired present status 1966. Responsible to the Ministry of Higher Education and Scientific Research.

Academic Year: October to July (October-February; March-July).

Admission Requirements: Secondary school certificate (baccalauréat).

Languages of Instruction: Arabic and French.

Degrees and Diplomas: Capacité en Droit, law, 2 yrs. Licence en Droit, 4 yrs. Diplôme (professional qualification) in–Pharmacy,5 yrs; Medicine, 6 yrs.

Academic Staff: c. 1000.

Student Enrolment: c. 9000.

49 **UNIVERSITÉ DES SCIENCES ET DE LA TECHNOLOGIE D'ORAN**

B.P.1505, El M'Naouer, Oran

Telex: 22701

Telephone: 34-19-63

Recteur: A. Abdellaoui

I. of Electronics
I. of Electrotechnology

Founded 1975. Responsible to the Ministry of Higher Education and Scientific Research. Residential facilities for academic staff and students.

Academic Year: September to June.

Admission Requirements: Secondary school certificate (baccalauréat) or equivalent.

Language of Instruction: French.

Degrees and Diplomas: Diplôme d'Ingénieur (in various fields). Magister.

Student Enrolment: c. 830.

50 **CENTRE UNIVERSITAIRE DE BATNA**

Batna

I. of Law and Administrative Sciences
I. of Arabic Language and Literature
I. of Biological Sciences
I. of Exact Sciences and Technology
I. of Economics
I. of Foreign Languages

Responsible to the Ministry of Higher Education and Scientific Research.

51 **CENTRE UNIVERSITAIRE DE MOSTAGANEM**

Mostaganem

I. of Biological Sciences
I. of Exact Sciences
I. of Physics

Responsible to the Ministry of Higher Education and ScientificResearch.

52 ***INSTITUTS NATIONAUX D'ENSEIGNEMENT SUPÉRIEUR DE SÉTIF**

Sétif

Telex: 86077 UNSET DZ

Telephone: 90-36-40

Président: Abdelhafid Khellaf (1985-)

Secrétaire général: Nadjib Bouguessa

I. of Electronics
Director: Abdelhafid Khellaf; *staff* 85 (5)
I. of Industrial Chemistry
Director: Farouk Tedjar; *staff* 46 (3)
I. of Mechanical Engineering
Director: Rabah Zegadi; *staff* 68 (5)
I. of Computer Sciences
Director: M. Akrouf; *staff* 53 (6)
I. of Economics
Director: Mohamed-Cherif Belmihoub; *staff* 60 (4)
I. of Medical Sciences
Director: M. Bouhali; *staff* 50 (11)
I. of Architecture
Director: Bouzid Aïssa; *staff* 50 (8)
I. of Modern Languages
Director: Saïd Belguidoum; *staff* 12 (4)
I. of Physics
Director: M. Belkhayat; *staff* 40 (10)

Ce. for Lifelong Education

Founded 1978 as Centre Universitaire, acquired present status and title 1985. The institutes are financially autonomous but maintain a joint structure presided over by a Conseil de Coordination. Responsible to the Ministry of Higher Education and Scientific Research. Limited residential facilities for academic staff and students.

Arrangements for co-operation with the Universities of: Rennes II; Paris VI; Strasbourg I; Institut national polytechnique de Grenoble.

Academic Year: September to June (September-January; March-June).

Admission Requirements: Secondary school certificate (baccalauréat).

Fees (Dinars): 50 per annum.

Languages of Instruction: Arabic and French.

Degrees and Diplomas: Licence, 4 yrs. Diplôme d'études supérieurs (D.E.S.), 4 yrs. Diplôme d'Ingénieur, 5 yrs. Magister, 2yrs after Licence.

Library: 100,000 vols.

Academic Staff, 1986-87:

Rank	Full-time	Part-time
Maîtres de conférences	50	–
Maîtres-Assistants	250	–
Assistants	356	72
Total	656	72

Student Enrolment, 1986-87:

	Men	Women	Total
Of the country	6500	5000	7100
Of other countries	50	10	60
Total	6550	5010	7160

53 **CENTRE UNIVERSITAIRE DE SIDI-BEL-ABBÈS**

Sidi-Bel-Abbès

I. of Biological Sciences
I. of Exact Sciences
I. of Physics

Responsible to the Ministry of Higher Education and Scientific Research.

54 **CENTRE UNIVERSITAIRE DE TIARET**

Tiaret (Tagdempt)

I. of Exact Sciences
I. of Biological Sciences

Responsible to the Ministry of Higher Education and Scientific Research.

55 **CENTRE UNIVERSITAIRE DE TIZI-OUZOU**

Hasnaoua, Tizi-Ouzou
Telex: 76079 UNIVE DZ
Telephone: 40-56-51

I. of Economics
I. of Law and Administrative Sciences
I. of Arabic Literature
I. of Agriculture
I. of Technology
I. of Electrical Engineering
I. of Computer Sciences
C. of Research and Development

Founded 1977. Responsible to the Ministry of Higher Education and Scientific Research.

Academic Year: September to June (September-January; February-June).

Admission Requirements: Secondary school certificate (baccalauréat) and entrance examination.

Languages of Instruction: Arabic and French.

Degrees and Diplomas: Licence. Diplôme d'études supérieures (D.E.S.). Diplôme d'Ingénieur. Magister. Doctorat in Medicine (University of Algiers).

Libraries: Central Library; libraries of the institutes.

Academic Staff: c. 470.

Student Enrolment: c. 4700.

56 **CENTRE UNIVERSITAIRE DE TLEMCEN**

Tlemcen
Telex: 18034 CUT DZ

I. of Economics
I. of Law
I. of Arabic Language and Literature
I. of Biological Sciences
I. of Exact Sciences

Founded 1974. Responsible to the Ministry of Higher Education and Scientific Research.

Other Institutions

57 **ÉCOLE NORMALE SUPÉRIEURE**

Kouba, Alger

Teacher Training

Attached to the University of Algiers.

Academic Year: October to June (October-December; January-April; April-June).

Admission Requirements: Secondary school certificate (baccalauréat) or recognized equivalent or entrance examination.

Languages of Instruction: Arabic and French.

Degrees and Diplomas: Teaching qualification, secondary level, 4 yrs.

58 **ÉCOLE NORMALE SUPÉRIEURE D'ENSEIGNEMENT POLYTECHNIQUE**

Es Senia, Oran

Teacher Training

Founded 1970.

59 **ÉCOLE POLYTECHNIQUE D'ARCHITECTURE ET D'URBANISME**

El-Harrach, Alger

Architecture
Town Planning

Founded 1970.

60 **ÉCOLE NATIONALE VÉTÉRINAIRE**

Avenue Pasteur, El-Harrach, Alger

Veterinary Medicine

61 **INSTITUT NATIONAL AGRONOMIQUE**

Avenue Pasteur, El-Harrach, Alger 10-2e
Telex: 54802 INA DZ
Telephone: 76-19-87

Agriculture (including Animal Husbandry and Forestry)

Founded 1905 as school, became Ecole nationale supérieure 1961. Acquired present status and title 1966. Responsible to the Ministry of Higher Education and Scientific Research. Residential facilities for students in Cité universitaire.

Academic Year: September to July (September-January; February-July).

Admission Requirements: Secondary school certificate (baccalauréat).

Language of Instruction: French.

Degrees and Diplomas: Diplôme d'Ingénieur d'agronome, 5 yrs.

Libraries: Central Library, *c.* 30,000 vols; Rural Engineering, *c.* 1500; Technology, *c.* 2000.

Publication: Annales de l'Institut national agronomique.

Academic Staff: c. 220.

Student Enrolment: c. 640.

62 **INSTITUT DES TÉLÉCOMMUNICATIONS D'ORAN**

Route d'Es Senia, Oran

Telecommunication Engineering

Founded 1972. Responsible to the Ministry of Higher Education and Scientific Research. Residential facilities for 800 students.

Academic Year: September to June (September-January; February-June).

Admission Requirements: Secondary school certificate (baccalauréat) and entrance examination (Technicien supérieur) plus 2 yrs university study (Ingénieur d'Etat).

Language of Instruction: French.

Degrees and Diplomas: Diplôme-d'Ingénieur d'Etat en Télécommunications, 7 sem; de Technicien supérieur, 5 sem.

Library: c. 15,000 vols.

Academic Staff: c. 120 (5).

Student Enrolment: c. 740.

ANGOLA

63 ***UNIVERSIDADE AGOSTINHO NETO**

University Agostinho Neto
Avenida 4 de Fevereiro 7, Caixa postal 815-C, Luanda
Telex: 3076 UNIVELA AN
Telephone: 37132
Reitor: Raul Neto Fernandes (1986-)

F. of Science
Director: Abílio Fernandes; *staff* 32 (20)
F. of Agriculture (including Veterinary Science)
Director: Fernando Manuel Girão Monteiro; *staff* 22 (17)
F. of Law
Director: Francisco Queiros; *staff* 9 (23)
F. of Economics
Director: Manuel José Nunes Júnior; *staff* 17 (32)
F. of Engineering (including Architecture)
Director: José Homero Basto Leitão; *staff* 70 (51)
F. of Medicine
Director: Silvio de Almeida; *staff* 50 (11)
I. of Education (Lubango)
Director: Vatomene Kukanda; *staff* 65 ()
I. for Correspondence Courses (Education)
Director: Vatomene Kukanda

Founded 1962 as Estudos Gerais Universitários, became University of Luanda 1968, University of Angola 1976 and acquired present title 1985. An autonomous State institution. Governing body: the Conselho Universitário. Some residential facilities for academic staff and students.

Arrangements for co-operation with the Universities of: Berlin (Humboldt); Patrice Lumumba, Moscow; São Paulo, Minho; Coimbra.

Academic Year: October to June (October-February; March-June).

Admission Requirements: Secondary school certificate and entrance examination.

Language of Instruction: Portuguese.

Degrees and Diplomas: Licenciado (in all fields), 5 yrs; Medicine, 6 yrs.

Libraries: Central Library, 8000 vols; faculty libraries.

Special Facilities (Museums, etc.): Museums of: Geology; Archaeology.

Academic Staff, 1986-87: 293 (129).

Student Enrolment, 1986-87:

Of the country	4481
Of other countries	12
Total	4493

ARGENTINA

Universities and Technical Universities

Governmental Establishments

64 ***UNIVERSIDAD DE BUENOS AIRES**
University of Buenos Aires
Calle Viamonte 430/444, Buenos Aires
Telex: 18.694
Telephone: 311-9030
Rector: Oscar J. Shuberoff (1986-90)
Secretaria General: Laura C. Musa

F. of Agriculture
Dean: Carlos Alberto M. Mundt
F. of Architecture and Town Planning
Dean: Juan Manuel Borthagaray; *staff* 5 (3000)
F. of Economics
Dean: Leopoldo Portnoy
F. of Exact and Natural Sciences
Dean: Héctor Torres
F. of Veterinary Science
Dean: Aníbal Juan Franco
F. of Philosophy and Letters
Dean: Norberto Rodríguez Bustamente
F. of Engineering
Dean: Félix Cernuschi; *staff* 104 (1636)
F. of Medicine (including Nursing and Midwifery)
Dean: Guillermo Jaime Etcheverry
F. of Dentistry
Dean: Pablo M. Bazerque; *staff* 14 (749)
F. of Psychology
Dean: Sara Slapak; *staff* 868
F. of Law and Social Science
Dean: Jorge A. Saenz; *staff* 80 (1710)
F. of Pharmacy and Biochemistry
Dean: Juana Pasquini
Course of Social Service
Head: Alicia R.W. Camilloni
Course of Political Science
Head: Edgardo R. Catterberg
Course of Social Communication
Head: Enrique Vázquez
Course of Sociology
Head: Mario Margullis; *staff* 5 (430)
Lifelong Education
Also 2 secondary level colleges.

Founded 1821. An autonomous State institution. Governing bodies: the Asamblea Universitaria; the Consejo Superior; the Consejos Directivos.

Academic Year: April to November (April-July; August-November).

Admission Requirements: Secondary school certificate (bachillerato) and entrance examination.

Language of Instruction: Spanish.

Degrees and Diplomas: Licenciado in various fields, 4-6 yrs. Professional titles of–Técnico; Traductor público, 2 yrs; Enfermera, nursing, 3 yrs; Procurador, law; Asistente social; Obstétrica, midwifery, 4 yrs; Farmacéutico; Abogado, law; Escribano, law; Odontólogo, dentistry; Bioquímico, 5 yrs; Contador público, accountancy; Ingeniero agrónomo, agriculture; Médico veterinario; Médico; Arquitecto; Actuario; Psicólogo; Ingeniero (various fields), 6 yrs. Doctorates by thesis. Also teaching qualifications.

Libraries: Central Library, *c.* 12,400 vols; faculty libraries.

Special Facilities (Museums, etc.): Ethnographic Museum.

Publications: Guía del Estudiante; Boletín de Informaciones; Revista de la Universidad; Síntesis 70.

Academic Staff: c. 12,600.

Student Enrolment, 1986-87:

	Men	Women	Total
Of the country	96,750	118,250	215,000

65 **UNIVERSIDAD NACIONAL DE CATAMARCA**
National University of Catamarca
República 350, 4700 San Fernando del Valle de Catamarca
Telephone: 2-5089

F. of Agriculture
F. of Applied Sciences and Technology
F. of Economics and Administration
F. of Exact and Natural Sciences
F. of Humanities
F. of Health Sciences
I. of Education
S. of Nursing

Founded 1972. An autonomous State institution.

Academic Year: March to November.

Admission Requirements: Secondary school certificate (bachillerato) or equivalent.

Language of Instruction: Spanish.

Degrees and Diplomas: Licenciado in–Geology; Physics; Mathematics; Biology; Geography; Chemistry; Philosophy; Nursing; Letters; Education; History; French; English, 5 yrs. Professional titles of–Enfermera, nursing; Técnico en–Administración pública; Administración privada; Hemoterapía, 2-3 yrs; Profesor (teaching qualification, secondary level), 4 yrs, Ingeniero agrónomo; Ingeniero agrimensor, surveying; Ingeniero en Minas, mining; Contador público, accountancy, 5-6 yrs.

Academic Staff: c. 300.

Student Enrolment: c. 1670.

66 **UNIVERSIDAD NACIONAL DEL CENTRO DE LA PROVINCIA DE BUENOS AIRES**
National University of the Centre of the Buenos Aires Province
Gral. Pinto 399, 70000 Tandil (Buenos Aires)
Telephone: 22062-3
Rector: Juan Carlos Pugliese (1986-89)
Secretario General: Alberto Horacio Somozo

F. of Exact Sciences
Dean: Fidel Alsina
F. of Veterinary Science
Dean: Carlos Alberto González
F. of Economics
Dean: Roberto Tassara
F. of Humanities
Dean: Mabel Berkunsky
F. of Engineering (Olavarría)
Dean: Carlos Nelson Lainz
F. of Agriculture (Azul)
Dean: José M. Rodríguez Silveira

Founded 1964 as University of Tandil, a private Foundation. Acquired present status and title 1974 and incorporating previously existing institutions in Olavarría and Azul. An autonomous State institution. Governing body: the Consejo Superior.

Academic Year: March to November (March-July; July-November).

Admission Requirements: Secondary school certificate (bachillerato) or equivalent.

Fees: None.

Language of Instruction: Spanish.

Degrees and Diplomas: Licenciado in–History, 5 yrs. Professional titles of–Asistente social, social work, 4 yrs; Ingeniero agrónomo, agriculture; Ingeniero electromecánico; Ingeniero en Construcciones; Ingeniero de Sistemas, 5 yrs; Médico veterinario, 6 yrs. Also teaching qualifications, 5 yrs.

Library: Central and branch libraries.

Publications: Revista (annually); Anuario del Institute du Estudios Históricos y Sociales (annually).

Academic Staff, 1986-87: 47 (978).

Student Enrolment, 1986-87:

	Men	Women	Total
Of the country	2563	1643	4206
Of other countries	11	7	18
Total	2574	1650	4224

67 **UNIVERSIDAD NACIONAL DEL COMAHUE**

National University of Comahue
Buenos Aires 1400, 8300 Neuquén
Telephone: 23596

F. of Economics and Administration (including Mathematics)
F. of Engineering
F. of Tourism
F. of Humanities
F. of Education
F. of Social Services (including Journalism)
F. of Agriculture
S. of Languages
I. of Marine Biology
S. of Biology

Founded 1965 as Universidad Provincial del Neuquén, became national State university with present title 1972. Governing bodies: the Asamblea Universitaria; the Consejo Superior.

Academic Year: March to December (March-July; August-December).

Admission Requirements: Secondary school certificate (bachillerato).

Language of Instruction: Spanish.

Degrees and Diplomas: Licenciado in–History; Tourism; Geography, 5 yrs. Professional titles of–Asistente social; Ingeniero in various fields; Contador público, accountancy, 5-6 yrs. Teaching qualification, secondary level, in various fields, 4 yrs.

Library: Central Library.

Academic Staff: c. 700.

Student Enrolment: c. 2950.

68 **UNIVERSIDAD NACIONAL DE CÓRDOBA**

National University of Córdoba
Obispo Trejo 242, 5000 Córdoba
Telex: 51822 BUCOR
Telephone: 46418
Rector: Luis A. Rébora (1986-89)
Secretario General: César Ignacio Aranega

F. of Architecture and Town Planning
Dean: Bernardino Taranto; *staff* 4 (286)
F. of Agriculture
Dean: osé Luis Pruneda; *staff* 105 (100)
F. of Economics
Dean: Carlos Perez-Mackeprang; *staff* 14 (77)
F. of Exact, Physical and Natural Sciences
Dean: Carlos Pratto; *staff* 36 (123)
F. of Medicine
Dean: Héctor Schroeder; *staff* 181 (291)
F. of Chemistry
Dean: Eduardo Staricco; *staff* 79 (28)
F. of Law and Social Sciences
Dean: Berta Kaller de Orchansky; *staff* 74 (10)
F. of Philosophy and Humanities
Dean: Gerardo Manzur; *staff* 36 (113)
F.of Mathematics, Astronomy, and Physics
Dean: Oscar Cámpoli; *staff* 74 (10)
F. of Dentistry
Dean: Mario Gotusso del Boca; *staff* 7 (106)
S. of Languages
Director: Cristina Elgué de Martini

Also secondary level college.

Founded 1613 as El Nuevo Colegio Máximo under the direction of the Society of Jesus; became university 1621. Recognized by Royal Decree 1680. In 1767 the Jesuits were expelled and the university was then directed by the Franciscans. Received the title of Royal University of San Carlos y Nuestra Señora de Monserrat in 1800 and became an autonomous State University by law in 1854. Governing bodies: the Asamblea Universitaria; the Consejo Superior.

Academic Year: February to December (April-July; August-November).

Admission Requirements: Secondary school certificate (bachillerato) or equivalent.

Language of Instruction: Spanish.

Degrees and Diplomas: Licenciado in–Dramatic Art; Cinematography, 4 yrs; Pharmacy, 4 ½ yrs; Administration; Economics; Philosophy; Letters; Education; History; Psychology; Physics; Mathematics; Astronomy, 5 yrs; Accountancy; Business Administration; Chemistry, 6 yrs. Professional titles of–Técnico en radiología; Bibliotecario, librarianship; Archivero; Kinesiólogo, kinesitherapy; Técnico de Laboratorio; Fonoaudiólogo, audiotherapy, 3 yrs; Enfermero universitario, nursing; Nutricionista-Dietista; Asistente social; Técnico in various fields; Perito traductor, translation; Profesor (teaching qualification, secondary level) in various fields; Contador público, accountancy; Geólogo; Procurador, law; Asistente en Pedagogía; Asistente en Psicología; Odontólogo, dentistry, 5 yrs; Actuario; Arquitecto; Ingeniero in various fields; Abogado, law; Notario, notarial studies; Bioquímico, 6 yrs. Médico cirujano, 6 yrs plus l yr internship. Doctorates by thesis.

Libraries: Central Library, 200,000 vols; libraries of the various faculties, institutes, and schools, c. 168,720.

Special Facilities (Museums, etc.): Museum of Natural Sciences.

Publications: Revista de la Universidad Nacional de Córdoba; Revista y Boletines de las Facultades e Institutos.

Academic Staff, 1986-87:

Rank	Full-time	Part-time
Profesores Titulares	150	280
Profesores Adjuntos	120	341
Jefe de Trabajos Prácticos	183	649
Auxiliaries	88	52
Total	541	1322

Student Enrolment, 1986-87:

	Men	Women	Total
Of the country	35,216	34,092	69,308
Of other countries	405	158	563
Total	35,621	34,250	69,871

69 **UNIVERSIDAD NACIONAL DE CUYO**

National University of Cuyo
Parque General San Martin, 5500 Mendoza
Telephone: 253219

F. of Agriculture
F. of Economics (including Administration)
F. of Medicine
F. of Political and Social Sciences
F. of Philosophy and Letters (including History and Geography)
F. of Petroleum and Industrial Engineering
I. of Physics (San Carlos de Bariloche)
S. of Dentistry
S. of Music
S. of Plastic Arts
S. of Industrial Design
S. of Drama
S. of Education

Founded 1939 as a State institution to serve the three provinces of Cuyo. Governing bodies: the Asamblea Universitaria; the Consejo Superior; the Consejo Académico. An autonomous State institution. Some residential facilities for students.

Academic Year: April to November (April-July; August-November).

Admission Requirements: Secondary school certificate (bachillerato) and entrance examination.

Language of Instruction: Spanish.

Degrees and Diplomas: Licenciado in–Psychology; Education; Physics; Mathematics; Philosophy; Letters; French and English Literature; Plastic Arts; Music; History; Geography; Political and Social Sciences and Public Administration; Sociology, 5 yrs; Chemistry; Bio-chemistry; Economics; Administration, 6 yrs. Professional titles of–Químico; Farmacéutico; Contador público y Perito partidor, accountancy, 4 yrs; Ingeniero agrónomo, agriculture; Diseñador, design n and industrial design, 5 yrs; Ingeniero, engineering in various fields; Arquitecto, 6 yrs; Bellas Artes, fine arts, 4-6 yrs; Odontólogo, dentistry, 5 yrs plus one year internship; Médico, 6 yrs plus one year internship. Profesor (teaching qualifications, secondary level), in various fields, 4 yrs. Doctorates by thesis.

Libraries: Central Library, *c.* 80,000 vols; libraries of various faculties and schools, *c.* 180,000.

Special Facilities (Museums, etc.): Museum of Archaeology and Ethnology; Museum of Natural Sciences.

Publications: Guia del Estudiante; Anuario Estadístico; Boletín Bibliográfico; Anales de Arqueología y Etnología; Boletín de la Biblioteca (Instituto de Filosofía); Filosofía; Boletín de Estudios Geográficos: Serie I, Fuentes Documentales (Instituto de Historia); Serie III, Ensayos (Instituto de Historia); Revista de Historia Americana y Argentina; Cuadernos de Historia del Arte; Cuadernos de Filosofía; Revista de Estudios Clásicos; Boletín de Estudios Germánicos; Revista de Literaturas Modernas; Anales del Instituto de Lingüística; Anales del Instituto de Investigaciones Psicopedagógicas; Cuadernos de la Escuela de Pedagogía; Boletín de Estudios Políticos y Sociales; Cuadernos del Instituto de Investigaciones Políticas y Sociales; Acta Cuyana de Ingeniería; Noticias de Ingeniería de Petróleos; Revista de la Facultad de Ciencias Agrarias; Serie de Cuadernos (Faculty of Economics); Boletín Bibliográfico (Faculty of Economics); Revista de la Facultad de Ciencias Económicas; Cuadernos de Psiquiatria; Nuestro Mundo (Faculty of Medicine); Anales (Department of Foreign Languages and Literature); Artes Plásticas; Publicación (Department of University Extension).

Academic Staff: c. 3300.

Student Enrolment: c. 11,290.

70 **UNIVERSIDAD NACIONAL DE ENTRE RÍOS**

National University of Entre Ríos

8 de Junio 600, 3260 Concepción del Uruguay (Entre Ríos)

Telephone: (442) 5573

Rector: Eduardo Alberto Barbagelata (1986-90)

Secretario General: Fabian Parlatto

F. of Education (Paraná)

Dean: Marta L. Saldias de Uranga; *staff* - (76)

F. of Agriculture (including Animal Husbandry) (Paraná)

Dean: Pedro Antonio Barbagelata; *staff* 5 (95)

F. of Engineering

Head: Elías Diaz Molano; *staff* 1 (36)

F. of Food Technology (Concordia)

Dean: Tito Augusto Lampazzi; *staff* 1 (36)

F. of Economics (Paraná)

Dean: Silvia Cuatran; *staff* - (82)

F. of Administration (including Accountancy) (Concordia)

Dean: César Gottfried; *staff* 1 (74)

F. of Social Service (Paraná)

Dean: Eloisa Elena De Jong de Garcia; *staff* 1 (53)

F. of Health Sciences (Nursing)

Dean: Teresa Marciana Corbalan de Robaina; *staff* 2 (22)

F. of Bromatology

Dean: Rubén Benito Peruzzo; *staff* 1 (51)

Founded 1973. An autonomous State institution. Governing body: the Consejo Superior.

Arrangements for co-operation with Universidad de la República, Uruguay.

Academic Year: April to November (April-July; August-November).

Admission Requirements: Secondary school certificate (bachillerato) or equivalent.

Fees: None.

Language of Instruction: Spanish.

Degrees and Diplomas: Licenciado in–Education; Administration; Social Service; Information Sciences; Bromatology, 5 yrs. Professional titles of–Enfermero(a), 3 yrs; Asistente social, 4 yrs; Contador público, accountancy, 5 yrs; Ingeniero agrónomo, agriculture; Bioingeniero; Ingeniero de Alimentos, food technology, 6 yrs. Profesorado in Economics, 1 further yr. Also teaching qualifications.

Library: Total, *c.* 27,000.

Academic Staff, 1986-87:

Rank	Full-time	Part-time
Profesores Titulares	27	285
Profesores Asociados	–	21
Profesores Adjuntos	–	110
Jefes de Trabajos Prácticos	–	228
Auxiliares	–	69
Total	27	713

Student Enrolment, 1986-87:

	Men	Women	Total
Of the country	2016	1936	3952
Of other countries	11	8	19
Total	2027	1944	3971

71 **UNIVERSIDAD NACIONAL DE JUJUY**

National University of Jujuy

Avenida Bolivia 2335, 4600 San Salvador de Jujuy

Telephone: 25617

F. of Agriculture

F. of Engineering

F. of Economics

F. of Humanities and Social Sciences

Extension D.

Founded 1972 as provincial university, acquired present status and title 1974. An autonomous State institution. Governing bodies: the Asamblea Universitaria; the Consejo Superior Universitario.

Academic Year: February to December (February-June; August-December).

Admission Requirements: Secondary school certificate (bachillerato) or equivalent.

Language of Instruction: Spanish.

Degrees and Diplomas: Licenciado in–Education; Anthropology; Letters; History. Professional titles of–Ingeniero, in several fields; Contador público; Bibliotecario. Also teaching qualifications.

Library: Total, *c.* 9560 vols.

Special Facilities (Museums, etc.): Museum of Palaeontology and Minerals.

Publications: Geological Sciences Review (every 3 months); Didactic Notes of the School of Agriculture (monthly); Financial Booklets (monthly).

Academic Staff: c. 40.

Student Enrolment: c. 4000.

72 **UNIVERSIDAD NACIONAL DE LA PAMPA**

National University of La Pampa

9 de Julio 149, 6300 Santa Rosa (La Pampa)

Telephone: 23109

F. of Humanities

F. of Economics

F. of Exact and Natural Sciences

F. of Agriculture

F. of Veterinary Science

I. of Labour Studies

Founded 1958 as a provincial university under an agreement with the Universidad Nacional de La Plata. Qualifications recognized nationally 1969, became national university 1973.

Academic Year: April to November (April-July; August-November).

Admission Requirements: Secondary school certificate (bachillerato) or equivalent.

Language of Instruction: Spanish.

Degrees and Diplomas: Licenciado in–Biology, Mathematics; Physics; Agricultural Chemistry; Land Development; Geology; Geography; Languages; Letters; History; Education, 4-5 years. Professional titles of–Contador público, accountancy; Médico veterinario; Administrador público; Ingeniero agrónomo, agriculture; Técnico en Cooperativas, 3-5 yrs. Profesor (teaching qualification, secondary level), in various fields.

Library: c. 25,000 vols.

Academic Staff: c. 630.

Student Enrolment: c. 2550.

73 **UNIVERSIDAD NACIONAL DE LA PATAGONIA 'SAN JUAN BOSCO'**

National University of La Patagonia 'San Juan Bosco'
25 de Mayo 427, 9000 Comodoro Rivadavia (Chubut)
Telex: 86022
Telephone: 23396
Rector: Manuel Vivas

F. of Engineering
Dean: Hugo Bersan
F. of Economics (including Accountancy)
Dean: Roberto Jones
F. of Humanities
Dean: Elsa Perfumo
F. of Engineering
Dean: Irene Ormachea
Ce. for Forestry Research
Director: Eduardo Malaspina
Micropaleontology L.
Director: Eduardo Musacchio
Chemical Engineering L. (Chemical Reactors)
Director: Enrique Rost
Aquaculture L
Director: Hector Zaisxo
Also Regional Centres at: Esquel, Puerto Madryn and Trelew.

Founded 1980, incorporating Universidad Nacional de la Patagonia, founded 1973, and Universidad de la Patagonia 'San Juan Bosco'(1963). An autonomous State institution.

Arrangements for co-operation with the Universities of: Mexico (UNAM); León and Islas Baleares, Spain. Colorado School of Mines.

Academic Year: March to November.

Admission Requirements: Secondary school certificate (bachillerato) or equivalent.

Fees: None.

Language of Instruction: Spanish.

Degrees and Diplomas: Licenciado, 5-6 yrs. Professional titles, 5-6 yrs. Teaching qualifications.

Library: Central Library, 100,000 vols.

Academic Staff, 1989:

Rank	Full-time	Part-time
Profesores Titulares	16	70
Profesores Asociados	14	92
Profesores Adjuntos	42	487
Jefes de Trabajos Prácticos	30	378
Auxiliares Primeras	10	515
Total	112	1542

Student Enrolment, 1989:

	Men	Women	Total
Of the country	2226	2099	4325
Of other countries	83	74	157
Total	2309	2173	4482

74 **UNIVERSIDAD NACIONAL DE LA PLATA**

National University of La Plata
Calle 7,776, 1900 La Plata (Buenos Aires)
Telex: 31151 BULAPAR
Telephone: 54-21-215501
Presidente: Angel Luís Plastino
Secretario General: Carlos Marcelo Rastelli

F. of Agriculture
Dean: Guillermo Hang
F. of Engineering
Dean: Luís Lima
F. of Humanities and Education
Dean: José Panettieri
F. of Law and Social Sciences
Dean: Pablo Reca
F. of Veterinary Science
Dean: Alberto Dibbern
F. of Exact Sciences
Dean: Guillermo Bibiloni
F. of Medicine
Dean: Jaime Traytemberg
F. of Natural Sciences
Dean: Abel Schalamuck
F. of Economics
Dean: Rogelio Simonatto
F. of Architecture and Town Planning
Dean: Tomás García
F. of Dentistry
Dean: Alfredo Ricciardi
F. of Fine Arts
Dean: Roberto Rollie
S. of Social Work
Director: Pedro García Cortina
F. of Astronomic Sciences and Geophysics
Dean: Cesar Mondinalli
S. of Journalism and Social Communication
Director: Jorge Bernetti
Also 43 Research Laboratories, Centres and Institutes, and primary and secondary colleges.

Founded 1890 by law as a provincial university with faculties of law, chemistry, medicine, and physical and mathematical sciences. Reorganized 1906 and became a national university. Governing bodies: the Asamblea Universitaria; the Consejo Superior.

Arrangements for co-operation with the Universities of: Quebec; Autónoma de Madrid; Complutense de Madrid; Siena; Bologna; Trieste; Reutlingen; Tokyo.

Academic Year: March to November (March-June; June-September; September-November).

Admission Requirements: Secondary school certificate (bachillerato) or equivalent. Foreign qualifications are recognized if covered byformal international agreements.

Fees: None.

Language of Instruction: Spanish.

Degrees and Diplomas: Licenciado in–Mathematics; Physics; Astronomy; Philosophy; Letters; History; Geography; Administration; Economics; Biology; Geophysics; Journalism; Library Science; Education; Plastic Arts; Chemistry; Geology; Social Service; Music; Zoology; Pharmacy; Biochemistry, 5 yrs. Professional titles of–Agrimensor, surveying; Bibliotecario; Obstétrica, midwifery, 3 yrs; Ingeniero agrónomo; Ingeniero aeronaútico; Ingeniero civil; Ingeniero en Construcciones; Ingeniero en Telecomunicaciones; Geofísico; Ingeniero electricista; Ingeniero hidraúlico; Ingeniero mecánico; Ingeniero mecánico electricista; Ingeniero metalúrgico; Ingeniero forestal; Ingeniero quimico; Abogado, law; Psicólogo; Médico veterinario; Farmacéutico; Diseñador industrial; Traductor en Lengua Inglesa; Contador público, accountancy; Odontólogo, 5 yrs; Arquitecto; Médico, 6 yrs; Bacteriólogo clínico e industrial. Doctorate (by thesis) in–Mathematics; Physics; Education; Geology; Philosophy; Letters; Education; History; Dentistry; Veterinary Science; Astronomy and Geophysics; Chemistry; Economics; Natural Sciences; Biochemistry; Pharmacy; Medicine; Law and Social Science. Teaching qualifications in–Psychology, 5 yrs; Plastic Arts; Physical Education, 4-6 yrs; Philosophy; Letters; History; Geography; Education; Law and Social Sciences; Languages and Literature; Music; Economics.

Library: Biblioteca Pública de la Universidad, 500,000 vols.

Special Facilities (Museums, etc.): Museum of Natural History; Colección 'Dr Emilio Azzarini' (Musical Instruments). Observatory.

Publications: Revista de la Universidad; publications of each faculty.

Press or Publishing House: Imprenta de la Universidad.

Academic Staff, 1990:

Rank	Full-time	Part-time
Profesores Titulares	150	750
Profesores Asociados	20	30
Profesores Adjuntos	100	1200
Jefes de Trabajos Prácticos	110	1200
Ayudantes de 1a Categoría	120	2200
Ayudantes de la Categoría	–	600
Total	500	5980

Student Enrolment, 1990: 52,000

75 **UNIVERSIDAD NACIONAL DEL LITORAL**

National University of the Litoral
Boulevard Pellegrini 2750, 3000 Santa Fe
Telephone: 34461

F. of Economics
F. of Chemical Engineering
F. of Law and Social Sciences
F. of Biochemistry
I. of Music

S. of Food Technology (Reconquista, Gálvez)
S. of Education
S. of Agriculture and Veterinary Science (Esperanza)
S. of Health Sciences

Founded 1889 as provincial university, became national university by law in 1919. An autonomous State institution. Governing bodies: the Asamblea Universitaria; the Consejo Superior. Residential facilities for students.

Academic Year: March to November.

Admission Requirements: Secondary school certificate (bachillerato).

Language of Instruction: Spanish.

Degrees and Diplomas: Licenciado in–Chemistry; Mathematics, 5-6 yrs. Professional titles of–Técnico, various fields, 2-3 yrs; Contador público y Perito partidor, accountancy; Notario, notarial studies; Médico veterinario; Ingeniero agrónomo, agriculture, 5 yrs; Abogado, law; Bioquímico, 6 yrs; Ingeniero, various fields of engineering, 5-7yrs. Profesor (teaching qualification, secondary level) in various fields, 3-5 yrs.

Library: c. 14,000 vols.

Publications: Revista Universidad; Boletín Informativo.

Academic Staff: c. 1330.

Student Enrolment: c. 8500.

76 **UNIVERSIDAD NACIONAL DE LOMAS DE ZAMORA**

National University of Lomas de Zamora

Camino de Cintara Km 2, Casilla de Correo 95, 1832 Lomas de Zamora (Buenos Aires)
Telex: 22067 CALOM-AR
Telephone: 244-4358
Rector: Eduardo José Crnko (1986-89)
Secretario General: Daniel Marcos Bubis

F. of Economics
Dean: Ricardo José María Pahlen; *staff* 2 (303)
F. of Social Sciences (including Education and Journalism)
Dean: Carlos A. Mendez
F. of Engineering and Agriculture
Dean: Eduardo Anastacio Barrandeguy
F. of Law
Dean: Mario Campos
F. of Mechanical and Industrial Engineering
Dean: Gabino Ríos

Founded 1972. An autonomous State institution. Governing bodies: the Asamblea Universitaria; the Consejo Superior.

Arrangements for co-operation with the Universities of: Quebec; McGill; Fluminense (Federal).

Academic Year: March to December (March-July; August-December).

Admission Requirements: Secondary school certificate (bachillerato) or equivalent.

Language of Instruction: Spanish.

Degrees and Diplomas: Licenciado in–Administration; International Letters; Labour Relations; Public Relations; Journalism; Education, 5 yrs. Professional titles of–Ingeniero rural; Ingeniero zoo tecnista; Ingeniero agrónomo, 5 yrs; Abogado, law, 6 yrs. Profesor (teaching qualification, secondary level) in various fields.

Libraries: Central Library, 10,000 vols; libraries of the faculties.

Special Facilities (Museums, etc.): Museo Pío Collivadino.

Academic Staff, 1986-87:

Rank	Full-time	Part-time
Profesores Titulares	1	177
Profesores Asociados	1	64
Profesores Adjuntos	–	402
Jefes de Trabajos Prácticos	–	178
Ayudantes	–	231
Total	2	1052

Student Enrolment, 1986-87: 17,454.

77 **UNIVERSIDAD NACIONAL DE LUJÁN**

National University of Luján

Ruta 5 km. 70, 6700 Luján (Buenos Aires)
Telephone: 23171

D. of Science and Technology (Food Production)
D. of Social Studies
D. of Education
Also 4 Regional Centres.

Founded 1972. An autonomous State institution.

Academic Year: March to November.

Admission Requirements: Secondary school certificate (bachillerato) or equivalent.

Fees: None.

Language of Instruction: Spanish.

Degrees and Diplomas: Licenciado in–Food Production; Food Technology; Administration; Social Service; History; Lifelong Education, 5 yrs. Doctorate in–Lifelong Education. Also technical qualifications, 3-4 yrs.

78 **UNIVERSIDAD NACIONAL DE MAR DEL PLATA**

National University of Mar del Plata

Boulevard Juan Bautista Alberdi 2695, 7600 Mar del Plata (Buenos Aires)
Telex: 39036 UNREC AR
Telephone: 39676
Rector: Javier Hernán Rojo (1989-92)
Secretario General: Daniel Katz

F. of Humanities (including Political Science and Education)
Dean: Ignacio Zuleta; *staff* 20 (92)
F. of Law
Dean: Omar Jorge; *staff* 3 (72)
F. of Architecture and Town Planning
Dean: Roberto Fernández; *staff* 2 (90)
F. of Agriculture (Balcarce)
Dean: Juan Patricio Miravé; *staff* 102 (36)
F. of Economics and Social Sciences (including Tourism)
Dean: Paulino Mallo; *staff* 9 (45)
F. of Engineering
Dean: Jorge Petrillo; *staff* 70 (71)
F. of Exact and Natural Sciences
Dean: Gustavo Daleo; *staff* 90 (43)
S. of Health Sciences
Dean: Amelia Dell'Anno; *staff* 2 (53)
C. of Psychology
Director: Cristina Di Doménico; *staff* 4 (47)
Materials Science and Technology Research I. (INTEMA)
Director: R. Williams
Ce. for Hispanomerican Letters
Director: I. Zuleta
Economic Research I.
Director: A. Rayó
Coastal Geology Ce.
Director: F. Isla
Regional Computer Ce.
Director: R. Tait
Political Science and Hispanoamerican Integration I.
Director: Javier Hernán Rojo
Biological Research I.
Director: R. Conde
Open U.
D. of Vocational Orientation
Also 13 Regional Centres.

Founded 1961 as provincial university, acquired present status and title 1975. An autonomous State institution. Governing body: the Consejo Superior.

Arrangements for co-operation with the Universities of: República Oriental del Uruguay; Alberta; Santiago deCompostela, Spain; Quebec; Pelotas; Río Grande do Sul; Delaware; La Habana; Caúca.

Academic Year: April to November (April-July; August-November).

Admission Requirements: Secondary school certificate (bachillerato) or equivalent.

Fees: None.

Language of Instruction: Spanish.

Degrees and Diplomas: Licenciado in–Business Administration; Economics; Mathematics; Geography; Letters; Biology; Tourism, 5 yrs; Professional titles of–Enfermera, nursing; Bibliotecario Documentalista; Cartógrafo, 3 yrs; Ingeniero agrónomo; Contador público; Terapista ocupacional, 5 yrs; Abogado, law; Arquitecto, 6 yrs; Ingeniero, various fields, 5-6 yrs. Teaching qualification, secondary and university levels, 4-5 yrs. Doctorates in–Economics; Psychology; Anthropology, by thesis.

Library: Central Library, c. 15,000 vols.

Publication: Revista.

Press or Publishing House: Editorial Universitaria de Mar del Plata.
Academic Staff, 1989-90:

Rank	Full-time	Part-time
Profesores Titulares	72	154
Profesores Asociados	28	14
Profesores Adjuntos	73	152
Jefes de Trabajos Prácticos	82	167
Ayudantes de Trabajos Prácticos	81	182
Total	336	669

Student Enrolment, 1989-90: 17,500.

79 **UNIVERSIDAD NACIONAL DE MISIONES**
National University of Misiones
Junín 2036, 3300 Posadas (Misiones)
Telephone: 26916

F. of Humanities and Social Sciences
F. of Exact and Natural Sciences, and Chemistry
F. of Economics
F. of Electromechanical Engineering (Oberá)
F. of Forestry (Eldorado)
I. of Aesthetic Studies (Oberá)
S. of Nursing

Founded 1973. An autonomous State institution. Governing body: the Consejo Superior Provisorio.

Academic Year: February to December (March-July; August-December).

Admission Requirements: Secondary school certificate (bachillerato) or equivalent.

Language of Instruction: Spanish.

Degrees and Diplomas: Licenciado in–Social Work; Social Anthropology; Business Administration; Cooperation Studies; Genetics; Literature; Tourism; History, 5 yrs. Professional titles of–Técnico, in various fields, 3-4 yrs; Bibliotecario, library science; Enfermera, nursing; Secretario ejecutivo; Guía de Turismo, 3 yrs; Ingeniero forestal; Contador público, accountancy, 5 yrs; Ingeniero electro-mecánico; Ingeniero químico; Bioquímico, 6 yrs. Profesor (teaching qualifications).

Library: Total, *c.* 16,400 vols.

Academic Staff: c. 80 (720).

Student Enrolment: c. 4050.

80 **UNIVERSIDAD NACIONAL DEL NORDESTE**
National University of the North-East
Calle 25 de Mayo 868, 3400 Corrientes
Telephone: 25060

F. of Agriculture
F. of Veterinary Science
F. of Law and Social and Political Sciences
F. of Exact and Natural Sciences and Surveying
F. of Humanities (Resistencia)
F. of Economics (Resistencia)
F. of Medicine
F. of Architecture and Town Planning (Resistencia)
F. of Engineering (Resistencia)
F. of Natural Resources (Forestry) (Formosa)
F. of Industrial Engineering (Presidente Roque Sáenz Peña)
F. of Dentistry

Founded 1956 and incorporating various schools attached to the National University of the Litoral. The institution, which enjoys academic and administrative autonomy, is responsible to the Ministry of Education and Culture. Governing bodies: the Asamblea Universitaria; the Consejo Superior; the Consejos Directivos. Some residential facilities for academic staff and students.

Academic Year: March to November (March-July; July-November).

Admission Requirements: Secondary school certificate (bachillerato) or equivalent.

Language of Instruction: Spanish.

Degrees and Diplomas: Licenciado in–Economics; Botany; Zoology; Geography; History; Mathematics; Physics; Philosophy; Literature; Education; Chemistry, 5-6 yrs. Professional titles of–Procurador, 3 yrs; Enfermero, 4 yrs; Contador público nacional, accountancy; Agrimensor nacional, surveying, 4 yrs. Ingeniero agrónomo, agriculture; Ingeniero forestal; Kinesiólogo; Odontólogo, dentistry; Médico veterinario, 4-5 yrs. Médico cirujano, surgery; Arquitecto, architecture; Ingeniero civil, civil engineer; Abogado, law, 6-7 yrs. Teaching qualification, secondary level (various fields), 4 yrs. Doctorate in–Veterinary Science, 5 yrs; Economics; Economics and Administration, 6 yrs. Doctor en-Derecho, doctor in law; Geography; Philosophy; Education; History, by theses.

Libraries: Central Library (Resistencia), *c.* 56,700 vols; Corrientes, *c.* 32,000.

Special Facilities (Museums, etc.): Anthropology and Archaeology.

Publications: Nordeste; Bomplandia; Revista de la Faculdad de Derecho (Law); Revista Veterinaria; Anales del Instituto de Patología Regional.

Academic Staff: c. 2330.

Student Enrolment: c. 25,000.

81 **UNIVERSIDAD NACIONAL DE RÍO CUARTO**
National University of Río Cuarto
Campus Universitario, Enlace 6 y 36-km. 603, 5800 Rio Cuarto (Córdoba)
Telephone: 24616

F. of Agriculture and Veterinary Science
F. of Engineering
F. of Exact and Natural Sciences, Physics, and Chemistry
F. of Economics
F. of Humanities
S. of Nursing
Graduate S.

Founded 1971. An autonomous State institution. Residential facilities for academic staff.

Academic Year: March to November (March-July; August-November).

Admission Requirements: Secondary school certificate (bachillerato) or equivalent.

Language of Instruction: Spanish.

Degrees and Diplomas: Licenciado in–Chemistry; Education; Philosophy; Mathematics; Journalism, 5 yrs; Business Administration; Economics, 5 ½ yrs. Professional titles of–Técnico, various fields, 2-3 yrs; Enfermera, nursing, 2 ½ yrs; Ingeniero agrónomo; Médico veterinario; Geólogo; Trabajador social; Contador público, accountancy, 4-5 ½ yrs; Ingeniero industrial; Ingeniero mecánico electricista, 6 yrs. Profesor (teaching qualification secondary level), 4 yrs.

Publications: Revista; Boletín.

Press or Publishing House: Imprenta.

Academic Staff: c. 940.

Student Enrolment: c. 4670.

82 **UNIVERSIDAD NACIONAL DE ROSARIO**
National University of Rosario
Córdoba 1814, 2000 Rosario (Santa Fe)
Telephone: 49492

F. of Medical Sciences
F. of Dentistry
F. of Biochemistry and Pharmacy
F. of Economics
F. of Agriculture
F. of Law
F. of Political Science and International Relations
F. of Exact Sciences and Engineering
F. of Architecture, Planning and Design
F. of Humanities and Arts
F. of Veterinary Science (Casilda)
I. of Music
S. of Plastic Arts
S. of Psychology
Extension D.

Also *c.* 100 schools, departments, and institutes of the faculties.

Founded 1968, incorporating various schools attached to the National University of the Litoral. Governing bodies: the Asamblea Universitaria; the Consejo Superior, composed of the Rector and Deans. Some residential facilities for medical students.

Academic Year: March to November (March-June; August-November).

Admission Requirements: Secondary school certificate (bachillerato).

Language of Instruction: Spanish.

Degrees and Diplomas: Licenciado in–Nursing; Midwifery; International Relations; Journalism; Industrial and Public Relations; Economics; Political Science; Physics; Mathematics; Philosophy; History; Letters; Visual Arts, 4-5 yrs. Professional titles of–Técnico en Ortóptica; Médico legista, 2 yrs; Enfermera, 2 ½ yrs; Fonoaudiólogo; Técnico radiólogo; Bibliotecario, 3 yrs; Contador público, accountancy; Farmacéutico; Estadístico; Ingeniero geógrafo; Odontólogo, dentistry; Médico veterinario; Ingeniero agrónomo; Ingeniero civil; Ingeniero electricista; Ingeniero mecánico; Psicólogo; Médico; Bioquímico; Abogado, law; Arquitecto, 4-6 yrs. Teaching qualifications (various fields), 2-5 yrs. Doctorates by thesis, 2 yrs after Licenciado.

Libraries: Faculty of Medicine, *c.* 32,170 vols; Faculty of Economics, *c.* 95,580; Faculty of Philosophy, *c.* 49,760; Faculty of Exact Sciences and Engineering, *c.* 40,830; Faculty of Dentistry, *c.* 3900; Faculty of Biochemistry, *c.* 2500; Faculty of Law, *c.* 3650; Faculty of Agriculture, *c.* 5070; Institute of Music, *c.* 1370.

Publications: Revista de la Universidad; Faculty publications.

Academic Staff: c. 4220.

Student Enrolment: c. 35,270.

83 **UNIVERSIDAD NACIONAL DE SALTA**

National University of Salta

Buenos Aires 177, 4400 Salta

Telex: 65121 UNSAT AR

Telephone: (87) 223200-220822

Fax: (87) 220822

Rector: Juan Carlos Gottifredi (1988-91)

Secretario General: Juan Carlos Martoccia

F. of Exact Sciences (including Computer Sciences)

Dean: Graciela Lesino; *staff* 79 (88)

F. of Technology

Dean: Osvaldo Demetrio Blesaf; *staff* 43 (217)

F. of Natural Sciences

Dean: Stella Maris Pérez de Bianchi; *staff* 65 (157)

F. of Humanities

Dean: Maria Julia Palacios, *staff* 43 (99)

F. of Health Sciences (Nutrition and Nursing)

Dean: Aldo José Maria Armesto; *staff* 21 (96)

F. of Economics, Law, and Social Sciences (including Accountancy and Business Administration)

Dean: Luis Alberto Martino; *staff* 8 (179)

Research I. of Industrial Chemistry

Director: Juan Carlos Gottifredi; *staff* 25

Solar Energy Research I.

Director: Luis Roberto Saravia; *staff* 17

Mineral Research I.

Director: Rubens Eduardo Pocovi; *staff* 17

I. for Regional Development

Director: Elio Rafael De Zuani; *staff* 1 (10)

Also Regional Centres at: Oran and Tartagal

Founded 1972, incorporating the Faculty of Natural Sciences, Department of Economics, and Institute of Endocrinology of the National University of Tucumán. An autonomous State institution. Governing body: the Asamblea Universitaria.

Arrangements for co-operation with other institutions of higher education in Latin America and Europe.

Academic Year: March to November (March-June; August-November).

Admission Requirements: Secondary school certificate (bachillerato) or equivalent.

Fees: None.

Language of Instruction: Spanish.

Degrees and Diplomas: Licenciado in–Anthropompgy; Administration; Nursing;Physics; Chemistry; Mathematics; Systems Analysis; Education; Letters; History; Nutrition; Biology; Natural Resources; Philosophy, 5 yrs. Professional titles of–Enfermera; Técnico Universitario en Perforaciones, 3 yrs; Químico; Ingeniero en Construcciones; Ingeniero industrial; Ingeniero agrónomo, 5-6 yrs. Profesor (teaching qualification), 4-5 yrs. Doctorate in–Chemistry; Physics; Geology, by thesis, a further 2 yrs.

Libraries: Central Library, *c.* 49,000 vols; libraries of the departments.

Special Facilities (Museums, etc.): Museum of Natural Sciences.

Publications: Revistas: Puerta Abierta (General); Capricornio (Geology); Cuaderno de Letras; Andes (Anthropology-History).

Press or Publishing House: Dirección de Publicaciones e Impresiones.

Academic Staff, 1989:

Rank	Full-time	Part-time
Profesores Titulares	47	37
Profesores Asociados	40	31
Profesores Adjuntos	99	272
Jefes de Trabajos Prácticos	101	389
Auxiliares Docentes de Primera	24	175
Total	311	904

Student Enrolment, 1989:

	Men	Women	Total
Of the country	5205	5122	10,327
Of other countries	316	190	506
Total	5521	5312	10,833

84 **UNIVERSIDAD NACIONAL DE SAN JUAN**

National University of San Juan

Avenida Libertador Gral. San Martín 1109 Oeste, 5400 San Juan

Telex: 59100

Telephone: 228750

F. of Engineering

F. of Exact, Physical and Natural Sciences

F. of Philosophy, Humanities and Arts

F. of Social Sciences (including Political Science)

F. of Architecture

S. of Industrial Engineering

S. of Commerce

Also 26 institutes of the faculties.

Founded 1973, incorporating faculties and schools of the National University of Cuyo. An autonomous State institution.

Academic Year: April to November (April-July; August-November).

Admission Requirements: Secondary school certificate (bachillerato) or equivalent.

Language of Instruction: Spanish.

Degrees and Diplomas: Licenciado in–Geology; Geophysics; School Administration; Business Administration; Political Science; Sociology; Social Service; Communication, 5 yrs. Professional titles of–Asistente social, 4 yrs; Ingeniero agrimensor, surveying, 5 yrs; Ingeniero electrónico; Ingeniero electricista; Ingeniero mecánico, 5 yrs; Arquitecto; Ingeniero civil; Ingeniero de Minas, mining, 6 yrs. Profesor (teaching qualifiation). Doctorate in Geology, by thesis.

Student Enrolment: c. 7130.

85 **UNIVERSIDAD NACIONAL DE SAN LUIS**

National University of San Luis

Lavalle 1189, 5700 San Luis

Telephone: 24639

F. of Engineering and Business Administration

F. of Mathematics, and Physical and Natural Sciences

F. of Chemistry, Biochemistry, and Pharmacy

F. of Education

F. of Engineering and Administration (Mercedes)

Founded 1973. An autonomous State institution.

Academic Year: March to November.

Admission Requirements: Secondary school certificate (bachillerato) or equivalent.

Language of Instruction: Spanish.

Degrees and Diplomas: Licenciado in–Physics; Chemistry; Biochemistry; Mathematics; Geology; Administration; Education; Psychology, 5 yrs. Professional titles of–Físico; Estadístico, statistics; Fonoaudiólogo; Técnico, various fields, 3 yrs; Químico; Farmacéutico, 4 yrs; Ingeniero agrónomo; Ingeniero electromecánico; Ingeniero químico, 5-6 yrs. Profesor (teaching qualification). Doctorates in–Education; Psychology, by thesis.

86 **UNIVERSIDAD NACIONAL DE SANTIAGO DEL ESTERO**

National University of Santiago del Estero

Avenida Belgrano 1912, 4200 Santiago del Estero

Telephone: 222595

F. of Basic Sciences

F. of Humanities

F. of Natural Resources (Agriculture, Forestry, Food Technology,) Hydrology

F. of Exact Sciences and Technology

Area of Health Sciences (Nursing and Health Education)
I. of Wood Technology
I. of Entomology
Ce. for Rural Education

Founded 1973. An autonomous State institution. Governing bodies: the Asamblea; the Consejo Superior; the Consejos Académicos.

Academic Year: February to December (March-July; August-December).

Admission Requirements: Secondary school certificate (bachillerato) or equivalent.

Language of Instruction: Spanish.

Degrees and Diplomas: Professional titles of–Educador sanitario, 2 yrs; Enfermería, nursing, 2 ½ yrs; Técnico, in various fields, 3 yrs; Ingeniero, in various fields, 5-6 yrs.

Library: Central Library, *c.* 20,000 vols.

Academic Staff: c. 400.

Student Enrolment: c. 2800.

87 **UNIVERSIDAD NACIONAL DEL SUR**

National University of the South

Avenida Colón 80, 8000 Bahía Blanca (Buenos Aires)
Telex: 81712 DUJOR AR
Telephone: (91) 24986
Fax: (91) 27876

Rector: Braulio Raúl Laurencena (1988-)
Secretario General: Cecilio Lucas

D. of Agriculture (including Horticulture and Animal Husbandry)
Director: Gustavo Orioli; *staff* 49 (12)
D. of Economics
Director: Ricardo Gutiérrez; *staff* 7 (21)
D. of Electrical Engineering
Director: Alberto Alvarez; *staff* 9 (28)
D. of Chemistry and Chemical Engineering
Director: Carlos Mayer; *staff* 54 (12)
D. of Humanities
Director: Hevel N. del Rio; *staff* 40 (24)
D. of Administration
Director: Fabio Rotstein; *staff* 5 (56)
D. of Biology
Director: Marcelo Sagardoy; *staff* 18 (21)
D. of Engineering
Director: Ricardo Casal; *staff* 24 (73)
D. of Geography
Director: Roberto Bustos Cara; *staff* 15 (11)
D. of Geology
Director: Eduardo Domínguez; *staff* 18 (9)
D. of Mathematics
Director: Edgardo Güichal; *staff* 36 (3)
D. of Physics
Director: Luis Ochoa; *staff* 4 (19)
I. of Oceanography
Director: Bruno Vuano; *staff* 7 (2)
I. of Biochemical Research
Director: Francisco José Barrantes; *staff* 10 (9)
Semi-Arid Zone Renewable Natural Resource Ce.
Director: Osvaldo Fernández; *staff* 32

Founded 1948 as Instituto Tecnológico del Sur, became university 1956. An autonomous State institution. Governing bodies: the Asamblea Universitaria; the Consejo Superior. Some residential facilities for visiting academic staff.

Arrangements for co-operation with the Universities of: Melbourne; Armidale; Gent State; Brasilia; Fluminense (Federal); São Paulo; Guelph; Concepción, Chile; Austral, Chile; Paris V; Karlsruhe; Hohenheim; Bielefeld; Göttingen; Bamberg; Dortmund; Würzburg; Trieste; Guadalajara; Barcelona; Santiago de Compostela; Valladolid; País Vasco; República Oriental del Uruguay; California, Riverside, Berkeley; Arizona; Idaho; Georgia; Massachusetts; Cornell; Minnesota; Yale; Indiana; Iowa State; Utah. Imperial College, London; Institut de Mécanique des Fluides, Toulouse.

Academic Year: March to November (March-June; August-November).

Admission Requirements: Secondary school certificate (bachillerato) or equivalent, and entrance examination.

Language of Instruction: Spanish.

Degrees and Diplomas: Licenciado in–Mathematics, 4 ½ yrs; Biology; Chemistry; History; Letters; Philosophy; Geography; Economics, 5 yrs; Geology, 5 ½ yrs; Biochemistry, 6 yrs. Professional titles of–Agrimensor, surveying, 3 yrs; Contador público, accountancy; Ingeniero, in various fields of engineering, 5-6 yrs. Profesor (teaching qualification, secondary level), in various fields, 4 yrs. Magister. Doctorates by thesis, 2-3 yrs after Licenciado.

Libraries: Central Library, 95,000 vols; institute libraries, *c.* 32,390.

Special Facilities (Museums, etc.): Museums of: Palaeontology; Mineralogy and Petroleum.

Publications: Notas de Algebra y Análisis; Notas de Geometría y Topología; Cuadernos del Sur.

Academic Staff, 1989:

	Full-time	Part-time
Profesores Titulares	101	45
Profesores Asociados	73	80
Profesores Adjuntos	106	207
Profesores Asistentes	109	265
Ayudantes	56	426
Total	445	1023

Student Enrolment, 1989:

Men	Women	Total
3532	2891	6423

88 **UNIVERSIDAD PROVINCIAL DE LA RIOJA**

Avenida Ortíz de Ocampo 1700, 5300 La Rioja
Telephone: 2-8836

Rector: Julio Argentino Romero
Secretario Administrativo: Juan Chade

D. of Basic Studies
Head: Cristina Fonseca de Uliana; *staff* – (10)
D. of Health Sciences (Psychology, Didactics, Pedagogy)
Head: Noemí Sacaba de Rivero; *staff* 9 (12)
D. of Social Sciences (including Accountancy, Economics, and Administration)
Head: Domingo Villafañe; *staff* 2 (13)
D. of Applied Sciences
Head: Alberto Brizuela
I. of Provincial Studies
Head: Hugo Martinasso; *staff* 3 (6)
Arid Zones Research I.
Head: Juan Carlos Gómez; *staff* 3 (2)
I. of Anthropology
Head: Amanda Rosa Giorano; *staff* 5 (1)
Extension D.
Head: Laura de León

Branches at Chamical, Chilecito.

Founded 1960 as school, and became provincial university 1972. Governing bodies: the Asamblea; the Consejo Superior; the Consejos Académicos.

Academic Year: March to November (March-July; August-November).

Admission Requirements: Secondary school certificate (bachillerato) and entrance examination.

Fees: None.

Language of Instruction: Spanish.

Degrees and Diplomas: Licenciado in–Nursing, 4 yrs; Administration, 5 yrs. Professional titles of–Enfermero Universitario, nursing, 3 yrs; Terapista ocupacional, 4 yrs; Contador público; Ingeniero de Minas, 5 yrs; Ingeniero agro-industrial; Ingeniero agrónomo; Ingeniero de Recursos Naturales Renovables para Zonas aridas, 6 yrs. Teaching qualification, secondary level, 4 yrs.

Libraries: Central Library, *c.* 7550 vols; Branch libraries, total, 2100; Science and Technology, *c.* 1500.

Academic Staff: c. 40 (70).

Student Enrolment, 1990: 2650.

89 **UNIVERSIDAD TECNOLÓGICA NACIONAL**

National Technical University

Sarmiento 440, 1041 Buenos Aires
Telex: 28210 UTN AR
Telephone: 394-9280

Rector: Juan Carlos Recalcatti
Secretario Administrativo: Abel Mauricio Domínguez

Aeronautical Engineering
Electrical Engineering
Construction Engineering
Mechanical Engineering
Chemical Engineering

Metallurgical Engineering
Textile Engineering
Naval Engineering
Regional faculties in: Avellaneda, Bahía Blanca, Buenos Aires, Campana, Concepción del Uruguay, Córdoba, General Pacheco, Haedo, La Plata, Mendoza, Paraná, Resistencia, Rosario, San Nicolás, Santa Fe, and San Miguel de Tucumán.

Founded 1953 as Universidad Obrera Nacional. Present title adopted 1959. Governing body: the Consejo Superior.

Arrangements for co-operation with the Universities of: Rome 'La Sapienza'; Trieste.

Academic Year: February to November (April-July; August-November).

Admission Requirements: Secondary school certificate (bachillerato) and certificate of work in a specialized field.

Fees: None.

Language of Instruction: Spanish.

Degrees and Diplomas: Professional title of Ingeniero, in various fields of engineering, 6 yrs. Postgraduate diplomas and certificates.

Library: Buenos Aires Faculty, *c.* 11,520 vols.

Publications: Bulletin (monthly); Administration and Management (annually).

Academic Staff, 1989: 6563.

Student Enrolment, 1989:

Of the country	59,376
Of other countries	126
Total	59,502

90 ***UNIVERSIDAD NACIONAL DE TUCUMÁN**
National University of Tucumán
Ayacucho 491, 4000 San Miguel de Tucumán
Telex: 61-143
Telephone: (81) 217123
Fax: (81) 311462
Rector: Rodolfo Martín Campero (1990-94)
Secretario Administrativo: Jorge Antonio Bascary

F. of Agriculture and Animal Husbandry
Dean: Pedro Miguel Mascaro
F. of Architecture and Town Planning
Dean Jorge Raúl Negrete
F. of Biochemistry, Chemistry, and Pharmacy
Dean César Atilio Catalán
F. of Economics
Dean: Héctor Carlos Ostengo
F. of Exact Sciences and Technology
Dean: Héctor Lencina
F. of Natural Sciences
Dean: Florencio Gilberto Aceñolaza
F. of Law and Social Sciences
Dean: Juan Carlos Veiga
F. of Philosophy and Letters
Dean: Vicente Atilio Billone
F. of Medicine
Dean: Carlos Fernández
F. of Dentistry
Dean: Jaime Steimberg
F. of Arts
Dean Carlos María Navarro
S. of Nursing
Director: Gladys Camargo de Guáraz
S. of Physical Education
Director: Dolores R. de Zelaya

Founded 1912, and inaugurated 1914 as a provincial university. Became a national university 1921. Governing bodies: the Consejo Superior; the Consejos Directivos.

Arrangements for co-operation with the Universities of: San Francisco Javier of Chuquisaca, Sucre; Münster; 'Juan Misael Sarachö' Bolivian University; Santa Catarina (Federal); Pernambuco (Federal); Antonio Abad del Cuzco; Laval; San Andrés, La Paz; Madrid; Salamanca; Valencia (Polytechnic); Hannover; Münich; Innsbruck; Rio Grande Do Sul (Federal); Valencia; Siena; Paris IX; 'Tomás Frías', Potosí; New Mexico.

Academic Year: February to December.

Admission Requirements: Secondary school certificate (bachillerato). Foreign qualifications are recognized if covered by formal international agreements.

Fees: None.

Language of Instruction: Spanish.

Degrees and Diplomas: Licenciado in–Physics; Mathematics; Biology; Chemistry; Economics; Philosophy; Letters; Education; History; French; English; Geography; Psychology; Nursing; Plastic Arts; Music, 4-6 yrs. Professional titles of–Químico, chemistry; Geólogo; Bioquímico; Farmacéutico; Contador, accountancy; Ingeniero agrónomo, agriculture; Abogado, law; Arquitecto; Agrimensor, surveying; Ingeniero, in various fields; Enfermero universitario, nursing; Odontólogo, dentistry, 3-6 yrs; Médico, 7 yrs. Profesor (teaching qualification, secondary level), in various fields. Doctorates by thesis.

Libraries: Central Library, *c.* 70,935 vols; libraries of faculties, 424,124.

Special Facilities (Museums, etc.): Museums of: Archaeology; Natural Sciences.

Publications: Revista Agronómica del Nordeste Argentino; Archivos de Bioquímica; Química y Farmacia; Revista Matemáticas y Física Teórica; Revista Jurídica; Humanitas; Lilloa; Acta Zoológica Lilloana; Revista de Medicina.

Academic Staff, 1990: 3545

Student Enrolment, 1990: 34,329

91 **ACADEMIA SUPERIOR DE ESTUDIOS POLICIALES**
Academy of Police Studies
Rosario 532, 1424 Buenos Aires
Telephone: 99-2426

Police Studies

Founded 1977.

Degrees and Diplomas: Licenciado in Criminology, 4 yrs.

92 **ESCUELA DE INGENIERÍA AERONÁUTICA**
School of Aeronautical Engineering
Avenida Fuerza Aérea Km. 5 ½, 5000 Córdoba
Telephone: 63958

Aeronautical Engineering

Founded 1971. An institution under the supervision of the Air Force. Residential facilities for single students.

Academic Year: February to December (February-June; July-October).

Admission Requirements: Successful completion of special preparatory year.

Fees: None.

Language of Instruction: Spanish.

Degrees and Diplomas: Professional titles of–Ingeniero Mecánico aeronáutico; Ingeniero Electrónico, 6 yrs.

Library: *c.* 3000 vols.

Academic Staff: *c.* 70.

Student Enrolment: *c.* 40.

Private Establishments

93 ***PONTIFICIA UNIVERSIDAD CATÓLICA ARGENTINA 'SANTA MARÍA DE LOS BUENOS AIRES'**
Pontifical Catholic University of Argentina
Juncal 1912, 1116 Buenos Aires
Telephone: 44-1035
Rector: Mgr Guillermo Pedro Blanco

F. of Theology
F. of Philosophy and Letters (including Psychology)
F. of Humanities and Education (Mendoza)
F. of Law and Political Science
F. of Law and Social Science (Rosario)
F. of Social Science and Economics (including Business Administration)
F. of Physical and Mathematical Sciences, and Engineering
F. of Agriculture
F. of Economics (Paraná)
F. of Arts and Music
I. of Culture and University Extension
I. of Integrated Studies (Science, Philosophy, and Theology)
I. of Health Sciences
I. for Extension
S. of Social Communications
C. of Education (Paraná)
Also 2 attached faculties and 2 Regional Centres.

Founded 1959 as a private university based on former Institute of Catholic Culture originated in 1922. Accorded status of Pontifical university by the Holy See 1960. The university and the degrees it awards are formally recognized by the national government. Financed by student fees and gifts. The Archbishop of Buenos Aires is Grand Chancellor of the university. Governing bodies: the Consejo Superior; the Consejo de Administración.

Academic Year: March to December.

Admission Requirements: Secondary school certificate (bachillerato) or equivalent, and competitive entrance examination.

Language of Instruction: Spanish.

Degrees and Diplomas: Licenciado in–Journalism; History; Political Science, 4 yrs; Economics; Agriculture (Animal Husbandry); Business Administration; Public Administration; Education; Psychopedagogy; Sociology; Letters; Arts and Music, 5 yrs; Philosophy; Psychology; Industrial Chemistry, 6 yrs; Theology, 8 yrs. Professional titles of Secretario ejecutivo; Traductorado público en Idioma Inglés; Bibliotecario; 3 yrs; Psicopedágogo, 4 yrs; Contador público, accountancy, 5 yrs; Ingeniero civil; Ingeniero industrial; Ingeniero mecánico electricista; Abogado, law, 6 yrs. Profesor (teaching qualification, secondary level) in various fields. Doctorates by thesis, a further 2 yrs.

Libraries: Central Library, *c.* 70,000 vols; faculty libraries.

Publications: Anuario; Universitas; Sapientia.

Academic Staff: c. 2900.

Student Enrolment: c. 11,000.

94 **UNIVERSIDAD ARGENTINA DE LA EMPRESA**

Argentine University of Business Administration

Libertad 1340, 1016 Buenos Aires

Telephone: 42-1546

Rector: Angel Daniel Vergera del Carril (1983-89)

Secretario Administrativo General: Armando Saúl Carlsson

F. of Administrative Studies

Dean: Carlos Manuel Giménez

F. of Agriculture (including Industrial Food Technology)

Dean: Gino Tomé

F. of Economics

Dean: Alfredo Gutiérrez Girault

F. of Law and Social Sciences

Dean: Eduardo Boneo Villegas

F. of Engineering

Dean: Ernesto G. Bendinger

I. of Economics

Director: José Angel Martelliti

I. of Computer Sciences

Director: Jorge Alberto Castro

Ce. for Vocational Orientation

Director Orlando Rafael Martín

Founded 1957 as a private Foundation, and officially recognized by the government 1962 as a private university. Governing bodies: the Consejo Académico, comprising 12 members; the Consejo de Administración, comprising 10 members.

Academic Year: March to December (March-July; July-December).

Admission Requirements: Secondary school certificate (bachillerato) or recognized equivalent.

Language of Instruction: Spanish.

Degrees and Diplomas: Licenciado in–Banking Organization and Techniques; Agricultural Administration, 3 yrs; Commerce; Business Administration; Public Administration; Insurance Organization and Techniques; International Commerce; Computer Sciences; Marine Economics; Public Relations; Industrial Relations; Organization of Production; Business Organization; Agricultural Economics; Agricultural Engineering; Food Technology, 4 yrs; Economics, 5 yrs. Professional titles of–Técnico en Capacitación, training technician; Técnico en Conducción de Producción, production techniques, 2 yrs; Analista en Informática, data analysis; Estadígrafo, statistics, 3 yrs; Contador público, accountancy; Traductor público, public translator, 5 yrs; Ingeniería en Organización de Empresas, business engineering and organization; Ingeniería industrial, industrial engineering, 7 yrs. Magister in Finance. Doctorate in Sociología del Trabajo.

Library: Central Library, 21,450 vols.

Publications: Estudios de Coyuntura (monthly, bimonthly, annually): Serie III: Utilización de la capacidad instalada; Serie IV: Situación monetaria y bancaria; Serie IX: Niveles de remuneraciones; Serie XII: Medición del poder de compra de los salarios industriales; Serie XIII: Niveles de actividad y ocupación en el sector industrial.

Academic Staff, 1986-87:

Rank	Full-time	Part-time
Profesores Titulares	–	936
Profesores Asociados	–	681
Profesores Adjuntos	–	1358
Jefes de Trabajos Prácticos	–	196
Profesores de Dedicación Exclusiva (Titulares)	2	–
Total	2	3171

Student Enrolment, 1986-87:

	Men	Women	Total
Of the country	3284	1449	4733
Of other countries	153	45	198
Total	3437	1494	4931*

*Also 15 external students.

95 **UNIVERSIDAD DEL ACONCAGUA**

University of Aconcagua

Catamarca 147, 5500 Mendoza

Telephone: 241257

F. of Social Sciences and Administration

F. of Economics (including Commerce)

F. of Psychology

D. of Postgraduate Studies

Founded 1973.

Degrees and Diplomas: Licenciado in–Business Administration, 4 yrs; Psychology, 5 yrs; Commerce; Accountancy; Economics, 6 yrs. Professional titles of–Técnico universitario administrativo contable, 3 yrs; Contador público, accountancy, 5 yrs. Doctorate in Psychology, by thesis.

Academic Staff: c. 250.

Student Enrolment: c. 890.

96 **UNIVERSIDAD ARGENTINA 'JOHN F. KENNEDY'**

Argentine University 'John F. Kennedy'

Calle Bartolomé Mitre 1407, 1037 Buenos Aires

Telephone: 45-4338

S. of Psychology

S. of Administration

S. of Accountancy

S. of Sociology

S. of Political Science

S. of Social Service

S. of Dramatic Art

S. of Education

S. of Journalism and Communication

S. of Public Relations

S. of Demography and Tourism

S. of Systems Analysis

S. of Graduate Studies (Sociology and Political Science)

Founded 1961 as college, became university 1968. A private institution authorized by governmental decree and responsible to the Ministry of Education and Justice.

Academic Year: April to October.

Admission Requirements: Secondary school certificate (bachillerato).

Language of Instruction: Spanish.

Degrees and Diplomas: Licenciado in all fields, 5 yrs, except Dramatic Art, 4 yrs. Professional titles of–Analista de Sistemas, 3 yrs; Asistente social, 4 yrs; Contador público, 5 yrs. Doctorates in–Sociology; Political Science; Social Psychology; Clinical Psychology, by thesis.

Library: c. 50,000 vols.

Academic Staff: c. 300.

Student Enrolment: c. 6000.

97 ***UNIVERSIDAD DE BELGRANO**

Federico Lacroze 1959, 1426 Buenos Aires

Telex: 18658

Telephone: 772-4014/18

Rector: Avelino José Porto (1964-)

Secretario General: Eustaquio Castro

F. of Law (including Political Science, Social Sciences, and International Relations)

Dean: Mario Molmenti; *staff* - (393)

F. of Architecture (including Urban Planning and Design)

Dean: Raúl Rica; *staff* - (465)

F. of Economics (including Accountancy and Administration)
Dean: José Aromando; *staff* - (379)
F. of Humanities (including Psychology and Education)
Dean: Alberto Bravo Larraburu; *staff* - (418)
F. of Technology
Dean: Gustavo Pollitzer; *staff* - (219)
F. of Engineering
Dean: Diego Pérsico; *staff* - (40)
F. of Graduate Studies
Dean: Aldo Pérez; *staff* - (85)
D. for Correspondence Courses
Director: Nélida Vuoto de Brigante; *staff* - (10)
Also 18 Research Institutes of the Faculties.

Founded 1964. A private institution recognized by the federal government 1965. Governing body: the Consejo Directivo.

Arrangements for co-operation with: Laval Université; The Johns Hopkins University; University of Maryland; University of North Carolina; University of Arkansas; Universidad Autónoma de México; Universidad Politécnica de Madrid; Universidad de Salamanca; Universidad de Santander; Hebrew University of Jerusalem; University of Tel-Aviv.

Academic Year: March to November (February-June; August-November).

Admission Requirements: Secondary school certificate (bachillerato) or equivalent.

Fees (Pesos): 103-124 per month.

Language of Instruction: Spanish.

Degrees and Diplomas: Licenciado in–Political Science; International Relations; Business Administration; Economics; Agricultural Economics; History; Psychology; Education; Systems Analysis; Business Statistics, 5 yrs. Professional titles in–Public Accountancy; Civil Engineering; Electromechanic Engineering, 5 yrs; Law; Architecture, 6 yrs. Magister, 2 yrs. Doctorates by thesis, a further 2 yrs. Profesor (teaching qualification, secondary level) in various fields.

Library: Total, 60,000 vols.

Publications: Ideas en Ciencias Sociales; Ideas en Arte y Tecnologia (both quarterly).

Press or Publishing House: Editorial Belgrano.

Academic Staff, 1986-87: 2600.

Student Enrolment, 1986-87: 16,000.

98 ***UNIVERSIDAD CATÓLICA DE CÓRDOBA**

Catholic University of Córdoba
Trejo 323, 5000 Córdoba
Telephone: 38389
Rector: Miguel A. Moreno, S.J. (1988-91)
Secretario Académico: Juan Sardo

F. of Architecture
Dean: Bernardo Marcelo Villasuso; *staff* – (78)
F. of Agriculture
Dean: Oscar Eduardo Melo; *staff* – (66)
F. of Economics and Administration
Dean: Raúl Carlos Enrique Bianchi; *staff* – (109)
F. of Political Science and International Relations
Dean: Jorge Edmundo Barbará *staff* – (51)
F. of Chemistry (including Pharmacy and Biochemistry)
Dean: Jorge Oscar Velasco; *staff* – (74)
F; of Law and Social Sciences
Dean: Armando Segundo Andruet; *staff* – (108)
F. of Philosophy and Humanities (including Education and Psychology)
Dean: Luisa Margarita Schweizer; *staff* – (26)
F. of Engineering
Dean: Aldo Oscar Sartori *staff* – (88)
F. of Medicine
Dean: José María Foscarini; *staff* – (177)
I. of Administration Sciences
Director: Eugenio Gimeno Balaguer; *staff* – (11)
Reality Research and Political Analysis I.
Director: Marta Díaz de Landa; *staff* – (10)

Founded 1956 as institute, became university and received government recognition 1959, authorized to award degrees and professional qualifications. A private institution operated under the direction of the Society of Jesus within the Archbishopric of Córdoba. Governing bodies: the Consejo Directivo; the Consejo Académico.

Arrangements for co-operation with Sophia University, Tokyo.

Academic Year: February-December (February-July; July-December).

Admission Requirements: Secondary school certificate (bachillerato) or recognized equivalent, and entrance examination.

Fees (US$): Registration, 60; tuition, 60-80 per month; foreign students, registration, 104; tuition, 104-135.20.

Language of Instruction: Spanish.

Degrees and Diplomas: Licenciado in–Educational Sciences, 3 yrs; Political Science; International Relations; Business Administration, 5 yrs. Professional titles of–Arquitecto Especialista en–Historia de la Arquitectura, 1 ½ yrs; Diseño del Paisaje, 2 yrs; Farmacéutico, 4 yrs; Ingeniero agrónomo, agriculture; Ingeniero (in various fields); Bioquímico; Contador público, accountancy; Notario, notarial studies; Abogado, law, 5 yrs; Arquitecto; Médico, medicine, 6 yrs. Profesor (teaching qualification, secondary level) in various fields, 2 yrs. Magister in–Business Administration; Public Administration, 2 yrs. Doctorates by thesis. Also diplomas of specialization, 2 yrs.

Library: c. 38,600 vols.

Publication: Acta Scientifica.

Academic Staff, 1989-90:

Rank	Part-time
Titulares	292
Encargados	86
Adjuntos	208
Jefes de Trabajos Prácticos	212
Total	798

Student Enrolment, 1990: 3650.

99 **UNIVERSIDAD CATÓLICA DE CUYO**

Catholic University of Cuyo
Avenida José de la Roxa 1516, Oeste, 5400 Rivadavia (San Juan)
Telephone: 230291

F. of Food Technology
F. of Economics
F. of Law and Social Sciences
F. of Philosophy and Humanities (including Psychology)
F. of Business Administration and Tourism (Mendoza)
F. of Social Service (San Luis)
S. of Nursing

Founded 1963.

Academic Year: March to November.

Admission Requirements: Secondary school certificate (bachillerato).

Language of Instruction: Spanish.

Degrees and Diplomas: Licenciado in–Food Technology, 4 yrs; Tourist Administration; Psychology; Psychopedagogy, 5 yrs. Professional titles of–Guía Turístico, 2 yrs; Enfermera, 3 yrs; Asistente social, 4 yrs; Contador público y Perito Partidor, 5 yrs; Abogado, 6 yrs. Profesor (teaching qualification, secondary level), 5 yrs.

Publication: Cuadernos.

Academic Staff: c. 340.

Student Enrolment: c. 1280.

100 **UNIVERSIDAD CATÓLICA DE LA PLATA**

Catholic University of La Plata
Calle 13 No. 1227, 1900 La Plata (Buenos Aires)
Telephone: 21-41291

F. of Architecture
F. of Applied Mathematics
F. of Economics
F. of Law
F. of Social Sciences
F. of Education

Founded 1971 as a private institution. Recognized by the government and authorized to award degrees.

Degrees and Diplomas: Licenciado in–Education, 2 yrs; Statistics; Systems Analysis; Applied Mathematics, 4 yrs; Sociology; Administration; Economics, 5 yrs. Professional titles of–Especialista en Computación, 2 yrs; Contador público, accountancy; Abogado, law, 5 yrs; Arquitecto, 6 yrs. Profesor (teaching qualification, secondary level), 4 yrs. Doctorates in–Economics; Law; Political Science, by thesis.

Academic Staff: c. 600.

Student Enrolment: c. 8270.

101 **UNIVERSIDAD CATÓLICA DE SALTA**

Catholic University of Salta

Casilla de Correo 18, 4428 Campo Castañares (Salta)

Telephone: 219000

F. of Arts and Science
F. of Economics and Administration
F. of Engineering
F. of Law
S. of Social Service
Extension D. (Economics and Business Administration)
Also branch at Metan.

Founded 1963 and began regular courses 1967. Recognized by the government 1968 and authorized to award degrees and professional qualifications. A private institution operated with the co-operation of the Society of Jesus. Governing bodies: the Directorio; the Consejo Académico; the Consejo Administrativo; the Consejo Estudiantil.

Academic Year: March to December (March-July; August-December).

Admission Requirements: Secondary school certificate (bachillerato) and entrance examination.

Language of Instruction: Spanish.

Degrees and Diplomas: Licenciado in–History; Philosophy; Literature; Mathematics; Psychology; Modern Languages; Economics; Business Administration; Social Service, 5 yrs. Professional titles of–Secretario ejecutivo, 5 sem; Asistente social, 4 yrs; Abogado, law, 5 yrs; Ingeniero civil; Ingeniero industrial, 6 yrs. Profesor (teaching qualification, secondary level), 4 yrs. Doctorates by thesis, 1-2 yrs after Licenciado.

Library: c. 20,000 vols.

Academic Staff: c. 340.

Student Enrolment: c. 1940.

102 **UNIVERSIDAD CATÓLICA DE SANTA FE**

Catholic University of Santa Fe

Echagüe 7151, 3000 Santa Fe

Telephone: 63030

F. of Philosophy
F. of Law
F. of Economics (including Accountancy)
F. of History
F. of Letters
F. of Architecture
F. of Education
F. of Soil Science

Founded 1957, became university 1960. Governing body: the Administrative Council, presided over by the Archbishop of Santa Fe, and the Academic Council, composed ofthe Rector, the Vice-Rector, the Secretary-General, and the deans of the Faculties.

Academic Year: March to April.

Admission Requirements: Secondary school certificate (bachillerato) or equivalent.

Language of Instruction: Spanish.

Degrees and Diplomas: Licenciado in–Co-operative Studies, 4 yrs; Philosophy; Soil Science, 5 yrs; Education; History; Letters, 6 yrs. Professional titles of–Abogado, law; Contador público, accountancy, 5 yrs; Psicopedágogo; Arquitecto, 6 yrs. Teaching qualifications, secondary level, 5 yrs, university level, 2 yrs after Licenciado. Doctorates by thesis.

Library: c. 6000 vols.

Academic Staff: c. 600.

Student Enrolment: c. 2200.

103 ***UNIVERSIDAD CATÓLICA DE SANTIAGO DEL ESTERO**

Catholic University of Santiago del Estero

Libertad 321, 4200 Santiago del Estero

Telephone: 213820

Rector: Pedro Fils Pierre

F. of Law and Political and Social Sciences
F. of Economics (Accountancy)
F. of Education (including Tourism)
D. of Applied Mathematics
Extension D.

Founded 1960 as a university institute attached to the Universidad Católica de Santa Fe. Recognized by the national government as an independent autonomous university 1969. Governing bodies: the Consejo Superior; the Consejo Académico.

Academic Year: April to November (April-June; August-November).

Admission Requirements: Secondary school certificate (bachillerato) or foreign equivalent.

Language of Instruction: Spanish.

Degrees and Diplomas: Licenciado in–Political Science; Sociology, 4 yrs; Education; Geography, 5 yrs. Professional titles of–Guía en Turismo, 2 yrs; Programador Universitario, 3 yrs; Analista de Sistemas, 4 yrs; Experto en Turismo; Procurador, 4 yrs; Ingeniero en Computación; Contador público, accountancy, 5 yrs; Abogado, law, 6 yrs. Teachingqualifications in–Geography, 4 yrs; Educational Sciences, 5 yrs.

Library: Central Library, c. 6200 vols.

Publication: Revista.

Academic Staff: c. 250.

Student Enrolment: c. 2000.

104 **UNIVERSIDAD DE CONCEPCIÓN DEL URUGUAY 'LA FRATERNIDAD'**

University of Concepción del Uruguay 'La Fraternidad'

8 de Junio 522, 3260 Concepción del Uruguay (Entre Ríos)

Telephone: 7721

F. of Economics (including Business Administration and Accountancy)
F. of Highway Engineering, Architecture, and Town Planning

Founded 1971.

Degrees and Diplomas: Licenciado in–Business Administration, 5 yrs; Economics, 6 yrs. Professional titles of–Perito en Administración de Empresas, business administration, 3 yrs; Contador público, accountancy, 5 yrs; Arquitecto, 6 yrs. Doctorates, by thesis.

105 **UNIVERSIDAD 'JUAN AGUSTÍN MAZA'**

University 'Juan Agustin Maza'

Salta 1690, 5500 Mendoza

Telephone: 251998

F. of Physical and Mathematical Sciences
F. of Pharmacy and Biochemistry
F. of Engineering (including Surveying)
F. of Journalism
F. of Oenology and Horticulture (Rodeo del Medio)
S. of Nutrition

Founded 1963.

Academic Year: April to March.

Language of Instruction: Spanish.

Degrees and Diplomas: Licenciado in–Oenology and Fruit-Growing; Industrial Chemistry, 4 yrs; Physics; Mathematics, 5 yrs; Industrial Pharmacy, 6 yrs. Professional titles of–Agrimensor, surveying, 3 yrs; Nutricionista; Farmacéutico, 4 yrs; Ingeniero Electromecánico; Ingeniero en Dirección de Empresas; Bioquímico, 6 yrs. Teaching qualification, secondary level, in Mathematics, Physics, and Cosmography; Chemistry, 4 yrs. Doctorates in–Oenology; Biochemistry, by thesis.

Academic Staff: c. 260.

Student Enrolment: c. 880.

106 **UNIVERSIDAD DE LA MARINA MERCANTE**

University of the Merchant Marine

Billinghurst 376, 1174 Buenos Aires

Telephone: 87-1130

F. of Engineering
F. of Administration and Economics

Founded 1974.

Degrees and Diplomas: Licenciado in–Engineering; Marine Administration, 4 yrs. Professional titles of–Perito en Administración naviera, 3 yrs; Ingeniero en Máquinas navales; Ingeniero en Electrónica naval, 6 yrs. Doctorate in Marine Administration, by thesis.

107 **UNIVERSIDAD DE MENDOZA**

University of Mendoza

Avenida Boulogne sur Mer 665, 5500 Mendoza

Telex: 18660 DELPHI AR

Telephone: 247017

Fax: 311100

Rector: Salvador Puliafito (1989-93)

Secretario Administrativo: Beatriz Celeste

F. of Law and Social Sciences
Dean: Juan C. Menghini; *staff* 7 (86)

F. of Architecture and Town Planning
Dean: Ricardo Beckerman; *staff* 18 (88)

F. of Engineering
Dean: Celeste d'Inca; *staff* 9 (69)
Ce. of Higher Studies (Environment, Democracy, Latin American Integration)
Head: Salvador Puliafito; *staff* 5 (8)
I. of Public Law
; *staff* 2 (3)
I. of Private Law
Head: Alejandro Baro; *staff* 1 (5)
I. of High Frequencies
Head: José Luis Puliafito
I. of Digital Techniques
Head: Raul A. Funes
I. of Informatics
Head: Salvador Navarria
I. of Special Microwave Applications (Submilimeter Waves)
Head: Carlos M. Puliafito

Founded 1960. A private institution officially recognized by the government. Governing bodies: the Asamblea Universitaria; the Consejo Superior; the Consejo Académico.

Arrangements for co-operation with the Universities of: Stuttgart; Concepción, Chile.

Academic Year: March to November (March-June; August-November).

Admission Requirements: Secondary school certificate (bachillerato) and entrance examination.

Language of Instruction: Spanish.

Degrees and Diplomas: Licenciado in–Systems Analyses. Professional titles of–Procurador, 3 yrs; Abogado, law, 5 yrs; Arquitecto; Ingeniero en Computación; Ingeniero en electrónica y electricidad, 6 yrs. Doctorate in Law and Social Sciences, by thesis, a further 2 yrs. Also diploma of specialization, by thesis, 1 ½ yrs.

Libraries: Faculty libraries: Law and Social Sciences, 14,817 vols; Architecture and Town Planning, 5917; Engineering, 4120.

Publications: Revista; Idearium (Law and Social Sciences publication).

Press or Publishing House: Editorial 'Idearium'.

Academic Staff: c. 300.

Student Enrolment: c. 2170.

108 UNIVERSIDAD DE MORÓN

University of Morón
Cabildo 134, 1708 Morón (Buenos Aires)
Telephone: 629-2404
Rector: Omar Lima Quintana
Secretario de Asuntos Administrativos: Miguel Angel Galán

F. of Law and Social Sciences
Dean: Albrané H. Malcervelli
F. of Engineering (including Surveying)
Dean: Celestino M. Arce
F. of Exact and Natural Sciences, and Chemistry
Dean: Enrique Vandersluis
F. of Architecture
Dean: Raúl von der Becke
F. of Economics (including Business Administration and Accountancy)
Dean: Mario Armando Mena
F. of Agriculture
Dean: Ulises Mitidieri
F. of Philosophy and Letters
Dean: Dina Picotti de Camara
F. of Tourism
Dean: Olga Villalba de Cesenj
F. of Computer Sciences and Communication
Dean: Pablo F.M. Ennis
S. of Social Service

Founded 1972. Governing bodies: the Asamblea Universitaria; the Consejo Superior.

Academic Year: April to November (April-July; August-November).

Admission Requirements: Secondary school certificate (bachillerato).

Language of Instruction: Spanish.

Degrees and Diplomas: Licenciado in–Taxation; Economics; Business Administration; Public Relations; Education; History; Philosophy; Letters; Tourism; Chemistry, 4-6 yrs. Professional titles in–Law; Notarial Studies; Accountancy; Agriculture; Civil Engineering; Electronic Engineering; Surveying; Architecture; Translation; Business Studies; Social Service. Doctorate in Chemistry, by thesis.

Library: University Library.

Publications: Air and Space Law Review; Philosophy and Letters Review; Logics and Methodology Review.

Academic Staff: c. 1350.

Student Enrolment: c. 13,500.

109 UNIVERSIDAD DEL MUSEO SOCIAL ARGENTINO

Avenida Corrientes 1723, 1042 Buenos Aires
Telephone: 40-6924

F. of Political Science, Law, and Economics
F. of Social Service
F. of Information Sciences (including Museology and Library Science)
F. of Therapeutic Sciences
S. of Choral Studies

Founded 1961.

Degrees and Diplomas: Licenciado in–Cooperative Studies; Library Science and Documentation, 3 yrs; Business Administration; Museology; Information, 4 yrs; Phonoaudiology, 5 yrs. Professional titles of–Bibliotecario, 2 yrs; Fonoaudiólogo, 3 yrs; Asistente social, 4 yrs; Abogado, law, 5 yrs. Teaching qualifications in Choral Studies, 2-5 yrs. Doctorates, 1-2 yrs after Licenciado and thesis.

110 UNIVERSIDAD DEL NORTE 'SANTO TOMÁS DE AQUINO'

University of the North 'Santo Tomás de Aquino'
9 de Julio 165, 4000 San Miguel de Tucumán
Telephone: 22 8805
Rector: Anibal Ernesto Fosbery, O.P.
Vice-Rector: Héctor Luis Partridge

F. of Humanities
Dean: Alejandro Llanes Navarro
F. of Economics (including Accountancy)
F. of Law and Social Sciences
Dean: Carlos Lorenzo Rosales
F. of Industrial Engineering
Dean: Juan Carlos Muzzo
F. of Administrative Studies (including Tourism)
Dean: Efrain Oscar David
F. of Philosophy
Dean: Alejandro Llanes Navarro
F. of Anthropology and Psychology
Dean: Alejandro Llanes Navarro
F. of Theology
Dean: Ernesto Parselis
I. of Social Work
I. of Political Science
I. of Letters
D. for Lifelong Education
Also University Centre at Concepción.

Founded 1956 as institute, acquired present status and title 1965. A private institution. Governing body: the Junta de Gobierno.

Academic Year: April to November (April-June; August-November).

Admission Requirements: Secondary school certificate (bachillerato).

Language of Instruction: Spanish.

Degrees and Diplomas: Licenciado in–Business Administration (Agriculture, Tourism); Psychology; Social Work; Letters; History; Philosophy; Political Science, 4-5 yrs. Professional titles of–Guía de Turismo, 2 yrs; Administrador de Empresas, business administration; Trabajador social, social work, 4 yrs; Ingeniero industrial, 5 yrs; Contador público, accountancy; Abogado, law, 6 yrs. Postgraduate diplomas of specialization. Doctorates by thesis. Also teaching qualifications.

Library: c. 13,780 vols.

Publications: Aportes para la Historia de Tucumán; Investigación y Docencia; faculty publications.

Academic Staff: c. 520.

Student Enrolment: c. 1930.

111 UNIVERSIDAD NOTARIAL ARGENTINA

Calle 51, No. 435, 1900 La Plata (Buenos Aires)
Telephone: 212-9283

Notarial Studies (postgraduate)
Branches in: Morón; Corrientes; Buenos Aires; Paraná; Rosario; Santa Fe.

Founded 1964 and recognized by the federal government as a private postgraduate institution 1968. Governing body: the Consejo Superior, comprising 7 members. Some residential facilities for academic staff and students.

Arrangements for co-operation with similar institutions in: Guatemala, Paraguay, and Puerto Rico.
Academic Year: March to December (March-July; August-December).
Admission Requirements: A University degree (Law and Social Sciences, Philosophy, Economics).
Language of Instruction: Spanish.
Degrees and Diplomas: Magister. Doctorates by thesis.
Library: c. 10,000 vols.
Special Facilities (Museums, etc.): Museo y Archivo 'Roberto Mario Arata'.
Academic Staff: c. 170.
Student Enrolment: c. 3640.

112 ***UNIVERSIDAD DEL SALVADOR**
Salvador University
Rodríguez Peña 640, 1020 Buenos Aires
Telex: 18691 EIRAS AR
Telephone: 49-5531
Rector: Juan Alejandro Tobias (1985-88)
Secretario General: Roberto López Rosas

F. of Law
Dean: Práxedes Sagasta; *staff* 8 (398)
F of Education and Communication Sciences
Head: María Mercedes M. Terrén; *staff* 8 (122)
F. of Social Sciences (including Political Science and International Relations)
Dean: Eduardo Suárez; *staff* 9 (192)
F. of Medicine
DEean: Luis González Montaner; *staff* 11 (69)
F. of Philosophy
Advisor: Cecilia Lynch Pueyrredón; *staff* 3 (26)
F. of Philosophy (San Miguel)
Dean: Jorge Seibold, S.J.
F. of Theology (San Miguel)
Dean: José Luis Lazzarini, S.J.
F. of History and Letters (including Geography and Tourism)
Dean: Juan C. Lucero Schmidt; *staff* 9 (250)
F. of Psychology
Dean: Saúl Miguel Rodríguez Amenabar; *staff* 5 (273)
F. of Psychopedagogy
Dean: María Isabel Oliver; *staff* 7 (294)
F. of Economics
Dean: Sergio García *staff* 5 (46)
F. of Administration (including Computer Sciences)
Dean: Aquilino López Diez; *staff* 5
S. of Oriental Studies
Director: Ismael Quiles, S.J.; *staff* 3 (30)
S. of Scenic Art
Director: Alice Darramón de Beitia; *staff* 2 (9)
Latin American I. for Medical Research
Director: Carlos A. Falasco; *staff* 8 (4)
Extension D

Founded 1944 as Instituto Superior de Filosofía, reorganized as faculty 1954 and officially recognized as university 1959. Operated under the authority of the Society of Jesus, which designates the Rector. Governing body: the Consejo Superior.
Academic Year: January to December (April-July; July-November).
Admission Requirements: Secondary school certificate (bachillerato) or equivalent.
Fees (Pesos): 120 per month.
Language of Instruction: Spanish.
Degrees and Diplomas: Licenciado in–International Relations; Business Administration; Geography; Political Science; Economics; Sociology; Philosophy; Psychology; History; Letters; Social Service; Tourism; Oriental Studies; Publicity; Computer Sciences; Audiotherapy; Business Administration; Psychopedagogy, 5 yrs; Theology, 6 yrs. Professional titles in–Music Therapy; Physical Therapy; Scenic Art, 3 yrs; Translation, 4-5 yrs; Law; Medicine, 6 yrs. Teaching qualifications in various fields, 5 yrs. Doctorate in–Law; Psychology; International Relations; Political Science; Philosophy; Theology; Medicine, by thesis.
Library: Central Library, 80,000 vols.
Publication: Revista (quarterly).

Academic Staff, 1986-87:

Rank	Full-time	Part-time
Profesores Consultos	–	38
Profesores Titulares	30	558
Profesores Asociados	10	520
Profesores Adjuntos	8	398
Profesores Auxiliares	7	377
Total	55	1891

Student Enrolment, 1986-87:

	Men	Women	Total
Of the country	2741	4835	7576
Of other countries	185	66	251
Total	2926	4901	7827

113 **CENTRO DE ALTOS ESTUDIOS EN CIENCIAS EXACTAS**
Avenida de Mayo 1396, 1085 Buenos Aires
Telephone: 373815

Exact Sciences
Founded 1968.
Degrees and Diplomas: Licenciado in–Applied Mathematics; Pure Mathematics; Administration; Systems Analysis, 4-5 yrs. Professional titles of–Analista de Valor, 2 ½ yrs; Calculista científico, 3 yrs; Estadígrafo, 3 ½ yrs; Investigador operativo, 4 yrs. Teaching qualification, 4-5 yrs. Doctorates by thesis.

114 **ESCUELA UNIVERSITARIA DE TEOLOGIA**
Pasaje Catedral 1750, 7600 Mar del Plata (Buenos Aires)
Telephone: 28633

Theology
Founded 1964.

115 **INSTITUTO TECNOLÓGICO DE BUENOS AIRES**
Buenos Aires Technology Institute
Avenida Emilio Madero 351, 1106 Buenos Aires
Telephone: 34-7748

D. of Marine and Mechanical Engineering
D. of Mathematics, Physics and Chemistry
D. of Electronics
D. of Computer Sciences
D. of Industrial Engineering
D. of Oceanography
Extension D.

Founded 1959 as a private institution, recognized by the federal government and operated under its supervision. Financed from private sources. Governing bodies: the Consejo de Regentes; the Consejo Académico.
Academic Year: February to December (March-July; August-November).
Admission Requirements: Secondary school certificate and entrance examination.
Language of Instruction: Spanish.
Degrees and Diplomas: Bachiller en Ingeniería, 4 yrs. Licenciado in Computer Sciences; Oceanography, 5 yrs. Professional title of Ingeniero (in various fields), 6 yrs; Magister, 2 yrs. Doctor en Ingeniería; Ciencias Geofísicas, 3 yrs.
Library: c. 1320 vols.
Publication: Revista (every four months).
Academic Staff: c.– (220).
Student Enrolment: c. 700.

Other Institutions

Professional Education

116 **ESCUELA NACIONAL DE BELLAS ARTES 'ROGELIO YRURTIA'**
Colón 428, Azul (Buenos Aires)

Fine Arts
Admission Requirements: Secondary school certificate (bachillerato) and entrance examination.
Degrees and Diplomas: Professional titles, 4 yrs.

117 **ESCUELA NACIONAL DE BELLAS ARTES 'MANUEL BELGRANO'**
Cerrito 1350, Buenos Aires

Fine Arts
Admission Requirements: Secondary school certificate (bachillerato) and entrance examination.
Degrees and Diplomas: Professional titles, 4 yrs.

118 **ESCUELA SUPERIOR DE BELLAS ARTES 'ERNESTO DE LA CÁRCOVA'**
Avenida Costanera esq. Brasil, Buenos Aires

Fine Arts
Degrees and Diplomas: Professional titles, 4 yrs.

119 **INSTITUTO NACIONAL DE BELLAS ARTES 'PRILIDIANO PUEYRREDON'**
Las Heras 1749, Buenos Aires

Fine Arts
Degrees and Diplomas: Professional titles, 3-4 yrs.

120 **INSTITUTO SANTA ANA**
Avenida del Libertador 6115/95, Buenos Aires

Design
Painting
Music
Founded 1960. A private institution.
Academic Year: March to December (March-May; May-July; August-September; September-December).
Admission Requirements: Secondary school certificate.
Language of Instruction: Spanish.
Degrees and Diplomas: Professional titles, 4-7 yrs. Teaching qualifications.
Academic Staff: c. 90.
Student Enrolment: c. 620.

121 **INSTITUTO 'MONSEÑOR JUAN M. TERRERO'**
Calle II No. 675, La Plata (Buenos Aires)

Visual Arts
Degrees and Diplomas: Professional titles, 7 yrs.

122 **INSTITUTO DEL PROFESORADO SECUNDARIO DE ARTES PLÁSTICAS**
La Rioja

Plastic Arts
Degrees and Diplomas: Professional titles, 4 yrs.

123 **ESCUELA DE ARTES VISUALES 'MARTÍN MALAHARRO'**
Funes 1357/71, Mar del Plata (Buenos Aires)

Visual Arts
Degrees and Diplomas: Professional titles, 7-10 yrs.

124 **INSTITUTO SUPERIOR DEL PROFESORADO 'ANTONIO RUÍZ DE MONTOYA'**
Buenos Aires 285, Posadas (Misiones)

Design
Painting
Degrees and Diplomas: Professional titles, 5 yrs.

125 **INSTITUTO SUPERIOR DEL PROFESORADO DE BELLAS ARTS**
Marcelo T. de Alvear 488, 3500 Resistencia (Chaco)
Telephone: 27228
Rector: María del Carmen Nievas

Fine Arts
Founded 1959.
Academic Year: March to December.
Admission Requirements: Secondary school certificate (bachillerato).
Fees: None.
Degrees and Diplomas: Professional titles, 3-4 yrs.
Library: 1277 vols.
Student Enrolment, 1990: 585.

126 **ESCUELA PROVINCIAL DE BELLAS ARTES 'TOMÁS CABERERA'**
Zuviría 465, Salta

Fine Arts
Degrees and Diplomas: Professional titles, 3-7 yrs.

127 **ACADEMIA NACIONAL DE BELLAS ARTES DEL NORTE 'JUAN YAPARI'**
Avenida Belgrano Sur 1289, Santiago del Estero
Telephone: 21-5799

C. of Fine Arts
Also secondary and preparatory schools.
Founded as secondary school 1959. Acquired present status and title 1973. A State institution.
Academic Year: March to December (March-May; June-August; September-December).
Admission Requirements: Secondary school certificate (bachillerato) and entrance examination.
Language of Instruction: Spanish.
Degrees and Diplomas: Professional titles of–Maestro nacional de Dibujo, 4 yrs; Profesor Nacional de Pintura; de Grabado; de Escultura.
Academic Staff: c. – (60).
Student Enrolment: c. 400.

128 **ESCUELA NACIONAL DE BIBLIOTECARIOS**
Biblioteca Nacional, Méjico 564, Buenos Aires

Library Science
Degrees and Diplomas: Professional titles, 2 ½ yrs.

129 **INSTITUTO SUPERIOR DE FORMACIÓN DOCENTE NO. 8**
Diagonal 74 No. 1052, La Plata, Buenos Aires 1900
Telephone: 21-3501
Director: Esther Arrastúa de Muõz

Library Science
Museology
Archive Studies
Founded 1948.
Academic Year: March to December.
Admission Requirements: Secondary school certificate (bachillerato).
Fees: None.
Degrees and Diplomas: Professional titles, 3 yrs.
Student Enrolment: c. 9125.

130 **ESCUELA DE BIBLIOTECOLOGÍA**
San Martín 3459, Santa Fe

Library Science
Degrees and Diplomas: Professional titles, 3 yrs.

131 **ESCUELA NACIONAL DE CERÁMICA**
Bulnes 43, Buenos Aires

Ceramic Art
Degrees and Diplomas: Professional titles, 5-6 yrs.

132 **ESCUELA DE CERÁMICA DE MAR DEL PLATA**
Dorrego 2081, 7600 Mar del Plata (Buenos Aires)

Ceramic Art
Founded 1951. A State institution.
Academic Year: April to November (April-June; July-September; September-January).
Admission Requirements: Secondary school certificate (bachillerato).
Fees: None.
Language of Instruction: Spanish.
Degrees and Diplomas: Professional titles, 3 yrs.
Academic Staff: c. 20.
Student Enrolment: c. 300.

133 **ESCUELA NACIONAL DE DANZAS**
Esmeralda 285, Buenos Aires

Dancing (Classical and Folkloric)
Founded 1929 as Classical Dancing section of the National Conservatory of Music and Scenic Art, incorporated the National School of Folkloric

Dancing and acquired present status and title 1949. A State institution under the jurisdiction of the Ministry of Education and Justice. Governing body: the Consejo Directivo.

Academic Year: March to November (March-May; May-July; July-September; October-November).

Admission Requirements: Secondary school certificate (bachillerato) and entrance examination.

Fees: None.

Languages of Instruction: Spanish and English.

Degrees and Diplomas: Professional titles of–Profesor de Danzas Nativas y Folklore, 3 yrs; Profesora de Danza Clásica, 10 yrs.

Academic Staff: c. 580.

Student Enrolment: c. 3780.

134 **ESCUELA DE DANZAS CLÁSICAS**
Calle 10 entre 51 y 53, Mar del Plata (Buenos Aires)

Classical Dancing

Founded 1948. A State institution.

Academic Year: April to November (April-June; June-September; September-November).

Fees: None.

Degrees and Diplomas: Professional title.

Academic Staff: c. 40.

135 **ESCUELA NACIONAL DE ARTE DRAMÁTICO**
French 3614, Buenos Aires

Dramatic Art

Degrees and Diplomas: Professional title, 4 yrs.

136 **ESCUELA DE CIENCIAS ECONÓMICAS**
La Rioja

Economics

Degrees and Diplomas: Professional title of Contador público, accountancy, 5 yrs.

137 **INSTITUTO SUPERIOR DE CIENCIAS ECONÓMICAS**
Ministerio de Gobierno, Justicia y Educación, Otero 369, San Salvador de Jujuy

Economics

Degrees and Diplomas: Professional title of Contador público, accountancy, 5 yrs.

138 **ESCUELA SUPERIOR DE ENFERMERÍA**
Saavedra 2149, Santa Fe

Nursing

Founded 1966. A State institution under the jurisdiction of the Ministry of Social Welfare and Public Health.

Academic Year: March to December (March-July; August-November).

Admission Requirements: Secondary school certificate (bachillerato).

Fees: None.

Language of Instruction: Spanish.

Degrees and Diplomas: Professional qualification in Nursing, 2-3 yrs. Also diploma of Nursing Assistant, 1 yr.

Library: c. 1980 vols.

Student Enrolment: c. 140.

139 **ESCUELA SUPERIOR DE CIENCIAS DE LA INFORMACIÓN Y RELACIONES PÚBLICAS**
Garibaldi 267, Mendoza

Journalism

Degrees and Diplomas: Professional titles, 3-5 yrs.

140 **CONSERVATORIO DE MÚSICA DE BAHÍA BLANCA**
Dorrego 1206, Bahía Blanca (Buenos Aires)
Telephone: 27290

Founded 1957. A State institution under the jurisdiction of the Ministry of Education and the Province of Buenos Aires.

Academic Year: April to November (April-June; June-August; August-November).

Admission Requirements: Secondary school certificate (bachillerato) or equivalent, and entrance examination.

Fees: None.

Language of Instruction: Spanish.

Degrees and Diplomas: Professional titles, 9-10 yrs.

Student Enrolment: c. 730.

141 **CONSERVATORIO DE MÚSICA 'JULIÁN AGUIRRE'**
Gral. Rodríguez 7672, Banfield (Buenos Aires)

Music

Degrees and Diplomas: Professional titles.

142 **CONSERVATORIO NACIONAL DE MÚSICA 'CARLOS LÓPEZ BUCHARDO'**
National Conservatory of Music
Callao 1521, Buenos Aires

Music

Degrees and Diplomas: Professional titles.

143 **CONSERVATORIO MUNICIPAL DE MÚSICA 'MANUEL DE FALLA'**
Sarmiento 1551, Centro Cultural Gral. San Martin, 1042 Buenos Aires
Telephone: 40-5898
Director: Mario A. Barabini

Music

Founded 1919 as school, acquired present status and title 1946.

Academic Year: April to November.

Admission Requirements: Secondary school certificate (bachillerato) and entrance examination.

Fees: None.

Language of Instruction: Spanish.

Degrees and Diplomas: Professional titles, 5-11 yrs.

Library: 20,000 vols.

Academic Staff, 1990: – (300).

Student Enrolment, 1990: 1860 (All external and including 15 foreign students).

144 **CONSERVATORIO DE MÚSICA DE CHASCOMUS**
Lavalle 281, Chascomus Buenos Aires)

Music

Founded 1963. A State institution under the jurisdiction of the Ministry of Education of the Province of Buenos Aires.

Academic Year: April to November (April-June; May-August; September-November).

Admission Requirements: Secondary school certificate (bachillerato) or equivalent, and entrance examination.

Fees: None.

Language of Instruction: Spanish.

Degrees and Diplomas: Teaching qualification, 3 yrs or 7-10 yrs for a particular instrument.

Academic Staff: c. – (30).

Student Enrolment: c. 160.

145 **CONSERVATORIO DE MÚSICA DE CHIVILCOY**
Calle Frias 37, Chivilcoy (Buenos Aires)

Music

Degrees and Diplomas: Professional titles.

146 **CONSERVATORIO DE MÚSICA DE LA PLATA**
Calle 7 No. 1141, La Plata (Buenos Aires)

Music

Degrees and Diplomas: Professional titles.

147 **CONSERVATORIO DE MÚSICA**
Dorrego 2071, Mar del Plata (Buenos Aires)

Music

Degrees and Diplomas: Professional titles.

148 **INSTITUTO CUYANO DE CULTURA MUSICAL**
Boulogne-sur-Mer 1685, Mendoza

Music

Degrees and Diplomas: Professional title, 7 yrs.

149 **CONSERVATORIO MUNICIPAL 'MANUEL AGUIRRE'**
Rauch y Salta, Morón (Buenos Aires)

Music
Degrees and Diplomas: Professional titles.

150 **ESCUELA DE MÚSICA**
Avenida 9 de Julio, Resistencia (Chaco)

Music
Degrees and Diplomas: Professional titles, 7-10 yrs.

151 **INSTITUTO DE SERVICIO SOCIAL DE AVELLANEDA**
French 146, Avellaneda (Buenos Aires)

Social Service
Degrees and Diplomas: Professional title, 3 yrs.

152 **ESCUELA DE SERVICIO SOCIAL**
Joaquín V. González 230, La Rioja

Social Service
Degrees and Diplomas: Professional title, 3 yrs.

153 **ESCUELA DE SERVICIO SOCIAL**
Julio A. Roca 343, Mendoza

Social Service
Degrees and Diplomas: Professional title, 4 yrs.

154 **INSTITUTO SUPERIOR DE SERVICIO SOCIAL**
Don Bosco 492, Gral. Roca, Río Negro

Social Service
Degrees and Diplomas: Professional title, 4 yrs.

155 **ESCUELA DE SERVICIO SOCIAL DE ROSARIO**
Córdoba 1770, Rosario (Santa Fe)

Social Service
Degrees and Diplomas: Professional title, 3-4 yrs.

156 **ESCUELA DE SERVICIO SOCIAL**
San Martin 2337, Santa Fe
Telephone: 25404

Social Service
Founded 1942. Under the jurisdiction of the Ministry of Health.
Academic Year: March to November (March-July; August-November).
Admission Requirements: Secondary school certificate (bachillerato).
Language of Instruction: Spanish.
Degrees and Diplomas: Professional titles, 4 yrs.
Library: c. 2000 vols.
Academic Staff: c. 30.
Student Enrolment: c. 90 (Women).

Teacher Training

157 **INSTITUTO NACIONAL DE ENSEÑANZA SUPERIOR NO. 1**
Córdoba 1951, Buenos Aires

Teacher Training

158 **INSTITUTO NACIONAL DE ENSEÑANZA SUPERIOR NO. 2**
Gral Urquiza 269, Buenos Aires

Teacher Training

159 **INSTITUTO NACIONAL DE ENSEÑANZA SUPERIOR'DR. JOAQUÍN V. GONZÁLEZ'**
Rivadavia 3577, (San Juan)

Teacher Training

160 **INSTITUTO NACIONAL DE ENSEÑANZA SUPERIOR'S. ECCLESTON'**
Figueroa Alcorta y Dorrego, Buenos Aires

Teacher Training

161 **INSTITUTO NACIONAL DE ENSEÑANZA SUPERIOR EN L.V. 'J.R. FERNÁNDEZ'**
Carlos Pellegrini 1455, Buenos Aires

Teacher Training

162 **INSTITUTO NACIONAL DE ENSEÑANZA SUPERIOR 'J.B. JUSTO'**
Lascana 3840, Buenos Aires 1417
Telephone: 566-9247
Rector: Miguel A. Gómez Wrow
Secretario General: María Luisa Segura

Teacher Training
Founded 1986.
Academic Year: April to November.
Admission Requirements: Secondary school certificate (bachillerato).
Language of Instruction: Spanish.
Degrees and Diplomas: Professional titles, 2-4 yrs.
Library: 3000 vols.
Academic Staff, 1990: – (48).
Student Enrolment, 1990:

	Men	Women	Total
Of the country	15	115	130

163 **INSTITUTO NACIONAL DE ENSEÑANZA SUPERIOR DE MORENO**
Ruta 7, Km.35, Moreno 7

Teacher Training

164 **INSTITUTO NACIONAL DE ENSEÑANZA SUPERIOR DE AZUL**
25 de Mayo 783, Azul (Buenos Aires)

Teacher Training

165 **INSTITUTO NACIONAL DE ENSEÑANZA SUPERIOR 'ROBERTO THEMIS SPERONI'**
Nirvana Esq. 23, City Bell 1896
Telephone: (21) 80-1263
Director: Velia J. Bianco
Secretario General: María Esperanza Montes

Teacher Training (Kindergarten and Primary Levels)
Founded 1960 as private institution. Became State in1984.
Academic Year: March to November.
Admission Requirements: Secondary school certificate (bachillerato).
Fees: None.
Language of Instruction: Spanish.
Degrees and Diplomas: Title of Profesor, 3 yrs.
Academic Staff, 1990: – (60).
Student Enrolment, 1990:

	Men	Women	Total
Of the country	352	325	677

166 **INSTITUTO NACIONAL DE ENSEÑANZA SUPERIOR DE LINCOLN**
Av. Leandro Alem 1950, Lincoln (Buenos Aires)

Teacher Training

167 **INSTITUTO NACIONAL DE ENSEÑANZA SUPERIOR DE PEHUAJÓ**
José Hernandez 250, Pehuajó, (Buenos Aires)

Teacher Training

168 **INSTITUTO NACIONAL DE ENSEÑANZA SUPERIOR DE PERGAMINO**
Av. Colón 725, Pergamino (Buenos Aires)

Teacher Training

169 **INSTITUTO NACIONAL DE ENSEÑANZA SUPERIOR DE SAN NICOLÁS**
Plaza 23 de Noviembre, San Nicolás (Buenos Aires)
Teacher Training

170 **INSTITUTO NACIONAL DE ENSEÑANZA SUPERIOR DE BELL VILLE**
25 de may 135, Bell Ville (Córdoba)
Teacher Training

171 **INSTITUTO NACIONAL DE ENSEÑANZA SUPERIOR DE CAPILLA DEL MONTE**
Hipólito Yrigoyen 450, Capilla del Monte (Córdoba)
Teacher Training

172 **INSTITUTO NACIONAL DE ENSEÑANZA SUPERIOR DE CÓRDOBA**
Av. Colón 951, Córdoba
Teacher Training

173 **INSTITUTO NACIONAL DE ENSEÑANZA SUPERIOR DE CRUZ DE EJE**
Sarmiento 1155, Cruz del Eje (Córdoba)
Teacher Training

174 **INSTITUTO NACIONAL DE ENSEÑANZA SUPERIOR DE LABOULAYE**
Independencia 4475, Laboulaye (Córdoba)
Teacher Training

175 **INSTITUTO NACIONAL DE ENSEÑANZA SUPERIOR DEL CENTRO DE LA REPÚBLICA**
Santiago del Estero 618, 5900 Villa María (Córdoba)
Telephone: (535) 21358
Rector: Angel Diego Márquez
Secretario Académico: Ricardo Martínez

Teacher Training (Tertiary Level)
I. of Physics
Co-ordinator: Leonardo Monti
I. of Mathematics
Co-ordinator: Concencio Coccioli
I. of Human Sciences
Co-ordinator: Hans Heiner Rudolph
I. of Biology
Co-ordinator: Silvia Moyano
I. of Chemistry
Co-ordinator: Luis Alvarez
S. of Education
Head: Ana Monti; *staff* 14
S. of Technology
Head: Rómulo Ballesteros; *staff* 43
S. of Agriculture
Head: Otto Wester; *staff* 21
S. of Health Sciences
Head (Acting): Angel Diego Márquez; *staff* 16
S. of Legal and Administrative Sciences:
Head: Carlos Seggiaro; *staff* 18
S. of Applied Social Sciences
Head: Bernardino Calvo; *staff* 67

Founded 1986. Governing bodies: the Asamblea Académica; the Consejo Superior.
Academic Year: April to November (April-June; August-November).
Admission Requirements: Secondary school certificate (bachillerato).
Fees: None.
Language of Instruction: Spanish.
Degrees and Diplomas: Professional titles, 3-4 yrs. Licenciado in Education, by thesis, 4 yrs.
Library: 445 volumes.
Publication: Research papers.
Student Enrolment, 1989: c. 440.

176 **INSTITUTO NACIONAL DE ENSEÑANZA SUPERIOR DE GUALEGUAY-MELITÓ**
Juárez 25, Gualeguay (Entre Rios)
Teacher Training

177 **INSTITUTO NACIONAL DE ENSEÑANZA SUPERIOR DE CONCEPCIÓN DEL URUGUAY**
Jordana 50, Concepción del Uruguay (Entre Rios)
Teacher Training

178 **INSTITUTO NACIONAL DE ENSEÑANZA SUPERIOR DE GUALEGUAYCHÚ 'MARÍA INÉS ELIZALDE'**
Gervasio Méndez 676, Gualeguaychú (Entre Rios)
Telephone: 0446-6448
Rector: Luis Alberto Murúa

Teacher Training
Founded 1988.
Academic Year: April to November.
Admission Requirements: Secondary school certificate (bachillerato).
Language of Instruction: Spanish.
Degrees and Diplomas: Teaching qualifications in various fields, 4 yrs.
Library: 6000 vols.
Academic Staff, 1990: 42.
Student Enrolment, 1990: 230.

179 **INSTITUTO NACIONALD ENSEÑANZA SUPERIOR DE PARANÁ**
Corrientes y Urquiza, Paraná (Entre Rios)
Teacher Training

180 **INSTITUTO NACIONAL DE ENSEÑANZA SUPERIOR DE VILLA HERNANDARIAS**
Eva Perón 220, Villa Hernandarias (Entre Rios)
Teacher Training

181 **INSTITUTO NACIONAL DE ENSEÑANZA SUPERIOR DE SAN SALVADOR DE JUJUY**
San Martin 750, San Salvador de Jujuy (Jujuy)
Teacher Training

182 **INSTITUTO NACIONAL DE ENSEÑANZA SUPERIOR DE LA RIOJA**
Pelagio B. Luna 749, 5300 La Rioja
Telephone: 0822-27803
Rector: Dominga Rombolá de Ortiz
Secretario: Blanca Lobato

Teacher Training (Secondary Level)
Founded 1960, acquired present status and title 1988.
Academic Year: April to December (April-July; August-November).
Admission Requirements: Secondary school certificate (bachillerato).
Language of Instruction: Spanish.
Degrees and Diplomas: Teaching qualification, secondary level, 4 yrs.
Library: c. 500 vols.
Academic Staff, 1990: – (90).
Student Enrolment, 1990: 400.

183 **INSTITUTO NACIONAL DE ENSEÑANZA SUPERIOR DE SAN RAFAEL**
Barcala 14, San Rafael (Mendoza)
Teacher Training

184 **INSTITUTO NACIONAL DE ENSEÑANZA SUPERIOR DE TUPUNGATO**
Alte. Brown s/n, Tupungato (Mendoza)
Teacher Training

185 **INSTITUTO NACIONAL DE ENSEÑANZA SUPERIOR DE EUGENIO BUSTOS**
Arenales y Belgrano, 5569 Eugenio Bustos (Mendoza)
Telephone: (622) 51108
Rector: Lucinda Ana María Gómez

Teacher Training (Pre-School)
Administrative Systems

Founded 1988.
Academic Year: April to October.
Admission Requirements: Secondary school certificate (bachillerato).
Fees: None.
Language of Instruction: Spanish.
Degrees and Diplomas: Professional titles, 2-3 yrs.
Academic Staff, 1990: c. 20.
Student Enrolment, 1990:

	Men	Women	Total
Of the country	34	131	165

186 **INSTITUTO NACIONAL DE ENSEÑANZA SUPERIOR DE SAN JUAN**
Av. Alem 31 Sur, an Juan

Teacher Training

187 **INSTITUTO NACIONAL DE ENSEÑANZA SUPERIOR DE SAN LUIS**
Rivadavia 774, San Luis

Teacher Training

188 **INSTITUTO NACIONAL DE ENSEÑANZA SUPERIOR DE ROSARIO**
Corrientes 1191, Rosario (Santa Fe)

Teacher Training

189 **INSTITUTO NACIONAL DE ENSEÑANZA SUPERIOR 'GALILEO GALILEI' DE ROSARIO**
Bv. Oroño 1145, Rosario (Santa Fe)

Teacher Training

190 **INSTITUTO NACIONAL DE ENSEÑANZA SUPERIOR DE SANTIAGO DEL ESTERO**
Independencia 751, Santiago del Estero

Teacher Training

191 **INSTITUTO NACIONAL DE ENSEÑANZA SUPERIOR DE SAN MIGUEL DE TUCUMÁN**
Muñecas 219, San Miguel de Tucumán

Teacher Training

192 **INSTITUTO NACIONAL DE ENSEÑANZA SUPERIOR DE USHUAIA**
12 de Octubre 383, Ushuaia (Tierra del Fuego)

Teacher Training

193 **INSTITUTO DE PERFECCIONAMIENTO DOCENTE**
Rivadavia 880, Azul (Buenos Aires)

Teacher Training

194 **INSTITUTO DE PERFECCIONAMIENTO DOCENTE**
Vieytes 51, Bahía Blanca (Buenos Aires)

Teacher Training (Differential and Pre-School)
Degrees and Diplomas: Professional qualifications, 2-3 yrs.

195 **INSTITUTO DE PERFECCIONAMIENTO DOCENTE**
9 de Julio 1158, Campana (Buenos Aires)

Teacher Training (Pre-School)
Degrees and Diplomas: Professional qualifications, 2 yrs.

196 **INSTITUTO DE PERFECCIONAMIENTO DOCENTE**
General Paz 8, Chivilcoy (Buenos Aires)

Teacher Training (Pre-School)
Degrees and Diplomas: Professional qualifications, 2 yrs.

197 **INSTITUTO DE PERFECCIONAMIENTO DOCENTE**
Calle 12 entre 67 y 68, La Plata (Buenos Aires)

Teacher Training (Pre-School)
Degrees and Diplomas: Professional qualifications, 2 yrs.

198 **INSTITUTO DE PERFECCIONAMIENTO DOCENTE**
25 de Mayo 254, Lincoln (Buenos Aires)

Teacher Training (Pre-School)
Degrees and Diplomas: Professional qualifications, 2 yrs.

199 **INSTITUTO DE PERFECCIONAMIENTO DOCENTE**
Garibaldi 253, Lomas de Zamora (Buenos Aires)

Teacher Training (Differential)
Degrees and Diplomas: Professional qualifications, 3 yrs.

200 **INSTITUTO DE PERFECCIONAMIENTO DOCENTE**
Calle 24 No. 338, Mercedes (Buenos Aires)

Teacher Training (Educational Psychology)
Degrees and Diplomas: Professional qualifications, 3 yrs.

201 **INSTITUTO DE PERFECCIONAMIENTO DOCENTE**
Gutiérrez 515, Pehuajó (Buenos Aires)

Teacher Training (Pre-School)
Degrees and Diplomas: Professional qualifications, 2 yrs.

202 **INSTITUTO DE PERFECCIONAMIENTO DOCENTE**
11 de Septiembre 812, Pergamino (Buenos Aires)

Teacher Training (Pre-School and Psychology)
Degrees and Diplomas: Professional qualifications, 2-3 yrs.

203 **INSTITUTO DE PERFECCIONAMIENTO DOCENTE**
Belgrano y Almafuerte, Saladillo (Buenos Aires)

Teacher Training (Pre-School)
Degrees and Diplomas: Professional qualifications, 2 yrs.

204 **INSTITUTO NACIONAL DE EDUCACIÓN FÍSICA 'DR. ENRIQUE ROMERO BREST'**
Avenida Libertador General San Martín 7101, Buenos Aires

Physical Education
Degrees and Diplomas: Titles of–Maestro Normal, kindergarten level, 1 yr; Profesora Nacional, secondary level, 3 yrs.

205 **INSTITUTO NACIONAL DE EDUCACIÓN FÍSICA 'GENERAL BELGRANO'**
Avenida Libertador 1800, 1646 San Fernando (Buenos Aires)
Rector: Juan Carlos Cutrera (1982-90)
Sub-Director: Martha Barbaccia

Physical Education

Founded 1906. A State institution.
Academic Year: March to December (April-June; July-November).
Admission Requirements: Secondary school certificate (bachillerato).
Fees: None.
Language of Instruction: Spanish.
Degrees and Diplomas: Titles of–Maestro Nacional, 3 yrs; Profesor Nacional, 4 yrs.
Academic Staff, 1986-87: – (223)
Student Enrolment, 1986-87:

	Men	Women	Total
Of the country	407	698	1105

206 **INSTITUTO DEL PROFESORADO EN EDUCACIÓN FÍSICA**
Ministerio de Educación y Cultura, Poeta Lugones 447, Córdoba

Physical Education
Degrees and Diplomas: Title of Profesor, 3 yrs.

207 **INSTITUTO NACIONAL DE EDUCACIÓN FÍSICA DE MENDOZA**
Belgrano 441, Mendoza
Physical Education
Degrees and Diplomas: Title of Profesor Nacional, 3 yrs.

208 **INSTITUTO SUPERIOR DEL PROFESORADO EN EDUCACIÓN FÍSICA**
Chacabuco 1365, Rosario (Santa Fe)
Physical Education
Degrees and Diplomas: Title of Profesor, 3 yrs.

209 **INSTITUTO NACIONAL DE EDUCACIÓN FÍSICA DE SANTA FE**
San Jerónimo 3139, Santa Fe
Physical Education
Degrees and Diplomas: Title of–Maestro Normal, kindergarten level, 1 yrs; Profesor Nacional, 3 yrs.

210 **INSTITUTO NACIONAL DEL PROFESORADO SECUNDARIO**
Boulevard Belgrano y Junín, Catamarca
Teacher Training
Founded 1943.
Academic Year: March to December.
Admission Requirements: Secondary school certificate (bachillerato) or elementary teaching certificate or diploma of a National Schoolof Commerce, or recognized foreign equivalent.
Degrees and Diplomas: Title of Profesor, secondary level, in various fields, 4 yrs.

211 **INSTITUTO SUPERIOR DEL PROFESORADO**
Avenida de Mayo 1396, Buenos Aires
Teacher Training

212 **INSTITUTO SUPERIOR DEL PROFESORADO**
San Martín 1152, Corondo (Santa Fe)
Teacher Training (Secondary Level)
Academic Year: March to November (March-July; August-November).
Admission Requirements: Secondary school certificate (bachillerato) and entrance examination.
Language of Instruction: Spanish.
Degrees and Diplomas: Teaching qualifications, in various fields, 4 yrs.
Academic Staff: c. 70.

213 **INSTITUTO SUPERIOR DEL PROFESORADO 'JOSÉ MANUEL ESTRADA'**
Mariano 1, Loza 824, Goya (Corrientes)
Teacher Training (Secondary Level)
Degrees and Diplomas: Teaching qualifications, in various fields, 4 yrs.

214 **INSTITUTO SUPERIOR DEL PROFESORADO (IDIOMAS E LETRAS)**
Mitre 929, Gral. Roca (Río Negro)
Teacher Training (Secondary Level)
Degrees and Diplomas: Teaching qualifications, in various fields, 4 yrs.

215 **INSTITUTO SUPERIOR DEL PROFESORADO DE MISIONES**
Tucumán 448, Posadas (Misiones)
Teaching Training (Secondary Level)
Degrees and Diplomas: Teaching qualifications, in various fields, 4 yrs.

216 **INSTITUTO SUPERIOR DEL PROFESORADO**
Alvear y Ludueña, Casilla de Correo 35, Reconquista (Santa Fe)
Teacher Training (Secondary Level)
Degrees and Diplomas: Teaching qualifications, in various fields, 4 yrs.

217 **INSTITUTO SUPERIOR DEL PROFESORADO 'BIBLIOTECA D.F. SARMIENTO' (CIENCIAS EXACTAS)**
San Carlos de Bariloche (Río Negro)
Teacher Training (Secondary Level)
Degrees and Diplomas: Teaching qualifications, in various fields, 4 yrs.

218 **INSTITUTO NACIONAL DEL PROFESORADO SECUNDARIO 'D.F. SARMIENTO'**
Santiago del Estero 48 San Juan (Sur)
Teacher Training
Degrees and Diplomas: Title of Profesor, secondary level, in various fields, 4 yrs.

219 **INSTITUTO SUPERIOR DEL PROFESORADO SECUNDARIO**
Avenida Estrugamous 250, Venado Tuerto (Santa Fe)
Teacher Training (Secondary Level)
Degrees and Diplomas: Teaching qualifications, in various fields, 4 yrs.

220 **INSTITUTO SUPERIOR DEL PROFESORADO (HUMANIDADES)**
San Martín 246, Viedma (Río Negro)
Teacher Training (Secondary Level)
Degrees and Diplomas: Teaching qualifications, in various fields, 4 yrs.

221 **INSTITUTO SUPERIOR DEL PROFESORADO DE VILLA CONSTITUCIÓN**
Gral. López 1331, Villa Constitución (Santa Fe)
Teacher Training (Secondary Level)
Degrees and Diplomas: Teaching qualifications, in various fields, 4 yrs.

222 **INSTITUTO NACIONAL DE ENSEÑANZA SUPERIOR DE AZUL**
25 de Mayo 783, Azul (Buenos Aires)
Teacher Training

223 **FACULTAD DE ANTROPOLOGÍA ESCOLAR**
Martínez de Rosas 829, Ciudad de Mendoza
Teacher Training (including Differential Education and Education of the Handicapped)
Education Psychology
Founded 1963, became faculty 1970. Responsible to the provincial government. The institution is designed to provide courses not normally given in teacher training colleges and to offer training for educational administrators.
Academic Year: April to December (April-June; August-December).
Admission Requirements: Secondary school certificate (bachillerato).
Language of Instruction: Spanish.
Degrees and Diplomas: Licenciado in various fields of general and specialized education, and in Psychology, 4-5 yrs. Teaching qualifications.
Academic Staff: c. 100.
Student Enrolment: c. 650.

224 **ESCUELA NORMAL DE MAESTROS NO. 6 Y PROFESORADO DE ECONOMÍA DOMÉSTICA**
Güemes 3859, Buenos Aires
Telephone: 824-0383
Director: Juan Carlos Civile (1986-)
Teacher Training (Domestic Science)
Founded 1909 as primary and secondary school. Acquired present status 1926. A State institution.
Academic Year: April to November.
Admission Requirements: Secondary school certificate (bachillerato).
Fees: None.
Language of Instruction: Spanish.
Degrees and Diplomas: Title of Profesora, 3 yrs.
Academic Staff, 1986-87: – (28).
Student Enrolment, 1986-87: 200 (Women).

225 **INSTITUTO SUPERIOR DE EDUCACIÓN DE LA COMUNIDAD DE LA CAPITAL FEDERAL**
Rodríguez Peña 744, Buenos Aires
Education
Degrees and Diplomas: Professional title in Community Education, 3 yrs.

226 **INSTITUTO DE EDUCACIÓN RURAL**
Casilla de Correo 77, Tandil (Buenos Aires)
Teacher Training (Rural Education)
Degrees and Diplomas: Title of Maestro especializado en Educación rural, 3 yrs.

227 **ESCUELA NORMAL DE MAESTROS PARA CIEGPOS**
Hipólito Yrigoyen 2850, Buenos Aires
Teacher Training (for the Blind)
Degrees and Diplomas: Title of Maestro Normal Nacional para Ciegos, 3 yrs.

228 **INSTITUTO SUPERIOR DE FORMACIÓN DOCENTE NO. 9**
Calle 2 No. 639, 1900 La Plata (Buenos Aires)
Telephone: 21-5393
Director: Armando Domingo Delucchi
Teacher Training (including Differential Education and Education for the Handicapped)
Founded 1960. A State institution under the jurisdiction of the Ministry of Education of the Province of Buenos Aires.
Academic Year: April to November.
Admission Requirements: Secondary school certificate (bachillerato) or equivalent.
Language of Instruction: Spanish.
Degrees and Diplomas: Professional qualifications, 2-3 yrs.
Library: 1400 vols.
Academic Staff, 1990: c. 270.
Student Enrolment, 1990:

	Men	Women	Total
Of the country	143	1489	1632

229 **INSTITUTO EXPERIMENTAL DEL MOGÓLICO**
Carlos Calvo 3176, Buenos Aires
Teacher Training (Mongoloids)
Degrees and Diplomas: Title of Maestro, 1-3 yrs.

230 **INSTITUTO DE PSICOPEDAGOGÍA Y EDUCACIÓN ESPECIAL 'DR. DOMINGO CABRED'**
La Rioja 556, 5000 Córdoba
Telephone: (51) 221317
Rector: Perla Ferrer de Diaz
Secretaria: Josefina Belda
Teacher Training (for the Handicapped)
Founded 1960.
Academic Year: April to November.
Fees: None.
Language of Instruction: Spanish.
Degrees and Diplomas: Professional titles, 4-5 yrs.
Library: 3500 vols.
Academic Staff, 1990: 3 (90).

Student Enrolment, 1990:	Men	Women	Total
Of the country	41	1290	1331
Of other countries	–	5	5
Total	41	1295	1336

231 **INSTITUTO NACIONAL DE SORDOMUDOS 'PROF. BARTOLOMÉ AYROLO'**
Avenida Lincoln 4325, Buenos Aires
Teacher Training (for the Deaf and Dumb)
Degrees and Diplomas: Title of Profesor Normal, 3 yrs.

232 **INSTITUTO NACIONAL DE NIÑAS SORDOMUDAS**
Austria 2561-93, Buenos Aires
Teacher Training (for Deaf and Dumb Girls)
Degrees and Diplomas: Title of Profesora Normal, 3 yrs.

AUSTRIA

Universities

233 ***KARL-FRANZENS-UNIVERSITÄT GRAZ**

Karl Franzens University of Graz
Universitätsplatz 3, 8010 Graz
Telex: 31 1662 UBGRZ
Telephone: (316) 380-0
Fax: (316) 382130
Rektor: Thomas Kenner (1989-91)
Universitätsdirektor: Michel Suppanz

F. of Catholic Theology
Dean: Karl Woschitz; *staff* 49 (9)
F. of Law
Dean: Bernd-Christian Funk; *staff* 131 (9)
F. of Social Sciences and Economics
Dean: Lutz Beinsen; *staff* 91 (85)
F. of Medicine
Dean: Helmut Tritthart; *staff* 577 (82)
F. of Human Sciences (including Liberal Arts and Education)
Dean: Reinhard Kamitz; *staff* 217 (369)
F. of Natural Sciences (including Pharmacy)
Dean: Helmut Huber; *staff* 278 (70)
Data Processing Ce.
Head: Norbert Pucker; *staff* 9
I. for Fundamental History Research
Director: Reinhard Härtel; *staff* 2
Also 13 University clinics and language preparatory courses for foreign students.

Founded 1585/86 by the Society of Jesus. Following suppression of the Society, university status withdrawn in 1782. Re-established as Karl-Franzens Universität 1827. The University functions under the jurisdiction of the Ministry of Science and Research. Governing body: the Akademischer Senat.

Arrangements for co-operation with: University of Zagreb; University of Trieste; University of Leipzig; University of Minnesota at Minneapolis; Universty of Wuhan.

Academic Year: October to June (October-January; March-June).

Admission Requirements: Secondary school certificate (Reifezeugnis) or recognized equivalent.

Fees (Schillings): 4000 per semester for foreign students.

Language of Instruction: German.

Degrees and Diplomas: Magister-phil.; -theol.; -rer.nat., natural sciences; -rer.soc.oec., social sciences and economics; -iur, law, 4-5 yrs. Doctorates–Dr.theol., theology; Dr.iur., law; Dr.rer.soc.oec.; Dr.phil.; Dr.rer.nat., a further 1-2yrs. Dr.med., 6 yrs.

Libraries: Central Library, *c.* 1,100,000 vols; departmental andfaculty libraries, 1,100,000.

Special Facilities (Museums, etc.): Observatory; Solar Observatory Kanzelhöhe (Carinthia); Botanical Garden, Graz.

Academic Staff, 1989:

	Full-time	Part-time
Ordentliche Universitätsprofessoren	138	–
Ausserordentliche Universitätsprofessoren	77	–
Honorarporofessoren	29	–
Universitätsdozenten	193	–
Universitätsdozenten Assistenten	223	–
Universitätsassistenten	381	–
Vertrags-, Studienassistenten, Demonstratoren	191	–
Lektoren, Instruktoren, Tutoren	–	601
Total	1232	601

Student Enrolment, 1989:

	Men	Women	Total
Of the country	11,474	13,181	24,655
Of other countries	392	393	785
Total	11,866	13,574	25,440

234 **LEOPOLD-FRANZENS UNIVERSITÄT INNSBRUCK**

University of Innsbruck
Innrain 52, 6020 Innsbruck
Telephone: 33601
Rektor: Rainer Sprung (1987-89)

F. of Catholic Theology
F. of Law
F. of Social Sciences and Economics (including Political Science)
F. of Medicine (including Pharmacy)
F. of Human Sciences (including Physical Education)
F. of Natural Sciences
F. of Civil Engineering and Architecture
I. for Alpine Research (Obergurgl/Ötztal)
I. for Interpretation
America I.
Electron Microscopy I.
I. of Physical Education
Also *c.* 40 institutes of the faculties.

Founded 1669. The university functions under the jurisdiction of the Federal Ministry of Science and Research. Governing body: the Akademischer Senat.

Academic Year: October to July (October-February; March-July).

Admission Requirements: Secondary school certificate (Reifezeugnis) or foreign equivalent.

Language of Instruction: German.

Degrees and Diplomas: Diplom–Dolmetscher, interpreting, 7 sem; -Volkswirt, economics; -Ingenieur, 10 sem; Magister der Pharmazie, pharmacy, 6 sem; Dr.jur., law; Dr.rer.pol., political science; Dr.rer.oec., economics; Dr.phil., philosophy andnatural sciences, 8 sem; Dr.med., medicine, 10 sem; Dr.theol., theology, 12 sem.

Library: *c.* 875,000 vols.

Publication: Nachrichtenblatt der Universität Innsbruck (annually).

Academic Staff: *c.* 1000.

Student Enrolment: *c.* 19,000.

235 **UNIVERSITÄT SALZBURG**

University of Salzburg
Residenzplatz 1, 5010 Salzburg
Telephone: (0662) 8044-0
Rektor: Theodor Wolfram Köhler (1989-91)
Universitätsdirektor: Raimund Spruzina

F. of Theology
Dean: Albert Biesinger; *staff* 95 (3)
F. of Law
Dean: Alfred Kryrer; *staff* 261 (17)
F. of Philosophy (Arts)
Dean: Edgar Morscher; *staff* 641 (27)
F. of Natural Sciences
Dean: Georg Amthauer; *staff* 498 (26)
International Research Ce.
President: Franz Martin Schmölz
Interuniversity Research I. for Distance Education
Also *c.* 50 institutes of the different faculties.

Founded 1617 as school by Archbishop Paris Lodron, became university 1622, dissolved 1810. Re-established 1962. The university is an autonomous institution financed by the Federal Ministry of Science and Research. Governing body: the Academic Senate, comprising 18 members. Residential facilities for students in Studentenheime.

Arrangements for co-operation with: Jagiellonian University, Cracow; University of Rheims; University of Perugia; Bowling Green State University; University of the Pacific; the Universities of: Bergen; Trieste; Vilnius; Passau; Amiens; Warsaw; California at Irvine; Maine; León; Vilnius.

Academic Year: October to June (October-January; March-June).

Admission Requirements: Secondary school certificate (Reifezeugnis), or recognized foreign equivalent.

Fees (Schillings): 4000 per semester for foreign students.

Language of Instruction: German.

Degrees and Diplomas: Magister-Mag.theol.; Mag.phil; Mag.rer.nat., natural sciences; Mag.phil.fac.theol; Mag.jur., law, 5 yrs. Doctorates, Dr., 5-7 yrs. Lehramtsprüfung, teaching qualification, secondary level, 4 yrs.

Libraries: University Library, 600,000 vols; libraries of the institutes, 1m.

Publications: Universitätsreden; Jahrbuch (biennially).

Press or Publishing House: Universitätsdirektion.

Academic Staff, 1989-90:

Rank	Full-time
Ordentliche Universitätsprofessoren	88
Ausserordentliche Universitätsprofessoren	46
Emeritierte Universitätsprofessoren	23
Honorarprofessoren	17
Universitätsdozenten	213
Personen mit der Lehrbefugnis	8
Universitätsassistenten	405
Vertragsassistenten	155
Studienassistenten	43
Tutoren	5
Sonstige Mitarbeiter im Wissenschaftlichen Betrieb	76
Lehrbeauftragte (nicht in eines Dienstverhältnis)	259
Total	1338

Student Enrolment, 1989-90:

	Men	Women	Total
Of the country	6432	7580	14,012
Of other countries	965	1115	2080
Total	7397	8695	16,092*

*Also 858 external students.

236 ***UNIVERSITÄT WIEN**

University of Vienna

Dr. Karl Lueger-Ring 1, 1014 Wien

Telex: 115619

Telephone: (0222) 4300-0

Rektor: Wilhelm Holczabek (1985-)

Universitätsdirektor: Franz Skacel

F. of Catholic Theology
Dean: Wolfgang Langer; *staff* 70

F. of Protestant Theology
Dean: Hans-Christoph Schmidt-Lauber; *staff* 25

F. of Law
Dean: Theo Öhlinger; *staff* 154

F. of Social Sciences and Economics
Dean: Leopold Schmetterer; *staff* 195

F. of Medicine
Dean: Arnulf Fritsch *staff* 1893

F. of Basic and General Sciences
Dean: Karl Wernhart; *staff* 370

F. of Human Sciences
Dean: Gerhard Oberhammer; *staff* 794

F. of Mathematics and Natural Sciences (including Pharmacy)
Dean: Otmar Preining; *staff* 686

Founded 1365, reorganized 1377, 1384 and 1850. Under Austrian law the administration of the university is in part the responsibility of the Federal Ministry of Science and Research and in part the autonomous responsibility of the Academic Senate. Governing body: the Akademischer Senat.

Arrangements for co-operation with the Universities of: Budapest; Warsaw; Trieste; Berlin (Humboldt).

Academic Year: October to September (October-February; March-September).

Admission Requirements: Secondary school certificate (Reifezeugnis) or recognized foreign qualifications.

Fees (Schillings): 4000 per semester for foreign students.

Language of Instruction: German.

Degrees and Diplomas: Diplom Dolmetscher, interpreting, 4 yrs. Magister der–Pharmazie; Rechtswissenschaften, law; Katholische Theologie; Sozial-und Wirtschaftswissenschaften, social sciences and economics; Philosophie; Naturwissenschaften, natural sciences, 4-5 yrs. Magister artium. Doktor der Rechte, Dr.jur., law; Doktor der Philosophie, Dr.phil.; Doktor der Sozial-und Wirtschaftswissenschaften, social science and economics; Pharmazie; Naturwissen schaften, 4-6 yrs; Doktor der Katholischen Theologie, Dr.theol., 5-6 yrs; Doktor der Medizin, Dr.med., medicine, 5-7 yrs; Doktor der Evangelischen Theologie, Dr.theol., 6-7 yrs. Lehramtsprüfung, teaching qualification, secondary level, 5-6 yrs.

Libraries: University Library, *c.* 4,066,020 vols; libraries of the faculties.

Special Facilities (Museums, etc.): Institute of Medical History Museum.

Academic Staff, 1986-87:

Rank	Full-time
Ordentliche Professoren/ Ausserordentliche Professoren	394
Dozenten/Assistenten	1307
Studienassistenten/Demonstratoren	208
Wissenschaftliche Beamte	214
Lektoren	578
Gastprofessoren/Gastdozenten	28
Total	2729

Student Enrolment, 1986-87:

	Men	Women	Total
Of the country	35,700	42,000	77,700
Of other countries	4100	3600	7700
Total	39,800	45,600	85,400

237 **TECHNISCHE UNIVERSITÄT GRAZ**

Technical University of Graz

Rechbauerstrasse 12, 8010 Graz

Telex: 311221

Telephone: (316) 873-0

Fax: (316) 827679

Rektor: Günther Schelling (1989-91)

Universitätsdireiktor: Fritz Auer

F. of Architecture
Dean: Harald Egger; *staff* 63 (6)

F. of Civil Engineering
Dean: Peter Klement; *staff* 210 (20)

F. of Mechanical Engineering
Dean: Josef Wohinz; *staff* 123 (15)

F. of Electrical Engineering
Dean: Kurt Richter; *staff* 167 (15)

F. of Technical-Natural Sciences
Dean: Hartmunt Kahlert; *staff* 253 (28)

Computer and Information Services Ce.
Head: Rudolf Zuheir Domiaty

Electron Microscopy and Fine Structure Research I.
Head: Wolfgang Geymayer

Alternative Energy and Biomass Research I.
Head: August Raggam

Also 65 institutes and centres of the faculties.

Founded 1811, acquired university rank and new statute 1865/66 and right to award doctorate 1901. Reorganized 1955. Limited autonomy. Under Austrian Law the university is responsible to the Federal Ministry of Science and Research and is financed by the State. Governing body: the Gesamtkollegium. Some residential facilities for students.

Academic Year: October to June (October-February; March-June).

Admission Requirements: Secondary school certificate (Reifezeugnis) or recognized equivalent.

Fees (Schillings): 4000 per semester for foreign students.

Language of Instruction: German.

Degrees and Diplomas: Diplom-Ingenieur, Dipl.-Ing., 5 yrs; Magister rer.nat., natural sciences; Doktor der technischen Wissenschaften, Dr.Techn., a further 2 yrs.

Library: *c.* 90,000 vols.

Academic Staff, 1989-90:

Rank	Full-time	Part-time
Ordentliche Professoren	71	–
Ausserordentliche Professoren	32	–
Universitätsassistenten	356	–
Vertragsassistenten	51	68
Studienassistenten	1	52
Beamte u. Vertragsbedienstete des Wissenschaftlichen Dienstes	49	–
Bundeslehrer	9	–
Total	569	120

Student Enrolment, 1989-90:

	Men	Women	Total
Of the country	9125	1263	10,388
Of other countries	622	87	709
Total	9747	1350	11,097

238 **MONTANUNIVERSITÄT LEOBEN**

University of Mining and Metallurgy
Franz-Josef-Strasse 18, 8700 Leoben
Telex: 033322 MHBLEO
Telephone: (3842) 42555
Fax: (3842) 42555-308
Rektor: Franz Jeglitsch (1987-91)
Sekretär General: Adalbert Neuberg

Mining Engineering
Mine Surveying
Metallurgy
Petroleum Engineering
Refractories and Ceramics Engineering
Mining and Metallurgy Machinery
Plastics Technology
Materials Sciences
Mining Geology

Founded 1840 as a mining institute, achieved university status 1904, and acquired present title by law 1975. The university is an autonomous institution responsible to the Federal Ministry of Science and Research. Residential facilities for students.

Arrangements for co-operation with: Technical University of Clausthal; Technical University for Heavy Industry, Miskolc; Freiberg Mining Academy.

Academic Year: October to June (October-February; February-July).

Admission Requirements: Secondary school certificate (Reifezeugnis) or recognized foreign equivalent.

Fees (Schillings): 4000 per semester for foreign students.

Language of Instruction: German.

Degrees and Diplomas: Diplom-Ingenieur, Dipl.-Ing., 10 sem. Magister naturalium, Mag.rer.nat.,in Mining Geology, 10 sem. Doktor der montanistischen Wissenschaften, Dr.Mont., mining, by research and Rigorosum, 2-4 yrs.

Library: c. 160,000 vols.

Publications: Mitteilungsblatt; Berg-und Hüttenmännische-Monatshefte der Montanuniversität Leoben.

Academic Staff, 1989-90: 280.

Student Enrolment, 1989-90: c. 2200.

239 **TECHNISCHE UNIVERSITÄT WIEN**

University of Technology
Karlsplatz 13, 1040 Wien
Telex: 131.000 TVFWA
Telephone: 588-01
Rektor: Friedrich Moser (1989-91)
Universitätsdirektor: Ernst Schranz

F. of Land Developlment and Architecture
Dean: Dieter Bökemann
F. of Civil Engineering
Dean: William Reismann
F. of Mechanical Engineering
Dean: Alfred Kluwick
F. of Electrical Engineering
Dean: Rupert Patzelt
F. of Natural Sciences
Dean: Peter Skalicky

Also 110 institutes of the faculties.

Founded 1815 as institute of technology, acquired university rank 1872 and right to award doctorates 1901. Reorganized 1955. Under Austrian Law the administration of the university is in part the responsibility of the Federal Ministry of Science and Research and in part the autonomous responsibility of the university itself. Governing body: the Akademischer Senat.

Arrangements for co-operation with: University of Strasbourg I; Technical University, Budapest; University of Trieste; University of Tokyo.

Academic Year: October to September (October-January; March-June).

Admission Requirements: Secondary school certificate (Reifezeugnis) or recognized foreign equivalent.

Fees (Schillings): 4000 per semester for foreign students.

Language of Instruction: German.

Degrees and Diplomas: Diplom-Ingenieur, Dipl.-Ing., 5 yrs. Magister der Sozial-und Wirtschaftswissenschaft, 5 yrs; Magister der Naturwissenschaften, 5 yrs. Dr. Techn., technology; Dr.rer.nat., 7 yrs and thesis.

Library: University Library, *c.* 790,000 vols.

Publications: TU Aktuell; Mitteilungsblatt; Schriftenreihe.

Academic Staff, 1990:

Rank	Full-time
Ordentliche Universitätsprofessoren	132
Ausserordentliche Universitätsprofessoren	69
Universitätsassistenten	527
Vertragsassistenten	274
Studienassistenten	86
Sonstige	380
Total	1468

Student Enrolment, 1989-90:

Of the country	16,250
Of other countries	2250
Total	18,500

240 **UNIVERSITÄT FÜR BODENKULTUR**

University of Agriculture
Gregor Mendelstrasse 33, 1180 Wien
Cables: bodenkultur A-1180
Telephone: (222) 34-25-00
Fax: (222) 3691659
Rektor: Werner Biffl (1989-91)
Universitätsdirektor: Ilona Gälzer

D. of Agriculture
Head: Karl Pieber
D. of Forestry and Wood Technology
Head: Gerhard Glatzel
D. of Cultivation and Water Technology
Head: Erich Marx
D. of Food and Fermentation Technology
Head: Uwe B. Sleytr
D. of Landscape Ecology and Design

Also 37 institutes of the different departments.

Founded 1872 as Hochschule. Acquired present title 1975. The institution is responsible to the Federal Ministry of Science and Research. Governing body: the Rektorat. Some residential facilities for students.

Academic Year: October to July (October-February; February-July).

Admission Requirements: Secondary school certificate (Reifezeugnis).

Language of Instruction: German.

Degrees and Diplomas: Diplom-Ingenieur, in relevant fields, 9-11 sem. Doktor der Bodenkultur, a further 2 yrs.

Libraries: Central Library, *c.* 150,000 vols; institute libraries, *c.* 75,000.

Publications: Die Bodenkultur; Die Österreichische Wasserwirtschaft; Das Zentralblatt für das gesamte Forstwesen; Die Milchwirtschaft.

Academic Staff: c. 600.

Student Enrolment: c. 5000.

241 **VETERINÄRMEDIZINISCHE UNIVERSITÄT WIEN**
Vienna University of Veterinary Medicine
Linke Bahngasse 11, 1030 Wien
Telephone: 711 55 0
Fax: 713 68 95
Rektor: Oskar Schaller (1987-91)
Universitätsdirektor: Herber Maska

Veterinary Medicine
Also 25 institutes.

Founded 1767 as school, achieved university status 1908 and granted the same rights and privileges as other Austrian universities 1920. Acquired present title 1975.

Academic Year: October to June (October-January; March-June).

Admission Requirements: Secondary school certificate (Reifezeugnis) or equivalent.

Language of Instruction: German.

Degrees and Diplomas: Tierärztdiplom (Tzt.), 4 ½ yrs. Doktorat der Veterinärmedizin (Dr.med.vet.), by thesis, 5 yrs, and teaching qualification (university level).

Library: c. 55,000 vols.

Special Facilities (Museums, etc.): Museums: Anatomie, Hufkunde; Beschirrung und Sattelung; Fleisch-hygiene; Parasitologie.

Publication: Univet Wien (quarterly).

Academic Staff, 1990:

Rank	Full-time
Ordentliche Professoren	21
Ausserordentliche Professoren	7
Dozenten	14
Assistenten	130
Total	172

Student Enrolment, 1990:

	Men	Women	Total
Of the country	1065	1286	2351
Of other countries	96	78	174
Total	1161	1364	2525

242 ***WIRTSCHAFTSUNIVERSITÄT WIEN**
Augasse 2-6, 1090 Wien
Telex: 111-127 WUW A
Telephone: (222) 34-05-25
Fax: (222) 34-05-25/885
Electronic mail: EARN/BITNET: wupost@awiwuw11
Rektor: Fritz Scheuch (1991-)
Universitätsdirektor: Hans Dieter Libowitzky

D. of Business Administration
Head: Fritz Scheuch
D. of Economics
Head: J. Hanns Pichler
D. of Law
Head: Karl Hannak
D. of Human Sciences
Head: Gerhard Derflinger
Also 23 Institutes.

Founded 1898 as academy for foreign trade, became Hochschule für Welthandel with university rank 1919 and authorized to award doctorates 1930. Acquired present status and title 1975. Operated under the jurisdiction of the Federal Ministry of Science and Research. Governing body: the Universitätskollegium.

Special arrangements for co-operation with: Hochschule St. Gallen für Wirtschafts-und Sozialwissenschaften; Academy of Economics, Katowice; University of Economics, Berlin; Colleges of Economics, Bratislava and Prague; Institute of Commerce, Moscow; Escuela Superior de Administración y Dirección, Barcelona; Ecole des hautes Etudes commerciales, Paris; Universit Ľuigi Bocconi, Milan; Copenhagen School of Economics and Business Administration; Stockholm School of Economics. The Universities of: Louvain (Catholic); Erasmus, Rotterdam; NewYork; Illinois; Kentucky; Michigan; North Carolina; McGill; Alberta; Belgrano, Buenos Aires; Beijing.

Academic Year: October to June (October-January; March-June).

Admission Requirements: Secondary school certificate (Reifezeugnis) or foreign equivalent.

Fees (Schillings): 4000 per semester for foreign students.

Language of Instruction: German.

Degrees and Diplomas: Magister in Social Science and Economics, Mag. rer.soc.oec., 4-5 yrs. (Graduates in Commerce may also use the title Diplom-Kaufmann). Doctorates in–Business Administration, 4-5 yrs; Social Sciences and Economics, Dr.rer.soc.oec., 1 further yr.

Library: Central Library, *c.* 225,000 vols.

Publications: Der Österreichische Betriebswirt; Bankarchiv; Zeitschrift für Ganzheitsforschung.

Academic Staff, 1989:

Rank	Full-time
Ordentliche Universitätsprofessoren	47
Ausserordentliche Universitätsprofessoren	10
Universitätsassistenten	182
Wissenschaftliche Beamte	8
Bundeslehrer	6
Vertragslehrer	3
Total	256

Student Enrolment, 1989-90:

	Men	Women	Total
Of the country	12,739	9199	21,938
Of other countries	1362	683	2045
Total	14,101	9882	23,983

243 ***JOHANNES KEPLER UNIVERSITÄT LINZ**
Johannes Kepler University
Altenberger Strasse 69, 4040 Linz-Auhof
Telex: 2-2323 UNILIA
Telephone: (732) 2468
Fax: (732) 2468-10
Rektor: Ernst Kulhavy (1989-91)

F. of Law
Dean: Heribert Franz Köck; *staff* 65 (3)
F. of Social Sciences and Economics
Dean: Walter Sertl; *staff* 106 (23)
F. of Technology and Natural Sciences
Dean: Heinz Falk; *staff* 117 (30)
Computer Ce.
I. for Lifelong Education
Head: Harald Stiegler
Law Research I.
Head: Rudolf Strasser; *staff* 2
Microprocessing Techniques Research I.
Head: Jörg Mühlbacher; *staff* 2 (7)
Opto-Electronic Research I.
Head: Klaus Lischka; *staff* 2
Social Planning Research I.
Head: Josef Weidenhol
Interdisciplinary Research I. for Work Development
Head: Klaus Zapotoczky

Founded 1962 as Hochschule für Sozial-und Wirtschaftswissenschaften and opened 1966. Became university with present title 1975. The university is operated under the jurisdiction of the Federal Ministry of Science and Research. Financed by the Federal Government. Governing body: the Senat. Residential facilities for academic staff and students.

Arrangements for co-operation with: Emory University; University of Toronto; Texas A&M University; University of Strasbourg III; University of Paris VI; Freiburg University; Martin-Luther University, Halle.

Academic Year: October to July (October-February; March-June).

Admission Requirements: Completed secondary or commercial education or foreign equivalent.

Language of Instruction: German.

Degrees and Diplomas: Magister iuris, Mag.iur.; Magister rerum socialium oeconomicarumque, Mag.rer.soc.oec., economics; Magister rerum naturalium, Mag.rer.nat., natural sciences, 4 1/2 yrs. Diplom-Ingenieure, Dipl.-Ing., 5 yrs. Dr.rer.rer.soc.oec., 1 yr following Mag.rer.soc.oec.; Dr.rer.nat., 2 yrs following Mag.rer.nat. Doctor iuris, Dr.iur., law, 5 yrs. Also Doctor technicae, technology.

Libraries: Central Library, *c.* 160,000 vols; libraries of the institutes, 120,000.

Publications: Forschung und Lehre; Universitätsnachrichten (6 times a year).

Press or Publishing House: Pressestelle der Universität.

Academic Staff, 1990: 293 (62).
Student Enrolment, 1990:

	Men	Women	Total
Of the country	8340	4323	12,663
Of other countries	300	75	375
Total	8640	4398	13,038

244 **UNIVERSITÄT FÜR BILDUNGSWISSENSCHAFTEN**
University of Educational Sciences
Universitätsstrasse 65, 9021 Klagenfurt
Telephone: (463) 53-17
Fax: (463) 53-17-100
Rektor: Albert Berger (1989-91)
Universitätsdirektor: Arnulf Longin

I. for the Teaching of Contemporary History
Head: Norbert Schausberger; *staff* 4
I. for the Teaching of Geography
Head: Bruno Backé; *staff* 7
I. for the Teaching of History
Head: Günther Hödl; *staff* 10
I. for the Teaching of Mathematics
Head: Willibald Dörfler; *staff* 13
I. for the Teaching of Anglo-American Studies
Head: William J. Nemser; *staff* 10
I. for the Teaching of Germanic Languages and Literature
Head: Friedbert Aspetsberger; *staff* 12
I. for the Teaching of Romance Philology
Head: UlrichWandruszka; *staff* 8
I. for the Teaching of Slavic Studies
Head: Gerhard Neweklowsky; *staff* 6
I. for the Teaching of Educational Economics and Sociology
Head: Paul Kellerman; *staff* 6
I. for the Teaching of Curriculum Research and Organizational Development in Education
Head: Peter Posch; *staff* 10
I. of Psychology
Head: Erich Löschenkohn; *staff* 9
I. of Philosophy and Group Dynamics
Head: Uwe Arnold; *staff* 13
I. of General and Applied Linguistics
Head: Heniz-Dieter Pohl; *staff* 4
I. of Educational Technology and Media
Head: Klaus Boeckmann; *staff* 12
Interuniversity Research I. for Distance Education
Head: Peter Heintel; *staff* 10
Interuniversity Research I. for Technology Media Didactics and Engineering Education
Head: Arno Bammé; *staff* 8
I. for Comparative Literature
Head: Peter Václav Zima; *staff* 3
I. of Law
Head: Robert Rebhahn; *staff* 4
D. of Computer Sciences
Head: Roland Mittermeir; *staff* 11
S. of Business and Economics
Head: Dieter J.G. Schneider; *staff* 16
I. for Further Education
Head: Peter Gstettner; *staff* 7

Founded 1970 as college, acquired present status and title 1975. An institution operated under the jurisdiction of the Federal Ministry of Science and Research. Residential facilities for students.

Arrangements for co-operation with: University of Ljubljana; University of Udine.

Academic Year: October to June (October-January; March-June).

Admission Requirements: Secondary school certificate (Reifezeugnis).

Language of Instruction: German.

Degrees and Diplomas: Magister phil. and Magister rer.nat, natural sciences, in the relevant field, 9 sem. Doctorate, at least 1 further yr and thesis. Teaching qualifications.

Library: c. 400,000 vols.

Publications: Klagenfurter Universitätsreden; Klagenfurter sprach-wissenschaftliche Beiträge; Klagenfurter Beiträge zur bildungswissenschaftlichen Forschung; Schriftenreihe 'Ingenieur-pädagogik'.

Academic Staff, 1990: 174 (350).
Student Enrolment, 1990:

	Men	Women	Total
Of the country	2059	2727	4786
Of other countries	148	142	290
Total	2207	2869	5076

245 **AKADEMIE DER BILDENDEN KÜNSTE IN WIEN**
Academy of Fine Arts
Schillerplatz 3, 1010 Wien
Telephone: 58-81-16
Fax: 587-79-77
Rektor: Carl Pruscha (1988-)
Director of Administration: Alfred Sammer

Fine Arts (including Sculpture, Painting, History of Art, Town Planning, Conservation and Technology, Arts and Crafts, Colour Science, Graphic Arts, Architecture, Textile Arts and Tapestry, Stage Design, Art Education and Science of Art)

Founded 1692.

Academic Year: October to June (October-February; March-June).

Admission Requirements: Secondary school certificate (Reifezeugnis).

Language of Instruction: German.

Degrees and Diplomas: Magister artium, mag.art. Magister architecturae, mag.arch.

Library: 84,000 vols.

Special Facilities (Museums, etc.): Art Gallery.

Academic Staff, 1990: c. 174.
Student Enrolment, 1990:

Men	Women	Total
294	258	552*

*Including 127 foreign students.

246 **HOCHSCHULE FÜR MUSIK UND DARSTELLENDE KUNST IN WIEN**
College of Music and Dramatic Art
Lothringerstrasse 18, 1030 Wien
Telephone: (222) 58806
Rektor: Helmut Schwarz (1988-92)

Music and Dramatic Art

Founded 1812 as a Conservatory, became Academy and State institution 1920 and university institution with title of Hochschule 1970. A State instutution.

Academic Year: October to June (October-mid-February; March-June).

Admission Requirements: Secondary school certificate (Reifezeugnis) and entrance examination.

Language of Instruction: German.

Degrees and Diplomas: Diplom, 4-8 yrs; teaching qualifications, 3-4 yrs, including Magister artium, 4-5 yrs.

Libraries: Central Library; department libraries, c. 90,000 vols; c. 1700 gramophone records; c. 700 tapes.

Academic Staff: c. 390.

Student Enrolment: c. 2570.

247 **HOCHSCHULE FÜR MUSIK UND DARSTELLENDE KUNST IN GRAZ**
College of Music and Dramatic Art
Leonhardstrasse 15, 8010 Graz
Telephone: (316) 389-0
Fax: (316) 32504
Rektor/Präsident: Sebastian Benda (1987-)
Rektoratsdirektor: Hermann Becke

Music and Dramatic Art (including Music Ethnology, Jazz Researc0h, Electronic Music, and Music Aesthetics and Evaluation Research)

Founded as provincial School of Music 1803, became Conservatory 1815, Akademie 1963, and university institution with title of Hochschule 1970. The College enjoys the independence of a State institution, operated under the jurisdiction of the Federal Ministry of Science and Research. Governing body: the Gesamtkollegium.

Academic Year: October to June (October-January; March-June).

Admission Requirements: Secondary school certificate (Reifezeugnis) and entrance examination.

Fees (Schillings): 4000 per semester for foreign students.

Language of Instruction: German.

Degrees and Diplomas: Magister artium, mag.art., 5 yrs. Diplom, 3-6 yrs.

Library: c. 95,000 vols. Tapes, records.
Publication: Research publications.
Academic Staff, 1989-90:

Rank	
Ordentliche Hochschulprofessoren	91
Assistenten	16
Bundeslehrer	17
Sondervertragslehrer	17
Lehrbeauftragte	160
Total	301

Student Enrolment, 1989-90:

	Men	Women	Total
Of the country	686	472	1158
Of other countries	184	136	320
Total	870	608	1478

248 **HOCHSCHULE FÜR MUSIK UND DARSTELLENDE KUNST 'MOZARTEUM' IN SALZBURG**

Academy of Music and the Performing Arts 'Mozarteum'
Mirabellplatz 1, 5020 Salzburg
Telephone: (662) 75534-0
Rektor: Günther Bauer (1983-91)
Rektoratsdirektorin: Annemarie Lassacher-Sandmeier

Music and Dramatic Art

Founded 1841, transferred to the Mozarteum foundation 1881, became Conservatory 1914, a State institution 1921 and Akademie 1953 and university institution with title of Hochschule 1970. Financed by the State and responsible to the Federal Ministry of Science and Research. Some residential facilities for students.

Arrangements for co-operation with the College of Music, Munich.
Academic Year: October to June (October-February; February-June).
Admission Requirements: Entrance examination.
Fees (Schillings): 4000 per semester for foreign students.
Language of Instruction: German.
Degrees and Diplomas: Magister artium, mag.art.
Library: 111,246 vols.
Academic Staff, 1986-87:

Rank	Full-time	Part-time
Ordentliche Hochschulprofessoren	79	–
Gastprofessoren	24	4
Lehrbeauftragte	69	88
Lehrer	29	–
Sondervertragslehrer	25	–
Hochschulassistenten	6	–
Künstliche wissenschaftliche Hilftskräfte	2	–
Total	234	92

Student Enrolment, 1986-87:

	Men	Women	Total
Of the country	428	429	857
Of other countries	261	376	637
Total	689	805	1494

249 **HOCHSCHULE FÜR KÜNSTLERISCHE UND INDUSTRIELLE GESTALTUNG IN LINZ**

University of Artand Industrial Design
Hauptplatz 8, 4010 Linz
Telephone: (732) 273485
Fax: (732) 283508
Rektor: Fritz Goffitzer (1989-93)
Rektoratsdirektor (Registrar): Christine Windsteiger

D. of Aesthetic Education
Head: Erwin Reiter; *staff* 28 (49)
D. of Environmental Design
Head: Günther Feuerstein; *staff* 8 (33)
D. of Applied Graphic Arts
Head: Marek Freudenreich; *staff* 12 (20)

Founded as School of Art 1947, acquired present status and title 1973. Operated under the jurisdiction of the Federal Ministry of Science and Research. Financed by the Federal Government, the Land Oberösterreich and the City of Linz.

Academic Year: October to July (October-February; March-July).
Admission Requirements: Secondary school certificate (Reifezeugnis) and entrance examination.
Fees (Schillings): 4000 per semester.
Language of Instruction: German.
Degrees and Diplomas: Magister artium, mag. art., 4-5 yrs. Magister architecturae, mag.arch., 5 yrs.
Library: c. 24,000 vols.
Academic Staff, 1990:

Rank	Full-time	Part-time
Ordentliche Hochschulprofessoren	11	–
Professoren	6	–
Assistenzprofessoren	6	–
Lehrbeauftragte	–	80
Total	23	80

Student Enrolment, 1989:

	Men	Women	Total
Of the country	213	154	367
Of other countries	13	13	26
Total	226	167	393

250 **HOCHSCHULE FÜR ANGEWANDTE KUNST IN WIEN**

University of Applied Arts
Oskar-Kokoschka-Platz 2, 1010 Wien
Telephone: (1) 71-1111
Fax: (1) 71-1111-2858
Präsident: Wilhelm Holzbauer
Rektoratsdirektor: Heinz Adamek

F. of Architecture
Dean: Friedrich Achleitner
F. of Fine Arts
Dean: Adolf Frohner
F. of Plastic Arts and Design
Dean: Alfred Vendl
F. of Visual Communication
Dean: Axel Manthey
F. of Art and Art Education
Dean: Peter Gorsen

Founded 1868 as school, reorganized 1940 and 1945, and became Academie 1948 and university institution with title of Hochschule 1970. Under Austrian Law the institution is responsible to the Federal Ministry of Science and Research. Governing body: the Gesamtkollegium.

Academic Year: October to June (October-February; March-June).
Admission Requirements: Secondary school certificate (Reifezeugnis) or equivalent, and entrance examination.
Fees (Schillings): 4000 per semester for foreign students.
Language of Instruction: German.
Degrees and Diplomas: Magister architecturae, mag.arch., 5 yrs; Magister artium, mag.art., 4-5 yrs. Doctorats-Dr.phil.; Dr.rer.nat.
Libraries: University Library, *c.* 75,000 vols; Museums, *c.* 180,000.
Special Facilities (Museums, etc.): Archives; Art Gallery.
Publications: Studienführer (annually); Prospekt (quarterly); Catologues (15 per year).
Academic Staff, 1989-90:

	Full-time	Part-time
Ordentliche Professoren	28	–
Assistente Professoren	38	–
Assistenten	15	–
Lektoren	56	100
Gastprofessoren	14	–
Total	151	100

Student Enrolment, 1989-90:

	Men	Women	Total
Of the country	420	480	900
Of other countries	140	160	300
Total	560	640	1200

BAHRAIN

251 ***UNIVERSITY OF BAHRAIN**

P.O. Box 32038, Isa Town
Telex: 9552 JAMEA BN
Telephone: 68-12-34
Fax: 68-14-65
President: Marwan R. Kamal (1968-)

C. of Arts and Science
Dean: Abdulla Sabt
D. of Arabic and Islamic Studies
Chairman: Hilal Al-Shaiji; *staff* 28
D. of Biology
Chairman: Saeed A. Mohamed; *staff* 13
D. of Chemistry
Chairman: Ahmed Yousif Ali Mohamed; *staff* 13
D. of Physics
Chairman: Waheeb Al-Naser; *staff* 13
D. of English
Chairman: R.J. Wigzell; *staff* 17
D. of General Studies
Chairman: A. Latif Al-Rumaihi; *staff* 10
D. of Mathematics
Chairman: A.Y. Al-Hawaj; *staff* 44
C. of Business Administration
Dean: George Najjar; *staff* 37
D. of Business Management
Chairman: Paris Andreou; *staff* 24
D. of Office Management
Chairman (Acting): Margaret Arnold; *staff* 13
D. of Cont. Management Education
Co-ordinator: Seref Turen; *staff* 2
C. of Education
Dean: Rafiqa Hammoud
D. of Education
Chairman: Abbas Adiby; *staff* 31
D. of Physical Education
Chairman: Aida A. Asim El-Banna; *staff* 8
D. of Psychology
Chairman: Jihan Al-Umran; *staff* 5
C. of Engineering
Dean: Nizar Al-Baharna
D. of Civil Engineering
Chairman Hanna Makhlouf; *staff* 12
D. of Electrical Engineering and Computer Sciences
Chairman: Ali K. Khan; *staff* 28
D. of Mechanical and Chemical Engineering
Chairman: Emad Taqi; *staff* 22
Continuing Engineering Education P.
Co-ordinator: Naji M. Ahmed; *staff* 2
English Language Ce.
Director: Husain Dhaif; *staff* 49

Founded 1986, incorporating the University College of Arts, Science and Education, founded 1978 as the Gulf Polytechnic. Governing body: the Board of Trustees of which the Minister of Education is ex officio chairman.

Academic Year: September to August (September-January; February-June; June-August).

Admission Requirements: Secondary school certificate (Twajihia) or equivalent.

Languages of Instruction: Arabic and English.

Degrees and Diplomas: Bachelor of–Arts; Science; Education; Physical Education, 4 yrs. Master of–Education; Business Administration. Postgraduate diploma.

Libraries: Arts, Science and Education, 58,000 vols; Polytechnic, 60,000.

Academic Staff, 1989-90: c. 320.

Student Enrolment, 1989-90:

	Men	Women	Total
Of the country	1760	2186	3946
Of other countries	132	164	296
Total	1892	2350	4242

252 **ARABIAN GULF UNIVERSITY**

P.O. Box 26671, Manama
Telex: 73119 AGU BN
Telephone: (973) 440044
Fax: (973) 440002
President: Ibrahim Sayed Jamal Alhashemi
General Director: Riyadh Yousuf Hamza

C. of Medicine and Medical Sciences
Dean: W. Lammers; *staff* 28 (48)
C. of Education
Dean: Fathi Al Sayyed Abdulrahim; *staff* 12
C. of Applied Sciences (including Desert and Arid Zones Sciences)
Dean: Ibrahim J. Al Hashemi; *staff* 24

Founded 1980 by the seven Gulf States. A regional autonomous scientific institution with public status. Jointly managed by the member countries on the basis of equal representation in the General Conference and on the Board of Trustees. Residential facilities for academic staff and students.

Academic Year: September to July.

Admission Requirements: Secondary school certificate with minimum average of 80%. 30% of total admission is reserved for member stateswhose local universities do not offer same programmes.

Fees (Bahrain Dinar): 1800-3000 per annum.

Languages of Instruction: English and Arabic.

Degrees and Diplomas: Bachelor in Medicine and Surgery, 7 yrs. Master in–Education; Science, 2 yrs. Higher Diploma in Education forthe Mentally Retarded, 1 yr.

Library: 25,000 vols.

Academic Staff, 1990:

Rank	Full-time	Part-time
Professors	11	2
Associate Professors	9	7
Assistant Professors	38	31
Lecturers	2	3
Language Teachers	–	4
Total	60	47

Student Enrolment, 1990:

	Men	Women	Total
Of the country	165	253	418
Of other countries	11	11	22
Total	176	264	440

253 **COLLEGE OF HEALTH SCIENCES**

Salmania Medical Centre, P.O. Box 12, Manama
Telex: 8511 HEALTH BN
Dean: Faisal Al Hamer

Health Sciences

Founded 1976. A State institution financially supported by the Ministry of Health. Governing body: the Board of Education.

Admission Requirements: Intermediate or secondary school certificate and entrance examination. For Nursing/Midwifery, general nursing Diploma.

Language of Instruction: English.

Degrees and Diplomas: Degree in Nursing, 2 yrs. Associated Degree (professional titles) of–Diagnostic Radiography Technician; Medical Equipment Technician; Medical Laboratory Technician; Pharmacy Technician; Bachelor in Nursing and Public Health Inspector, 2 yrs; General Nurse, 3 yrs. Dental Hygiene; Sports Therapy; Medical Secretary; Diploma of Nurse-Midwifery, 2 further yrs.

Library: 18,654 vols.

Academic Staff, 1986-87: 80.

Student Enrolment, 1986-87: 624 (Also 220 part-time students).

254 **HOTEL AND CATERING TRAINING CENTRE**
P.O. Box 22088, Muharraq
Telex: HTC MUHARRAQ
Telephone: 320191
Principal: Abdel Rahim El Khaja (1984-)
Registrar: Mohamed Al-Ansary

Hotel and Catering Studies

Founded 1975 following an agreement between the State of Bahrain, United Nations Development Programme, and the International Labour Organization. A State institution affiliated to the Ministry of Information. Residential facilities for academic staff and students.

Academic Year: October to June (October-February; February-June).

Admission Requirements: Secondary school certificate and entrance examination.

Fees (Dinars): c. 250-500 per semester.

Language of Instruction: English.

Degrees and Diplomas: Diploma, 2 yrs.

Library: c. 9,000 vols.

Academic Staff, 1986-87: 23.

Student Enrolment, 1986-87:

	Men	Women	Total
Of the country	127	62	189
Of other countries	15	2	17
Total	142	64	206

BELGIUM

255 ***UNIVERSITÉ LIBRE DE BRUXELLES**

Free University of Brussels

Avenue Franklin D. Roosevelt 50, 1050 Bruxelles

Telex: UNILIB 230-69

Telephone: (2) 650-2111

Fax: (2) 649-4070

Président: Hervé Hasquin (1990-)

Recteur: Françoise Thys-Clément

Secrétaire-général: Christian Dejean

F. of Philosophy and Letters (including Philology and Oriental and Slavonic History, and Journalism)
Chairman: Pierre de Maret; *staff* 62 (146)
F. of Law (including Criminology)
Chairman: Bernard Glansdorff; *staff* 14 (160)
F. of Science
Chairman: Gisèle Van de Vyver; *staff* 183 (80)
F. of Psychology and Education
Chairman: Alex Lefevbre; *staff* 21 (45)
F. of Medicine (including Dentistry)
Chairman: J.L. Vanherweghem; *staff* 124 (344)
F. of Applied Sciences (including Town Planning and Computer Sciences)
Chairman: Jean-Louis Van Eck; *staff* 98 (111)
F. of Social, Political, and Economic Sciences
Chairman: J.J. Droesbeke; *staff* 46 (137)
I. of Pharmacy
Chairman: Michel Hanocq; *staff* 24 (10)
I. of Physical Education
Chairman: R. Vanfraechem-Raway; *staff* 11 (76)
I. of Statistics
Director: Guy Louchard; *staff* 12 (5)
I. of Labour
Chairman; Pierre Salengros; *staff* 1 (20)
I. of European Studies
Director: Jean-Victor Louis; *staff* 3 (19)
I. of Oriental Languages and Civilizations
Director: Robert Anciaux
I. of Religious Studies and of Secularity
Chairman: Hervé Hasquin
I. of Phonetics
Director: Max Wajskop
S. of Public Health
Chairman: André Laurent; *staff* 30 (75)
S. of Nursing (annexed to the University)
Chairman: Jacques Henry
S. of Criminology
Chairman: Pierre Vandervort
I. of Sociology
Director: Jacques Nagels
Computer Ce.
Director: Jacques Grassart
I. of Philosophy
Chairman: Guy Haarscher
I. of Higher Studies of Belgium
Secretary-General: Pierre Goffin
Also three hospitals.

Founded 1834, the Free University of Brussels was transformed under the law of 28 May 1970 into separate Dutch and French speaking universities. The Rector is elected for a term of two years from among the titular professors. As a private autonomous institution with five campuses: Solbosch, Plaine, Porte de Hall in Brussels; Rhode-St-Genèse, Nivelles (province of Brabant), this university receives substantial public financial support. Governing bodies: the Conseil d'administration, composed of the Rector and, in varying proportions, representatives of the academic staff, research workers, students, technical staff, and social and public life; the Faculty Councils enjoying a considerable degree of autonomy and including representatives of all categories of academic staff and students. Residential facilities for *c.* 700 students in Cités universitaires.

Arrangements for co-operation with the Universities of: Paris VII; Montpellier; Sussex; Budapest; Belgrade; Cracow; Bénin; Togo; Gabon; Tunisia; Zaïre; Montréal; Sofia; Malta; Beirut; Baghdad; Qaraouiyine, Fès; Mohammed V, Rabat; Ouagadougou; Yaoundé; Marien Ngouabi, Brazzaville, etc.

Academic Year: October to September (October-January; January-May).

Admission Requirements: Secondary school certificate or recognized foreign equivalent, and entrance examination. Entrance examinationobligatory for the Faculty of Applied Sciences.

Fees (Francs): 21,000 per annum.

Language of Instruction: French.

Degrees and Diplomas: Candidat in–Philosophy and Letters; Philosophy and Letters (History and Archaeology); Philosophy (grade scientifique); Philology and Oriental History; Slavonic Philology and History; Science; Physical Education; Social Science; Education; Psychology, 2 yrs; Natural and Medical Sciences, 3 yrs. Licencié in–Philosophy and Letters; Philosophy and Letters (History and Archaeology); Philosophy (grade scientifique); Journalism and Communications; Oriental Philology and History; Languages; Slavonic Philology and History; Law; Notarial Studies; Criminological Science; Science and Linguistics; Science; Dentistry; Physical Education; Social Science; Political and International Relations; Political Theory; Informatics and Human Sciences; Political and Administrative Sciences; Economics; Education; Psychology, 2 yrs after Candidat; Maritime Law, 1 yr after Doctorat in Law; Econometry, 1 yr after Licence in Economics or diploma of Ingénieur commercial; Commerce and Finance, 1 yr after diploma of Ingénieur commercial; Actuarial Science, 2 yrs after Licence in Science or diploma of Ingénieur civil;Town Planning, 2 yrs after Licence; European Studies, 2 yrs after diploma; Applied Nuclear Science; Insurance. Doctorate in–Philosophy and Letters; Philosophy and Letters (History and Archaeology); Philosophy (grade scientifique); Physical Education; Social Science; Political Science and International Relations Political Theory; Informatics and Human Sciences; Political and Administrative Sciences; Economics; Education; Psychology, 1 yr after Licence and thesis; Science, 2 yrs and thesis; Law, 3 yrs; Medicine, Surgery and Midwifery, 4 yrs; Pharmacy, 1 yr after diploma of Pharmacien; Applied Sciences, after diploma of Ingénieur civil or equivalent; Applied Economics, after diploma of Ingénieur commercial. Agrégation de l'enseignement secondaire et supérieur (teaching qualifications, secondary and university level) in–Philosophy and Letters; Philosophy and Letters (History and Archaeology); Science; Physical Education; Commerce; Political and Social Sciences. Professional titles of–Pharmacien; Infirmière, nursing, 3 yrs;Ingénieur commercial, 4 yrs; Ingénieur civil (mining, constructional, mechanical and electrical, chemical, metallurgical, computer and physical engineering), 5 yrs; Médecin-Hygiéniste, 1 yr after docteur; Ingénieur géologue, 1 yr after diploma of Ingénieur civil (mining); Ingénieur urbaniste, 2 yrs after diploma of Ingénieur civil (construction); Architecte urbaniste, 2 yrs after diploma of Architecte; Ingénieur en Constructions aéronautiques; Ingénieur des Télécommunications et d'Electronique, after diploma of Ingénieur civil; Ingénieur in Sciences nucléaires appliquées.

Library: Total, *c.* 2,000,000 vols.

Publications: Revue (monthly); Telex, including Bulletin d'Information (bimonthly).

Press or Publishing House: Les Editions de l'Université de Bruxelles.

Academic Staff, 1989-90:

Rank	Full-time	Part-time
Professeurs ordinaires	144	–
Professeurs extraordinaires	–	11
Professeurs	50	16
Chargés de cours	72	367
Agrégés de Faculté	27	–
Chefs de travaux	167	–
1ers Assistants	83	85
Assistants	158	491
Total	701	970

Student Enrolment, 1989-90:

	Men	Women	Total

Of the country	5816	5446	11,262
Of other countries	3264	2039	5303
Total	9080	7485	16,565

256 ***VRIJE UNIVERSITEIT BRUSSEL**

Free University of Brussels
Campus Oefenplein Pleinlaan 2, 1050 Brussel
Telex: 61.051 VUBCO-B
Telephone: (2) 64-21-11
Fax: (2) 16-41-22-82
Rector: Sylvain J. Loccufier

F. of Philosophy and Letters
Dean: W. Van Rengen
F. of Law
Dean: M. Magits
F. of Science (including Agriculture, Engineering, Water Pollution Studies, Veterinary Medicine, and Astronomy)
Dean: C. Susanne
F. of Medicine and Pharmacy (including Dentistry)
Dean: L. Vanhaelst
F. of Applied Sciences (Civil, Electronic, Mechanical, and Biomedical Engineering)
Dean: R. Jonckheere
F. of Social, Political, and Economic Sciences
Dean: R. Lesthaeghe
F. of Psychology and Education
Dean: H. Rigaux
I. of Physical Education
President: M. Hebbelink

Founded 1970 when the former Free University of Brussels, founded 1834, was replaced by separate Dutch and French-speaking universities. A private autonomous institution receiving substantial financial support from the State. Governing body: the Raad van Beheer (Board of Directors), comprising the Rector, Pro-Rectors, 21 members of the Academic and scientific staff, 7 students and 7 co-opted members. Residential facilities for students.

Academic Year: October to July (October-February; February-July).

Admission Requirements: Secondary school certificate or recognized foreign equivalent, and entrance examination.

Languages of Instruction: Dutch and English.

Degrees and Diplomas: Kandidaat in all fields, 2 yrs, except Medicine, 3 yrs. Licentiaat in–Philosophy and Letters (various fields); Science (various fields); Physical Education; Social, Political or Economic Sciences, 4 yrs; Law; Dentistry; Clinical Psychology, 5 yrs. Professional qualifications in–Dentistry; Engineering (various fields), 5 yrs; Medicine, 7 yrs. Doctorates by thesis, 2 yrs after Licentiaat or Professional qualification. Geaggregeerde voor het Hoger Secundair Onderwijs (teaching qualification, higher secondary level), after Licentiaat; Geaggregeerde voor het Hoger Onderwijs (teaching qualification, university level), 2 yrs after Doctorate.

Library: Faculty Libraries, total, *c.* 147,000 vols.

Publications: Aula; Tijdschrift Vrije Universiteit Brussel.

Academic Staff, 1989-90: 333 (187).

Student Enrolment, 1989-90: 7700.

257 ***RIJKSUNIVERSITEIT TE GENT**

State University of Ghent
Sint-Pietersnieuwstraat 25, 9000 Gent
Telex: 12.754 RUGENT
Telephone: (91) 64-31-11
Fax: (91) 64-35-97
Rector: L. De Meyer
Administrator: W. Van Espen

F. of Philosophy and Letters
Dean: R. Van Eenoo; *staff* 145 (23)
F. of Law (including Political and Social Sciences)
Dean: P. Ghysbrecht; *staff* 71 (81)
F. of Science
Dean: W. De Breuck; *staff* 308 (23)
F. of Medicine
Dean: M. Bogaert; *staff* 230
F. of Applied Sciences (including Structural, Electrotechnical, and Mechanical Engineering, Chemistry, Metallurgy, Architecture, Textiles, Naval Architecture, and Physics)
Dean: J. Willems; *staff* 193 (30)
F. of Economics
Dean: J. Denduyver; *staff* 44 (14)
F. of Veterinary Medicine
Dean: H. Lauwers; *staff* 74 (1)
F. of Psychology and Education
Dean: K. De Clerck; *staff* 61 (26)
F. of Agriculture
Dean: L. Martens; *staff* 119 (20)
F. of Pharmacy
Dean: A. De Leenheer; *staff* 38 (3)
I. of Physical Education
Director: J.-L. Pannier; *staff* 5 (9)
Inter-F. Ce. for Town Planning and Regional Development
Director: M. Anselin
S. of Management
Director: H. Ooghe; *staff* 7 (5)
S. of Criminology
Director: R. Dierkens; *staff* – (7)
D. of Teacher Training
Director: F. Decreus; *staff* 3 (35)

Founded 1816 under King William I of the Netherlands. The official language of the university was originally Latin; this was changed to French in 1830 and to Dutch in 1930. The university enjoys limited autonomy but is financially dependent on the Government. The Rector is appointed by the King on the nomination of the GoverningCouncil and serves for 4 years. Governing bodies: the Raad van Beheer (Governing Council), with the Rector as Chairman, and comprising elected representatives of the professorial, the lecturer, research and administrative and technical staff, elected representatives of the students, as well as the business community, the trade unions and the public administration; the Academieraad (Academic Council). Residential facilities for students.

Arrangements for co-operation with institutions of higher education in Europe.

Academic Year: October to September.

Admission Requirements: Secondary school certificate or recognized foreign equivalent, and entrance examination for engineering.

Fees (Francs): 15,650 per annum.

Language of Instruction: Dutch.

Degrees and Diplomas: Candidate in all fields, 2 yrs, except Medicine, Veterinary Medicine, 3 yrs. Licentiate in all fields, a further 2 yrs, except Law, Dentistry, Psychological and Pedagogical Sciences, 3 yrs. Title of-Ingénieur, ir., in various fields; Pharmacist, 3 yrs following Candidate. Doctor of–Veterinary Medicine, 3 yrs following Candidate; Medicine, Surgery and Obstetrics, 4 yrs following Candidate. Agrégé for Education (upper secondary level), 1 yr following Licentiate, ir., Pharmacist, Doctor of Medicine, Surgery and Obstetrics. Postgraduate studies, 1-2 yrs, according to field of study. Doctorate, dr., 1-3 yrs and thesis. Special Doctorate and Agrégé for Higher Education, 2 yrs after Doctorate.

Libraries: Central Library (RUGent), *c.* 3,000,000 vols; faculty and laboratory libraires.

Special Facilities (Museums, etc.): History of Science Museum; Observatory; Botanical Garden.

Publication: Gent Universiteit (monthly).

Academic Staff, 1989-90: 310 (63).

Student Enrolment, 1989-90:

	Men	Women	Total
Of the country	7462	6111	13,573
Of other countries	491	258	749
Total	7953	6369	14,322

258 ***UNIVERSITÉ DE L'ÉTAT À LIÈGE**

State University of Liège
7, place du 20 août, 4000 Liège
Telex: 41397 UNIVLG
Telephone: (41) 66-21-11
Fax: (41) 22-41-08
Recteur: Arthur Bodson (1989-93)
Administrateur: René Grosjean

F. of Philosophy and Letters
Dean: A. Motte
F. of Law
Dean: P. Lewalle
F. of Science
Dean: Ch. Jeuniaux

F. of Medicine (including Dentistry and Pharmacy)
Dean: H. Kulbertus
F. of Veterinary Medicine (Cureghem)
Dean: A. Dewaeme
F. of Applied Sciences (Engineering and Architecture)
Dean: G. L'Homme
F. of Psychology and Educational Science
Dean: Mme. V.-M. Dekeyser
F. of Economics, Business, Administration, and Social Science
Dean: L. Bragard
S. of Criminology
President: G. Kellens

Founded 1816 under King William I of the Netherlands. Following the independence of Belgium designated in 1835 as a State university. In 1959 provision was made for the transfer of the university to a new campus. The university enjoys limited autonomy and receives the major portion of its income from the Communatué françaisede Belgique. Governing body: the Conseil d'administration, composed of the Rector as Chairman, a Vice-Rector, professors elected by each faculty, members of the scientific staff, representatives of the student body, representatives of administrativeand technical staff, and representatives prominent in social, political and economic life. Some residential facilities for students.

Special arrangements for co-operation with the Universities of: Cracow; Łódź; Poznań; Bucharest; Amiens; Aachen; Limburg; Budapest; Lille; Nancy; Montréal; Naples; Fribourg; Geneva; Lausanne; College of Mechanical and Electrical Engineering, Plzeň.

Academic Year: October to June (October-December; January-June).

Admission Requirements: Secondary school certificate or recognized foreign equivalent, and entrance examination.

Fees (Francs): 17,500 per annum.

Language of Instruction: French.

Degrees and Diplomas: Candidat in–Philosophy and Letters; Law; Social Science; Economics; Science; Medicine; Physical Education; Psychology; Veterinary Medicine; Civil Engineering; Architecture. Licence in–Philosophy and Letters; Economics; Social Science; Political Science; Criminology; Business Administration; Science; Dentistry; Physical Education; Chemistry; Architecture, 4 yrs; Law; Psychology; Education, 5 yrs. Professional titles of–Pharmacien; Ingénieur, 5 yrs. Doctorate, at least 1 further yr. Doctorate in Medicine, 7 yrs.

Libraries: Central Library, *c.* 1,400,000 vols; Bibliothèque Léon Graulich (Law), *c.* 200,000.

Special Facilities (Museums, etc.): Museum and Aquarium of the Institute of Zoology; Musée en plein air du Sart Tilman; Musée de la Science.

Academic Staff, 1989-90: 400.

Student Enrolment, 1989-90:

	Men	Women	Total
Of the country	4954	4171	9125
Of other countries	1231	512	1743
Total	6185	4683	10,868

259 **UNIVERSITÉ CATHOLIQUE DE LOUVAIN**
Catholic University of Louvain
Place de l'Université 1, 1348 Louvain-la-Neuve
Telex: 59516
Telephone: (10) 47-21-11
Fax: (10) 47-29-99
Recteur: Pierre Macq (1986-91)
Administrateur général: Jean Moulart

F. of Theology and Canon Law
Dean: J-M. Sevrin; *staff* 17 (24)
F. of Law
Dean: F. Delperee; *staff* 40 (82)
F. of Economic, Political, and Social Sciences
Dean: Anne-Marie Kumps; *staff* 160 (116)
F. of Medicine (including Dentistry, Public Health, and Physical Education)
Dean: L. Cassiers; *staff* 516 (200)
F. of Philosophy and Letters
Dean: D. Donnet; *staff* 92 (77)
F. of Psychology and Education
Dean: J.Ph. Leyens; *staff* 46 (35)
F. of Science
Dean: D. Laduron; *staff* 353 (109)
F. of Applied Sciences (including Mining Construction, Metallurgical, and Chemical Engineering, Architecture, and Applied Mathematics)
Dean: M. Giot; *staff* 221 (70)
F. of Agriculture
Dean: E. Persoons; *staff* 164 (24)
I. of Philosophy
Dean: Cl. Troisfontaines; *staff* 28 (6)
Ce. for Theatre Studies
Director: J. Florence
Ce. for Operations Research and Econometrics
President: J. Jaskold-Gabszewicz
I. of Modern Languages
Director: J. Van Roey
I. of Logography
President: J. Van Den Eeckhaut
International I. for Cellular and Molecular Pathology
Director: C. de Duve
Open F. for Adult Education Teachers
Director: E. Bockstael
Open F. for Economics and Social Sciences
Director: G. Lienard
International I. of Cellular and Molecular Pathology
Director: C. de Duve
Ce. for Operations Research and Econometrics
President: J. Jaskold Gabszewicz

Founded 1425 by Bull of Pope Martin V on the initiative of Duke John IV of Brabant, Collegium Trilingue established by Erasmus 1517. Suppressed 1797 under French occupation and closed during the reigns of Napoleon and William I of Holland. Re-established 1834 as Catholic University by Belgian episcopate. Reorganized 1969 with two divisions, the Katholieke Universiteit te Leuven and the Université catholique de Louvain which became separate legal entities in 1970. The titular head of the university is the Cardinal Archbishop of Malines-Bruxelles. The university is independent of direct State control but receives a full State subvention. Governing bodies: the Conseil d'administration, composed of 6 university and 6 non-university members; the Conseil académique. Residential facilities for students.

Arrangements for co-operation with the universities of: Vienna; Madrid (Complutense); Malaga; Strasbourg III; Aix-Marseilles I; Paris I; Paris II; Paris IX; Edinburgh; Bologne; Hitotsubashi; Leiden; Porto; Fribourg; Mannheim; Cologne; Münster; Montreal; Western Ontario; South Carolina; Chicago; Constantine, Algeria; Córdoba, Argentina; Burundi; Kinshasa; Pontifical University of Salamanca; Pontifical University Comillas, Madrid; University and Polytechnic Federation of Lille; Catholic Institute of Paris; Maynooth College, Ireland; Sophia University, Japan; Technical University of Eindhoven; Erasmus University; University 'Al.I. Cuza', Iasi; Federal Polytechnic School of Lausanne; Imperial College of Science and Technology, London; McGill University; Queen's University; Louisiana State University; New York University; Brandeis University; Texas A & M University; Cornell University; National Polytechnic School of Alger; National University of Rwanda; Universidad Academía de Humanismo Cristiano, Chili; Fujian Agricultural College; Colegio de Mexico; Escuela de Administración de Negocios para Graduados, Peru; Fu Jen Catholic University; Ecole nationale supérieure agronomique, Montpellier; Institut national polytechnique de Grenoble; Université commerciale 'Luigi Bocconi', Milan.

Academic Year: September to May (September-February; February-July).

Admission Requirements: Appropriate secondary school certificate and entrance examination, or foreign qualifications if formally recognized under agreement concluded with the Belgian Government. Other foreign qualifications subject to the approval of the faculty concerned.

Fees (Francs): Registration, 600; tuition, 17,100; undergraduate students from developing countries and all student

Fees: s from industrialized countries, 100,000-300,000 according to Faculty.

Language of Instruction: French.

Degrees and Diplomas: Candidat in–Law; Philosophy; Economics and Social Sciences; History; Philology; Medicine; Dentistry; Physical Education; Natural Sciences; Engineering; Pharmacy. Licence in–Religious Sciences; Canon Law; Criminology; Comparative International Relations and Politics; Public Administration; Social Sciences; Sociology; Social Communication; Economics; Applied Economics; Physical Education; Philosophy; History; Letters; Philology; Musicology; Mathematics; Physics; Chemistry; Geology and Mineralogy; Zoology; Botany; Geography, 4 yrs; Theology; Law; Notarial Studies; Medicine; Dentistry; Applied Sciences; Labour Studies; Psychology; Education, 5 yrs. Maîtrise in–Business Administration; Economics; Theology; Sociology; Demography; Science; Applied Sciences, 1 further yr. Doctorates by thesis. Professional qualification of Ingénieur in various fields, 5 yrs. Diplôme of Pharmacien, 5 yrs. Title of Doctor of Medicine, 7 yrs. Agrégé de l'enseignement secondaire supérieur (teaching qualification, higher secondary level), 4 yrs, together with Licence.Agrégé de l'enseignement supérieur (teaching qualification, university level), by thesis, at least 2 yrsafter Doctorate.

Library: Total, *c.* 1m. vols.

Special Facilities (Museums, etc.): Museums: Art and Archaeology; Histoire de la Médecine.

Publications: Nouvelles Brèves; UCL-Informations; Bulletin des Amis de Louvain; Le Porte-parole; Faculty publications (Centre général de Documentation, Pl. Card. Mercier, 31, B-1348 Louvain-la Neuve).

Press or Publishing House: Presses universitaires de Louvain.

Academic Staff, 1990-91: 915 (72).

Student Enrolment, 1990:

	Men	Women	Total
Of the country	7920	6819	14,739
Of other countries	2159	1379	3538
Total	10,079	8198	18,277

260 ***KATHOLIEKE UNIVERSITEIT LEUVEN**

Catholic University of Leuven

Naamsestraat 22, 3000 Leuven

Telex: 25715

Telephone: (16) 28-38-11

Rector: Roger Dillemans (1985-)

F. of Theology
Dean: J. Delobel
F. of Canon Law
Dean: L. De Fleurquin
F. of Law
Dean: R. Verstegen
F. of Economics and Applied Economics
Dean: J. Vander Eecken
F. of Social Sciences (including Political Science)
Dean: K. Dobbelaere
F. of Medicine (including Dentistry)
Dean: N. Casteels
F. of Philosophy and Letters
Dean: H. Van Gorp
F. of Psychology and Education
Dean: L. Delbeke
F. of Science
Dean: A. Dupré
F. of Applied Sciences (including Mining, Construction, Metallurgical, Chemical, Electrical, Architectural, and Nuclear Engineering, and Computer Sciences)
Dean: E. Aernoudt
F. of Agriculture
Dean: V. Goedseels
I. of Religious Sciences
Chairman: L. Leijssen
I. of Philosophy
Chairman: U. Dhondt
I. of Modern Languages
Chairman: M. Debrock
I. of Physical Education
Chairman: D. Van Gerven
I. of Labour Studies
Chairman: L. Lagrou
I. of Actuarial Studies
Chairman: L. D'Hooge
I. of Literary Studies
Chairman: J. Lambert
I. of Oriental and Slavonic Studies
Chairman: U. Vermeulen
I. of Medieval Studies
Chairman: A. Welkenhuysen
S. of Public Health
Chairman: H. Van de Voorde
I. of Family and Sex Studies
Chairman: F.A. Van Assche
I. of Pharmaceutical Sciences
Chairman: C. De Ranter
I. for the Study of Developing Countries
Chairman: L. Baeck

Founded 1425 by Bull of Pope Martin V on the initiative of Duke John of Brabant. Collegium Trilingue established by Erasmus 1517. Suppressed 1797 under French occupation and closed during the reigns of Napoleon and William I of Holland. Re-established 1834 as Catholic University by Belgian episcopate. Reorganized 1969 with two divisions, the Katholieke Universiteit te Leuven and the Université catholique de Louvain which became separate legal entities in 1970. The titular head of the university is the Cardinal Archbishop of Malines. The university is independent of direct State control but receives a full State subvention. Governing bodies: the Beheerraad (Board of directors) composed of university and non-university members; the Academic Board, including the Rector, Vice-Rector, Administrator, the deans and representatives of the academic staff, the students and the administrative personnel. University-owned residential facilities for about 15 per cent of the students.

Arrangements for the exchange of academic staff with the Universities of Fribourg and Nijmegen and a special agreement with the University of Chicago, Graduate School of Business. It also has special arrangements for co-operation with: Université du Zaïre; University of Wrocław. Postgraduate student exchange with the Universities of: Chicago; Cornell; Lublin; Jassy; Cologne; Bonn; Münster; Genoa.

Academic Year: October to June (October-January; February-June).

Admission Requirements: Appropriate secondary school certificate or foreign qualifications if formally recognized under agreements concluded with the Belgian Government. Other foreign qualifications subject to the approval of the faculty concerned.

Fees (Francs): *c.* 10,000 per annum.

Languages of Instruction: Dutch and English.

Degrees and Diplomas: Kandidaat, 2 yrs, Medicine, 3 yrs. Licentiaat, in various fields, a further 2 yrs. Geaggregeerde Hoger Secundair Onderwijs (teaching qualification, higher secondary level) together with Licentiaat. Professional titles in–Pharmacy; Civil Engineering; Agriculture; Chemical Engineering, 3 yrs and Medicine, 4 yrs after Kandidaat. Doctorates by thesis, 2 yrs after Licentiaat or Professional title. Geaggregeerde Hoger Onderwijs (teaching qualification, university level), at least 2 yrs after Doctorate. Magister in–Theology; Canon Law; Philosophy, 2 yrs after Doctorate. Degrees awarded under English Programme: Degree of Bachelor of–Arts in Theology, 2 yrs; Theology, 3 yrs. Master of–Moral and Religious Sciences, 1 yr after Bachelor; Business Administration, 1 yr after Licentiaat in Applied Economics; Engineering, 1 yr after diploma equivalent to Professional title of Civil Engineer; Agricultural Sciences (for foreign students). Degree of Doctor in Theology, 2 yrs after Bachelor of Artsin Theology.

Libraries: Central Library; also specialized faculty libraries, total, *c.* 370,000 vols.

Special Facilities (Museums, etc.): University Museum.

Publications: Jaarverslag; Academische Tijdingen; Campuskrant; also collections and reviews of various faculties and institutes.

Press or Publishing House: University Press.

Academic Staff: c. 800.

Student Enrolment: c. 23,000.

261 ***UNIVERSITÉ DE MONS-HAINAUT**

University of Mons-Hainaut

Place du Parc, 20, 7000 Mons

Telex: 57764 UE MONS-B

Telephone: (65) 37-31-11

Fax: (65) 37-30-54

Recteur: Yves Van Haverbeke (1981-93)

Administrateur: José Quenon

F. of Science
Dean: Philippe de Gottal; *staff* 66 (14)
F. of Economic and Social Sciences
Dean: Maurice Lefebure *staff* 41 (19)
F. of Medicine (including Pharmacy)
Dean: Jeanine-Anne Heuson Stiennon; *staff* 336 (98)
F. of Psychology and Education
Dean: Marie-Louise Moreau; *staff* 44 (24)
S. of Translation and Interpretation
Director: Marcel Voisin; *staff* 52 (10)

Founded 1899 as an institute, became college 1920 and faculty 1963. Acquired university status as Centre universitaire 1965 and present title 1971. Under the jurisdiction of the Ministry of Education and financed by the State. Governing bodies: the Conseil d'administration; the Conseil académique; the Commission administrative du Patrimoine. Residential facilities for students.

Academic Year: October to September (October-January; February-July).

Admission Requirements: Secondary school certificate or recognized equivalent, and entrance examination.

Fees (Francs): 18,650 per annum; School of Interpretation, 7500.

Language of Instruction: French.

Degrees and Diplomas: Candidat in–Pharmacy; Biology; Psychology and Education, 2 yrs; Medicine, 3 yrs. Licence in–Physics; Chemistry; Mathematics; Economic and Social Sciences; Psychology and Education; Applied Economics; Translation; Interpretation, 4 yrs. Professional titles of–Analyste-informaticien, 3 yrs; Ingénieur commercial, 5 yrs. Agrégation de l'enseignement secondaire supérieur (teaching qualification, higher secondary level) in Chemistry; Mathematics; Psychology and Education; Physics; Applied Economics; Economic and Social Sciences, 1 yr after corresponding Licence. Doctorate in–Applied Economics; Economic and Social Sciences; Psychology and Education;Science. Postgraduate diplomas in–Humanities; Linguistics. Also postgraduate certificates of specialization.

Libraries: Central Library, 531,304 vols; Science and Medicine library, 27,623; Economic and Social Sciences library, 81,425; Psychology and Education library, 25,246; Linguistics library, 22,619.

Publications: Revue de Phonétique Appliquée; Cahiers Internationaux du Symbolisme; Réseaux.

Academic Staff, 1989-90:

Rank	Full-time	Part-time
Professeurs ordinaires	36	–
Professeurs extraordinaires	–	2
Professeurs	9	5
Professeurs associés	3	–
Chargés de cours	3	46
Chargés de cours associés	3	–
Chargés de cours suppléants	–	8
Professeurs (Ecole)	11	–
Chargés de cours (Ecole)	9	1
Personnel scientifique	130	10
Personnel scientifique (Ecole)	32	9
Total	236	81

Student Enrolment, 1989-90:

	Men	Women	Total
Of the country	1043	1510	2553
Of other countries	292	330	622
Total	1335	1840	3175

Other Institutions

Institutions with full University Status

262 **RIJKSUNIVERSITAIR CENTRUM TE ANTWERPEN**

State University Centre of Antwerp

Kastreel 'Den Brandt', Beukenlaan 12, 2020 Antwerpen

Telephone: (3) 827-38-07

F. of Science (including Medical Sciences)

F. of Applied Economics

I. for Developing Countries (including Agriculture, Economics, Sociology and Administration)

I. of Translation and Interpretation

Founded 1965 incorporating the former State College of Commerce founded 1852 and the Institute of Tropical Medicine 1931, and absorbing the academic staff of the former Institute for Overseas Territories 1920. A State institution enjoying partial autonomy under the jurisdiction of the Ministry of Education. Financed by the State. Governing body: the Conseil d'administration. Some residential facilities for students.

Academic Year: October to July (October-December; January-April; April-July).

Admission Requirements: Secondary school certificate or recognized foreign equivalent.

Language of Instruction: Dutch.

Degrees and Diplomas: Kandidaat in–Science, 2 yrs; Natural and Medical Sciences, 3 yrs. Kandidaat in Applied Economics, 2 yrs followed by Licentiaat, a further 2 yrs, and Doctorate by thesis. Geaggregeerde voor het Hoger Secundair Onderwijs (teaching qualification, higher secondary level) in Applied Economics. Title of Handelsingenieur, business administration and industrial organization, 5 yrs. Kandidaat in Translation, 2 yrs followed by Licentiaat in Translation or Interpretation, a further 2 yrs.

Libraries: Central Library, *c.* 35,000 vols; library of Institute of Translation and Intepretation, *c.* 5,000.

Publication: Linguistica Antwerpensia (annually).

Academic Staff: *c.* 180.

Student Enrolment: *c.* 2950.

263 **UNIVERSITAIRE FACULTEITEN SINT-IGNATIUS TE ANTWERPEN**

Prinsstraat 13, 2000 Antwerp

Telex: 33599 UFSIA B

Telephone: (3) 220-41-11

Rector: J. Van Houtte

Voorzitter: M. Willems

F. of Philosophy and Letters

Dean: X. De Keyser

F. of Law

Dean: F. Van Neste

F. of Political and Social Sciences

Dean: F. Van Loon

F. of Applied Economics (including Accountancy, Commercial Engineering and Maritime Law)

Dean: C. Reyns

C. for Business Administration (MBA)

Programme Director: W. Van Grembergen

D. of Philosophy and Religious Studies

President: J. Leilich

D. of History

President: R. Van Uytven

D. of Linguistics and Literature

President: V.Claes

Ce. of History of Law

Director: J. Van Den Broeck

D. of Sociology and Social Policy

President: J. Breda

D. of Economic and Social Research

President: B. De Borger

D. of Third World Studies

President: R. Embrechts

D. of Business Economics

President: E. Claessens

I. for Post-University Studies

Director: L. De Rijcke

I. of Didactics

Director: E. Maurice

Founded 1852, authorized to award degrees 1933. Acquired present university status 1965. Administered by the Society of Jesus, an autonomous institution financially supported by the State. Governing bodies: the General Assembly; the Board of Governors. Residential facilities for *c.* 180 students.

Academic Year: October to July (October-January; January-June).

Admission Requirements: Secondary school certificate or recognized equivalent.

Fees (Francs): Registration, 350; tuition, 13,000 per annum.

Language of Instruction: Dutch.

Degrees and Diplomas: Kandidaat in–Law; Philosophy and Letters; Political and Social Sciences, 2 yrs. Licentiaat in–Applied Economics; Commerce, a further 2 yrs. Doktor in–Applied Economics or Commerce by thesis. Title of Handelsingenieur, business administration and organization, 5 yrs. Geaggregeerde voor het Hoger Secundair Onderwijs (teaching qualification, higher secondary level) in Applied Economics or Commerce. Diploma in Maritime and Inland Water Law; Diplomas in Business Economics.

Libraries: Central Library, *c.* 480,000 vols; Ruusbroec library, *c.* 104,000.

Special Facilities (Museums, etc.): Art Gallery; Radio and T.V. Studio.

Publications: Economisch en Sociaal Tijdschrift; Economische Didactik; Tijdschrift voor Managementvorming; Tijdschrift Universiteit Antwerpen;

Academic Staff, 1989-90: 380.

Student Enrolment, 1989-90: 3800.

264 **UNIVERSITAIRE FACULTEITEN SINT-ALOYSIUS (UFSAL BRUSSELS)**

Vrijheidslaan 17, 1080 Brussel

Telephone: (2) 427-99-60

Fax: (2) 427-99-61

Rector: Fernand Vanhemelryck

Hoofd Administratieve Diensten: Maurits Serneels

F. of Law
Dean: Marc Van Hoecke
F. of Philosophy and Letters
Dean: Jozef Janssens; *staff* 7 (17)
F. of Economic, Political and Social Sciences
Dean: Erik Raymaekers; *staff* 3 (13)
D. of Philosophy
President: Wilfried Goossens; *staff* 2 (2)
D. of Germanic Philology
President: Yvan Putseys; *staff* 4 (6)
D. of History
President: Jozef Janssens; *staff* 3 (9)

Founded 1858 as Section de Philosophie of the Institu Saint-Louis. First authorized to award degrees 1890; reorganized 1969 with separate Dutch and French sections which became legally distinct institutions in 1974. A fully autonomous institution recognized and financially supported by the State. Governing bodies: the Raad van Beheer; the Algemene Vergadering. Some residential facilities for students in private accommodation.

Academic Year: October to July (October-January; January-June).

Admission Requirements: Secondary school certificate or recognized equivalent.

Fees (Francs): 15,500 per annum.

Language of Instruction: Dutch.

Degrees and Diplomas: Kandidaat in–Law; Philosophy; Germanic Philology; Economics; Commercial Engineering; History; Communication Sciences, 2 yrs. Further 2 yr study in Law at a University.

Library: Central Library, *c.* 60,000 vols.

Publications: Study Guide (annuall); UFSAL-info (annually).

Academic Staff, 1989-90: 34 (56).

Student Enrolment, 1989-90:

	Men	Women	Total
Of the country	528	383	911

265 **FACULTÉS UNIVERSITAIRES SAINT-LOUIS**

Boulevard du Jardin Botanique 43, 1000 Bruxelles
Telephone: (2) 211-78-11
Fax: (2) 211-79-97
Recteur: Jacques Dabin
Secrétaire général: Michel van de Kerchove

F. of Philosophy and Letters
Dean: Jean-Marie Cauchies
F. of Law
Dean: François Ost
F. of Economic, Political, and Social Sciences
Dean: Jean-Paul Lambert
S. of Philosophical and Religious Studies
President: Michel van de Kerchove
Interdisciplinary Sem. of Law
Ce. of Sociological Studies
Ce. of Economic Research

Founded 1858 as Section de Philosophie. First authorized to award degrees 1890; reorganized 1969 with separate Dutch and French sections which became legally distinct institutions in 1974. Recognized and financially supported by the State. Governing bodies: the Conseil d'administration; the Conseil de direction.

Academic Year: September to September (October-December; February-May).

Admission Requirements: Secondary school certificate (humanités) or recognized equivalent.

Language of Instruction: French.

Degrees and Diplomas: Candidat in–Philosophy; History; Philology; Law; Economic, Political, and Social Sciences, 2 yrs. Graduat in Philosophy and Religious Studies, 3 yrs.

Library: *c.* 150,000 vols.

Publications: Revue interdisciplinaire d'Etudes juridiques (biannually); Revue Anthropoliques; Cahiers du SMASH (Séminairede Mathématiques appliquées aux Sciences humaines.

Academic Staff: *c.* 30 (40).

Student Enrolment, 1990: *c.* 1200.

266 **LIMBURGS UNIVERSITAIR CENTRUM**

Universitaire Campus, 3610 Diepenbeek
Telex: 39948 LUC B
Telephone: (11) 22-99-61
Fax: (11) 22-32-84
Electronic mail: lucearn@boilucol
Rector: Henri Martenshaegen (1988-92)
Vast Secretaris: Willy Goetstouwers

F. of Science (Mathematics, Physics, Computer Sciences, Chemistry and Biology)
Chairman: Klaus Schmidt; *staff* 33 (17)
F. of Medicine (including Dentistry)
Chairman: Paul Steels; *staff* 33 (17)
D. of Statistics
Co-ordinator: Herman Callaert; *staff* 4
Applied Computer Science L.
Co-ordinator: Eddy Flerackers; *staff* 9
D. of Chemistry
Co-ordinator: Jan Gelan; *staff* 8
Materials Physics Group
Co-ordinator: Lambert Stals; *staff* 7
Instructional Technology Group
Co-ordinator: Hubert Hendrickx; *staff* 6
D. of Applied Geology
Co-ordinator: Tony Van Autenboer; *staff* 2
D. of Applied Biology
Co-ordinator: Herman Clijsters; *staff* 2

Founded 1971. A self-governing public institution of university level. Governing body: the Board of Trustees, comprising 25 members.

Arrangements for joint undertakings in Research and Development with European Community.

Academic Year: October to September.

Admission Requirements: Secondary school certificate or recognized equivalent.

Fees (Francs): Tuition, 14,000.

Language of Instruction: Dutch.

Degrees and Diplomas: Kandidaat in–Mathematics; Physics; Computer Sciences; Chemistry; Biology; Dentistry, 2 yrs; Medicine, 3 yrs. Master of–Science in Biostastics; Integrale Kwaliteitszorg.

Library: *c.* 40,000 vols.

Publication: LUC-Nieuws (monthly).

Academic Staff, 1989-90:

Rank	Full-time	Part-time
Gewoon hoogleraar	18	1
Hoogleraar	4	6
Docenten	4	19
Faculteitsgeaggregeerde	2	–
Hoofdbibliothecaris	1	–
Werkleiders	11	5
Eerstaanwezend assistenten	3	–
Assistenten	28	2
Total	71	33

Student Enrolment, 1989-90:

	Men	Women	Total
Of the country	349	289	738
Of other countries	13	9	22
Total	362	298	760

267 **FACULTÉ DES SCIENCES AGRONOMIQUES DE GEMBLOUX**

Faculty of Agricultural Sciences of Gembloux
Passage des Déportés 2, 5800 Gembloux
Telex: 59482
Telephone: (81) 62-21-11
Fax: (81) 61-45-44
Recteur: C. Deroanne (1988-92)
Directeur administratif: B. Cuvelier

Agriculture (including Economics, Horticulture, Statistics, Meteorology, Geography, Forestry, and Animal Husbandry)

Founded 1860 as agricultural school, became institute 1920, acquired university status 1947 and present title 1965. A State institution responsible to the Ministry of Education of the French Community. Governing bodies: the Conseil d'administration, comprising 17 members; the Conseil académique; the Conseil de Faculté. Some residential facilities for academic staff and students.

Arrangements in co-operation with: Institut national agronomique, Alger; Université nationale du Bénin; National University of Agriculture, Lima; Institut agronomique et vétérinaire Hassan II, Rabat; Escola Superior de Agricultura de Piracicaba, Brazil; Ecole supérieure agronomique de Rennes; Ecole nationale supérieur des Sciences agronomiques d'Atananarivo; Universidad Nacional de San Martín, Tarapoto; Institut national agronomique Paris-Grignon; University of Udine; Ecole nationale supérieure des Sciences agronomiques appliquées de Dijon; Ecole nationale supérieure agronomique de Montpellier; Université de Lille; University of Perugia.

Academic Year: September to June (September-December; January-June).

Admission Requirements: Secondary school certificate or foreign equivalent or entrance examination.

Fees (Francs): 18,125.

Language of Instruction: French.

Degrees and Diplomas: Candidat Ingénieur agronome, 2 yrs. Ingénieur agronome; Ingénieur chimiste, et des industries agricoles, a further 3 yrs. Agrégation (teaching qualification, secondary level), 1 yr after Ingénieur. Docteur en Sciences agronomiques, at least a further 2 yrs. Agrégation (teaching qualification university level), at least 2 yrs after Ingénieur. Also postgraduate Certificates of specialization, 1-2 yrs after Ingénieur.

Library: c. 150,000 vols.

Special Facilities (Museums, etc.): Jardin botanique; Collections zoologiques, minérologiques; Collections végétales et animales.

Publication: Bulletin des Recherches agronomiques (quarterly).

Press or Publishing House: Les Presses agronomiques de Gembloux.

Academic Staff, 1989-90:

Rank	Full-time	Part-time
Professeurs ordinaires	21	–
Professeurs	7	–
Professeurs associés	3	–
Chargés de cours	5	10
Chargés de cours associés	8	–
Total	44	10

Student Enrolment, 1989-90:

Of the country	711
Of other countries	205
Total	916

268 *FACULTÉ POLYTECHNIQUE DE MONS

Polytechnical Faculty of Mons

Rue de Houdain, 9, 7000 Mons

Telephone: (65) 37-41-11

Fax: (65) 37-42-00

Recteur: C. Bouquegneau (1986-94)

F. of Applied Sciences (including Mining, Metallurgical, Chemical, Electrical and Mechanical Engineering, Architecture, Physics, and Mathematics, Computer Sciences and Management)

High Technology Research and Development Ce.

Director: H. Meunier

Founded 1837 as an institute of the Province of Hainaut. Independent since 1921. Financially supported by the State. The Rector is chosen by the Conseil d'administration from three candidates nominated by a combined electorate of representatives of the academic staff, students and technical personnel. He serves a four-year term,which may be renewed twice. Governing bodies: the Conseil d'administration, comprising 28 members; the Conseil de direction, comprising 18 members, representing all sections of the university community. Residential facilities for 288 students.

Arrangements for co-operation with: Brown University; Federal Institute of Technology of Lausanne; University of Mining, Ostrava.

Academic Year: September to June (September-December; February-May).

Admission Requirements: Special entrance examination for all applicants. The humanities section of this examination is not taken by candidates holding appropriate secondary school certificates.

Fees (Francs): 18,000 per annum.

Language of Instruction: French.

Degrees and Diplomas: Professional titles of–Candidat Ingénieur civil, 2 yrs; Ingénieur civil (mining, metallurgy, mechanical, electrical engineering, mathematics, computer sciences and management, energy, employment hygiene and security, geology, nuclear engineering, automatism, architecture, chemistry), a further 3 yrs. Maîtrise, 1 further yr. Docteur en Sciences appliquées. Agrégation de l'Enseignement supérieur (teaching qualification, university level), by thesis. Complementary certificates in–Nuclear Sciences; Industrial Management; Telecommunications; Automation; Quality Control.

Libraries: Central Library, 50,000 vols; Mathematics, Computer Sciences and Management, c. 3000; Architecture, 2000.

Special Facilities (Museums, etc.): Mineralogical and Geological Museum; permanent exhibition on Architecture and Town Planning, and on Ceramics.

Publications: Bulletin d'Information de l'Association des Ingénieurs; Rapport sur l'année académique.

Press or Publishing House: Mutuelle d'Editions des Etudiants de la Faculté de Mons.

Academic Staff, 1989-90:

Rank	Full-time	Part-time
Professeurs ordinaires	22	–
Professeurs	29	1
Chargés de cours	4	10
Chefs de travaux	20	–
Premiers Assistants	3	1
Assistants	24	–
Total	102	12

Student Enrolment, 1989-90:

	Men	Women	Total
Of the country	819	114	933
Of other countries	168	19	187
Total	987	133	1120

269 FACULTÉ UNIVERSITAIRE CATHOLIQUE DE MONS

Chaussée de Binche 151, 7000 Mons

Telephone: (65) 31-21-13

Applied Economics

Political Science and Public Administration

Founded 1896 and recognized by the State 1899. Granted legal status as institution of higher education 1921, institut supérieur 1934, and university 1965. Financially supported by the State. Governing bodies: the Conseil d'administration; the Comité de direction. Residential facilities for students.

Arrangements for co-operation with Université Laval.

Academic Year: September to June (September-January; January-May).

Admission Requirements: Secondary school certificate in relevant fields or recognized equivalent.

Language of Instruction: French.

Degrees and Diplomas: Candidat, 2 yrs. Licence in–Political Science and Administration; Applied Economics, 2 yrs. Maîtrise in Applied Economics, 1 further yr. Ingénieur commercial, 3 yrs. Doctorate by thesis. Agrégation de l'enseignement secondaire (teaching qualification, secondary level). Also Certificat in Data Processing.

Library: c. 12,000 vols.

Publications: FUCAM Informations; Liaisons.

Academic Staff: c. 20 (30).

Student Enrolment: c. 820.

270 *FACULTÉS UNIVERSITAIRES NOTRE-DAME DE LA PAIX

Rue de Bruxelles 61, 5000 Namur

Telex: 59.222 FAC NAM B

Telephone: (81) 22-90-61

Fax: (81) 23-03-91

Recteur: Jacques Berleur (1984-)

Secrétaire général: Raymond Paquay

F. of Philosophy and Letters (including History and Art and Archaeology)

Dean: P. Marchand; *staff* 13

F. of Law

Dean: P. Maon; *staff* 5 (7)

F. of Economics and Social Sciences (including Political Science)

Dean: M. Coipel; *staff* 16 (14)

F. of Science (including Physics, Chemistry, Biology, Mathematics, Geology, and Geography)

Dean: G. Cardinael; *staff* 48 (15)

F. of Medicine (including Pharmacy)

Dean: Robert Leloup; *staff* 8 (3)

I. of Computer Sciences

Director: Jean Ramaekers; *staff* 11 (3)

S. of Modern Languages
Head: P. Ostyn
D. of Education and Technology
Head: J.Donnay
Medico-Psychology Ce.
Head: J. Delville-Mercier
Inter-F. Ce. for Law, Ethics, and Health Sciences
Heads: J. Duchêne, X. Dijon, B. Feltz, J. Scheuer
Inter-F. Ut. of Electronic Microscopy
Head: R. Leloup
Analyses L. for Nuclear Reactions
Head: G. Demortier
I. for Studies in Interface Science:
Head: A. Lucas

Founded 1831 as college by the Society of Jesus and reconstituted under present title 1833. Independent but recognized and financially supported by the State. First authorized to award degrees 1929, accorded full university status 1971. Governing bodies: the Conseil d'administration; the Conseil académique. Residential facilities for academic staff and students.

Academic Year: September to September (September-January; January-June).

Admission Requirements: Secondary school certificate or recognized foreign equivalent.

Fees (Francs): 5700-16,500 per annum.

Language of Instruction: French.

Degrees and Diplomas: Candidat in–Law; History; Philosophy; Philology; Art and Archaeology; Political and Social Sciences; Science; Economics and Social Sciences; Pharmacy, 2 yrs; Veterinary Medicine; Medical Sciences, 3 yrs. Licence in–Science, 2 yrs; Licence spéciale et Maîtrise in–Economics; Computer Sciences, 3 yrs. Doctorat in–Science; Economics; Computer Sciences. Agrégation de l'Enseignement secondaire supérieur (teaching qualification, higher secondary level).

Libraries: Moretus Plantin Library, *c.* 900,000 vols; Centre de Documentation et de Recherche Religieuse, *c.* 400,000.

Publications: Les Etudes classiques (quarterly); Revue Régionale de Droit (quarterly); Revue des Questions scientifiques (quarterly); Annales de la Société Scientifique de Bruxelles (quarterly); Journal de Réflexion sur l'Informatique (quarterly); Cahier de Recherche de la Faculté de Sciences économiques et sociales (irregular); Cahiers de Formation continue de la Faculté des Sciences économiques et sociales (irregular); Documents et Points de Vue de la Faculté des Sciences économiques et sociales (irregular).

Press or Publishing House: Presses Universitaires de Namur.

Academic Staff, 1989-90:

Rank	Full-time	Part-time
Professeurs ordinaires	55	2
Professeurs	27	3
Professeurs associés	2	–
Chargés de cours	18	9
Chargés de cours associés	3	1
Chargés de cours horaires	–	5
Total	105	20

Student Enrolment, 1989-90:

	Men	Women	Total
Of the country	1950	1921	3871
Of other countries	193	128	321
Total	2143	2049	4192*

*Also 38 external students.

271 **UNIVERSITAIRE INSTELLING ANTWERPEN**
Universitetsplein 1, 2610 Wilrijk
Telex: 33646
Telephone: (3) 28-25-28
Fax: (3) 820-22-49
Rector: Freddy Adams
Vaste Sekretaris: Lode Lambeets

F. of Science
Dean: A. Dhondt
F. of Law and Political and Social Sciences
Dean: K Rimanque
F. of Philosophy and Letters
Dean: L. Goossens
F. of Medicine and Pharmacy
Dean: D. Brutsaert
D. of Mathematics and Computer Sciences
Chairman: J. Van Casteren
D. of Physics
Chairman: W. Malfiet
D. of Chemistry
Chairman: E. Vansant
D. of Biochemistry
Chairman: L. Moens
D. of Biology
Chairman: J.P. Verbelen
D. of Medicine
Chairman: S. Pattyn
D. of Pharmacy
Chairman: A. Haemers
D. of Romance Philology
Chairman: L. Tasmowski
D. of Germanic Philology
Chairman: C. Tindemans
D. of Law
Chairman: M. Rigaux
D. of Political and Social Sciences
Chairman: J. Lauwers
D. of Education
Chairman: A. Vermandel
Interdisciplinary P. in Occupational Health
Interdisciplinary P. in Environmental Sciences
I. for Materials Science
Head: J.Van Landuyt; *staff* 150

Founded 1971. A State institution enjoying partial autonomy under the jurisdiction of the Ministry of Education. Governing body: the Board of Directors. Residential facilities for students.

Arrangements for co-operation with the Universities of: Bucharest; Texas A & M; Georgia; East China Normal University, Shanghai; Shanghai Institute of Medicine No. 2; Utrecht; Granada: Paris VI; Dar es Salaam; Shaanxi Teachers; Padjadjaran State; Rwanda; Rabat. Chalmers University of Technology.

Academic Year: October to September (October-December; January-March; April-July; July-September).

Admission Requirements: Diploma of Kandidaat or equivalent.

Language of Instruction: Dutch.

Degrees and Diplomas: Licentiaat, 2-3 yrs. Professional qualifications in–Pharmacy, 3 yrs; Medicine, 4 yrs. Doctorates. Geaggregeerde voor het Hoger Secundair Onderwijs (teaching qualification, higher secondary level), 1 yr.

Library: *c.* 365,000 vols.

Publications: Studiegids; Antilope (catalogue of periodicals).

Academic Staff, 1989: 158 (270).

Student Enrolment, 1989:

	Men	Women	Total
Of the country	965	868	1833*

*Also 180 foreign students.

University Level Institutions

272 **HOGER ARCHITECTUURINSTITUUT VAN HET RIJK**
Mutsaetstraat 31, 2000 Antwerpen

Building and Town Planning

Founded 1952.

273 **INSTITUT SUPÉRIEUR D'ARCHITECTURE INTERCOMMUNAL VICTOR HORTA (I.S.A.I)**
Université libre de Bruxelles, boulevard du Triomphe, 1050 Bruxelles
Telephone: 512-12-96; 513-59-68
Director: Adrien Cools

Architecture

Founded 1763 as Ecole d'Architecture and officially recognized 1937. Acquired present status and title 1977. Associated with the Free University of Brussels 1984 and incorporated into the I.S.A.I. 1986. A State institution responsible to the Ministry of Education of the French Community. Governing body: the Conseil d'administration. Residential facilities for students.

Academic Year: October to July.

Admission Requirements: Secondary school certificate.

Fees (Francs): 9000 (Belgian and CEE); others, 60,000-80,000.

Language of Instruction: French.
Degrees and Diplomas: Candidat, 2 yrs. Diplôme d'Architecte, a further 3 yrs.
Library: Victor Horta et Urbanisme, *c.* 12,000 vols.
Publications: ISAB Bulletin (monthly); Catalogue exposition 'Poelaert et son temps'; 'Les Croisades de Victor Horta'; 200 ans d'Enseignement de l'Architecture'.
Academic Staff, 1990-91: 10 (37).
Student Enrolment, 1989-90: 238.

274 **INSTITUT SUPÉRIEUR D'ARCHITECTURE DE LA COMMUNAUTÉ FRANÇAISE-LA CAMBRE**
Place Flagey 19, 1050 Bruxelles
Telephone: (2) 648-96-19; 648-34-95
Directeur: Marcel Pesleux

Industrial Design
Applied and Monumental Arts
Cinematographic Technology

Founded 1926. A State institution responsible to the Ministry of Education of the French-speaking Community.
Academic Year: October to June (October-January; January-June).
Admission Requirements: Secondary school certificate and entrance examination.
Fees (Francs): EC students, 8000 per annum; others, 80,000.
Language of Instruction: French.
Degrees and Diplomas: Diplômes, 5 yrs.
Library: c. 500,000 vols.
Publications: Les Cahiers de La Cambre (biannually); La Cambre-Informatin (9 times a year).
Press or Publishing House: Imprimerie de l'Ecole.
Academic Staff: c. 90.
Student Enrolment: c. 450.

275 **INSTITUT SUPÉRIEUR D'ARCHITECTURE SAINT-LUC BRUXELLES**
57, rue d'Irlande, 1060 Bruxelles
Telephone: (02) 537-34-19
Directeur: Willy Serneels (1979-)
Secrétaire: Eddie Carton

Architecture
Ce. of Study, Research and Activity in Architecture
President: Jacques Masset

Founded 1904. Acquired present status and title 1977. A private institution of university level, receiving financial support from the State. Governing bodies: the Conseil d'administration; the Assemblée générale.
Arrangements for co-operation with: Ecole d'Architecture, Grenoble; Ecole d'Architecture, Paris; Université de Kaslik, Liban.
Academic Year: October to July (October-February; February-July).
Admission Requirements: Secondary school certificate or equivalent.
Fees (Francs): 15,000 per annum; foreign students, 60,000-80,000.
Language of Instruction: French.
Degrees and Diplomas: Diplôme de Candidat en Architecture, 2 yrs. Diplôme d'Architecte, a further 3 yrs.
Library: c. 10,000 vols.
Publications: Questions? (biannually); Références.
Academic Staff, 1989-90:

Rank	Full-time	Part-time
Professeurs	6	–
Chargés de cours	4	26
Chefs de travaux	4	2
Assistants	7	6
Total	21	34

Student Enrolment, 1989-90:

	Men	Women	Total
Of the country	181	110	291
Of other countries	55	17	72
Total	236	117	363

276 **HOGER ARCHITECTUURINSTITUUT SINT-LUKAS**
Zwartezustersstraat 34, 9000 Gent
Telephone: (091) 25-42-90
Directeur: Jozef Janssens (1978-89)
Beheerder-Secretaris: Paul Van Neck

I. of Architecture (including Urban Planning)

Founded 1862 as School of Architecture, Arts and Crafts. A private institution of university level financiallysupported by the State. Governing body: the Council, comprising 15 members.
Academic Year: September to July (September-January; January-July).
Admission Requirements: Secondary school certificate.
Fees (Francs): 7500 per annum; postgraduate, 2000.
Language of Instruction: Dutch.
Degrees and Diplomas: Titles in–Architecture; Interior Architecture. Postgraduate Diploma in–Restoration; Urban Planning.
Library: c. 7000 vols. Documentation Centre.
Publication: CAO Tijdingen (6 times a year).
Academic Staff, 1986-87:

Rank	Full-time	Part-time
Directeur	1	–
Adjunkt-Directeur	1	–
Hoogleraren	8	–
Docenten	15	9
Werkleiders	4	9
Leraren	13	19
Assistenten	8	7
Total	50	44

Student Enrolment, 1986-87:

	Men	Women	Total
Of the country	392	244	636
Of other countries	4	5	9
Total	396	249	645

277 **STEDELIJK HOGER ARCHITECTUURINSTITUUT 'DE BIJLOKE'**
Prof. J. Kluyskensstraat 6, 9000 Gent
Telephone: (91) 25-29-32
Directeur: Loys Vervenne
Beheerder-Secretaris: Frieda Van Driessche

D. of Architecture
Director: Loys Vervenne *staff* 21 (6)
D. of Town Planning
Dean: H. Verstraete; *staff* 9 (2)
D. of Interior Design
Dean: Frida Vaerewyck; *staff* 14 (8)

Created out of the Royal Academy of Fine Arts of Gent, established in the early 18th century.
Academic Year: September to June.
Admission Requirements: Secondary school certificate.
Fees (Francs): 500-5000.
Language of Instruction: Dutch.
Degrees and Diplomas: Kandidaat in Architecture, 2 yrs. Diplomas in–Interior Design, 4 yrs; Architecture, 5 yrs; Town Planning, a further 3 yrs.
Library: c. 2500 vols.

278 **PROVINCIAAL HOGER ARCHITECTUURINSTITUUT**
Provincial Institute of Architecture
Universitaire campus, Gebouw E, 3610 Diepenbeek
Telephone: (11) 22-83-12; 22-95-98
Fax: (11) 24-27-66
Directeur: M. Nivelle

D. of Architecture
D. of Interior Design
D. of Traffic Analysis and Planning

Founded 1955, acquired present status and title 1970. A provincial institution of university level financiallysupported by the State. Some residential facilities for students.
Participates in the ERASMUS programme.
Academic Year: October to July (October-January; February-July).
Admission Requirements: Secondary school certificate and entrance examination for Interior Design.
Language of Instruction: Dutch.
Degrees and Diplomas: Kandidaat in Architecture, 2 yrs. Diplomas in–Traffic Analyser and Planner, 3 yrs; Interior Design, 4 yrs; Architecture, a further 3 yrs.
Library: c. 4000 vols.

Academic Staff, 1989-90: c. 39 (19).
Student Enrolment, 1989-90:

	Men	Women	Total
Of the country	224	218	442
Of other countries	3	2	5
Total	227	220	447

279 **INSTITUT SUPÉRIEUR D'ARCHITECTURE ST.-LUC DE WALLONIE**

Rue Ste. Marie 30, 4000 Liège
Telephone: (41) 23-38-10
Fax: (41) 23-72-82
Directeur: André Verhulst (1987-)
Directeur-Adjoint: Michel Tilman

I. of Architecture
I. of Architecture (Tournai)
Director: Michel Tilman; *staff* 11 (10)

Founded 1880. Acquired present status and title 1977. A private institution of university rank financially supported by the State. Recently merged with Institut supérieur d'Architecture St. Luc, Ramegnies-Chin. Governing body: the Conseil d'administration.

Arrangements for co-operation with the Universté de Constantine, Algeria. Participates in the ERASMUS programme.

Academic Year: October to June (October-January; February-June).
Admission Requirements: Secondary school certificate.
Fees (Francs): 15,000.
Language of Instruction: French.
Degrees and Diplomas: Candidat, 2 yrs. Diplôme d'Architecte, a further 3 yrs.
Library: 200,000 vols.
Academic Staff, 1989-90:

Rank	Full-time	Part-time
Directeur	1	–
Directeur Adjoint	1	–
Professeurs	7	1
Chef du Bureau d'Etudes	1	–
Chargés de cours	9	11
Chefs de travaux	4	–
Assistants	2	9
Total	25	20

Student Enrolment, 1989-90:

	Men	Women	Total
Of the country	185	150	335
Of other countries	66	35	101
Total	251	185	436

280 **INSTITUT SUPÉRIEUR D'ARCHITECTURE LAMBERT LOMBARD**

Rue Saint-Gilles, 4000 Liège
Telephone: (041) 52-42-40
Directeur: Charles Burton (1972-90)

Architecture

Founded 1835. A State institution. Residential facilities for academic staff and students.

Academic Year: October to July.
Admission Requirements: Secondary school certificate.
Language of Instruction: French.
Degrees and Diplomas: Candidat, 2 yrs. Diplôme légal d'architecture, a further 3 yrs. Title of Urbaniste, a further 2 yrs.
Library: c. 8000 vols.
Academic Staff: c. 60.
Student Enrolment: c. 220.

281 **INSTITUT SUPÉRIEUR D'ARCHITECTURE DE LA VILLE DE MONS**

Rue d'Havre, 88, 7000 Mons
Telephone: (065) 31-46-20
Directeur: André Godart
Administrateur-Secrétaire: Emile Nisolle

Architecture

Founded 1780 as Académie Royale des Beaux-Arts. Acquired present status and title 1975. A State institution.

Academic Year: September to July (September-January; February-July).
Admission Requirements: Secondary school certificate.
Fees: Fees (Francs): Registration, 7500.
Language of Instruction: French.
Degrees and Diplomas: Candidat, 2 yrs. Diplôme légal d'architecte, a further 3 yrs.
Library: c. 2000 vols.
Publication: La Faluche (three times a year).
Academic Staff, 1986-87:

Rank	Full-time	Part-time
Directeur	1	–
Professeurs	3	–
Chefs de travaux	4	–
Chargés de cours	2	10
Assistants	4	3
Total	14	13

Student Enrolment, 1986-87:

	Men	Women	Total
Of the country	72	25	97
Of other countries	27	1	28
Total	99	26	125

282 **INSTITUT SUPÉRIEUR D'ARCHITECTURE ST.-LUC**

Chaussée de Tournai 50, 7721 Ramegnies-Chin

Architecture

Plans in progress to merge with Institut supérieur d'Architecture St. Luc, Liège.

283 **INDUSTRIËLE HOGESCHOOL VAN HET RIJK**

State College of Industrial Engineering
Nijverheidskaai 170, 1070 Brussel
Telephone: (2) 520-18-10
Fax: (2) 520-71-23
Directeur: W. Vansevenant
Beheerder: H. de Maeyer

D. of Mechanical Engineering
Head: J. Dooms; *staff* 13
D. of Electrical Engineering
Head: H. Steyaert; *staff* 7
D. of Mathematics and Physics
Head: H. d'Hollander; *staff* 10 (2)
D. of Electronics
Head: H. Lievens; *staff* 9

Founded 1977, incorporating 2 existing colleges of technical and nuclear engineering. A State institution.

Academic Year: October to July (October-February; February-July).
Degrees and Diplomas: Kandidaat, 2 yrs. Title of Industrieel Ingenieur, 4 yrs.
Library: Central Library, *c.* 6000 vols.
Academic Staff, 1989-90: 43 (3).
Student Enrolment, 1989-90: 429.

284 **INSTITUT GRAMME LIÈGE (INSTITUT SUPÉRIEUR INDUSTRIEL)**

Quai de Condroz, 28, 4900 Liège (Angleur)
Telephone: (41) 43-07-26
Directeur: Jules Dubois (1977-)
Directeur adjoint: M. Clotuche

Industrial Engineering

Founded 1906. A private institution of university level, recognized and financially supported by the State. Governing body: the Conseil d'administration. Residential facilities for students.

Academic Year: September to July (September-January; February-June).
Admission Requirements: Secondary school certificate.
Fees (Francs): Registration, 5000; tuition, 10,000.
Language of Instruction: French.
Degrees and Diplomas: Candidat. Title of Ingénieur industriel en– Section Industrie, Section Energie nucléaire, 4 yrs.
Library: Total *c.* 12,000 vols.

Academic Staff, 1986-87:

Rank	Full-time	Part-time
Directeur	1	–
Professeurs	10	–
Chargés de cours	6	13
Chefs de travaux	9	1
Assistants	8	8
Administratifs	7	–
Total	41	22

Student Enrolment, 1986-87:

	Men	Women	Total
Of the country	467	21	488
Of other countries	9	–	9
Total	476	21	497

285 **STEDELIJKE INDUSTRIËLE HOGESCHOOL ANTWERPEN**

Antwerp Municipal College of Industrial Engineering

Paardenmarkt 94, 2000 Antwerpen

Telephone: (3) 231 5036

Fax: (3) 231 8670

Directeur: W. Broeckhove (1982-)

Secretaris beheerder: J. Swygenhoven

Industrial Engineering (Energy, Electronics, Electro-Mechanics, Civil Engineering)

Founded 1977 with divisions in Antwerp and Mechelen. Detached 1982 to form separate college.

Academic Year: October to July (October-January; January-July).

Admission Requirements: Secondary school certificate.

Fees (Francs): 10,000 per annum.

Language of Instruction: Dutch.

Degrees and Diplomas: Kandidaat, 2 yrs. Title of Industrieel Ingenieur, 4 yrs.

Library: c. 10,000 vols.

Academic Staff, 1989-90:

Rank	Full-time	Part-time
Hoogleraaren	15	–
Docenter	13	–
Werkleiders	18	–
Assistenten	20	2
Total	66	2

Student Enrolment, 1989-90:

	Men	Women	Total
Of the country	748	74	822
Of other countries	28	–	28
Total	776	74	850

286 **INSTITUT SUPÉRIEUR INDUSTRIEL DE L'ÉTAT**

Chemin de Weyler 2, 6700 Arlon

Telephone: (63) 22-05-17

Directeur: Raymond Felten (1985-)

Administrateur-Secrétaire: Jacqueline Eppe

Industrial Engineering

Founded 1977. A State institution under the jurisdiction of the Minis-try of Education. Governing body: the Conseil d'administration. Some residential facilities for 83 students.

Arrangements for co-operation with Institut supérieur de Technologie, Luxembourg.

Academic Year: October to July (October-January; February-July).

Admission Requirements: Secondary school certificate.

Fees (Francs): 6250 per annum; foreign students, 60,000-80,000.

Language of Instruction: French.

Degrees and Diplomas: Candidat, 2 yrs. Title of Ingénieur industriel, 4 yrs.

Library: Central Library, *c.* 20000 vols.

Press or Publishing House: Imprimerie de l'I.S.I.E. d'Arlon.

Academic Staff, 1986-87:

Rank	Full-time	Part-time
Professeurs	4	–
Chefs de travaux	4	–
Assistants	9	4
Chargés de cours	4	6
Toteal	21	10

Student Enrolment, 1986-87:

	Men	Women	Total
Of the country	166	12	178
Of other countries	28	2	30
Total	194	14	208

287 **INSTITUT SUPÉRIEUR INDUSTRIEL DE BRUXELLES**

Rue Royale, 150, 1000 Bruxelles

Telephone: (2) 21-74-54

Président: Léonard Hocks

Sec. of Nuclear Science

Head: F. Jondeur; *staff* 4

Sec. of Electrical and Electonic Engineering

Head: A. Massin; *staff* 15

Sec. of Mechanical Engineering

Head: Cl. Van Leugenhaghe; *staff* 13

Sec. of Chemical Engineering

Head: P. Dieryck; *staff* 9

Founded 1956 as Institut supérieur des Sciences nucléaires, acquired present title 1977. A State institution under the jurisdiction of the Ministry of Education. Governing body: the Conseil d'administration. Residential facilities for students.

Academic Year: October to July (October-February; February-July).

Admission Requirements: Secondary school certificate.

Fees (Francs): 10,000 per annum.

Language of Instruction: French.

Degrees and Diplomas: Candidat, 2 yrs. Title of Ingénieur industriel, 2 yrs after Candidat.

Library: Central Library.

Academic Staff, 1989-90:

Rank	Full-time	Part-time
Professeurs	14	–
Chargés de cours	14	6
Chefs de travaux	8	1
Assistants	17	5
Total	53	12

Student Enrolment, 1989-90:

	Men	Women	Total
Of the country	623	67	690
Of other countries	55	1	56
Total	678	68	746

288 **INSTITUT SUPÉRIEUR INDUSTRIEL DE L'I.I.F.-I.M.C./I.S.I.**

Avenue Emile Gryzon 1, 1070 Bruxelles

Telephone: (2) 526-73-00

Fax: (2) 526-70-42

Président: D. Rober

Directeur: A. Weerens

Sec. of Industrial Bio-Engineering

Head: C.A. Masschelein; *staff* 6

Sec. of Catalysis

Head: G. Jannes; *staff* 5

Sec. of Organic and Polymer Chemistry

Head: J. Hanuise; *staff* 5 (3)

Sec. of Food Sciences and Technology

Head: P. Dysseler; *staff* 4 (3)

Sec. of Analytical Chemistry

Head: J. Vandegans; *staff* 5 (5)

Sec. of Computer Techniques

Head: A. Jaucot; *staff* 3 (2)

Sec. of Fermentation

Head: J.-P. Simon; *staff* 4

Sec. of Biochemistry-Microbiology
Head: J. Bechet *staff* 3

Founded 1954, incorporating Institut Meurice de Chimie (1892) and Institut des Industries de Fermentation (1930). Residential facilities for students.

Arrangements for student exchange with the Polytechnic of the South Bank, London.

Academic Year: October to July.

Admission Requirements: Diplôme d'Aptitude à Accéder à l'Enseignement supérieur-Niveau universitaire.

Fees (Francs): 10,000 per anuum.

Language of Instruction: French.

Degrees and Diplomas: Candidat, 2 yrs. Title of Ingénieur industriel, a further 2 yrs.

Academic Staff: c. 40 (10).

Student Enrolment, 1989-90:

	Men	Women	Total
Of the country	151	124	275

289 **ÉCOLE CENTRALE DES ARTS ET MÉTIERS (ECAM)**
Rue du Tir 14, 1060 Bruxelles
Telephone: (32-2) 539 3810
Fax: (32-2) 539 1163
Directeur: Gaston Decornet (1975-)
Secrétaire général: A. Huylenbroeck

Ut. of Mechanical Engineering
Head: Arthur Fritte; *staff* 7 (2)
Ut. of Electrical Engineering
Head: Georges Hennuy; *staff* 7 (2)
Ut. of Electronics
Head: Ernest De Pauw; *staff* 7 (5)
Ut. of Automation and Robotics
Head: Claude Dierickx; *staff* 3 (1)
Ut. of Civil Engineering
Head: Jacques De Jaeger; *staff* 5 (4)
Ut. of Sciences
Head: Lino Zandarin; *staff* 11 (1)
Ut. of ComputerSciences
Head: Jacques Taskin; *staff* 3 (2)
Ut. of Technology
Head: André Vanderbist; *staff* 12 (2)
Ut. of Human, Social, and Economic Studies
Head: Philippe Mercenier; *staff* 4

Founded 1898. Acquired present status 1977. A private institution of university level recognized and financially supported by the State. Governing bodies: the Conseil d'administration; the Conseil d'orientation et de perfectionnement.

Academic Year: September to July (September-January; February-May).

Admission Requirements: Secondary school certificate.

Fees (Francs): 11,500 per annum.

Language of Instruction: French.

Degrees and Diplomas: Candidat Ingénieur industriel, 2 yrs. Title of Ingénieur industriel, 4 yrs.

Library: Central Library, c. 3000 vols.

Academic Staff, 1989-90:

Rank	Full-time	Part-time
Professeurs	7	–
Chargés de cours	11	20
Chefs de travaux	11	–
Assistants	28	–
Total	57	20

Student Enrolment, 1989-90:

	Men	Women	Total
Of the country	695	15	710

290 **INSTITUT SUPÉRIEUR INDUSTRIEL DU HAINAUT**
Boulevard Solvay 31, 600 Charleroi

Industrial Engineering

291 **KATHOLIEKE INDUSTRIËLE HOGESCHOOL VOOR LIMBURG**
Catholic Institute of Industrial Engineering
Universitaire Campus, 3610 Diepenbeek
Telephone: (11) 22-21-42

Chemical Engineering
Electro-Mechanical Engineering

Founded 1977, incorporating the Hogere Scholen voor Technische Ingenieur in Sint-Truiden (1959) and Hasselt (1964). A private institution of university level recognized by and receiving financial support from the State. Governing body: the Board of Trustees.

Academic Year: September to July (September-February; February-July).

Admission Requirements: Secondary school certificate.

Language of Instruction: Dutch.

Degrees and Diplomas: Title of Industrieel Ingenieur, 4 yrs. Also Graduaat in de bedrijfsmechanisatie, 2 yrs.

Academic Staff: c. 70.

Student Enrolment: c. 790.

292 **KATHOLIEKE INDUSTRIËLE HOGESCHOOL DER KEMPEN**
Technische Schoolstraat 52, 2440 Geel
Telephone: (14) 58-55-75
President: Paul Martens

Industrial Engineering (Electromechanics, Electronics, Electrical Engineering, Agriculture)
Also 4 Research Institutes.

Founded 1957.

Academic Year: September to July (September-January; February-July).

Admission Requirements: Secondary school certificate.

Fees (Francs): 10,000.

Language of Instruction: Dutch.

Academic Staff, 1990: 91.

293 **KATHOLIEKE INDUSTRIËLE HOGESCHOOL OOST-VLAANDEREN**
Catholic College of Industrial Engineering
Campus Rabot, 9000 Gent
Telephone: (91) 23-60-01
Fax: (91) 25-62-69
Director: V. Van Haver

Industrial Engineering (including Chemistry, Biochemistry, Civil Construction, Electrical and Electronic Engineering, Physics, Mathematics, and Computer Sciences)

Founded 1977, incorporating 3 existing colleges of technical engineering. A private institution.

Participates in the ERASMUS programme.

Academic Year: September to July.

Admission Requirements: Secondary school certificate.

Fees (Francs): c. 9000.

Language of Instruction: Dutch.

Degrees and Diplomas: Kandidaat, 2 yrs. Title of Industrieel Ingenieur, 4 yrs.

Academic Staff, 1989-90: 140.

Student Enrolment, 1989-90:

	Men	Women	Total
Of the country	1472	310	1782*

Including c. 8 foreign students.

294 **INDUSTRIËLE HOGESCHOOL VAN HET RIJK C.T.L.**
State College of Industrial Engineering C.T.L.
Voskenslaan 270, 9000 Gent
Telephone: (91) 21-80-11
Directeur: W. Verheugen
Algemeen Beheerder: I. De Kuyper

Industrial Engineering (Chemistry, Textiles, Agriculture)

Founded 1977, incorporating institutes of textile engineering (1947), agriculture (1948) and chemistry (1960).

Academic Year: October to July.

Admission Requirements: Secondary school certificate.

Fees (Francs): Registration, 500; tuition, 5000 per annum.

Language of Instruction: Dutch.

Degrees and Diplomas: Kandidaat, 2 yrs. Title of Industrieel Ingenieur, 4 yrs.

Libraries: Central Library, c. 15,000 vols; Documentation Centre, c. 5000.

Publication: Cerevista (quarterly).
Academic Staff, 1986-87: 53 (40).
Student Enrolment, 1986-87:

	Men	Women	Total
Of the country	621	331	952
Of other countries	5	3	8
Total	626	334	960

295 **INDUSTRIËLE HOGESCHOOL VAN HET RIJK B.M.E.**
State Polytechnic B.M.E.
Schoonmeersstrasat 52, 9000 Gent
Telephone: (91) 21-38-31
Fax: (91) 21-19-37
President: Arthur Van Overberge
Vice-President: Gilbert Bartholomees

Engineering (Civil, Mechanical, Electrical, Electronic, and Surveying)

Founded 1827.

Arrangements for co-operation with: Eindhoven Polytechnic; Utrecht Polytechnic.

Academic Year: October to July.
Admission Requirements: Secondary school certificate.
Fees (Francs): 7000-12,000.
Language of Instruction: Dutch.
Degrees and Diplomas: Kandidaat, 2 yrs. Title of Industrieel Ingenieur, 4 yrs. Gegradueerde, 3 yrs.
Library: library: 14,000 vols.
Press or Publishing House: Indus VZW.
Academic Staff, 1990:

Rank	Full-time	Part-time
Hoogleraaren	17	7
Docenten	17	6
Werkleiders	16	11
Assistenten	22	13
Docenten	90	98
Total	162	135

296 **INDUSTRIËLE HOGESCHOOL VAN HET GEMEENSCHAPSONDERWIJS-LIMBURG**
Community Educational College of Industrial Engineering
Maastrichterstraat 100, 3500 Hasselt
Directeur: A. Queeckers
Beheerder-Secretaris: H. Piryns

Industrial Engineering (Civil, Electrical, Nuclear, Electronic Engineering)

Founded 1977 as a State college. Acquired present staatus and title 1989. Administered by the Flemisch Community. Governing body: the Administration Council. Residential facilities for students.

Academic Year: October to July.
Admission Requirements: Secondary school certificate.
Fees (Francs): 7000 per annum.
Language of Instruction: Dutch.
Degrees and Diplomas: Kandidaat, 2 yrs. Title of Industrieel Ingenieur, 4 yrs.
Library: c. 5000 vols.
Academic Staff, 1989-90: 37.
Student Enrolment, 1989-90:

	Men	Women	Total
Of the country	329	52	381
Of other countries	11	2	13
Total	440	54	394

297 **KATHOLIEKE INDUSTRIËLE HOGESCHOOL ANTWERPEN**
Salesianenlaan 1A, 2710 Hoboken
Telephone: (3) 828-16-40
Directeur: Alfred Popelier (1988-)
Beheerder-Secretaris: Francis Marien

D. of Electro-Mechanics
Head: B. De Koninck; *staff* 21
D. of Electrical Engineering
Head: F. Massie; *staff* 11
D. of Electronics
Head: B. Peeters; *staff* 5
D. of Biochemistry
Head: J. Apers; *staff* 5 (2)
D. of Industrial Chemistry
Head: J. Apers; *staff* 9
D. of Industrial and Chemical Chemistry
Head: W.Gunst

Founded 1960 as school, acquired present title and status 1977. A private institution of university level recognized and financially supported by the State. Governing body: the Board of Directors.

Academic Year: October to July (October-February; February-July).
Admission Requirements: Secondary school certificate.
Fees (Francs): 7000-9000 per annum.
Language of Instruction: Dutch.
Degrees and Diplomas: Kandidaat, 2 yrs. Title of Industrieel Ingenieur, 4 yrs. Gegradueerde in Chemistry, 3 yrs.
Library: Specialized libraries.
Academic Staff, 1989-90:

Rank	Full-time	Part-time
Directeur	1	–
Adjunkt-Directeur	1	–
Hoogleraren	17	–
Docenten	23	2
Werkleiders	29	2
Assistenten	15	1
Lesgevers	14	8
Total	100	13

Student Enrolment, 1989-90:

	Men	Women	Total
Of the country	944	296	1240
Of other countries	12	2	14
Total	956	298	1254

298 **INSTITUT SUPÉRIEUR INDUSTRIEL DE L'ÉTAT**
Rue St.-Victor 3, 4200 Huy

Industrial Engineering

Academic Year: October to July.
Admission Requirements: Secondary school certificate.
Language of Instruction: French.
Degrees and Diplomas: Candidat Ingénieur industriel, 2 yrs. Title of Ingénieur industriel, 4 yrs.

299 **PROVINCIALE INDUSTRIËLE HOGESCHOOL**
Graaf Karel de Goedelaan 5, 8500 Körtrijk
Telephone: (56) 21-54-65
Fax: (56) 21-04-13
Directeur: Gerard Verplancke (1977-)
Beheerder-Secretaris: Paul Dewerchin

Industrial Engineering (Electricity, Electronics, Chemistry, Biochemistry)

Founded 1957 as technical institute, acquired present status and title 1977. A provincial institution receiving financial support from the State. Governing body: the Board of Administrators.

Academic Year: October to July (October-January; February-July).
Admission Requirements: Secondary school certificate.
Fees (Francs): 5000 per annum.
Language of Instruction: Dutch.
Degrees and Diplomas: Kandidaat, 2 yrs. Title of Industrieel Ingenieur, 4 yrs.
Library: Central Library, c. 6000 vols.
Publication: Kontakt (quarterly).
Academic Staff, 1989-90:

Rank	Full-time	Part-time
Directeur, Adjunct-Directeur, Hoofd van studiebureau	3	–
Hoogleraren	5	–
Docenten	8	7
Werkleiders	4	–
Assistenten	11	5
Total	31	12

Student Enrolment, 1989-97:

	Men	Women	Total
Of the country	351	84	435

300 **INDUSTRIËLE HOGESCHOOL GROEP T LEUVEN**

Groep T College of Industrial Engineering

Campus Blauwput, Vuurkruisenlaan 4, 3000 Leuven

Telephone: (16) 23-08-50

Fax: (16) 22-83-43

Gedelegeerd Bestuurder-Directeur: Johan De Graeve

Adjunct-Directeur: Arthur d'Huys

D. of Mathematics
Head: Guido Claessens; *staff* 10
D. of Physics
Head: Fernand Dhoore; *staff* 15
D. of Chemistry
Head: Guido Van Orshaegen; *staff* 8
D. of Materials Science
Head Luc Vandenabeele; *staff* 6
D. of Electromechanical Engineering
Head: Juliaan Vuerinckx; *staff* 8 (2)
D. of Chemical and Biochemical Engineering
Head: Chantal Block; *staff* 7
D. of Economics-Management
Head: Guido Vercammen; *staff* 3 (5)
D. of Communication-Languages
Head: Yves Persoons; *staff* 6 (8)
D. of Information Technology
Head: Patrick de Ryck; *staff* 3 (1)

Founded 1960 as technical institute. Granted legal status as institution of university rank 1970 and amalgamated with Radio-en Filmtechnisch Instituut and Hoger Technisch Instituut Kardinaal Mercier 1977. Acquired present title 1980. A private institution financially supported by the State. Some residential facilities for students.

Academic Year: October to July (October-January; February-June).

Admission Requirements: Secondary school certificate or recognized foreign equivalent.

Fees (Francs): 14,800 per annum.

Language of Instruction: Dutch.

Degrees and Diplomas: Kandidaat, 2 yrs. Title of Industrieel Ingenieur, 4 yrs.

Library: c. 1000 vols.

Academic Staff, 1989-90:

Rank	Full-time	Part-time
Directeur	1	–
Adjunct-Directeur	1	–
Hoogleraaren	21	–
Docenten	18	2
Werkleiders	23	6
Assistenten	15	20
Total	79	28

Student Enrolment, 1989-90:

	Men	Women	Total
Of the country	979	308	1287
Of other countries	4	–	4
otal	983	308	1291

301 **INSTITUT SUPÉRIEUR INDUSTRIEL LIÉGEOIS**

Quai Gloesener 6, 4020 Liège

Telephone: (41) 41-13-85

Fax: (41) 41-50-27

Directeur: Servais Gardier (1985-)

Administrateur-Secrétaire: Guy Steyvers

Ut. of Agriculture and Food Technology
Ut. of Chemistry
Ut. of Civil Engineering
Ut. of Electrical Engineering
Ut. of Electronics
Ut. of Mechanical Engineering
Ut. of Computer Sciences
Ut. of Automation
Ut. of Socio-economics
Ut. of Physics
Ut. of Mathematics
Ut. of Design

Founded 1977. A State institution. Governing body: the Conseil d'administration. Some residential facilities for students.

Academic Year: October to July (October-January; February-July).

Admission Requirements: Secondary school certificate or foreign equivalent.

Fees (Francs): Registration, 6500 per annum; tuition for foreign students, 60,000-80,000 per annum.

Language of Instruction: French.

Degrees and Diplomas: Candidat Ingénieur industriel, 2 yrs. Title of Ingénieur industriel, 4 yrs.

Library: 4000 vols.

Press or Publishing House: Imprisil.

Academic Staff, 1989-90: c. 50.

Student Enrolment, 1989-90: c. 570.

302 **KATHOLIEKE INDUSTRIËLE HOGESCHOOL DE NAYER-MECHELEN**

Jan De Nayerlaan 5, 2580 Sint-Katelyne-Waver

Telephone: (15) 31-69-44

Fax: (15) 31-74-53

Directeur: C. Verwilt (1974-)

Beheerder-Secretaris: P. Liekens

S. of Chemistry
Head: M. Van Dyck; *staff* 32 (6)
S. of Electronics
Head: J. Compeers; *staff* 30 (1)
S. of Electro-Mechanics
Head: L. Devrieze; *staff* 35 (5)
S. of Construction Engineering
Head: L. Moris; *staff* 26 (3)
Graduate S. of Electro-Mechanics
Head: P. Felique; *staff* 14 (2)

Founded 1922. A private institution of university level recognized and financially supported by the State. Governing bodies: the General Council; the Board of Directors. Residential facilities for 100 men students.

Participates in the ERASMUS, COMETT and Eurotecnet programmes.

Academic Year: October to July (October-January; January-July).

Admission Requirements: Secondary school certificate.

Fees (Francs): Registration, 1000; tuition, 7110-9480.

Language of Instruction: Dutch.

Degrees and Diplomas: Kandidaat, 2 yrs. Title of Industrieel Ingenieur, 4 yrs. Also Gradué in Electro-Mechanics, 3 yrs.

Library: Library, 2000 vols.

Academic Staff, 1990: 134.

Student Enrolment, 1989-90:

	Men	Women	Total
Of the country	1325	238	1563
Of other countries	8	–	8
Total	1333	238	1571

303 **STEDELIJKE INDUSTRIËLE HOGESCHOOL MECHELEN**

Malines Municipal College of Industrial Engineering

Leopoldstraat 42, 2800 Mechelen

Telephone: (015) 41-22-11

Directeur: Armand Coppens (1977-)

Beheerder-Secretaris: Dirk Teugels

D. of Chemistry
Head: Roger De Wol; *staff* 6
D. of Electronics
Head: Robert Suykens; *staff* 8 (1)
D. of Electrical Engineering
Head: Jaques Geers; *staff* 5

Founded 1977 with divisions in Mechelen and Antwerpen. Detached 1982 to form separate college.

Academic Year: October to June (October-January; January-June).

Admission Requirements: Secondary school certificate.

Fees (Francs): Registration, 5000.

Language of Instruction: Dutch.

Degrees and Diplomas: Kandidaat, 2 yrs. Title of Industriel Ingenieur, 4 yr

Academic Staff, 1986-87:

Rank	Full-time-	Part-time
Hoogleraren	1	–
Docenten	11	1
Werkleiders	4	–
Assistenten	9	3
Total	25	4

Student Enrolment, 1986-87:

	Men	Women	Total
Of the country	311	26	337
Of other countries	11	–	11
Total	322	26	348

304 **INSTITUT SUPÉRIEUR INDUSTRIEL DE L'ÉTAT**

Avenue V. Maistriau 8, Bte. A., 7000 Mons
Cables: Isiem Mons
Telephone: (65) 338154

S. of Industrial Engineering
S. of Construction Engineering
S. of Electrical Engineering
S. of Electronics
S. of Automation, Radio and Television

Founded 1959 as technical institute, acquired present status and title 1977. A State institution. Governing body: the Conseil d'administration. Limited residential facilities for students.

Academic Year: October to July (October-January; February-July).

Admission Requirements: Secondary school certificate or foreign equivalent.

Language of Instruction: French.

Degrees and Diplomas: Candidat Ingénieur industriel, 2 yrs. Title of Ingénieur industriel, 4 yrs. Also Gradué in Automation and Radio/ Television, 2 yrs.

Library: Central Library.

Academic Staff: c. 30.

Student Enrolment: c. 330.

305 **INSTITUT SUPÉRIEUR INDUSTRIEL CATHOLIQUE DU HAINAUT**

Avenue de l'Hôpital, 22, 7000 Mons
Telephone: (65) 31-73-67/68
Fax: (65) 35-28-16
Directeur: André Lhost (1985-2001)

D. of Chemical Engineering and Biochemistry
Head: Jean-Paul Thibaut; *staff* 12 (15)
D. of Electro-mechanical Engineering
Head: René Seront; *staff* 22 (10)
D. of Electrical Engineering and Electronics
Head: Auguste Mousty; *staff* 10 (15)
Ce. for Computer Sciences
Ce. for Computer Sciences and Applied Mathematics

Founded 1977 incorporating the Institut Don Bosco de Tournai, Institut Reine Astrid de Mons, and Aumôniers de Travail de Charleroi. A private institution of university level receiving financial support from the Ministry of Education. Governing bodies: the Conseil d'administration; the Conseil de direction; the Conseil académique.

Arrangements for co-operation with: Université d'Aix-Marseille III; Institut de Génie chimique, Toulouse; Ecole nationale supérieure des Industries chimiques, Nancy.

Academic Year: September to June (September-January; February-June).

Admission Requirements: Secondary school certificate or foreign equivalent.

Fees (Francs): 12,000-15,000 per annum.

Language of Instruction: French.

Degrees and Diplomas: Candidat Ingénieur industriel, 2 yrs. Title of Ingénieur industriel, 4 yrs.

Academic Staff, 1989-90:

Rank	Full-time	Part-time
Direction	4	–
Professeurs	13	–
Chargés de cours	2	21
Chefs de travaux	8	17
Assistants	17	15
Total	44	53

Student Enrolment, 1989-90:

	Men	Women	Total
Of the country	460	56	516
Of other countries	83	6	89
Total	543	62	605

306 **KATHOLIEKE INDUSTRIËLE HOGESCHOOL WEST-VLAANDEREN**

Zeedijk 101, 8400 Oostende
Telephone: (59) 50-89-96
Fax: (59) 70-42-15
Directeur: Gerard Manderyck (1980-)

D. of Chemistry and Biochemistry
Dean: Jacques Perneel; *staff* 10 (4)
D. of Electronics
Dean: Johan Catrysse; *staff* 19 (7)
D. of Electro-Mechanical Engineering
Dean: André Dekeyser; *staff* 16 (5)
D. of Industrial Engineering
Dean: Leon Van Craeynest; *staff* 20 (6)
I. of Technology
Administrator: G. Manderyck *staff* 2 (12)

Founded 1948. Residential facilities for students.

Participates in the ERASMUS, COMETT, Eurotecnet, and Esprit programmes.

Academic Year: October to July (October-February; February-July).

Admission Requirements: Secondary school certificate.

Fees (Francs): 9100 per annum.

Language of Instruction: Dutch.

Degrees and Diplomas: Kandidaat, 2 yrs. Title of Industrieel Ingenieur, 4 yrs.

Library: c. 10,000 vols.

Academic Staff, 1989-90:

Rank	Full-time	Part-time
Hoogleraren	18	–
Docenten	44	1
Assistenten	27	1
Total	89	2

Student Enrolment, 1989-90:

Men	Women	Total
954	177	1131

307 **INSTITUT SUPÉRIEUR INDUSTRIEL CATHOLIQUE DU LUXEMBOURG**

Arts et Métiers, Rue de Pierrard 112, 6760 Virton
Telephone: (63) 57-63-27
Fax: (63) 57-67-62
Directeur: André Petitjean (1977-)
Administrateur secrétaire: Philippe Ninane

Ut. of Mathematics and Science
Head: Georges Hupet; *staff* 4 (3)
Ut. of Mechanical Engineering Construction
Head: Yvon Bodart; *staff* 2 (3)
Ut. of Mechanical Engineering Fabrications
Head: Alain Adam; *staff* 3 (2)
Ut. of Human Sciences and Business Administration
Head: Adelin Thomas *staff* – (8)
Ut. of Thermic and Fluid Engineering
Head: Raymond Maire; *staff* 1 (31)
Ut. of Electrical and Electronic Engineering
Head: Louis Romanini; *staff* 5 (1)
Ut. of Informatics and Automatics
Head: Hubert Coppens d'Eckenbrugge; *staff* 5

Research Ce. (CRISIP)
Chairman: Jean Van Droogenbroek; *staff* 14

Founded 1900 by the Congrégation des Aumôniers du Travail as Institut des Arts et Métiers, acquired present status and title 1977. A private institution of university level receiving financial support from the State. Governing body: the Commission administrative, including representatives from the industrial sectors. Some residential facilities for students.

Academic Year: September to July (September-January; January-May).

Admission Requirements: Secondary school certificate or foreign equivalent.

Fees (Francs): 8000-11,500; foreign students, 60,000-80,000.

Language of Instruction: French.

Degrees and Diplomas: Candidat Ingénieur industriel, 2 yrs. Title of Ingénieur industriel, 4 yrs. (Section Electromécanique).

Library: c. 6000 vols.

Publications: Revue (annually); Bulletin des Anciens (quarterly); Annuaire des Anciens (biannually).

Academic Staff, 1989-90:

Rank	Full-time	Part-time
Professeurs	2	–
Chargés de cours	57	109
Chefs de travaux	69	–
Assistants	79	1
Total	22	10

Student Enrolment, 1989-90:

	Men	Women	Total
Of the country	185	10	195
Of other countries	12		12
Total	197	10	207

308 **HANDELSCHOGESCHOOL**

Korte Nieuwstraat 33, 2000 Antwerp
Telephone: (3) 32-74-52

Business Administration and Economics

Founded 1925 as College of Commerce for Women. Officially recognized 1934 and acquired university status and present title 1969. Financially supported by the State.

Academic Year: October to July (October-December; January-March; April-July).

Admission Requirements: Secondary school certificate, or foreign equivalent.

Language of Instruction: Dutch.

Degrees and Diplomas: Kandidaat, 2 yrs. Licentiaat in Commercial and Consular Studies or Commercial Studies and Finance, a further 3 yrs. Geaggregeerde Hoger Secundair Onderwijs (teaching qualification, higher secondary level), 1 yr after Licentiaat. Also degree of Master.

Library: c. 25,000 vols.

Academic Staff: c. 30 (70).

Student Enrolment: c. 520.

309 **INSTITUT CATHOLIQUE DE HAUTES ÉTUDES COMMERCIALES**

2 boulevard Brand Whitlock, 1150 Bruxelles
Telephone: 739 3711
Fax: 738 3903
Président: Viscomte d'Avignon
Rector: P. Dupriel
Secrétaire général: Jacques Cornel

D. of International Commerce
Head: A. Huybrechts
D. of Financial Administration
Head: Ph. Van Namen
D. of Marketing Studies
Head: P. Van Vracem
D. of Computer Sciences
Head: J.M. Poncelet
Control and Revision D.
Head: P. Lurkin
D. of Human Resources
D. of Public Administration
D. of Commerce
Language Commission
Head: J. P. Callut
S. of Fiscal Studies
Head: P. Sibille
Ce. for Marketing Research
Head: P. Van Vracem
Ce. for Lifelong Education
Head: P. Van Vracem
Ce. for Management (Baccalauréat training)
Head: P. Flahaut

Founded 1931 and officially recognized 1931 under the name Institut supérieur de Commerce pour jeunes filles. Reorganized 1954 as a mixed institution and acquired present title. Additional schools and centres established 1957 and 1966. Financially supported by the State. Governing bodies: the Conseil académique; the Conseil d'administration, comprising 12 members. Some residential facilities for students.

Academic Year: September to June (September-January; February-June).

Admission Requirements: Secondary school certificate or teaching qualifications (secondary level), or foreign equivalents.

Fees (Francs): *c.* 21,000.

Language of Instruction: French.

Degrees and Diplomas: Candidat, 2 yrs. Licence–en Sciences commerciales et financières; en Sciences commerciales et consulaires, a further 2 yrs. Ingénieur commercial, 5 yrs. Agrégation de l'enseignement secondaire supérieur (teaching qualification, higher secondary level), 1 yr after Licence.

Library: Central Library and annex, *c.* 14,000 vols.

Publication: Reflets et perspectives de la vie économique (quarterly).

Academic Staff, 1990: c. 60 (80).

Student Enrolment, 1990: c. 1600 (Also *c.* 2000 adults in Lifelong Education).

310 **INSTITUT D'ENSEIGNEMENT SUPÉRIEUR LUCIEN COOREMANS**

Lucien Cooremans Institute of Higher Education
Place Anneessens 11, 1000 Bruxelles
Telephone: (2) 512-54-91
Directeur: Roger Van Damme (1978-)
Chef de travaux: Jacqueline Reumont

F. of Commerce
Chairman: Thierry Lambrecht; *staff* 19 (58)
F. of Administration
Chairman: Claude Wilwerth; *staff* 12 (35)
F. of Translation and Interpretation
Chairman: Michel Bastiaensen; *staff* 32 (17)

Founded 1971 incorporating the Institut supérieur de Commerce de Bruxelles (1911), the Ecole supérieure de Traducteurs et Interprétes (1962), the Ecole des hautes Etudes d'Administration (1924), and the Ecole de. All the constituent schools are recognized and financially supported by the State. Organized under the authority of the municipal council of Brussels. Governing bodies: the Conseil d'administration; the Conseil académique.

Academic Year: September to July (September-January; February-July).

Admission Requirements: Secondary school certificate or recognized equivalent.

Fees (Francs): 9000 per annum.

Language of Instruction: French.

Degrees and Diplomas: Candidat, 2-3 yrs. Licence–en Traduction; en Interprétation, 4 yrs; en Sciences commerciales et financières; en Sciences commerciales et consulaires; en Sciences commerciales appliquées aux pays en voie de développement; en Sciences commerciales et administratives; en Sciences administratives, 5 yrs (evenings). Title of Ingénieur commercial, 1 yr after Licence (evenings). Agrégation de l'enseignement secondaire supérieur (teaching qualification, secondary level), 1 yr after Licence.

Library: c. 7500 vols.

Academic Staff, 1989-90: 33 (88).

Student Enrolment, 1989-90:

Of the country	418
Of other countries	142
Total	560

311 **INSTITUT SUPÉRIEUR DE COMMERCE SAINT-LOUIS**
Rue du Marais, 113, 1000 Bruxelles
Telephone: (2) 2 18-33-52

Commerce (including Economics, Law, Computer Sciences, and Accountancy) (Evening courses)

Founded 1925 as Ecole de Commerce attached to the Institut Saint-Louis. Officially recognized 1934. A private institution of university rank financially supported by the State. Governing body: the Conseil d'administration.

Academic Year: October to April (October-January; February-April).

Admission Requirements: Secondary school certificate or recognized equivalent.

Language of Instruction: French.

Degrees and Diplomas: Candidat, 3 yrs. Licence–en Sciences commerciales et financières: en Sciences commerciales et consulaires, a further 2 yrs. Ingénieur commercial, 1 yr after Licence. Agrégation de l'enseignement secondaire supérieur (teaching qualification, higher secondary level), 1 yr after Licence.

Library: c. 2300 vols.

Academic Staff: c. 10.

Student Enrolment: c. 220.

312 **ÉCOLE DES HAUTES ÉTUDES COMMERCIALES**
Rue Sohet 21, 4000 Liège
Telephone: (41) 52-36-78; 52-38-01
Fax: (41) 52-66-69
Directeur: Marcel Aldenhoff (1968-)
Chef du Bureau d'Etudes: Christiane Henneghien-Orban

D. of Commerce and Applied Economics (including Accountancy, Law, Economics, and Management)
Heads: M. Eseh; M. Troufin; *staff* 50 (60)

D. of Commercial Engineering

D. for Lifelong Education
Head: Dujardin; *staff* 2 (4)

Founded 1898 and officially recognized 1934. Operated under the jurisdiction of the Ministry of Education and financially supported by the State. Governing bodies: the Conseil d'administration; the Commission administrative.

Arrangements for co-operation with the Universities of: Alabama;Aston; Reading: Barcelona; Madrid; Seville; Valladolid; Dublin; Bergamo; Lisbon (Technical); Maastricht; Trier. Institut Commercial de Nancy; Hochschule Bremen; Hochschule Düsseldorf.

Academic Year: September to July (September-January; January-July).

Admission Requirements: Secondary school certificate or recognized equivalent.

Fees (Francs): 20,000 per annum; foreign students, 80,000-100,000.

Languages of Instruction: French and English.

Degrees and Diplomas: Candidat, 2 yrs. Licence–en Sciences com merciales; en Sciences commerciales et financières; en Sciences commerciales et consulaires; en Sciences commerciales et administratives, a further 2 yrs. Title of Ingénieur commercial, 5 yrs. Agrégation de l'Enseignement secondaire supérieur (teaching qualification, higher secondary level), 1 yr after Licence.

Library: c. 10,000 vols.

Academic Staff: c.40 (70).

Student Enrolment, 1990:

	Men	Women	Total
Of the country	504	367	871
Of other countries	58	31	89
Total	562	398	960

313 **ECONOMISCHE HOGESCHOOL SINT-ALOYSIUS**
Sturmstraat 2, 1000 Brussel
Telephone: (2) 217-64-01; 217-64-68

Commerce (Evening courses)

Founded 1925. Officially recognized 1937. A private institution of university rank financially supported by the State.

Academic Year: September to June.

Admission Requirements: Secondary school certificate.

Fees (Francs): 10,000 per annum.

Language of Instruction: Dutch.

Degrees and Diplomas: Kandidaat, 3 yrs. Licentiaat in de–Handels-en Financiële Wetenschappen, commercial science and finance; Handels-en Consulaire Wetenschappen, commercial science and consular studies; Handels-en Bestuurswetenschappen, commercial science and administration, a further 2 yrs. Handelsingenieur, 1 yr after Licentiaat. Geaggregeerde voor het Hoger Secundair Onderwijs (teaching qualification, higher secondary level), 1 yr after Licentiaat.

Publications: Eclectica (quarterly); Didacta (quarterly).

Academic Staff: c. 100.

Student Enrolment: c. 750.

314 **ECONOMISCHE HOGESCHOOL LIMBURG**
Universitaire Campus, 3610 Diepenbeek
Telephone: (11) 22-99-61

Economics and Business Administration

Founded 1968. A private institution of university level recognized and financially supported by the State. Governing body: the Board of Trustees.

Academic Year: October to July (October-December; January-March; March-July).

Admission Requirements: Secondary school certificate or foreign equivalent.

Language of Instruction: Dutch.

Degrees and Diplomas: Kandidaat, 2 yrs. Licentiaat in de–Handels-en Financiële Wetenschappen, commerce and finance; Handels-en Consulaire Wetenschappen, commerce and consular studies; Handels-en Bestuurswetenschappen, commerce and administration, 4 yrs. Handelsingenieur, 4 yrs.

Library: c. 10,000 vols.

Academic Staff: c. 40 (30).

Student Enrolment: c. 600.

315 **VLAAMSE ECONOMISCHE HOGESCHOOL BRUSSEL**
Flemish College of Economics
284 Koningsstraat, 1210 Brussel
Telephone: (2) 217-65-10
Fax: (2) 219-05-57
President: S.F. Vandenhoeck (1969-)
Hoofd v/d Administratie: W. Grijseels

D. of Commerce and Business Administration
Head: F. Bostyn; *staff* 13 (67)

D. of Translation and Interpretation
Head: J. Vanhoucke; *staff* 18 (17)

Lifelong Education

Founded 1968. A private institution of university level recognized and financially supported by the State. Governing bodies: the Board of Directors; the General Assembly.

Arrangements for student exchange with the Universities of: Sheffield; Limerick; Tilburg; Grenoble; Stirling; Mesina; Cantabria; Toulon; Genoa. Technical College, Cologne; Ealing College, London; Moscow State Institute of Foreign Languages.

Academic Year: September to July (September-January; February-July).

Admission Requirements: Secondary school certificate.

Fees (Francs): 12,000-c. 30,000.

Languages of Instruction: Dutch and English.

Degrees and Diplomas: Kandidaat, 2 yrs. Licentiaat in de-Handels-en Financiële Wetenschappen, commerce and finance; Handels-en Consulaire Wetenschappen, commerce and consular studies; Vertaler-Tolk, translation and interpretation; Tolk, 4 yrs. Geaggregeerde voor het Hoger Secundair Onderwijs (teaching qualification, higher secondary level), 1 yr after Licentiaat. Post graduaat in de bedrijfseconomie, business management, 1 yr. Also degree of Master.

Library: c. 5500 vols.

Special Facilities (Museums, etc.): Auditorium with Interpreting Booths.

Publications: Interface (Journal of Applied Linguistics) (biannually); Didactic Working Schemes (3 times a year).

Academic Staff, 1989-90:

Rank	Full-time	Part-time
Hoogleraren	11	9
Docenten	18	73
Werkleiders	3	5
Assistenten	47	15
Total	79	102

Student Enrolment, 1989-90:

	Men	Women	Total
Of the country	718	617	1335
Of other countries	3	6	9
Total	721	623	1344

316 **PROVINCIAAL HOGER INSTITUUT VOOR BESTUURSWETENSCHAPPEN**

Provincial Institute of Administration

Koningin Elisabethlei 18, 2018 Antwerpen

Administration

Founded 1959.

317 **ADMINISTRATIEVE EN ECONOMISCHE HOGESCHOOL**

Business School for Commerce and Administration

Trierstraat 84, 1040 Brussel
Telephone: (2) 230-21-95; 45-02
Fax: (2) 231-16-60
Directeur: Alfons Roeck (1981-)
Hoofd Studiebureau: R. Fabre

Business Administration

Commerce

Founded 1938, acquired status as institution of higher education 1948. A private institution of university level, recognized and financially supported by the State, it provides evening courses for those employed during the day in the public and private sectors. Governing body: the Board of Trustees, comprising 12 members.

Academic Year: October to July (October-January; February-July).

Admission Requirements: Secondary school certificate.

Fees (Francs): 10,000 per annum.

Language of Instruction: Dutch.

Degrees and Diplomas: Kandidaat, 2 yrs. Licentiaat in–Bestuurs-wetenschappen, administration; Handels-en Financiële Wetenschappen, commerce and finance; Handels-en Consulaire Wetenschappen, commerce and consular studies; Handels-en Bestuurswetenschappen, commerce and administration, 5 yrs. Geaggregeerde voor het Hoger Secundair Onderwijs (teachingqualification, higher secondary level) in Commerce.

Library: 30,000 vols.

Publications: Tijdschrift voor Bestuurswetenschappen en Publiek Recht; H.I.B.H. Berichten.

Academic Staff, 1990:

Rank	Full-time	Part-time
Hoogleraren	3	–
Docenten	5	35
Assistenten	11	2
Total	19	37

Student Enrolment, 1990:

	Men	Women	Total
Of the country	180	100	2860

318 **PROVINCIALE HOGESCHOOL VOOR VERTALERS EN TOLKEN**

Brusselsepoortstraat 93, 9000 Gent
Telephone: (91) 23-94-51
Fax: (91) 23-97-05
Directeur: Paul Van Hauwermeiren (1987-)
Secretaris: Inge Van Leeuwen

Translation and Interpretation (Dutch, English, French, Spanish, German)

Ce. for Terminology

Head: E. Elyenbosch; *staff* – (4)

Founded 1937 as an independent school, became a provincial institution 1952 under the jurisdiction of the government of East-Flanders. Receives financial support from the Ministry of Education.

Participates in the ERASMUS and Comett II-Sovo programmes.

Academic Year: September to July (September-January; January-July).

Admission Requirements: Secondary school certificate.

Fees (Francs): 5000 per annum.

Language of Instruction: Dutch.

Degrees and Diplomas: Licentiaat in–Translation and Interpretation, 4 yrs. Postgraduate degree, 1 yr.

Library: Central Library, 12,000 vols.

Academic Staff, 1989-90:

Rank	Full-time	Part-time
Hoogleraren	8	–
Docenten	24	10
Assistenten	24	2
Total	56	12

Student Enrolment, 1989-90:

	Men	Women	Total
Of the country	232	609	841
Of other countries	4	6	10
Total	236	615	851

319 **INSTITUUT VOOR TROPISCHE GENEESKUNDE 'PRINS LEOPOLD'**

Nationalestraat 155, 2000 Antwerpen
Cables: metropical antwerpen
Telex: 31648 TROPIC B
Telephone: (3) 247-66-66
Fax: (3) 216-14-31
Directeur: Luc Eyckmans (1976-)
Secrétaire: Marc Van Boven

D. of Tropical Medicine

Head: M. Gigase

D. Tropical Veterinary Medicine

Head: M. Hardouin

D. of Tropical Medical Health

Head: M. Mercenier

Founded 1931 by Royal Decree replacing the Ecole de Médecine Tropicale, founded 1906. Acquired present status 1960. Governing body: the Board of Directors.

Academic Year: October to June.

Admission Requirements: Degree in Medicine, Science, Agriculture, or Veterinary Medicine. (Dependent on course to be followed).

Fees (Francs): 15,000-375,000.

Languages of Instruction: Dutch, French, and English.

Degrees and Diplomas: Postgraduate diplomas (M.P.H.; M.Sc.).

Library: c. 30,000 vols.

Publication: Annales de la Société de Médecine Tropicale.

Academic Staff, 1990-91: 24.

Student Enrolment, 1990-91:

Of the country	150
Of other countries	240
Total	390

320 **KATHOLIEKE VLAAMSE HOGESCHOOL**

Catholic Flemish Institute of Higher Education

St. Andriesstraat 2, 2000 Antwerpen
Telephone: (3) 225 06 40
Fax: (3) 231 30 60
Directeur: Rik Van Leuven

D. of Psychology

Head: Magda Wellens; *staff* 11 (34)

D. of Speech Therapy

Head: Magda Wellens; *staff* 6 (26)

D. of Translation and Interpretation

Head: Raoul Sinjan; *staff* 54 (35)

Research Ce. on Terminology and Lexicography

Head: F. Steurs

Research Ce. on Educational Software

Head: F. Steurs

Research Ce. on the Science of Translation

Head: R. Van den Broeck

Founded 1919. A private institution of university level recognized and financially supported by the State. Affiliated to the Catholic University of Leuven. Governing body: the Raad van Beheer (Board of Directors)

Participates in ERASMUS and Lingua programmes.

Academic Year: September to June (September-December; January-June).

Admission Requirements: Secondary school certificate or recognized foreign equivalent.

Fees (Francs): 8000-10,000 per annum.

Language of Instruction: Dutch.

Degrees and Diplomas: Kandidaat Vertaler, 2 yrs. Licentiaat Vertaler; Licentiat Tolk, 4 yrs. Assistent in de Psychologie. Geaggregeerde (teaching qualification) in de Logopedie, 3 yrs.

Library: c. 10,000 vols.

Academic Staff, 1989-90: c. 86 (83).

Student Enrolment, 1989-90:

	Men	Women	Total
Of the country	263	1095	1358
Of other countries	8	30	38
Total	271	1125	1396

321 **HOGER INSTITUUT VOOR VERTALERS EN TOLKEN**

Higher Institute of Translators and Interpreters

Schildersstraat 41, 2000 Antwerpen

Telephone: (3) 238 9833

Fax: (3) 248 1907

Electronic mail: (3) 248 1934

Directeur: J. Soenen

Secretaris: F. Crauwels

Translation and Interpretation

Founded 1961.

Academic Year: October to June.

Admission Requirements: Secondary school certificat.

Fees (Francs): 2150-9650.

Language of Instruction: Dutch.

Degrees and Diplomas: Kandidaat, 2 yrs. Licentiaat in-Translation or Interpretation, a further 2 yrs.

Library: c. 15,000 vols.

Publication: Linguistica Antverpiensia (annually).

Academic Staff, 1989-90:

Rank	Full-time	Part-time
Hoogleraren	8	1
Docenten	8	23
Werkleiders	2	2
Assistenten	8	13
Total	26	39

Student Enrolment, 1989-90:

	Men	Women	Total
Of the country	132	391	523
Of other countries	22	66	88
Total	154	457	611

322 **RIJKSHOGESCHOOL VOOR VERTALERS EN TOLKEN**

Trierstraat 84, 1040 Brussel

Telephone: (2) 230-12-60

Fax: (2) 230-99-90

Director: Herman J. Vermeylen

Assistant Director: Willy Bultereys

Translation and Interpretation (Dutch, English, French, Greek, Italian, Russian, Portuguese, Spanish.)

Ce. for Terminology and Terminography

Head: Rita Temmerman; *staff* 1 (9)

Ce. for Social and Business Communication, Intercultural Relations

Head: F. Simonis; *staff* 1 (9)

Ce. for European Law Terminology

Head: F. Taillieu; *staff* 1 (9)

Founded 1958 as school, acquired present status 1964. Financed by the State and tuition fees and responsible to the Ministry of Education and ARGO (Autonomous Council for the Flemish Community Education). Governing body: the Board of Directors.

Participates in the ERASMUS and Lingua programmes.

Academic Year: October to July (October-February; February-July).

Admission Requirements: Secondary school certificate and entrance examination.

Fees (Francs): 7000 per annum.

Language of Instruction: Dutch.

Degrees and Diplomas: Kandidat, 2 yrs. Licentiaat in–Translation or Interpretation, a further 2 yrs.

Library: Central Library, c. 10,000 vols.

Special Facilities (Museums, etc.): Art gallery for young Flemish artists.

Publication: Medium (quarterly).

Academic Staff, 1989-90:

Rank	Full-time	Part-time
Hoogleraren	13	–
Docenten	10	3
Werkleiders	5	–
Assistenten	23	9
Total	51	12

Student Enrolment, 1989-90:

	Men	Women	Total
Of the country	122	410	532
Of other countries	11	36	47
Total	133	446	579

323 **INSTITUT SUPÉRIEUR DE LA COMMUNAUTÉ FRANÇAISE DE TRADUCTEURS ET INTERPRÈTES**

Rue Joseph Hazard, 34, 1180 Bruxelles

Telephone: (2) 345-98-70; 345-51-33

Directeur: Georges Guislain (1988-)

Translation and Interpretation

Founded 1958 as a State institution. Authorized to award degrees 1965 and recognized as a university institution under the law of 1970. Financed by the State and responsible to the Ministry of Education. Governing bodies: the Conseil d'administration; the Conseil pédagogique.

Participates in the ERASMUS programme.

Academic Year: October to June (October-January; February-June).

Admission Requirements: Secondary school certificate or recognized equivalent.

Fees (Francs): 7500 per annum.

Language of Instruction: French.

Degrees and Diplomas: Candidat, 2 yrs, Licence in–Translation/Interpretation, a further 2 yrs.

Library: c. 18,000 vols.

Publication: Equivalences (quarterly).

Academic Staff, 1989-90:

Rank	Full-time	Part-time
Professeurs	8	–
Chargés de cours	21	5
Chefs de travaux	7	–
Assistants	23	10
Total	59	15

Student Enrolment, 1989-90:

	Men	Women	Total
Of the country	219	703	922
Of other countries	53	186	249
Total	272	889	1171

324 **INSTITUT LIBRE MARIE HAPS**

Rue d'Arlon 11, 1040 Bruxelles

Telephone: (2) 511-92-92

Directrice: Christiane de Galocsy-Giblet (1961-)

Translation and Interpretation

Psychology

Speech Therapy

Audio-Acoustics

Psychomotor Studies

Founded 1919 as a school, acquired present name 1963. Operated under the patronage of the Catholic University of Louvain. Financially supported by the State. Governing bodies: the Conseil de Direction; the Conseil académique.

Academic Year: September to June (September-December; January-June).

Admission Requirements: Secondary school certificate or recognized foreign equivalent.

Fees (Francs): 10,500 per annum.

Languages of Instruction: French. (The Department of Translation and Interpretation has two sections, one using French, and the other Dutch as the medium of instruction).

Degrees and Diplomas: Candidat, 2 yrs. Licencié-Traducteur; -Interprète, a further 2 yrs. Also titles of–Assistant en psychologie; Gradué en logopédie et/ou audio-acoustique, 3 yrs.

Library: 18,280 vols.

Publications: Revue 'Le Langage et l'Homme' (quarterly); Cahiers de Terminologie (4 times a year).

Academic Staff, 1986-87:

Rank	Full-time	Part-time
Professeurs	2	–
Chargés de cours	52	50
Assistants	19	8
Total	73	58

Student Enrolment, 1986-87:

	Men	Women	Total
Of the country	194	690	884
Of other countries	23	88	121
Total	217	778	1005

325 **ÉCOLE D'INTERPRÈTES INTERNATIONAUX**

Place Warocqué 17, 7000 Mons

Interpretation

326 **FONDATION UNIVERSITAIRE LUXEMBOURGEOISE**

rue des Déportés, 140, 6700 Arlon
Telephone: (63) 22-03-80
Fax: (63) 22-01-47
Directeur: Charles Debouche (1987-91)
Directeur administratif: Louis Hanin

Environmental Sciences (including Agro-Meteorology)

Founded 1971 under the provisions of the 1971 law on university expansion and recognized by Royal Decree. The purpose of the Foundation is to stimulate, in liaison with other university institutions, applied scientific research and postgraduate studies. Reorganized 1983. Governing body: the Conseil d'administration, comprising the Governor of the Province of Luxembourg, the Director-General of Higher Education and Scientific Research, the Secretary-General of the Prime Minister's Office for Science Policy, the Rectors of universities and university institutions, members of Parliament, professors, research workers, students and representatives of the economic, social and cultural sectors.

Special arrangements for co-operation with: Université de Metz; Centre Universitaire de Luxembourg; Universität des Saarlandes; Universität Trier; Universität Kaiserslautern; Université de Dakar.

Academic Year: September to June (September-January; February-June).

Admission Requirements: University degree or equivalent.

Fees (Francs): Registration, 18,000.

Language of Instruction: French.

Degrees and Diplomas: Doctorate in Environmental Sciences, 3 yrs. Maîtrise in Environmental Sciences, 1 yr.

Library: Documentation Centre, *c.* 25,000 vols.

Publication: Environment et Société (biannually).

Academic Staff, 1989-90: 9 (27).

Student Enrolment, 1989-90:

Of the country	38
Of other countries	26
Total	64

327 **UNIVERSITAIRE PROTESTANTE THEOLOGISCHE FACULTEIT BRUSSEL**

Bollandistenstraat 40, 1040 Brussel

328 **EVANGELISCHE THEOLOGISCHE FACULTEIT**

St. Jansbergsteenweg 97, 3030 Heverlee/Leuven
Telephone: (161) 20-08-95
Academisch Directeur/Decaan: Donald Moreland
Administratief Directeur: Jef De Vriese

Theology

Division of the Belgian Centre for Biblical Education, founded 1919. Recognized by the Government to give official degrees 1983. Residential facilities for students.

Academic Year: October to June (October-February; February-June).

Admission Requirements: Secondary school certificate.

Fees (Francs): 3,700 per month; Doctor, 17,000 per annum.

Languages of Instruction: Dutch, English and German.

Degrees and Diplomas: Kandidaat in de Godgeleerdheid, theology, 3 yrs. Licentiaat, a further 2 yrs. Doctor, a further 2-3 yrs.

Academic Staff, 1990: 6 (19).

Student Enrolment, 1990:

	Men	Women	Total
Of the country	1	–	1
Of other countries	12	4	16
Total	13	4	17

BENIN

329 ***UNIVERSITÉ NATIONALE DU BÉNIN**
B.P. 526, Cotonou
Telex: 5010
Telephone: 36-00-74
Recteur: Jean-Pierre O. Ezin (1990-)
Secrétaire général: Prudencia Zinsou

F. of Letters, Arts and Human Sciences
Dean: Francois Dossou; *staff* 81 (16)
F. of Law, Economics and Political Science
Dean: Robert Dossou; *staff* 65 (5)
F. of Science and Technology
Dean: Salifou Alidou; *staff* 81 (2)
F. of Agriculture (including Animal Husbandry)
Dean: Mama Adamou Ndiaye; *staff* 41 (31)
F. of Health Sciences (Medicine)
Dean: Eusebe Allihonou; *staff* 49
Also 8 colleges, institutes, schools and centres.

Founded 1970 as Université du Dahomey and incorporating departments of former Institut d'Enseignement supérieur du Bénin, established 1962. Acquired present title 1976. A State institution responsible to the Ministry of Higher Education and Scientific Research. Governing body: the Conseil Scientifique. Residential facilities for *c.* 600 students.

Arrangements for co-operation with Universities in: France, Netherlands, Germany, and Africa.

Academic Year: October to July (October-January; January-March; April-July).

Admission Requirements: Secondary school certificate (baccalauréat) or equivalent.

Fees (Francs C.F.A.): 5500 per annum; foreign students, 130,000-150,000.

Language of Instruction: French.

Degrees and Diplomas: Diplôme universitaire d'études–littéraires (D.U.E.L.); scientifiques (D.U.E.S.); juridiques générales (D.U.E.J.G.); économiques générales (D.U.E.S.G.), 2 yrs. Licence en Lettres, en Sciences humaines, 1 further yr. Diplôme d'Etudes techniques supérieures (D.E.S.). Maîtrise, 2 yrs. Diplôme–d'Ingénieur; d'Administrateur; de Magistrat, 5 yrs. Doctorat d'Etat en Médecine, 7 yrs. Also Certificat d'Aptitude (teaching qualification, secondary level), 2-4 yrs. Diplômes (lower level), 3 yrs. Certificat d'études spécialisées, 11 yrs.

Libraries: Central Library, 45,000 vols; Agriculture, 10,000; Medicine, 7000; Education, 5000.

Publications: Revue générale des Sciences juridiques, économiques et politique (quarterly); Annales de la Faculté des Lettres (annually).

Press or Publishing House: Centre national des Publications universitaires.

Academic Staff, 1989-90: 683.

Student Enrolment, 1989-90:

	Men	Women	Total
Of the country	8289	1464	9753*

*Also 396 foreign students.

330 **ÉCOLE NATIONALE D'ADMINISTRATION**
B.P. 990, Abomey-Calavi, 2231 Cotonou
Telephone: 36-01-43
Directeur: Théodor Holo

Administration

Founded 1984, incorporating the Institut national des Sciences juridiques et administratives and Centre de Formation administrative et de Perfectionnement. Attached to the Université nationale du Bénin. Residential facilities for students.

Arrangements for co-operation with: Ecole nationale d'Administration, Québec; Institut international d'Administration publique, Paris; similar institutions in Burkina Faso; Côte d'Ivoire; Niger; Togo.

Academic Year: October to July (October-December; January-April; April-July).

Admission Requirements: Secondary school certificate (baccalauréat) and entrance examination.

Fees (Francs C.F.A.): 5500 per annum.

Language of Instruction: French.

Degrees and Diplomas: Professional qualifications of–Technicien supérieur; Attachés des Services administratifs.

Academic Staff, 1986-87: 30 (100).

Student Enrolment, 1986-87:

	Men	Women	Total
Of the country	316	52	368
Of other countries	8	6	14
Total	324	58	382

331 **INSTITUT NATIONAL D'ÉCONOMIE**
Cotonou
Directeur: Félix Dansou

Economics (including Business Administration)

Attached to the Université nationale du Bénin.

Academic Year: October to June.

Admission Requirements: Secondary school certificate (baccalauréat) and entrance examination.

Language of Instruction: French.

Degrees and Diplomas: Professional qualifications.

332 **INSTITUT NATIONAL D'ENSEIGNEMENT D'ÉDUCATION PHYSIQUE ET SPORTIVE**
B.P. 169, Porto-Novo
Telephone: 21-30-87
Directeur: Gouda L. Souaïbou
Secrétaire principal: Alexis Ahissou

Physical Education and Sport

Attached to the Université nationale du Bénin

Arrangements for co-operation with the Université de Grenoble I.

Academic Year: October to June.

Admission Requirements: Secondary school certificate (baccalauréat) and entrance examination.

Language of Instruction: French.

Degrees and Diplomas: Professional titles, 3-4 yrs.

Academic Staff, 1990: 36 (2).

Student Enrolment, 1990:

	Men	Women	Total
Of the country	187	7	194

333 **COLLÈGE POLYTECHNIQUE UNIVERSITAIRE**
B.P. 2009, Abomey-Calavi, Cotonou
Directeur: Adékpédjou Akindes

Industrial Engineering
Civil Engineering
Radiology
Animal Husbandry

Founded 1977. Attached to the Université nationale du Bénin.

Academic Year: October to June.

Admission Requirements: Secondary school certificate (baccalauréat) and entrance examination.

Degrees and Diplomas: Professional qualifications.

Academic Staff, 1986-87: 80 (16).

334 **ÉCOLE NORMALE SUPÉRIEURE**
Porto-Novo
Directeur: Christian Dassou

Teacher Training

Attached to the Université nationale du Bénin

Academic Year: October to June.

Admission Requirements: Secondary school certificate (baccalauréat) and entrance examination.

Language of Instruction: French.

Degrees and Diplomas: Professional titles.

335 **CENTRE RÉGIONAL DE DÉVELOPPEMENT SANITAIRE**
Cotonou
Directeur: Samba Diop

Public Health

Founded 1977 jointly by the World Health Organization and the Government of Bénin. Open to doctors, midwives, and nurses from the African Region of WHO. Attached to the Université nationale du Bénin.

Academic Year: October to June.

Admission Requirements: Secondary school certificate and entrance examination.

Language of Instruction: French.

Degrees and Diplomas: Diplôme de Santé publique. Maîtrise. Doctorat.

Academic Staff, 1986-87: 2.

336 **CENTRE BÉNINOIS DE LANGUES ÉTRANGÈRES**
Cotonou
Directeur: Bienvenu Akoha

Foreign Languages

Attached to the Université nationale du Bénin.

Academic Year: October to June.

Admission Requirements: Secondary school certificate (baccalauréat) and entrance examination.

Language of Instruction: French.

Degrees and Diplomas: Professional qualifications.

Academic Staff, 1986-87: 4 (3).

337 **INSTITUT DES SCIENCES BIOMÉDICALES AVANCÉES**
Cotonou
Directeur: Vincent Dan

Medical and Biological Research

Attached to the Université nationale du Bénin.

Academic Year: October to June.

Admission Requirements: Secondary school certificate (baccalauréat) and entrance examination.

Language of Instruction: French.

Degrees and Diplomas: Professional qualifications.

BOLIVIA

Universities and Technical Universities

338 **UNIVERSIDAD CATÓLICA BOLIVIANA**
Avenida 14 de Septiembre 4807, Cajón postal 4805, La Paz
Telephone: 78-31-48
Rector: Luis Antonio Boza Fernández (1989-93)
Secretaria Académica: Elizabeth Alvarez R.

D. of Business Administration
Director: Alejandro Blacutt
D. of Economics
Director: Carlos Machicado
D. of Psychology
Director: Félix Via O.
D. of Communication Sciences
Director: Dulfredo Retamozo L.
D. of Public Relations and Tourism
Director: Luis Antonio Boza F.
I. of Rural Development
Director: Hugo Ossio
I. of Theology
Director: Miguel Manzanera
D. of Philosophy
Director: María Elisa Gantier
S. of Nursing
Director: Isabel Fierro
I. of Socio-Economic Research
Director: Juan Antonio Morales
Extension D.
Director Ana María Tineo
D. for Lifelong Education
Director: Luis F. Ocampo O.
D. of Basic Studies
Director: José Victor Arione
D. of Religious Sciences
Director: Luis Miguel Romero

Founded 1966. A private institution under the administration of the Conferencia Episcopal de Bolivia. Governing body: the Consejo Universitario.

Arrangements for co-operation with Arizona State University.

Academic Year: January to December (February-June; August-December).

Admission Requirements: Secondary school certificate (bachillerato) and entrance examination.

Language of Instruction: Spanish.

Degrees and Diplomas: Licenciado in–Social Communication; Psychology; Economics; Business Administration, 5 yrs. Professional titleof Técnico, 3 yrs. Magister en–Economía agrícola; Administración de Empresas, 6-7 yrs.

Library: Central Library, 14,600 vols.

Publication: Revista Boliviana Comunicación (quarterly).

Academic Staff, 1989-90: – (160).

Student Enrolment, 1989-90:

	Men	Women	Total
Of the country	1092	1339	2431*

*Also 1276 foreign students.

339 **UNIVERSIDAD AUTÓNOMA 'GABRIEL RENÉ MORENO'**
Plaza 24 de Septiembre, Casilla postal 702, Santa Cruz de la Sierra
Telephone: 4-2540
Rector: Manuel Jesús Angelo Parra (1987-)

F. of Law and Social Sciences
F. of Economics
F. of Agriculture
F. of Fishery
F. of Exact Sciences and Technology
I. of Technology
I. of Languages

Founded 1880 as University of Santo Tomás de Aquino. Became an autonomous institution in 1911. A State institution. Residential facilities for students.

Academic Year: February to December (February-June; July-December).

Admission Requirements: Secondary school certificate (bachillerato) and entrance examination.

Language of Instruction: Spanish.

Degrees and Diplomas: Licenciado in–Tropical Agricultural Engineering, 4 yrs; Business Administration; Accountancy; Law; Economics; Civil Engineering; Chemical Engineering; Animal Husbandry and Veterinary Medicine, 5 yrs. Professional title of Técnico in various fields, 3-4 yrs.

Libraries: Central Library, *c.* 70,000 vols; Campus library, *c.* 20,000.

Press or Publishing House: Imprenta Universitaria.

Academic Staff: c. 360.

Student Enrolment: c. 6620.

340 **UNIVERSIDAD BOLIVIANA 'JUAN MISAEL SARACHO'**
'Juan Misael Saracho' Bolivian University
Avenida Las Américas s/n, Casilla 51, Tarija
Telephone: 3110/11
Rector: Mario Rios Araoz

F. of Pure Sciences and Agriculture (including Forestry)
F. of Social Science (including Economics, Business Administration, and Law)
F. of Health Sciences (Dentistry and Nursing)

Founded 1886 as college, became university 1946. A State institution. Governing body: the Consejo Universitario. Some residential facilities for students.

Academic Year: March to December (March-July; August-December.

Admission Requirements: Secondary school certificate (bachillerato) and entrance examination.

Language of Instruction: Spanish.

Degrees and Diplomas: Licenciado in–Business Administration; Nursing, 4 yrs; Law; Auditing; Economics; Dentistry; Forestry; Agriculture, 5 yrs. Also professional titles in–General Accountancy; Nursing, 3 yrs; Agriculture; Forestry, 4 yrs.

Library: Central Library, *c.* 30,000 vols.

Special Facilities (Museums, etc.): Museums: Palaeontology; Archaeology.

Publication: Universidad (monthly).

Academic Staff: c. 100.

Student Enrolment: c. 740.

341 **UNIVERSIDAD MAYOR DE SAN ANDRÉS**
University of San Andrés
Avenida Villazón 1995, Casilla de Correo 6042, La Paz (Murillo)
Telephone: 35-94-90
Fax: 3438
Rector: Pablo Ramos Sánchez

F. of Health Sciences (including Medicine, Nursing, and Medical Technology)
Dean: Gustavo Leguía Iturri; *staff* 77 (64)
F. of Dentistry
Dean: Aldo Luna Maceda; *staff* 12 (29)
F. of Pharmacy and Biochemistry
Dean: Enrique Udaeta Velásquez; *staff* 12 (29)
F. of Exact and Natural Sciences (including Statistics and Computer Sciences)
Dean: Rubén Belmonte Coloma; *staff* 93 (21)
F. of Engineering
Dean: Adhemar Daroca Morales; *staff* 51 (14)
F. of Agriculture
Dean: Hugo Mendieta Pedraza; *staff* 25 (17)
F. of Geology
Dean: Antonio Saavedra Muñoz; *staff* 25

D. of Architecture and Arts
Dean: Alfonso Villegas Guzmán; *staff* 38 (13)
F. of Technology (Topography, Industrial Chemistry, Aviation, and Motor Mechanics)
Dean: Silverio Chávez Ríos; *staff* 36 (8)
F. of Social Sciences (including Anthropology and Archaeology)
Dean: María del Carmen Sánchez García; *staff* 31
F. of Law and Political Science
Dean: Abelardo Villarpando Retamoso; *staff* 17 (7)
F. of Humanities and Education (including Library Science, Psychology, Tourism, and Linguistics)
Dean: José Mendoza Quiroga; *staff* 51 (26)
F. of Economics and Finance (including Business Administration)
Dean: Hugo Argote Argote; *staff* 45 (20)
Also 21 Research Institutes.

Founded 1831. Acquired present title 1972. The university is an autonomous institution financially supported by the State and by special taxes. Governing body: Consejo Académico Universitario. Residential facilities for students.

Arrangements for co-operation with institutions of higher education in: Argentina, Brazil, Denmark, Federal Republic of Germany, France, Italy, Peru, Republic of China, Spain, United Kingdom, USA, USSR.

Academic Year: March to January.

Admission Requirements: Secondary school certificate (bachillerato) and entrance examination.

Language of Instruction: Spanish.

Degrees and Diplomas: Licenciado in–Social Work; Sociology; Social Communication; Anthropology; Archaeology; Economics; Business Administration; Education; History; Linguistics; Literature; Philosophy; Psychology; Tourism; Political Science; Law; Engineering, various fields; Biology; Statistics; Physics; Computer Sciences; Mathematics; Chemistry; Architecture; Arts; Geology; Geography; Agriculture; Nutrition and Dietetics; Nursing; Biotechnology; Dentistry; Pharmacy; Biochemistry, 4-5 yrs; Medicine, 6 yrs. Professional titles of Técnico Médico and Superior, 2-3yrs. Maestría in–Agricultural Development; Public Health, a further 2 yrs.

Libraries: Central Library, *c.* 120,000 vols; Economics, *c.* 5000; Law, *c.* 13,000; Sociology, *c.* 7000; Architecture, *c.* 1500; Genetics, *c.* 8000; Exact and Natural Sciences, *c.* 6000; Technology, *c.* 8000; Health Sciences, *c.* 9000; Humanities, *c.* 10,000.

Special Facilities (Museums, etc.): Archivo Histórico; El Planetario Max Schreier; Observatorio de Chacaltaya; Museo de Historia Natural; Nerbario Nacional de Bolivia.

Publication: Revista.

Academic Staff, 1990: 513 (761)

Student Enrolment, 1990:

Of the country	27,276
Of other countries	65
Total	27,341

342 **UNIVERSIDAD MAYOR DE SAN FRANCISCO XAVIER**
University of San Francisco Xavier
Calle Junín y Estudiantes 692, Casilla 212, Sucre
Telephone: 23245
Rector: Jorge Zamora Hernández

F. of Law and Political and Social Sciences
Dean: Ruffo Oropeza; *staff* 7 (8)
F. of Health Sciences (Medicine, Dentistry, Pharmacy, Biochemistry, Nursing, Physiotherapy and Radiology, and Clinical L.)
F. of Economics
Dean: Hugo Paniggua; *staff* 13 (4)
F. of Technology (Chemical Engineering, Mechanical Engineering, Industrial Engineering, and Food Industry)
F. of Humanities (including Languages and Tourism)
F. of Agriculture (including Animal Husbandry)
Dean: Sixto Cusicanqui; *staff* 19 (15)
Polytechnic I.
Director: Gerson Andrade; *staff* 6 (1)
Extension D.
Head: Mario Cespedes Toro; *staff* 8
I. of Economic Research
Director: Mario Gumiel; *staff* 2
I. of Bolivian Sociology
Director: Teresa Ramírez; *staff* 5
I. of Cancerology
Experimental I. of Biology

Founded 1624 by Father Juan de Frías y Herrán of the Society of Jesus and by Papal Bull and Royal Decree. Higher education came under State control in 1852 and the university was reorganized and granted autonomous status in 1930. Governing bodies: on which the academic staff and students have equal representation: the Claustro Universitario; the Consejo Universitario; the Asambleas de Facultades; the Consejos Directivos. Some residential facilities for students.

Academic Year: March to December (March-August; September-December).

Admission Requirements: Secondary school certificate (bachillerato) or equivalent, and entrance examination.

Language of Instruction: Spanish.

Degrees and Diplomas: Licenciado in–Political and Social Science; Law, 5 yrs, followed by Doctorate. Professional titles in–Tourism, 1 yr; Modern Languages; Chemistry and Pharmacy; Midwifery and Nursing; Agriculture, 4 yrs; Dentistry; Chemical Engineering; Accountancy, 5 yrs; Plastic Arts, 6 yrs; Medicine, 6 yrs.

Libraries: University Library, *c.* 60,000 vols; specialized faculty and school libraries, *c.* 20,000.

Special Facilities (Museums, etc.): Museums of: Colonial Art; Anthropology; Modern Art.

Publications: Revista de la Universidad; Revista de la Facultad de Derecho; Ciencias políticas y sociales; Revista de la Facultad de Ciencias médicas; Revista de la Facultad de Ciencias económicas; Revista del Instituto de Sociología Boliviana; Boletines estudiantiles; La Gaceta Universitaria; Boletín del Museo Antropológico; Boletín del Museo Colonial 'Charcas'; Boletín de la Universidad popular.

Academic Staff, 1989:

Rank	Full-time	Part-time
Catedráticos	70	22
Adjuntos	66	7
Asistentes	66	6
Total	202	35

Student Enrolment, 1989:

	Men	Women	Total
Of the country	6162	5042	11,204
Of other countries	99	66	165
Total	6261	5108	11,319

343 **UNIVERSIDAD MAYOR DE SAN SIMÓN**
University of San Simón
Avenida Oquendo-Sucre, Cochabamba
Telephone: 25501

F. of Biochemistry and Pharmacy
F. of Economics and Sociology
F. of Law and Political Sciences
F. of Medicine
F. of Dentistry
F. of Agriculture (including Forestry)
F. of Architecture
F. of Science and Technology
F. of Humanities and Education

Founded 1832 as school of science and arts. Accorded autonomous status by law 1930. The university is financedby the State, receiving 2.5% of the national budget. Governing bodies: the Consejo Universitario, composed of the deans of the faculties, an equivalent number of students, the Rector and Secretary-General; the Consejos Directivos of the faculties, each composed of the dean, three professorsand three students.

Academic Year: February to December (February-June; July-December).

Admission Requirements: Secondary school certificate (bachillerato) and entrance examination.

Language of Instruction: Spanish.

Degrees and Diplomas: Licenciado in all subjects, 4-5 yrs. Professional titles.

Libraries: Central Library, *c.* 29,310 vols; faculty libraries, *c.* 19,520.

Special Facilities (Museums, etc.): Archaeological Museum.

Publications: Disposiciones Universitarias; Boletín Estadístico.

Press or Publishing House: Imprenta Universitaria.

Academic Staff: c. 680 (10).

Student Enrolment: c. 17,330.

344 **UNIVERSIDAD NACIONAL SIGLO XX**
Edif. Fondo Exploración Minera, Avenida Ecuador 2007, La Paz
Founded 1984

345 **UNIVERSIDAD TÉCNICA DEL BENI**
Casilla 38, Trinidad-Beni
F. of Animal Husbandry
I. of Industrial Technology
Extension D.
Founded 1967. *Academic Staff: c.* 40.
Student Enrolment: c. 500.

346 **UNIVERSIDAD TÉCNICA DE ORURO**
Technical University of Oruro
Avenida 6 de Octubre 1209, Casilla 49, Oruro
Telephone: 50100
Rector: Antonio Salas Casado
F. of Economics and Finance (including Accountancy and Business Administration)
Dean: Raúl Arias Murillo; *staff* 25 (62)
F. of Engineering (Civil, Mechanical, and Electrical Engineering, Metallurgy, Architecture, and Chemical Processing)
Dean: Fidel Terrazas Camacho; *staff* 90 (79)
F. of Law and Political and Social Sciences (including Anthropology and Communication Sciences)
Dean: Oscar J. Quinteros; *staff* 14 (52)
F. of Agriculture
Dean: Nestor Suaznabar Ochoa; *staff* 32 (40)
F. of Technical Studies
Dean: Oscar Vargas Encinas; *staff* 19 (40)
F. of Architecture and Town Planning
Dean: Fernando Mendizabal Jara; *staff* 4 (17)
I. of Economic Research
Head: Freddy Snajinez Montan; *staff* 3
Social Research I.
Head: Amancio Valeriano; *staff* 3

Founded 1892 as provincial university. Became autonomous in 1937. Formerly known as the Universidad Autónomade San Agustín. Responsible to the Consejo Ejecutivo de la Universidad Boliviano. Financed by the State. Governing bodies: the Consejo Supremo Universitario; the Consejos Facultativos. Some residential facilities for students.

Academic Year: September to August.

Admission Requirements: Secondary school certificate (bachillerato en humanidades) and entrance examination.

Language of Instruction: Spanish.

Degrees and Diplomas: Licenciado and Professional titles of–Ingeniero de Minas; Ingeniero civil; Ingeniero metalurgía; Ingeniero eléctrico; Ingeniero mecánica; Químico; Abogado, law; Economista; Auditor; Perito agrícola, agriculture; Ingeniero industrial; Bachiller Industrial; Técnico; Técnico Superior.

Libraries: Central Library, *c.* 9088 vols; Law, *c.* 10,810; Economics, *c.* 7430; Engineering, *c.* 10,030; Agriculture, *c.* 1550; Polytechnic, *c.* 5070.

Special Facilities (Museums, etc.): Museums: History and Folklore; Archaeology; Mineralogy. Botanical Garden; Cultural House.

Publication: Cultura Boliviana (quarterly).

Press or Publishing House: Editora Universitaria.

Academic Staff, 1990:

Rank	Full-time	Part-time
Asistentes	16	18
Adjuntos	13	10
Catedráticos	35	28
Invitados	132	192
Total	195	248

Student Enrolment, 1990:

	Men	Women	Total
Of the country	5340	2317	7657

347 **UNIVERSIDAD AUTÓNOMA 'TOMÁS FRÍAS'**
Avenida del Maestro, Casilla 36, Potosí
Telephone: 2-7300
Rector: Félix Iñiguez Ayala
Secretario General: Julio Montoya Vargas
F. of Law, and Political and Social Sciences
Dean: Félix Goitia Aillón; *staff* 13 (29)
F. of Engineering
Dean: Damián Ponce; *staff* 17 (20)
F. of Economics (including Business Administration and Accountancy)
Dean: Abdón Soza Yañez; *staff* 26 (50)
F. of Mining Engineering
Dean: Eloy Espoza Villca; *staff* 20 (8)
F. of Plastic Arts and Music
Dean: Hipólito Taboada; *staff* 3 (23)
F. of Agriculture and Animal Husbandry
Dean: Germán Matos Leandro Vildozo; *staff* 11 (20)
F. of Science
Dean: Oscar Barrientos; *staff* 32 (11)
Polytechnic I
D. of Linguistics
Head: J. Alfredo Lenis Pórcel; *staff* 1 (6)

Founded 1892, the university was at first attached to the Universidad Francisco Xavier Sucre but became independent and autonomous 1931.

Academic Year: January to December (January-May; June-December).

Admission Requirements: Secondary school certificate (bachillerato).

Language of Instruction: Spanish.

Degrees and Diplomas: Licenciado, 5 yrs. Professional titles of Técnico, 3-4 yrs.

Libraries: Central Library, 25,450 vols; Technology, 6143; Economics, 5652; Law and Social Work, 3542; Agriculture, 659; Polytechnic, 442; Arts, 389.

Special Facilities (Museums, etc.): University Museum 'Ricardo Bohorquez'.

Publication: Journal of Science (annually).

Press or Publishing House: University Press.

Academic Staff, 1986-87: 109 (216).

Student Enrolment, 1986-87:

	Men	Women	Total
Of the country	2494	843	3337

Other Institutions

Technical Education

348 **ESCUELA INDUSTRIAL SUPERIOR DE LA NACIÓN 'PEDRO DOMINGO MURILLO'**
Avenida Chacaltaya 1001, La Paz
Telephone: 2-2565
I. of Mechanical Engineering
I. of Automobile Engineering
I. of Welding Technology
I. of Electrical Engineering
I. of Electronic Engineering (including Radio and Television)
I. of Chemical Engineering
I. of Building Engineering

Founded 1942. A State institution responsible to the Ministry of Education and Culture and the Council of Technical Education.

Academic Year: February to November (February-June; July-November).

Admission Requirements: Secondary school certificate (bachillerato) or Technical school certificate.

Language of Instruction: Spanish.

Degrees and Diplomas: Professional titles of–Técnico medio, 4 yrs; Técnico superior, 7 yrs.

Academic Staff: c. 120.

Student Enrolment: c. 900.

Professional Education

349 **ESCUELA SUPERIOR DE BELLAS ARTES DE LA PAZ**
Calle Rosendo Gutiérrez 323, La Paz
Fine Arts
Founded 1928.

350 **INSTITUTO COMERCIAL SUPERIOR DE LA NACIÓN 'FEDERICO ALVAREZ PLATE'**
Ayacucho 6737, Cochabamba City

Accountancy and Economics
Secretarial Studies

Founded 1944. A State institution operated by the Ministry of Education and Culture through the Dirección general de Educación (General Board of Education).

Academic Year: February to November.

Admission Requirements: Secondary school certificate (bachillerato).

Language of Instruction: Spanish.

Degrees and Diplomas: Professional titles of–Secretario comercial-cajero, commercial secretarial studies; Contador, accountancy; Contador general, 4 yrs.

Academic Staff: c. 30.

351 **INSTITUTO COMERCIAL SUPERIOR DE LA NACIÓN**

Calle Campero 94, La Paz
Cables: Incos
Telephone: 37-32-96
Rector: Armando de Palacios

Accountancy and Economics
Secretarial Studies

Founded 1944. A State institution operated by the Ministry of Education and Culture through the Dirección general de Educación (General Board of Education).

Academic Year: March to November.

Admission Requirements: Secondary school certificate (bachillerato).

Fees (Pesos Bolivianos): 10,000 per annum.

Language of Instruction: Spanish.

Degrees and Diplomas: Professional titles of–Secretario comercial-cajero, commercial secretarial studies; Contador, accountancy; Contador general, 3-4 yrs.

Library: 7500 vols.

Publication: Mercurio (annually).

Academic Staff, 1986-87: – (30).

Student Enrolment, 1986-87:

	Men	Women	Total
Of the country	900	600	1500

352 **COLEGIO NACIONAL DE COMERCIO 'FELIPE LEONOR RIVERA'**

Santa Cruz

Accountancy and Economics
Secretarial Studies

A State institution operated by the Ministry of Education and Culture through the Dirección general de Educación (General Board of Education).

Academic Year: February to November.

Admission Requirements: Secondary school certificate (bachillerato).

Language of Instruction: Spanish.

Degrees and Diplomas: Professional titles of–Secretario comercial-cajero, commercial secretarial studies; Contador, accountancy; Contador general, 4 yrs.

Academic Staff: c 30.

353 **INSTITUTO NACIONAL DE COMERCIO**

Oruro City

Accountancy and Economics
Secretarial Studies

A State institution operated by the Ministry of Education and Culture through the Dirección general de Educación (General Board oOf Education).

Academic Year: February to November.

Admission Requirements: Secondary school certificate (bachillerato).

Language of Instruction: Spanish.

Degrees and Diplomas: Professional titles of–Secretario comercial-cajero, commercial secretarial studies; Contador, accountancy; Contador general, 4 yrs.

Academic Staff: c. 30.

354 **COLEGIO NACIONAL DE COMERCIO**

Tarija City

Accountancy and Economics
Secretarial Studies

A State institution operated by the Ministry of Education and Culture through the Dirección general de Educación (General Board of Education).

Academic Year: February to November.

Admission Requirements: Secondary school certificate (bachillerato).

Language of Instruction: Spanish.

Degrees and Diplomas: Professional titles of–Secretario comercial-cajero, commercial secretarial studies; Contador, accountancy; Contador general, 4 yrs.

Academic Staff: c. 20.

355 **INSTITUTO SUPERIOR DE COMERCIO**

Trinidad City

Accountancy and Economics
Secretarial Studies

A State institution operated by the Ministry of Education and Culture through the Dirección general de Educación (General Board of Education).

Academic Year: February to November.

Admission Requirements: Secondary school certificate (bachillerato).

Language of Instruction: Spanish.

Degrees and Diplomas: Professional titles of–Secretario comercial-cajero, commercial secretarial studies; Contador, accountancy; Contador general, 4 yrs.

Academic Staff: c 20.

356 **ESCUELA NACIONAL DE ENFERMERÍA**

Calle 16 de Julio 83, Obrajes, La Paz

Nursing

Degrees and Diplomas: Title of Enfermera, 4 yrs.

357 **CONSERVATORIO NACIONAL DE MÚSICA**

Avenida 6 de Agosto 2092, La Paz

Music

Founded 1908, a State institution under the jurisdiction of the Ministry of Education and Culture.

Academic Year: February to October (February-June; June-October).

Admission Requirements: Special entrance examination.

Degrees and Diplomas: Titles and diplomas conferred by the Ministry of Education.

Academic Staff: c. 20.

Student Enrolment: c. 300.

Teacher Training

358 **ESCUELA NORMAL INTEGRADA CATÓLICA**

Casilla 849, Cochabamba
Telephone: 43165
Rector: Enrique Castro Rivero

Teacher Training (Primary level)

Founded 1956.

Admission Requirements: Secondary school certificate (bachillerato).

Fees (Pesos Bolivianos): 600 per annum.

Language of Instruction: Spanish.

Degrees and Diplomas: Diploma, 3 yrs.

Library: 5300 vols.

Special Facilities (Museums, etc.): Pre-History Museum.

Academic Staff, 1990: 12.

Student Enrolment, 1990: 102.

359 **INSTITUTO SUPERIOR DE EDUCACIÓN**

La Paz

Teacher Training

360 **ESCUELA NORMAL ESPECIALIZADA TÉCNICA**

Avenida Chacaltaya, Final, Casilla 2395, La Paz
Telephone: 37-32-91

Teacher Training (Technology)

Degrees and Diplomas: Diploma of Maestro normalista de Educación técnica.

361 **INSTITUTO NORMAL SUPERIOR 'SIMÓN BOLÍVAR'**
Villa IV Centenario, La Paz
Telephone: 30-03-04

Teacher Training

Founded 1917. A State institution under the jurisdiction of the Ministry of Education and Culture.

Academic Year: March to December (March-July; July-December).

Admission Requirements: Secondary school certificate (bachillerato).

Language of Instruction: Spanish.

Degrees and Diplomas: Diploma, 3-4 yrs.

Library: c. 60,000 vols.

Special Facilities (Museums, etc.): Museums of: Ethnography and Folklore; Natural Science.

Academic Staff: c. 140.

Student Enrolment: c. 1700.

362 **INSTITUTO NORMAL SUPERIOR DE EDUCACIÓN FÍSICA**
Calle Juande Vargas 311, La Paz
Telephone: 37-32-94

Teacher Training (Physical Education)

Degrees and Diplomas: Title of Profesor normalista de Educación física, 4 yrs.

363 **ESCUELA NORMAL INTEGRADA 'ENRIQUE FINOT'**
Avenida 'Ejército esq., Aba Barba', Santa Cruz
Telephone: 3416

Teacher Training

Founded 1959.

Academic Year: February to October.

Admission Requirements: Secondary school certificate (bachillerato) or equivalent.

Fees: None.

Language of Instruction: Spanish.

Degrees and Diplomas: Diploma of Maestro normal in various fields, 3 yrs.

364 **ESCUELA NORMAL INTEGRADA MAESTROS 'MARISCAL SUCRE'**
Avenida del Maestro 331, Casilla 137, Sucre

Teacher Training

Founded 1909. A State institution under the jurisdiction of the Ministry of Education and Culture.

Academic Year: February to December (February-June; July-December).

Admission Requirements: Secondary school certificate (bachillerato).

Language of Instruction: Spanish.

Degrees and Diplomas: Diploma, 4 yrs.

Library: Georges Rouma Library.

Publication: Revista Nuevos Rumbos (quarterly).

Academic Staff: c. 20 (160).

Student Enrolment: c. 1500.

365 **INSTITUTO SUPERIOR DE EDUCACIÓN RURAL**
Tarija

Teacher Training

BRAZIL

Universities

366 **UNIVERSIDADE FEDERAL DO ACRE**
Federal University of Acre
Avenida Getúlio Vargas 654, 69900 Rio Branco (Acre)
Telex: 69-2532
Telephone: (68) 2242397

I. of Human Science and Letters
F. of Law
F. of Economics
F. of Letters
Founded 1971. *Academic Staff: c.* 270.
Student Enrolment: c. 1600.

367 ***UNIVERSIDADE FEDERAL DE ALAGOAS**
Federal University of Alagoas
Br 101 Norte Km 14 Campus A.C., Simóes Tabuleiro do Martins, 57080 Maceió (Alagoas)
Telex: 822307
Telephone: (82) 241-6141
Reitor: Delza Leite Góes Gitai (1987-91)

Ce. for Exact and Natural Sciences
Director: Benedito de V. Pontes; *staff* 143 (14)
Ce. for Technology
Director: Amaro Monteiro de C. Filho; *staff* 66 (35)
Ce. for Biology
Director: Alfredo Raimundo C. Dacal; *staff* 80 (13)
Ce. for Health Sciences (Medicine, Dentistry, Physical Education, Nursing, Nutrition)
Director: Ana Dayse Rezende Dórea; *staff* 191 (67)
Ce. for Human Sciences, Letters and Arts
Director: Radjalma J. de A. Cavalcante; *staff* 147 (10)
Ce. for Applied Social Sciences
Director: Maria Valéria B. Lima; *staff* 92 (30)
Ce. for Agriculture
Director: Paulo Vanderlei Ferreira; *staff* 45 (3)
Ce. for Education
Director: Élcio de Gusmão Verçosa; *staff* 62 (10)
Also 41 departments, 8 centres, and Cultural Centre.

Founded 1961. Reorganized 1983 and faculties and institutes replaced by academic centres. A State institution financed by the federal government. Governing body: the Conselho Universitário, comprising the Rector, Vice-Rector, Directors, and representatives of the academic staff and students.

Academic Year: April to December (April-July; September-January).

Admission Requirements: Secondary school certificate and entrance examination.

Fees: None.

Language of Instruction: Portuguese.

Degrees and Diplomas: Licenciado in–Geography; Sciences; Philosophy; History; Education; Letters; Music, 3-4 yrs. Professional titles in–Civil Engineering; Chemical Engineering; Law; Economics; Business Administration; Accountancy; Social Studies; Dentistry; Medicine; Agriculture; Architecture; Meteorology; Sciences; Physical Education; Nursing andMidwifery; Nutrition; Journalism; Public Relations, 4-5 yrs.

Libraries: Central Library, 62,000 vols; libraries of the Centres and Departments, 160,000.

Special Facilities (Museums, etc.): Museum of Anthropology and Folklore.

Publications: Revista Scientia and Sapientia (biannually); Estudos Anuário do Centro de Ciências da Saúde; ProduçõCientíficas 1988.

Press or Publishing House: Editora Universitária.

Academic Staff, 1990:

	Full-time	Part-time
Titulares	12	2
Adjuntos	494	89
Assistentes	132	28
Auxiliares	186	62
Professores	2	1
Total	826	182

Student Enrolment, 1990:

Men	Women	Total
3385	3611	6996

368 ***UNIVERSIDAD DE ALFENAS**
University of Alfenas
Campus Universitária, Rodovia MG 179 Km.0, Alfenas (Minas Gerais)
Telex: (35) 2168
Telephone: (35) 921-1977
Fax: (35) 921-4403
Reitor: Edson Antônio Velano

F. of Law
Dean: Gilberto S. Filho; *staff* 1 (7)
F. of Medicine
Director: Adelino M. de Carvalho; *staff* 20 (29)
F. of Chemical and Pharmaceutical Sciences
Director: Lázaro Moscardini; *staff* 20 (28)
I. of Exact and Biological Sciences
Director: Julieta Maria Santos; *staff* 20 (28)
I. of Veterinary Medicine
Director: Paulo AfonsoFerreira; *staff* 11 (6)
I. of Arts and Technology
Director: Osvaldo Luis Mariano; *staff* 7 (22)
I. of Social and Human Sciences
Director: Sérgio Murad; *staff* 4 (25)
I. of Agriculture
Director: Hudson de Carvalho Bianchini; *staff* 10 (9)
I. of Dentistry
Director: José Velano; *staff* 2 (14)
Data Processing Ce.
Head: Alexandre M. Dias; *staff* 6 (22)

Founded 1979 as Faculdades Integradas da Região de Alfenas, became university 1988. Under the supervision ofthe Fundação de Ensino e Tecnologia de Alfenas.

Academic Year: February to December (February-June; August-December).

Admission Requirements: Secondary school certificate and entrance examination.

Fees (Cruzeiros): 250 per class.

Language of Instruction: Portuguese.

Degrees and Diplomas: Licenciado and Professional titles, 4-6 yrs. Mestrado, master, a further 2 yrs.

Library: c. 100,000 vols.

Special Facilities (Museums, etc.): Biological Garden.

Student Enrolment, 1990: 3010.

369 ***FUNDAÇÃO UNIVERSIDADE DO AMAZONAS**
University of the Amazonas
Avenida Getúlio Vargas 381, Centro, 69000 Manaus (Amazonas)
Telex: 92-2554
Telephone: (92) 2333600
Reitor: Marcus Luiz Barroso Barros
Diretor: Aluísio Augusto de Queiroz Braga

F. of Education
Director: José Dantas Cyrino Jr.; *staff* 74 (1)
F. of Technology
Director: Hélvio Neves Guerra; *staff* 57 (15)

F. of Health Sciences
Director: Alcidarta dos Reis Gadelha; *staff* 145 (37)
F. of Social Studies (including Law, Economics, Accountancy, and Administration)
Director: Humberto Coelho Batista; *staff* 59 (18)
I. of Exact Sciences
Director: Kléber Figueiras Bastos; *staff* 28 (10)
I. of Human Sciences and Letters (including Library Science)
Director: Odenildo Teixreira Sena; *staff* 157 (5)
I. of Biological Sciences
Director: Francisco Nailson Santos Pinto; *staff* 77 (4)
F. of Agriculture
Director: José Ferreira da Silva; *staff* 32 (22)
F. of Law
Director: Lourenço dos Santos P. Braga; *staff* 22 (22)
Ce. for Environmental Sciences
Director: Vicente Nogueira

Founded 1962. A State institution financed by the federal government. Governing body: the Conselho Universitário. Some residential facilities for students.

Academic Year: March to November (March-June; August-November).

Admission Requirements: Secondary school certificate and entrance examination.

Fees: None.

Language of Instruction: Portuguese.

Degrees and Diplomas: Bacharel or Licenciado in all fields, 3-9 yrs.

Library: Total, *c.* 90,270 vols.

Special Facilities (Museums, etc.): Amazonian Museum.

Press or Publishing House: Imprensa Universitária.

Academic Staff, 1990:

	Full-time	Part-time
Professores Titulares	125	15
Professores Adjuntos	213	50
Professores Assistentes	186	38
Professores Auxiliares	138	15
Total	662	118

Student Enrolment, 1990: 6706.

370 ***UNIVERSIDADE FEDERAL DA BAHIA**

Federal University of Bahia

Rua Augusto Viana s/n, 40140 Salvador (Bahia)
Telex: (71) 1978
Telephone: (71) 2452811
Fax: (71) 245-9002

Reitor: José Rogerio da Costa Vargens (1988-92)

Pró-Reitora para Assuntos de Planejamento e Administração: Evandro Walter de Sant'Anna Schneiter

I. of Biology
Director: Wanda Maria Pereira de Carvalho
I. of Earth Sciences
Director: Telésforo Martinez Marques; *staff* 81 (21)
I. of Letters
Director: Suzana Helena Longa Sampaio
I. of Mathematics
Director: Célia Maria Pitangueiras Gomes
I. of Physics
Director: Manoel Marcos Freire d'Aguiar Neto
I. of Health Sciences
Director: Luis Erlon de Araújo Rodrigues
I. of Chemistry
Director: Maria de Lourdes Botelho Trino
F. of Architecture
Director: Gilberto de Menezes Pedroso
F. of Economics
Director: Militno Rodrigues Peçanha Martinez
F. of Law
Director: Alberto Peçanha Martins
F. of Education
Director: Lucila Rupp de Magalhães
F. of Pharmacy
Director: Florentina Santos Diez del Corral
F. of Philosophy and Human Sciences
Director: Ubirajara Dórea Rebouças
F. of Medicine
Director: Heonir Pereira da Rocha
F. of Dentistry
Director: Urbino da Rocha Tunes
F. of Communication
Director: Ruy Alberto d'Assis E. Filho
S. of Administration
Director: Leopoldo Roberto Martins de Carvalho
S. of Agriculture
Director: Luiz Gonzaga Mendes
S. of Nursing
Director: Marisa Correia Hirata
S. of Veterinary Medicine
Director: Eliel Judson Duarte de Pinheiro
S. of Music
Director: Paulo Costa Lima
S. of Dance
Director: Eliana Rodrigues
S. of Theatre
Director: Paulo Lauro Nascimento Dourado
S. of Dietetics
Director: Nilze Barreto Villela
S. of Fine Arts
Director: Márcia de Azevedo Magno Baptista
S. of Library Science
Director: Francisco JoséLiberato de Mattos Carvalho
Polytechnic S.
Director: Carlos Emilio de Menezes Strauch
Ce. for Afro-Oriental Studies
Director: Iêda Castro
Ce. for Bahian Studies
Director: Fernando Rocha Peres
Ce for Interdisciplinary Studies for Public Services
Director: João Eurico Matta

Founded 1575 by the Society of Jesus, became university 1946 incorporating certain other institutions. Reorganized 1968. A State institution under the jurisdiction of the Ministry of Education and Culture. Governing bodies: the Assembleia Universitária; the Conselho de Curadores; the Conselho de Coordenação; the Conselho Universitário. Residential facilities for students.

Arrangements for co-operation with: Brown University; Harvard University; Cornell University; Universidade Técnica de Lisboa.

Academic Year: February to December (February-June; August-December).

Admission Requirements: Secondary school certificate and entrance examination.

Fees: Tuition, none.

Language of Instruction: Portuguese.

Degrees and Diplomas: Bacharel and Licenciado in–Mathematics; Physics; Chemistry; Geography; Biology; Philosophy; Social Science; History; Psychology; Letters; Languages, 4-5 yrs. Licenciado in–Science; Music; Ballet, 4 yrs. Professional titles of–Geologia; Arquitetura; Engenharia (various fields); Medicina; Enfermagem de Saúde pública; Enfermagem Obstétrica, midwifery; Farmácia Bioquímica; Odontologia; Nutrição; Medicina veterinária; Direito, law; Economia; Contador, accountancy; Administração de Emprêsas, business administration; Administração pública; Biblioteconomia e Documentação; Pedagogia; Secretariado; Museologia; Instrumento; Canto; Composição e Regência; Direcção Teatral; Dançarino profissional, 4-6 yrs. Mestrado. Doctorado in Geophysics.

Libraries: Central Library, 538,043 vols; Baianos Studies, 29,538; 32 libraries of the teaching sections.

Special Facilities (Museums, etc.): Museu de Arte Sacra; Archaeology and Ethnology Museum; Afro-Brazilian Museum.

Publication: Publications of the Faculties and Institutes.

Press or Publishing House: Gráfica Universitária.

Academic Staff, 1989-90: 1416 (623).

Student Enrolment, 1989-90: 15,175.

371 **UNIVERSIDADE DE BAURU**

Avenida Eng Luiz Edmundo Carrijo Coube, 17033 Bauru (São Paulo)
Telex: 14-2312
Telephone: (142) 232111

Engineering
Administration
Human Sciences
Physics, Chemistry and Computer Sciences
Mathematics
Education

Physical Education
Founded 1969. A municipal institution under the supervision of the Fundação Educacional de Bauru.

372 **UNIVERSIDADE REGIONAL DE BLUMENAU**
Rua Antonio da Veiga 140, 89010 Blumenau (Santa Catarina)
Telex: 47-3302
Telephone: (473) 228288
Reitor: José Tafner (1986-90)

Ce. for Applied Social Sciences (including Law, Economics and Administration)
Director: Gentil Telles
Ce. for Human Sciences, Letters and Arts
Director: Yolanda Tridapalli
Ce. for Exact and Natural Sciences
Director: Egon José Schramm
Ce. for Technology (including Data Processing)
Director: Wilson Lang
Ce. for Education (including Physical Education)
Director: Lorival Beckhauser

Founded 1968. Under the supervision of the Fundação Universidade Regional de Blumenau. Governing bodies: the Conselho Universitário; the Conselho de Ensino, Pesquisa e Extensão.

Academic Year: March to December (March-June; August-December).

Admission Requirements: Secondary school certificate and entrance examination.

Language of Instruction: Portuguese.

Degrees and Diplomas: Bacharel in–Economics; Administration; Accountancy, 4 yrs; Law, 5 yrs. Licenciado in–Science, 2 ½ yrs; Physical Education; Art Education, 3 yrs; Education; Letters; Mathematics; Chemistry; Biology, 4 yrs. Professional titles of–Tecnólogo em Processamento de Dados, 3 yrs; Engenheiro quimico; Engenheiro civil, 5 yrs.

Library: Central Library.

Publication: Revista de Divulgação Cultural.

Academic Staff, 1986-87:

Rank	Full-time	Part-time
Professores Responsável	53	124
Professores Colaboradores	8	64
Professores Assistentes	–	15
Professores Visitantes	1	–
Auxiliares de Ensino	–	2
Total	62	205

Student Enrolment, 1986-87:

	Men	Women	Total
Of the country	2400	2061	4461

373 ***FUNDAÇÃO UNIVERSIDADE DE BRASÍLIA**
University of Brasília
Campus Universitário, Asa Norte, 70910 Brasília, D.F.
Cables: unibras
Telex: 612730
Telephone: (61) 2740022
Fax: (61) 2733884
Reitor: Antônio Ibanez Ruiz

I. of Human Sciences
I. of Exact Sciences (including Statistics)
I. of Biology (including Psychology)
I. of Arts and Communication
I. of Architecture and Town Planning
F. of Technology (including Agricultural Engineering)
F. of Health Sciences (including Physical Education)
F. of Applied Social Sciences
F. of Education
Extension D.

Founded 1961. The university is constituted as a foundation and governed by a Conselho Director of 8 members who are appointed by the President of the Republic. The federal government provides 80% of the university's income. Residential facilities for academic staff and for students.

Academic Year: January to December (January-March; March-July; August-November).

Admission Requirements: Secondary school certificate and entrance examination.

Language of Instruction: Portuguese.

Degrees and Diplomas: Bacharel and Licenciado in–Physics; Mathematics; Chemistry; Statistics; Psychology; Biology; Economics; Social Sciences; Philosophy; History; Social Studies; International Relations; Geography; Language and Literature; Music; Letters; Design and Plastic Arts; Education; Physical Education; Nursing and Midwifery; Business Administration; Public Administration; Law; Accountancy; Library Science, 3-7 yrs. Professional titles in–Engineering (various fields); Agriculture; Geology; Nutrition; Dentistry; Architecture and Town Planning; Communication; Medicine; Data Processing, 3-7 yrs. Mestrado, master, 1-2 further yrs. Doctorado, doctorate, by thesis. Alsoteaching qualifications.

Library: Central Libraries, *c.* 457,090 vols.

Publications: Revista Humanidades (Quarterly); Diogens (biannually); Relações Internacionais (3 times a year); Documentação estualidade Politica (quarterly).

Press or Publishing House: Editora Universidade de Brasília.

Academic Staff: c. 900.

Student Enrolment: c. 10,000 (Also *c.* 6000 extension students and *c.* 40,000 attending Open University).

374 **UNIVERSIDADE 'BRAZ CUBAS'**
Rua Francisco Franco 133, 08700 Mogi das Cruzes (São Paulo)
Telex: 11-39267
Telephone: (11) 4696444

F. of Law
F. of Economics and Business Administration
F. of Engineering
F. of Philosophy, Science and Letters
F. of Architecture and Town Planning
F. of Social Communications
F. of Psychology
Also elementary and high schools.

Founded 1940 as private school, constituted as a federation 1972 and acquired present status and title 1984.

Academic Year: February to November (February-June; August-November).

Admission Requirements: Secondary school certificate and entrance examination.

Languages of Instruction: Portuguese and English.

Degrees and Diplomas: Professional titles. Mestrado, master. Also postgraduate diplomas of specialization.

Library: c. 92,000 vols.

Academic Staff: c. 140 (660).

Student Enrolment: c. 10,650.

375 **UNIVERSIDADE ESTADUAL DE CAMPINAS**
State University of Campinas
Cidade Universitária 'Zeferino Vaz', 13081 Campinas (São Paulo)
Telex: (019) 1150
Telephone: (192) 391301
Reitor: Carlos Alberto Vogt (1986-90)
Coordinador de Administração Geral: Vera Randi

I. of Biology
Director: Antonio Celso Nunes Magalhães; *staff* 153 (7)
I. of Fine Arts
Director: Bernardo Caro; *staff* 103 (20)
I. of Economics
Director: Mario Luis Possas; *staff* 94 (15)
I. of Language Studies
Director: Eduardo Roberto Jungueira Guimarães; *staff* 81 (1)
I. of Geosciences
Director: Bernardino Ribeiro Figueiredo; *staff* 40 (5)
I. of Mathematics, Statistics and Computer Science
Director: Marco Antonio Teixeira; *staff* 146 (29)
I. of Chemistry
Director: Paulo José Samenho Moran; *staff* 76 (1)
I. of Philosophy and Humanities
I. of Physics
Director: José Galvão de Pisapia Ramos; *staff* 133 (4)
S. of Mechanical Engineering
Director: José Tomaz Vieira Pereira; *staff* 83 (10)
S. of Food Engineering
Director: Theo Guenter Kickbusch; *staff* 75 (2)
S. of Civil Engineering
Director: Dayr Dchiozer; *staff* 64 (18)
S. of Electrical Engineering

S. of Physical Education
Director: Ademir Gebara; *staff* 43 (3)
S. of Dentistry
Director: Simonides Consani; *staff* 48 (43)
S. of Medical Sciences
Director: Marcelo de Carvalho Ramos; *staff* 305 (131)
S. of Education
Director: José Luis Sanfelice; *staff* 94 (26)
S. of Agricultural Engineering
Director: José Tadeu Jorge; *staff* 52 (1)
S. of Chemical Engineering
Director: Edson Biterncourt; *staff* 28 (8)
Also 25 Research Nucleü Centres, and Technical Cities at Campinas and Limeira.

Founded 1966 by the State legislature of São Paulo as an autonomous institution. Governing bodies: the University Board, comprising 44 members; the University Council, comprising 62 members.

Arrangements for co-operation with: Free University, Berlin; University of Rostock; Université de Quebec à Trois-Rivières and Rimouski; Technical University of Nova Scotia; University of Denver; University of Massachussets; State University of New York at Albany; Indiana University; Universuty of Miami; Florida University; Texas University; University of Boston; Colorado School of Mines; San Diego State University; University of California; Florida University; Texas A & M University; University of Texas at Austin; University of Tulsa; Imperial College; University of London; State University of Moscow; State University of Yerevan; Universidade Agostinho Neto; Université Catholique de Louvain; Université de Paris VII; Universidade Renê Descartes (Paris V); Ecole des hautes Etudes en Sciences sociales de Paris; Institut national des Sciences appliquées de Lyon; Université de Omar Bongo; University of Tel-Aviv; Israel Institute of Technology-Technion; Universitádegli studi di Trieste; Universitá degli Studi di Bologna; Universidade técnica de Lisboa;Universidade Nova de Lisboa; Universidade Coimbra; Universidade de Lisboa; Universidad de El Salvador; Universidad Nacional de Rosario; Universidad del Centro de La Província; Universidad Nacional de La Plata; Universidad Nacional de Entre Rios; Universidad de Buenos Aires; Universidad Mayor de San Andrés; Universidad Autónoma Gabriel René Moreno de Santa Cruz de La Sierra; Universidad Boliviana 'Tomás Frias'; Universidad de Chile; Universidad Católica de Valparaiso; Universidad de Santiago; Pontifícia Universidade Católica de Chile; Universidad de Concepción; Universidad de Tarapaca-Arica; Universidad Técnica Féderico Santa María; Instituto Profesional de Chile; Universidad Nacional de Colombia; Universidad Del Valle; Universidad Tecnológica de Pereira; Universidad de Caúca; Universidad de La Habana; Universidad de Costa Rica; Universidad de El Salvador; Universidad de Guayaquil; Escuela Politecnica Nacional de Quito; Universidad San Carlos da Guatemala; Universidad Autónoma de Honduras; Universidad Autónoma de Guadalajara;Instituto Politecnico Nacional, Mexico; Universidad Nacional Autónoma de Mexico; Universidad de Sonora; Universidad Nacional de Paraguay; Universidad Nacional de Assunción; Universidad Nacional de Assunción; Universidad Mayor de San Marco; Universidad de Tingo Maria; Universidad Nacional Agraria La Molina; Universidad Autónoma de Santo Domingo; Universidad Antom de Kom, Suriname; Universidad de La República de Uruguay (FEA) (ARQ); Universidad Central de Venezuela; Technical University of Budapest; University of Gifu; University of Tokyo.

Academic Year: March to December (March-June; August-December).

Admission Requirements: Secondary school certificate and entrance examination.

Fees: None.

Language of Instruction: Portuguese.

Degrees and Diplomas: Bacharel and Licenciado, 4-6 yrs. Professional titles, 3-6 yrs. Mestrado, master, a further 2-3 yrs. Doctorates by thesis.

Library: Total, 230,144 vols.

Special Facilities (Museums, etc.): Art Gallery; Observatory.

Publications: A total of *c.* 320 publications, including: Educação e Sociedade (quarterly); Cadernos CEDES (every 2 months); Relatório Interno-IMECC; Boletim do IMECC (monthly); Cadernos de Estudos Lingüísticos (annually); Estudos Portugueses e Africanos-EPA (biannually); Remate de Males; Trabalhos em Linguística Aplicada (biannually); CPG Informativo; Cadernos de História e Filosofia da Ciência (biannually); The Journal of Non-Classical Logic; Manuscrito: Revista de Filosofia (biannually); Cadernos do Arquivo Edgard Lenenroth; Cadernos IFCH; Boletim Informativo do Instituto de Física (weekly); Atvidades de Pesquisas Desenvolvidas (annually).

Press or Publishing House: Press and Publishing House: Editora Unicamp.

Academic Staff, 1989-90:

Rank	Full-time	Part-time
Professores Titulares	118	32
Professores Adjuntos	569	86
Professores Livres-Docentes	567	47
Professores Assistentes/Dout.	258	49
Professores Assistentes	125	72
Instrutores	200	48
Total	1834	334

Student Enrolment, 1989-90:

	Total
Of the country	10,108
Of other countries	495
Total	10,778

376 *PONTIFÍCIA UNIVERSIDADE CATÓLICA DE CAMPINAS

Pontifical Catholic University of Campinas
Rodovio D. Pedro I, Km. 112, 13100 Campinas (São Paulo)
Telex: 19-1806
Telephone: (192) 520899
Fax: (192) 528477
Reitor: Eduardo José Pereira Coelho (1989-92)
Secretário Geral: Marcel Dantas de Campos

I. of Arts and Communication (including Journalism, Marketing and Propaganda, and Tourism)
Director: Geny de Oliveira Lima; *staff* 164 (2)
I. of Biology
Director: Ermerson Cocco Lanaro; *staff* 73 (2)
F. of Law
Director: Alvaro Cesar Iglésias; *staff* 53 (2)
F. of Education
Director: Jamil Cury Sawaya; *staff* 60 (2)
F. of Physical Education
Director: José Agostinno Zugliani; *staff* 53 (2)
F. of Nursing
Director: Mara Regina Lemes de Sordi; *staff* 37 (2)
F. of Dentistry
Director: Thomaz Ferrara Fiori Wassal; *staff* 77 (2)
F. of Social Service
Director: Jeanette Liasch Martins de Sá; *staff* 29 (2)
C. of Commerce
Director: José Rachado Couto-Monsenhor; *staff* – (53)
I. of Informatics
Director: Otávio Roberto Jacobini

Founded 1941 as faculty of philosophy, formally constituted as university and recognized by the State 1955. Raised to the rank of Catholic university 1957. Reorganized 1972. The institution is responsible to the Metropolitan Archbishop of Campinas, its Grand Chancellor. Financially supported by federal and State governments and by municipal authorities. Governing bodies: the Conselho Universitário; the Conselho de Coordenação do Ensino e Pesquisa (Council of Coordination ofTeaching and Research).

Academic Year: March to November (March-June; August-November).

Admission Requirements: Secondary school certificate and entrance examination.

Fees (Cruzeiros): 5341-15,400 per annum.

Language of Instruction: Portuguese.

Degrees and Diplomas: Bacharel in–Journalism; Public Relations; Nutrition; Theology; Administration; Accountancy; Economics; Systems Analyses; Tourism; Library, 3-4 yrs; Biology; Law, 5 yrs. Licenciado in–Physical Education; Plastic Arts; Design; 3 yrs; Education; Nursing; Social Sciences; History; Geography; Science; Philosophy; Letters; Psychology; Mathematics; Biology, 4 yrs. Professional titles of–Farmácia-Bioquímica; Fisioterapéuta; Nutricionista; Cirurgião dentista; Assistente social, 4 yrs; Arquitecto; Psicólogo; Engenheiro civil, 5 yrs; Médico, 6 yrs. Mestrado, master, in–Psychology; Library Science; Letters; Philosophy, a further 2 yrs. Doctorado.

Library: 106,003 vols.

Special Facilities (Museums, etc.): Museu de Antropologia; Art and Cultural Theatre and Dance Group

Publications: Boletim Bibliográfico; Revista Notícia Bibliográfica e Histórica; Reflexão.

Academic Staff, 1989-90:

Rank	Full-time	Part-time
Professores Titulares	40	290
Professores Adjuntos	50	110
Professores Assistentes	30	440
Instructores	50	140
Total	200	980

Student Enrolment, 1989-90: c. 19,410.

377 **UNIVERSIDADE DE CAXIAS DO SUL**
University of Caxias do Sul
Rua Francisco Getúlio Vargas 1130, 95001 Caxias do Sul (Rio Grande do Sul)
Telex: 54-3734
Telephone: (542) 2224133
Reitor: Ruy Pauletti (1990-94)

Ce. for Biological and Health Sciences (including Nursing and Physical Education)
Director: Celso Picoli Coelho; *staff* 6 (9)
Ce. for Applied Social Studies (including Administration, Law, and Economics)
Director: Nelson Goularte Ramos; *staff* 6 (9)
Ce. for Exact Sciences and Technology
Director: Eliana do Sacramento Soares; *staff* 16 (9)
Ce. for Human Sciences and Arts
Director: Maria de Lourdes Skrebski; *staff* 13 (9)
I. of Biotechnology
Director: Juan Carrau; *staff* 1 (6)
I. of Administration and Technology
Director: Luiz Alberto Bertotto
S. of Hotel Administration
Director: André Poltronieri
Ce. of Philosophy and Education
Director: Nora Ordovás

Founded 1967 and incorporating previously existing faculties. A private institution constituted as a foundation and recognized by the federal government. Governing bodies: the Conselho Universitário; the Conselho de Ensino, Pesquisa e Extensão.

Academic Year: March to December (March-July; August-December).

Admission Requirements: Secondary school certificate and extrance examination.

Language of Instruction: Portuguese.

Degrees and Diplomas: Bacharel and Licenciado in all fields, 4 yrs; Business Administration; Communication; Computer Sciences; Accountancy; Economics; Psychology; Law, 5 yrs. Professional titles in–School Inspection; Nursing, 4 yrs; Engineering, various fields, 5 yrs; Medicine, 6 yrs. Postgraduate diplomas of specialization, 2 yrs. Also teaching qualifications.

Library: c. 80,000 vols.

Special Facilities (Museums, etc.): Natural Science Museum; Art Gallery.

Publication: Revista Chronos (biannually).

Press or Publishing House: Editora da Universidade de Caxias do Sul.

Academic Staff, 1989: c. 400.

Student Enrolment, 1990:

	Men	Women	Total
Of the country	3513	4297	7810

378 **UNIVERSIDADE ESTADUAL DO CEARÁ**
State University of Ceará
Paranjana, 1700, Campus do Itaperi, 60715 Fortaleza (Ceará)
Telex: 85-2295
Telephone: (85) 245113

Ce. for Applied Social Studies
Ce. for Human Sciences
Ce. for Science and Technology
Ce. for Health Services (Veterinary Science, Dietetics, Nursing)
Ce. for Administrative Studies

Founded 1977, incorporating previously existing private institutions. A State institution financed by the federal government. Governing bodies: the Conselho Universitário, comprising the Rector as President, the Vice-Rector, directors of the centres, students and non-university members; the Conselho de Pesquisa, Ensino e Extensão.

Academic Year: March to December (March-July; August-December).

Admission Requirements: Secondary school certificate and entrance examination.

Language of Instruction: Portuguese.

Degrees and Diplomas: Bacharel, 3-5 yrs. Licenciado, 3-7 yrs.

Libraries: Central Library, c. 15,140 vols; Human Sciences, c. 14,000; Applied Social Sciences, c. 10,000; Health Sciences, c. 5500; Science and Technology, c. 3000.

Academic Staff: c. 970.

Student Enrolment: c. 12,900.

379 **UNIVERSIDADE FEDERAL DO CEARÁ**
Federal University of Ceará
Avenida da Universidade 2853 Benfica, 60000 Fortaleza (Ceará)
Telex: 85-1077
Telephone: (85) 2230233
Reitor: Raimundo Helio Leite

Ce. for Human Sciences
Ce. for Science
Ce. for Agriculture Sciences (including Fishery, Home Economics, and Food Technology)
Ce. for Health Sciences (Medicine, Dentistry, Pharmacy, and Nursing)
Ce. for Applied Social Studies (Economics, Law, and Education)
Also 41 departments.

Founded 1955, the university is a State institution financed by the federal government. Governing body: the Conselho Universitário, comprising the Rector as President, the Vice-Rector and Pro-Rectors, directors of the centres, six students, and three non-university members. Residential facilities for students.

Academic Year: March to December (March-July; August-December).

Admission Requirements: Secondary school certificate or equivalent and entrance examination.

Fees: None.

Language of Instruction: Portuguese.

Degrees and Diplomas: Bacharel and Licenciado in all fields, 4 yrs; Medicine, 6 yrs. Mestrado, master, a further 2 yrs.

Libraries: Central Library, c. 155,000 vols; Health Sciences library.

Special Facilities (Museums, etc.): Museum of Art.

Publications: Revista de Ciências Sociais (biannually); Revista Agronómica (biannually); Revista de Medicina (biannually); Revista de Communicação Social (biannually); Revista Tecnologia; Arquivo do Centro de Ciências da Saúde.

Academic Staff: c. 1250.

Student Enrolment: c. 14,700.

380 **UNIVERSIDADE FEDERAL DO ESPÍRITO SANTO**
Federal University of Espirito Santo
Campus 'Dr. Alaor de Queiroz Araújo', Avenida Fernando Ferrari s/n, 29000 Vitória (Espirito Santo)
Telex: 27-2330
Telephone: (27) 227-7025
Reitor: Romulo Augusto Penina (1988-92)
Registrar: Lilian de Carvalho Pardo

Ce. for Arts (including Architecture and Town Planning)
Director: Seliegio Gomes Romalho; *staff* 72 (6)
Ce. for Law and Economics (including Business Administration, Library Science, and Social Communication)
Director: Roberto da Cunha Penedo; *staff* 125 (43)
Ce. for Biomedical Studies (Medicine, Dentistry, and Nursing)
Director: Fausto Edmundo Lima Pereira; *staff* 265 (38)
Ce. for Physical Education and Sport
Director: Conceição Aparecida Ferreira Viera; *staff* 39
Ce. for Education
Director: Dulce Castiglioni; *staff* 88 (3)
Ce. for General Studies (including Biology, Social Sciences, Statistics, Philosophy, Physics and Chemistry, Earth Sciences, Languages and Literature, and Psychology)
Director: Artelirio Bolsanello; *staff* 289 (13)
Ce. for Technology (including Civil, Mechanical, Electrical, Industrial Engineering, and Computer Sciences)
Ce. for Agriculture (including Animal Husbandry)
Director: José Geraldo Ferreira; *staff* 40 (2)
D. of Brazilian Studies
I of Technology
Head: Edson de Paula Ferreira
Computer Ce.
Director: José Fernando Robert Nunes

I. of Dental Medicine
Head: Rubens Sergio Rasseli
Ce. for Lifelong Educatin
Vice-Rector: Domingos Gomes de Azevedo
Also a Teaching Hospital and kindergarten, elementary and junior high schools.

Founded 1954 as a State university incorporating existing colleges. Became a federal institution 1961 and reorganized 1966. Financed by the federal government. Governing bodies: the Conselho Universitário, including students and representatives of the local community; the Conselho Ensino e Pesquisa.

Academic Year: March to December (March-July; August-November).

Admission Requirements: Secondary school certificate and entrance examination.

Fees: None.

Language of Instruction: Portuguese.

Degrees and Diplomas: Bacharel and Licenciado in all fields, 4-8 yrs. Professional titles. Mestrado, master in–Education; Environmental Engineering; Cardiovascular Physiology.

Libraries: Central Library, *c.* 94,273 vols; Biomedicine, *c.* 9000; Agriculture, 12,503.

Special Facilities (Museums, etc.): Museu Solar Monjardim; Museu Santa Luzia; Museu dos Reis Magos.

Publications: Revista de Cultura; UFES: Dados Estatísticos, Impresso II.

Press or Publishing House: Grafica Imprensa Universitária.

Academic Staff, 1989-90:

	Full-time	Part-time
Professores	38	8
Professores Adjuntos	713	116
Professores Asistentes	163	25
Professores Auxiliares	104	23
Total	1018	172

Student Enrolment, 1989-90:

	Men	Women	Total
Of the country	4128	4170	8298
Of other countries	35	18	53
Total	4163	4188	8351

381 UNIVERSIDADE ESTADUAL DE FEIRA DE SANTANA

State University of Feira de Santana
Km 3, BR-116, Campus Universitário, 44100 Feira de Santana (Bahia)
Telex: 75-2403
Telephone: (75) 2241521
Reitor: José Maria Nunes Marques (1983-87)

D. of Letters and Arts
D. of Health Sciences
D. of Biology
D. of Exact Sciences
D. of Education
D. of Civil Engineering
D. of Human Sciences and Philosophy (including Social Studies)

Founded 1970 by the State legislature of Bahia, recognized by the federal government 1976. Governing bodies: the Conselho Académico; the Conselho Superior de Ensino, Pesquisa e Extensão.

Academic Year: March to December (March-July; August-December).

Admission Requirements: Secondary school certificate and entrance examination.

Language of Instruction: Portuguese.

Degrees and Diplomas: Licenciado in–Languages and Letters; Social Studies; Science, 4 yrs. Professional titles in–Administration; Accountancy; Economics; Civil Engineering; Nursing, 4 yrs.

Library: c. 340,000 vols.

Academic Staff: c. 180 (60).

Student Enrolment: c. 3250.

382 *UNIVERSIDADE FEDERAL FLUMINENSE

Federal University of Fluminense
Rua Miguel de Frias 9, Icaraí, 24240 Niterói (Rio de Janeiro)
Telex: 21-32076
Telephone: (21) 7178080
Reitor: J.R. Martins-Romêo
Chefe de Gabinete: Dylva Araújo Moliterno

Ce. for Applied Social Studies
Director: José Carlos de Almeida
Ce. for General Studies
Director: Jorge da Silva Paula Gaimarães
Ce. for Medical Science (including Pharmacy, Dentistry and Nursing)
Director: Cresus Vinicius Depes de Gouveia
Ce. for Technology
Director: Carlos Prestes Cardoso
I. of Pharmacy and Biochemistry
I. of Arts and Social Communication
I. of Human Sciences and Philosophy
I. of Physics
I. of Earth Sciences
I. of Letters
I. of Mathematics
I. of Chemistry and Biomedical Studies
I. of Economics and Administration
I. of Medicine
I. of Dentistry
I. of Veterinary Science
I. of Law
I. of Education
S. of Engineering (including Architecture and Town Planning)
S. of Nursing
S. of Social Service
D. of Social Service (Campos)
S. of Industrial Metallurigial Engineering (Volta Redonda)
Conservatory of Music
Extension D.

Founded 1960, as Federal University of the State of Rio de Janeiro, acquired present title 1965. Reorganized 1983. An autonomous institution. Governing bodies: the Conselho Universitário; the Conselho de Curadores; the Conselho de Ensino e Pesquisa.

Academic Year: March to December (March-June; August-December).

Admission Requirements: Secondary school certificate and entrance examination.

Degrees and Diplomas: Bacharel and Licenciado in all subjects, 4-5 yrs. Professional titles, 3-6 yrs. Mestrado, master.

Library: Total, 491,960 vols.

Publications: Revista de Instituto de Educação (biannually); technological and didactic publications.

Press or Publishing House: Núcleo Editora.

Academic Staff, 1986-87:

Rank	Full-time	Part-time
Professores Titulares	174	57
Professores Adjuntos	1038	274
Professores Assistentes	646	251
Professores Auxiliares	193	168
Pessoal Técnico-Administrativo	4714	386
Total	6765	1136

Student Enrolment, 1986-87:

	Men	Women	Total
Of the country	9195	9592	18,787
Of other countries	55	33	88
Total	9250	9625	18,875

383 UNIVERSIDADE DE FORTALEZA

University of Fortaleza
Avenida Washington Soares 1321, 60810 Fortaleza (Ceará)
Telex: 85-37
Telephone: (85) 2392833
Reitor: Carlos Alberto Batista M. de Sousa (1981-89)
Secretário Geral: Epitácio Quezado Cruz

Ce. for Natural Sciences
Director: Godofredo de Castro Filho; *staff* 23 (77)
Ce. for Technology
Director: Lourenço Humberto Portela Reinaldo; *staff* 17 (76)
Ce. for Health Sciences
Director: José Antonio Carlos O. D. Morano; *staff* 14 (150)
Ce. for Administration
Director: José Maria Martins Mendes

Founded 1971. Under the supervision of the Fundação Educacional Edson Quieroz. A private institution recognized by the federal government.

Academic Year: March to December (March-July; August-December).

Admission Requirements: Secondary school certificate and entrance examination.

Fees (Cruzeiros): 2946 per semester.

Language of Instruction: Portuguese.

Degrees and Diplomas: Bacharel in–Chemistry; Geology; Computer Sciences; Civil Engineering; Mechanical and Electrical Engineering; Physical Education; Physiotherapy; Nursing; Occupational Therapy; Audiotherapy; Administration; Economics; Accountancy; Tourism; Law; Social Sciences; Psychology. Licenciado in–Education; Letters.

Library: Central Library, 51,000 vols.

Publications: Revista Tecnologia (biannually); Revista do Centro de Ciências da Saûde (biannually); Revista Humanidades (biannually).

Academic Staff, 1986-87: 87 (500).

Student Enrolment, 1986-87:

	Men	Women	Total
Of the country	7482	5871	13,353

384 **UNIVERSIDADE GAMA FILHO**

Gama Filho University

Rua Manoel Vitorino 625, 13 Piedade, 20740 Rio de Janeiro (Rio de Janeiro)

Telephone: (212) 2697272

Chancellor: Paulo Gama Filho (1984-94)

Ce. for Biology and Health Sciences (including Physical Education)

Ce. for Exact Sciences and Technology (including Architecture)

Dean: Sergio Flores da Silva

Ce. for Social Sciences (including Law, and Business Administration)

Dean: Henrique Luiz Arienti

Ce. for Human Sciences (including Physical Education)

Dean: Manoel José G. Tubino

Ce. for Business Administration

Director: Helio Duarte Nascimento

Ce. for Economics

Director: Paulo Di Tommaso

Ce. for Accounting

Director: Hermengildo S. Neto

Ce. for Social Work

Director: Heloina R. de Souza

Ce. for Social Commmunication

Director: Edson Schettine de Aguiar

Ce. for History

Director: Arno Wehling

Ce. for Law

Director: Celso Cesar Papaleo

Ce. for Biology

Director: João Baptista A. Carneiro

Ce. for Medicine

Co-ordinator: Jose Lisboa Miranda

Ce. for Dentistery

Co-ordinator: Roberto Schirmer

Ce. for Nutrition

Co-ordinator: Neuza Terezinha Cavalcante

Ce. for Nursing

Director: Leda Santos Pires

Ce. for Engineering

Directors: Hostilio Xavier Ratton; Fernando Flamarion Curvo; Edson Carvalho da Cruz

Ce. for Architecture

Co-ordinator: Maria Lucia M.Ribeiro

Ce. for Physical Education

Director: Claudio Macedo Reis

Ce. for Education

Director: Renato Cerqueira Zambrotti

Ce. for Psychology

Director: Italo Albizzati

Ce. for Letters and Arts

Director: Lucia Helena da S. Pereira

Founded 1972. A private institution recognized by the federal government and administered by the Sociedade Universitária Gama Filho. Governing bodies: the Conselho Universitário; the Conselho de Ensino e Pesquisa.

Arrangements for co-operation with Cleveland State University.

Academic Year: March to December (March-June; August-December).

Admission Requirements: Secondary school certificate and entrance examination.

Fees (Cruzeiros): 3298-9429

Language of Instruction: Portuguese.

Degrees and Diplomas: Bacharel. Licenciado in–Psychology; Nursing; Geography; Education; Letters; Biology; History; Physical Education. Professional titles in–Medicine; Engineering; Architecture; Nutrition; Dentistry; Business Administration; Social Work; Psychology, 5-6 yrs. Mestrado, master, in–Philosophy; Physical Education; Psychology; Law, 4-6 yrs. Doutorado, in Philosophy.

Libraries: Central Library, 137,665 vols; specialized libraries, *c.* 38,500.

Special Facilities (Museums, etc.): University Museum.

Publications: Guia Académico (annually); Revista Artus (quarterly); Revista Ciências Humanas (quarterly); Revista Ciências Biológicas; Catálogo Trabalhos Técnicos e Cientificos. Supplemento Acadêmico.

Press or Publishing House: Gráfica TEJU.

Academic Staff, 1990: c. 1570.

Student Enrolment, 1990: c. 20,400.

385 **UNIVERSIDADE CATÓLICA DE GOIÁS**

Catholic University of Goiás

Praça Universitária, 74000 Goiânia (Goiás)

Telex: 62-1276

Telephone: (62) 2251188

Ce. for Human Sciences

Ce. for Scientific Technology

Founded 1948 as faculty of philosophy, formally constituted as university and recognized by the State 1960. A private institution administered by the Catholic Archdiocese of Goiânia, but receives financial assistance from the State. Governing body: the Conselho Universitário.

Academic Year: March to December (March-July; August-December).

Admission Requirements: Secondary school certificate and entrance examination.

Language of Instruction: Portuguese.

Degrees and Diplomas: Bacharel in–Law; Social Service; Architecture; Economics; Accountancy; Public Administration; Business Administration; Nursing; Psychology. Licenciado in–Letters; History; Psychology; Education; School Administration; Mathematics; Physics; Natural History; Geography. Professional titles of–Psicólogo; Enfermeiro, nursing.

Libraries: Central Library, *c.* 10,500 vols; Social Service, *c.* 2000.

Special Facilities (Museums, etc.): Museums of: Anthropology, Archaeology, and History.

Publication: Revista (weekly).

Academic Staff: c. 560.

Student Enrolment: c. 11,500.

386 **UNIVERSIDADE FEDERAL DE GOIÁS**

Federal University of Goiás

Rodovia Gioânia Neropolis, 12, Caixa Postal 131, 74000 Goiânia (Goiás)

Telex: 62-2206

Telephone: (62) 205-1000

Fax: (62) 205-1510

Reitor: Ricardo Freva Bufáiçal (1990-94)

Chefe de Gabinete: Zezuca Pereira Da Silva

S. of Agriculture

Director: Ronaldo V. Naves; *staff* 44 (5)

S. of Veterinary Medicine

Director: Eurípedes L. Lopes; *staff* 49 (4)

S. of Engineering

Director: Armênia de Souza; *staff* 38 (36)

F. of Law

Director: Carlos Leopoldo Dayrell; *staff* 9 (37)

F. of Education

Director: Marlene de O. Faleiro; *staff* 140 (11)

F. of Pharmacy and Biochemistry

Director: Rui Hiroshi Yamada; *staff* 24 (6)

F. of Nursing and Nutrition

Director: Norma Leão Gonçalves; *staff* 36 (6)

F. of Medicine

Director: Maurício Sérgio Brasil Leite; *staff* 6 (163)

F. of Dentistry

Director: Edison Vivas de Resende; *staff* 14 (32)

I. of Arts

Director: Dalva Albernaz Nascimento; *staff* 65 (12)

I. of Biology

Director: Joaquim Tomé de Souza; *staff* 64 (19)

I. of Mathematics and Physics

Director: Ilka Maria A. Moreira; *staff* 72 (17)

I. of Tropical Pathology and Public Health
Director: Roberto Ruhman Daher; *staff* 50 (43)
I. of Chemistry and Earth Sciences
Director: Joaquim Lucas Araújo; *staff* 55 (4)
I. of Human Sciences and Letters
Director: Raquel Figueiredo A. Teixeira; *staff* 134 (21)
Extension D.
Pro-Rector: Ilsa Vitorio Rocha

Founded 1960. An autonomous institution falling under the jurisdiction of the Ministry of Education and Culture. Governing body: the Conselho Universitáno. Limited residential facilities for students.

Arrangements for co-operation with: University of Wyoming; Universidade de Aveiro; Ecole supérieure d'Agriculture d'Angers; Université de Strasbourg I; Universidad Nacional Autónoma do México.

Academic Year: February to December (February-June; August-December).

Admission Requirements: Secondary school certificate and entrance examination.

Language of Instruction: Portuguese.

Degrees and Diplomas: Bacharel and Licenciado, 3-5 yrs. Professional titles in–Economics; Visual Arts; Journalism; Public Relations; Law; Civil Engineering; Electrical Engineering; Pharmacy, 3-6 yrs; Medicine; Veterinary Medicine; Dentistry,3-9 yrs. Mestrado, master. Also teaching qualifications.

Library: Total, *c.* 63,390 vols.

Publications: Revistas; scientific publications.

Press or Publishing House: Centro Editorial e Gráfico da UFG-CEGRAF.

Academic Staff, 1989-90: c. 1240.

Student Enrolment, 1989-90: c. 11,300.

387 ***UNIVERSIDADE DE IJUÍ**

University of Ijuí

Rua São Francisco 501, Bairro São Geraldo, 98700 Ijuí (Rio Grande do Sul)
Telex: 55-2210
Telephone: (55) 3323211
Reitor: Telmo Rudi Frantz (1987-)
Pró-Reitor de Administração: Iraní Paulo Basso

I. of Philosophy, Letters and Arts
Director: Branca Cabeda Egger Moellwald; *staff* 15 (38)
I. of Social Sciences
Director: Jaeme Luiz Callai; *staff* 15 (17)
I. of Exact and Natural Sciences
Director: Telmo Luiz Uriarte; *staff* 22 (29)
Ce. for Education
Director: Lori Maria Frantz; *staff* 21 (25)
Ce. for Applied Social Studies
Director: David Basso; *staff* 31 (20)
Ce. for Health Sciences (Nursing, Midwifery, and Nutrition)
Director: Rejane Terezinha P. dos Santos; *staff* 14 (9)

Founded 1957 as Faculty of Philosophy, Sciences and Letters. Acquired present status and title 1985. A private institution under the supervision of the Fundação Integrada de Desenvolvimento da Educação Nordeste do Estado. Governing body: the Conselho Universitário.

Academic Year: March to November.

Admission Requirements: Secondary school certificate and entrance examination.

Fees (Cruzeiros): 1700 per semester.

Language of Instruction: Portuguese.

Degrees and Diplomas: Bacharel in–Co-operatives Administration, 4 yrs; Accountancy, 4 ½ yrs; Business Administration, 5 yrs. Licenciado in–Social Sciences; Arts; Science, 3 yrs; Plastic Arts; Scenic Arts; Philosophy; Geography; Letters; Nursing; Education, 4 yrs; Biology; Physics; Mathematics; Chemistry, 5 yrs. Professional titles of: Enfermeiro, nursing; Nutricionista, 4 yrs; Enfermagem–Obstetrica, midwifery, 5 yrs. Postgraduate diplomas of specialization. Also teaching qualifications.

Library: Central Library, 67,533 vols.

Special Facilities (Museums, etc.): Museu Antropológico.

Publication: Contexto e Educação (quarterly).

Press or Publishing House: Livraria UNIJUI Editora.

Academic Staff, 1986-87: 114 (141).

Student Enrolment, 1986-87:

	Men	Women	Total
Of the country	1496	3333	4829

388 **UNIVERSIDADE FEDERAL DE JUIZ DE FORA**

Federal University of Juiz de Fora

Rua Benjamin Constant 790, Caixa postal 656, 36100 Juiz de Fora (Minas Gerais)
Telephone: (32) 2125966

I. of Biological and Earth Sciences (including Medicine, Dentistry, and Pharmacy)
I. of Exact Sciences (including Engineering)
I. of Human Sciences and Letters (including Economics, Journalism, and Education)
F. of Law
F. of Medicine
F. of Economics
F. of Education
F. of Dentistry
F. of Engineering
F. of Pharmacy and Biochemistry

Founded 1960 by the federal government, incorporating five private institutions.

Academic Year: February to December (February-June; August-December).

Admission Requirements: Secondary school certificate and entrance examination.

Fees: None.

Language of Instruction: Portuguese.

Degrees and Diplomas: Bacharel in–Economics; Journalism, 4 yrs; Law, 5 yrs. Licenciado in–History; Geography; Philosophy; Mathematics; Design and Plastic Arts; Physics; Chemistry; Biology; Physical Education; Literature; Education, 4 yrs. Professional titles in–Pharmacy, 3 yrs; Dentistry, 4 yrs; Civil Engineering; Electrical Engineering, 5 yrs; Medicine, 6 yrs.

Library: c. 20,000 vols.

Special Facilities (Museums, etc.): Anatomy Museum.

Publications: 'Lumina Spargere'-Revista de Universidade Federal de Juiz de Fora; Anais; Selecção de Artigos do Boletim Alemão de Pesquisas; Tabulae.

Academic Staff: c. 780.

Student Enrolment: c. 6610.

389 **UNIVERSIDADE LUTERANA DO BRASIL**

Rua Miguel Tostes, 92420 Canões (Rio Grande do Sul)
Telex: (51) 3378 CELS BR
Telephone: (512) 725599
Fax: (512) 765205
Reitor: Ruben E. Becker

C. of Economic and Juridical Sciences
Director: Almo Dauber Menezes; *staff* 3 (50)
C. of Technology (Architecture, Agrarian Sciences, Civil Engineering and Transport)
Director: Mônica B.C. Russomano; *staff* 4 (62)
C. of Health Sciences (Nursing, Psychology, Social Work, Dentistry)
Director: Cristbristofoli Caberlon; *staff* 11 (82)
C. of Education, Sciences, and Literature
Director: Sirlei Dias Gomes; *staff* 11 (133)

Founded 1972 as Canõas College of Administration Sciences, became university 1989. Maintained by the Comunidade Evangelica Luterana São Paulo. Governing body: the Conselho de Ensino, Pesquisa e Extensão.

Academic Year: March to December (March-June; August-December).

Admission Requirements: Secondary school certificate and entrance examination.

Fees (Cruzeiros): 1576-2363 per credit. Maximum 20 credits per semester.

Language of Instruction: Portuguese.

Degrees and Diplomas: Bacharel and Licenciado, 4 ½-5 yrs. Postgraduate certificate of specialization, 1 ½-2 yrs.

Library: Central (Martin Luther) Library, 42,850 vols.

Publications: Jornal (4 times a year); Revista (biannually); Logos (Revista de Divulgação Científica, biannually).

Academic Staff, 1989: 33 (323).

Student Enrolment, 1989: 4760.

390 **UNIVERSIDADE ESTUDUAL DE LONDRINA**
State University of Londrina
Campus Universitário, 86100 Londrina (Paraná)
Telex: 43-2256
Telephone: (432) 275151

Ce. for Biological Sciences (including Psychology)
Ce. for Human Sciences and Letters
Ce. for Exact Sciences
Ce. for Applied Social Studies (Law, Economics, Business Administration, Social Services)
Ce. for Health Sciences (including Medicine, Pharmacy, Dentistry, Nursing, and Physiotherapy)
Ce. for Education, Communication Studies, and Arts (including Library Science and Physical Education)
Ce. for Agriculture (including Veterinary Medicine)
Ce. for Technology and Town Planning

Founded 1971 incorporating previously existing State faculties. The university is constituted as a State foundation. Governing bodies: the Conselho Universitário; the Conselho de Ensino, Pesquisa e Extensão; the Conselho de Administração; the Conselho de Curadores. Some residential facilities for students.

Academic Year: February to December (February-June; August-December).

Admission Requirements: Secondary school certificate and entrance examination.

Language of Instruction: Portuguese.

Degrees and Diplomas: Bacharel in–Library Science, 3 ½ yrs; Economics; Accountancy; Social Communication; Social Sciences; Psychology; Physics; Geography; Mathematics; Chemistry, 4 yrs; Law, 5 yrs. Licenciado in–Artistic Education, 2-4 yrs; Physical Education, 3 yrs; Education, 3 ½ yrs; Social Sciences; History; Letters; Psychology; Physics; Geography; Mathematics; Chemistry, 4 yrs. Professional titles of–Fisioterapéuta, 3 yrs; Farmacêutico, 3-4 yrs; Enfermeiro, 3 ½ yrs; Técnico em Administração; Assistente social; Cirurgião Dentista; Médico veterinário, 4 yrs; Engenheiro agrônomo, 4 ½ yrs; Arquitecto; Psicólogo, 5 yrs. Mestrado, master, in–Social Relations Law; Mathematics; Food Sciences; Biology/Histology.

Library: c. 43,000 vols.

Special Facilities (Museums, etc.): Folklore Museum.

Publications: Lemina (biannually); Boletim Oficial (monthly); Temática - Estudos de Administração (biannually); Boletim do Çentro de Letras e Ciências Humanas.

Press or Publishing House: Editora.

Academic Staff: c. 640 (430).

Student Enrolment: c. 10, 360.

391 **UNIVERSIDADE MACKENZIE**
Mackenzie University
Rua Maria Antonia 403, Higienópolis, 01222 São Paulo (São Paulo)
Cables: Collemack
Telephone: (11) 2566611
Reitor: Aurora Catharina Giora Albanese
Secretário Geral: Ingrid Vieira Liebold

S. of Engineering
Director: Antonio de Oliveira; *staff* 173 (93)
F. of Architecture and Town Planning
Director: Walter Saraiva Kneese; *staff* 70 (27)
F. of Exact and Experimental Sciences
Director: Samuel Xavier; *staff* 94 (39)
F. of Technology
Director: Osny Rodrigues; *staff* 36 (72)
F. of Communication and Arts
Director: Itajahy Feitosa Martins; *staff* 38 (22)
F. of Letters and Education
Director: Regina Toledo Damião; *staff* 44 (25)
F. of Law
Director: Alvaro Villaça Azevedo; *staff* 69 (14)
F. of Economics, Accountancy and Administration
Director: Mario Dos Santos Veiga; *staff* 54 (62)
I. of Technology
Director: Eber de Aquino

Founded as college by American Presbyterian missionaries 1870. Became university and recognized by the State 1952. A private institution, under the inspection of the federal government. Since 1961, belongs to the Brazilian Presbyterian Church. Governing body: the Conselho Universitário.

Academic Year: February to December (February-June; August-December).

Admission Requirements: Secondary school certificate and competitive entrance examination.

Fees (Cruzeiros): 16,712.27 per annum for 67 maximum credits.

Language of Instruction: Portuguese.

Degrees and Diplomas: Bacharel in–Science; Visual Communication; Industrial Design; Economics; Business Administration; Accountancy; Languages and Education, 4 yrs; Law, 5 yrs. Licenciado in–Science; Arts; Languages and Education, 3 yrs. Professional titles in–Technology, 3 yrs; Engineering; Architecture, 5 yrs.

Library: Central Library (Biblioteca George Alexander), 71,000 vols.

Special Facilities (Museums, etc.): Observatory.

Publication: Mackenzie Magazine.

Press or Publishing House: Gráfica Universitária.

Academic Staff, 1990:

Rank	Full-time	Part-time
Professores Titulares	153	–
Professores Adjuntos	258	–
Professores Assistentes	267	354
Total	678	354

Student Enrolment, 1990:

	Men	Women	Total
Of the country	7506	5859	13,365

392 **UNIVERSIDADE FEDERAL DO MARANHÃO**
Federal University of Maranhão
Largo dos Amoles 351, 65000 São Luís (Maranhão)
Telex: 98-2214
Telephone: (98) 222334
Reitor: Jerônimo Pinheiro
Secretário Geral: Maria Da Graça Buhatem Medeiros

Ce. for Technology
Director: Vera Lúcia Lobato Almeida; *staff* 120 (16)
Ce. for Health Sciences (including Medicine, Pharmacy, Dentistry) Physical Education, and Nursing
Director: Carlos Alberto Salgado Borges; *staff* 271 (83)
Ce. for Basic Studies
Director: Mário Cella; *staff* 158 (17)
Ce. for Social Sciences
Director: Iacy Viana Dourado; *staff* 181 (75)

Founded 1966. An autonomous institution financially supported by the federal government. Residential facilities for students.

Academic Year: March to December (March-June; August-December).

Admission Requirements: Secondary school certificate and entrance examination.

Language of Instruction: Portuguese.

Degrees and Diplomas: Bacharel in–Library Science; Accountancy; Social Communication; Mathematics; Economics, 4 yrs; Law, 5 yrs. Licenciado in–Design and Plastic Arts; Physics; Letters; History; Education; Chemistry; Physical Education; Mathematics, 4 yrs. Professional titles of–Farmacêutico, 3 yrs; Farmacêutico-Bioquímico; Desenhista Industrial; Cirurgião dentista; Químico industrial; Assistente social, 4 yrs; Engenharia Elétrica, 5 yrs.

Libraries: Central Library, c. 73,030 vols; Medicine, c. 3290; Nursing, c. 1080; Dentistry and Pharmacy, c. 1870.

Academic Staff: c. 900.

Student Enrolment: 6530 (70).

393 **UNIVERSIDADE ESTADUAL DO MARANHÃO**
Campus Universitário Paulo VI, 65000 São Luis (Maranhão)
Telephone: (98) 2250865

Administration
Agriculture
Engineering
Veterinary Medicine
Education

Founded 1972 as Federação das Escolas superiores. A State institution.

394 **FUNDAÇÃO UNIVERSIDADE ESTADUAL DE MARINGÁ**

State University of Maringá

Avenida Colombo 3690, 87020 Maringá (Paraná)

Telex: 44-2198

Telephone: (442) 26-2727

Reitor: Fernando Ponte de Sousa (1986-90)

Ce. for Human Sciences, Letters, and Arts
Director: Tércio Selvino Grassmann; *staff* 237 (62)

Ce. for Exact Sciences
Director: Wilson Ricardo Weinand; *staff* 147 (24)

Ce. for Technology
Director: João Dirceu Nogueira de Carvalho; *staff* 80 (29)

Ce. for Biology and Health Sciences (including Pharmacy, Nursing, Physical Education, Agriculture, and Animal Husbandry)
Director: José Gilberto Catunda Sales; *staff* 312 (70)

Ce. for Economics and Social Sciences (including Business Administration, and Law)
Director: Fernande Noboru Miyata; *staff* 123 (57)

I. of Languages
Director: Sandra Maria Coelho de Souza Moser; *staff* – (25)

Ce. for Education
Director: Antonia Peres Fávero; *staff* 9

I. of Japanese
Co-ordinator: Renato Cardoso Nery; *staff* 3 (2)

Also 27 departments.

Founded 1970, incorporating previously existing State faculties. The university is constituted as a State foundation. Governing bodies: the Conselho Universitário; the Conselho de Ensino, Pesquisa e Extensão; the Conselho de Administração; the Conselho de Curadores.

Academic Year: February to December (February-June; August-December).

Admission Requirements: Secondary school certificate and entrance examination.

Language of Instruction: Portuguese.

Degrees and Diplomas: Bacharel in–Administration; Accountancy; Economics, 4 yrs; Law, 5 yrs. Licenciado in–Science, 2 ½ yrs; Biology; Education; Physical Education, 3 yrs; Physics; Geography; History; Letters; Social Studies; Mathematics, 3 ½ yrs. Professional titles of–Farmacêutico, 3 yrs; Enfermeiro-Obstetra, nursing and midwifery, 3 ½ yrs; Farmacêutico-Bioquímico; Engenheiro agrônomo, 4 yrs; Computer Science, 4 ½ yrs; Engenheiro civil; Engenheiro químico; Odontologia; Psicólogo, 5 yrs; Medicina, 6 yrs. Mestrado in–Applied Chemistry; Biology, 3 yrs. Postgraduate diplomas of specialization.

Library: 102,569 vols.

Special Facilities (Museums, etc.): Museu da Bacia do Paraná.

Publications: Revista Unimar (annually); Boletim Cultural (biannually); Relatório Anual.

Press or Publishing House: Imprensa Universitária.

Academic Staff, 1990:

Rank	Full-time	Part-time
Professores Titulares	23	–
Professores Adjuntos	280	19
Professores Assistentes	360	35
Professores Auxiliares	219	89
Professores Colaboradores	126	–
Visitantes	5	–
Estatutários	–	3
Total	1013	146

Student Enrolment, 1989:

	Men	Women	Total
Of the country	3614	4107	7721
Of other countries	118	225	343
Total	3732	4332	8064

395 **UNIVERSIDADE FEDERAL DE MATO GROSSO DO SUL**

Campus Universitária 649, 791000 Campo Grande (Mato Grosso do Sul)

Telex: 67-2331

Telephone: (67) 3873833

Reitor: Fuaze Scaff Gattass Filho

Vice-Reitor: Ceslo Vitório Pierezan

Ce. for Biological and Health Sciences (Pharmacy, Medicine, Veterinary Medicine, and Dentistry)

Ce. for Exact Sciences and Technology (Computer Sciences, Civil Engineering, Electrical Engineering, Physics, Mathematics, and Chemistry)

Ce. for Human and Social Sciences (Administration, Social Communication, Arts, Physical Education, Letters, and Education)

Ds. of Science, Geography, History, and Letters (Aquidauana)

Ds. of Administration, Accountancy, Biology, Geography, History, Letters, Mathematics, Education, and Psychology (Corumbá)

Ds. of Agriculture, Accountancy, Geography, History, Letters, Mathematics, and Education (Dourados)

Ds. of Geography, History, Letters, Biology, Mathematics, and Education (Três Lagoas)

Founded as Faculty of Pharmacy and Dentistry 1963, became Institute of Biology 1966, State university 1970, and federal university 1979.

Academic Year: March to December (March-June; August-December).

Admission Requirements: Secondary school certificate and entrance examination.

Language of Instruction: Portuguese.

Degrees and Diplomas: Licenciado in–Letters; Education; Mathematics; History; Geography; Chemistry; Psychology; Plastic Arts; Physics; Physical Education and Sports, 3 yrs. Professional titles of–Farmacêutico geral, 3 yrs; Engehnaria Civil, and Elétrica; Jornolismo; Farmacêutico bioquímico; Cirurgião dentista; Médico veterinário, 4 yrs; Engenheiro civil, 5 yrs; Médico, 6 yrs.

Library: Total, 130,971 vols.

Publication: Revista Científica e Cultural.

Academic Staff: c. 330.

Student Enrolment: c. 2600.

396 **UNIVERSIDADE FEDERAL DE MATO GROSSO**

Federal University of Mato Grosso

Avenida Fernando Corrêa da Costa s/n, 78000 Cuiabá (Mato Grosso)

Telex: 65-2371

Telephone: (65) 3612211

Ce. for Letters and Human Sciences

Ce. for Exact Sciences and Technology

Ce. for Social Sciences

Ce. for Agriculture

Ce. for Biological and Health Sciences

Founded 1970, incorporating the Federal Faculty of Law, founded 1934, the Faculty of Philosophy, Science and Letters of Mato Grosso and the Institute of Science and Letters of Cuiabá. A State institution financed by the federal government and responsible to the Ministry of Education and Culture. Governing body: the Conselho de Administração.

Academic Year: March to December (March-July; August-December).

Admission Requirements: Graduation from high school and entrance examination.

Languages of Instruction: Portuguese, French, and German.

Degrees and Diplomas: Bacharel and Licenciado, 4 yrs.

Library: Central Library, c. 15,000 vols.

Special Facilities (Museums, etc.): Museu Rondon (ethnographic exposition of the Indian population of the region); Audio-visual documentation of pre-Columbian cultures.

Academic Staff: c. 1004.

Student Enrolment: c. 6430.

397 **PONTIFÍCIA UNIVERSIDADE CATÓLICA DE MINAS GERAIS**

Pontifical Catholic University of Minas Gerais

Avenida Dom José Gaspar 500, 30000 Belo Horizonte (Minas Gerais)

Telex: 31-3339

Telephone: (31) 3191144

Reitor: Geraldo Magela Teixeira (1981-86)

Ce. for Human Sciences (including Law, Education, and Theology)

Ce. for Technology

Ce. of Biological and Health Sciences

Ce. of Social Sciences

Extension D.

Founded 1958, incorporating existing faculties and schools founded between 1943 and 1953. The title of Pontifical University was conferred in 1983. A private institution receiving an annual grant from the federal government. Governing bodies: the Conselho Executivo; the Conselho de Ensino e Pesquisa; the Conselho Universitário.

Academic Year: February to December (February-June; August-December).

Admission Requirements: Secondary school certificate or equivalent, and entrance examination.

Language of Instruction: Portuguese.

Degrees and Diplomas: Bacharel, 5 yrs. Licenciado, 4 yrs. Also Certificates of specialization, 2 yrs.

Library: Central Library, *c.* 100,000 vols.

Special Facilities (Museums, etc.): Museums of: Natural Sciences; History of the University.

Publications: Revista de Ciências Humanas; Bios (Biology).

Press or Publishing House: Fumarc-Publishing House.

Academic Staff: c. 150 (570).

Student Enrolment: c. 14,000.

398 ***UNIVERSIDADE FEDERAL DE MINAS GERAIS**

Federal University of Minas Gerais

Avenida Antônio Carlos, 31270 Belo Horizonte (Minas Gerais)

Telex: 31-2308 BR/MG

Telephone: (31) 4481000

Fax: (31) 443-6757

Reitor: Vanessa Guimarães Pinto (1990-94)

Pro-Reitor: Lair Aguilar Rennó

I. of Exact Sciences
Dean: Miriam Lourenço Maia; *staff* 307 (30)

I. of Biological Sciences
Dean: Ubirajara Gabriel de Castro; *staff* 252 (25)

I. of Earth Sciences
Dean: Paulo Rogério Junqueira Alvim; *staff* 79 (8)

S. of Education
Dean: Glaura Vásques de Miranda; *staff* 123 (6)

S. of Law
Dean: Washington Peluso Albino de Souza; *staff* 55 (26)

S. of Economic Sciences
Dean: José Alberto Magno de Carvalho; *staff* 96 (40)

S. of Letters
Dean: Melânia Silva Aguiar; *staff* 151 (1)

S. of Philosophy and Human Sciences (including History, Political Science, Sociology and Anthropology, Social Communication)
Dean: Paulo Roberto Saturnino Figueiredo; *staff* 229 (16)

S. of Pharmacy
Dean: Geraldo Hélio Coelho; *staff* 70 (13)

S. of Medicine
Dean: Benedictus Philadelpho de Siqueira; *staff* 311 (168)

S. of Dentistry
Dean: Arnaldo de Almeida Garrocho; *staff* 62 (61)

S. of Fine Arts
Dean: Evandro José Lemos da Cunha; *staff* 47 (4)

S. of Music
Dean: Sandra Loureiro de Freitas Reis; *staff* 48 (2)

S. of Physical Education
Dean: Alcione Raposo; *staff* 89 (10)

S. of Nursing
Dean: Alcinéa Eustáquia Costa; *staff* 89 (5)

S. of Veterinary Medicine
Dean: Paulo Roberto Carneiro; *staff* 91 (1)

S. of Architecture
Dean: Luciano Amédée Péret; *staff* 37 (35)

S. of Engineering (Civil, Mechanical, Electrical, Metallurgical, Mining, Nuclear, Chemical)
Dean: Enio Medeiros Cunha; *staff* 203 (103)

S. of Library Science
Dean: Marília Júnia de Almeida Gardini; *staff* 27 (3)

Ce. for Regional Development and Planning
Director: João Antônio de Paulo

Ce. for Minas Gerais Studies
Director: Beatriz Ricardina de Magalhães

Ce. for Maintenance and Restoration of Cultural Assets
Director: Beatriz Ramos de Vasconcelos Coelho

Ce. for Portuguese Studies
Director: Ana Maria de Almeida

Ce. for Contemporary Music Research
C-oordinator: Eduardo Ruan Bertola

Geology Ce. (Diamantina)
Director: Angelo Almeida Abreu

Aesthetics L.
Director: Moacyr Laterza

Ce. for Electronic Microscopy
Director: Thaisa de Almeida Maria

Scientific Computation L.
Head: Manoel Lopes de Siqueira

Founded 1927 as a university incorporating institutions established between 1892 and 1911. Reorganized 1968. A State institution financed by the federal government and responsible to the Ministry of Education and Culture. Governing body: the Conselho Universitário.

Academic Year: February to December (February-June; August-December).

Admission Requirements: Secondary school certificate and entrance examination.

Fees (Cruzeiros): 1145.48 per semester.

Language of Instruction: Portuguese.

Degrees and Diplomas: Bacharel in–Computer Sciences; Statistics; Dentistry; Library Science; Journalism; Accountancy; Economics, 4 yrs; Engineering (various fields); Geology; Architecture; Pharmacy; Psysiotherapy; Veterinary Medicine; Occupational Thearapy; Law; Business Administration, 5 yrs; Medicine, 6 yrs. Licenciado and Bacharel in–Letters; Physical Education, 4 yrs; Education, 5 yrs. Mestrado, Master. Doutordo, Doctor.

Libraries: Central Library, *c.* 500,000 vols; libraries of the schools and faculties.

Special Facilities (Museums, etc.): Museum of Natural History; Botanical Garden; Cultural Centre; Astronomical Observatory; Audio-visual Centre.

Publications: Revistas; publications of the faculties and schools.

Press or Publishing House: Editora da UFMG.

Academic Staff, 1990: c. 2109 (560).

Student Enrolment, 1990:

Men	Women	Total
9018	9319	18,337

399 **UNIVERSIDADE DE MOGI DAS CRUZES**

Avenida Cândido Almeida Souza 200, 08700 Mogi das Cruzes (São Paulo)

Telephone: (11) 4695333

Ce. for Human Sciences
Ce. for Exact Sciences and Technology
Ce. for Biomedical Sciences
F. of Education
F. of Economics (including Business Administration)
F. of Law
F. of Communication Studies
F. of Medicine
F. of Dentistry
F. of Physical Education
F. of Engineering
F. of Architecture and Town Planning
F. of Geology
F. of Production Engineering
I. of Philosophy and Social Science
I. of Letters and Fine Arts
I. of Biology
I. of Psychology
I. of Science
S. of Nursing

Founded 1964, incorporating a number of previously existing faculties. A State institution receiving financialsupport from the Ministry of Education and Culture.

Academic Year: March to December (March-July; August-December).

Admission Requirements: Secondary school certificate and entrance examination.

Language of Instruction: Portuguese.

Degrees and Diplomas: Licenciado in–Letters; Education; Social Sciences, 3 yrs; Philosophy; Mathematics; Physics; Chemistry; Fine Arts, 4 yrs. Professional titles in–Nutrition; Communication Studies; Nursing; Public Relations, 3 yrs; Architecture and Town Planning; Law; Fine Arts; Business Administration; Accountancy; Economics; Dentistry, 4 yrs; Psychology, 4-5 yrs; Engineering, 5 yrs; Medicine, 6 yrs. Also teaching qualifications.

Library: Central Library, *c.* 30,000 vols.

Publication: Diário de Mogi.

Academic Staff: c. 850.

Student Enrolment: c. 14,020.

400 **UNIVERSIDADE REGIONAL DO NORESTE**
Avenida Marechal Floriano Peixoto 718, 58100 Campina Grande (Paraiba)
Telex: 83-3226
Telephone: (83) 3210099

Ce. for Human Sciences, Letters and Arts
Ce. for Science and Technology
Ce. for Biological and Health Sciences

Founded 1967. *Academic Staff: c.* 450.
Student Enrolment: c. 7200.

401 **UNIVERSIDADE DO OESTE PAULISTA**
Rua José Bongiovani 700, Cidade Universitária, 19050 Presidente Prudente (São Paulo)
Telex: 182-529
Telephone: (182) 225666
Fax: (182) 225530
Reitor: Agripino de Oliveira Lima Filho

F. of Health Sciences (Physiotherapy and Psychology)
Principal: Carlo Ceriani
F. of Dentistry
Principal: Adilson de Oliveira
F. of Pharmacy and Biochemistry
Principal: João Carlos Grigoli
F. of Medicine
Principal: José Carlos de Oliveira Lima
F. of Veterinary Medicine
Principal: José Giometto
F. of Animal Husbandry and Agriculture
Principal: Alfredo José Fernandes
F. of Civil Engineering
Principal: Ivan Salomão Liboni
F. of Computer Sciences
Principal: Moacir del Trejo
F. of Law, Administration, and Accountancy
Principal: Waldir de Mello Quelho
F. of Science, Letters, and Education
Principal: Ondina Barbosa Gerbasi

Founded 19872, incorporating previously existing Faculties. Under the supervision of the Associação Prudentina de Educação e Cultura. Some residential facilities for students.

Academic Year: February to December (February-June; August-December).

Admission Requirements: Secondary school certificate and entrance examination.

Degrees and Diplomas: Licenciado and Professional titles. Postgraduate diplomas of specialization.

Library: Biblioteca Nair Fortes Abu-Mehri, 70,445 vols.

Publication: Scientific Magazine (annually).

Academic Staff, 1990: – (375).

Student Enrolment, 1990: 7691.

402 ***UNIVERSIDADE FEDERAL DE OURO PRÊTO**
Federal University of Ouro Prêto
Rua Diogo de Vasconcelos 122, 35400 Ouro Prêto (Minas Gerais)
Telex: 31-2954
Telephone: (31) 5512111
Fax: (31) 5511689
Reitor: Cristovam Paes de Oliveira (1989-)
Chefe de Gabinete: Marcelo Marinho Franco

S. of Mines
Director: Antônio Maria Claret de Gouveia; *staff* 119 (22)
S. of Pharmacy (including Biochemistry)
Director: Maria Elizabeth Souza Totti Silva; *staff* 47 (8)
I. of Social and Human Sciences
Director: Solange Ribeiro de Oliveira; *staff* 50
I. of Arts and Culture
Director: Arnaldo Fortes Drummond
I. of Biological and Exact Sciences
Director: Magno Dias; *staff* 74 (6)

Founded 1969 incorporating Escola de Minas de Ouro Prêto, founded 1876 and Escola de Farmácia e Bioquímica, 1839. Operated under the jurisdiction of the Ministry of Education and Culture and financially supported by the federal government. Governing bodies: the Conselho Universitário; the Conselho de Ensino, Pesquisa e Extensão. Some residential facilities for academic staff and students.

Arrangements for co-operation with: Colorado School of Mines; Porto University; Imperial College of Science and Technology, United Kingdom; Technical Unversity of Clausthal; University of Texas; University of Nancy.

Academic Year: March to November (March-June; August-November).

Admission Requirements: Secondary school certificate and entrance examination.

Language of Instruction: Portuguese.

Degrees and Diplomas: Bachelor–in History; Letters, 4 yrs. Licenciado in Nutrition, 4 yrs. Postgraduate diplomas of specialization.

Library: Total, *c.* 30,000 vols.

Special Facilities (Museums, etc.): Museum of Mineralogy.

Publications: Revista de Escola de Minas; Revista da Escola de Farmácia; Jornal.

Academic Staff, 1990: 296 (39).

Student Enrolment, 1990:

	Men	Women	Total
Of the country	1167	1007	2174
Of other countries	24	5	29
Total	1191	1012	2203

403 **UNIVERSIDADE FEDERAL DO PARÁ**
Federal University of Pará
Rua Augusto Correa, 66000 Belém (Pará)
Telex: 91-1013
Telephone: (91) 2292088

Ce. for Exact and Natural Sciences
Ce. for Biological Sciences
Ce. for Philosophy and Human Sciences
Ce. for Letters and Arts
Ce. for Biomedical Sciences
Ce. for Technology
Ce. for Socio-economic Studies
Ce. for Education

Founded 1957 and comprising a number of previously existing faculties. Reorganized 1970-71 with a structure comprising centres for professional education. An autonomous institution, but financially supported by the Stateand responsible to the Ministry of Education and Culture.

Academic Year: March to February (March-June; August-December).

Admission Requirements: Competitive entrance examination following secondary school certificate.

Fees: None.

Language of Instruction: Portuguese.

Degrees and Diplomas: Bacharel in Law, 5 yrs. Licenciado in–Library Science, 3 yrs; Education; Letters; Mathematics; Physics; Geography; History; Social Sciences, 4 yrs. Professional titles of–Farmacêutico comercial, 3 yrs; Farmacêutico bioquímico analista clínico; Odontólogo, dentistry; Economista; Contador, accountancy; Técnico em Administração; Assistente social; Químico industrial; Geólogo, 4 yrs; Arquitecto; Engenheiro civil; Engenheiro mecânico; Engenheiro electrotécnico; Engenheiro electrônico; Engenheiro químico, 5 yrs; Médico, 6 yrs.

Publications: Revista de Ciências Médicas; Revista de Letras e Artes; Revista de Ciências Jurídicas, Econômicas e Sociais.

Academic Staff: c. 1490.

Student Enrolment: c. 12,330.

404 **UNIVERSIDADE FEDERAL DE PARAÍBA**
Federal University of Paraíba
Campus Universitário, 58000 João Pessôa (Paraíba)
Telex: 83-2187
Telephone: (83) 2247200
Reitor: José Jackson Carneiro de Carvalho (1984-88)
Chefe de Gabinete: Damião Ramos Cavalcanti

Ce for Human Sciences, Letters and Arts
Director: Neroaldo Ponteso de Azevedo; *staff* 393 (30)
Ce. for Applied Social Sciences (including Library Sciences, Economics, Law and Administration)
Director: José Décio de Almedia Leite; *staff* 183 (84)
Ce. for Education
Director: José Soares; *staff* 134 (5)
Ce. for Health Sciences (including Medicine, Dentistry, Pharmacy and Nursing)
Director: Norberto de Castro Nogueira Filho; *staff* 433 (116)

Ce. for Technology (including Architecture)
Director: Jader Nuñes de Olivieira; *staff* 174 (27)
Ce. for Exact and Natural Sciences
Director: Josué Eugênio Viana; *staff* 263 (6)
Ce. for Humanities (Campina Grande)
Director: Albanita Guerra Araújo; *staff* 204 (19)
Ce. for Science and Technology (Campina Grande)
Director: Ademilson Montes Ferreira; *staff* 411 (14)
Ce. for Biology and Health Sciences (Campina Grande)
Director: Antonio Roberto Vaz Ribeiro; *staff* 58 (54)
Ce. for Agriculture (including Animal Husbandry) (Areia)
Director: João José de Oliveira Filho; *staff* 115 (5)
Ce. for Agricultural Technology (Bananeiras)
Director: Oseias Almeida Neto; *staff* 62 (8)
Ce. for Education (Cajazeiras)
Director: José Leite da Silva; *staff* 60 (2)
Ce. for Law (Sousa)
Director: Inaldo Rocha Leitão; *staff* 23 (20)
Ce. for Rural Health and Technology
Director: Francisco Marinho de Medeiros; *staff* 101 (4)

Founded 1955, incorporating faculties established 1947-52. Reorganized 1974 with a structure comprising centres for professional education situated in 7 campuses.

Academic Year: March to December (March-June; August-November).

Admission Requirements: Secondary school certificate and entrance examination.

Language of Instruction: Portuguese.

Degrees and Diplomas: Bacharel in–Geography; Physics; Mathematics; Chemistry; Philosophy; Biology; Music; Computer Sciences; Social Sciences. Licenciado in–Geography; Science; Art Education; Philosophy; History; Letters; Education; Physical Education; Physics; Mathematics; Chemistry; Social Sciences. Professional titles of–Arquitecto; Engenheiro (various fields); Químico industrial; Administração; Contador, accountancy; Economista; Biblioteconomia, library science; Direito, law; Psicólogo; Enfermeira, nursing; Farmacêutico; Médico; Nutrição; Odontologia; Desenho industrial; Zootecnista; Agrónomo; Técnico (various fields). Mestrado. Doutorado.

Libraries: Central Library, 132,346 vols; libraries of the campuses, 266,251.

Publications: Horizonte (monthly); Tecnologia e Ciência (monthly); Ciência, Cultura e Saúde (quarterly).

Press or Publishing House: Editora Universitária.

Academic Staff, 1986: 3008.

Of the country	19,746
Of other countries	116
Total	19,862

405 **PONTIFÍCIA UNIVERSIDADE CATÓLICA DO PARANÁ**
Pontifical Catholic University of Paraná
Rua Imaculada Conceição 1155, 80210 Curitiba (Paraná)
Telex: 41-0282 PUCP
Telephone: (41) 322-1515
Fax: (41) 225-4373
Reitor: Euro Brandão (1990-93)
Vice-Reitor: João Oleynik

Ce. for Theology and Human Sciences
Director: Jayme Ferreira Bueno; *staff* 14 (80)
Ce. for Law and Social Sciences
Director: Alvacir Alfredo Nicz; *staff* 6 (84)
Ce. for Exact Sciences and Technology (including Engineering, Architecture and Computer Sciences)
Director: Sergio Ricardo Schneider; *staff* 11 (134)
Ce. for Biology and Health Sciences (Medicine, Dentistry, and Biology)
Director: Alberto Accioly Veiga; *staff* 11 (262)
I. for Enviromental Sanitation
Director: Muguel Manaur Aisse; *staff* 5 (4)
I. of Technology
I. of Psychology
I. of Physical Therapy
Also 2 Clinics and a Hospital, and Biological Station at Morretes.

Founded 1959 incorporating institutions established between 1945 and 1956. The title of Pontifical University conferred 1985. A private institution under the supervision of the Sociedade Paranaense de Cultura and recognized by the federal government. Affiliated with the Roman Catholic Church. Governing bodies: the Conselho Universitário; the Conselho de Ensino, Pesquisa e Extensão; the Conselho de AdministraçãoEconômico-Financeira; the Conselho de Desenvolvimento.

Arrangements for co-operation with the Universities of: Cincinnati; Wright State; Dayton; Okayama; del Valle, Cali; ; Rosário, Santa Fe; Kibi, Japan; Lisbon (Catholic); Eichstatt; Compiègne. Corporación Universitaria de Boyacá, Tunja; Ecole national supérieur des Mines, Paris.

Academic Year: March to December (March-June; August-December).

Admission Requirements: Secondary school certificate and entrance examination.

Fees (Cruzeiros): 37,000-105,000 per annum, according to subject.

Language of Instruction: Portuguese.

Degrees and Diplomas: Bacharel in–Computer Sciences, 4 yrs. Licenciado in–Letters; Physical Education, 4 yrs; Psychology, 5 yrs. Bacharel and Licenciado in–Philosophy; Scenic Arts and Dance; Social Sciences; Mathematics; Nursing Biology, 4 yrs. Professional titles in–Industrial Design; Industrial Chemistry; Physical Therapy; Speak Training; Pharmacy; Executive Secretarial Studies; Education; Social Work; Journalism, 4 yrs; Law; Architecture and Town Planning; Civil Engineering; Computer Engineering, 5 yrs.

Libraries: Central Library, 70,881 vols; Environmental Engineering, 3307.

Publications: Boletim Informativo (monthly); Estudos de Biologia (quarterly); Estudos Jurídicos; Psicologia Argumento (biannually); Revista de Filosofia (annually; Circulode Estudos (biannually); Fisioterapia en Movimento (biannually).

Press or Publishing House: Editora Universitária Champagnat.

Academic Staff, 1989-90:

Rank	Full-time	Part-time
Professores Titulares	11	50
Professores Adjuntos	10	52
Professores Assistentes	19	250
Professores Auxiliares I and II	1	129
Professores de Contrato Especial	1	79
Total	42	560

Student Enrolment, 1989-90:

	Men	Women	Total
Of the country	3332	4983	8315
Of other countries	11	24	35
Total	3343	5007	8350

406 **UNIVERSIDADE FEDERAL DO PARANÁ**
Federal University of Paraná
Rua XV de Novembro 1299, 80000 Curitiba (Paraná)
Telex: 41-5100
Telephone: (41) 2642522

Sec. for Exact Sciences
Sec. for Biological Sciences
Sec. for Human Sciences, Letters and Arts (including Social Sciences)
Sec. for Education (including Library Science)
Sec. for Applied Social Sciences (including Economics and Law)
Sec. for Health Sciences (Medicine, Pharmacy, Dentistry, Nursing)
Sec. for Technology (including Architecture and Town Planning)
Sec. for Agricultural Sciences (including Forestry and Veterinary Medicine)

Founded 1912. Reorganized 1974 with a structure comprising sectors for professional education. An autonomous institution, but financially supported by the State, falling under the jurisdiction of the Ministry of Education and Culture. Governing bodies: the Conselho de Ensino e Pesquisa; the Conselho Universitário; the Conselho de Curadores; the Assembléia Universitária. Residential facilities for *c.* 130 women and *c.* 100 men students.

Academic Year: March to December (March-June; August-December).

Admission Requirements: Secondary school certificate.

Language of Instruction: Portuguese.

Degrees and Diplomas: Bacharel, 3-5 yrs. Mestrado, master, a further 1-2 yrs. Doutorado, doctorate, by thesis.

Libraries: Central Library; Medical Library.

Special Facilities (Museums, etc.): Archaeology and Popular Arts.

Publications: Fastos Universitários (monthly); Boletim do Centro de Estudos Leprológicos Souza Araújo.

Academic Staff: c. 2020.

Student Enrolment: c. 14,880.

407 **UNIVERSIDADE DE PASSO FUNDO**

University of Passo Fundo

Campus Universitário, 99050 Passo Fundo (Rio Grande do Sul)
Telex: 54-5394
Telephone: (54) 313-3400
Reitor: Elydo Alcides Guareschi (1986-)
Vice-Reitor: Ilmo Santos

I. of Exact and Earth Sciences
Director: Lorivan Figueiredo; *staff* 12 (44)
I. of Biology (including Nursing and Midwifery)
Director: Antonio A. Pretto; *staff* 7 (48)
I. of Philosophy and Human Sciences
Director: Antonio Ancines; *staff* 17 (57)
I. of Fine Arts
Director: Elba F. Costa; *staff* – (35)
F. of Education
Director: Rosa L. Kalil; *staff* 18 (38)
F. of Law
Director: Juarez T. Diehl; *staff* – (36)
F. of Economics (including Business Administration)
Director: Paulo Secco; *staff* 2 (35)
F. of Medicine
Director: Luis Fragomeni; *staff* – (70)
F. of Dentistry
Director: Tadeu R. Pereira; *staff* – (70)
F. of Agriculture
Director: Moises Soares; *staff* 13 (26)
F. of Physical Education
Director: Carlos Schlemmer; *staff* 1 (18)
F. of Engineering
Director: Luis F. Prestes; *staff* 2 (9)
S. of Nursing
Extension Centres at: Carazinho; Soledade; Lagoa Vermelha; Palmeira das Missões.

Founded 1968 incorporating Faculty of Law, established 1956, and Faculties of Philosophy and Political Science, established 1957. A private institution recognized by the federal government. Governing body: the Conselho Universitário.

Academic Year: March to December (March-July; August-December).

Admission Requirements: Secondary school certificate and entrance examination.

Fees (Cruzeiros): 777.57-1287.62 per semester.

Language of Instruction: Portuguese.

Degrees and Diplomas: Professional titles in all fields, 3-4 yrs; Medicine, 6 yrs. Also teaching qualifications.

Libraries: Central Library, *c.* 67,580 vols; Agriculture, 7600; Biomedicine, *c.* 9500.

Special Facilities (Museums, etc.): Museu Zoo-Botânico; Museu e Arquivo Histórico Regional; Galeria de Arte Laura Borges Felizzardo; Mini-Zoológico.

Publication: Cadernos da U.P.F.

Press or Publishing House: Gráfica e Editora UPF.

Academic Staff, 1990:

Rank	Full-time	Part-time
Professores Titulares	43	123
Professores Assistentes	7	97
Professores Adjuntos	11	80
Professores Auxiliares	3	156
Total	64	456

Student Enrolment, 1990:

	Men	Women	Total
Of the country	3113	4016	7129
Of other countries	10	6	16
Total	3123	4022	7145

408 ***UNIVERSIDADE ESTADUAL PAULISTA 'JULIO DE MESQUITA FILHO'**

Praça de Sé 108, 01001 São Paulo (São Paulo)
Telex: 11-19001
Telephone: (11) 327171
Fax: 551136-3449
Reitor: Paulo Milton Barbosa Landim (1989-93)
Secretário Geral: Darvin Beig

F. of Dentistry (Araçatuba)
Director: Acyr Lima de Castro; *staff* 77 (21)
F. of Pharmaceutical Sciences (Araraquara)
Director: Bruno Mancini; *staff* 69 (03)
F. of Dentistry (Araraquara)
Director: Tatsuko Sakima; *staff* 93 (16)
F. of Science and Letters
Director: José Enio Casalecchi; *staff* 177 (4)
I. of Chemistry
Director: Antonio Carlos Massabni; *staff* 74 (2)
I. of Sciences and Letters
Director: José Ribeiro Júnior; *staff* 149 (3)
F. of Agricultural Sciences
Director: Flávio Abranches Pinheiro; *staff* 95 (2)
F. of Medicine
Director: Dinah Borges de Almeida; *staff* 174 (22)
F. of Veterinary Medicine and Animal Husbandry
Director: Marcio Rubens G. Kuchembuck; *staff* 86
I. of Bio-Sciences
Director: Cecílio Linder; *staff* 157
I. of History, Law and Social Service (Franca)
Director: Antonio Quelce Salgado; *staff* 69 (21)
F. of Engineeering (Guratinguetá)
Director: Nelson Murcia; *staff* 85 (21)
F. of Engineering (Ilha Solteira)
Director: Nelson de Araujo; *staff* 178 (4)
F. of Agrarian and Veterinary Sciences
Director: Joji Ariki; *staff* 245 (4)
F. of Philosophy and Sciences
Director: Jayme Wanderley Gasparoto; *staff* 117 (16)
F. of Sciences and Technology
Director: Marcio Antonio Teixeira; *staff* 122 (64)
I. of Bio-Sciences (Rio Claro)
Director: Carminda da Cruz Landim; *staff* 103 (6)
I. of Geo-Sciences and Exact Sciences
Director: Irineu Bicudo; *staff* 141 (7)
I. of Arts
Director: Irineu de Moura; *staff* 50 (12)
F. of Dentistry
Director: Antenor de Araújo; *staff* 57 (37)
I. of Bio-Sciences (São José do Rio Prêto)
Director: Antonio Espada Filho; *staff* 158 (6)
F. of Technology
Director: José M. Souza das Neves; *staff* 6
F. of Technology (Sorocaba)
Director: Decio Cardoso da Silva; *staff* 2
F. of Textile Technology
Director: Milton do M. Marcello; *staff* 3
F. of Technology (Baixada Santista)
Director: Spencer de Mello; *staff* 1
F. of Sciences
Director: Sergio Nereu Pagano; *staff* 10 (25)
F. of Engineering and Technology
Director: Nivaldo José Bósio; *staff* 56 (23)
F. of Arts, Architecture and Communication
Director: Telmo Correia Arrais; *staff* 81 (19)
I. of Theoretical Physics
Director: Rubem Aldrovandi; *staff* 18
I. of Meteorologic Research
Also Teaching Hospital, 5 experimental farms, and 2 veterinary hospitals.

Founded 1976, incorporating previously existing faculties established 1923-1966. An autonomous institution under the jurisdiction of and financially supported by the State of São Paulo. Governing bodies: the Conselho Universitário; the Conselho de Ensino, Pesquisa e Extensão de Serviços à Comunidade. Residential facilities for students.

Arrangements for co-operation with: Université de Bordeaux; Universidad de Barcelona; Universidad de la Plata, Argentina; University of Colorado; Tropical Agriculture Research Centre, U.S.A.; Université de Quebec; Universidad Católica, Chile; University of Georgia; Kyushu School of Agronomy, Japan; Tropical Agriculture Research Centre, Japan; Kyorin University; Indiana State University; Southern Illinois University; Université de Laval; Universidad Nacional Autónoma, Mexico; Tokyo Agriculture and Technology University; Universidad Nacional de Jujuy, Argentina; Keio University; Centro Panamericano de Estudios Y Investigaciones Geográficas, Ecuador; Universidad de Oriente, Venezuela; Universidad de la República, Uruguay; Universidad Castilla-La Mancha;

Universidad de Córdoba, Spain; Universidad de la Habana; University of Constance; Universidad de Lisboa; Centro Latino-Americano y del Caribe de Informaciones en Ciencias de la Salud; Universidade Técnica de Lisboa; Universitá degli Studi de Roma La Sapienza; Texas University; Free University of Berlin; Fachhochschule Darmstadt; Institut d'Elevage et de Médecine vétérinaire des Pays tropicaux, Maison-Alfort; Chicago City Wide College; Universidad Iberoamericana de Postgrado, Spain; Tenri University; Instituto Nacional de Meteorologia e Geofisica, Portugal; Hebrew University of Jerusalem; Universidad de los Andes, Venezuela. New Mexico State University; Centro Internacional de Agricultura Tropical, Colombia; Universidad Nova de Lisboa; Institut national polytechnique de Grenoble; Universidade Técnica de Lisboa; Technical University of Szeczecin.

Academic Year: February to December (February-June; August-December).

Admission Requirements: Secondary school certificate or equivalent, and entrance examination.

Fees: Tuition, none.

Language of Instruction: Portuguese.

Degrees and Diplomas: Bacharel in–Biology; Social Sciences; Economics; Geography; History; Letters; Mathematics; Chemistry, 4 yrs. Licenciado in–Biology; Social Sciences; Music; Philosophy; Physics; Physical Education; Chemistry; Geography; History; Letters; Mathematics; Education; Psychology, 4 yrs. Professional titles in–Agriculture; Library Science; Ecology; Pharmacy; Piano; Dentistry; Social Service, 4 yrs; Engineering, various fields; Law; Geology; Veterinary Medicine; Animal Husbandry, 5 yrs; Composition; Medicine, 6 yrs. Mestrado, master. Doutorado, doctorate.

Library: Central Library (Marília), 1,164,523 vols. Specialized library.

Publications: Cientifica (biannually); Didática (Education, annually); Naturalia (Biology, annually); Revistas (Biomedicine, Pharmacy, Letters, Dentistry). História; Revista de Ciêncas Biomédicas; Trans/form/açâo (Revista de Filosofia); Geociêncas; Alimentos e Nutriçâo; Eclética; Quimica.

Press or Publishing House: Editora da UNESP (UNESP Publishing Hause).

Academic Staff, 1989:

Rank	Full-time	Part-time
Professores Titulares	223	4
Professores Adjuntos	180	10
Professores Assistentes Doutores	701	72
Professores Assistentes	917	73
Auxiliares de Ensino	549	183
Total	2570	342

Student Enrolment, 1989: 19,400

409 UNIVERSIDADE CATÓLICA DE PELOTAS

Catholic University of Pelotas

Rua Felix da Cunha 412, 96100 Pelotas (Rio Grande do Sul)
Telex: 53-2454
Telephone: (532) 253455
Reitor: Jandir João Zanotelli

Ce. for Human Sciences
Ce. for Exact Sciences and Technology
Ce. for Biological and Health Sciences
I. of Social Planning and Business Administration
Sea and Inland Water Research I.

Founded 1960. A private institution under the supervision of the Mitra Diocesana de Pelotas, but receives financial support from the federal government. Governing bodies: the Conselho Superior; the Conselho Universitário.

Academic Year: March to November (March-June; August-November).

Admission Requirements: Secondary school certificate or foreign equivalent and entrance examination.

Language of Instruction: Portuguese.

Degrees and Diplomas: Bacharel in–Social Communication; Business Administration; Accountancy; Economics; Social Sciences, 4 yrs. Licenciado in–Science, 2 yrs; Social Studies, 2 ½ yrs; Letters (1st grade), 3 yrs; Physics; Mathematics; Social Sciences; Geography; History; Philosophy; Letters; Chemistry; Biology; Education, 4 yrs. Professional titles of–Assistente social, social work; Farmacêutico e Bioquimico; Psicólogo; Médico; Engenheiro electricista; Engenheiro civil, 5 yrs.

Library: Central Library, *c.* 39,200 vols.

Academic Staff: c. 410.

Student Enrolment: c. 5250.

410 UNIVERSIDADE FEDERAL DE PELOTAS

Federal University of Pelotas

Campus Universitário, 96165 Pelotas (Rio Grande do Sul)
Telex: (532) 302
Telephone: (532) 212033
Fax: 21-5023
Reitor: Amilcar G. Gigante (1989-92)

I. of Human Sciences
Director: José Rubens Acevedo; *staff* 27 (5)
I. of Biological Sciences
Director: João Nelci Brandalise; *staff* 67 (8)
I. of Physics and Mathematics
Direcor: Cleusa Iara A. Morga; *staff* 42 (5)
I. of Chemistry and Earth Sciences
Director: Jorge Luiz Martins; *staff* 27 (1)
I. of Letters and Arts
Director: Angela Maria S.R. Gonzales; *staff* 48 (1)
F. of Veterinary Medicine
Director: Antonio L. Meleu Gomes; *staff* 51 (20)
F. of Education
Director: Ceres Maria Torres Bonatto; *staff* 33
F. of Home Economics
Director: Zilma da Costa Tambará; *staff* 30 (3)
F. of Law
Director: José Gilberto da C. Gastal; *staff* 23 (7)
F. of Medicine (including Nursing)
Director: Wandeerlei Rospide Motta; *staff* 62 (38)
F. of Agriculture (including Animal Husbandry)
Director: Moacir Cardoso Elias; *staff* 101 (3)
F. of Dentistry
Director: Adair L.S. Busatto; *staff* 56 (7)
S. of Physical Education
Director: Florismar Oliveira Thomaz; *staff* 21 (20)
I. of Sociology and Political Science
Director: Maria Amélia Soares D. da Costa; *staff* 10 (1)
Conservatory of Music
Director: Maria Elizabeth M. Salles; *staff* 12 (8)
F. of Architecture
Director: Paulo Afonso Rheingantz; *staff* 26 (3)
F. of Nursing and Obstetrics
Director: Claudio Mairan Brasil; *staff* 21 (1)
F. of Agricultural Engineering
Director: Eurico G. de Castro Neves; *staff* 16 (5)
F. of Meteorology
Director: Darci Pegoraro Casarin; *staff* 15
F. of Nutrition
Director: Marli Costa dos Santos; *staff* 17 (1)
F. of Biotechnology Ce.
Director: Carlos Gil Turnes

Founded 1883 as Imperial Escola de Medicina Veterinária e Agricultura, became Escola de Agronomia Eliseu Maciel 1926, Universidade Rural do Sul 1960, Universidade Federal Rural do Rio Grande do Sul 1967, and acquired present title and status 1969. Operated under the jurisdiction of the Ministry of Education and Culture and financially supported by the federal government. Governing body: the Conselho Universitário. Residential facilities for 204 students.

Arrangements for co-operation with: University of Entre Rios, Uruguay; University of Uruguay; University of Porto; Instituto Nacional de Meteorologiae Geofisica, Portugal; University of Chile; University of Guelph; University of Córdoba, Argentina.

Academic Year: March to December (March-July; August-December).

Admission Requirements: Secondary school certificate or equivalent, and entrance examination.

Language of Instruction: Portuguese.

Degrees and Diplomas: Bacharel in–Home Economics; Education; Plastic Arts; Music; Design; Nursing; Meteorology, 4 yrs; Law, 5 yrs. Licenciado in–Nursing; Physical Education; Social Studies; Artistic Education; Letters; Education, 4 yrs. Professional titles of–Médico veterinário; Nutricionista; Cirurgião dentista; Engenheiro agrônomo, 4 yrs; Arquitecto; Engenheiro agricola. Médico, 5 yrs. Mestrado. Postgraduate diplomas of specialization.

Libraries: Central Library, *c.* 5630 vols; faculty and institute libraries: Agriculture, *c.* 25,530; Law, *c.* 23,910; Dentistry, *c.* 3020; Medicine, *c.* 5210; Education, *c.* 2850; Physical Education, *c.* 630; Chemistry, *c.* 1960.

Special Facilities (Museums, etc.): Museum of Zoology.

Publication: Revista Agros.

Academic Staff, 1990:

Rank	Full-time	Part-time
Professores Titulares	50	11
Professores Adjuntos	412	128
Professores Assistentes	147	26
Professores Auxiliares de Ensino	101	15
Total	710	180

Student Enrolment, 1990: 5963.

411 **UNIVERSIDADE CATÓLICA DE PERNAMBUCO**

Catholic University of Pernambuco

Rua do Principe 526, 50058 Recife (Pernambuco)

Telex: 81-2776

Telephone: (81) 2317233

Fax: (81) 2164204

Reitor: Theodoro Paulo Severino Peters, S.J. (1990-94)

Diretor de Admissão e Registro: Ferdinando Pereira Régo

Ce. for Social Sciences
Dean: Mirian de Sá Pereira; *staff* 7 (191)
Ce. for Theology and Human Sciences
Dean: Benno João Lermen; *staff* 7 (196)
Ce. for Science and Technology
Dean: Reginaldo Lourenço Da Silva; *staff* 9 (135)
Extension D.
; *staff* – (23)
Research D. of History
Head: Maria José Pinheiro; *staff* – (8)
Research D. of Education
Head: Maria Lucia C. Galindo; *staff* – (6)
Research D. of Psychology
Head: Zélia Maria de Melo; *staff* – (2)
Research D. of Law
Head: João Poluca Araújo; *staff* – (8)
Research D. of Sociology
Head: Paulo Gaspar de Meneses; *staff* – (4)
Research D. of Chemistry
Head: Walter Jucá A. Pimentel; *staff* – (6)
Research D. of Physics
Head: Luiz Gonzaga de S. Cabral; *staff* – (2)

Founded 1951 incorporating Faculty of Economics, established 1942, Faculty of Philosophy, 1943, and School of Engineering, 1912. Reorganized 1973 with a structure comprising centres for professional education. A private institution under the supervision of the Society of Jesus and recognized by the federal government. Governing bodies: the Conselho Universitário; the Conselho de Ensino e Pesquisa.

Academic Year: (February to December (February-June; August-December).

Admission Requirements: Secondary school certificate and entrance examination.

Fees (Cruzeiros): 16,829.78-12,535.69 per semester, for 22 credits.

Language of Instruction: Portuguese.

Degrees and Diplomas: Bacharel in–Tourism, 3-4 yrs; Philosophy; Social Service; Physics; Chemistry; 3-7 yrs; Psychology; Industrial Chemistry; Mathematics, 3 ½-7 yrs; History; Geography; Journalism; Public Relations; Law, 4-7 yrs; Accountancy; Business Administration; 4-8 yrs; Chemistry Engineering; Civil Engineering, 4-9 yrs; Economics, 5-7 yrs; Statistics; Computer Sciences, 5-8 yrs; Speech Therapy, 5-9 yrs. Licenciado in–Biology, 3-6 yrs; Philosophy; Letters; Education; Social Sciences; Physics; Chemistry, 3-7 yrs; Psychology; Mathematics, 3 1/2-7 yrs; History, 4-7 yrs. Professional titles of–Assistente social, 3-7 yrs; Engenheiro químico, 4-9 yrs; Psicólogo e Fonoaudiólogo, 5-9 yrs.

Library: Biblioteca Central Padre Aloisio Mosca de Carvalho, S.J., 80,249 vols.

Special Facilities (Museums, etc.): Museum of Archaeology.

Publications: Revista Symposium; Cadernos.

Academic Staff, 1990:

Rank	Full-time	Part-time
Professores Titulares	4	36
Professores Adjuntos	1	54
Professores Assistentes	12	187
Professores Colaboradores	–	6
Professores Auxiliares de Ensino	6	239
Total	23	522

Student Enrolment, 1990:

	Men	Women	Total
Of the country	5742	7519	13,261
Of other countries	11	12	23
Total	5753	7531	13,284

412 **UNIVERSIDADE FEDERAL DE PERNAMBUCO**

Federal University of Pernambuco

Avenida Professor Moraes Rego, Cidade Universitária, 50739 Recife (Pernambuco)

Telex: 81-1267

Telephone: (81) 2710344

Ce. for Arts and Communication
Ce. for Exact and Natural Sciences
Ce. for Biology
Ce. for Philosophy and Human Sciences
Ce. for Education
Ce. for Social Sciences
Ce. for Health Sciences
Ce. for Technology
F. of Law

Founded 1946 as Universidade do Recife, incorporating faculties established 1827-1941. Acquired present title 1965. Operated under the jurisdiction of the Ministry of Education and Culture and financially supported by the federal government. Some residential facilities for students.

Academic Year: March to December (March-June; August-December).

Admission Requirements: Secondary school certificate and entrance examination.

Language of Instruction: Portuguese.

Degrees and Diplomas: Bacharel in–Education; Neo-Latin Letters; Anglo-Saxon Letters; Classical Letters; History; Natural History; Geography; Social Science; Mathematics; Philosophy; Library Science, 3 yrs; Economics; Accountancy; Actuarial Science, 4 yrs; Law, 5 yrs. Licenciado in–Education; Neo-Latin Letters; Anglo-Saxon Letters; Classical Letters; History; Natural History; Geography; Social Science; Public Administration; Mathematics, 4 yrs. Doutor em Direito, law, 2 yrs after Bacharel. Professional titles of–Enfermeira obstétrica; Nutricionista, 3 yrs; Professor de Desenho; Químico; Farmacêutico; Cirurgião dentista; Enfermeira, 4 yrs; Engenheiro civil; Engenheiro electricista; Engenheiro de minas; Engenheiro mecânico; Pintor; Escultor; Engenheiro quimico industrial, 5 yrs; Médico, 6 yrs.

Library: Central Library, *c.* 206,440 vols.

Publications: Jornal Universitário (monthly); Estudos Universitários (3 times a month); Boletim oficial (quarterly).

Academic Staff: *c.* 2280.

Student Enrolment: *c.* 18,500.

413 **UNIVERSIDADE FEDERAL RURAL DE PERNAMBUCO**

Federal Rural University of Pernambuco

Rua Don Manoel de Medeiros s/n, 50000 Recife (Pernambuco)

Telex: 81-1195

Telephone: (81) 2685477

Reitor: Waldecy Fernandes Pinto (1983-87)

D. of Physics and Mathematics
D. of Chemistry
D. of Biology
D. of Morphology and Animal Physiology
D. of Letters and Human Sciences (including Economics)
D. of Agriculture
D. of Rural Technology
D. of Veterinary Medicine
D. of Animal Husbandry
D. of Fishery
D. of Education

D. of Home Economics

Founded 1912 as school, became university by State decree 1947, acquired status as federal institution 1956. Under the jurisdiction of the Ministry of Education and Culture. Governing bodies: the Conselho Universitário; the Conselho de Curadores; the Conselho de Ensino, Pesquisa e Extensão. Residential facilities for students.

Arrangements for co-operation with the University of Georgia.

Academic Year: March to December (March-June; August-December).

Admission Requirements: Secondary school certificate and entrance examination.

Language of Instruction: Portuguese.

Degrees and Diplomas: Bacharel in–Biology, 3-6 yrs. Licenciado in–Home Economics; Science, 3-7 yrs. Professional titles in–Social Science; Forestry; Fishery, 3-7 yrs; Agricultural Engineering, 4-8 yrs; Animal Husbandry, 3-5 yrs. Mestrado, master, a further 1-4 yrs. Also teaching qualifications.

Library: Central Library, *c.* 22,800 vols.

Publications: Caderno Omega; Informativo; Anais.

Press or Publishing House: Imprensa Universitária.

Academic Staff: *c.* 110 (60).

Student Enrolment: *c.* 420.

414 ***UNIVERSIDADE CATÓLICA DE PETRÓPOLIS**

Catholic University of Petrópolis

Rua Benjamin Constant 213, 25610 Petrópolis (Rio de Janeiro)

Telex: 21-31637

Telephone: (242) 425062

Reitor: Maria da Gloria Rangel Sampaio Fernandes (1987-)

I. of Exact and Natural Sciences
S. of Engineering
I. of Theology, Philosophy, and Human Sciences
I. of Arts and Communication
F. of Law
F. of Education
F. of Economics, Accountancy, and Administration
S. of Rehabilitation

Founded as Faculty of Law 1954, became university 1961 with the Diocesan Bishop as Grand Chancellor. Receives some financial support from federal and State Governments. Governing bodies: the Conselho Superior de Administração e Finanças; the Conselho de Patronos; the Conselho Universitário; the Conselho de Coordenação do Ensino e Pesquisa. Some residential facilities for students.

Academic Year: February to December (February-June; August-December).

Admission Requirements: Secondary school certificate and entrance examination.

Language of Instruction: Portuguese.

Degrees and Diplomas: Bacharel in–Law; Economics; Administration; Accountancy. Licenciado in–Letters; Education; History; Geography; Science; Tourism. Professional titles of–Engenheiro; Fisioterapêuta; Fonoaudiólogo; Psicólogo; Enfermeiro. Mestre.

Library: Central Library, *c.* 69,420 vols.

Publications: Informativo de U.C.P.; Boletim Cepetur (monthly).

Academic Staff: *c.* 280.

Student Enrolment: *c.* 3330.

415 **UNIVERSIDADE METÓDISTA DE PIRACICABA**

Methodist University of Piracicaba

Rua Rangel Pestana 762, 13400 Piracicaba (São Paulo)

Telex: 19-1914

Telephone: (914) 335011

Ce. for Human Sciences
Ce. for Applied Sciences
Ce. for Biological and Health Sciences
Ce. for Exact Sciences and Technology
F. of Economics, Accountancy, and Administration
F. of Social Communication
F. of Law
F. of Physical Education
F. of Education
F. of Philosophy, Science, and Letters
F. of Technology

Founded 1881 as a school by the American Methodist Mission, became Faculdade de Ciências Econômicas, Contábeis e Administração de Emprêsas 1964. Faculty of Education added 1966 and Faculty of Law 1970. Became university with present structure 1975. An autonomous institution under the jurisdiction of the federal Ministry of Education and Culture.

Academic Year: February to December (February-June; August-December).

Admission Requirements: Secondary school certificate.

Language of Instruction: Portuguese.

Degrees and Diplomas: Bacharel in all fields, 3-5 yrs. Licenciado, 3-5 yrs. Mestrado, master, in Education, 2-4 yrs.

Library: *c.* 38,000 vols.

Academic Staff: *c.* 600.

Student Enrolment: *c.* 6600.

416 **UNIVERSIDADE FEDERAL DO PIAUÍ**

Federal University of Piauí

Campus Universitaria, 64000 Teresina (Piauí)

Telex: 86-2271

Telephone: (85) 2321212

Ce. for Health Sciences (Medicine, Dentistry, Nursing)
Ce. for Natural Sciences
Ce. for Human Sciences and Letters
Ce. for Education
Ce. for Agricultural Sciences (including Veterinary Medicine)
Ce. for Technology
Extension D.

Also branches in Paraíba, Floriano, Guadalupe, and Bom Jesus.

Founded 1971. Operated under the jurisdiction of the Ministry of Education and Culture and financially supported by the federal government. Governing body: the Conselho Universitário.

Academic Year: March to November (March-June; August-November).

Admission Requirements: Secondary school certificate and entrance examination.

Fees: None.

Language of Instruction: Portuguese.

Degrees and Diplomas: Licenciado in–Physical Education; Mathematics; Physics; Biology; Chemistry; Science; Letters; History; Geography; Social Studies; Philosophy; Education; Commerce, 2 1/2-8 yrs. Professional titles in–Nursing; Nutrition; Law; Business Administration; Economics; Accountancy; Social Service; Agricultural Technology; Art; Rural Administration; Cattle-raising; Agriculture; Veterinary Medicine; Construction; Civil Engineering; Education, 2-8yrs; Dentistry, 4-6 yrs; Medicine, 5-9 yrs.

Library: Central Library, *c.* 80,880 vols.

Academic Staff: *c.* 1050.

Student Enrolment: *c.* 9380.

417 **UNIVERSIDADE ESTADUAL DE PONTA GROSSA**

State University of Ponta Grossa

Praça Santos Andrade, 84100 Ponta Grossa (Paraná)

Telex: 42-2242

Telephone: (422) 243966

Reitor: Ewaldo Podolan (1983-87)

Sec. for Biological and Health Sciences
Sec. for Exact and Natural Sciences
Sec. for Letters and Human Sciences

Founded 1970 incorporating previously existing State faculties. Recognized by the federal government 1973. Governing bodies: the Conselho Universitário; the Conselho de Administração.

Academic Year: March to December (March-June; August-November).

Admission Requirements: Secondary school certificate and entrance examination.

Language of Instruction: Portuguese.

Degrees and Diplomas: Bacharel and Licenciado in–Geography; Civil Engineering; Agriculture; Dentistry; Pharmacy and Biochemistry; History; Economics; Administration; Accountancy; Law; Social Studies. Licenciado in–Physics; Chemistry and Biology. Also teaching qualifications.

Library: Central Library, *c.* 92,360 vols.

Special Facilities (Museums, etc.): Museu Campos Gerais.

Publications: Jornal Campos Gerais; Anuário; Perfil Sócio-Econômico; Levantamento Informativo.

Press or Publishing House: Imprensa Universitária.

Academic Staff: 100 (240).

Student Enrolment: *c.* 4090.

418 **UNIVERSIDADE DE RIBEIRÃO PRÊTO**

Avenida Costabile Romano 2201, 14095 Ribeirão Prêto (São Paulo)
Telex: 16-6036 ASEN
Telephone: (166) 6246300

Human Sciences
Art
Exact Sciences
Education
Health Sciences

Founded 1971. A private institution under the jurisdiction of the União da Associação de Ensino de Ribeirão Prêto.

419 **UNIVERSIDADE DO RIO GRANDE**

University of Rio Grande
Rua Eng. Alfredo Huch 475, 96200 Rio Grande (Rio Grande do Sul)
Telex: 53-2373
Telephone: (532) 323300
Reitor: Jomar Bessonat Laurino
Sub-Reitor Administrativo: Vitor Hugo da Silveira Vitola

D. of Biology and Morphology
Head: Guassenir Born; *staff* 23
D. of Law
Head: Marilena Karam Zogbi; *staff* 17 (6)
D. of Medicine (including Nursing)
Head: Jaime Copstein; *staff* 14 (20)
D. of Midwifery and Infant Nursing
Head: Luiz Carlos Mello Esperon; *staff* 8 (16)
D. of Physiology and Pharmacy
Head: Fernando Amarante Silva; *staff* 7 (7)
D. of Pathology
Head: Carlos Renan Varella Juliano; *staff* 9 (8)
D. of Library Science and History
Head: Alba Maria Dourado Correa; *staff* 15 (5)
D. of Earth Sciences
Head: Haroldo Erwin Asmus; *staff* 13 (4)
D. of Economics
Head: Aldo Lapolli; *staff* 22 (5)
D. of Oceanography
Head: Clovis Campos Alt; *staff* 44
D. of Mathematics
Head: Tabajara Lucas de Almeida; *staff* 35 (1)
D. of Education
Head: Marise Costa Prado; *staff* 19 (22)
D. of Letters and Arts
Head: Claudio Gabiatti; *staff* 23 (3)
D. of Chemistry (including Food Technology)
Head: Neusa Ribeiro Costa; *staff* 28 (2)
D. of Materials and Construction (including Architecture and Town Planning)
Head: Décio Rodrigues de Oliveira; *staff* 20 (15)
D. of Physics
Head: Ernesto Casares Pintop; *staff* 24 (4)
D. of Surgery
Head: Délicio Figueira dos Santos; *staff* 4 (21)

Founded 1969 incorporating previously existing faculties of industrial engineering, law, philosophy, science and letters, and political and economic sciences. A State institution under the jurisdiction of the Ministry of Education and Culture. Governing body: the Conselho Universitário.

Arrangements for co-operation with the University of the Republic, Montevideo.

Academic Year: March to November (March-June; August-November).

Admission Requirements: Competitive entrance examination following secondary school certificate.

Language of Instruction: Portuguese.

Degrees and Diplomas: Bacharel in–Library Science, 3 yrs; Accountancy; Economics, 4 yrs; Law, 5 yrs. Licenciado in–Social Studies, 2 yrs; Science, 3 yrs; History; Geography; Education; Letters; Mathematics; Chemistry; Biology; Nursing, 4 yrs. Professional titles of–Enfermeiro, nursing, 3 yrs; Administrador de Empresas, business administration, 4 yrs; Oceanólogo, 4-5 yrs; Engenheiro (various fields), 5 yrs; Médico, 6 yrs. Mestrado, master, in Oceanography. Postgraduate diplomas of specialization.

Library: Central Library, 32,500 vols.

Special Facilities (Museums, etc.): Museu Oceanográfico.

Publication: Revistas of the departments.

Press or Publishing House: Editora da FURG.

Academic Staff, 1986-87:

Rank	Full-time	Part-time
Professores Titulares	52	15
Professores Adjuntos	108	5
Professores Assistentes	133	13
Professores Auxiliares	95	9
Substitutos	–	10
Ensinos Médios	14	7
Total	402	59

Student Enrolment, 1986-87:

	Men	Women	Total
Of the country	1804	1895	3699
Of other countries	25	2	27
Total	1829	1897	3726

420 **UNIVERSIDADE FEDERAL DO RIO GRANDE DO NORTE**

Federal University of Rio Grande do Norte
Campus Universitário, Lagoa Nova Km 7, BR 101, 59000 Natal (Rio Grande do Norte)
Cables: Edreitor
Telex: 84-2296
Telephone: (842) 2311266

Ce. for Exact Sciences
Ce. for Humanities, Letters, and Arts
Ce. for Technology (including Architecture)
Ce. for Applied Social Sciences (including Law, Economics, Education, and Business Administration)
Ce. for Biosciences
Ce. for Health Sciences (including Medicine, Dentistry, Pharmacy, Nutrition, and Nursing)
I. of Marine Biology
I. of Anthropology
S. of Home Economics
S. of Music

Founded 1958 incorporating a number of previously existing faculties. Operated under the jurisdiction of the Ministry of Education and Culture and financially supported by the federal government. Residential facilities for students.

Academic Year: February to December (February-June; August-December).

Admission Requirements: Secondary school certificate and entrance examination.

Language of Instruction: Portuguese.

Degrees and Diplomas: Bacharel in–Law; Science and Letters. Professional titles of–Assistente social, 3 yrs; Farmacêutico; Cirurgião dentista; Engenheiro civil; Médico. Doutorado.

Libraries: Central Library, *c.* 150,000 vols; libraries of the departments and campuses, total, *c.* 28,000.

Special Facilities (Museums, etc.): Museu de Antropologia; Museu do Mar.

Publications: Revista; Boletim.

Press or Publishing House: Editora Universitária.

Academic Staff: c. 2260.

Student Enrolment: c. 14,000.

421 **UNIVERSIDADE REGIONAL DO RIO GRANDE DO NORTE**

Campus Universitário, 59600 Mossoró (Rio Grande do Norte)
Telex: 84-3211
Telephone: (84) 3214997

I. of Human Sciences, Arts, and Letters
F. of Economics
F. of Education and Social Services
S. of Agriculture

Founded 1968.

422 ***PONTIFÍCIA UNIVERSIDADE CATÓLICA DO RIO GRANDE DO SUL**

Pontifical Catholic University of Rio Grande do Sul

Avenida Ipiranga 6681, Caixa postal 1429, 90620 Pôrto Alegre (Rio Grande do Sul)
Telex: 51-3349
Telephone: (512) 39-15-11
Fax: 391564

Reitor: Norberto F. Rauch (1982-90)
Chefe de Gabinete: Eurico Saldanha de Lemos

I. of Theology and Religious Sciences
Director: Zeno Hastenteufel; *staff* 6 (40)
I. of Letters and Arts
Director: Irmão Mainar Longhi; *staff* 28 (66)
I. of Psychology
Director: Itala M. Suarez de Puga; *staff* 17 (121)
F. of Education
Director: Irmão Armando Bertolini; *staff* 22 (167)
I. of Philosophy and Human Sciences
Director: Odone José de Quadros; *staff* 35 (74)
F. of Social Service
Director: Jairo Melo Araújo; *staff* 8 (15)
F. of Communications Media
Director: Antônio Firmo Oliveira Gonzalez; *staff* 7 (124)
F. of Law
Director: Júpiter Torres Fagundes; *staff* 18 (160)
F. of Political Science and Economics (including Accountancy)
Director: Jorge Alberto Franzoni; *staff* 13 (98)
I. of Biology
Director: Milton Menegotto; *staff* 43 (53)
F. of Dentistry
Director: Raphael Onorino Carlos Loro; *staff* 5 (73)
F. of Medicine
Director: José Torquato Severo; *staff* 2 (242)
I. of Mathematics
Director: Delmar Basso; *staff* 29 (45)
I. of Physics
Director: Antônio Dias Nunes; *staff* 19 (22)
I. of Chemistry
Director: Ivo Vedana; *staff* 18 (21)
Polytechnic S. (Civil, Mechanical, Electrical, and Electronic Engineering)
Director: Dulcemar Coelho Lautert; *staff* 44 (200)
F. of Animal Husbandry, Veterinary Medicine and Agriculture (Campus II)
Director: Aurio Moncerat Braccini; *staff* 28 (31)
F. of Accountancy and Business Administration (Campus II)
Director: Wilson Valente Da Costa; *staff* 3 (31)
F. of Philosophy, Science and Letters (Campus II)
Director: Juarez Hernandez; *staff* 9 (74)

Founded 1931 by the Marist Brothers as faculty of economics. Incorporated faculties and schools established 1939-60. Recognized by the government as a university 1948, became Pontifical University 1950. An independent institution, but receives some financial support from the State. Governing bodies: the Conselho de Curadores (Board of Trustees); the Conselho Universitário; the Conselho de Coordenação ePesquisa.

Arrangements for co-operation with Sophia University, Tokyo.

Academic Year: March to December (March-July; August-December).

Admission Requirements: Secondary school certificate and entrance examination.

Fees (Cruzeiros): 778.61 per credit.

Language of Instruction: Portuguese.

Degrees and Diplomas: Bacharel in–Letters; Law; Journalism; Social Sciences; Economics; Accountancy; Business Administration; Public Administration; Systems Analysis; Geography. Licenciado in–Letters; Physics; Mathematics; Chemistry; Biology; History; Geography; Theology; Computer Sciences; Philosophy; Pedagogy; Social Studies; Religious Studies. Professional titles in–Medicine; Veterinary Medicine; Dentistry; Animal Husbandry; Agriculture; Social Work; Chemistry; Psychology; Engineering (various fields). Mestrado, master, in–Linguistics and Letters; Education; Sociology; Social Service; Bucco-Facial Dentistry; Philosophy; History; Zoology. Doctorates, by thesis.

Libraries: Central Library, 118,048; specialized libraries, *c.*40,000.

Special Facilities (Museums, etc.): Museu de Ciências; Museu de Arqueologia.

Publications: Veritas (quarterly); Letras de Hoje (quarterly); Anuário (annually); Mundo Jovem (monthly); Teocomunicação (quarterly); Estudos Ibero-Americanos (biannually); Psico (biannually); Direito e Justiça (annually); Educação (biannually); Revista Análise (biannually); Informativo PUCRS Informação (biannually); Informativo Agenda PUC (monthly); Revista OdontoCiência (biannually); Revista de Medicina da PUCRS (quarterly).

Press or Publishing House: Escola Professional Champagnat.

Academic Staff, 1989-90:

Rank	Full-time	Part-time
Professores Titulares	63	151
Professores Adjuntos	52	244
Professores Assistentes	44	1000
Professores Auxiliares	5	396
Professores Contratados	11	47
Total	175	1838

Student Enrolment, 1989-90:

	Men	Women	Total
Of the country	10,888	10,888	21,776
Of other countries	135	127	262
Total	11,023	11,015	22,038

423 **UNIVERSIDADE FEDERAL DO RIO GRANDE DO SUL**

Federal University of Rio Grande do Sul

Avenida Paulo Gama 110, 90049 Pôrto Alegre (Rio Grande do Sul)
Telex: 51-1055
Telephone: (512) 21-4133/25-7375
Fax: (512) 27-2295

Reitor: Tuiskon Dick (1990-92)

I. of Arts
Director: Raimundo M. da Silva Filho; *staff* 61 (25)
I. of Biology
Director: Renato Dutra Dias; *staff* 151 (57)
I. of Mathematics (including Statistics)
Director: Aron Taitelbaum; *staff* 65 (32)
I. of Food Technology
Director: Christophy Bernasiuk *staff* 9 (7)
I. of Philosophy and Human Sciences (including Psychology and Social Science)
Director: Alberto de Boni; *staff* 109 (45)
I. of Physics
Director: Fernando C. Zawislak; *staff* 82 (13)
I. of Earth Sciences
Director: Clovis Carlos Carraro; *staff* 60 (17)
I. of Letters
Director: Ana Maria M. Guimarães; *staff* 67 (34)
I. of Hydrology Research
Director: Marcos Imério Leão; *staff* 30 (11)
I. of Chemistry
Director: Raquel Santos Mauler; *staff* 45 (17)
I. of Informatics
Director: Clésio Saraiva dos Santos; *staff* 40 (35)
F. of Agriculture
Director: Ema M. Leboute; *staff* 65 (12)
F. of Architecture
Director: Roberto Py G. da Silveira; *staff* 35 (69)
F. of Library Science and Journalism
Director: Blásio H. Hickmann; *staff* 32 (20)
F. of Economics (including Business and Public Administration)
Director: Walter Meuci Nique; *staff* 52 (120)
F. of Law
Director: José Sperb Sanseverion; *staff* 8 (67)
F. of Pharmacy
Director: Paulo Roberto Saraiva; *staff* 32 (9)
F. of Medicine
Director: Ronaldo P. Souza; *staff* 24 (261)
F. of Dentistry
Director: Carlos A. Mundstock; *staff* 12 (55)
F. of Veterinary Science
Director: Rodolfo Voll; *staff* 39 (16)
F. of Education
Director: Balduino Andreola; *staff* 77 (24)
S. of Nursing
Director: Sonia Maria Agostini; *staff* 50 (38)
S. of Engineering
Director: Arno Müller; *staff* 92 (86)
S. of Physical Education
Director: Paulo G. Oliveira; *staff* 23 (19)

Observatory

Founded 1934 as Universidade do Pôrto Alegre as a State institution incorporating faculties established 1896-1910. Acquired status as federal institution and present title 1965. Governing bodies: the Conselho Universitário; the Conselho de Coordenação de Ensino e da Pesquisa. Some residential facilities for students.

Arrangements for co-operation with: Universidad Politécnica de Madrid; University of Kassel; University of Heidelberg; University of Cologne; University of Freiburg; Münster University; University of Hanover; Université de Grenoble; Universidad Nacional Nordeste; University Tucumán; Universidad de Rosário; Midwest University; Universidad República do Uruguay; Universidade Eduardo Mondlane.

Academic Year: March to November (March-June; August-November).

Admission Requirements: Secondary school certificate and entrance examination.

Language of Instruction: Portuguese.

Degrees and Diplomas: Bacharel in–Physics; Geography; Mathematics; Chemistry; Biology; Journalism; Business Administration; Public Administration; Library Science; Statistics; Economics; Accountancy; Actuarial Sciences; Computer Sciences; Plastic Arts; Philosophy and Human Sciences; History; Social Sciences; Drama; Letters, 4 yrs; Music; Law, 5 yrs. Licenciado in–Physical Education, 3 yrs; Geography; Physics; Chemistry; Social Science; Philosophy; History; Letters; Education; Science; Mathematics; Biology, 4 yrs; Professional titles of–Técnico em Administração; Engenheiro agrônomo; Enfermeiro; Cirurgião dentista, 4 yrs; Geólogo; Engenheiro; Farmacêutico; Arquiteto; Psicólogo; Médico veterinário, 5 yrs; Médico, 6 yrs. Mestrado, master. Doutorado, doctor. Also teaching qualifications.

Libraries: Central Library, 403,059 vols; 28 branch libraries, *c.* 486,340.

Special Facilities (Museums, etc.): Theatre; Cinema; Agronomic Experimental Station (experimental farm).

Publications: Faculties and Institutes Reviews, Jornal da UFRGS (monthly); UFRGS Newsletter (weekly); DP Informativo (monthly); Aplicação Review (annually).

Press or Publishing House: Gráfica e Editora da Universidade.

Academic Staff, 1989-92:

Rank	Full-time
Professores Titulares	276
Professores Adjuntos	1322
Professores Assistentes	470
Professores de Ensino	273
Total	2341

Student Enrolment, 1989-92: 17,553.

424 ***PONTIFÍCIA UNIVERSIDADE CATÓLICA DO RIO DE JANEIRO**

Pontifical Catholic University of Rio de Janeiro

Rua Marquês de São Vicente 225, 22453 Rio de Janeiro (Rio de Janeiro)
Telex: 21-31048
Telephone: (21) 529-9922
Fax: (0055) 021-274-4546

Reitor: Laércio Dias de Moura, S.J. (1982-)
Registro: Mario Antonio Monteiro

Ce. for Theology and Human Sciences (including Education, Psychology, Arts, Letters, Philosophy, and Theology)
Dean: Danilo Marcondes; *staff* 121 (106)
Ce. for Social Sciences (including Law, Business Administration, Economics, Journalism, Sociology and Political Science, Social Communication, Management, and International Relations)
Dean: Luiz Roberto de Azevedo Cunha; *staff* 108 (185)
Ce. for Science and Technological Studies (including Physics, Chemistry, Mathematics, Computer Sciences, Civil, Electrical Metallurgical and Mechanical Engineering, and Telecommunications)
Dean: Humberto Brandi; *staff* 244 (116)
Ce. for Health Sciences
Dean: Rinaldo de Lamare
I. of Applied Psychology
I. of Logic and Philosophy of Language
Language Ce. for Foreign Students

Founded 1941 by Cardinal D. Sebastião Leme and Father Leonel Franca, S.J. Acquired university status 1946. The title of Pontifical University was conferred in 1947. The university operates under the supervision of the Society of Jesus and under the supreme authority of the Cardinal Archbishop of Rio de Janeiro as Grand Chancellor. Receives some financial support from the federal government. Governing bodies: the Board; the University Council.

Arrangements for co-operation with: University of Arizona; University of Alabama; University of Maryland; University of Illinois; University of Florida; Universidad Regiomontana; Universidad Técnica 'Federico Santa María', Valparaíso; Catholic University of Valparaíso; University of Concepción, Chile; Universdad de Las Américas, Puebla; Instituto Nazionale di Fisica Nucleare, Italy; Universidad Católica de Córdoba, Argentina; Sharif University of Technology, Tehran; University of Alberta; University of Montreal; Emmanuel College, Boston; University of Eichstatt; Universidad de la República, Uruguay. Student exchanges with University of Illinois, Urbana-Champaign.

Academic Year: March to December (March-June; August-December).

Admission Requirements: Secondary school certificate and entrance examination.

Fees (Cruzeiros): 1317.29-6107.57 per semester.

Language of Instruction: Portuguese.

Degrees and Diplomas: Bacharel in–Philosophy; Theology; Arts and Letters; Geography; History; Sociology; Physics; Chemistry; Mathematics; Industrial Design; Law, 4 yrs. Licenciado in–Education; Philosophy; Letters; Psychology; Geography; History; Theology; Physics; Chemistry; Mathematics, 4 yrs. Professional titles in–Computer Sciences, 3 yrs; Business Administration; Economics; Journalism; Industrial Chemistry; Social Work, 4 yrs; Engineering (various fields). Mestrado, master, in–Theology; Philosophy; Psychology; Education; Law; Letters; Business Administration; Metallurgy; Cardiology; Plastic Surgery; Endocrinology; Otolaryngology; Economics; Physics; Mathematics; Chemistry; Engineering (various fields); Computer Sciences, 1-2 yrs after Bacharel or Licenciado. Doctorates in–Theology; Letters; Mathematics; Physics; Chemistry; Education; Philosophy; Psychology; Computer Sciences; Engineering, a further 3 yrs.

Libraries: Central Library, 180,000 vols; 3 branch libraries, 66,560.

Publications: Brasil Perspectiva Internacionais (bimonthly); Gavea (biannually); PUC News (monthly); PUC-CIÊNCIA (quarterly); PUC-Rio (annually).

Academic Staff, 1989-90:

Rank	Full-time	Part-time
Professores	21	8
Professores Adjuntos	203	86
Professores Assistentes	167	134
Professores Auxiliares	90	214
Total	481	442

Student Enrolment, 1989-90: 7963.

425 **UNIVERSIDADE DO ESTADO DO RIO DE JANEIRO**

State University of Rio de Janeiro

Avenida São Francisco Xavier 524, 20550 Rio de Janeiro (Rio de Janeiro)
Telephone: (21) 2848322

Ce. for Biomedical Studies
Ce. for Technology
Ce. for Science
Ce. for Education and Human Sciences
I. of Social Medicine
I. of Human Sciences
I. of Criminology
I. of Economic, Social and Political Studies
I. of Mathematics and Statistics
I. of Physics
I. of Chemistry
I. of Earth Sciences
I. of Design and Applied Arts
I. of Philosophy and Letters
I. of Psychology and Social Communication
F. of Economics
F. of Law
F. of Engineering
F. of Education
F. of Social Service
F. of Administration and Finance

Founded 1961. *Academic Staff: c.* 1820.
Student Enrolment: c. 14,620.

426 UNIVERSIDADE FEDERAL DO RIO DE JANEIRO

Federal University of Rio de Janeiro
Avenida Brigadeiro Trompowski s/n, 21941 Rio de Janeiro (Rio de Janeiro)
Telex: 21-22924
Telephone: (21) 2902112
Reitor: Alexandre Pinto Cardoso
Secretário: Ivan Rodrigues da Silva

I. of Physics
Director: Joaquim Lopes Neto; *staff* 108 (8)
I. of Earth Sciences
Director: Elmo da Silva Amador; *staff* 75 (18)
I. of Mathematics
Director: Augusto J.M. Wanderley; *staff* 107 (44)
I. of Chemistry
Director: Marco Antonio França Faria; *staff* 91 (17)
I. of Philosophy and Social Science
Director: Michel Misse; *staff* 107 (21)
I. of Psychology
Director: Marcos Jardim Freire; *staff* 42 (10)
I. of Industrial Economics
Director: Aloísio Feixeira; *staff* 1 (3)
I. of Biological and Health Sciences
Director: Octavio Aprigliano; *staff* 60 (17)
I. of Microbiology
Director: Fernando Steele da Cruz; *staff* 55 (3)
I. of Biology
Director: Déia Maria F. dos Santos; *staff* 47 (6)
I. of Nutrition
Director: Alcinda S. da Gama; *staff* 25 (5)
I. of Biophysics
Director: Wanderley de Souza; *staff* 67 (13)
F. of Architecture and Town Planning
Director: Luiz Paulo Conde; *staff* 2
F. of Letters
Director: José Carlos de Azeredo; *staff* 216 (35)
F. of Education
Director: Jorge Ferreira da Silva; *staff* 101 (21)
F. of Law
Director: Antonio V. da Costa Jr.; *staff* 33 (36)
F. of Pharmacy
Director: Alice Pereira Mattos; *staff* 28 (20)
F. of Medicine
Director: Vera Halfoun; *staff* 307 (128)
F. of Dentistry
Director: Nicola Tancredo; *staff* 64 (21)
F. of Economics
Dean: Margareth Hanson Costa
S. of Fine Arts
Director: Leonardo V. Cavalleiro; *staff* 94 (21)
S. of Music
Director: Diva Teixeira Mendes Abalada; *staff* 97 (18)
S. of Communication
Director: Carlos Alberto Messeder; *staff* 39 (13)
S. of Social Service
Director: Maria Helena Rauta Rampos; *staff* 18 (5)
S. of Nursing
Director: Raymunda Becker; *staff* 52 (17)
S. of Physical Education and Sports
Director: Vernon Furtado da Silva; *staff* 54 (27)
S. of Engineering
Director: Cláudio L. Baraúna Vieira; *staff* 159 (187)
S. of Chemistry
Director: Ricardo Medronho; *staff* 45 (11)

Founded 1920, reorganized 1937 as Universidade de Brasil with autonomous status. Acquired present title 1961. Under the administration and financial responsibility of the Ministry of Education and Culture. Governing body: the Conselho de Curadores. Residential facilities for students.

Arrangements for co-operation with the Universities of: Paris I, III, VI; Santiago de Chile; the Republic, Montevideo; Rome 'La Sapienza'; La Habana; Wuhan; Alabama; Maryland; Lisbon. Moscow State Pedagogical Institute; Rhine Technical College, Cologne; Universidad Nacional de Ingenieria 'Simón Bolívar', Managua.

Academic Year: March to December (March-June; August-December).

Admission Requirements: Secondary school certificate and entrance examination.

Language of Instruction: Portuguese.

Degrees and Diplomas: Bacharel in Psychology, 5 yrs. Licenciado in–Design and Plastics, 3 yrs; Biology; Education; Artistic Education; Physics; Geography; Mathematics; Music; Chemistry, 4 yrs; Physical Education, Psychology, 5 yrs. Professional titles in–Philosophy; History, 3 yrs; Administration; Scenic Art; Astronomy; Biology; Economics; Social Science; Social Communication; Industrial Design; Law; Nursing; Statistics; Pharmacy; Physics; Geography; Geology; Data Processing; Letters; Mathematics; Meteorology; Nutrition; Dentistry; Education; Chemistry; Social Service, 4 yrs; Architecture; Composition; Engineering; Sculpture; Instrumental Music, 5 yrs; Medicine, 6 yrs; Clarinet; Civics, 7 yrs. Mestrado, master. Doutorado, doctorate, by thesis.

Library: Total, *c.* 895,760 vols.

Special Facilities (Museums, etc.): Museu Nacional.

Publication: Boletim (weekly).

Press or Publishing House: Serviço Industrial Gráfico.

Academic Staff, 1986-87:

Rank	Full-time	Part-time
Professores Titulares	296	72
Professores Adjuntos	1374	364
Professores Assistentes	828	313
Professores Auxiliares	42	68
Professores de ½ Graus	45	43
Total	2585	860

Student Enrolment, 1986-87:

	Men	Women	Total
Of the country	11,000	11,350	22,350
Of other countries	290	205	504
Total	11,299	11,555	22,854

427 UNIVERSIDADE DO RIO DE JANEIRO

University of Rio de Janeiro
Avenida Pasteur, 22290 Rio de Janeiro (Rio de Janeiro)
Telephone: (21) 2957794
Reitor: Guilherme Oliveira Figueiredo (1984-88)

Ce. for Biological and Health Sciences (including Medicine, Nutrition, and Nursing)
Ce. for Arts and Languages
Ce. for Humanities (including Library Science)
Extension D.

Founded 1969 as Federação das Escolas Federais Isoladas do Estado Guanabara. Acquired present status and title 1979. Under the jurisdiction of the Ministry of Education and Culture and financially supported by the federal government. Governing bodies: the Conselho Universitário; the Conselho de Ensino e Pesquisa; the Conselho de Curadores.

Academic Year: March to December (March-June; August-December).

Admission Requirements: Secondary school certificate and entrance examination.

Language of Instruction: Portuguese.

Degrees and Diplomas: Bacharel and Licenciado; 3-6 yrs. Mestrado, master, a further 2 yrs.

Libraries: Central Library, *c.* 7170 vols; libraries of the centres, *c.* 34,700.

Publication: Catálogo da Produção Técnica-Cientifica e Artistica (annually).

Press or Publishing House: Printing Office.

Academic Staff: c. 250 (330).

Student Enrolment: c. 2510.

428 UNIVERSIDADE FEDERAL RURAL DO RIO DE JANEIRO

Federal Rural University of Rio de Janeiro
Km 47 de Antiga Rodovia Rio/São Paulo, 23460 Seropédica (Rio de Janeiro)
Cables: Unirural
Telex: 21-34411
Telephone: (21) 7821210

I. of Agriculture
I. of Biology
I. of Exact Sciences
I. of Human and Social Sciences (including Home Economics)

I. of Education
I. of Forestry
I. of Technology
I. of Veterinary Science
I. of Animal Husbandry
F. of Teacher Training

Founded 1943 as Universidade Rural do Brasil, acquired present status and title 1965. A State institution under the jurisdiction of and financially supported by the Ministry of Education and Culture. Governing bodies: the Conselho Universitário; the Conselho de Ensino, Pesquisa e Extensão. Residential facilities for academic staff and students.

Academic Year: March to December (March-July; August-December).

Admission Requirements: Secondary school certificate and entrance examination.

Language of Instruction: Portuguese.

Degrees and Diplomas: Licenciado in–Mathematics; Physics; Chemistry; Biology; Home Economics; Physical Education, 4 yrs. Professional titles in–Agriculture; Veterinary Science; Administration; Economics; Geology; Chemical Engineering; Agricultural Sciences; Animal Husbandry; Forestry Engineering, 4 yrs. Mestrado, master, in–Soil Sciences; Veterinary Science, a further 2 yrs. Doctorate in Parasitology, a further 3 yrs.

Library: Central Library, *c.* 46,350 vols.

Publications: Agronomia (bimonthly); Arquivos.

Academic Staff: c. 600.

Student Enrolment: c. 4500.

429 **UNIVERSIDADE FEDERAL DE RONDÔNIA**

Avenida Presidente Dutra 2965, 78900 Pôrto Velho (Rondônia)
Telex: 69-2152
Telephone: (69) 2233262

Economics
Accountancy
Administration

Founded 1982.

430 **UNIVERSIDADE DO SAGRADO CORAÇÃO**

Sacred Heart University
Rua Irma Arminda 1050, Caixa Postal 511 17001 Bauru (São Paulo)
Telex: 142315 ASCJ
Telephone: (142) 232311
Fax: (142) 34-4763
Reitora: Ir. Jacinta Turolo Garcia (1988-92)
Pro-Reitora Academica: Alice Garcia de Morais

Ce. for Human Sciences and Philosophy
Director: Luiza Catharina Della Torre; *staff* 41 (53)
Ce. for Exact and Natural Sciences
Director: Geni da Silva; *staff* 17 (16)
Ce. for Biology and Health Studies
Director: Clea Maria Simões; *staff* 26 (26)
I. of Theology
Director: Jacinta T. Garcia; *staff* 3 (2)

Founded 1953 as faculty, acquired present status and title 1986. A private institution recognized by the federal government and under the supervision of the Instituto das Apostolas do Sagrado Coração de Jesus. Governing bodies: the Conselho Universitário; the Conselho de Ensino, Pesquisa e Extensão

Arrangements for co-operation with the Universities of: Duquesne; Fordham; St. Louis. Pontificia Universitas Urbaniana; Pontificio Ateneo 'Antonianum'.

Academic Year: February to December (February-June; August-December).

Admission Requirements: Secondary school certificate and entrance examination.

Fees (Cruzeiros): 560.82-984.52 per credit per course.

Language of Instruction: Portuguese.

Degrees and Diplomas: Bacharel and Licenciado.

Library: Central Library.

Special Facilities (Museums, etc.): Arboreto; Museu de Zoologia.

Publications: Salusvita (annually); Mimesis (annually): Cadernos Culturais (quarterly); Boletins Culturais (biannually).

Academic Staff, 1990:

Rank	Full-time	Part-time
Professores Titulares	13	–
Professores Adjuntos	9	–
Professores Assistentes	22	53
Professores Auxiliares	40	42
Total	84	95

Student Enrolment, 1990:

	Men	Women	Total
Of the country	659	2754	3413

431 **UNIVERSIDADE CATÓLICA DO SALVADOR**

Catholic University of Salvador
Praça 2 de Julio 7, 40000 Salvador (Bahia)
Telephone: (712) 2452292

I. of Exact and Natural Sciences
I. of Philosophy
I. of Letters
I. of Music
I. of Theology
F. of Education
F. of Nursing
F. of Economics
F. of Law
S. of Engineering
S. of Social Service
S. of Business Administration

Founded 1961.

Degrees and Diplomas: Bacharel em Ciências econômicas, 4 yrs. Bacharel and Licenciado in–Philosophy; Education; Mathematics; Chemistry; Physics; Letters. Professional title of Assistente social, 3 yrs.

Academic Staff: c. 550.

Student Enrolment: c. 11,000.

432 ***UNIVERSIDADE FEDERAL DE SANTA CATARINA**

Federal University of Santa Catarina
Campus Universitário 'Trindade', 88049 Florianópolis (Santa Catarina)
Telex: 0482240
Telephone: (482) 319000
Fax: (482) 344069
Electronic mail: BITNET: listserv@brlncc
Reitor: Bruno Rodolfo Schlemper Júnior (1988-92)
Pró-Reitor de Administração: Fernando Cherem Fonseca

Ce. for Mathematics, Physics, and Chemistry
Director: Wilson Erbs; *staff* 173 (10)
Ce. for Biology
Director: Cândido Geraldo Freitas; *staff* 124 (16)
Ce. for Arts and Communication
Director: Felicio Wessling Margotti; *staff* 137 (22)
Ce. for Human Sciences (including Psychology, Sociology, and Earth Sciences)
Director: Anamaria Beck; *staff* 179 (19)
Ce. for Law
Director: Rogério Stoeterau; *staff* 33 (55)
Ce. for Agriculture and Animal Husbandry
Director: Mário Luiz Vincenzi; *staff* 62 (7)
Ce. for Technology (Mechanical, Civil, and Electrical Engineering, Architecture, and Computer Sciences)
Director: Antàäonio Diomário de Queiróz; *staff* 295 (64)

Ce. for Socio-economic Studies (including Administration)
Director: Mário de Oliveira Azambuja; *staff* 77 (54)
Ce. for Health Sciences (including Dentistry, Pharmacy, Nutrition, Nursing, and Medicine)
Director: Lumar Valmor Bertoli; *staff* 169 (168)
Ce. for Education
Director: Valpi Costa; *staff* 85 (8)
Ce. for Physical Education
Director: Joel Cardoso; *staff* 53 (8)
Extension D.
Director: Jôi Cletison Alves
Regional Ce. for Technology and Computer Sciences
General Superintendent: Carlos Alberto Schneider
Also Technical Schools of Agriculture at Camboriú and Araquari. Hospital Universitário; Núcleo de Desenvolvimento Infantil, Colégio de Aplicação.

Founded 1968 and comprising a number of previously existing faculties. Reorganized 1970 with a structure comprising centres for professional education and centres of basic studies. An autonomous institution financially supported by the State and responsible to the Ministry of Education and Culture. Governing bodies: the Conselho Universitário, comprising 44 members; the Conselho de Ensino, Pesquisa e Extensão, comprising30 members.

Arrangements for co-operation with: Virginia Commonwealth University; University of Guadalajara; University of Aachen; University of Münster; University of Virginia; Virginia Polytechnic Institute and State University; George Mason University, Fairfax; Michigan State University; University of Tennessee at Martin; George Washington University; University of Chile; Universidad de Magallanes, Punta Arenas; University of Morón; University of the Republic, Montevideo; University of Bordeaux I; University of Venice; National University of Tucumán; National University of Lomas de Zamora; Technical University of Lisbon; University of Minho; University of the Azores; State University of Mons; University of Buenos Aires; University of San Simón, Cochabamba; Italian University for Foreigners, Perugia; Institut National Polytechnique de Lorraine, Nancy; University of Cape Coast; Université nationale de Côte d'Ivoire; Universidad Nacional de Rosário; Universidad de Concepción, Chile; Universidad Nacional de Asunción, Paraguay; Universidad Nacional de Ingeniería, Peru; Universidad de Habana; Universidad Catàolica de Valparaíso; Universidad Nacional de Entre Rios, Argentina; Universidad Autónoma de México; Universidad Nacional de Costa Rica; Universidad del Valle, Colombia; Instituto Tecnológico deSanto Domingo; Universidad Metropolitana, México; Universidad de Antofagasta, Chile; Universidad del Caúca; Universidad del Norte, Antofagasta; Universidad Tecnológica de Santiago de Los Caballeros; University of Texas at Austin; Radford University, Virginia; Universit de Technologie de Compiègne; Université de l'Etat de Liège; Institut national polytechnique de Toulouse; Universidade de Lisboa; Universidade do Porto; Universidade Nova de Lisboa; Università Cattólica del Sacro Cuore, Milan; Université de Strasbourg II; Università degli Studi di Camerino; Southeast University, China; Hohay University, China;

Academic Year: March to December (March-June; August-December).

Admission Requirements: Secondary school certificate and entrance examination.

Fees (Cruzeiros): Tuition, none.

Language of Instruction: Portuguese.

Degrees and Diplomas: Bacharel and Licenciado, 3-4 yrs. Professional titles in–Library Science, 3 ½ yrs; Law; Administration; Economics; Accountancy; Dentistry; Nutrition; Nursing; Social Work; Engineering, (various fields); Architecture; Computer Sciences; Journalism; Agriculture, 4-5 yrs; Medicine, 6 yrs. Mestrado, master, in–Mechanical Engineering; Production and Systems Engineering; Electrical Engineering; Chemistry; Dentistry; Nursing; Letters (English and Portuguese); Mathematics; History; Law; Administration; Social Sciences; History; Mathematics. Doutorado, doctorate–in Mechanical Engineering; Electrical Engineering; Law; English and Portuguese Letters.

Library: Central Library and branch libraries, *c.* 250,000 vols.

Special Facilities (Museums, etc.): Anthropology Museum; Marine Museum; Biological Garden; Art Gallery; Movie Studies; Observatory.

Publications: Travessia (biannually); Revista de Ciências de Saúde (biannually); Revista do Centro de Língua e Literatura Estrangeira (biannually).

Press or Publishing House: Editora da Universidade.

Academic Staff, 1990:

Rank	Full-time	Part-time
Professores Titulares	139	33
Professores Adjuntos	855	292
Professores Assistentes	287	43
Professores Auxiliares	95	42
Professores Visitantes	11	1
Total	1387	411

Student Enrolment, 1990:

	Men	Women	Total
Of the country	6726	4897	11,623
Of other countries	49	16	65
Total	6775	4913	11,688

433 ***UNIVERSIDADE PARA O DESENVOLVIMENTO DO ESTADO DE SANTA CATARINA**
Santa Catarina State's Development University
Madre Benvenuta 499, 88000 Florianópolis (Santa Catarina)
Telex: 48-2485
Telephone: (482) 34-2000/34-1868

F. of Education
Director: Octacílio Schüller Sobrinho; *staff* 40 (51)
F. of Engineering
Director: Luiz Dalla Valentina; *staff* 75 (53)
F. of Agriculture and Veterinary Medicine
Director: Sérgio João Dalagnol; *staff* 69 (32)
S. of Physical Education
Director: Marino Tessari; *staff* 18 (22)
F. of Administration
Director: Gilson Luiz Leal de Meireles; *staff* 16 (27)
F. of Arts
Director: Milton Luiz Valente; *staff* 31 (23)
Technical I. of Administration and Management
Director: Gilberto Dias; *staff* 5
Educational Studies and Research Ce.
Director: Maria Aparecida Lemos Silva

Founded 1965. A multi-campus, public institutions maintained by the Santa Catarina Sate government. Governing bodies: the Conselho Universitário; the Conselho de Ensina, Pequisa e Extensão.

Arrangements for co-operation with: University of Hanover; Guelph University.

Academic Year: March to December (March-June; August-December).

Admission Requirements: Secondary school certificate and entrance examination.

Fees: None.

Language of Instruction: Portuguese.

Degrees and Diplomas: Bacharel and Licenciado, 4 yrs. Mestre, a further 2-4 yrs. Postgraduate diplomas and specializations.

Library: Total, 41,416 vols.

Special Facilities (Museums, etc.): Art Gallery

Publication: Universidade e Desenvolovimento (cultural and scientic journal).

Academic Staff, 1989: 243 (207).

Student Enrolment, 1989: 3915.

434 **UNIVERSIDADE SANTA CECÍLIA DOS BANDEIRANTES**
Rua Oswaldo Cruz 250, 11100 Santos (São Paulo)
Telephone: (132) 344925
Reitor: Milton Teixeira (1986-)
Diretora-Coordenadora: Lúcia Maria Teixeira Furlani

F. of Plastic Arts
Director: Aquelino José Vasques; *staff* 35 (54)
F. of Science and Technology
Director: Roberto Patella; *staff* 39 (71)
F. of Civil Engineering
Director: Antonio de Salles Penteado; *staff* 42 (63)
F. of Industrial Engineering
Director: Richard Ocaña Zangari; *staff* 63 (92)
F. of Physical Education
Director: Rubens Flávio de Siqueira Viegas Jr.; *staff* 27 (33)
F. of Commerce and Administration
Director: Manoel Claudius Gomes Pereira; *staff* 35 (38)

F. of Education and Human Sciences
Director: Domingos Consistre Rocca Netto; *staff* 28 (32)
F. of Dentistry
Director: Donato Luiz Perillo; *staff* 62 (83)
Computer Ce.
Director: César Augusto Furlani; *staff* 8 (5)
Extension D.
Co-ordinator: João Abel da Cunha; *staff* 2 (6)

Founded 1961 as College, became Instituto Superior de Educação Santa Cecilia 1969 and acquired present status and title 1986. A private institution recognized by the federal government and administered by the Sociedа Universitária de Santos.

Arrangements for co-operation with: University of Córdoba, Buenos Aires; University of Salvador, Buenos Aires; University of Pittsburgh; University of Minho.

Academic Year: February to December (February-June; August-December).

Admission Requirements: Secondary school certificate and entrance examination.

Fees (Cruzeiros): 800-1500.

Language of Instruction: Portuguese.

Degrees and Diplomas: Bacharel in–Computer Sciences; Biology; Business Administration; Administration, 4 yrs. Licenciado in–Artistic Education, 2 yrs; Science; Social Studies; Physical Education; Education, 3 yrs. Professional titles of–Desenhista industrial; Comunicação visual, 4 yrs; Engenheiro (various fields), 5-6 yrs; Cirurgião dentista, 5 yrs.

Library: Biblioteca 'Martins Fontes', 45,431 vols.

Special Facilities (Museums, etc.): Museu de Conchas; Museu Didático e do Folclore.

Academic Staff, 1986-87:

Rank	Full-time	Part-time
Professores Titulares	89	182
Professores Adjuntos	59	167
Professores Assistentes	157	94
Total	305	443

Student Enrolment, 1986-87:

	Men	Women	Total
Of the country	6386	2654	9040
Of other countries	23	19	42
Total	6409	2673	9082

435 *UNIVERSIDADE FEDERAL DE SANTA MARIA

Federal University of Santa Maria
Cidade Universitária Km 9, 97100 Santa Maria (Rio Grande do Sul)
Telex: 55-2230
Telephone: (55) 2261616
Reitor: Tabajara Gaucho da Costa
Chefe de Gabinete: Antonio Carlos Machado

Ce. for Natural and Exact Sciences
Director: Higidio Menegotto; *staff* 9
Ce. for Technology (Civil, Electrical, Chemical, and Mechanical Engineering)
Director: Erico Ant. Lopes Hehn
Ce. for Health Sciences (including Nursing, Dentistry, Pharmacy, and Medicine)
DIrector: Edson Nunes de Moraes
Ce. for Rural Sciences (Forestry, Agriculture, Veterinary Medicine, and Animal Husbandry)
Director: Enio Tanini *staff* 66 (90)
Ce. for Social and Human Sciences (including Law, Economics, Administration, and Philosophy)
Director: José Antonio Fernandes; *staff* 66 (100)
Ce. for Arts and Letters
Director: Ivone Mendes Richter
Ce. for Education
Director: Clovis R.J. Guterres
Ce. for Physical Education
Director: Aluisio Otavio V. Avila

Founded 1961, incorporating a number of existing faculties created since 1931. Reorganized 1970 with a structure comprising centres for professional education. A State institution under the jurisdiction of the Ministry of Education and Culture. Governing bodies: the Conselho Universitário; the Conselho de Curadores; the Conselho de Ensino, Pesquisa e Extensão. Residential facilities for academic staff and students.

Academic Year: March to December (March-July; August-December).

Admission Requirements: Secondary school certificate and entrance examination.

Language of Instruction: Portuguese.

Degrees and Diplomas: Bacharel in–Economics; Accountancy; Law; Philosophy; Communication, 4 yrs. Licenciado in–Physical Education; Physics; Geography; History; Mathematics; Chemistry; Education; Biology; Letters, 3 yrs; Industrial Chemistry; Plastic Arts; Music, 4 yrs. Professional titles of–Farmacêutico; Fonoaudiôlogo, 3 yrs; Cirurgião dentista; Médico veterinário; Zootecnista, animal husbandry; Agrónomo; Engenheiro florestal, forestry, 4 yrs; Engenheiro (various fields), 5 yrs; Médico, 6 yrs. Mestrado, master, in–Education; Agriculture; Rural Engineering; Agricultural Education; Animal Science; Veterinary Medicine; Electrical Engineering; Mechanical Engineering.

Library: c. 71,290 vols.

Special Facilities (Museums, etc.): Museu Educativo 'Gama D'Eça'.

Publications: Boletim de Pessoal; Revista do Centro de Ciências Pedagógicas; Revista do Centro de Tecnologia; Revista doCurso de Farmácia; Revista Ciências Biomédicas e Ciências Rurais; O Quero-Quero.

Academic Staff: c. 1360.

Student Enrolment: c. 9700.

436 *UNIVERSIDADE DE SANTA ÚRSULA

University Santa Úrsula
Rua Fernando Ferrari 75, 22231 Rio de Janeiro (Rio de Janeiro)
Telex: 21-34929
Telephone: (21) 5515542
Reitora: Maria de Fatima Maron Ramos

Ce. for Theology and Philosophy
Ce. for Human and Social Sciences (including Law and Psychology)
Ce. for Education
Ce. for Biology and Nutrition
Ce. for Library Science and Literature
Ce. for Exact Sciences and Technology
Ce. for Architecture and Arts
I. of Applied Psychology
Also high school.

Founded 1938 by the Ursulines as Catholic faculty of education, science, and letters. Recognized as a university 1975. A private institution under the supervision of the Associação Universitária Santa Úrsula. Governing bodies: the Conselho Superior de Administração; the Conselho Universitário; the Conselho de Ensino e Pesquisa.

Academic Year: March to November (March-June; August-November).

Admission Requirements: Secondary school certificate and entrance examination.

Language of Instruction: Portuguese.

Degrees and Diplomas: Bacharel in–Library Science; Business Administration; Accountancy; Biology; Mathematics; History; Letters, 3-4 yrs; Psychology; Law, 5 yrs. Licenciado in–Education; Biology; Psychology; Letters; Mathematics; History, 3-4 yrs. Professional titles in–Nutrition; Psychology; Architecture; Engineering, 4-5 yrs.

Libraries: Central Library, c. 62,820 vols; Theology, c. 350; Biology (2), c. 6540.

Publications: Boletim; Espaço-Cadernos de Cultura; Série Documentos e Letra (biannually).

Press or Publishing House: Serviço Gráfico.

Academic Staff: c. 760.

Student Enrolment: c. 10,100.

437 UNIVERSIDADE CATÓLICA DE SANTOS

Rua Euclides da Cunha 241, 11060 Santos (São Paulo)
Telex: 13-1978
Telephone: (132) 373435

Administration
Architecture
Science
Biology
Accountancy
Economics
Law
Nursing
Social Studies
Philosophy
Geography, History and Letters
Applied Mathematics

Education

Founded 1954. A private institution under the jurisdiction of the Sociedade Visconde de São Leopoldo.

438 **UNIVERSIDADE FEDERAL DE SÃO CARLOS**
Federal University of São Carlos
Rodovia Washington Luiz, Km. 235, 13560 São Carlos (São Paulo)
Telex: 16-2369
Telephone: (162) 71 1100
Fax: (162) 71 2081
Reitor: Sebastião Elias Kuri (1989-90)
Vice-Reitor: Newton Lima Reto

Ce. for Education and Human Sciences
Director: Pericles Trevisan
Ce. for Science and Technology
Director: Gilberto Della Nina
Ce. for Health Sciences and Biology
Director: Francisco Tadeu Rantim

Founded 1960 as Universidade Federal de São Paulo, acquired present title 1968. A State institution under the jurisdiction of the Ministry of Education and Culture. Governing body: the Conselho Universitário.

Academic Year: March to December (March-June; August-December).

Admission Requirements: Secondary school certificate and entrance examination.

Language of Instruction: Portuguese.

Degrees and Diplomas: Bacharel in–Biology; Chemistry; Physics; Mathematics; Computer Sciences; Statistics; Nursing, 4 yrs. Licenciado in–Biology; Chemistry; Mathematics; Physics; Education; Nursing, 4 yrs. Professional titles in–Physiotherapy; Occupational Therapy, 4 yrs; Engineering, 5 yrs. Mestrado, master, 2-3 yrs. Doutorado, 4-5 yrs.

Library: Central Library, *c.* 60,000 vols.

Special Facilities (Museums, etc.): Biological Garden.

Publication: Annual Report.

Press or Publishing House: Editora da Universidade Federal de São Carlos (EDUFSCAR).

Academic Staff, 1989: c. 500.

Student Enrolment, 1989: c. 2460.

439 **UNIVERSIDADE SÃO FRANCISCO**
Saint Francis University
Avenida Francisco de Assis 218, 12900 Bragança Paulista (São Paulo)
Telex: 11-79949
Telephone: (11) 4331500
Fax: (11) 433 1825
Reitor: Frei Constancio Nogara, O.F.M. (1989-93)
Secretário Geral: José Enio Triervailer

F. of Law
Director: José Nicola Jannuzzi
F. of Pharmacy
Director: José Antonio Garcia Sanches
F. of Medical Sciences
Director: José Luis Leon Ramirez
F. of Philosophy, Science and Literature
Director: Pythágoras de Alecar Olivotti
F. of Human Sciences (including Arts and Psychology)
Director: Konrad Lindmeier
F. of Economics and Administration
Director: Alcebíades Vieira
F. of Odontology
Director: Rossine Amorim Maciel
F. of Engineering
Director: Adilson Franco Penteado
F. of Education and Social Sciences
Director: Izabel Cristina Petraglia
F. of Business and Administration
Director: Hilda Maria Cordeiro
F. of Juridical Sciences
Director: Gilberto Sant'Anna
F. of Administrative and Exact Sciences
Director: Vania Franciscon Vieira
I. of Anthropology
Co-ordinator: Frei Agostino Salvador Picollo

Founded 1967 as institute, became Faculdades Franciscanas 1976 and acquired present status and title 1985. A private institution recognized by the federal government and under the supervision of the Casa de Nossa Senhorada Paz Acão Social Franciscana. There are 3 campuses (Bragança Paulista; Itatiba; São Paulo). Governing bodies: the Conselho Universitário; the Conselho de Ensino, Pesquisa e Extensão.

Academic Year: February to December (February-June; August-December).

Admission Requirements: Secondary school certificate and entrance examination.

Language of Instruction: Portuguese.

Degrees and Diplomas: Bacharel in–Law; Accountancy; Business Administration, 4 yrs; Economics, 5 yrs. Licenciado in–Education; Biology; Literature; Mathematics Science, 3 yrs; Pharmacy and Biochemistry; History and Geography, 4 yrs; Psychology, 4-5 yrs. Professional titles of–Cirurgião Dentista, dental surgery; Analista de Sistemas, systems analysis, 4 yrs; Engenheiro, engineering, 5-6 yrs; Médico, medicine, 6 yrs.

Library: Total, 61,136 vols.

Publication: Revista (3 times a year).

Press or Publishing House: Departamento Gráfico.

Academic Staff, 1990:

Rank	Full-time	Part-time
Professores Titulares	6	61
Professores Adjuntos	10	48
Professores Assistentes	26	272
Professores Auxiliares	6	210
Instructores	10	8
Total	58	599

Student Enrolment, 1990:

	Men	Women	Total
Of the country	5811	4029	9840
Of other countries	90	20	110
Total	5901	4049	9950

440 **UNIVERSIDADE SÃO JUDAS TADEU**
Rua Taquari 546, 31660 São Paulo (São Paulo)
Telephone: (11) 9481677
Reitor: José Christiano Altenfelder Silva Mesquita

F. of Letters, Arts, Communication and Education
Director: Lilian Brando Garcia Mesquita
F. of Biology and Health Sciences
Director: Emilio Atilo Marino
F. of Exact Sciences and Technology
Director: Roberto Batisa Mesquita
F. of Human Sciences (including Psychology, Administration, Economics, and Accountancy)
Director: José Reinaldo Altenfelder Silva Mesquita

Founded 1971 as Faculdades, acquired present title 1989.

Academic Year: February to December.

Admission Requirements: Secondary school certificate and entrance examinition.

Language of Instruction: Portuguese.

Degrees and Diplomas: Bacharel, 4-5 yrs.

Library: c. 110,000 vols.

Academic Staff, 1990: 369.

Student Enrolment, 1990:

	Men	Women	Total
Of the country	7264	5561	19,825

441 ***UNIVERSIDADE DE SÃO PAULO**
University of São Paulo
Rua da Reitoria 109, 05508 São Paulo (São Paulo)
Cables: C.P. 8191
Telex: 11-36950
Telephone: (11) 2110011
Reitor: Roberto Leal Lobo e Silva Filho

S. of Law
Polytechnic S.
S. of Engineering (São Carlos)
S. of Medicine
S. of Public Health
S. of Nursing
S. of Nursing (Ribeirão Prêto)
S. of Communications and Arts
S. of Agriculture (Piracicaba)
S. of Medicine (Ribeirão Prêto)

S. of Philosophy, Languages, and Human Sciences
S. of Philosophy, Science and Letters (Ribeirão Prêto)
S. of Pharmacy and Biochemistry
S. of Veterinary Medicine and Animal Husbandry
S. of Economics and Business Administration
S. of Architecture and Town Planning
S. of Education
S. of Dentistry
S. of Dentistry (Bauru)
S. of Physical Education
S. of Pharmacy and Dentistry (Ribeirão Prêto)
I. of Astronomy and Geophysics
I. of Mathematics and Statistics
I. of Biology
I. of Earth Sciences
I. of Physics
I. of Biomedical Sciences
I. of Oceanography
I. of Chemistry
I. of Psychology
I. of Physics and Chemistry (São Carlos)
I. of Mathematics (São Carlos)

Founded 1934. An autonomous institution under the jurisdiction of and financially supported by the State of São Paulo. Governing bodies: the Conselho Universitário, including the directors of the institutes and representatives of the academic staff and of the students; the Conselho de Ensino, Pesquisa e Extensão.

Arrangements for co-operation with the Universities of: Texas at Austin; Nihon; Osaka; Lagos; Ife; Abidjan; Benin; Guinea-Bissau; Lomé; Tsukuba; Angola; Tokyo; Laval; Indiana; Mexico; Chile; New Mexico; College of Chinese Culture, Taipei.

Academic Year: March to November (March-June; August-November).

Admission Requirements: Secondary school certificate and entrance examination.

Fees: None.

Language of Instruction: Portuguese.

Degrees and Diplomas: Bacharel in–Economics; Accountancy; Philosophy; Science, and Letters, 4 yrs; Law and Social Science, 5 yrs. Licenciado in Philosophy, Science, and Letters. Doutor in–Agriculture; Law and Social Science; Pharmacy and Biochemistry; Philosophy; Science and Letters; Public Health; Medicine. Professional titles in–Nursing, 3 yrs; Dentistry, 4 yrs; Engineering (various fields); Agriculture; Geology; Architecture; Pharmacy; Veterinary Medicine, 5 yrs; Medicine, 6 yrs.

Library: c. 786,010 vols.

Special Facilities (Museums, etc.): Museums of: Archaeology and Ethnology; Contemporary Art; Zoology.

Publications: Revistas; Boletims; Jornals; Anuários.

Press or Publishing House: University Press.

Academic Staff: c. 4750.

Student Enrolment: c. 44,200.

442 PONTIFÍCIA UNIVERSIDADE CATÓLICA DE SÃO PAULO

Pontifical Catholic University of São Paulo
984 Rua Monte Alegre, Perdizes, 05014 São Paulo (São Paulo)
Telephone: (11) 2630211

Ce. for Human Sciences (including Social Sciences, Social Work,) Communications and Philosophy, and Psychology
Ce. for Education
Ce. for Biomedical Sciences (including Nursing)
Ce. for Law, Economics and Business Administration
I. of Special Studies
I. of Studies of the Deaf
I. of Urban Planning
African-Brazilian Research I.

Founded 1946, incorporating extra faculties including Faculty of Science, Philosophy and Literature, founded 1908, by the Episcopate of the Province of São Paulo and recognized by government decree. The title of Pontifical University was conferred in 1947. Academic structure reorganized 1976. The university is responsible to the Fundação São Paulo with the Cardinal Archbishop of São Paulo as Grand Chancellor. Governing bodies: the Conselho Superior; the Conselho Universitário.

Academic Year: March to November (March-June; August-November).

Admission Requirements: Secondary school certificate and entrance examination.

Language of Instruction: Portuguese.

Degrees and Diplomas: Bacharel and Licenciado in all fields, 4 yrs, except Law, 5 yrs; Psychology; Medicine, 6 yrs. Mestrado, 1 further yr. Doutor by thesis.

Libraries: Central Library, *c.* 92,850 vols; Biomedical library; Exact Sciences library.

Publications: Revista da Universidade Católica de São Paulo; Prandubas; Boletim (monthly).

Academic Staff: c. 1530.

Student Enrolment: c. 15,930.

443 *UNIVERSIDADE FEDERAL DE SERGIPE

Federal University of Sergipe
Campus Universitário, 49100 São Cristovão (Sergipe)
Telex: 79-2189
Telephone: (79) 2241331
Reitor: Clodoaldo de Alencar Filho (1988-92)

Ce. for Exact Sciences and Technology
Director: Djalma Andrade; *staff* 90 (20)
Ce. for Biological and Health Sciences (including Medicine, Dentistry, Nursing, and Physical Education)
Director: Delso Bringel Calheiros; *staff* 111 (58)
Ce. for Applied Social Sciences (including Administration, Accountancy, Economics, Law, and Social Service)
Director: Roberto Rodrigues dos Santos; *staff* 78 (19)
Ce. for Education and Human Sciences
Director: Joelina Menezes de Souza; *staff* 127 (4)

Founded 1968. Reorganized 1978 with a structure comprising centres for professional education. An autonomous institution but financially supported by the State and responsible to the Ministry of Education and Culture. Governing bodies: the Conselho Universitário; the Conselho do Ensino e da Pesquisa. Residential facilities for students.

Academic Year: March to December (March-June; August-December).

Admission Requirements: Secondary school certificate.

Language of Instruction: Portuguese.

Degrees and Diplomas: Bacharel in–Biology; Physics; Geography; Chemistry; Social Service, 4 yrs; Law, 5 yrs; Administration; Accountancy; Economics, 6 yrs. Licenciado in–Biology; Physics; Geography; History; Mathematics; Education; Chemistry; Letters, 4 yrs. Professional titles of–Químico industrial, 4 yrs; Cirurgião dentista, 4 ½ yrs; Enfermeiro, nursing; Engenheiro civil; Engenheiro químico, 5 yrs. Mestrado, master.

Library: Central Library, *c.* 79,127 vols.

Special Facilities (Museums, etc.): Museu de Antropologia.

Publication: Geonordeste.

Academic Staff, 1989-90:

Rank	Full-time	Part-time
Titulares	87	21
Adjuntos	113	16
Assistentes	128	21
Auxiliares	78	43
Total	406	101

Student Enrolment, 1989:

Men	Women	Total
2798	2798	5596

444 UNIVERSIDADE ESTADUAL DO SUDOESTE DA BAHIA

Bahia Southwest State University
Estrada do Bem-Querer, Km. 4, 45100 Vitória da Conquista (Bahia)
Telephone: 422-1143

C. of Teacher Training
S. of Business Administration
S. of Agriculture
S. of Animal Husbandry (Itapetinga)
C. of Nursing and Midwifery (Jequié)
C. of Teacher Training (Jequié)

Founded 1980, incorporating previously existing Faculties. Recognized by the federal government 1987.

Academic Year: March to December (March-July; September-January).

Admission Requirements: Secondary school certificate and entrance examination.

Language of Instruction: Portuguese.

Degrees and Diplomas: Bacharel and Licenciado, 4-5 yrs.

Library: Total, 28,461 vols.

Academic Staff, 1990: 304.

Student Enrolment, 1990: 1500.

445 **UNIVERSIDADE DE TAUBATÉ**
University of Taubaté
Rua 4 de Marco 432, 12100 Taubaté (São Paulo)
Telex: 12-2251
Telephone: (122) 327555

F. of Social Service
F. of Philosophy, Science, and Letters
F. of Economics and Administration
F. of Law
S. of Physical Education
S. of Engineering
Founded 1976. A municipal institution.

Other Institutions

Private Institutions

446 **FACULDADE DE SERVIÇO SOCIALE DE SAÚDE**
Rua Itororo 800, Centro, 89500 Caçador (Santa Catarina)
Telephone: (49) 6620536

Social work
Health Studies
Founded 1977.

Universities

447 ***UNIVERSIDADE FEDERAL DE UBERLÂNDIA**
Federal University of Uberlândia
Avenida Engenheiro Diniz 1178, 38400 Uberlândia (Minas Gerais)
Telex: 34-3264
Telephone: (34) 2350355
Reitor: Ataulfo Marques Martins da Costa (1984-)
Vice-Reitor: Geraldo de Carvalho

Ce. for Biomedical Sciences (including Veterinary Medicine and Dentistry)
Director: Luiz Mário G. Gonçalves; *staff* 294 (16)
Ce. for Exact Sciences and Technology
Director: Francisco Paulo L. Neto; *staff* 204 (19)
Ce. for Human Sciences and Arts
Director: Marly Bernardes de Araújo; *staff* 372 (24)
S. of Physical Education

Founded 1969, incorporating a number of previously existing faculties. Recognized as a federal institution 1978. Governing body: the Conselho Universitário.

Arrangements for co-operation with Ohio State University.

Academic Year: March to December (March-June; August-December).

Admission Requirements: Secondary school certificate or equivalent, and entrance examination.

Language of Instruction: Portuguese.

Degrees and Diplomas: Bacharel in–Administration; Accountancy; Economics; Law; Psychology, 4-7 yrs. Licenciado in–Science; Design and Plastic Arts; Art; Physical Education; Social Studies; Geography; History; Letters; Music; Education, 2-7 yrs. Professional titles in–Visual Communication; Decoration; Engineering, various fields; Music; Medicine; Veterinary Medicine; Dentistry, 4-9 yrs.

Library: Total, 78,032 vols.

Publications: Informativo da Reitoria; Revistas: Letras e Letras; Economia; Psicologia e Trãnsito; Centro de Ciências Biomédicas; Curso de Direito.

Press or Publishing House: Editora da Universidade.

Academic Staff, 1984-85:

Rank	Full-time	Part-time
Professores Titulares	327	29
Professores Adjuntos	319	13
Professores Assistentes	158	8
Auxiliares de Ensino	66	8
Total	870	58

Student Enrolment, 1986-87:

	Men	Women	Total
Of the country	3357	3347	6704
Of other countries	9	6	15
Total	3366	3353	6719

448 **UNIVERSIDADE DO VALE DO ITAJAÍ**
Rua Uruguai 458, 88300 Itajaí (Santa Catarina)
Telex: 471113
Telephone: (473) 44-1500
Reitor: Edison Villela

F. of Administration, Economics and Accountancy
Director: Marília Soares; *staff* 3 (44)
F. of Law and Social Sciences
Director: Ronaldo Silva; *staff* 5 (34)
F. of Tourism and Hotel Administration
Director: Marlene Buratto; *staff* 3 (5)
F. of Nursing and Midwifery
Director: Agueda Lenita W. dos Santos; *staff* 22 (22)
F. of Philosophy, Science and Letters
Director: Benedito Galatto; *staff* 8 (72)
F. of Dentistry
Director: Telmoo Mezadri; *staff* 2 (8)
F. of Psychology
Director: Pedro Antônio Geraldi; *staff* 2 (8)

Founded 1989, incorporating previously existing faculties. Under the supervision of the municipal authorities. Governing bodies: the Conselho Universitário; the Conselho de Ensino, Pesquisa e Extensão.

Academic Year: February to December (February-June; July-December).

Admission Requirements: Secondary school certificate or equivalent, and entrance examination.

Language of Instruction: Portuguese.

Degrees and Diplomas: Bacharel and Licenciado, 4 yrs.

Academic Staff, 1990: 45 (203).

Student Enrolment, 1990:

	Men	Women	Total
Of the country	2092	2405	4497
Of other countries	29	80	109
Total	2121	2485	4606

449 **UNIVERSIDADE DO VALE DO RIO DOS SINOS**
Sinos Valley University
Avenida Unisinos 950, 93020 São Leopoldo (Rio Grande do Sul)
Telex: 524076 SAVS
Telephone: (512) 926333
Fax: (512) 921035
Reitor: Aloysio Bohnen (1990-93)
Registrar: José Marculano

Ce. for Education and Human Sciences
Director: José Jacinto da F. Lara
Ce. for Communication Studies (including Letters, Journalism, Public Relations)
Director: Aday M. Tesche
Ce. for Biomedical Studies (Biology, Nursing, Psychology, Nutrition)
Director: Carlos A. Wieck
Ce. for Juridical Studies
Director: Antonio P.C. de Medeiros
Ce. for Economic Studies
Director: Ernani Ott
Ce. for Exact Sciences
Director: Suzana S.C. Gianotti
Ce. for Technological Studies (Engineering, Geology, Architecture)
Director: Vicente de P.O. Sant'Anna
I. of Research (History, Archaeology, Botany)
Director: Pedro Ignácio Schmitz

I. of Planarian Research
Director: Josef Hauser
Ce. for Documentation and Research (Co-operativism, Religion and Society, Rural Development, Demography, Ecology)
Director: José Ivo Follmann
Technological Ce. (Antartic Studies (Geology), Sediment Fields, Architecture)
Director: Vicente P.O. Sant'Anna
Ce. for Biomedical Research
Director: Carlos Alberto Wieck

Founded 1954 as Faculdade de Filosofia, Ciências e Letras and operated under the direction of the Society of Jesus. Became university by government decree 1969. Reorganized 1970 with a structure comprising centres for professional education. An autonomous institution under the jurisdiction of the Ministry of Education and Culture. Governing bodies: the Conselho Superior de Administração; the Conselho Universitário; the Conselho de Ensino e Pesquisa.

Academic Year: March to December (March-July; August-December).

Admission Requirements: Secondary school certificate and entrance examination.

Fees (Cruzeiros): 1,093 per credit, per semester.

Language of Instruction: Portuguese.

Degrees and Diplomas: Bacharel in–Accountancy; Social Sciences; Law; Economics, 4-5 yrs. Licenciado in–Philosophy; Social Science; Biology; Letters, 4 yrs. Professional titles in–Education; School Supervision; Biology; Nursing; Nutrition; Psychology; Journalism; Public Relations; Business Administration; Foreign Trade; Physics; Mathematics; Data Processing; Architecture; Engineering; Geology, 3-5 ½ yrs.

Library: Central Library, *c.* 474,000 vols.

Special Facilities (Museums, etc.): Museums: Zoology, Botany, Geology, Archaeology. Audio-visual Centre; TV and Radio Studio.

Publications: Estudos Leopoldenses; Pesquisas; Perspectiva Teológica; Estudos Jurídicos; Vale do Rio dos Sinos, Estudos Tecnológicos; Perspectiva Econômica; Verso e Reverso.

Press or Publishing House: Gráfica Unisinos.

Academic Staff, 1990:

Rank	Full-time	Part-time
Professores Titulares	33	32
Professores Adjuntos	27	104
Professores Assistentes	32	288
Auxiliares de Ensino	5	379
Total	97	803

Student Enrolment, 1990:

	Men	Women	Total
Of the country	11.303	11,728	23,031
Of other countries	42	37	79
Total	11,345	11,765	23,110

450 ***UNIVERSIDADE FEDERAL DE VIÇOSA**
Federal University of Viçosa
Avenida Peter Henry Rolfs, s/n 36570 Viçosa (Minas Gerais)
Telex: 31-1587
Telephone: (31) 8992921/8992103
Fax: (31) 899 2108
Reitor: Geraldo Martins Chaves
Diretor: Geraldo Galdino de Paula Jr.

Ce. for Exact Sciences and Technology (including Food Technology)
Director: Laede Maffia de Oliveira; *staff* 164 (6)
Ce. for Biological and Health Sciences (including Nutrition and Veterinary Science)
Director: Evaldo Ferreira Vilela; *staff* 157 (3)
Ce. for Humanities, Letters and Arts
Director: Juraci Aureliano Teixeira; *staff* 117 (2)
Ce. for Agriculture (including Animal Husbandry and Forestry)
Director: Carlos Sigueyuki Sediyama; *staff* 215 (2)
Ce. for Research, Experimentation and Extension (Minas Tringle)
Director: Sebastião Luis de A.Filho; *staff* 3
Ce. for Grain Storage Training
Director: Alexandre Aad Neto; *staff* 10
Also elementary and high schools.

Founded 1927 as College of Agriculture, became Universidade Rural do Estado de Minas Gerais 1948 by State decree. Reorganized as a federal university with present title 1969. Governing bodies: the Conselho Universitário; the Conselho de Coordenação de Ensino, Pesquisa e Extensão; the Conselho de Curadores. Some residential facilities for academic staff and over 1380 students.

Academic Year: February to November (February-June; August-November).

Admission Requirements: Secondary school certificate and entrance examination.

Fees (Cruzeiros): 167.56 per month.

Language of Instruction: Portuguese.

Degrees and Diplomas: Bacharel and Licenciado, 2 ½-8 yrs. Professional titles, 4-9 yrs. Magister Scientiae, a further 1-4 yrs. Doctor Scientiae, 2-6 yrs.

Library: Central Library, *c.* 141,217 vols.

Special Facilities (Museums, etc.): Museum.

Publications: Revista Ceres; Experientiae.

Press or Publishing House: Imprensa Universitária.

Academic Staff, 1990:

Rank	Full-time	Part-time
Professores Titulares	93	1
Professores Adjuntos	177	5
Professores Assistentes	306	5
Professores Auxiliares	71	2
Total	647	13

Student Enrolment, 1990:

Men	Women	Total
3421	2095	5516

Other Institutions

Public Institutions

451 **CENTRO BRASILEIRO DE PESQUISAS FÍSICAS**
Brazilian Centre for Research in Physics
Rua Dr Xavier Sigaud, 150, 2290 Rio de Janeiro (Rio de Janeiro)
Telex: (21) 22563 CBPQ
Telephone: (21) 2959044/2959643
Fax: (21) 5412047
Electronic mail: BITNET: cbpf lncc
Diretor: Amos Troper

Physics

Founded 1949. A research centre under the National Council for Scientific and Technological Development (CNPq), a federal goverment institution.

Academic Year: March to November (March-June; August-November).

Admission Requirements: Degree of Bacharel.

Language of Instruction: Portuguese.

Degrees and Diplomas: Mestre. Doctorado.

Library: 68,389 vols.

Academic Staff, 1989: 104.

Student Enrolment, 1989:

	Men	Women	Total
Of the country	82	11	93
Of other countries	5	1	6
Total	87	12	99

452 **CENTRO DE EDUCAÇÃO TÉCNICA DA UTRAMIG**
Avenida Afonsa Peña 3400, 30000 Belo Horizonte (Minas Gerais)
Telephone: (31) 2213677

Education (Technology)

Founded 1966.

453 **CENTRO DE EDUCAÇÃO TÉCNICA DA BAHIA**
Estradas das Barreiras s/n, 40000 Salvador (Bahia)
Telephone: (71) 2311546

Industrial Design
Social Communication

Accountancy

Founded 1980. Under the jurisdiction of the Universidade do Estado da Bahia.

454 **CENTRO DE EDUCAÇÃO TECNOLÓGICA DA BAHIA**

Via Universitária, 43700 Simões Filho (Bahia)
Telex: 712335 CETF BR
Telephone: (71) 5948400

Petrochemical Engineering
Mechanical Engineering
Electrical Engineering
Electronics
Telecommunications
Hotel Administration

Founded 1976. Under the jurisdiction of the federal Ministry of Education and Culture.

455 **CENTRO DE ENSINO SUPERIOR DO VALE DO SÃO FRANCISCO**

Avenida Colonel Trapia 202, 56440 Belém do São Francisco (Pernambuco)
Telephone: (81) 9361248
Diretora: Fátima Maria Bezerra Caribé (1984-88)
Secretária: Maria Gorete Belfort Lustosa

Education

Founded 1976 by the municipal authorities as Faculdade de Formação de Professores de Primeiro Grau. Acquired present status and title 1985.

Academic Year: March to November (March-July; August-November).

Admission Requirements: Secondary school certificate and entrance examination.

Language of Instruction: Portuguese.

Degrees and Diplomas: Licenciado in–History; Geography; Letters, 4 yrs.

Library: c. 5000 vols.

Academic Staff, 1986-87: 14 (5).

Student Enrolment, 1986-87:

	Men	Women	Total
Of the country	95	507	602

456 **CENTRO FEDERAL DE EDUCAÇÃO TECNOLÓGICA DE MINAS GERAIS**

Avenida Amazonas 7675, Gamaleira, 30530 Belo Horizonte (Minas Gerais)
Telex: 313863 CF BR
Telephone: (31) 3331880
Diretor: Wilton da Silva Mattos

D. of Industrial Electrical Engineering
Head: Marcos Antônio da Silva; *staff* 17 (16)
D. of Industrial Mechanical Engineering
Head: José Guilherme da Silva; *staff* 16 (17)
D. of Education
Head: Othílio Magela Neto; *staff* 6 (2)

Also Unidade Ensino Descentralizada in Leopoldina.

Founded 1910 as school. Became Escola Técnica Federal de Minas Gerais and acquired present status and title 1978. Under the jurisdiction of the federal Ministry of Education and Culture.

Academic Year: January to December (January-June; August-December).

Admission Requirements: Secondary school certificate and entrance examination.

Language of Instruction: Portuguese.

Degrees and Diplomas: Professional titles of–Tecnólogo, 3 yrs; Engenheiro industrial electricista; Engenheiro industrial mecânico, 5 yrs. Also teaching qualifications.

Library: Total, 24,847 vols.

Academic Staff: c. 80 (60).

Student Enrolment: c. 940.

457 **CENTRO FEDERAL DE EDUCAÇÃO TECNOLOGICA DO PARANÁ**

Avenida 7 de Setembro 3165, Rebouças, 80230 Curitiba (Paraná)
Telex: (41) 5562 EFET BR
Telephone: (41) 2245333
Diretor: Artur Antonio Bertol

Industrial Engineering

Also branch in Medianeira.

Founded 1910 as school, became Escola Técnica Federal de Paraná 1959. Acquired present status and title 1978. Under the jurisdiction of the Federal Ministry of Education and Culture.

Academic Year: February to December (February-June; August-December).

Admission Requirements: Secondary school certificate and entrance examiniation.

Language of Instruction: Portuguese.

Degrees and Diplomas: Licenciado, 5 yrs. Professional title of Tecnólogo,3 yrs. Mestrado, master, a futher 2 yrs. Also Diploma of specialization in Industrial Automation, 1 yr and teaching qualifications.

Library: 22,755 vols.

Publications: O Informativo (weekly); O Destaque (monthly); Tecnólogia e Humanismo (biannually).

Press or Publishing House: Editora CEFET-PR

Academic Staff, 1990: 60 (102).

Student Enrolment, 1990:

	Men	Women	Total
Of the country	925	85	1005
Of other countries	11	1	17
Total	936	86	1022

458 **CENTRO FEDERAL DE EDUCAÇÃO TECNOLOGICA DO RIO DE JANEIRO**

Avenida Maracaña 229, 20271 Rio de Janeiro (Rio de Janeiro)
Telephone: (21) 2489873

Engineering

Founded 1978.

459 **CENTRO INTEGRADO DE ENSINO DE CONCORDIA**

Rua Lauro Mueller 21, 89700 Concordia (Santa Catarina)
Diretor: Hermogenes Balena

D. of Nursing
Director: Mariestela Stamm; *staff* 6 (8)
D. of Biology
Director: Iône Inês Pinsson Slongo; *staff* 1 (17)
D. of Accountancy
Director: Ricardo Angnes; *staff* – (15)
D. of Physical Education
Director: Marcus Winkel dos Santos; *staff* – (10)
D. of Education
Director: Ortenila Sopelsa Beltran

Founded 1976.

Academic Year: March to December (March-July; August-December).

Admission Requirements: Secondary school certificate and entrance examination.

Language of Instruction: Protuguese.

Degrees and Diplomas: Bachelor, 4 yrs. Teaching certificate.

Library: 8500 vols.

Academic Staff, 1990: 50

Student Enrolment, 1990:

	Men	Women	Total
Of the country	230	468	698

460 **CENTRO POLIVALENTE DE TECNOLOGIA DE SOBRAL**

Avenida da Universidade s/n, 62100 Sobral (Ceará)
Telephone: (85) 6110023

Engineering

Founded 1978.

461 **ESCOLA DE ARTES PLÁSTICAS**

Avenida Amazonas 6252, 30000 Belo Horizonte (Minas Gerais)
Telephone: (31) 3320807

Plastic Arts

Founded 1954. Under the supervision of the Fundação Universidade Mineira de Arte.

Academic Year: March to December (March-June; August-December).

Admission Requirements: Secondary school certificate and entrance examination.

Language of Instruction: Portuguese.

Degrees and Diplomas: Licenciado in Plastic Arts. Professional titles in–Industrial Design; Decoration; Visual Communication.

462 **ESCOLA DE BIBLIOTECONOMIA E DOCUMENTAÇÃO DE SÃO CARLOS**

Rua São Sebastião, 2828, 13560 São Carlos (São Paulo)
Telephone: (162) 721308
Diretora: Elisabeth Marcia Martucci

D. of Basic and Instrumental Training (Library Science, Documentation)
Director: Rosemeire Marino Nastri; *staff* – (8)
D. of Professional Training
Director: Maria Christina de A. Nogueira; *staff* 1 (12)

Founded 1959. A municipal institution under the supervision of the Fundação Educacional São Carlos. Governing body: the Congregação.

Academic Year: February to December (February-June; August-December).

Admission Requirements: Secondary school certificate and entrance examination.

Fees (Cruzeiros): 15,420 per semester.

Language of Instruction: Portuguese.

Degrees and Diplomas: Bachelor, 4 yrs.

Library: 5,000 vols.

Academic Staff, 1990: 1 (20).

Student Enrolment, 1990:

	Men	Women	Total
Of the country	4	101	105

463 **ESCOLA DE CIÊNCIAS MÉDICAS DE ALAGOAS**

Avenida Siqueira Campos 2095, 57000 Maceió (Alagoas)
Telephone: (82) 2214646
Diretor: Walter de Moura Lima (1987-91)
Secretário Geral: Maria Cicera Ferreira Aires

Medicine

Founded 1970. Under the supervision of the Fundação Governador Lamenha Filho.

Academic Year: March to December (March-June; August-December).

Admission Requirements: Secondary school certificate and entrance examination.

Fees: None.

Language of Instruction: Portuguese.

Degrees and Diplomas: Doutor em Medicina, 6 yrs.

Library: Central Library, *c.* 3000 vols.

Academic Staff, 1989: 3 (117).

Student Enrolment, 1989:

	Men	Women	Total
Of the country	227	204	431

464 **ESCOLA DE EDUCAÇÃO FÍSICA DE SÃO CARLOS**

Rua São Sebastião, 13560 São Carlos (São Paulo)
Telephone: (162) 721308
Directora: Haydée Pozzi Semeghini

Physical Education

Founded 1949. A municipal institution under the supervision of the Fundação Educacional São Carlos.

Academic Year: February to December (February-June; August-December).

Admission Requirements: Secondary school certificate and entrance examination.

Fees (Cruzeiros): 1024.38 per semester.

Language of Instruction: Portuguese.

Degrees and Diplomas: Licenciado, 4 yrs.

Academic Staff, 1986-87: 1 (24).

465 **ESCOLA DE ENFERMAGEM**

Rua Teresina 495, 69000 Manaus (Amazonas)
Telephone: (92) 2347088

Nursing (including Midwifery)

Founded 1951. Under the supervision of the Fundação Serviços de Saúde Pública of the Ministry of Health.

Academic Year: March to December (March-July; August-December).

Admission Requirements: Secondary school certificate and entrance examination.

Language of Instruction: Portuguese.

Degrees and Diplomas: Professional title, 4 yrs.

Library: c. 2930 vols.

Academic Staff: c. 40.

Student Enrolment: c. 130.

466 **ESCOLA DE ENFERMAGEM MAGALHÃES BARATA**

Avenida José Bonifácio 1289, 66000 Belém (Pará)
Telephone: (91) 2290236

Nursing

Founded 1949.

467 **ESCOLA DE ENGENHARIA DE PIRACICABA**

Avenida Mons. Martinho Salgot 560, 13400 Piracicaba (São Paulo)
Telephone: (194) 233444

Engineering

Founded 1969.

468 **ESCOLA DE FARMÁCIA E ODONTOLOGIA DE ALFENAS**

Rua Gabriel Monteiro da Silva, 37130 Alfenas (Minas Gerais)
Telex: 352105 EFOA BR
Telephone: (35) 9211011
Dean: João Batista Magalhães (1989-93)
Secretário-Geral: Angela Aparecida Reis e Medeiros

D. of Pharmacy
Co-ordinator: Hêber S. de Carvalho; *staff* 42 (2)
D. of Dentistry
Co-ordinator: Maciro Manoel Pereira; *staff* 48 (9)
D. of Nursing
Co-ordinator: Silvana Maria Coelho Leite; *staff* 17

Founded 1914 as a private school, became a federal institution 1960 enjoying academic and administrative autonomy, and formally recognized by the federal government 1972. Responsible to the Ministry of Education and Culture. Governing bodies: the Congregação da Faculdade; the Conselho Curador; the Congregação Departamental. Residential facilities for students.

Academic Year: February to December (February-June; August-December).

Admission Requirements: Secondary school certificate and entrance examination.

Language of Instruction: Portuguese.

Degrees and Diplomas: Professional titles of–Farmacêutico, 3 1/2 yrs; Enfermeiro, Cirurgião-Dentista, 4 yrs; Bioquímico, 4 1/2 yrs.

Library: 10,672 vols.

Publication: Revista da Escola de Farmâcia e Odontologia de Alfenas.

Academic Staff, 1990:

Rank	Full-time	Part-time
Professores Titulares	8	–
Professores Adjuntos	85	8
Professores Assistentes	7	1
Professores Auxiliares	18	2
Total	118	11

Student Enrolment, 1990:

Of the country	330	562	855

469 **ESCOLA DE MÚSICA**

Rua Ouro Prêto, 30000 Belo Horizonte (Minas Gerais)
Telephone: (31) 3373274

Music

Founded 1954. Under the supervision of the Fundação Universidade Mineira de Arte Aleijadinho.

Academic Year: March to December (March-June; August-December).

Admission Requirements: Secondary school certificate and entrance examination.

Language of Instruction: Portuguese.

Degrees and Diplomas: Bacharel de Música.

470 **ESCOLA DE MÚSICA DO ESPÍRITO SANTO**

Avenida Princesa Isabel 610, 29000 Vitória (Espírito Santo)
Telephone: (27) 2220195

Music

Founded 1971.

471 **ESCOLA DE MÚSICA E BELAS ARTES DO PARANÁ**

Rua Emiliano Perneta 179, 80000 Curitiba (Paraná)
Telephone: (41) 2231129

Music

Fine Arts

Founded 1948. Governed by the Secretariat for Education and Culture of the State of Paraná. Financed by the federal and State governments.

Academic Year: March to December (March-June; August-December).

Admission Requirements: Secondary school certificate.

Language of Instruction: Portuguese.

Degrees and Diplomas: Professional titles of–Pintor; Escultor; Cantor, 4 yrs; Instrumentista, 7 yrs; Professor de Canto; Professor de Educação musical, 8 yrs; Professor de Música e Instrumentos, 12 yrs; Compositor; Maestro, 13 yrs.

Library: School Library.

472 **ESCOLA FEDERAL DE ENGENHARIA DE ITAJUBÁ**

Rua Colonel Renno 7, 37500 Itajubá (Minas Gerais)
Telex: 31-3485 EFEI BR
Telephone: (35) 6221966

I. of Mechanical Engineering

I. of Electrical Engineering I. of Basic Studies (Physics, Mathematics, Chemistry and Computer Sciences)

Founded 1913. Operated under the authority of the federal government. Governing bodies: the Congregação; the Conselho Instituto.

Academic Year: February to December (February-June; August-December).

Admission Requirements: Secondary school certificate and entrance examination.

Fees: None.

Language of Instruction: Portuguese.

Degrees and Diplomas: Professional titles of–Engenheiro eletricista; Engenheiro mecânico, 5 yrs. Mestre, a further 1-2 yrs.

Library: Biblioteca Mauá, *c.* 14,310 vols.

Special Facilities (Museums, etc.): Museu Theodomiro Santiago.

Publication: Pesquisa (Revista) (quarterly).

Press or Publishing House: Editora da Efei.

Academic Staff: c. 90.

Student Enrolment: c. 1630.

473 **ESCOLA NACIONAL DE CIÊNCIAS ESTATÍSTICAS**

Rua André Cavalcanti 106, 20231 Rio de Janeiro (Rio de Janeiro)
Telephone: (21) 2247677
Diretor: Djalma Galvão Carneiro Pessoa
Secretário Geral: Ariadne Correia

Statistics (including Mathematics and Economics)

Founded 1953. Under the supervision of the Instituto Brasileiro de Geografia e Estatistica (Brazilian Bureauof Census).

Academic Year: January to December (January-February; March-June; August-December).

Admission Requirements: High school certificate and entrance examination.

Language of Instruction: Portuguese.

Degrees and Diplomas: Bacharel, in Statistics. Graduate Course (lato sensu).

Library: 7000 vols.

Academic Staff, 1989-90: 14 (12).

Student Enrolment, 1989-90: 274.

474 **ESCOLA PAULISTA DE MEDICINA**

Rua Botucatu 720, 04023 São Paulo (São Paulo)
Telephone: (111) 5726033

D. of Medicine
Head: Oswaldo L. Ramos
D. of Nursing
Head: Rosa Ap. P. de Castro
D. of Preventive Medicine
Head: Roberto G. Baruzzi
D. of Phonology
head: Raymundo Manno Vieira
D. of Orthotics
Co-ordinator: Maria Cecilia Saccomani
National I. of Pharmacology
Head: Luiz Juliano Neto
I. of Study and Research into Nephrology and Hypertension
Head: Oswaldo L. Ramos

Founded 1933 as a private institution, became public institution 1956. Responsible to the Ministry of Education and Culture 1964.

Academic Year: March to December (March-July; August-December).

Admission Requirements: Secondary school certificate and entrance examination.

Fees: None.

Language of Instruction: Portuguese.

Degrees and Diplomas: Bacharel in Biology. Professional titles in–Phonology; Orthopaedics; Nursing. Doutor in Medicine, 6 yrs.

Special Facilities (Museums, etc.): History School's Museum; Indian's Museum.

Academic Staff, 1990: 268

Student Enrolment, 1990:

	Men	Women	Total
Of the country	1307	1119	2426
Of other countries	18	9	27
Total	1325	1128	2453

475 **ESCOLA POLITÉCNICA DA FUNDAÇÃO DE ENSINO SUPERIOR DE PERNAMBUCO**

Praça do Internacional, 50000 Recife (Pernambuco)
Telephone: (81) 2272855

Civil Engineering
Electrical Engineering
Mechanical Engineering

Founded 1912.

Degrees and Diplomas: Professional title of Engenheiro, 5 yrs.

476 **ESCOLA SUPERIOR DE ADMINISTRAÇÃO E GERENCIA**

Avenida Madre Bevenuta s/n, 88000 Florianopólis (Santa Catarina)

Administration

Founded 1966.

477 **ESCOLA SUPERIOR DE AGRICULTURA DE LAVRAS**

Campus Universitário, 37200 Lavras (Minas Gerais)
Telex: 353007 ESAG BR
Telephone: (35) 8213900
Diretor: Juventino Júlio de Souza

Agriculture (including Forestry, Soil Science, Animal Science, Food Sciences, and Rural Administration)
Head: Guy Alvarenga: *staff* 63 (1)
D. of Crop Protection
Head: Luiz Onofre Salgado; *staff* 20 (1)
D. of Soil Science
Head: Mozart Martins Perreira; *staff* 28
D. of Biology
Head: Silas Costa Pereira; *staff* 31
D. of Chemistry
Head: Jander Pereira Freire; *staff* 31
D. of Forestry Science
Head: Nelson Ventorim; *staff* 12
D. of Animal Science
Head: Benedito Lemos de Oliveira; *staff* 50 (1)
D. of Agriculture Engineering
Head: Hélcio Alves Teixeira; *staff* 32
D. of Basic Science
Head: Gilnei de Souza Duarte; *staff* 21
D. of Food Sciences
Head: Eliana Pinheiro de Carvalho; *staff* 19
D. of Rural Administration and Economics
Head: José Mário Patto Guimarães; *staff* 24
D. of Sports
Head:DCarlos Magno Alvarenga; staff 7

Founded 1908 as a private institution under the supervision of the Instituto Gammon. Recognized by the federalgovernment 1963. Responsible to the Ministry of Education and Culture. Some residential facilities for academic staff and students.

Academic Year: March to December (March-July; August-December).

Admission Requirements: Secondary school certificate and entrance examination.

Fees (Cruzeiros): 157 per semester.

Language of Instruction: Portuguese.

Degrees and Diplomas: Professional titles, 4-5 yrs. Mestrado, master, in Science, a further 2-3 yrs. Doutorado, a further 2-4 yrs.

Library: Central Library, *c.* 26,000 vols.

Special Facilities (Museums, etc.): Museu de Mineralogia.

Publications: Ciência e Prática (3 issues per year); Revista de Administração Rural (biannually).

Press or Publishing House: Gráfica da ESAL.

Academic Staff, 1989-90:

Rank	Full-time	Part-time
Professores Titulares	28	1
Professores Adjuntos	140	1
Professores Assistentes	13	1
Professores Auxiliares	6	–
Total	187	3

Student Enrolment, 1989-90:

	Men	Women	Totla
Of the country	1561	451	2012
Of other countries	24	6	30
Total	1585	457	2042*

*Also 298 external students.

478 **ESCOLA SUPERIOR DE AGRICULTURA DE MOSSORO**
BR-110, Km-47, 59600 Mossoro (Rio Grande do Norte)
Telex: 84-3152
Telephone: (84) 3211765
Diretor: Jerônimo Vingt-un Rosado Maia (1988-92)

Agriculture (including Animal Husbandry)

Founded 1967. Recognized by the federal government 1969. Responsible to the Ministry of Education and Culture. Governing bodies: the Conselho Têcnico Administrativo; the Conselho Departamental; the Conselho de Curadores. Residential facilities for academic staff and students.

Academic Year: March to November (March-June; August-November).

Admission Requirements: Secondary school certificate and entrance examination.

Language of Instruction: Portuguese.

Degrees and Diplomas: Professional title of Engenheiro agrônomo, 4 yrs. Mestrado, Master, a further 2 yrs. Diplomas of specialization, 8 months.

Library: Library Orland Teixeira, 42,358 vols.

Special Facilities (Museums, etc.): Museums of: Zoology; Geology; Paleontology; Malacology; History of ESAM.

Publication: Caatinga (weekly).

Academic Staff, 1989-90:

Rank	Full-time	Part-time
Professores Titulares	9	–
Professores Adjuntos	62	1
Professores Assistentes	8	1
Professores Auxiliares	4	–
Total	83	2

Student Enrolment, 1989-90:

	Men	Women	Total
Of the country	307	38	345

479 **ESCOLA SUPERIOR DE CIÊNCIAS AGRARIAS DE RIO VERDE**
Rua São Sebastião, 76200 Rio Verde (Goiás)
Telephone: (62) 6212019

Agriculture

Animal Husbandry

Founded 1984.

480 **ESCOLA SUPERIOR DE CIÊNCIAS CONTÁBEIS E ADMINISTRATIVAS**
Campus Universitário, 88800 Criciúma (Santa Catarina)
Telephone: (484) 381411

Administrative Studies

Accountancy

Founded 1975.

Academic Year: March to December (March-July; August-December).

Admission Requirements: Secondary school certificate.

Language of Instruction: Portuguese.

Degrees and Diplomas: Bacharel, 4 yrs.

481 **ESCOLA SUPERIOR DE EDUCAÇÃO FÍSICA DE AVARE**
Praça Altino Arantes 163, 18700 Avare (São Paulo)
Telephone: (147) 221133

Physical Education

Founded 1973.

482 **ESCOLA SUPERIOR DE EDUCAÇÃO FÍSICA DE CRUZEIRO**
Rua Dr. José R.A. Sobrinho 191, 12700 Cruzeiro (São Paulo)
Telephone: (12) 5441865

Physical Education

Founded 1970.

483 **ESCOLA SUPERIOR DE EDUCAÇÃO FÍSICA DE GOIÁS**
Avenida Anhanguera 1420, 74000 Goiânia (Goiás)
Telephone: (62) 2611443

Physical Education

Founded 1963.

484 **ESCOLA SUPERIOR DE EDUCAÇÃO FÍSICA DE JUNDIAÍ**
Praça Lazaro Miranda Duarte, 13200 Jundiaí (São Paulo)
Telephone: (01) 4347955

Physical Education

Founded 1974.

485 **ESCOLA SUPERIOR DE EDUCAÇÃO FÍSICA DE RECIFE**
Rua Arnobio Marques 310, 50000 Recife (Pernambuco)
Telephone: (81) 2225075

Physical Education

Founded 1946.

Academic Year: March to November (March-June; August-November).

Admission Requirements: Secondary school certificate.

Language of Instruction: Portuguese.

Degrees and Diplomas: Licenciado em Educação Física, 4 yrs.

Academic Staff: c. 30.

Student Enrolment: c. 310.

486 **ESCOLA SUPERIOR DE EDUCAÇÃO FÍSICA DO PARÁ**
Avenida 1 de Dezembro 817, 66000 Belém (Pará)
Telephone: (91) 2260436
Diretor: Nagib Coelho Matni
Secretária: Eduarda Maria Matni de Sousa

Physical Education

Founded 1970. Under the supervision of the Fundação Educacional do Estado do Pará. Residential facilities for 15 academic staff and 120 students.

Arrangements for co-operation with the Universities of: Kokushikan; Rolla; Columbia.

Academic Year: March to December (March-June; August-December).

Admission Requirements: Secondary school certificate and entrance examination.

Language of Instruction: Portuguese.

Degrees and Diplomas: Licenciado en Educação Fisica, 4 yrs. Professional titles of–Técnico em Desportivos; Médico Desportivo.

Library: 4730 vols.

Special Facilities (Museums, etc.): Anatomy Laboratory; Biological Laboratory.

Academic Staff, 1990:

Rank	Full-time	Part-time
Professores Titulares	16	17
Professores Adjuntos	2	7
Professores Assistentes	4	–
Professores Auxiliares	7	10
Total	29	34

Student Enrolment, 1989:

	Men	Women	Total
Of the country	291	320	611

487 **ESCOLA SUPERIOR DE EDUCAÇÃO FÍSICA E DESPORTOS DE CRICIÚMA**

Rua Pascoal Meller, 88800 Criciúma (Santa Catarina)
Telephone: (484) 381411

Physical Education

Founded 1974.

Academic Year: March to December (March-July; August-December).

Admission Requirements: Secondary school certificate.

Language of Instruction: Portuguese.

Degrees and Diplomas: Licenciado em Educação Física, 4 yrs.

488 **ESCOLA SUPERIOR DE EDUCAÇÃO FÍSICA E DESPORTOS DE JOINVILLE**

Campus Universitário 144 Bom Reitro, 89200 Joinville (Santa Catarina)
Telephone: (474) 253200

Physical Education

Founded 1970. Under the supervision of the Fundação Educacional da Região de Joinville.

Academic Year: March to November (March-June; August-November).

Admission Requirements: Secondary school certificate and entrance examination.

Language of Instruction: Portuguese.

Degrees and Diplomas: Licenciado, 3 yrs. Professional title of Técnico em Desportos, 3 yrs.

Library: Central Library of the Foundation, *c.* 20,000 vols.

489 **ESCOLA SUPERIOR DE ESTUDOS SOCIAIS**

Rua Padre Galtone 112, 88350 Brusque (Santa Catarina)
Telephone: (473) 551200

Natural Sciences
Social Studies

Founded 1973. Under the supervision of the Fundação Educacional de Brusque. Governing bodies: the Conselho Administrativo; the Conselho Curador. Residential facilities for 2 academic staff and 30 students.

Academic Year: March to December (March-July; August-December).

Admission Requirements: Secondary school certificate and entrance examination.

Language of Instruction: Portuguese.

Degrees and Diplomas: Licenciado in–Natural Sciences, 2-4 yrs; Social Studies, 3-7 yrs.

Library: *c.* 16,500 vols.

Academic Staff: *c.* 30.

Student Enrolment: *c.* 230.

490 **ESCOLA SUPERIOR DE TECNOLOGIA DE CRICIÚMA**

Rua Pascoal Meller s/n, 88000 Criciúma (Santa Catarina)
Telephone: (484) 381411

Agricultural Engineering

Founded 1975. Under the supervision of the Fundação Educacional de Criciúma.

Academic Year: March to December (March-July; August-December).

Admission Requirements: Secondary school certificate.

Language of Instruction: Portuguese.

Degrees and Diplomas: Professional title of Engenharia Agrimensura, 4 yrs.

491 **FACULDADE DE ADMINISTRAÇÃO DE EMPRESAS DO ALTO VALE DO ITAJAÍ**

Rua Dr. Guilherme Gemballa 13, 89160 Rio do Sul (Santa Catarina)
Telephone: (47) 8220988

Business Administration

Founded 1967.

492 **FACULDADE DE ADMINISTRAÇÃO E DE CIÊNCIAS CONTÁBEIS DE ARAPONGAS**

86700 Arapongas (Paraná)
Telephone: (432) 523730

Administration
Accountancy

Founded 1980.

493 **FACULDADE DE ADMINISTRACÃO ECONÓMICAS DE SÃO JOÃO DA BOA VISTA**

Avenida Dr. Oscar Pirajá Martins 15, 13870 São João da Boa Vista (São Paulo)
Telephone: (196) 233022

Economics

Founded 1965. Formally recognized by the federal government 1971.

Academic Year: March to December (March-June; August-December).

Admission Requirements: Secondary school certificate and entrance examination.

Language of Instruction: Portuguese.

Degrees and Diplomas: Bacharel em Ciências econômicas, 4 yrs.

494 **FACULDADE DE AGRONOMIA DO MÉDIO SÃO FRANCISCO**

Avenida Edgard Chastinet Guimarães s/n, 48900 Juázeiro (Bahia)
Telephone: (75) 8112363

Agriculture (including Animal Husbandry)

Founded 1960 as private foundation. Recognized as a State institution by the federal government 1970.

Academic Year: March to November (March-June; August-November).

Admission Requirements: Secondary school certificate and entrance examination.

Language of Instruction: Portuguese.

Degrees and Diplomas: Licenciado, 3-4 yrs. Professional title of Engenheiro agrônomo, 4-5 yrs.

Library: *c.* 18,320 vols.

Academic Staff: *c.* 30.

495 **FACULDADE DE AGRONOMIA LUIZ MENEGHEL**

Rodovia BP. 369, KM-54-Saida P/Andira, 86360 Bandeirantes (Paraná)
Cables: Agrofal
Telephone: (437) 421123

Agriculture (including Animal Husbandry)

Founded 1970. A municipal institution recognized by the federal government and financed by tuition fees. Governing body: the Congregação.

Academic Year: February to December (February-July; August-December).

Admission Requirements: Secondary school certificate.

Language of Instruction: Portuguese.

Degrees and Diplomas: Professional title of Engenheiro agrônomo, 4 yrs.

Library: Central Library, *c.* 8200 vols.

Publication: Poliagro.

Academic Staff: *c.* 60.

Student Enrolment: *c.* 770.

496 **FACULDADE DE CIÊNCIAS ADMINISTRATIVAS DE JOINVILLE**

Campus Universitário 144, Dom Retiro, 89200 Joinville (Santa Catarina)
Telephone: (474) 253200

Administration
Accountancy

Founded 1971. Under the supervision of the Fundação Educacional da Região de Joinville.

Academic Year: March to November (March-June; August-November).

Admission Requirements: Secondary school certificate and entrance examination.

Language of Instruction: Portuguese.

Degrees and Diplomas: Bacharel, 4 yrs.

Library: Central Library of the Foundation, *c.* 20,000 vols.

Academic Staff: *c.* 40.

497 **FACULDADE DE CIÊNCIAS ADMINISTRATIVAS DE POÇOS DE CALDAS**

Avenida Padre Francisco Cletos s/n, 37700 Poços de Caldas (Minas Gerais)
Telephone: (35) 7214954
Diretor: Rafael Acconcia
Secretário: Agenor dos Passos

Administration

Founded 1979. A municipal institution under the supervision of the Autarquia Municipal de Ensino de Poços deCaldas.

Academic Year: February to November (February-June; August-November).

Admission Requirements: Secondary school certificate and entrance examination.
Language of Instruction: Portuguese.
Degrees and Diplomas: Bacharel, 4 yrs.
Academic Staff, 1986-87: 20 (88).
Student Enrolment, 1986-87:

	Men	Women	Total
Of the country	183	67	250

498 **FACULDADE DE CIÊNCIAS AGRARIAS DE PARÁ**
Avenida Perimetral s/n, 66000 Belém (Pará)
Telex: 911892 FAGP
Telephone: (91) 2261922
Diretor: Jose Fernando Lucas de Oliveira (1986-)
Chefe de Gabinete: Marlina Santos

Agriculture (including Forestry, Veterinary, Medicine, and Animal Husbandry)

Founded 1951.
Academic Year: March to December (March-June; August-December).
Admission Requirements: Graduation from high school and entrance examination.
Language of Instruction: Portuguese.
Degrees and Diplomas: Bachelor in–Agriculture; Veterinary Medicine; Forestry, 5 yrs. Mestrado, Master, a further 2 yrs.
Publication: Boletim da FCAP
Academic Staff, 1989-90: 111 (11).
Student Enrolment, 1989-90: 1333.

499 **FACULDADE DE CIÊNCIAS BIOLOGICAS DE ARARAS**
Avenida Universitária s/n, 13600 Araras (São Paulo)
Telephone: (195) 411411
Diretor: Sylvio Alves de Aguiar (1990-94)
Secretário Geral: Angélica Apa. do Carmo Baptistella

Biological Sciences (including Dentistry, Pharmacy, and Nursing)

Founded 1975.
Academic Year: March to December (March-June; August-December).
Admission Requirements: Graduation from high school or recognized equivalent, and entrance examination.
Fees (Cruzeros): 5000 per month.
Language of Instruction: Portuguese.
Degrees and Diplomas: Bacharel, 4 yrs.
Library: Central Library, 5830 vols.
Special Facilities (Museums, etc.): Museum; Biological Garden.
Academic Staff, 1989-90: 125.
Student Enrolment, 1990:

	Men	Women	Total
Of the country	388	694	1082

500 **FACULDADE DE CIÊNCIAS CONTÁBEIS DE CURITIBANOS**
Avenida Leoberto Leal, 89520 Curitibanos (Santa Catarina)
Telephone: (482) 450724

Accountancy

Founded 1976.

501 **FACULDADE DE CIÊNCIAS CONTÁBEIS DE SOBRAL**
Avenida de Universidade, 62100 Sobral (Ceará)
Telephone: (85) 6111827

Accountancy

Founded 1970.

502 **FACULDADE DE CIÊNCIAS CONTÁBEIS E ADMINISTRATIVAS DE CACHOEIRO DO ITAPEMIRIM**
Rodovia Cachoeira Muqui, 29300 Cachoeiro do Itapemirim (Espírito Santo)

D. of Administration
D. of Accountancy
D. of Law
D. of Economics
D. of Mathematics

Founded 1968. Recognized by the federal government 1970. Governed by the municipal authorities and financed byfederal and State governments. Governing body: the Congregação.
Academic Year: March to December.
Admission Requirements: Secondary school certificate and entrance examination.
Language of Instruction: Portuguese.
Degrees and Diplomas: Bacharel in–Public Administration; Business Administration; Accountancy.
Library: c. 5000 vols.
Publication: Revista de Administração, Direito e Contabilidade.
Academic Staff: c. -(50).
Student Enrolment: c. 380.

503 **FACULDADE DE CIÊNCIAS CONTÁBEIS, ECONÔMICAS E ADMINISTRATIVAS DE VIDEIRA**
Rua 10 de Marco, 89560 Videira (Santa Catarina)
Telephone: (49) 5330488

Economics
Administration
Accountancy

Founded 1973.

504 **FACULDADE DE CIÊNCIAS DE ADMINISTRAÇÃO DE LIMOEIRO**
Avenida Jeronimo Heraclio, 55700 Limoeiro (Pernambuco)
Telephone: (81) 6280563

Administration

Founded 1976.

505 **FACULDADE DE CIÊNCIAS DE ADMINISTRAÇÃO DE PERNAMBUCO**
Avenida Abdias de Carvalhos s/n, 50000 Recife (Pernambuco)
Telephone: (81) 2285644

Administration

Founded 1956.

506 **FACULDADE DE CIENCIAS DA ADMINISTRAÇÃO DE PETROLINA**
Avenida Dom Bosco, 56300 Petrolina (Pernambuco)
Telephone: (81) 9611075

Administration

Founded 1976.

507 **FACULDADE DE CIÊNCIAS E EDUCAÇÃO DE CRICIÚMA**
Rua Pasoal Meller s/n, 88800 Criciúma (Santa Catarina)
Telephone: (484) 381090

Biological Sciences
Design
Social Studies
Letters
Mathematics
Education

Founded 1975. Under the supervision of the Fundação Educacional de Criciúma.
Academic Year: March to December (March-July; August-December).
Admission Requirements: Secondary school certificate.
Language of Instruction: Portuguese.
Degrees and Diplomas: Licenciado, 4 yrs.
Academic Staff, 1990: – (30).

508 **FACULDADE DE CIÊNCIAS E HUMANIDADES DE PATO BRANCO**
Rua Itacolomi 1550, Balbinotti, 85500 Pato Branco (Paraná)
Telephone: (462) 241348

Administration
Accountancy
Humanities

Founded 1975.

509 **FACULDADE DE CIÊNCIAS E LETRAS DE AVARE**
Praça Altino Arantes 163, 18700 Avare (São Paulo)
Telephone: (147) 221133
Diretor: Antonio Pompeu (1989-)
Secretário-Geral: Maria Celia Lopes Vieira

D. of Science
Head: João Alberto; *staff* – (5)
D. of Letters
Head: Vicente Dell'Agnolo; *staff* – (10)
D. of Education
Head: Conceição M. Bijeira; *staff* – (11)
D. of History
Head: Paulo P.D. de Almeida *staff* – (9)
D. of Geography
Head: Jose Alcides Muller; *staff* – (5)
D. of Artist Education
Head: Cleone L.Borin *staff* – (7)

Founded 1969.

Academic Year: February to December

Admission Requirements: Secondary school certificate and entrance examination.

Fees (Pesos): 880 per month.

Language of Instruction: Portuguese.

Degrees and Diplomas: Bachelor, 4 yrs.

Library: Library of Fundação Regional Education Avaré, 38,000 vols.

Academic Staff, 1989-90: – (55).

510 **FACULDADE DE CIÊNCIAS E LETRAS DE BRAGANÇA PAULISTA**
Rua Conselheiro Rodrigues Alves 249, 12900 Bragança Paulista (São Paulo)
Telephone: (11) 4332418

Science
Letters

Founded 1968.

511 **FACULDADE DE CIÊNCIAS E LETRAS DE CAMPO MOURÃO**
Avenida Comendador N. Marcondes 1972, 87300 Campo Mourão (Paraná)
Telephone: (44) 8231880

Science
Letters

Founded 1974.

512 **FACULDADE DE CIÊNCIAS E LETRAS DE MAFRA**
Avenida Presidente Nereu Ramos 1071, 89300 Mafra (Santa Catarina)
Telephone: (476) 420059

Science
Letters

Founded 1973.

513 **FACULDADE DE CIÊNCIAS ECONÔMICAS, ADMINISTRATIVAS E CONTÁBEIS DE BELO HORIZONTE**
Cobre, 30310 Belo Horizonte (Minas Gerais)
Telephone: (31) 2271388

Economics
Administration
Accountancy

Founded 1966.

514 **FACULDADE DE CIÊNCIAS ECONÔMICAS, CONTÁBEIS E ADMINISTRATIVAS DE LAGES**
Avenida Castelo Branco 170, 37, 88500 Lages (Santa Catarina)
Telephone: (492) 221020

Economics
Accountancy
Administration
Law and Social Sciences

Founded 1964.

515 **FACULDADE DE CIÊNCIAS ECONÔMICAS, ADMINISTRATIVAS E CONTÁBEIS DE SÃO JOÃO DEL REI**
Praça Frei Orlando 170, 36300 São João del Rei (Minas Gerais)
Telephone: (32) 3711397

Economics
Administration
Accountancy

Founded 1972.

516 **FACULDADE DE CIÊNCIAS ECONÔMICAS DE ANÁPOLIS**
Avenida Juscelino Kubitschek 146, 77100 Anápolis (Goiás)
Telephone: (62) 3243962

Economics

Founded 1962.

517 **FACULDADE DE CIÊNCIAS ECONÔMICAS DE JOINVILLE**
Campus Universitário 144, 89200 Joinville (Santa Catarina)
Telephone: (474) 253200

Economics

Founded 1965. Under the supervision of the Fundação Educacional da Região de Joinville.

Academic Year: March to November (March-June; August-November).

Admission Requirements: Secondary school certificate and entrance examination.

Language of Instruction: Portuguese.

Degrees and Diplomas: Bacharel, 4 yrs.

Library: Central Library of the Foundation, *c.* 20,000 vols.

Academic Staff: c. 30.

518 **FACULDADE DE CIÊNCIAS ECONÔMICAS E ADMINISTRATIVAS DE FRANCA**
Avenida Major Nicacio 2433, 14400 Franca (São Paulo)
Telephone: (16) 7224104

Economics
Administration

Founded 1951.

519 **FACULDADE DE CIÊNCIAS ECONÔMICAS E ADMINISTRATIVAS DE OSASCO**
Rua Narciso Sturlini 111, 06000 Osasco (São Paulo)
Telephone: (11) 8032955

Economics
Administration

Founded 1965.

520 **FACULDADE DE CIÊNCIAS ECONÔMICAS E ADMINISTRATIVAS DE SANTO ANDRÉ**
Principe de Galles 821, 09000 Santo André (São Paulo)
Telephone: (11) 4493093

Economics
Administration

Founded 1954.

521 **FACULDADE DE CIÊNCIAS HUMANAS ARNALDO BUSATO**
Rua de Faculdade 2550, 85900 Toledo (Paraná)
Telephone: (452) 52-3535
Diretor: Flávio Vendelino Scherer (1984-88)
Secretário Geral: Célio Escher

D. of Economics
Co-ordinator: Maria Conceição Gonzatto; *staff* 4 (11)
D. of Philosophy
Co-ordinator: Hugo José Rhoden; *staff* 4 (11)
D. of Secretarial Studies
D. of Social Service

Founded 1980. Under the supervision of the municipal authorities.

Academic Year: February to December (February-June; August-December).

Admission Requirements: Secondary school certificate and entrance examination.

Language of Instruction: Portuguese.

Degrees and Diplomas: Bacharel in Economics, 5 yrs. Licenciado in Philosophy, History and Psychology, 3 yrs.

Library: c. 8000 vols.

Academic Staff, 1986-87: 8 (22).

Student Enrolment, 1986-87: 460.

522 **FACULDADE DE CIÊNCIAS HUMANAS DA FUMEC**
Rua Cobre 200, 30310 Belo Horizonte (Minas Gerais)
Telephone: (31) 2217451
Diretor: Amâncio Fernandes Caixeta
Secretário Geral: Thais Estevanato

Psychology
Education

Founded 1971. Under the supervision of the Fundação Mineira de Educação e Cultura.

Academic Year: February to December (February-June; August-December).

Admission Requirements: Secondary school certificate and entrance examination.

Fees (Cruzeros): 17,465.68-19,125.12 per semester.

Language of Instruction: Portuguese.

Degrees and Diplomas: Bacharel in Psychology, 4 yrs. Licenciado in–Psychology, 2 yrs and practical experience; Education, 3 yrs. Professional title of Psychologist, 5 yrs.

Press or Publishing House: Lógica da Lógica; Qùólóquio; Plural.

Academic Staff, 1990: – (85).

Student Enrolment, 1990:

	Men	Women	Total
Of the country	136	909	1045

523 **FACULDADE DE CIÊNCIAS HUMANAS DE FRANCISCO BELTRÃO**

Rua João de Barro 212, 85600 Francisco Beltrão (Paraná)
Telephone: (465) 221233

Social Sciences
Home Economics

Founded 1974. Under the supervision of the municipal authorities.

Academic Year: March to December (March-July; August-December).

Admission Requirements: Secondary school certificate.

Language of Instruction: Portuguese.

Degrees and Diplomas: Licenciado, 3-4 yrs.

Library: Library Professor Bernardo Reisdorfer, *c.* 6500 vols.

Academic Staff: c. 10.

Student Enrolment: c. 30.

524 **FACULDADE DE CIÊNCIAS HUMANAS DE MARECHAL CANDIDO RONDON**

Rua Costa e Silva s/n, 85960 Marechal Candido Rondon (Paraná)
Telephone: (45) 543216

Human Sciences

Founded 1980.

525 **FACULDADE DE CIÊNCIAS HUMANAS DE CABO**

Rua do Campo, 54500 Cabo (Pernambuco)
Telephone: (81) 5210400

Human Sciences

Founded 1981.

526 **FACULDADE DE CIÊNCIAS MÉDICAS DE PERNAMBUCO**

Rua Arnobio Marques, 50000 Recife (Pernambuco)
Telephone: (081) 2211554

Medicine

Founded 1956, recognized by the government 1958. Under the supervision of the Fundação de Ensino Superior de Pernambuco and receiving some financial support from the government. Governing body: the Congregação. Residential facilities for students.

Academic Year: February to December.

Admission Requirements: Secondary school certificate and entrance examination.

Language of Instruction: Portuguese.

Degrees and Diplomas: Professional title of Médico, 6 yrs.

Library: c. 5000 vols.

Academic Staff: c. 140.

Student Enrolment: c. 1500.

527 **FACULDADE DE CIÊNCIAS SOCIAIS APLICADAS DE FOZ DO IGUAÇU**

Rua Silvino dal Bo, 85890 Foz do Iguaçu (Paraná)
Telephone: (455) 732290

Social Sciences

Founded 1979.

528 **FACULDADE DE DIREITO DE CACHOEÏRO DA ITAPEMIRIM**

Rua Mário Imperial 56, 29300 Cachoeiro da Itapemirim (Espírito Santo)
Telephone: (27) 5220128
Diretora: Marilia Villela de Madeiros Mignoni
Secretária: Maria José Machado Medina

Law

Founded 1965. Under the supervision of the municipal authorities.

Academic Year: March to December (March-June; August-December).

Admission Requirements: Secondary school certificate and entrance examination.

Language of Instruction: Portuguese.

Degrees and Diplomas: Bacharel em Direito, 5 yrs.

Academic Staff, 1986-87: 27.

Student Enrolment, 1986-87:

	Men	Women	Total
Of the country	300	128	428

529 **FACULDADE DE DIREITO DE CONSELHEIRO LAFAIETE**

Praça Barão de Queluz 11, 36400 Conselheiro Lafaiete (Minas Gerais)
Telephone: (31) 7211069

Law

Founded 1970.

530 **FACULDADE DE DIREITO DE FRANCA**

Avenida Major Niçacio 2377, 14400 Franca (São Paulo)
Telephone: (16) 222010

Law

Founded 1961.

531 **FACULDADE DE DIREITO SÃO BERNARDO DO CAMPO**

Rua Java 425, 09700 São Bernardo do Campo (São Paulo)
Telephone: (11) 4580222

Law

Founded 1965 and responsible to the municipal authorities. Governing bodies: Congregação de Faculdade, composed of the director and titular professors; the Conselho Técnico Administrativo, composed of the director and 3 professors.

Academic Year: March to December (March-July; August-December).

Admission Requirements: Secondary school certificate or equivalent and entrance examination.

Language of Instruction: Portuguese.

Degrees and Diplomas: Bacharel em Ciências jurídicas e sociais, 5 yrs.

Library: c. 4000 vols.

Publications: Jornal Acadêmico Vinte de Agosto 'Java'; Revista Acadêmica Vinte de Agosto 'Reviva'.

532 **FACULDADE DE EDUCAÇÃO, CIÊNCIAS E LETRAS DE CASCAVEL**

Rua Jardim Universitário, 85800 Cascavel (Paraná)
Telex: 451091 FUEO BR
Telephone: (452) 23-4961
Presidente: Carlos Roberto Calssavara (1986-90)
Secretário Geral: Carmen Lúcia Marcante Rossoni

D. of Education
Co-ordinator: Zulméa Müller Reis; *staff* 14 (3)

D. of Science, Biology, Chemistry, and Physics
Co-ordinator: Zélia Josefa Muraro Miotto; *staff* 14 (10)

D. of Letters
Co-ordinator: Rosane Beyer do Nascimento; *staff* 9 (6)

D. of Mathematics
Co-ordinator: Sérgio Flávio Schmits; *staff* 17 (7)

D. of Biomedicine
Co-ordinator: Alcy Aparecida Leite de Souza; *staff* 10 (5)

D. of Agronomy
Co-ordinator: João Francisco Back; *staff* 7 (10)

D. of Business Administration
Co-ordinator: Terezinho Lino de Oliveira; *staff* 5 (6)

D. of Economics
Co-ordinator: Sérgio Lopes; *staff* 9 (2)

Founded 1972 and supported by the municipal authorities. Acquired present status supported by the State 1987.

Academic Year: March to November.

Admission Requirements: Secondary school certificate.

Fees: None.
Language of Instruction: Portuguese.
Degrees and Diplomas: Licenciado, 4-5 yrs.
Academic Staff, 1990: 82 (57).
Student Enrolment, 1990:

	Men	Women	Total
Of the country	787	1006	1793

533 **FACULDADE DE EDUCAÇÃO, CIÊNCIAS E LETRAS DE IRATI**
Rua Cel Pires 826, 84500 Irati (Pernambuco)
Telephone: (424) 221381

Education
Science
Letters
Founded 1974.

534 **FACULDADE DE EDUCAÇÃO DE MOSSORÓ**
Praça Miguel Faustino, 59600 Mossoró (Rio Grande do Norte)
Education

535 **FACULDADE DE EDUCAÇÃO DE SOBRAL**
Avenida da Universidade, 62100 Sobral (Ceará)
Telephone: (85) 6112213

Education
Founded 1980.

536 **FACULDADE DE EDUCAÇÃO FÍSICA DA ALTA ARARQUERENSE**
Rua Oito 854, 15777 Santa Fe do Sul (São Paulo)
Telephone: (17) 6312921

Physical Education
Founded 1972.

537 **FUNDAÇAO FACULDADE DE ARTES DO PARANÁ**
Rua Almirante Barroso 78, 80510 Curitiba (Paraná)
Telephone: (41) 2237490
Diretora: Rosiliza M.S. Agibert
Secretária Geral: Maria do Carmo F. Silva

D. of Music:
Head: Cristina B. Santana; *staff* – (12)
D. of Plastic Arts
Head: Rosane Schloegel; *staff* – (11)
D. of Music Therapy
Coordinator: Eulide Meibel; *staff* – (14)

Founded as Faculdade de Educaçao Musical 1968. Acquired present status and title 1989. Governing bodies: the Congregação; the Conselho Departamental.

Academic Year: March to December (March-June; August-December).
Admission Requirements: Graduation from high school or recognized equivalent, and entrance examination.
Fees: None.
Language of Instruction: Portuguese.
Degrees and Diplomas: Bacherel in Music Therapy, 4 yrs. Licenciado in–Music; Plastic Arts, 4 yrs.
Library: c. 4500 vols.
Academic Staff, 1989-90: – (54).
Student Enrolment, 1989-90:

	Men	Women	Total
Of the country	180	362	542

538 **FACULDADE DE ENFERMAGEM E OBSTETRÍCIA DE PASSOS**
Rua Juca Stockler 1130, 37900 Passos (Minas Gerais)
Telephone: (35) 5212714

Nursing
Midwifery
Founded 1981.

539 **FACULDADE DE ENFERMAGEM E OBSTETRÍCIA DE SOBRAL**
Avenida da Universidade, 62100 Sobral (Ceará)
Telephone: (55) 6112583

Nursing
Midwifery
Founded 1972.

540 **FACULDADE DE ENFERMAGEM NOSSA SENHORA DAS GRAÇAS**
Rua Arnabio Marques, 50000 Recife (Pernambuco)
Telephone: (81) 2221933

Nursing
Founded 1945. Under the supervision of the Fundação de Ensino Superior de Pernambuco.

541 **FACULDADE DE ENGENHARIA CIVIL DE ITAJUBÁ**
Rua Zequinha Luiz, 37500 Itajubá (Minas Gerais)
Telephone: (035) 6222315

Civil Engineering
Founded 1973. Under the supervision of the Fundação de Ensino e Pesquisa de Itajubá.

Academic Year: February to December (February-June; August-December).
Admission Requirements: Secondary school certificate.
Language of Instruction: Portuguese.
Degrees and Diplomas: Professional title of Engenheiro civil, 5 yrs.
Academic Staff: c. 50.
Student Enrolment: c. 280.

542 **FACULDADE DE ENGENHARIA CIVIL DE PASSOS**
Avenida Juca Stockler, 37900 Passos (Minas Gerais)
Telephone: (35) 5212971

Civil Engineering
Founded 1976.

543 **FACULDADE DE ENGENHARIA DE BARRETOS**
Avenida Prof. Roberto Frade Monte, 14780 Barretos (São Paulo)
Telephone: (173) 226411

Engineering
Founded 1966.

544 **FACULDADE DE ENGENHARIA DE JOINVILLE**
Campus Universitário, 89200 Joinville (Santa Catarina)
Engineering
Founded 1965.

545 **FACULDADE DE ENGENHARIA INDUSTRIAL DE SÃO JOÃO DEL REI**
Praça Frei Orlando 170, 36300 São João del Rei (Minas Gerais)
Telephone: (32) 3711397

Engineering
Founded 1976.

546 **FACULDADE DE FARMACIA E BIOQUÍMICA DO ESPÍRITO SANTO**
Avenida Cleto Nuñes 133, 29000 Vitória (Espírito Santo)
Telephone: (27) 2234344

Pharmacy
Biochemistry
Founded 1975.

547 **FACULDADE DE FILOSOFIA, CIÊNCIAS E LETRAS DE ADAMANTINA**
Rua Nova de Julho 730, 17800 Adamantina (São Paulo)
Telephone: (189) 211176

Philosophy
Science
Letters
Founded 1968.

548 **FACULDADE DE FILOSOFIA, CIÊNCIAS E LETRAS DE ALEGRE**
Rua Belo Amorim 100, 29500 Alegre (Espírito Santo)
Telephone: (27) 5521412

Philosophy
Science
Letters
Founded 1973.

549 **FACULDADE DE FILOSOFIA, CIÊNCIAS E LETRAS DE ARAXA**
Avenida Amazonas, 38180 Araxa (Minas Gerais)
Telephone: (34) 6611920

Philosophy
Science
Letters
Founded 1973.

550 **FACULDADE DE FILOSOFIA, CIÊNCIAS E LETRAS DE BOA ESPERANÇA**
Rua Marechal Floriano Peixoto, 37170 Boa Esperança (Minas Gerais)
Telephone: (35) 9611223

Philosophy
Science
Letters
Founded 1973.

551 **FACULDADE DE FILOSOFIA, CIÊNCIAS E LETRAS DE CABO FRIO**
Avenida Prof. Julio Kubitschek s/n, 28900 Cabo Frio (Rio de Janeiro)
Telephone: (246) 431567

Philosophy
Science
Letters
Founded 1974. *Academic Staff:* c. 10.
Student Enrolment: c. 300.

552 **FACULDADE DE FILOSOFIA, CIÊNCIAS E LETRAS DE CARANGOLA**
Praça dos Estudiantes 23, 36800 Carangola (Minas Gerais)
Telephone: (32) 7411969

Philosophy
Science
Letters
Founded 1972.

553 **FACULDADE DE FILOSOFIA, CIÊNCIAS E LETRAS DE CATANDUVA**
Rua Maranhão, 15800 Catanduva (São Paulo)
Telephone: (175) 5222323

Philosophy
Science
Letters
Founded 1967.

554 **FACULDADE DE FILOSIFIA, CIÊNCIAS E LETRAS DE GUARABIRA**
P.B. 75 Km. 1, 58200 Guarabira (Paraíba)
Telephone: (83) 2711451

Philosophy
Science
Letters
Founded 1970.

555 **FACULDADE DE FILOSOFIA, CIÊNCIAS E LETRAS DE ITAJUBÁ**
Rua Zequinha Luiz, 37500 Itajubá (Minas Gerais)
Telephone: (35) 6221291

Philosophy
Science
Letters
Founded 1965. Under the supervision of the Fundação de Ensino e Pesquisa de Itajubá.
Academic Year: February to December (February-June; August-December).
Admission Requirements: Secondary school certificate.
Language of Instruction: Portuguese.
Degrees and Diplomas: Licenciado, 3-4 yrs.
Academic Staff: c. 50.

556 **FACULDADE DE FILOSOFIA, CIÊNCIAS E LETRAS DE ITUMBIARA**
Avenida de Furnas, 76100 Itumbiara (Goiás)
Telephone: (62) 4313609

Philosophy
Science
Letters
Founded 1979.

557 **FACULDADE DE FILOSOFIA, CIÊNCIAS E ARTES DE JOINVILLE**
Campus Universitário, 89200 Joinville (Santa Catarina)
Telephone: (474) 253200
Diretor: Achiles Julio Schünemann
Diretor de Administração: Romeu Brammer

Philosophy
Science
Lettersand Arts
Founded 1968 by the Fundação Educacional de Região de Joinville.
Academic Year: March to November (March-June; August-November).
Admission Requirements: Secondary school certificate and entrance examination.
Language of Instruction: Portuguese.
Degrees and Diplomas: Bacharel and Licenciado, 4 yrs. Mestrado, Master, a further 2 yrs. Diplomas and specialization, 2 yrs.
Library: Central Library (Alire Gomes Carneiro) of the Foundation, 20,000 vols.
Academic Staff, 1989: c. 60.
Student Enrolment, 1989: c. 770.

558 **FACULDADE DE FILOSOFIA, CIÊNCIAS E LETRAS DE MANDAGUARI**
Rua São Paulo 315, 86970 Mandaguari (Paraná)
Telephone: (442) 331356
Diretora: Clara Katsuda (1985-89)
Secretária: Terezinha Mosconi

D. of History
Chairman: Thereza de Castro Secron; *staff* – (6)
D. of Letters
Chairman: Maria Aparecida Zaneta Peres; *staff* – (7)
D. of Education
Chairman: Maria Pereira de Souza; *staff* – (14)
D. of Science and Mathematics
Chairman: Loadyr Assumpta Brancalhõa; *staff* – (7)
D. of Economics and Accountancy
Chairman: Ivo Miguel Karling; *staff* – (5)
Founded 1966. Under the supervision of the municipal authorities.
Academic Year: March to December.
Admission Requirements: Secondary school certificate and entrance examination.
Fees (Cruzeiros): 2002.44-2640.
Language of Instruction: Portuguese.
Degrees and Diplomas: Bacharel, 4-5 yrs.
Library: 17,433 vols.
Academic Staff, 1986-87: – (35).
Student Enrolment, 1986-87:

	Men	Women	Total
Of the country	270	833	1103

559 **FACULDADE DE FILOSOFIA, CIÊNCIAS E LETRAS DE PATOS DE MINAS**
Rua Irmão Exuperancio 800, 38700 Patos de Minas (Minas Gerais)
Telephone: (34) 8213561

Philosophy

Science
Letters
Founded 1970.

560 **FACULDADE DE FILOSOFIA, CIÊNCIAS E LETRAS DE PATROCÍNIO**
Rua Artur Botelho 403, 38740 Patrocínio (Minas Gerais)
Telephone: (34) 8313737

Philosophy
Science
Letters
Founded 1974.

561 **FACULDADE DE FILOSOFIA, CIÊNCIAS E LETRAS DE POÇOS DE CALDAS**
Avenida Padre Francis Cletus Cox, 37700 Poços de Caldas (Minas Gerais)
Telephone: (34) 7214954

Philosophy
Science
Letters
Founded 1966.

562 **FACULDADE DE FILOSOFIA, CIÊNCIAS E LETRAS DE SANTO ANDRÉ**
Avenida Principe de Gales 821, 09000 Santo André (São Paulo)
Telephone: (11) 4493158

D. of Education
D. of Mathematics
D. of Science
D. of Social Studies
D. of Languages
Founded 1966.

563 **FACULDADE DE FILOSOFIA, CIÊNCIAS E LETRAS DE SÃO JOSÉ DO RIO PARDO**
Avenida Dep. Eduardo Vicente Nasser 1020, 13720 São José do Rio Pardo (São Paulo)
Telephone: (19) 8611704

Philosophy
Science
Letters
Founded 1966.

564 **FACULDADE DE FILOSOFIA DE CIDADE DE GOIÁS**
Rua Maximiana Mendes s/n, 76600 Goiás (Goiás)

Philosophy
Founded 1972.

565 **FACULDADE DE FILOSOFIA DE PASSOS**
Avenida Juca Stockler 1130, 37900 Passos (Minas Gerais)
Telephone: (35) 5212714

Philosophy
Founded 1967.

566 **FACULDADE DE FILOSOFIA DE RIO VERDE**
Rua Senador Martins Borges 269, 76200 Rio Verde (Goiás)
Telephone: (62) 6211839

Philosophy
Founded 1973.

567 **FACULDADE DE FORMAÇÃO DE PROFESSORES DE ALAGOINHAS**
Praça Rui Barbosa s/n, 48100 Alagoinhas (Bahia)
Telephone: (75) 421139

Education
Founded 1972.

568 **FACULDADE DE FORMAÇÃO DE PROFESSORES DE ARARIPINA**
Rua 11 de Setembro 163, 56280 Araripina (Pernambuco)
Telephone: (81) 9311283

Education
Founded 1977.

569 **FACULDADE DE FORMAÇÃO DE PROFESSORES DE ARCOVERDE**
Rua Gumercindo Cavalcante s/n, 56500 Arcoverde (Pernambuco)
Telephone: (81) 8210574

Education

Founded 1970. A municipal institution under the supervision of the Autarquia de Ensino Superior de Arcoverde. Residential facilities for academic staff and students.

Academic Year: March to December (March-July; August-December).

Admission Requirements: Secondary school certificate and entrance examination.

Language of Instruction: Portuguese.

Degrees and Diplomas: Licenciado in–Natural Sciences; Letters; History; Geography, 4 yrs. Postgraduate diplomas of specialization.

Academic Staff, 1986-87: – (45).

Student Enrolment, 1986-87:

	Men	Women	Total
Of the country	480	1581	2061

570 **FACULDADE DE FORMAÇÃO DE PROFESSORES DE BELO JARDIM**
Dr. Henrique do Nascimento s/n, Boa Vista, 55150 Belo Jardim (Pernambuco)
Telephone: (81) 7261929

Education
Founded 1976.

571 **FACULDADE DE FORMAÇÃO DE PROFESSORES DE GARANHUNS**
Praça Souto Filho 696, Heliopolis, 55399 Garanhuns (Pernambuco)
Telephone: (81) 7611343

Education
Founded 1967.

572 **FACULDADE DE FORMAÇÃO DE PROFESSORES DE GOIANA**
Rua Poco do Rei s/n, 55900 Goiana (Pernambuco)
Telephone: (81) 6260517

Education
Founded 1978.

573 **FACULDADE DE FORMAÇÃO DE PROFESSORES DE JACOBINA**
Rua da Aurora, 44700 Jacobina (Bahia)
Telephone: (71) 6212307

Education
Founded 1981.

574 **FACULDADE DE FORMAÇÃO DE PROFESSORES DE MATA SUL**
BR 101 km. 117 Sul, 55545 Palmares (Pernambuco)
Telephone: (81) 6610086

Education

575 **FACULDADE DE FORMAÇÃO DE PROFESSORES DE NAZARÉ DA MATA**
Rua Professor Americo Brandão 43, 55800 Nazaré da Mata (Pernambuco)
Telephone: (81) 6331350

Education
Founded 1967.

576 **FACULDADE DE FORMAÇÃO DE PROFESSORES DE PRIMEIRO GRAU DE PENEDO**
Rua 15 de Novembro, 57200 Penedo (Alagoas)
Telephone: (82) 5512694

Education
Founded 1972.

577 **FACULDADE DE FORMAÇÃO DE PROFESSORES DE PRIMEIRO GRAU DE SERRA TALHADA**
Avenida Afonso Magalhães, 56900 Serra Talhada (Pernambuco)
Telephone: (81) 8311090

Education

578 **FACULDADE DE FORMAÇÃO DE PROFESSORES DE SANTO ANTONIO DE JESUS**
Santo Antonio de Jesus, 44570 Santo Antonio de Jesus (Bahia)
Telephone: (75) 731-2855
Diretor: José Raimundo Galvão

Education; *staff* 7 (18)
Founded 1980.
Academic Year: March to December (March-July; August-December).
Admission Requirements: Graduation from high school or foreign equivalent, and entrance examination.
Language of Instruction: Portuguese.
Degrees and Diplomas: Licenciado.
Library: 3000 vols.
Academic Staff, 1989-90: 4 (21).
Student Enrolment, 1990:

	Men	Women	Total
Of the country	46	132	178

579 **FACULDADE DE FORMAÇÃO DE PROFESSORES DE SÃO GONÇALO**
Rua Dr. Francisco Portela 794, 24400 São Gonçalo (Rio de Janeiro)
Telephone: (21) 7122005

Education
Founded 1973.

580 **FACULDADE DE MEDICINA DE JUNDIAÍ**
Rua Francisco Telles 250, 13200 Jundiaí (São Paulo)
Telephone: (11) 4375726
Diretor: Raymundo Manno Vieira
Secretário Geral: Oswaldo Willy Fehr

Medicine
Founded 1969. Recognized by the federal authorities 1973. Financially supported by the State and municipal authorities.
Academic Year: February to December (February-June; August-December).
Admission Requirements: Secondary school certificate and entrance examination.
Fees (Cruzeiros): 9530 per month.
Language of Instruction: Portuguese.
Degrees and Diplomas: Professional titles in Medicine, 2-6 yrs.
Library: Central Library, *c.* 5145 vols.
Publication: Perspectivas Médicas (quarterly).
Academic Staff, 1990: – (92).
Student Enrolment, 1990:

	Men	Women	Total
Of the country	171	158	329

581 **FACULDADE DE MEDICINA DO TRIÂNGULO MINEIRO**
Praça Manoel Terra, s/n, 38100 Uberaba (Minas Gerais)
Telex: 343206
Telephone: (34) 3333800
Diretor: Valdemar Hial
Registrar: José Henrique Nunes.

Medicine (including Surgery, Pharmacy, Nursing, and Midwifery)
Founded 1954 as a private institution, became federal institution 1972 enjoying academic and administrative autonomy. Financed by the Ministry of Education and Culture.
Academic Year: March to November (March-June; August-November).
Admission Requirements: Secondary school certificate (bachillerato) and entrance examination.
Fees: : None.
Language of Instruction: Portuguese.
Degrees and Diplomas: Professional title of Enfermagem e Obstetricas, 4 yrs; Médico, 6 yrs. Postgraduate Course (lato sensu).
Library: 5942 vols.
Academic Staff, 1990: 117 (11).
Student Enrolment, 1990:

	Men	Women	Total
Of the country	307	247	554

582 **FACULDADE DE ODONTOLOGIA DE NOVO FRIBURGO**
Rua Sylvio H. Braune 22, 28600 Novo Friburgo (Rio de Janeiro)
Telephone: (245) 222916

Dentistry
Founded 1971.

583 **FACULDADE DE ODONTOLOGIA DE PERNAMBUCO**
Avenida Gal Newton Cavalcanti 146, 54730 Recife (Pernambuco)
Telephone: (822) 2713088

Dentistry
Founded 1955, authorized 1957 and officially recognized as a faculty by the federal government 1960. Under thesupervision of the Fundação de Ensino Superior de Pernambuco.
Academic Year: March to December (March-June; August-December).
Admission Requirements: Secondary school certificate and entrance examination.
Language of Instruction: Portuguese.
Degrees and Diplomas: Professional title of Cirurgião dentista, 4 yrs.
Library: *c.* 500 vols.
Publications: Boletim da Faculdade de Odontologia de Pernambuco; Revista de Faculdade de Odontologia de Pernambuco.
Academic Staff: *c.* 50.

584 **FACULDADE DE TECNOLOGIA DE SÃO PAULO**
Praça Cel. Fernando Prestes 30, 01124 São Paulo (São Paulo)
Telephone: (11) 2279443

Engineering
Founded 1970.

585 **FACULDADE DE TECNOLOGIA DE SOROCABA**
Avenida Eng. Carlos Reinaldo Mendes, 18100 Sorocaba (São Paulo)
Telephone: (152) 326881
Diretor: Antonio Carlos Pannunzio
Secretária: Dulce Robiola Salvi

D. of Mathematics and Physics
Head: José Angelo Pezzotta; *staff* 7 (11)
D. of Systems Analysis
Head: Bernardino de Jesus Sanches; *staff* – (7)
D. of Mechanics
Head: Paulo Bona Filho; *staff* 11 (20)
Founded 1970 and incorporated in the Universidade Estadual Paulista 'Júlio de Mesquita Filho' 1976.
Academic Year: February to December (February-June; August-December).
Admission Requirements: Secondary school certificate and entrance examination.
Fees: None.
Language of Instruction: Portuguese.
Degrees and Diplomas: Bacharel, 3 yrs.
Academic Staff, 1986-87: 18 (38).
Student Enrolment, 1986-87:

	Men	Women	Total
Of the country	567	76	643
Of other countries	2	–	2
Total	569	76	645

586 **FACULDADE ESTADUAL DE CIÊNCIAS ECONÔMICAS DE APUCARANA**
Rodovia do Café BR 376, 86800 Apucarana (Paraná)
Telephone: (434) 222071

Economics
Accountancy

Administration
Founded 1961.

587 **FACULDADE ESTADUAL DE DIREITO DO NORTE PIONEIRO**
Avenida Manoel Ribas 711, 86400 Jacarèzinho (Paraná)
Telephone: (437) 220862

Law

Founded 1967 by a decree of the State of Paraná. Under the supervision of the Fundação Faculdade Estadual de Direito do Norte Pioneiro. Financially supported by the State and federal governments. Residential facilities for academic staff and for *c.* 40 students.

Academic Year: February to November (February-June; August-November).

Admission Requirements: Secondary school certificate or equivalent.

Language of Instruction: Portuguese.

Degrees and Diplomas: Bacharel em Direito, 4 yrs.

Library: c. 4950 vols.

Academic Staff: c. 20.

Student Enrolment: c. 280.

588 **FACULDADE ESTADUAL DE EDUCAÇÃO FÍSICA DE JACARÈZINHO**
Avenida Getúlio Vargas 2, 86400 Jacarèzinho (Paraná)
Telephone: (437) 220498

Physical Education
Founded 1972.

589 **FACULDADE ESTADUAL DE FILOSOFIA, CIÊNCIAS E LETRAS DE CORNÉLIO PROCÓPIO**
Avenida Portugal 340, 86300 Cornélio Procópio (Paraná)
Telex: 432624 FFEF
Telephone: (435) 232922
Diretor: Darci Ribeiro da Silva
Secretário Geral: Expedito Pegoraro

D. of Education
Head: Carmen Aparecida Prado Albino
D. of Social Studies
Head: Iokako Hatisuka
D. of Letters
Head: Anibal Campi
D. of Exact Sciences
Head: Ildeu Silvério Filgueiras
D. Administration
Head: Pedro Paulo Barbosa Resende
D. of Economics
Head: Orlando Batista da Fonseca
D. of Accountancy
Head: José do Carmo Benatti Sobrinho
D. of Biological Sciences
Head: Jonhy Roberto Prazeres

Founded 1966. Governing body: the Congregqção

Academic Year: February to December (February-July; August-December.

Admission Requirements: Secondary school certificate and entrance examination.

Fees: None.

Language of Instruction: Portuguese.

Degrees and Diplomas: Bacharel, 3-5 yrs.

Library: 22,679 vols.

Special Facilities (Museums, etc.): Biological Garden.

Academic Staff, 1989-90: 137.

Student Enrolment, 1989-90:

	Men	Women	Total
Of the country	608	1139	1747

590 **FACULDADE ESTADUAL DE FILOSOFIA, CIÊNCIAS E LETRAS DE GUARAPUAVA**
Presidente Zacarias 875, Santa Cruz, 85100 Guarapuava (Paraná)
Telex: 427092
Telephone: (427) 231869
Diretor: Wilson Luiz Camargo (1987-91)
Secretário Geral: José Luiz Andrade Vigil

D. of Letters
Head: Neonila Demczuk Gomes; *staff* 8 (19)
D. of History
Head: Waldemar Feller; *staff* 9 (12)
D. of Geography
Head: Amaury Antonio Martini; *staff* 7 (6)
D. of Education
Head: Clarice Linhares Zoschke; *staff* 13 (16)
D. of Social Studies
D. of Exact and Natural Sciences
Head: Vitor Hugo Zanette; *staff* 13 (16)
D. of Economics
Head: Ernesto Odilo Franciosi; *staff* 1 (7)
D. of Administration
Head: Wilson O. C. Milanez; *staff* 3 (9)
D. of Accountancy
Head: Valdir Michels; *staff* 5 (4)
D. of Law
Head: Sttela Maris N. Lacerda; *staff* 3 (11)
D. of Methodology and Teaching Practice
Head: Deris de Souza·Matos; *staff* 9 (2)

Founded 1970. Under the supervision of the Fundação Estadual.

Academic Year: March to December (March-June; August-December).

Admission Requirements: Secondary school certificate and entrance examination.

Language of Instruction: Portuguese.

Degrees and Diplomas: Licenciado, 3-4 yrs. Mestrado, Master, a further 2 ½ yrs. Diplomas of specialization, 2 yrs.

Library: c. 20,731 vols.

Special Facilities (Museums, etc.): Museum of Entomology.

Publication: Guairacá (literary and scientific magazine).

Academic Staff, 1990:

Rank	Full-time	Part-time
Professores Titulares	26	–
Professores Adjuntos	1	1
Professores Assistentes	28	17
Professores Auxiliares	23	33
Total	78	51

Student Enrolment, 1989:

	Men	Women	Total
Of the country	718	1149	1867

591 **FACULDADE ESTADUAL DE FILOSOFIA, CIÊNCIAS E LETRAS DE JACARÈZINHO**
Rua Padre Melo 1200, 86400 Jacarèzinho (Paraná)
Telephone: (437) 220643

Science
Letters
Education
Founded 1960.

592 **FACULDADE ESTADUAL DE FILOSOFIA, CIÊNCIAS E LETRAS DE PARANAGUÁ**
Rua Comendador Corrêa Júnior 81, 83300 Paranaguá (Paraná)
Telephone: (414) 221242
Diretor: José Carlos Rohn (1976-)
Secretária Geral: Jandira Xavier Gonzaga

D. of Letters
Head: Neide Cury da Paz; *staff* 6 (3)
D. of Education
Head: Brasilio R. Castilho; *staff* 4 (8)
D. of Human Sciences
Head: Abrão Matheus Celestino; *staff* 2 (4)
D. of Natural and Exact Sciences
Head: Luiz Carlos dos Santos; *staff* 3 (8)
D. of Administration and Accountancy
Head: Manoel Pedro Fogagnoli; *staff* 2 (19)

Founded 1956 and authorized by federal decree 1960. Financed by the State.

Academic Year: March to December (March-June; August-December).

Admission Requirements: Graduation from high school and entrance examination.

Fees: None.

Language of Instruction: Portuguese.

Degrees and Diplomas: Bacharel and Licenciado, 4 yrs.
Library: Biblioteca Prof. Guilherme Guímbala, 15,656 vols.
Academic Staff, 1990:

Rank	Full-time	Part-time
Professores Collaboratores	–	3
Professores Auxiliares	1	29
Professores Assistentes	14	11
Professores Adjuntos	3	2
Total	18	45

Student Enrolment, 1990:

	Men	Women	Total
Of the country	519	758	1277
Of other countries	5	–	5
Total	524	758	1282

593 **FACULDADE ESTADUAL DE FILOSOFIA, CIÊNCIAS E LETRAS DE UNIÃO DE VITÓRIA**
Praça Coronel Amazonas s/n, Caixa postal 234, 84600 União de Vitória (Paraná)
Telephone: (425) 224433
Diretor: Nelson Antônio Sicuro (1983-87)
Secretário Geral: Isael Pastuch

D. of Education
Head: Delci Aparecida Hausen Christ; *staff* – (14)
D. of History
Head: Estephano Makiak; *staff* – (8)
D. of Geography
Head: João Hort; *staff* – (5)
D. of Letters
Head: Sandra Regina Moura Konell; *staff* – (8)
D. of Science
Head: Valdir Vieira; *staff* – (6)

Founded 1960.
Academic Year: March to December (March-June; August-December).
Admission Requirements: Secondary school certificate and entrance examination.
Language of Instruction: Portuguese.
Degrees and Diplomas: Licenciado in all fields, 4 yrs.
Library: Central Library, 22,000 vols.
Academic Staff, 1986-87: – (46).
Student Enrolment, 1986-87:

	Men	Women	Total
Of the country	164	652	816

594 **FACULDADE ESTADUAL DE MEDICINA DO PARÁ**
Trav. 14 de Abril 1462, 66000 Belém (Pará)
Telephone: (91) 2293046

Medicine

Founded 1971.

595 **FACULDADE FEDERAL DE CIÊNCIAS MÉDICAS DE PROTO ALÊGRE**
Prof. Sarmento Leite 245, 90000 Porto Alêgre (Rio Grande do Sul)
Telephone: (51) 2248615

Medicine

Founded 1961.

596 **FACULDADE FEDERAL DE ODONTOLOGIA DE DIAMANTINA**
Rua da Glória 187, Caixa Postal 38, 39100 Diamantina (Minas Gerais)
Telex: 387044
Telephone: (37) 9311024
Diretor: Agnus Aécio de Meira (1990-94)
Secretário Geral: José da Purificacão Miranda

Dentistry

Founded 1953. Financially supported by the Ministry of Education and Culture. Governing body: the Congregação. Residential facilities for *c.* 20 students.

Arrangements for co-operation with the University of Northern Colorado.

Academic Year: February to December (February-July; August-December).
Admission Requirements: Secondary school certificate.
Language of Instruction: Portuguese.
Degrees and Diplomas: Professional title of Cirurgião Dentista, 4 yrs.
Library: *c.* 4400 vols.
Academic Staff, 1986-87: *c.* 30 (10).
Student Enrolment, 1986-87:

	Men	Women	Total
Of the country	96	85	181
Of other countries	4	1	5
Total	100	86	186

597 **FACULDADE MUNICIPAL DE ADMINISTRAÇÃO E CIÊNCIAS ECONÔMICAS DE UNIÃO DA VITÓRIA**
Avenida Bento Munhoz da Rocha Neto 3856, União da Vitória (Paraná)
Telephone: (42) 5221837

Administrative Studies
Economics

Founded 1975.

598 **FACULDADE MUNICIPAL DE EDUCAÇÃO, CIÊNCIAS E LETRAS DE PARANAVAÍ**
Avenida Gabril Esperidião, 87700 Paranavaí (Pakaná)
Telephone: (444) 220943

Education
Science
Letters

Founded 1966.

599 **FACULDADE OLINDENSE DE FORMAÇÃO DE PROFESSORES**
Avenida Getúlio Vargas 1360, Novo, 53000 Olinda (Pernambuco)
Telephone: (81) 4290957

Education

Founded 1973.

600 **FACULDADES REUNIDAS DE ADMINISTRAÇÃO, CIÊNCIAS CONTÂBEIS E CIÊNCIAS ECONÔMICAS DE PALMAS**
Rua Dr. Bernardo Ribeiro Viana 903, 84670 Palmas (Paraná)
Telephone: (462) 621287

Administration
Accountancy
Economics

Founded 1980.

601 **INSTITUTO DE CIENCIAS LETRAS E ARTES DE TRES CORAÇÕES**
Avenida Castelo Branco 82, Chaeara das Rosas, 37410 Tres Corações (Minas Gerais)
Telephone: (35) 2313924

Science
Letters
Arts

Founded 1967.

602 **INSTITUTO DE EDUCAÇÃO DE MINAS GERAIS**
Rua Pernambuco s/n, 30130 Belo Horizonte (Minas Gerais)
Telephone: (31) 2229637

Education

Founded 1970.

603 **INSTITUTO DE ENSINO SUPERIOR DE CACERES**
Praça Duque de Caxias s/n, 78700 Caceres (Minas Gerais)

Science
Languages
Social Studies

Founded 1970.

604 **INSTITUTO DE ENSINO SUPERIOR DE MOCACA**
Praça Madre Cabrini 87, Vila Mariano, 13730 Mococa (São Paulo)
Telephone: (19) 6550340

Library Science
Education

Founded 1973.

605 **INSTITUTO DE MATEMÁTICA PURA E APLICADA**
Edifício Lélio Gama, 22460 Rio de Janeiro (Rio de Janeiro)
Telex: 2121145 IAMP
Telephone: (21) 2949032
Fax: (21) 5124115
Diretor: Elon Lages Lima (1989-93)

Pure and Applied Mathematics

Founded 1952 by the National Council for Scientific and Technological Development. An institution of graduate studies financially supported by the federal government. Governing body: the Conselho Técnico Científico.

Academic Year: January to November (January-February; March-June; July-November).

Admission Requirements: Degree of Bachelor in Mathematics.

Fees: None.

Language of Instruction: Portuguese.

Degrees and Diplomas: Mestre em: Matemática; Matemática Aplicada, 2-3 yrs. Doutor em Ciências, a further 3-5 yrs.

Library: c. 55,000 vols.

Publications: Projeto Euclides; Monografias de Matématica.

Academic Staff, 1990: 38.

Student Enrolment, 1990: 94.

606 **INSTITUTO DE PESQUISAS ESPACIAIS DE SÃO JOSÉ DOS CAMPOS**
Avenida dos Astronauts 1758, 12200 São José dos Campos (São Paulo)
Telex: 11-33530
Telephone: (12) 2228333

Computer Science
Education
Engineering

Founded 1961. A postgraduate institution.

607 **INSTITUTO MUNICIPAL DE ENSINO SUPERIOR DE PRESIDENTE PRUDENTE**
Rua Robert Simonsen 300, 19100 Presidente Prudente (São Paulo)

Physical Education
Physics and Biology
Human Sciences and Education

Founded 1971.

608 **INSTITUTO MUNICIPAL DE ENSINO SUPERIOR DE SÃO CAETANO DO SUL**
Avenida Goiás 3400, Barcelona, 09500 São Caetano do Sul (São Paulo)
Telephone: (11) 4531577

D. of Economics
D. of Business Administration
D. of Quantitative Methods
D. of Law
D. of Social and Political Sciences
D. of International Business Administration

Founded 1968. Under the supervision of the municipal authorities.

Academic Year: March to December.

Admission Requirements: Secondary school certificate and entrance examination.

Language of Instruction: Portuguese.

Degrees and Diplomas: Licenciado, 4 yrs.

Library: c. 7200 vols.

Academic Staff: c. – (100).

Student Enrolment: c. 3000.

609 **INSTITUTO RIO BRANCO**
Brazilian Diplomatic Academy
Esplanada dos Ministérios, 70170 Brasília (Distrito Federal)
Cables: Exteriores
Telex: (61) 1311/1319
Telephone: (61) 2116194
Fax: 2237362
Diretora: Thereza Maria Machado Quintella (1987-)
Chefe da Sercretária: Ana Candida Perez

Diplomatic Studies

Founded 1945. A State institution under the jurisdiction of the Ministry of Foreign Affairs. Residential facilities for students.

Academic Year: February to November (February-July; August-November).

Admission Requirements: Three years of undergraduate study and entrance examination.

Fees: None.

Language of Instruction: Portuguese.

Degrees and Diplomas: Certificate, 2 yrs.

Publication: Yearbook (annually).

Academic Staff, 1990: – (38).

Student Enrolment, 1990:

	Men	Women	Total
Of the country	32	5	37
Of other countries	9	3	12
Total	41	8	49

610 **INSTITUTO SUPERIOR DE CIÊNCIAS, ARTES E HUMANIDADES DE LAVRAS**
Rua Padre José Poggel 506, Centenario, 37200 Lavras (Minas Gerais)
Telephone: (35) 821-2233
Diretora: Vera Aparecida Guerra (1990-)
Secretária: Carmen Lúcia Coelho dos Passos

D. of Dentistry
Head: Ronaldo de Carvalho; *staff* – (34)
D. of Language and Literature
Head: Maria Aparecida Possato; *staff* – (6)
D. of Biology
Head: Antonio Claret Guimarães; *staff* – (8)
D. of Exact Sciences
Head: José Francisco Faria; *staff* – (6)
D. of Human Sciences
Head: Rosangela Moura Cortez; *staff* – (7)
D. of Education
Head: Sérgio Wagner de Oliveira; *staff* – (7)

Founded 1969.

Academic Year: February to Dceember.

Admission Requirements: Secondary school certificate and entrance examination.

Language of Instruction: Portuguese.

Degrees and Diplomas: Bacharel in Dentistry, 4 yrs. Licenciado in–Philosophy; Letters; Education, 3 yrs; Science, 4 yrs.

Library: c. 12,000 vols.

Special Facilities (Museums, etc.): Museum of Geology (in process of development).

Academic Staff, 1990: – (68).

Student Enrolment, 1990:

	Men	Women	Total
Of the country	237	1033	1270

611 **INSTITUTO TECNOLÓGICO DE AERONÁUTICA**
Institute of Aeronautical Technology
C.T.A. - I.T.A. 12225 São José dos Campos (São Paulo)
Telex: 11-33393
Telephone: (123) 21-2575
Fax: (123) 22-6638
Reitor: Jessen Vidal
Diretor Administrativo: Mauro Gonçalves de Oliveira

D. of Basic Studies and Humanities (including Mathematics, Physics, Chemistry)
D. of Aeronautical Engineering (including Astronomy)
D. of Electrical Engineering
D. of Aeronautical Civil Engineering
D. of Aeronautical Mechanical Engineering

D. of Data Processing
Postgraduate D.
Junior C. of Engineering

Founded 1950, the institute is a State institution under the jurisdiction of the Air Ministry. Financed by thefederal government. Residential facilities for academic staff and students.

Academic Year: March to December (March-July; August-December).

Admission Requirements: Secondary school certificate.

Language of Instruction: Portuguese.

Degrees and Diplomas: Professional title of–Engenheiro, in various fields, 5 yrs. Mestre–em Ciência; em Engenharia, a further 1-2 yrs. Doutor, a further 2 yrs.

Library: 81,463 vols.

Publication: ITA-Engenharia Journal.

Academic Staff, 1989-90: 153 (7).

Student Enrolment, 1989-90:

	Men	Women	Total
Of the country	960	88	1048

Private Institutions

612 **CENTRO CIBERNETICO GAY-LUSSAC**
Rua Eduardo Luiz Gomes 134, 24020 Niterói (Rio de Janeiro)
Telephone: (21) 719747

Economics
Administration

Founded 1976. Under the supervision of the Gay-Lussac Instituto de Ensino Superior.

Academic Year: March to December (March-July; August-December).

Admission Requirements: Secondary school certificate and entrance examination.

Language of Instruction: Portuguese.

Degrees and Diplomas: Bacharel, 4 yrs.

Library: c. 5000 vols.

Academic Staff: c. 50.

Student Enrolment: c. 680.

613 **CENTRO DE CIÊNCIAS HUMANAS E SOCIAIS**
Rua Mariz e Barros 612, 20270 Rio de Janeiro (Rio de Janeiro)
Telephone: (21) 2843749

Human Sciences
Social Sciences

Founded 1973.

614 **CENTRO DE ENSINO SUPERIOR**
Estrada Chapeco, São Carlos Km. 07, 89800 Chapeco (Santa Catarina)
Telephone: (49) 7222033

D. of Administration
D. of Accountancy
D. of Education
D. of Exact Sciences
D. of Human and Social Sciences
Extension D.

Founded 1971. Under the supervision of the Fundação de Ensino do Desenvolvimento do Oeste.

Academic Year: March to December (March-July; August-December).

Admission Requirements: Secondary school certificate.

Language of Instruction: Portuguese.

Degrees and Diplomas: Bacharel in–Administration; Accountancy. Licenciado in–Education; Science; Social Studies; Letters.

Academic Staff: c. 80.

Student Enrolment: c. 550.

615 **CENTRO DE ENSINO SUPERIOR DE EREXIM**
Avenida Sete de Setembro 1621, 99700 Erexim (Rio Grande do Sul)
Telephone: (54) 3211943
Diretor: João Dautartas

D. of Education
Head: Maria Lourdes Bortolanza; *staff* – (12)
D. of Letters
Head: Paulo Marçal Mescka; *staff* 4 (8)
D. of Social Studies
Head: Neide Lourdes Piran; *staff* 6 (2)
D. of Science
Head: Alice Teresa Valduga; *staff* 5 (13)
D. of Economics and Business Administration
Head: Luiz Fernando Rohenkol; *staff* – (12)
D. of Agrarian Sciences
Head: Alice Teresinha Valduga; *staff* 1 (8)
Teaching Techniques D.
Head: Glênio Renan Cabral; *staff* 4 (11)
Accounting and Law D.
Head: Hélio Milton Severo;
Research and Extension D.
Head: Alindo Butzke; *staff* 2 (10)

Founded 1975. Under the supervision of the Fundação Alto Uruguai para a Pesquisa e o Ensino Superior. Some residential facilities for students.

Academic Year: March to December (March-June; August-December).

Admission Requirements: Secondary school certificate and entrance examination.

Fees (Cruzeiros): 185.78 per course.

Language of Instruction: Portuguese.

Degrees and Diplomas: Bacharel in Administration, 5 yrs. Licenciado in–Science, 3 yrs; Commercial and Work Techniques; Agriculture,3 ½ yrs; Administration; Education; Letters and Social Studies, 4 yrs; Accounting Sciences, 5 yrs.

Library: c. 24,166 vols.

Publications: Perspectiva (quarterly); Pesquisas Regionais (series).

Academic Staff, 1989: 52 (109).

Student Enrolment, 1989:

	Men	Women	Total
Of the country	415	582	997

616 **CENTRO DE ENSINO SUPERIOR DE JARAGUA DO SUL**
Avenida dos Immigrantes, 89250 Jaragua do Sul (Santa Catarina)
Telephone: (473) 720983

Education
Philosophy
Mathematics
Economics
Administration

Founded 1985.

617 **CENTRO DE ENSINO SUPERIOR DE JUIZ DE FORA**
Rua Halfeld 1179, 36100 Juiz de Fora (Minas Gerais)
Telephone: (32) 2118683

Science
Arts
Social Science
Letters
Education
Psychology
Biology

Founded 1972.

618 **CENTRO DE ENSINO SUPERIOR DE SANT'ANA DO LIVRAMENTO**
Avenida Daltro Filho 1537, 97570 Sant'Ana do Livramento (Rio Grande do Sul)
Telephone: (55) 2421621

I. of Agro-Technology
F. of Economics and Accountancy
F. of Education

Founded 1981.

619 **CENTRO DE ENSINO SUPERIOR DE SÃO CARLOS**
Avenida José Pereira Lopes 252, 13560 São Carlos (São Paulo)
Telephone: (16) 2711255

Social Science
Administration
Accountancy
Industrial Arts
Exact Sciences
Education

Law
Founded 1972.

620 **CENTRO DE ENSINO SUPERIOR PLINIO MENDES DOS SANTOS**
Rua Ceará 333, 79100 Campo Grande (Mato Grosso do Sul)
Telephone: (67) 3827660

Accountancy
Administration, Economics, and Commerce
Law
Founded 1976.

621 **CENTRO DE ENSINO UNIFICADO DE BRASÍLIA**
EQN 707/707, Campus Universitário Asa Norte Comercial, 70351 Brasília (Distrito Federal)
Telephone: (612) 272-1000
President: João Herculino de Souza Lopes
General Co-ordinator: Mauricio de Souza Neves Filho

F. of Law
Director: Amaury Serralvo
F. of Philosophy
Director: Carlos Alberto Cruz
F. of Education
Director: Neide Fonseca de Oliveira; *staff* 5 (25)
F. of Economics and Administration (including Accountancy)
Director: Luiz Edmar Lima; *staff* 8 (30)
D. of Software Technology
Director: José Pereira; *staff* 5 (15)
Founded 1967.
Academic Year: February to December (February-June; August-December).
Admission Requirements: Secondary school certificate and entrance examination.
Language of Instruction: Portuguese.
Degrees and Diplomas: Bacharel in–Economics; Accountancy; Administration; Social Communication, 4 yrs; Law, 5 yrs. Licenciado in–Psychology; Geography; History; Letters; Science; Social Studies; Education, 2-4 yrs. Professional title in Psychology, 5 yrs.
Libraries: Central Library, *c.* 60,000 vols; Book Bank, *c.* 33,000 vols.
Publication: Universitas (quarterly).
Academic Staff: c.– (320).
Student Enrolment, 1989-90:

	Men	Women	Total
Of the country	6125	4375	10,500
Of other countries	83	17	100
Total	6208	4392	10,600

622 **CENTRO DE ESTUDOS SUPERIORES DO CARMO**
Rua Egydio Martins 181, 11030 Santos (São Paulo)
Telephone: (132) 361735

Physics
Science
Chemistry
Education
Founded 1929.

623 **CENTRO DE ESTUDOS SUPERIORES DE LONDRINA**
Rua Juscelino Kubitschek 1260, 86100 Londrina (Paraná)
Telephone: (432) 272150

D. of Psychology
D. of Social Sciences
D. of Architecture and Town Planning
D. of Education
D. of Science
D. of Data Processing
D. of Nursing and Midwifery
Founded 1972. Under the supervision of the Evangelical Churches of Londrina.
Academic Year: February to December.
Admission Requirements: Secondary school certificate or equivalent.
Language of Instruction: Portuguese.
Degrees and Diplomas: Licenciado.
Publication: Terra e Cultura.
Academic Staff: c. 80.
Student Enrolment: c. 1100.

624 **CENTRO DE ESTUDOS SUPERIORES DE MACEIÓ**
Rua Conego Machado, 57055 Maceió (Alagoas)
Telephone: (82) 2215008

F. of Law
F. of Philosophy, Science and Letters
I. of Psychology
F. of Administration and Accountancy
S. of Science and Education
S. of Technology
Founded 1974. Under the supervision of the Fundação Educacional Jayme de Altavila.

625 **CENTRO DE ESTUDOS SUPERIORES DO ESTADO DO PARÁ**
Avenida Alcindo Cacela 287, 66000 Belém (Pará)
Telephone: (91) 2232100

D. of Law
D. of Public and Business Administration
D. of Economics
Founded 1974. Under the supervision of the Associação Paraense de Ensino e Cultura.
Academic Year: February to December (February-June; August-December).
Admission Requirements: Secondary school certificate and entrance examination.
Language of Instruction: Portuguese.
Degrees and Diplomas: Bacharel. Professional titles of Técnico.
Library: Central Library, *c.* 20,000 vols.
Publication: Roteiros.
Academic Staff: c. 130.
Student Enrolment: c. 2580.

626 **CENTRO DE FORMAÇÃO DE PROFESSORES DE DISCIPLINAS ESPECIALIZADAS**
Avenida Cussy de Almeida 187, 16100 Araçatuba (São Paulo)
Telephone: (186) 231188

Education
Founded 1976.

627 **CENTRO EDUCACIONAL LA SALLE DE ENSINO SUPERIOR**
Avenida Victor Barreto 2288, 92000 Canõas (Rio Grande do Sul)
Telephone: (512) 724411
Diretor: Irmão Sérgio Silveira Dias (1984-88)
Secretário: Gregório Menegat

D. of Philosophy, Political Science, Sociology, and Theology
Head: Solon Eduardo Annes Viola; *staff* 7 (18)
D. of Portuguese Language and Literature
Head: Clarice T. Arenhart Menegat; *staff* – (12)
D. of Didactics
Head: Mari Margarete dos Santos; *staff* – (21)
D. of Fundamentals of Education
Head: Bruno Edgar Ries; *staff* – (12)
Founded 1972. Under the supervision of the Sociedade Porvir Científico (Civil Society of the Christian Brothers).
Academic Year: March to November (March-July; August-November).
Admission Requirements: Secondary school certificate and entrance examination.
Fees (Cruzeiros): 113.04 per credit per semester.
Language of Instruction: Portuguese.
Degrees and Diplomas: Licenciado, 4 yrs.
Library: 55,120 vols.
Publications: Bulletins; Revista Integração.
Academic Staff, 1986-87: 26 (63).
Student Enrolment, 1986-87:

	Men	Women	Total
Of the country	89	827	916

628 **CENTRO INTEGRADO DE ENSINO SUPERIOR DE ALEGRETE**
Praça Getulio Vargas, 97540 Alegrete (Rio Grande do Sul)
Telephone: (55) 4221105

Education
Social Sciences
Philosophy and Psychology
Letters
Sciences
Administration
Economics
Statistics

Founded 1973.

629 **CENTRO SUPERIOR DE CIÊNCIAS SOCIAIS DE VILA VELHA**
Rua Sete de Setembro 70, Centro, 92010 Vila Velha (Espírito Santo)
Telephone: (27) 2291661

Social Science

Founded 1976.

630 **CENTROS INTEGRADOS DE ENSINO SUPERIOR FARIAS BRITO**
Praça Teresa Cristina 1, 07000 Guarulhos (São Paulo)
Telephone: (11) 2093688
Diretor Geral: João Cipriano de Freitas (1980-88)
Secretário Geral: Raul Virginio da Silva Filho

Ce. of Exact and Natural Sciences
Ce. of Health Sciences (Nursing and Psychology)
Ce. of Arts and Architecture
Ce. of Human Sciences
Ce. of Education
Ce. of Technology

Also secondary college.

Founded 1982, incorporating faculties created since 1970. Under the supervision of the Associação Paulistade Educação e Cultura.

Academic Year: February to December (February-June; August-December).

Admission Requirements: Secondary school certificate and entrance examination.

Language of Instruction: Portuguese.

Degrees and Diplomas: Bacharel and Licenciado in all fields, 4 yrs. Professional titles of–Arquiteto; Químico industrial; Psicólogo; Enfermeiro médico-cirurgico; Artista plástico; Desenhista industrial; Geógrafo; Historiador; Fisico; Sociólogo. Postgraduate diplomas of specialization.

Library: Central Library 'Fernando G. da Fonseca'.

Special Facilities (Museums, etc.): Mineralogy Museum.

Publications: Earth Sciences Bulletin (annually); Informativo Farias Brito (monthly).

Academic Staff: c. 100.

Student Enrolment: c. 5220.

631 ***CONJUNTO UNIVERSITARIO CANDIDO MENDES**
Candido Mendes University Conglomerate
Praça XV de Novembro 101, Centro, 20010 Rio de Janeiro (Rio de Janeiro)
Telephone: (21) 2226201
Presidente: Candido Mendes

F. of Political Science and Economics (2)
F. of Law (2)
F. of Law, Economics, Administration, Accountancy, and Education
F. of Economics, Administration, and Accountancy (Campos)
F. of Business Administration (Friburgo)

Also 12 Centres for Study and Research.

Founded 1981, incorporating independent faculties, established between 1919 and 1978, and consisting of 4 teaching units, 12 centres for study and research, 2 cultural centres and 2 art galleries. Under the supervision of the Sociedade Brasileira Instrução, founded 1902, and recognized by the Federal authorities.

Academic Year: February to December (February-June; August-December).

Admission Requirements: Secondary school certificate and entrance examination.

Language of Instruction: Portuguese.

Degrees and Diplomas: Bacharel, 4-5 yrs. Degree of Mestre, a further 2-3 yrs. Doutorado, 4-5 yrs.

Library: Total, c. 40,000 vols.

Special Facilities (Museums, etc.): Mineralogy Museum.

Academic Staff: c. 500.

Student Enrolment: c. 9800.

632 **CONSERVATÓRIO BRASILEIRO DE MÚSICA**
Brazilian Conservatory of Music
Graça Aranha Avenida 57, 12-andar, 20030 Rio de Janeiro (Rio de Janeiro)
Telephone: (212) 2406131
General Director: Marina Helena Lorenzo Fernandez Silva (1990-94)

Music
Music Therapy
Research Ce.

Co-ordinator: José Maria Neves

Founded 1936.

Academic Year: March to December (March-June; August; November).

Admission Requirements: Secondary school certificate.

Language of Instruction: Portuguese

Degrees and Diplomas: Bacharel in–Music; Music Therapy. Postgraduate in Musicology, Ethnomusicology and Music Education.

Library: Library, 6,500 vols.

Academic Staff, 1990: 25 (103).

Student Enrolment, 1990:

	Men	Women	Total
Of the country	475	845	1320

633 **CONSERVATÓRIO DRAMÁTICO E MUSICAL DE SÃO PAULO**
Rua Conselheiro Crispincano, 01037 São Paulo (São Paulo)
Telephone: (11) 2239231

Dramatic Art
Music

Founded 1941.

634 **CONSERVATÓRIO DE MÚSICA**
Rua São Pedro 96, 24000 Niterói (Rio de Janeiro)
Telephone: (21) 7192330

Music

Founded 1965.

635 **CONSERVATÓRIO MUSICAL DE SANTOS**
Rua Dr. Egydio Martins, 11100 Santos (São Paulo)
Telephone: (132) 361735

Music

Founded 1927.

636 **CURSO DE ESTUDOS SOCIAIS DE JAGUARÃO**
Rua 15 de Novembro, 96300 Jaguarão (Rio Grande do Sul)
Telephone: (532) 611868

Social Studies

Founded 1984.

637 **ESCOLA BRASILEIRA DE ADMINISTRAÇÃO PÚBLICA**
Praia de Botafogo 190, 5o andar, 22253 Rio de Janeiro (Rio de Janeiro)
Cables: fugevar
Telephone: (21) 551-35-99
Fax: (21) 23-840
Diretor: Bianor Scelza Cavalcanti
Secretária Geral: Vania Marilda S. Piçarra da Cru

Public Administration

Founded 1952 by the Fundação Getúlio Vargas. A private postgraduate institution. Governing bodies: the Congregaçao; the Conselho Departamental.

Arrangements for co-operation with: Centre d'Enseignement supérieurs des Affaires, Jouy-en-Josas; Université de Paris I; Universidad del Valle, Cali; Universidad Externado de Colombia; Pittsburgh University; London Graduate Business School; University of Seville.

Academic Year: March to December (March-June; June-August; September-December).

Admission Requirements: University degree.

Language of Instruction: Portuguese.

Degrees and Diplomas: Mestrado, master, 2 yrs.

Library: Central library, 96,660 vols.
Publication: Revista de Administração Pública (quarterly).
Academic Staff, 1990: c. 25 (4).
Student Enrolment, 1990:

	Total
Of the country	60
Of other countries	300
Total	360

638 **ESCOLA DE ADMINISTRAÇÃO DE EMPRESAS DE SÃO PAULO**
São Paulo Business School
Avenida Nove de Julho 2029, 01313 São Paulo (São Paulo)
Telex: 11-37563
Telephone: (11) 284-23-11
Fax: (11) 284-17-89
Electronic mail: BITNET: fcvsp02@6abrfapesp
Dean: Marcos Cintra Cavalcanti de Albuquerque (1987-91)
Secretária: Hamilton Madureira Villela

Business Administration
Public Administration
Economics

Founded 1954 by the Fundação Getúlio Vargas.

Arrangements for co-operation with: London Graduate Business School; Escuela Superior de Administración y Dirección de Empresas, Barcelona; Ecole des hautes Etudes commerciales, Lille; Centre d'Enseignement supérieur des Affaires, Jouy-en-Josas; Stockholm School of Economics; PIM Network.

Academic Year: March to December (March-June; August-December).

Admission Requirements: Secondary school certificate and entrance examination.

Language of Instruction: Portuguese.

Degrees and Diplomas: Bacharel in–Business Administration; Public Administration, 4 yrs. Mestrado, master in–Business Administration; Public Administration; Economics, a further 2 yrs. Doutorado, doctorate in–Businesss Administration; Pulic Administratino; Economics. Also postgraduate diploma of specialization.

Library: 117,532 vols.
Publication: Revista de Administração de Empresas.
Press or Publishing House: Editora da FGV.
Academic Staff, 1988-89:

Rank	Full-time	Part-time
Professores Titulares	40	8
Professores Adjuntos	22	5
Professores Assistentes	29	5
Professores Contratados	–	17
Professores Horistas	–	142
Total	91	177

Student Enrolment, 1988-89: 3220.

639 **ESCOLA DE ADMINISTRAÇÃO E INFORMATICA DE SANTA RITA DO SAPUCAÍ**
Avenida Antonio de Cassisa 472, 37540 Santa Rita do Sapucaí (Minas Gerais)

Administration and Computer Sciences

Founded 1971.

640 **ESCOLA DE BIBLIOTECONOMIA**
Avenida Dr. Arnaldo de Senna, 37290 Formigá (Minas Gerais)
Telephone: (37) 3212997

Library Science

Founded 1968. Under the supervision of the Fundação de Ensino Superior de Oeste de Minas.

Academic Year: February to November (February-June; August-November).

Admission Requirements: Secondary school certificate or equivalent and entrance examination.

Language of Instruction: Portuguese.

Degrees and Diplomas: Bacharel em Biblioteconomia, 4 yrs.

Academic Staff: c. 20.

641 **ESCOLA DE CIÊNCIAS CONTÁBEIS**
Fazenda Tres Poçis s/n, 27180 Volta Redonda (Rio de Janeiro)
Telephone: (243) 422313
Diretor: Luiz Gonzaga Balbi

Accountancy

Founded 1974. Under the supervision of the Fundação Oswaldo Aranha.

Academic Year: February to December (February-July; August-December).

Admission Requirements: Secondary school certificate and entrance examination.

Language of Instruction: Portuguese.

Degrees and Diplomas: Bacharel in Accountancy, 4 yrs.

Library: c. 2250 vols.

Academic Staff: c. 310.

642 **ESCOLA DE CIÊNCIAS MÉDICAS DE VOLTA REDONDA**
Fazenda Tres Poços-est., Pinheiral/Volta Redonda, 27180 Volta Redonda (Rio de Janeiro)
Telephone: (243) 426404
Diretor: Walter Luiz M.S. da Fonseca

Medicine

Founded 1968. Under the supervision of the Fundação Oswaldo Aranha.

Academic Year: February to December (February-July; August-December).

Admission Requirements: Secondary school certificate and entrance examination.

Language of Instruction: Portuguese.

Degrees and Diplomas: Professional title of Médico, 6 yrs.

643 **ESCOLA DE EDUCAÇÃO FÍSICA DE ASSIS**
Avenida Doctor Doria 204, 19800 Assis (São Paulo)
Telephone: (183) 222552

Physical Education

Founded 1970.

644 **ESCOLA DE EDUCAÇÃO FÍSICA DE BAURU**
Praça 9 de Julho 1-51, 17100 Bauru (São Paulo)
Telephone: (0142) 233911

Physical Education

Founded 1952.

645 **ESCOLA DE EDUCAÇÃO FÍSICA DE SÃO CARLOS**
Rua S. Sebastião s/n, 2828, 13560 São Carlos (São Paulo)
Telephone: (162) 721320
Diretor: Haydée Pozzi Semeghini

Physical Education

Founded 1949. Governing body: the Congregação.

Admission Requirements: Secondary school certificate and entrance examination.

Fees: 15,100 per semester.

Language of Instruction: Portuguese.

Degrees and Diplomas: Licenciado, 4 yrs.

Library: 5000 vols.

Academic Staff, 1990: – (25).

	Men	Women	Total
Of the country	235	323	558

646 **ESCOLA DE EDUCAÇÃO FÍSICA DE VOLTA REDONDA**
Rua 21 s/n, Santa Cecília, 27180 Volta Redonda (Rio de Janeiro)
Telephone: (243) 421560
Diretor: Nize Santiago Imbruglia

Physical Education

Founded 1971. Under the supervision of the Fundação Oswaldo Aranha.

Academic Year: February to December.

Admission Requirements: Secondary school certificate and entrance examination.

Language of Instruction: Portuguese.

Degrees and Diplomas: Licenciado, 4 yrs.

647 **ESCOLA DE ENFERMAGEM SANTA EMILIA DE RODAT**
Praça Caldas Brandão s/n, 58000 João Pessoa (Paraíba)
Telephone: (83) 2212925

Nursing (including Midwifery)

Founded 1959.

648 **ESCOLA DE ENFERMAGEM WENCESLAU BRAZ**
Avenida Cesário Alvim 566, 37500 Itajubá (Minas Gerais)
Telephone: (35) 622-09-30
Diretor: Lucyla Junqueira Carneiro

D. of Nursing (including Midwifery)
Co-ordinator: Débora V.A. Lisboa Vilela; *staff* 15 (2)
D. of Social and Human Sciences
Co-ordinator: Maria Ligia M. Carneiro; *staff* 3 (5)
D. of Basic Sciences
Co-ordinator: Agostinha Silva; *staff* – (9)

Founded 1955 by the Santa Casa de Misericórdia de Itajubá. A private institution recognized and financially assisted by the federal government. Residential facilities for academic staff.

Academic Year: March to November (March-June; August-November).

Admission Requirements: Secondary school certificate.

Language of Instruction: Portuguese.

Degrees and Diplomas: Professional titles of–Enfermeiro, 4 yrs; Enfermeiro de Saúde pública do Trabalho, 5 yrs.

Library: c. 4430 vols.

Academic Staff, 1989-90: 15 (12).

Student Enrolment, 1989-90:

	Men	Women	Total
Of the country	11	153	164
Of other countries	3	49	52
Total	14	202	216

649 **ESCOLA DE ENGENHARIA DE LINS**
Avenida Nicolau Zarvos 1925, 16400 Lins (São Paulo)
Telephone: (145) 222300

D. of Civil Engineering
Head: Aziz Kalaf Filho; *staff* 02 (32)
D. of Electrical Engineering
Head: Aziz Kalaf Filho; *staff* 2 (32)
D. of Electronic Engineering
Head: Aziz Kalaf Filho; *staff* 2 (23)
D. of Data Processing Technology
Head: Maria Emilce Ferreira Villela *staff* 2 (17)

Founded 1964.

Academic Year: March to November (March-June; August-November).

Admission Requirements: Secondary school certificate and entrance examination.

Fees (Cruzeiros): 186 per credit.

Language of Instruction: Portuguese.

Degrees and Diplomas: Professional titles of–Tecnólogo em Processamento de Dados, 3 yrs; Engenheiro civil; Engenheiro electricista, 5 yrs.

Library: c. 10,000 vols.

Academic Staff, 1989-90: 7 (81).

Student Enrolment: c. 1300.

	Men	Women	Total
Of the country	670	183	853

650 **ESCOLA DE ENGENHARIA DE VASSOURAS**
Avenida Expedicionario Oswaldo de Almeida Ramos 280, 27700 Vassouras (Rio de Janeiro)
Telephone: (244) 711595
Diretor: Othon Guilherme Pinto Bravo

Mechanical Engineering
Electrical Engineering

Founded 1984. Under the supervision of the Fundação Educacional Severino Sombra.

Academic Year: Febuary to December (February-June; August-December).

Admission Requirements: Secondary school certificate and entrance examination.

Fees (Cruzeiros): 6835.48 per month;

Language of Instruction: Portuguese.

Degrees and Diplomas: Professional titles, 5 yrs.

Academic Staff, 1989-90: 61.

651 **ESCOLA DE ENGENHARIA CIVIL**
Estrada Volta Redonda-Pinheiral, Tres Pocos, Volta Redonda (Rio de Janeiro)
Telephone: (243) 422313
Diretor: Carlos August Marcondes

Civil Engineering

Founded 1970. Under the supervision of the Fundação Oswaldo Aranha.

Academic Year: February to December.

Admission Requirements: Secondary school certificate and entrance examination.

Language of Instruction: Portuguese.

Degrees and Diplomas: Professional title.

652 **ESCOLA DE ENGENHARIA ELECTRO-MECÂNICA DA BAHIA**
Avenida Joana Angelica 1381, 40000 Salvador (Bahia)
Telephone: (71) 2416922

Engineering

Founded 1934.

653 **ESCOLA DE ENGENHARIA INDUSTRIAL DE SÃO JOSÉ DOS CAMPOS**
Avenida Barão do Rio Branco 882, 12200 São José dos Campos (São Paulo)
Telephone: (123) 219144

D. of Mechanical Engineering
D. of Research and Development
D. of Industrial Administration and Basic Sciences
D. of Electronic Engineering
D. of Human Sciences

Founded 1956, acquired present status and title 1968. Financed by tuition fees and income from development projects. Governing body: the Congregação, including representatives of industry.

Academic Year: January to December (January-July; August-December).

Admission Requirements: Secondary school certificate and entrance examination.

Language of Instruction: Portuguese.

Degrees and Diplomas: Professional titles of–Engenheiro operacional, 3 yrs; Engenheiro industrial, 5 yrs.

Library: c. 24,250 vols.

Academic Staff: c. 30 (40).

Student Enrolment: c. 490.

654 **ESCOLA DE ENGENHARIA KENNEDY**
Rua José Días Vieira 46, 30000 Belo Horizonte (Minas Gerais)
Telephone: (31) 4471761

Engineering

Founded 1963.

655 **ESCOLA DE ENGENHARIA MAUÁ**
Estrada das Lágrimas 2035, 09580 São Caetano do Sul (São Paulo)
Telex: 1145234 AUAT BR
Telephone: (11) 442-1900
Fax: (11) 441-6113
Diretor: Antonio de Oliveira (1988-92)
Secretário: Eder Moreira

Engineering

Founded 1961. Under the supervision of the Instituto Mauá de Tecnologia.

Academic Year: February to December (February-June; August-December).

Admission Requirements: Secondary school certificate and entrance examination.

Fees (Cruzeiros): 7025.41 per annum.

Language of Instruction: Portuguese.

Degrees and Diplomas: Professional title of Engenheiro–civil; –electricista; –mecânico; –metalurgista; –químico; –sanitarista; –de alimentos, 5 yrs.

Library: 36,000 vols.

Academic Staff, 1990:

Rank	Full-time	Part-time
Professores Plenos	2	69
Professores Associados	2	33
Professores Assistentes	6	67
Instrutores	8	98
Auxiliares de Ensino	–	5
Total	18	272

Student Enrolment, 1990:

	Men	Women	Total
Total	1958	581	2539

656 **ESCOLA DE ENGENHARIA VEIGA DE ALMEIDA**
Rua Ibiturana 108, 20271 Rio de Janeiro (Rio de Janeiro)
Telephone: (21) 2646172

Engineering
Founded 1972.

657 **ESCOLA DE MEDICINA DE SANTA CASA DE MISERICORDIA DE VITÓRIA**
Avenida N. Sra. da Penha s/n, Caixa postal 36, 29000 Vitória (Espírito Santo)
Telephone: (27) 2278679

Medicine
Founded 1968.

658 **ESCOLA DE MEDICINA E SAÚDE PÚBLICA**
Rua Frei Henrique 08, 40000 Salvador (Bahia)
Telephone: (71) 2434623

Medicine
Public Health
Founded 1953.

659 **ESCOLA DE MEDICINA SOUZA MARQUÊS**
Rua do Catete 6, 22220 Rio de Janeiro (Rio de Janeiro)
Telephone: (21) 2524172

Medicine
Founded 1970. Under the supervision of the Fundação Souza Marques. Receives some financial support from the Ministry of Education and Culture.
Academic Year: March to November.
Admission Requirements: Secondary school certificate and entrance examination.
Language of Instruction: Portuguese.
Degrees and Diplomas: Professional title of Médico, 6 yrs.

660 **ESCOLA DE ODONTOLOGIA DE VOLTA REDONDA**
Rua Luiz A. Pereira 76, 27180 Volta Redonda (Rio de Janeiro)
Telephone: (243) 431556
Diretor: Antonio D'Apparecida B. Silva

Dentistry
Founded 1970. Under the supervision of the Fundação Oswaldo Aranha.
Academic Year: February to December.
Admission Requirements: Secondary school certificate and entrance examination.
Language of Instruction: Portuguese.
Degrees and Diplomas: Professional title of Cirurgião dentista.

661 **ESCOLA DE SOCIOLOGIA E POLÍTICA DE SÃO PAULO**
Rua General Jardim 522, Vila Buarque, 01223 São Paulo (São Paulo)
Telephone: (11) 2561552

Sociology
Political Science
Founded 1933.

662 **ESCOLA GUIGNARD**
Avenida Alfonso Peña, 30130 Belo Horizonte (Minas Gerais)
Telephone: (31) 2268511

Education (Artistic)
Founded 1983.

663 **ESCOLA SUPERIOR DE ADMINISTRAÇÃO DE NEGÓCIOS**
Avenida Humberto de Alencar Castelo Branco 3740, 09700 São Bernardo do Campo (São Paulo)
Telephone: (11) 4195833

Business Administration
Founded 1965.

664 **ESCOLA SUPERIOR DE ADMINISTRAÇÃO DE NEGÓCIOS ESAN**
Rua São Joaquim 163, Liberdade, 01508 São Paulo (São Paulo)
Telephone: (11) 2780955

Business Administration
Founded 1941.

665 **ESCOLA SUPERIOR DE AGRIMENSURA DE MINAS GERAIS**
Rua Aquiles Lobo 524, 30000 Belo Horizonte (Minas Gerais)
Telephone: (31) 2246494

Agriculture
Founded 1968.

666 **ESCOLA SUPERIOR DE AGRONOMIA E CIÊNCIAS DE MACHADO**
Praça Olegario Maciel 25, 37750 Machado (Minas Gerais)
Telephone: (35) 9311866

Agriculture (including Animal Husbandry)
Science
Founded 1974.

667 **ESCOLA SUPERIOR DE AGRONOMIA DE PARAGUAÇU PAULISTA**
Rua Prof. Jayme Monteira, 19700 Paraguaçu Paulista (São Paulo)
Telephone: (18) 3611953

Agriculture
Founded 1974.

668 **ESCOLA SUPERIOR DE ARTES SANTA MARCELINA**
Rua Dr. Costa Leite 548, 18600 Botucatu (São Paulo)
Telephone: (14) 9220577

Fine Arts
Founded 1974.

669 **ESCOLA SUPERIOR DE CIÊNCIAS CONTÁBEIS E ADMINISTRATIVAS DE ITUIUTABA**
Avenida Geraldo Alves Tavares 1980, 38300 Ituiutaba (Minas Gerais)
Telephone: (34) 2612838

Business Administration
Founded 1970.

670 **ESCOLA SUPERIOR DE EDUCAÇÃO FÍSICA DA ALTA PAULISTA**
Rua Mandaguaris 274, 17600 Tupá (São Paulo)
Telephone: (144) 421218

Physical Education
Founded 1970.

671 **ESCOLA SUPERIOR DE EDUCAÇÃO FÍSICA DE MUZAMBINHO**
Rua Dinah s/n, 37890 Muzambinho (Minas Gerais)
Telephone: (35) 5711155

Physical Education
Founded 1971.

672 **ESCOLA SUPERIOR DE EDUCAÇÃO FÍSICA DE SÃO CAETANO DO SUL**
Rua Amazonas 2000, 09500 São Caetano do Sul (São Paulo)
Telephone: (11) 4413233

Physical Education
Founded 1971.

673 **ESCOLA SUPERIOR DE EDUCAÇÃO FÍSICA E DESPORTOS DE CATANDUVA**
Avenida Paulo de Faria s/n, 15800 Catanduva (São Paulo)
Telephone: (175) 227-656
Diretor: Constante Frederico Ceneviva Junior
Secretário: João Alfredo Gimenez

Physical Education

Founded 1973.

Academic Year: February to December (February-July; August-December).

Admission Requirements: Secondary school certificate.

Fees (Cruzeiros): 959,288.40 per annnum.

Language of Instruction: Portuguese.

Degrees and Diplomas: Bacharel, 4 yrs.

Library: 1000 vols.

Academic Staff, 1990: 25.

Student Enrolment, 1990:

	Men	Women	Total
Of the country	174	156	330

674 **ESCOLA SUPERIOR DE EDUCAÇÃO FÍSICA E TÉCNICAS DESPORTIVAS DE ANDRADINA**
Rua Amazonas 571, 16900 Andradina (São Paulo)
Telephone: (187) 222706

Physical Education

Founded 1973.

675 **ESCOLA SUPERIOR DE EDUCAÇÃO FÍSICA E TÉCNICAS DESPORTIVAS DE ARAÇATUBA**
Rua Francisco Braga 414, 16100 Araçatuba (São Paulo)
Telephone: (186) 235128

Physical Education

Founded 1971.

676 **ESCOLA SUPERIOR DE ESTATÍSTICA DA BAHIA**
Avenida Levigildo Filgueiras, 40000 Salvador (Bahia)
Telephone: (71) 2450611

Statistics

Founded 1966.

Academic Year: March to December (March-June; July-December).

Admission Requirements: Secondary school certificate.

Language of Instruction: Portuguese.

Degrees and Diplomas: Bacharel em Ciências estatísticas.

677 **ESCOLA SUPERIOR DE PROPAGANDA E MARKETING DE SÃO PAULO**
Avenida Rui Barbosa, 01326 São Paulo (São Paulo)
Telephone: (11) 2846388

Social Communication

Founded 1951.

678 **ESCOLA SUPERIOR DE RELAÇÕES PÚBLICAS DE PERNAMBUCO**
Avenida Conselheiro Rosa e Silva 839, 50000 Recife (Pernambuco)
Telephone: (81) 2225802

Public Relations

Founded 1973.

679 **FACULDADE ADVENTISTA DE EDUCAÇÃO**
Est Itapecerica da Serra Km-23, 05835 São Paulo (São Paulo)
Telephone: (11) 5114011

Education

Founded 1973. Under the supervision of the Instituto Adventista de Ensino.

Academic Year: February to December (February-June; August-December).

Admission Requirements: Secondary school certificate or equivalent.

Language of Instruction: Portuguese.

Degrees and Diplomas: Bacharel, 4 yrs.

Academic Staff: c. 30.

Student Enrolment: c. 50.

680 **FACULDADE ADVENTISTA DE ENFERMAGEM**
Est Itapecerica da Serra Km-23, 05835 São Paulo (São Paulo)
Telephone: (11) 5114011

Nursing

Founded 1968. Under the supervision of the Instituto Adventista de Ensino.

Academic Year: February to December (February-June; August-December).

Admission Requirements: Secondary school certificate or equivalent.

Language of Instruction: Portuguese.

Degrees and Diplomas: Bacharel, 4 yrs.

Academic Staff: c. 50.

Student Enrolment: c. 130.

681 **FACULDADE ANHANGUERA DE CIÊNCIAS HUMANAS**
Rua Piragibe Leite 456, Cidade Jardim, 74000 Goiânia (Goiás)
Telephone: (62) 2513688

Human Sciences

Founded 1972.

682 **FACULDADE ANHEMBI MORUMBI**
Rua Casa do Ator 90, 04546 São Paulo (São Paulo)
Telephone: (11) 5330588

Tourism

Social Communication

Founded 1970. Under the supervision of the Instituto Superior de Communicação Publicitaria.

Academic Year: March to December (March-June; August-December).

Admission Requirements: Secondary school certificate and entrance examination.

Language of Instruction: Portuguese.

Degrees and Diplomas: Bacharel, 4 yrs.

Library: c. 10,910 vols.

Academic Staff: c. – (130).

Student Enrolment: c. 2330.

683 **FACULDADE 'AUXILIUM' DE FILOSOFIA, CIÊNCIAS E LETRAS**
Rua Nicolau Zarvos 754, 16400 Lins (São Paulo)
Telephone: (145) 222733

D. of Education

D. of Letters and Modern Languages

D. of Geography

D. of History and Social Studies

D. of Mathematics

D. of Design and Plastic Arts

D. of Biology

Founded 1957 as a private institution supported by the Congregation of the Daughters of Mary Auxiliatricis. Formally recognized by the federal government 1950 and 1962.

Academic Year: March to December (March-July; August-December).

Admission Requirements: Secondary school certificate.

Language of Instruction: Portuguese.

Degrees and Diplomas: Bacharel in all fields, 4 yrs, except Education, 3 yrs; Social Studies, 1 ½ yrs.

684 **FACULDADE BRASILEIRA DE CIÊNCIAS JURÍDICAS**
Praça de República 60, 20211 Rio de Janeiro (Rio de Janeiro)
Telephone: (21) 2311965

Law

Founded 1956.

685 **FACULDADE CAMAQUENSE DE CIÊNCIAS CONTÁBEIS E ADMINISTRATIVAS**
Rua Alvaro Macedo 105, 96180 Camaquã (Rio Grande do Sul)

Accountancy

Administration

Founded 1970.

686 **FACULDADE CATÓLICA DE ADMINISTRAÇÃO E ECONOMIA**
Rua 24 de Maio 135, 80000 Curitiba (Paraná)
Telephone: (41) 2334222

D. of Economics
D. of Administration
D. of Accountancy

Founded 1957 as integrated faculty of the Catholic University of Paraná. Acquired present status 1977. Underthe supervision of the Associação Franciscana de Ensino Senhor Bom Jesus.

Academic Year: February to December (February-June; August-December).

Admission Requirements: Secondary school certificate and entrance examination.

Language of Instruction: Portuguese.

Degrees and Diplomas: Bacharel in–Administration; Accountancy, 8 sem; Economics, 10 sem. Specialization in–Business Administration; Systems Analyses.

Library: c. 23,300 vols.

Academic Staff: c. – (130).

Student Enrolment: c. 2500.

687 **FACULDADE CATÓLICA DE CIÊNCIAS ECONÔMICAS DA BAHIA**
Avenida Joana Angélica, 40000 Salvador (Bahia)
Telephone: (71) 2435832

Economics

Founded 1960. Formerly recognized by federal government 1968.

Academic Year: February to December (February-July; August-December).

Admission Requirements: Secondary school certificate and entrance examination.

Language of Instruction: Portuguese.

Degrees and Diplomas: Licenciado, 4 yrs.

Library: Central Library.

Academic Staff: c. – (30).

Student Enrolment: c. 990.

688 **FACULDADE DE ADMINISTRAÇÃO CHAMPAGNAT**
Rua Professor Estevão Pinto 400, Serra, 30000 Belo Horizonte (Minas Gerais)
Telephone: (31) 2234998

Administration

689 **FACULDADE DE ADMINISTRAÇÃO, CIÊNCIAS CONTÁBEIS E ECONÔMICAS DE TERESÓPOLIS**
Avenida Alberto Torres 11, 25950 Teresópolis (Rio de Janeiro)
Telephone: (21) 7423152
Diretor: Rodolpho Peixoto Mader Gonçalves

D. of Administration
Dean: Luiz Alfredo Caldeira; *staff* 14 (5)
D. of Accountancy
Dean: Lucio Luiz de Lima; *staff* 13 (4)
D. of Law
Dean: José Vieira Furtado; *staff* 5 (3)
D. of Exact Sciences
Dean: Ronald Vasconcellos Braga; *staff* 7 (1)
D. of Social, Political, and Economic Sciences
Dean: Oswaldo Pereira de Oliveira; *staff* 12 (3)

Founded 1975. Under the supervision of the Fundação Educacional Serra Dos Orgaõs.

Academic Year: March to December (March-June; August-December).

Admission Requirements: Secondary school certificate and entrance examination.

Language of Instruction: Portuguese.

Degrees and Diplomas: Bacharel, 4 yrs.

Academic Staff, 1990:

Rank	Full-time	Part-time
Professores Titulares	18	4
Professores Adjuntos	2	20
Professores Auxiliares de Ensino	10	2
Professores Assistentes	2	1
Total	32	27

Student Enrolment, 1990:

	Men	Women	Total
Of the country	383	244	627

690 **FACULDADE DE ADMINISTRAÇÃO, CIÊNCIAS ECONÔMICAS E CONTÁBEIS DE NATAL**
Rua Serido, 59000 Natal (Rio Grande do Norte)
Telephone: (84) 222314

Administration
Economics
Accountancy

Founded 1981.

691 **FACULDADE DE ADMINISTRAÇÃO DA FUNDAÇÃO ARMANDO ALVARES PENTEADO**
Rua Alagoas 903, 01242 São Paulo (São Paulo)
Telephone: (11) 8264233
Diretor: Lauro Ramalho Gurgel

Administration

Founded 1973. Under the supervision of the Fundação Armando Alvares Penteado.

Academic Year: March to December.

Admission Requirements: Secondary school certificate and entrance examination.

Fees: Fees (Cruzeiros): 8387.54.

Language of Instruction: Portuguese.

Degrees and Diplomas: Bacharel, 4 yrs.

692 **FACULDADE DE ADMINISTRAÇÃO DA GUANABARA**
Rua General Severino 159, Botafogo, 20000 Rio de Janeiro (Rio de Janeiro)
Telephone: (21) 2953099

Administration

Founded 1977.

693 **FACULDADE DE ADMINISTRAÇÃO DE CAPIVARI**
Rua Barão do Rio Branco 374, 13360 Capivari (São Paulo)
Telephone: (194) 911694

Administration

Founded 1972.

694 **FACULDADE DE ADMINISTRAÇÃO DE EMPRESAS AMADOR AGUIAR**
Rua Narcisco Sturlini 883, 06010 Osasco (São Paulo)
Telephone: (11) 8016840

Business Administration

Founded 1972.

695 **FACULDADE DE ADMINISTRAÇÃO DE EMPRESAS DE ARAÇATUBA**
Rua Mato Grosso, 16100 Araçatuba (São Paulo)
Telephone: (186) 235128

Business Administration

Founded 1969.

696 **FACULDADE DE ADMINISTRAÇÃO DE EMPRESAS DE CATANDUVA**
Rua do Seminario 281, 15800 Catanduva (São Paulo)
Telephone: (175) 222405
Diretor: Guiilherme Leguth Júnior

Business Administration

Founded 1972. Under the supervision of the Fundaçõ Padro Albino.

Academic Year: March to November (March-June; August-November).

Admission Requirements: Secondary school certificate and entrance examination.
Fees (Cruzeiros): 2129.73.
Language of Instruction: Portuguese.
Degrees and Diplomas: Professional title, 4 yrs.
Library: 4033 vols.
Academic Staff, 1990: – (17).

697 **FACULDADE DE ADMINISTRAÇÃO DE EMPRESAS DE GOVERNADOR VALADARES**
Rua José de Tassis s/n, Vila Bretas, 35100 Governador Valadares (Minas Gerais)
Telephone: (332) 213006
Business Administration
Founded 1975.

698 **FACULDADE DE ADMINISTRAÇÃO DE EMPRESAS DE JAHÚ**
Rua Tenente Navarro 642, 17200 Jahú (São Paulo)
Telephone: (146) 223435
Business Administration
Founded 1972.

699 **FACULDADE DE ADMINISTRAÇÃO DE EMPRESA**
BR 230 Km. 22, 58000 João Pessão (Paraíba)
Telephone: (83) 231-14-18
Diretor: Emerson Moreira de Oliveira
Secretária: Maria de Lourdes Ramalho de Mendonça
Business Administration
Founded 1973.
Academic Year: February to December (February-June; August-December).
Admission Requirements: Secondary school certificate.
Fees (Cruzeiros): 3500.
Language of Instruction: Portuguese.
Degrees and Diplomas: Bacharel, 4 yrs.
Library: 50,000 vols.
Academic Staff, 1989-90: 30.
Student Enrolment, 1989-90:

	Men	Women	Total
Of the country	482	360	842

700 **FACULDADE DE ADMINISTRAÇÃO DE EMPRESAS DE SANTOS**
Rua Armando de S. Oliveira 150, 11050 Santos (São Paulo)
Telephone: (13) 351311
Business Administration
Founded 1969. Under the supervision of the Fundação Lusiada.
Academic Year: March to December (March-June; August-December).
Admission Requirements: Secondary school certificate and entrance examination.
Language of Instruction: Portuguese.
Degrees and Diplomas: Bacharel, 4-5 yrs.

701 **FACULDADE DE ADMINISTRAÇÃO DE EMPRESAS E CIÊNCIAS CONTÂBEIS CAMPOS SALLES**
Rua Nossa Senhora da Lapa 284, 05072 São Paulo (São Paulo)
Telephone: (11) 2606477
Business Administration
Accountancy
Founded 1973.

702 **FACULDADE DE ADMINISTRAÇÃO DE JOAÇABA**
Campus Universitário, 89600 Joaçaba (Santa Catarina)
Telephone: (495) 220288
Diretor: Pedro Almeida
Administration (including Accountancy)
Founded 1972. A private institution under the supervision of the Fundação Educacional do Oeste Catarinense.
Academic Year: March to December (March-June; August to December).
Admission Requirements: Secondary school certificate and entrance examination.
Fees (Cruzeiros): 17,160 per semester.
Language of Instruction: Portuguese.
Degrees and Diplomas: Bacharel, 5 yrs.

703 **FACULDADE DE ADMINISTRAÇÃO DE PINHAL**
Avenida Hélio Vergueiro Leite s/n, 13990 Espírito Santo do Pinhal (São Paulo)
Telephone: (196) 513604
Administration
Founded 1972.

704 **FACULDADE DE ADMINISTRAÇÃO E INFORMÁTICA**
Avenida Antonio de Cassia 472, 37540 Santa Rita do Sapucaí (Minas Gerais)
Telephone: (35) 6311219
Diretor: Francisco Ribeiro de Magalhaes (1986-)
Secretária: Fausta Margherita Soares Andery
Business Administration
Computer Sciences
Founded 1970. Under the supervision of the Fundação Educandario Santarritense.
Academic Year: February to December (February-June; August-December).
Admission Requirements: Secondary school certificate and entrance examination.
Fees (Cruzeiros): 2184-3240.53.
Language of Instruction: Portuguese.
Degrees and Diplomas: Bacharel in Administration, 4 yrs. Professional title of Tecnólogo em Processamento de Dados, 3 ½ yrs.
Library: 6456 vols.
Academic Staff, 1986-87: 6 (32).
Student Enrolment, 1986-87:

	Men	Women	Total
Of the country	162	107	269
Of other countries	1	–	1
Total	163	107	270

705 **FACULDADE DE ADMINISTRAÇÃO E CIÊNCIAS CONTÁBEIS DE GUARULHOS**
Rua Doctor Solon Fernandes 155, Vila Rosalia, 07000 Guarulhos (São Paulo)
Telephone: (11) 2093233
Administrative Studies
Accountancy
Founded 1971.

706 **FACULDADE DE ADMINISTRAÇÃO E CIÊNCIAS CONTÁBEIS NOVE DE JULHO**
Rua Diamantina 302, 02117 São Paulo (São Paulo)
Telephone: (11) 2648843
Administration
Accountancy
Founded 1985.

707 **FACULDADE DE ADMINISTRAÇÃO E CIÊNCIAS CONTÁBEIS TIBIRIÇA**
Largo São Bento s/n, 01029 São Paulo (São Paulo)
Telephone: (111) 375-485
Diretor: Hilario Torloni
Secretária Geral: Tania S. Lara Costa
Business Administration
Accountancy
International Management
Founded 1972.
Academic Year: February to December (February-June; August-December).
Admission Requirements: Secondary school certificate and entrance examination.
Fees (Cruzeiros): 24,000 per semester.
Language of Instruction: Portuguese.
Degrees and Diplomas: Bacharel, 4 yrs.
Library: 14,000 vols.

Academic Staff, 1990: 64.
Student Enrolment, 1990:

	Men	Women	Total
Of the country	1164	527	1691
Of other countries	2	–	2
Total	1166	527	1163

708 **FACULTDADE DE ADMINISTRAÇÃO E FINANÇAS DE MACHADO**
Praça Olegario Maciel 25, 37750 Machado (Minas Gerais)
Telephone: (35) 9311866

Accountancy
Economics

Founded 1972. Under the supervision of the Fundação Educacional de Machado.
Academic Year: February to December (February-June; August-December).
Admission Requirements: Secondary school certificate.
Language of Instruction: Portuguese.
Degrees and Diplomas: Bacharel, 4-5 yrs.
Library: Biblioteca Central, *c.* 12,240 vols.
Academic Staff: c. 10.
Student Enrolment: c. 130.

709 **FACULDADE DE ADMINISTRAÇÃO E FINANÇAS DO NORTE DE MINAS**
Avenida Rui Braga, 39400 Montes Claros (Minas Gerais)
Telephone: (38) 2218687

Administration
Economics
Finance

Founded 1972.
Degrees and Diplomas: Bacharel, 4 yrs.
Academic Staff: c. 40.
Student Enrolment: c. 540.

710 **FACULDADE DE ADMINISTRAÇÃO HOSPITALAR**
Avenida Duquesa de Goias 735, 05686 São Paulo (São Paulo)
Telephone: (11) 5311620
Diretor: Domingos Marcos F. Fiorentini (1984-88)

Hospital Administration

Founded 1973.
Academic Year: February to December (February-July; August-December).
Admission Requirements: Secondary school certificate and entrance examination.
Fees (Cruzeiros): 6840.
Language of Instruction: Portuguese.
Degrees and Diplomas: Bacharel, 4 yrs.
Academic Staff, 1986-87: – (43).
Student Enrolment, 1986-87:

	Men	Women	Total
Of the country	78	90	168
Of other countries	2	–	2
Total	80	90	170

711 **FACULDADE DE ADMINISTRAÇÃO SÃO MARCOS**
Avenida Nazare 900, 04262 São Paulo (São Paulo)
Telephone: (11) 2745711

Administration

Founded 1972.

712 **FACULDADE DE ADMINISTRAÇÃO TRÊS DE MAIO**
Avenida Avai 370, 98910 Três de Maio (Rio Grande do Sul)
Telephone: (535) 1061

Administration

Founded 1970.

713 **FACULDADE DE AGRONOMIA E ZOOTÉCNICA MANOEL CARLOS GONÇALVES**
Avenida Helio Vergueiro Leite s/n, 13990 Pinhal (São Paulo)
Telephone: (196) 513579

Agriculture
Animal Husbandry

Founded 1969.

714 **FACULDADE DE ARQUITETURA DE BARRA DO PIRAI**
Rodovia Benjamin Ielpo, 27100 Barra do Pirai (Rio de Janeiro)
Telephone: (244) 421533
Diretor: Ralfe Pereira Lima
Secretário Geral: Adjalma Barbosa

Architecture

Founded 1972. Under the supervision of the Fundação Educacional Rosemar Pimentel.

715 **FACULDADE DE ARQUITETURA E URBANISMO DE TUPA**
Avenida dos Universitários, 17600 Tupa (São Paulo)
Telephone: (144) 421784

Architecture
Town Planning

Founded 1981.

716 **FACULDADE DE ARTES ALCANTARA MACHADO**
Praça Tres Corações 300, 05608 São Paulo (São Paulo)
Telephone: (11) 2702433

Fine Arts

Founded 1972.

717 **FACULDADE DE ARTES DA FUNDAÇÃO BRASILEIRA DE TEATRO**
SDS Bloco C Ed. FBT, 70300 Brasília (Distrito Federal)
Telephone: (61) 2260188

Scenic Arts

Founded 1980.

718 **FACULDADE DE ARTES PLÁSTICAS DA FUNDAÇÃO ARMANDO ALVARES PENTEADO**
Rua Alagoas 903, 01242 São Paulo (São Paulo)
Telephone: (11) 8264233
Diretor: Oswaldo d'Amora

Plastic Arts

Founded 1972. Under the supervision of the Fundação Armando Alvares Penteado.
Academic Year: March to December.
Admission Requirements: Secondary school certificate and entrance examination.
Fees (Cruzeiros): 8387.54.
Language of Instruction: Portuguese.
Degrees and Diplomas: Licenciado, 4 yrs. Professional titles.

719 **FACULDADE DE BELAS ARTES DE SÃO PAULO**
Praça da Luz 2, 01120 São Paulo (São Paulo)
Telephone: (11) 2299422

Fine Arts (Painting, Sculpture, Engraving, and Design)

Founded 1925. A private institution responsible to the federal government and Ministry of Education and Culture.
Academic Year: March to December (March-June; August-December).
Admission Requirements: Secondary school certificate or equivalent and entrance examination.
Language of Instruction: Portuguese.
Degrees and Diplomas: Licenciado in–Design and Plastic Arts. Professional titles in–Painting; Sculpture; Engraving, 4 yrs.
Library: José Carlos de Macedo Soares library.
Special Facilities (Museums, etc.): Fine Arts Museum.
Academic Staff: c. 60.
Student Enrolment: c. 1660.

720 **FACULDADE DE BIBLIOTECONOMIA E DOCUMENTAÇÃO**
Rua Martiniano de Carvelho, 01321 São Paulo (São Paulo)
Telephone: (11) 2842489

Library Science
Founded 1940.

721 **FACULDADE DE BIOLOGIA E PSICOLOGIA MARIA THERESA**
Rua Visconde do Rio Branco 869, 24020 Niterói (Rio de Janeiro)
Telephone: (21) 7190660

Biology
Psychology
Founded 1975.

722 **FACULDADE DE CIÊNCIAS ADMINISTRATIVAS, CONTÁBEIS E ECONÔMICAS DE UMUARAMA**
Praça Mascarenhas de Moraes s/n, 87500 Umuarama (Paraná)
Telephone: (446) 23164333

Administration
Accountancy
Economics
Founded 1980.

723 **FACULDADE DE CIÊNCIAS ADMINISTRATIVAS DE CANOINHAS**
Rua Robert Ehlke s/n, 89460 Canoinhas (Santa Catarina)
Telephone: (476) 220436

Administration
Founded 1973.

724 **FACULDADE DE CIÊNCIAS ADMINISTRATIVAS E COMERCIO EXTERIOR DE PARANÁ**
Rua Desembargador Westphalen, 80000 Curitiba (Paraná)
Telephone: (41) 2247375

Administration
Founded 1975.

725 **FACULDADE DE CIÊNCIAS ADMINISTRATIVAS E CONTÁBEIS E ATIBAIA**
Avenida de 9 de Julho 288, 12940 Atibaia (São Paulo)
Telephone: (11) 4844140

Administration
Accountancy
Founded 1972.

726 **FACULDADE DE CIÊNCIAS ADMINISTRATIVAS E CONTÁBEIS PAULO EIRO**
Rua Barão de Cotegipe 111, 04721 São Paulo (São Paulo)
Telephone: (11) 523-85-22
Diretora: Déa Carneiro Brag

Accountancy
Administration
Education
Founded 1972.
Arrangements for co-operation with the University of Montreal.
Academic Year: February to November (February-June; August-November).
Admission Requirements: Secondary school certificate and entrance examination.
Fees (Cruzeiros): 4887.82 per month.
Language of Instruction: Portuguese.
Degrees and Diplomas: Bacharel, 4 yrs.
Library: 12,000 vols.
Special Facilities (Museums, etc.): Museum of History
Academic Staff, 1990: 20 (38).
Student Enrolment, 1990:

	Men	Women	Total
Of the country	1200	800	2000

727 **FACULDADE DE CIÊNCIAS ADMINISTRATIVAS E CONTÁBEIS TABAJARA**
Avenida Jandira 455, 04080 São Paulo (São Paulo)
Telephone: (11) 2404397

Administration
Accountancy
Founded 1972. Under the supervision of the Institução Educacional Tabajara.
Academic Year: February to December (February-June; August-December).
Admission Requirements: Secondary school certificate and entrance examination.
Language of Instruction: Portuguese.
Degrees and Diplomas: Bacharel, 4 yrs.
Library: c. 15,000 vols.
Publication: Revista Rabajara (bimonthly).
Academic Staff: c. – (40).
Student Enrolment: c. 880.

728 **FACULDADE DE CIÊNCIAS ADMINISTRATIVAS E ECONÔMICAS**
Rua Itororo 800, Centro, 89500 Caçador (Santa Catarina)
Telephone: (49) 6620536

Administration
Economics
Founded 1977.

729 **FACULDADE DE CIÊNCIAS ADMINISTRATIVAS MARIA DE MAGALHÃES PINTO**
Ladeira da Freguesia 196, 22700 Rio de Janeiro (Rio de Janeiro)
Telephone: (21) 3926646

Administration
Founded 1976.

730 **FACULDADE DE CIÊNCIAS CONTÁBEIS, ADMINISTRATIVAS E ECONÔMICAS DO ICNPF**
Rua Tamoios 792, 30000 Belo Horizonte (Minas Gerais)
Telephone: (31) 2018811

Accountancy
Administration
Economics
Founded 1972.
Academic Year: February to December (February-June; August-December).
Admission Requirements: Secondary school certificate and entrance examination.
Language of Instruction: Portuguese.
Degrees and Diplomas: Bacharel, 3 yrs.

731 **FACULDADE DE CIÊNCIAS CONTÁBEIS DE ARAÇATUBA**
Rua Mato Grosso, 16100 Araçatuba (São Paulo)
Telephone: (186) 235128

Accountancy
Founded 1975.

732 **FACULDADE DE CIÊNCIAS CONTÁBEIS DE CARATINGA**
Rua João Pinheiro 286, 35300 Caratinga (Minas Gerais)
Telephone: (33) 3213377

Accountancy
Founded 1972.

733 **FACULDADE DE CIÊNCIAS CONTÁBEIS DE ITAPETININGA**
Avenida João Barth s/n, 18200 Itapetininga (São Paulo)
Telephone: (152) 710485

Accountancy
Founded 1966.
Academic Year: March to November (March-July; August-November).
Admission Requirements: Secondary school certificate.
Language of Instruction: Portuguese.
Degrees and Diplomas: Bacharel in Accountancy, 4 yrs.
Publication: Boletim.

Academic Staff: c. 30.
Student Enrolment: c. 720.

734 **FACULDADE DE CIÊNCIAS CONTÁBEIS DE LUCÉLIA**
Avenida Internacional 3000, 17780 Lucélia (São Paulo)
Telephone: (189) 511289

Accountancy
Founded 1972.

735 **FACULDADE DE CIÊNCIAS CONTÁBEIS DE PONTE NOVA**
Rua Dos Vereadores, 35430 Ponte Nova (Minas Gerais)
Telephone: (31) 8812580

Accountancy
Founded 1973.

736 **FACULDADE DE CIÊNCIAS CONTÁBEIS DE RIO CLARO**
Rua Nove 15, 13500 Rio Claro (São Paulo)
Telephone: (195) 342887

Accountancy
Founded 1971, by the Sociedade Rioclarense de Ensino Superior. Recognized by the federal government 1976.
Academic Year: February to December (February-June; August-December).
Admission Requirements: Secondary school certificate.
Language of Instruction: Portuguese.
Degrees and Diplomas: Bacharel. Professional title of Técnico.
Academic Staff: c. 20.
Student Enrolment: c. 200.

737 **FACULDADE DE CIÊNCIAS CONTÁBEIS DE SALVADOR**
Rua do Salete 50, 40000 Salvador (Bahia)
Telephone: (71) 2414861

Accountancy
Founded 1966. Recognized by the federal government 1972.
Academic Year: March to December (March-June; August-December).
Admission Requirements: Secondary school certificate and entrance examination.
Language of Instruction: Portuguese.
Degrees and Diplomas: Bacharel in Accountancy, 4 yrs.
Library: c. 6730 vols.

738 **FACULDADE DE CIÊNCIAS CONTÁBEIS E DE ADMINISTRAÇÃO DE EMPRESAS**
Avenida Ernani Cardoso 345, 21310 Rio de Janeiro (Rio de Janeiro)
Telephone: (21) 3906365

Accountancy
Business Administration
Founded 1971.

739 **FACULDADE DE CIÊNCIAS CONTÁBEIS E ADMINISTRATIVAS 'CRUZEIRO DO SUL'**
Avenida Dr. Ussiel Cirilo, 08060 São Paulo (São Paulo)

Accountancy
Business Administration
Founded 1973.

740 **FACULDADE DE CIÊNCIAS CONTÁBEIS E ADMINISTRATIVAS DE AVARE**
Praça Padre Tavares 46, 18700 Avare (São Paulo)
Telephone: (147) 221677

Administration
Accountancy
Founded 1975.

741 **FACULDADE DE CIÊNCIAS CONTÁBEIS E ADMINISTRATIVAS DE LINS**
Rua Dom Bosco 265, 16400 Lins (São Paulo)
Telephone: (14) 5121625

Accountancy
Administration
Founded 1972.

742 **FACULDADE DE CIÊNCIAS CONTÁBEIS E ADMINISTRATIVAS DE MARÍLIA**
Avenida Hygino Muzzy Filho 529, 17500 Marília (São Paulo)
Telephone: (144) 330833

Accountancy
Business Administration
Founded 1970.

743 **FACULDADE DE CIÊNCIAS CONTÁBEIS E ADMINISTRATIVAS DE ROLÂNDIA**
Rua Dom Pedro 11, 400, 86600 Rolândia (Paraná)
Telephone: (432) 562362

Accountancy
Administration
Founded 1974.

744 **FACULDADE DE CIÊNCIAS CONTÁBEIS E ADMINISTRATIVAS DE SANTA ROSA**
Rua Santos Dumont 820, 98900 Santa Rosa (Rio Grande do Sul)
Telephone: (55) 5121659

Accountancy
Administration
Founded 1970.

745 **FACULDADE DE CIÊNCIAS CONTÁBEIS E ADMINISTRATIVAS DE SOROCABA**
Avenida Gen. Osorio 215, 18165 Sorocaba (São Paulo)
Telephone: (152) 323062

Accountancy
Administration
Founded 1966.

746 **FACULDADE DE CIÊNCIAS CONTÁBEIS E ADMINISTRATIVAS DE TAQUARA**
Rua Julio de Castilhos 2084, 95600 Taquara (Rio Grande do Sul)
Telephone: (51) 6421256

Accountancy
Administration
Founded 1969.

747 **FACULDADE DE CIÊNCIAS CONTÁBEIS E ADMINISTRATIVAS DE VOTUPORANGA**
Rua Pernambuco 1624, 15500 Votuporanga (São Paulo)
Telephone: (174) 223700

Accountancy
Administration
Founded 1973.

748 **FACULDADE DE CIÊNCIAS CONTÁBEIS E ADMINISTRATIVAS 'MACHADO SOBRINHO'**
Rua Constantino Paleta 203, 36100 Juiz de Fora (Minas Gerais)
Telephone: (32) 2111477

Accountancy
Administration
Founded 1969.

749 **FACULDADE DE CIÊNCIAS CONTÁBEIS E ADMINISTRATIVAS 'MORAES JÚNIOR'**
Rua Buenos Aires 283, 20061 Rio de Janeiro (Rio de Janeiro)
Telephone: (21) 2245613

Accountancy
Administration
Founded 1964. Recognized by the federal government 1970.
Academic Year: February to December (February-July; August-December).
Admission Requirements: Secondary school certificate.
Language of Instruction: Portuguese.
Degrees and Diplomas: Bacharel em Ciências contábeis, 4 yrs. Professional title of Técnico de Administração, 4 yrs.
Library: c. 6300 vols.
Publication: Mensário Brasileiro de Contabilidade.

750 **FACULDADE DE CIÊNCIAS CONTÁBEIS E ADMINISTRATIVAS SÃO JUDAS TADEU**

Rua Dom Diego de Souza, 100-Bloc AB, 90000 Pôrto Alegre (Rio Grande do Sul)
Telephone: (512) 40-72-90
Reitor: Elisa Verinha Romak Alves
Diretor: Pedro Ruffoni Doval

Accountancy
Administration

Founded 1970.

Academic Year: March to November (March-June; August-November).

Admission Requirements: Secondary school certificate.

Fees (Cruzeiros): 10,350.

Language of Instruction: Portuguese.

Degrees and Diplomas: Bacharel, 4 ½ yrs.

Library: 17,000 vols.

Academic Staff, 1990: – (200).

Student Enrolment, 1990:

	Men	Women	Total
Of the country	920	850	1770

751 **FACULDADE DE CIÊNCIAS CONTÁBEIS E ADMINISTRATIVAS SÃO PAULO APOSTOLO**

Rua José Bonifacio 140, 20771 Rio de Janeiro (Rio de Janeiro)
Telephone: (21) 2492266

Accountancy
Administration

Founded 1974.

752 **FACULDADE DE CIÊNCIAS CONTÁBEIS E DE ADMINISTRAÇÃO DE TUPÃ**

Rua Cherentes 36, 17600 Tupã (São Paulo)
Telephone: (144) 42-26-20
Diretor: Massuyuki Kawano (1989-93)
Secretária: Miryan K. Andaku

Accountancy
Business Administration

Founded 1970. Under the supervision of the Organização Educacional Artur Fernandes and the Ministry of Education. Some residential facilities for academic staff.

Academic Year: February to December (February-June; August-December).

Admission Requirements: Secondary school certificate and entrance examination.

Fees (Cruzeiros): 1421.56 per semester.

Language of Instruction: Portuguese.

Degrees and Diplomas: Bacharel, 4 yrs.

Library: 10,000 vols.

Academic Staff, 1990:

Rank	Part-time
Professores Titulares	7
Professores Adjuntos	4
Professores Assistentes	9
Total	20

Student Enrolment, 1990:

	Men	Women	Total
Of the country	409	274	683

753 **FACULDADE DE CIÊNCIAS CONTÁBEIS E ADMINISTRATIVAS DE VARGINHA**

Rua Catanduvas 173, 37100 Varginha (Minas Gerais)

Accountancy
Administration

Founded 1970.

754 **FACULDADE DE CIÊNCIAS CONTÁBEIS E ATUARIAIS DO ALTA NOROESTE**

Avenida Cussy de Almeida 187, 16100 Araçatuba (São Paulo)
Telephone: (180) 231188

Accountancy
Actuarial Sciences

Founded 1974.

755 **FACULDADE DE CIÊNCIAS DA SAÚDE BARÃO DE MAUA**

Rua Ramos de Azevedo, 14100 Ribeirão Prêto (São Paulo)
Telephone: (16) 6254935

Nursing

Founded 1980. Under the supervision of the Organização Educacional Barão de Mauá.

Academic Year: February to December (February-June; August-December).

Admission Requirements: Secondary school certificate and entrance examination.

Language of Instruction: Portuguese.

Degrees and Diplomas: Professional title, 4 yrs.

756 **FACULDADE DE CIÊNCIAS DA SAÚDE DE INSTITUTO PÔRTO ALEGRE**

Cel Joaquim Pedro Salgado 80, 90000 Pôrto Alegre (Rio Grande do Sul)
Telephone: (51) 231300

Health Sciences

Founded 1971.

757 **FACULDADE DE CIÊNCIAS DA SAÚDE E SOCIAIS**

Rua Pereira da Silva, 20230 Rio de Janeiro (Rio de Janeiro)
Telephone: (21) 2254470

Health Sciences
Social Sciences

Founded 1980.

758 **FACULDADE DE CIÊNCIAS DA SAÚDE SÃO CAMILO**

Avenida Nazare 1501, 04263 São Paulo (São Paulo)
Telephone: (11) 2724760

Nutrition

Founded 1975.

759 **FACULDADE DE CIÊNCIAS DE ADMINISTRAÇÃO DE GARANHUNS**

Rua Ernesto Dourado, 55300 Garanhuns (Pernambuco)
Telephone: (81) 7611596

Administration

Founded 1977.

760 **FACULDADE DE CIÊNCIAS DE BARRETOS**

Avenida Prof. Roberto Frade Monte, 14780 Barretos (São Paulo)
Telephone: (17) 3226411

Sciences

Founded 1969.

761 **FACULDADE DE CIÊNCIAS E LETRAS 'CRUZEIRO DO SOL'**

Avenida Dr. Ussiel Cirilo, 08060 São Paulo (São Paulo)
Telephone: (011) 2871777

Science
Letters

Founded 1972.

762 **FACULDADE DE CIÊNCIAS E LETRAS DE ARARAS**

Rua Quadra H., 13600 Araras (São Paulo)
Telephone: (195) 413047

Science
Letters

Founded 1974.

763 **FACULDADE DE CIÊNCIAS E LETRAS DE MATÃO**

Rua Cesario Moto 644, 15990 Matão (São Paulo)
Telephone: (162) 821226

Science
Letters

Founded 1976.

764 **FACULDADE DE CIÊNCIAS E LETRAS DE OSORIO**

Rua Lobo da Costa 1042, 95520 Osorio (Rio Grande do Sul)

Science
Letters
Founded 1981.

765 **FACULDADE DE CIÊNCIAS E LETRAS DE RIBEIRÃO PIRES**
Rua Comendador João Ugliengo 12, 09400 Ribeirão Pires (São Paulo)
Telephone: (11) 4592634
Science
Letters
Founded 1973.

766 **FACULDADE DE CIÊNCIAS E LETRAS DE VOTUPORANGA**
Rua Pernambuco 1624, 15500 Votuporanga (São Paulo)
Telephone: (174) 223700
Science
Letters
Founded 1968.

767 **FACULDADE DE CIÊNCIAS E LETRAS PADRE ANCHIETA**
Rua Dom Jesus de Pirapora 140, 13200 Jundiaí (São Paulo)
Telephone: (11) 4348444
Science
Letters
Founded 1973.

768 **FACULDADE DE CIÊNCIAS E LETRAS PLINIO AUGUSTO DE AMARAL**
Rua Luiz Leite 232, 13900 Amparo (São Paulo)
Telephone: (192) 702918
Science
Letters
Founded 1971.

769 **FACULDADE DE CIÊNCIAS E PEDAGOGIA DE LAGES**
Avenida Castelo Branco, 88500 Lages (Santa Catarina)
Telephone: (492) 221216
Science
Social Sciences
Letters
Mathematics
Education
Founded 1970.

770 **FACULDADE DE CIÊNCIAS ECONÔMICAS, ADMINISTRATIVAS E CONTÁBEIS DE SÃO SEBASTIÃO DO PARAÍSO**
Avenida Wenceslau Braz, 37950 São Sebastião do Paraíso (Minas Gerais)
Telephone: (35) 5311998
Economics
Administration
Accountancy
Founded 1971.

771 **FACULDADE DE CIÊNCIAS ECONÔMICAS, CONTÁBEIS E ADMINISTRAÇÃO DE EMPRESAS CAMILO CASTELO BRANCO**
Rua Carolina Fonseca, 08230 São Paulo (São Paulo)
Telephone: (11) 2050099
Economics
Business Administration
Accountancy
Founded 1972.

772 **FACULDADE DE CIÊNCIAS ECONÔMICAS, CONTÁBEIS E ADMINISTRAÇÃO DE EMPRESAS PADRE ANCHIETA**
Avenida Dr. Andoniro Ladeira 94, 13200 Jundiaí (São Paulo)
Telephone: (11) 4376165
Economics
Accountancy
Business Administration
Founded 1966.
Academic Year: March to November (March-June; August-November).
Admission Requirements: Secondary school certificate.
Language of Instruction: Portuguese.
Degrees and Diplomas: Bacharel, 4 yrs.
Academic Staff: c. 30.
Student Enrolment: c. 950.

773 **FACULDADE DE CIÊNCIAS ECONÔMICAS, CONTÁBEIS E ADMINISTRATIVAS DE BARBACENA**
Rua Monsenhor José Augusto 203, Alto da Fabrica, Barbacena (Minas Gerais)
Telephone: (32) 3313182
Economics
Accountancy
Administration
Founded 1966.

774 **FACULDADE DE CIÊNCIAS ECONÔMICAS, CONTÁBEIS E ADMINISTRATIVAS DE VISCONDE DO RIO BRANCO**
Avenida Ruy Bouchardet s/n, 36520 Visconde do Rio Branco (Minas Gerais)
Telephone: (32) 5511600
Economics
Administration
Accountancy
Founded 1972.

775 **FACULDADE DE CIÊNCIAS ECONÔMICAS, CONTÁBEIS E ADMINISTRATIVAS NOVA IGUAÇU**
Rua Itaiara 301, 26150 Nova Iguaçu (Rio de Janeiro)
Telephone: (21) 7614440
Diretor: Valdir Vilela (1985-90)
Secretário Geral: Antonio Carlos de Santana Costa
Economics
Administration
Accountancy
Founded 1972.
Academic Year: February to December (February-July; August-December).
Admission Requirements: Secondary school certificate and entrance examination.
Fees (Cruzeiros): 3920.45.
Language of Instruction: Portuguese.
Degrees and Diplomas: Bacharel, 4 yrs.
Academic Staff, 1986-87: – (41).
Student Enrolment, 1986-87:

	Men	Women	Total
Of the country	600	414	1014
Of other countries	4	3	7
Total	604	417	1021

776 **FACULDADE DE CIÊNCIAS ECONÔMICAS, CONTÁBEIS E ADMINISTRATIVAS 'PROF. DE PLACIDO E SILVA'**
Avenida Dr. Vicente Machado, 80000 Curitiba (Paraná)
Telephone: (41) 2338423
Economics
Accountancy
Administration
Founded 1974.

777 **FACULDADE DE CIÊNCIAS ECONÔMICAS DA REGIÃO DOS VINHEDOS**
Alameda João dal Sasso, 95700 Bento Gonçalves (Rio Grande do Sul)
Telephone: (54) 2521188
Economics
Founded 1968.

778 **FACULDADE DE CIÊNCIAS ECONÔMICAS DE BAURU**
Praça 9 de Julho, 17100 Bauru (São Paulo)
Telephone: (142) 236290

Economics

Founded 1961.

779 **FACULDADE DE CIÊNCIAS ECONÔMICAS DE COLATINA**
Avenida Brasil, 29700 Colatina (Espírito Santo)
Telephone: (27) 7220533

Economics

Founded 1970.

780 **FACULDADE DE CIÊNCIAS ECONÔMICAS DE DIVINÓPOLIS**
Praça do Mercado 191, 35500 Divinópolis (Minas Gerais)
Telephone: (37) 2215921

Economics

Founded 1969.

781 **FACULDADE DE CIÊNCIAS ECONÔMICAS DE ITAÚNA**
Avenida Governador Magalhaes Pinto, 35680 Itaúna (Minas Gerais)
Telex: (37) 2121 UITA
Telephone: (37) 2419255
Diretor: Flavio Riani (1990-92)

Economics

Founded 1966. Under the supervision of the Fundação de Ensino Superior de Itaúna

Academic Year: February to December (February-June; August-December).

Admission Requirements: Secondary school certificate and entrance examination.

Language of Instruction: Portuguese.

Degrees and Diplomas: Bacharel, 5 yrs.

Academic Staff, 1990: – 29.

Student Enrolment, 1990: 380.

782 **FACULDADE DE CIÊNCIAS ECONÔMICAS DE PATOS GABRIEL**
Rua Antenor Navarro, 58700 Patos (Paraíba)
Telephone: (83) 4212819

Economics

Founded 1970.

783 **FACULDADE DE CIÊNCIAS ECONÔMICAS DE SÃO GABRIEL**
Rua Barão Cambai 550, 97300 São Gabriel (Rio Grande de Sul)

Economics

Founded 1977.

784 **FACULDADE DE CIÊNCIAS ECONÔMICAS DE SÃO PAULO**
Avenida da Libertade, 01502 São Paulo (São Paulo)
Telephone: (11) 2770122

Economics

Founded 1932.

785 **FACULDADE DE CIÊNCIAS ECONÔMICAS DE VALENÇA**
Praça Visconde do Rio Prêto 401, 27600 Valença (Rio de Janeiro)
Telephone: (244) 520910
Diretor: César Duque de Lima

Economics

Founded 1968.Under the supervision of the Fundação Educacional D. André Arcoverde.

Academic Year: January to December (January-June; August-December).

Admission Requirements: Secondary school certificate and entrance examination.

Fees (Cruzeiros): 234.18 per month.

Language of Instruction: Portuguese.

Degrees and Diplomas: Bacharel, 4 yrs.

786 **FACULDADE DE CIÊNCIAS ECONÔMICAS DO ALTO TAQUARI**
Rua João Tallini, 95900 Lajeado (Rio Grande do Sul)
Telephone: (51) 7142835

Economics

Founded 1969.

787 **FACULDADE DE CIÊNCIAS ECONÔMICAS DO SUL DE MINAS**
Avenida Presidente Tancredo de Almeida Neves, 37500 Itajubá (Minas Gerais)
Telephone: (35) 6221122

Economics

Founded 1965 as a private institution by the Colégio de Itajubá Society. Recognized 1966.

Academic Year: March to December (March-July; August-December).

Admission Requirements: Secondary school certificate and entrance examination.

Languages of Instruction: Portuguese, English and French.

Degrees and Diplomas: Bacharel em Ciências econômicas, 4 yrs.

788 **FACULDADE DE CIÊNCIAS ECONÔMICAS DO TRIÂNGULO MINEIRO**
Praça Tomas Ulhoa 07, 38100 Uberaba (Minas Gerais)
Telephone: (34) 3324043
Diretor: André Bortoletto Júnior (1985-)
Secretário: João de Almeida Pinto

Economics
Administration
Social Sciences
Accountancy

Founded 1966.

Academic Year: February to December (February-July; August-December).

Admission Requirements: Secondary school certificate and entrance examination.

Language of Instruction: Portuguese.

Degrees and Diplomas: Bacharel, 4-5 yrs.

Academic Staff, 1986-87: – (32).

Student Enrolment, 1986-87:

	Men	Women	Total
Of the country	347	349	696

789 **FACULDADE DE CIÊNCIAS ECONÔMICAS 'DOM BOSCO'**
Estrada Resende Riachuelo, 27500 Resende éRio de Janeiro)
Telephone: (243) 541140

Economics

Founded 1968.

790 **FACULDADE DE CIÊNCIAS ECONÔMICAS E CONTÁBEIS DE GUARATINGUETÁ**
Avenida Pedro de Toledo 195, 12500 Guaratinguetá (São Paulo)
Telephone: (12) 5222911

Economics
Administration

Founded 1974. Under the supervision of the Organização Guará de Ensino.

Academic Year: February to December.

Admission Requirements: Secondary school certificate and entrance examination.

Language of Instruction: Portuguese.

Degrees and Diplomas: Bacharel em Ciências econômicas, 4 yrs. Title of Técnico em Administração de Empresas, 4 yrs.

791 **FACULDADE DE CIÊNCIAS ECONÔMICAS E ADMINISTRATIVAS DE PRESIDENTE PRUDENTE**
Praça Raul Furquim s/n, 19100 Presidente Prudente (São Paulo)
Telephone: (182) 33-47-44
Diretora: Vera Alice Asperti Spera
Secretário: Milton Pennacchi

Economics
Administration

Accountancy

Founded 1970.

Academic Year: February to December.

Admission Requirements: Secondary school certificate and entrance examination.

Fees (Cruzeiros): 2684.22 per 24 credits, per annum.

Language of Instruction: Portuguese.

Degrees and Diplomas: Bacharel in Economics, 5 yrs.

792 **FACULDADE DE CIÊNCIAS ECONÔMICAS E DE ADMINISTRAÇÃO DE EMPRESAS DE SÃO JOSÉ DO RIO PRÊTO**

Avenida Bady Bassitt, 15100 São José do Rio Prêto (São Paulo)
Telephone: (172) 321622

Economics
Business Administration

Founded 1962.

793 **FACULDADE DE CIÊNCIAS GERENCIAIS DA UNA**

Rua Aimores, 30140 Belo Horizonte (Minas Gerais)
Telephone: (31) 2265677

Administration
D. of Accountancy
D. of Juridical Sciences
D. of Industrial Relations
D. of Economics
D. of Marketing.

Founded 1961. Under the supervision of the União de Negocios e Administração.

Academic Year: February to December (February-June; August-December).

Admission Requirements: Secondary school certificate and entrance examination.

Language of Instruction: Portuguese.

Degrees and Diplomas: Professional titles in–Business Administration; Accountancy; International Commerce, 4 yrs.

Library: Central Library, *c.* 8710 vols.

Publication: Tempos e Movimentos (monthly).

Academic Staff: c. – (90).

Student Enrolment: c. 1670.

794 **FACULDADE DE CIÊNCIAS HUMANAS DE CURVELO**

Raimunda de Souza Marques, 35790 Curvelo (Minas Gerais)

Human Sciences

Admission Requirements: Secondary school certificate and entrance examination.

Language of Instruction: Portuguese.

795 **FACULDADE DE CIÊNCIAS HUMANAS DE ITABIRA**

Rua Dr. Sizenando de Barros 90, 35900 Itabira (Minas Gerais)
Telephone: (31) 8313770

Teacher Training (secondary level)

Founded 1967 and associated with the Catholic University of Minas Gerais. Acquired present status as independent institution 1981. Under the supervision of the Fundação Itabirana Difusora de Ensino de 1, 2, e 3 Graus.

Academic Year: February to December (February-June; August-December).

Admission Requirements: Secondary school certificate and entrance examination.

Language of Instruction: Portuguese.

Degrees and Diplomas: Teaching qualifications, 3 yrs.

Academic Staff: c. – (20).

Student Enrolment: c. 360.

796 **FACULDADE DE CIÊNCIAS HUMANAS DE OLINDA**

Largo de Misericordia s/n, 53000 Olinda (Pernambuco)
Telephone: (81) 4292679
Diretor: José Adailson de Medeiros (1985-87)
Secretária: Irmã Marta de Vasconcelos

Education
Psychology
Letters

Founded 1973. Under the supervision of the Associação Instructora Missionaria.

Academic Year: March to November (March-June; August-November).

Admission Requirements: Secondary school certificate and entrance examination.

Language of Instruction: Portuguese.

Degrees and Diplomas: Licenciado. Teaching qualifications.

Academic Staff, 1986-87: – (72).

Student Enrolment, 1986-87: *

1288 external students.

797 **FACULDADE DE CIÊNCIAS HUMANAS DO SUL PAULISTA**

Rua Prof. Rivadavia Marques Júnior 338, 18400 Itapeva (São Paulo)
Telephone: (155) 220605

Human Sciences

Founded 1976.

798 **FACULDADE DE CIÊNCIAS HUMANAS E SOCIAIS DE CURITIBA**

Rua Tobias de Macedo Júnior 333, Bairro de Santo Inacio, 80000 Curitiba (Paraná)
Telephone: (41) 2328683

Human Sciences
Social Sciences

Founded 1975.

799 **FACULDADE DE CIÊNCIAS HUMANAS ESUDA**

Avenida João de Barros, Boa Vista, 50000 Recife (Pernambuco)
Telephone: (81) 2214866

Psychology
Economics
Administration

Founded 1974.

Degrees and Diplomas: Bacharel. Licenciado in Psychology.

Library: c. 5000 vols.

Academic Staff: c. 125.

Student Enrolment: c. 1790.

800 **FACULDADE DE CIÊNCIAS JURÍDICAS**

Campus Universitário s/n, Flor de Serra, 89600 Joaçaba (Santa Catarina)
Telephone: (495) 220288
Diretor: Jerri José Brancher

Law

Founded 1986. A private institution under the supervision of the Fundação Educacional do Oeste Catarinense.

Academic Year: March to December (March-June; August-December).

Admission Requirements: Secondary school certificate and entrance examination.

Fees (Cruzeiros): 1580 per semester.

Language of Instruction: Portuguese.

Degrees and Diplomas: Bacharel, 4-5 yrs.

801 **FACULDADE DE CIÊNCIAS JURÍDICAS E SOCIAIS**

João Luiz Ribeiro de Morais, 58000 João Pessoa (Paraíba)
Telephone: (83) 2241418

Law
Social Studies

Founded 1972.

802 **FACULDADE DE CIÊNCIAS JURÍDICAS E SOCIAIS DE BARBACENA**

Rua Monsenhor José Augusto 203, 36200 Barbacena (Minas Gerais)
Telephone: (32) 3313102

Law

Founded 1974.

803 **FACULDADE DE CIÊNCIAS JURÍDICAS E SOCIAIS VIANNA JUNIOR**

Avenida dos Andradas 415, 36100 Juiz de Fora (Minas Gerais)
Telephone: (32) 2122940

Law

Founded 1970.

804 **FACULDADE DE CIÊNCIAS MÉDICAS DE MINAS GERAIS**

Alameda Ezequiel Dias 275, 30000 Belo Horizonte (Minas Gerais)
Telephone: (31) 222-90-66
Diretor: José Rafael Guerra Pinto Coelho (1987-91)
Secretário Geral: João Daniel Fernandes Iglésias

S. of Medicine
Director: Adilson Savi; *staff* 29 (239)
D. of Occupational Therapy
; *staff* 6 (51)
D. of Physiotherapy
Head: Walace Flora; *staff* 4 (55)
Immunology L.
Head: Glaucus de Oliviera Andrade
Cytogenetic L.
Head: Luiz Eustáquio Lopes Pinheiro; *staff* – (6)

Founded 1950. Under the supervision of the Fundação Educacional Lucas Machado.

Arrangements for co-operation with Université de Tours.

Academic Year: February to December (February-July; July-December).

Admission Requirements: Secondary school certificate and entrance examination.

Fees (Cruzeiros): 5722 per annum.

Language of Instruction: Portuguese.

Degrees and Diplomas: Professional titles of–Fisioterapéuta; Terapéuta ocupacional, 5 yrs; Médico, 6 yrs.

Library: Central Library, 11,540 vols.

Academic Staff, 1990:

Rank	Full-time	Part-time
Professores Titulares	3	42
Professores Assistentes	7	104
Professores Auxiliares	4	115
Professores Colaboradores	2	85
Total	16	346

Student Enrolment, 1990:

	Men	Women	Total
Of the country	333	488	821
Of other countries	2	–	2
Total	335	488	823

805 **FACULDADE DE CIÊNCIAS MÉDICAS DE 'SANTA CASA DE SÃO PAULO'**

Rua Dr. Cesário Motta Júnior 112, 01221 São Paulo (São Paulo)
Telephone: (11) 2207288

Medicine

Founded 1963. Under the supervision of the Fundação Arnaldo Vieira de Carbalho. Residential facilities for *c.* 260 students.

Academic Year: February to December (February-July; August-December).

Admission Requirements: Secondary school certificate and entrance examination.

Language of Instruction: Portuguese.

Degrees and Diplomas: Professional title of Médico, 6 yrs.

Libraries: Central Library, *c.* 9330 vols; Gynaecology, *c.* 1250; Orthopaedics, *c.* 460.

806 **FACULDADE DE CIÊNCIAS MÉDICAS DE SANTOS**

Rua Oswaldo Cruz, 11045 Santos (São Paulo)
Telephone: (132) 351148

Medicine

Founded 1967. Under the supervision of the Fundação Lusíada.

Academic Year: March to December (March-June; August-December).

Admission Requirements: Secondary school certificate and entrance examination.

Language of Instruction: Portuguese.

Degrees and Diplomas: Professional title of Médico, 6 yrs.

Library: *c.* 3660 vols.

Special Facilities (Museums, etc.): Anatomy.

Publication: Ars Médica.

Academic Staff: *c.* 160.

Student Enrolment: *c.* 750.

807 **FACULDADE DE CIÊNCIAS MÉDICAS 'DR. JOSÉ ANTÔNIO GARCIA COUTINHO'**

Avenida Alfredo Custodio de Paula 320, 37550 Pouso Alegre (Minas Gerais)
Telex: 354093
Telephone: (35) 421-35-04
Diretor: Eduardo Chibeni Fernandes Ramones
Secretária: Marcia Maria Ribeiro do Valle

Medicine

Founded 1969.

Academic Year: March to December (March-July; August-December).

Admission Requirements: Secondary school certificate and entrance examination.

Language of Instruction: Portuguese.

Degrees and Diplomas: Professional title of Médico, 6 yrs.

Student Enrolment, 1990:

	Men	Women	Total
Of the country	234	185	419

808 **FACULDADE DE CIÊNCIAS POLÍTICAS E ECONÔMICAS DE CRUZ ALTA**

Parada Benito, 98100 Cruz Alta (Rio Grande do Sul)
Telephone: (55) 3223933

Political Science
Economics

Founded 1960.

809 **FACULDADE DE COMUNICAÇÃO DE FAAP**

Rua Alagoas 903, 01242 Pacaembu (São Paulo)
Telephone: (11) 8264233
Diretor: Bernando Issler (1986-88)
Secretário Geral: José Antonio Coutinho Caje

Social Communication

Founded 1972. Under the supervision of the Fundação Armando Álvares Penteado.

Academic Year: February to December (February-June; August-December).

Admission Requirements: Secondary school certificate and entrance examination.

Fees (Cruzeiros): 3540.73 per annum.

Language of Instruction: Portuguese.

Degrees and Diplomas: Bacharel, 4 yrs.

Academic Staff, 1986-87: – (97).

Student Enrolment, 1986-87:

	Men	Women	Total
Of the country	544	822	1366
Of other countries	6	3	9
Total	550	825	1375

810 **FACULDADE DE CIÊNCIAS SAÚDE DE NOVA IGUAÇU**

Avenida Abilio Augusto Tavora 2134, 26000 Nova Iguaçu (Rio de Janeiro)
Telephone: (21) 767-86-05
Diretor: Paulo Fraga Filho
Secretária: Sandra Regina Pinheiro Barbosa

Medicine
Dentistry

Founded 1976 as Faculdade de Ciências Médicas, acquired present title, 1988. Under the supervision of the Sociedade de Ensino Superior de Nova Iguaçu and subject to the control of the Federal Council for Education.

Academic Year: February to December (February-July; August-December).

Admission Requirements: Secondary school certificate and entrance examination.

Fees (Cruzeiros): 30,000 per semester.

Language of Instruction: Portuguese.

Degrees and Diplomas: Professional title of Médico, 6 yrs.

Libraries: Biblioteca Central Nair Fontes Abu-Mehry; 2 departmental libraries.

Academic Staff, 1990: 478.
Student Enrolment, 1990:

	Men	Women	Total
Of the country	537	411	948

811 **FACULDADE DE COMUNICAÇÃO E TURISMO HÉLIO ALONSO**
Rua Muniz Barreto, 22251 Rio de Janeiro (Rio de Janeiro)
Telephone: (21) 5515695

D. of Social Communication
Tourism
Also high school.
Founded 1971.
Academic Year: March to December (March-June; August-December).
Admission Requirements: Secondary school certificate.
Language of Instruction: Portuguese.
Degrees and Diplomas: Bacharel.
Library: c. 6200 vols.
Publications: Contodu Newspaper (monthly); Comum Magazine (biannually).
Press or Publishing House: Hélio Alonso Press.
Academic Staff: c.– (90).
Student Enrolment: c. 2270.

812 **FACULDADE DE COMUNICAÇÃO SOCIAL CASPER LÍBERO**
Avenida Paulista 900, 01310 São Paulo (São Paulo)
Telex: 35 914
Telephone: (11) 2874322
Diretor: Amaury Moraes de Maria
Secretário Geral: Alipio Rodriguez Linẽira

D. of Journalism
Head: João Alvas das Neves; *staff* – (15)
D. of Public Relations
Head: Maria Alice Maluf; *staff* – (13)
D. of Publicity
Head: Sandra Coti Lewin; *staff* – (15)
Founded 1947 as school of journalism. Acquired present status and title 1972. Under the supervision of the Fundação Casper Libero.
Arrangements for co-operation with: University of Navarra; University of Porto.
Academic Year: March to December (March-June; August-December).
Admission Requirements: Secondary school certificate and entrance examination.
Language of Instruction: Portuguese.
Degrees and Diplomas: Bacharel, 4 yrs. Mestrado, a further 2 yrs. Post-graduate diplomas of specialization, 1 yr.
Library: c. 7000 vols.
Academic Staff, 1990: – (54).
Student Enrolment, 1990:

	Men	Women	Total
Of the country	434	782	1216
Of other countries	7	8	15
Total	441	790	1231

813 **FACULDADE DE COMUNICAÇÃO SOCIAL E TURISMO DE SANTO AMARO**
Rua Prof. Eneas de Siqueiro Neto 340, 04829 São Paulo (São Paulo)
Telephone: (11) 5209611

Social Communication
Founded 1975.

814 **FACULDADE DE DESENHO INDUSTRIAL DE MAUÁ**
Rua Alonso Vasconcelos Pacecho, Vila Vitória, 09300 Mauá (São Paulo)
Telephone: (11) 4162166
Diretor: Renato Andreghetto (1983-87)
Secretária: Celina Souza

Industrial Design
Founded 1975. Under the supervision of the Centro de Ensino Superior de Mauá.
Academic Year: February to December (February-June; August-December).
Admission Requirements: Secondary school certificate.
Fees (Cruzeiros): *c.* 600,000 per month.
Language of Instruction: Portuguese.
Degrees and Diplomas: Bacharel, 4 yrs.
Library: 4000 vols.
Academic Staff, 1986-87: – (21).
Student Enrolment, 1986-87:

	Men	Women	Total
Of the country	133	16	149

815 **FACULDADE DE DIREITO DA ALTO PAULISTA**
Rua Mandaguaris 1010, 17600 Tupã (São Paulo)
Telephone: (144) 421862

Law
Founded 1970.

816 **FACULDADE DE DIREITO DE ANÁPOLIS**
Avenida Universitária, 77100 Anápolis (Goiás)
Telephone: (623) 3246517

Law
Founded 1968. Under the supervision of the Associação Educativa Evangélica.
Academic Year: February to November (February-June; August-November).
Admission Requirements: Secondary school certificate.
Language of Instruction: Portuguese.
Degrees and Diplomas: Bacharel em Direito, 5 yrs.
Library: c. 5000 vols.
Academic Staff: c. – (30).
Student Enrolment: c. 600.

817 **FACULDADE DE DIREITO DE ARAÇATUBA**
Rua Mato Grosso 1146, 16100 Araçatuba (São Paulo)
Telephone: (186) 234088

Law
Founded 1971.

818 **FACULDADE DE DIREITO DE BAURU**
Praça 9 de Julho 1-51, 17100 Bauru (São Paulo)
Telephone: (142) 233911

Law
Founded 1953.

819 **FACULDADE DE DIREITO DE CAMPOS**
Rua Tenente Coronel Cardoso 349, 28100 Campos (Rio de Janeiro)
Telephone: (247) 233350

Law
Founded 1960.

820 **FACULDADE DE DIREITO DE CARUARÚ**
Avenida Portugal 385, 55100 Caruarú (Pernambuco)
Telephone: (81) 7212155

Law
Founded 1959. Under the supervision of the Sociedade Caruarense de Ensino Superior.

821 **FACULDADE DE DIREITO DE COLATINA**
Avenida Guarapari s/n, 29700 Colatina (Espírito Santo)
Telephone: (27) 7222311

Law
Founded 1967.

822 **FACULDADE DE DIREITO DE CRUZ ALTA**
Parada Benito, 98100 Cruz Alta (Rio Grande do Sul)
Telephone: (55) 3223933

Law
Founded 1969.

823 **FACULDADE DE DIREITO DE CURITIBA**
Rua Emiliano Perneta 268, 80000 Curitiba (Paraná)
Telephone: (41) 2232986

Law
Founded 1952.

824 **FACULDADE DE DIREITO DE GUARULHOS**
Rua Dr. Solon Fernandes 155, 07000 Guarulhos (São Paulo)
Telephone: (11) 2093233

Law
Founded 1968.

825 **FACULDADE DE DIREITO DE ITAÚNA**
Rua São Sebastião 676, 35680 Itaúna (Minas Gerais)
Telephone: (37) 2412788
Diretor: Plínio Salgado (1988-90)

Law
Founded 1966. Under the supervision of the Fundação de Ensino Superior de Itaúna.
Academic Year: February to December (February-June; August-December).
Admission Requirements: Secondary school certificate and entrance examination.
Language of Instruction: Portuguese.
Degrees and Diplomas: Bacharel, 5 yrs.
Academic Staff, 1990: – 39.
Student Enrolment, 1990: 587.

826 **FACULDADE DE DIREITO DE ITÚ**
Avenida de Tiradentes s/n, 13300 Itú (São Paulo)
Telephone: (11) 409114

Law
Founded 1968.

827 **FACULDADE DE DIREITO DE JOINVILLE**
Rua São José 490, 89200 Joinville (Santa Catarina)
Telephone: (474) 228577

Law
Founded 1980.

828 **FACULDADE DE DIREITO DE MARÍLIA**
Avenida Hygino Muzzy Filho 529, 17500 Marília (São Paulo)
Telephone: (144) 330833

Law
Founded 1970.

829 **FACULDADE DE DIREITO DE NOVA IGUAÇU**
Avenida Abilio Augusto Tavora 2134, 26000 Nova Iguaçu (Rio de Janeiro)
Telephone: (21) 7677176

Law
Founded 1971.

830 **FACULDADE DE DIREITO DE OLINDA**
Rua de São Bento 200, 53000 Olinda (Pernambuco)
Telephone: (81) 4291300

Law
Founded 1971.

831 **FACULDADE DE DIREITO DE OSASCO**
Rua Narcisco Sturlini 883, 06000 Osasco (São Paulo)
Telephone: (11) 8016507

Law
Founded 1969.

832 **FACULDADE DE DIREITO DE PINHAL**
Avenida Helio Vergueiro Leite s/n, 13990 Pinhal (São Paulo)
Telephone: (196) 513604

Law
Founded 1966.

833 **FACULDADE DE DIREITO DE PRESIDENTE PRUDENTE**
Praça Raúl Furquim s/n, 19100 Presidente Prudente (São Paulo)
Telephone: (182) 334744

Law
Founded 1961.

834 **FACULDADE DE DIREITO DE SANTO ÂNGELO**
Rua Gaspar da Silveira Martins s/n, 98800 Santo Ângelo (Rio Grande do Sul)
Telephone: (55) 3121477

Law
Founded 1963.

835 **FACULDADE DE DIREITO DE SÃO CARLOS**
Rua Dr. Marino de Costa Terra, 13560 São Carlos (São Paulo)
Telephone: (162) 717222

Law
Founded 1968.
Academic Year: February to December (February-June; August-December).
Admission Requirements: Secondary school certificate and entrance examination.
Language of Instruction: Portuguese.
Degrees and Diplomas: Bacharel em Direito, 5 yrs.
Library: c. 6000 vols.
Academic Staff: c. – (35).
Student Enrolment: c. 1300.

836 **FACULDADE DE DIREITO DE SETE LAGOAS**
Avenida Marechal Castelo Branco, 35700 Sete Lagoas (Minas Gerais)
Telephone: (31) 9212022

Law
Founded 1970. Under the supervision of the Fundação Educacional 'Monsenhor Messias'.
Academic Year: February to January.
Admission Requirements: Secondary school certificate.
Language of Instruction: Portuguese.
Degrees and Diplomas: Bacharel em Direito, 5 yrs.
Academic Staff: c. – (50).

837 **FACULDADE DE DIREITO DE SÃO JOÃO DA BOA VISTA**
Rua Gen. Osorio 433, 13870 São João da Boa Vista (São Paulo)
Telephone: (19) 6233012

Law
Founded 1967.

838 **FACULDADE DE DIREITO DE SOROCABA**
Rua Dr. Ursulina L. Torres 123, 18100 Sorocaba (São Paulo)
Telephone: (152) 322975
Diretor: Helio Rosa Baldy (1986-90)
Secretário: Ademar Adade

Law
Founded 1957.
Academic Year: March to December (March-July; August-December).
Admission Requirements: Secondary school certificate and entrance examination.
Language of Instruction: Portuguese.
Degrees and Diplomas: Bacharel en direito, 4 yrs.
Library: 4275 vols.
Academic Staff, 1986-87: – (23).
Student Enrolment, 1986-87:

	Men	Women	Total
Of the country	340	300	640

839 **FACULDADE DE DIREITO DE TEÓFILO OTÔNI**
Rua Frei Dimas 111, 39800 Teófilo Otôni (Minas Gerais)
Telephone: (33) 5213111

Law
Founded 1971.

840 **FACULDADE DE DIREITO DE UMUARAMA**
Praça Mascarenhas de Moraes s/n, 87500 Umuarama (Paraná)
Telephone: (446) 231643

Law
Founded 1980.

841 **FACULDADE DE DIREITO DE VALENÇA**
Rua Sargento Victor Hugo 219, 27600 Valençia (Rio de Janeiro)
Telephone: (244) 52-14-12
Diretor: José Ivanir Gussem
Secretária: Maria Eugênia Furtado Teixeira

Law
Founded 1968. Under the supervision of the Fundação Educacional D. André Arcoverde.
Academic Year: January to December (January-June; August-December).
Admission Requirements: Secondary school certificate and entrance examination.
Fees (Cruzeiros):1784.89 per month.
Language of Instruction: Portuguese.
Degrees and Diplomas: BachAREL, 5 yrs.
Library: 10,449 vols.
Academic Staff, 1990: – (29)
Student Enrolment, 1990:

	Men	Women	Total
Of the country	270	247	517

842 **FACULDADE DE DIREITO DE VARGINHA**
Rua José Gonçalves Pereira, 37100 Varginha (Minas Gerais)
Telephone: (35) 2211900

Law
Founded 1966.

843 **FACULDADE DE DIREITO DO NORTE DE MINAS**
Avenida Rui Braga, 39400 Montes Claros (Minas Gerais)
Telephone: (38) 2212400

Law
Founded 1965.

844 **FACULDADE DE DIREITO DO OESTE DE MINAS**
Rua Minas Gerais 900, 35500 Divinópolis (Minas Gerais)
Telephone: (37) 2215975

Law
Founded 1961.

845 **FACULDADE DE DIREITO DO SUL DE MINAS**
Avenida João Beraldo 430, 37550 Pouso Alegre (Minas Gerais)
Telephone: (35) 4211339

Law
Founded 1960.

846 **FACULDADE DE DIREITO DO VALE DO RIO DOCE**
Rua Arturo Bernardes, 35100 Governador Valadares (Minas Gerais)
Telephone: (33) 2600621

Law
Founded 1969.

847 **FACULDADE DE DIREITO PADRE ANCHIETA**
Rua Bom Jesus de Pirapora 140, 13200 Jundiaí (São Paulo)
Telephone: (11) 4348444

Law
Founded 1969.

848 **FACULDADE DE DIREITO MILTON CAMPOS**
Avenida Carandai 587, 30000 Belo Horizonte (Minas Gerais)
Telephone: (31) 2248543

Law
Founded 1975.

849 **FACULDADE DE ECONOMIA DA FUNDAÇÃO ARMANDO ALVARES PENTADO**
Rua Alagoas 903, Picaembu, 01242 São Paulo (São Paulo)
Telephone: (11) 8264233
Diretor: Walter Alves

Economics
Founded 1977. Under the supervision of the Fundação Armando Alvares Penteado.
Academic Year: March to December.
Admission Requirements: Secondary school certificate and entrance examination.
Fees (Cruzeiros): 8387.54 per annum.
Language of Instruction: Portuguese.
Degrees and Diplomas: Bacharel, 4 yrs.

850 **FACULDADE DE ECONOMIA E FINANÇAS DO RIO DE JANEIRO**
Praça da República 62, 20211 Rio de Janeiro (Rio de Janeiro)
Telephone: (21) 2311965

Economics
Finance
Founded 1916.

851 **FACULDADE DE ECONOMIA, FINANÇAS E ADMINISTRAÇÃO DE SÃO PAULO**
Rua Altinopolis 147, 02334 São Paulo (São Paulo)
Telephone: (11) 2676244

Economics
Finance
Business Administration
Founded 1943.

852 **FACULDADE DE ECONOMIA 'SÃO LUÍS'**
Rua Haddok Lobo 400, 01414 São Paulo (São Paulo)
Telephone: (11) 2573022

Economics
Founded 1948 by the Society of Jesus.
Academic Year: March to Decmber (March to July; August-December).
Admission Requirements: Secondary school certificate.
Language of Instruction: Portuguese.
Degrees and Diplomas: Bacharel in–Economics; Accountancy; Actuarial Sciences; Business Administration; Public Administration, 5 yrs.
Library: c. 80,000 vols.
Special Facilities (Museums, etc.): Museums of: Natural History; Mineralogy; Palaeontology.

853 **FACULDADE DE EDUCAÇÃO**
Campus do Ipe, 58000 João Pessoa (Paraíba)
Telephone: (83) 2241418

Education
Founded 1980.

854 **FACULDADE DE EDUCAÇÃO ANTONIO A. REIS NEVES**
Rua 20, 383, 14780 Barretos (São Paulo)
Telephone: (173) 225733

Education
Founded 1973.

855 **FACULDADE DE EDUCAÇÃO CAMPOS SALLES**
Rua Nossa Senhora da Lapa 284, 05072 São Paulo, (São Paulo)
Telephone: (11) 2606472

Education
Founded 1971.

856 **FACULDADE DE EDUCAÇÃO, CIÊNCIAS E ARTES DOM BOSCO**
Rua Augusto Chiesa 679, 15150 Monte Aprazivel (São Paulo)
Telephone: (17) 2751736

Education
Arts
Social Studies
Founded 1972.

857 **FACULDADE DE EDUCAÇÃO, CIÊNCIAS E LETRAS**
SEP SUL EQ 912/712 Lote 4, Plano Piloto, 70390 Brasília (Distrito Federal)

Education
Science
Letters
Founded 1973.

858 **FACULDADE DE EDUCAÇÃO, CIÊNCIAS E LETRAS DA REGIÃO DOS VINHEDOS**
Alameda João dal Sasso, 95700 Bento Gonçalves (Rio Grande do Sul)
Telephone: (54) 2521188

Education
Science
Letters
Founded 1974.

859 **FACULDADE DE EDUCAÇÃO, CIÊNCIAS E LETRAS DO ALTO TAQUARI**
Rua Avelino Tallini 171, Caixa Postal 155, Bairro Universitário 95900 Lejeado (Rio Grande do Sul)
Telephone: (51) 714-21-66

Education
Letters
Science
Founded 1969.
Academic Year: March to December (March-July; August-December).
Admission Requirements: Secondary school certificate and entrance examination.
Fees (Cruzeiros): 30,000.
Language of Instruction: Portuguese.
Degrees and Diplomas: Bacharel, 4 ½ yrs.
Academic Staff, 1990: 8 (39).
Student Enrolment, 1990:

	Men	Women	Total
Of the country	50	350	400

860 **FACULDADE DE EDUCAÇÃO, CIÊNCIAS E LETRAS DE MOJI MIRIM**
Praça da Bandeira 11, 13800 Moji Mirim (São Paulo)
Telephone: (192) 620839

Education
Science
Letters
Founded 1973.

861 **FACULDADE DE EDUCAÇÃO, CIÊNCIAS E LETRAS DE UBERLÂNDIA**
Rua Barão de Camargos 695, 38400 Uberlândia (Minas Gerais)
Telephone: (34) 2364066

Education
Founded 1975.

862 **FACULDADE DE EDUCAÇÃO, CIÊNCIAS E LETRAS DON DOMENICO**
Rua Dr. Arthur Costa Filho 20, 11400 Guaruja (São Paulo)
Telephone: (132) 862617

Education
Science
Letters
Founded 1973.

863 **FACULDADE DE EDUCAÇÃO, CIÊNCIAS E LETRAS HEBRAICO BRASILEIRA RENASCENÇA**
Rua Prates 790, Bom Retiro, 01120 São Paulo (São Paulo)

Education
Science
Letters
Founded 1975.

864 **FACULDADE DE EDUCAÇÃO, CIÊNCIAS E LETRAS NOTRE DAME**
Barão da Torre 308, Ipanema, 22411 Rio de Janeiro (Rio de Janeiro)
Telephone: (21) 2873740

Education
Letters
Social Studies
Founded 1973. Under the supervision of the Sociedade Nacional Notre Dame.
Academic Year: March to November (March-July; August-November).
Admission Requirements: Secondary school certificate or equivalent, and entrance examination.
Language of Instruction: Portuguese.
Degrees and Diplomas: Licenciado, 4 yrs.
Library: Central Library, *c.* 21,000 vols.
Publication: Legenda.
Academic Staff: c. 60.
Student Enrolment: c. 650.

865 **FACULDADE DE EDUCAÇÃO, CIÊNCIAS E LETRAS OLAVIO BILAC**
Avenida Lusitania 169, 21011 Rio de Janeiro (Rio de Janeiro)
Telephone: (21) 2605552

Education
Science
Letters
Founded 1975.

866 **FACULDADE DE EDUCAÇÃO, CIÊNCIAS E LETRAS URUBUPUNGA**
Avenida Cel. Jonas Alves de Mello 1660, 15370 Pereira Barretos (São Paulo)
Telephone: (18) 611825

Education
Science
Letters
Founded 1973.

867 **FACULDADE DE EDUCAÇÃO DA BAHIA**
Rua da Mangueira, 40000 Salvador (Bahia)
Telephone: (71) 243-88-26
Diretor: Marcelo August Carvalho Rocha
Secretária Geral: Juzete Sá Barreto Vergne

Education
Founded 1967.
Academic Year: March to December (March-July; August-December).
Admission Requirements: Secondary school certificate and entrance examination.
Fees (Cruzeiros): 2655-3600 per month.
Language of Instruction: Portuguese.
Degrees and Diplomas: Licenciado, 4 yrs.
Library: Biblioteca da Faculdade de Educação da Bahia, 10,471 vols.
Academic Staff, 1990: – (23).
Student Enrolment, 1990:

	Men	Women	Total
Of the country	43	672	715

868 **FACULDADE DE EDUCAÇÃO DE FATIMA DO SUL**
Rua Tenente Antonio João 1410, 79700 Fatima do Sul (Mato Grosso do Sul)
Telephone: (67) 4237544

Education
Founded 1980.

869 **FACULDADE DE EDUCAÇÃO DE GUARATINGUETÁ**
Avenida Pédro de Toledo 195, 12500 Guaratinguetá (São Paulo)
Telephone: (12) 5222284

Education
Founded 1974.

870 **FACULDADE DE EDUCAÇÃO DE JAOÇABA**
Campus Universitário, 896000 Jaoçaba (SantaCatarina)
Diretor: Luiz de Lorenzi Dinon

Education
Founded 1976. Under the supervision of the Fundaĝo Educacional do Oeste Catarinense.

871 **FACULDADE DE EDUCAÇÃO DE JOÃO MONLEVADA**
Rua Tiete 100, 35930 João Monlevada (Minas Gerais)
Telephone: (31) 8514784

Education
Founded 1972.

872 **FACULDADE DE EDUCAÇÃO DE JOINVILLE**
Rua São José 490, 89200 Joinville (Santa Catarina)
Telephone: (474) 228577

Education
Founded 1973.

873 **FACULDADE DE EDUCAÇÃO E CIÊNCIAS PINHEIRENSE**
Rua Cardeal Aroverde 1097, Pinheiros, 05407 São Paulo (São Paulo)
Telephone: (11) 8136570

Education
Science
Founded 1975.

874 **FACULDADE DE EDUCAÇÃO E LETRAS SÃO JUDAS TADEU**
Clarimundo de Melo 79, 20740 Rio de Janeiro (Rio de Janeiro)
Telephone: (21) 2898749

Education
Letters
Founded 1974.

875 **FACULDADE DE EDUCAÇÃO FÍSICA**
Campus Universitário, 58000 João Pessoa (Paraíba)
Telephone: (83) 2241418

Physical Education
Founded 1972.

876 **FACULDADE DE EDUCAÇÃO FÍSICA DE BARRA BONITA**
Rua João Gerin 275, 17340 Barra Bonita (São Paulo)
Telephone: (146) 410300

Physical Education
Founded 1973.

877 **FACULDADE DE EDUCAÇÃO FÍSICA DE BATATAIS**
Rua Dom Bosco 466, 14300 Batataista (São Paulo)

Physical Education
Founded 1970.

878 **FACULDADE DE EDUCAÇÃO FÍSICA DE CRUZ ALTA**
Parada Benito, 98100 Cruz Alta (Rio Grande do Sul)
Telephone: (55) 3223933

Physical Education
Founded 1972.

879 **FACULDADE DE EDUCAÇÃO FÍSICA DE LINS**
Rua Dom Bosco 265, 16400 Lins (São Paulo)
Telephone: (14) 5221625

Physical Education
Founded 1972.

880 **FACULDADE DE EDUCAÇÃO FÍSICA DE SANTO AMARO**
Rua Prof. Eneas de Siqueira Netto 340, Rio Bonito Santo Amaro, 04829 São Paulo (São Paulo)
Telephone: (11) 5209611

Physical Education
Founded 1976.

881 **FACULDADE DE EDUCAÇÃO FÍSICA DE SANTO ANDRÉ**
Travessa Cisplatina 20, 09000 Santo André (São Paulo)
Telephone: (11) 4490700

Physical Education
Founded 1970.

882 **FACULDADE DE EDUCAÇÃO FÍSICA DE SOROCABA**
Rua da Penha 680, 18100 Sorocaba (São Paulo)
Cables: caracter
Telephone: (152) 320684

Physical Education
Founded 1971. Under the supervision of the YMCA of Sorocaba City.
Academic Year: February to December (February-June; August-December).
Admission Requirements: Secondary school certificate and entrance examination.
Language of Instruction: Portuguese.
Degrees and Diplomas: Licenciado.
Library: George Williams Library, c. 3000 vols.
Academic Staff: c. – (30).
Student Enrolment: c. 490.

883 **FACULDADE DE EDUCAÇÃO FÍSICA DO CLUBE NAÚTICO MOGIANO**
Rua Cabo Diogo Oliver 758, Ponte Grande, 08700 Mogi das Cruzes (São Paulo)
Telephone: (11) 469588

Physical Education
Founded 1972.

884 **FACULDADE DE EDUCAÇÃO FÍSICA DO NORTE DO PARANÁ**
Rua Piauí 399, 86100 Londrino (Paraná)
Telephone: (43) 2234202

Physical Education
Founded 1973.

885 **FACULDADE DE EDUCAÇÃO OSORIO CAMPOS**
Rua Prof. Alfredo G. Filgueiras, 28500 Nilopolis (Rio de Janeiro)
Telephone: (21) 791-33-34
Diretor: Valdir Vilela
Secretário: Josàe Roberto

D. of Education
Head: Júlio César F. dos Santos; *staff* – (27)
D. of Administration
Head: Ronaldo Cavalcante Gondim; *staff* – (50)
D. of Informatics
Head: Paulo Eduardo de O.S. Andrade; *staff* – (15)
Founded 1974.
Academic Year: February to November.
Admission Requirements: Secondary school certificate and entrance examination.
Language of Instruction: Portuguese.
Degrees and Diplomas: Licenciado, 4 yrs. Specialization, 1 yr.
Academic Staff, 1990: – (26).
Student Enrolment, 1990:

	Men	Women	Total
Of the country	408	292	600

886 **FACULDADE DE EDUCAÇÃO PADRE ANCHIETA**
Avenida Dr. Adoniro Ladeira, 13200 Jundiaí (São Paulo)
Telephone: (11) 4376165

Education
Founded 1968.

887 **FACULDADE DE EDUCAÇÃO SÃO LUÍS**
Rua Floriano Peixoto 873, 14870 Jaboticabal (São Paulo)
Telephone: (11) 220530

Education
Founded 1972.

888 **FACULDADE DE ENFERMAGEM E OBSTETRÍCIA DE ARARAS**
Avenida Universitaria, 13600 Araras (São Paulo)
Nursing (including Midwifery)

889 **FACULDADE DE ENFERMAGEM E OBSTETRÍCIA DE FERNANDÓPOLIS**
Avenida Teoronio Vilela, 15600 Fernandópolis (São Paulo)
Telephone: (174) 42-44-75
Diretor: Aldo José Moscardini Jr.
Nursing
Midwifery
Funded 1976.
Academic Year: February to December.
Admission Requirements: Secondary school certificate.
Fees (Cruzeiros): 14,500 per annum.
Language of Instruction: Portuguese.
Degrees and Diplomas: Professional title of Enfermeiro, 4 yrs.
Library: 1,512 vols.
Academic Staff, 1990: 7 (13).
Student Enrolment, 1990:

	Men	Women	Total
Of the country	13	99	112

890 **FACULDADE DE ENFERMAGEM E OBSTETRÍCIA DE GUARULHOS**
Rua Barão de Mauá 600, 07000 Guarulhos (São Paulo)
Telephone: (11) 2093719
Nursing
Midwifery
Founded 1979.

891 **FACULDADE DE ENFERMAGEM E OBSTETRÍCIA DOM DOMENICO**
Rua Dr. Arthur Costa Filho 20, 11400 Guaruja (São Paulo)
Telephone: (132) 862617
Nursing
Midwifery
Founded 1979.

892 **FACULDADE DE ENFERMAGEM LUIZA MARILLAC**
Rua Dr. Satamini 245, 20270 Rio de Janeiro (Rio de Janeiro)
Telephone: (21) 2343692
Diretor: Augusto Antonio Mezzomo
Secretária Geral: Lucia Maria Kemper Baptista
Nursing
Founded 1939 as school, acquired present title 1967. Under the supervision of the Sociedade Beneficente São Camilo.
Academic Year: February to December (February-June; August-December).
Admission Requirements: Secondary school certificate and entrance examination.
Language of Instruction: Portuguese.
Degrees and Diplomas: Professional title of Enfermeiro, 4 yrs.
Academic Staff, 1986-87: 13 (40).
Student Enrolment, 1986-87:

	Men	Women	Total
Of the country	39	351	390

893 **FACULDADE DE ENFERMAGEM NOSSA SENHORA MEDIANEIRA**
Avenida Presidente Vargas 2377, 97100 Santa Maria (Rio Grande do Sul)
Telephone: (55) 2211726
Nursing (including Midwifery)
Founded 1955.

894 **FACULDADE DE ENFERMAGEM SÃO JOSÉ**
Avenida Nazare, 04263 São Paulo (São Paulo)
Telephone: (11) 2724760
Nursing
Founded 1959.

895 **FACULDADE DE ENGENHEIRO CIVIL DE ALFENAS**
Rodovia MG 179 Km 0, 37130 Alfenas (Minas Gerais)
Telephone: (35) 9211977
Civil Engineering
Founded 1974. Under the supervision of the Fundação de Ensino e Tecnologia de Alfenas.
Academic Year: February to December (February-June; August-December).
Admission Requirements: Secondary school certificate and entrance examination.
Language of Instruction: Portuguese.
Degrees and Diplomas: Professional title of Engenheiro civil, 5 yrs.

896 **FACULDADE DE ENGENHARIA CIVIL DE ARARAQUARA**
Avenida Brasil 782, 14800 Araraquara (São Paulo)
Telephone: (162) 32-17-48
Diretor: Walter Logatti Filho
Secretária: Palmyra Logatti Segnini
Civil Engineering
Founded 1969 incorporating the former Escola de Agrimensura (School of surveying), founded 1966. Under the supervision of the Associação Escola de Agrimensura de Araraquara.
Academic Year: February to December (February-June; August-December).
Admission Requirements: Secondary school certificate and entrance examination.
Fees (Cruzeiros): 43,200 per annum.
Language of Instruction: Portuguese.
Degrees and Diplomas: Professional title of Engenheiro civil, 5 yrs.
Academic Staff: c. – (30).

897 **FACULDADE DE ENGENHARIA CIVIL DE BARRA DO PIRAÍ**
Rodovia Benjamin Ielpo, Km-11, 27100 Barra do Piraí (Rio de Janeiro)
Telephone: (244) 421243
Diretor: Paulo Jorge Mukarzel
Secretário Geral: Ubiratan Batista da Silva
Civil Engineering
Founded 1968 Under the supervision of the Funcação Educacional Rosemar Pimentel.
Degrees and Diplomas: Professional title of Engenheiro civil, 5 yrs.

898 **FACULDADE DE ENGENHARIA DA FUMEC**
Rua Cobre, 30000 Belo Horizonte (Minas Gerais)
Telephone: (31) 2212800
Civil Engineering
Founded 1966. Under the supervision of the Fundação Mineira de Educação e Cultura.
Academic Year: March to December (March-June; August-December).
Admission Requirements: Secondary school certificate.
Language of Instruction: Portuguese.
Degrees and Diplomas: Professional titles.
Library: c. 6520 vols.
Academic Staff: c. 20 (120).
Student Enrolment: c. 870.

899 **FACULDADE DE ENGENHARIA DA FUNDAÇÃO ARMANDO ALVARES PENTEADO**
Rua Alagoas 903, 01242 São Paulo (São Paulo)
Telephone: (11) 665918
Engineering
Founded 1967.

900 **FACULDADE DE ENGENHARIA DE AGRIMENSURA DE ARARAQUARA**
Avenida Brasil 782, 14800 Araraquara (São Paulo)
Telephone: (162) 22-42-81
Diretor: Alarico Haikel Junior
Secretária: Palmyra Logatti Segnini
Agricultural Surveying
Founded 1965, recognized by the federal government 1968. Under the supervision of Associação Escola de Agrimensura de Araraquara.

Academic Year: February to December (February-June; August-December).
Admission Requirements: Secondary school certificate and entrance examination.
Fees (Cruzeiros): 40,114 per annum.
Language of Instruction: Portuguese.
Degrees and Diplomas: Professional title, 5 yrs. Technical diplomas, 3 yrs.
Library: 16,000 vols.
Academic Staff: c. – (20).

901 **FACULDADE DE ENGENHARIA DE AGRIMENSURA DE PIRASSUNUNGA**
Avenida dos Academicos 1, 13630 Pirassununga (São Paulo)
Telephone: (195) 613845

Agriculture
Founded 1972.

902 **FACULDADE DE ENGENHARIA DE ITAÚNA**
Rua São Sebastião, 35680 Itaúna (Minas Gerais)
Telex: (37) 2121 UITA
Telephone: (37) 2412788
Diretor: Antônio Lombardo (1988-90)

Engineering
Founded 1968. Under the supervision of the Fundação de Ensino Superior de Itaúna.
Academic Year: February to December (February-June; August-December).
Admission Requirements: Secondary school certificate and entrance examination.
Language of Instruction: Portuguese.
Degrees and Diplomas: Professional title of Engenheiro Industrial Mecânico, 6 yrs.
Academic Staff, 1990: – 35.
Student Enrolment, 1990: 321.

903 **FACULDADE DE ENGENHARIA DE SOROCABA**
Rodovia Sen. José Ermirio de Moraes, Km. 1.5, 18100 Sorocaba (São Paulo)
Telephone: (152) 32-97-12
Diretor: Antonio Fábio-Beldi
Secretário Geral: José Aurélio Figueiredo

Engineering
Founded 1976. Under the supervision of the Associação Cultural de Renovação Tecnológica Sorocabana.
Academic Year: March to December (March-June; August-December).
Admission Requirements: Secondary school certificate and entrance examination.
Fees (Cruzeiros): *c.* 84,000 per annum.
Language of Instruction: Portuguese.
Degrees and Diplomas: Professional titles, 5 yrs.
Library: 10,000 vols.
Academic Staff, 1990: 5 (60).
Student Enrolment, 1990:

	Men	Women	Total
Of the country	669	110	779

904 **FACULDADE DE ENGENHARIA INDUSTRIAL**
Avenida Humberto de Alencar Castelo Branco 3972, 09700 São Bernardo do Campo (São Paulo)
Telephone: (11) 4190220

Industrial Engineering
Founded 1946.

905 **FACULDADE DE ENGENHARIA QUÍMICA DE LORENA**
Rodovia Lorena/Itajuba, 12600 Lorena (São Paulo)
Telex: 125-579 FTEI BR
Telephone: (125) 523113
Fax: (125) 523875
Diretor: Carlos Roberto Oliveira Almeida
Secretário Geral: Marco Antonio Pereira

Chemical Engineering
; *staff* 56 (25)

Industrial Engineering
; *staff* 54 (25)

Founded 1970. Under the supervision of the Fundação de Tecnologia Industrial.
Arrangements for co-operation with: Tampere University of Technology; Helsinki University of Technology; University of Padua; University of New York; University of Newcastle-upon-Tyne.
Academic Year: February to December (February-July; August-December).
Admission Requirements: Secondary school certificate and entrance examination.
Fees (Cruzeiros): 3670 per month.
Language of Instruction: Portuguese.
Degrees and Diplomas: Professional titles of–Engenheiro químico; Engenheiro industrial, 5 yrs. Mestrado, Master. Doutorado. Postgraduate Certificate in Alcohol Distilling; Chemistry; Computer Sciences, 1 yr.
Library: c. 100,000 vols.
Academic Staff, 1990: 78 (44).
Student Enrolment, 1990:

Men	Women	Total
502	227	729

906 **FACULDADE DE ENGENHARIA SÃO JOSÉ DO RIO PRÊTO**
Avenida Bady Bassitt 3777, 15100 São José do Rio Prêto (São Paulo)
Telephone: (172) 321622

Engineering
Founded 1976.

907 **FACULDADE DE ENGENHARIA SÃO PAULO**
Rua Arabe, 04042 São Paulo (São Paulo)
Telephone: (11) 8811022

Engineering
Founded 1975.

908 **FACULDADE DE ENGENHARIA SOUZA MARQUÊS**
Avenida Ernani Cardoso 335, 20000 Rio de Janeiro (Rio de Janeiro)
Telephone: (21) 3906365

Engineering
Founded 1967.

909 **FACULDADE DE ESTUDOS SOCIAIS APLICADOS DE ARACAJÚ**
Rua Estancia 362, 49000 Aracajú (Sergipe)
Telephone: (79) 2224477

Social Studies
Founded 1976.

910 **FACULDADE DE ESTUDOS SOCIAIS REGINA COELI**
Rua Conselheiro Ferraz, 20710 Rio de Janeiro (Rio de Janeiro)
Telephone: (21) 2646172

Social Studies
Founded 1976.

911 **FACULDADE DE FILOSOFIA 'BERNARDO SAYÃO'**
Avenida Universitária Km-3, 77100 Anápolis (Goiás)
Telephone: (62) 3244025

Philosophy
Founded 1961. Under the supervision of the Associação Educativa Evangélica.
Academic Year: February to November (February-June; August-November).
Admission Requirements: Secondary school certificate.
Language of Instruction: Portuguese.
Degrees and Diplomas: Licenciado.

912 **FACULDADE DE FILOSIFIA, CIÊNCIAS E LETRAS 'BARÃO DE MAUÁ'**
Rua Ramos de Azevedo 423, 4100 Ribeirão Prêto (São Paulo)
Telephone: (16) 6254935

Philosophy
Science

Letters

Founded 1968. Under the supervision of the Organização Educacional Barão de Mauá.

Academic Year: February to December (February-June; August-December).

Admission Requirements: Secondary school certificate and entrance examination.

Language of Instruction: Portuguese.

Degrees and Diplomas: Bacharel, 4 yrs.

Academic Staff, 1984-85: – (99).

913 **FACULDADE DE FILOSOFIA, CIÊNCIAS E LETRAS CAMILO CASTELO BRANCO**

Rua Caroline Fonseca, 08230 São Paulo (São Paulo)
Telephone: (11) 2005009

Philosophy
Science
Letters

Founded 1971.

914 **FACULDADE DE FILOSOFIA, CIÊNCIAS E LETRAS CARLOS QUEIROZ**

Avenida Cel Clementino Gonçalves 1651, 18900 Santa Cruz do Rio Pardo (São Paulo)
Telephone: (143) 721173

Philosophy
Science
Letters

Founded 1971.

915 **FACULDADE DE FILOSOFIA, CIÊNCIAS E LETRAS DA FUNDAÇÃO DE ENSINO SUPERIOR DE ITAÚNA**

Rua Professor Francisco Santiago 275, 35680 Itaúna (Minas Gerais)
Telephone: (37) 2413921

Philosophy
Science
Letters

Founded 1966.

916 **FACULDADE DE FILOSOFIA, CIÊNCIAS E LETRAS DO NORTE DE MINAS**

Rua Coronel Celestino 75, 39400 Montes Claros (Minas Gerais)
Telephone: (38) 2212651

Philosophy
Science
Letters

Founded 1964.

917 **FACULDADE DE FILOSOFIA, CIÊNCIAS E LETRAS DE ARAÇATABA**

Rua Mato Grosso 1141, 16100 Araçatuba (São Paulo)
Telephone: (186) 234088

Philosophy
Science
Letters

Founded 1966.

918 **FACULDADE DE FILOSOFIA, CIÊNCIAS E LETRAS DE ARAGUARI**

Avenida Minas Gerais 1889, 38440 Araguari (Minas Gerais)
Telephone: (34) 2413900

Philosophy
Science
Letters

Founded 1968.

919 **FACULDADE DE FILOSOFIA, CIÊNCIAS E LETRAS DE ARAPONGAS**

Rua das Garças 290, 86700 Arapongas (Paraná)
Telephone: (432) 521056

D. of Letters
D. of Social Studies (including Political Science)
D. of Mathematics
D. of Chemistry
D. of Sports
D. of Biomedical Sciences
D. of Education and Psychology

Founded 1968. Under the supervision of the Sociedade Educacional Centro Norte do Paraná.

Academic Year: February to December (February-June; August-December).

Admission Requirements: Secondary school certificate and entrance examination.

Language of Instruction: Portuguese.

Degrees and Diplomas: Licenciado in–Letters; Social Science; Physical Education, 3 yrs; Mathematics; Chemistry, 4 yrs.

Library: c. 8260 vols.

Academic Staff: c. 70.

Student Enrolment: c. 460.

920 **FACULDADE DE FILOSOFIA, CIÊNCIAS E LETRAS DE BARRA DO PIRAÍ**

Rodovia Benjamin Ielpo, Km. 11, 27100 Barra do Piraí (Rio de Janeiro)
Telephone: (244) 421533
Diretor: Walter Di Biase
Secretário Geral: Mário César Di Biase

D. of Letters
Head: José Geraldo Lamarca; *staff* 9
D. of Education
Head: José Maria Calife da Luz *staff* 7

Founded 1968. Under the supervision of the Fundação Rosemar Pimentel.

Degrees and Diplomas: Licenciado, 4 yrs.

921 **FACULDADE DE FILOSOFIA, CIÊNCIAS E LETRAS DE BEBEDOURO**

Rua Prof. Orlando F. de Carvalho 325, 14700 Bebedouro (São Paulo)
Telephone: (173) 421100

Philosophy
Science
Letters

Founded 1970.

922 **FACULDADE DE FILOSOFIA, CIÊNCIAS E LETRAS DE BELO HORIZONTE**

Avenida Antônio Carlos 521, 30000 Belo Horizonte (Minas Gerais)
Telephone: (31) 4426955

D. of Social Communication
D. of History
D. of Letters
D. of Mathematics
D. of Education
Extension D.

Founded 1964. Under the supervision of the Fundação Cultural de Belo Horizonte.

Academic Year: February to December (February-June; August-December).

Admission Requirements: Secondary school certificate and entrance examination.

Language of Instruction: Portuguese.

Degrees and Diplomas: Bacharel and Licenciado. Mestrado.

Library: c. 25,950 vols.

Academic Staff: c. – (130).

Student Enrolment: c. 2560.

923 **FACULDADE DE FILOSOFIA, CIÊNCIAS E LETRAS DE CARATINGA**

Avenida São José 49, 35300 Caratinga (Minas Gerais)
Telephone: (33) 3212930

Philosophy
Science
Letters

Founded 1968.

924 **FACULDADE DE FILOSOFIA, CIÊNCIAS E LETRAS DE CARUARÚ**
Rua Azevedo Coutinho, 55100 Caruarú (Pernambuco)
Telephone: (81) 7212611
Diretor: Mário Menezes

D. of Education
Head: Delma Evaneide Silva; *staff* – (18)
D. of Letters
Head: Márcia Duarte de Oliveira; *staff* – (10)
D. of History
Head: Antonio Claudio Pedrosa; *staff* – (7)
D. of Social Sciences
Head: Antonio Guedes de Queiroz; *staff* – (8)
Ce. for Research and Documentation
Head: Josué Euzébio Ferreira; *staff* – (4)

Founded 1961. Under the supervision of the Associação Diocesana de Ensino e Cultura de Caruarú.

Academic Year: February to November (February-June; July-November).

Admission Requirements: Secondary school certificate and entrance examination.

Language of Instruction: Portuguese.

Degrees and Diplomas: Licenciado in all fields, 4 yrs.

Library: 23,024 vols.

Academic Staff, 1990: 43.

Student Enrolment, 1990:

	Men	Women	Total
Of the country	413	1524	1937

925 **FACULDADE DE FILOSOFIA, CIÊNCIAS E LETRAS DE CATAGUASES**
Praça Rui Barbosa 86, 36770 Cataguases (Minas Gerais)
Telephone: (32) 4213109

Philosophy
Science
Letters

Founded 1971.

926 **FACULDADE DE FILOSOFIA, CIÊNCIAS E LETRAS DE COLATINA**
Avenida Brasil, 29700 Colatina (Espírito Santo)
Telephone: (27) 7220533

Philosophy
Science
Letters

Founded 1965.

927 **FACULDADE DE FILOSOFIA, CIÊNCIAS E LETRAS DE CRUZ ALTA**
Campus Universitário, 98100 Cruz Alta (Rio Grande do Sul)

Philosophy
Science
Letters

Founded 1969.

928 **FACULDADE DE FILOSOFIA, CIÊNCIAS E LETRAS DE DUQUE DE CAXIAS**
Avenida President Kennedy 9422, 25000 Duque de Caxias (Rio de Janeiro)
Telephone: (21) 7713942

Philosophy
Science
Letters

Founded 1969.

Academic Year: February to December (February-July; July-December).

Admission Requirements: Secondary school certificate and entrance examination.

Language of Instruction: Portuguese.

Degrees and Diplomas: Licenciado in–History; Geography; Social Studies; Portuguese and English Literature, 4 yrs.

Library: Biblioteca Castro Alves, *c.* 10,000 vols.

Academic Staff: c. 10.

Student Enrolment: c. 450.

929 **FACULDADE DE FILOSOFIA, CIÊNCIAS E LETRAS DE FORMIGA**
Avenida Dr. Arnaldo de Senna, 37290 Formiga (Minas Gerais)
Telephone: (37) 3212997

Philosophy
Science
Letters

Founded 1967. Under the supervision of the Fundação de Ensino Superior do Oeste de Minas.

Academic Year: February to November (February-June; August-November).

Admission Requirements: Secondary school certificate and entrance examination.

Fees (Cruzeiros): 85,000 per month.

Language of Instruction: Portuguese.

Degrees and Diplomas: Licenciado in Education, 3 yrs. Teaching qualifications, 3-4 yrs.

930 **FACULDADE DE FILOSOFIA, CIÊNCIAS E LETRAS DE GOVERNADOR VALADARES**
Campus Universitário, 35030 Governador Valadares (Minas Gerais)
Telephone: (332) 213090

Philosophy
Science
Letters

Founded 1971.

931 **FACULDADE DE FILOSOFIA, CIÊNCIAS E LETRAS DE GUARULHOS**
Rua Barão de Maua 600, 07000 Guarulhos (São Paulo)
Telephone: (11) 2093533

Philosophy
Science
Letters

Founded 1971.

932 **FACULDADE DE FILOSOFIA, CIÊNCIAS E LETRAS DE GUAXUPE**
Avenida D. Floriana s/n, 37800 Guaxupe (Minas Gerais)
Telephone: (35) 5511696

Philosophy
Science
Letters

Founded 1964.

933 **FACULDADE DE FILOSOFIA, CIÊNCIAS E LETRAS DE ITAPETININGA**
Avenida João Barth s/n, 18200 Itapetininga (São Paulo)
Telephone: (15) 2710503

D. of Letters
D. of Education
D. of Exact Sciences
D. of History
D. of Social Sciences

Founded 1968 and authorized by federal decree. Under the supervision of the Associação de Ensino de Itapetininga.

Academic Year: March to February (March-July; August-February).

Admission Requirements: Secondary school certificate.

Language of Instruction: Portuguese.

Degrees and Diplomas: Bacharel, 3 yrs. Licenciado, 4 yrs.

Library: c. 14,960 vols.

Academic Staff: c. – (70).

Student Enrolment: c. 550.

934 **FACULDADE DE FILOSOFIA, CIÊNCIAS E LETRAS DE ITARARÉ**
Rua João Batista Veiga 1725, 18460 Itararé (São Paulo)
Telephone: (155) 321330/321329
Diretor: Clovis Machado
Secretário: José Maria Aparecido de Almeida

Pedagogy

Founded 1973. Under the supervision of the Associação Itararéense de Ensino.

Academic Year: January to December (January-June; August-December).
Admission Requirements: Secondary school certificate.
Fees (Cruzeiros): 1570 per month.
Language of Instruction: Portuguese.
Degrees and Diplomas: Licenciado.
Library: c. 7600 vols.
Academic Staff, 1990: c. 20.
Student Enrolment, 1990:

	Men	Women	Total
Of the country	10	228	238
Of other countries	5	312	317
Total	15	540	555

935 **FACULDADE DE FILOSOFIA, CIÊNCIAS E LETRAS DE ITAÚNA**
Rua Prof Francisco Santiago 275, 35680 Itaúna (Minas Gerais)
Telephone: (37) 2412921
Diretor: Arno Balduino Weschenfelder (1990-92)

Education

Founded 1966. Under the supervision of the Fundação de Ensino Superior de Itaúna.
Academic Year: February to December (February-June; August-December).
Admission Requirements: Secondary school certificate and entrance examination.
Language of Instruction: Portuguese.
Degrees and Diplomas: Licenciado, 4 yrs.
Academic Staff, 1990: – (21).
Student Enrolment, 1990: 238.

936 **FACULDADE DE FILOSOFIA, CIÊNCIAS E LETRAS DE ITUVERAVA**
Rua Cel. Flausino Barbosa Sandoval 1259, 14500 Ituverava (São Paulo)
Telephone: (16) 7292326

Philosophy
Science
Letters

Founded 1971.
Academic Year: February to December (February-June; August-December).
Admission Requirements: Secondary school certificate.
Language of Instruction: Portuguese.
Degrees and Diplomas: Licenciado, 3-4 yrs.
Library: c. 5660 vols.
Academic Staff: c. 15 (20).
Student Enrolment: c. 960.

937 **FACULDADE DE FILOSOFIA, CIÊNCIAS E LETRAS DE JAHÚ**
Rua Tenente Navarro 642, 17200 Jahú (São Paulo)
Telephone: (146) 223435

Philosophy
Science
Letters

Founded 1966.

938 **FACULDADE DE FILOSOFIA, CIÊNCIAS E LETRAS DE JALES**
Avenida Francisco Jales 567, 15700 Jales (São Paulo)
Telephone: (17) 6321620

Philosophy
Science
Letters

Founded 1970.

939 **FACULDADE DE FILOSOFIA, CIÊNCIAS E LETRAS DE JANDAIA DO SUL**
Rua dos Patriotas, 86900 Jandaia do Sul (Paraná)
Telephone: (43) 4321113
Diretor: Wilson José Pontara
Secretária: Maria José Paduan Balarini

Philosophy
Science
Letters
Geography
Education

Founded 1967.
Academic Year: March to February.
Admission Requirements: Secondary school certificate and entrance examination.
Language of Instruction: Portuguese.
Degrees and Diplomas: Licenciado, 4 yrs.
Library: 9000 vols.

940 **FACULDADE DE FILOSOFIA, CIÊNCIAS E LETRAS DE MACAE**
Rua Tenente Rui Ribeiro 2001, 18700 Macae (Rio de Janeiro)
Telephone: (247) 620965

Philosophy
Science
Letters

Founded 1973.

941 **FACULDADE DE FILOSOFIA, CIÊNCIAS E LETRAS DE MOEMA**
Avenida Divino Salvador 12, 04078 São Paulo (São Paulo)
Telephone: (11) 5425888

Philosophy
Science
Letters

Founded 1971.

942 **FACULDADE DE FILOSOFIA, CIÊNCIAS E LETRAS DE NOVA IGUAÇU**
Avenida Abilio Augusto Tavora, 26000 Nova Iguaçu Rio de Janeiro)
Telephone: (21) 7677221

Philosophy
Science
Letters

Founded 1970.

943 **FACULDADE DE FILOSOFIA, CIÊNCIAS E LETRAS DE OURO FINO**
Rodovia MG 290 Km 59 Ouro Fino, 37570 Ouro Fino (Minas Gerais)
Telephone: (35) 4411426

Philosophy
Science
Letters

Founded 1972.

944 **FACULDADE DE FILOSOFIA, CIÊNCIAS E LETRAS DE PALMAS**
Rua Dr. Bernardo Ribeiro Viana 903, 84670 Palmas (Paraná)
Telephone: (462) 621287
Diretor: Agostinho José Sartori
Secretária: Tompson Eloi Schneider

Philosophy
Social Studies
Letters
Education

Founded 1969.
Academic Year: February to December (February-June; August-December).
Admission Requirements: Secondary school certificate and entrance examination.
Language of Instruction: Portuguese.
Degrees and Diplomas: Licenciado, 3-4 yrs.
Library: 40,000 vols.
Academic Staff, 1990: 10 (26)
Student Enrolment, 1990:

	Men	Women	Total
Of the country	110	1115	1225

945 **FACULDADE DE FILOSOFIA, CIÊNCIAS E LETRAS DE PATOS**
Rua Horacio Nobrega, 58700 Patos (Paraíba)
Telephone: (83) 4212606

Philosophy
Science
Letters
Founded 1970.

946 **FACULDADE DE FILOSOFIA, CIÊNCIAS E LETRAS DE PENÁPOLIS**
Campus Universitário, 16300 Penápolis (São Paulo)
Telephone: (186) 522315

D. of Mathematics
D. of Letters
D. of Science
D. of Design
D. of Education
D. of Social Science
S. of Art (Teacher Training)
Founded 1967. Under the supervision of the Fundação Educacional de Penápolis. Governing bodies: the Conselho Diretor; the Congregação da Faculdade; the Conselho Departamental. Residential facilities for students.
Academic Year: March to December (March-June; August-December).
Admission Requirements: Secondary school certificate or equivalent.
Language of Instruction: Portuguese.
Degrees and Diplomas: Licenciado, 4 yrs.
Library: c. 3000 vols.
Special Facilities (Museums, etc.): Museum of Geology and Mineralogy.

947 **FACULDADE DE FILOSOFIA, CIÊNCIAS E LETRAS DE PIRAJÚ**
Rua João Haiter 408, 18800 Pirajú (São Paulo)
Telephone: (143) 512078

Philosophy
Science
Letters
Founded 1975.

948 **FACULDADE DE FILOSOFIA, CIÊNCIAS E LETRAS DE PRESIDENTE WENCESLAU**
Avenida Carlos Platzeck, 19400 Presidente Wenceslau (São Paulo)
Telephone: (182) 712373

Philosophy
Science
Letters
Founded 1972.

949 **FACULDADE DE FILOSOFIA, CIÊNCIAS E LETRAS DE REGISTRO**
Rua São Francisco Xavier 165, 11900 Registro (São Paulo)
Telephone: (138) 212411

Philosophy
Science
Letters
Founded 1972.

950 **FACULDADE DE FILOSOFIA, CIÊNCIAS E LETRAS DE RIO DE JANEIRO**
Avenida Ernani Cardoso 335, 21310 Rio de Janeiro (Rio de Janeiro)

Philosophy
Science
Letters
Founded 1968.

951 **FACULDADE DE FILOSOFIA, CIÊNCIAS E LETRAS DE SANTIAGO**
Vinte de Setembro 2410, 97700 Santiago (Rio Grande do Sul)
Telephone: (55) 2511715

Philosophy
Science
Letters
Founded 1969.

952 **FACULDADE DE FILOSOFIA, CIÊNCIAS E LETRAS DE SANTO AMARO**
Rua Prof. Eneas de S. Neto 340, 04829 São Paulo (São Paulo)
Telephone: (11) 5209611

Philosophy
Science
Letters
Founded 1970.

953 **FACULDADE DE FILOSOFIA, CIÊNCIAS E LETRAS DE SÃO BERNARDINO DO CAMPO**
Rua Americo Brasilense 49, 09700 São Bernardino do Campo (São Paulo)
Telephone: (11) 4433277

Philosophy
Science
Letters
Founded 1971.

954 **FACULDADE DE FILOSOFIA, CIÊNCIAS E LETRAS DE SÃO BORJA**
Avenida Bernardo de Mello, 97670 São Borja (Rio Grande do Sul)
Telephone: (55) 4311687

Philosophy
Science
Letters
Founded 1970 as a private institution by the Fundação Educacional de São Borja. Receives some financial support from the municipal authorities.
Academic Year: March to December (March-June; August-December).
Admission Requirements: Secondary school certificate.
Language of Instruction: Portuguese.
Degrees and Diplomas: Licenciado, 3-4 yrs.
Library: c. 5790 vols.
Academic Staff: c. 30.
Student Enrolment: c. 450.

955 **FACULDADE DE FILOSOFIA, CIÊNCIAS E LETRAS DE SÃO CAETANO DO SUL**
Rua Amazonas, 95000 São Caetano do Sul (São Paulo)
Telephone: (11) 4413233

Philosophy
Science
Letters
Founded 1969.

956 **FACULDADE DE FILOSOFIA, CIÊNCIAS E LETRAS DE SÃO JOÃO DA BOA VISTA**
Rua Cristião Osorio 10, 13870 São João da Boa Vista (São Paulo)
Telephone: (196) 233833

Philosophy
Science
Letters
Founded 1971.

957 **FACULDADE DE FILOSOFIA, CIÊNCIAS E LETRAS DE SETE LAGOAS**
Avenida Marechal Castelo Branco, 35700 Sete Lagoas (Minas Gerais)
Telephone: (31) 9212022

Philosophy
Science
Letters
Founded 1970. Under the supervision of the Fundação Educacional 'Monsenhor Messias'.
Academic Year: February to January.
Admission Requirements: Secondary school certificate.
Language of Instruction: Portuguese.
Degrees and Diplomas: Bacharel.

958 **FACULDADE DE FILOSOFIA, CIÊNCIAS E LETRAS DE SOROCABA**
Avenida General Osório 35, 18165 Sorocaba (São Paulo)
Telephone: (152) 327153

Philosophy
Science

Letters
Founded 1954.

959 **FACULDADE DE FILOSOFIA, CIÊNCIAS E LETRAS DE TATUI**
Rua Prof. Cracy Gomes, 18270 Tatui (São Paulo)
Telephone: (152) 510460

Philosophy
Science
Letters
Founded 1971.

960 **FACULDADE DE FILOSOFIA, CIÊNCIAS E LETRAS DE TUPÃ**
Avenida dos Universitários, 17600 Tupã (São Paulo)
Telephone: (144) 421784

D. of Letters
D. of Exact Sciences
D. of Social Sciences
D. of Education
Founded 1968. Recognized by the federal government 1973. Under the supervision of the Instituição Tamoios de Ensino e Cultura. Governing body: the Congregação.
Academic Year: February to December (February-June; August-December).
Admission Requirements: Secondary school certificate and entrance examination.
Language of Instruction: Portuguese.
Degrees and Diplomas: Licenciado in all fields. Certificates of specialization.
Library: c. 20,000 vols.
Academic Staff: c. 40.
Student Enrolment: c. 1250.

961 **FACULDADE DE FILOSOFIA, CIÊNCIAS E LETRAS DE UBÁ**
Praça São Januario 276, 36500 Ubá (Minas Gerais)
Telephone: (32) 532-4657
Diretor: Luiz Alberto Duarte Martins

Pedagogy
Mathematics
Letters
History
Founded 1970. Under the supervision of the Fundação José Bonifácio.
Academic Year: February to December.
Admission Requirements: Secondary school certificate and entrance examination.
Language of Instruction: Portuguese.
Degrees and Diplomas: Licenciado, 4 yrs.
Library: 15,000 vols.
Academic Staff, 1990: – (40)
Student Enrolment, 1990:

	Men	Women	Total
Of the country	80	360	440

962 **FACULDADE DE FILOSOFIA, CIÊNCIAS E LETRAS DE UMUARAMA**
Praça Mascarenhas de Moraes 29, 87500 Umuarama (Paraná)
Telephone: (446) 231643

Philosophy
Science
Letters
Founded 1972.

963 **FACULDADE DE FILOSOFIA, CIÊNCIAS E LETRAS DE URUGUAIANA**
Domingos de Almeida 3225, 97500 Uruguaiana (Rio Grande do Sul)
Telephone: (55) 4121683

Philosophy
Science
Letters
Founded 1958.

964 **FACULDADE DE FILOSOFIA, CIÊNCIAS E LETRAS DE VALENÇA**
Rua Sargento Vitor Hugo 219, 27600 Valença (Rio de Janeiro)
Telephone: (244) 52-1888
Diretor: Marieta José Arbex
Secretário: Alcino Lima Guedes

D. of Pedagogy
Head: Therezinha P. Menezes
D. of Science (Mathematics)
Head: Dario Medeiros Toledo
D. of Letters
Head: José Geraldo Lamarca
D. of Social Sciences
Head: Consuelo Lago de Vasconcelos
D. of History
Head: Rogério da Silva Tjader
Founded 1965. Supported by the Fundação Educacional D. André Arcoverde and supervised by the Ministry ofEducation.
Academic Year: January to December (January-June; August-December).
Admission Requirements: Secondary school certificate and entrance examination.
Fees (Cruzeiros): 1326.97 per month.
Language of Instruction: Portuguese.
Degrees and Diplomas: Licenciado, 4 yrs.
Library: 50,065 vols.
Special Facilities (Museums, etc.): Museu de Arte Regional; Arte Sacra e Antropologia.
Academic Staff, 1990: – (45)
Student Enrolment, 1990:

	Men	Women	Total
Of the country	56	341	397

965 **FACULDADE DE FILOSOFIA, CIÊNCIAS E LETRAS DE VARGINHA**
Rua Maria B. Resende 78, 37100 Varginha (Minas Gerais)
Telephone: (35) 2212358

Philosophy
Science
Letters
Founded 1966.

966 **FACULDADE DE FILOSOFIA, CIÊNCIAS E LETRAS DE VASSOURAS**
Avenida Exp. Oswaldo de A. Ramos, 27700 Vassouras (Rio de Janeiro)
Telephone: (244) 711595
Diretor: Marilda Corrêa Ciribelli

Philosophy
Science
Letters
Founded 1971. Under the supervision of the Fundação Educacional Sevelino Sombra.
Academic Year: February to December (February-June; August-December).
Admission Requirements: Secondary school certificate and entrance examination.
Fees (Cruzeiros): 5272.05 per month.
Language of Instruction: Portuguese.
Degrees and Diplomas: Licenciado, 4 yrs.
Academic Staff, 1989-90: 77.

967 **FACULDADE DE FILOSOFIA, CIÊNCIAS E LETRAS DE VOLTA REDONDA**
Rua Gov. Luiz Monterra 81, 27180 Volta Redonda (Rio de Janeiro)
Telephone: (243) 424530
Diretor: Raimundo Pinheiro
Secretário Geral: Milton Carlos de Souza e Silva

D. of Letters
Head: Mário de Jesus Palheta Nunes; *staff* 9
D. of Mathematics and Physics
Head: Robeto Marinho Cardoso; *staff* 14 (1)
D. of Biology and Chemistry
Head: Geraldo Assis Cardoso; *staff* 14
D. of Education
Head: Francisco de Assis D.Cunha; *staff* 7

D. of Geography and History
Head: José Maria Calife da Luz; *staff* 11 (f1)
D. of Social Studies
Founded 1972. Under the supervision of the Fundação Educacional Rosemar Pimente.
Academic Year: March to December (March-July; August-December).
Admission Requirements: Secondary school certificate and entrance examination.
Language of Instruction: Portuguese.
Degrees and Diplomas: Licenciado, 4 yrs.
Library: Biblioteca 'Jair de Paula', 8500 vols.
Academic Staff: c. – (60).
Student Enrolment: c. 1110.

968 **FACULDADE DE FILOSOFIA, CIÊNCIAS E LETRAS DO ALTO SÃO FRANCISCO**
Avenida Formiga, 35595 Luz (Minas Gerais)
Telephone: (37) 4211494

Philosophy
Science
Letters
Founded 1979.

969 **FACULDADE DE FILOSOFIA, CIÊNCIAS E LETRAS DO ICNPF**
Rua Tamoios, 30000 Belo Horizonte (Minas Gerais)
Telephone: (31) 2018811

Philosophy
Science
Letters
Founded 1972. Under the supervision of the Instituto Cultural Newton Paiva Ferreira.
Academic Year: February to December (February-June; August-December).
Admission Requirements: Secondary school certificate and entrance examination.
Language of Instruction: Portuguese.
Degrees and Diplomas: Bacharel, 3 yrs.

970 **FACULDADE DE FILOSOFIA, CIÊNCIAS E LETRAS DOM BOSCO**
Rua Santa Rosa 536, 98900 Santa Rosa (Rio Grande do Sul)
Telex: 553804 DOMB BR
Telephone: (55) 5121183
Diretor: Faustino Chiamenti

D. of Philosophy
Head: Arcângelo Deretti; *staff* 2 (13)
D. of Science
Head: Anor Elias Lenzi; *staff* 10 (4)
D. of Letters
Head: Loiva Blum; *staff* 14 (2)
D. of Education
Head: Geraldo P, d'Ávila; *staff* 10 (3)
D. of Social Studies
Head: Tereza Christensen; *staff* 5 (14)
D. of Religious Sciences
Head: Severino Piccinini; *staff* 6 (7)
Founded 1969. Under the supervision of the Instituto Educacional Dom Bosco.
Academic Year: March to December (March-July; July-December).
Admission Requirements: Secondary school certificate and entrance examination.
Fees (Cruzeiros): 1650 per month.
Language of Instruction: Portuguese.
Degrees and Diplomas: Licenciado, 3-4 yrs.
Library: Biblioteca Central P. Faustino Chiamenti, 33,336 vols.
Academic Staff, 1990: 8 (47).
Student Enrolment, 1990:

	Men	Women	Total
Of the country	98	524	622

971 **FACULDADE DE FILOSOFIA, CIÊNCIAS E LETRAS EUGENIO PACELLI**
Rua Joaquim Roberto Duarte, 37550 Pouso Alegre (Minas Gerais)
Telephone: (35) 4211736

Philosophy
Science
Letters
Founded 1972.

972 **FACULDADE DE FILOSOFIA, CIÊNCIAS E LETRAS IMACULADA CONCEIÇÃO**
Rua Andradas 1614, 97100 Santa Maria (Rio Grande do Sul)
Telephone: (55) 2212792

Philosophy
Science
Letters
Founded 1955.

973 **FACULDADE DE FILOSOFIA, CIÊNCIAS E LETRAS JOSÉ OLYMPIO**
Rua Dom Bosco 466, 14300 Batatais (São Paulo)

Philosophy
Science
Letters
Founded 1973.

974 **FACULDADE DE FILOSOFIA, CIÊNCIAS E LETRAS 'MADRE GERTRUDES DE SÃO JOSÉ'**
Avenida Monte Castelo 03, 29300 Cachoeiro do Itapemirim (Espírito Santo)
Telephone: (27) 5225425

Philosophy
Social Science
Letters
Founded 1966.

975 **FACULDADE DE FILOSOFIA, CIÊNCIAS E LETRAS 'MATER DIVINAE GRATIAE'**
Rua Monsenhor J. Augusto 203, 36200 Barbacena (Minas Gerais)
Telephone: (32) 3313182

D. of Letters
D. of Education
D. of Mathematics
D. of History
Founded 1966 and recognized by the State. Recognized by the federal government 1972.
Academic Year: March to December (March-June; August-December).
Admission Requirements: Secondary school certificate.
Language of Instruction: Portuguese.
Degrees and Diplomas: Licenciado, 4 yrs.

976 **FACULDADE DE FILOSOFIA, CIÊNCIAS E LETRAS MINISTRO TARSO DUTRA**
Avenida Alcides Chacon Couto 395, 17900 Dracena (São Paulo)
Telephone: (18) 8211191

Philosophy
Science
Letters
Founded 1969.

977 **FACULDADE DE FILOSOFIA, CIÊNCIAS E LETRAS 'NOSSA SENHORA DO PATROCINIO'**
Rua Madre Maria Basilia 965, 13300 Itú (São Paulo)
Telephone: (11) 4822547

Letters
Education
Science
Founded 1958.
Academic Year: March to December (March-June; August-November).
Admission Requirements: Secondary school certificate.
Language of Instruction: Portuguese.
Degrees and Diplomas: Bacharel. Licenciado. Doutor.
Special Facilities (Museums, etc.): Museu de Ciências Naturais.

978 **FACULDADE DE FILOSOFIA, CIÊNCIAS E LETRAS 'NOSSA SENHORA DO SION'**
Rua Padre Nattuzzi, 37400 Campanha (Minas Gerais)
Telephone: (35) 2611187

Education
Letters
Geography
History

Founded 1975. Under the supervision of the Fundação Cultural Campanha da Princesa.
Academic Year: March to November (March-June; August-November).
Admission Requirements: Secondary school certificate.
Language of Instruction: Portuguese.
Degrees and Diplomas: Licenciado in all fields, 3 yrs.
Academic Staff: c. 20.
Student Enrolment: c. 150.

979 **FACULDADE DE FILOSOFIA, CIÊNCIAS E LETRAS NOVE DE JULHO**
Rua Diamantina 302, 02117 São Paulo (São Paulo)
Telephone: (11) 2648843

Philosophy
Science
Letters

Founded 1972.

980 **FACULDADE DE FILOSOFIA, CIÊNCIAS E LETRAS PROF. CARLOS PASQUALE**
Rua Oriente 123, 03016 São Paulo (São Paulo)
Telephone: (11) 2279239
Diretor: Wladimir Donatto
Secretário Geral: Izo Valini

D. of Pedagogy
Co-ordinator: Maria Salete Cruz; *staff* – (17)
D. of Science
Co-ordinator: João Paulo Fadelone; *staff* – (14)
D. of Letters
Co-ordinator: Marli Silva; *staff* – (11)
D. of Mathematics
Co-ordinator: João Paulo Fordelone; *staff* – (6)
D. of Biology
Co-ordinator: Celso Melo; *staff* – (7)
D. of Chemistry
Co-ordinator: Paulo Finotti; *staff* – (7)
D. of Social Studies
Co-ordinator: Odir José de Oliveira; *staff* – (15)

Founded 1972. Under the supervision of the Sociedade Educacional Liceu Academico São Paulo.
Academic Year: February to December (February-June; August-December).
Admission Requirements: Secondary school certificate and entrance examination.
Fees (Cruzeiros): 5000 per month.
Language of Instruction: Portuguese.
Degrees and Diplomas: Licenciado, 4 yrs.
Library: Biblioteca Francisco Pasetto, 12,859 vols.
Academic Staff, 1990: – (55).
Student Enrolment, 1990:

	Men	Women	Total
Of the country	506	674	1180

981 **FACULDADE DE FILOSOFIA, CIÊNCIAS E LETRAS 'PROF. JOSÉ A. VIEIRA'**
Praça Olegario Maciel 25, 37750 Machado (Minas Gerais)
Telephone: (35) 9311866

Education
Social Studies
Letters

Founded 1968. Under the supervision of the Fundação Educacional de Machado.
Academic Year: February to December (February-June; August-December).
Admission Requirements: Secondary school certificate.
Language of Instruction: Portuguese.

982 **FACULDADE DE FILOSOFIA, CIÊNCIAS E LETRAS 'PROF. NAIR FORTES ABU-MERHY'**
Avenida 18 de Julho 210, 36660 Além Paraiba (Minas Gerais)
Telephone: (32) 4622951

Philosophy
Science
Letters

Founded 1973. Under the supervision of the Fundação Educacional de Além Paraiba.

983 **FACULDADE DE FILOSOFIA, CIÊNCIAS E LETRAS 'SANTA MARCELINA'**
Rua do Bomfim, 36880 Muriaé (Minas Gerais)
Telephone: (32) 7211026

Philosophy
Letters (Neo-Latin)
Education

Founded 1927 as college, acquired present status 1961.
Academic Year: March to December (March-June; August-December).
Admission Requirements: Secondary school certificate and entrance examination.
Language of Instruction: Portuguese.
Degrees and Diplomas: Bacharel.

984 **FACULDADE DE FILOSOFIA, CIÊNCIAS E LETRAS SÃO MARCOS**
Avenida Nazare, 04262 São Paulo (São Paulo)
Telephone: (11) 2745711

Philosophy
Science
Letters

Founded 1971.

985 **FACULDADE DE FILOSOFIA, CIÊNCIAS E LETRAS TIBIRIÇA**
Largo São Bento, 01405 São Paulo (São Paulo)
Telephone: (11) 2808531

Philosophy
Science
Letters

Founded 1972.

986 **FACULDADE DE FILOSOFIA, CIÊNCIAS E LETRAS TUIUTI**
Rua Marcelino Champagnat, 80000 Curitiba (Paraná)
Telephone: (41) 2253131

D. of Philosophy
D. of Education
D. of Letters

Founded 1973.
Academic Year: February to December (February-July; August-December).
Admission Requirements: Secondary school certificate and entrance examination.
Language of Instruction: Portuguese.
Degrees and Diplomas: Licenciado in all fields.
Publication: O Garatuja.
Academic Staff: c. 80.
Student Enrolment: c. 1730.

987 **FACULDADE DE FILOSOFIA, CIÊNCIAS E LETRAS VEIGA DE ALMEIDA**
Rua Rua São Francisco Xavier 124, 20550 Rio de Janeiro (Rio de Janeiro)
Telephone: (21) 2646172

Philosophy
Science
Letters

Founded 1974.

988 **FACULDADE DE FILOSOFIA DE CAMPO GRANDE**
Estrada da Caroba 685, Campo Grande, 23000 Rio de Janeiro (Rio de Janeiro)
Telephone: (21) 3941230

Philosophy
Founded 1961.

989 **FACULDADE DE FILOSOFIA DE CAMPOS**
Avenida Visc. de Alvarenga s/n, 28100 Campos (Rio de Janeiro)
Telephone: (247) 228043

D. of Letters
D. of Education
D. of Social Communication
D. of Science
D. of History
Extension Teacher Training D.
Founded 1961. Under the supervision of the Fundação Cultural de Campos.
Academic Year: March to December (March-June; August-December).
Admission Requirements: Secondary school certificate and entrance examination.
Language of Instruction: Portuguese.
Degrees and Diplomas: Bacharel in Journalism, 4 yrs. Licenciado in all fields, 4 yrs.
Library: c. 15,000 vols.
Academic Staff: c. 100.
Student Enrolment: c. 1210.

990 **FACULDADE DE FILOSOFIA DE ITAPERUNA**
Rua Major Porphiro Henriques 41, 28300 Itaperuna (Rio de Janeiro)
Telephone: (249) 220610

Philosophy
Founded 1968.

991 **FACULDADE DE FILOSOFIA DO CRATO**
Rua del Antonio Luiz, 63100 Crato (Ceará)
Telephone: (85) 5210511

Philosophy
Founded 1960.

992 **FACULDADE DE FILOSOFIA DO RECIFE**
Avenida Conde da Boa Vista 921, 50000 Recife (Pernambuco)
Telephone: (81) 2226344

Philosophy
Founded 1940.

993 **FACULDADE DE FILOSOFIA DO VALE DO SÃO PATRICIO**
Praça Alvaro de Melo, Rua 21, 76700 Ceres (Goiás)
Telephone: (62) 7211318

Philosophy
Science
Letters
Under the supervision of the Associação Educativa Evangélica.
Academic Year: February to November (February-June; August-November).
Admission Requirements: Secondary school certificate.
Language of Instruction: Portuguese.
Degrees and Diplomas: Licenciado, 4 yrs.
Academic Staff: c. – (20).

994 **FACULDADE DE FILOSOFIA DOM JOSÉ DE SOBRAL**
Avenida da Universidade s/n, 62100 Sobral (Ceará)
Telephone: (85) 6112213

Philosophy
Founded 1961.

995 **FACULDADE DE FILOSOFIA E LETRAS**
Travessa Mercedes Mourão 77, 39100 Diamantina (Minas Gerais)
Telephone: (37) 9311922

Philosophy
Letters
Founded 1968.

996 **FACULDADE DE FILOSOFIA NOSSA SENHORA IMACULADA CONCEIÇÃO**
Rua Senador Salgado Filho 7427, 94400 Viamão (Rio Grande do Sul)
Telephone: (51) 2851177

Philosophy
Founded 1957.

997 **FACULDADE DE FILOSOFIA 'NOSSA SENHORA MEDIANEIRA'**
Rua Haddock Lobo 440, 01414 São Paulo (São Paulo)
Telephone: (11) 2573022

Philosophy
Science
Letters
Education
Founded 1955.
Degrees and Diplomas: Bacharel and Licenciado in–Social Sciences; Religious Culture; Philosophy; Physics; Geography; History; Letters (Classical and Neo-Latin); Mathematics; Education.

998 **FACULDADE DE FILOSOFIA 'SANTA DOROTÉIA'**
Rua Monsenhor Miranda 86, 28600 Novo Friburgo (Rio de Janeiro)
Telephone: (245) 222900

Philosophy
Founded 1967.

999 **FACULDADE DE FISIOTÉRAPIA DE PRESIDENTE PRUDENTE**
Rua José Bongiovani 700, 19100 Presidente Prudente (São Paulo)
Telephone: (18) 2225666

Physiotherapy
Founded 1981. Under the supervision of the Associação Prudentina de Educação e Cultura. Some residential facilities for academic staff.
Academic Year: February to December (February-June; August-December).
Admission Requirements: Secondary school certificate and entrance examination.
Degrees and Diplomas: Professional title of Fisioterapeuta, 3 yrs.
Academic Staff: c. 20.

1000 **FACULDADE DE FONDAUDIOLOGIA**
Rua de 18 Octubro, Rio de Janeiro (Rio de Janeiro)
Telephone: (21) 2082095

Founded 1980.

1001 **FACULDADE DE FORMACÃO DE PROFESSORES BETHENCOURT DA SILVA**
Rua Frederico Silva, 20230 Rio de Janeiro (Rio de Janeiro)
Telephone: (21) 2215708

Education
Founded 1981.

1002 **FACULDADE DE FORMAÇÃO DE PROFESSORES DE PETROLINA**
BR 203 Km 2 s/n, Predio, 56300 Petrolina (Pernambuco)

Education
Founded 1969.

1003 **FACULDADE DE FORMAÇÃO DE PROFESSORES DE PRIMEIRO GRAU DE ARAPIRACA**
Rua Governador Luiz Cavalcante s/n, Alto do Cruzeiro, 57300 Arapiraca (Alagoas)
Telephone: (82) 5213786

Education
Founded 1971.

1004 **FACULDADE DE FORMAÇÃO DE PROFESSORES DE VITÓRIA DE SANTO ANTÃO**

Lot São Vicente Ferrer s/n, Caja, 55600 Vitória de Santo Antão (Pernambuco)
Telephone: (81) 5231020

Education

Founded 1972.

1005 **FACULDADE DE FORMAÇÃO DE PROFESSORES E ESPECIALISTAS EM EDUCAÇÃO**

Rua Julio de Castilhos, 96180 Camaqua (Rio Grande do Sul)
Telephone: (51) 6711640

Education

Founded 1980.

1006 **FACULDADE DE FORMAÇÃO D PROFESSORES DO INSTITUTO AMERICANO DE LINS**

Rua Tenente Florencio Puppo Neto 200, Jardim Americano, 16400 Lins (São Paulo)
Telephone: (14) 5222223

Education

Founded 1970.

1007 **FACULDADE DE FORMAÇÃO DE PROFESSORES SÃO JUDAS TADEU**

Rua Dom Diego de Souza 100, Cristo Redentor, 90000 Pôrto Alegre (Rio Grande do Sul)
Telephone: (512) 40-72-90
Diretor: Pedro Ruffoni Doval

Education

Founded 1976.
Academic Year: March to November (March-June; August-November).
Admission Requirements: Secondary school certificate and entrance examination.
Fees (Cruzeiros): 10,350 per semester.
Language of Instruction: Portuguese.
Degrees and Diplomas: Bacharel.
Library: 17,000 vols.
Academic Staff, 1990: – (14).
Student Enrolment, 1990:

	Men	Women	Total
Of the country	18	42	60

1008 **FACULDADE DE FORMAÇÃO PROFESSIONAL INTEGRADA**

Avenida Ernani do Amaral Peixoto 836, 24020 Niterói (Rio de Janeiro)
Telephone: (21) 7194455

Letters
Science
Social Studies
Art
Accountancy
Administration
Economics
Statistics

Founded 1973.

1009 **FACULDADE DE HUMANIDADES PEDRO II**

Rua Piraúba s/n, 20940 São Cristovão (Rio de Janeiro)
Telephone: (21) 5806426
Reitor: Antonio José Chediak
Secretária: Helaisse Chagas Lobo

Human Sciences

Founded 1970.Under the supervision of the Sociedade Educadora Pedro II.
Academic Year: March to December (March-July; August-December).
Admission Requirements: Secondary school certificate and entrance examination.
Fees (Cruzeiros): 2476.39-2833.98 per semester.
Language of Instruction: Portuguese.
Degrees and Diplomas: Bacharel and Licenciado in–Biology; Physics; History; Letters; Mathematics; Psychology; Chemistry, 4 yrs.
Library: 20,000 vols.
Special Facilities (Museums, etc.): Museum of Marine Biology.
Publication: Omnia (biennially).
Academic Staff, 1986-87: 19 (145).
Student Enrolment, 1986-87:

	Men	Women	Total
Of the country	967	1366	2333
Of other countries	15	21	36
Total	982	1387	2369

1010 **FACULDADE DE LETRAS E EDUCAÇÃO DE VACARIA**

Avenida Presidente Kennedy 2020, Vila Militar, 95200 Vacaria (Rio Grande do Sul)
Telephone: (54) 2312055

Letters
Education

Founded 1974.

1011 **FACULDADE DE MEDICINA DE BARBACENA**

Praça Antonio Carlos s/n, 36200 Barbacena (Minas Gerais)
Telephone: (32) 3312966

Medicine

Founded 1971.

1012 **FACULDADE DE MEDICINA DE CAMPOS**

Rua Alberto Torres 217, 28100 Campos (Rio de Janeiro)
Telephone: (24) 7226788

Medicine

Founded 1967. Recognized by the federal government and financially supported by the Fundação Benedito Pereira Nunes. Governing bodies: the Conselho Superior; the Conselho Departamental; the Conselho Diretor.
Academic Year: March to December (March-July; August-December).
Admission Requirements: Secondary school certificate and entrance examination.
Language of Instruction: Portuguese.
Degrees and Diplomas: Professional title of Médico, 6 yrs.

1013 **FACULDADE DE MEDICINA DE CATANDUVA**

Rua Belém 647, 15800 Catanduva (São Paulo)
Telephone: (175) 22-1165
Diretor: Sleman Soubhia

Medicine

Founded 1970. Under the supervision of the Funcação Padre Albino.
Academic Year: March to November (March-June; August-November).
Admission Requirements: Secondary school certificate and entrance examination.
Fees (Cruzeiros): 11,227.79.
Language of Instruction: Portuguese.
Degrees and Diplomas: Professional title of Médico, 6 yrs.
Academic Staff, 1990: – (109).

1014 **FACULDADE DE MEDICINA DE ITAJUBÁ**

Rua Cel. Reno Júnior 368, 37500 Itajubá (Minas Gerais)
Telephone: (35) 6221100

Medicine

Founded 1968.
Academic Year: March to December (March-June; August-December).
Admission Requirements: Secondary school certificate and entrance examination.
Language of Instruction: Portuguese.
Degrees and Diplomas: Professional title of Médico, 6 yrs.
Library: c. 9210 vols.
Publication: Boletim.
Academic Staff: c. – (90).
Student Enrolment: c. 560.

1015 **FACULDADE DE MEDICINA DE MARÍLIA**

Avenida Monte Carmelo, 17500 Marília (São Paulo)
Telephone: (144) 331744
Diretor: Roberto de Queiroz Padiha
Secretário-Geral: Jácomo de Rossi Netto

Medicine (including Nursing)

Founded 1967. Under the supervision of the Fundação Municipal de Ensino Superior de Marília.

Academic Year: January to December (January-June; July-December).

Admission Requirements: Secondary school certificate and entrance examination.

Language of Instruction: Portuguese.

Degrees and Diplomas: Professional titles of–Enfermeiro, nursing, 4 yrs; Médico, 6 yrs.

Library: 3633 vols.

Academic Staff, 1986-87: – (137).

Student Enrolment, 1986-87:

	Men	Women	Total
Of the country	331	308	639
Of other countries	1	–	1
Total	332	308	640

1016 **FACULDADE DE MEDICINA DE PETRÓPOLIS**

Rua Machado Fagundes 326, 25710 Petrópolis (Rio de Janeiro)
Telephone: (242) 427017

Medicine

Founded 1967.

1017 **FACULDADE DE MEDICINA DE SANTO AMARO**

Rua Prof. Eneas de Sequeira Netto 340, 04829 São Paulo (São Paulo)
Telephone: (11) 5209611

Medicine

Founded 1970.

1018 **FACULDADE DE MEDICINA DE TERESÓPOLIS**

Avenida Alberto Torres 111, 25950 Teresópolis (Rio de Janeiro)
Telephone: (21) 7423152

Medicine

Founded 1970. Under the supervision of the Fundação Educacional Serra Dos Orgãos.

Academic Year: March to December (March-June; August-December).

Admission Requirements: Secondary school certificate and entrance examination.

Language of Instruction: Portuguese.

Degrees and Diplomas: Professional title of Médico, 6 yrs.

1019 **FACULDADE DE MEDICINA DE VALENÇA**

Praça Balbina Fonseca 186, 25960 Valença (Rio de Janeiro)
Telephone: (244) 520163
Diretor: Agnello Alves Filho

Medicine

Founded 1968. Under the supervision of the Fundação Educacional D. André Arcoverde.

Academic Year: January to December (January-June; August-December).

Admission Requirements: Secondary school certificate and entrance examination.

Fees (Cruzeiros): 1061.17 per month.

Language of Instruction: Portuguese.

Degrees and Diplomas: Professional title of Médico, 6 yrs.

1020 **FACULDADE DE MEDICINA DE VASSOURAS**

Rua Dr. Joaquin Teixeira Leite 53, 27700 Vassouras (Rio de Janeiro)
Telephone: (244) 711595
Diretor: João Carlos de Souza Cortes

Medicine

Founded 1969. Under the supervision of the Fundação Educacional Severino Sombra.

Academic Year: February to December (February-June; August-December).

Admission Requirements: Secondary school certificate and entrance examination.

Fees (Cruzeiros): 10,420.75 per month.

Language of Instruction: Portuguese.

Degrees and Diplomas: Professional title of Médico, 6 yrs.

Academic Staff, 1989-90: 148.

1021 **FACULDADE DE MEDICINA DO 'ABC'**

Avenida Principe de Gales, 09000 Santo André (São Paulo)
Telephone: (11) 4493347

Medicine

Founded 1969.

1022 **FACULDADE DE MEDICINA DO NORTE DE MINAS**

Avenida Rui Braza, 39400 Montes Claros (Minas Gerais)
Telephone: (38) 2216355

Medicine

Founded 1969.

1023 **FACULDADE DE MÚSICA CARLOS GOMES**

Rua Pirapitingui 162, 01508 São Paulo (São Paulo)
Telephone: (11) 5713100

Music

Founded 1963.

1024 **FACULDADE DE MÚSICA 'MÃE DE DEUS'**

Avenida São Paulo 651, 86100 Londrina (Paraná)
Telephone: (432) 235440

Music

Founded 1965.

1025 **FACULDADE DE MÚSICA PALESTRINA**

Rua Gen. Vitorino 305, 90000 Pôrto Alegre (Rio Grande do Sul)
Telephone: (51) 2273811

Music

Founded 1968.

1026 **FACULDADE DE MÚSICA SANTA CECÍLIA**

Praça Barão do Rio Branco 59, 12400 Pindamonhangaba (São Paulo)
Telephone: (12) 2425755

Music

Founded 1975.

1027 **FACULDADE DE MÚSICA SANTA MARCELINA**

Rua Dr. Costa Leite 548, 18600 Botucatu (São Paulo)
Telephone: (14) 9220577

Music

Founded 1963.

1028 **FACULDADE DE NUTRIÇÃO**

Rua Dr. Lauro de Oliveira 71, 90000 Pôrto Alegre (Rio Grande do Sul)
Telephone: (51) 2317720

Nutrition

Founded 1978.

1029 **FACULDADE DE ODONTOLOGIA CAMILO CASTELO BRANCO**

Rua Carolina Fonseca, 08230 São Paulo (São Paulo)
Telephone: (11) 2050099

Dentistry

Founded 1981.

1030 **FACULDADE DE ODONTOLOGIA DE BARRETOS**

Avenida Prof. Roberto Frede Monte 389, 14700 Barretos (São Paulo)
Telephone: (173) 226411

Dentistry

Founded 1984.

1031 **FACULDADE DE ODONTOLOGIA DE CAMPOS**

Avenida Visc. de Alvaranga 143, 28100 Campos (Rio de Janeiro)
Telephone: (247) 230616

Dentistry

Founded 1972.

1032 **FACULDADE DE ODONTOLOGIA DE CARUARU**
Avenida Portugal 385, 55100 Caruaru (Pernambuco)
Telephone: (81) 7210258

Dentistry
Founded 1959.

1033 **FACULDADE DE ODONTOLOGIA DE GOVERNADOR VALADARES**
Rodovia MG.-4 Km. 3, 35100 Governador Valadares (Minas Gerais)
Telephone: (332) 700430

Dentistry
Founded 1975.

1034 **FACULDADE DE ODONTOLOGIA DE ITAÚNA**
Rodovia MG-Trevo Itaúna/Pará de Minas, 35680 Itaúna (Minas Gerais)
Telephone: (37) 2412289
Diretor: Jair Raso (1988-90)

Dentistry
Founded 1966. Under the supervision of the Fundação de Ensino de Itaúna.
Academic Year: February to December (February-June; August-December).
Admission Requirements: Secondary school certificate and entrance examination.
Language of Instruction: Portuguese.
Degrees and Diplomas: Professional title of Cirurgião Dentista, 4 yrs.
Academic Staff, 1990: – 55.
Student Enrolment, 1990: 203.

1035 **FACULDADE DE ODONTOLOGIA DE LINS**
Rua Tenente Florencia Pupo Neto 200, 16400 Lins (São Paulo)
Telephone: (145) 222223

Dentistry
Founded 1954. Under the supervision of the Instituto Americano de Lins da Igreja Metodista.

1036 **FACULDADE DE ODONTOLOGIA DE SANTO AMARO**
Rua Prof. Eneias de Siqueira Neto 340, Santo Amaro, 04829 São Paulo (São Paulo)
Telephone: (11) 5209611

Dentistry
Founded 1971.

1037 **FACULDADE DE ODONTOLOGIA DE VALENÇA**
Rua Carneiro de Mendonça 139, 27600 Valença (Rio de Janeiro)
Telephone: (244) 521216
Diretor: Getúlio do Reis Maia

Dentistry
Founded 1968. Under the supervision of the Fundação Educacional D. André Arcoverde.
Academic Year: January to December (January-June; August-December).
Admission Requirements: Secondary school certificate and entrance examination.
Fees (Cruzeiros): 725.59 monthly.
Language of Instruction: Portuguese.
Degrees and Diplomas: Bacharel, 4 yrs.

1038 **FACULDADE DE ODONTOLOGIA JOÃO PRUDENTE**
Avenida Universitária Km-3, 77100 Anápolis (Goiás)
Telephone: (62) 3244729

Dentistry
Founded 1971. Under the supervision of the Associação Educativa Evangélica.
Academic Year: February to November (February-June; August-November).
Admission Requirements: Secondary school certificate.
Language of Instruction: Portuguese.
Degrees and Diplomas: Bacharel em Odontologia, 4 yrs.

1039 **FACULDADE DE PEDAGOGIA, CIÊNCIAS E LETRAS DE CAÇADOR**
Rua Itoro, 89500 Caçador (Santa Catarina)
Telephone: (49) 6620536

Education
Science
Letters
Administration
Social Service
Founded 1971. Under the supervision of the Fundação Educacional do Alto Vale do Rio de Peixe.
Academic Year: March to December (March-June; August-December).
Admission Requirements: Secondary school certificate and entrance examination.
Language of Instruction: Portuguese.
Degrees and Diplomas: Licenciado.

1040 **FACULDADE DE REABILITAÇÃO**
Rua Uaruma 80, Higienopolis, 21050 Rio de Janeiro (Rio de Janeiro)
Telephone: (21) 2601556

Physical Therapy
Founded 1977.

1041 **FACULDADE DE REABILITAÇÃO TUIUTI**
Rua Marcelino Champagnat, 80000 Curitiba (Paraná)
Telephone: (41) 2253131

Physical Therapy
Founded 1981.

1042 **FACULDADE DE SERVIÇO SOCIAL DE ARARAQUARA**
Rua Padre Duarte 1463, 14800 Araraquara (São Paulo)
Telephone: (162) 220733

Social Work
Founded 1972.

1043 **FACULDADE DE SERVIÇO SOCIAL DE BAURU**
Praça 9 de Julho 1-51, 17100 Bauru (São Paulo)
Telephone: (142) 236319

Social Work
Founded 1963.

1044 **FACULDADE DE SERVIÇO SOCIAL DE LINS**
Rua Dom Lucio 165, 16400 Lins (São Paulo)
Telephone: (145) 223966

Social Work
Founded 1958.

1045 **FACULDADE DE SERVIÇO SOCIAL DE PIRACICABA**
Rua Boa Morte 1865, 13400 Piracicaba (São Paulo)
Telephone: (194) 222332

Social Work
Founded 1963.

1046 **FACULDADE DE SERVIÇO SOCIAL DE UBERLÃNDIA**
Rua Mercedes Brasileiro 129, 38400 Uberlãndia (Minas Gerais)
Telephone: (34) 2364066

Social Work
Founded 1972.

1047 **FACULDADE DE SERVIÇO SOCIAL DO RIO DE JANEIRO**
Rua Conselheiro Ferraz, 20710 Rio de Janeiro (Rio de Janeiro)
Telephone: (21) 2646172

Social Work
Founded 1955.

1048 **FACULDADE DE TECNOLOGIA DE RIO CLARO**
Rua Nove 1864, 13500 Santa Cruz (São Paulo)
Telephone: (195) 346320
Diretor: Aldo Zottarelli Jr.

Technology
Founded 1981.
Admission Requirements: Secondary school certificate and entrance examination.
Language of Instruction: Portuguese.
Degrees and Diplomas: Professional titles of Tecnólogos.
Library: c. 5000 vols.

1049 **FACULDADE DE TURISMO EMBAIXADOR PASCHOEL CARLOS MAGNO**
Rua Ibituruna, 20271 Rio de Janeiro (Rio de Janeiro)
Telephone: (21) 2646172

Tourism
Founded 1979.

1050 **FACULDADE DE ZOOTÉCNICA DE UBERABA**
Rua Dom Luiz Santana 115, 38100 Uberaba (Minas Gerais)
Telephone: (34) 3331188

Animal Husbandry
Founded 1975.

1051 **FACULDADE DOM BOSCO DE FILOSOFIA, CIÊNCIAS E LETRAS**
Praça D. Helvécio 74, 36300 São João del Rei (Minas Gerais)
Telephone: (32) 3714744

D. of Science
D. of Philosophy
D. of Letters (Modern Languages)
D. of Education
Founded 1954 by the Salesian Order.
Residential facilities for academic staff and students.
Academic Year: March to November (March-July; August-November).
Admission Requirements: Secondary school certificate and entrance examination.
Language of Instruction: Portuguese.
Degrees and Diplomas: Bacharel, 3 yrs, and Licenciado, 4 yrs, in all fields.

1052 **FACULDADE ESPÍRITO SANTENSE DE ADMINISTRAÇÃO**
Rua Anselmo Serrat 199, 29000 Vitória (Espírito Santo)
Telephone: (27) 2225344

Administration
Founded 1973.

1053 **FACULDADE EVANGÉLICA DE MEDICINA DO PARANÁ**
Rua Princesa Isabel 1580, 80000 Curitibá (Paraná)
Telephone: (44) 2232633
Diretor: Carlos Augusto Moreira
Secretária Geral: Denise Gomara Cavallin

Medicine (including Surgery and Midwifery)
Founded 1969. Under the supervision of the Sociedade Evangélica Beneficente.
Arrangements for co-operation with the Université libre de Bruxelles.
Academic Year: March to November.
Admission Requirements: Secondary school certificate and entrance examination.
Fees (Cruzeiros): 56,018.40.
Language of Instruction: Portuguese.
Library: 6467 vols.
Academic Staff, 1990: – (120).
Student Enrolment, 1990:

	Men	Women	Total
Of the country	192	160	352
Of other countries	4	2	6
Total	196	162	358

1054 **FACULDADE IBERO-AMERICANA DE LETRAS E CIÊNCIAS HUMANAS**
Avenida Brigadeiro Luiz Antônio 871, 01317 São Paulo (São Paulo)
Telephone: (11) 370071

Letters
Human Sciences
Founded 1971.

1055 **FACULDADE LUZWELL**
Avenida Chibaras 74, Moema, 04076 São Paulo (São Paulo)
Telephone: (11) 5491611
Diretor: José Rage Zaher
Secretária: Ivete Fantinate Ammirabile

Business Administration
Accountancy
Founded 1972.
Academic Year: February to December (February-June; August-December).
Admission Requirements: Secondary school certificate and entrance examination.
Language of Instruction: Portuguese.
Degrees and Diplomas: Bacharel, 4 yrs.
Academic Staff, 1990: – (40).
Student Enrolment, 1990:

	Men	Women	Total
Of the country	797	347	1144

1056 **FACULDADE MARCELO TUPINAMBA**
Rua Vergueiro, 04010 São Paulo (São Paulo)
Telephone: (11) 5496899

Music
Founded 1974.

1057 **FACULDADE MOZARTEUM DE SÃO PAULO**
Rua Nova dos Portugueses, 02462 São Paulo (São Paulo)
Telephone: (11) 9500788

Music
Founded 1974.

1058 **FACULDADE NITEROIENSE DE EDUCAÇÃO, LETRAS E TURISMO**
Rua Visconde do Rio Branco 123, 24020 Niterói (Rio de Janeiro)
Telephone: (21) 7170513

Education
Letters
Tourism
Founded 1976.

1059 **FACULDADE NITEROIENSE DE FORMAÇÃO DE PROFESSORES**
Rua Visconde do Rio Branco 123, 24020 Niterói (Rio de Janeiro)
Telephone: (21) 7170513

Education
Founded 1972.

1060 **FACULDADE OLINDENSE DE ADMINISTRAÇÃO**
Rua do Bonfim 37, 53000 Olinda (Pernambuco)
Telephone: (81) 4291052

Administration
Founded 1972.

1061 **FACULDADE PARA EXECUTIVOS**
Avenida Junqueira Aires, 59000 Natal (Rio Grande do Norte)
Telephone: (84) 2226557

Executive Secretarial Studies
Founded 1981.

1062 **FACULDADE PAULISTA DE ARTE**
Rua Martiniano de Carvalho 864, 01321 São Paulo (São Paulo)
Telephone: (11) 2873213

Art
Music
Founded 1957.

1063 **FACULDADE PAULISTA DE SERVIÇO SOCIAL DE SÃO CAETANO DO SUL**

Avenida Paraiso 600, 09500 São Caetano do Sul (São Paulo)
Telephone: (11) 4532911

Social Work

Founded 1966.

1064 **FACULDADE PAULISTA DE SERVIÇO SOCIAL**

Paulista School of Social Work
Rua Lopes Chaves 273, 01154 São Paulo (São Paulo)
Telephone: (11) 66-0246
Diretor: Heliton Betetto
Secretário Geral: Alfio Elmo Minniti

Social Work

Founded 1940. Under the supervision of the Sociedade de Serviço Social.
Academic Year: March to December (March-June; August-December).
Fees (Cruzeiros): 4303.08 per annum.
Language of Instruction: Portuguese.
Degrees and Diplomas: Bacharel, 4 yrs.
Library: 5800 vols.
Academic Staff, 1990: – (21).
Student Enrolment, 1990:

	Men	Women	Total
Of the country	29	334	363

1065 **FACULDADE PAULISTANA DE CIÊNCIAS E LETRAS**

Rua Madre Cabrini 36, 04020 São Paulo (São Paulo)
Telephone: (11) 5493033

Science
Letters

Founded 1972.

1066 **FACULDADE PÔRTO-ALEGRENSE DE CIÊNCIAS CONTÁBEIS E ADMINISTRATIVAS**

Avenida Arnaldo Bohrer 253, 90000 Pôrto Alegre (Rio Grande do Sul)
Telephone: (512) 343533

Accountancy
Administrative Studies

Founded 1971.

1067 **FACULDADE PÔRTO-ALEGRENSE DE EDUCAÇÃO, CIÊNCIAS E LETRAS**

Avenida Manoel Elias 2001, 1300 Pôrto Alegre (Rio Grande do Sul)
Telephone: (512) 344522
Director: Darci Zanfeliz
Secretário: Walter Koller

Education
Science
Letters
History

Founded 1968. Under the supervision of the Sociedade Educacional Sul-Rio-Grandense.
Academic Year: March to December (March-July; August-December).
Admission Requirements: Secondary school certificate and entrance examination.
Fees (Cruzeiros): 14,157 per semester.
Language of Instruction: Portuguese.
Library: 19,000 vols.
Academic Staff, 1990: – (92).
Student Enrolment, 1990:

	Men	Women	Total
Of the country	279	1401	1680

1068 **FACULDADE REGIONAL DE MEDICINA DE SÃO JOSÉ DO RIO PRÊTO**

Avenida Brigadeiro Faria Lima, 15100 São José do Rio Prêto (São Paulo)
Telephone: (172) 325733

Medicine

Founded 1968.

1069 **FACULDADE RIOPRETENSE DE FILOSOFIA, CIÊNCIAS E LETRAS**

Rua Ipiranga 3460, 15100 São José do Rio Prêto (São Paulo)
Telephone: (17) 321646

Philosophy
Science
Letters

Founded 1972.

1070 **FACULDADE SALESIANA DE EDUCAÇÃO FÍSICA**

Rua Santa Rosa, 98900 Santa Rosa (Rio Grande do Sul)
Telex: 553804 DOMB BR
Telephone: (55) 5121683
Diretor: Faustino Chiamenti

Physical Education

Founded 1979. Under the supervision of the Instituto Educacional Dom Bosco.
Academic Year: March to December (March-July; July-December).
Admission Requirements: Secondary school certificate and entrance examination.
Fees (Cruzeiros): 1750 per month.
Language of Instruction: Portuguese.
Degrees and Diplomas: Licenciado, 4 yrs.
Library: Biblioteca Central P. Faustino Chiamenti, 33,336 vols.
Academic Staff, 1990: 2 (25).
Student Enrolment, 1990:

	Men	Women	Total
Of the country	60	134	194

1071 **FACULDADE SALESIANA DE FILOSOFIA, CIÊNCIAS E LETRAS**

Rua Dom Bosco 284, Caixa postal 29, 12600 Lorena (São Paulo)
Telephone: (12) 5522033

Ce. for Philosophy
Ce. for Psychology
Ce. for Education
Ce. for Social Studies
Ce. for Sciences
Ce. for Letters
Ce. for Religious Studies

Founded 1892 as a college by the Salesian Order. Became faculty 1952. A private autonomous institution. Governing body: the Conselho Departamental Administrativo.
Academic Year: January to December (January-July; August-December).
Admission Requirements: Secondary school certificate or equivalent.
Language of Instruction: Portuguese.
Degrees and Diplomas: Licenciado. Professional title of Psicólogo.

1072 **FACULDADE SALESIANA DE TECNOLOGIA**

Avenida Almeida Garret, 267 13085 Campinas (São Paulo)
Telephone: (192) 412188
Presidente: Milton Braga de Rezende

Industrial Electronics
Control and Instrumentation

Founded 1953. Under the supervision of the Escola Salesiana São José. Acquired present status and title 1981.
Academic Year: February to December (February-June; August-December).
Admission Requirements: Secondary school certificate and entrance examination.
Fees (Cruzeiros): 6800 per month.
Language of Instruction: Portuguese.
Degrees and Diplomas: Professional titles, 3 yrs.
Library: 4580 vols.
Academic Staff, 1990: 8 (41)
Student Enrolment, 1990:

	Men	Women	Total
Of the country	500	176	676

1073 **FACULDADE SANTA MARCELINA**

Rua Dr. Emilio Ribas, 89, 05006 São Paulo (São Paulo)
Telephone: (11) 8269718
Diretora: Angela Rivero

D. of Plastic Arts
Head: Silvia Rodrigues
D. of Design
Head: Vera Sigia Gisbert
D. of Music
Head: Laura Abrahâo

Founded 1929. Recognized by the federal authorities 1938.

Academic Year: February to December (February-July; August-December).

Admission Requirements: Secondary school certificate and entrance examination.

Fees (Cruzeiros): 7000 per month.

Language of Instruction: Portuguese.

Degrees and Diplomas: Bacharel and Licenciado, 3-7 yrs.

Library: 15,000 vols.

1074 **FACULDADES ASSOCIADOS DO IPIRANGA**
Avenida Nazare 993, 04263 Ipiranga (São Paulo)
Telephone: (11) 2748555

F. of Philosophy, Science, and Letters (including Education)
F. of Accountancy
F. of Administration

Founded 1971 and recognized by the federal government.

Academic Year: February to December (February-June; August-December).

Admission Requirements: Secondary school certificate and entrance examination.

Language of Instruction: Portuguese.

Degrees and Diplomas: Bacharel and Licenciado, 4 yrs. Postgraduate diplomas of specialization in Special Education.

Library: c. 28,580 vols.

Academic Staff: c. – (130).

Student Enrolment: c. 2450.

1075 **FACULDADES ASSOCIADAS DE SÃO PAULO**
Rua José Antonio Coelho 879, Vila Mariana, 04011 São Paulo (São Paulo)
Telephone: (11) 5498233
Fax: (11) 5727671
Diretor Geral: Mara Manrubia Trama
Secretário Geral: Marcos Cassiano Senna

F. of Administration
Director: Leonardo Prota
F. of Computer Sciences
Director: Cecilia Puerta Veruli

Founded 1975. Under the supervision of the Sociedade Civil Ateneu Brasil.

Academic Year: February to December.

Admission Requirements: Secondary school certificate and entrance examination.

Language of Instruction: Portuguese.

Degrees and Diplomas: Bacharel, 3-5 yrs.

Library: 8799 vols.

Academic Staff, 1990: – (109).

Student Enrolment, 1990:

	Men	Women	Total
Of the country	2181	936	3117

1076 **FACULDADES CAPITAL**
Rua Colonel Joviniao Brandão, 03127 São Paulo (São Paulo)

F. of Administration (including Economics and Accountancy)
F. of Statistics
F. of Letters and Human Sciences

Founded 1971.

Academic Year: March to December (March-June; August-December).

Admission Requirements: Secondary school certificate and entrance examination.

Language of Instruction: Portuguese.

Degrees and Diplomas: Bacharel and Licenciado, 4 ½-5 yrs.

1077 **FACULDADES DA ASSOCIAÇÃO EDUCACIONAL DO LITORAL SANTISTA**
Avenida Rangel Pestana, 11500 Cubatão (São Paulo)
Telephone: (132) 322060

Tourism
Accountancy

Founded 1970.

1078 **FACULDADES DA ZONA LESTE DE SÃO PAULO**
Rua Cesario Galero 432, 03071 São Paulo (São Paulo)
Telephone: (11) 9413499

Law, Accountancy, and Administration
Philosophy, Science, and Letters
Education

Founded 1972.

1079 **FACULDADES DE BARRA MANSA**
Rua Vereador P. de Carvalho 267, 27400 Barra Mansa (Rio de Janeiro)
Telephone: (243) 220222

Administration
Social Communication
Nursing and Midwifery
Law
Philosophy, Science and Letters

Founded 1966.

1080 **FACULDADES DE ITAPETININGA**
Rodovia Raposo Tavares 161, 18200 Itapetininga (São Paulo)
Telephone: (152) 2710284

Law
Social Communication
Administration
Physical Education

Founded 1969.

1081 **FACULDADES DO GRANDE DOURADOS**
Rua Balbina de Matos 2121, 79100 Dourados (Mato Grosso)
Telephone: (67) 4213121

1082 **FACULDADES DO INSTITUTO EDUCACIONAL TERESA MARTIN**
Rua Antonieta Leitão 129, 02925 São Paulo (São Paulo)
Telephone: (11) 8578222

F. of Science and Letters
F. of Library Science

Founded 1981.

1083 **FACULDADES INTEGRADAS ALCANTARA MACHADO**
Praça Tres Coraçoes 300, 05608 São Paulo (São Paulo)
Telephone: (11) 8145044

Communication
Science and Letters

Founded 1972.

1084 **FACULDADES INTEGRADAS AUGUSTO MOTTA**
Avenida Paris 72, 21041 Rio de Janeiro (Rio de Janeiro)
Telephone: (21) 2809422

Social Studies
Human Sciences, Letters and Arts
Education
Engineering
Rehabilitation

Founded 1972.

1085 **FACULDADES INTEGRADAS BENNETT**
Rua Marquês de Abrantes 55, 22230 Rio de Janeiro (Rio de Janeiro)
Telephone: (21) 2458000

Administration
Architecture and Town Planning
Economics
Law
Education

Founded 1971. Under the supervision of the Instituto Metodista Bennett.

1086 **FACULDADES INTEGRADAS CASTELO BRANCO**

Avenida Santa Cruz 1665, Realengo, 21710 Rio de Janeiro (Rio de Janeiro)
Telephone: (21) 3311207
Diretora Geral: Vera Costa Gissoni

Education, Science and Letters
Physical Education

Founded 1973. Under the supervision of the Centro Educacional de Realengo.

Academic Year: February to December (February-July; August-December).

Admission Requirements: Secondary school certificate and entrance examination.

Fees (Cruzeiros): 846-3312 per semester.

Language of Instruction: Portuguese.

Degrees and Diplomas: Bacharel in Physiotherapy. Licenciado in–Science; Mathematics; Physical Education. Teaching qualifications.

Library: Biblioteca Manuel Bandeira (Physical Education), 19,716 vols.

Publication: Revista Enfoque (biannually).

Academic Staff, 1986-87: – (368).

Student Enrolment, 1986-87:

	Men	Women	Total
Of the country	2952	3367	6317

1087 **FACULDADES INTEGRADAS COLEGIO MODERNO**

Trav. Quintino Bocaiuva 1808, 66040 Belém (Pará)
Telephone: (91) 2232111

Administration
Accountancy
Economics

Founded 1974.

1088 **FACULDADES INTEGRADAS DA CATÓLICAS DE BRASÍLIA**

Areas Complimentares, 72000 Taguatinga (Distrito Federal)
Telephone: (61) 5635000

Technology
Human Sciences
Social Sciences

Founded 1972.

1089 **FACULDADES INTEGRADAS DE CRUZEIRO**

Rua Dom Bosco 35, Centro, 12700 Cruzeiro (São Paulo)
Telephone: (125) 441603

Administration
Philosophy, Science, and Letters

Founded 1972.

1090 **FACULDADES INTEGRADAS DE EDUCAÇÃO FÍSICA E TÉCNICAS DESPORTIVAS**

Rua Solon Fernandes 155, 07000 Guarulhos (São Paulo)
Telephone: (11) 2093233

Physical Education

Founded 1972.

1091 **FACULDADES INTEGRADAS DE MARÍLIA**

Avenida Hygino Muzzi Filho 1001, 17500 Marília (São Paulo)
Telephone: (14) 338088

Economics
Education
Physical Education
Psychology
Social Service
Dentistry

Founded 1956.

1092 **FACULDADES INTEGRADAS DE OURINHOS**

Rua Arlindo Luz 800, 19900 Ourinhos (São Paulo)
Telephone: (14) 3222033

Science and Letters
Business Administration

Founded 1970.

1093 **FACULDADES INTEGRADAS DE SANTA CRUZ DO SUL**

Rua Cel. Oscar J. Jost 1551, 96800 Santa Cruz do Sul (Rio Grande do Sul)
Telephone: (51) 7131011
Diretor Geral: Wilson Kniphoff da Cruz (1987-91)
Secretário Geral: Nelci Gauciniski

F. of Accountancy and Administration
Director: Flavio Haas; *staff* 2 (38)

F. of Philosophy, Science, and Letters (including Social Sciences and Pedagogy)
Director: Maria H. Kipper; *staff* 28 (55)

F. of Law
Director: Aquilano J. Bergonsi; *staff* 2 (20)

S. of Physical Education
Director: Miria Suzana Burgos; *staff* 3 (17)

Founded 1980, incorporating faculties created since 1964. Under the supervision of the Associacão Pró-Ensino em Santa Cruz do Sul.

Academic Year: March to December (March-June; August-November).

Admission Requirements: Secondary school certificate and entrance examination.

Fees (Cruzeiros): 834.80-1085.24.

Language of Instruction: Portuguese.

Degrees and Diplomas: Bacharel in–Administration; Accountancy, 4 ½ yrs; Economics; Chemistyr; Law, 5 yrs. Licenciado in–Physical Education; Social Studies; Science; Education; Letters, 6-10 sem. Teaching qualifications. Also postgraduate certificates of specialization.

Library: 61,460 vols.

Special Facilities (Museums, etc.): Archaeological Centre.

Publications: Revista do Centro de Ensino e Pesquisas Arqueológicas (biannually); Revista do Centro de Estudos e Pesquisas Linguísticas e Literárias (biannually); Revista do Centro de Estudos e Pesquisas Pedagógicas (annually); Caderno Pesquisa; Série Botânica (biannually).

Press or Publishing House: Gráfica Universitária.

Academic Staff, 1990:

Rank	Full-time	Part-time
Professores Titulares	32	72
Professores Assistentes	2	24
Professores Auxiliares de Ensino	1	31
Professores Adjuntos	–	2
Total	35	129

Student Enrolment, 1990:

	Men	Women	Total
Of the country	1409	2434	3843

1094 **FACULDADES INTEGRADAS DE SANTO ANGELO**

Rua Universidade das Missoes 393, 98800 Santo Angelo (Rio Grande do Sul)
Telephone: (55) 3121599

Accountancy and Administration
Philosophy, Science, and Letters

Founded 1976.

1095 **FACULDADES INTEGRADAS DE SÃO GABRIEL**

Rua Barao do Cambai 550, 97300 São Gabriel (Rio Grande do Sul)
Telephone: (55) 2321042

Science
Social Sciences
Communication
Education
Economics and Administration

Founded 1970.

1096 **FACULDADES INTEGRADAS DE SÃO GONÇALO**

Rua Lambari 10, Trindade, 24400 São Gonçalo (Rio de Janeiro)
Telephone: (21) 7010505

Nutrition
Physical Education
Science and Letters

Founded 1976.

1097 **FACULDADES INTEGRADAS DE SÃO JOSÉ DOS CAMPOS**

Praça Candido Dias Castejon, 12200 São José dos Campos (São Paulo)
Telephone: (123) 222355

Applied Social Sciences
Exact Sciences and Technology
Human Sciences

Founded 1954.

1098 **FACULDADES INTEGRADAS DE UBERABA**

Avenida Guilherme Ferreira 217, 38100 Uberaba (Minas Gerais)
Telephone: (34) 3323322

Law
Physical Education
Civil Engineering
Social Studies
Dentistry

Founded 1972.

1099 **FACULDADES INTEGRADAS DO INSTITUTO RITTER DOS RIES**

Rua Santos Dumont, 92120 Canoas (Rio Grande do Sul)
Telephone: (512) 724149

Law
Architecture and Town Planning

Founded 1977.

1100 **FACULDADES INTEGRADAS ESTACÍO DE SÁ**

Rua Bispo 83, 20261 Rio de Janeiro (Rio de Janeiro)
Telephone: (21) 2843321

Administration
Economics
Communication
Law
Archaeology and Musicology
Education

Founded 1970.

1101 **FACULDADES INTEGRADAS HEBRAICO-BRASILEIRA RENASCENÇA**

Rua Prates 790, 101121 São Paulo (São Paulo)
Telephone: (11) 2286450
Diretor: Abrão Bernardo Zweiman (1988-92)
Secretário Geral: Celso Stott Pacheco

F. of Languages (Portuguese and English)
Head: Ida Mekler; *staff* – (25)
F. of Education
Head: Edith Gross Hojda; *staff* – (12)
F. of Science
Head: Mariano Meliani; *staff* – (22)
F. of Hotel Management
Head: Jonas Juliani Oliva; *staff* – (27)
F. of Computer Sciences
Head: Cesar Teixeira Mendes; *staff* – (18)

Founded 1975. Under the supervision of the Sociedade Hebraico Brasileira Renascença.

Academic Year: February to December (February-June; August-December).

Admission Requirements: Secondary school certificate and entrance examination.

Language of Instruction: Portuguese.

Degrees and Diplomas: Bacharel in–Hotel Management; Computer Sciences. Licenciado in–Science, 2 yrs; Education; Letters, 3 yrs.

Library: 25,000 vols.

Academic Staff, 1990: – (82).

Student Enrolment, 1990:

	Men	Women	Total
Of the country	458	825	1283
Of other countries	31	43	74
Total	489	868	1357

1102 **FACULDADES INTEGRADAS IBIRAPUERA**

Avenida Irai, 04082 São Paulo (São Paulo)
Telephone: (11) 5332022
Diretor: Jorge Bastos
Secretário Geral: Dalton Heitor Ferriello

Business Administration
Accountancy
Social Studies
Letters Education
Data Processing
Physics and Biology

Founded 1969. Under the supervision of the Asociação Princesa Isabel de Educação e Cultura.

1103 **FACULDADES INTEGRADAS MOACYR SREDER BASTOS**

Rua Engenheiro Trindade 229, 23000 Rio de Janeiro (Rio de Janeiro)
Telephone: (21) 3941063
Diretor Geral: Marfydio Vieira Machado Júnior
Secretária Geral: Elisabete Pereira Pinto

F. of Law
Director: Adilson Rodrigues Pinto; *staff* 2 (30)
F. of Economics (including Administration and Accountancy)
Director: Newton Rodrigues Alvarez; *staff* 3 (34)
F. of Science (including Physics and Mathematics)
Director: Nelson Fraire da Rocha; *staff* 3 (25)
F. of Geography
Director: Kleber Duarte Vasconcellos; *staff* – (22)
F. of Physical Education
Director: Wagner Domingos Fernandes Gomes; *staff* – (10)
F. of Computer Sciences
Director: José Maria de Figueiredo Guedes; *staff* – (5)

Founded 1970. Under the supervision of the Associação de Ensino de Campo Grande.

Academic Year: February to December (February-July; August-December).

Admission Requirements: Secondary school certificate and entrance examination.

Fees (Cruzeiros): 499 per month.

Language of Instruction: Portuguese.

Degrees and Diplomas: Bacharel in–Economics; Administration; Physical Education, 4 yrs; Law; Computer Sciences, 5 yrs. Licenciado in–Physics; Mathematics; Physical Education; Geography; History, 4 yrs.

Library: 25,551 vols.

Academic Staff, 1986-87:

Rank	Full-time	Part-time
Professores Titulares	8	82
Professores Adjuntos	–	–
Professores Assistentes	–	40
Professores de Nível Médio	8	–
Total	16	122

Student Enrolment, 1986-87:

	Men	Women	Total
Of the country	2506	3172	5678
Of other countries	913	1118	2031
Total	3419	4290	7709

1104 **FACULDADES INTEGRADAS RIOPRETENSE**

Rua Saldanha Marinho 2038, 15030 São José do Rio Prêto (São Paulo)
Telex: 172774
Telephone: (172) 325355
Diretor Geral: Halim Atique Junior

F. of Business Administration
Dean: Anete Maria Lucas V. Schiavinatto
F. of Hospital Administration
F. of Accountancy
F. of Law

Founded 1989, incorporating faculties created since 1965.

Academic Year: February to December (February-June; August-December).

Admission Requirements: Secondary school certificate and entrance examination.

Fees (Cruizeiros): 2600-5910.

Language of Instruction: Portuguese.
Degrees and Diplomas: Bacharel, 4 yrs. Postgraduate certificates of specialization, a further 1 1/2 yrs.
Library: 15,723 vols.
Academic Staff, 1989-90: – (84).
Student Enrolment, 1989-90: 1806.

1105 **FACULDADES INTEGRADAS RUI BARBOSA**
Rua Rodrigues Alves 932, Centro, 16900 Adradina (São Paulo)
Telephone: (18) 6223492
Philosophy, Science, and Letters
Economics
Founded 1966.

1106 **FACULDADES INTEGRADAS SILVA E SOUZA**
Rua Uranos 735, Ramos, 21060 Rio de Janeiro (Rio de Janeiro)
Telephone: (21) 2606422
F. of Architecture and Town Planning
F. of Industrial Design
F. of Statistics
Founded 1971.

1107 **FACULDADES INTEGRADAS TERESA D'AVILA**
Avenida Peixoto de Castro, 12600 Lorena (São Paulo)
Telephone: (125) 522888
F. of Arts
F. of Library Science and Documentation
F. of Domestic Science and Rural Education
Founded 1975, recognized by the federal government 1978.
Academic Year: February to December (February-June; August-December).
Admission Requirements: Secondary school certificate and entrance examination.
Language of Instruction: Portuguese.
Degrees and Diplomas: Bacharel in–Library Science, 3 yrs. Licenciado, 2-4 yrs.
Library: c. 47,000 vols.
Academic Staff: c. 5 (40).
Student Enrolment: c. 180.

1108 **FACULDADES INTEGRADAS TERESA D'AVILA**
Rua Siqueira Campos 483, 09020 Santo André (São Paulo)
Telephone: (11) 4497477
Diretora Geral: Theresina Carvalho Castro
F. of Arts
F. of Library Science and Documentation
F. of Domestic Science and Rural Education
Founded 1976. Under the supervision of the Instituto Coração de Jesus.
Academic Year: February to December (February-June; August-December).
Admission Requirements: Secondary school certificate and entrance examination.
Fees (Cruzeiros): 2300 per semester.
Language of Instruction: Portuguese.
Degrees and Diplomas: Bacharel in–Library Science, 3 yrs. Licenciado, 2-4 yrs.
Library: 18,000 vols.
Academic Staff, 1986-87: 75 (35).
Student Enrolment, 1986-87:

	Men	Women	Total
Of the country	500	1300	1800
Of other countries	–	5	5
Total	500	1305	1805

1109 **FACULDADES INTEGRADAS TIRADENTES**
Rua Lagarto 264, 49000 Aracajú (Sergipe)
Telephone: (79) 2223288
Economics, Administration, and Accountancy
Social Communication
Law
Founded 1972.

1110 **FACULDADES METODISTAS INTEGRADAS IZABELA HENDRIX**
Rua Bahia 2020, 30000 Belo Horizonte (Minas Gerais)
Telephone: (31) 3376973
Philosophy, Science, and Letters
Architecture and Town Planning
Founded 1972.

1111 **FACULDADES METROPOLITANAS UNIDAS**
Rua Tagua 150, 01508 São Paulo (São Paulo)
Telephone: (11) 2702433
Economics
Letters
Administration
Accountancy
Education
Social Service
Psychology
Law
Founded 1968.

1112 **FACULDADES OSWALDO CRUZ**
Rua Brigadeiro Galvão 540, Barra Funda, 01152 São Paulo (São Paulo)
Telephone: (11) 8254266
Philosophy, Science, and Letters
Administration, Economics, and Accountancy
Chemistry
Founded 1967.

1113 **FACULDADES REUNIDAS NUÑO LISBÔA**
Avenida Ministro Edgard Romero 807, 21361 Rio de Janeiro (Rio de Janeiro)
Telephone: (21) 3276515
D. of Civil Engineering
D. of Telecommunications and Electrical Engineering
D. of Electronics
D. of Physics
D. of Architecture and Town Planning
D. of Chemistry
D. of Business Administration and Social Sciences
D. of Law, Sociology, Social Service, and Letters
D. of Economics, Philosophy, and Psychology
D. of Statistics
D. of Cybernetics
D. of Physical Education
Extension D.
Founded 1970 as school of engineering and developing through addition of new schools as an independent university institution recognized by the Ministry of Education and Culture.
Academic Year: March to November (March-June; August-November).
Admission Requirements: Secondary school certificate.
Language of Instruction: Portuguese.
Degrees and Diplomas: Professional titles in–Civil Engineering; Electronics; Telecommunication Engineering; Accountancy; Business Administration.
Library: Central Library, *c.* 15,250 vols.
Publication: Ciência e Técnica (every 3 months).
Academic Staff: c. 300.
Student Enrolment: c. 4560.

1114 **FACULDADES SALVADOR S/C**
Avenida Cardeal da Silva 132, 40220 Salvador (Bahia)
Telephone: (71) 2352068
Diretor: Sérgio Viana
F. of Business Administration
F. of Data Processing
F. of Social Communication
F. of Accountancy
Founded 1972. A private institution recognized by the federal government and financed by fees.
Academic Year: March to December (March-June; August-December).
Admission Requirements: Secondary school certificate or recognized equivalent, and entrance examination.
Fees (Cruzeiros): 75,000 per annum.

Language of Instruction: Portuguese.
Degrees and Diplomas: Bacharel, 4-5 yrs.
Library: c. 8000 vols.
Academic Staff, 1990: – (96).
Student Enrolment, 1990:

	Men	Women	Total
Of the country	776	689	1465

1115 **FACULDADES UNIDAS CATÓLICAS DE MATO GROSSO**
Avenida Mato Grosso, 79100 Campo Grande (Mato Grosso do Sul)
Telex: (67) 2575 FUMT
Telephone: (67) 3824261
Fax: (67) 721-4640
Diretor: Angel Adolfo Sanchez y Sanchez
Secretário: Segismundo Martinez Alvarez

F. of Philosophy, Science, and Letters
Director: Guillermo Moralez Velazquez; *staff* 6 (7)
F. of Law
Director: Luigi Favero; *staff* 5 (4)
F. of Economics, Accountancy, and Administrative Sciences (including Data Processing)
Director: Luigi Favero; *staff* 5 (4)
F. of Social Sciences (including Psychology)
Director: Geraldo Grendene; *staff* 3 (2)

Founded 1975, incorporating faculties created since 1961. A private institution recognized by the federal government and financed by fees and contributions of the Missão Salesiana de Mato Grosso.
Academic Year: March to December (March-June; August-December).
Admission Requirements: Secondary school certificate and entrance examination.
Languages of Instruction: Portuguese and English.
Degrees and Diplomas: Bacharel in–Economics; Administration; Accountancy; Social Work; Geography, 4 yrs; Law, 5 yrs. Licenciado in–Science, 3 yrs; Literature; Education; History; Mathematics; Biology; Geography; Psychology, 4 yrs. Professional title in Psychology, 5 yrs. Also teaching qualification.
Library: 113,840 vols.
Special Facilities (Museums, etc.): Museu Regional 'Dom Bosco' (Ethnology, Mineralogy, Melacology, Zoology, and Ethnography).
Publications: Revista da Faculdade de Direito (annually); Estudos Universitarios (annually).
Press or Publishing House: Gráfica e Editora Dom Bosco.
Academic Staff, 1990: 45 (78)
Student Enrolment, 1990:

	Men	Women	Total
Of the country	2055	3044	5099

1116 **FACULDADES UNIDAS DE BAGÉ**
Avenida Tupy Silveira 2099, 96400 Bagé
Telephone: (532) 422244
Pró-Reitor: Morvan Meirelles Ferrugem (1985-89)

F. of Agriculture
Director: José Teixeira Kluwe; *staff* 7 (20)
F. of Fine Arts
Director: Marly Ribeiro Meira; *staff* 7 (17)
F. of Economics (including Administration and Accountancy)
Director: Roberto Nocchi Cachapuz; *staff* 6 (21)
F. of Law
Director: Carlos Rodolfo M.T. Flores; *staff* 6 (25)
F. of Physical Education
Director: Wagner Britto Previtalli; *staff* 2 (11)
F. of Philosophy, Science and Letters
Director: Angelina Feltrin Quintana; *staff* 18 (55)
F. of Veterinary Medicine (including Animal Husbandry)
Director: João Cezer Jardim de Quadros; *staff* 10 (36)

Founded 1969. Under the supervision of the Fundação Attila Taborda.
Academic Year: March to December (March-July; August-December).
Admission Requirements: Secondary school certificate and entrance examination.
Language of Instruction: Portuguese.
Degrees and Diplomas: Bacharel in–Music; Economics; Administration; Accountancy; Agriculture; Music; Veterinary Medicine; Law, 4-5 yrs. Licenciado in–Social Studies, 2 yrs; Education; Plastic Arts; Biology, 3 ½ yrs; Physical Education; Social Sciences; Philosophy; Letters, 4 yrs. Professional titles in–Veterinary Medicine, 4 yrs; Agricultural Engineering, 5 yrs. Also teaching qualification.
Libraries: Central Library, *c.* 27,000 vols; Agriculture and Veterinary Medicine, *c.* 2000.
Special Facilities (Museums, etc.): Museu Dom Diego de Souza; Museu Patrício Corrêa de Câmara; Museu of Brazilian Engraving.
Academic Staff, 1986-87: 57 (188).
Student Enrolment, 1986-87:

	Men	Women	Total
Of the country	1427	784	2211
Of other countries	347	950	1297
Total	1774	1734	3508

1117 **FACULDADES UNIDAS GRANDE RIO**
Rua Marques de Herval 1160, 25000 Duque de Caxias (Rio de Janeiro)
Telephone: (217) 7714251

Social Studies
Education, Science, and Letters
Health Sciences

Founded 1972.

1118 **FEDERAÇÃO DAS ESCOLAS SUPERIORES DE ILHÉUS E ITABUNA**
Rodovia Ilhéus-Itabuna, Km. 16, 45660 Ilhéus (Bahia)
Telephone: (73) 2313222

F. of Philosophy (Itabuna)
F. of Economics (Itabuna)
F. of Law (Ilhéus)

Founded 1973, incorporating previously existing faculties.
Academic Year: March to December (March-June; August-December).
Admission Requirements: Secondary school certificate and entrance examination.
Language of Instruction: Portuguese.
Degrees and Diplomas: Bacharel in–Administration; Economics; Law, 4 yrs. Licenciado in–Letters; Education; Science; Social Studies; Philosophy, 4 yrs.
Library: Central Library, *c.* 26,590 vols.
Press or Publishing House: Imprensa Universitária.
Academic Staff: c. 20 (90).
Student Enrolment: c. 2860.

1119 **FEDERAÇÃO DAS FACULDADES CELSO LISBOA**
Rua 24 de Mãio 797, 20951 Rio de Janeiro (Rio de Janeiro)
Telephone: (21) 201-47-22
Presidente: Celso Lisboa
Registrar: Rafael Maia Pereira

Administration
Accountancy
Letters and Education
Biology
Mathematics
Computer Sciences
Psychology

Founded 1970.
Academic Year: March to December (March-June; August-December).
Admission Requirements: Secondary school certificate.
Fees (Cruzeiros): 22,939-46,387 per annum.
Language of Instruction: Portuguese.
Degrees and Diplomas: Bacharel, 4-5 yrs.
Library: Central library, 51,048 vols.
Academic Staff, 1990: 186.
Student Enrolment, 1990:

	Men	Women	Total
Of the country	1327	4237	5564

1120 **FEDERAÇÃO DAS FACULDADES ISOLADAS DE ARARAQUARA**
Rua Voluntarios de Patria 1309, Centro, 14800 Araraquara (São Paulo)
Telephone: (16) 220499

Education and Social Studies
Economics and Administration
Law

Founded 1972.

1121 **FEDERAÇÃO DE ESCOLAS FACULDADES INTEGRADAS SIMOSEN**
Rua Ibitiuva 151, 21710 Rio de Janeiro (Rio de Janeiro)
Telephone: (21) 3313022

Economics, Administration, and Accountancy
Education, Science, and Letters
Founded 1971.

1122 **FEDERAÇÃO DE ESCOLAS SUPERIORES DO ABC**
Rua do Sacramento, 09720 São Bernardo do Campo (São Paulo)
Telephone: (11) 4573733

Administration
Human Sciences
Social Communication
Founded 1971.

1123 **FEDERAÇÃO DE ESTABELECIMENTOS DE ENSINO SUPERIOR EM NOVO HAMBURGO**
Rua Mauricio Cardoso 510, 93300 Novo Hamburgo (Rio Grande do Sul)
Telephone: (512) 933144

F. of Education
S. of Accountancy
F. of Fine Arts
F. of Social Communication
F. of Physical Education
S. of Administration
Ce. of Leather Technology
Ce. for Urban Sociology
Ce. for Lifelong Education

Founded 1970 incorporating the Instituto de Belas Artes, founded 1968, and other faculties and schools of the region. Under the jurisdiction of the Federal Ministry of Education and Culture. Governing body: the Board of Trustees.

Academic Year: March to November (March-June; August-November).

Admission Requirements: Secondary school certificate.

Language of Instruction: Portuguese.

Degrees and Diplomas: Bacharel in–Administration; Accountancy; Public Relations, 3 ½-4 ½ yrs. Licenciado in Physical Education, 3 ½ yrs; Design and Plastic Arts; Education, 4 yrs. Professional titles in Leather and Footwear Production,3 yrs.

Library: Central Library, *c.* 17,960 vols.

Special Facilities (Museums, etc.): Museum of Arts; Indian Museum.

Academic Staff: c. 10.

Student Enrolment: c. 1860.

1124 **INSTITUTO BRASILEIRO DE ESTUDOS E PESQUISAS GASTROENTEROLOGICAS**
Rua Dr. Seng 320, 01331 São Paulo (São Paulo)
Telephone: (11) 2882119

Medicine (Gastro-enteritis)
Founded 1963.

1125 **INSTITUTO DE CIÊNCIAS HUMANAS DE SANTO AMARO**
Rua Prof. Eneas de S. Neto 340, Santo Amaro, 03071 São Paulo (São Paulo)
Telephone: (11) 5209611

Human Sciences
Founded 1976.

1126 **INSTITUTO DE CIÊNCIAS SOCIAIS**
EQS 704/904, BL A LOTES ABC, 70390 Brasília (Distrito Federal)
Telephone: (61) 2232055

Social Sciences
Founded 1967.

1127 **INSTITUTO DE CIÊNCIAS SOCIAIS DE AMERICANA**
Rua Dom Bosco 100, 13470 Americana (São Paulo)
Telephone: (194) 613367

Social Sciences
Founded 1972.

Degrees and Diplomas: Bacharel in–Social Service, 3 yrs; Business Administration, 4 yrs. Licenciado in Education, 3 yrs.

Library: c. 25,000 vols.

Student Enrolment: c. 910.

1128 **INSTITUTO DE CIÊNCIAS SOCIAIS DO PARANÁ**
Rua General Carneiro 216, 80000 Curitiba (Paraná)
Telephone: (41) 2643311

Business Administration
Economics
Accountancy
Actuarial Sciences
Hospital Administration

Founded 1937. Under the supervision of the Fundação de Estudos Sociais do Paraná.

Arrangements for co-operation with School of Business Administration, Miami University.

Academic Year: March to December.

Admission Requirements: Secondary school certificate and entrance examination.

Language of Instruction: Portuguese.

Degrees and Diplomas: Bacharel. Licenciado.

Library: c. 8000 vols.

Academic Staff: c. 70.

Student Enrolment: c. 2350.

1129 **INSTITUTO DE CIÊNCIAS SOCIAIS E APLICADAS**
SGAS 910 LOTE 32, 70390 Brasília, (Distrito Federal)
Telephone: (51) 2439241
Diretor: Sergio Faria (1984-90)

D. of Economics
D. of Administration
D. of Accountancy
D. of Humanities

Founded 1979 as a private institution under the jurisdiction of the União Educacional de Brasília. Recognized by the federal government.

Academic Year: March to December (March-June; August-December).

Admission Requirements: Secondary school certificate and entrance examination.

Language of Instruction: Portuguese.

Degrees and Diplomas: Bacharel.

Library: c. 8000 vols.

Academic Staff: c. 10 (80).

Student Enrolment: c. 810.

1130 **INSTITUTO DE ENSINO DE ENGENHARIA PAULISTA**
Rua Doctor Bacelar, Mirandopolis, 04043 São Paulo (São Paulo)
Telephone: (11) 5786455

Engineering
Founded 1977.

1131 **INSTITUTO DE ENSINO SUPERIOR DO ALTO URUGUAÍ**
Rua Assis Brasil, 98400 Frederico Westphalen (Rio Grande do Sul)
Telephone: (55) 3441168

Letters
Administration
Accountancy
Law
Statistics
Social and Human Sciences
Founded 1970.

1132 **INSTITUTO DE ENSINO SUPERIOR E PESQUISA**
Campus Universitario, 35500 Divinopolis (Minas Gerais)
Telephone: (37) 2212799

D. of Human Sciences (including Social Sciences)
D. of Education
D. of Letters
I. of Languages
Extension Ce.

Founded 1965. Under the supervision of the Fundação Educacional de Divinopolis.

Academic Year: February to November (February-June; August-November).

Admission Requirements: Secondary school certificate and entrance examination.

Languages of Instruction: Portuguese and English.

Degrees and Diplomas: Licenciado in all fields, 4 yrs. Teaching qualification.

Library: Central Library, *c.* 13,760 vols.

Publication: Revistas (biannually).

Academic Staff: c. 40.

Student Enrolment: c. 850.

1133 **INSTITUTO DE ENSINO SUPERIOR SANTO ANDRÉ**

Rua Delfim Moreira 40, Centro, 09000 Santo André (São Paulo)
Telephone: (11) 4499277

Social Sciences
Accountancy

Founded 1972.

1134 **INSTITUTO DE FÍSICA TEÓRICA DE SÃO PAULO**

Rua Pamplona 145, 01405 São Paulo (São Paulo)
Cables: Físicateorica
Telephone: (11) 288-56-43
Presidente: Chaim S. Hönig

Physics

Founded 1952 as a foundation. Partly incorporated 1987 into the State University of São Paulo. Became a postgraduate institution 1969.

Arrangements for co-operation with: University of Paris VII; National Autonomous University of Mexico; National University of La Plata; International Centre for Theoretical Physics, Trieste; Centro de Estudios Científicos de Santiago, Chile.

Academic Year: March to December (March-June; August-December).

Admission Requirements: University degree.

Fees: None.

Language of Instruction: Portuguese.

Degrees and Diplomas: Mestrado, master, in Science, 2-3 yrs. Doutorado, a further 3-5 yrs.

Library: c. 20,000 vols.

Academic Staff: 23.

Student Enrolment, 1990:

	Men	Women	Total
Of the country	30	5	35

1135 **INSTITUTO DE ODONTOLOGIA PAULISTA**

Rua Doctor Bacelar, 04026 São Paulo (São Paulo)
Telephone: (11) 5786455

Dentistry

Founded 1981.

1136 **INSTITUTO DE PSICOLOGIA**

BR 230 Km. 22 Blocos E/F, 58000 João Pessoa (Paraíba)
Telephone: (83) 2241418

Psychology

Founded 1972.

1137 **INSTITUTO DE TECNOLOGIA DE GOVERNADOR VALADARES**

Rua Moreira Sales, 35030 Governador Valadares (Minas Gerais)
Telephone: (332) 213090

Engineering
Science

Founded 1978.

1138 **INSTITUTO NACIONAL DE TELECOMUNICAÇÕES DE SANTA RITA DO SAPUCAÍ**

Avenida João Camargo 510, 37540 Santa Rita do Sapucaí (Minas Gerais)
Telex: (35) 4364 FNNT BR
Telephone: (35) 631-17-88
General Director: Navantino Dionízo Barbosa Filho
Executive Secretary: Maria Helena Brusamolin

D. of Telecommunications
Head: José Paulo Falsarella; *staff* 5 (3)

D. of Electronics and Electrotechnics
Head: Arthur François de Gruiter; *staff* 6 (6)

D. of Physics and Mathematics
Head: José Carlos H. de Siqueira; *staff* 2 (10)

D. of Auxiliary Sciences
Head: Helio Mokarzel; *staff* – (7)

Technology and Development Ce.
Head: Pedro Sérgio Monti; *staff* 13 (26)

Founded 1965.

Academic Year: February to December (February-June; August-December).

Admission Requirements: Secondary school certificate and entrance examination.

Fees (Cruzeiros): *c.* 6000 per month.

Language of Instruction: Portuguese.

Degrees and Diplomas: Bacharel, 5 yrs.

Library: c. 30,000 vols.

Academic Staff, 1990: 13 (26).

Student Enrolment, 1990:

Men	Women	Total
978	48	1026

1139 **INSTITUTO SUPERIOR DE CIÊNCIAS APLICADAS**

Via 147 Limeira Piracicaba, 13480 Limeira (São Paulo)
Telephone: (19) 4415367

D. of Social Sciences
D. of Social Service
D. of Economics
D. of Business Administration
D. of Accountancy

Founded 1968 as a private institution under the supervision of the Associação Limeirense de Educação 'Alie'. Recognized by the federal government 1970.

Academic Year: March to December (March-July; August-December).

Admission Requirements: Secondary school certificate or foreign equivalent, and entrance examination.

Language of Instruction: Portuguese.

Degrees and Diplomas: Bacharel in all fields, 4 yrs. Licenciado in Social Sciences.

Library: c. 5870 vols.

Academic Staff: c. 30.

Student Enrolment: c. 720.

1140 **INSTITUTO SUPERIOR DE ENSINO E PESQUISA DE ITUIUTABA**

Avenida Rio Grande c/ Rua Bahia, 38300 Ituiutaba (Minas Gerais)
Telephone: (35) 2613344

Biology
Engineering
Exact Sciences
Human Sciences
Languages and Literature

Founded 1979.

1141 **INSTITUTO SUPERIOR DE ESTUDOS SOCIAIS CLOVIS BEVILACQUA**

Avenida Lusitania 169, 21011 Rio de Janeiro (Rio de Janeiro)
Telephone: (21) 2605552

Social Studies

Founded 1973.

1142 **INSTITUTO UNIFICADO PAULISTA**

Rua Luis Goes 2211, Mirandopolis, 04043 São Paulo (São Paulo)
Telephone: (11) 5786455

Psychology
Letters
Social Communication
Education

Founded 1972.

1143 **UNIÃO DAS FACULDADES FRANCANAS**

Anel Viario, 14400 Franca (São Paulo)
Telephone: (16) 7221444

Science, Education, and Technology
Plastic Design

Philosophy, Science, and Letters
Founded 1972.

1144 **UNIDADES ESCOLARES DA INSTITUIÇÃO MOURA LACERDA**
Rua Padre Euclides 995, Campos Elisios, 14085 Ribeirão Prêto (São Paulo)
Telephone: (16) 6361010
F. of Philosophy, Science and Letters
F. of Economics
F. of Physical Education (Jaboticabal)
F. of Architecture and Town Planning
Polytechnical I.
Founded 1969.

1145 **UNIDADES INTEGRADAS DE ENSINO SUPERIOR DO VALE DO JACUI**
Rua Major Ouriques 2284, 96500 Cachoeira do Sul (Rio Grande do Sul)
Telephone: (51) 722-43-99
Presidente: Augusto Antonio Torres da Costa
Diretora-Geral: Vera Lucia Moraes Almeida
F. of Economics, Accountancy and Administration
Head: Rui Carlesso; *staff* 3 (42)
F. of Philosophy, Science and Letters
Head: Pedrinho Michelin; *staff* 4 (48)
S. of Physical Education
Head: Rogerio Hamester; *staff* 2 (40)
S. of Arts
Head: Marucia Pinto Castagnino; *staff* 8 (16)
Founded 1970.
Academic Year: March to November (March-June; August-November).
Admission Requirements: Secondary school certificate and entrance examination.
Fees (Cruzeiros): 81.50 per month per class.
Languages of Instruction: Portuguese, English and French.
Degrees and Diplomas: Licenciado, 4 yrs.
Library: Central Library, 24,000 vols.
Special Facilities (Museums, etc.): Giceli Ribeiro Saraiv Museum

BULGARIA*

Universities

1146 ***PLOVDIVSKI UNIVERSITET 'PAISSII HILENDARSKI'**
University of Plovdiv
Ul. 'Tsar Assen' 24, Plovdiv 4000
Telex: 44251
Telephone: 22-62-38
Rector: Nikola Petkov Balabanov (1989-93)
Administration Officer: Jordan Ganchev Bakalov

F. of Chemistry
Dean: Georgi Andreev; *staff* 54 (4)
F. of Biology
Dean: Dimitar Vodenicharov; *staff* 41 (1)
F. of Mathematics
Dean: Georgi Zlatanov; *staff* 70 (15)
F. of Physics
Dean: Georgi Mekishev; *staff* 67 (4)
F. of Philology and Education
Dean: Georgi Petkov; *staff* 228 (38)
F. of Public Professions
Dean: Ivan Kutsarov
Also 5 Institutes of Teacher Training.

Founded 1961 as teacher training institute, became university 1972. A State institution with the right of autonomy. Governing bodies: the General Assembly, comprising 170 members; the Academic Council, comprising 38 members. Residential facilities for academic staff and 400 students.

Arrangements for co-operation with: Moscow State Pedagogical Institute; Adam Mickiewicz University in Poznań; Jana Ev. Purkyně University, Brno; University of Novi Sad; Kishinev State University; József Attila University, Szeged; College of Agriculture and Teacher Training, Siedlce.

Academic Year: September to May (September-December; February-May).

Admission Requirements: Secondary school certificate and entrance examination.

Fees: None.

Language of Instruction: Bulgarian.

Degrees and Diplomas: Diploma of Specialist in relevant fields, 4-5 yrs. Kandidat na Naukite, Candidate of the Sciences, a further 3yrs and thesis. Doktor na Naukite. Also teaching qualifications, 4 yrs.

Library: Central Library, 167,000 vols.

Publication: Nauchni Trudove (5 times a year).

Press or Publishing House: University Printing Office.

Academic Staff, 1990-91:

	Full-time	Part-time
Professors	14	1
Associate Professors	115	15
Research Workers	10	12
Assistants	285	2
Lecturers	36	33
Total	460	63

Student Enrolment, 1990-91:

	Men	Women	Total
Of the country	993	4753	5746
Of other countries	11	4	15
Total	1004	4757	5761

1147 ***SOFIISKI UNIVERSITET 'KLIMENT OHRIDSKI'**
University of Sofia
Boul. Ruski 5, Sofia 1000
Telex: 23296
Telephone: 85-81
Rector: Mintcho Semov

F. of Philosophy (including Education)
F. of History
F. of Slavonic Philology
F. of Western Philology
F. of Mathematics and Theoretical Mechanics
F. of Physics
F. of Chemistry
F. of Biology
F. of Geology and Geography
F. of Law
F. of Journalism
F. of Social Professions

Founded 1888 with one faculty, became a university 1904 and number of faculties increased to seven by 1938. Reorganized 1944, when the faculties of medicine and agriculture were detached from the university and established as separate institutions. A State institution. Governing bodies: the University Council presided over by the Rector who is elected by the professors and lecturers for a two-year period; the Rector and five Pro-Rectors; and the Faculty Councils which elect the titular professors. Some residential facilities for students.

Academic Year: September to June (September-December; February-May).

Admission Requirements: Secondary school certificate and entrance examination.

Fees: None.

Language of Instruction: Bulgarian.

Degrees and Diplomas: Diploma of Specialist in all fields, 4-5 yrs. Kandidat na Naukite, Candidate of the Sciences, a further 3 yrs and thesis. Doktor na Naukite, by thesis after Kandidat.

Library: c. 920,250 vols.

Special Facilities (Museums, etc.): Museum of Palaeontology.

Academic Staff: c. 1400.

Student Enrolment: c. 14,000.

1148 ***VELIKOTARNOVSKI UNIVERSITET 'KIRIL I METODI'**
University 'Cyril and Methodius'
Ul. Theodosius Tirnovo 1, Veliko Tarnovo 5000
Telephone: 2-01-89
Rector: Stanio Gheolguiev

F. of History
F. of Philology (Slavonic and Western)
F. of Fine Arts
F. of Education

Fouded 1963 s teacher training institute, became university 1971. A State institution. Governing body: the Academic Council. Residential facilities for academic staff and students.

Academic Year: September to May (September-December; February-May).

Admission Requirements: Secondary school certificate and entrance examination.

Fees: None.

Language of Instruction: Bulgarian.

Degrees and Diplomas: Diploma of Specialist in relevant fields, 4 yrs. Also teaching qualifications.

Libraries: Central Library, *c.* 153,000 vols; Philological Reading Room, *c.* 1000; History, *c.* 1000; Ideological Centre, *c.*5000; Specialized textbooks, *c.* 10,000.

*Major changes have affected the higher education system of the country and individual institutions during the preparation of this edition. These are reflected as far as they have been communicated to IAU before 30 September 1990.

Special Facilities (Museums, etc.): Ronsar Museum; Museum of Fine Arts.
Publication: Trudove na VTU Kiril i Metodii (annually).
Academic Staff: c. 300.
Student Enrolment: c. 3700.

Other Institutions

Technical Education

1149 **VISŠ HIMIKOTEHNOLOGIČESKI INSTITUT**
Higher Institute of Chemical Technology
Ul. Prof. Jakimov 1, Bourgas 8010
Cables: vhti
Telex: 83689
Telephone: (56) 6-01-19
Fax: (56) 8-61-41
Rector: Aristotel Dimov

F. of Organic Chemical Technology
Dean: Trojan Georgiev
F. of Inorganic Chemical Technology
Dean: Danail Bonchev
Research L.
Head: Bogdan Bogdanov; *staff* 21
Research Sec. (including New Materials, Optical Electronics and Laser Equipment, and Environmental Protection)
Head: Jivko Tasev; *staff* 87
D. for Foreign Students
Head: Petko Tanev; *staff* 25

Founded 1963, the institution operates under the jurisdiction of the Ministry of Education and is financed by the State. It is independent of the municipal authorities but co-operates closely with local and national industrial undertakings. Governing bodies: the General Assembly; the Academic Council. Residential facilities for academic staff and 1000 students.

Arrangements for co-operation with: Technical University, Leuna-Merseburg; College of Technical Techology, Pardubice; Veszprém Technical University of Chemical Engineering; Leningrad Polytechnic Institute; Institute of Precision Chemical Technology, Moscow; Technical University of Warsaw; Technical University of Szczecin. Research Institutes in France, Germany, India, and Japan.

Academic Year: October to May (October-December; February-May).
Admission Requirements: Secondary school certificate and competitive entrance examination.
Fees: None.
Language of Instruction: Bulgarian.
Degrees and Diplomas: Title of Chemical Engineer, 9 sem. Doctorate by thesis.
Library: c. 25,000 vols.
Publication: Annuales.
Academic Staff, 1990: c. 220.
Student Enrolment, 1990:

	Men	Women	Total
Of the country	432	616	1048
Of other countries	61	–	61
Total	493	616	1109*

*Also 348 external students.

1150 **VISŠ HIMIKOTEHNOLOGIČESKI INSTITUT**
Institute of Chemical Technology
8 bld. Climent Ohridski, Sofia 1156
Telex: (67) 23084 VHTI
Telephone: (3592) 68-10-43
Fax: (3592) 68-54-88
Rector: Ivan Bozhov
Director: Vesselin Vassilev

F. of Inorganic Technology and Automation of Industry
Dean: Ivan Grancharov; *staff* 115 (4)
F. of Organic Technology and Chemical Engineering
Dean: Kiril Stanulov; *staff* 160 (4)
F. of Metallurgy
Dean: Mincho Chimbulev; *staff* 161 (3)
F. of Liberal Professions
Dean: Stephan Dobrev; *staff* 32 (–)
F. for Foreign Students
Dean: Raina Draganova; *staff* 32 (–)
Central Research L.
Dean: Rodimir Nikolov; *staff* 6 (–)
D. of Postgraduate Studies
Dean: Stoyan Stoyanov; *staff* 15 (–)

Founded 1945 as department of State Polytechnical Institute, became faculty 1951 and acquired present status 1953, when the Polytechnical Institute was divided into four separate institutions. Now an independent State institution under the jurisdiction of the Ministry of Science and Higher Education. Governing body: the Rector's Council.

Arrangements for co-operation with similar institutions in: Moscow; Leningrad; Kiev; Tbilisi; Łódź; Wrocław; Szczecin; Dresden; Merzeburg; Prague; Košice; Budapest; Athens; Patras; Helsinki; Kyoto; Leeds; Swansea; Oslo.

Academic Year: October to July (October-February; March-July).
Admission Requirements: Secondary school certificate and competitive entrance examination.
Fees: None.
Language of Instruction: Bulgarian.
Degrees and Diplomas: Diploma and Professional titles in–Chemical Engineering; Metallurgical Engineering; Automation Engineering, 5yrs. Candidate of the Sciences, a further 3 yrs and thesis. Doctorate by thesis after Candidate.
Library: c. 20,000 vols.
Publication: Directory.
Academic Staff, 1990:

Rank	Full-time	Part-time
Profesori (Professors)	41	4
Dotsenti (Associate Professors)	143	7
Assistenti (Assistent Professors)	231	–
Nauchni Satrudnitsi (Researchers)	26	–
Total	441	11

Student Enrolment, 1990:

	Men	Women	Total
Of the country	1212	1671	2883
Of other countries	107	13	120
Total	1319	1684	3003*

*Also 925 external students

1151 **VISŠ INSTITUT PO HRANITELNA I VKUSOVÁ PROMIŠLENOST**
Institute of the Food Industry
Bul. Vladimir I. Lenin 26, 40000 Plovdiv
Telephone: 4-18-11

Food Technology

Founded 1948 as department of agricultural technology of the former University of Plovdiv, became a faculty of food technology 1950 and acquired present status 1953. A State institution under the jurisdiction of the Ministries of Education and of Food. Residential facilities for students.

Academic Year: September to May (September-December; February-May).
Admission Requirements: Secondary school certificate.
Fees: None.
Language of Instruction: Bulgarian.
Degrees and Diplomas: Diploma of Engineer-Technologist, 5 yrs. Kandidat na tehničeskite nauki, Candidate of the Technical Sciences, K.T.N., a further 3 yrs and thesis. Doctor of Science.
Library: c. 60,000 vols.
Publication: Nauchni Trudove na Vissiya institut po hranitelna i vkusová promišlenost (Scientific report).
Academic Staff: c. 240.
Student Enrolment: c. 2200.

1152 **VISŠ INSTITUT PO ARKITECTURA I STOITELSTVO**
Institute of Architecture and Civil Engineering
Boul. Christo Smirnenski 1, Sofia 1421
Rector: Ganio St. Ganev Stilianov (1979-87)
Registrar: Mincho Minchev

F. of Constructional Engineering
Dean: Jordan Totev; *staff* 174 (9)

F. of Hydro-Technology
Dean: Ilia Ninov; *staff* 91 (10)
F. of Architecture
Dean: Stefan Stephanov; *staff* 91 (11)
F. of Geodesy
Dean: Georgi Kolev
F. of Foreign Studies
Dean: Altimir Popov
D. for Extramural Studies
Head: J. Sotirov

Founded 1942 as technical school, became polytechnic institute 1947, acquired present status 1953. Residential facilities for academic staff and students.

Arrangements for student exchange with: Algeria; Czechoslovakia; German Democratic Republic; Greece; Hungary; Poland; Tunisia; USSR.

Academic Year: September to June (September-December; February-June).

Admission Requirements: Secondary school certificate or foreign equivalent, and entrance examination.

Language of Instruction: Bulgarian.

Degrees and Diplomas: Diplomas of Specialist and Professional title of Engineer, 9-11 sem. Doctor of Science.

Academic Staff, 1986-87:

Rank	Full-time	Part-time
Professors	86	18
Associate Professors	115	18
Professor Assistants	229	–
Lecturers	38	–
Total	468	36

Student Enrolment, 1986-87:

	Men	Women	Total
Of the country	1822	1600	3422
Of other countries	574	40	614
Total	2396	1640	4036

1153 **VISŠ MAŠINNO-ELEKTROTEHNIČESKI INSTITUT 'V. I. LENIN'**

Institute of Mechanical and Electrical Engineering
Hristo Botev Student Township, Sofia 1000
Telephone: 88-43-51
Rector: D. Butčkov

F. of Mechanical Engineering
F. of Energetics and Mechanical Construction
F. of Transport Engineering
F. of Electrical Engineering
F. of Radio Electronics
F. of Automation
F. of Machine Building
F. of Social Professions

Founded 1945 as faculty of mechanical engineering which formed the Ecole polytechnique with the institute of civil engineering (See above). Detached and re-established as a separate institution 1953. A State institution. Governing bodies: the Academic Council; the Faculty Councils; the Departmental Councils. Residential facilities for *c.* 1200 students.

Academic Year: September to June (September-December; February-May).

Admission Requirements: Secondary school certificate and entrance examination.

Fees: None.

Language of Instruction: Bulgarian.

Degrees and Diplomas: Diploma and Professional title of Engineer, 11 sem. Candidate of the Technical Sciences, a further 3 yrs and thesis.

Publication: Izvestia na VMEI (quarterly).

Academic Staff: c. 890.

Student Enrolment: c. 11,000.

1154 **VISŠ MAŠINNO-ELEKTROTEHNIČESKI INSTUTUT**

Institute of Mechanical and Electrical Engineering
Kvartel Levski, 010 Varna
Cables: Vmei
Telephone: 8-01-61

F. of Electrical Engineering (including Electronics and Automation)
F. of Mechanical Engineering
F. of Marine Construction
F. of Machine Building
F. of Social Professions
Research Ce.

Founded 1963. A State institution financed by and under the jurisdiction of the Ministry of Science of High Education. Governing body: the Academic Council. Residential facilities for academic staff and *c.* 960 students.

Academic Year: September to August (September-January; March-June).

Admission Requirements: Secondary school certificate and entrance examination.

Language of Instruction: Bulgarian.

Degrees and Diplomas: Diploma and Professional title of Engineer, 9 sem. Candidate of the Technical Sciences, a further 3 yrs and thesis. Doctorate by thesis, a further 3-4 ½ yrs.

Library: Central Library, *c.* 225,360 vols.

Publications: Annual Reports; Transactions.

Academic Staff: c. 380.

Student Enrolment: c. 4400.

1155 **VISŠ MINNO-GÉOLOŽKI INSTITUT**

Institute of Mining and Geology
Dărvénitza, Sofia 1156
Telephone: 6-25-81
Rector: Tsvetan Tsekov
Registrar: Stancho Georgiev

F. of Geology
Dean: Vasil Balinov *staff* 95 (40)
F. of Mining Electromechanics
Dean: Mento Menteshev; *staff* 123 (14)
F. of Mining Technology
Dean: Lilian Draganov; *staff* 127 (20)
Ce.for Mineral Biotechnology
Head: S. Grudev; *staff* 13
L. for Flexible Automated Production Systems and Robotics
Head: Sl. Totev; *staff* 8
Research L. for Explosion-proof Equipment
Head: K. Zaimov; *staff* 6
L. of Underground Buildings
Head: B. Bojinov; *staff* 5
L. of Mining Microprocessor Techniques
Head: Iv. Lalov; *staff* 6
L. for Vibroacoustic Intensification and Technology
Head: St. Stoev; *staff* 8
L. for Granulometric Preparation of Raw Materials
Head: S. Denev; *staff* 8
L. for Oil-Water Emulsions
Head: Sht. Djendova; *staff* 8
Drilling Equipment L.
Head: G. Georgiev; *staff* 13
L. of Strata Control
Head: R. Parashkevov; *staff* 15
L. for Geochemistry
Head: V. Kojuharov; *staff* 3
Blasting Techniques L.
Head: Sl. Lazarov; *staff* 11
Scientific Research Ce. (Kardjali)

Founded 1953, a State institution. Financed by the State through the activities of its research department andfrom subsidies from mining undertakings. Governing bodies: the Academic Council; Faculty Councils, and the Rector's Board for economic and administrative matters. Residential facilities for most students.

Academic Year: October to June (October-January; March-June).

Admission Requirements: Secondary school certificate.

Fees: None.

Language of Instruction: Bulgarian.

Degrees and Diplomas: Diplomas of Specialist and Professional title of Engineer, 9 sem. Also Candidate of the Sciences, a further 3 yrs and thesis. Doctor of Science.

Libraries: Central Library, *c.* 450,000 vols; specialized library, 73,000.

Special Facilities (Museums, etc.): Museums of: Mineralogy, Petrologyand Exploitable Minerals; Palaeontology and Geology.

Publication: Annuaire.

Academic Staff, 1990:

	Full-time	Part-time
Professors	54	
Assistant Professors	93	
Assistants	136	
Research Assistants	27	
Teachers	90	
Total	400	104

Student Enrolment, 1990:

	Men	Women	Total
Of the country	1671	779	2450
Of other countries	100	2	102
Total	1771	781	2552

1156 **VISŠ MAŠINNO-ELEKTROTEHNIČESKI INSTITUT**
Institute of Mechanical and Electrical Engineering
Ul. Hadji Dimitr 4, Gabrovo 5300
Telex: 67513
Telephone: 2-19-31
Rector: P. Stojanov
Registrar: M. Nenkov

F. of Electrical Engineering
Dean: L. Cekov
F. of Mechanical Engineering
Dean: J. Jordanov
F. of Social Professions
Dean: E. Skopalik

Founded 1964.

Academic Year: September to July.

Admission Requirements: Secondary school certificate.

Degrees and Diplomas: Diplomas and Professional titles.

Academic Staff: c. 170.

Student Enrolment: c. 2800.

1157 **VISŠE TEHNIČESKO UČILIŠČE 'ANGEL KANČEV'**
Ul. Komsomolska 8, Roussé 7004
Telex: 62462
Telephone: 4-40-71
Fax: 55145
Rector: A.L. Mitkov (1987-90)

F. of Agricultural Mechanization
Dean: Gancho Goujgoulov *staff* 97 (14)
F. of Mechanical Engineering
Dean: Boris Tomov; *staff* 119 (30)
F. of Electrotechnology, Electronics and Automation
Dean: G. Harizanov; *staff* 215 (47)
F. for Foreign Students
Dean: D. Simeonov; *staff* 44 (10)
F. of Social Professions
Dean: G. Mihailova
Scientific Research Sec.
Director: V. Penchev; *staff* 128 (3)
I. of Energo-ecological Problems of Internal Combustion Engines
Director: T. Petkov; *staff* 14 (1)
Scientific Research I. of Drives
Director: I. Dimitrov; *staff* 42 (3)
I. of High Engergy Technologies and Systems
Director: V. Etarski; *staff* 11

Founded 1954 as institute, acquired present status and title 1981. A state institution under the jurisdiction of the Ministry of Science and Higher Education and financed by the State. Governing body: the Academic Council. Some residential facilities for academic staff and students.

Arrangements for co-operation with: Institute of Agricultural Production, Moscow; Riga Polytechnical Institute; Institute of Steel and Alloys Technology, Moscow; Moscow Polytechnical Institute; Technical University of Dresden; Otto von Guericke Technical College, Magdeburg; University of Rostock; Technical University of Bratislava; College of Agriculture, Nitra; College of Engineering, Radom; University of Innsbruck.

Academic Year: September to July (September-January; February-July).

Admission Requirements: Secondary school certificate and entrance examination.

Fees: None.

Language of Instruction: Bulgarian.

Degrees and Diplomas: Professional title of Engineer, 11 sem. Candidate of the Technical Sciences, a further 3 ½ yrs and thesis.

Library: c. 40,000 vols.

Publication: Scientific Works.

Academic Staff, 1989-90:

Rank	Full-time	Part-time
Professors	19	2
Associate Professors	123	3
Assistants	341	69
Lecturers	51	24
Scientific Collaborators	38	15
Total	572	113

Student Enrolment, 1989-90:

	Men	Women	Total
Of the country	2638	1863	4501
Of other countries	133	2	135
Total	2771	1865	4636*

*Also 514 extramural students.

1158 **VISŠ LESOTEHNIČESKI INSTITUT**
Institute of Forestry
Bul. Kl. Ohridsky 10, Dărvénitza, Sofia 1156,
Telephone: 63-01
Rector: Nikola Christov Botev (1987-90)

F. of Wood Technology
F. of Forestry Economics and Landscape Architecture

Founded 1925, reorganized 1953. A State institution financed by and under the jurisdiction of the Ministry of Education. Some residential facilities for students.

Academic Year: September to June (September-January; March-June).

Admission Requirements: Secondary school certificate and entrance examination.

Fees: None.

Language of Instruction: Bulgarian.

Degrees and Diplomas: Professional title of Engineer, 5 yrs. Candidate–of the Technical Sciences; of the Agricultural Sciences, a further 3 yrs and thesis. Doctor of Science by thesis after Candidate.

Library: Central Library, c. 100,000 vols.

Special Facilities (Museums, etc.): Central Museum: Cynegetic; Dendrology; Forest Protection; Woodwork Industry.

Publication: Scientific Works: Series–Forestry, Forestry Technology, Landscape Architecture and Conservation of the Environment (annually).

Academic Staff, 1986-87:

Rank	Full-time
Professors	25
Associate Professors	64
Assistants	58
Lecturers	9
Total	156

Student Enrolment, 1986-87:

	Men	Women	Total
Of the country	593	554	1147
Of other countries	45	3	48
Total	638	557	1195*

*Also 305 external students.

Professional Education

1159 **VISŠ IKONOMIČESKI INSTITUT 'KARL MARK'**
'Karl Marx' Institute of Economics
Studentski grad Christov Botev, Sofia 1185
Rector: Danaïl Danaïlov

F. of General Economics
F. of Specialized Economics (Industrial Economics, Transport, Foreign Trade, and Domestic Trade)
F. of Social Professions

Founded 1920.

Degrees and Diplomas: Diploma of Specialist in relevant fields, 4-5 yrs. Kandidat na Naukite, Candidate of the Sciences, a further 3yrs and thesis.

Academic Staff: c. 400.
Student Enrolment: c. 7200.

1160 **VISŠ FINANSOVO-STOPANSKI INSTITUT 'D.A. TSENOV'**
Institute of Finance and Economics
Ul. Emanuil Tchakurov 2, Svichtov 5250
Telex: 66684
Telephone: (0631) 2-27-2
Rector: Svetlozar Kaltchev Tsonev (1979-87)

F. of Accountancy
Dean: Vassil Bozhkov
F. of Finance and Economics (including Insurance)
Dean: Metodi Kunnev; *staff* 103 (79)
F. of F. of Social Professions
Dean: Bogomil Geshev
Computing Ce.

Founded 1936 as school of commerce, became school of economic and social studies 1948-49, acquired present status and title 1952-53. A State institution financed by and under the jurisdiction of the Ministry of Science of High Education. Governing bodies: the General Assembly; the Academic Council; the Faculty Council. Some residential facilities for academic staff and students.

Arrangements for co-operation with: Institute of Finance, Moscow; University of Economics, Berlin; College of Engineering, Radom; Prague College of Economics, etc.

Academic Year: September to June (September-January; February-June).

Admission Requirements: Secondary school certificate and entrance examination.

Fees: None.

Language of Instruction: Bulgarian.

Degrees and Diplomas: Diplomas and Professional title of Economist, 4 yrs. Candidate of the Sciences, a further 3 yrs and thesis. Doctorate by thesis after Candidate.

Library: 176,000 vols.

Special Facilities (Museums, etc.): Institute Museum.

Publications: Narodnostopanski archiv (quarterly); Annual.

Press or Publishing House: Publishing House (Off-set).

Academic Staff, 1986-87:

Rank	Full-time
Professors	8
Assistant Professors	48
Lecturers	28
Assistants	98
Total	182

Student Enrolment, 1986-87:

	Men	Women	Total
Of the country	2469	2821	5290
Of other countries	13	4	18
Total	2482	2825	5308*

*Also 1485 external students.

1161 **VISŠ INSTITUT ZA NARODNO STOPANSTVO 'DIMITRE BLAGOEV'**
Institute of National Economics
77 Lenin Blvd., Varna 9002
Telex: 77382
Telephone: 2-13-51
Rector: Kalju Donef (1990-93)
Administrative Director: Stefko Ivanov

F. of Accountancy (including Management Studies and Political Economy)
Dean: Nikola Bakalov; *staff* 112 (65)
F. of Commerce and Commodity Sciences
Dean: Bojko Atanassov; *staff* 129 (80)
F. of Social Sciences
Dean: Stefan Kirov; *staff* 12 (10)

Founded 1920 as trade school. Became Faculty of Economics of University of Varna 1945. Detached as independentinstitute under present title 1953. A State institution under the jurisdiction of the Ministry of Education. Governing body: the Academic Council.

Arrangements for co-operation with: Institute of Economics, Odessa; Institutes of Economics, Minsk, Moscow; Institute of Economics and Trade, Kiev; College of Economics, Bratislava; Budapest University of Economic Sciences; Academies of Economics, Katowice and Poznań.

Academic Year: September to June (September-December; February-June).

Admission Requirements: Secondary school certificate and entrance examination.

Fees: None.

Language of Instruction: Bulgarian.

Degrees and Diplomas: Diploma of Specialist, 4 ½ yrs. Candidate of Economic Sciences, a further 3 yrs and thesis. Doctorate.

Library: c. 226,000 vols.

Publications: Troudové na Visš institut za narodno stopanstvo; Izvestia na Visš institut za narodno stopanstvo.

Academic Staff, 1989-90:

Rank	Full-time	Part-time
Professors	7	2
Associate Professors	69	14
Assistants/Lecturers	165	129
Total	241	145

Student Enrolment, 1989-90:

	Men	Women	Total
Of the country	2317	2261	4578*

*Also 2580 external students and students by correspondence.

1162 **VISŠ MEDICINSKI INSTITUT**
Institute of Medicine
Ul. Georgi Sofiiski 1, Sofia

Medicine (including Pharmacy and Dentistry)

Founded 1918 as faculty, acquired present status and title 1979. Forms part of the Academy of Medicine, Sofia.

Academic Year: October to June (October-January; March-June).

Admission Requirements: Secondary school certificate and entrance examination.

Fees: None.

Language of Instruction: Bulgarian.

Degrees and Diplomas: Professional qualifications. Title of Candidate of the Medical Sciences. Doctorate.

Academic Staff, 1986-87: c. 3000.
Student Enrolment, 1986-87: c. 5200.

1163 **VISŠ MEDICINSKI INSTITUT**
Institute of Medicine
Bul. Vassil Aprilov 15, Plovdiv
Telex: 044440
Telephone: 44-38-39
Rector: Petar Botouchanov
Registrar: Anton Chterev

F. of Medicine
Dean: Atanas Jourjev
F. of Stomatology
Dean: Gueorgui Gueorguiev
Branch at Pazardjik.

Founded 1945 as faculty, acquired present status and title 1979. An autonomous institute in direct relationship with the Ministry of Health and the Ministry of Science and Higher Education.

Arrangements for co-operation with similar insititutions in: Leningrad; Kiev; Vienna; Berlin; Munich.

Academic Year: September to June (September-January; February-June).

Admission Requirements: Secondary school certificate and entrance examination.

Fees: None.

Language of Instruction: Bulgarian.

Degrees and Diplomas: Bachelor of–Stomatology; Medicine, 6 yrs. Master, a further 2-3 yrs. Doctorate, Ph.D., 3 yrs.

Academic Staff, 1989-90:

Rank	Full-time
Professors	26
Associate Professors	98
Assistants	598
Total	722

Student Enrolment, 1989-90:

	Men	Women	Total
Of the country	776	1031	1807
Of other countries	368	119	487
Total	1144	1150	2294

1164 **VISŠ MEDICINSKI INSTITUT**
Institute of Medicine
Ul. Karl Marx 1, 5800 Pleven
Telex: 34590
Telephone: 29175
Rector: Marin Ganchev (1989-93)

Medicine (including Pharmacy, Psychology, and Ophthamology)
L. of Immunology
Head: P. Petrova
L. for Electron Microscopy
Head: K. Koichev

Founded 1974 as faculty, acquired present status and title 1979. Forms part of the Academy of Medicine, Sofia. Some residential facilities for academic staff and for students.

Arrangements for co-operation with similar institutions in: Czechoslovakia; France; Poland; German; Germany; USSR; Yugoslavia.

Academic Year: October to June (October-January; March-June).

Admission Requirements: Secondary school certificate and entrance examination.

Fees: None.

Language of Instruction: Bulgarian.

Degrees and Diplomas: Doctor of Medicine, 6 yrs. Ph.D., a further 3 yrs. Doctor of Sciences, D.Sc., 3 yrs following Ph.D..

Library: c. 80,000 vols.

Publication: Scientific Works.

Academic Staff, 1989-90: 515.

Student Enrolment, 1989-90:

	Men	Women	Total
Of the country	688	616	1304
Of other countries	231	62	293
Total	919	678	1597

1165 **VISŠ MEDICINSKI INSTITUT**
Institute of Medicine
Ul. Armeiska 27, Stara Zagora

Medicine

Founded 1982. Forms part of the Academy of Medicine, Sofia.

Academic Year: October to June (October-January; March-June).

Admission Requirements: Secondary school certificate and entrance examination.

Fees: None.

Language of Instruction: Bulgarian.

Degrees and Diplomas: Professional qualifications. Title of Candidate of Medical Sciences. Doctorate.

Academic Staff, 1986-87: c. 150.

Student Enrolment, 1986-87: c. 900.

1166 **VISŠ MEDICINSKI INSTITUT**
Institute of Medicine
Ul. Marin Drinov 55, Varna

Medicine
Branch at Toulbouhin.

Founded 1961 as faculty, acquired present status and title 1979. Forms part of the Academy of Medicine, Sofia.

Academic Year: October to June (October-January; March-June).

Admission Requirements: Secondary school certificate and entrance examination.

Fees: None.

Language of Instruction: Bulgarian.

Degrees and Diplomas: Professional qualifications. Title of Candidate of the Medical Sciences. Doctorate.

Academic Staff, 1986-87: c. 450.

Student Enrolment, 1986-87: c. 2000.

1167 **VISŠ SELSKOSTOPANSKI INSTITUT 'VASSIL KOLAROV'**
V. Kolarov Institute of Agriculture
bul. D. Mendeleev 12, Plovdiv 4000
Cables: Vsi Plovdiv.
Telex: 044405
Telephone: 2-34-98
Rector: Kiro Kostov
Assistant Rector: Atanas Landzev

F. of Agronomy
Dean: Stephan Gorbanov; *staff* 101 (10)
F. of Horticulture
Dean: Geno Pepeljankov; *staff* 82 (10)
F. of Plant and Soil Protection
Dean: Stojcho Karov; *staff* 71 (7)
F. of Tropical and Subtropical Agriculture
Dean: Atanas Stojanov; *staff* 15 (3)
Also 24 departments of the faculties.

Founded 1945. Governing body: the Rector's Council. Residential facilities for academic staff and students.

Academic Year: October to June (October-January; March-June).

Admission Requirements: Secondary school certificate and entrance examination.

Fees: None.

Language of Instruction: Bulgarian.

Degrees and Diplomas: Professional titles, 5 yrs. Postgraduate qualifications.

Library: Central Library, *c.* 230,000 vols.

Special Facilities (Museums, etc.): Pedagogical Museum; Botanical Garden; Video Club.

Publication: Scientific Works (annually, in four issues).

Press or Publishing House: Offset Printing Base.

Academic Staff, 1990:

Rank	Full-time	Part-time
Professors	33	28
Associate Professors	69	2
Teachers	24	–
Assistants and Researchers	107	–
Doctors	115	–
Total	348	30

Student Enrolment, 1990:

	Men	Women	Total
Of the country	1490	960	2450
Of other countries	331	69	400
Total	1821	1029	2850*

*Also 733 external students.

1168 **VISŠ INSTITUT PO ZOOTEHNIKA I VETERINARNA MEDICINA**
Institute of Animal Husbandry and Veterinary Medicine
Ul. 'D. Blagoev' 62, Stara Zagora 60000
Telex: 88465
Telephone: (042) 28-03

F. of Animal Husbandry Technology
F. of Veterinary Medicine
Research L.
D. for Correspondence Courses

Founded 1922 as faculty of University of Sofia. Reorganized 1948 and 1953. Became independent institution 1974. A State institution under the jurisdiction of the National Agricultural Complex. Governing body: the General Assembly. Residential facilities for academic staff and students.

Arrangements for co-operation with: College of Veterinary Medicine, Košice; College of Agriculture, Niťra; Academy of Agriculture, Moscow; Institute of Agriculture, Kujbyšev; Karl-Marx University, Leipzig; Warsaw Agricultural University; Academy of Agriculture and Technology, Olsztyn-Kortowo; College of Agriculture, Kaposvár; University of Ghent; University of Camaguëy, Cuba.

Academic Year: October to July (October-January; February-July).

Admission Requirements: Secondary school certificate and entrance examination.
Fees: None.
Language of Instruction: Bulgarian.
Degrees and Diplomas: Professional titles, 5 yrs. Candidate of the Sciences, a further 3-3 ½ yrs and thesis. Doctorate by thesis after Candidate.
Library: c. 110,000 vols.
Special Facilities (Museums, etc.): Museum of Animal Breeding.
Publication: Scientific Works.
Academic Staff: c. 300.
Student Enrolment: c. 2300.

Teacher Training

1169 **VISŠ INSTITUT ZA FISIČESKA KULTURA 'GUÉORGUI DIMITROV'**
Institute of Physical Culture
Ul. Tina Kirkova 1, Sofia 1001
Telephone: 88-15-11/13
Rector: Nikola Hadjiev (1979-87)

Physical Education and Sport

Founded 1942 as school, reorganized 1944, raised to present status and title 1953. A State institution under the jurisdiction of the Ministry of Education. Governing bodies: the Administrative Board, composed of the Rector, Pro-Rector, and Assistant Rector; the Academic Council, composed of the professors and other members of the academic staff. Some residential facilities for students.

Academic Year: September to June (September-January; February-June).
Admission Requirements: Secondary school certificate and entrance examination.
Fees: None.
Language of Instruction: Bulgarian.
Degrees and Diplomas: Teaching qualification in Physical Education, 4 yrs. Candidate of the Educational Sciences, a further 3 yrs and thesis. Doctor of Science.
Library: c. 70,000 vols.
Special Facilities (Museums, etc.): Museum of History of Physical Education.
Publication: Scientific works.
Academic Staff, 1986-87:

Rank	Full-time
Professors	20
Associate Professors	74
Assistants	172
Total	266

Student Enrolment, 1986-87:

Of the country	1400
Of other countries	268
Total	1668*

*Also 795 external students.

1170 **VISŠ PEDAGOGIČESKI INSTITUT**
Institute of Education
Ul. Maritsa 16, Blagoevgrad

Education

Founded 1983.
Academic Staff: c. 280.
Student Enrolment: c. 3500.

1171 **VISŠ PEDAGOGIČESKI INSTITUT 'KONSTANTIN PRESLAVSKY'**
Institute of Education
Choumen 9700
Telex: 73421
Telephone: 63151
Rector: D.A. Kamenov (1988-92)
Director: S. Nickolova

F. of Education (kindergarten and primary levels)
Dean: I.I. Stoilov; *staff* 95 (42)
F. of Philology
Dean: A.T. Alexandrov; *staff* 65 (24)
F. of Natural Sciences
Dean: S.V. Slavov; *staff* 94 (19)
Science Research Ce.
Head: C.M. Angelov

Founded 1964 as a faculty of the University of Sofia. Detached as independent institute under present title 1971. A State institution under the jurisdiction of and financed by the Ministry of Science and Higher Education. Governing body: the Academic Council. Residential facilities for academic staff and students.

Arrangements for co-operation with: Kossuth Lajos University, Debrecen; College of Education, Cracow; College of Education, Kielce; State Pedagogical Institute, Kiev; University Pierre and Marie Curie (Paris VI); University of Salzburg; University of Vienna; State Pedagogical Institutes of Tallin, and Izmail; College of Education, Magdeburg.

Academic Year: September to June (September-January; February-June).
Admission Requirements: Secondary school certificate.
Fees: None.
Languages of Instruction: Bulgarian and Russian.
Degrees and Diplomas: Diplomas, 4-5 yrs.
Library: c. 120,000 vols.
Special Facilities (Museums, etc.): Medieval Centre 'Prslavska skola'; Mushroom Production Laboratory.
Academic Staff, 1989-90: 339.
Student Enrolment, 1989-90: 1922 (Also c. 1950 external students).

1172 **INSTITUT ZA ČUŽDESTRANNI STUDENTI**
Institute for Foreign Students
Ul. Assen Velchev 27, Sofia
Telephone: 72-34-81

Preparatory F. for Foreign Students
Reader: Stefka Petrova; *staff* 280 (100)
F. for Foreign Language Teaching (English, German, French, Spanish, Portuguese, Greek, Italian, Arabic, Japanese)
Reader: Maria Grozeva; *staff* 100 (150)

Founded 1963. Governing bodies: the General Assembly; the Academic Council. Residential facilities for students.

Arrangements for joint research with: Leningrad State University.

Academic Year: October to June.
Admission Requirements: Secondary school certificate, recognized in respective country of student.
Fees (US$): Tuition, 3500 per annum.
Language of Instruction: Bulgarian.
Degrees and Diplomas: Certificate in Bulgarian. Diplomas in foreign languages.
Library: c. 65,000 vols.
Publication: Journal: Bulgarian for Foreigners (quarterly).
Academic Staff, 1990: 83.

General Education

1173 **VISŠ INSTITUT ZA ISOBRAZITELNI IZKUSTVA 'N. PAVLOVIČ'**
Institute of Fine Arts
Ul. Šipka 1, Sofia 1000

Fine Arts
Applied Arts

Founded 1921, reorganized 1954.

1174 **VISŠ INSTITUT ZA THEATRALNO IZKUSTVO 'KRISTU SARAFOV'**
Institute of Dramatic Art
Ul. G S Rakovski 108, Sofia 1000
Telephone: 87-98-62

Dramatic Art (including Cinema)

Founded 1948.
Academic Year: September to June (September-January; February-June).
Admission Requirements: Competitive entrance examination following secondary school certificate.
Fees: None.
Language of Instruction: Bulgarian.
Degrees and Diplomas: Diploma.
Library: c. 56,000 vols.
Publication: Godishnic (annually).

Academic Staff: c. 90.
Student Enrolment: c. 460 (Also c. 70 external students).

1175 **BALGARSKA DARŽAVNA KONSERVATORIA**
Bulgarian State Conservatory
Ul. Klément Gotvald 11, Sofia 1505
Telephone: 44-21-97
Rector: Georgi Kostov (1989-93)

D. of Instrumental Music
Dean: Savka Shopova; *staff* 85 (84)
D. of Vocal Music
Dean: Resa Koleva; *staff* 46 (25)
D. of Theory, Composition and Conducting
Dean: Zvezoa Ionova; *staff* 74 (43)
D. of Variety Music
Dean: Tomi Dimchev; *staff* 30 (21)

Founded 1921 as academy, acquired present status and title 1954. Governing body: the Academic Council. Some residential facilities for students.
Academic Year: September to May (September-December; February-May).
Admission Requirements: Secondary school certificate and entrance examination.
Fees: None.
Language of Instruction: Bulgarian.
Degrees and Diplomas: Teaching and Professional qualifications, 4 yrs plus 2 yrs specialization. Candidate of the Sciences, by thesis after professional qualification.
Library: 68,400 vols.
Academic Staff: c. 255 (200).
Student Enrolment: c. 840.

1176 **INSTITUTE OF COMMUNICATION SCIENCES**
Avram Stoyanov University Town, Sofia

1177 **VISŠ MUZIKALNO-PEDAGOGIČESKI INSTITUT**
Higher Institute of Music Education
Ul. Todor Samodumov 2, Plovdiv 4025
Telephone: (32) 22-83-10/11
Rector: Ivan Purvanov Spasov (1989-93)
Assistant Rector: Stephan Dimitrov Ivanov

Music Education
Folk Group Directing
Folk Music Choreography

Founded 1964 as branch of the Bulgarian State Conservatory, Sofia, became independent 1972. Governing bodies: the General Assembly; the Academic Council. Some residential facilities for students in hostels.
Arrangements for co-operation with similar institutions in: Leningrad, Moscow, Gdansk, Weimar, and Havana.
Academic Year: September to May (September-December; February-May).
Admission Requirements: Secondary school certificate and entrance examination.
Fees: None.
Language of Instruction: Bulgarian.
Degrees and Diplomas: Teaching and Professional qualifications, 4 yrs plus 2 yrs specialization.
Library: c. 760,000 vols.
Academic Staff, 1989-90:

Rank	Full-time	Part-time
Professors	5	2
Assistant Professors	14	–
Chief Assistants	20	–
Lecturers	3	104
Senior Lecturers	12	–
Senior Assistants	12	–
Assistants	8	–
Total	74	106

Student Enrolment, 1989-90:

	Men	Women	Total
Of the country	174	439	613
Of other countries	5	2	7
Total	179	441	620*

*Also 342 external students.

1178 **INSTITUTE OF INTERNATIONAL TOURISM**
Ul. St. Karadja 32, Varna

BURKINA FASO

1179 ***UNIVERSITÉ DE OUAGADOUGOU**

B.P. 7021, Ouagadougou
Cables: uniouaga uv 5270
Telephone: 30-70-64
Recteur: Alain N. Savadogo (1984-)
Secrétaire général: Galli Medah

I. of Letters and Human Sciences
Director: Hamidou Diallo; *staff* 43 (12)
I. of Natural Sciences
Director: Nindoura Alain Sawadogo; *staff* 23 (32)
I. of Mathematics and Physics
Director: Akry Coulibaly; *staff* 38
C. of Economics
Director: Dembo Gadiaga; *staff* 31 (7)
I. of Technology
Director: Sibiri Sarambé; *staff* 27 (7)
I. of Cinematography
Director: André Nyamba; *staff* 8 (4)
C. of Law
Director: Filiga Michel Sawadago; *staff* 28 (9)
C. of Health Sciences
Director: Rambré Moumouni Ouiminga; *staff* 39 (14)
I. of Rural Development
Director: Guillaume Sessouma; *staff* 29 (10)
I. of Chemistry
Director: Laou Bernard Kam; *staff* 22
I. of Languages, Letters, and Arts
Director: Sié Alain Kam; *staff* 49 (14)
I. of Education
Director: Théophile Bambara; *staff* 1 (3)

Founded 1965 as Ecole normale supérieure, became Centre d'Enseignement supérieur 1969. Acquired present title and status 1974. Reorganized 1985. An autonomous institution under the jurisdiction of the Ministry of Education and Culture. Governing body: the Assemblée. Residential facilities for academic staff.

Arrangements for co-operation with the Universities of: Paris VII; Paris XII; Amiens; Bordeaux II and III; Tours; Groningen; Heidelberg; Namur; Côte d'Ivoire; Niamey; Ghana. Ecole normale supérieure de Fontenay-aux-Roses.

Academic Year: September to June (September-December; January-March; April-June).

Admission Requirements: Secondary school certificate (baccalauréat) or recognized equivalent, or entrance examination

Fees (Francs CFA): 6000-10,000; foreign students, 125,000-200,000

Language of Instruction: French.

Degrees and Diplomas: Diplôme d'études universitaires générales (D.E.U.G.), 2 yrs; Licence, 1 yr after D.E.U.G.; Maîtrise, 1 yr after Licence. Diplôme–d'Ingénieur des Techniques du Développement rural, 3 yrs; d'Ingénieur du Développement rural, 5 yrs. Diplôme d'études approfondies (D.E.A.); Diplôme d'études supérieures spécialisées (D.E.S.S.), 1 yr after Maîtrise. Doctorats de 3è cycle et d'Etats en Economie; en Chimie; en Mathématiques. Diplôme universitaire de technologie (D.U.T.), 2 yrs. Teaching qualification, secondarylevel, 2 yrs.

Libraries: Central Library, *c.* 56,000 vols; libraries of the Colleges and Institutes, *c.* 9030.

Publications: Annales de l'Ecole supérieure des Lettres et des Sciences humaines; Revue Burkinabe de Droit (biannually); Bulletin du Laboratoire universitaire pour la tradition orale (quarterly).

Academic Staff, 1986-87:

Rank	Full-time	Part-time
Professeurs	7	–
Maîtres de Conférences	27	–
Maîtres-Assistants	54	–
Assistants	112	–
Chargés d'Enseignement	18	–
Enseignants	29	–
Vacataires	–	65
Total	247	65

Student Enrolment, 1986-87:

	Men	Women	Total
Of the country	3131	982	4113
Of other countries	197	40	237
Total	3328	1022	4350

1180 **INSTITUT DE LA RÉFORME ET DE L'ACTION PÉDAGOGIQUE**

B.P. 7043, Ouagadougou
Telex: MINEDUC 52 93
Telephone: 3363-63

Educational Research

Founded 1964 as Centre de Documentation et de Perfectionnement, attached to the Université de Ouagadougou 1970, became national institute of education 1976 and acquired present title 1983. A State institution under thejurisdiction of the Ministry of Education.

Academic Year: October to July (October-December; January-March; April-July).

Admission Requirements: Teaching qualification (school level) and entrance examination.

Fees: None.

Language of Instruction: French.

Degrees and Diplomas: Professional titles of–Conseiller pédagogique itinérant; Inspecteur de l'Enseignement du Premier Degré,2-3 yrs.

Library: c. 16,000 vols.

Publication: Revue 'Action, Réflexion, Culture' (monthly).

Academic Staff: c. 5 (20).

Student Enrolment: c. 60.

1181 **ÉCOLE NATIONALE D'ADMINISTRATION ET DE MAGISTRATURE**

B.P. 7024, Ouagadougou
Telephone: 33-46-10

Administration
Magistracy

Founded 1959 as Ecole nationale d'Administration. Acquired present title 1984.

Arrangements for cooperation with: Institut international d'Administration publique, Paris; University of Syracuse; University of Pittsburgh.

Academic Year: October to July (October-December; January-March; April-July).

Admission Requirements: Secondary school certificate (baccalauréat) and entrance examination or Diplôme (Licence or Maîtrise) and entrance examination.

Language of Instruction: French.

Degrees and Diplomas: Brevet and Certificat, 2 yrs. Diplôme, 2-3 yrs following Licence or Maîtrise.

Academic Staff: c. 2 (60).

Student Enrolment: c. 340.

1182 **INSTITUT NATIONAL DES SPORTS**

B.P. 7035, Ouagadougou

1183 **ÉCOLE INTER-ETATS D'INGÉNIEURS DE L'ÉQUIPEMENT RURAL**

B.P. 7023, Ouagadougou
Telex: 5266 EI ER
Telephone: (33) 35-28
Directeur: Jacques de Boissezon

Rural Engineering

Founded 1968 following an agreement between thirteen francophone African States. Admitted first students 1970. An inter-State institution under the jurisdiction of the Burkina Faso Ministry of Education and Culture. Receives financial support from France and African States. Governing body: the Conseil d'administration. Residential facilities for academic staff and students.

Academic Year: October to June (October-December; January-March; April-June).

Admission Requirements: Secondary school certificate (baccalauréat) and entrance examination, or Diplôme (D.U.E.S.) (Mathematics or Physics).

Fees: None.

Language of Instruction: French.

Degrees and Diplomas: Diplôme d'Ingénieur (Maîtrise), 3 yrs.

Library: Documentation Centre, *c.* 2000 vols.

Publication: Bulletin technique.

Academic Staff: *c.* 15 (20).

Student Enrolment: *c.* 80.

1184 **ÉCOLE INTER-ETATS DE TECHNICIENS SUPÉRIEURS DE L' HYDRAULIQUE ET DE L'ÉQUIPEMENT RURAL**

B.P. 594, Ouagadougou

Telex: 5266 UV

Telephone: (33) 42-47

Directeur: Hugues Devevey (1981-87)

Directeur administratif: M. Muguet

Hydrology

Rural Engineering

Founded 1974 following an agreement between thirteen francophone African States. An inter-State institution. Receives financial support from African States. Governing body: the Conseil d'administration. Residential facilities for academic staff and students.

Academic Year: October to June (October-December; January-March; April-June).

Admission Requirements: Secondary school certificate (baccalauréat) or special entrance examination.

Language of Instruction: French.

Degrees and Diplomas: Diplôme, 2 yrs.

Academic Staff: *c.* 7 (1).

Student Enrolment, 1986-87:

	Men	Women	Total
Of the country	11	1	12
Of other countries	77	2	79
Total	88	3	91

BURUNDI

1185 ***UNIVERSITÉ DU BURUNDI**
B.P. 1550, Bujumbura
Telex: 5161
Telephone: (22) 3288
Recteur: Evaiste Ndabanezé (1989-)

F. of Law
Dean: Gervais Gatunange; *staff* 9 (2)
F. of Letters and Human Sciences
Dean: Henri Boyi *staff* 38 (8)
F. of Sciences
Dean: Theodore Mubamba; *staff* 59 (2)
F. of Agriculture (including Animal Husbandry)
Dean: Pontien Ndabanezé; *staff* 11 (6)
F. of Medicine (including Pharmacy)
Dean: Evariste Ndabanezé; *staff* 21 (14)
F. of Education and Psychology
Dean: Gabriel Ntunaguza; *staff* 9 (4)
F. of Applied Sciences
Dean: Théophile Ndikumana; *staff* 23 (2)
I. of Technology
Dean: Théophile Ndikumana; *staff* 11
I. of Physical Education
Dean: Tharcisse Niyonzima; *staff* 6 (1)
I. of Education
Dean: Domitien Nizigiyimana; *staff* 25
Also 3 Research Centres.

Founded 1960, incorporating the Institut agronomique du Ruanda-Urundi, previously Faculty of Agriculture of the Université officielle du Congo belge et du Ruanda-Urundi founded 1958 and the Centre universitaire Rumuri founded 1960. Title of Université officielle de Bujumbura adopted 1964, acquired present title 1977. Largelyfinanced by the State. Governing body: the Conseil d'administration of 15 members, appointed by the President of the Republic. Residential facilities for students.

Arrangements for co-operation with the Universities of: Wisconsin-Madison; Pennsylvania; Paris I and II; Rennes; Tours; Brussels (Free); Louvain (Catholic); Mons; Donets State; Lusaka; Dar es Salaam; Alger; Marien Ngouabi, Congo. Ecole polytechnique de Montréal; Fachhochschule Köln.

Academic Year: October to July (October-December; January-April; April-July).

Admission Requirements: Secondary school certificate (Certificat d'humanités complètes) or foreign equivalent.

Fees (Burundi Francs): Registration, 3010.

Language of Instruction: French.

Degrees and Diplomas: Candidature in preparation for a Licence or professional qualification in–Law; Letters and Human Sciences (various fields); Economic and Social Sciences; Pure and Applied Sciences (various fields); Education and Psychology; Agriculture; Physical Education. Medical Sciences, 2 yrs; Civil Engineering, 3 yrs. Licence in–Law; Mathematics and Physics; Education; Psychology; Economics; Administration; Physical Education, 2 yrs after Candidature. Professional titles of–Ingénieur agronome; Ingénieur technicien; Pharmacien. Doctorat de spécialité (3e cycle). Doctorat en Médecine. Also Diplôme.

Library: c. 100,000 vols.

Publications: Revue de l'Université (Séries: Sciences humaines; Sciences exactes, naturelles, et médicales).

Academic Staff, 1986-87: 170 (45).

Student Enrolment, 1986-87:

	Men	Women	Total
Of the country	1502	413	1915
Of other countries	190	132	322
Total	1692	545	2237

1186 **ÉCOLE DE JOURNALISME**
B.P. 2393, Bujumbura

Journalism
Under the jurisdiction of the Ministry of Information.

1187 **ÉCOLE DE POLICE**
B.P. 105, Bujumbura

Police Studies
Under the jurisdiction of the Ministry of Justice.

1188 **ÉCOLE SUPÉRIEURE DE COMMERCE**
B.P. 1440, Bujumbura

Commerce
Founded 1982. Under the jurisdiction of the Ministry of Education.

Academic Year: September to June (September-December; January-March; April-June).

Admission Requirements: Secondary school certificate.

Language of Instruction: French.

Degrees and Diplomas: Diplôme, 2 yrs.

Academic Staff: c. 10 (30).

Student Enrolment: c. 330.

1189 **INSTITUT SUPÉRIEUR DES TECHNIQUES D'AMÉNAGEMENT ET D'URBANISME**
B.P. 2720, Bujumbura

Town Planning and Development
Under the jurisdiction of the Ministry of Public Works, Energy and Mines.

CAMBODIA

Universities

1190 **SAKÂL VITYALAY PHNÔM PENH**
University of Phnôm Penh
133 Moha Vithei Preah Bat Norodam, Phnôm Penh
Cables: uniphnompenh
Telephone: 2-3572

F. of Law and Economics
F. of Medicine and Paramedical Studies
F. of Pharmacy
F. of Letters and Human Sciences
F. of Science
F. of Education
F. of Commerce
F. of Dentistry
I. of Modern Languages
S. of Education

Founded 1960 incorporating faculties established between 1946 and 1949. Present title adopted 1970. A State institution responsible to the Ministry of Education and Fine Arts. Governing body: the Conseil d'administration. Some residential facilities for academic staff.

Academic Year: September to June (September-January; January-May).

Admission Requirements: Secondary school certificate (baccalauréat). Entrance examination for Faculty of Commerce.

Languages of Instruction: Khmer and French.

Degrees and Diplomas: Licence–ès Lettres, Sciences, Sciences économiques, Sciences juridiques, Sciences commerciales, 4 yrs. Doctorat–en Chirurgie dentaire, 6 yrs; en Médecine, 7 yrs. Diplôme de Pharmacien, 5 yrs. Also Brevet d'enseignement commercial, 3 yrs.

Libraries: Faculty libraries: Letters and Human Sciences, *c.* 14,180 vols; Science, *c.* 3400; Law and Economics, *c.* 8690; Medicine, *c.* 5890; Commerce, *c.* 4430.

Academic Staff: c. 350.

Student Enrolment: c. 8400.

1191 **UNIVERSITÉ TECHNIQUE**
Technical University
Angle Vithei Moat Chrouk et Vithei Hing Pén, Phnôm Penh

F. of General Engineering
F. of Civil Engineering
F. of Electrical Engineering
I. of Technology (Electrical, Building, Hydraulic, Textile, and Mining Engineering)
S. of Chemical Engineering
S. of Civil Aviation

Founded 1964 incorporating Khmero-Soviet Institute of Technology, founded 1961, and People's University, 1965.The university is a State institution responsible to the Minister of Education. Governing body: the Conseil d'administration. Some residential facilities for academic staff.

Academic Year: October to June (October-December; January-March; April-June).

Admission Requirements: Secondary school certificate (baccalauréat) and competitive entrance examination.

Fees (Riels): 450 per annum.

Languages of Instruction: Khmer and French.

Degrees and Diplomas: Diplôme d'Ingénieur, 4 yrs. Also Brevet supérieur, 3 yrs.

Academic Staff: c. 150.

Student Enrolment: c. 950.

1192 **UNIVERSITÉ DES SCIENCES AGRONOMIQUES**
Chamcar Daung (Kandal)
Cables: ursa

F. of Agriculture
F. of Forestry
F. of Veterinary Medicine
F. of Sociology and Rural Economy
F. of Fishery
Pasteur I.
Fishery Research I.
Animal Husbandry Research Station
Agricultural Research Station

Founded 1965. Reorganized 1970. Under the jurisdiction of the Ministry of Agriculture and financed by the State. Some residential facilities for academic staff and students.

Academic Year: October to July (October-February; March-July).

Admission Requirements: Secondary school certificate (baccalauréat) or equivalent.

Language of Instruction: French.

Degrees and Diplomas: Professional titles of Ingénieur and Vétérinaire.

Library: c. 1000 vols.

Special Facilities (Museums, etc.): Herbarium (Institute of Forestry Research).

Academic Staff: c. 20.

Student Enrolment: c. 100.

1193 **UNIVERSITÉ BOUDDHIQUE**
B.P. 117, Quai Sisowath, Phnôm Penh
Telephone: 2-3914

F. of Religion
F. of Philosophy
F. of Linguistics
F. of Khmer Civilization
F. of Classical Languages (Sanskrit and Pali)
F. of Modern Languages
F. of History and Geography

Founded 1954. Reorganized 1970. Under the jurisdiction of the Ministry of Religious Affairs and financed by the Ministry of Finance.

Academic Year: May to February.

Admission Requirements: Secondary school certificate.

Fees: None.

Language of Instruction: Khmer.

Degrees and Diplomas: Diplôme d'Etudes supérieures du Premier Degré, 3 yrs. Licence, 4 yrs. Doctorate, a further 3 yrs.

Library: c. 10,000 vols.

Publications: Buddikasksa; Culture et civilisation khmères.

Academic Staff: c. 20.

Student Enrolment: c. 180 (Men).

1194 **UNIVERSITÉ DES BEAUX-ARTS**
Boulevard U.R.S.S., Phnôm Penh
Telephone: 2-3125

F. of Choreography
F. of Plastic Arts
F. of Music
F. of Archaeology
F. of Architecture and Town Planning

Founded 1965 incorporating existing schools of art and music. A State institution under the jurisdiction of the Ministry of Culture. Governing bodies: the Conseil d'administration; the Conseil de perfectionnement; the Conseil de discipline; the Conseil des professeurs. Residential facilities for foreign academic staff.

Arrangements for cooperation with the Unités pédagogiques d'Architecture in France.

Academic Year: October to June (September-December; January-March; April-June).

Admission Requirements: Secondary school certificate (baccalauréat). Entrance examination for foreign students.

Languages of Instruction: Khmer and French.

Degrees and Diplomas: Diplôme and Baccalauréat ès Arts. Licence ès Arts plastiques, d'Archéologie.

Library: Central Library, *c.* 9420 vols.
Academic Staff: c. 50 (150).

CAMEROON

1195 ***UNIVERSITÉ DE YAOUNDÉ**
University of Yaoundé
B.P. 337, Yaoundé
Telex: 8384 U Y KN
Telephone: 22-07-44
Chancelier: Laurent Esso
Vice-Chancelier: Jacob Nguh Lifangi

F. of Law and Economics
F. of Sciences
F. of Letters and Human Sciences
S. of Education
S. of Journalism
Polytechnical S.
I. of International Relations
Ce. for Health Sciences

Founded 1962 and replacing Institut national d'Etudes supérieures, founded 1961. A State institution responsible to the Minister of Education. Governing bodies: the Conseil de l'Enseignement supérieur, presided over by the President of the Republic, and including representatives of all interested Ministries, the Directors of Education, the Heads of university institutions–there is also provision for academic and student participation; the Conseil d'administration, presided over by the Chancellor of the University. Financed by the State. Residential facilities for students.

Academic Year: October to July (October-December; January-March; April-July).

Admission Requirements: Secondary school certificate (baccalauréat) or foreign equivalent, and entrance examination.

Languages of Instruction: French and English.

Degrees and Diplomas: Licence–ès Sciences; ès Lettres; en Droit, law; ès Sciences économiques, 3-4 yrs. Maîtrise, 2 further yrs. Diplôme–en Relations internationales; en Soins Infirmiers supérieurs, 2 yrs; d'Ingénieur de travaux; supérieur de Journalisme, 3 yrs. Doctorat en Médecine, 6 yrs. Teaching qualification, lower secondary level, 2 yrs, higher secondary level, 4 yrs.

Library: Central Library, *c.* 85,000 vols.

Publications: Annales des Facultés; Revue camerounaise de Droit.

Academic Staff: c. 560.

Student Enrolment: c. 13,090.

1196 **CENTRE UNIVERSITAIRE DE DOUALA**
B.P. 2071, Douala
Telex: 6140 KN
Telephone: 42-62-19
Directeur général: Marc Bopelet
Secrétaire général: Bruno Bekolo Ebé

S. of Economics and Commerce
Director: Jérémie Ndioro A. Moumbock; *staff* 16 (28)
S. of Teacher Training (Technical)
Director: Elienida II; *staff* 34 (46)

Founded 1977. Previously part of the University of Yaoundé. Governing body: the Conseil d'Administration. Residential facilities for academic staff and students.

Arrangements for co-operation with: Ecole des hautes Etudes commerciales, Montréal; Ecole polytechnique, Montréal; Ecoles supérieures de Commerce Paris, Rouen; Ecoles normales supérieures de l'Enseignement technique, Cachan, Tunis.

Academic Year: October to July (October-December; January-March; April-July).

Admission Requirements: Competitive entrance examination following secondary school certificate (baccalauréat).

Fees (Francs CFA): 3300.

Languages of Instruction: French and English.

Degrees and Diplomas: Diplôme d'études supérieures de Commerce, 4 yrs. Teaching qualifications (technical), 3-5 yrs. Also Brevet, 2 yrs.

Libraries: Central Library, 5570 vols; libraries of the schools, 3906.

Academic Staff, 1986-87:

Rank	Full-time
Chargés de cours	20
Assistants	33
Total	53

Student Enrolment, 1986-87:

	Men	Women	Total
Of the country	600	245	845
Of other countries	7	3	10
Total	607	248	855

1197 **CENTRE UNIVERSITAIRE DE DSCHANG**
Dschang
Telex: 7013 KN

Agriculture

Founded 1977. Previously part of the University of Yaoundé.

1198 **CENTRE UNIVERSITAIRE DE NGAOUNDÉRÉ**
B.P. 454, Ngaoundéré
Telex: 7645 KN
Telephone: 25-12-45
Fax: 25-25-73
Directeur général: Samuel Domngang (1984-)
Secrétaire général: Pascal Bekolo

S. of Agriculture and Food Technology
Head: Samir Arabi; *staff* 70 (10)

Founded 1982. A State institution. Governing body: the Conseil d'Administration. Residential facilities for students.

Arrangements for cooperation with the Institut National Polytechnique de Lorraine.

Academic Year: October to July (October-December; January-April; April-July).

Admission Requirements: Competitive entrance examination following secondary school certificate (baccalauréat).

Fees (Francs CFA): 5,380,000 per annum.

Languages of Instruction: French and English.

Degrees and Diplomas: Diplômes, 3-5 yrs.

Library: 9000 vols.

Academic Staff, 1989-90: 70 (10).

Student Enrolment, 1989-90:

	Men	Women	Total
Of the country	401	14	415

1199 **CENTRE UNIVERSITAIRE DE BUÉA**
Buéa
Telex: 5155 KN
Telephone: 21-21-34
Directeur-général: Dorothy L. Njeuma
Secrétaire-général: Kashim I. Tala

Advanced S. of Translation and Interpretation
Head: Daniel Onana; *staff* 3 (23)

Founded 1977, admitted first students 1986. Governing body: the Board of Governors. Residential facilities for students.

Academic Year: October to June (October-December; January-March; April-June).

Admission Requirements: Competitive entrance examination following Licence (Translation) and Diploma in Translation (Interpretation).

Languages of Instruction: English, French and Spanish.

Degrees and Diplomas: Diploma in–Translation, 2 yrs; Interpretation, a further 1 yr.

Library: ASTI Documentation Unit.

Publication: Epasa Moto (Bilingual Journal of Language, Letters and Culture, annually).

Academic Staff, 1989-90: 4 (23).
Student Enrolment, 1989-90:

	Men	Women	Total
Of the country	53	8	61
Of other countries	2	2	4
Total	55	10	65

1200 **ÉCOLE NATIONALE D'ADMINISTRATION ET DE MAGISTRATURE**
B.P. 1180, Yaoundé
Telephone: 22-37-54

D. of Administrative Studies
D. of Magistracy

Founded 1959 as Ecole Camerounaise d'Administration and reorganized 1962. A State institution.

Academic Year: November to October.

Admission Requirements: Competitive entrance examination following secondary school certificate (baccalauréat), except for students admitted to special preparatory year.

Languages of Instruction: French and English.

Degrees and Diplomas: Diplôme, 3 yrs, including 1 yr of specialization in France. Also lower level qualifications, 1 yr.

Library: c. 8000 vols.

Academic Staff: c. 80.

Student Enrolment: c. 150.

1201 **ÉCOLE NATIONALE SUPÉRIEURE DE POLICE**
B.P. 148, Yaoundé

Police Science

1202 **ÉCOLE SUPÉRIEURE DES POSTES ET TÉLÉCOMMUNICATIONS**
B.P. 1186, Yaoundé

Telecommunications

1203 **ÉCOLE NATIONALE SUPÉRIEURE DES TRAVAUX PUBLICS**
B.P. 510, Yaoundé
Telex: 8653 KN
Telephone: 22-04-06
Directeur: John Patrick Navti (1986-)
Chef de Service administratif: John Fondzenyuy

D. of Civil Engineering
Head: Robert Fromenteau; *staff* 24 (25)
D. of Rural Engineering
Head: Etienne Kapto; *staff* 17 (25)
D. of Topography and Surveying
Head: Patrice Moineau; *staff* 11 (14)
D. of Town Planning
Head: Henri Golstain; *staff* 16 (13)
Also branches at Buéa and Akonolinga.

Founded 1970 as Ecole nationale de Technologie, acquired present status and title 1982. A State institution responsible to the Ministry of Equipment.

Arrangements for co-operation with: Ecole nationale supérieure des Travaux publics, Yamoussoukro; Ecole nationale des Ponts et Chaussées, Paris.

Academic Year: October to July (October-February; February-July).

Admission Requirements: Secondary school certificate (baccalauréat) and entrance examination.

Languages of Instruction: French and English.

Degrees and Diplomas: Title of Ingénieur des Travaux de Génie civil, 3 yrs. Also Diplômes, 2 yrs.

Academic Staff: c. 35 (30).

Student Enrolment: c. 520.

1204 **INSTITUT DE DÉVELOPPEMENT INFORMATIQUE AFRICAIN**
B.P. 6316, Yaoundé
Telex: 8653 KN
Telephone: 22-04-06

Computer Sciences

Founded 1982.

1205 **INSTITUT DE FORMATION ET DE RECHERCHE DÉMOGRAPHIQUES**
B.P. 1556, Yaoundé
Telephone: 22-24-71
Directeur: M. Sala-Diakanda (1986-87)
Administrateur: A. Bassené

Demographic Studies

Founded 1972 following an agreement between the Government and the United Nations. Under the supervision of the Ministry of Planning and Land Development. Reorganized 1982.

Arrangements for cooperation with: Institut de Démographie, Paris; Université Catholique de Louvain.

Academic Year: October to July (October-December; January-April; April-June).

Admission Requirements: University qualification.

Language of Instruction: French.

Degrees and Diplomas: Diplôme, 2 yrs.

Library: 12,000 vols.

Publications: Annales; Bulletin de Liaison de Démographie Africaine (both three times a year).

Academic Staff, 1986-87: 6 (10).
Student Enrolment, 1986-87:

	Men
Of the country	1
Of other countries	18
Total	19

1206 **INSTITUT INTERNATIONAL DES ASSURANCES**
B.P. 1575, Yaoundé
Telex: 8730 KN
Telephone: 22-49-81
Directeur: Julien Jean Codjovi

Insurance Studies

Founded 1972 at Yamoussoukro, Côte d'Ivoire. An Inter-State institution.

Academic Year: November to July (November-December; January-March; April-July).

Admission Requirements: Secondary school certificate (baccalauréat).

Language of Instruction: French.

Degrees and Diplomas: Diplôme du cycle moyen. Diplôme d'Etudes supérieres d'Assurances, 5 yrs.

Academic Staff, 1988-89: 44.

Student Enrolment, 1988-89: 42.

1207 **INSTITUT NATIONAL DE LA JEUNESSE ET DES SPORTS**
B.P. 1016, Yaoundé

Physical Education and Sports

1208 **INSTITUT DE STATISTIQUE, DE PLANIFICATION ET D'ÉCONOMIE APPLIQUÉE**
B.P. 294, Yaoundé
Cables: CIFS yaoundé
Telephone: 22-01-34

Statistics
Applied Economics

Founded 1961. A State institution serving other African countries. Residential facilities for students.

Arrangements for co-operation with: Ecole de Statistique d'Abidjan; Institut national de Statistique et d'Economie appliquée, Rabat; Institut Africain et Mauricien de Statistiques et d'Economie appliquée, Kigali.

Academic Year: October to June (October-December; January-March; April-June).

Admission Requirements: Competitive entrance examination following secondary school certificate (baccalauréat).

Language of Instruction: French.

Degrees and Diplomas: Diplômes, 3 yrs.
Library: ISPEA Library.

Academic Staff: c. 20 (40).
Student Enrolment: c. 150.

CENTRAL AFRICAN REPUBLIC

1209 ***UNIVERSITÉ DE BANGUI**

Avenue des Martyrs, B.P. 1450, Bangui
Telephone: (61) 20-00/20-05
Recteur: Joachim Raynaldy Sioke (1986-)
Secrétaire général: Auguste Magba

F. of Law and Economics
Dean: Antoine Adame; *staff* 1414
F. of Letters and Humanities
Dean: Faustin-Désiré Teguedère; *staff* 25
F.of Sciences
Dean: Joachim Raynaldy Sioke; *staff* 20
F. of Health Sciences
Dean: Raymond-Max Siopathis; *staff* 7
S. of Education
Director: Louis Quandet; *staff* 14
I. of Business Administration
Director: Odile Laurens *staff* 4
I. of Rural Development
Director: Raymond Baguida; *staff* 10
Polytechnic I.
Director: Jean-Bernard Minot; *staff* 3
I. of Applied Linguistics
Director: Michel Koyt
I. of Mathematics (Research)
Director Joachim Raynaldy Sioke

Founded 1969. Formerly Institut d'Etudes juridiques of Fondation de l'Enseignement supérieur en Afrique centrale. A State institution responsible to the Ministry of Education and Research and receiving some financial assistance from France. Governing body: the Conseil d'Administration. Residential facilities for students.

Arrangements for co-operation with the Universities of: Marien Ngouabi, Congo; Orléans; Paris XII; Strasbourg I; Limoges; Aix-Marseille I and II; Bordeaux I, II and III; Lille; Chad.

Academic Year: September to June (September-December; January-March; April-June).

Admission Requirements: Secondary school certificate (baccalauréat) or special entrance examination.

Fees (Francs CFA): 125,000-350,000.

Language of Instruction: French.

Degrees and Diplomas: Law and Economics: Licence en Droit, law; ès Sciences économiques, 3 yrs. Also Certificat de Capacité en Droit, 2 yrs. Science: Diplôme universitaire d'études scientifiques (D.U.E.S.), 2 yrs. Letters and Human Sciences: Licence ès Lettres, 3 yrs. Diplôme universitaire d'études littéraires (D.U.E.L.), 2 yrs. Health Sciences: Doctorat en Médecine, 6 yrs. Diplôme de Technicien supérieur de Santé, 4 yrs. Diplôme–d'Infirmier; de Sage-Femme, midwifery, 3 yrs. Also Diplôme supérieur de Gestion, D.S.G., 3 yrs; Diplômed'Ingénieur, in various fields, 3-4 yrs.

Libraries: Central Library, *c.* 28,000 vols; Health Sciences, *c.* 3500.

Academic Staff, 1986-87:

Rank	Full-time
Professeurs	6
Maîtres de conférences	5
Maîtres-Assistants	58
Assistants	34
Total	103

Student Enrolment, 1986-87:

	Men	Women	Total
Of the country	1941	195	2136
Of other countries	240	56	296
Total	2181	251	2432

CHAD

1210 ***UNIVERSITÉ DU TCHAD**
University of Chad
B.P. 1117, N'Djaména
Telephone: 21-76
Recteur: Jacques Yoguerna Dono-Horngar

F. of Letters, Modern Languages, and Human Sciences
F. of Law, Economics, and Business Administration
F. of Exact and Applied Sciences
I. of Stockraising

Founded 1971, comprising institutions formerly of the Fondation de l'-Enseignement supérieur en Afrique centrale. A State institution receiving some financial assistance from France. Governing body: the Conseil de l'-Université, composed of government representatives and members of the academic staff and student body. Residential facilities for foreign members of the academic staff.

Academic Year: October to June (October-February; March-June).

Admission Requirements: Secondary school certificate (baccalauréat).

Language of Instruction: French.

Degrees and Diplomas: Diplôme universitaire, 2 yrs; Licence, 3 yrs; Maîtrise, 4 yrs.

Library: Central Library, *c.* 3500 vols.

Academic Staff: *c.* 90.

Student Enrolment: *c.* 1370.

1211 **ÉCOLE NATIONALE D'ADMINISTRATION ET DE MAGISTRATURE**
B.P. 758, N'Djaména

Administration and Magistracy

Founded 1963.

1212 **ÉCOLE NATIONALE DES TRAVAUX PUBLICS**
N'Djaména

Public Works

Founded 1965.

1213 **INSTITUT DE TECHNIQUES DE L'ÉLEVAGE**
B.P. 433, N'Djaména

Tropical Stockraising and Veterinary Medicine

Founded 1952.

1214 **INSTITUT DE RECHERCHES DU COTON ET DES TEXTILES EXOTIQUES**
Route de Farcha, B.P. 764, N'Djaména

Cotton Research

Founded 1939.

1215 **OFFICE DE LA RECHERCHE SCIENTIFIQUE ET TECHNIQUE D'OUTRE-MER (ORSTOM)**
B.P. 65, N'Djaména

Geology
Pedology
Hydrology
Hydrobiology
Botany
Archaeology
Geophysics

CHILE

Universities and Technical Universities

1216 **UNIVERSIDAD DE ANTOFAGASTA**
Antonio Toro 851, Casilla 170, Antofagasta
Telephone: 226652

F. of Engineering
F. of Education and Humanities
F. of Health Sciences
I. of Oceanography Research
I. of Anthropological Research

Founded 1981, incorporating previous regional branches at Antofagasta of the University of Chile and the University of Santiago de Chile. Governing body: the Consejo Académico. Residential facilities for students.

Academic Year: March to December (March-July; August-December).

Admission Requirements: Secondary school certificate (Licencia de Educación Media) and entrance examination.

Language of Instruction: Spanish.

Degrees and Diplomas: Licenciado in Civil Engineering, 5 yrs. Professional titles, 4-6 yrs.

Libraries: Central Library, *c.* 23,500 vols; Engineering, *c.* 14,230; Oceanography, *c.* 500; Anthropology, *c.* 1160; Medicine, *c.* 1530.

Publications: Cuadernos de Filologia (annually); Estudos de Arqueologia (biannually); Apuntes de Oceanologia (quarterly); Forma y Función (annually).

Academic Staff: c. 225 (20).

Student Enrolment: c. 3670.

1217 **UNIVERSIDAD ARTURO PRAT**
Casilla 121, Iquique
Telex: 323126 UNAPIQ CK
Telephone: 22472; 21309
Rector: René Piantini Castillo
Vice-Rector for Administrative Affairs: Raúl Lara Carrasco

D. of Economics and Management
Director: Francisco Vergara Boggero; *staff* 12
D. of Education and Humanities
Director: Juan Jacob Fernández; *staff* 19 (23)
D. of Marine Sciences
Director: Carlos Merino Pinochet; *staff* 22 (1)
D of Engineering
Director: Oscar Castro Soto *staff* 9 (4)
D. of Science (including Computer Sciences)
Director Manuel Sovera Gutiérrez; *staff* 22 (11)
Ce. for Desert Studies
Director: José Delatorre Herrera; *staff* 6 (1)

Founded 1984. Previously regional branch of University of Chile and Instituto Profesional. A State institution. Governing bodies: the Junta Directiva (Board of Trustees); the Consejo Académico.

Academic Year: March to December (March-July; August-December).

Admission Requirements: Secondary school certificate (Licencia de Educación Media) and entrance examination.

Fees (Pesos): Registration, 10,000; tuition, 70,800-123,900 per annum.

Language of Instruction: Spanish.

Degrees and Diplomas: Licenciado in–Education, 2 yrs; Marine Sciences, 5 yrs. Professional titles of–Contador auditor; Administrador de Empresas, business administration, 4 yrs; Ingeniero (various fields), 4-6 yrs; Biólogo, 5 yrs; Estadistico, 5 ½ yrs. Profesor de Estado (teaching qualification), 5 yrs.

Libraries: Central Library, 16,000 vols; Marine Sciences, 2000.

Special Facilities (Museums, etc.): Museum of Anthropology.

Publications: Nuestro Norte (quarterly); Colosos de Iquique (annually).

Press or Publishing House: University Press.

Academic Staff, 1986-87:

Rank	Full-time	Part-time
Profesores Titulares	11	4
Profesores Asociados	33	6
Profesores Asistentes	42	26
Instructores	14	24
Ayudantes	–	57
Total	100	117

Student Enrolment, 1986-87:

	Men	Women	Total
Of the country	902	665	1567
Of other countries	2	1	3
Total	904	666	1570

1218 **UNIVERSIDAD DE ATACAMA**
Avenida J.F. Kennedy 485, Copiapó
Telephone: (52) 212005
Fax: (52) 212662
Rector: Mario Maturana Claro
Secretario General: Alejandro Alvarez Davies

F. of Engineering (including Mining Technology and Geological Sciences)
Dean: Mario Meza Maldonado; *staff* 75 (86)
F. of Humanities and Education
Dean: Juan Inglesias Diaz; *staff* 24 (28)
S. of Technology
Director: Timur Padilla Bocic; *staff* 12 (18)
I. of Scientific and Technological Research
Director: Germán Caceres Arenas; *staff* 8
I. of Postgraduate Studies
Director: Juan Iglesias Diaz; *staff* 1 (20)

Founded 1857 as school of mining and became regional branch of State Technical University 1947. Became independent and acquired present status and title 1981. An autonomous institution financially supported by the State. Governing body: the Junta Directiva (Board of Trustees). Residential facilities for *c.* 250 men students.

Academic Year: March to December (March-June; August-December).

Admission Requirements: Secondary school certificate (Licencia de Educación Media) and entrance examination.

Language of Instruction: Spanish.

Degrees and Diplomas: Professional title of Ingeniero, 4-6 yrs. Magister, a further 2 yrs. Teaching qualifications.

Special Facilities (Museums, etc.): Mineralogical Museum of Copiapó.

Press or Publishing House: Editorial de la Universidad de Atacama.

Academic Staff, 1990:

Rank	Full-time	Part-time
Profesores Titulares	5	2
Profesores Asociados	12	–
Profesores Asistentes	36	4
Instructores	11	4
Asistentes	5	3
Total	69	13

Student Enrolment, 1990:

	Men	Women	Total
Of the country	1084	453	1537
Of other countries	1	1	2
Total	1085	454	1539*

*Also 350 external students.

1219 **UNIVERSIDAD DEL BÍO BÍO**
Casilla 5C, Avenida Collao 1202, Concepción
Telex: 260086 UNBIO CL
Telephone: 238984
Fax: 238984-anexo 344
Rector: Guillermo Schaffeld Graniffo (1988-)
Vicerrector de Asuntos Económicos: Daniel Epprecht

F. of Architecture, Construction, and Design (Concepción and Chillán)
Dean: Ricardo Hempel Holzapfel; *staff* 38 (39)
F. of Engineering
Dean: Franciso Ramis Lanyon; *staff* 71 (59)
F. of Sciences (Concepción and Chillán)
Dean: Justo Lisperguer Muñoz; *staff* 35 (20)
F. of Administration (Concepción and Chillán)
Dean Carlon Román Yañez; *staff* 28 (43)
F. of Education (Chillán)
Dean: María Ipinza Tapia; *staff* 61 (25)
F. of Natural Resources (Agribusiness, Nutrition, and Nursing) (Chillán)
Dean: Nora Plaza Ceballos; *staff* 51 (24)
Ce. for General Studies
Director: Bernardo Arévalo Vilugrón; *staff* 6 (3)

Founded 1988 from the merging of the former Universidad de Bío Bío (until 1980 a branch of the State Technical University) and the Instituto Profesional de Chillán (previously branch of Universidad de Chile). Governing body: the Junta Directiva.

Arrangements for co-operation with the University of Nottingham.

Academic Year: March to December.

Admission Requirements: Secondary school certificate (Licencia de Educación Media) or recognized equivalent, and entrance examination.

Fees (Pesos): 210,000-300,000 per annum.

Language of Instruction: Spanish.

Degrees and Diplomas: Professional titles of–Administrador de Empresas, business administration; Contador Auditor, accountancy; Nutricionista; Ingeniero de Ejecución, 4 yrs; Profesor de Estado; Diseñador Gráfico; Constructorcivil; Ingeniero en Alimentos, 5 yrs; Arquitecto; Ingeniero civil, 6 yrs.

Libraries: 29,000 vols (Chillán); 22,000 (Concepción).

Special Facilities (Museums, etc.): T.V. Studio, Channel 10 (Chillán Campus). Radio Station.

Publications: Boletín (monthly); Arquitecturas del Sur (biannually).

Academic Staff, 1990:

Rank	Full-time	Part-time
Profesores Titulares	3	1
Profesores Asociados	39	2
Profesores Asistentes	117	13
Profesores Instructores	45	–
Total	204	16

Student Enrolment, 1990:

Men	Women	Total
3714	2079	5793

1220 **UNIVERSIDAD CENTRAL**
Avenida José Joaquín Prieto 10001, San Bernardo
Telephone: 5585621
Rector: Hugo Galvez Gajardo
Secretario General: Gonzalo Hernández Uribe

F. of Architecture and Fine Arts
Dean: René Martínez Lemoine; *staff* 3 (96)
F. of Law
Dean: Ruben Celis Rodríguez; *staff* 7
F. of Social Sciences
Dean: Aristides Giavellii Iturriaga; *staff* 4
F. of Economic and Administrative Sciences (including Accountancy and Engineering in Administration and Agrarian Business)
Dean: Fernando Escobar Cerda; *staff* 4 (55)
F. of Physical and Mathematical Sciences (including Engineering Design, and Administration and Development of Computational Systems of Information)
Dean: Luis Lucero Alday; *staff* 1 (20)
S. of Political Science and Administration
; *staff* 4 (53)
S. of Early Childhood Education
Dean: Selma Simonstein Fuentes; *staff* 4
Ce. for Social Housing Architecture
Head: Edwin Haramoto Nishikimoto; *staff* – (4)

Founded 1983.

Academic Year: April to January.

Admission Requirements: Secondary school certificate (Licencia de Educación Media) and entrance examination.

Language of Instruction: Spanish.

Degrees and Diplomas: Professional titles, 5-9 yrs.

Library: Total, 7025 vols.

Publications: Revistas (annually); Parthenon (annually).

Academic Staff, 1990:

Rank	Full-time	Part-time
Profesores	32	326
Profesores Ayudantes	–	196
Total	32	522

Student Enrolment, 1990:

Men	Women	Total
2311	1560	3871

1221 **UNIVERSIDAD DE CHILE**
University of Chile
Alameda Bernardo O'Higgins 1050, Santiago
Telephone: 6989539
Rector: Juan de Dios Vial (1987-)
Vice-Rector: Marino Pizarro P.

F. of Architecture and Town Planning
Dean: Hernán Monteciones
F. of Arts
Dean: Luis Merino
F. of Science
Dean: Camilo Quezeda
F. of Agriculture and Forestry
Dean: Antonio Lizana
F. of Economics and Administration
Dean: Sergio Melnick
F. of Physics and Mathematics (including Civil Engineering)
Dean: Atilano Lamana
F. of Chemistry and Pharmacy
Dean: Hugo Zunino
F. of Veterinary Medicine (including Stockraising)
Dean: Hugo González
F. of Law
Dean: Mario Mosquera
F. of Philosophy, Humanities, and Education (including Archaeology and Journalism)
Dean: Fernando Valenzuela
F. of Medicine (including Nursing)
Dean: Alejandro Goic
F. of Dentistry
Dean: Hernán Barahona
I. of Political Science
Director Gustavo Cuevas
I. of International Studies
Director: Pilar Armanet
I. of Nutrition and Food Technology
Director: Gustavo Moonckeberg
Extension D.
Head: Teresa Irarte G.

Founded 1738 by Philip V of Spain as Universidad de San Felipe. Replaced by present institution 1839, present title adopted 1842. Became autonomous under the law on higher education 1931. Reorganized 1981 when the University's 9 regional branches became separate universities and institutes. Governing body: the Consejo Universitario. Some residential facilities for students.

Academic Year: March to December (March-July; August-December).

Admission Requirements: Secondary school certificate (Licencia de Educación Media) and entrance examination.

Fees (Pesos): 68,000-160,000 per annum.

Language of Instruction: Spanish.

Degrees and Diplomas: Licenciado in–Psychology, 2 yrs; Architecture; Geography; Music; Theory and History of Art; Plastic Arts; Physics; Mathematics; Chemistry; Agriculture; Forestry; Economics; Business Administration; Science; Engineering; Biochemistry; Chemistry and Pharmacy; Veterinary Medicine; Anthropology; Social Communication; Sociology; Philosophy; History; Language and Literature; Dentistry, 4 yrs; Medicine, 4-5 yrs; Law and Social Sciences; Theory and History of Art, 5 yrs. Professional titles of–Interpretación en Danza, 3 yrs; Diseño teatral;

Enfermera(o); Fonaudiólogo(a); Kinesiólogo, 4 yrs; Periodista, 4 ½ yrs; Geógrafo; Contador Auditor; Administrador; Químico; Médico veterinario; Sociólogo, 5 yrs; Bioquímico; Químico y Farmacia; Cirujano dentista, 5 ½ yrs; Arquitecto; Geólogo; Psicólogo, 6 yrs; Médico-Cirujano, 7 yrs. Degree of Magister. Doctorado in–Science; Chemistry; Biochemistry; Pharmacy.

Libraries: Central Library, 223,450 vols; libraries of the faculties and institutes, 874,280.

Special Facilities (Museums, etc.): Museum of Popular Art; Museum of Modern Art.

Publications: Actualidad Universitaria (monthly); Anales de la Universidad de Chile (annually); Cuadernos Universidad de Chile (quarterly); Boletín Interamericano de Educación Musical (annually); Revista Musical Chilena (biannually); Desarrollo Rural (biannually); Terra Aridae (biannually); Comentarios sobre la Situación Económica; Taller de Coyuntura; Ocupación y Desocupación Encuesta nacional (biannually); Ocupación y Desocupación en el Gran Santiago (quarterly); Anuario Astronómico (annually); Tralka; Revista Chilena de Historia del Derecho; Revista de Derecho Económico; Revista de Derecho Público; Bizantion Nea Hellas; Boletín de Filología (biannually); Cuadernos de Historia (annually); Revista Chilena de Antropología (annually); Revista Chilena de Humanidades (annually); Revista de Filosofía (annually); Boletín Chileno de Parasitología (quarterly); Revista Psiquiátrica Clínica (annually); Estudios Internacionales (quarterly); Publicaciones Científicas-INTA (annually); Cuadernos de Ciencia Política (quarterly); Política (biannually).

Academic Staff: c. 5880.

Student Enrolment, 1986-87:

	Men	Women	Total
Of the country	10,949	5861	16,810
Of other countries	88	73	161
Total	11,037	5934	16,971

1222 **UNIVERSIDAD AUSTRAL DE CHILE**

Southern University of Chile

Campus Universitario Isla Teja, Casilla 567, Valdivia
Cables: independencia 641
Telex: 71035 UNAUS CL
Telephone: 3961
Rector: Juan Jorge Ebert Kronenberg (1987-)

F. of Medicine (including Nursing and Midwifery)
Dean: Alejandro Foradori Curtarelli
F. of Veterinary Medicine
Dean: Edmundo Butendieck Burattini
F. of Agriculture (including Animal Husbandry)
Dean: Javier Troncoso Correa
F. of Forestry
Dean: Eduardo Morales Verdugo
F. of Philosophy and Humanities (including Education)
Dean: Erwin Haverbeck Ojeda
F. of Economics and Business Administration
Dean: Carol Pinto-Agüero Barria
F. of Science
Dean: Justo Zamora Baragaño
F. of Judicial and Social Sciences
Dean: Félix Urcullú Molina
F. of Fishery and Oceanography
Dean: Fernando Berroeta Sánchez
F. of Engineering
Dean: Fredy Rios Martinez

Founded 1955, the university is a private institution, but receives a subvention from the State. Governing body: the Directorio dealing with administrative matters, and the Consejo Académico dealing with academic affairs. Residential facilities for academic staff and students.

Academic Year: March to December (March-July; August-December).

Admission Requirements: Secondary school certificate (Licencia de Educación Media) or recognized equivalent, and entrance examination.

Language of Instruction: Spanish.

Degrees and Diplomas: Bachiller or Licenciado in–Arts; Philosophy; Anthropology; Mathematics; Science; Physics, 3 yrs. Professional titles in–Nursing; Midwifery; Statistics, 4 yrs; Agricultural Engineering; Veterinary Medicine; Business Administration, 5 yrs; Forestry, 5 ½ yrs; Medicine, 7 yrs. Also teaching qualifications (primary and secondary levels). Degree of Magister in–Science; Philosophy; English; Technological Education; Letters; Linguistics; English; Physics; Immunology; Medicine.

Libraries: Central Library, c. 67,500 vols; Technology, c. 2800.

Special Facilities (Museums, etc.): History and Archaeology Museum; Biological Garden.

Publications: Estudios Filológicos; Archivos de Medicina Veterinaria; Agrosur; Bosque; Medio Ambiente (all biannually).

Academic Staff, 1990: c. 500 (120).

Student Enrolment, 1990:

	Men	Women	Total
Of the country	4053	2589	6642
Of other countries	43	19	62
Total	4096	2608	6704*

*Also 177 external students.

1223 **PONTIFICIA UNIVERSIDAD CATÓLICA DE CHILE**

Catholic University of Chile

Alameda 340, Casilla 114-D, Santiago
Cables: Alameda 340
Telex: 240395 PUCVA CL
Telephone: 222 4516
Rector: Juan de Dios Vial Correa (1985-)
Secretario General: Raúl Lecaros Zegers

F. of Agriculture
Dean: Juan Ignacio Dominguez Covarrubias; *staff* 42 (30)
F. of Architecture and Fine Arts
Dean: Renato Parada B.; *staff* 59 (112)
F. of Biology
Dean: Jorge Lewin C.; *staff* 79 (2)
F. of Economics and Administration
Dean: Juan Ignacio Varas Castellón *staff* 31 (56)
F. of Physics
Dean: Ricardo Ramírez L.: *staff* 28 (3)
F. of History, Geography, and Political Science
Dean: Ricardo Riesco J.; *staff* 37 (53)
F. of Letters
Dean: Jaime Martínez W.; *staff* 51 (75)
F. of Mathematics
Dean: José López; *staff* 48 (24)
F. of Chemistry
Dean: Rafael Gana O.: *staff* 41 (41)
F.of Social Sciences
Dean: Gabriel Gyarmati K.; *staff* 35 (63)
F. of Law
Dean: Arnoldo Gorziglia B.; *staff* 13 (68)
F. of Education
Dean: Josefina Aragoneses A.; *staff* 70 (116)
F. of Philosophy
Dean: Juan de Dios Vial; *staff* 19 (25)
F. of Engineering
Dean: Bernardo Domínguez C.; *staff* 87 (114)
F. of Medicine
Dean: Ricardo Ferretti; *staff* 122 (177)
F. of Theology
Dean: Eliseo Escudero; *staff* 9 (31)
Ce. for Tele-Education
Director: Alfonso Gómez

Also centres in Del Maule, Talcahuano, Temuco, and Villarrica.

Founded 1888 by decree of Archbishop of Santiago. Recognized by Pope Leo XIII 1889; became Pontifical University 1930. It is a private, autonomous institution, but its degrees are recognized by Chilean Law. Financially supported by State subsidy and tuition fees. Governing body: the Consejo Superior, presided over by the Rector and including the Secretary-General, the Vice-Rectors, the deans, a student representative, and 4 representatives of the university staff.

Arrangements for co-operation with: Universidad José Cecilio del Valle, Tegucigalpa; Universidade Estadual de Campinas; Pontifícia Universidade Católica de Rio de Janeiro; Universidade de São Paulo; Universidad Católica Boliviana; Universidad Mayor de San Andrés; Universidad Mayor de San Francisco Xavier de Chuquisaca; Universities of: Buenos Aires; Morón; Kiel; Madrid; Navarra; Barcelona; Pontifical Salamanca; Rennes; Purdue; Catholic of America; Pennsylvania; Institut national polytechnique de Toulouse; Facultés UniversitairesNotre-Dame de la Paix, Namur; MIT.

Academic Year: March to December (March-July; August-Decem-ber).

Admission Requirements: Secondary school certificate (Licencia de Educación Media) and entrance examination.

Language of Instruction: Spanish.

Degrees and Diplomas: Bachiller in–Religious Science; Theology; Philosophy, 3 yrs. Licenciado in–Religious Science; Theology; Philo-sophy; Education; Aesthetics; Agriculture; Architecture; Music; Arts; Biochemistry; Psychology; Law; Engineering; Letters; History; Geography; Mathematics; Physics; Chemistry; Biology; Economics and Management Science, 5 yrs; Medicine, 7 yrs; Professional titles in–Engineering (various fields); Social Work, 4 yrs; Translation; Journalism; Biochemistry; Design; Geography; Economics; Business Administration, 5 yrs; Psychology; Nursing; Law, 6 yrs; Medicine, 7 yrs. Degree of Magister. Teaching qualifications in various fields. Doctorado in–Theology; Exact Sciences; Biology; History.

Library: Total, 861,500 vols.

Publications: Revista Universitaria (quarterly); Revista Geografía (annually); Teología y Vida (quarterly); Anales de Teología (annually); Trabajo Social (3 times a year); Serie de Estudios Sociológicos (annually); Revista Eure (biannually); Revista Chilena de Derecho (3 times a year); Apuntes de Teatro (3 times a year); Aisthesis (biannually); Anales de Educación (3 times a year); Cuadernos de Economía (3 times a year); Apuntes de Ingeniería (quarterly); Filosofía (annually); Ediciones Gráficas (annually); Monografías Biológicas (annually); Biología Pesquera (biannually); Ciencia Política (annually); Historia (annually); Letras (annually); Notas Matemáticas (biannually); Boletín de la Escuela de Medicina (biannually); Ciencia e InvestigaciónAgraria (biannually); Arq (Arquitectura) (annually).

Press or Publishing House: Editorial Universidad Católica.

Academic Staff, 1986-87:

Rank	Full-time
Profesores Titulares	483
Profesores Adjuntos	549
Profesores Auxiliares	475
Instructores	164
Ayudantes	27
Total	1698

Student Enrolment, 1986-87:

Men	Women	Total
7479	7865	15,344

1224 **UNIVERSIDAD DE CONCEPCIÓN**

University of Concepción

Caupolicán 518, Casilla 20-C, Concepción

Telex: 260005 TEUCO CL (RECTORÍA)

Telephone: 225346

Rector: Carlos von Plessing Baentsch (1980-)

Secretario General: Gustavo Villagrán Cabrera

F. of Science

Dean: Moisés Silva Triviño

F. of Agricultural Sciences and Forestry (including Veterinary Medicine)

Dean: Alejandro Valenzuela Avilés

F. of Biology and Natural Resources (including Oceanology)

Dean: Luis Bardisa Ubeda

F. of Economics and Administration

Dean: Carlos René Mansilla Steinmeyer

F. of Law and Social Sciences

Dean: Hernán Troncoso Larronde

F. of Education, Humanities and Art (including Physical Education)

Dean: Astrid Raby Barros

F. of Pharmacy

Dean: Marco Antonio Montes Guyot

F. of Engineering

Dean: Uwe Schotte Schroeder

F. of Medicine (including Nursing and Midwifery)

Dean: John Pomeroy Franklin

F. of Dentistry

Dean: Humberto Trabucco Stratta

Also Centres at Chillán and Los Angeles.

Founded 1919 as a private institution and recognized by the State 1920. Financed from State subsidies. The Rector is elected for a period of 6 yrs by the government. Governing bodies: the Consejo Académico; the Comité Directivo. Residential facilities for students.

Academic Year: March to December (March-August; August-December).

Admission Requirements: Secondary school certificate (Licencia de Educación Media) or recognized equivalent, and entrance examination.

Fees (Pesos): 63,000-158,000 per annum.

Language of Instruction: Spanish.

Degrees and Diplomas: Bachiller in Mathematics, 4 yrs. Licenciado in–Economics; Education; Music; Engineering; Physics; Chemistry; Mathematics, 4 yrs; Law and Social Sciences, 5 yrs. Professional titles of: Contador Auditor, accountancy; Nutricionista; Matrona; Asistente social; Topógrafo; Traductor, 4 yrs; Ingeniero (various fields), 5-6 yrs; Biólogo; Biólogo Marino; Médico veterinario, 5 yrs; Bioquímico; Cirujano dentista; Químico farmacéutico; Sociólogo, 5 ½ yrs; Médico cirujano, 7 yrs. Magister in–Arts; Science; Statistics; Engineering; Education; Nursing; Agricultural Engineering, a further 2 yrs. Doctorado in–Chemistry; Metallurgy, a further 3 yrs. Teaching qualifications in various fields, 3-5 yrs. Postgraduate titles in various fields.

Libraries: Central Library, 319,000 vols; Agriculture and Forestry, 13,500; Centre at Los Angeles, 7300.

Special Facilities (Museums, etc.): Museums of: Anthropology; Botany; Zoology; Palaeontology; Mineralogy; Anatomy.

Publications: Antenea (biannually); Gayana; RLA (annually); Acta Literaria (annually); Revista de Derecho (biannually); Boletín Sociedad de Biología (annually).

Press or Publishing House: Editorial Universidad de Concepción.

Academic Staff: c. 1350.

Student Enrolment, 1986-87:

	Men	Women	Total
Of the country	6927	4506	11,433
Of other countries	5	1	6
Total	6932	4507	11,439

1225 **UNIVERSIDAD 'FINIS TERRAE'**

Pedro de Valdivia 1530, Santiago

Telephone: 494135

Rector: Pablo Baraona

Secretario General: Roberto Guerrero

F. of Business Administration

Dean: Patricio Rojas Gutiérrez; *staff* 20 (170)

F. of Law

Dean: Roberto Guerrero; *staff* – (20)

F. of Commercial Engineering

Dean: Daniel Tapia *staff* – (23)

F. of Social Sciences

Dean: Hermógenes Perez de Arce; *staff* – (13)

F. of Architecture and Design

Dean: Daniel Ballacey; *staff* – (25)

Founded 1988. A private institution. Governing body: the Consejo Superior.

Academic Year: March to December (March-July; August-December).

Admission Requirements: Secondary school certificate (Licencia de Educación Media) and entrance examination.

Fees (Pesos): 520,000 per annum.

Language of Instruction: Spanish.

Degrees and Diplomas: Licenciado, 5 yrs.

Library: Central Library.

Academic Staff, 1990: –(81).

Student Enrolment, 1990:

	Men	Women	Total
Of the country	365	292	657

1226 **UNIVERSIDAD DIEGO PORTALES**

Avenida Ejército 260, Santiago

Telephone: 6964331

Rector: Manuel Montt Balmaceda

F. of Business Administration

Dean: Patricio Rojas Gutiérrez; *staff* 20 (170)

F. of Law

Dean: Jorge Correa Sutil; *staff* 4 (35)

F. of Human Sciences

Dean: Domingo Asún Salazar *staff* 4 (30)

Founded 1982. A private institution. Governing body: the Consejo Académico.

Arrangements for co-operation with the Université de Louvain.

Academic Year: March to January (March-July; August-January).

Admission Requirements: Secondary school certificate (Licencia de Educación Media) and entrance examination.

Fees (Pesos): 160,000-220,000 per annum.

Language of Instruction: Spanish.

Degrees and Diplomas: Licenciado in–Law; Business Adminis-tration; Psychology; Journalism, 3 yrs. Professional titles of–Psicólogo; Ingeniero comercial; Contador auditor, Accountancy; Ingeniero de Ejecución en Comercialización; Ingeniero de Ejecución en Finanzas, 4 yrs.

Library: Central Library, *c.* 5000 vols.

Publications: Boletín (quarterly); Boletín Académico (biannually).

Academic Staff, 1986-87: 43 (240).

Student Enrolment, 1986-87:

	Men	Women	Total
Of the country	2000	1000	3000
Of other countries	20	2	22
Total	2020	1002	3022

1227 **UNIVERSIDAD GABRIELA MISTRAL**

Avenida Ricardo Lyon 1177, Santiago
Telephone: 2257497
Rector: Alicia Romo Román (1981-)
Director de Administración: Carlos Fuentes B.

S. of Law
Director: Lisandro Serrano; *staff* 5 (47)
S. of Business and Economics
Director: Rodrigo de la Cuadra; *staff* 3 (67)
S. of Psychology
Director: Hernán Berwart; *staff* 3 (43)
S. of Education
Director: Sylvia Sailer; *staff* 4 (28)
S. of Social Communication
Director: Loreto Caviedes; *staff* 6 (46)
S. of Civil Engineering
Director: Fernando Garcia; *staff* 2 (10)

Founded 1981. A private institution.

Academic Year: March to January.

Admission Requirements: Secondary school certificate (Licencia de Educación Media) and entrance examination.

Fees (Pesos): Registration, 45,000-30,000; tuition, 430,000 per annum; Accountancy, 300,000.

Language of Instruction: Spanish.

Degrees and Diplomas: Bachiller in Social Sciences, 2 yrs. Licenciado in–Law and Social Sciences; Economics and/or Administration; Education, 5 yrs; Psychology, 6 yrs. Professional titles of–Periodista; Contador Auditor, 5 yrs.

Library: (In development), 10,000 vols.

Publications: Revista del Instituto de Estudios del Pacífico (biannually); Temas de Derecho (quarterly).

Academic Staff, 1990: 25 (243).

Student Enrolment, 1986-87:

	Men	Women	Total
Of the country	1292	1074	2366*

*Also 108 foreign students.

1228 **UNIVERSIDAD DE LA FRONTERA**

Avenida Francisco Salazar 01145, Temuco
Telex: 267038
Telephone: 241418
Fax: 241231
Rector: Reginaldo Zurita Chávez
Secreetaria Ruth Aedo San Martín

F. of Medicine (including Nutrition and Nursing)
Dean: Ronald Gebert Oisel; *staff* 90 (163)
F. of Engineering
Dean: Roberto Gesche Robert; *staff* 121 (102)
F. of Education and Humanities
Dean: Hugo Carrasco Muñoz; *staff* 64 (64)
F. of Law, Administration, and Social Sciences
F. of Agriculture
Dean: Javier Fuenzalida Pavón; *staff* 10 (19)
I. of Informatics
Head: Aldo Vergara Cubillos

Founded 1981, incorporating previous regional branches at Temuco of the University of Chile and University of Santiago de Chile. An autonomous institution financed by the State. Governing bodies: the Consejo Directivo; the Consejo Académico. Residential facilities for women students.

Academic Year: March to December (March-July; August-December).

Admission Requirements: Secondary school certificate (Licencia de Educación Media) and entrance examination.

Fees (Pesos): 250,000-300,000 per annum.

Language of Instruction: Spanish.

Degrees and Diplomas: Professional titles of–Enfermería, nursing; Matrona; Kinesiólogo; Tecnólogo médico Nutricionista, 4 yrs; Ingeniero, in various fields, 4-6 yrs; Constructor civil; Contador público, accountancy; Asistente social, 4 ½-5 yrs; Psicólogo, 6 yrs; Médico cirujano, 7 yrs. Profesor de Estado (teaching qualification, secondary level), 4-5 yrs.

Libraries: Central Library, *c.* 22,600 vols; Engineering, *c.* 8800; Medicine, 780.

Publications: Revista Frontera; Revista Anales (both annually).

1229 **UNIVERSIDAD DE LAS AMÉRICAS**

Manuel Montt 948, Providencia, Santiago
Telephone: (2) 225-9896
Fax: (2) 225-8520
Electronic mail: BITNET
Rector: Mario E. Albornoz

F. of Engineering
F. of Economics and Administration
Dean: Luis Arturo Fuenzalida; *staff* 4 (13)
F. of Agriculture (including Fruit Cultivation and Horticulture)
Dean: Olivia Prado M.; *staff* 1 (6)

Also DATVM, a business enterprise providing short specialized courses and using computational equipment.

Founded 1988. A private institution sharing a common campus with the Instituto Profesional 'Campus'. Governing bodies: the Consej Superior; the Consejo Académico.

Academic Year: March to January (March-August; August-January).

Admission Requirements: Secondary school certificate (Licencia de Educación Media) and entrance examination).

Fees (Pesos): Registration, 32,000; tuition, 392,535-416,325 per annum.

Language of Instruction: Spanish.

Degrees and Diplomas: Licenciado in–Agricultural Engineering; Advertising, 5 yrs; Civil Engineering, 6 yrs. Professional titles in–Business Management; Advertising, 5 yrs.

Libraries: Central Library, 2956 vols;

Academic Staff, 1989-90: 6 (39).

Student Enrolment, 1989-90:

	Mean	Women	Total
Of the country	367	159	256

1230 **UNIVERSIDAD 'LAS CONDES'**

Avenida Las Condes 12500, Las Condes

S. of Economics
S. of Business Administration
S. of Law

Founded 1988.

1231 **UNIVERSIDAD 'LEONARD DA VINCI'**

Avenida República de Chile 592, Rancagua
Telephone: (562) 224-491
Fax: (72) 222-440
Rector: Laura Baxa

D. of Computer Engineering
Director: Edgard Shipley

Founded 1989. Under the supervision of the Fundación Leonardo Da Vinci.

Academic Year: March to January (March-August; August-January).

Admission Requirements: Secondary school certificate (Licencia de Educación Media) and entrance examination.

Language of Instruction: Spanish.

Degrees and Diplomas: Professional titles, 5 yrs.

Academic Staff, 1990: 3 (6).

Student Enrolment, 1990:

Men	Women	Total
36	16	52

1232 **UNIVERSIDAD DE LA SERENA**

Colina El Pino s/n, Casilla 599, La Serena
Telex: 220044 UNISE CL
Telephone: 211868
Rector: Luis J. Ramírez (1986-)
Secretario General: José Aguilera

F. of Engineering (including Food Technology)
Dean: Claudio Ihl; *staff* 61 (27)
F. of Sciences
Dean: Jaime Pozo; *staff* 70 (32)
F. of Humanities (including Education)
Dean: Edgardo Zelaya; *staff* 85 (27)

Founded 1981, incorporating previous regional branches at La Serena of the University of Chile and University of Santiago de Chile. An autonomous institution financed by the State. Governing bodies: the Consejo Directivo (Board of Trustees); the Consejo Académico. Residential facilities for students.

Arrangements for co-operation with: Colorado School of Mines; New Mexico State University; University of RhodeIsland; Indiana University of Pennsylvania; Universidad Politécnica de Madrid.

Academic Year: March to December (March-July; August-December).

Admission Requirements: Secondary school certificate (Licencia de Educación Media) and entrance examination.

Fees (Pesos): 98,600-135,000 per annum.

Language of Instruction: Spanish.

Degrees and Diplomas: Licenciado in–Engineering, 14 sem. Professional titles in Engineering, 8-12 sem. Teaching qualifications, 6-9sem.

Library: Central Library, 49,719 vols.

Special Facilities (Museums, etc.): Mineralogy.

Academic Staff, 1986-87:

Rank	Full-time
Profesores Titulares	17
Profesores Asociados	78
Profesores Asistentes	84
Profesores Instructores	17
Total	196

Student Enrolment, 1986-87:

	Men	Women	Total
Of the country	807	417	1224

1233 **UNIVERSIDAD DE MAGALLANES**

Casilla 113-D, Punta Arenas
Cables: 380004 umag
Telephone: (61) 224523
Fax: (61) 212973
Rector: Nestor Hernández Fuentes (1987-90)
Secretario: Jorge Fuenzalida Acuña

F. of Engineering
Dean: Jorge Reyes; *staff* 32 (16)
F. of Humanities and Social Sciences (including Education, Nursing, and Accountancy)
Dean: Luis Poblete Davanzo
F. of Science
Dean: Alejandro Figueroa Cortes *staff* 20 (4)
I. of Patagonia Studies
Director: Edmundo Pisano Valdes *staff* 10 (1)

Founded 1961 and attached to the State Technical University, became regional branch of it in 1964. Became institute of professional studies March 1981 and acquired present status and title October 1981. Institute of Patagonia Studies, formerly private research institution, incorporated 1985. An autonomous institution financed bythe State. Governing body: the Board of Directors.

Arrangements for co-operation with the Universities of: Santa Catarina, Brazil; Reading. National University of La Patagonia San Juan Bosco, Comodoro Rivadavia.

Academic Year: March to December (March-July; July-December).

Admission Requirements: Secondary school certificate (Licencia de Educación Media) and entrance examination.

Fees (US$): 1000-1500, according to field of study.

Language of Instruction: Spanish.

Degrees and Diplomas: Professional titles in–Nursing; Biology; Accountancy, 4 yrs; Engineering, 4-6 yrs. Teaching qualifications, 3-3 ½ yrs.

Libraries: Faculty of Engineering, 7000 vols; Humanities and Social Sciences, 10,000; Instituto de la Patagonia, 8000.

Special Facilities (Museums, etc.): Museo del recuerdo; Estación Climática 'Jorge Schythe'; Jardín Botàanico 'Carl Skottsberg'; Observatoio Astronómico 'Cruz delSur'.

Publications: Austrouniversitario (biannually); Anales del Instituto de la Patagonia (Natural and Social Sciences) (annually).

Academic Staff, 1990:

Rank	Full-time
Profesores Titulares	3
Profesores Asociados	25
Profesores Asistentes	52
Instructores	10
Total	90

Student Enrolment, 1990:

	Men	Women	Total
Of the country	663	321	984

1234 **UNIVERSIDAD 'MAYOR'**

Pedro de Valdivia 624, Providencia

S. of Architecture and Construction
S. of Forestry
S. of Engineering
S. Technical Education

Founded 1988.

1235 **UNIVERSIDAD METROPOLITANA DE CIENCIAS DE LA EDUCACIÓN**

Avenida José Pedro Alessandri 774, Santiago
Telephone: 2257731
Rector: Héctor Herrera Cajas (1986-)
Secretario General: Enrique López Bourasseau

F. of Arts and Physical Education
Dean: Alfonso Letelier Llona; *staff* 73 (23)
F. of Philosophy and Education
Dean: Bruno Rychlowski; *staff* 123 (64)
F. of Science
Dean: José Herrera Gonzáles; *staff* 80 (22)
F. of History, Geography, and Letters
Dean: Gonzalo Vial Correa; *staff* 74 (32)
I. of Entomology
Director: René Covarrubias Berríos; *staff* 4 (3)

Founded 1986. Previously Institute of Education of University of Chile (1889) and Academia Superior de Ciencias Pedagógicas (1980). A State institution. Governing bodies: the Junta Directiva (Board of Trustees); the Consejo Académico.

Academic Year: March to December (March-July; August-December).

Admission Requirements: Secondary school certificate (Licencia de Educación Media) and entrance examination.

Fees (Pesos): Registration, 8000; tuition, 95,000 per annum.

Language of Instruction: Spanish.

Degrees and Diplomas: Teaching qualifications, 4-5 yrs. Postgraduate titles of–Consejo educacional y vocacional; Administrador educacional, 5 sem.

Library: 38,000 vols.

Publications: Revista Academia (annually); Revista Corpus (quarterly); Revista Educación Física Chile (quarterly).

Academic Staff, 1986-87:

Rank	Full-time	Part-time
Profesores Titulares	37	34
Profesores Asociados	160	34
Profesores Asistentes	125	41
Instructores	28	32
Total	350	141

Student Enrolment, 1986-87:

	Men	Women	Total
Of the country	1431	3417	4848
Of other countries	8	16	24
Total	1439	3433	4872

1236 **UNIVERSIDAD DEL NORTE**
University of the North
Avenida Angamos 0610, Apartado postal 23, Antofagasta
Cables: Udelnorte
Telex: 225097
Telephone: 222040; 223752

F. of Architecture
F. of Science
F. of Economics and Administration
F. of Education
F. of Marine Sciences
F. of Engineering
Extension D.
Also centres in Coquimbo, Iquique, Salitre.

Founded 1956 under the control of the Universidad Católica de Valparaíso. Recognized by the State as an independent and autonomous institution 1964. Reorganized 1969. Residential facilities for *c.* 120 women and *c.* 130 men students.

Academic Year: March to December (March-July; August-December).

Admission Requirements: Secondary school certificate (Licencia de Educación Media) and entrance examination.

Language of Instruction: Spanish.

Degrees and Diplomas: Licenciado in–Mathematics; Chemistry; Business Administration; Marine Sciences, 5 yrs; Architecture; Engineering; Computer Sciences, 6 yrs. Professional titles of–Contador público, 4 ½ yrs; Ingeniero (in various fields); Geólogo. Also teaching qualifications, secondary level. Postgraduate certificates and titles in various fields.

Library: Central Library, *c.* 72,820 vols.

Special Facilities (Museums, etc.): Archaeological Museum (San Pedro de Atacama).

Publications: Boletín de Educación; Revista de Matemáticas; Proyecciones.

Press or Publishing House: Imprenta Universidad del Norte.

Academic Staff: c. 230 (110).

Student Enrolment: c. 3020.

1237 **UNIVERSIDAD DE PLAYA ANCHA DE CIENCIAS DE LA EDUCACIÓN**
Avenida Playa Ancha 850, Valparaiso

D. of Humanities
D. of Physical Education and Arts
D. of Natural and Exact Sciences
D. of Education

Founded 1985.

1238 **UNIVERSIDAD DE SANTIAGO DE CHILE**
University of Santiago de Chile
Avenida Sur 3469, Santiago Poniente, Casilla 4637, Correo 2, Santiago
Telephone: 761011-761009
Rector: Patricio Gualda Tiffaine

F. of Engineering
Dean: Lautaro Retamales Araya; *staff* 188 (281)
F. of Humanities
Dean: Isidoro Vazquez de Acuña; *staff* 36 (58)
F. of Science
Dean: Carlos Thomas Garfias; *staff* 187 (183)
F. of Economics and Administration
Dean: Luis A. Fuenzalida Asmusen; *staff* 60 (184)
S. of Technology
Director: Carlos Forray Rojas; *staff* 46 (188)
Computer Ce.

Founded 1947 as State Technical University, incorporating schools established 1849-1944. Admitted first students 1952. Acquired present title 1981. An autonomous institution financed by the State. Residential facilities for academic staff and students.

Academic Year: March to December (March-July; August-December).

Admission Requirements: Secondary school certificate (Licencia de Educación Media) and entrance examination.

Language of Instruction: Castellano.

Degrees and Diplomas: Licenciado in–Business Administration; Economics; Biochemistry; Education; Applied Physics; Mathematics; Chemistry; Engineering, 4-6 yrs. Magister in–Mathematics; Chemistry; Education; Physics; Applied Geography; Arts.Doctorado in Chemistry.

Library: Total, 95,500 vols.

Publications: Avances; Presencia.

Academic Staff, 1986-87: 557 (764).

Student Enrolment, 1986-87:

	Men	Women	Total
Of the country	9706	3622	13,328
Of other countries	22	16	38
Total	9728	3638	13,366

1239 **UNIVERSIDAD SANTO TOMÁS**
Santo Tomás University
Biarritz 1970, Providencia, Santiago
Telephone: 6970359
Presidente: Esteban Gerardo Rocha Vera
Secretario General: Patricio Cepeda Silva

F. of Sylviculture (including Veterinary Medicine)
Dean: Jorge Crossley; *staff* 2 (4)
F. of Economics and Administration
Dean: Pedro Johansen B.; *staff* 2 (4)
F. of Humanities (including Social Work, Psychology, and Journalism)
Dean: Marisol Roa; *staff* 2 (6)
F. of Education
Dean: Carmen Fisher; *staff* – (2)

Founded 1988. A private institution under the supervision of the Corporación Santo Tomás.

Academic Year: March to December.

Admission Requirements: Secondary school certificate (Licencia de Educación Media).

Fees (Pesos): Registration, 20,000; tuition, 400,000 per annum.

Language of Instruction: Spanish.

Degrees and Diplomas: Bachiller, 2-3 yrs. Licenciado, 4 yrs. Magister, 5 yrs. Professional titles.

Library: 3500 vols.

Student Enrolment, 1990:

Men	Women	Total
230	170	400

1240 **UNIVERSIDAD DE TALCA**
Avenida Lircay s/n, Talca
Telephone: (56) 71-31682
Rector: Guillermo Monsalve Mercadal (1986-90)
Secretario General: Juan Robertson Herrera

F. of Science (including Nursing)
Dean: Jorge Ossandón Gaete
F. of Humanities and Education
Dean: Luis Rojas Faúndez
F. of Engineering and Administration
Dean: Osvaldo Medina Setti
F. of Agriculture and Forestry
Dean: Virgilio Mannarelli Montgomery
I. of Environmental Research
Director: Virgilio Mannarelli Montgomery
I. of Molinianos Studies
President: Walter Hanish

Founded 1981, incorporating regional branches of the University of Chile and University of Santiago de Chile. A State institution. Governing bodies: the Junta Directiva (Board of Trustees); the Consejo Académico. Residential facilities for students.

Academic Year: March to December (March-July; August-December).

Admission Requirements: Secondary school certificate (Licencia de Educación Media) and entrance examination.

Fees (Pesos): *c.* 60,000 per semester.

Language of Instruction: Spanish.

Degrees and Diplomas: Licenciado in–Mathematics; Biology, 4 yrs. Professional titles of–Ingeniero de Ejecución en Mécanica; Contador público y Auditor; Tecnólogo Médico, 4 yrs; Enfermera Matrona, nursing, 5 yrs Ingeniero forestal, 6 yrs. Magister in Education. Teaching qualifications, 4 yrs.

Library: 50,000 vols.

Special Facilities (Museums, etc.): Pinacoteca Universidad de Tacna.

Publications: Revista Universum (biannually); Panorama Económico (quarterly); Boletín Informativo (monthly).

Academic Staff, 1986-87:

Rank	Full-time	Part-time
Profesores Titulares	8	
Profesores Asociados	25	
Profesores Asistentes	50	
Instructores	93	
Total	176	138

Student Enrolment, 1986-87:

	Men	Women	Total
Of the country	1977	1950	3927

1241 **UNIVERSIDAD DE TARAPACÁ**

Avenida 18 de Septiembre 2222, Arica
Cables: Untar Cl
Telex: 221036
Telephone: 42600
Rector: Carlos Raúl M. Valcarce (1981-)
Secretario: Ana Cecilia O. Rodríguez

F. of Administration and Economics
Dean: Normán C. Reyes; *staff* 26
F. of Science
Dean: Hernán M. Carrasco; *staff* 81 (11)
F. of Education
Dean: Rafael D. Montecinos; *staff* 59 (12)
F. of Humanities and Letters
Dean: Waldo B. Ríos; *staff* 37 (4)
F. of Engineering
Dean: Roberto O. Gibson; *staff* 57 (3)
I. of Agriculture
Director: Amador H. Torres; *staff* 11 (1)
I. of Anthropology and Archaeology
Director: Mario D. Rivera; *staff* 11

Founded 1982, incorporating Instituto Profesional de Arica, a regional branch of the University of Chile and Universidad del Norte. An autonomous institution. Governing body: the Consejo Académico. Residential facilities for *c.* 200 students.

Academic Year: March to January (March-July; August-January).

Admission Requirements: Secondary school certificate (Licencia de Educación Media) or equivalent, and entrance examination.

Fees (Pesos): 68,700-111,300 per annum.

Language of Instruction: Spanish.

Degrees and Diplomas: Professional titles, 4-6 yrs. Magister in Education, a further 2 yrs. Teaching qualifications (primary, elementary, and secondary levels), 3-5 yrs.

Libraries: Central Library, *c.* 70,000 vols; specialized libraries.

Academic Staff, 1985-86: 282 (31).

Student Enrolment, 1986-87:

	Men	Women	Total
Of the country	2414	1674	4088
Of other countries	12	8	20
Total	2426	1682	4108

1242 **UNIVERSIDAD TÉCNICA 'FEDERICO SANTA MARÍA'**

Avenida Placeres 401, Casilla 110-V, Valparaíso
Cables: Casilla 110-V
Telex: 230338 UTFSM-CL
Telephone: 660176
Rector: Gustavo Chianes

F. of Engineering (including Computer Sciences)
Dean: José Gundelach L.; *staff* 91 (35)
F. of Science
Dean: Juan Garbarino B.; *staff* 45 (40)
F. of Economics and Administration
Dean: Gustavo Fonck; *staff* 15 (30)

Founded 1932 as a private institution, generously endowed by Federico Santa María Carrera. Recognized by the State as technical university 1935. Mainly financed by the government, but enjoying administrative and academic autonomy. Governing bodies: the Consejo Superior; the Consejo Universitario; the Consejo Académico. Some residential facilities for students.

Arrangements for co-operation with: University of Southampton; Technical University of Aachen; Pittsburgh University; Ecole polytechnique de Lausanne.

Academic Year: March to December (March-July; August-December).

Admission Requirements: Secondary education (Licencia Secundaria) and entrance examination.

Fees (Pesos): 115,000 per annum.

Language of Instruction: Spanish.

Degrees and Diplomas: Licenciado in–Mathematics; Physics; Chemistry. Professional titles of–Técnico; Ingeniero civil; Ingeniero químico; Ingeniero mecánico; Ingeniero electricista; Ingeniero informático; Ingeniero electrónico; Ingeniero metalúrgico, 6 yrs. Magister in Engineering; Science. Doctorado en–Ingeniería eléctrica; Ingeniería mecánica; Ingeniería química, a further 2-3 yrs.

Libraries: Central Library, 70,000 vols; branch libraries, *c.* 35,000.

Publications: Scientia; Gestión Tecnológica.

Academic Staff, 1986-87:

Rank	Full-time
Profesores Titulares	14
Profesores Adjuntos	29
Profesores Auxiliares	62
Instructores Académicos	31
Ayudantes Académicos	3
Docentes	90
Ayudantes Docentes	7
Total	236

Student Enrolment, 1986-87:

	Men	Women	Total
Of the country	4100	300	4400
Of other countries	45	–	45
Total	4145	300	4445

1243 **UNIVERSIDAD DE VALPARAÍSO**

University of Valparaíso
Errázuriz 2190, Casilla 123-V, Valparaíso
Telephone: (56-32) 213071
Fax: (56-32) 252125

F. of Medicine (including Pharmacy and Nursing)
Dean: Fernando González L.; *staff* 66 (180)
F. of Law, Economics and Social Sciences
Dean: Italo Paolinelli M.; *staff* 25 (52)
F. of Architecture
Dean: Jaime Farías C.; *staff* 31 (69)
I. of Mathematics and Physics
Director: José Pantoja M.; *staff* 18 (14)
I. of Humanities
Director: Julio Castro; *staff* 11 (6)
I. of Economic and Management Sciences
Director: Roberto Maldonado V.; *staff* 18 (25)
I. of Oceanology Research
Director: Hellmuth Sievers; *staff* 13 (3)

Founded 1912 as regional branch of the University of Chile. Became an independent institution 1981. Governing body: the Junta Directiva.

Academic Year: March to December (March-July; August-December).

Admission Requirements: Secondary school certificate (Licencia de Educación) and entrance examination.

Fees (Pesos): 350,000-202,000 per annum.

Language of Instruction: Spanish.

Degrees and Diplomas: Licenciado in–Statistics, 4 yrs; Mathematics, 5 yrs; Biology, 6 yrs. Professional titles of–Asistente social; Meteorologie, 4 yrs; Ingeniero comercial; Auditor; Abogado, law; Diseñador; Constructor civil; Enfemera-Obstetricia, 5 yrs; Biologie marine; Psicologe; Cirujano dentista; Químico farmacéutico; Arquitecto, 6 yrs; Médico cirujano, 7 yrs.

Library: Faculty and Institute libraries.

Publications: Revista de Biología Marina; Revista de Ciencias Sociales; Boletín Micológico.

Academic Staff, 1990:

Rank	Full-time	Part-time
Profesores Titulares	65	50
Profesores Adjuntos	85	86
Profesores Auxiliares	43	186
Total	193	322

Student Enrolment, 1990:

	Men	Women	Total
Of the country	1761	1622	3383*

*Also 8 foreign students.

1244 **UNIVERSIDAD CATÓLICA DE VALPARAÍSO**
Avenida Brasil 2950, Casilla 4059, Valparaíso
Telex: 230389 UCVAL CL
Telephone: (32)251024
Fax: (32) 212746
Rector: Juan Enrique Froemel Andrade (1985-90)
Secretario General: Claudio Moltedo

F. of Architecture and Town Planning
Dean: Juan Purcell; *staff* 24 (5)
F. of Basic Science and Mathematics
Dean: Victoriano Campos; *staff* 82 (39)
F. of Law and Social Sciences
Dean: Alex Avsolomovich; *staff* 18 (25)
F. of Philosophy and Education (including Music and Physical Education)
Dean: Pedro Ahumada; *staff* 82 (33)
F. of Engineering
Dean: Raimundo Villarruel; *staff* 94 (19)
F. of Natural Resources (including Food Technology, Oceanography, and Marine Sciences)
Dean: Gabriel Yany; *staff* 31 (7)
F. of Economics and Administration
Dean: Fernando Alvarado; *staff* 33 (11)
I. of Religious Sciences
Director: Gonzalo Ulloa Rübke; *staff* 9 (13)
F. of Agriculture (including Stockraising)
Dean: Eduardo Salgado; *staff* 12 (2)
Also courses for foreign students.

Founded 1928, recognized by official decree 1929. Recognized as Catholic university by the Holy See 1961. Governing body: the Consejo Superior. Some residential facilities for students.

Arrangements for co-operation with: Oregon State University; Florida International University; Drew University; State University of New York; Rice University; University of Missouri-Rolla; Universidad Católica de Minas Gerais; University of Munich; Universidad Católica 'Nuestra Señora de la Asunción', Paraguay; Universities of Cantabria, Granada, Salamanca (Spain).

Academic Year: March to December (March-July; August-December).

Admission Requirements: Secondary school certificate (Licencia de Educación Media) or foreign equivalent, and entrance examination.

Fees (Pesos): 26,076-37,152 per semester, according to field of study.

Language of Instruction: Spanish.

Degrees and Diplomas: Bachiller in Religious Sciences, 4 yrs; Licenciado, 1 further yr. Licenciado in–Biology; Physics; Mathematics; Chemistry; Hispanic Language and Literature; History; Music, 4 yrs; Agriculture; Biochemistry; Commerce and Economics; Business Administration; Law; Philosophy, 5 yrs; Architecture; Engineering, 6 yrs. Professional titles of–Diseño gráfico; Estadístico; Asistente social, 4 yrs; Diseño industrial, 4 ½ yrs; Ingeniero agrónomo; Químico; Ingeniero comercial; Abogado, law; Constructor civil; Oceanógrafo, 5 yrs; Ingeniero, various fields, 5-6 yrs; Arquitecto, 6 yrs. Magister in–Philosophy; History; Hispanic Literature; Science (Chemistry, Physics); Mathematics; Statistics; Applied Linguistics; Biology, a further 2-3 yrs. Doctorado in Science (Chemistry), a further 4 yrs. Postgraduate diplomas in–Educational Administration; French; Industrial Engineering; Business Administration; Finance, a further 2 yrs. Also teaching qualifications.

Library: 200,000 vols.

Publications: Revista Geográfica; Revista Signos; Revista Philo-sophica; Revista de Estudios Histórico-Jurídico; Revista de Derecho; (all annually); Revista de Investigaciones Marinas (biannually).

Press or Publishing House: Ediciones Universitarias de Valparaíso.

Academic Staff, 1989:

Rank	Full-time	Part-time
Profesores Titulares	167	26
Profesores Asociados	142	33
Profesores Asistentes	54	67
Instructores	9	16
Total	372	142

Student Enrolment, 1989: 6806.

Other Institutions

Public Institutions

1245 **INSTITUTO PROFESIONAL DE OSORNO**
Avenida Fuchslocher s/n, Osorno
Telephone: 2194-5377

D. of Food Technology
D. of Exact and Natural Sciences
D. of Social Sciences and Administration
D. of Education
D. of Humanities and Art
Founded 1981.

1246 **INSTITUTO PROFESIONAL DE SANTIAGO**
Dieciocho 161, Santiago
Telephone: 6964123
Rector: Félix Lagreze Byrt (1986-89)
Secretario General: Eduardo Hajna Rifo

S. of Administration
Director: Osvaldo Flores Weber *staff* 11 (71)
S. of Library Science
Director: Amalia Rodríguez de la Presa; *staff* 7 (20)
S. of Civil Engineering
Director: Nelso Avila Rivera: *staff* 12 (40)
S. of Design
Director: Mario Mora Concha; *staff* 12 (34)
S. of Computer Sciences
Director: Rainer Puvogel Hirsch; *staff* 13 (15)
S. of Cartography
Co-ordinator: Octavio Flores Castelli; *staff* 5 (17)
S. of Technology
Director: Tomás Lassardo Pérez; *staff* 11 (46)
S. of Social Work
Director: Jaime Indo López; *staff* 7 (6)
D. of General Studies
Director: José Avila Chanía; *staff* 34 (36)

Founded 1981. An autonomous institution financed by the State.

Academic Year: March to December (March-August; August-December).

Admission Requirements: Secondary school certificate (Licencia de Educación Media) or equivalent, and entrance examination.

Fees (Pesos): 94,000 per annum.

Language of Instruction: Spanish.

Degrees and Diplomas: Professional titles, 4 ½-5 yrs.

Libraries: Central Library, 13,000 vols; Social Work, 4704; Technology, 1000.

Publication: Trilogia (Ciencia, Técnica, Espíritu) (biannually).

Academic Staff, 1986-87: 112 (285).

Student Enrolment, 1986-87:

	Men	Women	Total
Of the country	2410	1338	3748

Private Institutions

1247 **CENTRO INTERAMERICANO DE EDUCACIÓN Y CULTURA CIDEC**
Barcelona 2011, Providencia, Santiago
Telephone: 2330741
Presidente: Estebán Gerardo Rocha Vera
Secretario General: Laura Nora Schulz Dubreuil

Business Administration
Architecture
Secretarial Studies
Also branches in: Antogagasta, Arica, Chillán, Concepción, Curicó, Iquique, La Serena, Ovalle, Puerta Montt, Punta Arenas, Rancagua, Talca, Temuco, Valdivia.

Founded 1976, acquired present status and title 1982. A private institution under the supervision of the Corporación Santo Tomás.

Academic Year: March to December.

Admission Requirements: Secondary school certificate (Licencia de Educación Media).

Fees (Pesos): Registration, 8000; tuition 150,000 per annum

Language of Instruction: Spanish.

Degrees and Diplomas: Professional title of Técnico, 2-3 yrs.

Library: 5000 vols.

Student Enrolment, 1990:

Men	Women	Total
2900	2000	4900

1248 **CENTRO NACIONAL DE ESTUDIOS PARAMÉDICOS 'PROPAM'**

Huérfa 1463, Providencia 139, Santiago
Telephone: 726200
Presidente: Esteban Gerardo Rocha Vera
Secretario General: Laura Nora Schulz Dubreuil

Paramedical Studies
Also branches in: Antofagasta, Arica, Chillán, Concepción, Curicó, Iquique, La Serena, Ovalle, Puerto Montt, Punta Arenas, Rancagua, Talca, Temuco, Valdivia, Viña.

Founded 1975, acquired present status and title 1982. A private institution under the supervision of the Corporación Santo Tomás.

Academic Year: March to December.

Admission Requirements: Secondary school certificate (Licencia de Educación Media).

Fees (Pesos): Registration, 8000; tuition, 150,000 per annum.

Language of Instruction: Spanish.

Degrees and Diplomas: Professional title of Técnico, 2-3 yrs.

Library: 5000 vols.

Student Enrolment, 1990:

Men	Women	Total
1400	1800	3200

1249 **INSTITUTO PROFESIONAL AGRARIO 'ADOLFO MATTHEI'**

Casilla 58-A, Orsono
Telephone: 232640
Rector: Alfredo Neumann Kuschel

Agriculture
Founded 1932 as school, became institute 1964 and acquired present status and title 1981.

Arrangements for co-operation with the University of Munich.

Academic Year: March to December.

Admission Requirements: Secondary school certificate (Licencia de Educación

Fees (Pesos): 120,000 per semester.

Language of Instruction: Spanish.

Degrees and Diplomas: Professional titles (Técnico, Profesional), 2 yrs.

Library: 6392 vols.

Special Facilities (Museums, etc.): Estación Meteorológica; Parque Botánico y Zoológico.

Publication: Boletín de Observaciones Meteorológicas (every 5 years).

Academic Staff, 1990: 7 (48)

Student Enrolment, 1990:

	Men	Women	Total
Of the country	467	100	567*

*Also 7 foreign students.

1250 **INSTITUTO PROFESIONAL 'ADVENTISTA'**

Fundo Las Mariposas, Camino Tanilvoro, Km 12, Coihueco

Founded 1982.

1251 **INSTITUTO PROFESIONAL DE LA ARAUCANÍA**

Avenida Alemania 0587, Temuco
Telephone: 7238327
Presidente: Esteban Gerardo Rocha Vera
Secretario General: Patricio Ruiz-Tagle

Publicity, Design, and Public Relations
Accountancy and Auditing
Tourism and Hotel Administration
International Commerce
Teacher Training (pre-school level)

Founded 1987. A private institution under the supervision of the Corporación Santo Tomás.

Academic Year: March to December.

Admission Requirements: Secondary school certificate (Licencia de Educación Media).

Fees (Pesos): Registration, 14,000; tuition, 240,000 per annum.

Language of Instruction: Spanish.

Degrees and Diplomas: Professional titles, 2-4 yrs.

Library: 2000 vols.

Student Enrolment, 1990:

Men	Women	Total
300	155	455

1252 **INSTITUTO PROFESIONAL 'BLAS CAÑAS'**

Carmen 160, Santiago
Telephone: 393032

Education
Founded 1981.

Academic Year: March to December (March-July; August-December).

Admission Requirements: Secondary school certificate (Licencia de Educación Media) and entrance examination.

Language of Instruction: Spanish.

1253 **INSTITUTO PROFESIONAL 'CAMPUS'**

Manuel Montt 948, Providencia, Santiago
Telephone: (2) 223-1135
Fax: (2) 225-8520
Rector: Sergio Aguilera

Area of Computer Sciences
Head: Hernán Campos; *staff* 6 (32)
Area of Business Administration
Head: Juan Carlos; *staff* 8 (38)
Also DATVM, a business enterprise providing short specialized courses and use in computational equipment.

Founded 1981. A private institution recognized by the State 1983. Became an autonomous institution 1989. Shares a campus with the Universidad de Las Américas.

Academic Year: March to January (March-August; August-January).

Admission Requirements: Secondary school certificate (Licencia de Educación Media) and entrance examination.

Fees (Pesos): Registration, 21,000; tuition, 307,000 per annum.

Language of Instruction: Spanish.

Degrees and Diplomas: Professional titles of Ingeniero, various fields; Contador, accountancy, 4 yrs.

Libraries: Central Library, 2000 vols;

Academic Staff, 1989-90: 17 (96).

Student Enrolment, 1989-90:

	Mean	Women	Total
Of the country	1172	443	1615

1254 **INSTITUTO PROFESIONAL 'DIEGO PORTALES'**

Maipú 301, Concepción

Founded 1988.

1255 **INSTITUTO PROFESIONAL 'D.U.O.C.'**

Darío Urzúa 2100, Providencia, Santiago
Telephone: 40203
Fax: 40203
Rector: Rodrigo Alarcón Jara
Secretario General: Jorge López Pinochet

Public Relations
Design
Administration
Computer Sciences

Accountancy
Business Administration

Founded 1983. A private institution under the supervision of the Fundación DUOC of the Catholic University of Chile, which also controls a Centro de FormaciónTénica, and Centro de Educación de Adultos.

Academic Year: March to December (March-July; August-December).

Admission Requirements: Secondary school certificate (Licencia de Educación Media) and entrance examination.

Fees (Pesos): 141,000-190,000 per annum.

Language of Instruction: Spanish.

Degrees and Diplomas: Professsional titles, 4 yrs. Title of Técnico, 2 yrs.

Library: 2500 vols.

Academic Staff, 1990: 436.

Student Enrolment, 1990: 9685.

1256 **INSTITUTO PROFESIONAL CHILENO BRITÁNICO DE CULTURA**

British Institute Teacher Training College
Santa Lucía 124, Casilla 3900, Santiago
Telephone: 382-156
Presidente: Victor Braun (1970-)
Rector: Anthony Adams

English Studies
Director: Miriam Rabinovich
Teacher Training
Co-ordinator: María Donoso
Also courses for Business English, for Executives, and Spanish courses for Foreign Executives.

Founded 1938 as language institute, acquired present status and title 1982. A private institution whose teaching degree is recognized by the Ministry of Education. Governing bodies: the Board of Directors, comprising 18 members; the Executive Committee, comprising 8 members.

Academic Year: March to December (March-July; August-December).

Admission Requirements: Secondary school certificate (Licencia de Educación Secundaria) and linguistic Aptitude Test.

Fees (Pesos): 249,000 per annum.

Languages of Instruction: English and Spanish.

Degrees and Diplomas: Diploma in–Advanced English Studies, 2 yrs. Degree in Teaching of English as a Foreign Language, 4 yrs.

Library: 17,000 vols.

Academic Staff: c.20 (15).

Student Enrolment: c.100.

1257 **INSTITUTO PROFESIONAL 'DE LA ARANCANIA'**

Andrés Bello esq, General Lagos s/n, Temuco

Founded 1987.

1258 **INSTITUTO PROFESIONAL 'DEL PACÍFICO'**

Arturo Prat 386, Santiago
Telephone: 395655
Rector: Julio Ortúzar Prado
Secretario General: Mauricio Feliú Ramírez

S. of Social Communication
Director: Manuel Segura C.; *staff* 27 (9)
S. of Design
Director: José Korn Bruzzone; *staff* 24 (3)
S. of Education
Director: Mireya Gálvez; *staff* 15 (8)

Founded 1982. A private institution.

Academic Year: March to December.

Admission Requirements: Secondary school certificate (Licencia de Educación Media) and entrance examination.

Fees (Pesos): 180,000.

Language of Instruction: Spanish.

Degrees and Diplomas: Professional titles.

Library: 2500 vols.

Academic Staff, 1986-87: 11 (122).

Student Enrolment, 1986-87:

	Men	Women	Total
Of the country	315	565	886
Of other countries	3	5	8
Total	318	570	894

1259 **INSTITUTO PROFESIONAL 'EDUCARES'**

Luis Rodríguez Velasco 4746, Santiago
Telephone: 2232677

Founded 1981.

1260 **INSTITUTO PROFESIONAL 'ESCUELA DE COMUNICACIÓN'**

Avenida Ricardo Lyon 227, Santiago
Telephone: 2315335
Rectora: Mónica Herrera (1980-90)

Social Communication
Public Relations
Drama
Design
Audio-visual Technology
Marketing

Founded 1980 as college, acquired present status and title 1982.

Admission Requirements: Secondary school certificate (Licencia de Educación Media) and entrance examination.

Language of Instruction: Spanish.

Degrees and Diplomas: Professional titles.

1261 **INSTITUTO PROFESIONAL 'ESCUELA DE CONTADORES AUDITORES DE SANTIAGO'**

Providencia 1933, Providencia
Telephone: 2323985
Rector: Germán Cerón López
Director Académico: Luis A. Werner-Wilder

D. of Quanitative Methods
Director: Enrique Caputo L. *staff* – (46)
D. of Accountancy
Director: Milenko Norero *staff* 1 (42)
D. of Management
Director: Hugo O. Inostroza; *staff* – (33)
D. of Law
Director: Iván Poklépovic V.; *staff* – (6)
D. of Tax Law
Director: Bernardo Lara B.; *staff* – (8)
D. of Management Accountancy
Director: María Luisa Toro R.; *staff* – (5)
D. of Economics
Director: Félix Durán F.; *staff* – (8)
D. of Social Sciences
Director: Sergio Jorquera R.; *staff* – (8)
D. of Computer Sciences
Director: Max Wacchotz Avalos; *staff* – (9)
D. of Finance
Director: Carlos Acevedo *staff* – (9)
D. of Auditing
Director: Pedro Peña Pérez; *staff* – (5)

Founded 1982.

Academic Year: March to December (March-July; August-December).

Admission Requirements: Secondary school certificate (Licencia de Educación Media) and entrance examination.

Fees (Pesos): 130,000 per annum.

Language of Instruction: Spanish.

Degrees and Diplomas: Professional title of Contador auditor, 4 yrs.

Academic Staff, 1990:

Rank	Full-time	Part-time
Profesores Titulares	5	20
Profesores Asociados	–	70
Profesores Asistentes	–	30
Ayudantes	–	42
Total	5	162

Student Enrolment, 1990:

	Men	Women	Total
Of the country	909	467	1376

1262 **INSTITUTO PROFESIONAL 'GUILLERMO SUBERCASEAUX'**

Agustinas 1476, Santiago

Banking

Founded 1982.

1263 **INSTITUTO PROFESIONAL 'IACC'**
Avenida Salvador 1222, Providencia
Founded 1987.

1264 **INSTITUTO PROFESIONAL 'INACAP'**
Chesterton 7028, Las Condes, Santiago
Telephone: 2299000
Director: Patricio Escudero Troncoso (1984-)
Secretario General: Jorge Barrenechea Fernández

Engineering

Founded 1966. Acquired present status 1982. Responsible to the Ministries of Economics, Education and Labour. Governing body: the Consejo Superior.

Academic Year: March to January (March-August; September-January).

Admission Requirements: Secondary school certificate (Licencia de Educación Media) and extrance examination.

Fees (Pesos): 90,000-120,000 per annum.

Language of Instruction: Spanish.

Degrees and Diplomas: Professional titles of–Ingeniero, 4 yrs; Técnico, 2-3 yrs.

Library: Central Library, *c.* 7200 vols.

Publication: Revista de INACAP (3 times a year).

Academic Staff, 1986-87: 143 (566).

Student Enrolment, 1986-87:

	Men	Women	Total
Of the country	9379	3103	12,482

1265 **INSTITUTO PROFESIONAL 'IPEVE'**
República 237, Santiago
Founded 1981.

1266 **INSTITUTO PROFESIONAL 'LIBERTADOR DE LOS ANDES'**
Avenida Libertador Bernardo O'Higgins 197, Los Andes
Founded 1981.

1267 **INSTITUTO PROFESIONAL 'LUIS GALDAMES'**
María Luisa Santander 466, Providencia
Founded 1984.

1268 **INSTITUTO PROFESIONAL 'MANPOWER'**
Avenida Ricardo Lyon 891, Santiago
Telephone: 2514359
Rector: Alberto Finlay (1990-)
Director Académico: Pablo Persico

S. of Business Administration
Director: Alicia Moena *staff* 5 (30)

S. of Auditing
Director: Fortunato Bobilla *staff* 5 (15)

Founded 1968. Acquired present status 1981.

Academic Year: March to December (March-July; August-December).

Admission Requirements: Secondary school certificate (Licencia de Educación Media) and entrance examination.

Fees (Pesos): 270,000 per annum.

Language of Instruction: Spanish.

Degrees and Diplomas: Professional titles, 2-4 yrs.

Library: 4000 vols.

Academic Staff, 1990: 5 (45).

Student Enrolment, 1990:

	Men	Women	Total
Of the country	280	204	484*

*Also 3 foreign students.

1269 **INSTITUTO PROFESIONAL DE PROVIDENCIA**
Dr. Hernán Alessandri 644, Providencia, Santiago
Telephone: (562) 223-8635
Fax: (562) 223-3664
Rector: Laura Baxa

S. of Special Education
Head: Alicia Diaz; *staff* 2

S. of Education (kindergarten levels)
Head: Fernando de la Jara

S. of Design
Head: Arturo Molina; *staff* 1

Sec. of Computer Engineering
Head: Victor Godoy; *staff* 2

Sec. of Accountancy and Auditing
Head: Milton Figueroa; *staff* 1

Sec. of Food Engieering
Head: Gloria Valiente; *staff* 1

Branch in Rancagua.

Founded 1981. Under the supervision of the Fondación Leonardo Da Vinci.

Academic Year: March to January (March-August; August-January).

Admission Requirements: Secondary school certificate (Licencia de Educación Media) and entrance examination.

Language of Instruction: Spanish.

Degrees and Diplomas: Professional titles, 4-5 yrs.

Academic Staff, 1990: 19 (138).

Student Enrolment, 1990:

Men	Women	Total
278	780	1058

1270 **INSTITUTO PROFESIONAL SANTO TOMÁS**
Biarritz 1970, Providencia, Santiago
Telephone: 2744748
Presidente: Esteban Gerardo Rocha Vera
Secretario General: Patricio Cepeda Silva

Design, Public Relations, and Audio-visual Communication
Agro-Industrial Engineering
Accountancy and Auditing
Computer Sciences
Social Work
Business Administration

Also Branches in: Concepción, Iquique, La Serena, Ovalle, Puerto Montt, Rancagua, Talca, Viña del Mar.

Founded 1975, acquired present status and title 1987. A private institution under the supervision of the Corporación Santo Tomás.

Academic Year: March to December.

Admission Requirements: Secondary school certificate (Licencia de Educación Media).

Fees (Pesos): Registration, 14,000; tuition, 240,000 per annum.

Language of Instruction: Spanish.

Degrees and Diplomas: Professional titles, 2-4 yrs.

Library: 2000 vols.

Student Enrolment, 1990:

Men	Women	Total
300	100	400

1271 **INSTITUTO PROFESIONAL 'TEATRO LA CASA'**
Romero 2421, Santiago
Telephone: 92672
Founded 1982.

1272 **INSTITUTO PROFESIONAL DEL 'VIÑA DEL MAR'**
Montana 800, Viña del Mar
Founded 1985.

1273 **INSTITUTO PROFESIONAL 'VIPRO'**
Padre Mariano 94, Providencia
Founded 1988.

1274 **INSTITUTO PROFESIONAL 'WILHELM VON HUMBOLDT'**
Avenida Kennedy 6150, Las Condes
Founded 1988.

1275 **INSTITUTO PROFESIONAL 'DEL MAULE'**
4 Oriente 1279, Talca
Rector Luis Rojas Faundez
Secretario General: Héctor Avila Campos

Education (including Teaching of English)
Social Sciences

Management and Trading

Founded 1988. A private institution under the supervision of the Sociedad Educacional Del Maule Ltda.

Academic Year: March to December (March-July; August-December).

Admission Requirements: Secondary school certificate (Licencia de Educación).

Fees (Pesos): 116,000-212,000 per annum.

Language of Instruction: Spanish. English for English Teaching Programme.

Degrees and Diplomas: Professional titles, 3-5 yrs.

CHINA
(People's Republic)

Universities and Technical Universities

1276 **ANHUI UNIVERSITY**
Hefei (Anhui Province)

1277 **ANHUI NORMAL UNIVERSITY**
Wuhu (Anhui Province)
Cables: 1234
Telephone: 2065
President: Du Yijin

D. of Chinese Language and Literature
Dean: Fang Kewei; *staff* 125
D. of Political Science
Dean: Wen Binmo; *staff* 73
D. of History
Dean: Wang Hongyu; *staff* 67
D. of Music and Fine Arts
Dean: Zhen Zheng; *staff* 83
D. of Chemistry
Dean: Jia-Liang; *staff* 125
D. of Education
Dean: Xia Rui-Sing; *staff* 63
D. of Biology
Dean: Tao Kai-Xi; *staff* 89
D. of Geography
Dean: Zhou Hou-Shun; *staff* 73
D. of Mathematics
Dean: Nan Chao-Shun; *staff* 125
D. of Physics
Dean: Dui Ke-Fan; *staff* 111
D. of Physical Education
Dean: Wang Yong-An; *staff* 111
Chinese Language Research I.
Head: Zhang Zi-Wen; *staff* 40
Education Science Research I.
Head: Dai Ben-Bo; *staff* 5 (10)
Higher Education Research I.
Head: Chen Yi; *staff* 7
Organic Chemistry Research I.
Head: Ye Zhong-Wen; *staff* 16
D. for Correspondence Courses
Head: Deng Qi-Feng; *staff* 18
U. for Evening Studies
Director: Deng Qi-Feng; *staff* 21

Founded 1949, incorporating Anhui National University and Anhui Provincial University. Acquired present status 1970 and present title 1972. under the jurisidiction of the National Education Commission and of the Provincial Government. Residential facilities for academic staff and students.

Arrangements for co-operation with the University of Osnabrück.

Academic Year: September to July (September-January; February-July).

Admission Requirements: Graduation from senior middle school and entrance examination.

Language of Instruction: Chinese.

Degrees and Diplomas: Bachelor of-Arts; Science, 4 yrs. Master, a further 3 yrs.

Libraries: Central Library, 1,800,000 vols; Library of Chinese Classical Books and Calligraphic Models, 231,000.

Publications: Journal of Anhui Normal University; Bulletin; Learning the Chinese Language; Literary Periodical; High Education Exploration.

Academic Staff, 1986-87:

Rank	Full-time
Professors	32
Associate Professors	163
Lecturers	310
Assistants	416
Total	921

Student Enrolment, 1986-87:

	Men	Women	Total
Of the country	4194	1480	5674

1278 **ANHUI UNIVERSITY OF LABOUR**
District of Xuancheng (Anhui Province)

1279 **BEIJING UNIVERSITY**
Beijing (Beijing Municipality)
Telex: 22239 PKUNI CN
Telephone: 28471
President: Ding Shisun (1984-)
Secretary-General: Wen Zhong

D. of Mathematics
Head: Li Zhong
D. of Mechanics
Head: Chen Bin
D. of Physics
Head: Zhao Kaihua
D. of Technical Physics
Head: Zhao Weijiang
D. of Radio Electronics
Head: Wang Chu
D. of Geophysics
Head: Liou Xita
D. of Chemistry
Head: Sun Yitong
D. of Biology
Head: Gu Xiaocheng
D. of Geology
Head: He Guoqi
D. of Geography
Head: Hu Zhaoliang
D. of Computer Science and Technology
Head: Yang Fuqing
D. of Psychology
Head: Xu Zhengyuan
D. of Chinese Language and Literature
Head: Fei Zhengang
D. of History
Head: Ma Keyao
D. of Archaeology
Head: Su Bai
D. of Philosophy
Head: Huang Nansen
D. of Economics
Head: Chen Tehua
D. of Law
Head: Zhang Guohua
D. of International Politics
D. of Library Science
Head: Zhou Wenjun
D. of Sociology
Head: Pan Naigu
D. of Western Languages and Literature (German, French, Spanish)
Head: Sun Kunrong

D. of English Language and Literature
Head: Hu Zuanglin
D. of Russian Language and Literature
Head: Li Mingbin
Beijing I. of Modern Physics
I. of Mathematics
I. of Solid State Physics
I. of Theoretical Physics
I. of Heavy Ion Physics
I. of Physical Chemistry
I. of Molecular Biology
I. of Computer Science and Technology
I. of Afro-Asian Studies
I. of Foreign Philosophy
I. of Marxism-Leninism Studies
I. of International Law
I. of Economic Law
I. of Higher Education
I. of Chinese Ancient Classics
Ce. for Research in Chinese Medieval History
Ce. for Comparative Literature Studies
I. of Demography

Founded 1898. Reorganized 1945, 1952, 1977. A Key institution. Residential facilities for academic staff and all students.

Academic Year: September to July (September-January; March-July).

Admission Requirements: Graduation from senior middle school and entrance examination.

Language of Instruction: Chinese.

Degrees and Diplomas: Bachelor of–Arts, Science, 4 yrs. Master, 3 further yrs. Doctor.

Library: 3,300,000 vols.

Publication: University Journal (quarterly).

Press or Publishing House: University Press and Publishing House.

Academic Staff, 1986-87:

Rank	Full-time
Professors	164
Associate Professors	612
Lecturers	1268
Assistants	416
Others	409
Total	2869

Student Enrolment: c. 7400 (Also *c.* 150 foreign students).

1280 **BEIJING AGRICULTURAL UNIVERSITY**

Yuanmingyuan West Road 2, Haidian District, Beijing 100094
Cables: 5832 beijing
Telex: 222487 BAU CN
Telephone: (1) 258-2330
Fax: (1) 258-2332
President: Shi Yuan-Chun
Honorary President: Yu Da-Fu

D. of Agronomy
Head: Dai Jing-Rui; *staff* 88 (9)
D. of Horticulture
Head: Li Guang-Chen; *staff* 62 (5)
D. of Plant Protection
Head: Shen Zuo-Rui; *staff* 89 (6)
D. of Soil and Plant Nutrition
Head: Xu Zheng; *staff* 112 (6)
D. of Animal Husbandry
Head: Zhang Yuan; *staff* 121 (7)
C. of Veterinary Medicine
Head: Jiang Jin-Shu; *staff* 124 (6)
C. of Agricultural Economics and Management
Head: Zhao Dong-Huan; *staff* 72 (12)
D. of Agrometeorology
Head: Gong Shao-Xian; *staff* 41 (3)
D. of Food Science
Head: Cai Tong-Yi; *staff* 39 (2)
C. of Biological Sciences
Head: Mao Yan-Lin; *staff* 207 (11)
D. of Land Resource Science
Head: Lin Pei; *staff* 48 (12)
D. of Agricultural Applied Chemistry
Head: Li Zeng-Min; *staff* 33 (8)
National Agrobiotechnology L.
Head: Chen Yong-Fu; *staff* 40 (15)
National I. of L. Animal Science for Agriculture and Biology
Head: Wang Jing-Lan; *staff* 14 (9)
Research I.
Head: Zeng Shi-Mai; *staff* 8 (35)
Agricultural Economics Research I.
Head: Dong Kai-Chen; *staff* 6 (24)
I. of Preplanting and Dost Harvest Technology
Head: Li Jin-Yu; *staff* 5 (12)
Plant Ecological Engineering I.
Head: Chen Yan-Xi; *staff* 9 (6)
I. of Applied Chemistry
Head: Shang He-Yan; *staff* 8 (33)
I. of Agricultual Resources, Environment and Remote Sensing
Head: Lin Pei; *staff* 10 (40)
National Application and Training Ce. for Agricultural Remote Sensing
staff 34 (10)
I. for Agricultural Education
Head: Yang Shi-Mu; *staff* 5 (3)
Research and Planning I. of Agricultural Engineering Installational
Head: Wang Yun-Long; *staff* 4 (12)

Also Postdoctoral Research Circulating Station, receiving fellows from China and abroad.

Founded 1905, as Agricultural College of Capital University merged with the agricultural college of Beijing University, and North China University 1949. Became Key institution 1954. Under the jurisdiction of the Ministryof Agriculture, and has adopted the presidential responsibility system. Residential facilities for academic staff and students.

Academic Year: September to July (September-January; February-July).

Admission Requirements: Graduation from senior middle school and entrance examination.

Fees: None.

Languages of Instruction: Chinese. Also English, Japanese, Russian, German, French, and Latin.

Degrees and Diplomas: Bachelor of–Agronomy, B.Agr.; Science, B.Sc.; Economics, B.Eco.; Engineering, B.E., 4-5 yrs. Master, a further 3 yrs. Doctor, Ph.D., 3 yrs.

Library: 97,000 vols.

Special Facilities (Museums, etc.): Botanical Garden and Museum of Agricultural Science; University Museum.

Publications: Acta Agricuturae Universitatis Pekinensis in Latin, (quarterly); Chinese Journal of Veterinary Medicine (monthly); The Journal of Rural Social Economics (quarterly); Chinese Journal of Animal Sciences (bimonthly); Acta Phytophylacica Sinica in Latin, (quarterly); Acta Phytopathologica Sinica (in Latin) (The Chinese Journal of Plant Pathology) (quarterly).

Press or Publishing House: Publishing House of BAU.

Academic Staff, 1990:

Rank	Full-time	Part-time
Professors	150	7
Associate Professors	253	–
Lectures	352	–
Assistants	189	–
Total	944	7

Student Enrolment, 1990:

Men	Women	Total
2042	875	2917*

*Also 4400 external students.

1281 **BEIJING AGRICULTURAL ENGINEERING UNIVERSITY**

Qinghua Donglu, Beijing 100083
Cables: 9125
Telex: 222573 RIMET CN
Telephone: (1) 201-6303
Fax: (1) 201-6320
President: Wing Zhi-Xin
Secretary-General: Jiang Xiao-San

D. of Agricultural Mechanization
Head: Chen Ji-Qin
D. of Farm Power and Machinery
Head: Ma Ting-Xi
D. of Water Conservancy and Building Engineering
Head: Zhou Jun

D. of Electronics and Electric Power Engineering
Head: Wang Hui-Min
D. of Food Engineering
Head: Chen Shi-Liang
I. of Rural Development
Head: Wan He-Qun
I. of Agricultural Mechanization
Head: Chen Ji-Qin
I. of New Feedstuff Resources Development
Head: Guo Pei-Yi
I. of Livestock Engineering
Head: Lü Zhong-Xiao

Founded 1952 as Beijing Institute of Agricultural Mechanization. Under the juridiction of the Ministry of Agriculture. Residential facilities for academic staff and students.

Arrangements for co-operation with: Silsoe College, United Kingdom; Asian Institute of Technology, Bangkok; Darling Downs Institute of Advanced Education, Toowoomba; University of Melbourne.

Academic Year: September to July (September-January; February-July).

Admission Requirements: Graduation from senior middle school and entrance examination.

Fees: None.

Language of Instruction: Chinese.

Degrees and Diplomas: Diploma, 2 ½-3 yrs. Bachelor, 4 yrs. Master, a further 2 ½-3 yrs. Doctor, Ph.D., 3 yrs.

Library: 600,000 vols.

Special Facilities (Museums, etc.): Museum of Agricultural Machinery and Tractors; Movie Studio.

Publications: Journal (every 3 months); Agricultural Engineering Abstract (every 2 months).

Press or Publishing House: BAEU Press House.

Academic Staff, 1990: – (610).

Student Enrolment, 1990: 3700 (Also 400 external students).

1282 **BEIJING MEDICAL UNIVERSITY**
Xue Yan Lu, Beijing
Telex: 222782 BMU CN
Telephone: (861) 2017601
Fax: (861) 2015681
President: Qu Mianyu

S. of Basic Medicine
Dean: Wu Bingquan; *staff* 605
A. of Nursing
Dean: Zhao Binghua; *staff* 35
S. of Public Health
Dean: Zhuang Hui; *staff* 227
S. of Oral Medicine
Dean: Zhang Zhengkang; *staff* 750
S. of Pharmaceutical Studies
Dean: Wang Kui; *staff* 250
S. of Medicine
Dean: Fang Yuqian; *staff* 1323
I. of Clinical Pharmacology
Head: Jia-Tai Li; *staff* 54
I. of Clinical Medicine
Head: Rong Xie; *staff* 144
I. of Urology
Head: Fang-Lu Gu; *staff* 45
I. of Hematology
Head: Dao-pei Lu; *staff* 45
Beijing I. for Cancer Research
Head: Gnang-wei Xu; *staff* 187
I. of Basic Medical Sciences
Head: Nai-heng Zhang; *staff* 138
I. of Environmental Medicine
Head: Hui Zhuang; *staff* 54
I. of Pharmaceutical Research
Head: Lihe Zhang; *staff* 54
I. of Stomatology
Head: Zhenkang Zhang; *staff* 56
I. of Mental Health
Head: Yu-cun Shen; *staff* 60
I. of Sports Medicine
Head: Mianyu Qu; *staff* 40
I. of Child and Adolescent Research
Head: Quang-jun Ye; *staff* 30
Research I. for Medical Education
Head: Hua Chen; *staff* 8
I. of Hepatology
Head: Qi-min Tao; *staff* 14
Also 3 affiliated hospitals.

Founded 1912, as school, became college 1952 and acquired present title 1985. A Key institution. Residential facilities for academic staff and students.

Arrangements for co-operation with University Medical Faculties in: Federal Republic of Germany; Netherlands; Sweden; Japan; USA; Canada; Iran.

Academic Year: August to July.

Admission Requirements: Graduation from senior middle school and entrance examination.

Fees: None.

Languages of Instruction: Chinese and English.

Degrees and Diplomas: Bachelor, 6 yrs. Master, a further 3 yrs. Doctor, Ph.D., 3 yrs.

Publications: The Journal of Beijing Medical University (bimonthly); Foreign Medicine (fascicle of hospital management, quarterly); Medical Education (monthly).

Academic Staff, 1989-90: *c.* 1480.

Student Enrolment, 1989:

Of the country	4835
Of other countries	80
Total	4925

1283 **BEIJING SHIFAN DAXUE**
Beijing Normal University
19 Xin Jie Kou Wai Street, Beijing 100875
Telex: 222701 BNU CN
Telephone: (1) 201-2288
Fax: (1) 201-3929
President: Fang Fu-Kang
Provost: Zhang Lan-Sheng

D. of Mathematics
Head: Zhao Zhen; *staff* 130
D. of Physics
Head: Yang Zhan-Ru; *staff* 177
D. of Chemistry
Head: Wu Yong-Ren; *staff* 147
D. of Chinese Language
Head: Liu Qing-Fu; *staff* 153
D. of History
Head: Gong Shu-Duo; *staff* 89
I. of Low Energy Nuclear Physics
Head: Han Zhu-En; *staff* 107
I. of Modern Education Technology
I. of History (Historiography, History of Ancient China;)
Head: Bai Shou-Yi; *staff* 13
I. of Foreign Education
Head: Bi Shu-Zhi; *staff* 44

Founded 1902. A Key institution. Under the direction of the State Education Commission. Residential facilities for academic staff and students.

Arrangements for co-operation with *c.* 50 universities worldwide, including: Japan, United States, and United Kingdom.

Academic Year: September to July (September-January; February-July).

Admission Requirements: Graduation from high school and entrance examination.

Fees: None.

Language of Instruction: Chinese.

Degrees and Diplomas: Bachelor of–Arts, B.A.; Education, B.Ed.; Philosophy, B.Ph.; Science, B.S., 4 yrs. Master, a further 3 yrs. Doctor, Ph.D., a further 3 yrs.

Library: Central Library, 2,700,000 vols.

Publication: Beijing Shifan Daxue Xuebao (Social Science and Science Editions) (6 and 4 times a year, respectively).

Press or Publishing House: Beijing Shifan Daxue Chubanshe (Beijing Normal University Press).

Academic Staff, 1989:

Rank	Full-time
Professors	175
Associate Professors	620
Lecturers	900
Total	1695

Student Enrolment, 1989:

Of the country	8000
Of other countries	100
Total	8100*

*Also 8000 external students.

1284 **BEIJING POLYTECHNICAL UNIVERSITY**

Ping Le Yuan 100, Chao Yang District, Beijing 100022
Cables: 2971 beijing
Telex: (1) 771-4088
Telephone: (1) 771-1177
President: Wang Hu
Secretary-General: Li Shi-Wei

D. of Mechanical Engineering
Head: Ying De-Yi; *staff* 99
D. of Industrial Automation
Head: Gong Wei-Ting; *staff* 122
D. of Radio Electronics
Head: Ge Ming-Hao; *staff* 108
D. of Civil Engineering (including Architecture)
Head: Xuan Yi-Tao; *staff* 123
D. of Environmental Engineering
Head: Li Ti-Chuan; *staff* 168
D. of Applied Physics
Head: Hua Bao-Ying; *staff* 111
D. of Computer Sciences
Head: Gu Qing-Zuo; *staff* 87
D. of Applied Mathematics
Head: Lü Hong-Bo *staff* 68
D. of Metallurgy
Head: Xiong Di-Jing; *staff* 77
D. of Thermal Engineering
Head: Ma Chong-Fa; *staff* 99
D. of Business Management
Head: Guang Wei-Li; *staff* 20
D. of Basic Studies
Head: Zeng Yan-Jun; *staff* 105
D. of Architecture
Head: Wang Su-Chun; *staff* 22
Computer Ce.
Head: Yang Lin; *staff* 45
Also 8 Research Sections.

Founded 1960. Under the jurisdiction of the Beijing Municipality and financially supported by the Central Government. Residential facilities for academic staff and students.

Academic Year: September to July (September-January; February-July).

Admission Requirements: Graduation from senior middle school and entrance examination.

Fees: None.

Language of Instruction: Chinese.

Degrees and Diplomas: Bachelor of Engineering, 4-5 yrs. Double Bachelor, a futher 2 yrs. Master, a further 2-3 yrs.

Library: c. 700,000 vols.

Publications: Journal; Academic Journal (monthly).

Academic Staff, 1989:

Rank	Full-time
Professors	45
Assistant Professors	297
Lecturers	461
Teachers	151
Teaching Assistants	174
Total	1128

Student Enrolment, 1989:

	Men	Women	Total
Of the country	3061	1383	4444

1285 **BEIJING UNIVERSITY OF AERONAUTICS AND ASTRONAUTICS**

37 Xue Yuan Road, Beijing 100083
Cables: 0085
Telex: 22036 BIAAT CN
Telephone: (1) 201-7251
President: Shen Shi-Tuan (1982-)
Secretary-General Liu Bao-Jun

D. of Materials Science and Engineering
Director: Cheng Chang-Qi; *staff* 170 (7)
D. of Electronics
Director: Shao Ding-Rong; *staff* 293 (8)
D. of Automatic Control
Director: Wang Zhan-Lin; *staff* 286
D. of Thermal Power Engineering
Director: Wu Shou-Sheng; *staff* 301
D. of Aeronautical Engineering
Director: Yuan Xiu-Gang; *staff* 301 (5)
D. of Computer Sciences
Director: Zhao Xing-Ping; *staff* 123
D. of Manufacturing Technology
Director: Shen Fu-Zheng; *staff* 219 (1)
D. of Applied Mathematics and Physics
Director: Guang Ke-Ying; *staff* 209 (8)
D. of Mechanical and Electrical Engineering
Director: Zhu Guo-Cui; *staff* 168 (1)
D. of Social Sciences
Director: Gao Jing-Liang; *staff* 65 (2)
D. of Foreign Languages
Director: Gao Yuan; *staff* 80
D. of Systems Engineering
Director: Yang Wei-Min; *staff* 79
C. for Evening Studies
Principal: Diao Zhen-Ban; staff 1 (35)
C. of Management
Director: Gu Chang-Yao; *staff* 104
D. for Correspondence Courses
Director: Chen Xiao-Dai; *staff* 2 (50)
Also 15 Research Institutes.

Founded 1952 as Institute. A Key institution under the jurisdiction of the Ministry of Aerospace Industry. Residential faciliteies for academic staff and students.

Arrangements for co-operation with: Carolo-Wilhelmina Technical University of Brunswick; Rhenish-Westphalian Technical University; University of Manchester; University of Southampton; University of Toronto; University of Alberta; University of Manitoba; Kyoto University; Ohio State University. Massachusetts Institute of Technology; Georgia Institute of Technology; Institut supérieur des Matériaux et de la Construction mécanique, Saint-Ouen.

Academic Year: September to July (September-January; February-July).

Admission Requirements: Graduation from senior middle school and entrance examination.

Fees: None.

Language of Instruction: Chinese.

Degrees and Diplomas: Bachelor of–Arts; Science; Engineering, 4 yrs. Master of–Arts; Science; Engineering, a further 2 ½ yrs. Doctor of–Science; Engineering.

Library: University Library *c.* 780,000 vols.

Special Facilities (Museums, etc.): Beijing Aviation Museum.

Publication: Journal (quarterly).

Press or Publishing House: BUAA Publishing House.

Academic Staff, 1986-87:

Rank	Full-time	Part-time
Professors	112	18
Associate Professors	478	11
Lecturers	607	–
Assistant Professors	161	–
Assistants	504	2
Total	1862	31

Student Enrolment, 1986-87:

	Men	Women	Total
Of the country	4920	1331	6251*

*Also 1282 external students.

1286 **BEIJING UNIVERSITY OF FOREIGN STUDIES**

2 North Xisanhuan Avenue, Haidan District (Beijing Municipality)
Telephone: 890351
President: Wang Fuxiang (1984-88)

Languages and Literature (Chinese, English, Russian, French, Italian, Spanish, Portuguese, German, Swedish, Polish, Czech, Romanian, Hungarian, Bulgarian, Serbian, Albanian, Vietnamese, Laotian, Cambodian, Thai, Malay, Indonesian, Burmese, Sinhalese, Hausa, Swahili, Turkish, Japanese, Arabic)

Founded 1941 as School, acquired present status and title 1954. A Key institution under the jurisdiction of the Ministry of Education.

Arrangements for co-operation with the Universities of: Massachusetts, Amherst; Griffith; Daito Bunka; Heidelberg; Missouri-Kansas; Mons; Madrid (Autonomous).

Academic Year: September to July (September-January; February-July).

Admission Requirements: Graduation from senior middle school and entrance examination.

Language of Instruction: Chinese.

Degrees and Diplomas: Bachelor of Arts. Master of Arts in–English; French; German; Spanish; Russian; Arabic. Doctor, Ph.D., in English.

Library: Central Library, *c.* 580,000 vols.

Publications: Foreign Language Teaching and Research; Foreign Literature.

Press or Publishing House: Foreign Language Teaching and Research Press.

Academic Staff: c. 180.

1287 **BEIJING UNIVERSITY OF SCIENCE AND TECHNOLOGY**

30 Xuyuan Lu, Beijing 100083 (Beijing Municipality)
Cables: 7441
Telex: 22036 BIAAT CN EXT, UST BEIJING
Telephone: (1) 201744½019944
Fax: 86-1-2017283
President: Run Wang
Provost: Wudi Huang

D. of Geology
Chairman: Huaiyu Yuan; *staff* 34 (1)
D. of Mining and Mineral Engineering
Chairman: Tiangui Ren; *staff* 178 (2)
D. of Metallurgy
Chairman: Tianjun Yang; *staff* 160 (5)
D. of Metal Forming
Chairman: Xianjin Wang; *staff* 84 (3)
D. of Materials Science and Engineering
Chairman: Guoliang Chen; *staff* 138 (6)
D. of Surface Sciences and Corrosion Engineering
Chairman: Rizhang Zhu; *staff* 47 (6)
D. of Thermal Energy Engineering
Chairman: Sijun Wang; *staff* 64
D. of Mechanical Engineering
Chairman: Kexing Chen; *staff* 196 (3)
D. of Automation and Control Engineering
Chairman: Yikang Sun; *staff* 201 (3)
D. of Computer Sciences
Chairman: Xuyan Tu; *staff* 79 (2)
D. of Mathematics and Mechanics
Chairman: Erqian Rong; *staff* 103 (6)
D. of Physics
Chairman: Zhe Gao; *staff* 89 (3)
D. of Chemistry
Chairman: Yuankai Zhu; *staff* 59 (3)
D.of Physical Chemistry
Chairman: Shengbi Zhang; *staff* 68 (1)
I. of Materials Physics
Director: Shi Lin; *staff* 71 (4)
D. of Management
Chairman: Fu Sun; *staff* 66 (11)
D. of Social Sciences
Chairman: Wuben Guo; *staff* 66 (6)
D. of Foreign Languages
Chairman: Shusheng Pan; *staff* 95 (4)
Mining Research I.
Directors: Tian Gui Ren, Ming Han Feng; *staff* 80
I. of Metallurgy
Director: Rong Zhang Zhou; *staff* 24 (30)
I. of Metal Forming
Director: Xian Jin Wang; *staff* 12 (24)
I. for Rolling Technology Innovation
Director: Ting Zheng Zhgong; *staff* 10 (25)
I. of Mechanical Engineering
Director: Ke Xing Chen; *staff* 36 (140)
I. of Automatic Control
Director: Yi Kang Sun; *staff* 20 (15)
I. of Robotics
Director: Da Tai YU; *staff* 48 (6)
I. of Computer and System Sciences
Director: Xu Yang Tu; *staff* 14 (24)
I. of Thermal Energy Engineering
Director: Shi Jun Wang; *staff* 17 (6)
I. of Materials Science
Director: Guo Liang Chen; *staff* 24 (32)
I. of Applied Physics
Director: Nan Xian Chen; *staff* 4 (1)
I. of Physics of Metals and Materials
Directors: Tsun Ko; Shi Lin; *staff* 15 (20)
I. of Physical Chemistry of Metallurgy
Directors: Shou Kun Wei; Sheng Bi Zhang; *staff* 20 (10)
I. of Materials Failure
Director: Ji Mei Xiao; *staff* 10 (10)
Technical Training and Consulting Ce. of Metal Corrosion and Protection
Director: Ri Zhang Zhu; *staff* 15 (1)
I. of Historical Metallurgy
Director: Ru Bin Han; *staff* 9 (10)
I. of Management Science
Director: Fu Sun; *staff* 11 (66)
I. for Research in Higher Education
Directors: Jing Bo LI; Xing Zhang; *staff* 12 (64)

Founded 1952. A Key institution. Under the jurisdiction of the Ministry of Metallurgical Industry and the State Committee of Education.

Arrangements for co-operation with: Rhinish-Westphalian Technical University; McMaster University; University of Pennsylvania; Kanagawa University; University of Wollongong; Lehigh University; Umeå University; Hokkaido University; University of Dortmund; University Paul-Sabatier, Toulouse III; Tokyo Institute of Technology; Kyushu Kogyo Daigaku; The Royal Institute of Technology, Stockholm.

Academic Year: September to July (September-January; February-July).

Admission Requirements: Graduation from senior middle school and entrance examination.

Language of Instruction: Chinese.

Degrees and Diplomas: Bachelor of–Arts; Science, Engineering. Master of–Arts; Science; Engineering. Doctor of–Engineering; Science; Arts.

Library: c. 700,000 vols.

Publications: Journal; Higher Education Research; Metal World.

Academic Staff, 1986-87:

Rank	Full-time	Part-time
Professors	46	20
Associate Professors	260	27
Lecturers	700	–
Assistants	300	–
Total	1306	47

1288 **BEIJING UNIVERSITY OF POSTS AND TELECOMMUNICATIONS**

42 Xueyuan Road, Hai Dian District, Beijing 100088
Cables: 02699
Telex: 222341 BUPTF CN
Telephone: 2011974
President: Zhu Xiang-Hua (1989-)
Secretary-General: Zhao Er-yuan

F. of Telecommunication Engineering
Director: Yue Guang-xin; *staff* 103
F. of Radio Engineering
Director: Zhou Ji-xin; *staff* 123
F. of Computer Engineering
Director: Sha Fai; *staff* 93

F. of Mechanical Engineering
Director: Wang Shi-Geng; *staff* 62
F. of Management Engineering
Director: Liang Xong-jian; *staff* 58
F. of Information Engineering
Director: Zhang Hui-Min; *staff* 42
F. of Applied Science and Technology
Director: Song Jun-de; *staff* 70
F. of Foreign Languages
Director (Deputy): Cheng Wen-de; *staff* 67
Computer Ce.
Director (Deputy): Zhu Zhen-ging; *staff* 32
Training Ce. for Cadres
Director: Ding Wei; *staff* 64
Also 60 teaching and research sections, 30 laboratories and 2 branches in Ping Gu County and Fu Zhou City.

Founded 1955. A Key institution under the jurisdiction of the Ministry of Posts and Telecommunications. Residential facilities for academic staff and students.

Arrangements for co-operation with: Université Pierre-et-Marie Curie (Paris VI); Ecole nationale supérieure des Télécommunications de Bretagne, Brest; Institut national des Télécommunications, Evry; Ecole nationale supérieure des Télécommunications, Paris.

Academic Year: September to July (September-January; March-July).

Admission Requirements: Graduation from senior middle school and entrance examination.

Fees: None.

Language of Instruction: Chinese.

Degrees and Diplomas: Bachelor of–Science; Management, 4 yrs. Master of Science, a further 2 ½ yrs. Doctor, 3 yrs after Master.

Library: Central Library, *c.* 700,000 vols.

Publication: Journal of Beijing University of Posts and Telecommunications.

Press or Publishing House: The University Press.

Academic Staff, 1990:

Rank	Full-time
Professors	66
Associate Professors	299
Lecturers	353
Assistants	182
Teachers	14
Total	914

Student Enrolment, 1990:

	Men	Women	Total
Of the country	2256	1322	3578
Of other countries	38	4	42
Total	2294	1326	3620*

*Also 440 external students.

1289 **ZHONGNAN GONGYE DAXUE**

Central South University of Technology
Yuelushan, Changsha 410085 (Hunan Province)
Cables: 4349 Changsha
Telex: 98190 CSUOT CN
Telephone: (731) 83111
Fax: (731) 82817
President: Wang Dianzuo

C. of Mining and Metallurgy
Dean: Zuo Tieyong; *staff* 755
C. of Mechanical and Electrical Engineering
Dean: Liu Yexiang; *staff* 414
C. of Science and Liberal Arts (including Foreign Languages and Social Science)
Dean: Mei Zhi; *staff* 494
C. for Correspondence Courses
Dean: Wang Shixun; *staff* 113
C. of Graduate Studies
Dean: Wang Dianzuo; *staff* 284 (40)
Research I. of Higher Education
Director: Liao Caiying; *staff* 10
Research I. of Powder Metallurgy
Director: Huang Peiyun; *staff* 242
Research I. of Diwa Theory Metallurgy
Director: Chen Guoda; *staff* 7
Robotics Research Ce.
Director: Li Tan; *staff* 10
Ce. of Applied Quantum Chemistry
Director: Gao Xiaohui; *staff* 25

Founded 1951, as Institute. Acquired present status and title 1955. A Key institution, under the jurisdiction of the China National Non-ferrous Metals Industry Corporation, and also under the instruction of the State Education Commission. Residential facilities for 3000 academic staff and 7000 students.

Arrangements for co-operation with: University of Melbourne; Luleå University of Technology; The Royal Institute of Technology, Sweden; Technische Universität Clausthal; University of Technology, Aachen; University of Alaska-Fairbanks; Colorado School of Mines; Texas A&M University; Rensselaer Polytechnic Institute; University of Minnesota; University of Utah; Columbia University; University of Manchester, Insitute of Science and Technology; Chulalongkorn University, Thailand; Université de Sherbrook, Canada; Fukui Institute of Technology; Nagoya University; Akita University; Faculté polytechnique de Mons.

Academic Year: February to January (February-July; September-January).

Admission Requirements: Graduation from senior middle school and entrance examination.

Fees: None.

Language of Instruction: Chinese.

Degrees and Diplomas: Bachelor of–Science; Arts, 4 yrs. Master of–Science; Arts, a further 2-3 yrs. Doctor of Engineering, 2-3 yrs.

Libraries: Central Library, 1,170,000 vols; department libraries, *c.* 100,000.

Special Facilities (Museums, etc.): Exhibition Centre of the University History; Museum of Minerals and Geology; Museum of Mining and Metallurgical History of China.

Publications: Journal of Central South Institute of Mining and Metallurgy (bimonthly); Campus News (weekly).

Press or Publishing House: Central South University of Technology Press.

Academic Staff, 1990:

Rank	Full-time	Part-time
Professors	143	33
Honorary Professors	–	7
Research Fellows	2	–
Associate Professors	325	–
Associate Research Fellows	58	–
Lecturers	425	–
Engineers	302	–
Lecture Assistants and Other Staff Members	763	–
Total	2018	40

Student Enrolment, 1990:

	Men	Women	Total
Of the country	5829	1171	7000*

*Also 2000 external students.

1290 **CHENGDU UNIVERSITY OF SCIENCE AND TECHNOLOGY**

Mozi Bridge, Chengdu 610065 (Sichuan Province)
Cables: 1331
Telex: 60166
Telephone: 581554
Fax: 582670
President: Wang Jian-Hua
Registrar: Wang Yin-Qing

C. of Electrohydraulic Engineering
Head: Teng Fusheng
C. of Light Industry
Head: Sun Qi-Cai
C. of Textile Engineering
Head: Li Sheng-Ping
C. of Urban Construction and Environmental Science
Head: Li Cheng-Dian

S. of Graduate Studies
Head: Xu Xi
S. of Lifelong Education
Head: Wang Yin-Qing
D. of Mechanical Engineering
Chairwoman: Liu Wen-Fang; *staff* 190
D. of Electrical Engineering
Head: Wang Gui-De; *staff* 111
D. of Computer and Automation Technology
Head: You Ke-Wei; *staff* 119
D. of Chemical Engineering
Head: Dang Ji-Xiu; *staff* 207
D. of Hydraulic Engineering
Head: Chen Jia-Yuan; *staff* 155
D. of Metallic Materials
Head: Yang Chuan-Yun; *staff* 73
D. of Polymer Materials
Head: Wang Gui-Heng; *staff* 57
D. of Engineering Mechanics
Head: Li Yong-Nian; *staff* 80
D. of Applied Mathematics and Management
Head: Yang De-Rong; *staff* 32
D. of Applied Physics
Head: Zheng Xi-Te; *staff* 84
D. of Chemistry
Head: Huang Wen-Hui; *staff* 154
D. of Social Sciences and Humanities
Head: Zhang Di-Ming; *staff* 34
Foreign Language Ce. (English, Japanese, Russian)
Head: Hu Yun-Jiang; *staff* 61
Audio-visual Ce.
Head: Li Bi-Zheng; *staff* 18
Computer Ce.
Head: Tang De-Qing; *staff* 39
D. of Mathematics
Head: Zhang Guang-Cheng; *staff* 78
D.of Leather Technology and Engineering
Head: Li-Ying; *staff* 56
D.of Food Science and Engineering
Head: Sun Qi-Cai; *staff* 19
D. of Textile Engineering
Head: Gu Da-Zhi
D. of Environmental Engineering
Head: Zhu Lian-Xi; *staff* 37
Polymeric Research I.
Head: Xu Xi; *staff* 72
High-Technical Research I.
Head: Tu Ming-Jing
High-Speed Hydraulics National L.
Head:Zhao Wen-Qian; staff 4
Physical Education Division
Head: Shen Ji-Rong *staff* 40

Founded 1954 as Institute, incorporating faculty of Sichuan University and Sichuan Chemical Engineering College. Acquired present status and title 1978. A Key institution. Under the jurisdiction of the State Education Commission and the Provincial Government. Governing body: the Board of Trustees. Residential facilities for academic staff and students.

Academic Year: September to July (September-January; February-July).

Admission Requirements: Graduation from senior middle school and entrance examination.

Fees: None.

Languages of Instruction: Chinese and English.

Degrees and Diplomas: Bachelor of–Engineering; Science, 4 yrs. Master, a further 2-3 yrs. Doctor, 2-3 yrs.

Library: Central Library, *c.* 1,050,000 vols.

Special Facilities (Museums, etc.): University closed-circuit TV system (University TV station).

Publications: Journal; Bulletin; Chinese Information; Oil-field Chemistry; CUST Journal; Journal of Atomic and Molecular Physics; Journal of Biomedical Engineering; Polymeric Material Science and Technology.

Press or Publishing House: Chengdu University of Science and Technology Press.

Academic Staff, 1989-90:

Rank	Full-time	Part-time
Professors	58	11
Senior Engineers	27	–
Senior Scientists	17	–
Associate Professors	333	25
Lecturers	629	–
Assistant Lecturers	416	–
Engineers	107	33
Total	1587	69

Student Enrolment, 1989-90:

	Men	Women	Total
Of the country	5473	1715	7188
Of other countries	6	1	7
Total	5479	1716	7195*

*Also 2024 external students.

1291 **CHINA CAPITAL MEDICAL UNIVERSITY**
Beijing (Beijing Municipality)

1292 **CHINA TEXTILE UNIVERSITY**
1882 Yanan West Road, Shanghai (Shanghai Municipality)
Telephone: (21) 522430

Founded 1951.

1293 **CHINA UNIVERSITY OF MINING AND TECHNOLOGY**
Xuzhou 221008 (Jiangsu Province)
Cables: 2233
Telex: 34076 XPTTB CN
Telephone: (516) 88653
Fax: (516) 30393
President: Peng Shiji (1982-)

D. of Mining Engineering
Chairman: Qian Ming-gao; *staff* 105
D. of Mine Construction
Chairman: Shi Tiansheng; *staff* 91
D. of Coal Geology
Chairman: Shao Zhenjie; *staff* 83
D. of Mining Surveying and Geophysical Prospecting
Chairman: Guo Dazhi; *staff* 54
D. of Automation Engineering
Chairman: Xu Shifan; *staff* 123
D. of Mechanical Engineering
Chairman: Liu Changqing; *staff* 63
D. of Mining Machinery
Chairman: Li Changxi; *staff* 71
D. of Coal Preparation and Utilization
Chairman: Ou Zeshen; *staff* 85
D. of Social Sciences
Chairman: Li Jinyao; *staff* 41
D. of Applied Mathematics and Mechanics
Chairman: Li Anchang; *staff* 107
D. of Foreign Languages for Science and Technology (English)
Chairman: Sha Qixiqn; *staff* 48
D. of Physical Education
Chairman: Ma Zhonghua; *staff* 32
Graduate S. (Beijing)
Director: Ba Zhaolun; *staff* 275
C. of Economics and Trade
Chairman: Chen Baoshu; *staff* 69
C. of Adult Education
Chairman: Li Jinyao; *staff* 29
Briquette Research Ce.
Director: Zhang Guofan; *staff* 5
Dry Coal Preparation Research Ce.
Director: Chen Qingru; *staff* 8
Scientific Research I.
Director: Cui Guangxin; *staff* 22
Also Blasting Technique Development Corporation.

Founded 1909. A Key institution. Under the jurisdiction of the China National Coal Corporation. Residential facilities for academic staff and students.

Arrangements for co-operation with: West Virginia University; Colorado School of Mines; University of Missouri-Rolla; Southern Illinois University; Technical University of Berlin; Leningrad Mining Institute; Ballarad College of Advanced Education, Australia; Technical University of Wrocław; University of Queensland.

Academic Year: September to July (September-January; February-July).

Admission Requirements: Graduation from senior middle school and entrance examination.

Fees: None.

Language of Instruction: Chinese.

Degrees and Diplomas: Bachelor, in all fields, 4 yrs. Master, a further 2 ½ yrs. Doctor, Ph.D., a further 3 yrs.

Library: Central Library, 840,000 vols.

Publication: Journal (quarterly).

Academic Staff, 1989-90:

Rank	Full-time
Professors	108
Associate Professors	404
Lecturers	511
Assistant Teachers	422
Total	1445

Student Enrolment, 1989-90:

	Men	Women	Total
Of the country	4583	890	5473
Of other countries	2	–	2
Total	4585	890	5475*

*Also 1907 external students.

1294 **CHINESE UNIVERSITY OF POLITICAL SCIENCE AND LAW**

Beijing (Beijing Municipality)

1295 **CHONGQING UNIVERSITY**

Shapingba, Chongqing 630044 (Sichuan Province)
Cables: Chongqing 6234
Telex: 62216 CQUY CN
Telephone: 661185; 664893
President: Gu Leguan (1987-91)

D. of Mechanical Engineering I
Chairman: Zhang Jisheng; *staff* 227
D. of Mechanical Engineering II
Chairman: Zhou Jichang; *staff* 79
D. of Thermal Power Engineering
Chairman: Chen Yuanguo; *staff* 99
D. of Electrical Engineering
Chairman: Zhen Xiangren; *staff* 200
D. of Mining
Chairman: Tang Xueshu; *staff* 143
D. of Metallurgy
Chairman: Zhang Binghuai; *staff* 171
D. of Radio Engineering
Chairman: Lu Gongzan; *staff* 104
D. of Computer Sciences
Chairman: Chen Daijie; *staff* 80
D. of Applied Mathematics
Chairman: Yang Wannian; *staff* 82
D. of Applied Physics
Chairman: Chen Xinrong; *staff* 95
D. of Applied Chemistry
Chairman: Ling Weihua; *staff* 77
D. of Foreign Languages (including English)
Chairman: Jiang Ziwen; *staff* 94
D. of Physical Education
Chairman: Chen Chuiran; *staff* 47
D. of Social Science
Chairman: Yang Delin; *staff* 37
D. of Engineering
Chairman: He Yusheng; *staff* 18
D. of Automation
Chairman: Wang Xuejin; *staff* 115
C. of Management Engineering
Dean: Yang Xuetai; *staff* 54
C. for Evening Studies
Dean: Wu Zhongfu; *staff* 24
I. of Bioengineering
Director: Wu Yunpeng; *staff* 18
I. of Optical-Electronic Precision Mechanics
Director: Huang Shanglian

Founded 1929. A Key institution under the jurisdiction of the State Education Commission. Residential facilities for academic staff and students.

Arrangements for co-operation with the Universities of: California; San Diego; Virginia; Western Washington; Washington; Gonzaga; Strathclyde; Leicester; Karlsruhe; Valenciennes and Hainaut-Cambrésis; Tohoku. ImperialCollege of Science and Technology, London.

Academic Year: September to July (September-January; February-July).

Admission Requirements: Graduation from senior middle school and entrance examination.

Fees: None.

Language of Instruction: Chinese.

Degrees and Diplomas: Bachelor of–Science; Engineering, 4 yrs. Master of–Science; Engineering, a further 2 ½-3 yrs. Doctor of Engineering, 2-3 yrs.

Library: Central Library, *c.* 1,200,000 vols. Southwest China Foreign Textbooks Centre.

Publication: Journal (bimonthly).

Press or Publishing House: Publishing House of Chongqing University.

Academic Staff, 1990:

Rank	Full-time
Professors	128
Associate Professors	472
Lecturers	608
Total	1208

Student Enrolment, 1990:

	Men	Women	Total
Of the country	8260	2064	10,324
Of other countries	3	–	3
Total	8263	2064	10,327*

*Also *c.* 70 external students.

1296 **EAST CHINA NORMAL UNIVERSITY**

3663 Zhongshan Road (North), Shanghai 200062 (Shanghai Municipality)
Cables: 0187
Telephone: 548461
President: Yuan Yun-kai
Secretary-General: Hua Yu-xian

D. of Education
; *staff* 69
D. of Political Education
Head: Wang Song; *staff* 108
D. of Philosophy
Head: Zhang Tian-fei
D. of Economics
Head: Shu Tong-shu; *staff* 53
D. of Chinese Language and Literature
Head: Qi Sen-hua; *staff* 136
D. of History
Head: Chen Chong-Wu; *staff* 84
D. of Foreign Languages
Dean: Huang Yuan-shen *staff* 180
D. of Library and Information Sciences
Dean: Chen Yu; *staff* 45
D. of Mathematics
Dean: Hu Qi-di; *staff* 124
D. of Mathematic Statistics
Dean: Mao Shi-song; *staff* 39
D. of Physics
Head: Xu Zai-xin; *staff* 144
D. of Electronic Science and Technology
Head: Weng Mao-ying; *staff* 96
D. of Chemistry
Head: Chen Bang-lin; *staff* 171
D. of Biology
Head: Zhang Shan-qing; *staff* 156
D. of Computer Science
Head: Tao Zen-le; *staff* 111

D. of Psychology
Dean: Miao Siao-chun; *staff* 55
D. of Geography
Head: Liu Shu-ren; *staff* 116
D. of Computer Technology in Education
Head: Wan Jia-ruo; *staff* 70
D. of Environmental Sciences
Head: Son Yong-chang; *staff* 22
D. of Physical Education
Head: Xia De-li; *staff* 48
D. of Fine Arts
Head: Shen Rou-jian; *staff* 29
Graduate I.
I. of Educational Management
D. for Lifelong Education;
staff 93 (13)

Founded 1951. A Key institution under the jurisdiction of the National Educational Commission.

Academic Year: September to July (September-February; February-July).

Admission Requirements: Graduation from senior middle school and entrance examination.

Language of Instruction: Chinese.

Degrees and Diplomas: Bachelor of–Arts; Science, 4-5 yrs. Master of–Arts; Science, a further 3 yrs.

Libraries: Central Library, 2,453,000 vols; department libraries, *c.* 10,000.

Publications: Journal of ECNU (Philosophy and Social Science) (bimonthly); (Educational Science) (quarterly); (Physics) (quarterly); Physics Teaching (bimonthly); Chemistry Teaching (bimonthly); Mathematics Teaching (bimonthly); Geography Teaching (bimonthly); Research in Theory in Literature and Arts (bimonthly); Problems of History Teaching (bimonthly); Foreign Educational Materials (bimonthly); Foreign Language Teaching Abroad (quarterly); Guide to Chinese Self-Teaching (monthly); Applied Probability and Statistics (quarterly); Biology Teaching (quarterly).

Academic Staff, 1986-87:

Rank	Full-time
Professors	128
Associate Professors	431
Lecturers	645
Total	1204

Student Enrolment, 1986-87:

Of the country	8264
Of other countries	118
Total	8382

1297 **EAST CHINA TECHNICAL UNIVERSITY OF WATER RESOURCES**

Hehai University
Xikang Road 1, Nanjing 210024 (Jiangsu Province)
Cables: 5478 nanjing
Telex: 34101 ECTUW CN
Telephone: 632106
President: Liang Rui-Ju

D. of Hydraulic Engineering
D. of Navigation and Ocean Engineering
Head: Xi Yu-Yao; *staff* 145
D. of Irrigation and Drainage Engineering
Head: Li Shou-Sheng; *staff* 59
D. of Hydrology and Water Resouces
Head: Cong Shu-Zhen; *staff* 112
D. of Engineering Surveying
Head: Dai Ming-Shen; *staff* 104
D. of Architectural Engineering
Head: Liu Rui; *staff* 65
D. of Management Engineering
Head: Li Kai-Yun; *staff* 102
D. of Mechanics
Head: Wu Shi-Wei; *staff* 102
D. of Hydraulic Engineering Automation
D. of Basic Studies
Head: He Chai-Fa; *staff* 114
D. for Correspondence Courses
D. of Foreign Languages
Head: Guo Kun; *staff* 60
D. of Social Science
Head: Fu Bei-Da; *staff* 56
Research I. of Coast and Ocean Engineering
Head: Fan Zhi-Ming; *staff* 34
Research I. of Environmental Engineering
Head: Cong Shu-Zheng; *staff* 41
Research I. of Water Resources and Hydroelectric Power
Head: Xia Shong-You; *staff* 100

Founded 1952 incorporating existing hydraulic engineering faculties of universities in eastern China. A Key institution under the jurisdiction of and financially supported by the Ministry of Water Resources and Electric Power. Governing body: the Academic Council. Residential facilities for academic staff and students.

Arrangements for co-operation with seven universities in the U.S.A. and the Federal Republic of Germany.

Academic Year: September to July (September-February; February-July).

Admission Requirements: Graduation from senior middle school or equivalent and entrance examination.

Fees: None.

Language of Instruction: Chinese.

Degrees and Diplomas: Bachelor of Engineering, 4 yrs. Master, a further 3 yrs. Doctor. Also Diploma in English, 2 yrs.

Library: c. 450,000 vols.

Publication: Journal.

Press or Publishing House: Hehai Press House.

Academic Staff, 1990:

Rank	Full-time
Professor and Associate Professors	400
Lecturers	600
Others	500
Total	1500

Student Enrolment, 1990:

	Men	Women	Total
Of the country	5100	900	6000
Of other countries	79	–	79
Total	5179	900	6079

1298 **EAST CHINA UNIVERSITY OF CHEMICAL TECHNOLOGY**

130 Meilong Road, Shanghai 200237 (Shanghai Municipality)
Cables: 9006
Telex: 33428 ECICT CN
Telephone: 439-4280
President: Chen Min-Heng (1990-)
Secretary-General: Lin Zhu-Yuan

D. of Chemical Engineering
Head: Ren De-Cheng; *staff* 114
D. of Chemical Engineering for Energy Resource
Head: Ge Wei-Huan; *staff* 15
D. of Biochemical Engineering
Head: Tu Tian-Xiang; *staff* 46
D. of Fine Chemical Engineering
Head: Cheng Zhu-Sun; *staff* 42
D. of Polymer Science and Engineering
Head: Zhou Da-Fei; *staff* 46
D. of Inorganic Materials Science
Head: Zhou Shi-Gui; *staff* 31
D. of Environmental Engineering
Head: Xu Chuan-Ning; *staff* 34
D. of Mechanical Engineering
Head: Zhuang Shui-Yuan; *staff* 40
D. of Automation and Electronic Engineering
Head: Pan Ri-Fang; *staff* 86
D. of Mathematics
Head: Yu Wen-Ci; *staff* 15
D. of Physics
Head: Pan Xiao-Ren; *staff* 17
D. of Chemistry
Head: Feng Yang-Ji; *staff* 79
D. of Foreign Languages for Science and Technology
Head: Zhao Jian-Cheng; *staff* 32
D. of Social Sciences
Head: Ruan Shun-Xiong

D. of Computer Sciences
Head: Yang Ming-Fu; *staff* 15
D. of Process Equipment
Head: Wang Jia-Xian; *staff* 54
D. of Management
Head: He Shu-Jian; *staff* 16
D. of Industrial Design
Head: Chen Ping; *staff* 20
S. of Fundamental Education
Head: Zhang Zhao-Kui; *staff* 300
D. of Petroleum Processing
Head: Weng Huo-Xin; *staff* 23
Research I. of Biochemical Engineering
Head: Yu Jin-Tang; *staff* 60
Research I. of Chemical Reaction Engineering
Head: Yuan Wei-Kang; *staff* 40
Research I. of Chemical Engineering
Head: Shi Ya-Qun; *staff* 40
Research I. of Materials Science and Engineering
Head: Yin Sheng-Kang; *staff* 36
Also 16 further Research Institutes.

Founded 1952, incorporating previously existing departments of Chiaotung, Tatung, Aurora, Soochow and KiangnanUniversities. A Key institution. Under the jurisdiction of the State Education Commission.

Arrangements for co-operation with the Universities of: Washington; Queensland; McMaster. Massachusetts Institute of Technology; Tokyo Institute of Polytechnics; Institut national des Sciences appliquées de Lyon; Technical University of Clausthal; University Stuttgart; Ohio State University; D.I.Mendeleev Moscow Institute of Chemical Engineering.

Academic Year: September to July (September-February; February-July).

Admission Requirements: Graduation from senior middle school and entrance examination.

Language of Instruction: Chinese.

Degrees and Diplomas: Bachelor, 4 yrs. Master. Doctor.

Library: Central Library, *c.* 1,100,000 vols.

Publication: Journal (bimonthly).

Press or Publishing House: Press of East China University of Chemical Technology.

Academic Staff, 1989-90:

Rank	Full-time
Professors	79
Associate Professors	395
Lecturers	601
Research Staff	425
Total	1500

Student Enrolment, 1989-1990:

	Men	Women	Total
Of the country	5502	2382	7884
Of other countries	53	2	55
Total	5555	2384	7939*

*Also 910 external students.

1299 **FUDAN UNIVERSITY**
Shanghai (Shanghai Municipality)

A Key institution.

1300 **FUJIAN NORMAL UNIVERSITY**
Fuzhou (Fujian Province)

Education

1301 **FUZHOU UNIVERSITY**
Industrial Road, Fuzhou (Fujian Province)
Cables: 8383
Telephone: 55874
President: Jin-Ling Huang (1984-)

D. of Mathematics
D. of Computer Science
D. of Physics
D. of Chemistry
D. of Civil and Architectural Engineering
D. of Radio Engineering
D. of Geology and Mining Engineering
D. of Mechanical Engineering
D. of Light Industry
D. of Electrical Engineering
D. of Chemical Engineering
D. of Foreign Languages
D. of Industrial Management
C. of Finance and Economics

Founded 1958. Under the jurisdiction of the Provincial Government and the Ministry of Power. Residential facilities for academic staff and students.

Academic Year: August to June (August-February; March-June).

Admission Requirements: Graduation from senior middle school and entrance examination.

Language of Instruction: Chinese.

Degrees and Diplomas: Bachelor in all subjects, 4 yrs. Master, a further 2 yrs.

Library: Central Library, *c.* 750,000 vols.

Publication: Journal of Fuzhou University (quarterly).

Press or Publishing House: Fuzhou University Press.

Academic Staff: c. 1280.

1302 **GANSU AGRICULTURAL UNIVERSITY**
District of Wuwei (Gansu Province)

1303 **GANSU NORMAL UNIVERSITY**
Lanzhou (Gansu Province)

Education

1304 **GANSU UNIVERSITY OF TECHNOLOGY**
57 LanGongPing, Lanzhou 730050 (Gansu Province)
Cables: 3695
Telex: 72135 UOTNG CN
Telephone: 35951-35958 or 34386
President: Chen Jian-Hong
Head of President Office: Wu Yu-Cai

D. of Mechanical Engineering I
Dean: Zhu Pin-Shun; *staff* 44
D. of Mechanical Engineering II
Dean: Wang Min-Zhi; *staff* 109
D. of Automatic Control
Dean: Liu Xiu-Yuan; *staff* 45
D. of Architecture and Structural Engineering
Dean: Xu Tie-Sheng; *staff* 37
D. of Management Engineering
Dean: Zhong Yong-Long; *staff* 21
Instructional and Research D. of Basic Science
Dean: Zhou Yi-Tong; *staff* 135
D. of Evening Studies
Dean: Chen Jian-Hong; *staff* 10
Training D. for Cadres
Dean: Wang Fa-Lie; *staff* 5
I. of Machine Manufacturing Engineering
Director: Wang Min-De; *staff* 39
I. of Welding Techniques
Director: Wang Zheng; *staff* 30
I. of Fracture Technology
Director: Lang Fu-Yuan; *staff* 6
I. of Fluid Power Machinery
Director: Wang Ming Ming-Zhi; *staff* 30

Founded 1958 as Polytechnic School. Under the jurisdiction of the Ministry of Machine Building Industry and the Provincial Government. Residential facilities for academic staff and students.

Arrangements for co-operation with: Lander College Greenwood, South Caroline; Strathclyde University; Liverpool University; Osaka University.

Academic Year: September to July (September-January; March-July).

Admission Requirements: Graduation from senior middle school and entrance examination.

Fees: None.

Language of Instruction: Chinese.

Degrees and Diplomas: Bachelor, 4 yrs. Master, a further 2-3 yrs.

Library: 300,000 vols.

Publication: Transaction of Gansu University of Technology (bimonthly).

Academic Staff, 1990:

Rank	Full-time
Professors	15
Associate Professors	117
Lecturers	184
Teachers	182
Total	498

Student Enrolment, 1990:

	Men	Women	Total
Of the country	2154	584	2738

1305 **GUANGXI UNIVERSITY**
Nanning, Zhuang (Guangxi Autonomous Region)

1306 **GUANGXI NORMAL UNIVERSITY**
Guilin (Guangxi Autonomous Region of Zhuang Nationality)

1307 **GUIZHOU UNIVERSITY**
Guizhou (Guizhou Province)

1308 **HANGZHOU UNIVERSITY**
Tien Mu Shan Road, No 34, Hangzhou (Zhejiang Province)
Telex: 9600
Telephone: 81224
President: Shen Shanhong (1986-)

D. of Politics
Head: Wang Xueqi; *staff* 64
D. of Philosophy
Head: Xue Kecheng; *staff* 33
D. of Economics
Head: Zhang Minliang; *staff* 103
D. of Law
Head: Huang Huansheng; *staff* 45
D. of Chinese Language and Literature
Head: Zheng Zekui; *staff* 101
D. of Foreign Languages
Head: Ren Shaozeng; *staff* 202
D. of History
Head: Jin Puseng; *staff* 70
D. of Education
Head: Pei Wenmin; *staff* 37
D. of Psychology
Head: Wang Ansheng; *staff* 45
D. of Mathematics
Head: Wang Silei; *staff* 94
D. of Physics
Head: Geo Qin; *staff* 115
D. of Chemistry
Head: Zhang Yonmin; *staff* 103
D. of Biology
Head: Din Kenrui; *staff* 80
D. of Geography
Head: Wang Dehan; *staff* 110
D. of Computer Sciences
Head: Zhang Song; *staff* 30
D. of Physical Culture
Head: Wang Minghai; *staff* 124
Sect. of Library Science and Higher Education Management
I. of Biology Research
Ancient Books Research I.
Also 12 Research Sections.

Founded 1958. Under the jurisdiction of the Zhejiang Provincial Government. Residential facilities for academic staff and students.

Arrangements for co-operation with: Indiana University; San Diego State University; Missouri University; Harvard University; Indiana University of Pennsylvania; University of Central Florida; University of Montana; University of the Pacific; California State University-Fresno; Christian-Albrechts-Universität Kiel; Bayerische Julius-Maximilians-Universität Würzburg; Shimane University; University of Sussex; California State College, Stanislaus.

Academic Year: September to July (September-February; March-July).

Admission Requirements: Graduation from senior middle school and entrance examination.

Language of Instruction: Chinese.

Degrees and Diplomas: Bachelor in all fields, 4 yrs. Master a further 3 yrs. Doctor in–Industrial Psychology; Fundamental Mathematics; Chinese Classics; Comparative Education, 2-3 yrs after Master.

Library: c. 1,255,833 vols.

Publications: Academic Journal (quarterly); Psychology Abroad (monthly); Study of Chinese Language (monthly).

Academic Staff, 1986-87:

Rank	Full-time
Professors	74
Associate Professors	300
Lecturers	615
Teachers	8
Assistants	497
Total	1494

Student Enrolment, 1986-87:

	Men	Women	Total
Of the country	4205	2366	6571
Of other countries	3	12	15
Total	4208	2378	6586*

*Also 2640 external students.

1309 **HAINAN UNIVERSITY**
Haikou (Guandong Province)

1310 **HARBIN POLYTECHNICAL UNIVERSITY**
Harbin (Heilong Jiang Province)

A Key institution.

1311 **HARBIN NORMAL UNIVERSITY**
Harbin (Heilong Jiang Province)

Education

1312 **HARBIN MEDICAL UNIVERSITY**
Harbin (Heilong Jiang Province)

1313 **HARBIN UNIVERSITY OF SCIENCE AND TECHNOLOGY**
22 Xue Fu Road, Nangang District, Harbin 150080 (Heilong Jiang Province)
Cables: 2500
Telephone: (451) 61081
Fax: (451) 61849
President: Wang Ren Shu
Director: Liu Bai Tao

D. of Mechanical Engineering I
Director: Li Zhengjia; *staff* 126
D. of Mechanical Engineering II
Director: Meng Fanyu; *staff* 71
D. of Electronic Engineering
Director: Liu Zhidong; *staff* 85
Computer D.
Director: Chen Shiyoung; *staff* 53
D. of Technological Physics
Director: Wang Shuqian; *staff* 79
D. of Management Engineering
Director: Zhu Ying Shan; *staff* 43
D. of Basic Studies
Director: Wang Tingfu; *staff* 133
C. of Adult Education
President: Ren Shanzhi; *staff* 60
Scientific Research I. of Computer Auxiliary Design
Director: Wang Zhiyan; *staff* 29
Mechanical Engineering I.
Director: Li Zhengjia; *staff* 25
Research I. of Optimization Design and Laser
Director: Zhu Jilin; *staff* 7
Research I. of Function Analysis
Director: Wang Tingfu; *staff* 6

Founded 1958, as Heilongjiang Institute of Engineering. Acquired present status and title 1978. Under the jurisdiction of the State Ministry of Machinery and Electronics.

Academic Year: September to July (Spetember-January; February-July).
Admission Requirements: Graduation from senior middle school and entrance examination.
Fees: None.
Language of Instruction: Chinese.
Degrees and Diplomas: Bachelor of Engineering, 4 yrs. Master, a further 2 ½-3 yrs
Library: 350,000 vols.
Publications: Newspaper (monthly); Journal.
Academic Staff, 1989:

Rank	Full-time
Professors	14
Associate Professors	143
Lecturers	387
Assistants	179
Total	723

Student Enrolment, 1989:

	Men	Women	Total
Of the country	1698	580	2278

1314 **HEBEI UNIVERSITY**
He Zuolu Road, Baoding 071002 (Hebei Province)
Cables: 0181 baoding
Telex: 26294 BDPBL CN
Telephone: (312) 22929
President: Yu Shan-rui (1983-)

D. of Physics
Dean: Ge Yun-zao; *staff* 101
D. of Mathematics
Dean: Wang Zhen-yuan; *staff* 74
D. of Electronics
Dean: Li Xing-wen; *staff* 103
D. of Chemistry
Dean: Han Wen-yan; *staff* 97
D. of Biology
Dean: Li Qing-yu; *staff* 78
D. of Chinese Language
Dean: Cui Jian-ping; *staff* 79
D. of History
Dean: Hu bing-quan; *staff* 50
D. of Philosophy (including Sociology)
Dean: Bao Xun-wu; *staff* 47
D. of Education
Dean: Yan Guo-hua; *staff* 47
D. of Foreign Languages (including English, Japanese, Russian)
Dean: Ma Zhung-yuan; *staff* 56
D. of Economics
Dean: Yang Huan-jin; *staff* 126
D. of Law
Dean: Cui Yun-peng; *staff* 54
D. of Library Science and Informatics
Dean: Xu Yan-yun; *staff* 23
I. of History
Director: Qi-Xia; *staff* 23
Japan and Research I.
Director: Guo Shi-xin; *staff* 17
I. of Bioengineering
Director: Wu Jing-zai; *staff* 23
Analytical Ce. of Physics and Chemistry
Directors: Fu Chen-guang; Jiang Shou-gui; *staff* 24
Computer Ce.
Dean: Li Tian-zhu; *staff* 23
Also branch in Qinhuangdao City.

Founded 1921, as Tianjin Industrial and Commercial University. Acquired present title 1960. Residential facilities for academic staff and students.

Arrangements for co-operation with: Iowa State University; City University of New York; San Diego University.

Academic Year: August to July (August-January; March-July).
Admission Requirements: Graduation from senior middle school and entrance examination.
Fees: None.
Language of Instruction: Chinese.
Degrees and Diplomas: Bachelor of–Arts; Social Science; Science, 4 yrs. Master, a further 2 yrs. Doctor of–Arts; History; Pedagogy, a further 2 yrs.
Library: 1,520,000 vols.
Special Facilities (Museums, etc.): Chinese Cultural Relics Gallery.
Publications: Journals; Bulletin of Physics; Studies for Japan Topics (all bimonthly).
Press or Publishing House: Hebei University Press.
Academic Staff, 1989-90:

Rank	Full-time
Professors	18
Associate Professors	191
Lecturers	343
Assistant Teachers	238
Total	790

Student Enrolment, 1989-90:

	Men	Women	Total
Of the country	2714	2415	5129
Of other countries	—	1	1
Total	2714	2416	5130*

*Also 2875 external students.

1315 **HEBEI AGRICULTURAL UNIVERSITY**
Baoding (Hebei Province)

1316 **HEBEI TEACHERS' UNIVERSITY**
Yuhua Zhonglu, Shijiazhuang 050016 (Hebei Province).
Cables: 2345
Telephone: 49941
President: Li Mengxing
Registrar: Gu Jiancheng

D. of Education
Deputy Dean: He Pu; *staff* 44
D. of Mathematics
Dean: Gu Shi-Qin; *staff* 104
D. of Chemistry
Dean: Zhang Wen-Zhi; *staff* 119
D. of Geography
Dean: Yang Ji-Yu; *staff* 82
D. of Physical Culture
Dean: Li De-Xiao; *staff* 98
D. of Chinese Language and Literature
Dean: Wang Yu-Jun; *staff* 83
Hebei Audio-visual Technology Research Ce.
Director: Gao Mao-Quan; *staff* 45
Population Research I.
Deputy Director: Gu Shu-Lan; *staff* 20
Education Science Research I.
Director: Jia Yu-Wu; *staff* 10
Substitute Fuel Research I.
Director: Hu Jiao-Ping; *staff* 10

Founded 1906 as school. Acquired present status and title 1956. Under the jurisdiction of the Provincial Government. Residential facilities for academic staff and students.

Arrangements for co-operation with: University of Northern Iowa; Drake University.

Academic Year: August to July (August-January; February-July).
Admission Requirements: Graduation from high school and entrance examination.
Fees: None.
Language of Instruction: Chinese.
Degrees and Diplomas: Bachelor of–Arts; Science, 4 yrs. Master, a further 3 yrs.
Library: 101,6885 vols.
Special Facilities (Museums, etc.): Plant Garden; Art Gallery 'Yihai'.
Publication: Journal (quarterly).

Rank	Full-time
Professors	32
Associate Professors	202
Lecturers	408
Assistant Lecturers	199
Teachers	5
Foreign Teachers	3
Total	849

Student Enrolment, 1990:

	Men	Women	Total
Of the country	2252	2779	5031
Of the countries	1	1	2
Total	2253	2780	5033*

*Also 3256 external students.

1317 **HEBEI UNIVERSITY OF NEW MEDICINE**
5 Changan West Road, 050017 Shijiazhuang (Hebei Province)
Telephone: 48744
Fax: (631) 161-4092
Vice-President: Wu Shenchun

F. of Medicine Sciences
Dean: Zhang Guozhen; *staff* 274
F. of Stomatology
Dean: Du Jiejun; *staff* 46
F. of Pharmacy
Dean: Zhang Like; *staff* 99
F. of Public Health
Dean: Liu Maosong; *staff* 86
F. of Paediatrics (in preparation)
I. of Basic Medicine
Dean: He Rirong; *staff* 73
I. of Cardiovascular and Cerebrovascular Diseases
Dean: Liu Zhenhua; *staff* 50
I. of Tumor Research
Dean: Du Xicun; *staff* 26
I. of Orthopaedics
Dean: Lin Zhenfu; *staff* 25

Founded 1915, as provincial college. Acquired present status and title 1932.

Arrangements for co-operation with: Shinshu University; Okayama University; Totori University; New York Medical College; Iowa University.

Academic Year: September to July (September-January; March-July).

Admission Requirements: Graduation from senior middle school and entrance examination.

Fees: None.

Language of Instruction: Chinese.

Degrees and Diplomas: Bachelor, 4-5 yrs. Master, a further 3 yrs. Doctor, Ph.D., in Psychology, a further 3 yrs.

Library: 245,000 vols.

Publications: Acta Academiae Medicinae Hebei; Foreign Medicine: Section of Respiratory System.

Academic Staff, 1990: 181.

Student Enrolment, 1990:

	Men	Women	Total
Of the country	2735	1471	4206*

*Also 354 external students.

1318 **HEFEI POLYTECHNICAL UNIVERSITY**
Hefei (Anhui Province)

A Key institution.

1319 **HEILONGJIANG UNIVERSITY**
24 Xue Fu Road, Nankang District, Harbin (Heilongjiang Province)
Telephone: 64940-9
President: Xu Lan Xu (1985-89)
Vice-President: Li Zupei

D. of Chinese
Chairman: Qu Mei Ruo; *staff* 84
D. of History
Chairman: Duan Jing Xuan; *staff* 68
D. of Philosophy
Chairman: Sun Yun; *staff* 55
D. of Economics
Chairman: Chen Gong Lin
D. of Law
Chairman: Li Yuan Zhi; *staff* 58
D. of Russian Studies
Chairman: Long Xiang; *staff* 45
D. of English
Head: Chen Chuan Guo; *staff* 64
D. of Japanese
Chairman: Jin Wan Ging; *staff* 40
D. of Library and Information Sciences
Chairman: Li Xiu Yu
D. of Mathematics
Chairman: Sun De Bao; *staff* 67
D. of Computer Sciences
Chairman: Lang Yan; *staff* 67
D. of Physics
Chairman: Li Zong Ze; *staff* 130
D. of Chemistry
Chairman: Li Fu Xiang; *staff* 120
I. of Lexicography
Director: Li Xi Yin; *staff* 14
I. of Applied Mathematics
Director: Han Zhi Gang; *staff* 17
I. of Soviet Studies
Director: Jiang Chang Bin; *staff* 4
I. of Foreign Literature
Director: Diao Shao Hua; *staff* 7
I. of Sensor and Sensing Techniques
Director: Huang De Xing; *staff* (19)
I. of Linguistics
Director: Lü Ji Ping; *staff* 5
I. of Russian
Director: Hau Shao; *staff* (3)
I. of Economics
Director: Xiong Ying Wu
S. for Evening Studies
President: Cheng Dao Xi; *staff* 100

Founded 1942 as Russian Language School, acquired present status and title 1958 and incorporated Harbin Institute of Foreign Languages 1972. Under the jurisdiction of the Provincial Government. Residential facilities for academic staff and students.

Academic Year: September to July (September-January; March-July).

Admission Requirements: Graduation from senior middle school and entrance examination.

Languages of Instruction: Chinese; English and Russian for language departments.

Degrees and Diplomas: Bachelor of–Arts, Sciences, 4 yrs. Master of–Arts, Sciences, a further 3 yrs. Doctor of–Arts, Sciences, 3 yrs after Master.

Library: 700,000 vols.

Publications: Journal of Foreign Languages (bimonthly); Journal of Natural Sciences (quarterly); Higher Education Studies; Soviet Studies.

Academic Staff, 1986-87:

Rank	Full-time
Professors	27
Associate Professors	152
Lecturers	234
Teaching Assistants	464
Total	877

Student Enrolment, 1986-87:

	Men	Women	Total
Of the country	2297	1831	4128
Of other countries	13	12	25
Total	2310	1843	4153*

*Also 2621 external students.

1320 **HEILONGJIANG AUGUST 1ST UNIVERSITY OF LAND RECLAMATION**
District of Mishan (Heilongjiang Province)
Telex: 1331
President: Zhang Wanshuang (1984-)

D. of Agriculture
D. of Mechanical Engineering

D. of Farm Economics
D. of Veterinary Medicine (including Animal Husbandry)
F. of English Language Training
F. of Farm Management Training

Founded 1958. Under the jurisdiction of the Department of Agriculture. Arrangements for co-operation with the University of Alberta.

Academic Year: March to January (March-July; September-January).

Admission Requirements: Graduation from senior middle school.

Language of Instruction: Chinese.

Degrees and Diplomas: Bachelor in–Agriculture; Animal Husbandry and Veterinary Medicine; Farm Management; Engineering; Economics. Master in–Agriculture; Animal Husbandry and Veterinary Medicine.

Libraries: Central Library (Reddly Hall); department libraries.

Publications: NongDa Xue Bae (monthly); NongDa Review (weekly).

Press or Publishing House: Nong Da Press.

Academic Staff: c. 430.

Student Enrolment: c. 1200 (Also c. 300 external students).

1321 **HENAN NORMAL UNIVERSITY**
Kaifeng (Henan Province)

Education

1322 **HUANAN NORMAL UNIVERSITY**
Guangzhon (Guandong Province)

Education

1323 **HUAZHONG AGRICULTURAL UNIVERSITY**
Wuhan (Hubei Province)
Telephone: 028-715681
President: Sun Ji-Zhong (1984-)
Secretary-General: Wang Guang-Mu

D. of Agriculture
Dean: Liu Dao-Hong; *staff* 128
D. of Plant Protection
Dean: Wan Dao-Ben; *staff* 66
D. of Soil Science and Agricultural Chemistry
Dean: Yu Zi-Niu; *staff* 75
D. of Animal Husbandry and Veterinary Medicine
Dean: Peng Hong-Ze; *staff* 90
D. of Horticulture and Sericulture
Dean: Wan Shu-Yuan; *staff* 68
D. of Agricultural Engineering
Dean: Pang Seng-Hai; *staff* 59
D. of Food Science and Technology
Dean: Zhan Shen-Hua; *staff* 54
D. of Fisheries
Dean: Zhang Hai-Ming; *staff* 45
D. of Agricultural Economics
Dean: Guo You-Huan; *staff* 71
D. of Basic Studies
Dean: staff 129
D. of Social Science
Dean: Liu Chun-Ren; *staff* 34
Training Ce. of Agricultural Economics Management
Language Ce.
Deans: Ye Bao-Mei; Lu Shi-Rong; *staff* 27
Swine Breeding Ce.
Dean: Xiong Yuan-Zhu; *staff* 9 (24)
Cotton Ce.
Deans: Li Wan-Jiu; Liu Jin-Lan; *staff* 5
D. for Lifelong Education
Dean: Li Hong-xi; *staff* 10 (50)
Biotech Ce.
Head: Zhan Qi-Fa; *staff* 4 (12)

Founded 1925 as college, acquired present status and title 1985. A Key institution under the jurisdiction of the Ministry of Agriculture, Animal Husbandry and Fishery. Residential facilities for academic staff and students.

Arrangements for co-operation with: University of California-Davis; Kasetsart University; Massey University; University of Manitoba.

Academic Year: September to July (September-January; February-July).

Admission Requirements: Graduation from senior middle school and entrance examination.

Language of Instruction: Chinese.

Degrees and Diplomas: Bachelor of Science, 4 yrs. Master, a further 3 yrs. Doctor, 3 yrs after Master.

Library: University Library, 620,000 vols.

Publications: Journal; Huazhong Agricultural University Periodical.

Academic Staff, 1988-89:

Rank	Full-time
Professors	49
Associate Professors	179
Lecturers	268
Assistants	172
Teachers	84
Total	752

Student Enrolment, 1989-90:

	Men	Women	Total
Of the country	2643	572	3215*

*Also 1132 external students.

1324 **HUNAN UNIVERSITY**
Changsha (Hunan Province)

A Key institution.

1325 **HUNAN MEDICAL UNIVERSITY**
22 Beizhang Road, Changsha 410078 (Hunan Province)
Cables: 6829
Telex: 085-982017
Telephone: (731) 24411
Fax: (731) 44329
President: Luo Jia-dian (1987-94)

F. of Medicine
Dean: Liu Yu-min; *staff* 646
F. of Laboratory Science
Dean: Chen Zheng-yan; *staff* 32
F. of Anaesthesia
Dean: Xu Qi-ming; *staff* 45
F. of Stomatology
Dean: Liu Shu-fang; *staff* 76
F. of Medical Library and Information Sciences
Dean: Liu Xiao-chun; *staff* 24
F. of Preventive Medicine
Dean: Wang Xiang-pu; *staff* 117
F. of Mental Health
Dean: Yang Der-son; *staff* 86
I. of Cardiology
Dean: Zahng Yue; *staff* 50
I. of Mental Health
Dean: Yang Der-son; *staff* – (86)
I. of Oncology
Dean: Yao Kai-tai; *staff* 23
I. of Medical Genetics
Dean: Xia Jia-hui; *staff* 26
I. of Combined Western and Chinese Medicine
Dean: Wen Yao-fan; *staff* 59
I. of Medical Education Research
Dean: Lu Zhi-gang; *staff* 9
I. of Preventive Medicine
Dean: Wang Xiang-pu; *staff* – (117)
National English Training Ce.
Head: Chen Mu-zhu; *staff* 8

Also 2 affiliated hospitals and 6 teaching hospitals.

Founded 1914 as Hsiangya Medical College, became Hunan Medical College 1953. Acquired present status and title1988. Under the jurisdiction of the Ministry of Public Health. Residential facilities for academic staff and students.

Arrangements for co-operation with the Universities of: Yale; Colorado; Harvard; Iowa; San Francisco; Washington; Hong Kong; Nagasaki.

Academic Year: August to July (August-January; February-July).

Admission Requirements: Graduation from senior middle school and entrance examination.

Fees: None.

Languages of Instruction: Chinese and English.

Degrees and Diplomas: Bachelor of Medical Sciences, 5-6 yrs. Master, a further 3 yrs. Doctor, a further 2-3 yrs following Master. Also Diploma in Mental Health.

Library: Central Library, 460,000 vols.

Special Facilities (Museums, etc.): Experimental Animal Garden.

Publications: Bulletin of Hunan Medical University (quarterly); Journal of Foreign Medicine-Section of Psychiatry, Neurologyand Neuro-surgery, Physiology and Pathology (quarterly and bimonthly).

Academic Staff, 1989:

Rank	Full-time
Professors	154
Associate Professors	519
Lecturers	1509
Assistants	1354
Others	908
Total	4444

Student Enrolment, 1989-90: 4877.

1326 **INNER MONGOLIA UNIVERSITY**
Hohhot (Inner Mongolia Autonomous Region)

A Key institution.

1327 **INNER MONGOLIA NORMAL UNIVERSITY**
Hohhot (Inner Mongolia Autonomous Region)

Education

1328 **JIANGXI UNIVERSITY**
Nanchang (Jiangxi Province)
Telephone: 67800
President: Dai Zhi-zhong (1983-)

D. of Chinese Language and Literature
D. of Journalism
D. of Law
D. of History
D. of Economics
D. of Mathematics
D. of Physics
D. of Chemistry
D. of Biology
D. of Foreign Languages and Literatures
D. of Philosophy
I. of Computer Sciences
Audio-visual Ce.
D. for Evening Studies
Also 62 laboratories.

Founded 1958. A Key institution under the jurisdiction of the Ministry of Education. Residential facilities for academic staff and students.

Academic Year: September to July (September-February; March-July).

Admission Requirements: Graduation from senior middle school and entrance examination.

Language of Instruction: Chinese.

Degrees and Diplomas: Bachelor of–Arts; Science, 4 yrs. Master of–Arts in History of Ancient China; Science in Pure Mathematics, afurther 3 yrs.

Library: Central Library, *c.* 1,043,000 vols.

Publications: Journal (Section Natural Science); (Section Social Science) (quarterly).

Academic Staff: *c.* 730 (70).

Student Enrolment: *c.* 3050 (Also 9500 external students).

1329 **JIANGXI AGRICULTURAL UNIVERSITY**
Nanchang S(Jiangxi Province)

A Key institution.

1330 **JIANGXI NORMAL UNIVERSITY**
77, Beijing West Road, Nanchang (Jiangxi Province)
Telephone: 67801/67802
President: Zhang Chuanxian

D. of Chinese
; *staff* 93
D. of Political Education
; *staff* 59
D. of Foreign Languages
; *staff* 88
D. of History
; *staff* 50
D. of Education (including Psychology)
; *staff* 45
D. of Music
; *staff* 48
D. of Painting
; *staff* 28
D. of Mathematics
; *staff* 95
D. of Computer Sciences
; *staff* 27
D. of Physics
; *staff* 84
D. of Chemistry
; *staff* 81
D. of Geography
; *staff* 60
D. of Physical Education
;E69
D. of Education Communication
;E11
Also 11 Research Institutes.

Founded 1952 as teachers' college. Acquired present status and title 1983. Under the jurisdiction of the Provincial Government.

Arrangements for co-operation with: Oklahoma City University; Eastern Michigan University; University of Western Ontario.

Academic Year: September to July (September-January; March-July).

Admission Requirements: Graduation from senior middle school and entrance examination. Maximum age, 25 yrs and unmarried.

Language of Instruction: Chinese.

Degrees and Diplomas: Bachelor of–Arts; Science. Master of–Arts; Science.

Library: Central Library, 1,600,000 vols.

Publications: Journal (quarterly); Bulletin (monthly); Study of Middle School Mathematics; Study of Higher Education Administration; Coaching in Self-Study of Higher Education; Correspondence Education of Jiangxi Normal University.

Press or Publishing House: University Printing House.

Academic Staff, 1989-90:

Rank	Full-time
Professors	50
Associate Professors	250
Lecturers	*c.* 300
Assistants	*c.* 300
Total	*c.* 900

Student Enrolment, 1989-90: *c.* 4000 (Also *c.* 5300 external students).

1331 **JIAYING UNIVERSITY**
Mei Zi Gang (Hill), Mei Zhou City 514015 (Guangdong)
Cables: 2393
Telephone: 232539
President: liu Yun-Qian (1988-)

D. of Economics
Head: Hou Jing-heng; *staff* 21
D. of Finance
Head: Li Zhuo-neng; *staff* 12
D. of Foreign Languages
Head: Zeng Xiang-huan; *staff* 31
D. of Electronics
Head: He Guo-chang; *staff* 23
D. of Mathematics
Head: Liu Jing-wen; *staff* 29
D. of Physics
Head: Li Jin-sheng; *staff* 25
D. of Chemistry
Head: Luo Biao-xiang; *staff* 19
D. of Biology
Head: Ye Guang-yan; *staff* 16
D. of Geography
Head: Li Meng-hua; *staff* 12
D. of Chinese
Head: Xie You-xiang; *staff* 23
D. of Politics and History
Head: Liu Nan-biao; *staff* 16
I. for Research in Higher Learning
Head: Liu Jian Ling

I. for Customs and Culture of Hakka Research
Head: Chen Xiu

Founded 1982 as Normal Institute of Jiaying, acquired present title 1985. Residential facilities for academic staff and students.

Academic Year: September to July.

Admission Requirements: Graduation from senior middle school and entrance examination.

Fees: None.

Language of Instruction: Chinese.

Degrees and Diplomas: Diplomas, 2-3 yrs.

Library: c. 230,000 vols.

Special Facilities (Museums, etc.): Biological Garden; Movie Studio.

Publication: Jiaying University Journal (quarterly).

Academic Staff, 1986-87:

Rank	Full-time
Professors	1
Associate Professors	31
Teachers	180
Total	212

Student Enrolment, 1986-87:

	Men	Women	Total
Of the country	1377	393	1770*

*Also 676 external students.

1332 **JILIN UNIVERSITY**
83 Jiefang Road, Changchun 130023 (Jilin Province)
Cables: 1513
Telex: 83040 JLU CN
Telephone: (431) 22331
Fax: (431) 823907
President: Wu Zhuoqun (1986-)
Secretary-General: Fan Wanqing

D. of Mathematics
Head: Li Ronghua; *staff* 92
D. of Physics
Head: Liu Yunzuo; *staff* 155
D. of Chemistry
Head: Xu Ruren; *staff* 128
D. of Computer Sciences
Head: Ju Jiubin; *staff* 104
D. of Molecular Biology
Head: Li Wei; *staff* 39
D. of Chinese Language and Literature
Head: Yu Chaogang; *staff* 74
D. of History
Head: Li Dasheng; *staff* 51
D. of Economics
Head: Li Wenzhe; *staff* 27
D. of Law
Head: Gao Ge; *staff* 33
D. of Philosophy
Head: Gao Qinghai; *staff* 50
D. of Political Science
Head: Wang Huiyan; *staff* 39
D. of Foreign Languages and Literature
Head: Tan Lin; *staff* 82
D. of Marxism-Leninism Teaching and Research
Head: Shao Pengwen; *staff* 41
D. of Foreign Languages as a Second Language
Head: Chen Zhuan; *staff* 76
D. of International Economics
Head: Shen Xuemin; *staff* 18
D. of Management Science
Head: Zhao Zhenquan; *staff* 37
D. of Economic Management
Head: Zhang Jincai; *staff* 28
D. of Economic Law
Head: Li Zhongfang; *staff* 24
D. of Electronic Sciences
Head: Liu Shiyong; *staff* 100
D. of International Law
Head: Liu Shiyuan; *staff* 22
D. of Archaeology
Head: Lin Yun; *staff* 27
D. of Environmental Sciences
Head: Du Raoguo; *staff* 26
D. of Materials Science
Head: Wang Yuming; *staff* 8
Mathematics I.
Head: Li Ronghua; *staff* 32
I. of Atomic and Molecular Physics
Head: Zhou Guangtian; *staff* 71
I. of Theoretical Chemistry
Head: Sun Jiazhong; *staff* 64
I. of Materials Science
Head: Chen Xinfang; *staff* 57
Demography I.
Head: Wang Shengjin; *staff* 22
I. of Classical Works (including Chinese Ancient History, Archaeology)
Head: Lin Yun; *staff* 21
I. of Systems Science
Head: Dong Wenquan; *staff* 11
Japanese Affairs I.
Head: Li YuraN: *staff* 33
Graduate S.
Head: Wu Zhuoqun; *staff* 537
Computer Ce.
Head: Feng Guocheng; *staff* 50
Ce. for Modern Instrumental Analysis and Testing
Head: Qiu Zhuwen; *staff* 34

Founded 1946 as Northeast Administration Institute, became People's University 1950 and acquired present status and title 1958. Graduate School established 1984, College of Economic Management (1958), College of Law (1988) A Key institution under the jurisdiction of the State Education Commission. Residential facilities for academic staff and students.

Arrangements for co-operation with: Novosibirsk State University; Magoya University; Kwansei Gakuin University; Rutgers University; University of Minnesota; The State University of New Jersey; Simon Fraser University.

Academic Year: September to July (September-January; February-July).

Admission Requirements: Graduation from senior middle school and entrance examination.

Fees: None.

Language of Instruction: Chinese.

Degrees and Diplomas: Bachelor, 4 yrs, except in Biochemistry; Semiconductor Chemistry; Russian Language and Soviet Affairs, 5 yrs. Master, a further 3 yrs. Doctor, 3 yrs after Master.

Library: c. 2,070,000 vols (including *c.* 1,470,000 in Chinese and *c.* 600,000 in other languages).

Special Facilities (Museums, etc.): Exhibition Hall of Historical Relics and Archaeology.

Publications: Chemical Journal of Chinese University; Acta Scientiarum Naturalium Universitality; Northeastern Mathematical Journal Jilincesis; Jilin University Journal, Social Sciences Edition; Contemporary Economy in Japan; Collected Papers of Historical Science; Population Journal.

Press or Publishing House: Jilin University Press.

Academic Staff, 1989: 1203

Student Enrolment, 1989:

Of the country	7304
Of other countries	24
Total	7328*

*Also 660 external students and 5495 students by correspondence.

1333 **JILIN AGRICULTURAL UNIVERSITY**
The South of the East Ring Road, Changchun 130118 (Jilin Province)
Telephone: 42112 43923
President: Li Chao (1983-)

D. of Soil Science and Agricultural Chemistry
Head: Wu Dian-Wu; *staff* 148
D. of Agronomy
Head: Wu Xin-Kang; *staff* 113
D. of Animal Science
Head: Sun Xian-Tu; *staff* 133
D. of Agricultural Engineering
Head: Wang Wei-Zhong; *staff* 96
D. of Agricultural Economics
Head: Xu Shou-Shen; *staff* 46

D. of Horticulture and Local Special Products
Head: Li Xiang-Gao; *staff* 119
D. of Science
Head: Hu Xi-Yong; *staff* 51
D. for Professional Teachers
Head: Xu Cuen-Zhong; *staff* 13
Comprehensive Technology of Agricultural Modernization I.
Head: Sun Jui-Shi; *staff* 9
Cysticercosis I.
Head: Lou De-Hui; *staff* 13
Also 72 Teaching and Research Sections; 97 Laboratories; and 3 Basic Teaching and Research Departments.

Founded as college 1948. Acquired present status and title 1959, incorporating previously existing agricultural colleges. Under the jurisdiction of the Provincial Government.

Arrangements for co-operation with: University of Minnesota; Iowa University; Carleton University.

Academic Year: September to July (September-January; March-July).

Admission Requirements: Graduation from senior middle school and entrance examination.

Language of Instruction: Chinese.

Degrees and Diplomas: Bachelor in all subjects, 4 yrs, Master, a further 3 yrs.

Library: Central Library, *c.* 450,000 vols.

Publications: Journal of Jilin Agricultural University (quarterly); Furbearer Farming (quarterly). Fur Animal Raising; Study of Agricultural Higher Education.

Press or Publishing House: J.A.U. Publishing House.

Academic Staff, 1989-90:

Rank	Full-time
Professors	31
Associate Professors	175
Lecturers	186
Assistants	235
Total	627

Student Enrolment, 1989-90:

	Men	Women	Total
Of the country	1819	768	2587*

*Also 1100 external students.

1334 **JILIN POLYTECHNICAL UNIVERSITY**
Changchun (Jilin Province)

A Key institution.

1335 **JINAN UNIVERSITY**
Shipai, Guangzhou 510632 (Guangdong Province)
Cables: 0870 guangzhou
Telex: 44645 JUN CN
Telephone: 516511
Fax: 516941
President: Liang Lingguang (1983-)

C. of Economics
Dean: Wang Guangzhen; *staff* 298
C. of Medicine (including Stomatology)
Dean: Zhang Ronghua; *staff* 290
C. of Liberal Arts
Dean: Ke Muhuo; *staff* 341
C. of Science and Technology
Dean: Zou Han; *staff* 520
C. of Adult and Lifelong Education
Dean: Yun Guanping; *staff* 39
D. of Foreign Languages and Literature (including English, Japanese)
Chairman: Tang Ronhua; *staff* 63
D. of Chinese Language and Literature
Chairman: Lu Jingguang; *staff* 52
D. of Journalism
Chairman: Ma Yanxun; *staff* 51
D. of History
Chairman: Lu Wei; *staff* 46
D. of Chemistry
Chairman: Feng Dexiong; *staff* 104
D. of Applied Physics
Chairman: Chen Daisheng; *staff* 60
D. of Biology
Chairman: Lin Jian; *staff* 90
D. of Mathematics
Chairman: Yang Xinglong; *staff* 68
D. of Computer Sciences
Chairman: Wu Gongshun; *staff* 68
D. of Electronic Engineering
Chairman: Lui Tao; *staff* 45
D. of Economics
Chairman: Wang Fuchu; *staff* 50
D. of Finance
Chairman: Wang Tao; *staff* 51
D. of Business Administration
Chairman: He Zenxiang; *staff* 52
D. of Commerce
Chairman: Zhang Yong'an; *staff* 48
D. of Accountancy
Chairman: He Kenyuan; *staff* 50
D. of Statistics and Planning
Chairman: Xie Qinqn; *staff* 47
D. of Chinese as Foreign Language
Chairman: Rao Binbcai; *staff* 16
I. of Southeast Asia Studies
Director: Chen Qiaozhi; *staff* 23
I. of Overseas Chinese Studies
Director: Xu Xuanfu; *staff* 20
I. for Economic Studies of Hong Kong's Special Economic Zones
Director: He Jiasheng; *staff* 19
I. of Chinese Culture and History
Director: Chen Shaowun; *staff* 19
I. of Bioengineering Technology
Director: Zou Han; *staff* 30
Hydrophyte Research Ce.
Director: Qi Yuzao; *staff* 15
Research for Reproduction Immunology Ce.
Director: Liu Xuegao; *staff* 19
Also affiliated Teaching Hospital, Preparatory School, and Nursing School.

Founded 1906 as academy. Became university 1927. Mainly open to Chinese coming from abroad, to students from Hong Kong, Macao, Taiwan, and Chinese of foreign nationality. Under the supervision of the Office of Overseas Chinese Affairs of the State Council and the State Education Commission. Governing body: the Board of Trustees. Residential facilities for academic staff and students.

Arrangements for co-operation with: California State University; Miami University; Texas Tech University; University of Wisconsin-Eau Claire; East Carolina University; Saqinaw State University; Simon Fraser University; University of Alberta; Liverpool School of Tropical Medicine; University of Glasgow; Hanover Medical University; Kobe University of Commerce; University of Kyushu; University of Osaka. Similar relationships with: University of Hongkong; Chinese University of Hongkong; Hongkong Polytechnic; Hongkong Baptist College; University of East Asia, Macao.

Academic Year: September to July (September-January; February-July).

Admission Requirements: Graduation from senior middle school and entrance examination.

Fees: None.

Language of Instruction: Chinese.

Degrees and Diplomas: Bachelor of–Arts; Science, 4 yrs; Medicine, 6 yrs. Master, a further 3 yrs. Doctor of–Philosophy in Hematology; Science in Industrial Economics; Ocular Science, 3 yrs.

Library: Central Library, *c.* 930,000 vols.

Publications: Academic Journals (Natural Sciences and Medicine; Human Studies, both quarterly); Bulletin; Jinan Education; Southeast Asia Studies; Jinan University Newspapers (biweekly).

Academic Staff, 1989:

Rank	Full-time
Professors	97
Associate Professors	360
Lecturers	388
Assistant Masters	324
Total	1169

Student Enrolment, 1989:

Of the country	4970
Of other countries	1282
Total	6252*

*Also 2954 external students.

1336 **JISHOU UNIVERSITY**
District of Jishou (Hunan Province)

1337 **LANZHOU UNIVERSITY**
Lanzhou (Gansu Province)

A Key institution.

1338 **LIAONING UNIVERSITY**
Shenyang (Liaoning Province)
Cables: 6275
Telephone: 62541
President: Feng Yu Zhong (1983-86)

D. of Chinese
Head: Gao Sheng Dong; *staff* 124
D. of History
Head: Chen Chong Qiao; *staff* 112
D. of Philosophy
Head: Guo Guo Xiun; *staff* 71
D. of Law
Head: Zhao Yu Gang; *staff* 77
D. of Foreign Languages
Head: Ding Zhu Xin; *staff* 88
D. of Computer Technology
Head: Whang Shu Ren; *staff* 75
D. of Mathematics
Head: Liu Long Fu; *staff* 88
D. of Physics
Head: Wang Jin Xiang; *staff* 149
D. of Chemistry
Head: Ma Cheng Long; *staff* 126
D. of Biology
Head: Ding Shi Chong; *staff* 98
D. of Economics
Head: Wang Wen Yan; *staff* 252
D. of Industrial Administration
Head: Li Ying Lin; *staff* 28
D. of Planning and Statistics
Head: Zhang Jin Sheng; *staff* 33
D. of Finance and Insurance
Head: Wu Yao Zhong; *staff* 49
D. of Finance and Accounting
; *staff* 26
I. of Japanese
; *staff* 28
Research I. of Demographic Studies
; *staff* 11
Foreign Language Training and Research Sec.
; *staff* 61

Founded 1958, incorporating Northeast China Institute of Finance and Economics, Shenyang Teachers College, andShenyang Institute of Russian. Residential facilities for academic staff and students.

Arrangements for co-operation with: Southern Illinois University; University of Denver; Kansai University; Toyama University.

Academic Year: August to July (August-January; February-July).

Admission Requirements: Graduation from senior middle school and entrance examination.

Language of Instruction: Chinese.

Degrees and Diplomas: Bachelor of–Arts; Sciences. Master. Doctor.

Library: 1,200,000 vols.

Publication: Journal.

Press or Publishing House: University Publishing House and Printing Shop.

Academic Staff, 1986-87:

Rank	Full-time
Professors	21
Associate Professors	212
Lecturers	466
Teachers	30
Assistants	142
Total	871

Student Enrolment, 1986-87:

Of the country	6112
Of other countries	60
Total	6172

1339 **NANJING UNIVERSITY**
22 Hankou Road, Nanjing (Jiangsu Province)
Cables: 0909
Telex: 34151 PRCNU CN
Telephone: 37651; 37551
President: Qu Qinyue (1984-)

D. of Chinese Language and Literature
Chairman: Dong Jian; *staff* 103
D. of Foreign Languages and Literature
Chairman: Huang Zhongweng; *staff* 178
D. of History
Chairman: Qiu Shushen; *staff* 83
D. of Philosophy
Chairman: Ling Dehong; *staff* 53
D. of Law
Chairman: Li Qianhen; *staff* 31
D. of Political Science
Chairman: Zhang Yongtao; *staff* 56
D. of Economics
Chairman: Wang Xinheng; *staff* 75
D. of Management Science
Chairman: Zhou Shanduo; *staff* 38
D.of Library Scinece
Deputy Chairman: Zhou Zhiren; *staff* 12
D. of Mathematics
Chairman: Zheng Weide; *staff* 115
D. of Computer Sciences
Chairman: Sun Zhongxiu; *staff* 77
D. of Astronomy
Chairman: Liu Ling; *staff* 64
D. of Physics
Chairman: Gong Changde; *staff* 231
D. of Information Physics
Chairman: We Wenqiu; *staff* 114
D. of Chemistry
Chairman: Chen Yi; *staff* 215
D. of Biology
Chairman: Yu Qiqiang; *staff* 82
D. of Biochemistry
Chairman: Zhu Dexi; *staff* 37
D. of Geology
Chairman: Yu Jianhua; *staff* 167
D. of Geography
Chairman: Yang Wu; *staff* 117
D. of Atmospheric Science
Chairman: Wu Rongshen; *staff* 80
D. of Environmental Sciences
Chairman: Xu Ouyong; *staff* 27
Ce. for Chinese and American Studies
Directors: Wang Zhigang; Leon M.S. Slawecki; *staff* 24
Computer Ce.
Director: Chen Huasheng; *staff* 71
Materials Analysis Ce.
Director: Zai Hongru; *staff* 53
Audio-visual Ce.
; *staff* 55
D. of Foreign Language Instruction
Director: Yang Zhizhong; *staff* 63

D. for Lifelong Education
Director: Yan Yongquan

Founded 1902. A Key institution under the jurisdiction of the State Education Commission.

Academic Year: September to July (September-January; February-July).

Admission Requirements: Graduation from senior middle school and entrance examination.

Language of Instruction: Chinese.

Degrees and Diplomas: Bachelor in all fields. Master. Doctor.

Library: c. 3,000,000 vols.

Publications: Quarterly (Humanities and Social Sciences); (Natural Sciences); Computational Mathematics Journal; the Journalof Inorganic Chemistry; Progress in Physics and Contemporary Foreign Literature.

Academic Staff, 1986-87:

Rank	Full-time
Professors	181
Associate Professors	563
Lecturers	828
Assistants	470
Total	2042

Student Enrolment, 1986-87:

Of the country	10,300
Of other countries	200
Total	10,500

1340 **NANJING FORESTRY UNIVERSITY**
Longpan Road, Nanjing (Jiangsu Province)
Cables: 2651
Telex: 342234 JPEC CN
Telephone: 653231
Fax: (86-25) 502936
President: Wang Ming-xiu (1984-90)

D. of Forestry
Director: Chao Chi-Son; *staff* 132
D. of Wood Industry
Director: Zhang Gui-Ling; *staff* 73
D. of Forestry Engineering
Director: Su Jin-Yun; *staff* 50
D. of Chemical Engineering
Director: Li Zhong-Zheng; *staff* 56
D. of Forestry Machinery
Director: Seng Guan-Fu; *staff* 69
D. of Forestry Economics and Management
Director: Chen Guo-Liang; *staff* 31
Bamboo Research I.
Head: Zhou Fang-Zhun; *staff* 12
D. for Correspondence Courses
D. for Evening Studies
Head: Zheng Bing-Jin

Founded 1952 as Nanjing Institute of Forestry, acquired present status and title 1984. Under the jurisdiction of the Ministry of Forestry.

Arrangements for co-operation with: University of Washington; University of Quebec; University of Tokyo.

Academic Year: September to July (September-January; February-July).

Admission Requirements: Graduation from high school and entrance examination.

Fees: None.

Language of Instruction: Chinese.

Degrees and Diplomas: Bachelor of–Engineering; Agriculture, 4 yrs. Master of Science, a further 3 yrs. Doctor, 3 yrs after Master.

Library: c. 430,000 vols.

Publications: Bamboo Research (quarterly); Nanjing Forestry University Journal (quarterly).

Press or Publishing House: Nanjing Forestry University Press.

Academic Staff, 1989-90:

Rank	Full-time
Professors	43
Associate Professors	210
Lecturers	256
Assistants	222
Total	731

Student Enrolment, 1989: 2328 (Also 320 external students).

1341 ***NANKAI UNIVERSITY**
Weijin Road 94, Tianjin 300071 (Tianjin Municipality)
Cables: 0589
Telex: 23133 NANKI CN
Telephone: (22) 318825/315960 (661)
Fax: (22) 344853
President: Mu Guoguang (1986-90)
Secretary-General: Weng Xinguang

D. of Chinese Language and Literature
Head: Hao Shifeng; *staff* 76
D. of History
Head: Liu Zehua; *staff* 60 (1)
D. of Philosophy
Head: Chen Yanqing; *staff* 45 (1)
D. of Economics
Head: Cai Xiaozhen; *staff* 55
D. of International Economics
Head: Xue Jingxiao; *staff* 25 (5)
D. of Economic Management
Head: Ji Kailin; *staff* 49
D. of Foreign Languages and Literature
Head: Chang Yaoxin; *staff* 60
D. of Mathematics
Head: Ding Guanggui; *staff* 42
D. of Physics
Head: Zhang Guangyin; *staff* 128 (3)
D. of Chemistry
Head: Shen Hanxi; *staff* 209
D. of Biology
Head: Shang Kejin; *staff* 105 (2)
D. of Electronics
Head: Zhou Qing; *staff* 79
D. of Computer Sciences
Head: Wang Zhibao; *staff* 69
D. of Environmental Science
Head: Dai Shugui; *staff* 32
D. of Library Science
Head: Lai Xinxia; *staff* 16
D. of Political Science
Head: Che Mingzhou; *staff* 26 (3)
D. of Law
Head: Liu Chunmao; *staff* 32 (1)
D. of Finance
Head: Wang Jizu; *staff* 55 (4)
D. of Tourism
Head (Deputy): Li Weishu; *staff* 45
D. of Sociology
Head: Feng Chengbo; *staff* 28
D. of Accounting
Head: Zhou Gairong; *staff* 23
D. of Oriental Art
Head: Fan Zeng; *staff* 16
Research I. of Economics
Director: Gu Shutang; *staff* 38 (2)
Research I. of International Economics
Director: Shu-Chin Yang; *staff* 25 (7)
Research I. of Demography
Director: Li Jingmeng; *staff* 13
Research I. of History
Director: Zhang Youlun; *staff* 3 (1)
Research I. of Ancient Chinese Bibliographical Collation
Director: Zheng Kecheng; *staff* 15
Research I. of Law
Director: Liu Chunmao; *staff* 7
Research I. of Elemento-Organic Chemistry
Director: Li Zhengming; *staff* 98
Research I. of Modern Optics
Director: Mu Guoguang; *staff* 20
Research I. of Polymer Chemistry
Director: He Binglin; *staff* R38 (1)
Research I. of Molecular Biology
Director: Yu Yaoting; *staff* 35
Research I. of Applied Chemistry
Director: Zhang Daxin
Research I. of Transportation Economics
Director: Heng-Kang Sang; *staff* 6

Research I. of Taiwan Economy
Director: Bao Juemin; *staff* 1 (3)
Nankai I. of Mathematics
Director: Shing-Shen Chern; *staff* 8 (3)
Also Ce. for Teaching Chinese as a Second Language; Intensive Chinese Language P.; Chinese Studies P. (conducted in English) (all for foreign students).

Founded 1919. A Key institution under the jurisdiction of the State Commission of Education. Residential facilities for academic staff and students.

Arrangements for co-operation with the Universities of: Minnesota; State New York, Albany; Pennsylvania State; Kansas; Temple; Moorhead; Indiana; Michigan State; South Florida; Brown; Columbia; Illinois; Quinnipiac; Hamilton; Western Michigan; Michigan; New Jersey; East Carolina; Wisconsin-Madison; Swarthmore; Sarajevo; Skopje; Jena; Heidelberg; Münster; Orleans; Kent; Queen Mary; Pavia; Venice; McGill; Laval; McMaster; York; Montreal; Calgary; Australian National; Melbourne; New South Wales; Salahaddin; Waseda; Hitotsubashi; Ritsumeikan; Aichi; Okayama; Rikkyo; Bunkyo; Nagoya-Nagoyagakuin.

Academic Year: September to July (September-January; February-July).

Admission Requirements: Graduation from senior middle school and entrance examination.

Fees: None.

Language of Instruction: Chinese.

Degrees and Diplomas: Bachelor, 4 yrs. Master, a further 3 yrs. Doctor of–Economics; Philosophy; Arts; History; Science, 2-3 yrs after Master.

Library: Central Library, 2,050,000 vols.

Special Facilities (Museums, etc.): Archives; Gymnasium; Exhibition Hall for Historic Relics.

Publications: Nankai Journal (bimonthly); Nankai History (bimonthly).

Press or Publishing House: Nankai University Press; Nankai University Publishing House.

Academic Staff, 1989-90:

Rank	Full-time	Part-time
Professors	151	39
Associate Professors	554	3
Lecturers	957	2
Teachers	293	–
Total	1955	44

Student Enrolment, 1989-90:

	Men	Women	Total
Of the country	5182	2888	8070
Of other countries	63	31	94
Total	5245	2919	8164

1342 **NINGXIA UNIVERSITY**
21 Wenchi Road, Yinchunan (Hui Ningxia Autonomous Region)

1343 **NORMAN BETHUNE UNIVERSITY OF MEDICAL SCIENCES**
6 Xinmin Street, Changchun 130021 (Jilin Province)
Telex: 886410
Telephone: 55911
President: Shu-zheng Liu (1983-)

S. of Basic Medical Sciences
Dean: Jia-xiang Wu; *staff* 497
S. of Preventive Medicine
Dean: Hong-xue Fan; *staff* 222
S. of Dentistry
Dean: Jie Ouvang; *staff* 278
F. of Library and Information Science
Dean: Zhao-an Wang; *staff* 21
D. of Social Sciences
Director: Sheng-xian Dong
Research I. of Basic Medical Sciences
Director: Jia-xiang Wu *staff* 91
Research I. of Environmental Medicine
Director: Zhang Li; *staff* 27
Research I. of Radiation Medicine
Director: Shu-zheng Liu; *staff* 40
Research I. of Endemic Diseases
Director: Ru-guo An; *staff* 70
Research I. of Cerebrovascular Diseases
Director: Ming-li Rao; *staff* 12
Research I. of Surgery
Director: Fu-min Zheng; *staff* 2
Research I. of Respiratory Diseases
Director: Guo-zhi He; *staff* 10
Research I. of Hepatic Diseases
Director: Mei-de Liu; *staff* 10
Research I. of Gerontology
Director: Ping-ru Zheng; *staff* 8
Research I. of Pharmaceutical Sciences
Director: Guang-sheng Li; *staff* 13
Research I. of Higher Medical Education Management
Director: Shu-zheng Liu; *staff* 4
Health School
Principal: Jing-hua Chi; *staff* 70
D. of Adult Education
Director: Li-ping Chen; *staff* 12
D. of Animal Medicine
Director: Zhao-ming Liu; *staff* 41
National Training Ce. of Neurology
Director: Duo-san Liu; *staff* 12
Audiovisual Ce.
Director: Bao-chun Jin; *staff* 25
Computer Ce.
Director: Yong Fang; *staff* 13
Molecular Biology Ce.
Director: Yin-qiao Mai; *staff* 21
Radioisotope Ce.
Director: Zhi-min Ji; *staff* 3
Electronmicroscopy Ce.
Director: Zhen-bao Li; *staff* 7
Japanese Language Training Ce. for Sasakawa Medical Scholars
Director: Xuan-gang Wu; *staff* 17
Also 3 Clinical Colleges.

Founded 1939 as medical school, became college 1958 and acquired present status and title 1978. Under the jurisdiction of the Ministry of Public Health. Residential facilities for academic staff and students.

Arrangements for co-operation with: Tohoku University; Laval University; University of Saskatchewan; Kitasato University; Akita University; Tokyo Medical and Dental University; Mie University; Asahikawa University; Hirosaki University; Kyushu University; Aichi Medical Unversity.

Academic Year: September to July (September-January; March-July).

Admission Requirements: Graduation from senior middle school and entrance examination.

Fees: None.

Languages of Instruction: Chinese, English, and Japanese.

Degrees and Diplomas: Bachelor of Medical Sciences, 5 yrs. Master, a further 3 yrs. Doctor, 3 yrs after Master.

Library: Central Library, 455,000 vols.

Special Facilities (Museums, etc.): Movie Studio; Pharmaceutical Factory.

Publications: Journal of Norman Bethune University of Medical Sciences (bimonthly); Foreign Medicine-Gerontology (bimonthly); Journal of Stroke and Neurological Diseases (quarterly); Journal of Hepatobiliary Diseases (quarterly).

Academic Staff, 1989-90:

Rank	Full-time
Professors	164
Associate Professors	413
Lecturers	1281
Assistants	1520
Total	3378

Student Enrolment, 1989-90:

	Men	Women	Total
Of the country	1323	1405	2728*

*Also 846 external students.

1344 **NORTHEAST AGRICULTURAL UNIVERSITY**
Gongbin Road, Xiangfang District, District of Acheng Harbin 150030 (Heilongjiang Province)
Cables: 1333
Telephone: 55981-588
President: Shi Bo-Hong

D. of Bioengineering
Director: Qin Peng-Chun; *staff* 48 (4)

D. of Agricultural Engineering
Director: Xu Hong-Ji; *staff* 193 (30)
D. of Laboratory Centre
Director: Wang Fu-Li; *staff* 30
D. of Horticulture
Director: Cui Cong-Shi; *staff* 68 (30)
D. of Agricultural Economics
Director: Li You-Hua; *staff* 32
D. of Food Science
Director: Liu Xi-Liang; *staff* 29
D. of Plant Protection
Director: Cheng Zhi-Ming; *staff* 32
D. of Agricultural Education
Director: Ma Zhan-Feng; *staff* 7
D. of Social Sciences
Director: Liang Xi-Xian; *staff* 27
D. of Basic Disciplines
Director: Xu Zhong-Ru; *staff* 99
D. of Physical Training
Director: Jiang Tian-Ri; *staff* 22
D. of Animal Husbandry
Director: Zhang Da-Peng; *staff* 89 (6)
D. of Veterinary Medicine
Director: Liu Wen-Zhou; *staff* 94 (1)
D. of Agronomy
Director: Wang Yun-Sheng; *staff* 119 (20)
Branch College at Acheng.

Founded 1948. Residential facilities for academic staff and students.

Arrangements for co-operation with: University of Wisconsin-Madison; Michigan State University; Colorado StateUniversity; University of Alberta; Instituto Agronomico Mediteranco Italy; University of Hokkaido.

Academic Year: September to July (September-January; March-July).

Admission Requirements: Graduation from high school and entrance examination.

Language of Instruction: Chinese.

Degrees and Diplomas: Bachelor, 4 yrs. Master, a further 3 yrs. Doctor, Ph.D., 3 yrs.

Library: 620,000 vols.

Press or Publishing House: Editorial Department of Journal.

Academic Staff, 1990:

Rank	Full-time
Professors	63
Associate Professors	179
Lecturers	177
Assistants	209
Total	628

Student Enrolment, 1990:

	Men	Women	Total
Of the country	1389	656	2045*

*Also 690 external students.

1345 **NORTHEAST NORMAL UNIVERSITY**

Changchun (Jilin Province)
Telephone: 27056; 22336
President: Qichang Huang (1986-90)
Vice-President: Jingsi Zhou

D. of Education
Chairman: Shun Wenlong; *staff* 95 (6)
D. of Chinese Language and Literature
Chairman: Liu He; *staff* 130 (6)
D. of History
Chairman: Tang Chengyun; *staff* 100 (11)
D. of Mathematics
Chairman: Wang Mingwen; *staff* 115
D. of Biology
Chairman: He Mengyuan; *staff* 114 (3)
I. of Japanese Studies
Director: Song Shaoyeng; *staff* 24 (5)
I. of the History of Ancient Civilization
Director: Lin Zhicun; *staff* 10
Graduate S.
Dean: Zhan Ziqing; *staff* 69
C. for Lifelong Education
Dean: He Yanru; *staff* 59 (144)

Founded 1946 as comprehensive school, acquired present status and title 1950. Under the jurisdiction of the Ministry of Education. Residential facilities for academic staff and students.

Arrangements for co-operation with the Universities of: Wisconsin at Milwaukee; Saskatchewan; Mississippi; California; Michigan; Southern Illinois; Miyagi; Okayawa; Stanford. Obirin Colleges and Schools.

Academic Year: September to July (September-January; February-July).

Admission Requirements: Graduation from senior middle school and entrance examination.

Language of Instruction: Chinese.

Degrees and Diplomas: Bachelor. Master.

Libraries: Central Library, 2,300,000 vols; specialized libraries, 132,115.

Special Facilities (Museums, etc.): Museum of Biology; Museum of China's Ancient History.

Publications: Journal (bimonthly); Foreign Problems Studies (quarterly); Journal of Ancient Books (quarterly); Foreign Education Studies (quarterly); Physics Experiments (bimonthly).

Press or Publishing House: University Press.

Academic Staff, 1986-87:

Rank	Full-time	Part-time
Professors	97	29
Associate Professors	372	20
Instructors	570	–
Teaching Assistants	334	–
Total	1373	49

Student Enrolment, 1986-87:

	Men	Women	Total
Of the country	3265	3042	6307
Of other countries	50	44	94
Total	3315	3086	6401

1346 ***NORTHEAST UNIVERSITY OF TECHNOLOGY**

Chenyang (Liaoning Province)
Cables: 2168
Telex: 80033 NEIT CN
Telephone: 482157
President: Lu Zhongwu (1984-)

D. of Mining Engineering
D. of Mineral Engineering
D. of Metallurgy
D. of Non-Ferrous Metallurgy
D. of Metallic Materials
D. of Metal Processing
D. of Thermal Engineering
D. of Mechanical Engineering I
D. of Mechanical Engineering II
D. of Automation
D. of Computer Sciences and Engineering
D. of Physics
D. of Chemistry
D. of Mechanics
D. of Foreign Languages
D. of Physical Education
D. of Social Science
D. for Correspondence Courses
Also 8 Research Institutes and 26 Research Sections.

Founded 1923 as college. Acquired present status and title 1950. A Key institution under the jurisdiction of the Ministries of Education and Metallurgical Industry. Residential facilities for academic staff and students.

Arrangements for co-operation with the Universities of: Tohoku; Nagoya; Kansai; Pittsburgh; Appalachian State;Linköping; Wollongong. The Chinese University of Hong Kong; Royal Institute of Technology, Sweden.

Academic Year: September to August (September-January; February-July).

Admission Requirements: Graduation from senior middle school and entrance examination.

Language of Instruction: Chinese.

Degrees and Diplomas: Bachelor of–Science; Engineering, 4 yrs. Master, a further 2 ½-3 yrs. Doctor, 3 yrs.

Library: Central Library, *c.* 1,000,000 vols.

Publication: Journal.

Press or Publishing House: University Press.

Academic Staff: c. 1670 (20).

Student Enrolment: c. 8920 (Also *c.* 3250 external students).

1347 ***NORTHERN JIAOTONG UNIVERSITY**
Beijing (Beijing Municipality)
Telephone: 890561
President: Zhang Shujing (1983-)
Vice-President: Dong Shilin

D. of Telecommunications
Director: Li Chengshu; *staff* 153
D. of Civil Engineering
Director: Tang Yeqing; *staff* 116
D. of Mechanical Engineeering
Director: Qi Qisheng; *staff* 87
D. of Computer Sciences and Technology
Director: Tan Weikang; *staff* 49
D. of Industrial Management
Director: Bi Ruxiang; *staff* 51
D. of Railway Transportation
Director: Shen Qinyan; *staff* 82
D. of Electronic Engineering
Director Hao Rongtai; *staff* 31
D. or Management Engineering
Director: Sun Jinhua; *staff* 52
D. of Physics
Director: Shi Jiren; *staff* 43
D. of Mathematics
Director: Liu Yisheng; *staff* 52
D. of Economics
Director: Song Shuxun; *staff* 43
Sec. of Foreign Languages
Director: Zhang Zhiluo; *staff* 74
D. for Correspondence Courses
Director: Lin Junfeng; *staff* 11
D. for Evening Studies
Director: Lin Demao; *staff* 2
Training D. for Cadres
Director: Lu Shenyou; *staff* 2
Also 4 Research Institutes.

Founded 1909. A Key institution under the jurisdiction of the State Education Committee and the Ministry of Railways. Residential facilities for staff and students.

Arrangements for co-operation with 3 U.S. universities and 1 German university.

Academic Year: September to July (September-February; March-July).

Admission Requirements: Graduation from senior middle school and entrance examination.

Language of Instruction: Chinese.

Degrees and Diplomas: Bachelor of Science, 4 yrs. Master, a further 3 yrs. Doctor, 2 yrs.

Library: Central Library, *c.* 650,000 vols.

Publications: Newspaper (weekly); Journal (quarterly).

Academic Staff, 1986-87:

Rank	Full-time
Professors	43
Associate Professors	226
Lecturers	326
Assistant Lecturers	330
Total	925

Student Enrolment, 1986-87:

	Men	Women	Total
Of the country	2333	921	3254
Of other countries	50	1	51
Total	2383	922	3305*

*Also 1891 external students.

1348 **NORTHWEST UNIVERSITY**
Xi'an (Shaanxi Province)

A Key institution.

1349 **NORTHWESTERN AGRICULTURAL UNIVERSITY**
Yangli (Shaanxi Province)
Cables: 6007 Yanling
President: Zhang Yue
Secretary-General: Feng Shiliang

D. of Agriculture
Dean: Wang Hongjun; *staff* 102
D. of Plant Protection
Dean: Zhang Jianyu; *staff* 95
D. of Soil Science and Agrochemistry
Dean: Freng Lixiao; *staff* 75
D. of Horticulture
Dean: Li Jiari; *staff* 81
D. of Agricultrual Economics
Dean: Zhang Dongan; *staff* 77
D. of Agricultural Machinery
Dean: Ren Wenhui; *staff* 114
D. of Hydraulics
Dean: Zhu Wenyong; *staff* 103
D. of Animal Husbandry
Dean: Lu Xingzhong; *staff* 82
D. of Veterinary Medicine
Dean: Cao Guangrong; *staff* 105
D. of Food Technology
Dean: Chen Jingping; *staff* 30
D. of Basic Studies
Dean: Zhang Zhenying; *staff* 178
Research Ce. for Agriculture in Arid and Semi-Arid Areas
Director: Wan Jianzhong
Ce. for Rural Economics and Management
Director: Zhang Dongan
Computer Ce.
Director: Wang Naixin
Training Sec. for Cadres
Head: Liu Xiaoqian
Also 12 Research Units.

Founded 1934 as school, acquired present status and title 1985. A Key institution under the jurisdiction of the Ministry of Agriculture, Animal Husbandry and Fishery. Residential facilities for academic staff and students.

Arrangements for co-operation with: Justus-Liebig-Universität-Giessen; University of Idaho; University of Edinburgh; Université Laval.

Academic Year: September to July (September-January; February-July).

Admission Requirements: Graduation from senior middle school and entrance examination.

Language of Instruction: Chinese.

Degrees and Diplomas: Bachelor of Science, 4 yrs. Master, a further 3 yrs. Doctor, 3 yrs after Master.

Library: c. 600,000 vols.

Special Facilities (Museums, etc.): Insect Specimen Museum.

Publications: Acta Universitatis Septentrionali Occidentali Agriculturae (quarterly); Agricultural Research in the Arid Areas (quarterly); Entomotaxonomia (quarterly); Journal of Animal Husbandry and Veterinary Medicine (quarterly); Foreign Veterinary Medicine-Livestock and Poultry Diseases (quarterly); China Yellow Cattle (quarterly); Agricultural Education (biannually); Milk Goat and Goat Milk (biannually).

Academic Staff, 1986-87:

Rank	Full-time
Professors	65
Associate Professors	214
Teachers	188
Lecturers	418
Assistants	356
Total	1241

Student Enrolment, 1986-87:

	Men	Women	Total
Of the country	2618	748	3366*

*Also 226 external students.

1350 ***NORTHWESTERN POLYTECHNICAL UNIVERSITY**
127 West Youyi Road, Xi'an 710072 (Shaanxi Province)
Cables: Xi'an 5300
Telex: 70185 NWTUY CN
Telephone: (29) 53351
Fax: (29) 711959
President: Fu Hengzhi (1984-)
Secretary-General: Tao Guojin

C. of Astronautics
Dean: Cai Timin; *staff* 86 (16)

C. of Management Science
Dean: Wu Xinping; *staff* 75 (7)
C. of Marine Engineering
Head: Yang Binzheng; *staff* 79 (1)
Graduate S.
Dean: Wu Xinping; *staff* 21 (2)
D. of Aero-Engineering
Chairman: Liu Songlin; *staff* 800 (8)
D. of Aircraft Engineering
Chairman: Zhu Depei; *staff* 75 (8)
D. of Aircraft Manufacture Engineering
Chairman: Ren Jingxin; *staff* 105 (10)
D. of Applied Mathematics
Chairman: Zhang Yongshu; *staff* 77 (2)
D. of Applied Physics
Chairman: Bao Yinluan; *staff* 47
D. of Architecture and Civil Engineering
Chairman: Wang Shangwen; *staff* 23 (5)
D. of Automatic Control
Chairman: Jin Xiyue; *staff* 98 (1)
D. of Computer Sciences and Engineering
Chairman: Kang Jichang; *staff* 82 (2)
D. of Mechanical Engineering
Chairman: Bai Zhenlin; *staff* 57 (1)
D. of Electronic Engineering
Chairman: Chen Xingeng; *staff* 95 (5)
D. of Flight Vehicles and Propulsion
Chairman: Wen Bingheng; *staff* 42 (7)
D. of Foreign Languages
Chairman: Shu Xiangxi; *staff* 72
D. of Marine Control Engineering
Chairman: Chen Jingxi; *staff* 23 (1)
D. of Marine Electronic Engineering
Chairman: Li Zhishun; *staff* 45
D. of Marine Mechanical Engineering
Chairman: Wang Minzhu; *staff* 101 (1)
D. of Space Flight and Control
Chairman: Chen Xinhai *staff* 44 (9)
D. of Social Sciences
Chairman: Wang Wenbin; *staff* 57 (1)
D. for Correspondence Courses
Dean: Mao Yuzeng; *staff* 21
I. of Aircraft Construction
Director: Zhao Lingcheng; *staff* 30 (23)
I. of Pilotless Aircraft
Director: Wang Tinrui; *staff* 184 (1)
I. of Marine Equipment
Director:Huang Jingquan; staff 14 (18)
I. of Heat Materials Technology
Director: Li Yuzhong; *staff* 5 (72)
I. of Computer Sciences and Information Engineering
Director: Kang Jichang; *staff* 3 (122)
I. of Natural Dialectics
Director: Shui Yunhua; *staff* 3 (30)
D. for Lifelong Education
Dean: Zhang Qin'en; *staff* 3 (2)
I. of Vibration Engineering
Director: Gu Jialiu; *staff* 15
Research Ce. for Automatic Control
Director: Chen Xinhai; *staff* 5 (15)
Research Ce. for Composite Materials
Director: Ma Zukang; *staff* 2 (7)
Research Ce. for Industrial Robotics
Director: Peng Yanwu; *staff* 5 (8)
Research Ce. for Computational Thermophysics
Director: Wu Xinping; *staff* 4 (10)
Research Ce. for Moulding
Director: Ren Jinxin; *staff* 3 (9)
Research Ce. for Electromagnetics
Director: Tang Zhizhong; *staff* 4 (20)
Research Ce. for Aerospace Technology
Director: Liu Yuanyong; *staff* 6 (15)
Research Ce. for Aerofoil
Director: Qiao Zhide; *staff* 7 (12)
Also 14 Research Sections.

Founded 1957, incorporating previously existing engineering colleges, institutes and departments. A Key institution, under the jurisdiction of the Ministry of Aero-space Industry.

Arrangements for co-operation with the Universities of: Maryland; Lehigh; Tennessee; Eastern Illinois; South Carolina; Stuttgart; Braunschweig; Oxford; Lancaster. Georgia Institute of Technology; Technical University of Berlin.

Academic Year: September to July (September-January; February-July).

Admission Requirements: Graduation from senior middle school and entrance examination.

Fees: None.

Language of Instruction: Chinese.

Degrees and Diplomas: Bachelor in all subjects, 4 yrs. Master, a further 2 ½ yrs and thesis. Doctor, 3 yrs after Master.

Library: Central Library, *c.* 1,200,000 vols.

Special Facilities (Museums, etc.): Museum of Aero-Space Science.

Publications: University Journal (quarterly); Machine Design (quarterly).

Press or Publishing House: The NPU Publishing House.

Academic Staff, 1989-90:

Rank	Full-time	Part-time
Professors	126	103
Associate Professors	501	23
Lecturers	583	–
Assistants	395	–
Total	1605	126

Student Enrolment, 1989-90:

	Men	Women	Total
Of the country	5899	1548	7557*

*Also 2438 external and correspondence students.

1351 **OVERSEAS CHINESE UNIVERSITY**
Quanzhou (Fujian Province)

1352 **PEOPLE'S UNIVERSITY OF CHINA**
39 Haidian Road, West Suburb, Beijing (Beijing Municipality)
Cables: 0086 beijing
Telex: 222653 PUCBJ CN
Telephone: (1) 285431
Fax: (1) 2566374
President: Yuan Baohua (1985-)
Secretary-General: Chen Guang

Graduate S.
Associate Dean: Zhou Xincheng
C. of Economics
Dean: Huang Da
C. of Economic Planning and Statistics
Dean: Li Zhenzhong
C. of Industrial And Commercial Management (including Agricultural Economics, and Accountancy)
Dean: Shi Liming
C. of Labour and Personnel Administration
Associate Dean: Zhao Lukuan
C. of Law
Associate Dean: Gu Chunde
C. of Journalism
Associate Dean: He Zihua
C. of Archives (including Philosophy, History of the Chinese Communist Party, International Politics, Population Studies, Chinese Language and Literature, Sociology, Physical Education)
Associate Dean: Chen Zhaowu
I. of the History of Development of Marxism-Leninism
Director: Xi Guangqing; *staff* 28
I. of Population History
Director: Liu Zheng; *staff* 30
I. of Chinese Language and Writing
Deputy Director: Hu Ruichang; *staff* 12
I. of the History of Qing (Manchurian) Dynasty
Director: Wang Junyi; *staff* 41
I. of Administration Studies
Director: Huang Daqiang; *staff* 16
I. of Sociology
Director: Zheng Hangsheng; *staff* 23
I. of Soft Science
Director: Li Zhongshang; *staff* 6

I. of Education in Marxist Theory
Director: Xu Zhengfan; *staff* 9
Information Ce.
Director: Jiang Zhao; *staff* 11
Ce. of Chinese (for foreign students)
Chairman: Liu Jin; *staff* 25
C. for Correspondence Courses
Dean: Fang Jia
Audio-visual Ce.

Founded 1937, as school. Acquired present title 1950. A Key institution. Residential facilities for academic staff and students.

Arrangements for co-operation with: Karl-Marx University, Leipzig; Tokai University; University of Hawaii; University of Economic Sciences, Budapest; Concordia University, Canada; Colby College, USA; Cedarville College, USA; University of Durham; Universidad Nacional Autoónoma de México; Universidad Inca Garcilaso de la Vega, Peru; Instituto Universitatio Orientale, Naples; Central School of Planning and Statistics, Warsaw; Institutsupérieur de Gestion, Paris.

Academic Year: September to July.

Admission Requirements: Graduation from senior middle school and entrance examination.

Fees: None.

Language of Instruction: Chinese.

Degrees and Diplomas: Bachelor, 4 yrs. Master, a further 3 yrs. Doctor, Ph.D., 3 yrs and thesis.

Library: 2,500,000 vols.

Publications: Teaching and Research (bimonthly); Economic Theory and Business Management (bimonthly); Population Studies (bimonthly; boyh Chinese and English edition); Foreign Economy and Management (bimonthly); World Press (quarterly); History of Qing Dynasty Research Newsletter (quarterly); Intelligence and Material Work (bimonthly); Learned Journal of the People's University of China (bimonthly).

Press or Publishing House: PUC Publishing House; PUC Book, Newspaper and Periodical Information Centre.

Academic Staff, 1990:

Rank	Full-time
Professors	200
Associate Professors	515
Lecturers	582
Assistant Professors	286
Total	1583

Student Enrolment, 1990:

	Men	Women	Total
Of the country	4817	2183	7000
Of other countries	86	40	126
Total	4903	2223	7126*

*Also 7848 students by correspondence.

1353 **QINGHAI UNIVERSITY**
40 Ning Zhang Road, Xining 810016 (Qinghai Province)
Cables: 2239
Telephone: 40948, 40117
President: Pang Yi-Sheng (1986-)
Registrar: Chen Chang-Jun

D. of Mechanical Engineering
Dean: Xu Wu-Yang; *staff* 24
D. of Chemical Engineering
Dean: Qiu Zhong-Qing; *staff* 35
D. of Plant Protection
D. of Agronomy
Dean: Li Hua-Ying; *staff* 73
D. of Mining
D. of Hydroelectrical Engineering
Dean: Chen Zong-An; *staff* 34
D. of Civil Engineering
Dean: Fang Hong-Da; *staff* 37
D. of Chinese Language
Dean: Zhang Yong-Long; *staff* 15
D. of Administrative Engineering
Dean: Wan Shi-Chun; *staff* 24
Soft Science Research Ce.
Director: Sun Qin-Yi; *staff* 3
Scientific and Technical Information Ce.
Director: Cai Guo-Dong; *staff* 4
Computer Ce.
Director: Chen Min; *staff* 6
D. for Elementary Courses (Teaching and Research P.)
Vice-Dean: Wu Jian-Gong; *staff* 39
Also middle school.

Founded 1958. Under the jurisdiction of the Provincial Government. Residential facilities for academic staff and students.

Academic Year: September to July (September-February, March-July).

Admission Requirements: Graduation from senior middle school and entrance examination.

Fees: None.

Language of Instruction: Chinese.

Degrees and Diplomas: Bachelor, 4 yrs, and thesis.

Library: Central Library, *c.* 400,000 vols.

Special Facilities (Museums, etc.): Movie Studio.

Publication: Periodical.

Press or Publishing House: Printing Shop.

Academic Staff, 1990:

Rank	Full-time
Professors	5
Associate Professors	45
Lecturers	116
Assistants	82
Total	248

Student Enrolment, 1990:

	Men	Women	Total
Of the country	852	567	1419

1354 **QINGHAI NORMAL UNIVERSITY**
38 Wu Si Street, Xining (Qinghai Province)
Telex: 5400
Telephone: 55451

Teacher Training
Training Sec. for Cadres
Also 3 Research Sections.

Founded 1956 as school, became college 1958. Acquired present status and title 1984. Under the jurisdiction ofthe Ministry of Education and the Provincial Government. Residential facilities for academic staff and students.

Academic Year: August to July (August-January; March-July).

Admission Requirements: Graduation from senior middle school and entrance examination.

Language of Instruction: Chinese.

Degrees and Diplomas: Bachelor of–Arts; Science.

Library: Central Library, *c.* 505,460 vols.

Publication: Journal.

Academic Staff: c. 400.

Student Enrolment: c. 1670.

1355 **SHAANXI TEACHERS UNIVERSITY**
Foreign Affairs Department, Xi'an 710062 (Shaanxi Province)
Telephone: (29) 711212
Fax: (29) 711212
President: Guo-jun Wang
Registrar: An-min Gao

D. of Education
Head: An-min Zhang; *staff* 44
D. of Chinese Language and Literature
Head: Xi-ming Pu; *staff* 99 (2)
D. of Political Education
Head: Wen-zhou Song; *staff* 87 (2)
D. of History
Head: Qing-yun Zheng; *staff* 55 (2)
D. of Geography
Head: Zhi-xun Zhang; *staff* 52 (1)
D. of Biology
Head: Mei-xiang Gui; *staff* 68 (2)
D. of Mathematics
Head: Xin-min Wang; *staff* 84 (2)
D. of Physics
Head: Ke-de Fu; *staff* 98 (3)
D. of Computer Sciences
Head: Yue Cao; *staff* 17 (2)

D. of Chemistry
Head: Qian-guang Liu; *staff* 78 (1)
D. of Physical Education
Head: Zhi-yi Zhang; *staff* 27 (1)
D. of Arts and Music
Head: Zheng Zhou; *staff* 14 (1)
D. of Foreign Languages
Head (Acting): Ji-guo Dai; *staff* 39 (2)
D. of Audio-visual Education
Head: Ming-sheng Zhang; *staff* 16 (1)
S. for Adult Education
Head: Cheng-quan Su; *staff* 5 (1)
D. for Correspondence Courses
Evening S.
Also 7 Research Institutes.

Founded 1944, as normal college. Acquired present status and title 1960. Under the jurisdiction of the National Education Commission.

Arrangements for co-operation with: University of Massachusetts, Amherst; California State University; Northridge; University of Northern Iowa; Western Oregon State College; Ohio State University; New Mexico State University; New York State University; Shikoku Women's University; Meiji University; International Christian University, Japan; South Australian College of Advanced Education; La Trobe University; University of Antwerp; The Chinese University of Hong Kong.

Academic Year: September to July (September-January; March-July).

Admission Requirements: Graduation from senior middle school and entrance examination.

Fees: None.

Language of Instruction: Chinese.

Degrees and Diplomas: Certificate, 1-3 yrs. Bachelor, 4 yrs. Master, a further 3 yrs. Doctor, Ph.D., 3 yrs.

Library: 1,920,000 vols.

Publication: Philosophy and Science (quarterly).

Press or Publishing House: Shaanxi Teachers University Press.

Academic Staff, 1990:

Rank	Full-time
Professors	52
Associate Professors	235
Lecturers	406
Total	693

Student Enrolment, 1990: 12,351 (Also 6090 part-time students and students by correspondence).

1356 **SHANDONG UNIVERSITY**
Jinan (Shandong Province)
Telephone: 43861
President: Conhao Deng (1984-)

D. of Chinese Language and Literature
Chairman: Zhian Dong; *staff* 88
D. of History
Chairman: Maochun Ge; *staff* 87
D. of Foreign Languages and Literature
Chairman: Delin Hu; *staff* 67
D. of Economics
Chairman: Dejun Zang; *staff* 46
D. of Philosophy
Chairman: Lishen Zhou; *staff* 41
D. of Social Sciences
Chairman: Mingyi Zhao *staff* 33
D. of Sociology
Head: Jingze Xu; *staff* 17
D. of Mathematics
Chairman: Dajun Guo; *staff* 92
D. of Physics
Chairman: Liangmu Mei; *staff* 113
D. of Chemistry
Chairman: Yongjia Yin; *staff* 136
D. of Optics
Chairman: Wenji Chen *staff* 58
D. of Law
Chairman: Wei Qiao; *staff* 38
D.of Computer Sciences
Chairman: Jiaye Wang; *staff* 41
D. of Biology
Chairman: Long Wang; *staff* 68
D. of Microbiology
Chairman: Xinmin Qian; *staff* 36
D. of Management
Head: Wenchan Mo; *staff* 13
D. of Electronics
Chairman: Gangwu Cheng; *staff* 85
D. of Library Science
Head: Jingqi Lu; *staff* 5
D. of Aerospace Technical English
Head: Huan Wu; *staff* 44
D. of Marxism-Leninism
Head: Xuesheng Xu; *staff* 25

Founded 1901 as high school, acquired present status and title 1926. Moved to Jinan from Qingdao 1958. A Key institution under the jurisdiction of the Ministry of Education. Residential facilities for academic staff and students.

Arrangements for co-operation with: Harvard University; Indiana University; New York City College; University of Regina; Yamaguchi University; University of Adelaide.

Academic Year: September to July (September-January; February-July).

Admission Requirements: Graduation from senior middle school and entrance examination.

Language of Instruction: Chinese.

Degrees and Diplomas: Bachelor of Science, 4 yrs. Master, a further 3 yrs. Doctor, 3 yrs after Master.

Libraries: Central Library, *c.* 1.7 m. vols; department and institute libraries.

Publications: Journals: Natural Sciences; Social Sciences; Literature, History, and Philosophy (all quarterly).

Press or Publishing House: Shandong University Publishing House.

Academic Staff, 1986-87:

Rank	Full-time
Professors	72
Associate Professors	375
Lecturers	538
Assistants	383
Total	1368

Student Enrolment, 1986-87:

	Men	Women	Total
Of the country	1622	761	2383
Of other countries	79	28	107
Total	1701	789	2490

1357 **SHANDONG NORMAL UNIVERSITY**
Jinan (Shandong Province)

Education

1358 **SHANDONG POLYTECHNICAL UNIVERSITY**
Jinan (Shandong Province)
Telex: 1260
Telephone: 23901
President: Xia Tianjiu (1984-)

D. of Mechanical Engineering
D. of Metallurgy
D. of Thermal Power Engineering
D. of Electrical Engineering
D. of Electric Power Engineering
D. of Electronics
D. of Computer Sciences and Engineering
D. of Hydraulic Engineering
D. of Industrial Management
D. of Basic Studies
D. for Evening Studies
D. for Correspondence Courses
Also Research Institute and 6 Research Laboratories.

Founded as college 1951. Acquired present status and title 1984. Under the jurisdiction of the Provincial Government. Residential facilities for academic staff and students.

Arrangements for co-operation with Coventry (Lanchester) Polytechnic.

Academic Year: September to July (September-February; March-July).

Admission Requirements: Graduation from senior middle school and entrance examination.

Language of Instruction: Chinese.

Degrees and Diplomas: Bachelor, 4 yrs. Master, a further 3 yrs. Also Diploma.

Library: Central Library, *c.* 480,000 vols.

Publications: Proceedings of Shandong Polytechnic University (quarterly); Teaching Study (biannually).

Academic Staff: *c.* 920 (40).

Student Enrolment: *c.* 4590 (Also *c.* 940 external students).

1359 **SHANGHAI UNIVERSITY**

1220 Xin Zha Road, Shanghai (Shanghai Municipality)

Vice-Chancellor: Lin Jiongru (1987-)

C. of Liberal Arts
Deputy President: Weng Si-Rong
C. of Engineering
President: Maguo-Ling
C. of Business Management
President: Jiang Jia-Jun
C. of Fine Arts
President: Li Tian-Xian
C. of International Business
President: Guan-Quan
C. of Political Science
President: Chen Xian-Hong
Research I. of Sociology
Research I. of Archaeology

Founded 1920 as Shanghai University, acquired present status and title 1983. Under the jurisdiction of the Municipal Government of Shanghai.

Academic Year: September to July.

Admission Requirements: Graduation from senior middle school and entrance examination.

Language of Instruction: Chinese.

Library: 600,000 vols.

Academic Staff, 1986-87:

Rank	Full-time	Part-time
Professors	7	20
Associate Professors	68	15
Lecturers	700	40
Assistants	230	–
Total	1005	75

Student Enrolment, 1986-87:

	Men	Women	Total
Of the country	4200	2800	7000
Of other countries	20	5	25
Total	4220	2805	7025

1360 **SHANGHAI FISHERIES UNIVERSITY**

334 Jun Gong Road, Shanghai 200090
Cables: 4347
Telephone: (2) 5431090 (Ex.)
Fax: (21) 5434358
President: Lo Mei-Long (1984-)
Secretary-General: Wang Tian-Sheng

D. of Aquaculture
Director: Zhu Xue-Bao; *staff* 79
D. of Food Science
Director: Ge Mao-Quan; *staff* 63 (2)
D. of Fisheries Engineering
Director: Lin Hui-Huang; *staff* 79
D. of Fishery Economics and Management
Director: Ge Guang-Hua; *staff* 25
D. of Basic Studies
Director: Hua Ku-Chen; *staff* 54
Training D. for Cadres
Director: Ge Guang-Hua; *staff* 2 (5)
Distant Water Fisheries Research I.
Director: Wang Yao-Geng; *staff* 10
Ichthyology L.
Director: Wu Han-Lin; *staff* 7
Food Science and Technology L.
Director: Wang Zhao; *staff* 5
Fisheries Education Research Sec.
Director: Wang Tian-Sheng
Also Fish Farms in Nanhui and Fonghua Countys, and Fishing Fleet.

Founded as school 1912, became college 1952 and acquired present status and title 1985. Under the jurisdictionof the Ministry of Agriculture. Residential facilities for academic staff and students.

Academic Year: September to July (September-February; February-July).

Admission Requirements: Graduation from senior middle school and entrance examination.

Language of Instruction: Chinese.

Degrees and Diplomas: Bachelor of–Agriculture; Engineering, 4 yrs. Master, a further 3 yrs.

Library: Central Library, *c.* 380,000 vols.

Special Facilities (Museums, etc.): Museum of Ichthyology.

Publications: Bulletin; Journal of Fisheries of China, (quarterly).

Academic Staff, 1989-90:

Rank	Full-time	Part-time
Full Professors	18	4
Associate Professors	115	–
Lecturers	145	–
Assistants	145	–
Total	423	4

Student Enrolment, 1989-90:

	Men	Women	Total
Of the country	1153	456	1609

1361 **SHANGHAI INTERNATIONAL STUDIES UNIVERSITY**

550 Da Lian Road(W), Shanghai
Cables: 0369
Telex: 33505 SISU CN
Telephone: (86-21) 5420900
Fax: (86-21) 5420225
President: Dai Wei-Dong

D. of Languages and Literature (English, Japanese, German, French, Russian, Spanish, Arabic, Italian, Greek and Portugese.)
D. of International Trade
D. of Foreign Affairs Management
D. of Chinese as a Foreign Language
D. of Educational Communication and Technology
D. of International Journalism
D. of International Economic Law
D. of Linguistics and Applied Linguistics
Research Ce. for Foreign Languages and Literatures
Research I. for Soviet Studies
Research I. for Middle East Culture
German-Speaking Areas Research Ce.
Also secondary school.

Founded 1949. Became Shanghai Foreign Language Institute 1956 and has since acquired present status and title.A Key institution. Under the jurisdiction of the State Commission of Education. Residential facilities for academic staff and students.

Arrangements for co-operation with: University of Pittsburgh; Heidelberg Whitman College; Indiana University of Pennsylvania; Canberra College of Advanced Education; Université de l'Etat, Mons; Université Laval; Institut national des Langues et Civilisations orientales, Paris.

Academic Year: September to July (September-February; February-July).

Admission Requirements: Graduation from senior middle school and entrance examination.

Language of Instruction: Chinese.

Degrees and Diplomas: Bachelor of Arts, 4 yrs. Master. Doctor, Ph.D. Also Advanced Teacher Training qualification.

Library: Central Library, *c.* 806,000 vols.

Publications: Journal of Foreign Languages; Comparative Literature in China; Russian Teaching in China; Foreign Language World; Media in Foreign Langua Instruction; Teach Yourself English; Arab World; Shanghai Students' Post.

Press or Publishing House: Shanghai Foreign Language Education Press; Shanghai Foreign Language Audio-Visual Publishing House.

Academic Staff, 1989-90:

Rank	Full-time
Professors	43
Associate Professors	140
Total	183

Student Enrolment, 1989-90:

	Men	Women	Total
Of the country	915	1052	1967
Of the countries	72	48	120
Total	987	1100	2087

1362 **SHANGHAI JIAOTONG UNIVERSITY**
Shanghai (Shanghai Municipality)

A Key institution.

1363 **SHANGHAI POLYTECHNICAL UNIVERSITY**
Shanghai (Shanghai Municipality)

1364 **SHANGHAI SECOND MEDICAL UNIVERSITY**
280 Chong Qing Nan Road, Shanghai 200025
Telephone: 260760
President: Wang Yi-Fei
Vice-President: Xue Chun-Liang

F. of Medicine (I)
Dean: Li Hong-Wei; *staff* 51
F. of Medicine (II)
Dean: Li Xue-Min; *staff* 18
F. of Medicine (III)
Dean: Wang Zhi-Jin; *staff* 23
S. of Stomatology
Rector: Qiu Wei-Liu; *staff* 34
F. of Pediatrics
Dean: Ding Wen-Xiang; *staff* 33
D. of Biomedical Engineering
Director: Qin Jia-Nan; *staff* 99
D. of Medical Sciences
Director: Wang Hong-Li; *staff* 70
D. of Social Sciences
Director: Ding Yin-Kuai; *staff* 51
D. of Nursing
Director: Liu Guo-Yuan; *staff* 8
Night U.
President: Wang Yi-Fei
S. of Basic Medical Sciences
Rector: Tang Xue-Min; *staff* 689
D. of Medical Nutrition
Director: Shi Kui-Xiong
D. of Health Management
Director: Yang Xin-Tian; *staff* 19

Also 16 Research Institutes and Centres, and 5 affiliated hospitals.

Founded 1952, incorporating Medical School of St. John's University, Medical College of Aurora University, Tong-Teh Medical College, and Shanghai Dentistry Special School. Under the jurisdiction of the Municipal authorities.

Arrangements for co-operation with: University of Missouri-Kansas City; University of California-San Francisco; Osaka-Dental University; Université René Descartes (Paris V); Université d'Aix-Marseille II; Université de Nancy I; State University Centre of Antwerp; Université de Paris VII; Université de Strasbourg; Université de Paris VI; University of Hamburg.

Academic Year: September to July (September-February; February-July).

Admission Requirements: Graduation from senior middle school and entrance examination.

Fees: None.

Languages of Instruction: Chinese, English and French.

Degrees and Diplomas: Bachelor of Medicine, 5 yrs. Master, a further 3-4 yrs. Doctor of Medicine, *c.* 3 yrs after Master.

Library: Health Sciences Library and Information Centre, *c.* 465,195 vols.

Publications: Shanghai Journal of Immunology; Acta Universitatis Medicinalis Secundae Shanghai; The Journal of Clinical Pediatrics; Chinese Journal of Endocrinology and Metabolism; Shanghai Journal of Endocrinology and Metabolism; Shanghai Journal of Andrology; Shanghai Journal of Medical Laboratory.

Press or Publishing House: SSMU Press.

Academic Staff, 1989-90:

Rank	Full-time
Professors	279
Associate Professors	733
Lecturers	1747
Total	2759

Student Enrolment, 1989-90:

	Men	Women	Total
Of the country	2173	2608	4781
Of other countries	47	6	53
Total	2220	2614	4844

1365 **SHANGHAI UNIVERSITY OF ENGINEERING SCIENCE**
435 Xin Chun Road, Shanghai (Shainghai Municipality)
Telex: 142
Telephone: 6611420
President: Jiang Shang Xin

D. of Managerial Engineering
D. of Textile Engineering
D. of Mechanical Engineering
D. of Electrical Engineering
D. of Clothing Technology

Founded 1985, incorporating the Shanghai School Textile Industry. Under the jurisdiction of the Provincial authorities.

Academic Year: February to January (February-July; September-January).

Admission Requirements: Graduation from senior middle school and entrance examination.

Language of Instruction: Chinese.

Degrees and Diplomas: Bachelor of Engineering, 4 yrs.

Library: 5200 vols.

Publication: Journal.

Academic Staff, 1990: 330.

Student Enrolment, 1990: 1414.

1366 **SHANGHAI UNIVERSITY OF SCIENCE AND TECHNOLOGY**
Shanghai (Shanghai Municipality)

1367 **SHANTOU UNIVERSITY**
Tuopu Town, Shantou 515063 (Guandong Province)
Cables: 2828
Telex: 45448 STUNI CN
Telephone: (754) 221128
Fax: (754) 221120
President: Dai Jing Chen

D. of Chinese Language and Literature
; *staff* 31 (3)
D. of Foreign Languages and Literature
; *staff* 45
D. of Mathematics
; *staff* 25 (4)
D. of Physics
; *staff* 25 (6)
D. of Chemistry
; *staff* 26 (1)
D. of Biology
; *staff* 21
D. of Architectural Engineering
; *staff* 19 (2)
D. of Computer and Information Engineering
; *staff* 39 (3)
D. of Art Design
; *staff* 21 (2)
D. of Electro-Mechanic Engineering
; *staff* 7
D. of Economics
; *staff* 24 (4)
D. of History
; *staff* 16 (1)
D. of Law
; *staff* 29 (1)

Medical C.
Dean: Zhong Yong Sheng; *staff* 176
Chinese Language Training Ce. for Foreign Students
Taiwan, Hong Kong and Overseas Chinese Literature Research Ce.
Vice-Director: Chen Xian Mao; *staff* 6
Tumor Pathology Research I.
Director: Zhong Yong Sheng; *staff* 9
Applied Computer Science Research I.
Director: Chen Mu Tian; *staff* – (8)
Research Office of Laws Concerning China's SEZ (and those of Hong Kong and Macao)
Director: Lin Yong Nian; *staff* – (6)
Also 2 hospitals.

Founded 1981. Accepted first students 1981. Under the jurisdiction of the Provincial authorities.

Arrangements for co-operation with: University of Hong Kong; University of Glasgow.

Academic Year: September to July (September-January; February-July).

Admission Requirements: Graduation from senior middle school and entrance examination.

Fees: None.

Language of Instruction: Chinese.

Degrees and Diplomas: Bachelor of–Arts, B.A.; Law, B.L.; Economics, B.E.s.; History, B.H.; Science, B.S.; Engineering, B.E., 4 yrs;Medicine, B.M., 5 yrs.

Libraries: University Library, 386,761 vols; Medical College Library, 149,055.

Special Facilities (Museums, etc.): Marine Biology Experimental Base.

Publications: Journals (Humanities, Science, quarterly); Taiwan, Hong Kong and Overseas Literature; University Newspaper.

Academic Staff, 1989:

Rank	Full-time	Part-time
Professors	20	11
Associate Professors	129	22
Lecturers	234	–
Teaching Assistants	203	–
Total	586	33

Student Enrolment, 1989:

	Men	Women	Total
Of the country	2441	1099	3540
Of other countries	4	3	7
Total	2445	1102	3547*

*Also evening students and students by correspondence.

1368 **SHANXI UNIVERSITY**

Taiyuan (Shanxi Province)
Cables: 0982
Telephone: 773441
President: Li Zhenxi

D. of Chinese
Chairman: ; *staff* 79
D. of History
Chairman: Du Shiduo; *staff* 68
D. of Chemistry
Chairman: Xia Zhizong; *staff* 128
D. of Foreign Languages
Chairman: Wang Zhengren; *staff* 102
D. of Physics
Chairman: Su Dachun; *staff* 106
Teachers' C.
I. of Photo-Electron Research
Director: Peng Kunchi; *staff* 29
I. of Molecular Science Research
Director: Yang Ping; *staff* 27
I. of the Loess Plateau (Economic and Natural Geography, Ecology)
Director: Zhang Weibang; *staff* 32
History Research I.
Director: Qiao Zhiqiang; *staff* 7

Founded 1920 by a British missionary, Timothy Richard. Acquired present name 1900, and status 1943.

Arrangements for co-operation with: University of South Carolina; Rikkyo University.

Academic Year: September to July (September-January; February-July).

Admission Requirements: Graduation from senior middle school and entrance examination.

Fees: None.

Language of Instruction: Chinese.

Degrees and Diplomas: Bachelor of–Arts; Science, 4 yrs. Master, a further 3 yrs.

Library: The North Library, 1,260,000 vols.

Publications: Research on Higher Education; Campus News (bimonthly); Shanxi University Journal.

Academic Staff, 1989-90:

Rank	Full-time	Part-time
Professors	55	45
Associate Professors	287	20
Lecturers	416	–
Teaching Assistants	443	–
Total	1201	65

Student Enrolment, 1989-90:

	Men	Women	Total
Of the country	2830	2494	5324
Of other countries	7	8	15
Total	2837	2502	5339*

*Also 3375 external students.

1369 **SHANXI AGRICULTURAL UNIVERSITY**

Taigu (Shanxi Province)

A Key institution.

1370 **SHANXI UNIVERSITY OF COAL AND CHEMICAL TECHNOLOGY**

Taiyuan (Shanxi Province)

In process of development.

1371 **SHENZHEN UNIVERSITY**

Nantou, Shenzhen (Guandong Province)
Cables: 3356
Telex: 420706 SZN CN
Telephone: 660277
Fax: 660462
President: Wei You-Hai
Director: Liang Shu-Ping

D. of Economics
Director: Zhang Minru; *staff* 33
D. of Management
Director: Yu Zhong-Wen; *staff* 33
D. of Law
Director: Zhong Wu; *staff* 25
D. of Chinese Language and Literature
Director: Hu Jing-Zhi; *staff* 29
D. of Foreign Languages
Director: Tan Zai-Xi; *staff* 52
D. of Social Sciences
Director: Guo Yongxian; *staff* 20
D. of Precision Machinery and Instruments
Director: Gao Li-Sheng; *staff* 14
D. of Electronic Engineering
Director: Ying Qi-Rui; *staff* 29
D. of Architecture
Director: Xu An-Zhi; *staff* 31
D. of Construction Engineering
Director: Yu Ping-Jing; *staff* 11
D. of Applied Mathematics
Director: Liao Ke-Ren; *staff* 17
D. of Applied Chemistry
Director: Luo Yunzhu; *staff* 12
D. of Applied Physics
Director: Wang Jian-Sheng; *staff* 18
Computer Ce.
Director: Huang Yun-Sen; *staff* 33
Audio-visual Ce.
Director: Liu Hui-Yuan; *staff* 20
C. of Adult Education
Director: Liao Han-Guang; *staff* 41

D. for Evening Studies
Dean: Liao Hanguang; *staff* 10
Founded 1983. Residential facilities for academic staff and students.
Academic Year: September to July.
Admission Requirements: Graduation from senior middle school and entrance examination.
Language of Instruction: Chinese.
Library: c. 200,000 vols.
Publications: Journal (quarterly); World Architecture Review (quarterly).
Academic Staff, 1986-87:

Rank	Full-time
Professors	4
Associate Professors	31
Lecturers	137
Assistant Professors	46
Assistants	69
Total	287

Student Enrolment, 1986-87:

	Men	Women	Total
Of the country	1368	686	2054
Of other countries	–	–	64
Total	–	–	2118*

*Also c. 2000 external students.

1372 **SICHUAN INSTITUTE OF FOREIGN LANGUAGES**
Lieshimu, Shapingba Chongqing (Sichuan Province)
Cables: 1818
Telex: 62218 SIFL CN
Telephone: 661737, 664940
President: Lan Ren-Zhe (1990-1994)

D. of English
Head: Tan Shao-Qing; *staff* 96
D. of Teacher Education
Head: Li Wan-Shui; *staff* 65
D. of Russian
Head: Shen Rong-Hui; *staff* 28
D. of French
Head: Huang Xin-Cheng; *staff* 28
D. of German
Head: Diao Cheng-Jun; *staff* 20
D. of Japanese
Head: Wang Tin-Kai; *staff* 28
D. of Chinese as a Foreign Language
Head: Zhu Hong-Guo; *staff* 23
D. of Foreign Trade
Head: Tang Ping-De; *staff* 18
D. for Students Preparing to Study Abroad
Head: Huang Guan-Bin; *staff* 30
Chinese D. for International Students
Head: Huang Guan-Bin; *staff* 7
D. of Adult Education
Head: Zeng Xiang-Lu; *staff* 8
I. of Higher Education Research
Head: Cao Guang-Jiu; *staff* 2
Canadian Studies Ce.
Head: Lan Ren-Zhe; *staff* 5
I. of Foreign Language Lexicography Research
; *staff* 3 (24)
I. of Foreign Children's Literature
Head: Cheng Xian-Guang; *staff* 5 (18)
Research I. of Sinology Abroad
Head: Zhang Liang-Chun; *staff* 2
Audio-visual Ce.
Also middle school and foreign languages middle school.
Founded 1950. Residential facilities for academic staff and students.
Arrangements for exchange with: University of Mons; Beebu University, Japan; Bethune College, Canada; Washington State University; Whiteman College; Linfield College, Oregon.
Academic Year: September to July (September-January; February-July).
Admission Requirements: Graduation from high school and entrance examination.
Fees: None.
Languages of Instruction: Chinese. Also English, French, German, Rusian and Japanese.
Degrees and Diplomas: Bachelor, 4 yrs. Master, a further 3 yrs.
Publications: SISU, Biweekly; Foreign Lanuguage Teaching (academic quarterly); World Children (literary quarterly).
Academic Staff, 1990:

Rank	Full-time
Professors	12
Associate Professors	86
Lecturers	128
Assistants	132
Teachers	10
Total	368

Student Enrolment, 1990:

	Men	Women	Total
Of the country	649	977	1654
Of other countries	14	5	19
Total	663	982	1673*

*Also 535 external students.

1373 **SICHUAN UNIVERSITY**
Chengdu (Sichuan Province)
A Key institution.

1374 **SICHUAN TEACHERS' UNIVERSITY**
Chengdu, Sichuan
Telephone: 42612-341
President: Wang Jun Neng (1983-87)

D. of Chinese Language and Literature
Head: Su Heng
D. of Political Education
Head: Zhou Gang
D. of Foreign Languages
Head: Zhang Yu Du
D. of Mathematics
Head: Kang Shi Xiang
D. of Physics
Head: Zhao Min Guang
D. of Chemistry
Head: Wang Bao
D. of Geography
Head: Xu Zhong Lu
D. of Education
Head: Wei Mao Yun
D. of Biology
Head: Ren Yun Qing
D. of Chinese (for Foreign Students)
Director: Zhang Liang Bin
Electronic Computer Ce.
Director: Yao Liang Wen
D. for Lifelong Education
Directors: Luo Yong Lin; Pi Chao Gang
Founded as college 1952, acquired present status and title 1986. A Key institution under the jurisdiction of the Ministry of Education. Residential facilities for academic staff and students.
Admission Requirements: Graduation from senior middle school and entrance examination.
Language of Instruction: Chinese.
Degrees and Diplomas: Bachelor. Master.
Publication: Journal.
Academic Staff, 1987-87: 700.
Student Enrolment, 1986-87:

Of the country	5000
Of other countries	34
Total	5034

1375 **SOUTH CHINA AGRICULTURE UNIVERSITY**
Wushan (Guangzhou Province)
Cables: 6340 Guangzhou
Telephone: 774881
President: Lu Yong-gen (1983-87)

D. of Agriculture
Director: Zhang Le-qing; *staff* 154

D. of Soil and Agricultural Chemistry
Director: Liu Shu-ji; *staff* 74
D. of Plant Protection
Director: Mo Meng-yi; *staff* 120
D. of Horticulture
Director: Wu Ding-hua; *staff* 105
D. of Forestry
Director: Tu Shi-liang; *staff* 124
D. of Sericulture
Director: Lu Keng-ming; *staff* 70
D. of Agricultural Economics
Director: Ten Jin-wei; *staff* 44
D. of Animal Husbandry and Veterinary Medicine
Director: Wu Xian-hua; *staff* 259
D. of Agricultural Engineering
Director: Shao Yao-jian; *staff* 128
D. of Agricultural Biology
Director: Xiao Jingping; *staff* 92
Sec. of Fundamental Courses of Teaching and Research
Director: Chen Zhen-quan; *staff* 117
Sec. of Marxism-Leninism
Director: Song Tian-quan; *staff* 38
Sec. of Physical Education
Director: Chen Shi-zhang; *staff* 25
D. for Lifelong Education
Directors: Hu Shou-xun; Ke Kai-li; *staff* 17
Also 22 Research Laboratories.

Founded as college 1952, acquired present status and title 1984. A Key institution under the jurisdiction of the Ministry of Agriculture, Animal Husbandry and Fishery and the Provincial Government. Residential facilities for academic staff and students.

Arrangements for co-operation with the Universities of: Pennsylvania State; California; Davis, Kyushu; Sydney;Massey; Kasetsart; Philippines. Riverina-Murray Institute; Silsoe College.

Academic Year: September to July (September-January; March-July).

Admission Requirements: Graduation from senior middle school and entrance examination.

Language of Instruction: Chinese.

Degrees and Diplomas: Bachelor of Science, 4-5 yrs. Master of Science, a further 3 yrs. Doctor, a further 3 yrs.

Library: Central Library, 630,000 vols.

Publication: Journal (quarterly).

Academic Staff, 1986-87:

Rank	Full-time
Professors)	41
Associate Professors	109
Lecturers	488
Teaching Assistants	325
Teachers	97
Total	1060

Student Enrolment, 1986-87:

	Men	Women	Total
Of the country	800	200	1000
Of other countries	35	1	36
Total	835	201	1036*

*Also 150 external students.

1376 **SOUTHWEST CHINA JIAOTONG UNIVERSITY**
District of Emei (Sichuan Province)

A Key institution.

1377 **SOUTHWEST CHINA TEACHERS UNIVERSITY**
2 Tiansheng Road, Chongqing 630715 (Sichuan Province)
Cables: 0350
Telephone: 3901, 3902
President: Zhong Zhang-Cheng
Secretary-General: Wang Chang-Kai

D. of Chinese Languagu and Literature
Dean: Cao Ting-Hua; *staff* 107
D. of Foreign Languages and Literature
Dean: Cheng Zhi-An; *staff* 145
D. of Education
Dean: Yang Zhong-Yi; *staff* 118
D. of Political Education
Dean: Zou Xue-Rong; *staff* 95
D. of History
Dean: Cheng Zi-Hua; *staff* 81
D. of Library and Information Sciences
Dean: Wu Chao-Yuan; *staff* 25
D. of Mathematics
Dean: Zhou Zhong-Qun; *staff* 97
D. of Physics
Dean: Wan Zhong-Yi; *staff* 122
D. of Chemistry
Dean: Huang Zhi-Gui; *staff* 125
D. of Biology
Dean: Zhang Guo-Zheng; *staff* 112
D. of Geography
Dean: Liu Qing-Quan; *staff* 90
D. of Computer Sciences
Dean: Qiou Yu-Hui; *staff* 55
D. of Audio-visual Education
Dean: Cheng Cheng-Zhi; *staff* 49
D. of Music
Dean: Xue Shi-Min; *staff* 79
D. of Physical Culture
Dean: Feng Xiao-Fa; *staff* 90
D. of Arts
Dean: Fu Yu-Ben; *staff* 86
Also 10 Research Institutes.

Founded 1950, incorporating National Women Teachers' College and Sichuan Province Education College. Under thejurisdiction of the State Education Commission. Residential facilities for academic staff and students.

Arrangements for co-operation with: West Illinois University; Hydaburg College; Tennessee University; West Washington University; Friendship University; West Chester University; Utrecht University.

Academic Year: September to July (September-January; Febuary-July).

Admission Requirements: Graduation from high school and entrance examination.

Fees: None.

Language of Instruction: Chinese.

Degrees and Diplomas: Bachelor, 4 yrs. Master, a further 3 yrs. Doctor, a further 2 yrs.

Library: 1,300,000 vols.

Special Facilities (Museums, etc.): The Museum of History, Art Gallery.

Publication: Journal of Southwest China Teachers University (quarterly).

Press or Publishing House: Southwest China Teachers University Press.

Academic Staff, 1989:

Rank	Full-time
Professors	44
Associate Professors	241
Lecturers	446
Assistants	383
Others	43
Total	1157

Student Enrolment, 1989-90:

	Men	Women	Total
Of the country	3559	2396	5955*

*Also 5940 external students.

1378 **SOUTHWEST UNIVERSITY OF FORESTRY**
District of Anning, Kunming (Yunnan Province)
Telex: 2825
Telephone: 28606
President: Wang Chun-lin (1984-)

Forestry
Training Sec. for Cadres
Also middle school.

Founded 1939 as department of Agricultural College, Yunnan University. Acquired present status and title 1983. A Key institution under the jurisdiction of the Ministry of Forestry.

Academic Year: September to July (September-February; March-July).

Admission Requirements: Graduation from senior middle school and entrance examination.

Language of Instruction: Chinese.

Degrees and Diplomas: Bachelor, 4 yrs. Master, a further 3 yrs.

Library: Central Library, *c.* 200,000 vols.

Publication: Journal.

Academic Staff: c. 500.
Student Enrolment: c. 1000.

1379 **SUZHOU UNIVERSITY**
Suzhou (Jiangsu Province)

1380 ***TAIYUAN UNIVERSITY OF TECHNOLOGY**
Taiyuan (Shanxi Province)
Cables: 0560
Telephone: 66701
President: Yang Guitong (1984-)

D. of Hydraulic Engineering
Head: Pan Guangzai; *staff* 111
D. of Mechanical Engineering I
Head: Feng Zhaoxi; *staff* 174
D. of Mechanical Engineering II
Head: Dong Zonglu; *staff* 117
D. of Electrical Engineering
Head: Guo Gennai; *staff* 156
D. of Thermal Energy Engineering
Head: Pan Yintang; *staff* 32
D. of Information Systems Engineering
Head: Chen Yanyi; *staff* 91
D. of Computer Sciences and Engineering
Head: Jiang Lizhang: *staff* 41
D. of Chemical Engineering
Head: Chen Binquan *staff* 160
D. of Applied Chemistry
Head: Duan Ruizheng; *staff* 118
D. of Mathematics and Mechanics
Head: Sun Jue; *staff* 139
D. of Civil and Environmental Engineering
Head: Qiu Yihui; *staff* 189
D. of Basic Theory
Head: Li Qunzhu; *staff* 133
D. of Management Engineering
Head: Zhou Guirong; *staff* 25
D. for Evening Studies
Head: Xu Rongliang; *staff* 4
Also 7 Research Institutes and primary school.

Founded as college of Shanxi University 1902. Became independent institute 1953. Acquired present status and title 1984. Under the jurisdiction of the Provincial Government. Residential facilities for academic staff and students.

Arrangements for co-operation with: Oberlin College; South Carolina University; Georgia Institute of Technology; Newcastle-upon-Tyne Polytechnic.

Academic Year: September to July (September-January; February-July).

Admission Requirements: Graduation from senior middle school and entrance examination.

Language of Instruction: Chinese.

Degrees and Diplomas: Bachelor of Science, 4 yrs. Master, a further 3 yrs. Doctor. Also Diploma.

Library: Central Library, c. 1,200,000 vols.

Publication: Journal (quarterly).

Academic Staff, 1986-87:

Rank	Full-time
Professors	51
Associate Professors	226
Lecturers	347
Assistants	676
Total	1300

Student Enrolment, 1986-87:

	Men	Women	Total
Of the country	3801	1540	5341

1381 **TALIMU UNIVERSITY OF AGRICULTURE AND LAND RECLAMATION**
District of Akesu (Oygur Xingjian Autonomous Region)

1382 **TIANJIN UNIVERSITY**
92 Weijin Road, Nankai District, Tianjin 300072 (Tianjin Municipality)
Telex: 23288 TUICO CN
Telephone: (22) 31-8715
Fax: 318329
President: Wu Yongshi
Secretary-General: Wang Yutin

Graduate S.
Head: Zhou Heng
S. of Management
Head: Liu Bao
S. of Petrochemical Engineering
Head: Chen Hongfang
D. of Chemical Engineering
Head: Chen Hongfang; *staff* 148
D. of Applied Chemistry
Head: Guo Hetong; *staff* 82
D. of Chemistry
Head: Tian Ruchuan; *staff* 101
D. of Precision Instruments Engineering
Head: Zhang Guoxiong; *staff* 178
D. of Electronic Engineering
Head: Yu Sile; *staff* 154
D. of Electrical Engineering and Automation
Head: Xu Lingan; *staff* 157
D. of Physics
Head: Ma Shining; *staff* 102
D. of Mechanical Engineering
Head: Zhu Mengzhou; *staff* 198
D. of Thermophysics Engineering
Head: Xu Sidu; *staff* 63
D. of Architecture
Heaed: Hu Dejun
D. of Civil Engineering
Head: Yu Qingrong; *staff* 140
D. of Water Resources and Harbour Engineering
Head: Cui Guangtao; *staff* 134
D. of Ocean Engineering and Naval Architecture
Head: Liu Defu; *staff* 59
D. of Management Engineering
Head: He Bosen; *staff* 56
D. of Mathematics
Head: Qi Zhilan; *staff* 89
D. of Mechanics
Head: Shu Wei; *staff* 77
D. of Humanities and Social Sciences
Head: Feng Huaibi; *staff* 66
D. of Foreign Languages
Head: Zhang Zhongying; *staff* 94
D. of Industrial Economics and System Engineering
Head: Xu Datu; *staff* 51
D. of Material Science and Engineering
Head: Yuan Qiming; *staff* 86
D. of Computer Engineering and Science
Head: Wang Lei; *staff* 44
Thermal Energy I.
Head: Su Sidu; *staff* 64
System Engineering Institute
Head: Liu Bao; *staff* 40
Chemical Engineering I.
Head: Yu Guozong; *staff* 34
I. of Modern Optical Instruments
Head: Wu Jizong; *staff* 21 (40)
Internal Combustion Engine Research I.
Head: Yao Shouren; *staff* 220
Higher Education I.
Head: Wang Zhihe; *staff* 8
S. of Adult Education
Head: Xu Leping; *staff* 16
Training Ce. for Managerial Cadres of Higher Engineering Education
Head: Wang Zhihe; *staff* 7 (7)

Founded 1895 as Peiyang University. Acquired present title 1952. A Key institution under the jurisdiction of the State Education Commission of China. Residential facilities for academic staff and students.

Arrangements for co-operation with 37 institutions in 12 countries, including: USA; Canada; Japan; United Kingdom; France; Federal Republic of Germany; Poland; India; Italy; Finland; Sweden.

Academic Year: September to July (September-January; February-July).

Admission Requirements: Graduation from senior middle school and entrance examination.

Language of Instruction: Chinese.

Degrees and Diplomas: Bachelor, 4 yrs. Master, a further 2 ½ yrs. Doctor, 3 yrs after Master.

Library: Central Library, *c.* 1,500,000 vols.

Publication: Journal.

Press or Publishing House: Publishing House of Tianjin University.

Academic Staff, 1990:

Rank	Full-time
Professors	195
Associate Professors	756
Lecturers	1070
Assistant Teachers	474
Total	2495

Student Enrolment, 1990:

Of the country	12293
Of other countries	56
Total	12,349

1383 **TIANJIN NORMAL UNIVERSITY**
Tianjin (Tianjin Municipality)

Education

1384 **TIANJIN UNIVERSITY OF COMMERCE**
East Entrance of Jinba Road, Northern Suburbs of Tianjin, Tianjin
Cables: 3614
Telex: 23174 TIPTB CN (53)
Telephone: 573169
Fax: 573169
President: Li Bing-Wei

D. of Commercial Enterprise Management
Head: Zhou Tie; *staff* 71
D. of Management Engineering
Head: Li Yun; *staff* 47
D. of Refrigeration Engineering
Head: Gao Zu-Kun; *staff* 59
D. of Food Engineering
Head: Jin Tie-Sheng; *staff* 93
D. of Packing Engineering
Head: Fan Zhu-Xiao; *staff* 67
D. of Politics and Laws
D. of Basic Studies
D. of Training Cadres
D. of Hotel and Catering Management
I. of Commercial Comprehensive Designs
Head: Fang Qi-Wu; *staff* 17
I. of Freezing Technology
Head: He Shao-Shu; *staff* 16

Founded 1984. Under the jurisdiction of the Ministry of Commerce and Provincial Government. Residential facilities for academic staff and students;

Academic Year: September to July (September-January; February-July).

Admission Requirements: Graduation from high school and entrance examination.

Fees: None.

Language of Instruction: Chinese.

Degrees and Diplomas: Bachelor, 4 yrs. Master, a further 2 yrs. Also Dipomas, 2 yrs.

Library: 400,000 vols.

Publications: Campus periodical; University newspaper; Higher Education Research.

Press or Publishing House: Printing House of Tianjin University of Commerce.

Academic Staff, 1990:

Rank	Full-time
Professors	5
Associate Professors	75
Lecturers	160
Assistants	173
Total	413

Student Enrolment, 1990: 5000 (Also 365 students by correspondence).

1385 **TONGJI UNIVERSITY**
1239 Siping Road, Shanghai (Shanghai Municipality)
Cables: 3658
Telex: 33488 TJIDC CN
Telephone: 5455080
Fax: 0086-021-545
President: Gao Tingyao (1989-93)

S. of Mechanical Engineering
Head: Xi Shiguang; *staff* 271
S. of Structural Engineering
Head: Fan Lichu; *staff* 202
S. of Architecture and Urban Planning
Head: Tao Shonglin; *staff* 185 (17)
Shanghai Research I. for Disaster, Prevention, and Relief
Head: Shen Zuyan; *staff* 2 (62)
I. of Environmental Protection Technology
Head: Gu Guowei; *staff* 50
I. of Acoustics
Head: Zhao Shonglin; *staff* 49
Shanghai I. of Radiation and Immunity Analytical Technology
Head: Huang Zude; *staff* 12
Computer Ce.
Head: Chen Fumin; *staff* 47
Graduate S.
Head: Gao Tingyao; *staff* 23
Correspondence and Continuation Education S.
Head: Tu Chengsong; *staff* 51

Also 24 departments of the faculties and 18 research institutes and centres.

Founded 1927. A Key institution under the jurisdiction of the National Education Commission. Residential facilities for some academic staff and for students.

Arrangements for co-operation with: Ruhr University, Bochum; Darmstadt Technical University.

Academic Year: September to July (September-January; February-June;June-July).

Admission Requirements: Graduation from senior middle school and entrance examination.

Fees: None.

Language of Instruction: Chinese.

Degrees and Diplomas: Bachelor of Engineering, 4-5 yrs. Master, a further 2 ½ yrs. Doctor, 3-4 yrs after Master. Post-doctorate.

Library: 1,400,000 vols.

Publication: Tongji Journal (monthly).

Press or Publishing House: Tongji University Press.

Academic Staff, 1989:

Rank	Full-time
Professors	142
Associate Professors	584
Lecturers	776
Assistants	416
Total	1918

Student Enrolment, 1989:

Of the country	8481
Of other countries	156
Total	8637*

*Also 63 external students by correspondence.

1386 **TONGJI MEDICAL UNIVERSITY**
Hang Kong Lu, Wuhan (Hubei Province)
Telephone: 356811
President: Wu Zaide (1984-87)

F. of Basic Medical Sciences
Director: Wang Dishun; *staff* 524
S. of Public Health
Dean: Wen Liyang; *staff* 263
F. of Pharmacy
Dean: Shi Chaozhou; *staff* 106
F. of Forensic Medicine
Dean: Huang Guangzhao; *staff* 31
I. of Family Planning
Director: Wu Xirui; *staff* 63
I. of Organ Transplantation
Director: Xia Shuisheng; *staff* 64

I. of Cardiovascular Disease
Director: Dan Hongjun; *staff* 96
I. of Basic Medicine
Director: Wang Dixun
I. of Chinese and Western Medicine
Director: Li Mingzhen; *staff* 45
I. of Environmental Medicine
Director: Lu Sheng yie; *staff* 65
I. of Social Medicine
Director: Liang Haozhai
Experimental Medicine Research Ce.
Director: Deng Zhongduan; *staff* 113
Ce. for Medical Training
Director: Li Zhongzheng; *staff* 20
Sec. for Lifelong Education
Director: Zhen Hongzhang; *staff* 3

Founded as school 1907, acquired present status and title 1985. A Key institution under the jurisdiction of Ministry of Health and the Provincial Government. Residential facilities for academic staff and students.

Arrangements for co-operation with the Universities of: Ohio State, Boston; Pittsburgh; Heidelberg; Ulm; Saar;Essen; Munich; Berlin (Free); Kanazawa.

Academic Year: September to August (September-January; February-July).

Admission Requirements: Graduation from senior middle school and entrance examination.

Language of Instruction: Chinese.

Degrees and Diplomas: Bachelor of Medical Sciences, 5 yrs. Master, a further 3 yrs. Doctor, 3 yrs.

Library: Central Library, 369,000 vols.

Press or Publishing House: University Press.

Academic Staff, 1986-87:

Rank	Full-time
Professors	156
Associate Professors	335
Lecturers	994
Assistants	1400
Total	2885

Student Enrolment, 1986-87:

	Men	Women	Total
Of the country	2192	1103	3295
Of other countries	10	1	11
Total	2202	1104	3306*

*Also 208 external students.

1387 **TSINGHUA UNIVERSITY**

Beijing 100084 (Beijing Municipality)
Telex: 22617 QHTSC CN
Telephone: (1) 2567733
Fax: (1) 2562768
President: ZhangXianowen (1988-)
Provost: Zhou Yuanqing

S. of Sciences
Dean: Zhou Guangzhao
S. of Economics and Management
Dean: Zhu Rongji
S. of Architecture
Dean: Li Daozeng
S. of Lifelong Education
Dean: Lu Sen
Graduate S.
Dean: Liang Youneng
D. of Architecture
Head: Gao Yilan
D. of Urban Planning and Design
Head: Zhao Bingshi
D. of Automation
Head: Wang Sen
D. of Automobile Engineering
Head: Liu Weixin
D. of Chemical Engineering
Head: Dai Youyuan
D. of Civil Engineering
Head: Jiang Jianjing
D. of Computer Sciences and Technology
Head: Wang Erqian
D. of Electrical Engineering
Head: Han Yingduo
D. of Electronic Engineering
Head: Zhang Keqian
D. of Engineering Mechanics
Head: Yu Shouwen
D. of Engineering Physics
D. of Environmental Engineering
Head: Jing Wenyong
D. of Materials Science and Engineering
Head: Jianguang Wu
D. of Mechanical Engineering
Head: Pan Jiluan
D. of Precision Instrumentation and Mechanology
Head: Jin Guofan
D. of Thermal Engineering
Head: Ye Dajun
D. of Applied Mathematics
Head: Xiao Shutie
D. of Chemistry
Head: Wu Guoshi
D. of Modern Applied Physics
Head: Xiong Jiajong
D. of Economics
Head: Dong Xinbao
D. of International Trade and Finance
Head: Zhao Jiahe
D. of Management Engineering
Head: Xu Guohua
D. of Management Information Systems
Head: Zhao Jiahe
D. of Chinese Language and Literature
Head (Acting): Zhang Zhengquan
D. of Foreign Language
Head: Wu Guhua
D. of Social Sciences
Head: Jia Guan
Also 31 Research Institutes and 146 Laboratories.

Founded 1911. A Key institution.

Arrangements for co-operation with 46 universities in 17 countries.

Academic Year: Bachelor, 5 yrs. Master, a further 2-3 yrs. Doctor, Ph.D., 3 yrs.

Academic Year: September to July.

Admission Requirements: Graduation from senior middle school and entrance examination.

Fees: None.

Language of Instruction: Chinese.

Library: 2,300,000 vols.

Academic Staff, 1990: 3901.

Student Enrolment, 1990: 13,287 (Including 164 international students from 39 countries).

1388 **UNIVERSITY OF ELECTRONIC SCIENCE AND TECHNOLOGY OF CHINA**

Chengdu
Cables: 6061
Telex: 60202
Telephone: 33312
Fax: 334131
President: Liu Sheng-Gang (1986-90)

D. of Radio and Telecommunications Technology
Head: Liu Ya-Kang; *staff* 180
D. of Electromagnetic Field Engineering
Head: Ruan Ying-Zheng; *staff* 78
D.of Electronic Mechanics
Head: Xiong Shi-He; *staff* 150
D. of Opto-Electronics Technology
Head: Xiang Jing-Cheng; *staff* 150
D. of Foreign Languages
Head: Chen Zhi-Yuan; *staff* 93
D. of Electronic Engineering
Head: Xiang Jing-Cheng; *staff* 170
D. of Computer Sciences
Head: Gong Tian-Fu; *staff* 102

High Energy and Micro-Electronic Research I.
Head: Li Hong-Fu; *staff* 64
Applied Physics Research I.
Head: Guan Benkang; *staff* 97
Computation Ce.
Head: Li Shi-Cheng; *staff* 50
Microwave Test Ce.
Head: Zhang Qi-Zhao; *staff* 48
Also branches in: Kun Ming, De Yang, Mie Yang, Pan Zi-Hua.

Founded 1956. A Key institution under the jurisdiction of the Ministry of Machinery and Electronic Industry. Residential facilities for academic staff and students.

Arrangements for co-operation with: Keio University; Fachhochschule Aachen; Technische Universität Hamburg-Harburg; Simon Fraser University; Arizona State University; Technische Universität Braunschweig; Universitéscientifique et médicale de Grenoble.

Academic Year: September to July (September-February; March-July).

Admission Requirements: Graduation from senior middle school and entrance examination.

Fees: None.

Language of Instruction: Chinese.

Degrees and Diplomas: Bachelor, 4 yrs. Master, a further 2-3 yrs. Doctorate, 2-3 yrs after Master.

Library: c. 1 m. vols

Publication: Academic Journal.

Press or Publishing House: University Publishing House.

Academic Staff, 1990:

Rank	Full-time
Professors	97
Assistent Professors	432
Lecturers	926
Assistents	432
Total	1887

Student Enrolment, 1990: 6984.

1389 **UNIVERSITY OF INTERNATIONAL BUSINESS AND ECONOMICS**

He Ping Jie Beikou, Beijing (Beijing Municipality) 100029
Cables: 2161
Telex: 22019 CCHDP CN
Telephone: 4212022/4212186
President: Sun Weiyan (1984-)

F. of International Business Communications
Dean: Huang Zhen-hua; *staff* 204
F. of Foreign Languages (French, Spanish, Russian, Italian, German, Arabic, Korean, and Vietnamese)
Dean: Wang Hanming; *staff* 115
F. of International Business
Dean: Li Kanghua; *staff* 94
F. of Customs Administration
Dean: Du Congde; *staff* 58
F. of International Business Management
Dean: Gao Guopei; *staff* 72
F. of International Economic Co-operation
Dean: Chu Xiangyin; *staff* 48
F. of International Economic Law
Dean: Feng Datong; *staff* 35
F. of Political Science
Dean: Jiang Yonghe; *staff* 39
F. of German
Dean: Wang Zhenfu; *staff* 34
F. of Economic Information Management
Dean: Cao Zelan; *staff* 28
Paçific Asian Business I.
Director: Liu Fangtian; *staff* 5
Audio-visual Ce.
Director: Sheng Yueshan; *staff* 14
Business English Training Ce.
Head: Chen Zhunming; *staff* 45
Ce. for Lifelong Education
Director: Ma Guangde; *staff* 7
D. for Correspondence Courses
Director: Cai Yuanling; *staff* 11
Teacher Training Ce
Director: Ding Henggi; *staff* 5
International Business Research I.
Director: Yu Shimao; *staff* 49
Also branch school in Hainan Province.

Founded 1954 as institute, acquired present status and title 1984. A Key institution under the jurisdiction ofthe Ministry of Foreign Trade. Residential facilities for academic staff and students.

Arrangements for co-operation with: George Washington University; Seton Hall University; Pace University; State University of New York System; Carleton University; St. Mary's University; Tokyo Keizai University; Hitotsubashi University; American Graduate School of International Management, Glendale, Arizona; Winona State University; University of Connecticut; Loyola Law School; University of South Carolina; University of British Columbia; University of Lancaster; Victoria University; University of Wellington; Moscow State Institute of International Relations; Central School of Statistics and Planning, Warsaw; College of Foreign Trade, Budapest; Prague School of Economics.

Academic Year: September to July (September-January; March-July).

Admission Requirements: Graduation from senior middle school and entrance examination.

Languages of Instruction: Chinese and English.

Degrees and Diplomas: Bachelor. Master. Doctor.

Library: 440,000 vols.

Special Facilities (Museums, etc.): Movie Studio.

Publications: Journal of International Trade (bimonthly); Japanese Study, Translation of International Trade Articles; Journal UIBE (bimonthly).

Press or Publishing House: International Business Educational Press.

Academic Staff, 1990:

Rank	Full-time
Professors	47
Associate Professors	163
Lecturers	276
Assistant Professors	293
Teachers	57
Total	836

Student Enrolment, 1990:

Of the country	2362
Of other countries	87
Total	2449*

*Also 11,000 external students.

1390 **UNIVERSITY OF MEDICINE OF CHINA**

Shenyang (Liaoning Province)
Cables: 3257
Telephone: 32578
President: He Wei-Wei (1984-)

Medicine

Founded 1931 as school. Acquired present status and title 1948, incorporating Shenyang Medical College and Liaoning Medical College. Under the jurisdiction of the Ministry of Health. Residential facilities for academic staff and students.

Arrangements for co-operation with the Universities of: Jichi; Sapporo; Tohoku; Kurume; Mie; Kanazawa; Fukuoka.

Academic Year: September to August (September-February; March-August).

Admission Requirements: Graduation from senior middle school and entrance examination.

Language of Instruction: Chinese.

Degrees and Diplomas: Bachelor, 5-6 yrs. Master. Doctor, 2 ½-3 yrs.

Library: Central Library, *c.* 340,000 vols.

Publications: Journal (bimonthly); Journal of Pediatrics, Chinese Health Statistics (quarterly); Practical Ophthalmology (bimonthly).

Academic Staff: c. 1080.

Student Enrolment: c. 3340.

1391 **UNIVERSITY OF PETROLEUM**

149 Taian Street Dongying 257062 (Shandong Province)
Cables: 7108
Telex: 39314 FAOSL CN
Telephone: (5461) 221011
Fax: 222923
President: Yang Guanghua (1984-)

Secretary-General: Wang Yaobin
D. of Petroleum Engineering (including Computer Sciences)
Dean: Chen Tinggen; *staff* 72
D. of Petroleum Exploration
Dean: Liu Zhongyi; *staff* 124
D. of Chemical Engineering
Dean: Lin Shixiong; *staff* 145
D. of Mechanical Engineering
Dean: Lu Yongming; *staff* 168
D. of Automation
Dean: Chai Qinzhong; *staff* 68
D. of Management Engineering
Dean: Shi Zhaofu; *staff* 34
D. of Mathematics and Physics
Dean: Yan Zhipei; *staff* 137
Zell Drilling I.
Head: Shen Zhonghou; *staff* 45
Heavy Oil I.
Head: Fan Yaohua; *staff* 33
Petroleum Exploration I.
Head: Huang Longji; *staff* 22
Applied Tribology I.
Head: Zhai Yusheng; *staff* 9 (5)
UN-Assisted Training Ce. Oil Exploration and Development Techniques
Dean: Xia Yuequan; *staff* 26 (33)
Computer Ce.
Also 54 Laboratories and 22 Research Divisions.

Founded 1953 as Beijing Petroleum Institute, became China Petroleum Institute 1969. Acquired present status and title 1988. A Key institution under the jurisdiction of the National Petroleum Corporation and Shandong Education Committee. Residential facilities for academic staff and students.

Arrangements for co-operation with: Texas A&M University; Heriot-Watt University.

Academic Year: September to July (September-January; February-July).

Admission Requirements: Graduation from senior middle school and entrance examination.

Fees: None.

Language of Instruction: Chinese.

Degrees and Diplomas: Bachelor of Engineering, 4 yrs. Master, a further 3 yrs. Doctor, 3 yrs.

Library: Central Library, *c.* 1,000,000 vols.

Special Facilities (Museums, etc.): Museum for University Development; Cinema.

Publications: High Education (quarterly); Journal of the University of Petroleum (editions of Natural Science and Social Science, quarterly).

Press or Publishing House: The Publishing House of University of Petroleum.

Academic Staff, 1990:

Rank	Full-time
Professors	96
Assistant Professors	308
Lecturers	373
Others	526
Total	1303

Student Enrolment, 1990: 6980 (Also 3300 external students).

1392 **UNIVERSITY OF SCIENCE AND TECHNOLOGY OF CHINA**
24 Jin Zhai Road, Hefei (Anhui Province)
Cables: 4430
Telephone: 63300

D. of Mathematics
D. of Physics
D. of Modern Chemistry
D. of Modern Physics
D. of Modern Mechanics
D. of Radio and Electronics
D. of Earth and Space Sciences
D. of Biology
D. of Precision Technology
D. of Science Management (in preparation)
Also 38 laboratories and 6 Research Divisions.

Founded 1958.

Admission Requirements: Graduation from senior middle school and entrance examination.

Language of Instruction: Chinese.

Degrees and Diplomas: Bachelor of Science, 5 yrs. Master. Doctor, Ph.D.

Library: *c.* 500,000 vols.

Academic Staff: *c.* 1460.

Student Enrolment: *c.* 3520.

1393 **WEST CHINA UNIVERSITY OF MEDICAL SCIENCES**
Chengdu
Cables: 7777 Chengdu
Telex: 60251 UCUMS CN
Telephone: (28) 581130
Fax: (28) 583252
President: Yang Guang-Ha (1988-)

S. of Medicine
Dean: Tang Xiao-Da; *staff* 666
S. of Stomatology
Dean: Chen An-Yu; *staff* 112
S. of Public Health
Dean: Ni Zong-Zan; *staff* 192
S. of Pharmacy
Dean: Zheng-Hu; *staff* 258
S. of Basic Medical Studies
Dean: Bao Ding-Yuan; *staff* 505
D. of Professional Retraining
Director: Chen Shaoji
D. of Forensic Medecine
Director: Wu Jia-Wen; *staff* 52
D. of Foreign Languages
Director: Wu Shu-Kai; *staff* 54
D. of Sociology
Director: Ji Tie-Jian; *staff* 30
I. of Stomatology
Deputy Director: Zhao Yun-Fong
I. of Oncology (2)
Also 12 research centres and institutes.

Founded 1910 as a missionary institution. Became Medical College 1959 and later University. A Key institution under the jurisdiction of the Ministry of Public Health. Residential facilities for academic staff and students.

Arrangements for co-operation with: University of Toronto; University of British Columbia; University of Washington.

Academic Year: September to July (September-February; March-July).

Admission Requirements: Graduation from senior middle school and entrance examination.

Languages of Instruction: Chinese and English.

Degrees and Diplomas: Bachelor of Medical Sciences, 6 yrs. Master, a further 3 yrs. Doctor, 2 yrs after Master.

Library: *c.* 319,000 vols.

Publications: Acta Academica Medicinae Sichuan; West China Journal of Stomatology; Heredity and Disease.

Press or Publishing House: Press House.

Academic Staff, 1990:

Rank	Full-time
Professors	223
Associate Professors	475
Assistant Professors	679
Total	1377

Student Enrolment, 1990:

	Men	Women	Total
Of the country	2072	1707	3779

1394 **WUHAN UNIVERSITY**
Wuhan (Hubei Province)

A Key institution.

1395 **WUHAN TECHNICAL UNIVERSITY OF SURVEYING AND MAPPING**

39 Luoyu Road, Wuhan 430070 (Hubei Province)
Cables: 6852
Telex: 40210 WTUSM CN
Telephone: 715571
Fax: 714185
President: Ning Jinsheng
Secretary-General: Zhang Shaoduo

D. of Engineering Surveys
Chairman: Ding Jungwang; *staff* 109
D. of Photogrammetry and Remote Sensing
Chairman: Li Deren; *staff* 117 (5)
D. of Geodesy
Chairman: Tao Benzao; *staff* 97 (4)
D. of Cartography
Chairman: Zhu Guorui; *staff* 74 (1)
D. of Printing Enginering
Chairman: Zou Yujun; *staff* 55 (1)
D. of Optical Instrumentation
Chairman: Chen Xiaodong; *staff* 154
D. of Electronic Engineering
Chairman: Yuan Yuzheng; *staff* 52 (1)
D. of Computer Sciences and Engineering
Chairman: Li Jingxiang; *staff* 67 (2)
D. of Architectural Engineering
Chairman: Zhao Xingren; *staff* 48
National L. for Remote Sensing Information Engineering in Surveying and Mapping
Director: Zhang Zuxun; *staff* 72 (58)
Education Ce. for Urban and Rural Surveys, Planning and Management
Director: Yang Ren; *staff* 24 (3)
D. of Social Sciences
Director: Hiang Xianguang; *staff* 31
D. of Basic Studies
Director: Hu Weimin; *staff* 104 (1)
Research I. of Surveying and Mapping
Diretor: Zhang Zuxun
Computer Ce.
Director: Yang Quanxing; *staff* 33

Founded 1958 as college, acquired present status and title 1984. Under the jurisdiction of the State EducationCommission. Residential facilities for academic staff and students.

Arrangements for co-operation with: University of New Brunswick; University of North Dakota; University of Washington State; Technical University for Surveying and Mapping, Moscow; Hong Kong Polytechnic; International Institute for Aerospace Survey and Earth Sciences, Netherlands; University of Queensland; Queensland University of Technology.

Academic Year: September to July (September-January; February-July).

Admission Requirements: Graduation from senior middle school and entrance examination.

Fees: None.

Languages of Instruction: Chinese and English.

Degrees and Diplomas: Bachelor of Engineering, 4 yrs. Master, a further 2 ½ yrs. Doctor, a further 3 yrs.

Libraries: Central Library, *c.* 480,000 vols; Social Science Library, 24,000; various departmental libraries, 50,000

Publications: Journal of Wuhan Technical University of Surveying and Mapping (quarterly); Science and Technology at WTUSM (quarterly); Sci-Tech Translations at WTUSM (quarterly); Cartography (quarterly).

Press or Publishing House: Publishing House of Wuhan Technical University of Surveying and Mapping.

Academic Staff, 1989-90:

Rank	Full-time	Part-time
Professors	50	15
Associate Professors	158	1
Lecturers	197	–
Assistants	210	–
Total	615	16

Student Enrolment, 1989-90:

	Men	Women	Total
Of the country	2580	828	3408
Of other countries	10	–	10
Total	2590	828	3418*

*Also 1363 external students.

1396 **WUHAN UNIVERSITY OF HYDRAULIC AND ELECTRIC ENGINEERING**

Wuhan 430072 (Hubei Province)
Cables: 5750 wuhan
Telex: C/O 40170 WCTEL CN
Telephone: (027) 812212
Fax: (027) 814496
President: Liu Zhao-Yi

D. of Hydraulic Engineering
Dean: Lei Sheng-Long; *staff* 154
D. of River Engineering
Dean: Xu Chen-Xian; *staff* 97
D. of Water Power Engineering
Dean: Xiao Huan-Xiong; *staff* 207
D. of Civil Engineering
Dean: Tian Chuang-Qian; *staff* 107
D. of Mechanical Engineering
Dean: Guo Ying-Long; *staff* 121
D. of Electrical Engineering
Dean: Li Guang-Xi; *staff* 146
D. of Computer and Electronic Engineering
Dan: Lin Tian-Chen; *staff* 98
D. of Hydraulic Power Engineering
Dean: Li Yu-Xing; *staff* 79
D. of Thermal Power Engineering
Dean: He Zhi; *staff* 130
D. of Management Engineering
Dean: Zhang Shao-Qiang; *staff* 25
D. of Basic Science
Dean: Zhou Xue-Liang; *staff* 194
D. of Foreign Languages (English, French)
Dean: Ji Hong-Chang; *staff* 50
D. of Social Science
Dean: Yuan Yao-Dong; *staff* 65
Research I. of Water Conservancy and Hydraulic and Electric Power
Director: Liang Zhai-Chao; *staff* 83
Research I. of Electrical Engineering
Director: Chen Chi-Xuan; *staff* 44
Research I. of Hydraulic Construction
Director: Xiao Huan-Xiong; *staff* 62
Research I. of Irrigation and Drainage
Director: Shen Yong-Kai; *staff* 46
I. of Electro-mechanical Pumping Station Research
Director: Lu Hong-Qi; *staff* 46
River Engineering Research I.
Director: Wang Yun-Hui; *staff* 29
Hydraulic Power Engineering Research I.
Director: Li Yu-Xing; *staff* 24
Thermal Power Science Research I.
Director: He Zhi; *staff* 39
Computer and Electronic Application Research I.
Director: Li Chuan-Xiang; *staff* 29
Social Science Research I.
Director: Liu Xin-Bin; *staff* 20
Higher Learning Education Research I.
Director: Wang Hong-Shuo; *staff* 6

Founded 1954. A Key institution. Residential facilities for academic staff and students.

Arrangements for co-operation with: University of Iowa; University of Manchester Institute of Science and Technology; University of Queensland; Leningrad Polytechnic Institute; Institut national polytechnique de Toulouse.

Academic Year: September to July (September-February; February-July).

Admission Requirements: Graduation from high school and entrance examination.

Fees: None.

Language of Instruction: Chinese.

Degrees and Diplomas: Bachelor of–Arts; Science, 4 yrs. Master, a further 2-3 yrs. Doctor, Ph.D., 3 yrs.

Library: *c.* 800,000 vols.

Special Facilities (Museums, etc.): Audio-visual Educaton Centre; Closed Circuit TV Systems.

Publications: Irrigation and Drainage and Small Hydropower Station; Sprinkler Irrigation and Technique; Journal; Bulletin onHydraulic and Electrical Engineering.

Press or Publishing House: Publishing House of Wuhan University of Hydraulic and Electric Engineering.

Academic Staff, 1990:

Rank	Full-time
Professors	109
Associate Professors	366
Lecturers	440
Total	915

Student Enrolment, 1990: 10,311 (Also 2800 students by correspondence).

1397 **WUHAN UNIVERSITY OF IRON AND STEEL TECHNOLOGY**

Wuhan (Hubei Province)
Cables: 7006
Telephone: 663212

D. of Mining and Ore Technology
D. of Metallurgy
D. of Machinery
D. of Industry Automation
D. of Chemical Engineering
D. of Industrial Management
Also 3 Research Institutes.

Founded 1958 as college, acquired present status and title 1984. Under the jurisdiction of the Ministry of Metallurgy. Residential facilities for academic staff and students.

Academic Year: September to July (September-January; February-July).

Admission Requirements: Graduation from senior middle school and entrance examination.

Language of Instruction: Chinese.

Degrees and Diplomas: Bachelor in all fields, 4 yrs. Master, a further 3 yrs.

Library: Central Library, 300,000 vols.

Publications: Journal of Natural Sciences (quarterly); Journal of Social Scienices (annually).

Academic Staff: c. 630.

Student Enrolment: c. 3220.

1398 **XIAMEN UNIVERSITY**

Shi Ming Road South, Xiamen (Fujian Province)
Cables: 0633 xiamen
Telex: 93003 BTHXM CN
Telephone: 25102
Fax: 0086-0592-27402

President (Acting): Lin Zu-Geng (1989-)
Secretary-General: Chen Shi-Yuan

D. of Chinese Language and Literature
Dean: Zheng Wen-Zhen; *staff* 66
D. of History
Dean: Shun Fu-Sheng; *staff* 67
D. of Anthropology
Dean: Li Jian-Tian; *staff* 38
D. of Foreign Languages and Literature (English, Japonese, Russian, French)
Dean: Lin Yu-Ru; *staff* 94
D. of Journalism and Communication Sciences
Vice-Dean: Xu Dong-Liang; *staff* 38
D. of Economics
Dean: Li Xuai; *staff* 30
D. of Planning and Statistics
Dean: Huang Yi-Mu; *staff* 73
D. of Accountancy
Dean: Cheng Shou-Wen; *staff* 48
D. of Business Management
Dean: Liao Quan-Wen; *staff* 29
D. of Finance and Banking
Dean: Zhang Yi-Chun; *staff* 83
D. of Foreign Trade
Dean (Acting): Zhuge Shu-Ying; *staff* 44
D. of Philosophy
Dean: Shang Ying-Wei; *staff* 50
D. of Politics
Dean: Huan Qiang; *staff* 66
D. of Law
Dean: Liao Yi-Xing; *staff* 80
D. of Mathematics
Dean: Lin Hong-Qing; *staff* 103
D. of Physics
Dean: Huang Qi-Sheng; *staff* 162
D. of Chemistry
Dean: Zhang Qian-Er; *staff* 333
D. of Biology
Dean: Zheng Ding; *staff* 172
D. of Oceanography
Dean: Li Shao-Qing; *staff* 153
D. of Electronic Engineering
Vice-Dean: Chen Cai-Sheng; *staff* 58
D. of Computer Sciences
Vice-Dean: Cai Wei-Xian; *staff* 98
D. of Instruments Technology
Dean: Huang Chang-Yi; *staff* 47
D. of Music
Vice-Dean: Zhou Chang; *staff* 36
D. of Fine Arts
Vice-Dean: Hong Rui-Sheng; *staff* 37
I. of Southeast Asia Studies
Director: Liao Shao-Lian; *staff* 45
I. of Taiwan Problems
Director: Chen Kong-Li; *staff* 42
Higher Education I.
Director: Pan Mao-Yuan; *staff* 25
I. of Chinese Language and Literature
Director: He Geng-Feng; *staff* 13
I. of Anthropology
Director: Jiang Bing-Zhao
D. of Architecture
Dean: Guo Hu-Sheng; *staff* 26
Cancer Research Ce.
Director: Wang De-Yao; *staff* 38
I. of Environmental Science
Director: Wu Yu-Duan; *staff* 11
C. of Overseas Correspondence
Dean: Zhuang Ming-Xian; *staff* 75

Founded 1921. A Key institution under the jurisdiction of the State Education Committee. Residential facilities for academic staff and students.

Arrangements for co-operation with: Australian National University; Université de Nice; University College, Cardiff; University of Amsterdam; State University of Leiden; Osaka University of Foreign Studies; Dalhousie University; Emory University; University of Rhode Island; University of Washington; Williamette University; University of Oregon; Syracuse Unversity.

Academic Year: October to June (October-January; February-June).

Admission Requirements: Graduation from senior middle school and entrance examination.

Fees: None.

Languages of Instruction: Chinese and English.

Degrees and Diplomas: Bachelor of–Arts; Science, 4 yrs. Master of–Arts, Science, a further 3 yrs. Doctor of–Arts, Science, 3 yrs after Master. Also University certificates and diplomas.

Library: 1,700,000 vols.

Special Facilities (Museums, etc.): Museum of Anthropology; Museum of Lu Xun.

Publications: Journal; The Problems of Southeast Asia; The Problems of the Chinese Economy; Study on Chinese Socio-Economic History; Transaction.

Press or Publishing House: University Publishing House.

Academic Staff, 1989-90:

Rank	Full-time
Professors	125
Associate Professors	520
Lecturers	1245
Assistants	726
Total	2616

Student Enrolment, 1989-90: 7719 (Also 1891 external students).

1399 **XI'AN JIAOTONG UNIVERSITY**
26 Xianning Road, Xi'an 710049 (Shaanxi Province)
Cables: 2827
Telex: 70123 XJTU CN
Telephone: 335011
Fax: 335471
President: Jiang De-Ming (1990-)
Li Neng-Gui

D. of Management
Director: Li Huai-Zu; *staff* 52
D. of Mechanical Engineering
Director: Shi Yao-Wu; *staff* 132
D. of Energy and Power Engineering
Director: Zhang Yong-Shao; *staff* 151
D. of Electrical Engineering
Director: Zhu Ren-Chu; *staff* 147
D. of Electronic Engineering
Director: Yao Xi; *staff* 59
D. of Information and Control Engineering
Director: Li Ren-Hou; *staff* 86
D. of Computer Science
Director: Shi Hong-Bao; *staff* 65
D. of Materials Engineering
Director: He Jia-Wen *staff* 38
D. of Architecture and Construction
Director: Xiao Yong-Ning; *staff* 28
D. of Chemical Engineering
Director: Yu Yong-Zhang; *staff* 29
D. of Mathematics
Director: You Zhao-Yong; *staff* 33
D. of Physics
Director: Wang Yong-Chang; *staff* 11
D. of Foreign Languages (English, Japanese)
Director: Hao Ke-Qi; *staff* 40
D. of Social Sciences
Director: Lu Lie-Yi; *staff* 114
D. of Economic Management
Director: Wang Wei-Wu; *staff* 36
D. of Engineering Mechanics
Director: Shen Ya-Peng; *staff* 26
D. of Machinery Science
Director: Xu Zeng-Yin; *staff* 81
Ce. for Foreign Students (Chinese Language and Cultural Studies)
Also 18 Research Institutes.

Founded 1896. A Key institution. Under the jurisdiction of the State Education Commission. Residential facilities for academic staff and students.

Arrangements for co-operation with the Universities of: Cornell; Minnesota; Pittsburgh; Syracuse; Pennsylvania State, Ohio; Keio; Kyoto; Tokyo; Alberta; Toronto; Manitoba; Birmingham; Manchester; Strathclyde; Eindhoven (Technology). Georgia Institute; Kanazawa Engineering College; Institut national polytechnique de Lorraine; Ecole polytechnique de Lausanne.

Academic Year: September to July (September-January; February-July).

Admission Requirements: Graduation from senior middle school and entrance examination.

Language of Instruction: Chinese.

Degrees and Diplomas: Bachelor, 4 yrs, Master, a further 2 ½-3 yrs. Doctor, Ph.D., 2-3 yrs.

Library: Central Library, *c.* 1,300,000 vols.

Publication: Journal (bimonthly).

Academic Staff, 1990:

Rank	Full-time
Professors	169
ssociate Professors	540
Lecturers	614
Assistants	856
Total	2179

Student Enrolment, 1990:

Of the country	11,500
Of the countries	14
Total	11,514*

*Also 1148 students by correspondence.

1400 **XINGJIANG UNIVERSITY**
Urumqi (Oygur Xingjiang Autonomous Region)
A Key institution.

1401 **XINGJIANG NORMAL UNIVERSITY**
Urumqi (Oygur Xingjiang Autonomous Region)
Education

1402 **XIANGTAN UNIVERSITY**
Xiangtan (Hunan Province)
A Key institution.

1403 **XIZANG (TIBET) UNIVERSITY**
Lhasa (Xizang Autonomous Region)
Founded 1984. Previously Xizang College of Education. In process of development.
Student Enrolment: c. 1000.

1404 **YAN'AN UNIVERSITY**
Yan'an (Shaanxi Province)

1405 **YANBIAN UNIVERSITY**
Yanji (Jilin Province)

1406 **YUNNAN UNIVERSITY**
Kunming (Yunnan Province)
A Key institution.

1407 **YUNNAN AGRICULTURAL UNIVERSITY**
District of Xundian (Yunnan Province)

1408 **ZHEJIANG UNIVERSITY**
20 Yugu Road Hangzhou 310027 (Zhejiang Province)
Cables: 0420
Telex: 35040 ZUFAO CN
Telephone: (86) 572244
Fax: (86) 0571-571797
Electronic mail: dma zunet/china.ira.uka.de
President: Lu Yong-xiang (1988-92)

D. of Applied Mathematics
Dean: Lu Shi-jie; *staff* 128
D. of Physics
Dean: Sun Wei; *staff* 140
D. of Chemistry
Dean: Feng Lin-xian; *staff* 183
D. of Mechanics
Dean: Ding Hao-Jian; *staff* 122
D. of Earth Science
Dean: Lan Yu-gi; *staff* 68
D. of Electrical Engineering
Dean: Li Ju; *staff* 274
D. of Chemical Engineering
Dean: Wu Zhao-li; *staff* 320
D. of Civil Engineering
Dean: Qian Zai-chi; *staff* 145
D. of Mechanical Engineering
Dean: Tong Zhong-fang; *staff* 252
D. of Information and Electronic Engineering
Dean: Gu Wei-kang; *staff* 141
D. of Optics Engineering
Dean: Tang Jin-fa; *staff* 169
D. of Materials Science and Engineering
Dean: Lei Yongquan; *staff* 270
D. of Energy Engineering
Dean: Xu Hang; *staff* 173
D. of Scientific Instruments
Dean: Wang Le-yu; *staff* 111
D. of Computer Sciences and Engineering
Dean: Yu Rui-zhao; *staff* 115
D. of Management Engineering
Dean: Huang Qing-ming; *staff* 68

D. of Philosophy and Social Sciences
Dean: Sun Yu-zheng; *staff* 46
D. of Chinese Language and Literature
Dean: Luo Han-chao; *staff* 30
D. of Biological Sciences and Technology
Dean: Zhang Wei-jie; *staff* 50
D. of Foreign Languages
Dean: Zhang Qing-yan; *staff* 120
D. of Economics
Dean: Yao Xian-guo; *staff* 31
D. of Architecture
Dean: Shen Ji-huang; *staff* 52
Computer and Information Ce.
Director: Hu Shang-xu; *staff* 60
Ce. for Analysis and Measurement
Director: Huang Bang-da; *staff* 85
Audio-visual and News Ce.
Director: Ji Feng; *staff* 41
Also 12 interdisciplinary Research Centres and 18 Institutes of the Departments.

Founded 1897 as academy. Acquired present status and title 1928. A Key institution under the jurisdiction of the State Commission of Education. Residential facilities for academic staff and students.

Arrangements for co-operation with the Universities of: Berlin (Technical); Würzburg; Utah; Massachusetts; Maryland; Rutgers; Indiana; Hawaii; Purdue; Valparaiso; Liverpool; Reading; Sussex; Murdoch; Newcastle; Montreal; Nova Scotia (Technical); Lund; Ghent; Odense; Gifu; Tohoku; Hokkaido. Georgia Institute of Technology; Rochester Institute of Technology; Rose-Hulman Institute of Technology; Friends World College; Quinnipiac College; Imperial College of Science and Technology; Queen Mary College, London; Musashi Institute of Technology; CityPolytechnic of Hong Kong.

Academic Year: August to July (August-January; February-July).

Admission Requirements: Graduation from senior middle school and entrance examination.

Fees: None.

Language of Instruction: Chinese.

Degrees and Diplomas: Bachelor of–Science; Philosophy; Economics; Arts; History, 4 yrs; Engineering, 4-5 yrs. Master of–Science; Engineering, a further 2-3 yrs. Doctor of–Philosophy; Science, 2-3 yrs after Master.

Library: Central Library, *c.* 1,300,000 vols.

Publications: Journals (Natural Science and Social Science, bimonthly); Chinese Journal of Industrial Engineering and Engineering Management; Chemical Reaction Engineering and Technology; Applied Mathematics A Journal of Chinese Universities; Journal of Chemical Engineering of Chinese Universities; Journal of Materials Science and Engineering; Light World.

Press or Publishing House: Zhejiang University Press.

Academic Staff, 1989-90:

Rank	Full-time
Professors	150
Associate Professors	616
Lecturers	1106
Assistants	248
Teachers	274
Total	2394

Student Enrolment, 1989-90:

	Men	Women	Total
Of the country	8680	2110	10,790
Of other countries	41	–	41
Total	8721	2110	10,831*

*Also 2022 external students.

1409 **ZHEJIANG AGRICULTURAL UNIVERSITY**
172 Kai Xuan Road, Hangzhou 310029 (Zhejiang Province)
Cables: 2418
Telex: 351016 ZAU CN
Telephone: 42605
President: Li Debao (1989-)

D. of Agronomy
Head: Ding Shouren; *staff* 66
D. of Plant Protection
Head: Fan Defan; *staff* 52
D. of Soil Science and Agrochemistry
Head: Wang Renchao; *staff* 57
D. of Horticulture
Head: Zhang Shanglong; *staff* 45
D. of Sericulture
Head: Xu Junliang; *staff* 20
D. of Tea Science
Head: Liu Zushen; *staff* 30
D. of Animal Husbandry and Veterinary Medicine
Head: Shen Shuben; *staff* 66
D. of Agricultural Engineering
Head: Wang Junjie; *staff* 74
D. of Economics and Management
Head: Xu Liyu; *staff* 35
D. of Environmental Sciences
Head: Yu Xiu-e; *staff* 32
D. of Food Science and Technology
Head: Je Liyong; *staff* 28
D. of Social Science
Director: Chen Liejong; *staff* 35
D. of Nuclear-Agricultural Sciences
Director: Sun Jinhe; *staff* 22
D. of Basic Studies
Head: Zhen Yungiu; *staff* 159
China Agricultural Administration C.
Dean: Ding Yuanshu
Sec. for Correspondence Courses
Biotechnology Research I.
Director: Li Debao; *staff* 12
Pesticide Environmental Toxicology Research I.
Director: Fan Defang; *staff* 20
Agro-Ecology I.
Director: Wang Zhaoqian; *staff* 9 (22)
Food Science I.
Director: Xu Zirong; *staff* 8
Edible Fungus Research I.
Director: Cao Ruo-bin; *staff* 10
Silk Research Ce.
Director: Chen Ziyuan; *staff* 5
Plant Quarantine Training Ce.
Director (Acting): Fan Defang; *staff* 3

Founded 1910 as school, acquired present status and title 1960. A Key institution under the jurisdiction of the Provincial Government.

Arrangements for co-operation with: University of Maryland; Oregon State University; Virginia Polytechnic Institute and State University; University of Hawaii, Manoa; Technical University of Berlin; Christian-Albrechts-University, Kiel; Tokyo University of Agriculture and Technology; Shimane University; University of Newcastle upon Tyne; University of British Columbia.

Academic Year: September to July (September-January; February-July).

Admission Requirements: Graduation from senior middle school and entrance examination.

Fees: None.

Language of Instruction: Chinese.

Degrees and Diplomas: Bachelor of Agriculture, 4 yrs. Master, a further 3 yrs. Doctor, Ph.D., 3 yrs after Master.

Library: 400,000 vols.

Publications: University Journal (quarterly); New Village (monthly); Zhejiang Agricultural Sciences (bimonthly).

Press or Publishing House: University Publishing House.

Academic Staff, 1989-90:

Rank	Full-time
Professors	56
Associate Professors	202
Lecturers	283
Teaching Assistants	230
Total	771

Student Enrolment, 1989-90:

	Men	Women	Total
Of the country	2556	732	3288
Of other countries	59	4	63
Total	2615	736	3351*

*Also 872 external students.

1410 **ZHEJIANG UNIVERSITY OF MEDICINE**
157 Yian Road, Hangzhou 310006 (Zhejiang Province)
Cables: Hangzhou, PRC
Telex: 35036 ZMU CN
Telephone: 722700
President: Zheng Shu (1984-)
Administrative Officer: Yao Zhu-Xiu

D. of Medicine
Chairmen: Huang Hue-De; Wu Jin-Ming; *staff* 217
D. of Pharmacy
Dean: Liu Zhi-Qang; *staff* 115
D. of Stomatology
Chairman: Yang Ming-Da; *staff* 80
D. for Premedical Courses
; *staff* 355
D. of Biomedical Engineering
Chairman: Hua Yun-Buo; *staff* 28
S. of Public Health
Chairman: Huang Xin-Shu; *staff* 65
D. of Nutrition
Dean: Zhu Shou-Ming; *staff* 30 (2)
Tumour Research I.
President: Zheng Shu; *staff* 47
I. of Infectious Diseases
Deputy Director: Liu Ke-Zhou; *staff* 26
I. of Cardiology
Vice-President: Jin Gan
I. of Demography
Vice-President: Yao zhu-Xiu; *staff* 13
D. of Nursing
Director: Wang Xi-Tian; *staff* 13
D. for Lifelong Education
Director: Tu Zhong-Yuan; *staff* 10
I. of Cardio- cerebro-vascular Problems
Director, Vice-President: Jin Gan
I. of Geriatrics
Director: Tong Zhong-Hang; *staff* 35 (58)
I. of Materia Medica
Director: Fan Rui-Ying

Founded 1912. Acquired present title 1960. Under the jurisdiction of the Provincial Government. Residential facilities for academic staff and students.

Arrangements for co-operation with the Universities of: Stanford; Jifu; Missouri; Kiel; Yamagata; Mons; Lubeck.

Academic Year: September to July (September-January; February-July).

Admission Requirements: Graduation from senior middle school and entrance examination.

Fees: None.

Language of Instruction: Chinese.

Degrees and Diplomas: Bachelor of–Pharmacy, 4 yrs; Medicine; Dentistry, 5 yrs. Master, a further 3-4 yrs. Doctor in Infectious and Blood Diseases.

Library: Central Library, 290,000 vols.

Special Facilities (Museums, etc.): Anatomy Museum.

Publications: Journal (bimonthly); Population and Eugenics (quarterly); Medical Education Research (bimonthly).

Academic Staff, 1986-87:

Rank	Full-time
Professors	64
Associate Professors	217
Assistant Professors	388
Total	669

Student Enrolment, 1989-90:

	Men	Women	Total
Of the country	1563	1062	2625

1411 **ZHEJIANG NORMAL UNIVERSITY**
Beishan Road, Jinhua City (Zhejiang Province)
Telex: 3800
Telephone: 41801
President: Xue Ke-Cheng (1988-)

D. of Chinese Language and Literature
Dean: Ren Yuan;; *staff* 98
D. of Foreign Languages
Deputy Deans: Chen Chang-Yi; Hu Mei-Hua; Yang Yong-Qing; *staff* 61
D. of Political Education
Deans: Zhou Zu-Liang; Qiang Yu-Ming; Shi Yi-Qing; *staff* 60
D. of History
Dean: Zhang Guan-Zhao; *staff* 35
D. of Mathematics
Dean: Zhang You-Xun; *staff* 93
D. of Physics
Deputy Deans: Li He-Nian; Feng Jia-Xian; Jiang Le-Chao; *staff* 99
D. of Chemistry
Dean: Ma Xin-Zong; *staff* 83
D. of Biology
Deputy Deans: Zhou Yu-Chan; Wang Min-Xing; *staff* 51
D. of Geography
Dean: Wang Du; *staff* 41
D. of Physical Education
Dean: Hu Zong-Yuan; *staff* 65
D. of Arts
Dean: Hu Yao-Hua; *staff* 42
D. of Education
Dean: Cheng Gong; *staff* 21
D. for Correspondence Courses
Chief: Dong Xing-Sen; *staff* 10
Research I. of Mathematics
Director: Xu Shi-Ying
Research I. of Children's Literature
Director: Jiang Feng
Research I. of Pedagogical Science
Director: Zhu Yu

Founded 1956 as school, acquired present status and title 1985. A Key institution under the jurisdiction of the Provincial Government. Residential facilities for academic staff and students.

Arrangements for co-operation with Bethany College, West Virginia.

Academic Year: September to July (September-January; February-July).

Admission Requirements: Graduation from senior middle school and entrance examination.

Fees: None.

Language of Instruction: Chinese.

Degrees and Diplomas: Bachelor of–Arts; Science, 4 yrs. Master, a further 3 yrs.

Library: Shao Yifu Library, 1,070,000 vols.

Special Facilities (Museums, etc.): Movie Studio.

Publications: ZNU Learned Journal (quarterly); Education of Higher Pedagogical Colleges (biannually); Higher Pedagogical Education by Correspondence (quarterly); Teaching and Research of Secondary School Education (monthly).

Press or Publishing House: Printing House.

Academic Staff, 1989-90:

Rank	Full-time
Professors	10
Associate Professors	131
Lecturers	306
Assistant Professors	274
Total	721

Student Enrolment, 1989-90:

	Men	Women	Total
Of the country	2351	1759	4110*

*Also 2000 external students.

1412 **ZHENGZHOU UNIVERSITY**
Zhengzhou (Henan Province)

1413 ***ZHONGSHAN (SUN YAT-SEN) UNIVERSITY**
Guangzhou (Guangdong Province)
Cables: 8775
Telex: 44604 ZSUFO CN
Telephone: 446300
President: Li Yueshing (1984-88)

D. of Management
Head: Wang Zhengxian; *staff* 27
D. of Anthropology
Head: Feng Jiajun; *staff* 17
D. of Mathematics
Head: Lin Wei; *staff* 77

D. of Computer Sciences
Head: Wu Zigian; *staff* 35
D. of Mechanics
Head: Zhang Diming; *staff* 39
D. of Physics
Head: Mo Dang; *staff* 120
D. of Radioelectronics
Head: Lin Yikun; *staff* 35
D. of Chemistry
Head: Den Yunxiang; *staff* 130
D. of Biology
Head: Lin Haoran; *staff* 103
D. of Geography
Head: Huang Jin; *staff* 56
D. of Geology
Head: Huang Yukun; *staff* 34
D. of Meteorology
Head: Luo Huibang; *staff* 40
D. of Chinese Language and Literature
Head: Huang Tianji; *staff* 60
D. of History
Head: Chen Shenglin; *staff* 50
D. of Law
Head: Duanmu Zheng; *staff* 31
D. of Philosophy
Head: Li Jiquan; *staff* 47
D. of Economics
Head: Tang Zhaolian; *staff* 33
D. of Foreign Languages and Literature
Head: Li Genzhou; *staff* 85
D. of Sociology
Head: He Zhaofa; *staff* 4
D. of Library Science
Head: Luo Wei; *staff* 12
I. of Materials Science
Head: Zeng Hanmin; *staff* 11
I. of Computer Software
Head: Yao Qingda; *staff* 6
I. of Polymer Science
Head: Lin Shanggan; *staff* 24
Entomology Research I.
Head: Pu Zhelong; *staff* 23
Environmental Science Research I.
Head: Zhang Zhanxia; *staff* 8
I. of Microelectronics
Head: Mo dang; *staff* 17
I. of Southeast Asian History
Head: Zhang Yingqiu; *staff* 15
I. of Hong Kong and Macao Studies
Head: Lei Jiang; *staff* 5
I. of Demography
Head: Zhu Yuncheng; *staff* 9
I. of Ancient Chinese Books and Records
Head: Huang Qi; *staff* 5
I. of Marxist Philosophy History
Head: Liu Rong; *staff* 4
D. for Lifelong Education
Heads: Wu Junqiang; He Huanquan; *staff* 7

Founded 1924 as Guangdong University. Acquired present title 1926. Reorganized 1952. A Key institution under the jurisdiction of the Ministry of Education. Residential facilities for academic staff and students.

Academic Year: September to July (September-February; March-July).

Admission Requirements: Graduation from senior middle school and entrance examination.

Language of Instruction: Chinese.

Degrees and Diplomas: Bachelor, 4 yrs. Master, a further 3 yrs. Doctor, 3 yrs after Master.

Library: c. 2,300,000 vols.

Special Facilities (Museums, etc.): Anthropology Museum.

Publications: Periodical of History (monthly); Journal (quarterly); Journal of Sun Yetsun University; Studies of Hong Kong and Macao; Population in the South; Studies on Higher Education; Journal of the Graduate (Social Sciences Edition); Journal of the Graduates (Natural Sciences Edition).

Academic Staff, 1986-87:

Rank	Full-time	Part-time
Professors	110	–
Associate Professors	334	–
Lecturers	555	–
Assistants	496	–
Total	1495	38

Student Enrolment, 1986-87:

Of the country	9758
Of other countries	63
Total	9821

Other Institutions

Anhui (Province)

1414 **ANHUI INSTITUTE OF TECHNOLOGY**
111 Luan Road, Hefei 230069 (Anhui Province)
Telephone: (551) 255553
Fax: (551) 253494
President: Shu De-Lin

D. of Machinery Engineering
Head: Xue Yao-Qing
D. of Power Machinery
Heads: Wu Hin; Yao Tie-Cheng
D. of Materials Engineering
Head: Chen Jian-Ming
D. of Electrical Engineering
Head: Wang Jing-Mei
D. of Management Engineering
Head: Fan Jia-Ren

Founded 1958. Under the jurisdiction of the Ministry of Mechanical and Electronic Industry. Residential facilities for c. 1200 academic staff and c. 2000 students.

Academic Year: September to July (September-January; February-July).

Admission Requirements: Graduation from senior middle school and entrance examination.

Fees: None.

Languages of Instruction: Chinese and English.

Degrees and Diplomas: Bachelor. Master.

Library: 350,000 vols.

Publications: Journal of Anhui Institute of Technology; Research about Higher Education.

Academic Staff, 1990: 420.

Student Enrolment, 1990: 2400.

1415 **ANHUI ELECTRICAL AND MECHANICAL INSTITUTE**
Wuhu

1416 **HUAINAN MINING INSTITUTE**
Huainan

1417 **EAST CHINA INSTITUTE OF METALLURGY**
Hu Dong Road, Maanshan 243002
Cables: 2699
Telephone: (0555) 73235
President: Wang Duan-Qing
Vice-President: Li Da-Jing

D. of Metallurgical Engineering
Director: Zhu Ben-Li; *staff* 107
D. of Chemical Engineering
Deputy Director: Xu Han-Chu; *staff* 75
D. of Mechanical Engineering
Deputy Director: He Jian; *staff* 78
D. of Industrial Automation
Director: Hong Nai-Gang; *staff* 74
D. of Economics and Management Engineering
Deputy Director: Wang Jia-Qi; *staff* 74

Metallurgical Technology and Material Research I.
Director: Zhu Ben-Li; *staff* 3 (15)
Automation Research I.
Director DHong Nai-Gang; *staff* 2 (10)
Energy Sources Utilization and Monitor Ce.
Head: Yan Wen-Fu; *staff* 1 (7)
Numerical Display and Control Ce.
Head: Zhou Jia-An; *staff* 1 (5)

Founded 1958 as Maanshan School of Iron and Steel, acquired present title 1985. Under the jurisdiction of the Ministry of Metallurgical Industry and Anhui Provincial Government. Residential facilities for academic staff and students.

Academic Year: September to July (September-January; Febuary-July).

Admission Requirements: Graduation from high school and entrance examination.

Fees: None.

Language of Instruction: Chinese.

Degrees and Diplomas: Bachelor, 4 yrs. Master, a further 2 yrs.

Library: 320,000 vols.

Special Facilities (Museums, etc.): Movie Studio.

Publications: Journal (quarterly); Higher Education Research (quarterly); Newspaper (bimonthly).

Academic Staff, 1989:

Rank	Full-time
Professors	13
Associate Professors	195
Lecturers	158
Teaching assistants	149
Total	515

Student Enrolment, 1989:

	Men	Women	Total
Of the country	1653	476	2129*

*Also 1300 external students.

1418 **HEFEI INSTITUTE OF GEOLOGY**
Hefei

1419 **ANHUI AGRICULTURAL INSTITUTE**
Hefei

1420 **WANNAN AGRICULTURAL INSTITUTE**
Xuancheng

1421 **ANHUI MEDICAL COLLEGE**
Hefei

1422 **BENGBU MEDICAL COLLEGE**
108 Zhi Huai Road, Bengbu 233000
Cables: 6200
Telephone: 4243, 4412
President: Liu Naiyan (1983-)

F. of Medicine

Founded 1958. Under the jurisdiction of the Provincial Goverment. Residential facilities for academic staff and students.

Academic Year: September to July (September-February; March-July).

Admission Requirements: Graduation from senior middle school and entrance examination.

Language of Instruction: Chinese.

Degrees and Diplomas: Bachelor of Medicine, 5 yrs. Master, a further 3 yrs.

Library: Central Library, *c.* 157,000 vols.

Publication: Acta Academiae Medicinae Bengbu (quarterly).

Academic Staff: c. 250.

Student Enrolment: c. 1300.

1423 **WANNAN MEDICAL COLLEGE**
Wuhu

1424 **ANHUI COLLEGE OF TRADITIONAL CHINESE MEDICINE**
Wuhu

1425 **ANQING TEACHERS' COLLEGE**
Anqing

1426 **FUYANG TEACHERS' COLLEGE**
Fuyang

1427 **HUAIBEI TEACHERS' COLLEGE FOR COAL**
Huaibei

1428 **CHAOHU TEACHERS' SCHOOL**
Chaou

1429 **CHUZHOU TEACHERS' SCHOOL**
Chuzhou

1430 **HUAINAN TEACHERS' SCHOOL**
Huainan

1431 **HUIZHOU TEACHERS' COLLEGE**
Tunxi
Telephone: 3130
President: Ye Guang-li (1983-88)

Teacher Training
Training Sec. for Cadres

Founded 1978 as school, acquired present status and title 1980. Residential facilities for academic staff and students.

Arrangements for co-operation with Lund University.

Academic Year: September to July (September-January; March-July).

Admission Requirements: Graduation from senior middle school and entrance examination.

Language of Instruction: Chinese.

Degrees and Diplomas: Diploma, 3 yrs.

Library: 149,000 vols.

Publications: Journal (Arts Edition) (quarterly); (Science Edition) (biannually).

Academic Staff, 1986-87:

Rank	Full-time	Part-time
Professors	2	–
Associate Professors	10	8
Lecturers	17	26
Assistants	97	–
Total	116	34

Student Enrolment, 1986-87:

	Men	Women	Total
Of the country	1063	353	1416*

*Also 109 external students.

1432 **LIUAN TEACHERS' SCHOOL**
District of Liuan

1433 **WUHU TEACHERS' SCHOOL**
Wuhu

1434 **XUZHOU TEACHERS' SCHOOL**
Xuzhou

1435 **ANHUI INSTITUTE OF FINANCE**
Bengbu

1436 **MAANSHAN SCHOOL OF COMMERCE**
Maanshan

1437 **TONGLING SCHOOL OF FINANCE AND ECONOMICS**
Tongling

Beijing (Municipality)

1438 **BEIJING INSTITUTE OF CHEMICAL FIBRES**
Heping Street, Chaoyang District, Beijing

1439 **BEIJING INSTITUTE OF CHEMICAL TECHNOLOGY**
Beisanuaun East Road, Chaoyang District Beijing

1440 **BEIJING INSTITUTE OF CIVIL ENGINEERING AND ARCHITECTURE**
Beijing

1441 **BEIJING INSTITUTE OF FORESTRY**
Beijing

A Key institution.

1442 **BEIJING INSTITUTE OF LIGHT INDUSTRY**
3 Fucheng Road, Beijing 100037
Cables: 8765
Telephone: 892497
President: Wang Yi-Duan (1988-)
Vice-Presidents: Han Gui-Jeng

D. of Mechanical Engineering
Director: Qiao Wu-Zhi *staff* 77
D. of Chemical Enginnering
Director: Xu Li-Yuan; *staff* 103
D. of Automatic Engineering
Director: Chen Wei-Zhi; *staff* 100
D. of Management Engineering
Director: Bao Wei; *staff* 34
D. of Basic Courses
Director: Zhou Zun-Rong; *staff* 45
D. of Foreign Languages
Director: Yu Song-Xi; *staff* 48
Foreign Languages Training Ce.
Director: Yu Song-Xi; *staff* 48
Research I. of Plastics
Director: Qian Han-Ying; *staff* 56
D. for Evening Studies
Director: Hu Xian-Jun

Founded 1958. Under the jurisdiction of the Ministry of Light Industry. Residential facilities for academic staff and students.

Academic Year: September to July (September-January; February-July).

Admission Requirements: Graduation from senior middle school and entrance examination.

Language of Instruction: Chinese.

Degrees and Diplomas: Bachelor, 4 yrs. Master, 3 yrs.

Library: c. 200,000 vols.

Publication: The journal of the Beijing Institute of Light Industry (quarterly).

Academic Staff, 1989-90:

Rank	Full-time
Professors	10
Associate Professors	109
Lecturers	248
Total	367

Student Enrolment, 1989-90:

	Men	Women	Total
Of the country	1135	610	1745

1443 **BEIJING INSTITUTE OF TECHNOLOGY**
P.O. Box 327, Beijing
Cables: 0055 beijing
Telex: 22011 BITCN
Telephone: (1) 841-6688
President: Zhu He-Sun (1984-)
Secretary-General: Ji Duo-Zhi

D. of Applied Mathematics
Chairman: Shi Rong-Chang; *staff* 72
D. of Applied Physics
Chairman: Zhang Ju; *staff* 76
D. of Applied Mechanics
Chairman: Mei Feng-Xiang; *staff* 56
D. of Aerodynamics
Chairman: Miao Rui-Shen; *staff* 112
D. of Automatic Control
Chairman: Hu You-De; *staff* 97
D. of Fluid Dynamics
Chairman: Qin Yao-Fang; *staff* 108
D. of Optics
Chairman: Yu Xin; *staff* 134
D. of Electronics
Chairman: Li Shi-Zhi; *staff* 148
D. of Chemical Engineering
Chairman: Huang Yao-Zhi; *staff* 153
D. of Mechanical Engineering
Chairman: Liu Xuan-Er; *staff* 168
D. of Safety Engineering
Chairman: Xu Geng-Guang; *staff* 103
D. of Computer Science
Chairman: Chen Wei-Zheng; *staff* 66
D. of Industrial Management
Chairman: Gu Bao-Gui; *staff* 52
D. of Industrial Design
Chairman: Jian Zhao-Quan; *staff* 25
D. of Foreign Languages
Chairman: Zhang Shu-Liang; *staff* 68
D. of Social Science and Humanities
Chairman: Liu Nai-Xin; *staff* 59
D. for Lifelong Education
Chairman: Li Shao-Lin; *staff* 13 (2)
Material Science Research Ce.
Guidance Research Ce.
Artificial Intelligence Research Ce.
Robotics Research Ce.
Vehicular Engineering Research Ce.
Radio-Electronics Research Ce.

Also 6 Further Research Centres and 2 branch colleges.

Founded 1940, acquired present name 1951. A Key institution. Residential facilities for academic staff and students.

Arrangements for co-operation with: Technische Universität Berlin; Penn. State University; University of Iowa; Eidgenössische Technische Hochschule Zürich; Tokyo Institute of Technology.

Academic Year: September to July (September-January; February-July).

Admission Requirements: Graduation from senior middle school and entrance examination.

Fees: None.

Language of Instruction: Chinese.

Degrees and Diplomas: Bachelor of–Science; Engineering, 4 yrs. Master of–Science; Engineering, a further 2 ½ yrs. Doctor of–Science; Engineering, 2-2 ½ yrs after Master.

Library: c. 874,000 vols.

Publications: Journal (quarterly); Education at B.I.T. (quarterly).

Academic Staff, 1989-90:

Rank	Full-time
Professors	144
Associate Professors	518
Lecturers	728
Total	1390

Student Enrolment, 1989-90:

	Men	Women	Total
Of the country	4804	1252	6056*

*Also 3198 external students.

1444 **BEIJING METALLURGICAL INSTITUTE OF MECHANICAL AND ELECTRICAL ENGINEERING**
Beijing

1445 **BEIJING TECHNICAL SCHOOL OF ELECTRONICS**
Beijing

1446 **BEIJING SCHOOL OF METEOROLOGY**
Beijing

1447 **BEIJING TECHNICAL SCHOOL OF PETROCHEMICAL TECHNOLOGY**
Beijing

1448 **BEIJING PRINTING INSTITUTE**
Daxing County, Huangcun
Telex: 3469
Telephone: 9233981/9233983
President: Zhou Xinghua (1986-94)

Printing Technology
D. for Correspondence Courses

Founded as Institute 1978. Under the jurisdiction of the Department of State Information and Publishing. Residential facilities for academic staff and students.

Academic Year: September to June (September-February; March-June).

Admission Requirements: Graduation from senior middle school and entrance examination.

Language of Instruction: Chinese.

Degrees and Diplomas: Bachelor of Engineering, 4 yrs.

Library: 500,000 vols.

Publication: Bulletin (quarterly).

Academic Staff, 1986-87:

Rank	Full-time
Professors	2
Associate Professors	32
Lecturers	56
Assistants	84
Total	174

Student Enrolment, 1986-87:

	Men	Women	Total
Of the country	424	216	640

1449 **BEIJING MEDICAL COLLEGE NO. 2**
Beijing

1450 **BEIJING COLLEGE OF TRADITIONAL CHINESE MEDICINE**
11 Beihuandong Road, Chaoyang District, Beijing

A Key institution.

1451 **BEIJING TEACHERS COLLEGE**
Huayuancun, Haidian District, Beijing 100037
Telephone: (841) 4411
Fax: (841) 8536

D. of Social Sciences
Associate Dean: Li Chunnan; *staff* 577
D. of Natural Sciences
Associate Dean: Yang Xueli; *staff* 353
I. of Educational Sciences
Director: Yan Ligin; *staff* 52
Also high school.

Founded 1955. A Key institution.

Arrangements for co-operation with: State University of New York College at Crotland; Oswego College; Whittier College; Central Connecticut State University; University of Massachusetts; Duke University; La Trobe University.

Academic Year: September to July (September-January; February-July).

Admission Requirements: Graduation from senior middle school and entrance examination.

Fees: None.

Language of Instruction: Chinese.

Degrees and Diplomas: Bachelor, 4 yrs. Master, a further 3 yrs. Doctor, Ph.D., 3 yrs.

Library: 1,410,000 vols.

Publication: Journals (Social and Natural Sciences, bimonthly).

Press or Publishing House: Beijing Teachers College Press.

Academic Staff, 1989:

Rank	Full-time
Professors	43
Associate Professors	302
Lecturers	368
Assistant Lecturers	116
Total	829

Student Enrolment, 1989: 3664 (Also 373 students by correspondence).

1452 **BEIJING TEACHERS' COLLEGE OF PHYSICAL EDUCATION**
No. 21 Bei San Huan West Road, Hai Dian District, Beijing
Telephone: (201) 5522
President: Sun Minzhi (1982-)
Vice-President: Yu Gang

Physical Education
D. for Lifelong Education and Correspondence Courses

Founded 1956. Under the jurisdiction of Beijing Municipality. Residential facilities for academic staff and students.

Academic Year: September to July (September-January; February-July).

Admission Requirements: Graduation from senior middle school and entrance examination.

Language of Instruction: Chinese.

Degrees and Diplomas: Bachelor, 4 yrs. Master, a further 3 yrs. Certificates.

Library: c. 200,000 vols.

Publication: The Teaching of Physical Education (bimonthly).

Press or Publishing House: College Printing House.

Academic Staff, 1986-87:

Rank	Full-time
Professors	8
Associate Professors	55
Lecturers	135
Assistants	105
Total	303

Student Enrolment, 1986-87:

	Men	Women	Total
Of the country	234	76	310*

*Also 125 external students.

1453 **BEIJING SECOND FOREIGN LANGUAGES INSTITUTE**
Dingfuzhuang, Chaoyang District, Beijing

1454 **BEIJING LANGUAGE INSTITUTE**
Xueyuan Road, Haidian District, Beijing

1455 **BEIJING BROADCASTING INSTITUTE**
Dinfuzhuang, Beijing

1456 **BEIJING INSTITUTE OF COMMERCE**
11 Fu Cheng Road, Beijing
Telex: 1018
Telephone: 89-0341
President: He ming-lun (1983-)

D. of Business Economics
D. of Finance and National Planning
D. of Mercantile Storage
D. of Mathematics and Electronics
D. of Chinese and Foreign Languages
D. for Evening Studies

Founded 1960. Under the jurisdiction of the Ministries of Education and of Commerce. Residential facilities for academic staff and students.

Academic Year: September to July (September-January; March-July).

Admission Requirements: Graduation from senior middle school and entrance examination.

Language of Instruction: Chinese (some courses in English).

Degrees and Diplomas: Bachelor of Arts, 4 yrs. Also Diploma for Evening students.

Library: Central Library, c. 300,000 vols (c. 6000 in foreign languages).

Publications: Bulletin (quarterly); Business Economics (quarterly).

Academic Staff: c. 210 (30).
Student Enrolment: c. 990.

1457 **BEIJING INSTITUTE OF ECONOMICS**
Hongmiao, Chaoyangmen, Beijing

1458 **BEIJING INSTITUTE OF FOREIGN TRADE**
68 Tsao Ling Front Street, Hsuan Wu District Beijing

1459 **BEIJING FINANCE AND TRADE COLLEGE**
68 Tsao Ling Front Street, Hsuan Wu District, Beijing
Telephone: (36) 1631
President: Jiang Che-fu (1983-)
Registrar: Kuan Hsiao-yuen

D. of Chinese and Foreign Languages
Banking and Trade (including Finance, Accountancy, Business Economics, and Management)
C. for Evening Studies
Sec. for Correspondence Courses

Founded 1978. Under the jurisdiction of the Beijing Municipality. Residential facilities for academic staff and students.

Academic Year: September to July (September-January; March-July).

Admission Requirements: Graduation from senior middle school and entrance examination.

Language of Instruction: Chinese.

Degrees and Diplomas: Bachelor of Arts. Also Diploma.

Library: 250,000 vols.

Publications: Journal; Study of Finance and Trade.

Press or Publishing House: College Press House.

Academic Staff, 1986-87:

Rank	Full-time	Part-time
Professors	1	–
Associate Professors	16	1
Lecturers	158	14
Assistants	194	–
Total	369	15

Student Enrolment, 1986-87:

	Men	Women	Total
Of the country	171	210	381

1460 **BEIJING INSTITUTE OF PROCUREMENTS AND HANDLING OF COMMODITES**
Beijing

1461 **CENTRAL INSTITUTE OF FINANCE**
19 Xueyuan South Road, Xizhimenwai, Beijing

1462 **FOREIGN AFFAIRS COLLEGE**
24 Zhan Lan Road, Beijing
Telephone: 890151
President: Zhou Nan (1986-)
Vice-President: Mei Ping

Diplomatic Studies
Also evening courses.

Founded 1955. Under the jurisdiction of the Ministry of Foreign Affairs. Residential facilities for academic staff and students.

Arrangements for co-operation with: University of Oxford; The Johns Hopkins University; Georgetown University;Institut d'Etudes politiques, Paris.

Academic Year: September to July (September-January; February-July).

Admission Requirements: Graduation from senior middle school and entrance examination.

Language of Instruction: Chinese.

Degrees and Diplomas: Bachelor, 4 yrs. Master, a further 3 yrs. Doctor, a further 3 yrs.

Library: Central Library.

Publication: Journal.

Academic Staff, 1986-87:

Rank	Full-time
Professors and Associate Professors	60
Lecturers	130
Total	190

Student Enrolment, 1986-87:

	Men	Women	Total
Of the country	500	240	740*

*Also 7 foreign students.

1463 **INSTITUTE OF INTERNATIONAL POLITICS**
Beijing

1464 **INSTITUTE OF INTERNATIONAL RELATIONS**
Beijing

1465 **BEIJING INSTITUTE OF PHYSICAL CULTURE**
Yuanmingyuan East Road, Beijing

1466 **CENTRAL ACADEMY OF ARTS AND CRAFTS**
134 Donghuan North Road, Beijing

1467 **CENTRAL ACADEMY OF FINE ARTS**
Donghuan Beilu 34, Beijing
Cables: 4457
Telephone: 596391

Fine Arts

Founded 1956. A Key institution.

Arrangements for co-operation with: National Institute of Design, India; Pennsylvania State University; Tokyo College of Art and Design; California State University, Long Beach; Bath Academy of Art; Osaka University of Arts; Tokyo University of Arts; National School of Arts and Crafts, Oslo; Academy of Fine Arts, Stuttgart.

Academic Year: September to July (September-February; March-July).

Admission Requirements: Graduation from senior middle school and entrance examination.

Language of Instruction: Chinese.

Publication: Decoration (quarterly).

Student Enrolment: c. 520.

1468 **CENTRAL CONSERVATORY OF MUSIC**
43 Bao Jia Street, Xicheng District Beijing
Cables: 7299
Telephone: 66.7120
President: Wu Zu-Qiang

Music

Founded 1950, incorporating previously existing music colleges. A Key institution. Residential facilities for academic staff and students.

Academic Year: September to July (September-January; Febuary-March).

Admission Requirements: Graduation from senior middle school and entrance examination.

Language of Instruction: Chinese.

Degrees and Diplomas: Bachelor of Arts, 4-5 yrs. Master, a further 3 yrs. Doctor, 3 yrs.

Libraries: Central Library, 1,300,000 vols; 1,400,000 gramophone records and cassettes.

Publication: Journal.

Academic Staff, 1986-87:

Rank	Full-time
Professors	33
Associate Professors	69
Lecturers	132
Assistants	65
Instructors	95
Total	274

Student Enrolment, 1986-87: c. 550.

1469 **INSTITUTE OF CHINESE MUSIC**
Beijing

1470 **INSTITUTE OF CHINESE OPERA**
Beijing

1471 **CENTRAL ACADEMY OF DRAMA**
39 Dong Mianhua Lane, Jiaodaoku, Beijing

1472 **BEIJING FILM ACADEMY (BFA)**
Zhu-xin-zhuang, Beijing
Cables: 9111
Telephone: 65 7231
President: Shen Song-sheng (1983-)

Cinema

Founded 1950 as institute. Acquired present status and title 1956. Under the jurisdiction of the Ministry of Culture. Residential facilities for academic staff and students.

Arrangements for co-operation with: Australian Film and Television School; Ryerson Polytechnical Institute.

Academic Year: September to July (September-February; March-July).

Admission Requirements: Graduation from senior middle school and entrance examination.

Language of Instruction: Chinese.

Degrees and Diplomas: Bachelor, 4 yrs.

Academic Staff: c. 130.

Student Enrolment: c. 230.

1473 **BEIJING DANCING ACADEMY**
Beijing

1474 **CENTRAL INSTITUTE FOR NATIONALITIES**
27 Baishiqiao Road, Haidian District Beijing

A Key institution.

Fujian (Province)

1475 **FUJIAN SCHOOL OF CIVIL ENGINEERING**
Fuzhou

1476 **JIMEI NAVIGATION INSTITUTE**
1, Jiageng Road, Jimei, Xiamen 361021
Cables: 5300 xiamen
Telephone: (592) 48155
Fax: 48415 xiamen
President: Yu Zhi-Cheng (1990-)

D. of Navigation
Director: Shi Zhu-Lie; *staff* 108
D. of Marine Engineering
Director: Qian Tian-Zhi; *staff* 99
D. of Electrical Engineering
Director: Chen Cong-Gui; *staff* 54
Sec. of Basic Studies
Director: Chen Bing-Zhong; *staff* 73
Sec. for Lifelong Education
Director: Lin Han-Zu; *staff* 3

Founded 1920. Under the jurisdiction of the Ministry of Communication. Residential facilities for academic staff and students from Ministry of Communications.

Academic Year: September to July (September-January; February-July).

Admission Requirements: Graduation from senior middle school and entrance examination.

Language of Instruction: Chinese.

Degrees and Diplomas: Diplomas, 3-5 yrs.

Library: Central Library, 229,386 vols.

Publications: Journal; Research of Marine Higher Education.

Academic Staff, 1989-90:

Rank	Full-time
Professors	2
Associate Professors	48
Lecturers	121
Assistant Lecturers	71
Teachers	17
Total	259

Student Enrolment, 1989-90: 1151 (Also 70 students by correspondence).

1477 **FUJIAN COLLEGE OF FORESTRY**
Xiqin, Nanping
Cables: 710B
Telephone: (599) 25677
President: Zhang Jianguo (1988-)

Forestry

Also 3 Research Institutes.

Founded 1940 as department of Fujian Agricultural College, acquired present status and title 1958. Under the jurisdiction of the Provincial Government. Residential facilities for academic staff and students.

Academic Year: September to July (September-February; March-July).

Admission Requirements: Graduation from senior middle school and entrance examination.

Fees: None.

Language of Instruction: Chinese.

Degrees and Diplomas: Bachelor of–Agriculture; Engineering, 4 yrs. Master, a further 2 yrs.

Library: c. 368,000 vols.

Publications: Journal of Fujian College of Forestry (quarterly); Problems of Forest Economics (quarterly).

Academic Staff, 1990:

Rank	Full-time
Professors	9
Associate Professors	60
Lecturers	131
Assistants	103
Total	303

Student Enrolment: c. 1020.

1478 **FUJIAN AGRICULTURAL COLLEGE**
Fuzhou
Telephone: 50721
President: Wu zhong-Fu (1984-87)

Agriculture (including Horticulture, Animal Husbandry and Veterinary Science, and Beekeeping)

Founded 1935. Acquired present title 1952, incorporating previously existing agricultural colleges. Under the jurisdiction of the Provincial Government.

Academic Year: September to July (September-February; March-July).

Admission Requirements: Graduation from senior middle school and entrance examination.

Language of Instruction: Chinese.

Degrees and Diplomas: Bachelor of Science, 4 yrs. Master, a further 3 yrs. Doctor, 3 yrs.

Library: Central Library, c. 400,000 vols.

Publication: Journal (quarterly).

Academic Staff: c. 600.

Student Enrolment: c. 2200.

1479 **XIAMEN INSTITUTE OF AQUATIC PRODUCTS**
Xiamen

1480 **FUJIAN MEDICAL COLLEGE**
Central 817 Road, Fuzhou
Telephone: 57861
President: Yin Feng-Zhi (1986-)
Dean: Fang Li-sheng

Medicine (including Public Hygiene and Stomatology)
Sec. for Lifelong Education

Also 4 research sections.

Founded 1937 as school, became college 1949 and university 1970. Renamed as college 1982. Under the jurisdiction of the Provincial Government. Residential facilities for academic staff and students.

Arrangements for co-operation with University of Minnesota of Minneapolis Saint Paul.

Academic Year: September to July (September-January; March-July).

Admission Requirements: Graduation from senior middle school and entrance examination.

Language of Instruction: Chinese.

Degrees and Diplomas: Bachelor of Medicine, 5 yrs. Master of Medicine, a further 3 yrs.

Library: Central Library, 258,448 vols.

Publications: Journal (quarterly); Medical Education Study (biannually).

Academic Staff, 1986-87:

Rank	Full-time
Professors	27
Associate Professors	124
Lecturers	122
Assistants	188
Total	461

Student Enrolment, 1986-87:

	Men	Women	Total
Of the country	1484	659	2143

1481 **FUJIAN COLLEGE OF TRADITIONAL CHINESE MEDICINE**
Fuzhou

1482 **FUQING TEACHERS' SCHOOL**
Fuqing

1483 **FUZHOU TEACHERS' SCHOOL**
Fuzhou

1484 **JIMEI TEACHERS' SCHOOL**
Xiamen

1485 **NNANPING TEACHERS' SCHOOL**
Nanping

1486 **NINGDE TEACHERS' SCHOOL**
District of Ningde

1487 **QUANZHOU TEACHERS' SCHOOL**
Quanzhou

1488 **ZHANGZHOU TEACHERS' SCHOOL**
Zhangzhou

1489 **FUJIAN INSTITUTE OF PHYSICAL CULTURE**
Xiamen

Gansu (Province)

1490 **LANZHOU RAILWAY INSTITUTE**
Lanzhou

1491 **LANZHOU MEDICAL COLLEGE**
Lanzhou

1492 **LANZHOU COLLEGE OF TRADITIONAL CHINESE MEDICINE**
Lanzhou

1493 **NORTHWEST TEACHERS' COLLEGE**
Lanzhou

1494 **LANZHOU TEACHERS' SCHOOL**
Lanzhou

1495 **QINGYANG TEACHERS' SCHOOL**
District of Qingyang

1496 **TIANSHUI TEACHERS' SCHOOL**
Tianshui

1497 **ZHANGYE TEACHERS' SCHOOL**
District of Zhangye

1498 **LANZHOU INSTITUTE OF COMMERCE**
Lanzhou

1499 **NORTHWEST INSTITUTE FOR NATIONALITIES**
Xi Bei Xin Cun, Lanzhou 730030
Cables: 1111
Telephone: (931) 464011
President: Yan Si-Sheng

D. of Animal Husbandry and Veterinary Science
D. of Medical Treatment
D. of Chinese Language and Literature
D. of Languages and Literatures of National Minorities
D. of History
D. of Politics
D. of Mathematics, Physics and Chemistry
D. of Trade Between Nationalities
D. of Arts
D. of Foreign Languages
Cadre Training D.
Evening C.

Founded 1950. Under the jurisdiction of the State Nationalities Affairs Commission. Residential facilities for academic staff and students.

Academic Year: September of July (September-January; March-July).

Fees: None.

Degrees and Diplomas: Bachelor, 4 yrs. Master in Ancuebt Tibetan Speciality, a further 2 yrs.

Library: c. 500,000 vols.

Publications: Journal; Research of Northwest Nationalities; The Occasional Papers on Teaching and Reseach; Newspaper.

Academic Staff, 1990:

Rank	Full-time
Professors	7
Associate Professors	104
Lectures	197
Others	662
Total	970

Student Enrolment, 1990: 3000.

Guangdong (Province)

1500 **GUANGDONG INSTITUTE OF TECHNOLOGY**
729 East Dong Feng Road, Guangzhou
Telephone: 776597
President: Liang Shi (1985-)

D.of Electrical and Electronic Engineering
Deputy Head: Zhang Zhen-Zhao; *staff* 119
D. of Mechanical Engineering
Deputy Head: Li Zhu-Jian; *staff* 88
D. of Chemical Engineering
Head: Li Zhong Ling; *staff* 98
D. of Mineral Engineering
Deputy Head: Wang Yin-Biao; *staff* 63
D. of Civil Engineering
Head: Huang Shen-Yao; *staff* 19

D. of Management
Head: Guo Ming-Zhang; *staff* 13
D. of Basic Studies
Head: Zie Rong-Xiang *staff* 99
I. of Marxism-Leninism
Head: Li Sen: *staff* 17
I. of Moral and Character Teaching and Research
Head: Zhang Xiaoan; *staff* 2

Founded 1958. A Key institution. Under the jurisdiction of the State Education Commission.

Academic Year: September to July (September-January; February-July).

Admission Requirements: Graduation from senior middle school and entrance examination.

Language of Instruction: Chinese.

Degrees and Diplomas: Bachelor of Science. Master.

Library: Central Library, 279,000 vols.

Publication: Journal.

Academic Staff, 1986-87:

Rank	Full-time
Professors	11
Associate Professors	62
Lecturers	206
Assistants	138
Total	417

Student Enrolment, 1986-87:

	Men	Women	Total
Of the country	1883	390	2273

1501 **GUANGDONG INSTITUTE OF MECHANICAL ENGINEERING**

Guangzhou
Cables: 4076
Telephone: 776024

Vice-Presidents: Yang Bao-Quan; Liu Jin-yun; Chen Ting-Shu

D. of Mechanical Engineering
Head: Li Ding-Hua
D. of Management Engineering
Head: Shao Jing-Hua
D. of Electrical Engineering
Head: Mao Huan-Quan
D. for Lifelong Education
Chancellor: Chen Ting-Shu

Founded 1978. Under the jurisdiction of the provincial Government. Residential facilities for academic staff and students.

Academic Year: September to July (September-January; March-July).

Admission Requirements: Graduation from senior middle school and entrance examination.

Language of Instruction: Chinese.

Degrees and Diplomas: Bachelor, 4 yrs.

Library: Central Library, 96,000 vols.

Publication: Journal (biannually).

Academic Staff, 1986-87:

Rank	Full-time
Professors	3
Associate Professors	48
Lecturers	136
Assistants	101
Total	288

Student Enrolment, 1986-87:

	Men	Women	Total
Of the country	1399	293	1692

1502 **SOUTH CHINA INSTITUTE OF TECHNOLOGY**

Wushan, Guangzhou
Cables: Guangzhou 7003
Telephone: 77461

President: Liu Zhen-qun (1981-)

D. of Mechanical Engineering I (Machine Building, Automotive Engineering)
D. of Mechanical Engineering II (Foundry, Forging, and Welding Technology)
D. of Architecture
D. of Architectural Engineering
D. of Shipbuilding
D. of Radio Engineering
D. of Electric Power Engineering
D. of Automation
D. of Computer Sciences and Engineering
D. of Chemical Machinery
D. of Polymer Studies
D. of Inorganic Materials
D. of Chemical Engineering I (Organic and Inorganic Chemistry)
D. of Chemical Engineering II (Papermaking Technology, Sugar Technology, Food Technology, Microbiology)
D. of Mathematics and Applied Mechanics
D. of Physics
D. of Chemistry
D. of Engineering Management
D. for Correspondence Courses

Also Research Institutes and kindergarten, primary, and middle schools.

Founded 1952, incorporating colleges and departments of engineering from 11 universities and colleges in the 5Provinces of South-Central China. A Key institution under the jurisdiction of the Ministry of Education.

Arrangements for co-operation with: Texas Tech University; University of Pittsburgh; Edinboro State College; Southern Methodist University; Georgia Institute of Technology; The City University, London; Hong Kong Polytechnic; University of Braunschweig.

Academic Year: September to July (September-February; March-July).

Admission Requirements: Graduation from senior middle school and entrance examination.

Language of Instruction: Chinese.

Degrees and Diplomas: Bachelor, 4 yrs. Master, a further 2-3 yrs. Doctor.

Library: Central Library, *c.* 1,000,000 vols.

Publication: Journal.

Press or Publishing House: SCIT Press House.

Academic Staff: c. 2380.

Student Enrolment: c. 2730.

1503 **ZHANJIANG FISHERIES COLLEGE**

40 Jiefang Road, Xiashan, Zhanjiang
Cables: 8110
Telephone: 21233, 21370
President: Gu Xuewen (1984-)
Secretary-General: Lu Jinlun

D. of Marine Fishing Technology
Head: Zhong Bailing; *staff* 51
D. of Aquaculture
Head: Cai Ying ya; *staff* 94
D. of Pearl Research
Head: Chen Ming yao; *staff* 13
D. of Marine Engineering
Head: Chen Bingguang; *staff* 52
D. of Food Processing and Technology of Refrigeration
Head: Wang Minghe; *staff* 46
D. for Lifelong Education
Head: Liu Sijian

Founded 1935 as school, became college 1979. Under the jurisdiction of the Ministry of Agriculture, Animal Husbandry and Fishery. Residential facilities for academic staff and students.

Academic Year: September to July (September-January; February-July).

Admission Requirements: Graduation from senior middle school and entrance examination.

Language of Instruction: Chinese.

Degrees and Diplomas: Bachelor, 4 yrs.

Library: Central Library, 180,000 vols.

Publications: Journal; Teaching Research; Fisheries Translation Series.

Academic Staff, 1986-87:

Rank	Full-time
Professors	6
Associate Professors	40
Lecturers	115
Assistants	89
Total	250

Student Enrolment, 1986-87:

	Men	Women	Total
Of the country	766	203	969

1504 **ZHANJIANG AGRICULTURAL SCHOOL**
Zhanjiang

1505 **FOSHAN JUNIOR VETERINARY COLLEGE**
Dali, Foshan Nanhai, Guangdong
Telephone: 41337
President: Zhen Jiming
Director: Lin Chaoxin

D. of Veterinary Medicine
Head: Hu Hanming; *staff* 36
D. of Animal Husbandry
Head: Li Jinyu; *staff* 21
D. of Agronomy
Head: Deng Guohan; *staff* 39
D. of Agricultural Economics
Head: Chen Jieyang; *staff* 8

Founded 1958 as Foshan Branch College of South China Agricultural Institute. Acquired present title 1962. Under the jurisdiction of provincial authorities. Residential facilities for academic staff and students.

Academic Year: September to July (September-January; February-July).

Admission Requirements: Graduation from senior middle school and entrance examination.

Fees: None.

Language of Instruction: Chinese

Library: 135,936 vols.

Academic Staff, 1990: 207.

Student Enrolment, 1990:

	Men	Women	Total
Of the country	223	65	288*

*Also 90 external students.

1506 **GUANGZHOU MEDICAL COLLEGE**
Guangzhou

1507 **ZHANJIANG MEDICAL COLLEGE**
Zhanjiang
Telex: 9990
Telephone: 4745
President: Xiang Fan (1983-)

Medicine
Nursing

Founded 1958 as a Department of Zhonshan Medical College. Acquired present status and title 1964. Under the jurisdiction of the Provincial Government. Residential facilities for academic staff and students.

Academic Year: September to August (September-February; March-August).

Admission Requirements: Graduation from senior middle school and entrance examination.

Language of Instruction: Chinese.

Degrees and Diplomas: Bachelor of Medicine.

Library: Central Library, *c.* 400,000 vols.

Publication: Acta of Zhanjiang Medical College.

Academic Staff: c. 160.

Student Enrolment: c. 310.

1508 **ZHOGSHAN (SUN YATSEN) MEDICAL COLLEGE**
Guangzhou

1509 **GUANGZHOU COLLEGE OF TRADITIONAL CHINESE MEDICINE**
San Yuan Li, Guangzhou
Cables: 3901
Telephone: 661233
President: Zhida Tao (1984-)
Vice-President: Ou Ming

Traditional Chinese Medicine
S. of Nursing
D. for Lifelong Education
Also 6 Research Centres.

Founded 1956. Under the jurisdiction of the Ministry of Public Health. Residential facilities for academic staff and students.

Arrangements for co-operation with the University of Illinois Medical Center at Chicago.

Academic Year: September to July (September-January; February-July).

Admission Requirements: Graduation from senior middle school and entrance examination.

Language of Instruction: Chinese.

Degrees and Diplomas: Bachelor, 5 yrs. Master, a further 3 yrs. Doctor, 3 yrs after Master.

Library: c. 200,000 vols.

Special Facilities (Museums, etc.): Chinese Materia Medica Herbarium and Herb Garden.

Publications: Journal of New Traditional Medicine (monthly); Journal of Guangzhou College of Traditional Medicine (quarterly); Teaching and Investigation (quarterly).

Press or Publishing House: College Publishing House.

Academic Staff, 1986-87:

Rank	Full-time
Professors	17
Associate Professors	81
Lecturers	200
Assistants	200
Total	498

Student Enrolment, 1986-87:

	Men	Women	Total
Of the country	1019	455	1474
Of other countries	15	2	17
Total	1034	457	1491*

*Also 235 external students.

1510 **GUANGDONG MEDICAL AND PHARMACEUTICAL COLLEGE**
Baoggang, Haizhu District, Guangzhou
Telex: 0976
Telephone: 429040
President: Chen Ying-Yang (1983-)

F. of Public Health
Head: Chen Jiong-Ran; *staff* 102
F. of Medicine
Head: Zhang Yi-yuan; *staff* 71
F. of Pharmacy
Head: Du Qi-Zhang; *staff* 102
F. of Fundamental Medicine
Head: Wang Qi-Hua; *staff* 128

Founded 1978. Under the jurisdiction of the Provincial Government. Residential facilities for academic staff and students.

Academic Year: September to July (September-January; February-July).

Admission Requirements: Graduation from senior middle school and entrance examination.

Language of Instruction: Chinese.

Degrees and Diplomas: Bachelor of–Pharmacy, 4 yrs; Medicine, 5 yrs.

Library: Central Library, 100,000 vols.

Publication: Journal.

Academic Staff, 1986-87:

Rank	Full-time
Professors	5
Associate Professors	53
Lecturers	164
Assistants	170
Total	392

Student Enrolment, 1986-87:

	Men	Women	Total
Of the country	334	186	520

1511 **GUANGZHOU TEACHERS' COLLEGE**
Guangzhou

1512 **FOSHAN TEACHERS' SCHOOL**
Foshan

1513 **HANSHAN TEACHERS' SCHOOL**
District of Chaoan

1514 **HUIYANG TEACHERS' SCHOOL**
Huiyang

1515 **LEIZHOU TEACHERS' COLLEGE**
Zhanjiang 524048
Telephone: 38255
President: Liang Jing (1985-)

D. of Physics
Dean: Zhang Guan-Qun; *staff* 19
D. of Mathematics
Dean: Liu Xu-Guo; *staff* 28
D. of Chemistry
Dean: Wan Chao-Shen; *staff* 19
D. of Physical Education
Dean: Li Xiang; *staff* 30
D. of Chinese
Dean: Pei Shu-Hai; *staff* 28
D. of Politics and History
Dean: Sheng Xiong-Fei; *staff* 23
D. of English
Dean: Peng Yu-Chen: *staff* 22
D. of Biology
Dean (Acting): Huang Dong-Yun; *staff* 13

Founded 1978. Under the jurisdiction of the Ministry of Education and the Provincial Government. Residential facilities for academic staff and students.

Academic Year: September to July (September-January; February-July).

Admission Requirements: Graduation from senior middle school and entrance examination.

Language of Instruction: Chinese.

Library: Central Library, 270,000 vols.

Publication: Journal (quarterly).

Academic Staff, 1989-90:

Rank	Full-time
Professor	2
Associate Professors	37
Lecturers	104
Assistants	58
Total	201

Student Enrolment, 1989-90:

	Men	Women	Total
Of the country	546	277	826

1516 **SHAOGUAN TEACHERS' COLLEGE**
Da Tang Road, Shaoguan 512005
Telephone: 85707
President: Yu Bo-Xi (1984-)
Director: Yang Zheng-Biao

D. of Chinese
Dean: Yu Nai-Qiu; *staff* 24
D. of Politics
Dean: Chen Chong; *staff* 20
D. of English
Dean: Wang Cheng-Ji; *staff* 19
D. of Mathematics
Dean: Chen Chong; *staff* 24
D. of Physics
Dean: Wu Hong-Bin; *staff* 18
D. of Chemistry and Biology
Dean: Yang Shu-Geng; *staff* 22
D. of Physical Education
Dean: Huang Fu-Yun; *staff* 24
Antique Literature Research Sec.
Director: Huang Zhi-Hui

Founded 1958. Acquired present status and title 1978. Under the jurisdiction of the Provincial Government. Residential facilities for academic staff and students.

Academic Year: September to July (September-January; March-July).

Admission Requirements: Graduation from senior middle school and entrance examination.

Fees: None.

Language of Instruction: Chinese.

Degrees and Diplomas: Diploma, 2 yrs.

Library: Central Library, 250,000 vols.

Publication: Journal of Shaoguan Teachers' College (quarterly).

Academic Staff, 1989-90:

Rank	Full-time	Part-time
Associate Professors	12	4
Lecturers	69	5
Assistants	80	–
Total	161	9

Student Enrolment, 1989-90:

	Men	Women	Total
Of the country	1067	673	1740*

*Also 1055 external students and students by correspondence.

1517 **TEACHERS' SCHOOL FOR HAINAN LI AND MIAO AUTONOMOUS ZHOU**
Tongshen

1518 **ZHAOQING EDUCATION COLLEGE**
Xing Huz, Zhaoqing 52602
Telephone: 23-22-16
President: Zhou Yao-xin (1984-90)
Secretary-General: Tang Zhi-ji

D. of English
Dean: Lin Lian-qiu; *staff* 10
D. of Chemistry
Dean: Lu Song-ling; *staff* 10
D. of Physics
Dean: Wu Xiao-chuan; *staff* 12
D. of Biology
Dean: Chen Xiong-wei; *staff* 11
D. of Politics and History
Dean: Wu Bing-shi; *staff* 13
D. of Physical Education
Vice-Dean: He Guo-lin; *staff* 8
D. of Psychology
Vice-Dean: Zheng Xue-yan; *staff* 5
D. of Mathematics
Dean: Huang Wen-qing; *staff* 18
D. of Chinese
Vice-Dean: Huang Huo-you; *staff* 17
D. of Geography
Dean: Huang Chi-sheng; *staff* 8
D. for Lifelong Education (by correspondence)
Dean: Luo Qin-Ji; *staff* 5

Founded 1977 as teacher training school, acquired present status and title 1983.

Academic Year: September to July (September-January; March-July).

Admission Requirements: Graduation from senior middle school and entrance examination.

Language of Instruction: Chinese.

Degrees and Diplomas: Bachelor, 4 yrs.

Library: Central Library, 120,000 vols.

Publication: Journal (biannually).

Academic Staff, 1986-87:

Rank	Full-time
Lecturers	21
Teachers	43
Assistants	51
Total	115

Student Enrolment, 1986-87:

	Men	Women	Total
Of the country	508	141	649*

*Also 2690 external students.

1519 **GUANGZHOU INSTITUTE OF FOREIGN LANGUAGES (GIFL)**
Huangpodong, Guangzhou
Cables: 0009
Telephone: 62303
President: Gui Shi-chun (1984-88)

Foreign Languages (English, French, German, Spanish, Russian, Thai,Indonesian, Japanese, Vietnamese)
Evening Studies

Ce. for Correspondence Courses (English)
Also Research Institute (Linguistics).

Founded 1964. Under the jurisdiction of the Ministry of Education.

Arrangements for co-operation with: Murdoch University, Perth; University of Paderborn.

Academic Year: September to July (September-January; February-July).

Admission Requirements: Graduation from senior middle school and entrance examination.

Language of Instruction: Chinese.

Degrees and Diplomas: Bachelor of Arts, 4 yrs. Master, a further 3 yrs.

Library: Central Library, *c.* 270,000 vols.

Publication: Modern Foreign Languages (quarterly).

Press or Publishing House: Guangzhou Foreign Language Audio-visual Publishing House.

Academic Staff: c. 420.

Student Enrolment: c. 760 (Also *c.* 9820 external students).

1520 **GUANGDON INSTITUTE OF FINANCE AND ECONOMICS**
Guangzhou

1521 **GUANGZHOU INSTITUTE OF FOREIGN TRADE**
Dalang, 510450 Guangzhou
Telephone: 60-16-60
Fax: 60-19-07
President: Shi Weisan
Director: Xiao Peixiong

F. of International Trade
Dean: Fang Zhenfu; *staff* 40
F. of Business English
Dean: Lu Ruixiang; *staff* 59
F. of International Business Management
Dean: Ma Junlin; *staff* 36
I. of International Trade
Director: Tong Liangao
Evening C.
Head: Wang Yuqi; *staff* 7 (23)

Founded 1980. Through affiliation of the Foreign Trade Dept. of Jinan University and Guangdong School of Foreign Trade, the Institute is under the dual leadership of the Ministry of Foreign Economic Relations and Trade and the Provincial People's Government of Guangdong. Residential facilities for academic staff and students.

Arrangements for co-operation with: Institut supérieur de Gestion, Paris; University of Houston.

Academic Year: September to July (September-February; February-July).

Admission Requirements: Graduation from senior middle school and entrance examination.

Fees: None.

Languages of Instruction: Chinese and English.

Degrees and Diplomas: Bachelor, 4 yrs.

Publication: Journal (quarterly).

Academic Staff, 1990:

Rank	Full-time
Professors	4
Associate Professsors	29
Lecturers	63
Assistant Lecturers	106
Total	202

Student Enrolment, 1990:

	Men	Women	Total
Of the country	626	562	1188

1522 **GUANGZHOU INSTITUTE OF PHYSICAL EDUCATION**
Maoer Hill, Shaheding, Guangzhou

Physical Education
Also 4 Research Sections.

Founded 1958. Under the jurisdiction of the Ministry of Education and the State Commission of Physical Education and Sports.

Academic Year: September to July.

Admission Requirements: Graduation from senior middle school and entrance examination.

Language of Instruction: Chinese.

Degrees and Diplomas: Bachelor, 4 yrs.

Library: Central Library, *c.* 95,000 vols.

Publication: Journal.

Academic Staff: c. 220.

Student Enrolment: c. 1300.

1523 **GUANGZHOU CONSERVATORY OF MUSIC**
Guangzhou

1524 **GUANGZHOU ACADEMY OF FINE ARTS**
Guangzhou

1525 **GUANGDONG INSTITUTE OF NATIONALITIES**
Guangzhou

Guangxi (Zhuang Autonomous Region)

1526 **GUANGXI INSTITUTE OF TECHNOLOGY**
Nanning

1527 **GUILIN INSTITUTE OF ELECTRONICS**
Guilin

1528 **GUILIN INSTITUTE OF GEOLOGY**
Guilin
Cables: 2699
Telephone: 2796
President: Yuan Kuirong (1984-)
Secretary-General: Fan Xuegin

Geology (including Petroleum Technology)

Academic Year: September to July (September-February; March-July).

Admission Requirements: Graduation from senior middle school and entrance examination.

Language of Instruction: Chinese.

Degrees and Diplomas: Bachelor of Science, 4 yrs. Master, a further 3 yrs.

Library: Central Library, 240,000 vols.

Special Facilities (Museums, etc.): Geological Museum

Publication: Journal (quarterly).

Academic Staff, 1986-87:

Rank	Full-time	Part-time
Professors	6	13
Associate Professors	49	15
Lecturers	113	–
Assistants	168	–
Total	336	28

Student Enrolment, 1984-85:

	Men	Women	Total
Of the country	1428	315	1743

1529 **GUANGXI AGRICULTURAL COLLEGE**
Nanning
Cables: 5100
Telephone: 4101; 4280
President: Ru-Cong Luo

Agriculture (including Veterinary Medicine, Animal Husbandry, Horticulture, and Sericulture)
Also 7 Research Sections.

Founded 1932 as college. Acquired present status and title 1952. Under the jurisdiction of Ministry of Education and Provincial Government. Residential facilities for academic staff and students.

Academic Year: September to July (September-January; February-July).

Admission Requirements: Graduation from senior middle school and entrance examination.

Language of Instruction: Chinese.

Degrees and Diplomas: Bachelor, 4 yrs. Master, a further 3 yrs.

Library: Central Library, *c.* 335,000 vols.

Publication: Journal (biannually).

Academic Staff: c. 570.

Student Enrolment: c. 2300.

1530 **GUANGXI MEDICAL COLLEGE**
Nanning

1531 **GUANGXI COLLEGE OF TRADITIONAL CHINESE MEDICINE**
Nanning

1532 **YOUIJIANG MEDICAL COLLEGE FOR NATIONALITIES**
Baise

1533 **GUILIN MEDICAL SCHOOL**
Guilin

1534 **NANNING TEACHERS' COLLEGE**
Nanning

1535 **HECHI TEACHERS' SCHOOL OF EDUCATION**
Yishan

1536 **NANNING TEACHERS' SCHOOL**
District of Longzhou

1537 **YULIN TEACHERS' SCHOOL**
Yulin

1538 **GUANGXI YOUJIANG TEACHERS' SCHOOL FOR NATIONALITIES**
Baise

1539 **GUANGXI ACADEMY OF ARTS**
Nanning

1540 **GUANGXI INSTITUTE FOR NATIONALITIES**
Nanning

Guizhou (Province)

1541 **GUIZHOU INSTITUTE OF TECHNOLOGY**
Guiyang
Cables: 1114
President: Hu Guo Gen (1984-)
Secretary-General: Gu Xi Min

Geology
Mining
Metallurgy
Mechanical and Electrical Engineering Chemistry
Civil Engineering
Light Industrial Technology

Founded 1958. Under the jurisdiction of the Provincial Government. Arrangements for co-operation with the University of Lille.

Academic Year: September to July (September-January; March-July).

Admission Requirements: Graduation from senior middle school and entrance examination.

Language of Instruction: Chinese.

Degrees and Diplomas: Bachelor of Science, 4 yrs.

Library: Central Library, 310,000 vols.

Publications: Journal (quarterly); Academic Discussion (biannually).

Academic Staff, 1986-87:

Rank	Full-time
Professors	12
Associate Professors	147
Lecturers	404
Assistants	211
Total	774

Student Enrolment, 1986-87:

	Men	Women	Total
Of the country	2396	762	3158

1542 **GUIZHOU AGRICULTURAL COLLEGE**
Guiyang

1543 **GUIYANG MEDICAL COLLEGE**
Guiyang

1544 **ZUNYI MEDICAL COLLEGE**
Zunyi

1545 **GUIYANG COLLEGE OF TRADITIONAL CHINESE MEDICINE**
Shidong Road, Guiyang 55000
Telephone: 22633

D. of Traditional Chinese Medicine
Dean: Shi Enquan; *staff* 283
D. of Traditional Chinese Materia Medica
Dean: Lo Xianjin; *staff* 83
D. of Acupuncture and Moxibustion
Dean: Lu Shaozhu; *staff* 27
D. of Orthopedics and Traumatology
Dean: An Yixian; *staff* 35
I. of Trace Elements
Dean: Zhu Meiniah; *staff* 18
I. of Orthopedics and Traumatology
Dean: Shi Guangda; *staff* 9
Also 2 affiliated hospitals and 2 teaching hospitals.

Founded 1965. Under the jurisdiction of the Education Comission of Guizhou Province.

Academic Year: September to July (Spetember-January; March-July).

Admission Requirements: Graduation from senior middle school and entrance examination.

Fees: None.

Language of Instruction: Chinese.

Degrees and Diplomas: Bachelor, 4-5 yrs. Master, a further 3 yrs.

Library: 170,000 vols.

Special Facilities (Museums, etc.): Herbarium of Medicinal Plants; Medicinal Animal Specimen Room.

Publications: Journal; Trace Elements.

Academic Staff, 1990:

Rank	Full-time
Professors	32
Associate Professors	73
Lecturers	197
Assistants	73
Total	375

Student Enrolment, 1990:

	Men	Women	Total
Of the country	640	388	1028

1546 **GUIYANG TEACHERS' COLLEGE**
Guiyang

1547 **ANSHUN TEACHERS' SCHOOL**
Anshun

1548 **BIJIE TEACHERS' SCHOOL**
Bijie

1549 **TONGREN TEACHERS' SCHOOL**
District of Tongren

1550 **XINGYI TEACHERS' SCHOOL**
District of Xingyi

1551 **ZUNYI TEACHERS' SCHOOL**
Zunyi

1552 **SOUTHEAST GUIZHOU SCHOOL FOR NATIONALITIES**
District of Kaili

1553 **SOUTH GUIZHOU TEACHERS' SCHOOL FOR NATIONALITIES**
Duyun

1554 **GUIZHOU INSTITUTE OF FINANCE AND ECONOMICS**
Guiyang

1555 **GUIZHOU INSTITUTE OF NATIONALITIES**
Guiyang

Hainan (Province)

1556 **SOUTH CHINA COLLEGE OF TROPICAL CROPS**
Baodao Xincun, Danxian
Cables: 7108 danxian
President: Huang Zong-Dao (1981-)

D. of Tropical Crops Cultivation
Director: Huang Wen-Zheng; *staff* 87
D. of Tropical Plant Protection
Director: Zhang Kai-Ming; *staff* 27
D. of Horticulture and Gardening
Director: Ai Ding-Zeng; *staff* 8
D. of Tropical Crops Production Mechanization
; *staff* 41
D. of Tropical Crops Products Processing
Director: Ye Long-Jun; *staff* 58

Founded 1958. Under the jurisdiction of the Ministry of Agriculture. Residential facilities for academic staff and students.

Academic Year: September to August (September-February; March-August).

Admission Requirements: Graduation from senior middle school and entrance examination.

Fees: None.

Language of Instruction: Chinese.

Degrees and Diplomas: Bachelor, 4 yrs. Master, a further 3 yrs.

Library: Central Library, 218,000 vols.

Special Facilities (Museums, etc.): Botanical Garden of Tropical Crops.

Publication: Chinese Journal of Tropical Crops (biannually).

Press or Publishing House: Printing House of South China College of Tropical Crops.

Academic Staff, 1989:

Rank	Full-time
Professors	10
Associate Professors	65
Lecturers	129
Assistants	156
Total	360

Student Enrolment, 1989-90:

	Men	Women	Total
Of the country	1300	390	1789

Hebei (Province)

1557 **HEBEI INSTITUTE OF CHEMICAL TECHNOLOGY**
Shijiazhuang

1558 **HEBEI INSTITUTE OF CIVIL ENGINEERING AND ARCHITECTURE**
Zhangjiakou

1559 **HEBEI INSTITUTE OF COAL MINING**
Xingtai

1560 **HEBEI INSTITUTE OF MECHANICAL AND ELECTRICAL ENGINEERING**
65 Xinhua Xi Lu, Shijiazhuang
Telex: 3456
Telephone: 22072
President: Ma Jia-Qi

Automation Engineering
Mechanics
Electronics
Industrial Management

Founded 1971.

Language of Instruction: Chinese.

Library: Central Library, 250,000 vols.

Publication: Journal.

Academic Staff, 1986-87: 497.

Student Enrolment, 1986-87: 2373.

1561 **HEBEI INSTITUTE OF MINING AND METALLURGY**
Tangshan

1562 **HEBEI INSTITUTE OF TECHNOLOGY**
No.1 Road, Dingzigu, District Hongqiao, Tianjin 300130
Cables: 3010
Telephone: 570-244
President: Zhang Min
Secretary-General: Zhan Yingmin

D. of Mechanical Engineering I
Head: Yin Zingwei
D. of Mechanical Engineering II
Head: Wang Jianan
D. of Electrical Engineering
Head: Yan Weili
D. of Chemical Engineering
Head: Zhang Lincheng
D. of Civil Engineering
Head: Jiang Zhiren
D. of Industrial Management Engineering
Head: Zhang Xianmo
D. of Computer Sciences and Engineering
Head: Yang Wenlin
Ut. of Fundamental Science
Head: Yang Guochen
Materials Research Ce.
Head: Xu Yueshung
Computer Ce.
Head: Jiang Guozhang

Founded 1903. A Key institute.

Admission Requirements: Graduation from senior middle school and entrance examination.

Fees: None.

Languages of Instruction: Chinese and English.

Degrees and Diplomas: Bachelor, 4 yrs. Master, a further 2-3 yrs.

Library: 650,000 vols.

Special Facilities (Museums, etc.): Movie studio; Video-Audio Room.

Publications: Journal of HIT (quarterly); Newspaper (each 2 weeks); Science and Engineering Teaching (quarterly); Higher Education Research (quarterly).

Academic Staff, 1990:

Rank	Full-time
Professors	19
Associate Professors	305
Lecturers	360
Senior Engineers	26
Engineers	200
Total	910

Student Enrolment, 1990:

	Men	Women	Total
Of the country	3000	1500	4500

1563 **HEBEI SCHOOL OF WATER CONSERVANCY**
Cangzhou

1564 **NORTH CHINA INSTITUTE OF ELECTRICAL POWER**
Baoding

A Key institution.

1565 **NORTH CHINA INSTITUTE OF INDUSTRIAL AGRICULTURAL ENGINEERING**
Xingtai

A Key institution.

1566 **SHIJIAZHUANG INSTITUTE OF TECHNOLOGY FOR RAILWAY CORPS**
Shijiazhuang

1567 **HEBEI INSTITUTE OF GEOLOGY**
Zhangjiakou

1568 **HEBEI SCHOOL OF FORESTRY**
Yixian

1569 **ZHIANGJIAKOU SCHOOL OF AGRICULTURE**
District of Xuanhua

1570 **CHENGDE MEDICAL SCHOOL**
Chengde

1571 **ZHANGJIAKOU MEDICAL COLLEGE**
Zhangjiakou

1572 **TANGSHAN COAL MEDICAL COLLEGE**
Tangshan

1573 **HEBEI COLLEGE OF CHINESE TRADITIONAL MEDICINE**
Shijiazhuang

1574 **HEBEI TEACHERS' COLLEGE**
Shijiazhuang

1575 **BAODING TEACHERS' SCHOOL**
Baoding

1576 **CHENGDE TEACHERS' SCHOOL**
Chengde

1577 **HANDAN TEACHERS' SCHOOL**
Handan

1578 **HENGSHUI TEACHERS' SCHOOL**
Hengshui

1579 **LANGFANG TEACHERS' SCHOOL**
District of Anci

1580 **SHIJIAHUANG TEACHERS' SCHOOL**
Shijiahuang

1581 **TANGSHAN TEACHERS' SCHOOL**
Tangshan

1582 **ZHANGJIAKOU TEACHERS' SCHOOL**
Zhangjiakou

1583 **HEBEI INSTITUTE OF FINANCE AND TRADE**
Shijiazhuang

Heilongjiang (Province)

1584 **DAQING PETROLEUM INSTITUTE**
Anda

A Key institution.

1585 **HARBIN ARCHITECTURAL AND CIVIL ENGINEERING INSTITUTE**
144 Da Zhi Street, Harbin 150006
Cables: 2049
Telephone: 33512
President: Shen Shi-Zhao

D. of Building Engineering
Director: Zhang Tie-Zheng; *staff* 122
D. of Environment Engineering
Director: Wang Bao-Zhen; *staff* 93
D. of Construction Materials
Director: Fan Cheng-Mou; *staff* 75
D. of Machinery and Electrical Engineering
Director: Gu Di-Min; *staff* 80
D. of Architecture
Director: Chang Huai-Sheng; *staff* 95
D. of Construction Management
Director: Ren Yu-Feng; *staff* 83
D. of Highway Engineering
Director: Wang Ze-Ren; *staff* 32
D. of Energy Supply Engineering
Director: Lu Ya-Jun; *staff* 108
C. of Adult and Lifelong Education
Dean: Yu Wen-zeng; *staff* 30
Research Ce. for Engineering Science
Dean: Wang Guang-Yuan
Research Ce. for Environment Engineering
Research Ce. for Energy Supply and Thermoisolation
Research Ce. for Utilization of New Materials

Founded 1920. Under the jurisdiction of the Ministry of Construction. Residential facilities for academic staff and students.

Arrangements for co-operation with University of Iowa; University of Hanover; Waseda University; Wageningen Agricultural University.

Academic Year: September to July (September-January; February-July).

Admission Requirements: Graduation from high school and entrance examination.

Fees: None.

Language of Instruction: Chinese.

Degrees and Diplomas: Bachelor, 4 yrs. Master, a further 3 yrs. Doctor, 3 yrs.

Library: 65,000 vols.

Rank	Full-time
Professors	41
Associate Professors	194
Lecturers	304
Assistants	204
Total	743

Student Enrolment, 1989-90:

Of the country	3294
Of the counties	7
Total	3301*

*Also 2600 external students and students by correspondence.

1586 **HARBIN INSTITUTE OF ELECTRICAL TECHNOLOGY**

Da Qing Road, Harbin 150040
Cables: 4015
Telephone: 55941; 51913
President: He Lian (1984-)
Head, Student Division: Lu Ming-Juan

D. of Electrical Machinery Engineering
Chairman: Li Zhe-Shing
D. of Electrical Material Engineering
Chairman: Yang Jia-Xiang
D. of Electromagnetic Measurement and Instrumentation
Chairman: Ma Huai-Jian
D. of Computer Science
Chairman: Sun Xing-Ru
D. of Mechanical Engineering
Chairman: Jiang Chen
D. of Administration Engineering (Industrial Economics)
Chairman: Guan Zhi-Yao
Adult Education I.
Chairman: Yang Qi
Wind Power Station Research Ce.
Director: Liu Zeng-Hu

Founded 1953 as school. Acquired present status and title 1958. Under the jurisdiction of the Ministry of Machinery and Electronics Industry. Residential facilities for academic staff and students.

Arrangements for co-operation with Chiba University.

Academic Year: September to July (September-January; March-July).

Admission Requirements: Graduation from senior middle school and entrance examination.

Fees: None.

Language of Instruction: Chinese.

Degrees and Diplomas: Bachelor of Science, 4 yrs. Master, a further 2 ½-3 years.

Library: Central Library, c. 250,000 vols.

Publication: Journal of Harbin Institute of Electrical Technology (quarterly).

Academic Staff, 1990:

Rank	Full-time
Professors	14
Associate Professors	115
Lecturers	201
Assistants	174
Senior Engineers	3
Others	30
Total	537

Student Enrolment, 1990:

	Men	Women	Total
Of the country	1581	434	2015*

*Also 401 students by correspondence.

1587 **HARBIN INSTITUTE OF SHIPBUILDING ENGINEERING**

Wenmiao Jie 11/F, Nangangqu, Harbin 150001
Cables: 5307
Telephone: 492570;492571
President: Wu De-Ming (1988-92)

D. of Naval Architecture and Ocean Engineering
Head: Huang Sheng; *staff* 29
D. of Aeronautical Engineering
Head: Qiu Hai-Ming; *staff* 28
D. of Marine Power Engineering
Head: Wang Zhi-Qiu; *staff* 34
D. of Automation Control
Head: Li Guo-Bin; *staff* 31
D. of Electronic Engineering
Head: Xiao Rong-Duan; *staff* 28
D. of Underwater Acoustical Engineering
Head: Hui Jun-Ying; *staff* 27
D. of Mechanical Engineeering
Head: Gan Jiu-An; *staff* 32
D. of Computer and Information Science
Head: Huang Hou-Kuan; *staff* 14
D. of Management Engineering
Head: Liu Xi-Song; *staff* 7
D. of Chemistry Engineering
Head: Zhao Feng-Lian; *staff* 13
D. of Social Sciences
Head: Zhang Ji-Zhi; *staff* 13
D. of Physics
Head: Chen Wei-Qing; *staff* 12
D. of Mathematics and Mechanics
Head: Zhang Zhen-Guo; *staff* 24
D. of Foreign Languages
Head: Han Zhe; *staff* 13
Underwater Acoustical Engineering Research I.
Director: Yang Shie
New Energy Source Research I.
Director: Wang Yin-Dong
C. of Adult Education
President: Chen Da-Yan
Computer Ce.
Director: Wu Chang-Ling

Founded 1953. A Key institution. Under the jurisdiction of the China State Shipbuilding Corporation. Residential facilities for academic staff and students.

Arrangements for co-operation with: Nagasaki Institute of Applied Sciences; Hamburg University; Southeastern Louisiana University; Loughborough University of Technology.

Academic Year: September to July (September-January; March-July).

Admission Requirements: Graduation from senior middle school and entrance examination.

Fees: None.

Language of Instruction: Chinese.

Degrees and Diplomas: Bachelor, 4 yrs. Master, a further 2-3 yrs. Doctor, 3 yrs.

Library: Central Library, 541,000 vols.

Publications: Journal (biannually); Science and Technology at HSEI (quarterly); Higher Education Research (biannually); Shipbuilding Education.

Academic Staff, 1990: c. 1200.

Student Enrolment, 1990: c. 6000.

1588 **HEILONGJIANG INSTITUTE OF MINING**

Jixi

1589 **HEILONGJIANG HYDRAULIC INSTITUTE**

Harbin
Telephone: 61903
President: Bin-Cheng (1985-)
Secretary-General: He Jin-Lu

Water Conservancy and Irrigation

Founded 1958, acquired present status and title 1983. Under the jurisdiction of the Ministry of Education. Residential facilities for academic staff and students.

Academic Year: September to July (September-January; February-July).

Admission Requirements: Graduation from senior middle school and entrance examination.

Language of Instruction: Chinese.

Degrees and Diplomas: Diploma.

Library: Central Library, 157,000 vols.

Publication: Hydraulic Power Technology.

Academic Staff, 1986-87:

Rank	Full-time
Associate Professors	9
Lecturers	57
Assistants	56
Total	122

Student Enrolment, 1986-87:

	Men	Women	Total
Of the country	451	163	614

1590 **JIAMUSI INSTITUTE OF TECHNOLOGY**
Jiamusi

1591 **NORTHEAST INSTITUTE OF HEAVY INDUSTRY**
Fulaerji

A Key institution.

1592 **QIQIHAR INSTITUTE OF LIGHT INDUSTRY**
Qiqihar

1593 **NORTHEAST COLLEGE OF FORESTRY**
Harbin
Cables: 1331
Telephone: 63163
President: Xiu Guohan (1983-)

Forestry (including Civil Engineering)
D. for Correspondence Courses

Founded 1952, incorporating previously existing colleges of agricul-ture and forestry. Under the jurisdiction of the Ministry of Forestry. Residential facilities for academic staff and students.

Arrangements for co-operation with Oregon State University.

Academic Year: September to July (September-January; March-July).

Admission Requirements: Graduation from senior middle school and entrance examination.

Language of Instruction: Chinese.

Degrees and Diplomas: Bachelor of–Agriculture; Engineering; Science, 4 yrs. Master of–Agriculture; Engineering, a further 3 yrs. Doctor, Ph.D., 3 yrs.

Library: Central Library, *c.* 400,000 vols.

Publications: Journal (quarterly); Bulletin of Botany Research (quarterly); Wildlife (bimonthly); Versions of Essays in Forestry (quarterly); Forest Protection (quarterly).

Academic Staff: c. 730.

Student Enrolment: c. 1220 (Also *c.* 600 external students).

1594 **JIAMUSI MEDICAL COLLEGE**
Jiamusi

1595 **HEILONGJIANG COLLEGE OF TRADITIONAL CHINESE MEDICINE**
Harbin

1596 **MUDANJIANG MEDICIAL SCHOOL**
Mudanjiang

1597 **QIQIHAR SCHOOL OF MEDICINE**
Qiqihar

1598 **MUDANJIANG TEACHERS' COLLEGE**
Mudanjiang

1599 **QIQIHAR TEACHERS' COLLEGE**
Qiqihar

1600 **DAQING TEACHERS' COLLEGE**
Daqing

1601 **HARBIN TEACHERS' SCHOOL**
Harbin

1602 **HULAN TEACHERS' SCHOOL**
Hulan

1603 **JIAMSU TEACHERS' TRAINING COLLEGE**
Jiamusi
Cables: 1857
Telephone: 21857
President: Gao Guang-fu (1985-)

Teacher Training

Founded 1949 as normal school, acquired present status and title 1958. Residential facilities for academic staff and students.

Academic Year: September to July (September-January; March-July).

Admission Requirements: Graduation from senior middle school and entrance examination.

Language of Instruction: Chinese.

Degrees and Diplomas: Diploma, 2-3 yrs.

Library: 180,000 vols.

Academic Staff, 1986-87:

Rank	Full-time	Part-time
Professors	–	2
Associate Professors	13	–
Lecturers	66	–
Assistants	145	–
Total	224	2

Student Enrolment, 1986-87:

	Men	Women	Total
Of the country	635	550	1185

1604 **KESHAN TEACHERS' SCHOOL**
Keshan

1605 **SUIHUA TEACHERS' SCHOOL**
Suihua

1606 **HEILONGJIANG NONG-KEN NORMAL COLLEGE**
Acheng
Telephone: 2546
President: He Zheng-qiang (1985-)
Secretary-General: Gao Yu-zhong

Teacher Training

Founded 1973, became secondary normal school 1981 and acquired present status and title 1983. Residential facilities for academic staff and students.

Academic Year: September to July (September-January; March-July).

Admission Requirements: Graduation from senior middle school and entrance examination.

Language of Instruction: Chinese.

Degrees and Diplomas: Diploma, 2-3 yrs.

Library: Central Library, 110,000 vols.

Publication: Journal (quarterly).

Academic Staff, 1986-87:

Rank	Full-time
Vice-Professors	2
Lecturers	26
Teachers	94
Assistants	20
Total	142

Student Enrolment, 1986-87:

	Men	Women	Total
Of the country	447	511	958

1607 **HEILONGJIANG INSTITUTE OF COMMERCE**
Harbin

1608 **HEILONGJIANG SCHOOL OF FINANCE**
Harbin

1609 **HARBIN MONETARY SCHOOL**
Harbin

Henan (Province)

1610 **ZHENGZHOU INSTITUTE FOR CEREAL PRESERVATION AND PROCESSING**
57 Songshan Road, Zhengzhou
Telephone: 49241
President: Gu Liangji (1983-)

Grain Processing Engineering

Founded 1960. Under the jurisdiction of the Ministry of Commerce. Residential facilities for academic staff and students.

Academic Year: September to July (September-January; February-July).

Admission Requirements: Graduation from senior middle school and entrance examination.

Language of Instruction: Chinese.

Degrees and Diplomas: Bachelor of Engineering. Master.

Library: College Library.

Publication: Academic Journal.

Academic Staff: c. 350.

Student Enrolment: c. 1960.

1611 **JIAOZUO MINING INSTITUTE**
Jiaozuo

1612 **LUOYANG INSTITUTE OF TECHNOLOGY**
Luoyang

1613 **ZHENGZHOU LIGHT INDUSTRY INSTITUTE**
5 Dongfeng Road, Zhengzhou 450002
Cables: 1331
Telephone: (371) 332076
Fax: (371) 332273
President: Tang Tian-Shu (1988-)
Secretary-General of the Party: Du Jun-Yi

D. of Food Engineering
Dean: CaoJun-Hui; *staff* 42
D. of Chemical Engineering
Dean: Shi Xin-Sheng; *staff* 85
D. of Mechanical Engineering
Dean: Pei Quan-An; *staff* 85
D. of Control Engineering
Dean: Liu Xian-Xin; *staff* 79
D. of Industrial art Design
Dean: Xu Pei-Jian; *staff* 87
D. of Administration Engineering
Dean: Guo Zu-He; *staff* 28
Bureau of Scientific Research (Food Engineering, Home Refrigeration, Chemical Engineering, Mechanical Engineering.)
Director: Cai Ming-Dou; *staff* 9

Founded 1977. Under the jurisdiction of the Ministry of Light Industry. Residential facilities for academic staff and students.

Arrangements for co-operation with the Universities of: Pittsburgh; Kansas; Wichita.

Academic Year: September to July (September-January; February-July).

Admission Requirements: Graduation from senior middle school and entrance examination.

Fees: None.

Language of Instruction: Chinese.

Degrees and Diplomas: Bachelor, 4 yrs.

Library: Central Library, 300,000 vols.

Publication: Journal (quarterly).

Press or Publishing House: Press of Zhengzhou Light Industry Institute.

Academic Staff, 1989-90:

Rank	Full-time
Professors	1
Associate Professors	99
Lecturers	178
Assistants	164
Total	442

Student Enrolment, 1989-90: 2673 (Also 200 external students).

1614 **ZHENGZHOU INSTITUTE OF TECHNOLOGY**
52 Wenhua Road, Zhengzhou
Cables: 7108
Telephone: 32113
President: Li Liangfu (1982-90)
Vice-President: Liu Dazhuang

D. of Mechanical Engineering
Dean: Wang Shangjun; *staff* 129
D. of Electrical and Computer Engineering
Dean: Wang Junkun; *staff* 111
D. of Civil Engineering and Architecture
Vice-Dean: Zhou Jianqing; *staff* 130
D. of Hydraulic Engineering
Dean: Brian Kaiyuan; *staff* 103
D. of Chemical Engineering
Dean: Xu Xucheng; *staff* 150
D. of Mathematics and Mechanics
Dean: Wang Guosen; *staff* 144
D. of Foreign Languages
Dean: Jian Zhizhong; *staff* 20
D. of Management
Lifelong Education

Founded 1959 as department of Zhengzhou University. Acquired present status and title 1963. Under the jurisdiction of the Ministry of Chemical Industry. Residential facilities for academic staff and students.

Arrangements for co-operation with the Universities of: Oakland; Delaware. Worcester Polytechnic Institute; Northeast University, Japan.

Academic Year: September to July (September-February; March-July).

Admission Requirements: Graduation from senior middle school and entrance examination.

Language of Instruction: Chinese.

Degrees and Diplomas: Bachelor of Engineering, 4 yrs. Master, a further 3 yrs.

Library: Central Library, 630,000 vols.

Publications: Newspaper (biweekly); Journal (quarterly).

Academic Staff, 1986-87:

Rank	Full-time
Professors	30
Associate Professors	110
Lecturers	300
Assistants	260
Engineers	24
Total	724

Student Enrolment, 1986-87:

	Men	Women	Total
Of the country	2373	479	2855

1615 **HENAN AGRICULTURAL INSTITUTE**
Zhengzhou

1616 **BAIQUAN AGRICULTURAL SCHOOL**
Hui County

1617 **YUXI AGRICULTURAL COLLEGE**
Xinan County

1618 **ZHENGZHOU SCHOOL OF ANIMAL HUSBANDRY AND VETERINARY MEDICINE**
Xinan County

1619 **HENAN MEDICAL COLLEGE**
Zhengzhou

1620 **XINXIAN MEDICAL COLLEGE**
Ji County

1621 **HENAN COLLEGE OF TRADITIONAL CHINESE MEDICINE**
Zhengzhou

1622 **KAIFENG MEDICAL SCHOOL**
Kaifeng

1623 **LUOYANG MEDICAL SCHOOL**
Luoyang

1624 **WEST HENAN SCHOOL OF MEDICINE**
District of Yanshi

1625 **XINXIANG TEACHERS' COLLEGE**
Xinxiang

1626 **XINYANG TEACHERS' COLLEGE**
Xinxiang

1627 **ANYANG TEACHERS' SCHOOL**
Anyang

1628 **LUOYUANG TEACHERS' SCHOOL**
Luoyang

1629 **SHANGQUI TEACHERS' SCHOOL**
Shangqui

1630 **XUCHANG TEACHERS' ACADEMY**
Xuchang
Telephone: 4853
President: Huang Huaqiang
Secretary-General: Gao Mingjun

Teacher Training

Founded 1949. Under the jurisdiction of the Provincial Government.

Admission Requirements: Graduation from senior middle school and entrance examination.

Language of Instruction: Chinese.

Degrees and Diplomas: Diplomas.

Library: Central Library, 300,000 vols.

Publication: Journal (biannually).

Academic Staff, 1986-87:

Rank	Full-time	Part-time
Professors	–	2
Associate Professors	8	15
Lecturers	75	–
Assistants	93	–
Total	176	17

Student Enrolment, 1986-87:

	Men	Women	Total
Of the country	1106	615	1721

1631 **ZHENGZHOU TEACHERS' SCHOOL**
Zhengzhou

1632 **ZHOUKOU TEACHERS' SCHOOL**
Zhoukou

1633 **HENAN INSTITUTE OF FINANCE AND ECONOMICS**
Zhengzhou

1634 **SCHOOL OF AERONAUTICAL ENGINEERING MANAGEMENT**
Zhengzhou

Hubei (Province)

1635 **GEZHOUBA INSTITUTE OF HYDROELECTRICAL ENGINEERING**
Yichang
Telex: 7108
Telephone: 22011-3615
President: Wu Guo-dong (1984-87)
Dean: Xu Zhi-ping

D. of Hydroelectrical Construction
Head: Guo Qi-dada; *staff* 112
D. of Mechanical Engineering
Head: Yang Xing-hai; *staff* 56
D. of Electrical Automation
Head: Chen Yiao-zhong; *staff* 60
D. of Basic Studies
Sec. of Marxism-Leninism
Sec. of Physical Culture

Founded 1978. Under the jurisdiction of the Ministry of Water Conservancy and Power. Residential facilities for academic staff and students.

Academic Year: September to July (September-February; March-July).

Admission Requirements: Graduation from senior middle school and entrance examination.

Fees: None.

Language of Instruction: Chinese.

Degrees and Diplomas: Bachelor of Engineering, 4 yrs.

Library: c. 220,000 vols.

Publications: Journal (biannually); Research on Academic Education.

Academic Staff, 1986-87:

Rank	Full-time
Professors	4
Associate Professors	34
Lecturers	160
Assistants	140
Total	338

Student Enrolment, 1986-87:

	Men	Women	Total
Of the country	1505	548	2053

1636 **HUAZHONG INSTITUTE OF TECHNOLOGY**
Wuhan

1637 **HUBEI INSTITUTE OF LIGHT ENGINEERING**
Ma-fang-shan Wuchang, Wuhan
Telephone: 73001

D. of Chemical Technology
D. of Mechanical and Electrical Engineering
D. of Basic Studies
Sec. of Arts and Crafts

Founded 1978. Under the jurisdiction of the Provincial Government. Residential facilities for academic staff and students.

Academic Year: September to July (September-January; February-July).

Admission Requirements: Graduation from senior middle school and entrance examination.

Language of Instruction: Chinese.

Degrees and Diplomas: Diploma, 4 yrs.

Library: c. 100,500 vols.

Academic Staff: c. 175.

Student Enrolment: c. 700.

1638 **WUHAN INSTITUTE OF BUILDING MATERIAL TECHNOLOGY**
Wuhan

A Key institution.

1639 **WUHAN INSTITUTE FOR CEREAL PRESERVATION AND PROCESSING**
Wuhan

1640 **WUHAN INSTITUTE OF CHEMICAL TECHNOLOGY**
Luxiang, Wuhan 430073
Telex: 5450
Telephone: 701351
President: Chen Gu-Shen (1988-91)
Secretary-General: Cheng Han-Yuan

D. of Chemical Engineering
Head: Yin Bin-Lie; *staff* 79
D. of Mining
Head: Zhang Jun-Quan; *staff* 72
D. of Mechanical Engineering
Head: Gao Yi-Tong; *staff* 78
D. of Automation
Head: Li Xu-zhi; *staff* 67

Founded 1972. Under the jurisdiction of the Ministry of Chemical Industry. Residential facilities for academic staff and students.

Academic Year: September to July (September-January; February-July).

Admission Requirements: Graduation from senior middle school and entrance examination.

Fees: None.

Language of Instruction: Chinese.

Degrees and Diplomas: Bachelor of Science, 4 yrs. Master, a further 2-5 yrs.

Library: Central Library, 240,000 vols.

Publication: Bulletin.

Academic Staff, 1989-90:

Rank	Full-time	Part-time
Professors	3	2
Associate Professors	65	–
Lecturers	183	–
Assistants	114	–
Total	365	2

Student Enrolment, 1989-90:

	Men	Women	Total
Of the country	1791	463	2254

1641 **WUHAN INSTITUTE OF TECHNOLOGY**
Wuhan

1642 **WUHAN INSTITUTE OF TEXTILE TECHNOLOGY**
Wuhan

1643 **WUHAN SCHOOL FOR BUILDING CONSTRUCTION FOR METALLURGICAL INDUSTRY**
Wuhan

1644 **WUHAN SCHOOL OF RIVER TRANSPORTATION**
Wuhan

1645 **WUHAN COLLEGE OF GEOLOGY**
Wuhan
Cables: 5378
Telephone: 70481
President: Zhao Pengda (1984-)

Geology (including Geophysics, and Applied Chemistry)
D. of Basic Studies
D. for Correspondence Studies
Computer Ce.

Founded 1952, incorporating departments of geology of the Uni-versities of Beijing, Qin Hua, Tien Jing, Northwest and Tang Shan Engineering College. Acquired present title 1975. A Key institution under the jurisdiction of the Ministries of Geology and Mineral Resources and Education. Residential facilities for academic staff and students.

Arrangements for co-operation with the Universities of: Hanover; Clausthal.

Academic Year: September to July (September-January; February-July).

Admission Requirements: Graduation from senior middle school and entrance examination.

Language of Instruction: Chinese.

Degrees and Diplomas: Bachelor of Science, 4 yrs. Master, a further 3 yrs. Doctor, 3 yrs after Master.

Library: Central Library, *c.* 530,000 vols.

Special Facilities (Museums, etc.): Geological Museum.

Publication: Earth Science (quarterly).

Press or Publishing House: Wuhan College of Geology Press.

Academic Staff: c. 1120.

Student Enrolment: c. 4390 (Also *c.* 750 external students)

1646 **HUBEI AGRICULTURAL MACHINERY INSTITUTE**
Wuhan

1647 **HUBEI MEDICAL COLLEGE**
Wuhan

1648 **HUBEI COLLEGE OF TRADITIONAL CHINESE MEDICINE**
Wuhan

1649 **WUHAN METALLURGICAL MEDICAL SCHOOL**
Wuhan

1650 **ENSHI MEDICAL SCHOOL**
District of Enshi

1651 **YICHANG MEDICAL SCHOOL**
Yichang

1652 **HUBEI COLLEGE OF EDUCATION**
23, Wuluo Road, Wuchang
Telephone: 71123
President: Ren Xijian

Education
D. for Evening Studies and Correspondence Courses
Also Research Institute.

Founded 1979. Under the jurisdiction of the Provincial Government. Residential facilities for academic staff and students.

Academic Year: September to July (September-January; February-June).

Admission Requirements: Graduation from senior middle school, 5 yrs teaching experience, and entrance examination.

Language of Instruction: Chinese.

Degrees and Diplomas: Diploma, 2 yrs.

Library: Central Library, *c.* 200,000 vols.

Publications: Journal (quarterly); Teaching Research (monthly).

Academic Staff: c. 230.

Student Enrolment: c. 520.

1653 **HUANGSHI TEACHERS' COLLEGE**
Huangshi

1654 **WUHAN TEACHERS' COLLEGE**
Wuhan

1655 **ENSHI TEACHERS' SCHOOL**
District of Enshi

1656 **HUANGGANG TEACHERS' SCHOOL**
District of Huanggang

1657 **JINGZHOU TEACHERS' SCHOOL**
District of Jiangling

1658 **XIAOGAN TEACHERS' COLLEGE**
Xiaogan
Telephone: 3906
President: Wu Changshu (1986-)

Teacher Training

Founded 1958, acquired present status and title 1981. Under the jurisdiction of the Provincial Government. Residential facilities for academic staff and students.

Academic Year: September to July (September-January; February-June).

Admission Requirements: Graduation from senior middle school and entrance examination.

Language of Instruction: Chinese.

Degrees and Diplomas: Diploma, 2-3 yrs.

Library: Central Library, 200,000 vols.

Publications: Journal (quarterly); Newspaper (monthly).

Press or Publishing House: College Press.

Academic Staff, 1986-87:

Rank	Full-time
Assistant Professors	20
Lecturers	55
Assistants	26
Teachers	103
Total	204

Student Enrolment, 1986-87:

	Men	Women	Total
Of the country	1027	200	1227

1659 **XIANNING TEACHERS' SCHOOL**
Xianning

1660 **YICHANG TEACHERS' SCHOOL**
Yichang

1661 **YINCHEN TEACHERS' SCHOOL**
Xiangfan

1662 **YUNYANG TEACHERS' SCHOOL**
Jun County

1663 **HUBEI INSTITUTE OF FINANCE AND ECONOMICSUC**
Wuhan

1664 **SOUTH CENTRAL INSTITUTE OF POLITICAL SCIENCE AND LAW**
Zheng Yuan road, Hongshan District, Wuhan
Telephone: 701-620
Fax: 703-056
President: Luo Yu Zhen

D. of Law
Head: Giao Keyu; *staff* 118
D. of Economic Law
Head: Wu Han Dong; *staff* 87
D. of Basic Studies
Head: Guan Dian Xi; *staff* 107
Jurisprudence Research I.
Dean: Wang Xian Shu *staff* 8

Founded 1953. Acquired present status and title, 1984 on the basis of the Law Department of Hubei Institute ofFinance and Law. Residential facilities for academic staff and students.

Academic Year: September to July (September-January; February-July).

Admission Requirements: Graduation from senior middle school and entrance examination.

Fees: None.

Language of Instruction: Chinese.

Degrees and Diplomas: Bachelor of Law, Ll.B, 4 yrs. Master of Law, LL.M., a further 3 yrs.

Library: Total, 384,000 vols.

Publication: Journal (quarterly)

Press or Publishing House: Printing House.

Academic Staff, 1989-90:

Rank	Full-time
Professors	12
Vice-Professors	54
Lecturers	49
Assistants	198
Total	313

Student Enrolment, 1989-90:

	Men	Women	Total
Of the country	1884	570	2454*

*Also 2995 external students.

1665 **WUHAN INSTITUTE OF PHYSICAL CULTURE**
Wuhan

1666 **HUBEI ACADEMY OF FINE ARTS**
38 Huazhongcun, Wuchang District, Wuhan 430060
Telephone: (27) 877201
Vice-President: Li Zhelin (1985-)

D. of Fine Arts
Head: Luo Pan; *staff* 30
D. of Design
Head: Deen Tongcheng; *staff* 32
D. of Art Teaching
Head: Wang Liantian; *staff* 23

Founded 1920 as private art school. Acquired present status and title 1985. Residential facilities for academic staff and students.

Academic Year: September to July.

Admission Requirements: Graduation from senior middle school and entrance examination.

Fees: None.

Language of Instruction: Chinese.

Degrees and Diplomas: Bachelor of Arts, 4-5 yrs. Master, a further 2 yrs.

Library: 89,000 vols.

Publication: Hubei Art Academy (monthly).

Academic Staff, 1990: 124.

Student Enrolment, 1990:

	Men	Women	Total
Of the country	320	118	438*

*Also 532 external students.

1667 **ZHONGNAN INSTITUTE OF NATIONALITIES**
Wuhan

Hunan (Province)

1668 **CHANGSHA TRANSPORTATION COLLEGE**
Changsha
Cables: 4002
Telephone: 32967

Civil Engineering (including Highway and Harbour Construction)
Mechanical Engineering (including Marine Engineering)
D. of Basic Studies

Founded 1956 as vocational school, acquired present status and title 1978. Under the jurisdiction of the Ministry of Communication.

Academic Year: September to July (September-January; February-July).

Admission Requirements: Graduation from senior middle school and entrance examination.

Academic Staff: c. 585.

Student Enrolment: c. 270.

1669 **CHANGSHA RAILWAY INSTITUTE**
Changsha

1670 **HENGYANG ENGINEERING COLLEGE**
Hengyang 421001
Cables: 7108
Telephone: 24931
President: Sun De-Lun
Secretary-General: Wang Chang-Chan

D. of Mechanical Engineering
Director: Yan Jin-Cheng; *staff* 54
D. of Computer Sciences
Director: He Sian; *staff* 66
C. of Civil Engineering
Director: Qin Xu-Sheng; *staff* 90
D. of Industrial Management Engineering
Director: Ren DE-Xi; *staff* 47
D. of Nuclear Electronics
Director: Liu Ji-Cai; *staff* 18
D. of Mining Engineering
Director: Wang Chang-Han; *staff* 14

Founded 1957 as Hengyang Engineering Institute of Mining and Metalluragy. Acquired present title 1980. Residential facilities for academic staff and students.

Academic Year: September to July (September-February; March-July).

Admission Requirements: Graduation from high school and entrance examination.

Fees: None.

Language of Instruction: Chinese.

Degrees and Diplomas: Bachelor, 4 yrs.

Library: 240,000 vols.

Special Facilities (Museums, etc.): Theatre.

Publication: Journal.

Academic Staff, 1989: 343.

Student Enrolment: 2500.

1671 **XIANGTAN MINING INSTITUTE**
Xiangtan
Cables: 7108
Telephone: 22357,Electronic Mail: 411201
President: Liu Guorong
Vice-President: Yu Liren

D. of Mining
Dean: Li Chengduan; *staff* 45
D. of Geology
Dean: Liu Zhan; *staff* 69
D. of Mechanical Engineering
Dean: Liu Liangguo; *staff* 49
D. of Automation
Dean: Liu Miaoshen; *staff* 42
D. of Civil Engineering
Dean: Li Chibo; *staff* 36
D. of Chemical Engineering
Dean: Li Zhong-ji; *staff* 36
D. of Economics
Dean: Zhu You-zhi; *staff* 25
D. of Basic Studies
Dean: Li Ming-qing; *staff* 77
D. of Social Sciences
Dean: Liu Fagui; *staff* 19
I. of Mine Design
Chief: Li Chengduan

Founded 1978. A Key institution. Residential facilities for academic staff and student

Academic Year: September to July (September-January; March-July).

Admission Requirements: Graduation from senior middle school and entrance examination.

Fees: None.

Language of Instruction: Chinese.

Degrees and Diplomas: Bachelor, 4 yrs. Master, a further 2-3 yrs.

Library: 22,000 vols.

Publications: Journal; Higher Education Research.

Academic Staff, 1990:

Rank	Full-time
Professors	7
Assistant Professors	45
Lecturers	146
Assistant Lecturers	106
Total	304

Student Enrolment, 1990:

	Men	Women	Total
Of the country	1452	364	1816*

*Also 313 external students.

1672 **SOUTH-CENTRAL CHINA INSTITUTE OF FORESTRY**
Zhuzhou

1673 **HUNAN AGRICULTURAL COLLEGE**
Changsha

1674 **HENGYANG MEDICAL COLLEGE**
Hengyang 421001
Cables: 7200
Telephone: 25661
President: Yang Yong-Zong (1984-89)
Director: Zhang Yi

D. of Medicine
Dean: Zhou Shao-Gin; *staff* 240 (30)
I. of Cardiovascular Diseases
Director: Yang Yong-Zong; *staff* 28 (29)
I. of Oncology
Director: Kuang Xi-Wei; *staff* 27 (30)
Also 2 affiliated hospitals.

Founded 1956. Under the jurisdiction of the Hunan Provincial Government. Residential facilities for 90% of the academic staff and for students.

Academic Year: September to July (September-February; February-July).

Admission Requirements: Graduation from senior middle school and entrance examination.

Language of Instruction: Chinese.

Degrees and Diplomas: Bachelor of Medicine, 5 yrs. Master, a further 3 yrs.

Library: Central Library, *c.* 191,000 vols.

Publication: Journal (quarterly).

Academic Staff, 1989-90:

Rank	Full-time	Part-time
Professors	20	–
Associate Professors	130	26
Lecturers	600	–
Assistants	960	–
Others	690	–
Total	2400	26

Student Enrolment, 1989-90:

	Men	Women	Total
Of the country	1200	600	1800*

*Also 900 external students.

1675 **HUNAN TEACHERS' COLLEGE**
Changsha

1676 **CHANGDE TEACHERS' SCHOOL**
Changde

1677 **CHENZHOU TEACHERS' SCHOOL**
Chenzhou

1678 **HENGYANG TEACHERS' COLLEGE**
Hunan Bai Road, Hengyang 421008
Telephone: 25971
President: Zeng Xibin (1983-)

D. of Chinese
Dean: Yao Yunxiang; *staff* 38

D. of English
Dean: Lin Yongfa; *staff* 35
D. of Physics
Dean: Dai Gang; *staff* 25
D. of Mathematics
Dean: Xiao Shuangfa; *staff* 25
D. of Chemistry
Dean: Hou Xinfa; *staff* 21
D. of Politics
Dean: Gao Ru; *staff* 22
D. of History
Dean: Zhou Hui Xiang; *staff* 21
D. of Geography
Dean: Yang Zai Tian; *staff* 19
D. of Music
Dean: Zhao Ting Wu; *staff* 22
D. of Arts
Dean: Peng Zhen Gui; *staff* 20

Founded 1958. Residential facilities for academic staff and students.

Academic Year: September to July (September-January; February-July).

Admission Requirements: Graduation from senior middle school and entrance examination.

Fees: None.

Language of Instruction: Chinese.

Degrees and Diplomas: Diploma, 3 yrs.

Library: Central Library, 390,000 vols.

Publication: Journal (quarterly).

Academic Staff, 1989:

Rank	Full-time
Vice-Professors	83
Lecturers	180
Teachers	15
Assistants	113
Total	391

Student Enrolment, 1989:

	Men	Women	Total
Of the country	1240	625	1865*

*Also 1548 external students.

1679 **SHAOYANG TEACHERS' SCHOOL**
Shaoyang

1680 **XIANGTAN TEACHERS' SCHOOL**
Xiangtan

1681 **YIYANG TEACHERS' COLLEGE**
Yiyang
President: Chen Hua-Dong (1985-)
Secretary-General: Den Min-Gao

D. of English
Head: Yang Yin-Ming; *staff* 34 (1)
D. of Chinese
Head: Tan Ke-Jing; *staff* 27
D. of Mathematics
Head: Xia Che-Miao; *staff* 21
D. of Physics
Head: Chai Xing-Gao; *staff* 21
D. of History
Head: Tao Yen-Xu; *staff* 20
D. of Physical Education
Head: Zhang Hong-Fang; *staff* 32 (1)
D. of Chemistry
Head: Li Yue-Er; *staff* 19

Founded 1970, acquired present status and title 1980. Residential facilities for academic staff and students.

Academic Year: September to July (September-January; February-July).

Admission Requirements: Graduation from senior middle school and entrance examination.

Fees: None.

Language of Instruction: Chinese.

Degrees and Diplomas: Diploma.

Library: Central Library, 289,000 vols.

Publication: Journal (quarterly).

Academic Staff, 1990:

Rank	Full-time	Part-time
Professors	61	–
Lecturers	135	–
Teachers	167	24
Total	363	24

Student Enrolment, 1989-90:

	Men	Women	Total
Of the country	938	534	1472*

*Also 822 students by correspondence and television.

1682 **YUEYANG TEACHERS COLLEGE**
Qijialing, East Suburbs of Yueyang City, Yueyang 414000
Telephone: 22611
President: Li Linyan
Secretary-General: Lin Zhi

D. of Political Education
Vice-Dean: Wen Yiwen; *staff* 20
D. of Chinese
Dean: Yu Shanding; *staff* 34
D. of Foreign Languages
Dean: Wang Jiasheng; *staff* 28
D. of Mathematics
Dean: Li Shaocu; *staff* 23
D. of Physics
Dean: Liu Yunlo; *staff* 23
D. of Physical Education
Dean: Zhou Tiejun; *staff* 24
D. of Art
Dean: Lo Enjun; *staff* 19

Founded 1972 as Yueyang Normal School. Acquired present title 1978. Under the jurisdiction of the Provincial Education Commission. Residential facilities for academic staff and students.

Academic Year: September to July (September-January; February-July).

Admission Requirements: Graduation from high school and entrance examination.

Fees: None.

Languages of Instruction: Chinese and English.

Degrees and Diplomas: Certificate, 3 yrs.

Library: Yueyang Teachers College Library, 250,000 vols.

Publications: Yunmen; School Weekly.

Press or Publishing House: Yueyang Teachers College Publishing House.

Academic Staff, 1990:

Rank	Full-time
Associate Professors	57
Lecturers	77
Assistants	49
Total	183

Student Enrolment, 1990:

	Men	Women	Total
Of the country	1057	661	1718*

*Also 806 students by correspondence.

1683 **HUNAN INSTITUTE OF FINANCE AND ECONOMICS**
Changsha

1684 **HUNAN SCHOOL OF COMMERCE**
Changsha

Nei Monggol (Inner Mongolian Autonomous Region)

1685 **BAOTOU IRON AND STEEL ENGINEERING INSTITUTE**
Baotou
President: Cuei Baolu (1982-)

Iron and Steel Engineering

Founded 1958. Under the jurisdiction of the Ministry of Metallurgical Industry.

Academic Year: September to July (September-January; February-July).

Admission Requirements: Graduation from senior middle school and entrance examination.
Language of Instruction: Chinese.
Degrees and Diplomas: Bachelor of Science, 4 yrs.
Library: Central Library, 300,000 vols.
Publication: Journal (biannually).
Academic Staff, 1986-87:

Rank	Full-time
Professors	4
Associate Professors	46
Lecturers	126
Assistants	140
Total	316

Student Enrolment, 1986-87:

	Men	Women	Total
Of the country	1675	683	2360

1686 **INNER MONGOLIAN ENGINEERING COLLEGE**
Hohhot 010062
Cables: 2699 hohhot
Telex: 85004 ITCC CN
Telephone: 664455
President: Li Xiyu (1983-)

Engineering (including Architecture)
D. of Basic Sciences
Director: Wen Jian
Livestock Machinery Research I.
Director: Jiang Zhi-Fan
Rare Earth Research I.
Director: Lin Bao-Jun
Natural Energy Research I.
Director: Liu Zhi-Zhang

Founded 1958. Under the jurisdiction of the Provincial Government. Residential facilities for academic staff and students.

Arrangements for co-operation with: University of Saskatchewan; Hawaii University.

Academic Year: September to July (September-January; February-July).
Admission Requirements: Graduation from senior middle school and entrance examination.
Language of Instruction: Chinese.
Degrees and Diplomas: Bachelor, 4 yrs. Master, a further 2-3 yrs.
Library: Central Library, 440,000 vols.
Publication: Journal of IMEC.
Academic Staff, 1989-90:

Rank	Full-time
Professors and Associate Professors	120
Lecturers	230
Assistants	250
Total	600

Student Enrolment, 1989-90: 3300 (Also 760 external students).

1687 **INNER MONGOLIA FORESTRY COLLEGE**
Hinjian Dongjie, Hohhot 010019
Telex: 85015 HUHE CN
Telephone: (471) 44665
President: Li Yun-Zhang (1983-)
Secretary-General: Liu Lian-Ming

D. of Forestry
Head: Zhang Shiying; *staff* 20
D. of Desert Control and Utilization
Head: Zhou Shiquan; *staff* 83
D. of Forest Economics Management
Head: Liu Lian-ming; *staff* 16
D. of Forest Logging Engineering
Head: Zhang Dian-zhong; *staff* 42
D. of Forest Machinery and Wood Industry
Head: Pan Shifeng; *staff* 73
Desert Research I.
Director: Wang Jiu-wen; *staff* 5

Founded 1958. Acquired present status 1978. Under the jurisdiction of the Provincial Government.

Arrangements for co-operation with Tottori University.

Academic Year: September to July (September-January; February-July).
Admission Requirements: Graduation from senior middle school and entrance examination.
Fees: None.
Language of Instruction: Chinese.
Degrees and Diplomas: Bachelor. Master. Certificates.
Library: Central Library, 250,000 vols.
Publication: Journal (biannually).
Academic Staff, 1990:

Rank	Full-time
Professors	7
Associate Professors	87
Lecturers	169
Assistants	389
Total	652

Student Enrolment, 1990: 1724.

1688 **INNER MONGOLIA INSTITUTE OF AGRICULTURE AND ANIMAL HUSBANDRY**
Hohhot

1689 **ZHELIMU ANIMAL HUSBANDRY INSTITUTE**
Tongliao

1690 **BAOTOU MEDICAL COLLEGE**
Baotou

1691 **INNER MONGOLIA MEDICAL COLLEGE**
Hohhot

1692 **MEDICAL COLLEGE FOR INNER MONGOLIA NATIONALITY**
Hohhot

1693 **ZHELIMU MEDICAL COLLEGE**
Tongliao

1694 **TEACHERS' COLLEGE OF INNER MONGOLIA NATIONALITY**
Tongliao

1695 **BAOTOU TEACHERS' SCHOOL OF EDUCATION**
Baotou

1696 **TEACHERS' SCHOOL OF ZHAOWUDAMENG NATIONALITY**
Chifeng

1697 **INNER MONGOLIA INSTITUTE OF FINANCE AND ECONOMICS**
Hohhot

Jiangsu (Province)

1698 **EAST CHINA INSTITUTE OF ENGINEERING**
Nanjing

A Key institution.

1699 **JIANGSU INSTITUTE OF CHEMICAL TECHNOLOGY**
Airport Road, Changzhou 213016
Cables: 4100
Telephone: 602615
Executive President: Gao Xiqi (1983-1993)
Head of Administrative Office: Zhou Yuangyuan

D. of Chemical Technology
Chairman: Zhao Chengbo; *staff* 56 (5)

D. of Materials' Science
Director: Sun Zaijian; *staff* 15 (3)
D. of Mechanical Engineering
Chairman: Huang Ao; *staff* 35 (3)
D. of Management Engineering
Chairman: Jing Guoming; *staff* 12
D. of Oil Storage and Transportation
Director: Gao Xiqi; *staff* 8 (3)
D. of Thermal Energy Engineering
Director: Shi Wenqing; *staff* 14 (2)
D. of Adult Education
Executive Director: Liu Peiyu; *staff* 4 (20)
I. of Design and Research in Chemical Technology
Director: Zhang Quanxing; *staff* 40 (6)

Founded 1978. Under the jurisdiction of the Jiangsu Principal Government. Residential facilities for academic staff and students.

Academic Year: September to July (September-January; February-July).

Admission Requirements: Graduation from senior middle school and entrance examination.

Fees: None.

Language of Instruction: Chinese.

Degrees and Diplomas: Bachelor of Engineering, 4 yrs.

Library: Central Library, 210,000 vols.

Publication: Journal (quarterly). Research in Higher Engineering Education (half-yearly).

Press or Publishing House: Press of JICT

Academic Staff, 1989-90:

Rank	Full-time
Professors	100
Lecturers	174
Assistants	254
Total	528

Student Enrolment, 1989-90:

	Men	Women	Total
Of the country	1648	527	2175*

*Also 159 external students.

1700 **ZHENJIANG INSTITUTE OF AGRICULTURAL ENGINEERING**
Zhenjiang

A Key institution.

1701 **LIANYUNGANG CHEMICAL MINING SCHOOL**
Lianyungang

1702 **NANJING AERONAUTICAL INSTITUTE**
29 Yu dao Street, Nanjing
Cables: 3057 nanjing
Telex: 34155 NANJ CN
Telephone: 46752; 46131
President: Yu Chengye (1983-)

Aeronautical Technology (Aircraft Design, Electronics and Aerodynamics)

Founded as technical college 1952, acquired present status and tite 1956. A Key institution under the jurisdiction of the Ministry of Aviation Industry. Residential facilities for academic staff and students.

Arrangements for co-operation with the Universities of: New Mexico; Tennessee; Glasgow; Nottingham; Oxford; Manchester. Institutes of Technology of: Georgia; Kyushu. Royal Institute of Technology, Stockholm.

Academic Year: September to July (September-January; February-July).

Admission Requirements: Graduation from senior middle school and entrance examination.

Language of Instruction: Chinese.

Degrees and Diplomas: Bachelor of Engineering, 4 yrs. Master, a further 2 ½ yrs. Doctor, a further 3 yrs.

Library: Central Library, 790,000 vols.

Publications: Journal (quarterly); Data Acquisition and Processing (quarterly).

Press or Publishing House: NAI Printing Press.

Academic Staff, 1986-87:

Rank	Full-time	Part-time
Professors and Associate Professors	300	31
Lecturers	570	–
Assistants	240	–
Total	1110	31

Student Enrolment, 1986-87:

	Men	Women	Total
Of the country	4050	1150	5200*

*Also 80 external students.

1703 **NANJING INSTITUTE OF CHEMICAL ENGINEERING AND ENERGETICS**
Nanjing

1704 **NANJING INSTITUTE OF CHEMICAL TECHNOLOGY**
Nanjing

1705 **NANJING ARCHITECTURAL AND CIVIL ENGINEERING INSTITUTE**
200 North Zhongshan Road, Nanjing 210009
Cables: 9098 nanjing
Telephone: 632002
President: Sun Jingwu
Administrator: Bao Shipbiao

D. of Architecture
Dean: Zhao Guoquan; *staff* 31
D. of Construction Engineering
Dean: Li Zhihao; *staff* 122
D. of Business Administration
Dean: Yin Zhijian; *staff* 27
D. of Surveying
Dean: Pan Yude; *staff* 70
D. of Machinery and Electrical Engineering
Dean: Mao Chenjun; *staff* 76
D. of Adult Education (Correspondence and Evening S.)
Dean: Zhang Yuanzhen; *staff* 11 (80)

Founded 1933. Under the jurisdiction of the Ministry of Construction. Residential facilities for academic staff and students.

Arrangements for co-operation with Fachhochschule, München; Pratt Institute, USA.

Academic Year: Spetember to July (September-January; February-July).

Admission Requirements: Graduation from senior middle school and entrance examination.

Fees: None.

Language of Instruction: Chinese.

Degrees and Diplomas: Bachelor, 4 yrs (5 yrs by correspondence). Professional Certificates, 2-3 yrs.

Library: c. 250,000 vols.

Publications: Journal (quarterly); Research on Education in Universities (bimonthly).

Academic Staff, 1990:

Rank	Full-time
Professors	9
Associate Professors	75
Lecturers	270
Assistants	210
Total	564

Student Enrolment, 1989:

	Men	Women	Total
Of the country	1787	356	2143*

*Also 275 external students and students by correspondence.

1706 **NANJING INSTITUTE OF METEOROLOGY**
Nanjing
President: Zhang Pei-Chang (1984-)

Meteorology

Founded 1960. A Key institution under the jurisdiction of the State Meteorological Bureau. Residential facilities for students.

Arrangements for co-operation with the University of Edinburgh.

Academic Year: September to July (September-February; March-July).

Admission Requirements: Graduation from senior middle school and ntrance examination.

Language of Instruction: Chinese.

Degrees and Diplomas: Bachelor of Science, 4 yrs. Master, a further 2-3 rs.

Library: c. 350,000 vols.

Publications: Journal (quarterly); Meteorological Education and Science quarterly).

Press or Publishing House: Publishing House.

Academic Staff: c. 170 (20).

Student Enrolment: c. 1170 (Also c. 250 external students).

707 **NANJING INSTITUTE OF POSTS AND TELECOMMUNICATIONS**

38 Guandong Road, Sampailon, Nanjing

708 **NANJING INSTITUTE OF TECHNOLOGY**

Nanjing

A Key institution.

709 **SUZHOU INSTITUTE OF SILK TEXTILE TECHNOLOGY**

District of Wuxian

Telephone: 25614

President: Wu Rong-Ru (1986-)

Silk and Fibre Technology

Founded 1912 as private sericulture school, acquired present status and itle 1960. Under the jurisdiction of the Ministry of Textile Industry.

Arrangements for co-operation with Shinshu University.

Academic Year: September to July (September-January; February-July).

Language of Instruction: Chinese.

Degrees and Diplomas: Bachelor of Science. Master.

Library: Central Library, 308,228 vols.

Publications: Journal (quarterly); Silk Technology Overseas (bimonthy); Educational Research (quarterly); News of Suzhou Institute of Silk Textile Technology (monthly).

Academic Staff, 1986-87:

Rank	Full-time
Professors	1
Associate Professors	22
Lecturers	202
Assistants	53
Total	278

Student Enrolment, 1986-87:

	Men	Women	Total
Of the country	1223	642	1865

710 **WUXI INSTITUTE OF LIGHT ENGINEERING**

170 Huihe Road, Wuxi 214036

Cables: Wuxi 6535

Telephone: 66-99-90

Fax: 66-79-76

President: Xiao-Lin Ding (1988-)

D. of Food Science and Engineering
Dean: Wen-sheng Wang; *staff* 77

D. of Fermentation Engineering
Dean: Ke-chang Zhang; *staff* 74

D. of Cereal and Oil Engineering
Dean: Jia-gen Wu; *staff* 60

D. of Chemical Engineering
Dean: Zhao-yuan Shen; *staff* 105

D. of Mechanical Engineering
Dean: Zhen-xi Lu; *staff* 104

D. of Textile Engineering
Dean: Ping-sheng Zong; *staff* 48

D. of Automation
Dean: Pin-ru Feng; *staff* 95

D. of Industrial Design
Dean: Wei-xing Cheng; *staff* 54

D. of Business Administration and International Trade
Dean: Chen-fu Liu; *staff* 25

D. of Basic Studies
Dean: He-sheng Tan; *staff* 103

D. of Adult Education
Dean: Zhi-Zhou; *staff* 6

Research Ce.
Director: Xian-zhang Wu; *staff* 47

Founded 1958, incorporating existing university departments. Under the jurisdiction of the Ministry of Light Industry. Residential facilities for academic staff and students.

Arrangements for co-operation with: Rutgers University; University of California-Davis; Kansas State University; Kyushu University; Gifu University; Leigh University; Tokyo University of Art and Design.

Academic Year: September to July (September-January; February-July).

Admission Requirements: Graduation from senior middle school and entrance examination.

Fees: None.

Language of Instruction: Chinese.

Degrees and Diplomas: Bachelor of Science, 4 yrs. Master, a further 2 ½-3 years. Doctor, Ph.D., 2 ½-3 yrs.

Library: Central Library, 410,000 vols.

Publication: Institute Journal (quarterly).

Press or Publishing House: Printing Shop.

Academic Staff, 1989:

Rank	Full-time
Professors	15
Associate Professors	143
Senior Engineers	13
Lecturers	281
Engineers	107
Teaching Assistants	206
Assistant Engineers	66
Total	831

Student Enrolment, 1989:

	Men	Women	Total
Of the country	2106	974	3080
Of other countries	38	3	41
Total	2144	977	3121*

*Also 612 external students and students by correspondence.

1711 **ZHENJIANG SHIPBUILDING INSTITUTE**

P.O. Box 414, Zhenjiang 212003

Cables: 5306

Telephone: 23-22-92

President: Ding Yu-Zhong

D. of Shipbuilding Engineering
Head: Xie Zho Shui; *staff* 64

D. of Thermal Power Mechanics and Equipment
Head: Zhu De-Shu; *staff* 33

D. of Industrial Management Engineering
Head: Xu Long Gui; *staff* 74

D. of Welding Technology and Equipment
Head: Song Sheng-Yang; *staff* 60

D. of Computer Systems and Applications
Head: Gu Zi-Tian; *staff* 46

D. of Mechanical Technology and Equipment
Head: Zhao Li-Che; *staff* 59

Training Sec. for Cadres
Director: Gu Fu-Xing; *staff* 5

D. for Evening Studies
Director: Hua Yu-fen; *staff* 4

Science Research Ce.
Director: Chen Jian-Fu

Noise and Vibration Research Ce.
Director: Ding Yu-Zhong; *staff* 16

Also 14 laboratories.

Founded 1952 as school in Shanghai. Moved to Zhenjiang 1970. Acquired present status and title 1978. Under thejurisdiction of the China State Shipbuilding Corporation. Residential facilities for academic staff and students.

Arrangements for co-operation with the Universities of: Michigan; Osaka; Osaka Prefecture; Strathclyde; Nagasaki Institute of Applied Science; Tokyo Institute of Technology; Nikolayev Shipbuilding Institute, USSR.

Academic Year: September to July (September-February; March-July).

Admission Requirements: Graduation from senior middle school and entrance examination.

Fees: None.
Language of Instruction: Chinese.
Degrees and Diplomas: Bachelor, 4 yrs. Master, a further 2 yrs.
Library: Central Library, c. 360,000 vols.
Special Facilities (Museums, etc.): Biological Garden; Art Gallery; Movie Studio.
Publication: Learned Journal (monthly).
Press or Publishing House: Zhenjiang Shipbuilding Institute Publishing House.
Academic Staff, 1989-90:

Rank	Full-time	Part-time
Professors	9	25
Associate Professors	110	–
Lecturers	365	
Total	484	25

Student Enrolment, 1989-90:

	Men	Women	Total
Of the country	1531	339	1870

1712 **NANJING SCHOOL OF RIVER NAVIGATION**
Nanjing

1713 **NANTONG TEXTILE SCHOOL**
Nantong

1714 **YANCHENG SCHOOL OF TECHNOLOGY**
District of Yancheng

1715 **YANGZHOU INSTITUTE OF TECHNOLOGY**
36 Yingxin Road, Yangzhou 225001
Telex: 2699
Telephone: 33513
President: Liu Bingkun (1988-)
Secretary-General: Ye Xingsheng

D. of Mechanical Engineering
Head: Cui Yongmao; *staff* 65
D. of International Economy, Trade and Management Engineering
Head: Zhang Yonglu; *staff* 36
D. of Civil Engineering
Director: Li Xuanhao; *staff* 57
D. of Environmental Engineering
Director: Zhou Daosheng; *staff* 12
D. of Electrical Engineering
Director: Gao Chengjing; *staff* 74
D. of Basic Studies
Director: Wang Jiayong; *staff* 70
Photoelectronic L.
Director: Liu Bingkun; *staff* 5 (4)
Computer-Assisted Designing L.
Director: Huang Heting; *staff* 2 (2)
L. of Basic Science Applications
Director: Li Shou Shong; *staff* – (8)
Machine Engineering L.
Director: Yuan Xiejue; *staff* 1 (4)
Environmental Science and Technology L.
Director: Zhou Daosheng; *staff* 1 (4)
Also branch at Changzhou.

Founded 1952. Under the jurisdiction of the Government of Jiangsu Province.

Arrangements for co-operation with educational and research institutions in Japan and Australia.

Academic Year: September to July (September-January; February-July).
Admission Requirements: Graduation from senior middle school and entrance examination.
Fees: None.
Language of Instruction: Chinese.
Degrees and Diplomas: Lower Bachelor, 3 yrs; Bachelor, 4 yrs.
Library: 320,000 vols.
Publication: Learned journal (quarterly)
Press or Publishing House: YIT Publishing House.

Academic Staff, 1989:

Rank	Full-time
Professors	2
Associate Professors	62
Teachers	192
Assistants	255
Total	511

Student Enrolment, 1989:

	Men	Women	Total
Of the country	1724	110	2164

1716 **JIANGSU AGRICULTURAL INSTITUTE**
Yangzhou

1717 **SUZHOU SERICULTURE SCHOOL**
District of Wuxian

1718 **NANJING MEDICAL COLLEGE**
Nanjing

1719 **NANTONG MEDICAL COLLEGE**
Nantong

1720 **SUZHOU COLLEGE OF MEDICINE**
Suzhou

1721 **XUZHOU MEDICAL COLLEGE**
Xuzhou
Telephone: 24932
Dean: Ping-Yu Wang (1982-87)

Medicine

Founded 1958 as Xuzhou branch of Nanjing Medical College. Acquired present status and title 1960. Under the jurisdiction of the Provincial Government. Residential facilities for academic staff and 1123 students.

Academic Year: September to July (September-January; February-July).
Admission Requirements: Graduation from senior middle school.
Language of Instruction: Chinese.
Degrees and Diplomas: Bachelor of Medicine, 5 yrs. Master, a further 3 yrs.
Library: c. 120,000 vols.
Publications: Acta Academiae Medicinae Xuzhou (4 times a year); Subdivision of Anesthesia and Resuscitation; Foreign Medicine (6 issues a year).
Academic Staff: c. 220.
Student Enrolment: c. 1120.

1722 **NANJING COLLEGE OF TRADITIONAL CHINESE MEDICINE**
Nanjing

1723 **NANJING RAILWAY MEDICAL COLLEGE**
87 Dingjiaqiao Road, Nanjing 210009
Cables: 0697 nanjing
Telephone: (25) 301508
President: Yujiao Zhou
Secretary-General: Zengtang Zhang

D. of Medicine
Director: Dongping Yin
D. of Health and Hygiene
Director: Gao Jingwu; *staff* 76 (7)
D. of Preclinical Medicine
Head: Sentang Zou; *staff* 96 (24)
Medical Science I.
Director: Chaochun Zhang; *staff* 21 (11)
Also 2 affiliated hospitals.

Founded 1958. Under the jurisdiction of the Ministry of Railways.

Academic Year: September to July (September-January; February-July).
Admission Requirements: Graduation from senior middle school and entrance examination.
Fees: None.

Languages of Instruction: Chinese. Also English, Russian, and Japanese.

Degrees and Diplomas: Bachelor of Medicine, 5 yrs. Master, a further 3 yrs.

Libraries: Central Library, 230,000 vols; specialized libraries, 50,000.

Publications: Acta of Nanjing Railway Medical College (quarterly); Railway Medical Journal (bimonthly); China Medical Abstracts, Internal Medicine (English edition, quarterly).

Press or Publishing House: Printing House of Nanjing Railway Medical College.

Academic Staff, 1989-90:

Rank	Full-time
Professors and Associate Professors	234
Lecturers	508
Total	742

Student Enrolment, 1989-90:

	Men	Women	Total
Of the country	1270	1014	2284

1724 **NANJING COLLEGE OF PHARMACY**

24 Tong Jia Xiang, Nanjing

Telephone: 34371

President: Zongjing Yin (1984-90)

Pharmacy (including Chinese Traditional Medicine)

Lifelong Education

Also 7 Research Divisions.

Founded 1936 as school. Acquired present status and title 1956. Under the jurisdiction of the State Pharmaceutical Administration of China. Residential facilities for academic staff and students.

Arrangements for co-operation with: Gifu College of Pharmacy; University of Pittsburgh.

Academic Year: September to July (September-January; February-July).

Admission Requirements: Graduation from senior middle school and entrance examination.

Language of Instruction: Chinese.

Degrees and Diplomas: Bachelor of Science, 4 yrs. Master, a further 3 yrs. Doctor, Ph.D., in Pharmacy, 2-3 yrs.

Library: Central Library, *c.* 220,000 vols.

Special Facilities (Museums, etc.): Medicinal Botanical Gallery.

Publication: Journal (quarterly).

Press or Publishing House: Publishing House.

Academic Staff: *c.* 350.

Student Enrolment: *c.* 310.

1725 **YANGZHOU MEDICAL SCHOOL**

Yangzhou

1726 **ZHENJIANG MEDICAL SCHOOL**

Zhenjiang

1727 **NANJING TEACHERS' COLLEGE OF EDUCATION**

Nanjing

1728 **XUZHOU TEACHERS' COLLEGE**

Xuzhou

Telephone: 88750

Teacher Training

Founded 1959. Under the jurisdiction of the Provincial Government.

Academic Year: September to July (September-January; February-July).

Language of Instruction: Chinese.

Degrees and Diplomas: Bachelor. Master.

Library: Central Library, 650,000 vols.

Publication: Journal.

Press or Publishing House: College Press.

Academic Staff, 1986-87:

Rank	Full-time
Professors	3
Associate Professors	33
Lecturers	152
Instructors	223
Assistants	39
Total	450

Student Enrolment, 1986-87:

	Men	Women	Total
Of the country	2023	992	3015

1729 **YANCHENG TEACHERS' COLLEGE**

District of Yancheng

1730 **YANGZHOU TEACHERS' COLLEGE**

The Shore of Slender West Lake, Yangzhou 225002

Telephone: 43011

President: Wu Jitao

Director: Su Hehu

D. of Chinese Language and Literature

Director: Zeng Huapeng; *staff* 72

D. of History

Deputy Director: Zhou Xinguo; *staff* 38

D. of Political Education

Deputy Director: Liu Congfu; *staff* 31

D. of Foreign Languages

Deputy Director: Zhai Ansong; *staff* 56

D. of Mathematics

Director: Zhang Hongyu; *staff* 66

D. of Physics

Director: Ding Jiansheng; *staff* 54

D. of Chemistry

Director: Mu Shaolin; *staff* 42

D. of Physical Education

Director: Huang Shuhuai; *staff* 68

D. of Business Economics

Deputy Director: Jiang Mingyue; *staff* 20

D. of Financial Accounting

Deputy Director: Yan Juhuai; *staff* 16

I. of Ancient Chinese Culture

Honorary Director: Ren Zhongmin; *staff* 10

Also 9 Research Groups, 2 middle schools, and courses for foreign students.

Founded 1952. Under the jurisdiction of the Jiangsu Education Commission.

Arrangements for co-operation with Kennesaw State College, Georgia.

Academic Year: September to July (September-January; February-July).

Admission Requirements: Graduation from senior middle school and entrance examination.

Fees: None.

Language of Instruction: Chinese.

Degrees and Diplomas: Bachelor of–Arts, B.A.; History; Law; Science; Education; Economics, 4 yrs. Master, a further 3 yrs. Doctor, Ph.D., 3 yrs.

Library: 1,060,000 vols.

Publication: Journals (Social Sciences, and Natural Science, quarterly).

Academic Staff, 1989:

Rank	Full-time
Professors	11
Associate Professors	101
Lecturers	264
Assistants	169
Others	88
Total	633

Student Enrolment, 1989:

	Men	Women	Total
Of the country	2015	1164	3179*

*Also 1544 external students.

1731 **SUZHOU RAILWAY TEACHERS' COLLEGE**

Shangfangshan, Suzhou 215009

Telephone: 333270

President: Hu Chengmin

Dean of Studies: Zhang Yanda

D. of Chinese
Dean: Huang Yiyuan; *staff* 30
D. of History
Dean: Yao Hai; *staff* 24 (1)
D. of Foreign Languages
Dean: Yu Changkai; *staff* 29 (1)
D. of Political Studies
Dean: Xu Zheng; *staff* 28
D. of Mathematics
Dean: Lei Zhongxie; *staff* 28 (2)
D. of Chemistry
Dean: Yao Chongfu; *staff* 27
D. of Geography
Dean: Xu Shuying; *staff* 15
D. of Physics
Dean: Zhong Shiduan; *staff* 21 (1)
D. of Music
Director: Jiang Ti; *staff* 4 (5)
D. of Biology
Dean: Zhao Kentang; *staff* 19
Research I. of Chinese Ancient Books
Director: Tang Wen; *staff* 3
Research I. of Modern Management
Director: Sun Zhang; *staff* 3

Founded 1980. Under the jurisdiction of the Ministry of Railways and the Jiangsu Provincial Government. Residential facilities for academic staff and *c.* 1600 students.

Academic Year: September to July (September-January; February-July).

Admission Requirements: Graduation from senior middle school and entrance examination.

Fees: None.

Language of Instruction: Chinese.

Degrees and Diplomas: Bachelor of–Arts; Science, 4 yrs.

Library: 300,000 vols.

Publication: Academic Journals (Social Sciences, and Science).

Academic Staff, 1990:

Rank	Full-time
Professors	4
Associate Professors	65
Lecturers	85
Assistants	53
Total	207

Student Enrolment, 1990:

	Men	Women	Total
Of the country	775	823	1598

1732 **HUAIYANG TEACHERS' SCHOOL**
Huaiyang

1733 **NANTONG TEACHERS' SCHOOL**
Nantong
President: Zhu Jia Yao
Secretary-General: Yang De Zhao

Teacher Training

Founded 1902. Residential facilities for academic staff and students.

Academic Year: September to July (September-January; February-July).

Admission Requirements: Graduation from senior middle school and entrance examination.

Language of Instruction: Chinese.

Degrees and Diplomas: Diploma, 3-5 yrs.

Library: Central Library, 100,000 vols.

Publication: Journal.

Academic Staff, 1986-87:

Rank	Full-time
Lecturers	20
Teachers	75
Total	95

Student Enrolment, 1986-87:

	Men	Women	Total
Of the country	118	189	307*

*Also 240 external students.

1734 **SUZHOU TEACHERS' SCHOOL**
Suzhou

1735 **ZHENJIANG TEACHERS' SCHOOL**
Zhenjiang

1736 **JIANGSU COMMERCIAL SCHOOL**
Yangzhou

1737 **NANJING COLLEGE OF FOOD ECONOMICS**
14 Hongmiao Lane, Fujian Road, Nanjing
Telephone: 025-86033
President: Niu Zheng-Jiang (1982-)

Food Technology and Economics

Founded 1957, acquired present status and title 1981. Under the jurisdic tion of the Ministry of Trade. Residential facilities for academic staff an students.

Academic Year: September to July (September-January; February-July).

Language of Instruction: Chinese.

Degrees and Diplomas: Bachelor.

Library: Central Library, 350,000 vols.

Publication: Food Economics Research.

Academic Staff, 1986-87:

Rank	Full-time
Professors	2
Associate Professors	14
Lecturers	82
Teachers	102
Total	200

Student Enrolment, 1986-87:

	Men	Women	Total
Of the country	436	321	757*

*Also 546 external students.

1738 **JIANGSU SCHOOL OF PUBLIC SECURITY**
Nanjing

1739 **NANJING INSTITUTE OF PHYSICAL CULTURE**
Nanjing

1740 **NANJING ACADEMY OF ARTS**
Nanjing

Jiangxi (Province)

1741 **EAST CHINA INSTITUTE OF GEOLOGY**
Nanchang

1742 **JIANGXI INSTITUTE OF TECHNOLOGY**
Nanchang

1743 **JINGDEZHEN CERAMIC INSTITUTE**
Xinghu Road, Eastern Suburb, Jingdezhen 333001
Cables: 0202 jingdezhen
Telephone: (0798) 441845 ext 301
President: Lu Wen-Sui

D. of Engineering
D. of Machinery
D. of Ceramic Fine Arts
D. of Business Management

Founded 1958. Under the jurisdiction of the Ministry of Light Industry. Residential facilities for academic staff and students.

Arrangements for co-operation with universities in Australia and Japan.

Academic Year: September to July (September-January; February-July).

Admission Requirements: Graduation from high school and entrance examination.

Fees: None.

Language of Instruction: Chinese.

Degrees and Diplomas: Bachelor, 4 yrs. Master, a further 2-3 yrs.
Academic Staff: c. 600.
Student Enrolment: c. 1430.

1744 **NANCHANG INSTITUTE OF AERONAUTICAL ENGINEERING**
11 Shanghai Road, Nanchang 330034
Cables: 0181 nanchang
Telephone: 331812
President: Liu Rong-Guang

D. of Materials Engineering
Dean: Wu Suo-Chun; *staff* 137 (7)
D. of Chemical Engineering
Dean: Chen Li-Feng; *staff* 85 (3)
D. of Mechanical Engineering
Vice-Dean: Ren Ji-Lin; *staff* 71
D. of Electronic Engineering
Dean: Su Da-Yi; *staff* 80
D. of Teacher Training
Dean: Huang Ning-Qing; *staff* 106

Founded 1978. Under the jurisdiction of the Ministry of Aerospace Industry. Residential facilities for academic staff and students.

Arangements for co-operation with: Vrije Universiteit Brussel; Laurentian University, Canada.

Academic Year: September to July (September-January; February-July).
Admission Requirements: Graduation from high school and entrance examination.
Fees: None.
Language of Instruction: Chinese.
Degrees and Diplomas: Bachelor, 4 yrs. Master, a further 2 ½ yrs.
Library: 400,000 vols.
Academic Staff, 1989:

Rank	Full-time	Part-time
Professors	12	8
Associate Professors	115	2
Lecturers	307	–
Assistants	133	–
Total	567	10

Student Enrolment, 1989:

	Men	Women	Total
Of the country	1358	540	1898*

*Also 574 external students.

1745 **JIANGXI MEDICAL COLLEGE**
Nanchang

1746 **JIANGXI COLLEGE OF TRADITIONAL CHINESE MEDICINE**
Nanchang

1747 **SOUTHERN INSTITUTE OF METALLURGY**
108 Red Flag Road, Ganzhou 341000
Cables: 1331 ganzhou
Telephone: (0797) 6711
President: Qi Hong-En
Director: Yang Zheng-Bing

D. of Mining
Dean: Ru Ju-Mei; *staff* 126
D. of Metallurgy
Dean: Wu Bing-Quan; *staff* 84
D. of Mechanical Engineering
Dean: Yao Jian-Qian; *staff* 95
D. of Automation
Dean: Zhong Meng-Hong; *staff* 103
D. of Administration Engineering
Dean: Liu Guang-Nan
D. of Social Science
Dean: Zhang Xiao-Ling
D. of Basic Studies
Dean: Chen Heng-Hong
Also 3 Research Institutes.

Founded 1958 as Jiangxi Metallurgical Institute. Acquired present title 1988. Under the jurisdiction of the China National Nonferrous Metals Industry Corporation. Residential facilities for academic staff and students.

Academic Year: September to July (September-January; March-July).
Admission Requirements: Graduation from high school and entrance examination.
Fees: None.
Language of Instruction: Chinese.
Degrees and Diplomas: Bachelor of Science, 4 yrs. Master, a further 3 yrs.
Publications: Journal (quarterly); Ye Yuan Ke Ji (Science and Technology).
Academic Staff, 1989-90:

Rank	Full-time
Professors	10
Associate Professors	132
Lecturers	327
Assistants	392
Total	861

Student Enrolment, 1990:

	Men	Women	Total
Of the country	2293	586	2879*

*Also 372 external students.

1748 **GANNAN MEDICAL SCHOOL**
Ganzhou

1749 **SHANGRAO TEACHERS' COLLEGE**
No. 1 Maojialing, Shangrao City
Telephone: 2440; 2480
President: Fang Cheng (1984-)
Secretary of Committee: Wang Bin

Teacher Training
Training Sec. for Cadres

Founded 1958 as Gandongbei University, incorporating Shangrao Teachers College and Shangrao Engineering College. Retitled Shangrao Teachers College 1961. Under the jurisdiction of the Provincial Government. Residential facilities for academic staff and students.

Academic Year: September to July (September-February; March-July).
Admission Requirements: Graduation from senior middle school and entrance examination.
Language of Instruction: Chinese.
Degrees and Diplomas: College Diploma.
Library: Central Library, *c.* 300,000 vols.
Publication: Journal (bimonthly).
Press or Publishing House: College's Publishing House.
Academic Staff, 1986-87:

Rank	Full-time
Professors	1
Associate Professors	3
Instructors	46
Assistant Instructors	245
Teachers	26
Total	321

Student Enrolment, 1986-87:

	Men	Women	Total
Of the country	2009	556	2565

1750 **GANNAN TEACHERS' SCHOOL**
Ganzhou

1751 **FUZHOU TEACHERS' SCHOOL**
Fuzhou

1752 **JIAN TEACHERS' SCHOOL**
Jian

1753 **JIUJIANG TEACHERS' COLLEGE**
Sanli Street, Juijiang
Telephone: 3591/92
President: Xiong Da-Cheng (1988-92)

D. of Chinese
Dean: Yang Zhen-Rong; *staff* 41 (1)
D. of Mathematics
Dean: Cheng Ping-Sun; *staff* 39 (2)
D. of Physics
Dean: Wang Sheng-Gui; *staff* 32 (3)
D. of Biology
Dean: Cai Zhu-Ping; *staff* 22 (1)
D. of Chemistry
Dean: Wen Xun-Guang; *staff* 26 (3)
D. of Foreign Languages
Dean: Lian Jie; *staff* 30
D. of Physical Education
Dean: Shu Xiao-Shan; *staff* 33 (3)
D. of Political Education and History
Dean: Fang Liang; *staff* 30 (3)
D. of Fine Arts
Dean: Luo Wan-Zhong; *staff* 11 (4)
Also 7 Research Centres and middle schools.

Founded 1977. Under the jurisdiction of the Provincial Government. Residential facilities for academic staff and students.

Academic Year: September to July (September-January; February-July).

Admission Requirements: Graduation from senior middle school and entrance examination.

Fees: None.

Language of Instruction: Chinese.

Degrees and Diplomas: Diploma.

Library: Central Library, 261,200 vols.

Publications: Journal (bimonthly); Jiujiang Teachers' College Press (monthly).

Academic Staff, 1988-90:

Rank	Full-time	Part-time
Professors	–	1
Lecturers	34	10
Engineers	115	8
Assistants	87	19
Total	236	38

Student Enrolment, 1989-90:

	Men	Women	Total
Of the country	1443	464	1907

1754 **YICHUN TEACHERS' SCHOOL**
Yichun

1755 **JIANGXI INSTITUTE OF FINANCE AND ECONOMICS**
Nanchang

Jilin (Province)

1756 **CHANGCHUN COLLEGE OF GEOLOGY**
27 Fu Jin Road, Changchun
Telex: 1967 CHANGCHUN
Telephone: 24781 Changchun
President: Zhang Yixia

D. of Geology
Director: Yang Zhensheng: *staff* 220
D. of Hydro-geology and Engineering
Director: Chao Yilin; *staff* 121
D. of Applied Earth Sciences
Director: Sun Yunsheng; *staff* 113
D. of Geological Instruments
Director: Li Mosun; *staff* 85
D. of Mineral Prospecting
; *staff* 154
D. for Basic Studies
Director: Ji Yinghan; *staff* 168
D. of Energy Resources
Director: Wang Dongpo; *staff* 68
D. of Drilling Engineering
Director: Zhang Zupei; *staff* 68
D. for Correspondence Courses

Founded 1952. Residential facilities for academic staff and students.

Arrangements for co-operation with: University of Adelaide; Universit of Queensland; Idaho State University; Institute of Mining and Geolog Sofia.

Academic Year: September to August (September-February; March August).

Admission Requirements: Graduation from senior middle school an entrance examination.

Language of Instruction: Chinese.

Degrees and Diplomas: Bachelor, 4 yrs. Master, a further 3 yrs. Doctor, yrs after Master.

Library: *c.* 700,000 vols.

Special Facilities (Museums, etc.): Geological Exhibition.

Publications: Journal (quarterly); World Geology (quarterly).

Press or Publishing House: Publishing House.

Academic Staff, 1986-87:

Rank	Full-time
Professors	23
Assistant Professors	118
Lecturers	350
Assistants	202
Total	693

Student Enrolment, 1986-87:

	Men	Women	Total
Of the country	2753	711	3464
Of other countries	7	–	7
Total	2760	711	3471*

*Also 1156 external students.

1757 **CHANGCHUN INSTITUTE OF OPTICS AND PRECISION MECHANICS**
7 Weixing Road, Changchun 130022
Cables: 2008
Telex: 883815
Telephone: 883402
President: Wu Shi-Ke

D. of Optical Engineering
Head: Mao Ying-Tai; *staff* 54
D. of Optical Physics
Head: Wang Kui-Xung; *staff* 75
D. of Electronic Engineering
Head: Zhang Shu-Ren; *staff* 58
D. of Optical Materials
Head: Chen Tie-Min; *staff* 43
D. of Management Engineering
Head: He Ting-Kai; *staff* 30
D. of Fine Mechanics Engineering
Head: Wang Jia-Ren; *staff* 56
D. of Foreign Languages
Head: Yan Fu-Jun; *staff* 47
D. of Chinese Language
Head: Liu Qiao; *staff* 22
D. of Basic Sciences
Head: Zhang Heng; *staff* 79
D. of Graduate Studies
Head: Wang Chang-Xing; *staff* 5
D. of Social Science
Head: Wang Zi-Ye; *staff* 24
D. of Computer Sciences
Head: Wang Xi-Long; *staff* 26
D. for Adult Education
Head: Kong Fan-Rong; *staff* 14
Also 3 Research Institutes.

Founded 1958. Under the jurisdiction of the Ministry of Machine-Build ing and Electronics Industry. Residential facilities for academic staff an students.

Academic Year: September to July (September-January; March-July).

Admission Requirements: Graduation from high school and entranc examination.

Fees: None.

Language of Instruction: Chinese.

Degrees and Diplomas: Bachelor, 4 yrs. Master, a further 2-3 yrs.
Library: 0.45 million vols.
Publications: Journal of Changchun Institute of Optics and Fine Mechanics (Natural Science Edition) (quarterly); Applied Writing (bimonthly); Research on Higher Education (quarterly).

1758 **CHANGCHUN INSTITUTE OF POSTS AND TELECOMMUNICATIONS**
20 South Lake Road Changchun 130012 (Jilin Province)
Cables: 02699
Telephone: 54223
President: Dai Yu-Zhuo
Vice-President: Wang Zhi-Huai

D. of Telecommunications Engineering
Head: Jia Yi-Yong; *staff* 38
D. of Radio Communications Engineering
Head: Tang Ru-Jin; *staff* 37
D. of Computer Sciences
Head: Jin Ren-Xun; *staff* 41

Academic Year: September to July (September-January; February-July).
Admission Requirements: Graduation from high school and entrance examination.
Fees: None.
Language of Instruction: Chinese.
Library: 285,000 vols.
Academic Staff, 1989-90: 919.
Student Enrolment, 1989-90: 1518.

1759 **JILIN INSTITUTE OF CHEMICAL TECHNOLOGY**
Jilin

1760 **JILIN INSTITUTE OF CIVIL ENGINEERING AND ARCHITECTURE**
Changchun

1761 **JILIN INSTITUTE OF FORESTRY**
Jilin
Telephone: 22375
President: Xing Shao-peng (1979-)

Forestry
Lifelong Education

Founded 1958 as school. Acquired present status and title 1978. Under the jurisdiction of the Provincial Departments of Higher Education and Forestry. Residential facilities for academic staff and students.
Academic Year: September to August (September-January; February-July).
Admission Requirements: Graduation from senior middle school and entrance examination.
Language of Instruction: Chinese.
Degrees and Diplomas: Bachelor of–Science; Agriculture, 4 yrs.
Library: Central Library, *c.* 124,760 vols.
Publication: Journal.
Press or Publishing House: Press of Jilin Institute of Forestry.
Academic Staff: c. 120.
Student Enrolment: c. 870.

1762 **JILIN INSTITUTE OF TECHNOLOGY**
Changchun

1763 **NORTHEAST CHINA INSTITUTE OF ELECTRIC POWER**
Changchun Road, Changchun 132012
Cables: 3443
Telephone: 242186
Vice-Chancellor: Wei Jia-Ding (1984-89)

D. of Electric Power Engineering (including Computer Sciences)
Dean: Song Jia-Hua
D. of Thermal Power Engineering
Dean: Yang Shan-Rang
D. of Applied Chemistry
Dean: Yao Ji-Xian
D. of Civil Engineering
Dean: Ma Shu-Xun
D. of Management Engineering
Dean: Zhang Chun
D. for Correspondence Courses
Director: Guo Chun-Guang
Electric Power Science Research I.
Director: Luo Ji-Shou
Survey and Design Ce. of Electric Power
Director: Sun Jian

Founded 1949 as school. Acquired present status and title 1978. Under the jurisdiction of the Ministry of Electric Power and Water Conservation Energy Resources. Residential facilities for academic staff and students.
Arrangements for co-operation with: Yamagata University; University of Lancaster.
Academic Year: September to July (September-January; February-July).
Admission Requirements: Graduation from senior middle school and entrance examination.
Fees: None.
Language of Instruction: Chinese.
Degrees and Diplomas: Bachelor of Engineering, 4 yrs. Master, a further 2 ½ yrs.
Library: Central Library, *c.* 500,000 vols.
Publication: Journal (biannually).
Academic Staff, 1989-90: 114.
Student Enrolment, 1989-90: c. 3000 (Also *c.* 2000 external students).

1764 **JILIN MECHANICAL AND ELECTRICAL SCHOOL**
Changchun

1765 **YANBIAN AGRICULTURAL INSTITUTE**
District of Yanji

1766 **YANBIAN MEDICAL COLLEGE**
District of Yanji

1767 **CHANGCHUN COLLEGE OF TRADITIONAL CHINESEMEDICINE**
Changchun

1768 **CHANGCHUN TEACHERS' COLLEGE**
Changchun

1769 **JILIN TEACHERS' COLLEGE**
Jilin

1770 **SIPING TEACHERS' COLLEGE**
Siping

1771 **TONGHUA TEACHERS' COLLEGE**
Tonghua

1772 **BAICHENG TEACHERS' SCHOOL**
Baicheng

1773 **YANBIAN TEACHERS' SCHOOL**
Yanbian

1774 **JILIN INSTITUTE OF FINANCE AND ECONOMICS**
Changchun

1775 **JILIN PHYSICAL CULTURE INSTITUTE**
Changchun

1776 **JILIN ACADEMY OF ARTS**
Changchun

Liaoning (Province)

1777 **ANSHAN INSTITUTE OF IRON AND STEEL TECHNOLOGY**
Anshan
Cables: 1331
Telephone: 25931
President: Shang Jiuliang (1983-)

Iron and Steel Technology (including Metallurgy and Mining)

Founded 1958. Under the jurisdiction of Ministry of Metallurgical Industry. Residential facilities for academic staff and students.

Arrangements for co-operation with Sheffield Polytechnic.

Academic Year: September to July (September-January; February-July).

Admission Requirements: Graduation from senior middle school and entrance examination.

Language of Instruction: Chinese.

Degrees and Diplomas: Bachelor of Science. Master.

Library: Central Library, 310,000 vols.

Publications: Journal (bimonthly); Studies of Higher Education.

Academic Staff, 1986-87:

Rank	Full-time
Professors	2
Associate Professors	48
Lecturers	248
Teaching Assistants	187
Total	485

Student Enrolment, 1986-87:

	Men	Women	Total
Of the country	1523	535	2058*

*Also 797 external students.

1778 **DALIAN INSTITUTE OF LIGHT INDUSTRY**
Dalian

1779 **DALIAN INSTITUTE OF TECHNOLOGY**
Dalian

A Key institution.

1780 **DALIAN MARITIME INSTITUTE**
Dalian

A Key institution.

1781 **DALIAN RAILWAY INSTITUTE**
Dalian

1782 **FUSHUN INSTITUTE OF PETROLEUM**
Fushun

1783 **FUXIN MINING INSTITUTE**
Fuxin

A Key institution.

1784 **JINZHOU INSTITUTE OF TECHNOLOGY**
Jinzhou

1785 **LIAONING INSTITUTE OF CONSTRUCTION ENGINEERING**
Shenyang

1786 **SHENYANG INSTITUTE OF AERONAUTICAL ENGINEERING**
52 North Huang-He Street, Shenyang
Cables: 6061
Telephone: 462574
President: Li Yuan-Qi

D. of Aeronautical Engineering
Head: Wei Y.L.; *staff* 92

D. of Mechanical Engineering
Head: Zhu T.M.; *staff* 98

D. of Electonic Engineering
Head: Yang Z.Q.; *staff* 90

D. of Safety Engineering
Head: Chang J.Z.; *staff* 50

D. of Industrial Design
Head: Liu R.J.; *staff* 23

Also 4 Research Centres and Institutes.

Founded 1952 as school. Acquired present status and title 1978. Under the jurisdiction of the Ministry of Aeronautical and Aerospace Industry. Residential facilities for academic staff and students.

Academic Year: September to July (September-January; March-July).

Admission Requirements: Graduation from senior middle school and entrance examination.

Fees: None.

Language of Instruction: Chinese.

Degrees and Diplomas: Bachelor of Engineering, 4 yrs.

Library: Central Library, *c.* 260,000 vols.

Publications: Journals; Research on Higher Education; Research on Science and Technology.

Academic Staff, 1989-90:

Rank	Full-time	Part-time
Professors	11	6
Associate Professors	74	–
Senior Lecturers	54	–
Lecturers	106	–
Tutors	135	–
Total	380	6

Student Enrolment, 1989-90:

	Men	Women	Total
Of the country	1399	233	1632

1787 **SHENYANG INSTITUTE OF CHEMICAL TECHNOLOGY**
Shenyang

1788 **SHENYANG INSTITUTE OF TECHNOLOGY**
Shenyang

A Key institution.

1789 **SHENYANG MECHANICAL AND ELECTRICAL INSTITUTE**
Shenyang

1790 **SHENYANG COLLEGE OF METALLURGICAL MACHINERY**
21 Wanghua South Street, Dadong District Shenyang
Cables: 4321
Telephone: 892183
Rector: Yu Qin-Zi

D. of Mechanics I (including Machine-making and Manufacturing, and Welding)
Director: Chen Min; *staff* 57

D. of Mechanics II (including Forging and Casting, Heat Treatment and Metal-Working Techniques)
Director: Zhang You-Wei; *staff* 50

D. of Management Engineering
Director: Jiang Fei-Fei; *staff* 41

D. of Basic Studies
Director: Yiang Chang-Shan; *staff* 63

D. of Electrical Engineering
Director: Meng De-Rie; *staff* 28

Founded 1906. Under the jurisdiction of the Ministry of Metallurgical Machinery. Residential facilities for academic staff and students.

Arrangements for co-operation with: Tokoyoto Senior Technical College; Fachhochschule Karlsruhe.

Academic Year: September to July (September-January; March-July).

Admission Requirements: Graduation from high school and entrance examination.

Fees: None.

Language of Instruction: Chinese.

Degrees and Diplomas: Diploma, 3 yrs.

Library: 230,000 vols.

Publications: College Magazine (monthly); College Newspaper (weekly).
Academic Staff, 1989:

Rank	Full-time
Professors	69
Associate Professors	146
Asistants	106
Total	321

Student Enrolment, 1989: 1709.

1791 **SHENYANG INSTITUTE OF GOLD TECHNOLOGY**
89 Wenhua East Road, Shenyang
Cables: 4141
Telephone: 483221
President: Ji Wei-Dong (1987-)

D. of Geology
Head: Zhang Zhong-Shen; *staff* 64
D. of Mining
Head: Li Chao-Dong; *staff* 50
D. of Metallurgy
Head: Li An-Guo; *staff* 37
D. of Basic Studies
Head: Liu Chi-Ting; *staff* 82
D. of Mechanical and Electrical Engineering
Head: Cha Ren-Yan; *staff* 59
D. for Adult Education
Head: Xiong Han-Bin; *staff* 12
Research I. of Gold and Silver
Head: Li An-Guo; *staff* 12

Founded 1952, acquired present status and title 1987. Under the jurisdiction of the National Gold Bureau. Residential facilities for academic staff and students.

Academic Year: September to July (September-January; February-July).

Admission Requirements: Graduation from senior middle school and entrance examination.

Fees: None.

Language of Instruction: Chinese.

Degrees and Diplomas: Diploma, 3 yrs. Bachelor, 4 yrs.

Library: Central Library, 300,000 vols.

Publications: Journal; Educational Research.

Academic Staff, 1989-90:

Rank	Full-time
Professors	7
Associate Professors	69
Lecturers	115
Assistants	73
Total	264

Student Enrolment, 1989-90:

	Men	Women	Total
Of the country	1259	305	1564*

*Also 800 Adult Education students.

1792 **SHENYANG AGRICULTURAL INSTITUTE**
Shenyang

A Key institution.

1793 **DALIAN INSTITUTE OF AQUATIC PRODUCTS**
Dalian

1794 **DALIAN MEDICAL COLLEGE**
220 Xinghai Street, Dalian
Cables: 4324 Dalian
Telephone: 491242
Director: Wu Gong-Kan (1986-89)
Secretary-General: Tan Yu-Xian

Medicine

Founded 1949, acquired present status and title 1978. Under the jurisdiction of the Provincial Government. Residential facilities for academic staff and students.

Arrangements for co-operation with: Boston University School of Medicine; Tokyo Medical University.

Academic Year: September to July (September-January; February-July).

Admission Requirements: Graduation from senior middle school and entrance examination.

Language of Instruction: Chinese.

Degrees and Diplomas: Bachelor of Medicine, 5 yrs. Master, a further 3 yrs. Doctor, a further 3 yrs.

Library: Central Library, 140,000 vols.

Publications: Journal; Research of Medical Education.

Academic Staff, 1986-87:

Rank	Full-time
Professors	19
Associate Professors	117
Lecturers	75
Assistants	139
Total	350

Student Enrolment, 1986-87:

	Men	Women	Total
Of the country	619	708	1317

1795 **JINZHOU MEDICAL COLLEGE**
Jinzhou

1796 **LIAONING COLLEGE OF TRADITIONAL CHINESE MEDICINE**
Shenyang

1797 **SHENYANG INSTITUTE OF PHARMACY**
Shenyang

1798 **SHENYANG SCHOOL OF PHARMACY**
Shenyang

1799 **JINZHOU TEACHERS' COLLEGE**
Jinzhou

1800 **LIAONING TEACHERS' COLLEGE**
Dalian

1801 **SHENYANG TEACHERS' COLLEGE**
Shenyang

1802 **TIELING TEACHERS' COLLEGE**
Tieling

1803 **YINGKOU TEACHERS' COLLEGE**
Yingkou

1804 **ANSHAN TEACHERS' COLLEGE**
Ping An Street, Anshan 114005
Telephone: 536743, 532564
President: Cai Xue-Pu

D. of Chinese
Head: Wei Lian-Cai; *staff* 39
D. of Political Studies
Head: Gu Xing-De; *staff* 25
D. of English
Head: Wang Chong-Man; *staff* 26
D. of Ecomomics
Head: Bian Xu-Kui; *staff* 16
D. of Mathematics
Head: Yang Qi-Chang; *staff* 41
D. of Physics
Head: Shong Ben-Xiang; *staff* 25
D. of Chemistry
Head: Shun Wei; *staff* 29
D. of Mechanical Engineering
Head: Zhao Nai-Xiang; *staff* 13
D. of Physical Education
Head: Yang Zhen-Qin; *staff* 20

Sec. for Basic Studies

Founded 1958. Became School 1962 and reverted to original title 1978. Under the jurisdiction of the City and Provincial Government.

Arrangement for co-operation with University of Wisconsin-Whitewater.

Academic Year: September to July (September-January; March-July).

Admission Requirements: Graduation from high school and entrance examination.

Fees: None.

Language of Instruction: Chinese.

Degrees and Diplomas: Diploma, 3 yrs.

Library: 260,000 vols.

Publication: Journal (every three month).

Student Enrolment, 1990:

	Men	Women	Total
Of the country	1421	1932	3353

1805 **CHAOYANG TEACHERS' COLLEGE**
Chaoyang

1806 **DANDONG TEACHERS' SCHOOL**
Dandong

1807 **DALIAN INSTITUTE OF FOREIGN LANGUAGES**
Dalian

1808 **LIAONING INSTITUTE OF FINANCE AND ECONOMICS**
Dalian
Telex: 6299 DALIAN
Telephone: 91101
President: Tong Zhe-hui

Economics
Finance

Founded 1950 as commercial college, acquired present status and title 1959. Under the jurisdiction of the Ministry of Finance. Residential facilities for academic staff and students.

Academic Year: September to August (September-February; March-August).

Admission Requirements: Graduation from senior middle school and entrance examination.

Language of Instruction: Chinese.

Degrees and Diplomas: Bachelor, 4 yrs. Certificates.

Library: *c.* 600,000 vols.

Publication: Bimonthly Magazine.

Academic Staff: *c.* 550.

Student Enrolment: *c.* 3230 (Also *c.* 3000 external students).

1809 **LIAONING SCHOOL OF COMMERCE**
Jinzhou

1810 **CHINESE INSTITUTE OF POLICY STUDIES**
Shenyang

1811 **SHENYANG INSTITUTE OF PHYSICAL EDUCATION**
Shenyang

1812 **SHENYANG CONSERVATORY OF MUSIC**
Shenyang

1813 **LU XUN ACADEMY OF FINE ARTS**
1 Sanhao Street, Heping District, Shenyang
Telephone: 482467
President: Wang Sheng-Lie (1981-)

Fine Arts (including Traditional Chinese Painting)

Founded 1938 as college. Acquired present status and title 1958.

Academic Year: September to July (September-January; March-July).

Admission Requirements: Graduation from senior middle school and entrance examination.

Language of Instruction: Chinese.

Degrees and Diplomas: Bachelor of Arts. Master.

Library: Central Library, *c.* 140,000 vols.

Publication: Journal (bimonthly).

Press or Publishing House: Lu Xun Academy's Publishing House.

Academic Staff: 230.

Student Enrolment: *c.* 590.

Ningxia (Hui Autonomous Region)

1814 **NINGXIA INSTITUTE OF TECHNOLOGY**
Yinchuan

1815 **NINGXIA AGRICULTURAL COLLEGE**
Yongning County, Ningxia
Telephone: 283

Agriculture (including Forestry, Animal Husbandry, and Veterinary Medicine)
Training Sec. for Cadres

Founded 1958. Became part of Ningxia University 1962-1971. Detached with present status and title 1972. Residential facilities for academic staff and students.

Academic Year: September to July (September-January; March-July).

Admission Requirements: Graduation from senior middle school and entrance examination.

Language of Instruction: Chinese.

Degrees and Diplomas: Bachelor of Agriculture. Diploma.

Library: Central Library, *c.* 250,000 vols.

Publication: Journal.

Academic Staff: *c.* 250 (10).

Student Enrolment: *c.*1160.

1816 **NINGXIA MEDICAL COLLEGE**
Sheng Li Nan jie Yinchuan 750004
President: Chen Shu-Lan (1983-90)

D. of Basic Medical Sciences
D. of Clinical Medical Sciences
D. of Preventive Medicine
D. of Traditional Chinese Medicine
I. of Cardiovascular Diseases
I. of Tumour Research
Immunity Research L.

Also affiliated hospital.

Founded 1958. Under the jurisdiction of the Provincial Government. Residential facilities for academic staff and students.

Academic Year: September to July (September-January; February-July).

Admission Requirements: Graduation from high school and entrance examination.

Fees: None.

Language of Instruction: Chinese.

Degrees and Diplomas: Bachelor of Medicine, 5 yrs. Master, a further 3 yrs.

Library: Central Library, 160,000 vols.

Publication: Journal of Ningxia Medical College (quarterly).

Academic Staff, 1990:

Rank	Full-time	Part-time
Professors	11	1
Associate Professors	50	4
Lecturers	70	3
Assistants	103	–
Instuctors	–	2
Total	234	10

Student Enrolment, 1989-90:

	Men	Women	Total
Of the country	736	565	1301

1817 **GUYUAN TEACHERS' SCHOOL**
District of Guyuan

1818 **YINCHUAN TEACHERS' SCHOOL**
Helan

Qinghai (Province)

1819 **QINHAI COLLEGE OF ANIMAL HUSBANDRY AND VETERINARY MEDICINE**

14 Ning Zhang Road, Xining 810003
Telex: 3757
Telephone: 40926
President: Li Xi-Hong
Secretary: Zhang Shao-Hua

D. of Animal Husbandry
Dean: Wei Zhu-Ye; *staff* 32 (3)
D. of Veterinary Medicine
Dean: Jia Bing-An; *staff* 43 (6)
D. of Grassland Studies
Dean: Liu Zhen-Kui; *staff* 34 (3)
D. of Basic Sciences
Dean: Gu Ming-Fu; *staff* 42
D. of Cadre Training
Vice-Dean: Yang Man-Shou; *staff* 2
Central L.
Director: Yu Shi-Fu

Founded 1958. Attached to Qinghai University 1964 and acquired present status and title 1978. Under the jurisdiction of the Provincial Government. Residential facilities for academic staff and students.

Arrangements for co-operation with: Hokkaido University; Royal Veterinary Medicine College of Denmark.

Academic Year: September to July (September-January; March-July.

Admission Requirements: Graduation from senior middle school and entrance examination.

Fees: None.

Language of Instruction: Chinese.

Degrees and Diplomas: Bachelor of Agronomy, 4 yrs. Professional Diplomas.

Publication: Journal (biannually).

Academic Staff, 1990:

Rank	Full-time
Professors	5
Associate Professors	35
Lecturers	87
Assistants	101
Total	228

Student Enrolment, 1990:

	Men	Women	Total
Of the country	480	150	630

1820 **QINGHAI MEDICAL COLLEGE**

84 Kun Lun Road, Xining
President: Song Ya-shan (1983-)

Medicine (including Traditional Chinese Medicine)

Founded 1958. Residential facilities for academic staff and students.

Academic Year: September to August (September-January; March-June).

Admission Requirements: Graduation from senior middle school and entrance examination.

Language of Instruction: Chinese.

Degrees and Diplomas: Bachelor of Medicine, 5 yrs. Also Diploma.

Library: Central Library, *c.* 180,000 vols.

Publication: Journal (biannually).

Academic Staff: c. 210.

Student Enrolment: c. 730.

1821 **QINGHAI EDUCATIONAL COLLEGE**

Xining
Telephone: 55137
President: Zhang Yang (1985-)

Teacher Training

Founded 1979. Under the jurisdiction of the Provincial Government. Residential facilities for academic staff and students.

Academic Year: September to July (September-January; March-July).

Admission Requirements: Graduation from senior middle school and entrance examination.

Language of Instruction: Chinese.

Degrees and Diplomas: Diploma, 2 yrs.

Library: Central Library, 280,000 vols.

Publication: Journal (biannually).

Academic Staff, 1986-87:

Rank	Full-time
Associate Professors	2
Lecturers	23
Assistants	82
Total	107

Student Enrolment, 1986-87:

	Men	Women	Total
Of the country	562	217	779*

*Also 432 external students.

1822 **QINGHAI COLLEGE OF NATIONALITIES**

25 Bayi Road, Xining
Cables: 2469
Telephone: 75340

Regional Studies
Basic Studies
Training Sec. for Cadres
Also middle school and Research Division.

Founded 1956. Under the jurisdiction of Provincial Government. Residential facilities for academic staff and students.

Arrangements for co-operation with Saskatchewan Indian Federated College.

Academic Year: September to July (September-January; March-July).

Admission Requirements: Graduation from senior middle school and entrance examination.

Language of Instruction: Chinese.

Degrees and Diplomas: Bachelor, 4 yrs. Master, a further 2 yrs. Also teaching qualifications, 2-3 yrs.

Library: Central Library, *c.* 470,000 vols.

Publication: Journal (quarterly).

Academic Staff: c. 320.

Student Enrolment: c. 1860.

Shaanxi (Province)

1823 **NORTHWEST INSTITUTE OF CIVIL ENGINEERING**

Xi'an

1824 **NORTHWEST INSTITUTE OF FORESTRY**

Wugong

1825 **NORTHWEST INSTITUTE OF LIGHT INDUSTRY**

Xianyang 712081
Cables: 5678
Telex: 71199 ACEST CN
Telephone: 4389
President: Peng Guo-Xun (1985-)
Vice-President: Yan Shu-Hui

D. of Mechanical Engineering
Director: Shang Jiu-Hao; *staff* 117
D. of Pulp and Paper-Making
Director: Ren Wei-Xian; *staff* 56
D. of Silicate Engineering
Director: Gao Li-Ming; *staff* 57
D. of Leather Engineering
Director: Chang Xing-Hua; *staff* 51

Founded 1958. A Key institution under the jurisdiction of the Ministry of Light Industry. Residential facilities for academic staff and students.

Arrangements for co-operation with: University of Wisconsin-Stout; North-Carolina State University; Universityof Missouri-Rola.

Academic Year: September to July (September-January; February-July).

Admission Requirements: Graduation from high school and entrance examination.

Fees: None.

Language of Instruction: Chinese.

Degrees and Diplomas: Bachelor of Science, 4 yrs. Master, a further 2 ½ yrs.

Library: Central Library, 500,000 vols.

Publication: Journal (quarterly).

Student Enrolment, 1990:

	Men	Women	Total
Of the country	1800	900	2700

1826 **NORTHWEST INSTITUTE OF TELECOMMUNICATION ENGINEERING**

Xi'an
Cables: Xi'an 1331
Telephone: 55801
President: Bao-Zheng (1984-88)

Telecommunication Engineering (including Computer Sciences)

Founded 1947. A Key institution under the jurisdiction of Ministry of Electronic Industry. Residential facilities for academic staff and students.

Academic Year: September to July (September-January; February-August).

Admission Requirements: Graduation from senior middle school and entrance examination.

Language of Instruction: Chinese.

Degrees and Diplomas: Bachelor. Master. Doctor.

Library: Central Library, 750,000 vols.

Publications: Bulletin; Higher Education in Electronics.

Academic Staff, 1986-87:

Rank	Full-time
Professors	29
Associate Professors	198
Instructors	335
Teachers	289
Assistants	107
Total	958

Student Enrolment, 1986-87:

	Men	Women	Total
Of the country	3852	1242	5094*

*Also 1860 external students.

1827 **XI'AN INSTITUTE OF TEXTILE SCIENCE AND TECHNOLOGY**

Jin Hwa Road, Xi'an 710048
Cables: 4762 xi'an
Telephone: 335561, 335562
Fax: 335671
President: Zhang Le-Shan

D. of Textile Engineering I
Vice-Director: Ren Xin-Xian; *staff* 80
D. of Automation
Vice-Director: Yang Yong-Guo; *staff* 67
D. of Textile Chemistry
Vice-Director: Yang Ding-Guo; *staff* 77
D. of Textile Engineering II
Director: Yu Xing-Gan; *staff* 58
D. of Clothing Engineering
Director: Zhu Song-Wen; *staff* 84
D. of Industrial Management Engineering
Director: Pan Zhao-Jun; *staff* 37
D. of Mechanical Engineering
Vice-Director: Wei Jun-Min; *staff* 89
D. of Basic Studies
Vice-Director: Yang Ding-Jun; *staff* 58
Also 4 Research Institutes.

Founded 1911 as textile department of Beijing Industrial Institute, attached to Peking University 1924, and acquired present status and title 1979. Under the jurisdiction of the Ministry of Textile Industries and financed by the Central Government. Residential facilities for academic staff (80%) and all students.

Arrangements for co-operation with: University of Leeds; Polytechnic Institute of Hong Kong; Nara Women's University.

Academic Year: September to July (September-January; February-July).

Admission Requirements: Graduation from senior middle school and entrance examination.

Fees: None.

Language of Instruction: Chinese.

Degrees and Diplomas: Diplomas. Bachelor of Engineering. Master.

Library: 200,000 vols.

Publications: Journal (quarterly); Translations of Textile Science and Technology (quarterly).

Academic Staff, 1989-90:

Rank	Full-time
Professors	14
Associate Professors	89
Assistant Professors	178
Others	936
Total	1217

Student Enrolment, 1989-90:

	Men	Women	Total
Of the country	1581	977	2558

1828 **SHAANXI INSTITUTE OF MECHANICAL ENGINEERING**

Jin Hua Road, Xi'an 710048
Cables: 8503
Telephone: 332933
Fax: 71244 sime cn
President: Shen Fu-San

D. of Materials Engineering
Head: Ma Si-Chun; *staff* 59
D. of Mechanical Engineering
Head: Li Zhun-Shuang; *staff* 81
D. of Precision Engineering
Head: Tang Jia-Ju; *staff* 36
D. of Printing Technology
Head: Xu Chang-Qing; *staff* 34
D. of Automation
Head: Chen Zhi-Ming; *staff* 117
D. of Economics Engineering
Head: Zhang Dao-Hong; *staff* 57
D. of Hydraulic Engineering
Head: Li Jian-Zhong; *staff* 134
Audio-visual Ce.
Head: Ma Zhen-Ping;
Training Sec. for Cadres
I. for Evening Studies
D. for Basic Studies
Head: Liu You-Bin; *staff* 180
Also 2 Research Institutes.

Founded 1972. Under the jurisdiction of the Ministry of Machine Building. Residential facilities for academic staff and students.

Arrangements for co-operation with: Rochester Institute of Technology; Northern Illinois University; Fukui University; Kyoto University; University of Rome.

Academic Year: September to July (September-January; February-July).

Admission Requirements: Graduation from senior middle school and entrance examination.

Fees: None.

Language of Instruction: Chinese.

Degrees and Diplomas: Bachelor, 4 yrs. Master, 2 ½ yrs. Doctor of Hydrology Engineering and Water Resources, 3 yrs.

Library: Central Library, 460,000 vols.

Publications: Journal; Research on Higher Education.

Press or Publishing House: Printing House.

Academic Staff, 1986-87:

Rank	Full-time
Professors	30
Associate Professors	163
Lecturers	297
Assistants	294
Total	784

Student Enrolment, 1989-90:

	Men	Women	Total
Of the country	2918	848	3766

1829 **SHAANXI INSTITUTE OF TECHNOLOGY**

Hedongdian Hanzhong 723003
Cables: 7810
Telephone: 2921
President: Wang Hua-Min
Director of President's Office: Guo Bu-Hua

D. of Mechanical Engineering
Head: Meng Zheng-Jiang; *staff* 108

D. of Electrical Engineering and Electronics
Head: Wang Da-Sen; *staff* 94
D. of Management Engineering
Head: Zuo Zhen-Xi; *staff* 31
D. of Civil Engineering
Head: Li Wen-Zhi; *staff* 19
D. of Social Sciences
Head: Cheng Xi-Tao; *staff* 20
D. Basic Studies
Head: Zhang Zhi-Hua; *staff* 60
Chemical Engineering Research F.
Head: Hu Zi-Long; *staff* 8

Founded 1978. Under the jurisdiction of Provincial Government. Residential facilities for academic staff and students.

Academic Year: September to July (September-February; March-July).

Admission Requirements: Graduation from senior middle school and entrance examination.

Fees: None.

Language of Instruction: Chinese.

Degrees and Diplomas: Bachelor of Engineering, 4 yrs. Also Associate Diploma, 2 yrs.

Library: Central Library, *c.* 370,000 vols.

Publication: Journal of Shaanxi Institute of Technology (1-4 times a year).

Academic Staff, 1990:

Rank	Full-time
Professors	1
Associate Professors	56
Lecturers	114
Assitants	176
Total	347

Student Enrolment, 1990:

	Men	Women	Total
Of the country	1256	420	1676

1830 **XI'AN INSTITUTE OF METALLURGY AND CONSTRUCTION ENGINEERING**
13 Yan'ta Road, Xi'an
Cables: 3555
Telephone: 51293
President: Zhao Hong-Zuo (1983-87)

Metallurgy and Civil Engineering (including Architecture and Environmental Engineering)

Founded 1955. Under the jurisdiction of the Ministry of Metallurgical Industry and Provincial Bureau of HigherEducation. Residential facilities for academic staff and students.

Arrangements for co-operation with: Kyushu University; University of Wollongong; Old Dominion University.

Academic Year: September to July (September-February; March-July).

Admission Requirements: Graduation from senior middle school and entrance examination.

Language of Instruction: Chinese.

Degrees and Diplomas: Bachelor of Science, 4 yrs. Master, a further 2 ½-3 yrs. Doctor, a further 3 yrs.

Library: Central Library, 450,000 vols.

Publications: Journal (quarterly); Science and Technology of Xian Institute of Metallurgy and Construction Engineering.

Academic Staff, 1986-87:

Rank	Full-time	Part-time
Professors	33	8
Associate Professors	206	2
Lecturers	438	–
Assistants	262	–
Total	939	10

Student Enrolment, 1986-87:

	Men	Women	Total
Of the country	3465	1091	4556*

*Also 1330 external students.

1831 **XI'AN INSTITUTE OF GEOLOGY**
Xi'an

1832 **XI'AN INSTITUTE OF HIGHWAY ENGINEERING**
Xi'an

1833 **XI'AN INSTITUTE OF PETROLEUM**
Xi'an

1834 **XI'AN INSTITUTE OF TECHNOLOGY**
Xi'an

1835 **XI'AN MINING INSTITUTE**
Xi'an

1836 **XI'AN MEDICAL COLLEGE**
Xi'an
Cables: 4000
Telex: 700204
Telephone: 711609
Fax: 711401
President: Ren Hui-Min (1986-)

D. of Medicine (including Pharmacy, Nursing, and Stomatology)
D. for Evening Studies
Also 9 Research Institutes.

Founded 1937 as school. Acquired present title 1956, under the jurisdiction of the Ministry of Public Health. Residential facilities for academic staff and students.

Academic Year: September to July (September-February; March-July).

Admission Requirements: Graduation from senior middle school and entrance examination.

Language of Instruction: Chinese.

Degrees and Diplomas: Bachelor of–Medicine; Stomatology, 5 yrs. Master, a further 3 yrs. Doctor of Medicine, 3 yrs after Master.

Library: Central Library, *c.* 260,000 vols.

Publications: Acta Academiae Medicinae Xian (quarterly); Medical Education Study (2-4 issues); Medical Geography Abroad (quarterly).

Academic Staff: c. 540.

Student Enrolment: c. 2520.

1837 **YANAN MEDICAL COLLEGE**
Yanan

1838 **SHAANXI COLLEGE OF TRADITIONAL CHINESE MEDICINE**
Xianyang

1839 **HUASHAN MEDICAL SCHOOL FOR METALLURGY**
Huayin

1840 **BAOJI TEACHERS' COLLEGE**
Baoji

1841 **HANZHONG TEACHERS' COLLEGE**
Hanzhong

1842 **WEINAN TEACHERS' SCHOOL**
District of Weinan

1843 **XIANGYANG TEACHERS' SCHOOL**
District of Zhouzhi

1844 **XI'AN INSTITUTE OF FOREIGN LANGUAGES**
Xi'an

1845 **SHAANXI PEDAGOGICAL INSTITUTE**
3 Xing Shan Si East Street, Xiao Zhai, Xi'an 710061
Telephone: 51594, 52143
Vice-President: Song Jing-Zong (1988-)
Director: Liu Jie

D. of Education
Dean: Li Li-Ming; *staff* 31
D. of Political Education
Dean: Zhang Jan-Yun; *staff* 33
D. of Chinese Language and Literature
Dean: Sha Zuo-Hong; *staff* 29
D. of Mathematics
Dean: Kong Qing-Sui; *staff* 28 (4)
D. of Physics
Dean: Cao Ting-Fen; *staff* 24
D. of Chemistry
Dean: Ge Qin-Cao; *staff* 22
D. of Biology
Assistant Dean: Yan Bao-Qi; *staff* 22
D. for Correspondence Courses
Deputy Director: Fu Zhi-Yi; *staff* 61 (45)
D. of Vocational Education
Director: Ding Ren-Zu; *staff* 8
Asian and the Pacific P. of Educational Innovation for Development (Associated Ce. of Unesco)
Head: Tian Jia-Sheng; *staff* 3 (5)
National Teacher Training Ce. of Population Education in Secondary Schools
Head: Tian Jia-Sheng; *staff* 3 (4)

Founded 1978. An institution of adult education and provincial training and centre of teachers and educationaladministrators for secondary schools. Under the jurisdiction of the Provincial Government. Residential facilities for academic staff and students.

Academic Year: September to July (September-January; February-July).

Admission Requirements: Graduation from middle school and entrance examination.

Fees: None.

Language of Instruction: Chinese.

Degrees and Diplomas: Teaching certificate, 1 yrs. University graduate diploma, 2 yrs.

Libraries: Central Library, 250,000 vols; libraries of the departments, total, 14,000.

Academic Staff, 1989:

Rank	Full-time
Professors	3
Associate Professors	49
Lecturers	93
Assistants	87
Total	232

Student Enrolment, 1989:

	Men	Women	Total
Of the country	714	320	1034*

*Also 3037 external students.

1846 **SHAANXI INSTITUTE OF FINANCE AND ECONOMICS**
Xi'an
Telephone: 5222
President: Feng Da-Ling (1980-)

Economics
Finance
Accounting
Banking

Founded 1960. Under the jurisdiction of the Central Bank of China.

Arrangements for co-operation with: Baylor University; State University of New York; Texas Tech University.

Academic Year: September to August.

Admission Requirements: Graduation from senior middle school and entrance examination.

Language of Instruction: Chinese.

Degrees and Diplomas: Bachelor, 4 yrs. Master, a further 3 yrs.

Library: Central Library, *c.* 300,000 vols.

Special Facilities (Museums, etc.): Currency History of China.

Publication: Journal (monthly).

Press or Publishing House: Printing House.

Academic Staff: c. 80.

Student Enrolment: c. 2300 (Also *c.* 300 external students).

1847 **NORTHWEST INSTITUTE OF POLITICAL SCIENCE AND LAW**
Xi'an

1848 **XI'AN INSTITUTE OF PHYSICAL CULTURE**
Xi'an

1849 **XI'AN MUSIC CONSERVATORY**
Xi'an

1850 **XI'AN ACADEMY OF FINE ARTS**
Xi'an

Shandong (Province)

1851 **SHANDONG INSTITUTE OF OCEANOGRAPHY**
Qingdao

A Key institution.

1852 **SHANDONG INSTITUTE OF AGRICULTURAL MECHANIZATION**
Zibo

1853 **SHANDONG INSTITUTE OF BUILDING MATERIALS**
Qixianzhuang of Shizong District, Zibo 250022
President: Lin Di-Sheng
Vice-President: Li Guo-Bao

D. of Inorganic Materials Engineering
Director: Zhao Zhong-Yu
D. of Automation Control
Director: Zhang Tong-Chun
D. of Mechanical Engineering
Director: Pan Xiao-Liang
D. of Applied Chemistry
Director: Xi Zheng-Kai
D. of Architectural Engineering
Director: Dong Ke-Jing

Also 4 Research Centres and Branch in Zibo.

Founded 1948. Residential facilities for academic staff and students.

Academic Year: September to July (September-January; March-July).

Admission Requirements: Graduation from high school and entrance examination.

Fees: None.

Languages of Instruction: Chinese and English.

Degrees and Diplomas: Bachelor of Science, 4 yrs.

Library: c. 220,000 vols.

Publication: Journal of Shandong Institute of Building Materials.

Academic Staff, 1990:

Rank	Full-time
Professors	51
Lecturers	111
Assistant Professors	182
Total	344

Student Enrolment, 1989:

	Men	Women	Total
Of the country	427	110	537

1854 **SHANDONG INSTITUTE OF CHEMICAL TECHNOLOGY**
Quingdao

1855 **SHANDONG INSTITUTE OF CIVIL ENGINEERING**
Jinan

1856 **SHANDONG INSTITUTE OF LIGHT ENGINEERING**
Jinan

1857 **SHANDONG INSTITUTE OF METALLURGY**
Quingdao

1858 **SHANDONG INSTITUTE OF TEXTILE TECHNOLOGY**
Quingdao

1859 **SHANDONG MINING INSTITUTE**
District of Taian

1860 **SHANDONG AGRICULTURAL INSTITUTE**
District of Taian

1861 **LAI YANG AGRICULTURAL COLLEGE**
Lai Yang
Telephone: 777
President: Xu Fang (1984-)

Agriculture (including Animal Husbandry, Veterinary Medicine,and Horticulture)
Training Sec. for Cadres

Founded 1951 as school. Acquired present status and title 1978. Residential facilities for academic staff and students.

Academic Year: September to July (September-February; March-July).

Admission Requirements: Graduation from senior middle school and entrance examination.

Language of Instruction: Chinese.

Degrees and Diplomas: Bachelor of–Agriculture; Engineering, 4 yrs.

Library: Central Library, *c.* 290,000 vols.

Publication: Journal (biannually).

Press or Publishing House: Lai Yang Agricultural College Publishing House.

Academic Staff: *c.* 190 (40).

Student Enrolment: *c.* 1330.

1862 **SHANDONG ACADEMY OF MEDICINE**
Jing Shi Road 35, Jinan
Telephone: 22098
President: Yuan Jing-chun (1984-)

Medicine

Founded 1981.

Language of Instruction: Chinese.

Degrees and Diplomas: Master, 3 yrs.

Publication: Acta of Shandong Medical Academy.

Student Enrolment: *c.* 20.

1863 **BINZHOU MEDICAL COLLEGE**
Binzhou

1864 **CHANGWEI MEDICAL COLLEGE**
Weifang

1865 **QINGDAO MEDICAL COLLEGE**
Jinan

1866 **TAISHAN MEDICAL COLLEGE**
Tian

1867 **SHANDONG INSTITUTE OF TRADITIONAL CHINESE MEDICINE**
Jinan

1868 **HEZE MEDICAL SCHOOL**
District of Heze

1869 **JINING MEDICAL SCHOOL**
Jining

1870 **YISHUI MEDICAL SCHOOL**
District of Yishui

1871 **LIAOCHENG TEACHERS' INSTITUTE**
Liaocheng

1872 **QUFU TEACHERS' INSTITUTE**
District of Qufu

1873 **BINZHOU TEACHERS' COLLEGE**
Binzhou

1874 **CHANGWEI TEACHERS' SCHOOL**
Weifang

1875 **DEZHOU TEACHERS' SCHOOL**
Dezhou

1876 **HEZE TEACHERS' SCHOOL**
Heze

1877 **JINING TEACHERS' SCHOOL**
Jining

1878 **LINYI TEACHERS' SCHOOL**
District of Feixian

1879 **TAIAN TEACHERS' SCHOOL**
Taian

1880 **YANTAI TEACHERS' COLLEGE**
Yantai 264000
Telephone: 246451
President: Wang Rong-Gang (1987-)

D. of Chinese Language and Literature
Head: Sun Yuan-Zhang; *staff* 48
D. of Politics
Head: Wang Guo-Hong; *staff* 31
D. of English
Head: Yang Yu-Lin; *staff* 32
D. of History
Head: Li Yong-Pu; *staff* 27
D. of Mathematics
Head: Wang Chang-Fan; *staff* 44
D. of Physics
Head: Wang Zhi-Zeng; *staff* 58
D. of Chemistry
Head: Liu Bing-Lan; *staff* 36
D. of Physical Education
Head: Yu Shi-Hao; *staff* 36
D. of Biology
Head: Guo Zhen-Yuan; *staff* 43
D. of Geography
Head: Cheng Xue-You; *staff* 29
D. of Art
Head: Qian Hu-Zuang; *staff* 7
D. for Adult Education
Head: Yang Yu-Qiang; *staff* 9
Environmental Science Research I.
Head: Cheng Xue-You; *staff* 4
Research Office of Applied Organic Chemistry
Head: Liu Bing-Lan; *staff* 5
Research I. of Modern and Contemporary Chinese History
Head: Li Yong-Pu; *staff* 9
Research Office of Modern Chinese Literature
Head: Han Ri-Xin; *staff* 3
Research Office of Nuclear Physics
Head: Wang Qi-Xin; *staff* 6

Founded 1958, acquired present status and title 1984. Under the jurisdiction of the Provincial Government. Residential facilities for academic staff and students.

Academic Year: September to July (September-January; February-July).

Admission Requirements: Graduation from senior middle school and entrance examination.

Fees: None.

Language of Instruction: Chinese.

Degrees and Diplomas: Bachelor, 4 yrs.

Library: Central Library, 550,000 vols.

Publication: Journal of Yantai Teachers' College (Social Science Edition and Natural Science, quarterly).

Academic Staff, 1989-90:

Rank	Full-time
Professors	6
Associate Professors	48
Lecturers	137
Assistants	195
Total	386

Student Enrolment, 1989-90:

	Men	Women	Total
Of the country	1649	1351	3000*

*Also 2650 external students and students by correspondance.

1881 **SHANDONG INSTITUTE OF ECONOMICS**

Jinan

Telephone: (0531) 44161

President: Zhang Wenjie (1984-)

Vice-President: Su Chaoliang

Economics

D. for Correspondence Courses

Founded 1958. Under the jurisdiction of Provincial Government.

Academic Year: September to August (September-February; March-July).

Admission Requirements: Graduation from senior middle school and entrance examination.

Language of Instruction: Chinese.

Degrees and Diplomas: Bachelor of Arts, 4 yrs.

Library: Central Library, 202,000 vols.

Publication: Shandong Economy (bimonthly).

Academic Staff, 1986-87:

Rank	Full-time
Professor	1
Associate Professors	13
Lecturers	61
Assistants	163
Teachers	27
Total	265

Student Enrolment, 1986-87:

	Men	Women	Total
Of the country	1288	414	1702

1882 **SHANDONG INSTITUTE OF PHYSICAL CULTURE**

Jinan

1883 **SHANDONG ACADEMY OF ARTS**

Jinan

Shanghai (Municipality)

1884 **SHANGHAI INSTITUTE OF MECHANICAL ENGINEERING**

516 Jun Gong Road, Shanghai 200093

Cables: 1191 shanghai

Telephone: (86-21) 5433040

Fax: (86-21) 5431258

President: Zhao Xue-Duan (1986-)

Dean of Studies: Wu Yi-Wen

D. of Systems Engineering

Dean: Che Hong-AN; *staff* 68

D. of Mechanical Engineering

Head: Duanmu Shi-Xia

D. for Adult Education (Correspondence and Evening courses)

Deputy Dean: Shen Chang-Yong

C. of Instrumentation

Dean: Zhou Peng-Fei; *staff* 244

C. of Power Engineering

Dean: Li Yan-Sheng; *staff* 189

C. of Arts and Sciences

Dean: Lu Si-Yuan; *staff* 182

C. of Commerce (Hu-Jiang)

Head: Chen Kang-Min; *staff* 14

Systems Engineering Research I.

Director: Chen Shou-Dao

Energy Conservation and Development Research I.

Director: Wang Nai-Ning

Precision Instruments Research I.

Director: Dai Xing-Qing

Information Management and Office Automation Research I.

Deputy Director: Deng Liang-Di

Founded as Baptist College 1906, renamed University of Shanghai 1915. Reorganized 1952. Under the jurisdictionof the Ministry of Machine Building. Residential facilities for academic staff and students.

Arrangements for co-operation with: University of Stuttgart; University of Siegen; Massachusetts Institute of Technology; Sloan School of Commerce; Indiana University; Iowa University; Tokyo University of Agriculture andTechnology; Hong Kong Polytechnic; University of Montreal.

Academic Year: September to July (September-January; February-July).

Admission Requirements: Graduation from senior middle school and entrance examination.

Language of Instruction: Chinese.

Degrees and Diplomas: Bachelor of Science, 4 yrs. Master, a further 2-5 yrs. Doctor of Engineering, 3 yrs after Master.

Library: 615,000 vols.

Publications: Institute Journal; Power Machine Dispatches; Instrumentation News; Automation Engineering; Education and Research; Energy Information and Research; Systems Engineering Research, HUJIANG News.

Press or Publishing House: SIME Printing Press.

Academic Staff, 1989-90:

Rank	Full-time
Professors	148
Lecturers	238
Assistants	117
Total	501

Student Enrolment, 1989-90:

	Men	Women	Total
Of the country	3139	1075	4214*

*Also 328 external students.

1885 **SHANGHAI MARITIME COLLEGE**

Shanghai

1886 **SHANGHAI INSTITUTE OF RAILWAY TECHNOLOGY**

1, Zhennen Road, Shanghai

Cables: 8135

Telephone: 506344

President: Xia Jian-Xin

Secretary-General: Zhang Cuan-Ming

Railways Technology (including Transport and Communication Engineering)

Founded 1958. Under the jurisdiction of the Ministry of Railways.

Academic Year: September to July (September-January; February-July).

Admission Requirements: Graduation from senior middle school and entrance examination.

Language of Instruction: Chinese.

Degrees and Diplomas: Bachelor of Engineering, 4 yrs. Master, a further 2-3 yrs.

Library: Central Library, 480,000 vols.

Publication: Journal (quarterly).

Academic Staff, 1986-87:

Rank	Full-time
Professors	19
Associate Professors	113
Lecturers	351
Assistants	274
Total	757

Student Enrolment, 1986-87: 2963.

1887 **SHANGHAI TECHNICAL COLLEGE OF METALLURGY**
121 Caobao Road, Shanghai 200233
Cables: 9052
Telephone: 4363051
President: Wang Yi-Cheng (1984-)
Vice-President: Xiang Zhong-Ming; Ma Shi-Ying; Ye Qin

D. of Automation
Director: Lu Zi-Xiong; *staff* 94
D. of Metal Technology
Director: Xu Yun-Xiang; *staff* 61
D. of Mechanical Engineering
Director: Feng Keng-Ling; *staff* 80
D. of Fundamental Sciences
Director: Tong Heng-Zhi; *staff* 75

Founded as school 1958. Acquired present status and title 1978. Under the jurisdiction of the Provincial Government. Residential facilities for academic staff and students.

Arrangements for co-operation with: Fachhochschule Giessen-Friedberg; Fachhochschule Coburg; Institute of Technology, Maassachusetts; East Tennessee State University; Capital College; Oregon Institute of Technology.

Academic Year: September to July (September-January; February-July).

Admission Requirements: Graduation from senior middle school and entrance examination.

Fees: None.

Language of Instruction: Chinese.

Degrees and Diplomas: Diploma, 3 yrs.

Library: Central Library, 192,000 vols.

Publications: Journal (biannually); Translated Series (quarterly).

Press or Publishing House: The Printing House, Educational Administration Office.

Academic Staff, 1989-90:

Rank	Full-time
Professors	3
Associate Professors	33
Lecturers	126
Assistants	100
Teachers	1
Total	263

Student Enrolment, 1989-90:

	Men	Women	Total
Of the country	886	331	1217*

*Also 418 external students.

1888 **SHANGHAI SCHOOL OF BUILDING MATERIALS**
Shanghai

1889 **SHANGHAI SCHOOL OF CHEMICAL TECHNOLOGY**
Shanghai

1890 **SHANGHAI SCHOOL OF OF MEDICAL APPARATUS AND INSTRUMENTS**
Shanghai

1891 **SHANGHAI SCHOOL OF PETROCHEMICAL TECHNOLOGY**
Shanghai

1892 **SHANGHAI SCHOOL OF SCIENCE AND TECHNOLOGY**
Shanghai

1893 **SHANGHAI AGRICULTURAL COLLEGE**
Qi Bao Town, Shanghai
Telephone: 389081
President: Shen Huanchen (1984-87)

Agriculture
Horticulture
Animal Husbandry and Veterinary Science

Founded 1978. Under the jurisdiction of the Provincial Government. Residential facilities for academic staff and students.

Arrangements for co-operation with the University of Osaka.

Academic Year: September to July (September-January; February-July).

Admission Requirements: Graduation from senior middle school and entrance examination.

Language of Instruction: Chinese.

Degrees and Diplomas: Licence in Agricultural Economics, 2 yrs. Bachelor, 4 yrs.

Library: Central Library, 140,000 vols.

Publication: Journal.

Academic Staff, 1986-87:

Rank	Full-time
Professors	4
Associate Professors	28
Lecturers	151
Assistants	111
Total	294

Student Enrolment, 1986-87:

	Men	Women	Total
Of the country	719	356	1075

1894 **SHANGHAI FIRST MEDICAL COLLEGE**
Shanghai

A Key institution.

1895 **SHANGHAI COLLEGE OF TRADITIONAL CHINESE MEDICINE**
530 Lingling Road, Shanghai 200032
Cables: 6276
Telephone: 4385400
Fax: (86-21) 4398290
President: Lu De-Ming (1985-)

D. of Basic Medical Science
D. of Social Science
D. of Chinese Medicine
D. of Postgraduate and Further Study
Also 10 Research Institutes and 3 Teaching Hospitals.

Founded 1956. Acquired present status 1984. Under the jurisdiction of the Ministry of Health. Residential facilities for academic staff and students.

Arrangements for co-operation with: Kawasaki Medical School; Harvard Medical School; Showa University; University of Groningen; University of San Francisco.

Academic Year: September to July (September-January; February-July).

Admission Requirements: Graduation from senior middle school and entrance examination.

Fees: None.

Language of Instruction: Chinese.

Degrees and Diplomas: Bachelor of–Pharmacy, 4 yrs; Medicine, 5 yrs. Master, a further 3 yrs. Doctor, Ph.D., a further 3 yrs.

Library: Central Library, 350,000 vols.

Special Facilities (Museums, etc.): Museum of Medical History; Exhibition Room of Herbal Specimens; Pharmaceutical Factory; Movie Studio.

Publications: Shanghai Journal of Chinese Medecine (monthly); Shanghai Journal of Acupuncture-Moxibustion (bimonthly).

Press or Publishing House: Publishing House of Shanghai College of Traditional Chinese Medicine.

Academic Staff, 1990:

Rank	Full-time
Professors	108
Associate Professors	376
Lecturers	800
Assistants	1142
Total	2426

Student Enrolment, 1990: 1420 (Also 30 foreign students and 400 students by correspondence).

1896 **SHANGHAI RAILWAY MEDICAL INSTITUTE**
Shanghai

1897 **SHANGHAI INSTITUTE OF FINANCE AND ECONOMICS**
Shanghai

1898 **SHANGHAI INSTITUTE OF FOREIGN TRADE**
620 Gu Bei Road, Shanghai
Cables: 3074
Telex: 33531 SIOFT CN
Telephone: 598181
President: Wang Zhong-Wu (1986-)
Vice-President: Feng Fu-Hai

Foreign Trade and Economics (including Languages and International Business Law)
Lifelong Education

Founded 1960. A Key institution under the jurisdiction of the Ministry of International Economic Relations andTrade.

Arrangements for co-operation with the Universities of: Colombia; San Francisco; Lincoln; Eastern Washington; Sydney; Tokyo. Southwestern College.

Academic Year: September to July (September-February; March-July).

Admission Requirements: Graduation from senior middle school and entrance examination.

Language of Instruction: Chinese.

Degrees and Diplomas: Bachelor, 4 yrs. Master, a further 3 yrs.

Library: Central Library, 170,000 vols.

Publications: International Business Research; Translations of International Business Publications.

Academic Staff, 1986-87:

Rank	Full-time	Part-time
Professors	40	10
Lecturers	130	50
Associate Professors	101	10
Researchers	33	–
Total	304	70

Student Enrolment, 1986-87:

	Men	Women	Total
Of the country	470	610	1080
Of other countries	28	12	40
Total	498	622	1120

1899 **SHANGHAI SCHOOL OF TOURISM**
Shanghai

1900 **SHANGHAI CUSTOMS COLLEGE**
45 Fenyang Road, Shanghai
Telex: 378623
Telephone: 378623
President: Liu Yi (1986-)

Customs Training

Founded 1953. Under the jurisdiction of the Direction of Customs General Administration.

Academic Year: September to July (September-February; March-July).

Admission Requirements: Graduation from senior middle school and entrance examination.

Language of Instruction: Chinese.

Degrees and Diplomas: Licence, 3 yrs.

Library: Central Library, 39,000 vols.

Academic Staff, 1986-87:

Rank	Full-time
Professors	2
Associate Professors	27
Lecturers	5
Assistants	61
Total	95

Student Enrolment, 1986-87:

	Men	Women	Total
Of the country	279	186	465*

*Also 369 external students.

1901 **EAST CHINA INSTITUTE OF POLITICAL SCIENCE AND LAW**
Shanghai

1902 **SHANGHAI INSTITUTE OF PHYSICAL CULTURE**
Shanghai

1903 **SHANGHAI CONSERVATORY OF MUSIC**
20 Fen Yang Road, Shanghai
Telephone: 370137
President: Sang Tong (1984-)
Vice-President: Li Mingqiang

Music (including Chinese Traditional Music)
C. for Evening Studies

Also Research Institute and primary school.

Founded 1927. Under the jurisdiction of the Ministry of Culture. Residential facilities for academic staff and students.

Academic Year: September to July (September-January; March-July).

Admission Requirements: Graduation from senior middle school and entrance examination.

Language of Instruction: Chinese.

Degrees and Diplomas: Bachelor of Arts, 4 yrs. Master, a further 3 yrs. Doctor, 2 yrs.

Libraries: Central Library, 150,000 vols; Sound Library and Video-Audio Recording Rooms.

Publication: Art of Music (quarterly).

Academic Staff, 1986-87:

Rank	Full-time
Professors	25
Associate Professors	89
Lecturers	160
Assistants	62
Teachers	92
Total	428

Student Enrolment, 1986-87:

	Men	Women	Total
Of the country	335	205	540
Of other countries	13	7	20
Total	348	212	560*

*Also 585 external students.

1904 **SHANGHAI DRAMA INSTITUTE**
Shanghai

Shanxi (Province)

1905 **TAIYUAN MACHINERY INSTITUTE**
Academic Road, Taiyuan 030051
Telephone: 359411
President: Zu Jing
Secretary-General: Wang San-Jin

D. of Mechanical and Electronic Engineering
Dean: Zhao Wen-Xung; *staff* 113
D. of Mechanical Engineering
Dean: Li Bo-Min; *staff* 45
D. of Chemical Engineering
Dean: Liang Shan-Jie; *staff* 82
Research I. of Mechanical Manufacture Technology
Principal: Wang Jun; *staff* 10
I. of Chemical Engineering Research
Principal: Wang Jian-Min; *staff* 7
I. of Applied Chemistry Research
Principal: Yang Zheng-De; *staff* 11
I. of Measure Technique Research
Principal: Lu Hong-Nian; *staff* 12 (30)
D. of Measurement Engineering
Dean: Lu Hong-Nian; *staff* 50
D. of Mechanics Engineering
Dean: Meng Xian-Chang; *staff* 40
D. of Safety Engineering
Dean: Zhang Jing-Lin; *staff* 35
D. of Computer Sciences
Dean: Tong Zhen-Ya; *staff* 65
D. of Mathematics and Physics
Dean: Sun Xian-Yi; *staff* 72

Training S.
Dean: Liu Zhen-Ning; *staff* 475
D. of Foreign Languages
Dean: Zhang Shi-Xin; *staff* 40
D. of Graduate Students
Dean: Liu Feng-Zheng; *staff* 10
D. of Social Science and Adult Education
Dean: Hao Zhi-Yin; *staff* 10

Founded 1940 as school. Acquired present status and title 1958. Under the jurisdiction of the Department of Mechanical and Electronic Industry. Residential facilities for academic staff and students.

Arrangements for co-operation with Chiba University.

Academic Year: September to July (September-January; March-July).

Admission Requirements: Graduation from high school and entrance examination.

Fees: None.

Language of Instruction: Chinese.

Degrees and Diplomas: Bachelor, 4 yrs. Master, a further 2 ½-3 yrs.

Library: 480,000 vols.

Publication: Journal of Taiyuan Machinery Institute (quarterly).

Academic Staff, 1989-90: 1600.

Student Enrolment, 1989-90:

	Men	Women	Total
Of the country	2130	670	2800

1906 **TAIYUAN INSTITUTE OF HEAVY MACHINERY**
Taiyuan

1907 **SHANXI MEDICAL COLLEGE**
Taiyuan

1908 **DATONG MEDICAL SCHOOL**
Datong

1909 **SOUTHEAST SHANXI MEDICAL SCHOOL**
Changzhi

1910 **SHANXI TEACHERS' COLLEGE**
Linfen

1911 **TAIYUAN TEACHERS' COLLEGE**
Taiyuan
Telephone: 22370
President: Jin Peiyi (1983-87)

Teacher Training

Founded as school 1958. Acquired present status and title 1977. Under the jurisdiction of the Provincial Government.

Academic Year: August to July (August-January; February-July).

Admission Requirements: Graduation from senior middle school, teaching experience, and entrance examination.

Language of Instruction: Chinese.

Degrees and Diplomas: Diploma, 2 yrs.

Library: Central Library, 230,000 vols.

Publication: Journal.

Academic Staff, 1986-87: 256 (2).

Student Enrolment, 1986-87:

	Men	Women	Total
Of the country	712	1094	1806

1912 **CENTRAL SHANXI SCHOOL OF EDUCATION**
Yuci

1913 **SOUTHEAST SHANXI SCHOOL OF EDUCATION**
Changzhi

1914 **XIN COUNTY TEACHERS' SCHOOL**
Xin County

1915 **YANBEI SCHOOL OF EDUCATION**
District of Shuoxian

1916 **YANBEI TEACHERS' SCHOOL**
District of Shuoxian

1917 **SHANXI INSTITUTE OF FINANCE AND COMMERCE**
Taiyuan

Sichuan (Province)

1918 **CHENGDU COLLEGE OF GEOLOGY**
Chengdu 610059
Cables: 0966
Telephone: 34712

Geology
D. for Retraining
D. for Correspondence Courses
Also 12 Research Institutes.

Founded 1956. Under the jurisdiction of the Ministry of Geology and Mineral Resources. Residential facilities for academic staff and students.

Arrangements for co-operation with: Adelaide University; Universities in Lower Saxony.

Academic Year: September to August (September-January; February-August).

Admission Requirements: Graduation from senior middle school and entrance examination.

Language of Instruction: Chinese.

Degrees and Diplomas: Bachelor of Science. Master. Doctor, Ph.D.

Library: Central Library, *c.* 500,000 vols.

Special Facilities (Museums, etc.): Geological Museum.

Publication: Journal (quarterly).

Academic Staff: c. 740.

Student Enrolment: c. 3000 (Also *c.* 860 external students).

1919 **CHENGDU INSTITUTE OF METEOROLOGY**
Chengdu

1920 **CHINA INSTITUTE OF MINING TECHNOLOGY**
District of Hechuan

A Key institution.

1921 **CHONGQING CIVIL ENGINEERING INSTITUTE**
Chongqing
Cables: 5120
Telephone: 661989
President: Lu Zhong-zheng (1983-87)

Architecture and Engineering
D. for Correspondence Courses

Founded 1952, incorporating previously existing colleges and departments of institutions in South-West China. A Key institution under the jurisdiction of the Ministry of Urban and Rural Construction and Environment Protection. Residential facilities for academic staff and students.

Arrangements for co-operation with the Universities of: Minnesota; Washington; Tennessee; Michigan; Manitoba; Waseda.

Academic Year: September to July (September-January; February-July).

Admission Requirements: Graduation from senior middle school and entrance examination.

Language of Instruction: Chinese.

Degrees and Diplomas: Bachelor of Engineering, 4 yrs. Master, a further 2-3 yrs. Doctor, 2-3 yrs.

Library: Central Library, *c.* 450,000 vols.

Publications: Journal; Interior Design (quarterly).

Academic Staff: c. 1200.

Student Enrolment: c. 5400.

1922 **CHONGQING INSTITUTE OF POST AND TELECOMMUNICATIONS**
Chongqing

1923 **CHONGQING INSTITUTE OF RIVER AND HIGHWAY TRANSPORT**
Chongqing

1924 **SICHUAN INSTITUTE OF BUILDING MATERIALS**
District of Mianyang

1925 **SICHUAN INSTITUTE OF CHEMICAL TECHNOLOGY**
Zigong

1926 **SICHUAN INSTITUTE OF TECHNOLOGY**
Chengdu
Telephone: 21271; 21287

D. of Mechanical Engineering I
D. of Mechanical Engineering II
D. of Mechanical Engineering III
D. of Architectural Engineering
D. of Automobile Engineering
D. of Power Engineering
D. of Basic Studies

Founded 1960. Acquired present title 1983. Under the jurisdiction of the Provincial Government. Residential facilities for academic staff and students.

Academic Year: September to August (September-January; March-July).

Admission Requirements: Graduation from senior middle school and entrance examination.

Language of Instruction: Chinese.

Degrees and Diplomas: Bachelor of Engineering, 4 yrs. Master, a further 3 yrs.

Library: Central Library, *c.* 350,000 vols.

Publication: Journal (biannually).

Academic Staff: c. 530.

Student Enrolment: c. 630.

1927 **SOUTHWEST CHINA PETROLEUM INSTITUTE**
6 Shiyou Donglu, Nanchong 637001
Telex: 2340
Telephone: (0817) 24433
Fax: 22362
President: Zhang Shao-Huai
Director of President Office: Xiang Xiao-Zhuang

D. of Petroleum Engineering
Head: Huang Yi-Ren; *staff* 140 (7)
D. of Geology
Head: Lei Xiao; *staff* 119 (3)
D. of Mechanical Engineering
Head: Ma De-Kun; *staff* 141 (5)
D. of Applied Chemistry
Head: Zhao Li-Zhi; *staff* 72 (2)
D. of Management Engineering
Head: Li Guang-Yao; *staff* 62 (3)
D. of Offshore Petroleum Engineering
Head: Zhang Ning-Sheng; *staff* 28 (2)
D. of Mathematics and Physics
Head: Dong Feng-Cheng; *staff* 85
D. of Foreign Languages
Head: Zen Yan-Yi; *staff* 62 (1)
D. of Further Education
Head: Shi Bao-De; *staff* 15
D. of Social Sciences
Head: Liang Ting-Wu; *staff* 31
Also *c.* 16 Research Centres.

Founded 1958. Under the jurisdiction of the China National Petroleum Corporation. Residential facilities for academic staff and students.

Arrangements fo co-operation with: Texas A & M University; Colorado School of Mines; University of Texas at Austin; University of Liverpool.

Academic Year: September to July (September-January; February-July).

Admission Requirements: Graduation from high school and entrance examination.

Fees: None.

Language of Instruction: Chinese.

Degrees and Diplomas: Bachelor of Science, 4 yrs. Master of Science, a further 2 ½ yrs. Doctor, Ph.D., 3 yrs.

Library: 75,000 vols.

Special Facilities (Museums, etc.): Geology Museum. Open-air Cinema.

Publications: Teaching and Studying; Journal of Southwest-China Petroleum Institute; SWPI Newspaper.

Press or Publishing House: Compus Printing House.

Academic Staff, 1990:

Rank	Full-time	Part-time
Professors	43	49
Associate Professors	155	–
Lecturers	356	–
Assistant Professors	324	30
Total	878	79

Student Enrolment, 1990:

	Men	Women	Total
Of the country	2927	738	3665*

*Also 291 external students.

1928 **CHINESE AVIATION PILOT SCHOOL**
Guanghan

1929 **SICHUAN AGRICULTURAL INSTITUTE**
District of Ya'an

1930 **SOUTHWEST AGRICULTURAL COLLEGE**
Beibei, Chongqing
Telex: 7762
Telephone: 3964; 3965

Agriculture (including Horticulture, Sericulture, Animal Husbandry and Veterinary Science)

Founded 1950, incorporating departments of Sichuan University, Yunnan University, Agricultural College of Guizhou, Sichuan College of Education, University of Northern Sichuan, and West China University. A Key institution under the jurisdiction of the Ministry of Agriculture, Animal Husbandry and Fishery. Residential facilities for academic staff and students.

Academic Year: September to July (September-February; March-July).

Admission Requirements: Graduation from senior middle school and entrance examination.

Language of Instruction: Chinese.

Degrees and Diplomas: Diploma, 4 yrs. Bachelor, 4 yrs. Doctor.

Library: Central Library, *c.* 700,000 vols.

Publications: Periodical (quarterly); Journal (monthly).

Press or Publishing House: College Publishing House.

Academic Staff: c. 680.

Student Enrolment: c. 720.

1931 **MIANYANG AGRICULTURAL SCHOOL**
District of Mianyang

1932 **XICHANG AGRICULTURAL COLLEGE**
Mapinba, Xichang
Telephone: 3334
President: Long Xin-Lin (1986-)

Veterinary Medicine and Animal Husbandry
Horticulture

Founded 1978. Under the jurisdiction of the Ministry of Education. Residential facilities for academic staff and students.

Academic Year: August to July (August-January; February-July).

Admission Requirements: Graduation from senior middle school and entrance examination.

Language of Instruction: Chinese.

Library: Central Library, 96,909 vols.

Publication: Teaching and Scientific Research.

Academic Staff, 1986-87:

Rank	Full-time	Part-time
Vice-Professor	1	–
Lecturers	32	18
Total	33	18

Student Enrolment, 1986-87:

	Men	Women	Total
Of the country	890	401	1291

1933 **CHONGQING MEDICAL COLLEGE**
Chongqing

1934 **LUZHOU MEDICAL COLLEGE**
Luzhou

1935 **CHENGDU COLLEGE OF TRADITIONAL CHINESE MEDICINE**
Chengdu

1936 **NANCHONG MEDICAL SCHOOL**
Nanchong

1937 **ABA TEACHERS' COLLEGE**
District of Wenchuan

Teacher Training

Founded 1979. Residential facilities for academic staff and students.

Academic Year: September to August (September-January; March-August).

Admission Requirements: Graduation from senior middle school and entrance examination.

Language of Instruction: Chinese.

Degrees and Diplomas: College Diploma.

Library: Central Library.

Academic Staff: c. 20.

1938 **CHONGQING TEACHERS' COLLEGE**
Chongqing

1939 **LIANGSHAN COLLEGE OF EDUCATION**
Xichang
President: Hu Zhong-ze

Teacher Training

Founded 1978.

Admission Requirements: Experienced teachers with no formal higher education.

Language of Instruction: Chinese.

Academic Staff: c. 80.

1940 **NANCHONG TEACHERS' COLLEGE**
Nanchong

1941 **DAXIAN TEACHERS' SCHOOL**
District of Daxian

1942 **FULING TEACHERS' SCHOOL**
Fuling

1943 **JIANJING TEACHERS' SCHOOL**
District of Yongchuan

1944 **LESHAN TEACHERS' SCHOOL**
Leshan

1945 **MIANYANG TEACHERS' SCHOOL**
Mianyang

1946 **NEIJIANG TEACHERS' SCHOOL**
Neijiang

1947 **SICHUAN INSTITUTE OF FINANCE AND ECONOMICS**
Chengdu

1948 **SOUTHWEST INSTITUTE OF LAW AND POLITICS**
Chongqing

A Key institution.

1949 **CHENGDU INSTITUTE OF PHYSICAL CULTURE**
Chengdu

1950 **SICHUAN CONSERVATORY OF MUSIC**
Chengdu

1951 **SICHUAN INSTITUTE OF FINE ARTS**
Chongqing
Cables: 7724
Telephone: 23423
President: Ye Yushan (1983-)

Fine Arts

D. of Teacher Training

Founded 1950 as college. Acquired present title 1959. Under the jurisdiction of the Provincial Government. Residential facilities for academic staff and students.

Arrangements for co-operation with: Ecole des Beaux-Arts, Toulouse; Pacific Northwest College of Art.

Academic Year: September to July (September-February; March-July).

Admission Requirements: Graduation from senior middle school and entrance examination.

Language of Instruction: Chinese.

Degrees and Diplomas: Bachelor of Fine Arts, 4 yrs. Master, a further 3 yrs.

Library: Central Library, *c.* 160,000 vols.

Publication: Modern Artist (quarterly).

Academic Staff: c. 160.

Student Enrolment: c. 300 (Also *c.* 140 external students).

1952 **SOUTHWEST INSTITUTE FOR NATIONALITIES**
Qinglongcun, Chengdu 610041
Cables: 7108
Telephone: 553811, 581093
President: Meng Zhu-Qun
Director: Wang Xiao-Hua

D. of History
Dean: Li zheng-qing; *staff* 31

D. of Politics
Dean: Yang Ming-Hen; *staff* 34

D. of Minority Language and Literature
Dean: Yu Hui-Bang; *staff* 57

D. of Law
Dean: Zhang Zi-Ping; *staff* 35

D. of Mathematics
Dean: Zheng Ke-Ming; *staff* 51

D. of Physics
Dean: Yang Guo-Xiang; *staff* 50

D. of Animal Husbandry and Veterinary Medicine
Dean: Wang Yun-Feng; *staff* 114

D. of Chinese
Dean: Liu Hang-Shu; *staff* 53

Also Experimental Farm; courses for foreign students (Chinese, Tibetan, Yi Language), and 3 Research Centres.

Founded 1951. A comprehensive institute training specialists, management cadres and middle school teachers for the Minority nationality regions in South West China. Under the jurisdiction of the State Nationalities Affairs Commission. Residential facilities for academic staff and students.

Arrangements fo co-operation with: University of Washington; Saskatchewan Indian Federated College; Park College of America.

Academic Year: September to July (September-January; February-July).

Admission Requirements: Graduation form high school and entrance examination.

Fees: None.

Languages of Instruction: Chinese, Tibetan and Yi Language.

Degrees and Diplomas: Bachelor of–Arts; Science, 4 yrs. Master, a further 3 yrs.

Libraries: Total, 750,000 vols (Chinese, 710,000; Foreign Langugage 40,000).

Publications: Journal of Philosophy and Social Science (quarterly); Journal of Animal Husbandry and Veterinary Medicine (quarterly); National Minority Education (bimonthly).

Rank	Full-time
Professors	10
Associate Professors	135
Lecturers	242
Assistants	125
Total	512

Student Enrolment, 1989: 3300 (Also 356 external students).

Tianjin (Municipality)

1953 **CIVIL AVIATION INSTITUTE OF CHINA (CAIC)**
East Suburbs, Tianjin
Telephone: 247602
President: Liu Depu (1985-)

Aeronautics Engineering
D. of Foreign Languages

Founded 1956 as professional school, acquired present status and title 1981. Residential facilities for academic staff and students.

Academic Year: September to July (September-January; February-July).

Admission Requirements: Graduation from senior middle school and entrance examination.

Language of Instruction: Chinese.

Degrees and Diplomas: Diploma, 3 yrs. Bachelor of–Science; Arts, 4 yrs.

Library: Central Library, 140,000 vols.

Publications: Journal; Study of Civil Aviation Education; Civil Aviation Institute of China (monthly).

Academic Staff, 1986-87:

Rank	Full-time	Part-time
Associate Professors	7	1
Lecturers	55	27
Assistants	127	–
Teachers	21	–
Total	210	19

Student Enrolment, 1986-87:

	Men	Women	Total
Of the country	1124	352	1476

1954 **TIANJIN INSTITUTE OF LIGHT INDUSTRY**
1486 Dagu Nanlu, Tianjin
Cables: 6400
Telephone: 82538

D. of Applied Liberal Arts
D. of Mechanical Engineering
D. of Electrical Engineering
D. of Chemical Engineering
D. of Food Technology
D. of Salt and Sea-water Industries
Extension D.

Founded 1958. Under the jurisdiction of the Ministry of Light Industry. Residential facilities for academic staff and students.

Academic Year: September to July (September-February; March-July).

Admission Requirements: Graduation from senior middle school and entrance examination.

Language of Instruction: Chinese.

Degrees and Diplomas: Speciality Diploma, 2 yrs. Bachelor, 4 yrs. Master, a further 2 ½-3 yrs. Doctor, 3 yrs.

Library: Central Library, *c.* 400,000 vols.

Academic Staff: c. 490.

Student Enrolment: c. 560.

1955 **TIANJIN INSTITUTE OF SCIENCE AND TECHNOLOGY**
Tianjin

1956 **TIANJIN INSTITUTE OF TEXTILE TECHNOLOGY**
Tianjin

1957 **TIANJIN AGRICULTURAL INSTITUTE**
Tianjin

1958 **TIANJIN MEDICAL COLLEGE**
62 Qi Xiang Tai Road, Tianjin
Telephone: 3-7790
President: Wu Hsien-Chung (1983-)

Medicine
Public Health
Stomatology
Nursing

Founded 1952. Under the jurisdiction of the Tianjin Municipality.

Academic Year: September to July (September-January; February-July).

Admission Requirements: Graduation from senior middle school and entrance examination.

Language of Instruction: Chinese.

Degrees and Diplomas: Bachelor, 5 yrs. Master, a further 3 yrs. Doctor, 3 yrs after Master.

Library: c. 200,000 vols.

Publication: Acta Academiae Medicinae Tianjin.

Academic Staff: c. 870.

Student Enrolment: c. 1870 (Also *c.* 70 external students).

1959 **TIANJIN COLLEGE OF TRADITIONAL CHINESE MEDICINE**
Tianjin

1960 **TIANJIN MEDICAL SCHOOL**
Tianjin

1961 **TIANJIN TEACHERS' SCHOOL**
Tianjin

1962 **TIANJIN TECHNICAL TEACHERS' INSTITUTE**
Tianjin

1963 **TIANJIN INSTITUTE OF FOREIGN LANGUAGES**
Tianjin

1964 **TIANJIN INSTITUTE OF FINANCE AND ECONOMICS**
Tianjin

1965 **TIANJIN INSTITUTE OF FOREIGN TRADE**
Tianjin

1966 **TIANJIN INSTITUTE OF PHYSICAL CULTURE**
Tianjin

1967 **TIANJIN MUSIC CONSERVATORY**
Tianjin

1968 **TIANJIN INSTITUTE OF FINE ARTS**
Tianjin

Xizang (Autonomous Region) (Tibet)

1969 **TIBET COLLEGE OF AGRICULTURE AND ANIMAL HUSBANDRY**
District of Linzhi

1970 **TIBET TEACHERS' COLLEGE**
Lhasa

1971 **TIBET INSTITUTE OF NATIONALITIES**
Xianyang, Province of Shaanxi

Xingjiang (Province)(Uygur Autonomous Region)

1972 **XINGJIANG AUGUST 1ST AGRICULTURAL COLLEGE**

Urumqi
Cables: 2470
Telephone: 42141
President: Zhang Xue-zu (1983-)

Agriculture (including Forestry, Animal Husbandry, and Veterinary Medicine)

Founded 1952. Under the jurisdiction of the Ministry of Education and the Provincial Government. Residential facilities for academic staff and students.

Arrangements for co-operation with Cornell University.

Academic Year: September to July (September-January; March-July).

Admission Requirements: Graduation from senior middle school and entrance examination.

Language of Instruction: Chinese.

Degrees and Diplomas: Bachelor of Science, 4-5 yrs. Master, a further 2-3 yrs.

Library: Central Library, *c.* 400,000 vols.

Publication: Journal (quarterly).

Press or Publishing House: College Printing House.

Academic Staff: *c.* 780.

Student Enrolment: *c.* 2630 (Also *c.* 810 external students).

1973 **XINGJIANG INSTITUTE OF PETROLEUM**

Urumqi

1974 **XINGJIANG INSTITUTE OF TECHNOLOGY**

Urumqi

1975 **SHIHEZI XINGJIANG AGRICULTURAL COLLEGE**

Shihezi

1976 **SHIHEZI MEDICAL COLLEGE**

The Second North Road, Shihezi 832002
Telephone: 22036
President: Chen Jia-Yu (1988-)
Director of Administration Office: Song Jia-Hua

D. of Clinical Medicine (including Pharmacy and Nursing)
Director: Zhu Yu-lu; *staff* 33 (120)
D. of Pharmacy
Director: Li Yu-Gian; *staff* 32
D. of Nursing Care
Director: Yang Gui-Bin; *staff* 8 (31)
D. of Basic Studies
Director: Zhuan Yi-Ping; *staff* 141
D. of Social Science
Director: Li Yun-Shun; *staff* 15
Training Sec. for Cadres
Director: Wang Xue-Jen; *staff* – (188)
Also Affiliated Hospitals and 4 Research Sections.

Founded 1949 as school. Acquired present status and title 1978. Under the jurisdiction of the Ministry of Agriculture, Animal Husbandry and Fishery. Residential facilities for academic staff and students.

Academic Year: September to July (September-January; February-July).

Admission Requirements: Graduation from senior middle school and entrance examination.

Fees: None.

Language of Instruction: Chinese.

Degrees and Diplomas: Diploma of–Pharmacy; Nursing, 3 yrs. Bachelor of Medicine, 5 yrs. Diploma of adult training 3 yrs.

Library: Central Library, 140,000 vols.

Publications: Journal of Shihezi Medical College (quarterly); Bulletin of Shihezi Medical College (monthly).

Press or Publishing House: Shihezi Medical College Printing House.

Academic Staff, 1990:

Rank	Full-time	Part-time
Professors	2	6
Associate Professors	43	20
Lecturers	77	55
Assistants	107	70
Total	229	151

Student Enrolment, 1989-90: 2070

1977 **XINGJIANG MEDICAL COLLEGE**

Urumqi

1978 **KESHI TEACHERS' COLLEGE**

Keshi

1979 **ILI TEACHERS' COLLEGE**

Ining

1980 **HETIAN TEACHERS' SCHOOL**

District of Hetian

1981 **XINGJIANG INSTITUTE OF FINANCE AND ECONOMICS**

Urumqi

Yunnan (Province)

1982 **KUNMING INSTITUTE OF TECHNOLOG**

38 Lianhuachi North Suburb, Kunming 650093
Cables: 1331
Telephone: 51322
President: Cai Qiao-Fang (1983-87)

D. of Geology
Dean: Zhuo Shi-Min; *staff* 117
D. of Mining Engineering
Dean: Chen Xiao-Hua; *staff* 80
D. of Metallurgy
Dean: Yang Xian-Wan; *staff* 123
D. of Metal Processing
Dean: Huang Guo-Qing; *staff* 74
D. of Mechanical Engineering
Dean: Ma Yun-Qi; *staff* 150
D. of Environmental Engineering
Dean: Huang Ruo-Hua; *staff* 74
D. of Automation
Dean: Yang Wei; *staff* 129
D. of Management
Dean: Zeng Xiang-Zheng; *staff* 46
D. of Basic Science
Dean: Jiang Tong-Li; *staff* 151
D. of Social Science
Dean: Han Shu-Zhen; *staff* 29
D. of Adult Education
Dean: Liu Gong-Hua; *staff* 40
D. of Foreign Languages
Dean: Zeng Xiu-Hua; *staff* 66
D. for Correspondence Courses
Vacuum Metallurgy I.
Director: Dan Yong-Nian

Founded 1954. Under the jurisdiction of the China National Non Ferrous Metals Industry Corporation. Residential facilities for academic staff and students.

Arrangements for co-operation with: South Dakota School of Mines and Technology; Lehigh University; Colorado State University; Institut National des Sciences appliquées de Lyon; University of Karlsruhe.

Academic Year: September to July (September-February; March-July).

Admission Requirements: Graduation from senior middle school and entrance examination.

Fees: None.

Language of Instruction: Chinese.

Degrees and Diplomas: Bachelor, 4 yrs. Master, a further 2 ½-3 yrs. Doctor, 3 yrs.

Library: Central Library, *c.* 700,000 vols.

Special Facilities (Museums, etc.): Geology Museum, Movie Studio.

Publications: Journal (quarterly); Science and Technology; Research in Higher Education.

Press or Publishing House: The Printing House of Kunming Institute of Technology.

Academic Staff, 1989:

Rank	Full-time
Professors	36
Associate Professors	264
Lecturers	125
Assistant Professors	350
Total	775

Student Enrolment: 8000.

1983 **YUNNAN INSTITUTE OF TECHNOLOGY**

Huancheng Donglu, Kunming

Cables: 2820

Telephone: 2903½9033

President: Yu Yi (1980-)

Vice-President: Zhou Xuexiang

D. of Basic Studies

Head: Li Congxian; *staff* 158 (1)

D. of Civil Engineering

Head: Luo Yongkang; *staff* 116 (3)

D. of Chemical Engineering

Head: Chan Chenghua; *staff* 154 (1)

D. of Electric Power Engineering

Head: Cheng Yuxian; *staff* 72 (1)

D. of Electric Engineering

Head: Liao Xiang-en; *staff* 91

D. of Mechanical Engineering

Head: Jiang Youcheng; *staff* 91

D. of Automobile Engineering

Head: Cai Jiaoxiao; *staff* 56

D. of Computer Applications and Management

Training Sec. for Cadres

Also 12 Research Institutes and Sections.

Founded in 1900s as school. Acquired present status and title 1974, incorporating previously existing colleges. Under the jurisdiction of the Provincial Government. Residential facilities for academic staff and students.

Arrangements for co-operation with the Universities of: Carnegie-Mellon; Colombia; California.

Academic Year: September to July (September-February; March-July).

Admission Requirements: Graduation from senior middle school and entrance examination.

Language of Instruction: Chinese.

Degrees and Diplomas: Certificate, 4 yrs. Bachelor of–Science; Engineering, 4 yrs. Master, a further 2-3 yrs.

Library: Central Library, *c.* 300,000 vols.

Publications: Journal (quarterly); Teaching Research (monthly).

Press or Publishing House: Printing House.

Academic Staff, 1986-87:

Rank	Full-time	Part-time
Professors	17	20
Associate Professors	95	15
Lecturers	287	–
Assistants	289	–
Total	688	35

Student Enrolment, 1986-87: 3280 (Also 86 external students).

1984 **DALI MEDICAL COLLEGE**

Dali

1985 **KUNMING MEDICAL COLLEGE**

Mynming

1986 **YUNNAN COLLEGE OF TRADITIONAL CHINESE MEDICINE**

Kunming

1987 **DALI TEACHERS' COLLEGE**

Dali Xia-guang, Dali Bai National Autonomous Prefecture

Teacher Training

Founded 1978. Acquired present title 1984. Under the jurisdiction of the Provincial Government. Residential facilities for academic staff and students.

Academic Year: September to August (September-February; March-July).

Admission Requirements: Graduation from senior middle school and entrance examination.

Language of Instruction: Chinese.

Degrees and Diplomas: Diploma, 3 yrs.

Library: Central Library, *c.* 130,000 vols.

Publication: Journal.

Academic Staff: c. 70 (20).

Student Enrolment: c. 380.

1988 **KUNMING TEACHERS' COLLEGE**

Kunming

1989 **BAOSHAN TEACHERS' SCHOOL**

District of Baoshan

1990 **KUNMING TEACHERS' SCHOOL**

Kunming

1991 **MENGZI TEACHERS' SCHOOL**

District of Mengzi

1992 **QUIJING TEACHERS' SCHOOL**

District of Quijing

1993 **SIMAO TEACHERS' SCHOOL**

District of Ouer

1994 **ZHAOTONG TEACHERS' SCHOOL**

District of Zhaotong

1995 **YUNNAN FINANCE AND TRADE INSTITUTE**

Shangmacun Kunming

Telephone: 51723

President: Wu Jian-An

Secretary-General: Cheng Jie-Shan

D. of Banking

Head: Zhou Hou-Wen; *staff* 25

D. of Finance

Head: Ding Zhi; *staff* 28

D. of Planning and Statistics

Head: Xu Shu-Long; *staff* 42

D. of Accounting

Head: Mo Guo-Jiang; *staff* 35

D. of Commercial Economics

Head: Zhou Gan; *staff* 37

Economic Research I.

Head: Nie Yuan-Kun; *staff* 10

Computer Ce.

Head: Zhou Tian-Yuan

Founded 1981. Under the jurisdiction of the Provincial Government. Residential facilities for academic staff and students.

Academic Year: September to July (September-January; February-July).

Admission Requirements: Graduation form high school and entrance examination.

Fees: None.

Language of Instruction: Chinese.

Degrees and Diplomas: Bachelor of Economics, 4 yrs.

Library: 25m. vols.

Publications: Institute Academic Journal; Foreign Economic Theory and Administration.

Academic Staff, 1989-90:

Rank	Full-time
Professors	2
Associate Professors	22
Lecturers	93
Assistants	136
Others	22
Total	275

Student Enrolment, 1989-90:

	Men	Women	Total
Of the country	1414	1206	2620*

*Also 1580 external students.

1996 **YUNNAN SCHOOL OF POLITICAL SCIENCE AND LAW**
Kunming

1997 **YUNNAN ACADEMY OF ARTS**
Kunming

1998 **YUNNAN INSTITUTE OF NATIONALITIES**
Kunming
Telephone: 24717

Regional Studies
Basic Studies
Foreign Languages
D. for Evening Studies
D. for Correspondence Courses
Also Research Institute.

Founded 1951. Under the jurisdiction of the Provincial Government. Residential facilities for academic staff and students.

Arrangements for co-operation with: Baylor University; University of Virginia.

Academic Year: August to July (August-February; February-July).

Admission Requirements: Graduation from senior middle school and entrance examination.

Language of Instruction: Chinese.

Degrees and Diplomas: Bachelor of–Arts; Science, 4 yrs. Master, a further 2 yrs.

Library: Central Library, *c.* 330,000 vols.

Special Facilities (Museums, etc.): Exhibition Halls of Minority Arts and Relics.

Publications: Journal; Journal of Nationality Researches.

Academic Staff: c. 780.

Student Enrolment: c. 1750 (Also *c.* 1000 external students).

Zhejiang (Province)

1999 **HANGZHOU INSTITUTE OF ELECTRONIC ENGINEERING**
Hangzhou 310037
Cables: 1565 Hangzhou
Telex: 35010 HEADT
Telephone: (571) 883214
Fax: (571) 887232
President: Zhou Xing-Quan (1988-1992)

D. of Mechanical Engineering
Director: Mo Hong-Xun; *staff* 70
D. of Industrial Economics
Director: Jin Pei-Liang; *staff* 76 (3)
D. of Management Engineering
Director: Zhou Hong-Nian; *staff* 46; (1)
D. of Electronic Engineering
Director: Tian Fu-Yong; *staff* 78
D. of Computer Science
Director: Ye You-Xin; *staff* 50; (1)
Computer and Audio-visual Ce.
Head: Sun Zu-De;E36
D. of Adult Education
Head: Chai Bing-Guan; *staff* 14; (40)
Also 3 Research Institutes

Founded 1956 as Hangzhou Aviation Industry School of Finance and Economics. Acquired present status and title in 1980. Under the jurisdiction of the Ministry of Mechanical and Electronic Industry. Residential facilities for academic staff and students

Arrangements for co-operation with Fachhochschule Aachen

Academic Year: September-July (September-January; February-July)

Admission Requirements: Graduation from high school and entrance examination.

Fees: None.

Language of Instruction: Chinese.

Degrees and Diplomas: Bachelor, 4 ½ yrs. Master, 2 ½ yrs.

Library: 328,800 vols

Publications: Journal of Hangzhou Institute of Electronics Engineering (quarterly); Higher Education Research of HIEE (annually).

Academic Staff, 1990:

Rank	Full-time	Part-time
Professors	23	12
Associate Professors	111	–
Lecturers	164	–
Assistant Lectures	114	–
Total	412	12

Student Enrolment, 1990:

	Men	Women	Total
Of the country	1741	746	2487*

*Also 30 evening students and 988 students by correspondance.

2000 **ZHEJIANG INSTITUTE OF FORESTRY**
District of Lin'an, Lin'an 311300
Telephone: 21231
President: Liu Mao-Chun
Vice-President: Lin Hua-Gang

Forestry (including Landscape Architecture)

Founded 1958. Under the jurisdiction of the Provincial Government. Residential facilities for academic staff and students.

Academic Year: September to July (September-January; February-July).

Admission Requirements: Graduation form high school and entrance examination.

Fees: None.

Language of Instruction: Chinese.

Degrees and Diplomas: Bachelor of Agronomy, 4 yrs. Also Diplomas, 2-3 yrs.

Library: 167,000 vols.

Publication: Journal of Zhejiang Forestry College (quarterly).

Academic Staff, 1989:

Rank	Full-time
Professors	1
Associate Professors	34
Lecturers	103
Assistants	125
Laboratory Technicians	51
Total	314

Student Enrolment, 1989:

	Men	Women	Total
Of the country	829	207	1036

2001 **ZHEJIANG FISHERIES INSTITUTE**
Putuo County
Cables: 7108
Telephone: 53851
President: Tang Yi-Min (1983-)
Secretary-General: Shi Qi-Cai

D. of Fisheries
Director: She Xian-Wei; *staff* 22
D. of Navigation
Director: Qian Tian-Kuang; *staff* 31
D. of Economics and Management
Head: Zhen Shu-Guang; *staff* 14
D. of Machinery Design and Manufacturing
Head: Shen Yun; *staff* 48
D. of Food Engineering
Head: Xia Xin-Lin; *staff* 48

D. of Fish Farming
Head: Xu Xin-Lin;
Branch at Ningbo.

Founded 1961 as school, acquired present status and title 1975. Under the jurisdiction of Provincial Government. Residential facilities for academic staff and students.

Academic Year: September to June (September-January; February-June).

Admission Requirements: Graduation from senior middle school and entrance examination.

Fees: None.

Language of Instruction: Chinese.

Degrees and Diplomas: Bachelor, 4 yrs.

Library: Central Library, 600,000 vols.

Publications: Journal (biannually); Fisheries Information (quarterly).

Academic Staff, 1986-87:

Rank	Full-time
Professors	2
Associate Professors	27
Lecturers	95
Assistants	90
Total	214

Student Enrolment, 1986-87:

	Men	Women	Total
Of the country	691	170	861

2002 **ZHEJIANG SILK ENGINEERING COLLEGE**
Wen Yi Road, Hangzhou
Cables: 4762
Telephone: 85814
President: Zhang You-mei (1983-87)

Silk Engineering
D. for Evening Studies
Training Sec. for Cadres

Founded 1897. Acquired present status and title 1964. Under the jurisdiction of the China Silk Corporation.

Academic Year: September to August (September-February; March-August).

Admission Requirements: Graduation from senior middle school and entrance examination.

Language of Instruction: Chinese.

Degrees and Diplomas: Bachelor of Science. Master.

Library: Central Library.

Publication: Journal.

Academic Staff: c. 300.

Student Enrolment: c.1200 (Also c. 460 external students).

2003 **ZHEJIANG INSTITUTE OF TECHNOLOGY**
Mishi Lane, Hangzhou
Cables: 8036
Telephone: 88514
President: Deng Hang-xin (1984-88)

D. of Mechanical Engineering
Head: Zhang Kan-da; *staff* 109
D. of Chemical Engineering
Head: Xu Chong-si; *staff* 127
D. of Electronic Engineering
Head: Yu Yun-tao; *staff* 69
D. of Civil Engineering
; *staff* 49
D. of Industrial Management
Head: Wu Tian-zu; *staff* 29
D. of Light Industry Engineering
Head: Li Xiang-Lin; *staff* 30
D. of Education (Technical)
; *staff* 68
D. of Computer Engineering
Head: Mao Pei-fa; *staff* 39
D. for Evening Studies
Head: Wang Lie-xieng; *staff* 20 (15)

Founded 1978. Incorporated Zhejiang Institute of Chemical Engineering 1980. Residential facilities for academic staff and students.

Arrangements for co-operation with Ashikaga Institute of Engineering.

Academic Year: September to July (September-January; February-July).

Admission Requirements: Graduation from senior middle school and entrance examination.

Language of Instruction: Chinese.

Degrees and Diplomas: Bachelor, 4 yrs. Master, a further 3 yrs.

Library: Central Library, 600,000 vols.

Publication: Journal (quarterly).

Academic Staff, 1984-85:

Rank	Full-time
Professors	8
Associate Professors	106
Lecturers	288
Assistants	249
Total	651

Student Enrolment, 1986-87:

	Men	Women	Total
Of the country	3142	561	3703

2004 **WENZHOU MEDICAL COLLEGE**
Yixue Yuan Road, Wenzhou 325003
Telex: 3547
Telephone: (0577) 334941
President: Li Ri-Qian
Secretary-General: Li Xun-Li

F. of Basic Sciences
Dean: Xia Lian; *staff* 211
F. of Medicine
Dean: Chi Ren-Yuen; *staff* 93
F. of Padiatrics
Dean: Hu Chong-Yi; *staff* 28
F. of Ophthalmology
Deputy Dean: Shi Min-Guang; *staff* 10
F. of Laboratory Examination
Deputy Dean: Lu Yong-Sui; *staff* 26
Also 9 Hospitals and 5 Research Groups.

Founded 1958. Under the jurisdiction of the Provincial Government Residential facilities for academic staff and students.

Academic Year: September to July (September-January; February-July).

Admission Requirements: Graduation from high school and entrance examination.

Fees: None.

Language of Instruction: Chinese.

Degrees and Diplomas: Bachelor, 5 yrs. Master, a further 3 yrs.

Library: 150,000 vols.

Publications: Journal of Wenzhou Medical College (quarterly); Ophthalmology News (quarterly); Medical Education Research.

Academic Staff, 1990:

Rank	Full-time
Professors	10
Associate Professors	54
Lecturers	113
Total	177

Student Enrolment, 1990:

	Men	Women	Total
Of the country	964	694	1658*

*Also 223 students by correspondence.

2005 **ZHEJIANG COLLEGE OF TRADITIONAL CHINESE MEDICINE**
Chingchun Road, Hangzhou
Telephone: 71568
President: Feng Heming (1983-88)

Traditional Chinese Medicine
D. for Correspondence Courses

Founded 1959. Under the jurisdiction of the Ministries of Public Health and Education and of the Provincial Government. Residential facilities for academic staff and students.

Academic Year: September to July (September-February; March-July).

Admission Requirements: Graduation from senior middle school and entrance examination.

Language of Instruction: Chinese.

Degrees and Diplomas: Bachelor, 5 yrs. Master, a further 2-3 yrs.

Library: Central Library, c. 140,000 vols.

Publication: Journal (bimonthly).

Academic Staff: c. 110.
Student Enrolment: c. 260 (Also c. 310 external students).

2006 **JIAXING TEACHERS' SCHOOL**
District of Wuxing

2007 **LISHUI TEACHERS' SCHOOL**
District of Lishui

2008 **NINGBO TEACHERS' SCHOOL**
Ningbo

2009 **SHAOXING TEACHERS' TRANING COLLEGE**
5 Huancheng Xilu, Shaoxing 312000
Telephone: (0571) 37050, 34138
President: Cheng Zu-Nan (1989-)
Vice-Presidents: Zhang Shu-Jian; Dong Wei-Zu

D. of Chinese
Director: Bao Xian-Luen; *staff* 28
D. of History
Director: Meng Wen-Yong; *staff* 13
D. of Political Education
Director: Xia Sheng-Yua; *staff* 18
D. of Foreign Languages
Director: Jiang Kun-Fang; *staff* 18
D. of Physics
Director: Jin Lie-Hou; *staff* 22
D. of Mathematics
Director: Yu Ding-Guo; *staff* 26
D. of Biochemistry
Director: Cai Xiu-Hua; *staff* 27
Bureau of Pedagogy
Director: Ma Zhao-Zhang; *staff* 7
Bureau of Physical Education
Director: Zhang Ying; *staff* 11
Ce. for Adult Education
Director: Cheng Sui-Zhong; *staff* 14
Ce. for Evening Studies
Vice-President: Xie De-Xi
Also 2 Research Centres.

Founded 1909 as teachers' school. Acquired present status and title 1980 Residential facilities for academic staff and students.

Academic Year: September to July (September-January; February-July).

Admission Requirements: Graduation from middle school and entrance examination.

Fees: None.

Language of Instruction: Chinese.

Degrees and Diplomas: Diploma.

Library: Central Library, 380,000 vols.

Publication: Journal of Shaoxing Teachers Training College (quarterly).

Academic Staff, 1990:

Rank	Full-time
Associate Professors	30
Lecturers	79
Others	65
Total	174

Student Enrolment, 1990: 1200 (Also 537 external students).

2010 **TAIZHOU TEACHERS' SCHOOL**
District of Linhai

2011 **WENZHOU TEACHERS' SCHOOL**
Wenzhou

2012 **HANGZHOU INSTITUTE OF COMMERCE**
Jiao Gong Road, Hangzhou
Telex: 5096
Telephone: 81024
President: Zhao Guozhu
Vice-President: Li Xueyin

Commerce (including Business Administration, Accountancy, FoodTechnology and Electronics)

Founded 1911 as school, acquired present status and title 1980. Under the jurisdiction of the Ministry of Commerce and Provincial Government. Residential facilities for academic staff and students.

Arrangements for co-operation with the University of South Florida.

Academic Year: September to July (September-January; February-July).

Admission Requirements: Graduation from senior middle school and entrance examination.

Language of Instruction: Chinese.

Degrees and Diplomas: Bachelor, 4 yrs.

Library: Central Library, 400,000 vols.

Publications: Economics and Business Administration (quarterly); Foreign Commerce (quarterly); Correspondence Education (monthly).

Academic Staff, 1986-87:

Rank	Full-time
Professors	26
Lecturers	131
Teachers	48
Assistants	171
Total	376

Student Enrolment, 1986-87:

	Men	Women	Total
Of the country	1800	600	2400*

*Also 2980 external students.

2013 **ZHEJIANG SCHOOL OF METALLURGICAL ECONOMICS**
District of Jiande

2014 **ZHEJIANG ACADEMY OF FINE ARTS**
218 Nanstan Road, Hangzhou
Telex: 9710
Telephone: 22316; 22634
President: Xiao Feng (1983-)

Fine Arts (including Chinese Traditional Painting and Industrial Design)

Founded 1928 as art institute. Acquired present status and title 1957. Under the jurisdiction of the Ministry of Culture. Governing body: the Executive Committee. Residential facilities for academic staff and 488 students.

Arrangements for co-operation with: University of Minnesota; University of Montana.

Academic Year: September to July (September-February; March-July).

Admission Requirements: Graduation from senior middle school and entrance examination.

Language of Instruction: Chinese.

Degrees and Diplomas: Bachelor of Arts, 4 yrs. Master, a further 2 yrs. Doctor of Arts, 3 yrs.

Library: c. 150,000 vols.

Publications: New Fine Arts (quarterly); Translations of Foreign Articles on Fine Arts (quarterly).

Academic Staff: c. 190.

Student Enrolment: c. 360 (Also c. 40 external students).

COLOMBIA

Universities and Other University Institutions

Public Institutions

2015 **COLEGIO MAYOR DE ANTIOQUIA**
Calle 65 Carrera 78 Robledo, AA, Apartado aéreo 5177, Medellín (Antioquia).
Telephone: 2334740
Rector: Lucia Duque de Vargas
Secretaria General: Rosa Elena de Buitrago

F. of Bacteriology and Clinical Laboratory Science
Dean: Amparo Cuartas de Jaramillo; *staff* – (20)
F. of Technology (including Architectural Design)
Dean: Jorge Iván Arango; *staff* – (20)
F. of Tourism Administration (Technology)
Dean: Maruja Vargas de Gómez; *staff* – (40)
F. of Bilingual Secretarial Studies (English, Spanish)
Dean: Gloria Lucía Urreta; *staff* – (30)
F. of Technology in Social Promotion
Dean: Inés Vásquez; *staff* – (22)

Founded 1945. Acquired present status 1986. A national institution. Governing bodies: the Consejo Superior; the Consejo Académico.

Academic Year: February to November (February-June; July-November).

Admission Requirements: Secondary school certificate and entrance examination.

Fees (Pesos): 15,000-60,000 per semester.

Language of Instruction: Spanish.

Degrees and Diplomas: Professional titles of Tecnólogo, 3 yrs.

Library: c. 3290 vols.

Student Enrolment, 1990: 280

Student Enrolment, 1990:

	Men	Women	Total
Of the country	30	770	800

2016 **COLEGIO MAYOR DE CUNDINAMARCA**
Calle 28 No. 6-02, Bogotá
Telephone: 2340257

Bacteriology and Laboratory Science
Architectural Design
Social Work

Founded 1945. A national institution.

Admission Requirements: Secondary school certificate (bachillerato) and entrance examination.

Language of Instruction: Spanish.

Degrees and Diplomas: Licenciado in Social Work, 4 yrs. Professional titles, 3-4 yrs.

Library: c. 2150 vols.

Student Enrolment: c. 1020 (Women).

2017 **ESCUELA DE CADETES DE POLICIA 'GENERAL SANTANDER'**
Autopista Sur Calle 42, Bogotá
Telephone: 2381674

2018 **ESCUELA SUPERIOR DE ADMINISTRACIÓN PÚBLICA 'ESAP'**
Diagonal 40 No. 46A-37, Bogotá
Telephone: 2699147

D. of Political and Administrative Sciences

Founded 1958. A national institution of university rank.

Academic Year: January to December.

Admission Requirements: Secondary school certificate (bachillerato) and entrance examination.

Language of Instruction: Spanish.

Degrees and Diplomas: Professional titles, 5 yrs.

Library: c. 24,810 vols.

Student Enrolment: c. 820.

2019 **ESCUELA SUPERIOR DE ADMINISTRACIÓN PÚBLICA**
Calle 56 (Bolivia) No 45-34, Medellín (Antioquia).
Telephone: 2543780

P. of Municipal Administration

2020 **INSTITUTO DEPARTAMENTAL DE BELLAS ARTES 'ANTONIO MARIA VALENCIA'**
Avenida 2 Norte No 7-38, Cali (Valle)
Telephone: 0803850
Rector: Cyrano Fernández
Secretaria General: Hilia David Pérez

P. of Plastic Arts
Head: Sonia Echeverry; *staff* 14 (16)
P. of Music
Head: Marjorie Tanaka; *staff* – (35)
P. of Theatre
Head: Myriam Cecilia Mora; *staff* 12 (7)

Founded 1932.

Academic Year: February to December.

Admission Requirements: Secondary school certificate (bachillerato) and entrance examination.

Fees (Pesos): According to income of parents.

Degrees and Diplomas: Maestro, teaching qualifications, 4-5 yrs. Bachilleres–Artistas del Ballet; Actores, 3-4 yrs.

Academic Staff, 1990: 60 (87).

Student Enrolment, 1990:

	Men	Women	Total
Of the country	165	260	425*

*Also 3 foreign students.

2021 **INSTITUTO UNIVERSITARIO DE CUNDINAMARCA 'ITUC'**
Diagonal 18 No. 20-29, Fusugasugá (Cundinamarca)
Telephone: 0002144
Rector: José del Carmen Castro Castillo

F. of Educational Administration
Dean: Amanda Gracia Martínez; *staff* 7 (21)
F. of Mathematics and Physics
Dean: Luís Hernando Piedrahita N.; *staff* 8 (11)
F. of Physical Education
Dean: Hernán López Riaño; *staff* 8 (31)
F. of Business Technology
Dean: Francisco Baquero A.; *staff* – (45)
F. of Agricultural Technology
Dean: Enrique Orlando Quevedo; *staff* 7 (16)
F. of Animal Husbandry
Dean: Héctor Caicedo; *staff* 7 (12)
F. of Biology and Chemistry
Dean: Rolando Maradey; *staff* 7 (25)
F. of Social Sciences
Dean: Maria Eugenia Saibatto; *staff* 9 (22)
F. of Nursing
Dean: Elsa Helena Espinosa; *staff* 12 (25)
F. of Languages (Ubaté)
Dean: Nubia Giomar Ballen; *staff* 7 (13)
F. of Mathematics and Physics
Dean: Alvaro Rosas E.; *staff* 6 (11)
F. of Business Technology
Dean: Fernando Castellanos O.; *staff* 6 (25)
Open U.
Head: Fladio Hernández; *staff* 4 (84)

Research Ce. (Socio-Economics, Afro-Industrial Studies)
Head: Gregorio Clavijo; *staff* 6

Founded 1969. An official provincial institution. Governing bodies: the Consejo Superior; the Consejo Académico.

Academic Year: February to December (February-June; August-December).

Admission Requirements: Secondary school certificate (bachillerato) and entrance examination.

Fees (Pesos): 50,000 per semester.

Language of Instruction: Spanish.

Degrees and Diplomas: Licenciado, 4 yrs. Professional titles, 5 yrs. Tecnólogo, 3 yrs.

Library: Total, *c.* 16,140.

Special Facilities (Museums, etc.): Natural History Museum (Girardot).

Publication: Episteme (Ubaté).

Academic Staff, 1990:

Rank	Full-time	Part-time
Profesores Titulares	40	10
Profesores Asociados	30	15
Profesores Asistentes	22	40
Profesores Auxiliares	3	260
Total	95	325

Student Enrolment, 1990:

	Men	Women	Total
Of the country	640	600	1240*

*Also 597 external students and students by correspondence.

2022 **INSTITUTO UNIVERSITARIO DE LA PAZ**

Calle 9 No.10-22, Santander
Telephone: 0021908

P. of Veterinary Medicine
P. of Animal Husbandry

2023 **UNIDAD CENTRAL DEL VALLE DEL CAUCA**

Carrera 26 No 30-58, Tuluá (Cauca)
Telephone: 0004375

F. of Education
F. of Business Administration
F. of Accountancy
F. of Law
D. of Physical Education
D. of Social Sciences

Founded 1971. A State institution. Governing body: the Consejo Superior.

Academic Year: February to December (February-June; July-December).

Admission Requirements: Secondary school certificate (bachillerato) and entrance examination.

Language of Instruction: Spanish.

Degrees and Diplomas: Licenciado in Education. Professional titles of–Abogado, law; Administrador de Empresas, business administration; Contador, accountancy.

Library: c. 5300 vols.

Academic Staff: c. 30 (100).

Student Enrolment: c. 1550.

2024 **UNIDAD UNIVERSITARIA DEL SUR DE BOGOTÁ (FORMACIÓN A DISTANCIA)**

Carrera 7a No 6-5A, Bogotá
Telephone: 2895063
Rectora: María Teresa Arias de Barrero (1986-)
Secretaria General: Betty Gongora Pedraza

F. of Administration
Dean: Marco Elàias Contreras; *staff* 12 (3)
F. of Engineering (Food Technology)
Dean: Gustavo Sandoval Valderrama; *staff* 15 (1)
F. of Agriculture (including Animal Husbandry) (in process of development)
Dean: Gonzalo Téllez Iregui; *staff* 11 (2)
F. of Social Sciences and Humanities
Dean: Roberto Salazar Ramos; *staff* 10 (2)

Founded 1981. A State institution. Governing body: the Consejo Superior.

Academic Year: February to December (February-June; July-December).

Admission Requirements: Secondary school certificate (bachillerato) and entrance examination.

Fees (Pesos): According to income of parents.

Language of Instruction: Spanish.

Degrees and Diplomas: Professional titles, 3-5 yrs.

Student Enrolment, 1986-87:

	Men	Women	Total
Of the country	2500	1500	4000

2025 **UNIVERSIDAD DE LA AMAZONIA**

Avenida Circunvalación, Barrio el Cedral, Florencia (Caquetá).
Telephone: 0002905

Education
Accountancy
Animal Husbandry

2026 **UNIVERSIDAD DE ANTIOQUIA**

University of Antioquia
Calle 67 No 53-108, Medellín
Telephone: 2334740
Fax: (4) 2638282
Rector: Saúl Mesa Ochoa (1985-)
Secretaria General: Martha Nora Palacio Escobar

F. of Arts (Drama, Visual Arts, Music)
Dean: Aníbal Vallejo R.; *staff* 39 (23)
F. of Economics
Dean: Gustavo A. López; *staff* 70 (56)
F. of Natural and Exact Sciences
Dean: Luiz Enrique Ruíz G.; *staff* 212 (27)
F. of Human Sciences
Dean: Alfonso Monsalve S.; *staff* 124 (12)
F. of Social Sciences
Dean: Olga Castaño M.; *staff* 124 (12)
F. of Law
Dean: Luis Fernando Restrepo; *staff* 89 (40)
F. of Education
Dean: César Morato H.; *staff* 56 (35)
F. of Nursing
Dean: Clara Ines Giraldo M.; *staff* 77 (26)
F. of Engineering
Dean: Abelardo Parra A.; *staff* 111 (88)
F. of Medicine
Dean: Luis Javier Giraldo M.; *staff* 106 (173)
F. of Veterinary Medicine and Animal Husbandry
Dean: Oscar Machado J.; *staff* 43 (11)
F. of Dentistry
Dean: Alejandro Boiero B.; *staff* 46 (46)
F. of Pharmacy
Dean: Rosalba Alzaie; *staff* 25 (17)
F. of Public Health
Dean: Francisco Correa U.; *staff* 62 (6)
S. of Bacteriology and Clinical Chemistry
Director: Luz Estella Londoño; *staff* 28 (3)
S. of Library Science
Director: Iván Rúa; *staff* 9 (3)
I. of Physical Education
Director: Benjamin Díaz L.; *staff* 17 (5)
D. for Distance Education
Head: Cipriano López H.
S. of Food and Nutrition
Director: Amparo Galeano H.
I. of Political Science
Director: William Restrepo R.
I. of Regional Studies
Director: Francisco Gómez P.
Medical Research Ce.
Chairman: Julian Betancur M.: *staff* 2 (128)
Natural and Exact Sciences Research Ce.
Chairman: Gustavo Quiniero
Economic Research Ce.
Chairman: Saul Mesa Ochoa; *staff* 1 (39)
Research Ce. for Environmental Sciences
Chairman: Jorge Humberto Sierra; *staff* 1 (26)
Research Ce. for Energy Sources
Chairman: Carlos E. Arroyave Posada; *staff* 1 (27)

Public Health Research Ce.
Chairman: Yolanda Torres de Galvis; *staff* 1 (62)

Founded 1801 as school by King Charles IV of Spain, became State university 1822. Governing bodies: the Consejo Superior; the Consejo Académico.

Arrangements for cooperation with the Universities of: Laval; Trieste; McGill; Montpellier.

Academic Year: February to December (February-June; July-December).

Admission Requirements: Secondary school certificate (bachillerato) and entrance examination.

Fees: According to income of parents.

Language of Instruction: Spanish.

Degrees and Diplomas: Licenciado, 4 yrs. Professional titles, 5 yrs. Magister, 6-7 yrs, and specialization in Medicine, 8-10 yrs. Also diplomas of Técnico, 2-3 yrs.

Libraries: Central Library, 108,266 vols; Health Sciences Library.

Special Facilities (Museums, etc.): Museum of Anthropology and History.

Publications: Iatreia; Investigación y Educ. en Enfermería; Temas Microbiológicas; Estudios de Filosofia; Estudios de Derecho; Tecnología Administrativa; Actualidades Biológicas; Revista Intermericana de Bibliotecologia, Linguística y Literatura; Boletín de Antropología.

Press or Publishing House: Editorial Universidad de Antioquia.

Academic Staff, 1989-90:

Rank	Full-time	Part-time
Profesores Titulares	816	67
Profesores Asociados	196	86
Profesores Asistentes	84	82
Instructores	2	6
Total	1098	241

Student Enrolment, 1989-90:

	Men	Women	Total
Of the country	7102	10,006	17,108

2027 **UNIVERSIDAD DEL ATLÁNTICO**
University of the Atlantic
Carrera 43 Nos. 50-53, Barranquilla (Atlántico).
Cables: Uniatlántico
Telephone: 313513

P. of Education
P. of Economics (including Business Administration and Accountancy)
P. of Architecture
P. of Chemical Engineering
P. of Chemistry and Pharmacy
P. of Dietetics and Nutrition
P. of Law
I. of Mathematics
S. of Painting
S. of Music

Founded 1941 as Museo del Atlántico, acquired present structure and status 1946. A State institution. Governing bodies: the Consejo Superior; the Consejo Directivo.

Academic Year: January to December (January-June; July-December).

Admission Requirements: Secondary school certificate (bachillerato) and entrance examination.

Fees: According to income of parents.

Language of Instruction: Spanish.

Degrees and Diplomas: Licenciado in–Education; Dietetics and Nutrition, 4 yrs. Professional titles of–Arquitecto; Abogado, law; Economista; Ingeniero químico; Químico farmacéutico; Dietista; Administrador de Empresas, business administration; Contador público, accountancy, 5 yrs. Maestro in Artes Plásticas, teaching qualification, 5 yrs.

Libraries: Central Library, *c.* 6000 vols; Fine Arts, *c.* 1850; Economic Research, *c.* 800; Education, *c.* 4390.

Special Facilities (Museums, etc.): Museo Antropológico.

Publication: Economía (quarterly).

Academic Staff: c. 280 (560).

Student Enrolment: c. 9000.

2028 **UNIVERSIDAD DE CALDAS**
University of Caldas
Calle 65 No. 26-10, Apartado aéreo 275, Manizales (Calda)
Telephone: 855240

S. of Medicine
S. of Veterinary Medicine and Animal Husbandry
S. of Agriculture
S. of Law
S. of Home Economics (including Dietetics)
S. of Nursing
D. of Education
S. of Fine Arts
S. of Philosophy and Letters
S. of Social Work
S. of Geology

Founded 1937 as Instituto Politécnico de Caldas, became Universidad Popular 1943, and national university 1967. Governing bodies: the Consejo Superior, composed of the State Governor, a representative of a Catholic clergy, a representative of the Ministry of Education, a representative of the academic staff, a student representative, the Rector and Secretary-General; the Consejo Directivo, composed of the Rector, the Secretary-General, deans of faculties, a representative of the academic staff, and a student representative. Financed by the central government. Residential facilities for *c.* 60 students.

Academic Year: February to December (February-June; (July-December).

Admission Requirements: Secondary school certificate (bachillerato) and entrance examination.

Fees: According to income of parents.

Language of Instruction: Spanish.

Degrees and Diplomas: Licenciado and Professional titles in all fields, 4 yrs. Specialization in Medicine.

Libraries: Central Library, *c.* 100,000 vols; School of Law, *c.* 40,000.

Publication: Aleph (quarterly).

Academic Staff: c. 400.

Student Enrolment: c. 3600.

2029 **UNIVERSIDAD DE CARTAGENA**
University of Cartagena
Carrera 6 No.36-100, Cartagena (Bolivar)
Telephone: 065503240118; 40262

F. of Medicine
F. of Dentistry
F. of Chemistry and Pharmacy
F. of Nursing
F. of Law
F. of Social Work
F. of Economics
F. of Civil Engineering
P. of Accountancy
P. of Business Administration

Founded 1774, became university 1827. A State institution. Governing bodies: the Consejo Superior; the Consejo Académico. Residential facilities for *c.* 60 students.

Arrangements for co-operation with the University of Dallas.

Academic Year: February to December (February-June; July-December).

Admission Requirements: Secondary school certificate (bachillerato) and entrance examination.

Fees: According to income of parents.

Language of Instruction: Spanish.

Degrees and Diplomas: Professional titles of–Enfermera, nursing, 4 yrs; Trabajadora social, social work, 4 yrs; Ingeniero civil; Odontólogo, dentistry; Economista; Administrador de Empresas, business administration; Contador público, accountancy; Químico farmacéutico; Abogado, law, 5 yrs; Médico cirujano, 7 yrs. Specialization in various fields.

Libraries: 'Fernández de Madrid' University Library, *c.* 44,510 vols; Medicine, *c.* 2830; Dentistry, *c.* 1100.

Special Facilities (Museums, etc.): Museo Los Corales 'Reynaldo Pfaff-2'.

Publications: Revista Jurídica; Revista de Ciencias Económicas; Boletín de Enfermería.

Academic Staff: c. 280 (260).

Student Enrolment: c. 4130.

2030 **UNIVERSIDAD DEL CAUCA**
University of Cauca
Calle 5, No. 4-70, Popayán (Cauca)
Cables: unicauca
Telex: 5966 UNCAN CO
Telephone: 23020

F. of Law and Political and Social Sciences
F. of Health Sciences
F. of Civil Engineering

F. of Electronics and Telecommunications
F. of Accountancy
F. of Humanities
F. of Education

Founded 1827 by decree of General Santander. Title changed to Colegio provincial in 1850 when higher education was suppressed. Reorganized and raised to the rank of Colegio mayor in 1857. Re-established as university in 1883, became a public autonomous institution 1964. Governing bodies: the Consejo Superior; the Consejo Académico.

Academic Year: January to December (January-June; August-December).

Admission Requirements: Secondary school certificate (bachillerato) and entrance examination.

Fees: According to income of parents.

Language of Instruction: Spanish.

Degrees and Diplomas: Licenciado, 4 yrs. Professional titles of–Enfermera, 3 yrs; Abogado, law; Ingeniero, 5 yrs; Médico, 7 yrs. Magister, a further 1 ½ yrs.

Library: Central Library, *c.* 35,000 vols.

Special Facilities (Museums, etc.): Natural History Museum.

Publication: Faculty publications.

Press or Publishing House: Editorial de la Universidad del Cauca.

Academic Staff: c. 440.

Student Enrolment: c. 3650.

2031 **UNIVERSIDAD DE CÓRDOBA**

University of Cordoba

Kilometro 3 via Ceretê, Apartado aéreo 354, Montería (Córdoba)
Cables: unicordoba
Telephone: 3278

Rector: Laureano Mestra Diaz
Vice-Rector Académico: Efrain Pastor Nieves

F. of Veterinary Medicine and Animal Husbandry
Dean: Francisco Aguilar M.; *staff* 34 (1)
F. of Agriculture
Dean: Maximiliano Espinosa P.; *staff* 36 (4)
F. of Sciences
Dean: Auiles Gonzalez Salaza; *staff* 59 (2)
F. of Health Sciences (Nursing)
Dean: Giselle Ferrer Ferrer; *staff* 9 (14)
F. of Education
Dean: José Morales Manchego; *staff* 39 (4)
F. of Fishery
Director: Rodolfo Montes Rhemals; *staff* 6

Founded 1966 by the provincial government, incorporating faculties of agriculture and veterinary medicine founded 1962. The university is autonomous in administrative and academic matters. Financed by the national and provincial governments. Governing bodies: the Consejo Directivo; the Consejo Académico.

Academic Year: February to November (February-June; July-November).

Admission Requirements: Secondary school certificate (bachillerato) and entrance examination.

Fees (Pesos): According to income of parents, 9000-100,000 per semester.

Language of Instruction: Spanish.

Degrees and Diplomas: Licenciado in–Biology and Chemistry; Mathematics and Physics; Social Sciences, 5 yrs. Professional titles in–Nursing, 4 yrs; Veterinary Medicine; Agricultural Engineering, 5 yrs.

Library: c. 6320 vols.

Special Facilities (Museums, etc.): Museum of Anthropology.

Academic Staff, 1986-87:

Rank	Full-time	Part-time
Titulares	10	–
Asociados	147	9
Agregados	18	6
Asistentes	5	–
Total	180	15

Student Enrolment, 1986-87:

	Men	Women	Total
Of the country	1682	654	2336

2032 **UNIVERSIDAD DISTRITAL 'FRANCISCO JOSÉ DE CALDAS'**

Carrera 8a No. 40-78, Bogotá
Telephone: 2457088

P. of Education

Founded 1950 under the authority of the municipality of Bogotá. Nationally recognized as an official university 1963. Governing bodies: the Consejo Superior; the Consejo Directivo.

Academic Year: February to December (February-June; August-December).

Admission Requirements: Secondary school certificate (bachillerato) and entrance examination.

Language of Instruction: Spanish.

Degrees and Diplomas: Licenciado, 4 yrs. Professional titles.

Library: c. 35,000 vols.

Academic Staff: c. 350.

Student Enrolment: c. 4500.

2033 **UNIVERSIDAD 'FRANCISCO DE PAULA SANTANDER'**

'Francisco de Paula Santander' University

Avenida Gran Colombia 12 E-96, Cúcuta (Norte de Santander)
Telephone: 0040072

F. of Technology (including Architecture)
F. of Engineering
F. of Business Administration (including Accountancy)
F. of Education
D. for Distance Education (primary education level)
Branch at Ocaña.

Founded 1962 as a private institution, recognized by the State 1970. Financed by the national, provincial, andlocal governments. Governing bodies: the Consejo Superior; the Consejo Académico.

Academic Year: February to December (February-June; August-December).

Admission Requirements: Secondary school certificate (bachillerato) and entrance examination.

Language of Instruction: Spanish.

Degrees and Diplomas: Licenciado in–Biology and Chemistry; Mathematics and Physics, 5 yrs. Professional titles of–Tecnólogo; Delineante de Arquitectura; Enfermera, nursing, 3 yrs; Ingeniero; Administrador de Empresas, business administration; Contador público, accountancy, 5 yrs.

Library: c. 15,000 vols.

Publication: Oriente Universitario.

Academic Staff: c. 140 (40).

Student Enrolment: c. 3450.

2034 **UNIVERSIDAD INDUSTRIAL DE SANTANDER 'UIS'**

Industrial University of Santander

Ciudad Universitaria, Apartado Aéreo 678, Bucaramanga (Santander)
Telephone: (973) 57131
Fax: (973) 51136

Rector: Rafael Serrano Sarmiento (1985-)
Secretario General: José Asthul Rangel Chacon

F. of Science
Dean: Graciela Chalela Alvarez; *staff* 90 (22)
F. of Human Sciences and Education (including Social Sciencs, Economics, and Languages)
Dean: Ernesto Rueda Suárez; *staff* 63 (70)
F. of Engineering (Mechanics)
Dean: Julio César Pava Barbosa; *staff* 89 (26)
F. of Engineering (Chemical)
Dean: Julio Elias Pedraza Rosas; *staff* 40 (11)
F. of Health Sciences (including Nursing, Nutrition, and Medicine)
Dean: Jorge Gómez Duarte; *staff* 78 (88)
F. of Distance Education
Dean: Gloria Inés Marin; *staff* 6
Extension and Lifelong Education D.
Director: Humberto Pradilla
Also Teaching Hospital.

Founded 1948 as a State institution with Faculties of Electrical, Chemical and Mechanical Engineering. The University has developed in different humanistic health and technological areas. Governing bodies: the Consejo Superior Universitario; the Consejo Académico. Residential facilities for students.

Arrangements for co-operation with institutions in: Brazil; France; Mexico; Peru; Spain; U.S.A; Venezuela.

Academic Year: February to December (February-June; August-December).

Admission Requirements: Secondary school certificace (bachillerato) and entrance examination.

Fees (Pesos): According to income of parents.

Language of Instruction: Spanish.

Degrees and Diplomas: Licenciado in–Vocational Studies, 4 sem; Mathematics; Biology; Languages; Music; Social Work, 8 sem. Professional titles of–Fisioterapéuta; Bacteriólogo y Lab. Clínico; Nutricionista y Dietista; Enfermera, nursing, 8 sem; Geólogo; Diseñador industrial; Ingeniero, various fields, 10 sem; Médico, 12 sem. Degrees of Magister and Specialization in–Sciences; Engineering; Medicine; Semiology Graduate Studies. Also TechnologicalDegrees in Distance Education.

Libraries: Central Library, 200,000 vols; faculty libraries, total, 49,549; Medical Library, 10,500.

Special Facilities (Museums, etc.): Museo Biología e Historia Natural; Museo Auditório 'Luis A. Calvo'.

Publications: Revista ION; Revista de Humanidades; Boletín de Geología; Revista de Medicina; Vida UIS; Revista de Investigaciones; Medical UIS; Boletín Ventana Informàatica.

Press or Publishing House: Centro de Publicaciones, UIS.

Academic Staff, 1989:

Rank	Full-time	Part-time
Profesores Titulares	55	1
Profesores Asociados	130	18
Profesores Asistentes	163	66
Profesores Auxiliares	13	4
Docentes Especiales	22	11
Instructores	3	–
Asociados	1	–
Asistentes	2	–
Total	389	100

Student Enrolment, 1988:

	Men	Women	Total
Of the country	4582	3040	7622
Of other countries	–	–	28
otal	4582	3040	7650*

*Also 952 external students.

2035 **UNIVERSIDAD DE LA GUAJIRA**

Calle 26 Salida a Valledupar, Apartado aéreo 172, Riohacha (La Guajira)
Telephone: 73856
Rector: Luis Arcasitas Rodríguez

F. of Business Administration
Dean: Enitso Martínez; *staff* 16 (5)
F. of Industrial Engineering
Dean: Facundo Blanco; *staff* 17 (6)
F. of Languages
Dean: Armando Granda G.; *staff* 7 (1)

Founded 1976. A State institution. Governing bodies: the Consejo Superior; the Consejo Académico.

Arrangements for co-operation with the University of Texas.

Academic Year: January to December (January-July; August-December).

Admission Requirements: Secondary school certificate (bachillerato) and entrance examination.

Fees (Pesos): 4000 per semester.

Language of Instruction: Spanish.

Degrees and Diplomas: Licenciado in Languages, 4 yrs. Professional titles in–Industrial Engineering; Business Administration, 5 yrs.

Academic Staff, 1986-87: 40 (12).

Student Enrolment, 1986-87:

	Men	Women	Total
Of the country	287	310	597

2036 **UNIVERSIDAD NACIONAL DE COLOMBIA**

National University of Colombia
Ciudad Universitaria, Bogotá
Cables: Apartado aereo 14490
Telex: 42531 INCCA CO.
Telephone: 2442830

F. of Arts (including Architecture)
F. of Science
F. of Human Sciences (including Education)
F. of Economics (including Administration)
F. of Law and Political and Social Sciences
F. of Engineering
F. of Nursing
F. of Medicine
F. of Dentistry
F. of Agriculture
F. of Veterinary Medicine and Animal Husbandry
F. of Agriculture (Medellín)
F. of Architecture (Medellín)
F. of Science (Medellín)
F. of Human Sciences (Medellín)
F. of Mining (Medellín)
F. of Engineering (Manizales)
F. of Agricultural Sciences (Palmira)

Founded 1825, the university was granted autonomy by the government in 1935. A State institution financed by the central government. Governing bodies: the Rector; the Consejo Superior Universitario, including a representative of the Ministry of Education, the Chancellor of the Exchequer, academic staff, and 2 students; the Consejo Académico. Residential facilities for students.

Special arrangements for co-operation with: Johannes Gutenberg University of Mainz; University of Kaiserslautern; Universities in the German Democratic Republic; State University of Campinas; Bouwcentrum International Education, Rotterdam; University of Sâo Paulo; University of Montpellier II; Ecole polytechnique fédérale de Lausanne.

Academic Year: February to December (February-June; August-December).

Admission Requirements: Secondary school certificate (bachillerato) and entrance examination.

Language of Instruction: Spanish.

Degrees and Diplomas: Licenciado in–Education (various fields); Philology, 4 yrs. Professional titles of–Tecnólogo forestal, 2 yrs; Terapéuta, 3 ½ yrs; Antropólogo; Diseñador gráfico; Filósofo; Sociólogo; Trabajador social, social work; Enfermero; Nutricionista-Dietista, 4 yrs; Odontólogo, 4 ½ yrs; Arquitecto; Diseñador industrial; Abogado, law; Biólogo; Estadístico; Químico farmacéutico; Físico; Geólogo; Matemático; Químico; Ingeniero, various fields; Psicólogo; Economista agrícola; Historiador; Economista; Administrator de Empresas, business administration; Contador público, accountancy; Médico veterinario; Zootecnista, animal husbandry, 5 yrs; Médico cirujano, 6 yrs. Music, 4-5 yrs. Magister, Magister Scientiae and specialization, in various fields, a further 1 ½-2 yrs. Maestro, teaching qualifications in–Arts; Music, 4-5 yrs.

Libraries: Bogotá: Central Library, *c.* 117,950 vols; Art, *c.* 200; Biology, *c.* 2290; Education, *c.* 1140; Natural Sciences, *c.* 2100; Conservatory, *c.* 1500; Engineering, *c.* 2500; Mathematics and Physics, *c.* 8500; Chemistry and Pharmacy, *c.* 7000; SINDU, *c.* 16,300; Economics, *c.* 3400; Veterinary Medicine, *c.* 390; libraries of the Sections, *c.*64,200.

Special Facilities (Museums, etc.): Museo de Arte; Museo de Criminología; Museo de Ciencias Naturales.

Publications: Revistas (Faculty publications); Anuario Colombiano de Historia; Anuario del Observatorio Astronómico Nacional; Acta Bibliográfica; Agronomía Colombiana; Alimentos (ICTA); Boletín de Matemáticas; Caldasia (Ciencias Naturales); Cuadernos de Economía; Forma y Función (Filología e Idiomas); Geología Colombiana; Geografía; Ideas y Valores; Ingeniería e Investigación; Lozania (Ciencias Naturales); Mutisia (Ciencias Naturales); Maguaré (Antropología).

Press or Publishing House: Empresa Editorial.

Academic Staff: c. 2210 (1020).

Student Enrolment: c. 26,640.

2037 **UNIVERSIDAD DE NARIÑO**

University of Nariño
Carrera 22 No. 18-109, y Ciudad Universitaria, Torobajo Pasto (Nariño)
Cables: uninariño
Telephone: (57277) 35652
Fax: (57277) 35175
Rector: Efren Coral Quintero
Secretario General: Alvaro Montenegro Calvachy

F. of Sciences and Education
Dean: Luis A. Ortega; *staff* 143 (2)
F. of Plastic Arts
Dean: Julio Cabrera Jiménez; *staff* 20 (1)
F. of Law
Dean: Carlos Santacruz Galeano; *staff* 9 (5)

F. of Civil Engineering
Dean: Armando Muñoz David; *staff* 15 (1)
F. of Agriculture
Dean: José Ovidio Zúñiga Ruales; *staff* 16
F. of Animal Husbandry
Dean: Jorge Nelson López Macías; *staff* 18
F. of Economics
Dean: Luis Alberto Arcos; *staff* 20
F. of Sciences and Technologies of the Pacific
Dean: Bernardo Calvache; *staff* – (1)
F. of Hydroculture (Distance Education)
Co-ordinator: Gloria González Guacán; *staff* – (2)
F. of Music
Director: Jaime Hernán Cabrera

Founded 1689 as college, became university 1904. Governing bodies: the Consejo Superior, composed of the Governor of the Department, the Rector, representatives of the Catholic Church, of the academic staff, and of the students, with the Secretary-General as Secretary; the Consejo Académico, composed of the Rector, representatives of the academic staff and of the students, and the deans of the faculties and institutes. Residential facilities for students.

Academic Year: February to December (February-June; August-December).

Admission Requirements: Secondary school certificate (bachillerato) and entrance examination.

Fees (Pesos): According to income of parents.

Language of Instruction: Spanish.

Degrees and Diplomas: Licenciado, 4 yrs. Doctor en Derecho y Ciencias Sociales, law and social sciences, 5 yrs. Professional titles of–Ingeniero agrónomo; Zootecnia, animal husbandry; Ingeniería civil, 5 yrs; Economista, 5-6 yrs. Maestro, teaching qualifications, in Plastic Arts, 5 yrs. Magister in Literature, a further 2 yrs. Degrees of Specialization. Also certificate in Languages.

Libraries: University Library, *c.* 23,921 vols; Agricultural library, *c.* 15,000.

Special Facilities (Museums, etc.): Museum of Arts. Botanical Garden.

Publication: Revistas of the Faculties.

Press or Publishing House: Centro de Publicaciones Universidad de Nariño.

Academic Staff, 1990:

Rank	Full-time	Part-time
Profesores Titulares	11	1
Profesores Asociados	87	5
Profesores Asistentes	127	3
Docentes Instructores	4	–
Others	8	–
Total	237	9

Student Enrolment, 1990:

	Men	Women	Total
Of the country	2359	1800	4159*

*Also 1675 external students.

2038 **UNIVERSIDAD DE PAMPLONA**
University of Pamplona
Calle 5 No. 3-23, Pamplona (Norte de Santander)
Telephone: 82960

F. of Education (including Physical Education)
F. of Food Technology

Founded as a private school 1960. Acquired present status and title 1970. A State institution. Governing bodies: the Consejo Superior, composed of the Rector, professors and students; the Consejo Directivo, composed of academic staff and students; the Comité Académico.

Academic Year: February to November (February-June; July-November).

Admission Requirements: Secondary school certificate (bachillerato) and entrance examination.

Language of Instruction: Spanish.

Degrees and Diplomas: Licenciado, 8-9 sem.

Library: *c.* 11,790 vols.

Academic Staff: *c.* 120 (10).

Student Enrolment: *c.* 1520.

2039 **UNIVERSIDAD PEDAGÓGICA NACIONAL**
National University of Education
Calle 723 No. 1186, Bogotá
Cables: Apartado aereo 75144
Telephone: 2352600

F. of Science and Technology (including Physical Education)
F. of Arts and Humanities
F. of Education
Education Research Ce.
Ce. for Adult Education

Founded as School of Education 1936, became university for women 1955 and co-educational 1962. A State institution. Governing bodies: the Consejo Superior, composed of seven members; the Consejo Académico, composed of the Rector as President and eight members.

Academic Year: January to December (January-May; August-December).

Admission Requirements: Secondary school certificate (bachillerato) and entrance examination.

Fees (Pesos): According to income of parents.

Language of Instruction: Spanish.

Degrees and Diplomas: Licenciado en Ciencias de la Educación, 4 yrs. Maestro, a further 2 yrs. Professional title of Experto en Enseñanza Prescolar, 2 yrs.

Libraries: Central Library, *c.* 30,000 vols; Documentation Centre, *c.* 7000.

Publications: Revista Colombiana de Educación; Documentación Educativa.

Academic Staff: *c.* 180.

Student Enrolment: *c.* 4870.

2040 **UNIVERSIDAD PEDAGÓGICA Y TECNOLÓGICA DE COLOMBIA**
University of Education and Technology of Colombia
Carretera Central del Norte, Tunja (Boyacá)
Cables: upetec
Telephone: 422173
Rector: Hugo Arias Castellanos
Secretario General: Jaime Guttiérez Peñuela

F. of Engineering (Highway, and Metallurgical)
Dean: Carlos Forero R.; *staff* 39 (22)
F. of Economics
Dean: Pedro Castro R.; *staff* 45 (55)
F. of Agricultural Engineering
Dean: Roberto Castelblanco B.; *staff* 23 (6)
F. of Education
Dean: Daniel Quintero Trujillo; *staff* 128 (156)
F. of Sciences (including Chemistry, Physics, Mathematics, and Biology)
Dean: Luis Alberto Cervantes Z.; *staff* 87 (85)
F. of Health Sciences
Dean: Carmen Sofía Gómez U.; *staff* 20 (3)
Open U.
Dean: Ricardo Tovar R.; *staff* – (126)
Also Branches at Chiquinquirá, Sogamoso, Duitama.

Founded 1872 as Escuela Normal de Tunja, became Facultad de Pedagogía 1933, Universidad 1953, and acquired present title 1968. A State institution. Governing bodies: the Consejo Superior Universitario; the Consejo Académico; the Consejo Directivo.

Arrangements for co-operation with: Technical University, Berlin; Universidad Autónoma de México.

Academic Year: February to December (February-July; August-December).

Admission Requirements: Secondary school certificate (bachillerato) and entrance examination.

Fees (Pesos): According to income of parents.

Language of Instruction: Spanish.

Degrees and Diplomas: Licenciado in–Educational Psychology and Administration; Social Sciences; Mathematics; Physics; Biology; Chemistry; Languages, 4 yrs. Professional title of Ingeniero in–Agriculture; Metallurgy and Engineering, 5 yrs.

Libraries: Central Library, *c.* 32,000 vols; faculty libraries, *c.* 2000.

Special Facilities (Museums, etc.): Archaeological Museum; Natural Sciences Museum; Art Gallery.

Publications: Revista 'Pensamiento y Acción' (monthly); Avance Universitario (quarterly); Acontecer (biweekly); Apertura (monthly).

Academic Staff, 1990:

Rank	Full-time	Part-time
Profesores Titulares	351	6
Profesores Asociados	106	4
Profesores Asistentes	33	2
Instructores	10	–
Primer Nombramientos	8	2
Cátedras	–	521
Tutores Universitarios a Distancia	–	126
Total	508	661

Student Enrolment, 1990:

	Men	Women	Total
Of the country	4078	4432	8510*

*Also 1459 Open University students.

2041 **UNIVERSIDAD POPULAR DEL CÉSAR**

Carrera 9 No. 14-32, Valledupar (César)
Telephone: 955-720001
Rector: Vicente Vaños Galvis
Secretario General: Normando José Suárez Fernández

F. of Education (Mathematics and Physics)
Dean: Ernesto Difilippo; *staff* 22 (2)
F. of Business Administration and Accountancy
Dean: Omar Londoño Uribe; *staff* 40 (5)
F. of Health Sciences (Nursing)
Dean: Emiro Lujan Salcedo; *staff* 24 (7)
Also 4 Research Centres.

Founded 1972 as institute of technology, acquired present status and title 1976. A State institution. Governing bodies: the Consejo Superior; the Consejo Académico; the Consejo de Facultad.

Academic Year: February to December (February-July; July-December).

Admission Requirements: Secondary school certificate (bachillerato) and entrance examination.

Language of Instruction: Spanish.

Degrees and Diplomas: Licenciado in–Education; Nursing, 4 yrs. Professional titles of–Administrador de Empresas, business administration; Contador público, 5 yrs.

Libraries: Central Library, *c.* 4470 vols; libraries of the faculties.

Publications: Revista Editada por el Centro de Investigaciones; Boletin Mensual de Rectoria.

Academic Staff, 1990:

Rank	Full-time	Part-time
Profesores Asociados	32	–
Profesores Asistentes	43	5
Instructores Asociados	7	8
Instructores Asistentes	4	1
Total	86	14

Student Enrolment, 1990:

	Men	Women	Total
Of the country	732	615	1347

2042 **UNIVERSIDAD DEL QUINDÍO**

University of Quindío
Carrera 15, Calle 12, Armenia (Quindío)
Telex: 8531CUQUIN CO
Telephone: 52181

P. of Education
P. of Public Accountancy
P. of Civil Engineering
P. of Mechanical Engineering
P. of Electrical Engineering
P. of Medicine
P. of Industrial Engineering
P. of Topography

Founded 1960 by the Municipality of Armenia with the assistance of the Universidad Nacional de Colombia and with the authorization of the Asociación Colombiana de Universidades. Receives financial support from nationaland provincial governments. Governing bodies: the Consejo Superior, including representatives of the national and provincial governments and of the academicstaff and students; the Consejo Directivo; the Consejos Académicos. Some residential facilities for students.

Admission Requirements: Secondary school certificate (bachillerato) and entrance examination.

Language of Instruction: Spanish.

Degrees and Diplomas: Licenciado. Professional titles of–Topógrafo geodesta, 3 yrs; Contador público, accountancy; Ingeniero civil, 5 yrs.

Library: c. 12,500 vols.

Special Facilities (Museums, etc.): Museum of Archaeology.

Publication: Revista.

Academic Staff: c. 160.

Student Enrolment: c. 3300.

2043 **UNIVERSIDAD DE SUCRE**

Calle 19 No. 22-58, Sincelejo (Sucre)
Telephone: (95) 821240
Rector: Ligia Verbel de Draz
Secretario General: Alfredo Salinas

F. of Sciences and Humanities
Dean: Orlando Arroyo; *staff* 33 (23)
F. of Agricultural Engineering
Dean: Guillermo Gutierrez; *staff* 15 (11)
F. of Agricultural Production
Dean: Vicente Periñan Petro; *staff* 8 (4)
F. of Health Sciences
Dean: Gladys Alvarez; *staff* 14 (3)

Founded 1978. A State institution. Governing body: the Consejo Superior.

Academic Year: February to December (February-July; August-December).

Admission Requirements: Secondary school certificate (bachillerato) and entrance examination.

Fees (Pesos): According to income of parents.

Language of Instruction: Spanish.

Degrees and Diplomas: Licenciado in Mathematics, 5 yrs. Professional titlesof–Tecnólogo en Producción agropecuaria, 3 yrs; Ingeniero agrícola; Enfermero, 5 yrs.

Library: Biblioteca Pompeyo Molina, 10,485 vols.

Publication: Avanzada (quarterly).

Academic Staff, 1990:

Rank	Full-time	Part-time
Profesores Asociados	8	–
Profesores Asistentes	54	–
Catedráticos	–	49
Total	62	49

Student Enrolment, 1990:

	Men	Women	Total
Of the country	623	313	936

2044 **UNIVERSIDAD SURCOLOMBIANA**

Avenida Pastrana Borrero Carrera 1, Neiva (Huila)
Telephone: 45444
Rector: Ricardo Mosquera Mesa
Secretario General: Edgar Machado

F. of Accountancy and Administration
Dean: Armando Criollo; *staff* 5
F. of Education (including Physical Education)
Dean: Jesús María Vidal Arias; *staff* 8
F. of Health Sciences (Medicine and Nursing)
Dean: Jaime Martín Ruiz Leal; *staff* 4
F. of Engineering
Dean: Jorge A. Polania P.; *staff* 5
D. for Distance Education
Head: Rafael Cortes; *staff* 3
Extension D.
Head: William Torres S.; *staff* 3

Founded 1968 as Instituto Universitario, acquired present status and title 1976. A State institution. Governing bodies: the Consejo Superior; the Consejo Académico.

Academic Year: February to December (February-June; July-December).

Admission Requirements: Secondary school certificate (bachillerato) and entrance examination.

Language of Instruction: Spanish.

Degrees and Diplomas: Licenciado, 5 yrs. Professional titles, 3-5 yrs.

Libraries: Central Library, 15,293 vols; Health Sciences, 2660.

Publications: Cuardernos Surcolombiano (3 times a year); Boletín de la Física (monthly); Revista (3 times a year).

Academic Staff, 1986-87:

Rank	Full-time	Part-time
Profesores Titulares	28	–
Profesores Asociados	76	–
Profesores Asistentes	37	–
Profesores Auxiliares	17	–
Instructores	8	–
Catedráticos	–	174
Total	116	174

Student Enrolment, 1986-87:

Of the country	3387
Of other countries	1
Total	3388

2045 **UNIVERSIDAD TECNOLÓGICA DEL CHOCÓ 'DIEGO LUIS CÓRDOBA'**

Carrera 2 No. 25-22, Apartado aéro 22, Quibdó (Chocó)
Telephone: 735

P. of Education
P. of Social Work
P. of Public Works Technology
P. of Business Administration
P. of Fishery Technology
P. of Agricultural Technology

Founded 1972 as college, acquired present status and title 1975. A State institution.

Academic Year: February to December (February-July; August-December).

Admission Requirements: Secondary school certificate (bachillerato) and entrance examination.

Language of Instruction: Spanish.

Degrees and Diplomas: Licenciado or Professional title, 3-4 1/2 yrs.

Library: c. 5500 vols.

Academic Staff: c. 100 (50).

Student Enrolment: c. 1790.

2046 **UNIVERSIDAD TECNOLÓGICA DE LOS LLANOS ORIENTALES**

Apartado aéreo 2621, Km. 11, Via Puerto López, Villavicencio (Meta)
Telephone: 23449

P. of Education
P. of Nursing
P. of Veterinary Medicine and Animal Husbandry
I. of Environmental Research

Founded 1974. A State institution.

Academic Year: February to December (February-June; July-December).

Admission Requirements: Secondary school certificate (bachillerato) and entrance examination.

Language of Instruction: Spanish.

Degrees and Diplomas: Licenciado in Education, 4 yrs. Professional titles in–Nursing, 3 yrs; Veterinary Medicine; Animal Husbandry;Agricultural Engineering, 5 yrs.

Library: c. 10,000 vols.

Special Facilities (Museums, etc.): Natural History Museum.

Publications: Bulletin (monthly); Revista (annually).

Academic Staff: c. 70 (30).

Student Enrolment: c. 840.

2047 **UNIVERSIDAD TECNOLÓGICA DEL MAGDALENA**

San Pedro Alejandrino, Apartado aéreo 731, Santa Marta (Magdalena)
Telephone: 36150

F. of Agricultural Engineering
F. of Agricultural Economics
F. of Fishing Technology
F. of Education
F. of Administration

Founded 1958. A State institution. Governing bodies: the Consejo Superior; the Consejo Académico.

Academic Year: February to December (February-July; August-December).

Admission Requirements: Secondary school certificate (bachillerato) and entrance examination.

Language of Instruction: Spanish.

Degrees and Diplomas: Licenciado, 5 yrs. Professional titles of–Tecnólogo en Administración agropecuaria, 3 yrs; Ingeniero agrónomo; Ingeniero pesquero, fishery; Economista agrícola, 5 yrs.

Library: c. 13,600.

Publications: Revista Ingeniero Pesquero; Revista Agronómica.

Academic Staff: c. 130 (20).

Student Enrolment: c. 1740.

2048 **UNIVERSIDAD TECNOLÓGICA DE PEREIRA**

Technological University of Pereira
La Julita, Apartado aéreo 97, Pereira (Risaralda)
Cables: universtec
Telephone: 34944

P. of Education
P. of Electrical Engineering
P. of Mechanical Engineering
P. of Industrial Engineering
P. of Medicine
Polytechnical I.

Founded 1958 as a State institution, supported by the central government and the federal and municipal authorities. Governing bodies: the Consejo de Regentes; the Consejo Directivo; the Consejo de Facultades.

Academic Year: January to December (January-May; June-July; August-December).

Admission Requirements: Secondary school certificate (bachillerato) and entrance examination.

Fees (Pesos): According to income of parents.

Language of Instruction: Spanish.

Degrees and Diplomas: Licenciado in–Physics; Mathematics. Professional titles of–Tecnólogo (in various fields), 3 yrs; Ingenieroindustrial; Ingeniero mecánico; Ingeniero electricista, 5 yrs.

Library: c. 14,200 vols.

Publication: Jornal.

Academic Staff: c. 300.

Student Enrolment: c. 3420.

2049 **UNIVERSIDAD DEL TOLIMA**

Barrio Santa Elena, Apartado aéreo 546, Ibagué (Tolima)
Telephone: (982) 644219
Fax: (982) 644869
Rector: Iván Melo Delvasto (1987-)
Secretario General: Héctor Villarraga Sarmiento

F. of Business Administration
Dean: Jorge Alirio Ortíz; *staff* 10 (2)
F. of Agricultural Engineering
Dean: Luis A. Ramirez; *staff* 35 (1)
F. of Forestry
Dean: Rosven Libardo Arevalo F.; *staff* 14 (1)
I. of Science
Director: Daniel Jauregui; *staff* 65
F. of Veterinary Medicine and Animal Husbandry
Dean: Rafael Iván Montoya R.; *staff* 27 (1)
F. of Education
Dean: Jaime Lozano Restrepo; *staff* 56
F. of Technology (including Architecture)
Dean: Alberto González Díaz; *staff* 25
I. of Science
Co-ordinator: José César Jaramillo; *staff* 71
D. for Distance Education
Head: Sandra Amaya de Pujana; *staff* 93
Extension D.
Head: León Cuartas

Founded 1945, opened 1954. A State institution. Governing bodies: the Consejo Superior Universitario, composed of representatives of the national and local governments, of the academic staff and of the students; the Consejo Académico, composed of the Rector, the deans and representatives of the academic staff and students. Residential facilities for students.

Arrangements for co-operation with the University of Costa Rica.

Academic Year: January to December (January-June; July-December).

Admission Requirements: Secondary school certificate (bachillerato) and entrance examination.

Fees (Pesos): According to income of parents.

Language of Instruction: Spanish.

Degrees and Diplomas: Licenciado in–Education; History and Geography; Spanish and English; Mathematics and Physics; Chemistry and Biology, 4 yrs. Professional titles of–Tecnólogo in–Agriculture; Topography; Architecture and Engineering, 3 yrs; Ingeniero agrónomo, agriculture; Ingeniero forestal, forestry; Médico veterinario; Administrador deEmpresas, 5 yrs. Degrees of Specialization.

Library: c. 25,000 vols.

Special Facilities (Museums, etc.): Museo Antropológico. Botanical Garden.

Publications: Revistas; Panorama.

Academic Staff, 1986-87:

Rank	Full-time	Part-time
Profesores Titulares	69	1
Profesores Asociados	70	–
Profesores Asistentes	86	4
Profesores Auxiliares	12	2
Total	237	7

Student Enrolment, 1986-87:

	Men	Women	Total
Of the country	2120	1634	3754
Of other countries	7	4	11
Total	2127	1638	3765

2050 **UNIVERSIDAD DEL VALLE**

University of Valle

Ciudad Universitaria, Meléndez, Apartado 25360 Cali (Valle del Cauca)
Cables: univalle
Telex: 57-923-398483
Telephone: 391486
Fax: 398457
Rector: Harold José Rizo Otero (1984-)
Secretario General: Iván Alberto Díaz

F. of Engineering
Dean: Silvio Delvasto; *staff* 131 (28)
F. of Health Sciences
Dean: Oscar Bolaños; *staff* 139 (157)
F. of Architecture
Dean: Jairo Mazorra; *staff* 39 (19)
F. of Social Sciences and Economics
Dean: Diego Roldán Luna; *staff* 34 (3)
F. of Humanities
Dean: Carlos Restrepo; *staff* 120 (31)
F. of Education
Dean Hernando Rivera; *staff* 61 (17)
F. of Science
Dean: Omar Velasquez; *staff* 121 (21)
F. of Business Administration
Dean: Rubén Dario Echeverry; *staff* 38 (3)
Also Regional Programmes in: Buenaventura; Buga; Caicedonia; Palmira; Roldanillo; Sevilla; Tuluá; Zarzal.

Founded 1945 as a State institution. Governing bodies: the Consejo Superior Universitario, composed of representatives of the national and local governments, of the academic staff, and of the students; the Consejo Académico, composed of the Rector, Vice-Rector, the deans and representatives of the academic staff and students. Residential facilities for students.

Arrangements for co-operation with: Tulane University; Metropolitan Autonomous University, Naucalpan de Juárez; Technical University of Madrid; University of Alabama.

Academic Year: September to June (September-January; February-June).

Admission Requirements: Secondary school certificate (bachillerato) and entrance examination.

Fees (Pesos): According to income of parents.

Language of Instruction: Spanish.

Degrees and Diplomas: Licenciado in–Drama; Philosophy; History; Music; Literature; Primary Education; Languages; Biology and Chemistry; Physical Education, 8 sem; Agriculture; Electrical Engineering; Mathematics and Physics; Social Sciences, 10 sem. Professional titles in–Physics; Mathematics; Chemistry; Social Communication; Social Work; Economics; Sociology; Physiotherapy; Nursing; Speech Therapy; Engineering, various fields; Dentistry; Biology; Business Administration; Accountancy; Statistics; Architecture; Psychology, 8-11 sem; Medicine, 12 sem. Degrees of Magister and specialization.

Libraries: Central Library, 218,927 vols; Health Sciences, 19,698.

Special Facilities (Museums, etc.): Museums of: Zoology; Marine Biology; Botany; Entomology; Prehispanic Museum.

Publications: Lenguage; Revista de la Universidad del Valle; Acta Medica del Valle (monthly); Boletín Coyuntura Socio-Económica; Cuardernos de Psicología; Diálogos Tecnología apropiada; Historia y Espacio; Poligramas; Reflexiones Pedagógicas; Praxis Filosofa (bimonthly); Historia y Espacio (annually); Neusitica (Ingeniería).

Academic Staff, 1986-87:

Rank	Full-time	Part-time
Profesores Titulares	110	23
Profesores Asociados	128	24
Profesores Asistentes	321	74
Profesores Auxiliares	99	76
Instructores	13	64
Auxiliares de Docentes	24	4
Total	696	265

Student Enrolment, 1986-87:

	Men	Women	Total
Of the country	4628	3090	7718
Of other countries	18	7	23
Total	4644	3097	7741*

*Also 10,500 external students.

Private Institutions

2051 **CENTRO DE INVESTIGACIÓN Y PLANEAMIENTO ADMINISTRATIVO**

Apartado aéro 6478, Carrera 43 No. 49-57, Medellín (Antioquia)
Telephone: 282-00-88
Fax: 239-16-45
Rector: Antonio Mazo Mejia
Secretario General: David Cardozo Gutierrez

F. of Business Administration
Dean: Juan Carlos Perez Perez

Founded 1972. A private institution.

Academic Year: February to December (February-June; July-December).

Admission Requirements: Secondary school certificate (bachillerato) and entrance examination.

Language of Instruction: Spanish.

Degrees and Diplomas: Licenciado in Education, 4-5 yrs. Professional title of Tecnólogo, 3 yrs.

Library: c. 8000 vols.

Publications: Linea Directa; Psicológia Educativa.

Academic Staff, 1989-90: 111

Student Enrolment, 1989-90:

Of the country	363	867	1230

2052 **COLEGIO DE ESTUDIOS SUPERIORES DE ADMINISTRACIÓN**

Diagonal 35 No. 5-41, Bogotá
Telephone: 2851026
Fax: 2885974
Rector: Marco Fidel Rocha R.

Business Administration

Founded 1975. A private institution.

Arrangements for co-operation with: College of St. Thomas, Minnesota; College of Insurance, New York.

Academic Year: January to December (January-June; July-December).

Admission Requirements: Secondary school certificate (bachillerato) and entrance examination.

Fees (Pesos): 300,000 per semester.

Language of Instruction: Spanish.

Degrees and Diplomas: Professional title, 4 ½ yrs.

Library: 5000 vols.

Academic Staff, 1990: 5 (60).

Student Enrolment, 1989-90:

	Men	Women	Total
Of the country	195	105	300

2053 **COLEGIO MAYOR DE NUESTRA SEÑORA DEL ROSARIO**
Calle 14 No. 6-25, Bogotá
Telephone: 282-00-88
Fax: 2818583
Rector: Roberto Arias Pérez (1986-90)
Secretario General: Angelica Uribe Gavira

P. of Business Administration
Dean: Beatriz Forero de Gómez; *staff* 6 (115)
P. of Economics
Dean: Sergio Callé; *staff* 6 (115)
P. of Law
Dean: Marcela de Posada; *staff* – (123)
P. of Medecine
Dean: Antonio Becerra; *staff* 68 (183)
F. of Physiology
Dean: Martha Sarmiento; *staff* – (59)
P. of Phonoaudiology
Dean: María Eugenia Fonseca *staff* – (28)
P. of Therapy
Dean: Cristina Paris; *staff* – (28)
P. of Philosophy and Letters
Dean: Luz Gloria Cárdenas; *staff* – (19)

Founded 1653.

Arrangements for co-operation with the Hague Academy of International Law.

Academic Year: February to December (February-June; July-December).

Admission Requirements: Secondary school certificate (bachillerato) and entrance examination.

Fees (Pesos): 146,790-368,793.

Language of Instruction: Spanish.

Degrees and Diplomas: Licenciado in-Physiotherapy; Speech Therapy; Occupational Therapy; Philosophy. Professional titles in Business Administration; Economics; Law; Medicine, 4-5 yrs. Diplomado in Philosophy. Degrees of Specialization.

Library: Biblioteca Antonio Rochar Alvira, 70,000 vols.

Publication: Revista (every three months).

Academic Staff, 1990: 75 (637).

Student Enrolment, 1990:

	Men	Women	Total
Of the country	1098	1670	2768
Of other countries	5	3	8
Total	1103	1673	2776

2054 **COLEGIO ODONTOLÓGICO COLOMBIANO**
Calle 13 No. 4-38, Bogotá
Telephone: 2421375

Dentistry

Founded 1975. A private institution. Governing body: the Consejo Directivo.

Arrangements for co-operation with: University of Michigan; University of Indiana; University of Buenos Aires.

Academic Year: January to December (January-June; July-December).

Admission Requirements: Secondary school certificate (bachillerato) and entrance examination.

Language of Instruction: Spanish.

Degrees and Diplomas: Professional title, 5 yrs.

Library: c. 400 vols.

Academic Staff: c. 20.

2055 **CORPORACIÓN AUTÓNOMA UNIVERSITARIA DE MANIZALES**
Antigua Estación del Ferrocarril, Manizales (Caldas)
Telephone: 83 61 01
Rector: Ernesto Gutiérez Arango
Secretario General: Olga del Socorro Serna de Quintero

P. of Dentistry
Dean: Jorge Gómez Ospina; *staff* 4 (18)
P. of Economics
Dean: Ignacio Restrepo Abondano; *staff* 5 (2)
P. of Systems Analyses
Dean: Camilo Rueda Calderón; *staff* 18 (3)
P. of Physiotherapy
Dean: Francia Restrepo de Mejia; *staff* 6 (8)
P. of Industrial Design
Dean: Juan Pablo Constain Van Reck; *staff* 4 (1)
P. of Coffee Economics (postgraduate)
Research and Enterprsie Guidance Ce.
Head: María Teresa Buitrago
Forestal Entomology Ce.
Head: Maria Cecilia Villegas

Founded 1978. A private institution. Governing body: the Asamblea General

Academic Year: February to November (February-June; July-November).

Admission Requirements: Secondary school certificate (bachillerato) and entrance examination.

Fees (Pesos): 66,600-278,953.

Language of Instruction: Spanish.

Degrees and Diplomas: Professional titles, 5 yrs.

Library: 5000 vols.

Student Enrolment, 1989-90:

	Men	Women	Total
Of the country	508	685	1193

2056 **CORPORACIÓN EDUCATIVA DEL CARIBE**
Carrera 19 No.28A-109, Sincelejo (Sucre)
Telephone: 21402
Rector: Roberto Arias Pérez (1986-90)
Secretario General: Santiago Jaramillo Villamizar

P. of Education

2057 **CORPORACIÓN EDUCATIVA MAYOR DEL DESARROLLO 'SIMÓN BOLIVAR'**
Carrera 59 No. 59-92, Barranquilla (Catlántico)
Telephone: 358963

Education
Social Work Sociology
Economics
Social Studies
Law

Founded 1972. A private institution.

Admission Requirements: Secondary school certificate (bachillerato) and entrance examination.

Language of Instruction: Spanish.

Degrees and Diplomas: Licenciado in–Social Work, 4 yrs; Social Science, 4 ½ yrs; Sociology, 5 yrs. Professional title of Economista, 5 yrs. Doctor en Derecho, law, 5 yrs.

Library: c. 12,000 vols.

Student Enrolment: c. 770.

2058 **ESCUELA DE ADMINISTRACIÓN DE NEGOCIOS**
Calle 72 No. 9-71, Bogotá
Telephone: 2112111-211
Rector: Eduardo Arias Osorio
Secretario Académico: Raúl Niño Caro

Business Administration

Founded 1968. A private institution.

Academic Year: January to December (January-July; August December).

Admission Requirements: Secondary school certificate (bachillerato) and entrance examination.

Fees (Pesos): 50,000.

Language of Instruction: Spanish.

Degrees and Diplomas: Professional title, 5 yrs. Degrees of specialization.

Library: 10,000 vols.

Academic Staff, 1986-87: 12 (56).

Student Enrolment, 1986-87: 1850.

2059 **ESCUELA COLOMBIANA DE MEDICINA**
Transversal 9A bis No. 133-25, Bogotá
Telephone: 2741662

Medicine

2060 **CORPORACIÓN TECNOLÓGICA DE BOLÍVAR**
Manga Calle del Bouquet, Carrera 21 No. 25-92, Cartagena (Bolívar)
Telephone: 62518

F. of Engineering
F. of Economics

Extension D.

Founded 1970. A private institution under the supervision of the city's five economic trade unions. Governing bodies: the Asamblea General; the Consejo Superior.

Academic Year: January to December (January-June; August-December).

Admission Requirements: Secondary school certificate (bachillerato) and entrance examination.

Language of Instruction: Spanish.

Degrees and Diplomas: Professional titles, 5 yrs.

Library: c. 10,000 vols.

Publication: Boletín Informativo.

Academic Staff: c. 20 (140).

Student Enrolment: c. 1220.

2061 **CORPORACIÓN UNIVERSIDAD PILOTO DE COLUMBIA**

Carrera 19 No. 17-33, Alto Magdalena (Santa Marta)
Telephone: 28505

2062 **CORPORACIÓN UNIVERSIDAD PILOTO DE COLOMBIA**

Carrera 9 No. 45A-44, Bogotá
Telephone: 2856450

F. of Architecture
Dean: Alberto Sánchez; *staff* 5 (4)
F. of Systems Engineering
Dean: Mauro Flórez; *staff* 5 (3)
F. of Economics
Dean: Héctor Oviedo Rojas; *staff* 2 (2)
F. of Accountancy
Dean: Ediberto Galeano
F. of Systems Engineering (Girardot)
Vicer-Rector: Hugo Aranguren; *staff* 4
F. of Administration (Girardot)
Dean: Mauricio Betancour; *staff* 6

Founded 1962. A private institution. Governing bodies: the Consiliatura; the Consejo Superior Académico.

Arrangements for co-operation with: University of Pittsburgh; Austin University, Texas.

Academic Year: January to December (January-July; August-December).

Admission Requirements: Secondary school certificate (bachillerato) and entrance examination.

Fees (Pesos): 54,714-82,163 per semester.

Language of Instruction: Spanish.

Degrees and Diplomas: Professional titles of–Arquitecto; Ingeniero de Sistemas; Economista; Contaduría Pública, accountancy, 5 yrs.

Academic Staff, 1986-87: 18 (15).

Student Enrolment, 1986-87:

	Men	Women	Total
Of the country	1537	1100	2637
Of other countries	8	5	13
Total	1545	1105	2650

2063 **CORPORACIÓN UNIVERSITARIA ADVENTISTA**

Carrera 84 No. 33AA-01, Medellín (Antioquia)
Cables: icolven
Telephone: 2508328
Fax: 2506428
Rector: Leonardo Suescún F.
Secretario General: Juan Alberto Díaz R.

F. of Theology
Dean: Miguel Angel López *staff* 3 (3)
F. of Business Administration
Dean: Hugo Visbal Díaz; *staff* 4 (4)
F. of Music
Dean: Mario Vera Muñoz; *staff* 4 (3)
F. of Secretarial Science
Dean: Hugo Visbal Díaz; *staff* 1 (3)
Research Ce.
Head: Aura Ruiz

Founded 1937 as Instituto Colombo Venezolano. A private institution administered by the Seventh Day Adventist Church since 1980, and fully accredited to the State. Governing body: the Board of Trustees. Residential facilities for academic staff and students.

Academic Year: February to November (February-June; July-November).

Admission Requirements: Secondary school certificate (bachillerato) and entrance examination.

Fees (Pesos): *c.* 60,000 per semester.

Language of Instruction: Spanish.

Degrees and Diplomas: Licenciado, 4-5 yrs. Professional titles.

Library: c. 18,000 vols.

Publication: Revista de Ingestigación.

Academic Staff, 1990: 26 (25).

Student Enrolment, 1990:

	Men	Women	Total
Of the country	143	103	246
Of other countries	49	21	70
Total	192	124	316

2064 **UNIVERSITARIA AUTÓNOMA DE BUCARAMANGA**

Calle 48 No. 39-234, Bucaramanga (Santander)
Telephone: 375111
Fax: (97) 334062
Rector: Gabriel Burgos Mantilla (1988-)
Secretario General: Hernán Prada Niño

F. of Law
Dean: Rodolfo Mantilla
F. of Social Communication
Dean: Carlos Humberto Gómez Mantilla
F. of Business Administration
Dean: Jorge Enrique Silva Duarte
F. of Accountancy
Dean: Eleazar Uribe Pinilla
F. of Education (pre-school level)
Dean: Luthing Ocazionez de Jaimes
Research Ce.
Director: Laureano Gómez Serrano

Founded 1952 as Instituto Caldas. A private institution. Governing body: the Board of Directors.

Arrangements for co-operation with the Universities of: Los Andes, Mérida; Iowa; Massachusetts, Amherst.

Academic Year: February to December (February-June; July-December).

Admission Requirements: Secondary school certificate (bachillerato) and entrance examination.

Fees (Pesos): 102,849-135,594.

Language of Instruction: Spanish.

Degrees and Diplomas: Licenciado in Education. Professional titles of–Comunicador; Periodista; Contador, accountancy, 5 yrs; Administrador de Empresas, business administration, 5 ½ yrs; Abogado, law, 5-6 yrs. Also title of Tecnólogo en Educación pre-escolar, 3 yrs. Degrees of Specialization.

Library: Central Library, 27,684 vols.

Special Facilities (Museums, etc.): Art Gallery.

Publication: Revistas.

Academic Staff, 1990: 40 (176).

Student Enrolment, 1990:

	Men	Women	Total
Of the country	966	1831	2797
Of other countries	–	4	4
Total	966	1835	2801

2065 **CORPORACIÓN UNIVERSITARIA AUTÓNOMA DE OCCIDENTE**

Calle 9B No. 29A-67, Cali (Valle del Cauca)
Telephone: 588191

Economics
Industrial Engineering
Mechanical Engineering
Electrical Engineering

Founded 1969. A private institution.

Academic Year: January to November (January-June; July-November).

Admission Requirements: Secondary school certificate (bachillerato) and entrance examination.

Language of Instruction: Spanish.

Degrees and Diplomas: Professional titles, 6 yrs.

Library: c. 2720 vols.

Academic Staff: c. 15.

Student Enrolment: c. 1530.

2066 **CORPORACIÓN UNIVERSITARIA DE BOYACÁ**

Calle 19 No. 11-64, Tunja (Boyacá)
Telephone: (982) 42-59-30
Fax: (982) 42-59-30
Rector: Osmar Correal Cabral
Secretario General: Enrique Cabral Rubaiano

F. of Business Administration
Dean: Mariela Vargas de Molina
F. of Industrial Relations
Dean: Mariela Vargas de Molina
Sanitary and Environmental Engineering
Dean: Jaime Díaz Gómez; *staff* 7 (1)

Founded 1979. A private institution. Governing bodies: the Consejo Académico; the Consejo Directivo.

Arrangements for co-operation with: Universidad del Valle, Colombia; Universidade Católica del Parana.

Academic Year: February to December (February-June; July-December).

Admission Requirements: Secondary school certificate (bachillerato) and entrance examination.

Fees (Pesos): 86,130-146,000.

Language of Instruction: Spanish.

Degrees and Diplomas: Professional titles, 3-5 yrs. Degree of specialization in Political Science, 1 ½ yrs.

Library: Politeca Corporación Universitaria de Boyacá.

Publications: Boletines; Proyección Universitaria.

Academic Staff, 1990: c. 16 (1).

Student Enrolment, 1990:

	Men	Women	Total
Of the country	393	555	948

2067 **CORPORACIÓN UNIVERSITARIA DE CIENCIAS AGROPECUARIAS'CUDCA'**

Avenida 40 No. 17-7490, Bogotá
Telephone: 2457551 Electronic Mail Box 34204

F. of Veterinary Medicine
Dean: Sonia de Uribe
F. of Animal Husbandry
Dean: Luz Delia Vera

Founded 1983.

Academic Year: January to December (January-June; July-December).

Admission Requirements: Secondary school certificate (bachillerato) and entrance examination.

Fees (Pesos): 250,000 per semester.

Language of Instruction: Spanish.

Degrees and Diplomas: Professional titles, 5 yrs.

Library: 10,000 vols.

Special Facilities (Museums, etc.): Bioterio Museum.

2068 **CORPORACIÓN UNIVERSITARIA DE COLUMBIA IDEAS**

Calle 69 No. 7-77, Bogotá
Telephone: 2494508

2069 **CORPORACIÓN UNIVERSITARIA DE IBAGUÉ**

Calle 14 No. 7-53, Barrio Ambalá (Ibagué)
Cables: coruniversitario
Telephone: 640616

S. of Finance Administration
S. of Industrial Engineering
S. of Accountancy
S. of Marketing
I. of Languages

Founded 1982. A private institution offering fields of study chosen according to local needs.

Arrangements for co-operation with the University of South Florida.

Academic Year: February to November (February-June; July-November).

Admission Requirements: Secondary school certificate (bachillerato) and entrance examination.

Languages of Instruction: Spanish and English.

Degrees and Diplomas: Associate in–Marketing; Accountancy; Engineering, 3 yrs. Bachelor, 5 yrs. Degrees of specialization.

Library: c. 2520 vols.

Publication: What's up (biweekly in English).

Press or Publishing House: Publicaciones Coruniversitaria.

Academic Staff: c. 10 (130).

Student Enrolment: c. 1680.

2070 **CORPORACIÓN UNIVERSITARIA DE LA COSTA (UNICOSTA)**

Carreras 54 y 58, Calle 58, Barranquilla (Atlántico)
Telephone: 328350

Education
Economics Business Administration
Architecture
Civil Engineering
Law

Founded 1969. A private institution.

Admission Requirements: Secondary school certificate (bachillerato) and entrance examination.

Language of Instruction: Spanish.

Degrees and Diplomas: Licenciado (evening course), 4 yrs. Professional titles, 5 yrs.

Library: c. 14,730 vols.

Student Enrolment: c. 2540.

2071 **CORPORACIÓN UNIVERSITARIA LASALLISTA**

Calle 54A No. 30-01, Medellín (Antioquia)
Telephone: 249-88-91
Fax: 239-7595
Rector: Octavio Martínez López (1983-)
Secretario General: Sergio Isaza Restrepo

P. of Education (pre-school level)
Dean: Sylvia Elena Rivera Escobar; *staff* 4 (33)
P. of Agricultural Administration
Dean: German Guillermo Correa Pezzotti; *staff* 3 (28)
P. of Food Technology
Dean: Georges Weinstein Velásquez; *staff* 5 (40)
Ce. of Education and Social Communication Techniques
Head: Libardo Mejia
Food Processing Research P.
Head: Georges Weinstein

Founded 1983. A private institution. Governing bodies: the Asamblea de Fundadores; the Consejo Superior; the Consejo Académico.

Academic Year: January to December (January-June; July-December).

Admission Requirements: Secondary school certificate (bachillerato) and entrance examination.

Fees (Pesos): 72,723-110,558 per semester.

Language of Instruction: Spanish.

Degrees and Diplomas: Licenciado in Education (pre-school level), 4 yrs. Professional titles in–Business Administration; Food Technology, 5 yrs.

Library: 5,168 vols.

Special Facilities (Museums, etc.): Museo de Ciencias Naturales y Mineralogía.

Publications: Comunicación Periódica; Prisma.

Academic Staff, 1990: 26 (71).

Student Enrolment, 1990:

	Men	Women	Total
Of the country	430	661	1091

2072 **CORPORACIÓN UNIVERSITARIA DEL META**

Carrera 32 No. 34A-31, Meta (Villavicencio).
Telephone: 31149
Rector: Rafael Mojica Garcia

S. of Administration
Computer Ce.

Founded 1985. A private institution. Governing bodies: the Consejo Superior; the Consejo Académico.

Academic Year: February to December (February-June; July-December).

Admission Requirements: Secondary school certificate (bachillerato) and entra

Fees (Pesos): Registration, 5500; tuition, 82,500.

Language of Instruction: Spanish.

Degrees and Diplomas: Professional title, 5 yrs.

Library: 15,000 vols.

Academic Staff, 1990: 3 (72).

Student Enrolment, 1990:

	Men	Women	Total
Of the country	289	299	588

2073 **CORPORACIÓN UNIVERSITARIA 'RAFAEL NUNEZ'**
Carrera 17 No. 25-90, Bolivar (Castagena).
Telephone: 655137

2074 **CORPORACIÓN UNIVERSITARIA SANTA ROSA DE CABAL**
Carrera 15 No. 12-75, Santa Rosa de Cabal (Risaralda)
Telephone: 64-12-23
Fax: 64-26-34
Rector: Carlos Manuel Osorio Vera
Secretario General: Carlos Eugenio Ocampo Ramirez

F. of Agricultural Administration
Dean: Luis Alfredo Lopéz Tovar
F. of Co-operative Business Administration
Dean: César Augusto Osorio Vera
F. of Animal Husbandry
Head: Hernando Gómez Correa

Founded in 1983. A private institution.

Academic Year: February to December (February-June; August-December).

Admission Requirements: Secondary school certificate (bachillerato) and entrance examination.

Language of Instruction: Spanish.

Degrees and Diplomas: Professional titles, 3-5 yrs.

Student Enrolment, 1990:

	Men	Women	Total
Of the country	500	100	600

2075 **CORPORACIÓN UNIVERSITARIA DEL SINU**
Carrera 3 No. 29-26, Montería (Córdoba).
Telephone: (9401) 2467
Fax: (9401) 2988
Presidente: Elías Bechara Zainum
Vice-Presidente: Ilse Bechara Catilla

F. of Law
Dean: Manuel Ramón Padilla; *staff* 10 (39)
F. of Business Administration
Dean: Carlos Hoyos López; *staff* 1 (24)
F. of Social Work
Dean: Betty Romero de Puerta; *staff* 1 (17)
F. of Education (pre-school level)
Dean: Luz Marina Brunal de Petro; *staff* 1 (22)
F. of Modern Languages
Dean: Magaly Cogollo de Pérez; *staff* 1 (15)
F. of Certified Public Accountancy
Dean: Conrado Parra Q.; *staff* 1 (16)

Founded 1974. Acquired present status and title 1983. A private institution. Governing bodies: the Consejo Superior; the Consejo Académico.

Academic Year: February to December (February-July; July-December).

Admission Requirements: Secondary school certificate (bachillerato) and entrance examination.

Fees (Pesos): 74,420-97,699 per semester; Law, 173,349 per annum.

Language of Instruction: Spanish.

Degrees and Diplomas: Licenciado in–Education (pre-school level), 4 yrs; Modern Languages, 4 ½ yrs. Professional titles of–Trabajo social, social work, 4 ½ yrs; Abogado, law, 5-6 yrs; Administrador de Empresas, business administration; Contador público, public accountancy, 5 yrs.

Library: Central Library, 8660 vols.

Academic Staff, 1989: 15 (88).

Student Enrolment, 1989:

	Men	Women	Total
Of the country	479	917	1396

2076 **ESCUELA COLOMBIANA DE INGENIERÍA 'JULIO GARAVITO'**
Autopista del Norte Km 13, Bogotá.
Telephone: 6760451

Civil Engineering
Electrical Engineering

Founded 1972. A private institution.

Admission Requirements: Secondary school certificate (bachillerato) and entrance examination.

Language of Instruction: Spanish.

Degrees and Diplomas: Professional title, 5 yrs.

Library: c. 1470 vols.

Student Enrolment: c. 560.

2077 **ESCUELA DE INGENIERÁ DE ANTIOQUIA**
Calle 25 Sur No. 42-73 Envigado Zúñiga, Medellín (Antioquia)
Telephone: 2764360

Civil Engineering
Geology

2078 **FUNDACIÓN EDUCATIONAL INTERAMERICANA 'UNIVERSIDAD CATÓLICA DE COLOMBIA'**
Diagonal 47 No. 1550, Bogotá
Telephone: 2853912

Architecture
Economics
Law
Civil Engineering
Industrial Engineering
Psychology

Founded 1970. A private institution.

Admission Requirements: Secondary school certificate (bachillerato) and entrance examination.

Language of Instruction: Spanish.

Degrees and Diplomas: Professional titles, 5-6 yrs.

Library: c. 6500 vols.

Student Enrolment: c. 3320.

2079 **FUNDACIÓN EDUCATIVA DE ESTUDIOS SUPERIORES**
Calle 63 No. 3-45, Bogotá
Telephone: 2359806D

2080 **FUNDACIÓN ESCUELA DE CIENCIAS DE LA SALUD DE LA SOCIEDAD DE CIRUGÍA DE BOGOTÁ**
Calle 10 No. 18-75, Bogotá
Telephone: 2473680

Nursing

Founded 1976. A private institution.

Admission Requirements: Secondary school certificate and entrance examination.

Language of Instruction: Spanish.

Degrees and Diplomas: Licenciado in Nursing, 4 yrs.

Library: c. 1340 vols.

Student Enrolment: c. 50.

2081 **FUNDACIÓN ESCUELA DE MEDICINA 'JUAN N. CORPAS'**
Avenida Flóres de los Andes, Suba Km.3, Bogotá
Telephone: 6813637
Rector: Jorge Piñeros Corpas (1970-92)

Medicine

Founded 1970. A private institution.

Arrangements for exchange programmes with Albert Einstein College of Medicine, New York.

Academic Year: February to December (February-July; August-December).

Admission Requirements: Secondary school certificate (bachillerato) and entrance examination.

Language of Instruction: Spanish.

Degrees and Diplomas: Professional title of Médico cirujano, 6 yrs.

Library: c. 3000 vols.

Academic Staff: c. 70 (60).

Student Enrolment: c. 250.

2082 **FUNDACIÓN INSTITUTO UNIVERSITARIO DE CIENCIA Y TECNOLOGÍA 'KONRAD LORENZ'**
Calle 77 No. 11-63, Bogotá
Telephone: 248-67-90
Rector: Juan Alberto Aragón Bateman

F. of Psychology
Dean: Patricia Valencia Posada

Founded 1979. A private institution. Governing body: the Consejo Superior.

Academic Year: January to December (January-June; July-December).

Admission Requirements: Secondary school certificate (bachillerato) and entrance examination.
Fees (Pesos): 121,304 per semester.
Language of Instruction: Spanish.
Degrees and Diplomas: Professional title of Psicólogo, 5 yrs.
Library: 5,000 vols.
Academic Staff, 1989: 3 (53)

2083 **FUNDACIÓN UNIVERSIDAD DE AMÉRICA**
Avenida de Los Cerros No. 19-91, Bogotá
Telephone: 2815715

P. of Architecture
P. of Economics
P. of Industrial Engineering
P. of Mechanical Engineering
P. of Chemical Engineering
P. of Petroleum Engineering
Founded 1952.
Degrees and Diplomas: Professional titles, 5 yrs.
Library: c. 3200 vols.
Student Enrolment: c. 1634.

2084 **FUNDACIÓN UNIVERSIDAD DE BOGOTÁ 'JORGE TADEO LOZANO'**
'Jorge Tadeo Lozano' University of Bogotá
Calle 23 No. 4-47, Bogotá
Telephone: 2834610

P. of Business Administration
P. of Agriculture
P. of Foreign Commercial Studies
P. of Public Accountancy
P. of Communication Sciences
P. of Economics
P. of Geography
P. of Marine Biology
P. of Publicity
P. of Architectural Design and Decoration
P. of Industrial Design
P. of Graphic Design
P. of Diplomatic and International Studies
P. of Food Technology
P. of Agricultural Administration
P. of Marketing Technology
P. of Systems Technology and Data Processing
P. of Architecture (Cartagena)
P. of Foreign Commercial Studies (Cartagena)
P. of Tourism (Cartagena)
Founded 1954, a private institution partly financed by the State. Some residential facilities for students.
Academic Year: February to December (February-June; August-December).
Admission Requirements: Secondary school certificate (bachillerato) and entrance examination.
Language of Instruction: Spanish.
Degrees and Diplomas: Licenciado in all fields, 4 yrs (evening courses, 5 yrs). Professional titles, 3-5 yrs.
Library: c. 30,000 vols.
Special Facilities (Museums, etc.): Museum of Marine Sciences.
Publication: Revistas de la Universidad.
Academic Staff: c. 50 (420).
Student Enrolment: c. 6530.

2085 **FUNDACIÓN UNIVERSIDAD CENTRAL**
Central University Foundation
Carrera No. 21-38, Bogotá
Telephone: 2848249

P. of Public Accountancy
P. of Economics
P. of Business Administration
P. of Publicity
Founded 1966, formerly known as Universidad Central Grancolombiana.
Academic Year: February to December (February-June; July-December).
Admission Requirements: Secondary school certificate (bachillerato) and entrance examination.
Language of Instruction: Spanish.
Degrees and Diplomas: Professional titles of–Administrador de Empresas; Contador público; Economista, 5 yrs.
Library: c. 6300 vols.
Publication: General Information.
Academic Staff: c. 20.
Student Enrolment: c. 2970.

2086 **UNIVERSIDAD DEL NORTE**
Apartado aéreo 1569, Barranquilla
Telex: UNINORTE
Telephone: (958)35-77-20
Fax: (958) 25-07-22
Rector: Jesús Ferro Bayona (1980-)
Secretaria Académica: Carmen Helena J. de Peña

D. of Engineering
Dean: Pedro Gutiérrez Visbal
D. of Business Administration
Dean: Miguel Pacheco
D. of Law
Dean: Adalberto Reyes Olivares
D. of Psychology
Dean: Beatriz A. de Torres
D. of Health Sciences (Medicine and Nursing)
Dean: Hugo Flórez
Ce. for Lifelong Education
Director: Emelina S. de Buitrago
Graduate Studies Ce.
Director: Ignacio Ramírez
Cayena Cultural Ce.
Director: Zandra Vasquez
Research Ce.
Director: Pedro Falco
Founded 1966 as a private institution, recognized by the State as a university 1973. Governing bodies: the Consejo Directivo; the Consejo Académico.
Arrangements for co-operation with: Clark University; University of Missouri.
Academic Year: January to December (January-May; July-December).
Admission Requirements: Secondary school certificate (bachillerato) or equivalent, and entrance examination.
Fees (Pesos): 119,615-254,620 per semester.
Language of Instruction: Spanish.
Degrees and Diplomas: Licenciado in Nursing, 4 yrs. Professional titles of–Ingeniero civil; Administrador de Empresas; Psicólogo; Abogado, law; Ingeniero mecánico; Ingeniero industrial; Ingeniero de Sistemas, 5 yrs; Médico, 6 yrs. Degree of Magister in–Business Administration; Biology and Microbiology. Also technical qualifications, 2-3 yrs.
Libraries: Central Library, 14,552 vols; Medicine, 1646.
Publications: Huellas (quarterly); Boletín Estadístico (annually); Salud (quarterly); Anuario Científico (annually).
Press or Publishing House: Ediciones Uninorte
Academic Staff, 1989: c. 190 (320).
Student Enrolment, 1989: c. 4230.

2087 **FUNDACIÓN UNIVERSITARIA AGRARIA DE COLOMBIA**
Calle 170 No. 50-90, Bogotá
Telephone: 672-16-30
Rector: Fernando Gaitan Arciniegas
Secretario General: Fidel Huertas Bernal

F. of Engineering (Food and Civil Engineering)
Dean: Hernando Vallejo Castaño; *staff* 1 (55)
F. of Administrative Economic Sciences
Dean: Alvaro Zuñiga Garcia; *staff* 1 (8)
F. of Animal Husbandry
Dean: Jorge Gaitan Arciniegas; *staff* 1 (10)
Founded 1986. A private institution. Governing bodies: the Asamblea General; the Consejo Superior; the Consejo Académico.
Academic Year: February to December (February-June; August-December).
Admission Requirements: Secondary school certificate (bachillerato) and entrance examination.
Fees (Pesos): 140,965-190,200.
Language of Instruction: Spanish.

Degrees and Diplomas: Professional titles, 5 yrs.
Library: 1200 vols.
Academic Staff, 1990: 3 (73).
Student Enrolment, 1990:

	Men	Women	Total
Of the country	250	321	571

2088 **FUNDACIÓN UNIVERSITARIA AUTÓNOMA DE COLOMBIA**
Carrera 5 No. 1143, Bogotá
Telephone: 2818624

F. of Economics
F. of Industrial Engineering
F. of Systems Engineering
F. of Law

Founded 1971. A private institution. Governing bodies: the Asamblea General; the Consejo Académico; the Consejo Directivo.
Arrangements for co-operation with the University of Warsaw.
Academic Year: January to December (January-June; July-December).
Admission Requirements: Secondary school certificate (bachillerato) and entrance examination.
Language of Instruction: Spanish.
Degrees and Diplomas: Professional titles, 5 yrs.
Library: c. 12,000 vols.
Publications: Criterio (quarterly); Boletín (monthly).
Academic Staff: c. 270.
Student Enrolment: c. 4110.

2089 **FUNDACIÓN UNIVERSITARIA CATÓLICA DE ORIENTE**
Calle 41 No. 45-201, Rionegro (Antioquia)
Telephone: 2715959

Agricultural Administration
Business Administration
Religious Science
External Commerce
Industrial Engineering

2090 **FUNDACIÓN UNIVERSITARIA DE GARCÍA ROVIRA NORTE Y GUTIÉRREZ**
Ciudad Universitaria, Málaga (Santander)
Telephone: 4753

Agricultural Administration
Forestry
Zoology

2091 **FUNDACIÓN UNIVERSITARIA 'LOS LIBERTADORES'**
Carrera 10 Calle No. 65-98, Bogotá
Telephone: 211-04-24
Rector: Luis Hernán Limares Angel

F. of Education (pre-school level)
F. of Hotel and Tourist Administration
F. of Economics and International Trade
F. of Tourism
F. of Social Communication and Journalism

Founded 1982. A private institution. Governing bodies: the Asamblea General; the Consejo Superior.
Academic Year: February to December (February-June; July-December).
Admission Requirements: Secondary school certificate (bachillerato) and entrance examination.
Fees (Pesos): 100,000 per semester.
Language of Instruction: Spanish.
Degrees and Diplomas: Professional titles, 5 yrs.
Library: 10,000 vols.
Academic Staff, 1989-90: 10 (200).
Student Enrolment, 1989-90: 1930

2092 **FUNDACIÓN UNIVERSITARIA 'LUIS AMIGO'**
Transversal 51A No. 67B-134, Medellín (Antioquia)
Telephone: 2301804

2093 **FUNDACIÓN UNIVERSITARIA DE MANIZALES**
Carrera 9 No. 1903, Manizales (Caldas)
Telephone: 841450
Rector: Alvaro Martínez Ocampo (1984-88)
Secretario General: Jhon Jairo Betancur Londoño

F. of Accountancy
Dean: Hector Osorio Gómez; *staff* 5 (28)
F. of Law
Dean: Guillermo Mejia Gutiérrez; *staff* 10 (21)
F. of Economics
Dean: Alfonso Delgadillo Parra; *staff* 97 (16)
F. of Psychology
Dean: Luis González López; *staff* 9 (17)
F. of Education (pre-school level)
Dean: Jorge Prieto Téllez; *staff* 10 (15)

Founded 1972. Acquired present status and title 1983. A private institution. Governing bodies: the Consejo Directivo; the Consejo Académico.
Academic Year: February to December (February-July; July-December).
Admission Requirements: Secondary school certificate (bachillerato) and entrance examination.
Fees: Fees (Pesos): 36,000 per semester.
Language of Instruction: Spanish.
Degrees and Diplomas: Professional titles.
Library: 10,000 vols.
Publication: Revista de Investigaciones (monthly).
Academic Staff, 1986-87: 50 (110).
Student Enrolment, 1986-87:

	Men	Women	Total
Of the country	875	1216	2091

2094 **FUNDACIÓN UNIVERSITARIA 'MARÍA CAÑO'**
Calle 52 No. 49-27, Medellín (Antioquia)

2095 **FUNDACIÓN UNIVERSITARIA MONSERRATE**
Calle 72 No. 11-41, Bogotá
Telephone: 2174912

Education (pre-school level)
Family and Social Education

2096 **FUNDACIÓN UNIVERSITARIA DE POPAYÁN**
Calle 5A No. 3-38 Sede Los Robles, Popayán (Cauca)
Telephone: 21920
Rector: Jorge Illera Fernández (1983-)
Vice-Rector Académico: Henry Paz Paz

F. of Agricultural Administration
Dean: Henry Maya; *staff* 4 (27)
F. of Ecology
Dean: Guillermo Vásquez; *staff* 7 (27)
F. of Mining
Dean: Alirio Alvarez;E6 (14)

Founded 1983. A private institution. Governing body: the Consejo de Regentes. Some residential facilities for academic staff.
Academic Year: August to May (August-December; February-May).
Admission Requirements: Secondary school certificate (bachillerato) and entrance examination.
Fees (Pesos): 50,000 per semester.
Language of Instruction: Spanish.
Degrees and Diplomas: Professional titles, 3-5 yrs.
Library: 1430 vols.
Special Facilities (Museums, etc.): Francisco José de Caldas Mineral Collection.
Publication: Quercus (monthly).
Academic Staff, 1986-87: 17 (68).
Student Enrolment, 1986-87:

	Men	Women	Total
Of the country	298	196	494
Of other countries	1	1	2
Total	299	197	496

2097 **FUNDACIÓN UNIVERSITARIA SAN MARTÍN**

Calle 61A No. 14-28, Bogotá
Telephone: 25555919

Dentistry

2098 **INSTITUTO DE CIENCIAS DE LA SALUD**

Institute of Health Sciences
Apartado aéro 054591,2Tr. Superior Calle 10, Medellín (Antioquia)
Telephone: 246-51-45
Fax: 266-60-46
Rector: Hernán Vélez A. (1982-)
Secretario General: Maria Adelaida Posada A.

F. of Medicine
Dean: Luis Alfonso Vélez C.
F. of Dentistry
Dean: Alpidio Jiménez G.

Founded 1978. A private institution. Governing bodies: the Consejo Directivo; the Consejo Académico.

Arrangements for co-operation with Boston University School of Medicine.

Academic Year: January to November (January-June; July-November).

Admission Requirements: Secondary school certificate (bachillerato) and entrance examination.

Fees (Pesos): 320,000 per semester.

Language of Instruction: Spanish.

Degrees and Diplomas: Professional titles, 5-6 yrs.

Library: Total, 7020 vols.

Publication: Reviews (biannually).

Academic Staff, 1989-90:

Rank	Full-time	Part-time
Profesores Honorarios	5	–
Profesores	2	5
Profesores Asistentes	15	21
Profesores Asociados	13	18
Instructores	38	14
Total	73	58

Student Enrolment, 1989-90:

	Men	Women	Total
Of the country	403	258	661

2099 **INSTITUTO UNIVERSITARIO DE HISTORIA DE COLOMBIA**

Carrera 9 No. 9-52, Bogotá
Telephone: 282-53-16
Rector: Antonio Cauca Prada
Secretario General: Roberto Velandia

Colombian History

Founded 1963 by the Academia Colombiana de Historia. A private institution.

Academic Year: February to December (February-June; August-December).

Admission Requirements: Secondary school certificate (bachillerato) and entrance examination.

Fees (Pesos): 85,000 per semester.

Language of Instruction: Spanish.

Degrees and Diplomas: Licenciado, 4 yrs. Extension courses, 1 yr.

Library: Biblioteca Educardo Santos, *c.*100,000 vols.

Academic Staff, 1990: 2 (10).

Student Enrolment, 1990:

	Men	Women	Total
Of the country	24	42	66

2100 **INSTITUTIÓN UNIVERSITARIA 'SERGIO ARBOLEDO**

Calle 74 No. 14-14, Bogotá
Telephone: 21239819

2101 **PONTIFICIA UNIVERSIDAD JAVERIANA**

Xavier Pontifical University
Carrera 7 No. 40-62, Bogotá
Cables: Apartado aéreo 56710
Telephone: 287-57-91
Fax: (571) 288-23-35
Rector: Gerardo Arango, S.J. (1989-)
Secretario General: Jaime Bernal E., S.J.

F. of Theology
Dean: Mario Gutiérrez, S.J.; *staff* 9 (15)
F. of Architecture and Design
Dean: Eduardo Castañeda; *staff* 2 (129)
F. of Economics and Administration
Dean: Hernando Arellano; *staff* 9 (166)
F. of Sciences
Dean: Ernesto Pachon; *staff* 58 (74)
F. of Law
Dean: Roberto Suárez; *staff* 2 (70)
F. of Social Sciences
Dean: Eduardo Uribe, S.J.; *staff* 3 (18)
F. of Canon Law
Dean: Roberto Suárez; *staff* – (6)
F. of Nursing
Dean: María Teresa de Vergara; *staff* 31 (10)
F. of Social Communication
Dean: Joaquín Sánchez, S.J.; *staff* 7 (37)
F. of Philosophy
Dean: Fabio Ramírez, S.J.; *staff* 11 (16)
F. of Psychology
Dean: Graciela Aldana de Conde; *staff* 6 (95)
F. of Engineering
Dean: Carlos Cuartas Chacón; *staff* 22 (148)
F. of Medicine
Dean: Arturo Marillo; *staff* 75 (173)
F. of Dentistry
Dean: Atenógenes Blanco; *staff* 7 (166)
F. of Interdisciplinary Studies
Dean: Pedro Polo; *staff* 6 (6)
F. of Humanities and Social Sciences (Cali)
Dean: Hernando Silva, S.J.
F. of Engineering (Cali)
Dean: Alvaro Enrique Alvarez, S.J.
F. of Economics and Administration (Cali)
Dean: Beatriz Castro de Posada
P. for Distance Education
Director: Omayra Parra de Maroquin
P. for Adult Education
Director: Josè Manuel Reyes
D. of Religious Sciences
Director: Antonio Josè Sarmiento, S.J.
D. of Modern Languages
Director: Angela de Toro
I. of Geophysics
Director: René van Hissenhoven, S.J.

Founded 1623 as Academia Javeriana by the Society of Jesus. Became university 1704. In 1767 the Jesuits were expelled and the university closed. Re-established 1930 with faculty of economics and law. Formally inaugurated as a Pontifical university in 1937. Privately financed. Its degrees and diplomas are formally recognized by the State. Governing bodies: Consejo de Regentes; the Consejo Directivo.

Arrangements for co-operation with 65 institutions in various countries.

Academic Year: January to November (February-May; August-November).

Admission Requirements: Secondary school certificate (bachillerato) and entrance examination.

Language of Instruction: Spanish.

Degrees and Diplomas: Licenciado in–Theology, 3 yrs; Nutrition; Bacteriology; Biology; Journalism; Education; Nursing; Philosophy; Letters; History; Ecclesiastical Philosophy; Mathematics; Library Science, 4 yrs; Canon Law; Philosophy. Professional titles of–Matemático; Arquitecto; Diseñador industrial; Biólogo; Administrador de Empresas, business administration; Contador público, accountancy; Economista; Ingeniero civil; Odontólogo; Abogado, law; Ingeniero industrial; Ingeniero electrónico; Psicólogo, 4-5 yrs; Médico cirujano, 6 yrs. Doctorado in–Canon Law; Philosophy and Letters; Philosophy; Theology, 5 yrs. Degrees of Magister and Specialization.

Libraries: Central Library, 112,000 vols; Ecclesiastic Studies, 150,000.

Publications: Theologica Xaveriana (biannually); Universitas Medica (biannually); Universitas Humanística (biannually); Universitas Economica (biannually); Universitas Canonica (biannually); Universitas Philosophica (biannually); Universitas Odontologica (biannually); Hoy en la Javeriana (weekly); Signo y Pensamiento (monthly).
Academic Staff, 1990: 298 (1613).
Student Enrolment, 1990:

Men	Women	Total
10,209	10,752	20,961

2102 **UNIVERSIDAD AUTÓNOMA DEL CARIBE**
Calle 90 No. 46-112, Barranquilla (Atlántica)
Cables: uniautonoma
Telephone: 452605

P. of Business Administration
P. of Architecture
P. of Communication
P. of Accountancy
P. of Sociology
P. of Hotel Administration

Founded 1967, formally recognized by the State as a university 1974. A private institution.
Academic Year: February to December (February-June; August-November).
Admission Requirements: Secondary school certificate (bachillerato) and entrance examination.
Language of Instruction: Spanish.
Degrees and Diplomas: Licenciado in Communication, 4 yrs. Professional titles of–Administrador de Empresas, business administration; Arquitecto; Contador público, accountancy; Sociólogo; Hotel Administration, 5 yrs.
Library: c. 4000 vols.
Publication: Galaxia.
Student Enrolment: c. 1900.

2103 **UNIVERSIDAD AUTÓNOMA LATINOAMERICANA 'UNAULA'**
Carrera 55 No. 4951, Medellín (Antioquia)
Telephone: 2311199

P. of Education
P. of Law
P. of Accountancy
P. of Industrial Engineering
P. of Economics
P. of Sociology

Founded 1966 as a private institution. Privately financed but receives some support from the State. Governing body: the Consejo Académico.
Academic Year: February to December.
Admission Requirements: Secondary school certificate (bachillerato) and entrance examination.
Language of Instruction: Spanish.
Degrees and Diplomas: Licenciado in Education, 4 yrs. Professional titles of–Sociólogo, 4 yrs; Economista; Contador público, 5 yrs; Ingeniero industrial; Abogado, law.
Libraries: Central Library, c. 20,000 vols; Law, c. 2000.
Student Enrolment: c. 2440.

2104 **UNIVERSIDAD CATÓLICA DE MANIZALES**
Catholic University of Manizales
Carrera 23 Nos. 60-63, Manizales (Caldas)
Telephone: 86-00-19
Fax: 85-41-41
Rectora: Mabel Jaramillo Restrepo (1984-89)
Secretaria General: Leonor Hurtado Jiménez

F. of Education
Dean: Jaime Ruiz López; *staff* 2 (36)
F. of Health Sciences
Dean: Jorge Raad Aljure; *staff* 22 (68)
Ut. of Technology (including Tourism)
Director: Nubia Inés Siera Cardona; *staff* 9 (26)
D. of Humanities
Director: Maria Teresa Yépez Avila; *staff* 3 (4)
D. of Foreign Languages
Director: Oscar Llano Idárraga; *staff* – (5)
Research Ce.
Ce. for Human Communication Studies.

Founded 1954 as Colegio Mayor, became university 1978 and acquired present status and title 1983. A private institution. Governing bodies: the Consejo Superior; the Consejo Académico.
Academic Year: February to November (February-June; July-November).
Admission Requirements: Secondary school certificate (bachillerato) and entrance examination.
Fees (Pesos): 52,000-15,000 per semester.
Language of Instruction: Spanish.
Degrees and Diplomas: Licenciado in–Education and Religious Sciences; Educational Administration; Counselling, 4 yrs. Professional titles in–Speech Training; Tourism; Publicity, 2-4 yrs.
Library: 10,000 vols.
Special Facilities (Museums, etc.): Tourism Museum 'Emilio Robledo'.
Publications: Revista de Investigación (annually); Reflejos (Facultad de Educación) (biannually); Boletín de la Escuela de Fonoaudiologàia (monthly).
Press or Publishing House: Taller de Publicaciones de la Corporación Universidad Católica de Manizales.
Academic Staff, 1990: 38 (99).
Student Enrolment, 1990:

	Men	Women	Total
Of the country	326	1334	1660

2105 **UNIVERSIDAD CATÓLICA POPULAR DEL RISARALDA**
Calle 20 No. 3-65, Pereira (Risaralda)
Telephone: 46524
Rector: Francisco Nel Jiménez Gómez (1975-)
Secretario Académico: Duffay Alberto Gómez

F. of Business Administration
Dean: Jaime Montoya *staff* 8 (15)
F. of Economics
Dean: Mariela Cardona; *staff* 5 (18)
P. of Religious Sciences

Founded 1975. A private institution. Governing bodies: the Consejo Superior; the Consejo Académico.
Academic Year: February to November (February-June; July-August).
Admission Requirements: Secondary school certificate (bachillerato) and entrance examination.
Language of Instruction: Spanish.
Degrees and Diplomas: Licenciado in Religious Sciences, 4 ½ yrs. Professional titles, 5-6 yrs.
Library: c. 3100 vols.
Publication: Páginas UCPR (monthly).
Academic Staff, 1986-87: 16 (44).
Student Enrolment, 1986-87:

	Men	Women	Total
Of the country	233	321	554*

*Also 27 external students.

2106 **UNIVERSIDAD COOPERATIVA DE COLOMBIA**
Carrera 15 No. 38-00, Bogotá
Telephone: 245-47-78
Rector: Cesar Pérez-García
Secretario-General: Alfonso Clavijo González

Educational Administration
Economics
Business Administration
Sociology
Educational Administration (Barrancabermeja)
Administration (Barrancabermeja)
Economics (Barrancabermeja)
Educational Administration (Bucaramanga)
Economics (Bucaramanga)
Business Administration (Bucaramanga)
Educational Administration (Medellín)
Administration and Planning (Medellín)
Economics (Medellín)
Commercial Engineering

Founded 1958. A private institution.
Admission Requirements: Secondary school certificate (bachillerato) and entrance examination.
Language of Instruction: Spanish.
Degrees and Diplomas: Licenciado, 4 yrs. Professional titles, 4-5 yrs.
Library: Total, c.25,000 vols.

Student Enrolment: c. 10,000.

2107 **UNIVERSIDAD ESCUELA DE ADMINISTRACIÓN Y FINANZAS Y TECNOLOGÍAS 'EAFIT'**

Carrera 49 No. 7 Sur, 50 Avenida Las Vegas, Medellín (Antioquia)
Telephone: 266-43-24
Fax: 266-42-84
Rector: Guillermo Sanín Arango
Secretario General: Luis Edouardo Gómez

S. of Administration (including Accountancy)
Dean: Jorge Posada; *staff* 60 (120)
S. of Engineering
Dean: Alberto Rodríguez; *staff* 45 (90)
S. of Graduate Studies
Dean: Javier del Rio

Branches in: Bogotá, Cali, Manizales, Bucaramanga.

Founded 1960 as institute. A private institution supported by industry and also partly financed by the State. Governing bodies: the Consejo Superior; the Consejo Académico.

Academic Year: January to December (January-June; July-December).

Admission Requirements: Secondary school certificate (bachillerato) and entrance examination.

Language of Instruction: Spanish.

Degrees and Diplomas: Professional titles of–Administrador de Negocios; Ingeniero de Producción; Ingeniero de Sistemas; Ingeniero civil; Contador público, accountancy; Geólogo, 5 ½ yrs. Magister in–Administration; Mathematics, a further 2 yrs.

Library: c. 14,000 vols.

Publication: Journal (quarterly).

Press or Publishing House: EAFIT

Academic Staff, 1990: c. 100 (210).

Student Enrolment, 1990: c. 5000.

2108 ***UNIVERSIDAD EXTERNADO DE COLOMBIA**

Calle 12 No. 1-17 Este, Bogotá
Telephone: 2413484
Rector: Carlos Mestrepo Piedrahita (1963-)
Secretario General: Manuel Cubides Romero

F. of Law and Social and Political Sciences
Dean: Fernando Hinestrosa Forero; *staff* 66 (106)
F. of Economics (including Administrative Sciences)
Dean: Enrique Low Murtra
F. of Finance and International Relations
Dean: Roberto Hinestrosa Rey; *staff* 1 (15)
F of Social Work
Dean: Lucero Zamudio; *staff* 13 (12)
F. of Education CDean: Jaime González Joves; *staff* 24 (60)
F. of Social Communication
Dean: José de Recasens *staff* 9 (32)

Founded 1886 as Faculty of Law, became university 1958. Privately financed but receives some support from the State. Governing body: the Consejo Directivo.

Academic Year: January to December (January-July; July-December).

Admission Requirements: Secondary school certificate (bachillerato) and entrance examination.

Fees (Pesos): 39,900-80,000 per semester; Law, 94,400-100,000 per annum.

Language of Instruction: Spanish.

Degrees and Diplomas: Licenciado in Education, 4 ½ yrs. Professional titles in–Social Work, 4 yrs; Social Communications (Journalism), 4 ½ yrs; Law; Economics; Business Administration; Finance and International Relations; Hotel Administration; Accountancy, 5 yrs. Degrees of Magister and Specialization.

Library: Central Library, 41,500 vols.

Publications: Externado; Revista Derecho Penal y Criminología (bi-annually); Boletín Estadístico (annually); Revista Papeles Económicos (quarterly); Revista Educación y Sociedad (annually); Revista Turismo y Sociedad (biannually).

Press or Publishing House: Editorial Universidad Externado de Colombia.

Academic Staff, 1986-87: 173 (470).

Student Enrolment, 1986-87:

	Men	Women	Total
Of the country	2536	3413	5949

2109 ***UNIVERSIDAD INCCA DE COLOMBIA**

Carrera 13 No. 24-15, Bogotá
Telex: 42531 INCCA CO
Telephone: 286-52-00
Rector: Jaime Quijano Caballero (1955-)
Secretario General: José Luis Robayo León

I. of Scientific Socialism
Head: Jaime Quijano Caballero; *staff* 12
I. of Mathematics and Cybernetics
Head: Myriam Gonzále; *staff* 13 (1)
I. of Natural Sciences
Head: Over Quintero Castillo; *staff* 19 (1)
I. of Human and Social Sciences
Head: Carlos Alberto Duffo Vallejo; *staff* 16 (10)
F. of Technology (including Food Technology and Systems Engineering)
Dean: Mario Martínez Rojas; *staff* 31 (6)
F. of Economic Sciences
Dean: Guillermo Rojas Sánchez; *staff* 3
F. of Education
Dean: Néstor Bravo Salinas; *staff* 7 (2)
Extension and Extramural D.
I. of Arts
Director: Gladys Alvarez; *staff* 1
I. of Biotechnology Development
Director: Over Quintero Castillo
I. of Informatic Development
Director: Mario Martínez Rojas
I. of Industrial Development
Director: Vladimir Gómez Calderón

Founded 1955 as institute of administrative sciences, recognized as a university by government decree 1970. A private institution. Governing bodies: the Academic Senate; the Administrative Senate.

Arrangements for co-operation with: Karl Marx University of Leipzig; Patrice Lumumba People's Friendship University, Moscow; University of Moscow; University of Rostock; University of Havana; University of Las Villas; Instituto Superior Politécnico 'José A. Echeverría', La Habana; Free University of Brussels; Universidade Estatal de Campinas; Universidade Federal de Viçosa; Université de Québec; Instituto de Ciencias 'Alejandro Lipschutz' de Santiago; Instituto Superior ARCIS de Chile; Instituto Superior de Ciencias Agropecuaria, Havana; Instituto Superiod de Cultura Física 'Manuel Fajardo', Havana; Universidad de Cuenca; Universidad de Guayaquil; Universidad Politécnica de madrid; Universidad de Alicante; Université de Paris-X, Nanterre; University of Delhi; Universidad Autónoma de México; Universidad del Valle de México; Universidad Autónoma Metropolitana; Universidad San Luis Gonzaga de Ica; Technical University of Dresden; University of Nanjing; Moscow State University; Universidad de Zulia, Venezuela.

Academic Year: January to November (January-May; July-November).

Admission Requirements: Secondary school certificate (bachillerato) and entrance examination.

Fees (Pesos): 109,140 per semester.

Language of Instruction: Spanish.

Degrees and Diplomas: Licenciado in Education, 5 yrs. Professional titles of–Ingeniero, engineering, various fields; Economista; Psicólogo; Abogado, law, 5 yrs. Magister in Philosophy, a further 2 yrs.

Library: Central Library, *c.* 30,000 vols.

Publication: Revista Científica.

Press or Publishing House: Unincca's Publishing Unit.

Academic Staff, 1990:

	Full-time	Part-time
Monitores Estudiantes	6	18
Lectores Monitores	6	16
Lectores Auxiliares	64	291
Docentes Instructores	57	20
Docentes Asistentes	24	94
Profesores Asociades	2	–
Total	159	439

Student Enrolment, 1990:

	Men	Women	Total
Of the country	4276	2672	6948
Of other countries	20	10	30
Total	4296	2682	6978

2110 **UNIVERSIDAD 'LA GRAN COLOMBIA'**
Avenida Bolivar 7-46, Bogotá
Telephone: 2438047

P. of Education
P. of Architecture
P. of Public Accountancy
P. of Law and Political Science
P. of Economics
P. of Civil Engineering
P. of Law (Armenia)
P. of Economics (Armenia)

Founded 1951.

Academic Year: February to November.

Admission Requirements: Secondary school certificate (bachillerato) and entrance examination.

Language of Instruction: Spanish.

Degrees and Diplomas: Licenciado in–Philosophy; Letters; Education, 4 yrs. Doctorado in–Law and Political Science, 5 yrs. Professional titles of–Economista; Contador público, accountancy, 5 yrs. Ingeniero civil; Arquitecto, 6 yrs and thesis.

Library: c. 26,000 vols.

Student Enrolment: c. 7330.

2111 **UNIVERSIDAD DE LA SABANA**
Calle 70 No. 11-79, Bogotá
Telex: 42574 INALD CO
Telephone: 249-56-93
Fax: 2-15-98-88
Rector: Rafael González Cagigas

F.of Education (including Social Sciences, Plastic Arts, Linguistics and Literature)
F. of Health Sciences (Psychology)
Head: Carmenza Peñaloza de Flóres
F. of Law
Dean: Edilberto Solis Escobar
F. of Administration and Economics
Dean: Iván Anzola Castillo
F. of Engineering
Dean: Evaristo Ayuso Martinez
F. of Social Communication
Dean: Victor Rodriguez Gallón

Founded 1971 as Institute for Higher Education. Acquired present status and title 1979.

Arrangements for co-operation with: University of Navarra; University of Piura, Peru.

Academic Year: February to November.

Admission Requirements: Secondary school certificate (bachillerato) and entrance examination.

Fees (Pesos): 54,000-192,300.

Language of Instruction: Spanish.

Degrees and Diplomas: Licenciado and Professional titles, 4-5 yrs. Degree of Magister in Education.

Library: Central Library, 32,000 vols.

Academic Staff, 1990: 27 (263).

Student Enrolment, 1990: 5091 (Also 2096 students of distance education).

2112 **UNIVERSIDAD DE LA SALLE**
Calle 11 No. 47, Carrera 2da. No. 10-70 Bogotá
Cables: unisalle
Telephone: 283-09-00
Fax: 242-21-83
Rector: Juan Vargas Muñoz
Secretario General: Fernando Galvis Gaitan

P. of Education
Dean: Gilberto Hernández Ceballos
P. of Business Administration
Dean: Ruben Martinezi
P. of Agricultural Administration
Dean: Mauricio Gonzalez Medina
P. of Library Science
Dean: Hugo Noel Parra Florez
P. of Economics
Dean: Luis Fernando Ramirez
P. of Civil Engineering
Dean: Jose Suarez Caro
P. of Architecture
Dean: Guillermo Gonález García
P. of Philosophy and Letters
Dean: Luis Enrique Ruíz López
P. of Languages
Dean: Stephen Colas
P. of Statistics
Dean: Antonio Velasco Muñoz
P. of Optometry
Dean: Oswaldo Vargas Garzón
P. of Social Work
Dean: Clara Ines Rodriguéz Hoyos
P. of Animal Husbandry
Dean: German Serrano Quintero
P. of Electrical Engineering
Dean: Gonzálo Estrada Vega
P. of Food Engineering
Dean: Maritza Richoux de Leal
P. of Sanitary Engineering
Dean: Carlos Fonseca Zarate
P. of Chemistry and Biology
Dean: Abraham Hadra Sauda
P. of Mathematics and Physics
Dean: Lucio Fernando Ruiz Guzman
D. of Advanced Studies
Dean: Augusta Franco Arbelaez

Also 5 research centres and institutes.

Founded 1964 as a private institution, formerly recognized by the State 1965. Governing body: the Consejo Directivo. Residential facilities for students.

Academic Year: February to November.

Admission Requirements: Secondary school certificate (bachillerato) and entrance examination.

Fees (Pesos): 77,000-230,335 per semester.

Language of Instruction: Spanish.

Degrees and Diplomas: Licenciado in–Philosophy and Letters; Education; Social Work, Religious Studies; Library Science, 4 yrs. Professional titles in–Agricultural Administration, 3 yrs; Civil Engineering; Optometry; Business Administration, Statistics; Accountancy; Economics; Architecture; Electrical Engineering; Food Engineering; Sanitary Engineering; Veterinary Science, 5 yrs.

Library: Central Library, c. 40,000 vols.

Special Facilities (Museums, etc.): Natural Sciences Museum.

Publication: Boletín Cientifico

Academic Staff, 1989-90: 27 (551).

Student Enrolment, 1989-90:

	Men	Women	Total
Of the country	4516	2978	7494

2113 **UNIVERSIDAD LIBRE DE COLOMBIA**
Free University of Colombia
Carrera 6a No. 8-54, Bogotá
Cables: unilibre
Telephone: 2869466
Rector: Jorge Enrique Córdoba P.

P. of Law
P. of Education
P. of Accountancy
P. of Metallurgical Engineering
P. of Industrial Engineering
P. of Law (Barranquilla)
P. of Medicine (Barranquilla)
P. of Dentistry (Barranquilla)
P. of Law (Cali)
P. of Business Administration (Cali)
P. of Accountancy (Cali)
P. of Medicine (Cali)
P. of Education (Cúcuta)
P. of Law (Cúcuta)
P. of Accountancy (Cúcuta)
P. of Economics (Pereira)
P. of Law (Pereira)
P. of Education (Socorro)

Founded 1923. Financed by the State and student fees.

Academic Year: February to December (February-June; July-December).
Admission Requirements: Secondary school certificate (bachillerato) and entrance examination.
Language of Instruction: Spanish.
Degrees and Diplomas: Licenciado in–Biology; Languages; Physics; Social Sciences; Mathematics; Chemistry, 4 yrs. Professional titles of–Derecho y Ciencias sociales, law and social sciences; Contador público, accountancy; Ingeniero metalúrgico; Ingeniero industrial; Médico cirujano; Economista; Abogado, law, 5 yrs. Doctor en Derecho, law, 5 yrs.
Library: c. 12,250 vols.
Publication: Revista de la Universidad Libre.
Academic Staff: c. 250.
Student Enrolment: c. 5480

2114 **UNIVERSIDAD DE LOS ANDES**
University of the Andes
Carrera l E No. 18-A-10, Bogotá
Telex: 42343 UNAND CO
Telephone: 243-74-74
Rector: Arturo Infante Villarreal (1985-)
Secretario General: Tica Laserna de Brando

S. of Engineering (including Computer Sciences)
Dean: Antonio García Roza; *staff* 55 (55)
S. of Economics
Dean: Eduardo Sarmiento; *staff* 21
S. of Law
Dean: Carlos Gustavo Arrieta; *staff* 12 (40)
S. of Sciences
Dean: Margarita de Meza; *staff* 33 (107)
S. of Humanities and Social Sciences
Dean: Gretel Wernher; *staff* 44 (105)
S. of Architecture
Dean: Carlos Morales; *staff* 1 (55)
S. of Management
Dean: Manuel Rodríguez; *staff* 20 (20)
Ce. of Studies on Economic Development
D. of Regional Development
P. for Lifelong Education

Founded 1948 as an independent private institution. Privately financed. Recognized as a university by the Ministry of Education and entitled to award legally valid degrees. Governing bodies: the Consejo Directivo, composed of 40 members; the Consejo Académico.

Arrangements for co-operation with the Universities of: Illinois; Stanford; Massachusetts; Johns Hopkins; Notre Dame; State New York at Stony Brook; Wake Forest; Harvard; Mainz; Erasmus, Rotterdam; Dublin; London; Barcelona; Grenoble III; Trieste; Ottawa; United Nations, Tokyo; Simón Bolivar, Caracas. Institute of Social Studies, The Hague.

Academic Year: January to December (January-May; August-December).
Admission Requirements: Secondary school certificate (bachillerato) and entrance examination.
Fees (Pesos): According to income of parents.
Language of Instruction: Spanish.
Degrees and Diplomas: Licenciado in–Psychology; Modern Languages; Physics; Mathematics; Biology; Bacteriology; Microbiology; Anthropology, 4 ½ yrs. Professional titles of–Matématico; Físico; Biólogo; Psicólogo; Bacteriólogo; Informático; Ingeniero; Economista; Economista industrial; Arquitecto; Administrador de Empresas; Abogado, law, 5 yrs. Degree of Magister, 1 ½-2 yrs after Licenciado in–Biology; Economics; Civil Engineering; Industrial Engineering; Electrical Engineering; Mathematics; Microbiology; Business Administration; Computer Sciences; Planning and Administration of Regional Development; University Administration; Ethnolinguistics.
Library: Total, c. 150,000 vols.
Publications: Texto y Contexto (quarterly); Cuadernos de filosofía; Desarrollo y Sociedad (quarterly).
Academic Staff, 1986-87: c. 200 (430).
Student Enrolment, 1986-87:

	Men	Women	Total
Of the country	3012	2508	5520
Of other countries	18	26	44
Total	3030	2534	5564

2115 **UNIVERSIDAD MARIANA**
Calle 18 No. 34-104, Pasto (Nariño)
Telephone: 33616

F. of Education
F. of Health Sciences (Nursing)
F. of Accountancy

Founded 1967 as institute, acquired present status and title 1983. A private institution. Governing bodies: the Consejo Superior; the Consejo Académico. Residential facilities for academic staff and students.

Academic Year: February to December (February-June; August-December).
Admission Requirements: Secondary school certificate (bachillerato) and entrance examination.
Language of Instruction: Spanish.
Degrees and Diplomas: Licenciado or Professional title, 4-5 yrs.
Library: c. 11,400 vols.
Academic Staff: c. 20 (120).
Student Enrolment: c. 1200.

2116 **UNIVERSIDAD DE MEDELLÍN**
Carrera 87 No. 30-65. Los Alpes (Belén), Medellín (Antioquia)
Cables: A.A. No. 19-83 Medellín
Telephone: 2383906

P. of Education
P. of Law
P. of Industrial Economics
P. of Administration
P. of Statistics
P. of Civil Engineering
P. of Accountancy

Founded 1950 as a private institution. Privately financed but receives some assistance from the State. Governing bodies: the Asamblea General de Socios (Founders' Assembly); the Conciliatura (University Council); the Consejo Directivo; the President; the Rector; the deans and directors.

Academic Year: January to December (February-June; August-December).
Admission Requirements: Secondary school certificate (bachillerato) and entrance examination.
Language of Instruction: Spanish.
Degrees and Diplomas: Licenciado in Education, 4 yrs. Professional titles of–Estadístico, statistics; Abogado, Law; Economista industrial; Profesional en Ciencias administrativas; Contador público, accountancy; Ingeniero civil, 5 yrs. Specialization in Penal Law and Criminology, 2 yrs postgraduate study.
Library: c. 18,000 vols.
Academic Staff: c. 450.
Student Enrolment: c. 5400.

2117 **UNIVERSIDAD METROPOLITANA**
Carrera. 42F No. 75B-169, Barranquilla (Atlántico)
Telephone: 353757
Rector: Eduardo Acosta Bendek B. (1982-)

P. of Medicine
Dean: Nestor Vazquez Macias; *staff* 81 (75)
P. of Dentistry
Dean José Puche; *staff* 21 (32)
P. of Bacteriology
Dean: Aida ortega de Pájaro; *staff* 31 (19)
P. of Physiotherapy
Dean: Margarita Rosales; *staff* (18)
P. of Psychology
Dean: Luís Camatin; *staff* 25 (22)
P. of Nursing
Dean: Alba Iinás de Reyes; *staff* 23 (12)
P. of Nutrition and Dietetics
Dean: Marta Charris de De Mier; *staff* 18 (8)
P. of Social Work
Dean: Miriam Jiménez de Calderón; *staff* 22 (6)
Ce. for Lifelong Education
Head: Nestor Vasquez Macías

Founded 1973. A private institution. Governing bodies: Consejo Directivo; the Consejo Académico. Residential facilities for academic staff.

Academic Year: February to December (February-June; August-December).

Admission Requirements: Secondary school certificate (bachillerato) and entrance examination.

Fees (Pesos): 45,155-135,057 per semester.

Language of Instruction: Spanish.

Degrees and Diplomas: Professional titles, 4-7 yrs. Degrees of Specialization.

Library: Central Library, 6762 vols.

Publications: Revista Unimetro (biannually); Boletín en Derecho (quarterly).

Academic Staff, 1986-87: 262 (192).

Student Enrolment, 1986-87:

	Men	Women	Total
Of the country	1064	2099	3163
Of other countries	4	2	6
Total	1068	2101	3169

2118 **UNIVERSIDAD PONTIFICIA BOLIVARIANA**

Pontifical Bolivariana University

Calle 52 No. 40-88, Medellín A(ntioquia)

Telex: 65047UPB CO

Telephone: (94) 249-71-99

Fax: (94) 239-66-83

Rector: Mgr Darío Munero Vélez (1988-91)

Secretario General: Pedro Posada Marín

F. of Social Sciences
Dean: Ana María Montoya; *staff* 13 (58)
F. of Architecture and Design
Dean: Augusto González V.; *staff* 15 (101)
F. of Law and Political Science
Dean: William Fernando Yarce Maya; *staff* 9 (67)
F. of Engineering (including Business Administration)
Dean: Luis Carlos Molina A.; *staff* 22 (83)
F. of Medicine
Dean: Jorge Benicio Tissnesh; *staff* 55 (52)
F. of Education and Humanities
Dean: Carlos Enrique Londoño; *staff* 16 (39)
F. of Religious Sciences
Dean: gonalo Soto Pasado; *staff* 10 (55)
D. for Lifelong Education
Head: Francisco Restrepo; *staff* 5 (132)
Ce. for Evening Studies
Ce. for Development Research
Director: Eugenio Betancur
Branch in Marinilla. Also primary and high school.

Founded 1936 by the Archbishop of Medellín. Governing body: the Consejo Directivo.

Arrangements for co-operation with the Catholic University of Washington.

Academic Year: January to December (January-June; July-December).

Admission Requirements: Secondary school certificate (bachillerato) and entrance examination.

Fees (Pesos): 83,600-269,000 per semester.

Language of Instruction: Spanish.

Degrees and Diplomas: Licenciado in–Theology, 3 yrs; Philosophy; Sociology; Social Work; Education; Religious Studies; Education, 4 yrs; Social Communication, 5 yrs. Professional titles of–Arquitecto; Ingeniero químico; Ingeniero mecánico; Ingeniero eléctrico; Ingeniero electrónico; Administrador de Empresas; Abogado, law; Diseñador industrial; Diseñador gráfico, 5 yrs; Medico cirujano, 7 yrs. Doctorado in Theology. Degrees of Specialization.Also teaching qualifications, 5-6 yrs.

Libraries: Central Library, 28,435 vols; Social Work, 8014; Engineering, 12,045; Architecture and Design, 6179; Business Administration, Social Communication, Theology, 10,082; Medicine, 3266.

Publications: Revista de la Universidad; Revista Sociología; Cuestiones Teológicas; Revistas of the Faculties: Medicine;Social Work; Social Communication; Law; Education; Administration.

Press or Publishing House: Procesos Editoriales U.P.B.

Academic Staff, 1990: 87 (724).

Student Enrolment, 1990:

	Men	Women	Total
Of the country	3326	2884	6210

2119 **UNIVERSIDAD DE SAN BUENAVENTURA**

Calle 73 No. 10-45, Bogotá

Cables: universidad buenaventura

Telephone: 2354942

Rector: Alberto Montealegre González, O.F.M.

P. of Education (including Distance Study)
P. of Philosophy
P. of Theology
P. of Education (including Distance Study) (Cali)
P. of Law (Cali)
P. of Accountancy (Cali)
P. of Economics (Cali)
P. of Electronic Engineering (Cali)
P. of Architecture (Cali)
P. of Religious Sciences (Cali)
P. of Special Education (Cali)
P. of Psychology (Medellín)
P. of Sociology (Medellín)
P. of Education (including Distance Study) (Medellín)

Founded 1708 by Royal decree. Closed in nineteenth century; officially reopened 1961 and recognized by the Ministry of Education 1964. A private institution under the supervision of the Franciscan Order.

Academic Year: Mid-January to mid-November (January-June; July-November).

Admission Requirements: Secondary school certificate (bachillerato) and entrance examination.

Language of Instruction: Spanish.

Degrees and Diplomas: Licenciado, 4-5 yrs. Magister in Lifelong Education. Doctorado in Engineering.

Libraries: Bogotá, *c.* 85,000 vols; Cali, *c.* 36,000; Medellín, *c.* 19,000.

Academic Staff: – (539).

Student Enrolment: *c.* 5200 (Also *c.* 2170 external students).

2120 **UNIVERSIDAD SANTIAGO DE CALI**

Calle 5, Carrera 62, Cali (Valle del Cauca)

Telephone: 515342

P. of Education
P. of Law
P. of Business Administration
P. of Accountancy

Founded 1958.

Degrees and Diplomas: Licenciado in Education, 4 yrs. Professional titles of–Administrador de Empresas; Contador público, accountancy, 5 yrs. Doctor en Derecho, law, 5 yrs.

Library: *c.* 3260 vols.

Student Enrolment: *c.* 5450.

2121 ***UNIVERSIDAD SANTO TOMÁS**

University Santo Tomás

Carrera 9a No. 51-23, Bogotá

Telephone: 210085

Rector: Alvaro Galvis Ramírez, O.P.

Secretario General: Jorge Vergel Villamizar

F. of Civil Engineering
Dean: Jairo Rojas Carvajal; *staff* 16 (55)
F. of Electronics
Dean: Demetrio Martínez Montoya; *staff* 14 (46)
F. of Accountancy
Dean: Alberto Yepes Mora; *staff* 18 (69)
F. of Economics and Administration
Dean: Héctor Devia Cortés; *staff* 16 (52)
F. of Sociology
Dean: Alfonso Morant González; *staff* 6 (7)
F. of Psychology
Dean: María Eugenia S. de Romero; *staff* 19 (70)
F. of Law and Political Science
Dean: Ricardo Calvete Rangel; *staff* 18 (10)
F. of Philosophy and Letters
Dean: Joaquín Zabalza Iriarte, O.P.
F. of Architecture (Bucaramanga)
Dean: Reynaldo Oruz Arenas; *staff* 7 (55)
F. of Dentistry (Bucaramanga)
Dean: Jaime Trillos Novoa; *staff* 10 (74)
F. of Economics (Bucaramanga)
Dean: Alejandro Rincón Uribe; *staff* 10 (34)

Founded 1580 by Pope Gregorio XIII. Closed 1861 by General Tomás Cipriano de Mosquera. Re-established 1965 and approved by government decree 1966. Privately financed. Governing bodies: the Consejo Superior; the Consejo Académico.

Arrangements for co-operation with: University of Münster; Universidad de Morón.

Academic Year: February to December (February-June; August-December).

Admission Requirements: Secondary school certificate (bachillerato) and entrance examination.

Fees (Pesos): 26,300-97,700 per semester; postgraduate, 90,000-98,000.

Language of Instruction: Spanish.

Degrees and Diplomas: Licenciado in Philosophy, 4 yrs. Professional titles in–Sociology, 4 yrs; Civil Engineering; Accountancy; Economics; Architecture; Dentistry; Electronics; Psychology; Law, 5 yrs. Magister in–Clinical Psychology; Economics and Administration; Accountancy; Teaching; Latin American Philosophy.

Libraries: Central Library, 50,000 vols; Bucaramanga, 30,000.

Publications: Cuadernos de: Filosofía; Sociología; Revista Análisis; Módulos; Revista Económica.

Press or Publishing House: University Press.

Academic Staff, 1986-87: 159 (728).

Student Enrolment, 1986-87:

	Men	Women	Total
Of the country	7937	9082	17,019*

*Also 6900 external students.

Other Institutions

Technical Education

2122 **CENTRO EDUCATIVO DE COMPUTOS Y SISTEMAS 'CEDESISTEMAS'**

Calle 54 No. 45-29, Medellín (Antioquia)
Cables: cedesistemas
Telephone: 241-81-32
Rector: Alvaro Gil Gil
Director: Flor Angela Giraldo

Founded 1976. Recognized by the Ministry of Education.

Academic Year: January to December (January-June; July-December).

Admission Requirements: Secondary school certificate (bachillerato) and entrance examination.

Fees (Pesos): 81,140 per semester.

Language of Instruction: Spanish.

Degrees and Diplomas: Professional titles, 3 yrs. Certificates, 1 yr.

Library: 2000 vols.

Publication: Cedeinformes (6 times a year).

Academic Staff, 1989-90: 20 (53).

Student Enrolment, 1990:

	Men	Women	Total
Of the country	400	600	1000

2123 **CENTRO DE INVESTIGACIONES Y RECREATIÓN DIRIGIDA 'CIRDI'**

Carrera 19 No. 75-86, Bogotá
Telephone: 2110262

Sociology of Leisure

Founded 1972. A private institution. Governing bodies: the Consejo Directivo; the Consejo Académico.

Academic Year: February to December (February-June; August-December).

Admission Requirements: Secondary school certificate (bachillerato) and entrance examination.

Language of Instruction: Spanish.

Degrees and Diplomas: Professional title of Tecnólogo en Recreación Dirigida, 6-7 sem.

Library: c. 1860 vols.

Academic Staff, 1986-87: 13 (39).

Student Enrolment: c. 80.

2124 **CENTRO NACIONAL DE LA CONSTRUCCIÓN 'SENA'**

Carrera 18A No. 2-18 sur, Bogotá
Telephone: 2463647

Constructionon
Topography
Architectural Design

2125 **COLEGIO MAYOR DE BOLÍVAR**

Calle de la Factoría 35-95, Cartagena (Bolívar)
Telephone: 44060

Educationation
Technology (including Architectural Design)
Secretarial Studies
Translation
Social Studies

Founded 1945. A national institution. Governing bodies: the Consejo Directivo; the Consejo Académico.

Academic Year: February to December (February-June; August-December).

Admission Requirements: Secondary school certificate (bachillerato) and entrance examination.

Language of Instruction: Spanish.

Degrees and Diplomas: Professional titles, 3 yrs.

Library: c. 1880 vols.

Student Enrolment: c 220 (Women).

2126 **COLEGIO MAYOR DE CULTURA POPULAR DEL CAUCA**

Calle 5 No. 4-33, Popayán
Telephone: 23562

P. of Architectural Design

Founded 1945. A national institution.

Admission Requirements: Secondary school certificate (bachillerato) and entrance examination.

Language of Instruction: Spanish.

Degrees and Diplomas: Professional title of Delineante de Arquitectura, architectural design, 3 yrs.

Library: c. 400 vols.

Student Enrolment: c. 60.

2127 **CORPORACIÓN ACADEMIA TECNOLÓGICA DE 'COLUMBIA**

Calle 55 No. 41-10, Medellín (Antioquia)
Telephone: 2399089

2128 **CORPORACIÓN DE EDUCACIÓN DEL NORTE DEL TOLIMA 'COREDUCACIÓN'**

Casa de los Virreyas (Calle el Retiro esq. de las Trampas), Honda
Telephone: 3266

Administration
Secretarial Studies
Agricultural Administration

2129 **CORPORACIÓN EDUCATIVA DE ADMINISTRACIÓN Y FINANZAS DE NARIÑO**

Carrera 26 No. 14-83, Nariño
Telephone: 32322

2130 **CORPORACIÓN EDUCATIVA CENTRO SUPERIOR DE CALI**

Calle 14 Norte No. 6-26 y Cra. 6 No. 8-49, Cali
Telephone: 615816

P. of Business Administration
P. of Industrial Engineering
P. of Accountancy
P. of Secretarial Studies (Bilingual)
P. of Secretarial Studies
P. of Industrial Technology
P. of Administrative Technology
P. of Marketing Technology

Founded 1964 as institute, acquired present status and title 1977. A private institution financially supportedby tuition fees.Founded 1964. A private institution. Governing body: the Consejo Superior.

Academic Year: February to December (February-June; August-December).
Admission Requirements: Secondary school certificate (bachillerato) and entrance examination.
Language of Instruction: Spanish.
Degrees and Diplomas: Professional title of Técnico, 2-3 yrs.
Library: c. 3090 vols.
Publication: c. El Mural (biannually).
Academic Staff: c. 15 (60).
Student Enrolment: c. 970.

2131 **CORPORACIÓN EDUCATIVA 'ESUMER'**
Calle 76 No. 80-126, Carretera al Mar, Medellín (Antioquia)
Telephone: 2344259

Marketing
Foreign Trade
Founded 1964.
Admission Requirements: Secondary school certificate (bachillerato).
Language of Instruction: Spanish.
Degrees and Diplomas: Professional title or Licenciado, 3 yrs.
Library: c. 1500 vols.
Student Enrolment: c. 200.

2132 **CORPORACIÓN EDUCATIVA-INSTITUTO DE EDUCACIÓN EMPRESARIAL 'IDEE'**
Avenida la Norte No. 3N-27, Cali (Valle del Cauca)
Telephone: 0813940

P. of Administrative Technology
Founded 1974. A private institution. Financially supported by tuition fees.
Academic Year: February to December (February; September-December).
Admission Requirements: Secondary school certificate (bachillerato) and entrance examination.
Language of Instruction: Spanish.
Degrees and Diplomas: Professional titles, 3 yrs.
Library: c. 1000 vols.
Academic Staff: c 50
Student Enrolment: c. 360.

2133 **CORPORACIÓN ESCUELA DE ADMINISTRACIÓN DE EMPRESAS 'EAE'**
Carrera 34 No. D29-09 Cali (Valle del Cauca)
Telephone: 541856

P. of Business Administration
Founded 1969. A private institution.
Admission Requirements: Secondary school certificate (bachillerato) and entrance examination.
Language of Instruction: Spanish.
Degrees and Diplomas: Professional title, 3 yrs.
Library: c. 1000 vols.
Student Enrolment: c. 390.

2134 **CORPORACIÓN TECNOLÓCA DE CIENCIAS EMPRESARIALES**
Calle 36 No. 1712, Bogotá

P. of Commerce

2135 **CORPORACIÓN DE ESTUDIOS TECNOLÓGICOS NORTE DEL VALLE**
Calle 10a No. 3-95, Cartago (Valle)
Telephone: 248-12-23
Rector: Orlando Restrepo (1990-92)
Secretario General: Rosalba Hurtado

P. of Accountancy
Head: Omar Betancourt; *staff* – (23)
P. of Agricultural Administration
Head: Johnson Cardona; *staff* – (22)
P. of Coffee Administration and Agricultural Diversification
Head: Eliana Villafañe *staff* – (8)
Founded 1971. A private institution. Governing bodies: the Asamblea General; the Consejo Executivo; the Consejo Académico.
Academic Year: February to December (February-June; August-December).
Admission Requirements: Secondary school certificate (bachillerato) and entrance examination.
Language of Instruction: Spanish.
Degrees and Diplomas: Professional title of Tecnológo, 3 ½ yrs.
Academic Staff, 1990: – (45).
Student Enrolment, 1990:

	Men	Women	Total
Of the country	89	131	220

2136 **CORPORACIÓN INSTITUTE COLOMBO-ALÉMAN PARA LA FORMACIÓN TECNOLÓGICA**
Carrera 52 No. 218-85, Bogotá
Telephone: 6760257

2137 **CORPORACIÓN TECNOLÓGICA DE BOGOTÁ**
Carrera 21 No. 54-85, Bogotá
Telex: 5189
Telephone: 248-12-23
Rector: Hernando Campos Rodriguez
Secretario General: Berenice del Castillo Martinez

S. of Industrial Chemistry
Director: Omar Moral; *staff* 10 (30)
S. of Pharmacology
Director: Ramon Arrunategui; *staff* 10 (30)
S. of Electrochemistry
Director: Hector A. Corredor; *staff* 5 (10)
S. of Computer Science
Director: Hector Gayon; *staff* 5 (8)
Founded 1958 as Escuela de Quimica Industrial, acquired present title, 1980. A private institution.
Academic Year: February to December (february-June; August-December)
Admission Requirements: Secondary school certificate (bachillerato) and entrance examination.
Fees (Pesos): 86,000 per semester.
Language of Instruction: Spanish.
Degrees and Diplomas: Professional titles of Tecnológo, 3 ½ yrs.
Library: 12,000 vols.
Publication: Technological Research Newsletters (6 per semester).
Academic Staff, 1990: 20 (35).
Student Enrolment, 1990:

	Men	Women	Total
Of the country	330	415	745
Of other countries	1	–	1
Total	331	415	746

2138 **CORPORACIÓN TECNOLÓGICA INDUSTRIAL COLOMBIANA**
Calle 13 No. 17-12, Bogotá
Telephone: 2606477

2139 **CORPORACIÓN DE CIENCIAS EMPRESARIALES**
Calle 36 No. 17-12, Bogotá
Telephone: 2879421

P. of Commerce

2140 **CORPORACIÓN TECNOLÓGICA DE SANTANDER**
Carrera 30 No. 53-16, Bucaramanga (Santander)
Telephone: 37-29-49
Presidente: Fernando Vargas Mendoza
Secretario General: Patricia Tangariffe Robledo

D. of Surgical Instrumentation
Head: Mauro Miguel Rivera; *staff* 3
D. of Textile Design
Head: Gonzalo González Vallé; *staff* 5 (20)
D. of Hotel Administration
Head: Ana Francisca Martinez Q.; *staff* 7 (22)
D. of Tourist Administration
Head: Ana Francisca Martinez Q.; *staff* 6 (19)
D. of Publicity and Marketing Techniques
Head: Jose Sanchez; *staff* 4 (9)

Research Ce. (Incoming Tourism and Surgical Material Research)
Head: Mauricio Salazar Londoño; *staff* 1 (2)

Founded 1984. A private institute. Governing bodies: the Consejo Superior; the Consejo Académico.

Academic Year: February to December (February-July; August-December).

Admission Requirements: Secondary school certificate (bachillerato) and entrance examination.

Languages of Instruction: Spanish, English and French.

Degrees and Diplomas: Professional title of Tecnólogo, 7 semesters.

Academic Staff, 1990: c. 65.

Student Enrolment, 1990:

	Men	Women	Total
Of the country	120	675	795

2141 **ESCUELA COLOMBIANA DE MERCADOTECNIA**
Calle 56 No. 46-39, Medellín (Antioquia)
Telephone: 2399854

Founded 1970.

2142 **ESCUELA TRIBUTARIA E TECNOLOGÍAS DE COLOMBIA**
Calle 62 No. 49-67, Medellín (Antioquia)
Telephone: 2543077

Taxation Studies

Founded 1975. A private institution.

Admission Requirements: Secondary school certificate (bachillerato) and entrance examination.

Language of Instruction: Spanish.

Degrees and Diplomas: Professional title, 3 yrs.

Library: c. 470 vols.

Student Enrolment: c. 100.

2143 **FUNDACIÓN CENTRO DE ESTUDIOS SUPERIORES 'MARÍA GORETTI'**
Avenida de Las Américas, Pasto (Nariño)
Telephone: 35357

P. of Administration
Director: Gustavo Cortes Burbano; *staff* 3 (39)
P. of Ceramics
Director: Horacio Mora Ordoñez; *staff* 3 (24)
P. of Physical Education
Director: Ricardo Ortiz Solarte; *staff* 2 (38)
P. of Education (pre-school level)
Director: Alicia Pérez de López; *staff* 2 (25)
P. of Architectural Drawing
Director: Carlos E. Trujillo Santacruz; *staff* 2 (21)
P. of Topography
Director: Carlos E. Trujillo Santacruz; *staff* 2 (20)

Founded 1980. A private institution.

Academic Year: January to December.

Admission Requirements: Secondary school certificate (bachillerato) and entrance examination.

Fees (Pesos): 18,950 per semester.

Language of Instruction: Spanish.

Degrees and Diplomas: Professional title of Tecnológo, 3 yrs.

Library: 5000 vols.

Special Facilities (Museums, etc.): María Goretti Museum; Volcanic Observatory; Funcega Art Gallery.

Press or Publishing House: María Goretti Publication Centre.

Academic Staff, 1989: 13 (167).

Student Enrolment, 1990:

	Men	Women	Total
Of the country	5566	689	1255

2144 **FUNDACIÓN DE ESTUDIOS SUPERIORES**
Calle 63 No. 3-45, Bogotá
Telephone: 2359806

2145 **FUNDACIÓN INSTITUTO TECNOLÓGICO 'CONFENALCO'**
Cartagena (Bolívar)
Telephone: 620889

2146 **FUNDACIÓN TECNOLÓGICA 'ANTONIO DE AREVALO'**
Calle de La Moneda No. 7-122, Bolívar (Cartagena)
Telephone: 647082

2147 **FUNDACIÓN TECNOLÓGICA DEL ÁREA ANDINA**
Calle 71 No.13-21, Bogotá
Telephone: 2489054

Civil Engineering
Food Technology
Mining

2148 **FUNDACIÓN TECNOLÓGICA POLITÉCNICO NACIONAL**
Calle 34A No. 76-35, Medellín (Antioquia)
Telephone: 2503481

2149 **INSTITUTO CENTRAL FEMENINO**
Calle 50 No. 41-55, Medellín (Antioquia)
Telephone: 2393756

2150 **INSTITUTO SUPERIOR DE CIENCIAS SOCIALES Y ECONÓMICO-FAMILIARES 'ICSEF'**
Calle 70 No. 13-12, Bogotá
Telephone: 2483309

Administrative Studies

Founded 1971. A private institution.

Admission Requirements: Secondary school certificate (bachillerato) and entrance examination.

Language of Instruction: Spanish.

Degrees and Diplomas: Professional title, 3 yrs.

Library: c. 6000 vols.

Student Enrolment: c. 130.

2151 **INSTITUTO SUPERIOR DE EDUCACIÓN RURAL 'ISER'**
Carrera 8 No. 8-155, Pamplona (Norte de Santander)
Telephone: 82597
Rector: César Carrasco Villamizar
Secretario General: Jorge Enrique Castillo Rami

Ut. of Social Science
Director: Tulio E. Villamizar Solano
Ut. of Agronomy and Animal Science
Director: Manuel F. Urbina Sierra
Ut. of Education (Open U.)
Director: Pablo A. Jaimes Montano
Research Ce.
Director: Dario A. Sequeda Rojas

Founded 1956. A national institution.

Academic Year: February to November (February-June; July-November).

Admission Requirements: Secondary school certificate (bachillerato) and entrance examination.

Fees: Pesos: 22,800 per semester.

Language of Instruction: Spanish.

Degrees and Diplomas: Professional title of Tecnológo, 3 yrs.

Library: c. 7000 vols.

Academic Staff: c. 40.

Student Enrolment: c. 470.

2152 **INSTITUTO TECNOLÓGICO 'PASCUAL BRAVO'**
Apartado aéro 6821, Transversal 73 No. 73A-226, Medellín (Antioquia)
Telephone: 2345082
Rector: Jaime Eladio Lopera Caro

Industrial Systems Technology
Electronic Technologygy
Mechanical Technology
Electrical Technology

Founded 1938 as a school, acquired present status andtitle 1950. A national institution.

Admission Requirements: Secondary school certificate (bachillerato) and entrance examination.
Language of Instruction: Spanish.
Degrees and Diplomas: Professional titles of Tecnólogo, 3 ½ yrs (evening courses).
Library: c. 7980 vols.
Student Enrolment: c. 470.

2153 **INSTITUTO TECNOLÓGICO DE ADMINISTRACIÓN Y ECONOMÍA**
Calle 35 No. 981, Bucaramanga (Santander)
Telephone: 21885
Rector: Eduardo Sierra Barreneche
Secretario General: Héctor Olaya Pedraza

Ut. of Business Administration
Director: Jaime Luis Gutiérrez
Ut. of Art and Decoration
Director: Gloria Riberos de Silva
Ut. of Fashion Design
Director: Gloria Riberos de Silva

Founded 1972. A private institution. Governing body: the Consejo Directivo.
Academic Year: February to December (February-June; August-December).
Admission Requirements: Secondary school certificate (bachillerato) and entrance examination.
Fees (Pesos): 70,555-82,755 per semester.
Language of Instruction: Spanish.
Degrees and Diplomas: Professional titles, 3 yrs.
Library: c. 3500 vols.
Academic Staff, 1990: c. 60

2154 **INSTITUTO TECNOLÓGICO COLOMBIANO DE INCOLDA**
Avenida Guadalupe No. 1B-71, Cali (Valle)
Telephone: 514322

2155 **INSTITUTO TECNOLÓGICO DE ELECTRÓNICA DE COMMUNICACIONES 'ITEC'**
Transversal 49 No. 105-84, Bogotá
Telephone: 253-60-40
Director: Victoria Kairuz Marquez

D. of Electronics and Communications Technology
Head: Hernán Caballero Herrera

Founded 1961. Authorized to grant higher education diplomas 1987. A national institution. Governing body: the Consejo Superior.
Admission Requirements: Secondary school certificate (bachillerato) and entrance examination.
Language of Instruction: Spanish.
Degrees and Diplomas: Professional titles, 2-3 yrs.
Library: c. 8000 vols.
Academic Staff, 1990: 36 (7).
Student Enrolment, 1990:

	Men	Women	Total
Of the country	159	19	178

2156 **POLITÉCNICO COLOMBIANO 'JAIME ISAZA CADAVID'**
Apartado Las Vegas Calle 10 No. 48-85, El Poblado, Medellín (Antioquia)
Telephone: 2665700
Rector: Norberto Guerra Vélez
Secretaria General Luz Emilia Gutiérrez Gil

Cost Accounting
Precision Engineering
Industrial Technology
Systems Analyses and Data Processing
Agricultural Technology
Civil Engineering

Branches at: Rionegro, Jericó, and Apartadó.
Founded 1964. An official provincial institution. Governing bodies: the Consejo Superior; the Consejo Académico.
Academic Year: February to November (February-June; July-November).
Admission Requirements: Secondary school certificate (bachillerato) and entrance examination.
Language of Instruction: Spanish.
Degrees and Diplomas: Professional titles, 3-5 yrs.
Library: Central Library, 20 222 vols.
Publication: Ciencia Tecnologia y Cultura (bimonthly).
Press or Publishing House: Editorial Politécnico.
Academic Staff, 1986-87:: 357 (300).
Student Enrolment, 1986-87:

	Men	Women	Total
Of the country	2600	2400	5000

2157 **POLITÉCNICO GRANCOLOMBIANO**
Calle 57 Carrera 3 Este, Bogotá
Telephone: 17-97-77
Fax: 17-42-28
Rector: César Tulio Delgado Hurtado
Secretario General: Maurício Canales Espinosa

D. of Agricultural Management
Head: Andres Romero Moreno
D. of Banking Management
Head: Douglas Bernal Saavedra
D. of Cost and Finance and Auditing
Head: Maurício Rubio García
D. of Systems Management
Head: Sergio Ibarnegaray
Research D. (Political Science)
Head: Alejandro Fernandez
D. of Planning and Statistics Research
Head: Clara Ines Martínez
Computer Ce.
Head: Camilo Garcia Peña

Founded 1980. Governing body: the Consejo Superior.
Academic Year: January to November (January-May; July-November).
Admission Requirements: Secondary school certificate (bachillerato) and entrance examination.
Fees (Pesos): 119,060-126,615.
Language of Instruction: Spanish
Degrees and Diplomas: Professional titles, 3-5 yrs.
Library: Library.
Academic Staff, 1990: 269
Student Enrolment, 1990: 4250.

2158 **POLITÉCNICO 'MARCO FIDEL SUÁREZ'**
Carrera 49 No. 52-29, Bello (Antioquia)
Telephone: 2751821

2159 **SERVICIO NACIONAL DE APRENDIZAJE 'SENA'**
Calle 52 No. 2bis-15, Cali (Valle del Cauca)
Telephone: 467198

P. of Topography

2160 **TECNOLÓGICO 'INPI'**
Calle 67 No. 5-27, Bogotá
Telephone: 2110928

2161 **UNIDADES TECNOLÓGICAS DE SANTANDER**
Apartado aéro 899, Calle 10 No. 28-77, Bucaramanga (Santander)
Telephone: 358366

CONGO

2162 ***UNIVERSITÉ MARIEN NGOUABI**

B.P. 69, Brazzaville
Telex: 5331 KG
Telephone: 8124-36
Recteur: Hilaire Bouhoyi (1986-)
Secrétaire générale: Marie-Rose Quenum

F. of Letters and Human Sciences
Dean: Elo Dacy; *staff* 114
F. of Sciences
Dean: Alphonse Ekouya; *staff* 135
F. of Law
Dean: Narcisse Mayetela
F. of Economics
Dean: Louis Bakabadio
I. of Management
Director: Mwaziby-Olingoba
I. of Rural Development
Director: Daniel Amboulou
I. of Education
Director: Bonaventure Mengho; *staff* 88
I. of Economic and Juridical Sciences (including Administration and Business Administration)
Director: Nestor Makoundzi-Wollo; *staff* 79
I. of Physical Education and Sport
Director: Paul Ebondzibato; *staff* 41
I. of Health Sciences
Director: Assori Itoua-Ngaporo; *staff* 51
S. of Technical Education
Director: Raphaël Batadila; *staff* 41
S. of Administration and Training for the Magistrature
Director: Firmin Kitsoro-Kinzounza; *staff* 23
I. of Teacher Training (Loubomo)
Director: Diendonas Hossié; *staff* 12
D. for Correspondence Courses
Directeur: Dongala Boundzeki

Founded 1959 as Centre d'Etudes administratives et techniques supérieures. Previously formed part of the Fondation de l'Enseignement supérieur en Afrique centrale. Became Université de Brazzaville 1971, acquired present title 1977. Governing body: the Comité de Direction.

Arrangements for co-operation with the Universities of: Omar Bongo, Gabon; Kinshasa; Bangui; Burundi; Rwanda; Pennsylvania; Howard; Louvain; Dijon; Montpellier; Strasbourg; Paris VII.

Academic Year: October to June (October-December; January-March; April-June).

Admission Requirements: Secondary school certificate (baccalauréat) or equivalent.

Language of Instruction: French.

Degrees and Diplomas: Licence, 3 yrs. Diplôme d'études supérieures (D.E.S.), a further 2 yrs. Diplôme d'Ingénieur, 2-5 yrs. Doctorat, 5 yrs after D.E.S. Certificat de Capacité en Droit; Teaching qualifications.

Library: Central Library, *c.*70,000 vols.

Publications: Annales; Dimi; Mélanges; La Saison des Pluies (all annually); Mbongi (quarterly); Sango (Bulletin) (bimonthly).

Academic Staff, 1986-87: c. 580.

Student Enrolment, 1986-87:

	Men	Women	Total
Of the country	8209	1499	9708
Of other countries	804	167	971
Total	9013	1666	10,679

COSTA RICA

Universities

Public Institutions

2163 **UNIVERSIDAD DE COSTA RICA**
University of Costa Rica
Ciudad Universitaria 'Rodrigo Facio', San Pedro de Montes de Oca, San José
Telex: 2544 UNICORI
Telephone: 25-55-55
Rector: Fernando Durán Ayanegui (1985-1989)

F. of Letters
Dean: Cristina Brenes Vega; *staff* 46 (60)
F. of Science
Dean: Alfonso Mata Jiménez; *staff* 138 (79)
F. of Fine Arts
Dean: Daniel Gallegos Troyo; *staff* 36 (41)
F. of Agriculture (including Animal Husbandry)
Dean: Miguel González Aguilar; *staff* 35 (17)
F. of Engineering (including Architecture)
Dean: Rodolfo Herrera Jiménez; *staff* 79 (148)
F. of Economics (including Business Administration)
Dean: Percival Kelso Baldioceda; *staff* 29 (84)
F. of Social Sciences
Dean: Zinnia Méndez Barrantes; *staff* 75 (153)
F. of Education
Dean: Fernando Castro Ramírez; *staff* 53 (79)
F. of Medicine (including Nursing)
Dean: Carlos Arguedas Chaverri; *staff* 67 (429)
F. of Dentistry
Dean: José Rafael Garita Salas; *staff* 22 (81)
F. of Microbiology
Dean: Misael Chinchilla Carmona; *staff* 29 (19)
F. of Pharmacy
Dean: Carlos Cubero Vega; *staff* 12 (17)
F. of Law
Dean: Bernardo Vanderlaat Echeverría; *staff* 29 (43)
S. of General Studies
Director: Estrella Cartín de Güier; *staff* 25 (94)
Centralamerican S. of Sociology
Centralamerican S. of Geology
Ce. for Lifelong Education
Head: Rodolfo Calderón

Also 38 schools of the faculties and 18 research centres and institutes. Regional Centres at : Guanacaste, Limón, Turrialba, and San Ramón.

Founded 1814 as Casa de Enseñanza de Santo Tomás and became Universidad de Santo Tomás in 1844. Closed 1887, with exception of school of law, and abolished by decree 1888. Re-established as Universidad de Costa Rica by decree of Congress 1940, and reopened in 1941 with the existing faculties of law, pharmacy, agriculture, fine arts, and education, together with new schools of philosophy and letters, and engineering. School of dentistry opened in 1942 and school of economics and social sciences in 1943. Titles of some schools changed as part of university reforms, 1957 and 1972. The university is an autonomous institution. Financially supported bythe central government which provides 10% of its Education budget for the university. Governing bodies: the Asamblea Universitaria; the Consejo Universitario, composed of the Rector, the Minister of Education, the Secretary-General, 6 members of the academic staff, a representative from each Regional Centre, a member of the administrative sector, and two student representatives. Residential facilities for students.

Arrangements for co-operation with the Universities of: Mexico; Carleton, Ottawa; Concordia; Aix-Marseille III; Toulouse III; Rome; Tacchiang, Taiwan; Northern Illinois; Kansas; California; New York, Albany. Gaullaudet College of Washington.

Academic Year: February to December (February-June; August-December).

Admission Requirements: Secondary school certificate (bachillerato) or equivalent, and entrance examination.

Fees (Colones): 750 per credit.

Language of Instruction: Spanish.

Degrees and Diplomas: Diplomado, 2-3 yrs. Bachiller (Bachillerato Universitario), 4-5 yrs. Licenciado, 5-6 yrs. Maestría, 6-7 yrs.Doctorado in–Philosophy; Chemistry. Degrees of Specialization.

Libraries: Central Library, *c.* 189,890 vols; specialized libraries, 297,000.

Special Facilities (Museums, etc.): Museums: Herbal; Entomology; Zoology.

Publications: Revista de Filosofía; Revista de Ciencias Jurídicas; Revista de Biología Tropical; Agronomía Costarricense; Revista de Ciencias y Tecnología; Revista de Educación; Revista de Filología y Linguística; Revista de Ciencias Sociales; Revista de Ciencias Económicas; Revista de Historia; Armario de Estudios Centroamericanos.

Press or Publishing House: Editorial de la Universidad de Costa Rica.

Academic Staff, 1986-87:

Rank	Full-time	Part-time
Catedráticos	212	121
Asociados	299	193
Adjuntos	120	134
Instructores	234	540
Total	865	988

Student Enrolment, 1986-87:

	Men	Women	Total
Of the country	16,977	17,605	34,582

2164 **UNIVERSIDAD ESTATAL A DISTANCIA**
Ap. 2 de Plaza González Víquez, San José
Telex: 3003 UNED CR
Telephone: 24-16-89
Fax: 53-49-90
Rector: Celedinio Ramírez Ramírez (1986-91)

S. of Education
Head: Lara González; *staff* 21 (4)
S. of Management
Head: Anabelle Castillo; *staff* 21 (4)
S. of Health Studies
S. of Natural and Applied Sciences
Head: Walter Araya; *staff* 21 (4)
S. of Social and Human Sciences
Head: Walter Araya; *staff* 21 (4)

Also 30 Regional Centres.

Founded 1977 to give access to higher education to those who are unable to attend university, particularly those living in rural areas. An autonomous institution financed by the State. Governing bodies: the Asamblea Universitaria, comprising 66 members; the Consejo Universitario, comprising 9 members.

Arrangements for co-operation with: Universidade Federal de Santa Maria, Brazil; Open University, Milton Keynes; Universidad Nacional de Educación a Distancia, Madrid; University of New Mexico.

Academic Year: March to November (March-June; August-November).

Admission Requirements: Secondary school certificate (bachillerato) or equivalent.

Fees (Colones): Tuition, 2400 per 12 credits; 1875 per 3 credits.

Language of Instruction: Spanish.

Degrees and Diplomas: Title of Diplomado. Bachillerato in: Education; Educational Administration; Finance and Banking; Business Administration; Agricultural Business Administration; Child Social Service Administration; Cooperative Business Administration, 4 yrs. Licenciado in Education; Education Administration, 5 yrs.

Library: Central Library, 125,045 vols.

Publication: Enlace (biannually).

Press or Publishing House: Editorial Universidad Estatal a Distancia.

Academic Staff, 1990: 90 (20).
Student Enrolment, 1986-87:

	Men	Women	Total
Of the country	4494	6206	10,700

2165 **UNIVERSIDAD NACIONAL**
National University
Apartado 86, Heredia
Telex: 7550 UNAVI CR
Telephone: 37-63-63
Fax: (506) 380086/377593
Rector: Rose Marie Ruíz Bravo
Secretario General: Jorge Mora Alfaro

Ce. for General Studies
Dean: Hazel Vargas
F. of Philosophy and Letters
Dean: Corra Ferro Calabrese
F. of Social Sciences
Dean: Vladimir de la Cruz
F. of Earth and Marine Sciences
Dean: Fernando Rivera
F. of Exact and Natural Sciences (including Computer Sciences)
Dean: Tatiana Lascaria
F. of Health Sciences (Veterinary Medicine and Physical Education)
Dean: Luis Vargas Aráuz
Ce. for Research and Teaching in Education
Dean: Oscar Besavides
Also Regional Centres at: Liberia, Pérez Zeledós.

Founded 1973. A State institution. Governing bodies: the Asamblea Universitaria; the Consejo Universitario.

Academic Year: March to November (March-June; August-November).

Admission Requirements: Secondary school certificate (bachillerato) and entrance examination.

Fees: According to parents' income.

Language of Instruction: Spanish.

Degrees and Diplomas: Bachillerato, 4 yrs. Licenciado, 5 yrs. Professional title of Técnico, 2 yrs. Doctorado, 7 yrs. Teaching qualification, 3 yrs.

Library: Total, *c.* 49,850 vols.

Publications: Repertorio Americano (every 4 years); Revista Geográfica (biennially); Praxis (Philosophy) (biennially); Revista de Historia (biennially).

Academic Staff, 1990: 1200.

Student Enrolment, 1990: 12,000.

2166 ***UNIVERSIDAD TECNOLÓGICA DE COSTA RICA**
Apartado 159, Cartago
Telex: 51-53-48
Telephone: 51-53-33
Rector: Arturo Jofré Vartanián (1987-91)
Vicerrector de Administración: Enrique Rivera Bianchini

D. of Business Administration
Director: Nidia Ullet Córdoba; *staff* 10 (60)
D. of Agricultural Administration
Director: Rodrigo Mata Solano; *staff* 11 (3)
D. of Electronics
Director: Victorino Rojas Madrigal; *staff* 15
D. of Agricultural Engineering
Director: Luis E. Obando Quesada; *staff* 71 (2)
D. of Industrial Engineering
D. of Forestry Engineering
Director: Freddy Rojas Rodríguez; *staff* 102 (3)
D. of Industrial Production
Director: Joaquín Solano Quesada; *staff* 13 (3)
D. of Industrial Design
Director: Sergio Rivas Porras; *staff* 8
D. of Computer Sciences
Director: Luis Montoya Poitevien; *staff* 14 (3)
D. of Civil Engineering
Director: Eduardo Paniagua Madrigal; *staff* 7 (14)
D. of Wood Technology
Director: Francisco Jiménez; *staff* 8 (2)
D. of Agriculture
Director: Férnando Gómez Sánchez; *staff* 16 (3)
D. of Metallurgy
Director: Juan F. Alvarez Castro; *staff* 8 (1)
D. of Drawing:
Director: Mario Cordero Palomo; *staff* 4 (10)
D. for Production Supervising
Head: Oscar Gamboa Calderón; *staff* – (7)
D. for Security and Occupational Hygiene
Head: Guillermo Rojas; *staff* 3 (4)
Computer Ce.
Director: Juan Mario Rodriguez
Contruction Experimental Ce.
Information Technology Ce.
Wood Experimental Ce.
Also Regional Centre at San Carlos and Academic Centre at San José.

Founded 1971. A State institution financed by the government. Governing bodies: the Asamblea Institucional; the Consejo Institucional, comprising the Rector, the Minister of Education, the Minister of Planning and Economics, 4 members of the academic staff, a member of the administrative sector, a graduate, and two student representatives. Residential facilities for academic staff and students at San Carlos.

Arrangements for co-operation with: Murray State University, Kentucky; University of Wisconsin.

Academic Year: February to November (February-May; August-November).

Admission Requirements: Secondary school certificate (bachillerato) or equivalent, and entrance examination.

Fees (Colones): Tuition, 2000 per semester; foreign students, 4000.

Language of Instruction: Spanish.

Degrees and Diplomas: Diplomado, 2 yrs. Bachiller, 4 yrs. Licenciado, 5 ½ yrs. Maestría in Computer Sciences, 6 yrs.

Library: Total, 545,040 vols.

Publications: Comunicación (biannually); Módulo; Tecnología en Marcha (quarterly).

Academic Staff, 1989-90:

Rank	Full-time	Part-time
Profesores Asociados	29	2
Profesores Adjuntos	102	13
Instructores	96	109
Profesores Técnicos	23	16
Total	250	140

Student Enrolment, 1990:

	Men	Women	Total
Of the country	3009	752	3761
Of other countries	158	39	197
Total	3958	791	3958

Private Institutions

2167 ***UNIVERSIDAD AUTÓNOMA DE CENTRO AMÉRICA**
Autonomous University of Central America
Apartado 7637, 1000 San José
Telex: 2907
Telephone: 23-58-22
Rector: Guillermo Malavassi Vargas (1981-)

D. of Business Administration
D. of Public Administration
D. of Accountancy
D. of Banking and Finance
D. of Human Resources
D. of Cooperative Studies
D. of Industrial Engineering
D. of Administrative Engineering
D. of Computer Sciences
D. of Architecture
D. of Fine Arts
D. of Law
D. of Economics
D. of Social Sciences
D. of Political Science
D. of International Relations
D. of Public Relations
D. of Design
D. of Classics
D. of Philosophy
D. of Geography

D. of History
D. of Humanities
D. of Education
D. of Medicine
D. of Music
D. of Journalism
D. of Catholic Theology

Founded 1976 as an independent institution authorized by the government. Governing bodies: the Senado Académico, comprising the Rector, deans, and the Minister of Education; the Board of Trustees.

Academic Year: January to December (January-April; May-August; September-December).

Admission Requirements: Secondary school certificate (bachillerato) or foreign equivalent, and entrance examination.

Language of Instruction: Spanish.

Degrees and Diplomas: Bachiller in all fields, 3 yrs, except Civil Engineering; Industrial Engineering; Psychology; Architecture, 4 yrs; Medicine, 5 sem. Licenciado and Magister, a further 2 yrs, except Medicine, 6 sem. Doctorado, in Law, 2 yrs after Licenciado or Magister. Doctor of Medicine, 3 ½ sem after Licenciado.

Library: c. 11,000 vols.

Publications: Ordenanzas Académicas; Anuario de la Universidad (both annually).

Academic Staff: c. 580.

Student Enrolment: c. 8360.

2168 **UNIVERSIDAD ADVENTISTA DE CENTRO AMÉRICA**

Carretera a Iriquís, La Ceiba, Alajuela
Cables: ucadve
Telex: 7034
Telephone: (506) 4156-22
Fax: (506) 4112-82
Rector: Tevni Grajales

S. of Business Administration
Director: Danny Jones *staff* 5
S. of Theology
Director; Julio Juárez; *staff* 3
S. of Education
Director: Alberto dos Santos; *staff* 10
Research Ce.
Secretary: Alberto dos Santos

Founded 1986. A private institution authorized by the government. Residential facilities for academic staff and students.

Academic Year: March to November (March-June; July-November).

Admission Requirements: Secondary school certificate (bachillerato).

Fees (Colones): 52,380-154,890 per annum.

Language of Instruction: Spanish.

Degrees and Diplomas: Bachiller, 4 yrs. Diplomado in Secretarial Studies, 2 yrs.

Library: Central Library, 28,755 vols.

Publications: Eco Universitario (biannually); Eco Estudiantil (annually).

Press or Publishing House: Imprenta Granix

Academic Staff, 1990: 18.

Student Enrolment, 1990:

	Men	Women	Total
Of the country	39	57	96
Of other countries	148	129	277
Total	187	186	373

2169 **UNIVERSIDAD INTERNACIONAL DE LAS AMÉRICAS**

Calle 23, Avenidas 7 y 7bis, San José
Telephone: 33-5304
Fax: 506-223216
Rector: Miguel Angel Gutiérrez
Director de Administración: Cristina Solís

D. of Business Administration
Director: Jorge E.Mora; *staff* 17 (30)
D. of International Trade
Director: Alvaro Apesteegui; *staff* 5 (8)
D. of Accountancy
Director: Carlos López; *staff* 4 (7)
D. of Systems Engineering
Director: Miguel A. Alfaro; *staff* 10 (13)
D. of Industrial Engineering
Director: Benigno Guiérrez; *staff* 8 (12)
D. of Law
Director: Máximo Sequeira; *staff* 9 (14)
D. of Education (pre-school level)
Director: Teres
D. of Electrical Engineering
Director: José Rod
D. of English
Director: Jimmy Hernández; *staff* 7 (14)
D. of Diplomacy
Director: Max Suárez; *staff* 3 (4)
D. of Risks and Assurance
Director: Victor Julio
D. of Advertising
Director: Eduardo Ching; *staff* 4 (7)
D. of Tourism
Director: Miguel Angel Gutiérrez; *staff* 8 (12)
Computer Ce.
Regional College at San Isidro del General.

Founded 1986 by the International American Foundation. A private institution authorized by the government.

Academic Year: January to December (January-April; May-August; September-December).

Admission Requirements: Secondary school certificate (bachillerato).

Fees (Colones): Registration, 5000; tuition, 20,000 per semester. Foreign students, registration, $US 100; tuition,

Fees: $US 400.

Language of Instruction: Spanish.

Degrees and Diplomas: Bachiller, 4 yrs. Licenciado, 5-6 yrs. Maestrá in–Business Administration; International Trade.

Library: 5000 vols.

Special Facilities (Museums, etc.): T.V. Channel.

Academic Staff, 1990: 930 (175).

Student Enrolment, 1990:

	Men	Women	Total
Of the country	1784	1581	3365
Of other countries	113	126	239
Total	1897	1707	3604

2170 **UNIVERSIDAD LATINOAMERICANA DE CIENCIAS Y TECNOLOGÍA**

Apartado 10235, 1000 San José
Telephone: 2391-55
Fax: 2245-42
President Alvaro Castro Harrigan

Business Administration
Accountancy
Tourism
Computer Sciences
Research and Development

Founded 1986. A private institution authorized by thegovernment.

Academic Year: January to December.

Admission Requirements: Secondary school certficate (bachillerato).

Fees (Colones): 5100-9500.

Language of Instruction: Spanish.

Degrees and Diplomas: Bachiller, 4 yrs. Licenciado, a further 2 yrs.Maestria, 6 yrs.

Library: Central Library, 10,000 vols.

Publication: Revista Cientifica (in preparation).

Academic Staff, 1990: 95.

Student Enrolment, 1990: 932.

2171 **UNIVERSIDAD PANAMERICANA**

Calle 23 entre avenida Central y la, Apartado 886, 1002 San José
Founded 1988.

Other Institutions

Professional Education

2172 **CENTRO AGRONÓMICO TROPICAL DE INVESTIGACIÓN Y ENSEÑANZA**

Tropical Agricultural Research and Training Centre
Turrialba 7170
Telex: 8005 CATIE
Telephone: 56-64-31
Director: Rodrigo Tarté (1984-88)
Jefe de Administración: Agustin López

Agriculture (including Forestry and Animal Husbandry)

Founded 1942 as Instituto Interamericano de Ciencias Agricolas, became autonomous centre under present title 1973. It is supported and financed by governments of the Organization of American States which are represented on its Board of Directors. Essentially a graduate school, its programme is conducted in cooperation with universities within and outside the area. Some residential facilities for academic staff and students.

Academic Year: September to September (September-December; January-March; April-June; June-September).

Admission Requirements: Degree of Bachelor of Science, Ingeniero agrónomo, Ingeniero forestal, Médico veterinario, or a corresponding professional qualification.

Fees ($US): 4320-5080 per annum.

Language of Instruction: Spanish.

Degrees and Diplomas: Magister Scientiae, Mag.Sc. (Master of Science), yrs.

Library: 80,000 vols.

Publications: Activities at Turrialba (quarterly); Informe de Progreso (annually).

Student Enrolment, 1986-87:

	Men	Women	Total
Of the country	9	3	12
Of other countries	27	5	32
Total	36	8	44

2173 **COLEGIO UNIVERSITARIO DE ALAJUELA CUNA**

Apartado 229, Alajuela
Telephone: 41-86-22
Dean: Hernán Gdo. Cordero G.

D. of Interior Design
D. of Industrial Health Studies
D. of Purchasing Technology
D. of Finance
D. of Public Administration
D. of Business Administration
D. of Foreign Trade

Founded 1977 and officially recognized by the government 1980. Governing body: the Consejo Directivo.

Academic Year: March to November (March-July; August-November).

Admission Requirements: Secondary school certificate (bachillerato) and entrance examination.

Language of Instruction: Spanish.

Degrees and Diplomas: Diplomado, 2-3 yrs.

Library: c. 3170 vols.

Academic Staff: c. 10 (70).

Student Enrolment: c. 630.

2174 **COLEGIO UNIVERSITARIO DE CARTAGO CUC**

Apartado postal 422, Alajuela

2175 **COLEGIO UNIVERSITARIO DE PUNTARENAS CUP**

Puntarenas

Founded 1980.

2176 **ESCUELA CENTROAMERICANA DE GANADERÍA**

Apartado postal 7, Atenas, Alajuela

Stock-raising

Founded 1969.

2177 **ESCUELA SUPERIOR DE ADMINISTRACIÓN DE NEGOCIOS**

Apartado postal 3510, San José

Business Administration

2178 **INSTITUTO DE TECNOLOGÍA ADMINISTRATIVA**

Apartado postal 1900, San José 1000
Cables: castrocazo costa rica
Telephone: 23-91-55
Director: Alvaro Castro Harrigan (1980-90)

S. of Business Administration
D. of Computer Sciences
Professional Retraining D.
D. for Correspondence Courses

Founded 1980. A private institution authorized by the government. Governing body: the Board of Directors.

Academic Year: February to December (February-July; July-December).

Admission Requirements: Secondary school certificate (bachillerato) or equivalent, and entrance examination.

Language of Instruction: Spanish.

Degrees and Diplomas: Title of Diplomado, 2-3 yrs.

Library: c. 10,000 vols.

Press or Publishing House: Editorial Técnica Comercial, Inc.

Academic Staff, 1990: 10 (80).

Student Enrolment, 1990:

	Men	Women	Total
Of the country	1215	691	1906
Of other countries	52	17	69
Total	1267	708	1975

2179 **INSTITUTO SUPERIOR DE ADMINISTRACIÓN DE EMPRESAS**

Apartado 31, San Francisco de Dos Rios, San José
Telephone: 21-42-67

Accountancy
Co-ordinator: Guillermo Sáenz G. *staff* – (5)
D. of Business Administration
Co-ordinator: Ramiro Arguedas V.; *staff* – (4)

Founded 1972. A private institution authorized by the government.

Academic Year: March to November.

Admission Requirements: Secondary school certificate (bachillerato) and entrance examination.

Language of Instruction: Spanish.

Degrees and Diplomas: Professional title of Contador, accountancy, 3 yrs.

Library: c. 250 vols.

Press or Publishing House: Departamento de Publicaciones-ISAE.

Academic Staff, 1990: c.–(12).

Student Enrolment, 1990:

	Men	Women	Total
Of the country	347	110	447

2180 **INSTITUTO TÉCNICO DE ADMINISTRACIÓN DE NEGOCIOS**

Apartado postal 1380, 1000 San José
Telephone: 25-58-78
Director: José J. Seco (1983-)

Business Administration
Industrial Electronics

Founded 1968. A private institution authorized by the government.

Academic Year: March to February (March-June; July-October; November-February).

Admission Requirements: Secondary school certificate (bachillerato).

Fees (Colones): 3100 per month.

Language of Instruction: Spanish.

Degrees and Diplomas: Diplomado, 2 yrs.

Library: c. 1000 vols.

Academic Staff, 1990: –(70).

Student Enrolment, 1990:

Of the country	1400
Of other countries	32
Total	1432

COTE D'IVOIRE

Universities

2181 ***UNIVERSITÉ NATIONALE DE CÔTE D'IVOIRE**
B.P.V. 34, Abidjan
Telex: 26138 RECTU CI
Telephone: (255) 43-90-00
Fax: (225) 44-35-31
Recteur: Bakary Touré (1983-)
Secrétaire général: Julienne Badia

F. of Sciences
Dean: Kore Diopoh; *staff* 212 (6)
F. of Medicine
Dean: Leopold Malan Kassi; *staff* 217 (9)
F. of Law
Dean: Segui Degni; *staff* 88 (7)
F. of Economics
Dean: ADama Bakayoko; *staff* 92 (9)
F. of Letters and Human Sciences
Dean: Barthelmy Kotchy; *staff* 179 (9)
F. of Pharmacy
Dean: Etienne Yapo Abbé; *staff* 25 (22)
I. of Dentistry
Dean: Joannes Egnankou Kouame; *staff* 18
I. of Tropical Ecology
Director: Yaya Sangare; *staff* 1 (6)
I. of Applied Linguistics
Director: Jeremy Kouadio N'Guessan; *staff* 24
I. of Negro-African Literature and Aesthetics
Director: Koffi Niamkey; *staff* 89
I. of Ethno-Sociology
Director: N'Guessan Kouame; *staff* 11 (6)
I. of Tropical Geography
Director: Abdoulaye Sawadogo; *staff* 4 (18)
Ce. of French for Foreign Students
Director: Balli Grodri; *staff* 18 (3)
I. of African History, Art, and Archaeology
Director: Bizan Semi; *staff* 13 (9)
I. of Criminology
Director: Alain Cissouko; *staff* 2 (4)
Ce. for Lifelong Education
Also 9 Research Centres.

Founded 1958 as Centre d'études supérieures, became Université d'Abidjan 1964. Linked to French university system by intergovernmental agreements concluded in 1961. Its degrees and diplomas are recognized in France. Residential facilities for academic staff and students.

Arrangements for co-operation with 40 French Universities and the Universities of: Brussels; Naples; Neuchâtel; Bayreuth; Salamanca; Louvain (Catholic); Cologne; Michigan; Illinois; Brasilia; São Paulo; Santa Catarina (Federal); Para; Montreal; McGill; Quebec; Sherbrook; Cape Coast; Liberia; Niamey; Ouagadougou. Ecole normale de Bénin.

Academic Year: September to June (October-February; March-June).

Admission Requirements: Secondary school certificate (baccalauréat) or equivalent, or special entrance examination.

Fees (Francs C.F.A.): Registration, 4200-50,000.

Language of Instruction: French.

Degrees and Diplomas: Law and Economics: Diplôme d'études universitaires générales (D.E.U.G.), 2 yrs; Licence, 1 yr after D.E.U.G.; Maîtrise, 1 yr after Licence; Diplôme d'études approfondies (D.E.A.), 1 yr after Maîtrise; Doctorat de spécialité (3e cycle), 1 yr after D.E.A.; Doctorat de l'Université; also Certificat de Capacité en Droit, law, 2 yrs. Science: Diplôme univesitaire d'études scientifiques (D.U.E.S.), 2 yrs; Licence, 1 yr following D.U.E.S.; Maîtrise, 1 yr after Licence; Diplôme d'études supérieures (D.E.S.); Diplôme d'études approfondies (D.E.A.), 1 yr after Maîtrise; Doctorat de spécialité (3e cycle), 1 yr after D.E.A. and thesis; Doctorat ès Sciences, at least 2 yrs after Maîtrise; Diplôme d'Ingénieur-Docteur; Doctorat de l'Université (Science). Letters and Human Sciences: Diplôme universitaire d'études littéraires (D.U.E.L.), 2 yrs; Licence ès Lettres, 1 yr after D.U.E.L.; Maîtrise, 1 yr after Licence; Diplôme d'études approfondies(D.E.A.), 1 yr after Maîtrise; Doctorat de spécialité (3e cycle) (Géographie, Sciences sociales). Medicine: Doctorat d'Etat; Doctorat de l'Université; also Diplôme in Pharmacy, 3 yrs; Doctorat d'Etat en Chirurgie dentaire (1ère, 2ème années).

Libraries: Central Library, *c.* 80,000 vols; libraries of the faculties, 38,897.

Special Facilities (Museums, etc.): Jardin botanique.

Publications: Annales de l'Université; Revue de Communication audio-visuelle; Revue de Littérature et Esthétique Négro-africaine; Revue Ivoirienne de Droit; Journal 'Ekomba'; Cahiers: de Recherches économiques et sociales; de Recherche linguistique; Revue de Géographie de Côte d'Ivoire; Revue Ivoirienne de Philosophie et de Culture.

Academic Staff, 1988-89: 861.

Student Enrolment, 1988-89:

	Men	Women	Total
Of the country	13,786	2891	16,677
Of other countries	1263	401	1664
Total	15,049	3292	18,341

Other Institutions

Technical Education

2182 **INSTITUT NATIONAL SUPÉRIEUR DE L'ENSEIGNEMENT TECHNIQUE**
B.P.V. 79, Abidjan 1083
Telex: 2288
Telephone: 44-42-88
Directeur général: Jean-Jonas Adou (1975-)
Secrétaire général: Kouakou Houssou

S. of Engineering
Director: Georges Collin
S. of Commerce
Director: Ouattara Aboulaye
I. of Industrial Technology
Director: Nahounou Bobouo
I. of Technology (Business Administration and Finance)
Director: Atsain Kouadio Ignace
I. of Computer Sciences
Director: Amon d'Aby
I. of Accountancy
Director: Coulibaly Kouhatien
S. of Engineering Specialization
Director: P. Veil
Ce. for Lifelong Education
Head: Kouao Kakou Sibinan

Founded 1975. A State institution. Residential facilities for academic staff and students. Residential facilities for academic staff and students.

Arrangements for co-operation with: Ecole nationale supérieure d'Art et Métiers, Paris; Centre d'Enseignement supérieure des Affaires, Paris; Collège Polytechnique Universitaire, Cotonou; Ecole nationale supérieure d'Enseignement technique, Cachan; Institut national des Techniques économiques et comptables, Paris.

Academic Year: September to July (September-February; February-July).

Admission Requirements: Secondary school certificate (baccalauréat) and entrance examination.

Fees (Francs C.F.A.): 5500.

Languages of Instruction: French and English.

Degrees and Diplomas: Diplôme d'Ingénieur, 5 yrs. Diplôme universitaire de technologie (D.U.T.). Qualifications as technician (B.T.S.). Diplômes in–Commerce; Accountancy; Programming.

Library: Central Library, 2500 vols.

Academic Staff, 1986-87: 74.
Student Enrolment, 1986-87:

	Men
Of the country	1192
Of other countries	101
Total	1293

2183 **INSTITUT NATIONAL DE LA JEUNESSE ET DES SPORTS**
B.P.V. 803, Abidjan 04

Physical Education
Founded 1961.

2184 **CENTRE D'ANIMATION ET DE FORMATION à L'ACTION CULTURELLE**
B.P.V. 39, Abidjan

Library Science
Museology
Cultural Techniques
Founded 1984.

2185 **ACADÉMIE DES SCIENCES ET TECHNIQUES DE LA MER**
B.P.V. 158, Abidjan

Navigation
Marine Transport
Founded 1986.

Professional Education

2186 **ÉCOLE NATIONALE D'ADMINISTRATION**
B.P.V. 20, Abidjan
Telephone: 41-52-25

Public Administration
Founded 1960.
Academic Year: November to July (November-February; February-July).
Admission Requirements: Competitive entrance examination following further studies after secondary school certificate, or 4 yrs publicservice.
Languages of Instruction: French. Degrees and diplomas: Diplôme; Certificat, 2 yrs.
Library: c. 10,500 vols.
Academic Staff: c. 80.
Student Enrolment: c. 450.

2187 **ÉCOLE NATIONALE SUPÉRIEURE AGRONOMIQUE**
B.P. 35, Km. 8 Route d'Adzopé, Abidjan 08
Telephone: 44-08-40

Agriculture
Founded 1965. A State institution attached to the National University of Côte d'Ivoire, and under the jurisdiction of the Ministry of Agriculture. Governing body: the Conseil d'administration, comprising 20 members. Residential facilities for academic staff and students.
Academic Year: October to June (October-December; January-April; April-June).
Admission Requirements: Secondary school certificate (baccalauréat) or entrance examination.
Fees: None.
Language of Instruction: French.
Degrees and Diplomas: Diplôme universitaire d'études scientifiques (D.U.E.S.), 2 yrs. Diplôme d'Agronomie générale (D.A.G.). Diplôme d'Ingénieur agronome. Doctorats de Spécialité.
Library: Central Library.
Academic Staff: c. 20.
Student Enrolment: c. 450.

2188 **ÉCOLE NATIONALE SUPÉRIEURE DE STATISTIQUE ET D'ÉCONOMIE APPLIQUÉE**
B.P. 3, Abidjan 08
Telephone: 44-08-42
Directeur: François Yattien-Amiguet

D. of Statistics and Economics
Director: C. Girier
Founded 1961 for students from all French-speaking African countries. Acquired present title and placed under the authority of the Ministry of Economics and Finance 1963. Reorganized 1969 and 1982. Now under the authority of the Ministry of Planning and Industry. Governing body: the Conseil d'administration. Residential facilities for academic staff and students.
Arrangements for co-operation with similar institutions in: Paris; Kigali; and Yaoundé.
Academic Year: October to June (October-December; January-March; April-June).
Admission Requirements: Secondary school certificate (baccalauréat) and entrance examination.
Fees (Francs C.F.A.): 40,000-50,000 per annum.
Language of Instruction: French.
Degrees and Diplomas: Professional title of–Ingéneiur statisticien economist, 3 yrs; Ingénieur des Travaux statistiques, 4 yrs. Also lower level qualifications of Adjoint-Technique de la Statistique, 2 yrs; Agent-Technique de la Statistique, 1 yr.
Library: c. 7500 vols.
Publication: Etudes et Recherches.
Academic Staff, 1989-90: 10 (99).
Student Enrolment, 1989-90:

	Men	Women	Total
Of the country	64	3	67
Of other countries	87	4	67
Total	151	7	158

2189 **ÉCOLE NORMALE SUPÉRIEURE**
B.P. 18, Abidjan 08
Directeur: Touré Vakaba

Teacher Training.
Founded 1964.

2190 **ÉCOLE NATIONALE DES POSTES ET TÉLÉCOMMUNICATIONS**
Abidjan 18

Telecommunication Engineering
Founded 1967.

2191 **ÉCOLE NATIONALE SUPÉRIEURE DES TRAVAUX PUBLICS**
B.P. 1483, Abidjan
Telex: 22606 ENSIPA CI
Telephone: 64-01-00
Directeur général: Ezan Akele (1982-)

S. of Civil Engineering
S. of Public Works
Ce. for Lifelong Education
Founded 1962 in Abidjan. Transferred to present location 1979. A State institution. Financed by the Ministry of Public Works. Some residential facilities for academic staff and students.
Arrangements for co-operation with: Ecole nationale des Ponts et Chaussées, Paris; Ecole nationale supérieure d'Electricité, d'Electronique, d'Informatique et d'Hydraulique, Toulouse; Ecole polytechnique fédérale de Lausanne.
Academic Year: September to June (September-December; January-Easter; Easter-June).
Admission Requirements: Secondary school certificate (baccalauréat) for S. of Civil Engineering; entry to S. of Public Works at lower level by competitive examination.
Language of Instruction: French.
Degrees and Diplomas: Qualification as technician, 2 yrs. Professional title of Ingénieur, 4-5 yrs.
Academic Staff: c. 120 (50).
Student Enrolment: c. 440.

2192 **INSTITUT NATIONAL DES ARTS**
B.P. V.39, Abidjan 08

S. of Fine Arts
S. of Music
S. of Drama

S. of Applied Arts (Bingerville)
Conservatoire of Music
Founded 1971. A State institution responsible to the Ministry of Cultural Affairs.

2193 **INSTITUT NATIONAL DE FORMATION SOCIALE**
B.P. 2625, Abidjan 01

Sec. for Social Studies
Sec. for Teacher Training (Pre-school level)
Sec. for Special Education
Founded 1978.

CUBA

Universities

2194 **UNIVERSIDAD DE CAMAGÜEY**
University of Camagüey
Carretera de Circunvalación, Camagüey

F. of Agriculture and Animal Husbandry
F. of Technology
I. of Economics
I. of Education

Founded 1967 as Centro Universitario de Camagüey, incorporating institutions previously forming part of the Universidad de Las Villas. Acquired present title 1974. A State institution financed by the Government and under the jurisdiction of the Ministry of Education. Governing bodies: the Rectoría; the Consejo Universitario.

Degrees and Diplomas: Diploma or Professional title in all fields, 5 yrs, except Education, 4 yrs; Medicine, 6 yrs. Candidato a Doctor en Ciencias, a further 3 yrs. Doctorado, by thesis.

Student Enrolment: c. 5000.

2195 ***UNIVERSIDAD DE LA HABANA**
University of Havana
L y San Lázaro, Ciudad de La Habana
Telex: 511277 ESC MATEMATICAS UH
Telephone: 73231
Rector: Fernando Rojas Avalos (1982-)

F. of Biology
F. of Geography
F. of Cybernetics
F. of Physics
F. of Chemistry
F. of Science and Nuclear Technology
F. of Philosophy and History
F. of Arts and Letters
F. of Journalism
F. of Foreign Languages
F. of Psychology
F. of Law
F. of Economic Planning
F. of Accountancy and Finance
F. of Political Economics
F. of Pharmacy and Food Technology
Preparatory F.
Ce. of Computer Sciences
Ce. of Demographic Studies
F. of Encounter Courses for Workers and Correspondence Courses
Also 6 Research Centres.

Founded 1728 by the monks of Santa Cruz of the Dominican Order of Preaching Friars following Papal Bull 1721. Approved by the Spanish Royal Council of the Indies 1722. Secularized 1842 and granted autonomy 1933. Reorganized 1959 and university reform law promulgated 1962. A State institution. Governing bodies: 7he Rectoria, comprising the Rector, the Vice-Rectors, the Secretary-General, and the first Secretary of the Communist Party in the university; the Consejo Universitario, composed of the members of the Rectoria, the deans of the faculties, directors of the research centres and of the branches of the university, and representatives of the academic staff and students; Consejo Científico; Comisión Central Metodológica. Residential facilities for students.

Academic Year: September to July (September-January; February-July).

Admission Requirements: Secondary school certificate or graduation from Preparatory Faculty.

Language of Instruction: Spanish.

Degrees and Diplomas: Licenciado in all fields, 5 yrs. Professional title of Ingeniero, 5 yrs. Candidato a Doctor en Ciencias, a further 3 yrs. Doctorado, by thesis.

Library: Central Library 'Rubén Martínez Villena', *c.* 600,000 vols.

Special Facilities (Museums, etc.): Museums: Anthropology; Fragua Martiana; History of the University.

Publication: Various publications (Revistas) of the faculties and institutes.

Academic Staff: c. 1820 (170).

Student Enrolment: c. 15,980 (Also *c.* 11,620 external students).

2196 ***UNIVERSIDAD CENTRAL DE LAS VILLAS**
University of Las Villas
Carretera a Camajuane Kilómetro 10, Santa Clara Las Villas
Telex: 41130 UNIV LAS VILLAS
Telephone: 4581/9
Rector: Luis Gómez Gutiérrez (1982-)

F. of Industrial Engineering
F. of Mechanical Engineering
F. of Electrical Engineering
F. of Chemical and Sugar Technology
F. of Civil Engineering and Architecture
F. of Chemistry and Physics
F. of Letters
F. of Economics
F. of Law
F. of Psychology
F. of Cybernetics and Mathematics
Preparatory F. of Languages
F. of Agriculture
F. of Veterinary Medicine
D. of Marxism-Leninism
I. of Computer Sciences
D. of Physical Education, Sport and Recreation
F. of Encounter Courses for Workers and Correspondence Courses

Founded 1952 and reorganized 1959. Faculty of Medicine and Institute of Education detached 1976 as independent institutions. A State institution financed by the government and under the jurisdiction of the Ministry of Education. Governing body: the Board, comprising the Rector, three Vice-Rectors, and student representation. Residential facilities forsome academic staff and 80% of the students.

Academic Year: September to July (September-January; February-July).

Admission Requirements: Secondary school certificate or graduation from Preparatory Faculty.

Fees: None.

Language of Instruction: Spanish.

Degrees and Diplomas: Licenciado or Professional title in all fields, 5 yrs. Maestría in Sciences, a further 1-2 yrs. Candidato a Doctor en Ciencias, a further 4 yrs. Doctorado, by thesis.

Libraries: Central Library, *c.* 141,213 vols; faculty and department libraries.

Special Facilities (Museums, etc.): Natural History Museum.

Publications: Centro Agricola; Centro Azúcar; Construcción de Maquinaria; Islas.

Academic Staff: c. 890 (220).

Student Enrolment: c. 6540 (Also *c.* 4030 students of the Workers' Encounter Courses and *c.* 2810 by correspondence).

2197 ***UNIVERSIDAD DE ORIENTE**
University of Oriente
Avenida Patricio Lumumba s/n, Apartado postal 436, Santiago de Cuba Oriente
Telex: 061-145
Telephone: 33011
Rector: Enrique Marañón Reyes

F. of Technology (including Architecture)
F. of Humanities
F. of Agriculture
F. of Sciences
I. of Economics

I. of Education
Ce. for Scientific Research

Founded 1947 as a private institution. Recognized by the State and reorganized 1948. Became an official institution 1949 and reorganized 1959. Operated under the supervision of the Ministry of Education. Governing bodies: the Consejo de Dirección; the Asamblea de Dirección y Claustro General de Profesores (General Assembly).

Academic Year: November to October (November-May; June-October).

Admission Requirements: Secondary school certificate or entrance examination.

Fees: None.

Language of Instruction: Spanish.

Degrees and Diplomas: Diploma or Professional title in all fields, 5 yrs, except Education, 4 yrs; Medicine, 6 yrs. Candidato a Doctor en Ciencias, a further 3 yrs. Doctorado, by thesis.

Library: c. 174,680 vols.

Special Facilities (Museums, etc.): Museums: Mineralogy; Cuban Archaeology; Zoology.

Publications: Revista Mamby de la Federación Estudiantil Universitaria; Taller Literario de la Escuela de Letras.

Academic Staff: c. 800.

Student Enrolment: c. 12,000.

Other Institutions

2198 **CENTRO NACIONAL DE INVESTIGACIONES CIENTIFÍCAS**

Avenida 25, Calle 158, Reparto Cubanacán, La Habana

Science

2199 **CENTRO UNIVERSITARIO DE HOLGUÍN**

Miró No. 125 e/Frexes y Aguilera, Holguín

Founded 1976.

2200 **CENTRO UNIVERSITARIO DE MATANZAS**

Calle Medio No. 100 e/Zaragoza y Manzaneda, Matanzas
Telephone: 2612

F. of Engineering
F. of Agricultural Sciences (including Sugar Cane Production)
F. of Economics and Social Sciences
F. of Medicine
Agricultural Experimental Station

Founded 1972. A State institution financed by the government and under the jurisdiction of the Ministry of Education. Residential facilities for academic staff and students from outside Matanza.

Academic Year: September to July (September-January; February-July).

Admission Requirements: Secondary school certificate or graduation from Preparatory Faculty, or recognized equivalent.

Fees: None.

Language of Instruction: Spanish.

Degrees and Diplomas: Diploma or Professional title in all fields, 5 yrs, except Medicine, 6 yrs. Candidato a Doctor en Ciencias, a further 3 yrs. Doctorado, by thesis.

Library: Centro de Información Científico-Técnica, *c.* 20,000 vols.

Publication: Journal of Pastures and Forages (every 4 months).

Academic Staff: c. 200.

Student Enrolment: c. 4470 (Also *c.* 1300 external students).

2201 **CENTRO UNIVERSITARIO DE PINAR DEL RÍO**

Martí No. 270 esq. a 27 de Noviembrie, Pinar del Río

Founded 1976.

2202 **INSTITUTO SUPERIOR AGRÍCOLA DE CIEGO DE AVILA**

Carretera a Morón, Km 9, Ciego de Avila 69450
Telex: 032-146
Telephone: (2) 5702
Rector: Carlos G. Borroto Nordelo
Secretario General: Reynaldo Rodríguez Alonso

Agriculture

Founded 1978.

Academic Year: September to July.

Admission Requirements: Secondary school certificate (bachillerato) and entrance examination.

Language of Instruction: Spanish.

Degrees and Diplomas: Bachelor. Master.

Library: 33,000 vols.

2203 **INSTITUTO SUPERIOR DE ARTE**

Calle 120 No. 1110 e/9na y 13, Cubanacán, Ciudad de La Habana

Art

Founded 1976.

2204 **INSTITUTO SUPERIOR DE CIENCIAS AGROPECUARIAS**

Km. 10 Carretera de Manzanillo, Bayamo Granma

Agriculture

Founded 1976.

2205 **INSTITUTO SUPERIOR DE CIENCIAS AGROPECUARIAS DE LA HABANA**

Quinta de los Molinos-Avenida Salvador Allende y Luaces, La Habana

Agriculture

Founded 1976.

2206 **INSTITUTO SUPERIOR DE CIENCIAS MÉDICAS DE CAMAGÜEY**

Hospital Provincial y Politécnico de la Salud, Camagüey 1
Telephone: 8536
Rector: Alberto Hatim Ricardo (1981-)
Secretario General: Maria E. Morales

Medicine (including Stomatology and Nursing)

Founded 1968 as school, became Faculty of Medicine of University of Camagüey 1971 and acquired present status and title 1981. A State institution under the jurisdiction of the Ministry of Health.

Arrangements for co-operation with the Universities of: Cuenca; San Andrés, La Paz.

Academic Year: September to July (September-January; February-July).

Admission Requirements: Secondary school certificate.

Fees: None.

Language of Instruction: Spanish.

Degrees and Diplomas: Licenciado in Nursing. Professional titles in Medicine and Stomatology, 5-6 yrs.

Academic Staff, 1986-87:

Rank	Full-time	Part-time
Profesores Titulares	2	10
Profesores Auxiliares	5	21
Asistentes	15	69
Instructores	53	306
Total	75	401

Student Enrolment, 1986-87:

	Men	Women	Total
Of the country	418	375	793
Of other countries	24	14	38
Total	442	389	831

2207 **INSTITUTO SUPERIOR DE CIENCIAS MÉDICAS DE LA HABANA**

146 No. 2504 e/31 y 25 Cubanacán, Ciudad de La Habana

Medicine (including Stomatology and Nursing)

Founded 1976. A State institution under the jurisdiction of the Ministry of Health.

Academic Year: September to July (September-January; February-July).

Admission Requirements: Secondary school certificate.

Fees: None.

Language of Instruction: Spanish.

Degrees and Diplomas: Licenciado in Nursing. Professional titles in Medicine and Stomatology, 5-6 yrs.

2208 **INSTITUTO SUPERIOR DE CIENCIAS MÉDICAS DE VILLA CLARA**

Arias No. 9 Hospital Provincial e/Doble Via y Circunvalación, Santa Clara Villa Clara
Telephone: 27820
Rector: Serafín Ruiz de Zarate Ruiz
Secretario General: Jorge Luis López López

Medicine (including Stomatology and Nursing)

Founded 1966 as school attached to the University of Havana, became Faculty of Medicine of University of Las Villas 1973 and acquired present status and title 1976. A State institution under the jurisdiction of the Ministry of Health.

Arrangements for co-operation with the Universities of: Patrice Lumumba, Moscow; Rostock; Nicaragua (Autónoma).

Academic Year: September to July (September-January; February-July).

Admission Requirements: Secondary school certificate.

Fees: None.

Language of Instruction: Spanish.

Degrees and Diplomas: Licenciado in Nursing. Professional titles in Medicine and Stomatology, 5-6 yrs.

Library: 5730 vols.

Academic Staff, 1986-87:

Rank	Full-time	Part-time
Profesores Titulares	8	17
Profesores Auxiliares	15	22
Asistentes	58	84
Instructores	112	348
Auxiliares	4	–
Auxiliares Técnica Docentes	22	6
Total	219	477

Student Enrolment, 1986-87:

	Men	Women	Total
Of the country	2795	3063	5858
Of other countries	89	19	108
Total	2884	3082	5966

2209 **INSTITUTO SUPERIOR DE CIENCIAS MÉDICAS DE SANTIAGO DE CUBA**

Avenida de las Américas e I, Santiago de Cuba
Telephone: 6679
Rector: Juan J. Ceballos Arrieta
Secretario General: Rigoberto Yuanis Verdecia

Medicine (including Stomatology and Nursing)

Founded 1962 as school, became Faculty of Medicine of University of Oriente 1964 and acquired present status and title 1976. A State institution under the jurisdiction of the Ministry of Health.

Arrangements for co-operation with the Universities of: Mexico; Rostock.

Academic Year: September to July (September-January; February-July).

Admission Requirements: Secondary school certificate.

Fees: None.

Language of Instruction: Spanish.

Degrees and Diplomas: Licenciado in Nursing. Professional titles in Medecine and Stomatology, 5-6 yrs.

Academic Staff, 1986-87:

Rank	Full-time
Profesores Titulares	51
Profesores Auxiliares	51
Asistentes	249
Instructores	321
Total	672

Student Enrolment, 1986-87:

	Men	Women	Total
Of the country	1532	2309	3841
Of other countries	182	91	273
Total	1714	2400	4114

2210 **INSTITUTO SUPERIOR DE CULTURA FÍSICA 'MANUEL FAJARDO'**

Sta. Catalina e/Primelles y Boyeros, Ciudad de La Habana
Telephone: 406171
Rector: Antonio Pozas Ramos (1985-)

Physical Education

Founded 1973. A State institution under the jurisdiction of the Ministry of Education. Residential facilities for 300 students.

Arrangements for co-operation with similar institutions in: Moscow; Germany; Bulgaria; Czechoslovakia; and Poland.

Academic Year: September to July (September-February; March-July).

Admission Requirements: Secondary school certificate.

Language of Instruction: Spanish.

Degrees and Diplomas: Licenciado, 5 yrs. Candidato a Doctor en Ciancias, a further 4 yrs.

Publication: Revista Cientifica (quarterly).

Academic Staff, 1986-87:

Rank	Full-time	Part-time
Profesores Titulares	2	–
Profesores Auxiliares	20	–
Profesores Asistentes	136	–
Instructores	507	–
Auxiliares Técnica docentes	7	–
Profesores Adjuntos	12	–
Profesores Invitados	–	2
Total	914	2

Student Enrolment, 1986-87:

	Men	Women	Total
Of the country	6334	4221	10,635
Of other countries	66	14	80
Total	6400	4235	10,715

2211 **INSTITUTO SUPERIOR MINERO METALÚRGICO DE MOA**

Moa Holguín

Mining

Metallurgy

Founded 1976.

2212 **INSTITUTO SUPERIOR PEDAGÓGICO**

Carretera de Circunvalación, Camagüey

Teacher Training

Founded 1976.

2213 **INSTITUTO SUPERIOR PEDAGÓGICO DE LENGUAS MODERNAS**

Ciudad Libertad, Marianao, Ciudad de La Habana

Teacher Training (Modern Languages)

Founded 1976.

2214 **INSTITUTO SUPERIOR PEDAGÓGICO DE LA EDUCACIÓN TÉCNICA Y PROFESIONAL**

Avenida Vantroi y Ranchos Boyeros, Ciudad de La Habana

Technical Teacher Training

Founded 1976.

2215 **INSTITUTO SUPERIOR PEDAGÓGICO DE GUANTÁNAMO**

Guantánamo

Teacher Training

2216 **INSTITUTO SUPERIOR PEDAGÓGICO DE HOLGUÍN**

Calle Quinta e/Maceo y Hospital, Holguín

Teacher Training

Founded 1976.

2217 **INSTITUTO SUPERIOR PEDAGÓGICO DE LA HABANA**

La Habana

Teacher Training

2218 **INSTITUTO SUPERIOR PEDAGÓGICO DE LAS VILLAS**
Universidad Central, Carretera de Camaguaní Km. 10, Santa Clara, Villa Clara

Teacher Training
Founded 1976.

2219 **INSTITUTO SUPERIOR PEDAGÓGICO DE MANZANILLO**
Veguitas, Manzanillo Granma

Teacher Training
Founded 1976.

2220 **INSTITUTO SUPERIOR PEDAGÓGICO DE MATANZAS**
Calle Rio e/Matanzas y Medio, Matanzas

Teacher Training
Founded 1976.

2221 **INSTITUTO SUPERIOR PEDAGÓGICO DE PINAR DEL RÍO**
Colón Rpto. Llamalari (Antigua Sec. Básica 'Frank País'), Pinar del Río

Teacher Training
Founded 1976.

2222 **INSTITUTO SUPERIOR PEDAGÓGICO DE SANTIAGO DE CUBA**
Avenida Patricio Lumumba s/n, Santiago de Cuba

Teacher Training
Founded 1976.

2223 **INSTITUTO SUPERIOR POLITÉCNICO 'JOSÉ A. ECHEVERRÍA"**
Calle 127 s/n CUJAE, Marianao, Ciudad de La Habana
Telex: 511153 CCFT CUJAE
Telephone: 20-6780
Rector: Antonio Romillo Tarque

F. of Architecture
Dean: Llourdes Ortega
F. of Civil Engineering
Dean: Norberto Marrero
F. of Machine Engineering
Dean: Francisco Benít
F. of Electrical Engineering
Dean: Marcos Rangel
F. of Industrial Engineering
Dean: Antonio Diaz
F. of Chemical Engineering
Dean: Raúl Boué
Ce. for Systems Engineering
Director: José A. Pérez Rivero
Ce. for Hydraulic Research
Director: Alcides León
Ce. for Tropical Architecture and Construction
Director: Ofelia Martínez
Ce. for Microelectronics Research
Director: Ofelia Martínez

Founded 1900 as school, acquired present status and title 1976. A State institution financed by the governmentand under the jurisdiction of the Ministry of Higher Education. Residential facilities for academic staff and students

Academic Year: September to July (September-January; March-July).

Admission Requirements: Secondary school certificate or graduation from Preparatory Faculty, and entrance examination.

Fees: None.

Language of Instruction: Spanish.

Degrees and Diplomas: Professional titles of–Ingeniero; Arquitecto, 5-6 yrs. Candidato a Doctor en Ciencias, a further 3-4 yrs. Doctor en Ciencias.

Library: c. 165,000 vols.

Publication: Research publications (quarterly).

Academic Staff, 1990: c. 1200.

Student Enrolment, 1990: c. 15,000.

2224 **INSTITUTO SUPERIOR DE SERVICIO EXTERIOR**
22 e/Ira y 3ra, Miramar, Ciudad de La Habana
Telephone: 25097 International Studies

Founded 1976.

Academic Year: September to July (September-February; February-July).

Admission Requirements: Graduation from Preparatory Faculty.

Language of Instruction: Spanish, English, French, Russian.

Degrees and Diplomas: Licenciado.

Student Enrolment, 1984-85:

	Men	Women	Total
Of the country	1000	400	1400

2225 **INSTITUTO SUPERIOR TÉCNICO DE CIENFUEGOS**
Carretera A. Rodas, Cienfuegos
Telex: 042141
Telephone: 21521
Rector: Eduardo Cruz González (1979-)
Secretaria General: Margarita Romeo Peña

F. of Engineering
Dean: José Saborido Loidi
F. of Economics
Dean: Antonio Valencia Lagar
D. for Professional Retraining

Founded 1971 as institute of the University of Las Villas, became independent 1979. A State institution under the jurisdiction of the Ministry of Education. Residential facilities for students.

Arrangements for co-operation with: Institute of Economics, Odessa; Odessa Polytechnical Institute; Universityof Rostock; College of Transport and Communications, Dresden; Lappeenranta University of Technology.

Academic Year: September to July (September-December; February-June).

Admission Requirements: Secondary school certificate or graduation from Preparatory Faculty.

Language of Instruction: Spanish.

Degrees and Diplomas: Licenciado in Economics, 5 yrs. Professional title of Ingeniero, 5-6 yrs.

Library: 6000 vols.

Publication: Boletín (quarterly).

Academic Staff, 1986-87:

Rank	Full-time	Part-time
Profesores Titulares	5	2
Profesores Auxiliares	13	2
Investigador Auxiliar	1	–
Asistentes	33	7
Instructores	124	52
Total	176	73

Student Enrolment, 1986-87:

	Men	Women	Total
Of the country	858	452	1310*

*Also 898 external students.

CZECHOSLOVAKIA*

Universities and Technical Universities

2226 ***UNIVERZITA KOMENSKÉHO**
Comenius University
Šafárikovo nám. 6 885 45, Bratislava
Telephone: 580-41/5
Rektor: Ladislav Melioris (1985-)
Kvestor: Jozef Guliš

F. of Medicine (including Dentistry)
Dean: Anton Molnár; *staff* 417
F. of Medicine (Martin)
Dean: Viliam Mézeŝ; *staff* 148
F. of Pharmacy
Dean: Milana Mandák; *staff* 124
F. of Law
Dean: Andrej Bajcura; *staff* 72
F. of Philosophy and Arts
Dean: Jozef Vladár; *staff* 274
F. of Natural Sciences
Dean: Štefan Toma; *staff* 226
F. of Mathematics and Physics
Dean: Michal Greguš; *staff* 195
F. of Physical Education and Sport
Dean: Jozef Hrčka; *staff* 84
F. of Education
Dean: Zdeněk Obdržálek; *staff* 58
I. of Marxism-Leninism
I. of Immunology
I. of Biochemistry
I. of Molecular and Subcellular Biology
Computer I.

Founded 1919 to replace the former Hungarian university established 1914. Known as Slovenská univerzita v Bratislave from 1939-1954. A State institution under the jurisdiction of the Ministry of Education of Slovakia. Governing bodies: the Rector; the Advisory Board; the Scientific Council. Residential facilities for students.

Arrangements for co-operation with: Moscow State University; Tbilisi State University; Erevan State University; Kiev State University; Martin-Luther University Halle Wittenberg; Eötvös Loránd University; University of Warsaw; Jagiellonian University; University of Ljubljana; University of Novi Sad; University of Skopje; University 'Cyril and Methodius', Veliko Turnovo; University of Sofia; University of Madrid; University of Perugia; University of Udine; State University of Ghent; University of Constantine; University of Mysore; Kim Il Sung University; University of Silesia.

Academic Year: October to September (October-February; February-September).

Admission Requirements: Secondary school certificate and entrance examination.

Fees: Tuition, none.

Language of Instruction: Slovak.

Degrees and Diplomas: Absolvent, graduate, Law; Science; Letters, 5 yrs; Medicine, 6 yrs. Title of Doctor in–Law, JUDr; Science, RNDr; Letters, PhDr, Medicine, MUDr, by examen rigorosum, after Absolvent. Higher degrees: Candidatus scientiarum, CSc., at least a further 3 yrs, and Doctor scientiarum, DrSc. after CSc.

Libraries: Faculty libraries: Medicine, *c.* 123,890 vols; Medicine (Martin), *c.* 29,760; Pharmacy, *c.* 73,800; Philosophy, *c.* 280,550; Law, *c.* 84,800; Science, *c.* 214,100; Physical Education, *c.* 29,260; Teacher Training, *c.* 122,200; Institute of Marxism-Leninism, *c.* 16,600.

Publications: Folia Facultatis Medicae Universitatis Comenianae Bratislavensis; Folia Medica Martiniana; Acta Facultatis Pharmaceuticae Universitatis Comenianae; Zborník FFUK (series: Graeco-latina et orientalia, Historica, Musaica, Oeconomica, Paedagogica, Paedagogica specialis, Žurnalistika); Acta Facultatis rerum naturalium Universitatis Comenianae (series: Anthropologia, Botanica, Chimia, Mathematica, Meteorologia, Mikrobiologia, Physiologia plantarum, Res sociales, Zoologia, Physica); Acta Geologica et Geographica Universitatis Comenianae (Geologica, Geographica); Zborník Pedagogickej fakulty UK, series: Spoločenské vedy (História, Pedagogika).

Academic Staff, 1989-90: 2100.

Student Enrolment, 1989-90: 18,500.

2227 **UNIVERZITA PALACKÉHO**
Palacký University
Křížkovského 10, 770 47 Olomouc
Telephone: (0042) 68-29134
Fax: (0042) 68-22731
Rektor: Josef Jařab (1989-)
Kvestor: Josef Dvořák

F. of Medicine (including Stomatology)
Dean: Lubomír Neoral; *staff* – (358)
F. of Natural Sciences
Dean: Otokar Štěrba; *staff* – (159)
F. of Philosophy (including Psychology)
Dean: Ludvik Václavek; *staff* – (145)
F. of Education
Dean: Bohuslav Hodaň; *staff* – (188)
F. of Theology
Dean: Vojtěch Tkadlčík
Optics L.
Head: Miroslav Hrabovský; *staff* 6
Computer Ce.
Director: Karel Dočekal; *staff* 2

Founded 1573 under the authority of Pope Gregory XIII and Emperor Maximilian II. Became a State institution in 1773 when the Society of Jesus was suppressed, and was subsequently transferred to Brno. Closed during the German occupation, reopened 1946. The university is under the jurisdiction of the Ministry of Education. Facultyof Theology reopened 1990. Governing body: the University Council. Residential facilities for students.

Arrangements for co-operation with: Volgograd State University; Moscow State Pedagogical Institute; Karl Marx University of Leipzig; Marie Curie-Skłodowska University, Lublin; University of Ljubljana; Volgograd Medical Institute; Medical University of Szeged; College of Education, Halle; Medical Academy of Silesia; Azerbaijan State University; Odessa State University; Technical University of Wrocław; Lvov State University; LeningradState University.

Academic Year: September to July (September-December; February-July).

Admission Requirements: Secondary school certificate and entrance examination.

Fees: None.

Language of Instruction: Czech.

Degrees and Diplomas: Absolvent, graduate, Philosophy; Science, 5 yrs; Medicine or Dentistry, 5-6 yrs. Title of Doctor in–Philosophy, PhDr; Science, RNDr; Medicine or Dentistry, MUDr; Education, PaeDR, by examen rigorosum, after Absolvent. Teaching qualifications, 5 yrs. Higher degrees: Candidatus scientiarum, CSc., at least a further 3 yrs, and Doctor scientiarum, after CSc.

Library: Total, *c.* 712,160 vols.

Publication: Acta Universitatis Palackianae.

Press or Publishing House: University Publishing Centre.

---

*Major changes have affected the higher education system of the country and individual institutions during the preparation of this edition. These are reflected as far as they have been communicated to IAU before 30 September 1990.

Academic Staff, 1989-90:

Rank	Full-time
Profesoři	55
Docenti	172
Odborní asistenti	502
Asistenti	17
Research Workers	28
Total	746

Student Enrolment, 1989-90:

	Men	Women	Total
Of the country	1848	3064	4912
Of other countries	78	61	139
Total	1926	3125	5051

2228 ***MASARYKOVA UNIVERZITA**

Masaryk University

Burešova 20, 60177 Brno

Cables: mu brno

Telephone: (42-5) 757000

Fax: (42-5) 750000

Rektor: Milan Jelínek (1989-)

Kvestor: Josef Burda

F. of Science
Dean: Lumír Sommer; *staff* 372 (74)
F. of Medicine (including Dentistry)
Dean: Lambert Klabusay; *staff* 589 (121)
F. of Arts
Dean: Josef Hladký; *staff* 213 (34)
F. of Law
Dean: Jiří Kroupa; *staff* 98 (17)
F. of Education
Dean: Stanislava Kučerová; *staff* 236 (51)
D. of Physical Education
Head: Václav Buzek; *staff* 30 (5)
D. of Languages
Head: Ludmila Pavlíková; *staff* 27 (6)
I. of Computer Sciences
Director: Václav Račanský; *staff* 44 (6)
I. for Economics and Management in the Non-productive Areas
Director: Yvonne Strecková

Founded 1919 with faculties of law and medicine; faculty of science added 1920 and faculty of letters 1921. Closed 1939 during German occupation, reopened 1945 as Jana Evangelista Purkyně University. Reverted to formername 1989. The university is under the jurisdiction of the Ministry of Education. Governing body: the University Council. Some residential facilities for students.

Arrangements for co-operation with: Semmelweis Medical University; University of Plovdiv; University of Sofia; University of Greifswald; Kiev State University; University of Voronezh; University of Wrocław; University of Medicine, Debrecen; College of Education, Dresden; College of Education, Magdeburg; Institute of Education,Voronezh; University of Jena; University of Regensburg; University of Fribourg.

Academic Year: September to August (September-January; February-June).

Admission Requirements: Secondary school certificate and entrance examination.

Fees: None.

Language of Instruction: Czech.

Degrees and Diplomas: Absolvent, graduate, and title of Doctor by examen rigorosum, 4-5 yrs. Medicine, MUDr, 6 yrs. Higher degrees: Candidatus scientiarum, CSc., at least a further 3 yrs, and Doctor scientiarum, DrSc.

Library: Total, 1,043,089 vols.

Special Facilities (Museums, etc.): Czechoslovak Collection of Microorganisms; Botanical Garden; Audio-visual Centre.

Publications: Universitas (6 times a year); Scripta medica (8 times a year); Archivum mathematicum (4 times a year); Scriptanaturalia (10 times a year).

Press or Publishing House: University Press.

Academic Staff, 1989-90:

Rank	Full-time	Part-time
Profesoři	106	23
Docenti	264	11
Odborní asistenti	639	64
Asistenti	27	5
Total	1036	113

Student Enrolment, 1989-90:

	Men	Women	Total
Of the country	2467	3956	6423
Of other countries	113	41	154
Total	2580	3997	6577*

*Also 2717 external students.

2229 ***UNIVERZITA KARLOVA**

Charles University

Ovocný trh 5, 116 36 Praha 1

Telex: 122818 UP PHO

Telephone: (42-2) 228-441/8

Fax: (42-2) 266503

Rektor: Radim Palouš (1990-)

Kvestor: Jan Winkler

F. of Mathematics and Physics
Dean: Karel Drbohlav; *staff* 200 (30)
F. of Natural Sciences
Dean: Vladimír Kořínek *staff* 219 (18)
F. of Law
Dean: Ivan Mucha; *staff* 137 (6)
F. of Journalism
Dean: Čestmír Suchý *staff* 40 (37)
F. of Philosophy and Letters
Dean: František Černý *staff* 365 (60)
F. of Medicine I (including Dentistry)
Dean: Vladimír Pacovský; *staff* 531
F. of Medicine II
Dean: Josef Kouteckày; *staff* 141 (12)
F. of Medicine III
Dean: Cyril Höschl ; *staff* 162 (6)
F. of General Medicine (Plzeň)
Dean: František Macků; *staff* 164
F. of General Medicine (Hradec Králové)
Dean: Lubor Vokrouhlický; *staff* 205 (28)
F. of Pharmacy (Hradec Králové)
Dean: Vladimír Semecký *staff* 84 (21)
F. of Education
Dean: Jiří Kotásek; *staff* 281 (158)
F. of Physical Education and Sport
Dean: Václav Hošek; *staff* 109 (6)
F. of Catholic Theology
Dean: Václav Wolf
F. of Goose Theology
Dean: Zdeněk Kučera
F. of Gospel Theology
Dean: Josef Smolík
I. of Social and Political Sciences
Director: Josef Alan
D. of Languages (for foreign students)
Director: Antonín Bytel; *staff* 18 (1)
I. of Economics
Director: Bohumil Urban
I. of Slavonic Studies
Director: Jan Kuklík; *staff* 12
Also 17 institutes and centres of the faculties.

Founded 1348 by King Charles IV. Became a State institution 1773 when the Society of Jesus was dissolved. Divided in 1882 into separate Czech and German universities each bearing the title Charles-Ferdinand. Present title adopted 1918. Closed in November 1939 during the German occupation; reopened 1945 at which time the German university was abolished. The university is under the jurisdiction of the Ministry of Education. Governing body: the University Council. Residential facilities for students.

Arrangements for co-operation with: Moscow State Pedagogical University; University of the Republic, Montevideo; A&M University, Texas; Beijing University; Beijing Language Institute; Catholic University of

Louvain; University of Lisbon; University of Vienna; University of Nebrasak; University of Algiers; Indiana University of Bloomington; Texas University at Austin; University of Siena; University of Amsterdam; City University of New York; Kyoto University; University of Würzburg; University of Freiburg; University of Heidelberg.

Academic Year: September to August (September-January; February-June).

Admission Requirements: Secondary school certificate and entrance examination.

Fees: None.

Language of Instruction: Czech.

Degrees and Diplomas: Absolvent, graduate and title of Doctor by examen rigorosum, 4-5 yrs. Medicine or Dentistry, MUDr, 5-6 yrs. Higher degrees: Candidatus scientiarum, CSc., at least a further 3 yrs, and Doctor scientiarum, DrSc.

Library: Faculty libraries, 3,712,840 vols.

Publications: Acta Universitatis Carolinae; Biologica, Geographica, Geologica, Iuridica, Mathematica and Physica, Medica, Oeconolica, Philologica, Philosophica and Historica, Psychology of Economic Practice. Historia Universitatis Carolinae Pragensis; Prague Bulletin of Mathematical Linguistics.

Press or Publishing House: Charles University Publishing House.

Academic Staff, 1989-90:

Rank	Full-time	Part-time
Profesoři	249	22
Docenti	726	41
Odborní asistenti	1752	87
Asistenti	44	–
Lektoři	4	–
Odborní instruktoři	10	–
Ostatní učitelé	–	279
Total	2785	429

Student Enrolment, 1989-90:

	Men	Women	Total
Of the country	6520	9996	16,516
Of other countries	561	352	913
Total	7081	10,348	17,429*

*Also 8337 external students.

2230 ***UNIVERZITA PAVLA JOSEFA ŠAFÁRIKA IN KOŠICE**

Pavel Josef Šafárik University

Šrobárova 57, 041-80 Košice

Telex: 77562

Telephone: 226-08

Fax: 669-59

Rektor: Rudolf Korec (1990-)

Kvestor: Marian Schmidt

F. of Medicine (including Pharmacy)
Dean: Michal Pichanič
F. of Natural Sciences
Dean: Dušan Podhradsky
F. of Education
Dean: Jan Košťálik
F. of Philosophy
Dean: Jan Sabol
F. of Law
Dean: Igor Paluš
F. of Theology (Greco-Catholic)
F. of Theology (Orthodox)
Dean: Milan Gerka
Computer Ce.
Head: V. Novitzky

Founded 1959, incorporating faculty of medicine (1948), faculty of education, and faculty of letters, Prešov (1952). The faculty of Law was established 1975, and those of Theology (2) 1990. The university is under the jurisdiction of the Ministry of Education, and is financed by the State. Governing bodies: the Senate; the Scientific Council. Residential facilities for students.

Arrangements for co-operation with the Universities of: Jena, Magdeburg, Łódź, Groningen, Debrecen, Užhorod, Kiev, Harkov.

Academic Year: September to August (September-February; February-August).

Admission Requirements: Secondary school certificate or recognized foreign equivalent, and entrance examination.

Fees: None.

Language of Instruction: Slovak.

Degrees and Diplomas: Absolvent, graduate, and title of Doctor by examen rigorosum, 4-5 yrs. Medicine, MUDr, 6 yrs. Higher degrees: Candidatus scientiarum, CSc., at least a further 3 yrs, and Doctor scientiarum, DrSc, for recognized scientific work.

Libraries: Central Library; libraries of the faculties.

Special Facilities (Museums, etc.): Biological Garden.

Publications: Recueil des travaux scientifiques (annually); Folia Facultatis Medicae Universitatis Safarikianae Cassoviensis; Acta Juridica Cassoviensia;

Press or Publishing House: Edičné stredisko UPJŠ.

Academic Staff, 1989-90:

Rank	Full-time
Profesoři	44
Docenti	209
Asistenti	473
Total	726

Student Enrolment, 1989-90:

	Men	Women	Total
Of the country	1363	2637	7000
Of other countries	83	25	108
Total	1446	2662	4108*

*Also 88 external students.

2231 ***ČESKÉ VYSOKÉ UČENÍ TECHNICKÉ V PRAZE**

Czech Technical University of Prague

Zikova 4, 166 35 Praha 6

Telex: 121711 OVC PC

Telephone: 332111

Fax: 3112768

Rektor: Stanislav Hanzl (1990-91)

Kvestor: Milam Cásenský

F. of Civil Engineering (including Engineering and Surveying)
Dean: Jiří Witzany; *staff* 739 (93)
F. of Mechanical Engineering
Dean: Jiří Sesták; *staff* 494 (54)
F. of Electrical Engineering
Dean: Jan Hlavička; *staff* 526 (22)
F. of Nuclear Science and Physical Engineering
Dean: Miloslav Havlíček; *staff* 68 (70)
F. of Architecture
Dean: Svatopluk Voděra; *staff* 90 (17)
Computer Ce
Director: Lubomír Ohera; *staff* 169 (36)
Building Research I.
Director: Pavel Novák; *staff* 105
I. of Architectural Planning and Development
Director: Jan Vaněck; *staff* 62
Research I. of Engineering
Director: Jiří Měřička; *staff* 51 (10)

Founded 1707 as Czech State Engineering School, became Polytechnic 1803. In 1864 the institution was granted university status. Closed 1939 during the German occupation, reopened 1945. The university is under the jurisdiction of the Ministry of Education. Governing bodies: the Academic Senate; the Scientific Council. Residential facilities for students.

Special arrangements for co-operation with: Leningrad Polytechnic Institute; Polytechnical Institute, Tbilisi; Technical University of Dresden; Technical University of Budapest; Technical University of Warsaw; Institute of Mechanical and Electrical Engineering, Sofia; Instituto Superior Politécnico 'José A. Echeverría', La Habana; Ecole nationale des Ponts et Chaussées, Paris; University of Lancaster; Johannes Kepler Universität, Linz; Université d'Ottawa; Instituto Superior Politécnico Julio Antonio Mella, Santiago de Cuba; Instituto Tecnológico de Querétaro.

Academic Year: September to June (September-February; February-June).

Admission Requirements: Secondary school certificate and entrance examination.

Fees: None for students of the country.

Language of Instruction: Czech.

Degrees and Diplomas: Doktor, Dr.

Library: Faculty libraries, 50-70,000 vols.

Publication: Acta Polytechnica–Práce Čvut v Praze.

Press or Publishing House: Edični středisko ČVUT.

Academic Staff, 1989-90:

Rank	Full-time
Profesoři	114
Docenti	403
Odborní asistenti	884
Odborní instruktoři	13
Total	1448

Student Enrolment, 1989-90:

	Men	Women	Total
Of the country	11,817	2154	13,971*

*Also 593 foreign students.

2232 ***SLOVENSKÁ VYSOKÁ ŠKOLA TECHNICKÁ V BRATISLAVE**

Slovak Technical University of Bratislava

Gottwaldovo nám. 17, 81243 Bratislava

Cables: SVŠT Bratislava

Telephone: 53740

Rektor: Norbert Fristacky (1990-)

F. of Electrical Engineering
Dean: Ladislav Hruškovič; *staff* 406
F. of Chemical Engineering
Dean: Ján Garaj; *staff* 508
F. of Civil Engineering (including Building Engineering)
Dean: Milan Bielek; *staff* 454
F. of Architecture
Dean: Ján Antal; *staff* 94
F. of Mechanical Engineering
Dean: Igor Jaššo; *staff* 398
F. of Machine Technology (Trnava)
I. of Marxism-Leninism
Director: Koloman Slivka; *staff* 120
Computer I.
Director: Pavol Horváth; *staff* 92
I. of Biotechnology
Director: Anton Blažej; *staff* 31
D. of Cybernetics
Head: Karol Horváth; *staff* 44
D. of Engineering and Human Sciences
Head: Dušan Driensky; *staff* 26
D. of Languages
Head: Elena Beranová; *staff* 5 (6)
D. of Physical Education
Head: Ján Greššo; *staff* 69
Also 15 institutes and laboratories.

Founded 1938 at Košice, removed to Martin and to Bratislava in 1939. All faculties offer facilities for external studies. Governing body: the Scientific Council, including the Rector, Secretary-General, professors, and student representatives. Residential facilities for academic staff and students.

Arrangements for co-operation with similar institutions in: USSR (Moscow, Minsk); Germany (Ilmenau, Magdeburg, Weimar); Poland (Wrocław, Gliwice); Hungary (Budapest); Netherlands (Eindhoven); United Kingdom (Salford); France (Université Paris-Sud).

Academic Year: September to June (September-January; February-June).

Admission Requirements: Secondary school certificate and entrance examination.

Fees: None.

Languages of Instruction: Slovak and Czech.

Degrees and Diplomas: Professional titles of Inženýr in–Electrical Engineering; Chemistry; Mechanical Engineering; Civil Engineering; Machine Technology; and Architecture, 8-10 sem. Candidatus scientiarum, CSc., at least a further 3 yrs and thesis, and Doctor scientiarum, DrSc., by thesis after CSc.

Libraries: Faculty libraries: Electrical, *c.* 115,600 vols; Chemical Engineering, *c.* 133,050; Mechanical Engineering, *c.* 98,850; Civil Engineering, *c.* 114,060; Machine Technology, *c.* 13,700. Institute of Marxism-Leninism, *c.* 23,250.

Academic Staff, 1986-87:

Rank	Full-time
Profesoři	97
Docenti	435
Odborní asistenti	506
Asistenti	60
Lektoři	2
Total	1100

Student Enrolment, 1986-87:

	Men	Women	Total
Of the country	8126	3824	11,950
Of other countries	400	72	472
Total	8526	3896	12,422*

*Also 3478 external students.

2233 **VYSOKÁ ŠKOLA TECHNICKÁ V KOŠICIACH**

Technical University of Košice

Švermova 9, 042 00 Košice

Telex: 77410 VSTKO C

Telephone: 399-063-075

Fax: 327 48

Rektor: F. Zábranský

Secretary-General: Igor Zibrínyi

F. of Mining Engineering
Dean: Teodor Szuttor; *staff* 47
F. of Metallurgical Engineering
Dean: Ivan Imriš; *staff* 166
F. of Mechanical Engineering
Dean: Vladimir Klimo; *staff* 336
F. of Electrical Engineering
Dean: Karol Marton; *staff* 265 (58)
F. of Civil Engineering
Dean: Ludovít Nad; *staff* 104 (47)
High Voltage L.
Head: Karl Marton; *staff* 8 (4)
Research I. of Materials and Metallurgy
Head: Karel Tomášek; *staff* 35

Founded 1864 as the Mining and Metallurgical School at Banská Bystrica. Divided in 1919 into two parts, one at Sopron, Hungary, and the other at Příbram, Czechoslovakia. The latter was later transferred to Ostrava and its non-ferrous branch and part of the metallurgy department was finally established in Košice. The mining department at Banská Bystrica was incorporated in the Technical University of Bratislava and then in 1952 moved to Košice. The university is a State institution under the jurisdiction of the Ministry of Education and financed by the State. Residential facilities for academic staff and 70 per cent of the students.

Academic Year: October to June (October-January; February-June).

Admission Requirements: Secondary school certificate and entrance examination.

Fees: None.

Language of Instruction: Slovak.

Degrees and Diplomas: Professional title of Inženýr, 5-5 ½ yrs. Higher degrees: Candidatus scientiarum, CSc., at least a further 3 yrs, and Doctor scientiarum, DrSc.

Library: Central Library, *c.* 110,000 vols.

Publication: Recueil des travaux scientifiques (biannually).

Student Enrolment, 1989-90:

	Men	Women	Total
Of the country	4736	1666	6402
Of other countries	143	5	148
Total	4879	1671	6550

2234 **VYSOKÉ UČENÍ TECHNICKÉ V BRNĚ**

Technical University of Brno

Burešova 20, Brno

Cables: vutrk c

Telex: 62536

Telephone: (42-5) 757-000

Fax: (42-5) 755-252

Rektor: Arnošt Hönig

Kvestor: Miroslav Kledus

F. of Civil Engineering
Dean: Alois Materna; *staff* 747 (30)

. of Mechanical Engineering
)ean: Jaromír Slavík; *staff* 666 (28)
. of Electrical Engineering
)ean: Zdeněl Chjallupa; *staff* 514 (20)
. of Technology (Zlín)
)ean: Jan Kupec: *staff* 172 (1)
. of Architecture
lead: Ivan Ruler; *staff* 112 (6)
esign and Development I.
irector: Karel Bárek; *staff* 101
omputer Ce.
lead: Jan Dvořák; *staff* 82
udio-visual Ce.
lead: Tomáă Čermk; *staff* 11
ntegrated Scientific and Research I. (including Hydraulic Engineering and Water Management, Nuclear Non-destructive Testing, Theory and Methods of Management)
lead: František Kouřil

Founded 1849 as a State institution, reorganized 1899. Closed during the erman occupation, reopened 1945. The university is under the jurisdicion of the Ministry of Education. Financed by the State the university also erives income from research undertaken for industry. Residential facilies for more than 3000 students.

Academic Year: September to August.

Admission Requirements: Secondary school certificate and entrance xamination.

Fees: None for students of the country.

Language of Instruction: Czech.

Degrees and Diplomas: Professional title of Inženýr, 5 yrs. Higher derees, at least a further 3 yrs. Dr.Ing.

Library: c. 303,620 vols.

Publications: Sborník VUT; Knižnice VUT.

Academic Staff: c. 820.

Student Enrolment, 1989-90:

	Men	Women	Total
Of the country	10,499	2656	13,155
Of other countries	359	41	400
Total	10,858	2697	13,555*

Including 1780 external students.

Other Institutions

Technical Education

235 **VYSOKÁ ŠKOLA CHEMICKO-TECHNOLOGICKÁ V PRAZE**

College of Chemical Technology
Suchbátárova 1905, 166 28 Praha 6
Telex: 122744 VSCH/C
Telephone: 332
Rector: Jiří Mostecký (1985-90)
Kvestor: Jan Mrásek

. of Chemical Technology
)ean: J. Matoušek
. of Petroleum, Gas, and Water Technology
)ean: J. Pelikán
. of Food Technology and Biochemistry
)ean: J. Davídek
. of Chemical Engineering
)ean: S. Valenta

Founded 1806 and functioned as a faculty of the Czech Technical Univrsity in Prague. Detached and re-established as separate institutions 1952. State institution under the jurisdiction of the Ministry of Education ndCulture. Some residential facilities for students.

Arrangements for co-operation with institutions in: USSR (Moscow, eningrad); Germany (Berlin, Leuna-Merseburg, Freiberg, Leipzig, hemnitz, Dresden); Poland (Wrocław); Yugoslavia (Belgrade).

Academic Year: October to August (October-February; Februaryeptember).

Admission Requirements: Secondary school certificate and entrance xamination.

Fees: None.

Language of Instruction: Czech.

Degrees and Diplomas: Professional title of Inženýr Chemie, inž. chem., 4 yrs. Higher degrees: Candidatus scientiarum, CSc., at least a further 3 yrs, and Doctor scientiarum, DrSc.

Libraries: Central Library, *c.* 85,000 vols; department libraries, *c.* 150,000.

Special Facilities (Museums, etc.): Mineralogy.

Publication: Sborník Vysoké školy chemicko-technologické v Praze.

Academic Staff, 1986-87:

Rank	Full-time
Profesoři	50
Docenti	80
Asistenti	270
Total	400

Student Enrolment, 1986-87:

	Men	Women	Total
Of the country	1400	1200	2600
Of other countries	100	40	140
Total	1500	1240	2740

2236 **VYSOKÁ ŠKOLA CHEMICKO-TECHNOLOGICKÁ V PARDUBICÍCH**

College of Chemical Technology
Nám Čs. Legií 565, 532 10 Pardubice
Cables: všcht pardubice
Telephone: (40) 513221
Rektor: Josef Panchártek (1990-)
Kvestor: Milena Čeganová

D. of Inorganic Chemistry
Head: M. Frummer; *staff* 18
D. of Analytical Chemistry
Head: J. Churáček; *staff* 15
D. of Physics
Head: F. Kosek; *staff* 5
D. of Mathematics
Head: S. Kolda; *staff* 6
D. of Physical Chemistry
Head: K. Komers; *staff* 8
D. of Inorganic Technology
Head: Z. Šolc; *staff* 9
D. of Organic Chemistry
Head: V. Macháček; *staff* 9
D. of Chemical Engineering
Head: J. Stejskal; *staff* 11
D. of Automation of Chemical Processes
Head: S. Krejči; *staff* 12
D. of Chemical Industry Economics and Management
Head: Z. Skřivánek; *staff* 7
D. of Environmental Protection
Head: T. Sàakra; *staff* 7
D. of Organic Technology
Head: J. Kulič; *staff* 6
D. of Theory and Technology of Explosives
Head: B. Vetlický; *staff* 5
D. of Plastics
Head: V. Čermák; *staff* 6
D. of Textiles and Fibres
Head: J. Růžička; *staff* 8
D. of Pulp and Paper
Head: M. Milichovský; *staff* 5
D. of Printing Technology
Head: V. Kadeřábek; *staff* 5

Founded 1950 as school, acquired present status and title in 1953. A State institution under the jurisdiction of the Ministry of Education. Residential facilities for *c.* 1100 students.

Arrangements for co-operation with: Veszpremi Technical University of Chemical Engineering; 'Carl Schorlemmer' Technical University Leuna-Merseburg; Technical University of Łódź; Institute of Chemical Technology, Bourgas; Institute of Technology, Leningrad; Institute of Chemical Technology, Moscow; Technical University, Dresden; University of Halle; Technical University of Munich; Tashkent Polytechnical Institute; Institute of Textile Technology, Tashkent; Azerbaijan State University.

Academic Year: September to July (September-February; February-July).

Admission Requirements: Secondary school certificate and entrance examination.

Fees: None.
Language of Instruction: Czech.
Degrees and Diplomas: Professional title of Inženýr Chemie, inž.chem., 4 yrs. Higher degrees: Candidatus scientiarum, CSc., at least a further 3 yrs, and Doctor scientiarum, DrSc. (Planned from 1990: Bachelor, 3 yrs. Inž., a further 2yrs. Dr., a further 2-3 yrs).
Library: Central Library, *c.* 140,000 vols.
Publication: Sbornik vědeckých (Scientific Papers, twice a year).
Academic Staff, 1989-90:

Rank	Full-time
Profesoři	11
Docenti	50
Odborní asistenti	96
Asistenti	3
Total	160

Student Enrolment, 1989-90: 854 (Also 121 external students).

2237 **VYSOKÁ ŠKOLA STROJNÍ ELEKTROTECHNICKÁ V PLZNI**
College of Mechanical and Electrical Engineering
Nejedlého sady 14, 30614 Plzeň
Telex: 154 292
Telephone: 36881
Rektor: František Pláníčka
Kvestor: Antonín Vyšinka

F. of Mechanical Engineering
Dean: Josef Rosenberg; *staff* 150 (35)
F. of Electrical Engineering
Dean: Jaroslav Svakcr; *staff* 141 (42)

Founded 1949 as part of the Czech Technical University of Prague. Detached and re-established as separate institution 1953. A State institution under the jurisdiction of the Ministry of Education. Some residential facilities for students.

Arrangements for co-operation with: Institutes of Technology (Gabrovo, Gliwice, Sverdlovsk, Volgograd); Technical University, Chemnitz; Brunel University, London.

Academic Year: September to July (September-January; February-July).
Admission Requirements: Secondary school certificate.
Language of Instruction: Czech.
Degrees and Diplomas: Professional title of Inženýr, 4-5 yrs. Higher degrees: Candidatus scientiarum, CSc., at least a further 3-5 yrs, and Doctor scientiarum, DrSc.
Library: Central Library, *c.* 212,000 vols.
Publication: Recueil des travaux scientifiques (biennially).
Academic Staff, 1986-87:

Rank	Full-time	Part-time
Profesoři	11	4
Docenti	36	2
Odborní asistenti	223	7
Asistenti	3	–
Total	273	13

Student Enrolment, 1986-87:

	Men	Women	Total
Of the country	2553	357	2910
Of other countries	50	3	53
Total	2603	360	2963*

*Also 284 external students.

2238 **VYSOKÁ ŠKOLA STROJNÍ A TEXTILNÍ V LIBERCI**
Technical University of Mechanical and Textile Engineering
Hálkova 6, Liberec I
Telephone: (48) 25441

F. of Mechanical Engineering (including Machine-Industry Technology Systems with Industrial Robots and Manipulators; Chemical, Food Industries, and Materials Engineering)
Dean: Zdeněk Kovář; *staff* 227 (26)
F. of Textile Engineering
Dean: Jaroslav Nosek; *staff* 161 (46)

Founded 1953 as college.
Academic Year: September to June (September-January; February-June).
Admission Requirements: Secondary school certificate.
Fees: None.
Language of Instruction: Czech.
Degrees and Diplomas: Professional title of Inženýr, ing. Higher degrees: Candidatus scientiarum, CSc., at least a further 3 yrs, and Doctor scientiarum, DrSc.
Library: Central Library, *c.* 45,000 vols.
Publication: Annals of the University (annually).
Academic Staff, 1990:

Rank	Full-time	Part-time
Profesoři	19	–
Docenti	63	–
Odborní asistenti	159	117
Asistenti	7	–
Total	248	117

Student Enrolment, 1990:

	Men	Women	Total
Of the country	1356	1097	2453
Of other countries	47	29	76
Total	1403	1126	2529*

*Also 339 external students.

2239 ***VYSOKÁ ŠKOLA BÁŇSKÁ V OSTRAVĚ**
College of Mining and Metallurgy
třída 17 Listopadu, 70833 Ostrava-Poruba
Telex: 52568 VSBOS
Telephone: 424111
Rektor: Tomáš Čermák (1990-)
Kvestor: Jan Černota

F. of Mining Engineering and Geology
Dean: Vitězslav Zámarský; *staff* 17 (44)
F. of Metallurgy
Dean: Petr Jelinekc; *staff* 97 (36)
F. of Engineering and Electrotechnics
Dean: Zdeněk Rýc; *staff* 156 (96)
F. of Economics
Dean: Josef Jünger; *staff* 146 (109)

Founded 1716 as School of Mining and Metallurgy at Jáchymov in Bohemia, became part of the University of Prague 1763. Moved to Slovakia 1770 as Mining Academy in Stiaynica, and to Příbram in Bohemia 1849. Acquired university status 1894 and moved to present location 1945. Governing body: the Academic Council. Residential facilities for academic staff and students.

Arrangements for co-operation with: Institute of Steel and Alloys Technology, Moscow; Donets Polytechnical Institute; Freiberg Mining Academy; Academy of Mining and Metallurgy, Cracow; Technical University for Heavy Industry, Miskolc; Eberhard-Karls-Universität Tübingen; Universidade Federal do Rio de Janeiro; Instituto Tecnológico de Morelia.

Academic Year: September to August (September-December; February-May).
Admission Requirements: Secondary school certificate and entrance examination.
Fees: None.
Language of Instruction: Czech.
Degrees and Diplomas: Professional titles of–Economist; Banský Inženýr, mining engineering; Hutný Inženýr, metallurgical engineering; Strojný Inženýr, mechanical engineering, 4-5 yrs. Higher degrees: Candidatus scientiarum,CSc., in Engineering and Economics, at least a further yrs, and Doctor scientiarum, DrSc.
Library: Central Library, 520,000 vols.
Special Facilities (Museums, etc.): Collection of Geological Minerals.
Publication: Recueil des travaux scientifiques.
Academic Staff, 1989-90:

Rank	Full-time	Part-time
Professors	47	5
Assistant Professors	132	13
Senior Lecturers	382	267
Lecturers	14	–
Total	575	285

Student Enrolment, 1989-90:

	Men	Women	Total
Of the country	4120	2330	4450
Of other countries	90	3	93

	Full-time	Part-time	
Total	4210	2333	4543

2240 **VYSOKÁ ŠKOLA DOPRAVY A SPOŽOV**
College of Transport Engineering and Communications
Moyzesova 20, 01088 Žilina
Cables: všd
Telephone: 20392
Rektor: Pavol Kluvánek

F. of Operation and Economics of Transport and communications
Dean: Hynek Sertler; *staff* 220 (11)
F. of Mechanical and Electrical Engineering
Dean: Jaroslav Cáp; *staff* 350 (35)

Founded 1953 as Faculty of Railway Engineering of the Czech Technical University in Prague. Detached and re-established as separate institution 1959 and moved to Žilina 1960. A State institution. Governing bodies: the Academic Senate; the Faculty Senates and Councils. Residential facilities for academic staff and students.

Academic Year: October to September (October-January; February-June).

Admission Requirements: Secondary school certificate and entrance examination.

Fees: None.

Languages of Instruction: Slovak and Czech.

Degrees and Diplomas: Professional title of Inženýr, inž. in–Transport Engineering; Communications Engineering; Constructional Engineering; Mechanical Engineering, 5 yrs. Higher Degrees: Candidatus scientiarum, CSc., at least a further3 yrs, and Doctor scientiarum, DrSc.

Library: Central Library, *c.* 181,830 vols.

Publication: Sborník prác a študií VŠD.

Academic Staff, 1990:

Rank	Full-time	Part-time
Professors	28	4
Associate Professors	138	8
Assistant Professors	396	32
Instructors	8	1
Researchers	90	2
Total	660	47

Student Enrolment, 1990:

	Men	Women	Total
Of the country	3509	1062	4571
Of other countries	54	3	57
Total	3563	1065	4628*

*Also 1220 external students.

Professional Education

2241 **VYSOKÁ ŠKOLA ZEMĚDĚLSKÁ V BRNĚ**
College of Agriculture
Zemědělská 1, 61300 Brno
Telex: 62489
Telephone: 604

F. of Agriculture (including Animal Husbandry)
F. of Agricultural Economics
F. of Forestry

Founded 1919. A State institution. Residential facilities for students.

Arrangements for co-operation with: Institute of Agriculture, Tbilisi; Institute of Agriculture, Krasnojarsk; Academy of Forestry and Wood Technology, Leningrad; Academy of Agriculture and Technology, Olsztyn-Kortowo; Academy of Agriculture, Wrocław; Wilhelm Pieck University Rostock; Technical University of Dresden; University of Agriculture, Gödöllö; Institute of Agriculture, Plovdiv; University of Horticulture, Budapest; Universidad Politécnica, Madrid.

Academic Year: September to August (September-January; February-August).

Admission Requirements: Secondary school certificate and entrance examination.

Fees: None.

Language of Instruction: Czech.

Degrees and Diplomas: Professional titles of–Zemědělský Inženýr; Lesní Inženýr, 4 yrs. Higher Degrees: Candidatus scientiarum, CSc., at least a further 3 yrs and Doctor scientiarum, DrSc.

Library: Central Library, *c.* 340,000 vols.

Publications: Acta Universitatis Agriculturae, Series A, C, D. (quarterly); Informační zpravodaj (Bulletin).

Academic Staff: c. 380.

Student Enrolment: c. 3350 (Also *c.* 900 external students).

2242 ***VYSOKÁ ŠKOLA POL'NOHOSPODÁRSKA V NITRA**
College of Agriculture
Lomonosova ul. 2 949 76, Nitra
Cables: Všp
Telex: 98445
Telephone: 23501/5
Rektor: Ladislav Kabát (1990-)

F. of Agriculture (including Animal Husbandry)
Dean: Viktor Sidor; *staff* 190 (2)
F. of Agricultural Economics and Management
Dean: Július Ševčík; *staff* 126
F. of Agricultural Engineering
Dean: Bohumil Procházka; *staff* 105
I. of Marxism-Leninism
Director: Milan Balážik; *staff* 42
Computer Ce.
Director: Tibor Koščo
I. of Biology
Head: Emil Špaldon
I. of Measuring and Evaluating Technology
Head: Josef Lobotka
D. of Educational Sciences
Head: Ján Bakša

Founded 1941 as part of the Technical University of Bratislava. Department of Agriculture moved to Košice 1946 and to Nitra 1952, when departments of animal husbandry, and economics added, and department of forestry detached. A State institution. Residential facilities for most of the academic staff and students.

Special arrangements for co-operation with 13 similar institutions in other countries.

Academic Year: September to September (September-January; February-September).

Admission Requirements: Secondary school certificate and entrance examination.

Fees: None.

Language of Instruction: Slovak.

Degrees and Diplomas: Professional titles of–Pol'nohospodársky Inženýr, in various specializations, 4 yrs. Candidatus scientiarum, CSc., at least a further 3 yrs, and Doctor scientiarum, DrSc.

Library: Central Library, 500,000 vols.

Special Facilities (Museums, etc.): Pol'nohospodárske muz'eum v Nitre.

Publications: Acta fytotechnica; Acta zootechnica; Acta operativo-oeconomica; Acta technologica agriculturae.

Press or Publishing House: Edičné stredisko (Publishing Centre).

Academic Staff, 1986-87:

Rank	Full-time	Part-time
Profesoři	30	3
Docenti	147	1
Odborní asistenti	258	5
Asistenti	12	–
Lektoři a Instruktoři	11	–
Total	458	9

Student Enrolment, 1986-87:

	Men	Women	Total
Of the country	1980	1265	3245
Of other countries	–	–	92
Total	1980	1265	3337*

*Also 1307 external students.

2243 **VYSOKÁ ŠKOLA ZEMĚDĚLSKÁ**
University of Agriculture
Kamýcká ul. 129, 16521 Praha-Suchdol 6
Telex: 122323
Telephone: 323-641/9
Rektor: Jiří Petr
Kvestor: Pavel Blažek

F. of Agriculture (including Animal Husbandry, Soil Conservation, and Land Improvement)
Dean: Vàněk; *staff* 419
F. of Agricultural Economics and Management
Dean: Josef Fojtl; *staff* 208
F. of Agricultural Mechanization
Dean: J. Havlíček; *staff* 189
I. of Tropical and Subtropical Agriculture
Director: Jiří Houska; *staff* 41
I. of Applied Ecology and Ecotechnology
Director: Miriam Čech; *staff* 75
F. of Agriculture (České Budějovice)
Dean: Jaroslav Kursa; *staff* 304

Founded 1906 as part of the Czech Technical University in Prague. Closed 1939 during the German occupation, reopened 1945. A State institution. Detached and re-established as separate institution 1952. Governing body: the University Council, including the Rector, Vice-Rector, and deans. Residential facilities for *c.* 2000 students.

Academic Year: October to September (October-March; March-September).

Admission Requirements: Secondary school certificate or certificate from agricultural school, and entrance examination.

Fees: None.

Language of Instruction: Czech.

Degrees and Diplomas: Professional title of Zemědělský Inženýr, inž. in–Agricultural Engineering; Agriculture; Economics, 5 yrs. Master of Science in Tropical and Sub-tropical Agriculture, 5 yrs. Higher degrees: Candidatus scientiarum, CSc., at least a further 3 yrs, and Doctor scientiarum, DrSc.

Libraries: Central Library, *c.* 200,000 vols; Institute of Forestry Research, *c.* 20,000.

Publication: 15 Scientific periodicals (mostly annually).

Academic Staff, 1990:

Rank	Full-time
Profesoři	64
Docenti	124
Odborní asistenti, asistenti	288
Lektoři	5
Total	481

Student Enrolment, 1989-90: 3928 (Also 1098 external students).

2244 **VYSOKÁ ŠKOLA LESNÍCKA A DREVÁRSKA**
College of Forestry and Wood Technology
Štúrova 2, 96053 Žvolen
Cables: Vsld
Telex: 72267 VSLD Z
Telephone: 223-12; 15; 26

F. of Forestry
F. of Wood Technology
I. of Computer Techniques

Founded 1807 at Banská Stiaynica as School of Forestry. Became Faculty of Forestry at Bratislava Technical University 1939, and moved to Žvolen and acquired present status 1952. A State institution under the jurisdiction of the Ministry of Education. Residential facilities for *c.* 1000 students.

Arrangements for co-operation with similar faculties in: USSR; Poland; Germany; Hungary; Romania; Cuba; Bulgaria; Yugoslavia.

Academic Year: September to August (September-February; February-August).

Admission Requirements: Secondary school certificate.

Fees: None.

Languages of Instruction: Czech and Slovak.

Degrees and Diplomas: Professional title of Inženýr, 5 yrs. Higher degrees: Candidatus scientiarum, CSc., at least a further 3 yrs, and Doctor scientiarum, DrSc.

Library: *c.* 600,000 vols.

Publication: Acta Facultatis Forestalis Zvolen (annually).

Academic Staff: *c.* 180.

Student Enrolment: *c.* 1670 (Also *c.* 470 external students).

2245 **VYSOKÁ ŠKOLA VETERINÁRNÍ**
University of Veterinary Science
Palackého 1-3, 61242 Brno
Cables: 445
Telex: 63039
Telephone: 7110
Rektor: Jaroslav Konrád (1990-)
Kvestor: Jiří Tureček

F. of Veterinary Medicine (including Tropical Veterinary Medicine)
F. of Hygiene and Ecology
D. of Diagnosis, Therapy and Control of Animal Diseaeases
Head: Bohumír Hofírek
D. of Epizootiology, Microbiology and Immunology
Head: Vladimír Celer
D. of Animal Husbandry
Head: Eduard Kudláč
D. of Food Hygiene and Technololgy
Head: Vladimír Pažout

Founded 1918. Became university 1969. A State institution. Governing bodies: the Scientific Council; the Academic Senate. Residential facilities for 500 students.

Arrangements for co-operation with similar institutions in: Cuba; Germany; Mexico; Poland; Yugoslavia; Hungary; USSR; Switzerland; Mozambique; Algeria; Denmark.

Academic Year: September to August (September-December; February-June).

Admission Requirements: Secondary school certificate and entrance examination.

Fees: None.

Language of Instruction: Czech.

Degrees and Diplomas: Doctorat of Veterinary Medicine, MVDr, 6 yrs. Candidatus scientiarum, CSc., as further 3-5 yrs. Doctor scientiarum, DrSc.

Library: Central Library, 203,198 vols.

Special Facilities (Museums, etc.): Museums: Pathological; Anatomical; History of Veterinary Science.

Publication: Acta Veterinaria.

Press or Publishing House: Publishing Centre.

Academic Staff, 1989-90:

Rank	Full-time	Part-time
Professors	16	2
Associate Professors	34	–
Assistant Professors	74	–
Research Fellows	10	–
Total	134	2

Student Enrolment, 1989-90:

	Men	Women	Total
Of the country	522	296	818
Of other countries	60	23	83
Total	582	319	901*

*Also 147 external students.

2246 **VYSOKÁ ŠKOLA VETERINÁRSKA**
College of Veterinary Medicine
Komenského ul. 73, 04181 Košice
Telex: VSVKE-177322
Telephone: 321-11/15
Fax: 67675

Veterinary Medicine
Experimental Research Ce. (Zemplínska Teplica)
Also 2 School Farms.

Founded 1949 as school, became faculty of College of Agriculture in Nitra 1952, detached and acquired present status 1969. A State institution. Governing body: the Senate. Residential facilities for 15 academic staff and *c.* 780 students.

Academic Year: September to July (September-February; February-July).

Admission Requirements: Secondary school certificate and entrance examination.

Fees: None.

Language of Instruction: Slovak.

Degrees and Diplomas: Doctor of Veterinary Medicine, MVDr, 6 yrs and thesis. Candidatus scientiarum, CSc. Doctor scientiarum, DrSc.

Library: Central Library and Information Centre, *c.* 77,000 vols.

Special Facilities (Museums, etc.): Veterinary Medicine Museum.

Publications: Folia Veterinaria; Veterinársky časopis.

Academic Staff, 1990:

Rank	Full-time	Part-Time
Profesoři	21	–
Docenti	66	–
Asistenti	83	4
Total	170	4

Student Enrolment, 1990:

	Men	Women	Total
Of the country	475	309	784
Of other countries	36	8	44
Total	511	317	828

2247 **VYSOKÁ ŠKOLA EKONOMICKÁ V BRATISLAVE**

School of Economics in Bratislava

ul. Odbojárov 10, 832 20 Bratislava

Telephone: 605 615

Fax: 630 45

Rektor: Ján Petrenka (1990-)

Finance Officer: Gejza Böhm

F. of Commerce (including Foreign Trade Relations, World Economy, and Law)

Dean: Peter Baláž; *staff* 119

F. of National Economy

Dean: Jozef Košnár; *staff* 128

F. of Management (including Accountancy, Mathematical Economic Methods, Data Processing, and Statistics)

Dean: Hedviga Bakytová; *staff* 158

F. of Applied Management

Dean: Mikuláš Sedlák; *staff* 91

F. of Economics of Services and Tourism (including Economics of Non-productive Sphere and Social Development Specializations) (Banská Bystrica)

Dean: Miroslav Abrahám; *staff* 61

I. of Computer Sciences

Director: Anton Zdarílek; *staff* 59 (6)

I. of Advanced Economic Education and Training

Director: Ján Šimkovic; *staff* 10 (15)

Research I. of National Economy

Director: Marta Šimunková; *staff* 41 (1)

Research I. of Services (Banská Bystrica)

Director: Ľubica Švantnerová; *staff* 9 (3)

Branches in Banská Bystrica and Košice.

Founded 1940 as school, acquired present status and title 1952. A State institution under the jurisdiction of the Ministry of Education. Residential facilities for students.

Arrangements for co-operation with institutions of higher education in: USSR (5); Bulgaria (1); Hungary (4); Germany (3); Poland (4); Yugoslavia (1); Cuba (1); Greece (1); Austria (1).

Academic Year: September to June (September-January; February-June).

Admission Requirements: Secondary school certificate and entrance examination.

Fees: None.

Degrees and Diplomas: Professional title of Inžinier, 4-5 yrs. Higher degrees: Candidatus scientiarum, CSc., at least a further 3 yrs, and Doctor scientiarum, DrSc.

Library: Total, 406,493 vols.

Publications: Economic Survey; Collection of Research Works (quarterly).

Academic Staff, 1989-90:

Rank	Full-time
Profesoři	43
Docenti	219
Odborní asistenti, Asistenti	375
Total	637

Student Enrolment, 1989-90:

	Men	Women	Total
Of the country	3532	5196	8728
Of other countries	121	45	166
Total	3653	5241	8894*

*Also 2073 external students.

2248 **VYSOKÁ ŠKOLA EKONOMICKÁ V PRAZE**

Prague College of Economics

Nám. Ant. Zápotockého 4, 13067, Praha 3

Cables: VŠE Prague 3

Telex: 122310

Telephone: 2125111

Rektor: Antónia Bržek (1985-90)

Kvestor: Václav Dejm

F. of Economics and Planning

Dean: Jiří Petřivalský; *staff* 123 (45)

F. of Applied Economics

Dean: Vladimír Líbal; *staff* 120 (15)

F. of Commerce (including Tourism)

Dean: Petr Semeniuk; *staff* 160 (8)

F. of Management

Dean: Stanislav Adamec; *staff* 103 (13)

I. of Marxism-Leninism

Head: Jiří Bauer; *staff* 92 (12)

Computer Ce.

Director: Jiří Beck; *staff* 90 (5)

Founded 1949, a State institution. Acquired present status 1953. Under the jurisdiction of the Ministry of Education. Governing body: the Scientific Council, comprising 43 members. Residential facilities for students.

Arrangements for co-operation with: Karl Marx Institute of Economics, Sofia; University of Havana; University of Economics, Berlin; College of Commerce, Leipzig; Humboldt University of Berlin; Karl Marx University of Economic Sciences, Budapest; Central School of Planning and Statistics, Warsaw; Academy of Economics, Cracow; Academy of Economics, Poznán; Leningrad State University; Institute of Industrial Organization and Economics, Moscow; Institute of Economic Statistics, Moscow; University of Rijeka.

Academic Year: September to June (September-January; February-June).

Admission Requirements: Secondary school certificate and entrance examination.

Fees: None.

Language of Instruction: Czech.

Degrees and Diplomas: Professional title of Inženýr, 4 yrs. Higher degrees: Candidatus scientiarum, CSc., at least a further 3 yrs, and Doctor scientiarum, DrSc.

Library: Central Library which is part of the State Library, *c.* 760,000 vols.

Publication: Acta Economica Pragensia (biannually).

Academic Staff, 1986-87:

Rank	Full-time	Part-time
Profesoři	31	8
Docenti	134	4
Lektoři	360	120
Total	525	132

Student Enrolment, 1986-87:

	Men	Women	Total
Of the country	4500	5385	9885
Of other countries	239	86	325
Total	4739	5471	10,210

2249 **VYSOKÁ ŠKOLA MÚZICKÝCH UMĚNÍ V BRATISLAVE**

College of Arts

Jiráskova 3, Bratislava 813 01

Cables: všmu

Telephone: (42-7) 332306

Fax: (42-7) 335913

Rektor: Miloš Jurkovič (1986-)

F. of Dramatic Art

F. of Music

F. of Cinema and Television

Founded 1949, a State institution. Governing body: the Council. Some residential facilities for students.

Arrangments for co-operation with similar schools in: Poland, German Democratic Republic, Hungary, USSR, United Kingdom, and France.

Academic Year: October to September (October-January; February-September).

Admission Requirements: Secondary school certificate.

Fees (US$): 5000-700 per annum.

Language of Instruction: Slovak.

Degrees and Diplomas: Diploma and degree of Magister, 4-5 yrs.

Library: c. 38,000 vols.
Academic Staff, 1989-90: 145 (226).
Student Enrolment, 1989-90: 307 (Also 120 external students).

2250 **JANÁČKOVA AKADEMIE MÚZICKÝCH UMĚNÍ**
The Janáček Academy of Music and Dramatic Art
Komenského nám. 6, 662 15 Brno
Telephone: 26842
Rektor: František Šolc (1975-90)
Kvestor: Marie Snášelová

Music and Dramatic Art

Founded 1947 as a State institution.

Arrangements for co-operation with the State Conservatories of Gdańsk, Novosibirsk, and Riga.

Academic Year: September to June (September-December; February-June).

Fees: None.

Language of Instruction: Czech.

Degrees and Diplomas: Diploma, 4-5 yrs.

Library: 30,000 vols.

Academic Staff, 1986-87:

Rank	Full-time	Part-time
Profesoři	7	–
Docenti	17	4
Odborní asistenti	26	23
Asistenti	2	1
Odborní instruktoři	1	–
Externí učitel	–	52
Total	53	80

Student Enrolment, 1986-87:

	Men	Women	Total
Of the country	100	61	161
Of other countries	1	1	2
Total	101	62	163

2251 **AKADEMIE MÚZICKÝCH UMĚNÍ**
Academy of Music
Smetanovo nábř 2, Praha 1
Telephone: 23-42-54

F. of Music
F. of Dramatic Art
F. of Film and Television Techniques

Founded 1945. Some residential facilities for students.

Academic Year: October to June.

Admission Requirements: Secondary school certificate and entrance examination.

Fees: None.

Language of Instruction: Czech.

Degrees and Diplomas: Diploma, 5 yrs.

Student Enrolment: c. 500 (Also *c.* 250 external and part-time students).

2252 **VYSOKÁ ŠKOLA VÝTVARNÝCH UMĚNÍ**
Academy of Fine Arts
Hviezdoslavovo nám. 18, Bratislava 81437
Telephone: 332-431
Rektor: Jozef Jankovič
Kvestor: Juraj Jankovič

D. of Painting
Head: Ludovit Hološka
D. of Sculpture
Head: Ján Hoffstädter
D. of History and Theory of Art
Head: Lubica Belohradská
D. of Free Graphc Art and Illustration
Head: Karol Ondreička
D. of Art and Design
Head: Peter Paliatka
D. of Architecture
Head: Rastislav Janák
D. of Restoration and Conservation
Head: Vladimir Plekanec

Founded 1949 as a State institution and operated under the jurisdiction of the Ministry of Education. Residential facilities for students.

Academic Year: September to June (September-January; February-June).

Admission Requirements: Secondary school certificate and entrance examination.

Fees: None.

Degrees and Diplomas: Professional titles of–Akademický architekt; Akademický malíř, painting; Akademický sochař, sculpture, 6 yrs.

Library: c. 25,000 vols.

Academic Staff, 1990-91: 60.

Student Enrolment, 1990-91: 248.

2253 **AKADEMIE VÝTVARNÝCH UMĚNÍ**
Academy of Fine Arts
Ul. Akademie 4, Praha 7
Telephone: 373-641-8
Rektor: Mulan Knižák (1990-)
Kvestor: Mirolav Tajč

Painting
Sculpture
Graphic Art
Restoration of Fine Arts
Architecture

Founded 1799 as a private school of art, became State institution 1896 and extended to include sculpture. Extended to include architecture 1910. Reorganized 1945 and 1990.

Arrangements for co-operation with similar institutions in: Antwerp, Berlin, Budapest, Leningrad, Vienna.

Academic Year: September to June (September-January; February-June).

Admission Requirements: Secondary school certificate and entrance examination.

Fees: None.

Language of Instruction: Czech.

Degrees and Diplomas: Professional titles of–Akademický malíř, painting; Akademický sochař, sculpture; Akademický architekt, 6 yrs.

Library: Central Library, *c.* 30,000 vols.

Academic Staff, 1989-90:

Rank	Full-time	Part-time
Profesoři	10	2
Docenti	10	3
Asistenti	19	7
Total	39	12

Student Enrolment, 1989-90:

	Men	Women	Total
Of the country	121	63	184
Of other countries	14	1	15
Total	135	64	199

2254 **VYSOKÁ ŠKOLA UMĚLECKOPRŮMYSLOVÁ**
Academy of Applied Arts
Jan Palach Square 80, Praha 1 110 00
Cables: Všup
Telex: 232 6884
Telephone: 231 9512
Rektor: Ladislav Vrátník (1990-)

S. of Architecture I (Town Planning)
Head: Martin Rajniš; *staff* 14 (12)
S. of Architecture II (Interior Architecture)
Head: Jan Fišer; *staff* 14 (12)
S. of Architecture III (Interior Design)
Head: Ladislav Vrátník; *staff* 14 (12)
S. of Design I
Head: Bořek Siipek; *staff* 12 (9)
S. of Design II (Product Design)
Head: Otto Diblik; *staff* 12 (9)
S. of Design III (Industrial Design)
Head: Pavel Škarka; *staff* 13 (9)
S. of Sculpture and Applied Plastics
Head: Kurt Gebauer; *staff* 14 (9)
S. of Painting
Head: Pavel Nešlenha; *staff* 13 (9)
S. of Glass Creative Art
Head: Vladimír Kopecký; *staff* 14 (9)
S. of Ceramics and China
Head: Václav Šerák; *staff* 13 (6)

S. of Metals and Jewels
Head: Jiří Harcuba; *staff* 13 (6)
S. of Textile Creative Art I (Industrial Design)
Head: Adéla Matasová; *staff* 14 (8)
S. of Textile Creative Art II (Textiles)
Head: Bohdan Mrázek; *staff* 13 (8)
S. of Fashion Design
Head: Zdeňka Bauerová; *staff* 9 (10)
Also 4 Graphic Studios.

Founded 1885 as Royal and Imperial School of Industrial Art. Reorganized and granted present status 1946. A State institution. Governing bodies: the Academic Senate; the Artistic Council.

Arrangements for co-operation with several institutions in: Austria, Belgium, Germay, Finland, France, Israel,Italy, United Kingdom, USSR.

Academic Year: October to June (October-January; February-June).

Admission Requirements: Secondary school certificate and entrance examination.

Fees: None.

Language of Instruction: Czech.

Degrees and Diplomas: Professional titles of–Akademický architekt; Akademický malíř, painting; Akademický sochař, sculpture, 6 yrs. New title in preparation.

Library: Central Library, *c.* 42,000 vols.

Academic Staff, 1989-90:

Rank	Full-time	Part-time
Professors	8	
Associate Professors	19	
Professional Assistants	21	
Assistants	2	
Instructors	2	
Professional Workers	3	
Total	55	30

Student Enrolment, 1989-90:

	Men	Women	Total
Of the country	146	132	278
Of other countries	6	11	17
Total	152	143	295

Teacher Training

2255 **PEDAGOGICKÁ FAKULTA**
Tajovského 3, 97549 Banská Bystrica
Telephone: 345-45-59

Teacher Training (Humanities and Sciences)

Founded 1954 as a school, acquired present status 1965. A State institution financed by and under the jurisdiction of the Ministry of Education. Residential facilities for students.

Academic Year: October to July (October-January; February-June).

Admission Requirements: Secondary school certificate and entrance examination.

Fees: None.

Language of Instruction: Slovak.

Degrees and Diplomas: Teaching qualification, middle secondary level, 5 yrs.

Library: 124,000 vols.

Publication: Sborník (Recueil d'études) (biannually).

Academic Staff: *c.* 210.

Student Enrolment: *c.* 2700.

2256 **PEDAGOGICKÁ FAKULTA**
Ul. Jeronýmova 10, České Budějovice
Telephone: 0042-38-23453
Děkan: Jiří Divísek
Tajemník: Václav Přibán

Teacher Training

Founded 1948 as institute, acquired present status 1964. A State institution under the jurisdiction of the Ministry of Education.Will be incorporated in the planned University of South Bohemia.

Arrangements for co-operation with: Johannes Kepler University, Linz; College of Education, Halle-Köthen; Kalinin State University.

Academic Year: September to May (September-December; February-May).

Admission Requirements: Secondary school certificate.

Fees: None.

Language of Instruction: Czech.

Degrees and Diplomas: Teaching qualification, 5 yrs.

Library: 156,000 vols.

Academic Staff, 1990: 162.

Student Enrolment, 1990: 1600.

2257 **PEDAGOGICKÁ FAKULTA**
301 nám. V.I. Lenina, 50191 Hradec Králové
Telephone: 25226/8

Teacher Training (Humanities and Sciences)
D. for Correspondence Courses
I. of Applied Education

Founded 1959 as institute, acquired present status 1964. A State institution under the jurisdiction of the Ministry of Education. Residential facilities.

Academic Year: October to June (October-January; February-June).

Admission Requirements: Secondary school certificate.

Fees: None.

Language of Instruction: Czech.

Degrees and Diplomas: Teaching qualification, middle secondary level, 8 sem.

Library: Central Library, *c.* 160,000 vols.

Publication: Recueil d'études.

Academic Staff: *c.* 130.

Student Enrolment: *c.* 2140 (Also *c.* 950 external students).

2258 **PEDAGOGICKÁ FAKULTA**
Lomonosova 1, Nitra
Telephone: 73-59

Teacher Training

Founded as an institute 1959, acquired present status 1964. A State institution under the jurisdiction of the Ministry of Education. Residential facilities for students.

Academic Year: October to June (October-February; February-June).

Admission Requirements: Secondary school certificate and entrance examination.

Fees: None.

Language of Instruction: Slovak.

Degrees and Diplomas: Teaching qualification, middle secondary level, 8 sem.

Library: Central Library, *c.* 150,000 vols.

Publications: Sborník Pedagogickej fakulty v Nitre; Studentský vedecký sborník; Zo svitania (writing by students).

Academic Staff: *c.* 180.

Student Enrolment: *c.* 1000 (Also *c.* 850 external students).

2259 **PEDAGOGICKÁ FAKULTA**
Dvořákova 7, Ostrava I
Telephone: 245-51; 252-31

Teacher Training

Founded 1953 as School of Education at Opava. Became an institute 1959 and moved to Ostrava, acquired present status 1964. A State institution under the jurisdiction of the Ministry of Education. Some residential facilities for students.

Academic Year: October to September (October-February; February-September).

Admission Requirements: Secondary school certificate.

Fees: None.

Language of Instruction: Czech, Polish, Russian, Slovak.

Degrees and Diplomas: Teaching qualification, middle secondary level, 4 yrs.

Library: *c.* 46,500 vols.

Publications: Acta Facultatis Paedagogicae Ostraviensis, series A-D (Natural Sciences and Mathematics; Education and Psychology; Geography and History; Philology, Linguistics and Literature) (quarterly); Spisy Pedagogickej fakulty v Ostrava (2-3 times a year).

Academic Staff: *c.* 160.

Student Enrolment: *c.* 1000 (Also *c.* 1300 external students).

2260 **PEDAGOGICKÁ FAKULTA**
Veleslavínova 42, Plzeň
Telephone: 379-51
Dean: Jiří Pyšel

Teacher Training

Founded 1948 as Faculty of Education of the University of Prague, became school 1953, and institute 1959. Acquired present status 1964.

Arrangements for co-operation with: Szczecin University; Janus Pannonious University of Pécs; Colleges of Education, Zwickau, Odessa.

Academic Year: September to June (September-January; February-June).

Admission Requirements: Secondary school certificate.

Fees: None.

Degrees and Diplomas: Teaching qualification, middle secondary level, 4 yrs; secondary level, 5 yrs.

Academic Staff, 1990: c.150.

Student Enrolment, 1990: 1580 (Also *c.* 460 external students).

2261 **PEDAGOGICKÁ FAKULTA**
České mládeže 8, Ústí nad Labem
Telephone: 26441

Teacher Training (Humanities and Sciences)

Ce. for Correspondence Courses (Liberec)

Founded 1954 as school of education, became an institute 1959 and acquired present status 1964. A State institution under the jurisdiction of the Ministry of Education. Residential facilities for *c.* 520 students.

Academic Year: October to June (October-December; January-June).

Admission Requirements: Secondary school certificate.

Fees: None.

Language of Instruction: Czech.

Degrees and Diplomas: Teaching qualification, middle secondary level, 4 yrs.

Library: *c.* 90,000 vols.

Publication: Sborník Pedagogickej fakulty v Ustí n.L.

Academic Staff: *c.* 130.

Student Enrolment: *c.* 1540 (Also *c.* 580 external students).

DENMARK

Universities and Technical Universities

2262 ***AALBORG UNIVERSITETSCENTER**

The University of Aalborg

Langagervedl 2, 9100 Aalborg

Telephone: (98) 15-91-11

Fax: (98) 15-22-01

Rektor: Sven Caspersen (1976-91)

Administrationschef: Peter Plenge

F. of Social Sciences (including Economics and Business Administration)

Dean: Hans Güllestrup; *staff* 102 (11)

F. of Technology and Science (including Computer Sciences)

Dean: Finn Kjærsdam; *staff* 353 (12)

F. of Arts and Humanities (including Music, Business Languages)

Dean: Ole Prehn; *staff* 61 (17.)

Founded 1971, admitted first students 1974. A State institution incorporating previously established centres of education in Aalborg and employing new teaching and learning methods based on an 'integrated' approach to higher education, with emphasis on project work in groups. Financed by the State. Governing body: the Konsistorium (University Council), comprising representatives of the academic staff (50%), students (25%) and members of the technical and admininistrative staff (25%). Some residential facilities for foreign academic staff and students.

Arrangements for co-operation with universities worldwide. Participates in the ERASMUS programme.

Academic Year: September to August (September-January; February-June).

Admission Requirements: Secondary school certificate (studentereksamen) or Høhere-Forberedelseseksamen, -Handelseksamen, or -Tekniskeksamen.

Fees: Tuition, none.

Language of Instruction: Danish.

Degrees and Diplomas: Professional titles of–Bilingual Correspondent, 2 ½ yrs; Akademiingeniør; Socialrådgiver, 3 ½ yrs; Almene erhvervsøkonomiske eksamen, H.A.; Erhvervsjuridisk afgangseksamen; economics and business law, 3 yrs; Candidatus philosophiae, cand.phil., 4 yrs; Candidatus magisterii, cand.mag., 5 yrs; cand.oecon., economics; cand.scient.adm., public administration, 5 yrs; cand.merc., commerce; cand.polyt., 5 yrs; cand.geom., 5 yrs; Candidatus scientiarum, cand.scient., 5 yrs. Postgraduate Licentiate in all faculties, a further 2-3 yrs. Doctorates by thesis.

Library: Central Library, 363,500 vols.

Special Facilities (Museums, etc.): NordjyllandsVidenpark (Novi). (Science Park)

Publications: Årsberetning (biannually); Center-NYT (10 times a year).

Press or Publishing House: Aalborg Universitetsforlag (autonomous).

Academic Staff, 1990:

Rank	Full-time
Professorer	92
Adjunkter/lektorer	339
Stipendiater	65
Total	496

Student Enrolment, 1986-87:

	Men	Women	Total
Of the country	3809	2415	6224
Of other countries	216	70	286
Total	4025	2485	6510

2263 ***AARHUS UNIVERSITET**

Aarhus University

Ndr. Ringgade 1, 8000 Aarhus C

Telephone: (86) 13-43-11

Fax: (86) 19-70-2999

Rektor: Henning Lehmann (1983-89)

Direktør: Stig Møller

F. of Arts (Humanities including Archaeology)

Dean: Ole Høiris Nielsen; *staff* 189 (40)

F. of Medicine

Dean: Søren Mogensen; *staff* 270 (115)

F. of Social Sciences (Economics, Law, Political Science, and Psychology)

Dean; Niels Chr. Sidenius; *staff* 177 (40)

F. of Theology

Dean: Viggo Mortensen; *staff* 45 (15)

F. of Natural Sciences (including Biology)

Dean: Karl Pedersen; *staff* 266 (50)

Postgraduate S. of Home Economics

Inspector: Nina Kiesling; *staff* 5

S. of Advanced Nursing Education

Rector: Inge Andersen; *staff* 55

Founded 1928 by municipal authorities, recognized by Parliament 1931, and awarded government grant. Achieved full university status 1934. Became a State institution 1970 under the supervision of the Ministry of Education. Governing bodies: the Konsistorium (Senate), comprising 32 members, including 16 members of the academic staff, 8 of the technical and administrative staff, and 8 representatives of the student body; the Faculty Councils; the Institute Councils; the Study Committees. Some residential facilities for students.

Academic Year: September to June (September-December; February-June).

Admission Requirements: Secondary school certificate (studentereksamen) or equivalent.

Fees: Tuition, none.

Language of Instruction: Danish.

Degrees and Diplomas: Candidatus magisterii, cand.mag.; Magister artium, mag.art., humanities; Candidatus medicinae, cand.med., medicine; Candidatus juris, cand.jur., law; Candidatus oeconomices, cand.oecon., economics; Candidatus scientiarum politicarum, cand. scient.polit., political science; Candidatus psychologiae, cand.psych., psychology; Candidatus theologiae, cand.theol., theology; Candidatus scientiarum, cand.scient., science. Magister scientiarum, mag.scient., science, 5-6 yrs, except Candidatus medicinae, 8 yrs. Doctorates and Licentiates (Ph.D.s) in all fields by thesis.

Library: State and University Library, *c.* 1,740,000 vols.

Special Facilities (Museums, etc.): Museums: History of Science; Prehistoric; Natural History; Medical History; Classical Archaeology.

Publications: Acta Jutlandica (annually): Årsberetning (yearbook); Information og Debat (Gazette).

Academic Staff, 1988-89: c. 840 (700).

Student Enrolment, 1988-89:

	Men	Women	Total
Of the country	6792	5899	12,691
Of other countries	238	160	398
Total	7030	6059	13,089

2264 **DANMARKS INGENIØRAKADEMI**

Engineering Academy of Denmark

Bygning 101, 2800 Lyngby

Telex: 37529 DTH DIAD

Telephone: (42) 88-22-22

Rektor: Hans Peter Jensen

Administrationschef: Henrik Moltke

D. of Chemical Engineering

Head: Uwe Nissen; *staff* 43

D. of Mechanical Engineering
Head: Ove Bogø; *staff* 42
D. of Civil Engineering
Head: Ole Brink-Usar; *staff* 43
D. of Electrical Engineering
Head: Otto Mortensen; *staff* 45

Founded 1957 and associated with Danmarks Tekniske Højskole, Copenhagen. A State institution under the supervision of the Ministry of Education. Governing body: the Konsistorium, comprising students, academic staff and representatives of the administrative and technical personnel.

Academic Year: August to July (August-January; January-July).

Admission Requirements: Secondary school certificate (studentereksamen) in appropriate subjects.

Fees: None.

Language of Instruction: Danish.

Degrees and Diplomas: Professional title of–Akademiingeniør (chemical, civil, mechanical, and electrical engineering), 3 ½-4 yrs.

Academic Staff, 1989-90:

Rank	Full-time
Ingeniørdocenter	26
Lektorer	147
Total	173

Student Enrolment, 1989-90:

	Men	Women	Total
Of the country	1534	644	2178
Of other countries	142	28	170
Total	1676	672	2348

2265 ***DEN POLYTEKNISKE LÆREANSTALT, DANMARKS TEKNISKE HØJSKOLE**

Technical University of Denmark
Lundtoftevej 100, Bygning 101A, 2800 Lyngby
Telex: 37529 DTH DIA
Telephone: (45) 42-88-22-22
Fax: (45) 42-88-17-99
Rektor: Hans Peter Jensen (1989-92)
Administrationschef: Henrik Moltkeer

D. of Chemical Engineering
Chairman: John Villadsen
D. of Electrical Engineering
Chairman: Erik Lintz Christensen
D. of Civil Engineering
Chairman: Esben Byskov
D. of Mechanical Engineering
Chairman: Frithiof Niordson
D. of Basic Science
Chairman: Vagn Lundsgaard Hansen

Founded 1829 as a State institution under the supervision of the Ministry of Education. Governing body: the Konsistorium.

Arrangements for co-operation with universities and institutions of higher education in Scandinavia, EEC countries, and other countries.

Academic Year: September to July (September-January; February-July).

Admission Requirements: Secondary school certificate (studentereksamen) in appropriate subjects.

Fees: Tuition, none.

Language of Instruction: Danish.

Degrees and Diplomas: Title of Civilingeniør (Master of Science in: chemical, mechanical, civil, and electrical engineering), 5 yrs. Ph.D., a further 2 ½-3 yrs. Dr.techn., doctorate, by thesis.

Library: Central Library, 547,000 vols.

Academic Staff, 1989-90: 511.

Student Enrolment, 1989-90:

	Men	Women	Total
Of the country	3864	983	4847
Of other countries	259	34	293
Total	4123	1017	5140

2266 ***KØBENHAVNS UNIVERSITET**

University of Copenhagen
Frue Plads/Nørregade 10, Postboks 2177, 1017 København K
Cables: univcop
Telex: 22221 NNICOP DK
Telephone: (45)33-91-08-28
Fax: (45) 33-91-18-28
Rektor: Ove Nathan (1973-)
Universitetsdirektør: Niels Jørgen Hertzum

F. of Theology
F. of Social Sciences (including Law, Economics and Social Sciences)
F. of Medicine
F. of Humanities
F. of Natural Sciences

Founded 1479. Financed by the State. Governing bodies: the Konsistorium (Senate); the Faculty Councils; the Institute Councils with equal representation of academic staff (50%), students (25%), and members of the technical and administrative staff (25%). Some residential facilities for students.

Arrangements for exchange with the Universities of: Lund; Göteborg; Bergen; Helsinki; Oulu; Lancaster; Sheffield; Sussex; Caen; Lille III; Paris IV; Madrid; Santiago de Compostela; Zaragoza; Kiel; Tübingen; Berlin Free; Moscow; Leipzig; Rostock; Zürich; Alaska-Fairbanks; California; Wisconsin-Madison; Washington State; Washington; McGill; McMaster; Western Ontario; York, Ontario; British Columbia; Cracow; Gdańsk; Poznań; Warsaw; Ghana; Nagoya; Baja California; Mansoura; Tel Aviv; Birzeit. Daido Institute of Technology, Nagoya.

Academic Year: September to July (September-December; February-June).

Admission Requirements: Secondary school certificate (studentereksamen), or foreign equivalent, and entrance examination in Danish language.

Fees: None.

Language of Instruction: Danish.

Degrees and Diplomas: Candidatus artium/examinatus artium, cand. art./exam.art., 2 yrs. Candidatus -juris, cand.jur., law, 4-5 yrs; -theologiae, cand.theol.; -politices, cand.polit. (economics); -statisticae, cand.stat.; -scientiarum socialium, cand.adm.pol., cand.scient.soc.; -scientiarum, cand.scient., -medicinae, cand.med., 5-6 yrs; -magisterii, cand.mag., 6-7 yrs. Magister -scientiarum socialium, mag.scient.soc.; -artium, mag.art.; -scientiarum, mag.scient., 7-8 yrs. Postgraduate Ph.D. in all faculties, a further 3 yrs. Doctorates by thesis. Bachelor of-Arts; Science, 3 yrs.

Library: University Libraries (Humanities and Science and Medicine), c. 1,000,000 vols.

Special Facilities (Museums, etc.): Botanical Museum; Zoological Museum; Medical History Museum; Mineralogical Museum.

Publications: Årbog for Københavns universitet (yearbook); Lektionskatalogen: Foreloesning øvelser ved Københavns Universitet (lecture lists published twice a year); Universitetsavisen (University gazette).

Academic Staff, 1990: c. 2000.

Student Enrolment, 1990: c. 25,000.

2267 ***ODENSE UNIVERSITET**

University of Odense
Campusvej 55, 5230 Odense M
Telex: OUBIBL-59918
Telephone: +4566158428
Rektor: Carl Th. Pedersen (1983-89)
Universitetsdirektør: Helge Muhle Larsen

F. of Natural Sciences
Dean: Jørgen Munkholm; *staff* 185 (16)
F. of Medicine
Dean: Mogenshørder; *staff* 157 (161)
F. of Humanities
Dean: Carlbache; *staff* 177 (56)
F. of Social Sciences (including Economics)
Dean: Mogens N. Pedersen; *staff* 55

Also Scandinavian Studies for Foreign Students.

Founded 1966. A State institution. Governing bodies: the Konsistorium; the Faculty Councils; the Departmental Councils; the Study Boards.

Arrangements for co-operation with: University of Sterling; Ohio University; University of Minnesota; Gothenburg University; University of Uppsala; Mahidol University, Bangkok; University of California, Berkeley; Humboldt University; Wonkwang University; University of Cracow.

Academic Year: September to June (September-January; February-June).

Admission Requirements: Secondary school certificate (studentereksamen) or Højere-Forberedelseseksamen or Handelseksamen, or recognized foreign equivalent.

Fees: Tuition, none.

Language of Instruction: Danish.

Degrees and Diplomas: Examinatus artium, exam.art., 2 yrs. Candidatus philosophiae, cand.phil; Candidatus negot, cand.negot., 4 yrs; Candidatus mercaturae, cand.merc.; Candidatus mercaturae et auditoris, cand.merc.aud.; Candidatus rerum socialium, cand.rer.soc., 5 yrs; Candidatus scientiarum, cand.scient., 5 ½ yrs; Candidatus magisterii, cand.mag., 6 yrs. Magister artium, mag.art., 6 yrs; Candidatus medicinae, cand.med., 6 yrs. Licentiatus–Philosophiae, lic.phil.; –Medicinae, lic.med., –Scientiarum, lic.scient. Doctor Medicinae, dr.med.; Doctor Philosophiae, dr.phil.

Library: Central Library, 800,000 vols.

Publication: University Handbooks (annually).

Press or Publishing House: Odense University Press.

Academic Staff, 1989:

Rank	Full-time	Part-time
Professorer	56	–
Lektorer/Adjunkter	383	–
Ekstern Lektorer/Undervisning assistenter	–	281
Total	439	281

Student Enrolment, 1989:

Men	Women	Total
4425	3039	7464

2268 **ROSKILDE UNIVERSITETSCENTER**

Roskilde University

Marbjergvej 35, Postbox 260, 4000 Roskilde

Telephone: (46) 75-77-11

Fax: (46) 75-74-01

Rektor: Henrik Toft Jensen (1989-)

Administrationschef: Erik Ebbe

Humanities

Natural Sciences

Social Sciences

Ce. for Integrated Education

Ce. for Media Communications (including Journalism, Radio, and Public Relations)

Ce. for Social Sciences

Founded 1970 by government decree, admitted first students 1972. A State institution employing new teaching and learning methods based on an 'integrated' approach to higher education, and placing emphasis on group work. Governing body: the Konsistorium (Senate) of 24 member, comprising representatives of the academic staff (50%), students (25%)and members of the technical and administrative staff (25%).

Academic Year: September to June (September-January; February-June).

Admission Requirements: Secondary school certificate (studentereksamen), or appropriate educational level reached through formal or non-formal education.

Fees: Tuition, none.

Language of Instruction: Danish.

Degrees and Diplomas: The structure provides for a first degree in the field of Humanities, Natural Sciences, or Social Sciences after 3-4 yrs study. Candidatus, 5-5 ½ yrs. Doctorate, 3 yrs. Licentiate.

Library: c. 325,000 vols.

Publications: RUC-NYT (biweekly); Fructus (annually).

Academic Staff, 1990: 262.

Student Enrolment, 1990: 3618.

Other Institutions

Technical Education

2269 **INGENIØRHØJSKOLEN, AARHUS TEKNIKUM**

Engineering College of Aarhus

Dalgas Avenue 2, 8000 Aarhus C

Telephone: (86) 13-62-11

Fax: (86) 13-64-88

Rektor: Harry Svanhede Pedersen (1990-)

Administrator: Aa. Tjørnager

D. of Civil Engineering

Head: P. Neergaard

D. of Electrical Power

Head: Erling Johansen

D. of Electronic Engineering

Head: K. Møller Petersen

D. of Mechanical Engineering

Head: Poul Erik Møllenberg

Founded 1915. Reorganized 1938. An independent institution entirely financed by the State. Its governing body includes representatives from industry, trade unions, municipal authorities and the State.

Academic Year: August to June (August-December; January-June).

Admission Requirements: 1 yr practical training following secondary school certificate (studentereksamen) or 2-4 yrs practical training following realeksamen.

Fees: Tuition, none.

Language of Instruction: Danish.

Degrees and Diplomas: Title of Ingeniør, 3 yrs.

Library: 18,000 vols.

Academic Staff, 1990-91:

Rank	Full-time	Part-time
Fagrådsformænd	5	–
Lærere	107	16
Total	112	16

Student Enrolment, 1990-91:

	Men	Women	Total
Of the country	1131	116	1247
Of other countries	81	3	84
Total	1212	119	1331

2270 **INGENIØRHØJSKOLEN, ESBJERG TEKNIKUM**

Esbjerg Teknikum

Niels Bohrs Vej 8, 6700 Esbjerg

Telephone: (75) 12-76-66

Fax: (75) 45-36-43

Rektor: Kurt Kallestrup

Administrator: Bent Lemche

D. of Civil and Construction Engineering

Head: Jørn Thorsen; *staff* 12 (5)

D. of Mechanical Engineering

Head: Preben Hansen; *staff* 11 (6)

D. of Chemical Engineering

Head: Birgit Storm; *staff* 12 (10)

Founded 1964. An independent institution entirely financed by the State. Its governing body includes representatives from industry, trade unions, municipal authorities and the State. Some residential facilities for students.

Participates in the ERASMUS and Comett programmes in co-operation with the Universities of: London; Loughorough; Dublin; Reading; Santander; Cantabria.

Academic Year: August to June (August-January; February-June).

Admission Requirements: 1 yr practical training following secondary school certificate (studentereksamen) or 2-4 yrs practical training following realeksamen.

Fees: Tuition, none.

Language of Instruction: Danish.

Degrees and Diplomas: Title of Teknikumingeniør, 4 yrs.

Library: Esbjerg Tekniske Bibliotek, c. 15,000 vols.

Academic Staff, 1990-91:

Rank	Full-time	Part-time
Professors	2	–
Assistants	10	2
Senior Lecturers	28	5
Lecturers	5	14
Total	45	21

Student Enrolment, 1989-90:

	Men	Women	Total
Of the country	330	300	630
Of other countries	20	–	20
Total	350	300	650

2271 **INGINIØRHØJSKOLEN, HASLEV TEKNIKUM**

College of Technical Engineering
Bråbyvej 45, 4690 Haslev
Telephone: (03) 69-14-00

D. of Civil Engineering

Founded 1963. An independent institution entirely financed by the State. Its governing body includes representatives from industry, trade unions, municipal authorities and the State.

Academic Year: August to July.

Admission Requirements: 1 yr practical training following secondary school certificate (studentereksamen) or 2-4 yrs practical training following realeksamen.

Fees: Tuition, none.

Language of Instruction: Danish.

Degrees and Diplomas: Title of Ingeniør in Civil and Construction Engineering, 3 yrs.

Library: c. 8000 vols.

Academic Staff: c. 20.

Student Enrolment: c. 100.

2272 **INGENIØRHØJSKOLEN, HELSINGØR TEKNIKUM**

College of Technical Engineering
Rasmus Knudsensvej 50, 3000 Helsingør
Telephone: 02-216622

Marine Architecture

Mechanical Engineering

Founded 1962. An independent institution entirely financed by the State. Its governing body includes representatives from industry, trade unions, municipal authorities and the State. Residential facilities for students.

Academic Year: August to June (August-January; January-June).

Admission Requirements: 1 yr practical training following secondary school certificate (studentereksamen) or 2-3 yrs practical training following realeksamen.

Fees: Tuition, none.

Language of Instruction: Danish.

Degrees and Diplomas: Titles, 4 yrs.

Library: c. 10,000 vols.

Academic Staff: c. 40.

Student Enrolment: c. 380.

2273 **INGENIØRHØJSKOKEN, HORSENS TEKNIKUM**

Engineering College of Horsens
Chr.M. Østergaards Vej 4, 8700 Horsens
Telephone: (75) 62-88-11
Fax: (75) 62-64-56
Rektor: Poul Holm Nielsen (1988-91)
Administrator: Hans Loft

D. of Civil and Construction Engineering
Head: Werner Bai; *staff* 35 (15)

D. of Agricultural and Mechanical Engineering
Head: Hans Jørn Hansen; *staff* 27 (12)

D. of Export Engineering
Head: Anker Stæ-Jørgensen; *staff* – (2)

Founded 1915. An independent institution entirely financed by the State. Its governing body includes representatives from industry, trade unions, municipal authorities and the State.

Academic Year: August to July (August-February; February-July).

Admission Requirements: 1 yr practical training following secondary school certificate (studentereksamen) or 2-4 yrs practical training following realeksamen.

Fees: Tuition, none.

Language of Instruction: Danish.

Degrees and Diplomas: Title of Teknikumingeniør, 3 yrs.

Library: 25,000 vols.

Academic Staff, 1989-90:

Rank	Full-time	Part-time
Rektor	1	–
Afdelingsforstandere	2	–
Lærere	60	29
Total	63	29

Student Enrolment, 1989-90:

	Men	Women	Total
Of the country	433	151	584
Of other countries	27	–	27
Total	460	151	611

2274 **INGENIØRHØJSKOLEN, KØBENHAVNS TEKNIKUM**

College of Technical Engineering
Prinsesse Charlottes Gade 38, 2200 København N
Telephone: (31) 39-48-11
Fax: (31) 39-48-65
Rektor: Verner Daugaard (1989-)

D. of Civil Engineering
Head: Olav Aaen; *staff* 12 (27)

D. of Mechanical Engineering
Head: Peter Ulrik Andersen; *staff* 20 (9)

D. of Electrical Power Engineering
Head: Ib Dyring Kledal; *staff* 10 (5)

D. of Electronic Engineering
Head: Flemming Krogh; *staff* 26 (10)

D. of Production Engineering
Head: Gorm Hemmingsen; *staff* 16 (14)

D. of Export Engineering
Head: Knud Holm Hansen; *staff* 17 (20)

Founded 1876 as technical school, acquired present status and title 1963. An independent institution entirely financed by the State. Its governing body includes representatives from industry, trade unions, municipal authorities and the State.

Academic Year: August to June (August-January; February-June).

Admission Requirements: Secondary school certificate (studentereksamen) or equivalent, or minimum 2 yrs practical training and 1-yr preparatory course in Mathematics, Physics, Chemistry, Danish, History, and 2 foreign languages, following folkeskolens udvidede afgangsprøve.

Fees: Tuition, none.

Language of Instruction: Danish.

Degrees and Diplomas: Title of Teknikumingeniør, 3 yrs. Export Engineering, 5 yrs.

Library: 32,900 vols.

Academic Staff, 1990:

	Full-time	Part-time
Lektorer	110	5
Adjunkter	16	11
Timelønnede lærere	–	44
Total	126	60

Student Enrolment, 1990:

	Men	Women	Total
Of the country	1377	407	d1784
Of other countries	99	10	109
Total	1476	417	1893

2275 **INGENIØRHØJSKOLEN, ODENSE TEKNIKUM**

College of Technical Engineering
Niels Bohrs Allé 1, 5230 Odense
Telephone: (45) 66-13-08-27
Fax: (45) 66-13-48-27
Rektor: B. Poulsen (1988-91)
Administrator: F. Johansen

D. of Civil Engineering
Head: J. Møllerhøj; *staff* 14 (8)

D. of Electrical Engineering
Head: Th. Kier; *staff* 29 (20)

D. of Mechanical Engineering
Head: N.O. Clausen; *staff* 31 (1)

D. of Production Engineering
Head: J. Banke; *staff* 17 (8)

D. of Chemical Engineering
Head: Th. Shrøder; *staff* 4 (1)

Founded 1905. An independent institution entirely financed by the State. Its governing body includes representatives from industry, trade unions, municipal authorities and the State.

Academic Year: August to June (August-January; February-June).

Admission Requirements: 1 yr practical training following secondary school certificate (studentereksamen) or 2-4 yrs practical training following realeksamen.

Fees: Tuition, none.

Language of Instruction: Danish.

Degrees and Diplomas: Title of Teknikumingeniør (Bachelor of Science in Engineering), 3-4 yrs.

Library: c. 30,000 vols.

Academic Staff: c.100 (30).

Student Enrolment, 1990:

	Men	Women	Total
Of the country	756	347	1103
Of other countries	145	5	150
Total	901	352	1253

2276 **INGENIØRHØJSKOLEN, SØNDERBORG TEKNIKUM**

College of Technical Engineering
Voldgade 5, 6400 Sønderborg
Telephone: 74425550
Fax: 74431735
Rektor: Kjeld Clemen Jørgensen (1975-81)
Administrator: Mathias L. Madsen

D. of Electrical Engineering
Head: Erik Urth; *staff* 16 (1)
D. of Mechanical Engineering
Head: Hans Brandt; *staff* 14 (1)

Founded 1963. An independent institution entirely financed by the State. Its governing Board includes representatives from industry, trade unions, municipal authorities and the State.

Academic Year: August to June (August-December; January-June).

Admission Requirements: 1 yr practical training following secondary school certificate (studentereksamen) or 2-4 yrs practical training following realeksamen.

Fees: Tuition, none.

Language of Instruction: Danish.

Degrees and Diplomas: Title of Teknikumingeniør, 3 yrs.

Library: Central Library.

Academic Staff, 1986-87: 38 (33).

Student Enrolment, 1989-90:

	Men	Women	Total
Of the country	265	21	286
Of other countries	19	1	20
Total	284	22	306

Professional Education

2277 **ARKITEKTSKOKEN I AARHUS**

Aarhus School of Architecture
Nørreport 20, 8000 Aarhus C
Telephone: (86) 13-08-22
Fax: (86) 19-06-45
Rektor: Mogens Brandt Poulsen (1985-)
Administrator (Acting): Ole Graah

D. of Architecture
D. of Town Planning
D. of Garden and Landscape Design
D. of Interior Design (Furniture)
D. of Restoration
D. of Industrial Design

Founded 1965, a State institution under the jurisdiction of the Ministry of Cultural Affairs. The Rector is appointed by the Crown. Governing bodies: the Council of the School, comprising 30 members representing the academic staff (12), the student body (12), and technical and administrative staff (6); the Academic Council.

Participates in the ERASMUS and NORDPLUS programmes.

Academic Year: October to May (October-January; February-May).

Admission Requirements: Secondary school certificate (studentereksamen) or equivalent.

Fees: Tuition, none.

Language of Instruction: Danish.

Degrees and Diplomas: Diploma, 5-6 yrs.

Library: 20,000 vols.

Academic Staff, 1986-87:

Rank	Full-time
Professorer	6
Lektorer	5
Faglige assistenter	75
Total	86

Student Enrolment, 1986-87:

	Men	Women	Total
Of the country	407	302	709
Of other countries	22	16	38
	C		
Total	429	318	747

2278 **DANMARKS BIBLIOTEKSSKOLE**

Royal School of Library Science
6 Birketinget, 2300 København S
Telephone: (31) 58-60-66
Fax: (32) 84-02-01
Rektor: Ole Harbo (1983-)
Administrator: Edvard Jeppesen

Library and Information Sciences
Branch in Aalborg.

Founded 1956. Reorganized 1985, with a new curriculum offering a multi-purpose programme. Master course introduced 1990. A State institution under the jurisdiction of the Ministry of Cultural Affairs. Governing body: the Council.

Arrangements for co-operation with the Technical College of Library Science, Stuttgart. Participates in the ERASMUS and NORDPLUS programmes.

Academic Year: September to August (September-December; January-June).

Admission Requirements: Secondary school certificate (studentereksamen) or Højere Forberedelseseksamen or equivalent. Research and University Libraries; university degree and practical experience.

Fees: Tuition, none.

Language of Instruction: Danish.

Degrees and Diplomas: Diplomas in Library and Information Studies, 4 yrs. Master in Library and Information Science (M.L.I.Sc.), a further 2 yrs university degree.

Library: 142,403 vols.

Publication: Biblioteksarbejde (Library Journal) (quarterly).

Academic Staff, 1989-90: 62

Student Enrolment, 1989-90:

	Men	Women	Total
Of the country	178	485	663
Of other countries	–	1	1
Total	178	486	664

2279 **DANMARKS FARMACEUTISKE HØJSKOLE**

The Royal Danish School of Pharmacy
2 Universitetsparken, 2100 København
Telephone: 45(01) 37-08-50
Rektor: Henning Gjelstrup Kristensen
Administrator: Otto Jarl

Pharmacy

Founded 1892, acquired university status 1941. Under the financial and administrative jurisdiction of the Ministry of Education. Financed by the State.

Academic Year: September to June (September-December; January-June).

Admission Requirements: Secondary school certificate (studentereksamen) or equivalent.

Fees: Tuition, none.

Language of Instruction: Danish.

Degrees and Diplomas: Candidatus pharmaciae, cand.pharm., 5 yrs. Licentiatus pharmaciae, lic.pharm., a further 3 yrs. Doctor pharmaciae, dr.pharm., by thesis, at least a further 2 yrs. Also diploma of Pharmacy Assistant, 2 yrs.

Library: c. 30,500 vols.
Academic Staff, 1986-87: c. 110.
Student Enrolment, 1986-87:

Of the country	816
Of other countries	23
Total	839

2280 **HANDELSHØJSKOLEN I AARHUS**

Aarhus School of Business
Fuglesangs Allé 4, 8210 Aarhus V
Telephone: (86) 15-55-88
Fax: (86) 15-01-88
Rektor: Bent Provostgaard (1988-)
Administrator: Chr. Lorenzen

F. of Business Administration and Economics
Dean: Steen Lund-Thomsen; *staff* 97 (270)
F. of Modern Languages
Dean: Birger Andersen; *staff* 61 (87)

Founded 1939. A semi-private institution under the jurisdiction of the Ministry of Education and financed by the State.

Academic Year: September to June (September-December; January-June).

Admission Requirements: Secondary school certificate (studentereksamen), HF-eksamen or HH-eksamen.

Fees: Tuition, none.

Language of Instruction: Danish.

Degrees and Diplomas: Almen erhvervsøkonomisk uddannelse, business economics and administration; Erhvervsøkonomisk uddannelse med datalogi, business economics and dataprocessing; Erhvervsøkonomisk-sproglig uddannelse, business economics and modern languages; Erhvervsretlig uddannelse, business law, 3 yrs. Candidatus mercaturae, cand.merc., a further 2 yrs. Licentiatus mercaturae, lic.merc., postgraduate degree after Candidatus. Qualification as bilingual commercial correspondent, 2 ½ yrs. Candidatus linguae mercaturae, cand.ling.merc., a further 3 yrs. Also diplomas for part-time (evening) students.

Library: 138,000 vols.
Academic Staff, 1990:

Rank	Full-time	Part-time
Professorer	19	–
Lektorer/Adjunkter	139	–
Undervisningsassistenter	–	357
Total	158	357

Student Enrolment, 1989-90: 7200.

2281 **HANDELSHØJSKOLEN I KØBENHAVN**

Copenhagen School of Economics and Business Administration
Nansensgade 19, 1366 København K
Telephone: (01) 14-44-14
Rektor: Finn Junge Jensen (1981-)
Administrator: Kurt Poder

F. of Economics (including Marketing, Business Administration, Commercial Law, Sociology, Transport and Tourism, and Foreign Trade)
Dean: Lauge Stetting
F. of Modern Languages
Dean: Bente Kristensen

Founded 1917 as a private institution. Received approval of Ministry of Commerce. Between 1926 and 1965 the school was financed partly by student fees and partly by government subsidies. Since 1965 the institution, though remaining independent, has been entirely financed by the State. Governing body: the Konsistorium, comprising 21 members.

Arrangements for co-operation with: London Business School; University of Texas at Austin; Northwestern University; University of New York; Oregon State Universities.

Academic Year: September to June (September-December; January-June).

Admission Requirements: Secondary school certificate (studentereksamen), HF-eksamen, or HH-eksamen.

Fees: Tuition, none.

Language of Instruction: Danish.

Degrees and Diplomas: Almene erhvervsøkonomiske eksamen, H.A., economics and business administration, 3 yrs; Handelsvidenskabelige kandidateksamen, cand.merc., 5 yrs. Handelsvidenskabelige licentiatgrad, lic.merc., postgraduate degree, 3 yrs after candidatus. Erhvervsøkonomiske doktorgrad, by thesis after licentiat. Bilingual commercial correspondent, 2-3 yrs; Erhvervssproglige afgangseksamen, E.A., modern languages, 4 yrs; Erhvervssproglige kandidateksamen, cand.ling.merc., a further 2 yrs. Dr.merc.; Dr.ling.merc. Licentiate in business Administration; Languages. Also diplomas for part-time (evening) students.

Library: c. 212,863 vols.
Academic Staff, 1986-87:

Rank	Full-time	Part-time
Professors	23	–
Associate Professors	221	–
Research Fellows	28	–
Instructors	–	861
Total	272	861

Student Enrolment, 1986-87:

Of the country	13,500
Of other countries	361
Total	13,861

2282 **DANMARKS JORDEMODERSKOLEN, AFDELINGEN I KØBENHAVN**

Danish School of Midwifery
Righospitalet, afsnit 7211,Tagensvej 18, 2100 København N
Telephone: (31) 38-66-33
Rektor: Mogens Osler

Midwifery
Also department at Aalborg.

Founded 1787. A State institution under the jurisdiction of the Ministry of Education. Residential facilities for students.

Academic Year: April to September (April-March; October-September).

Admission Requirements: Secondary school certificate (studentereksamen).

Fees: None.

Language of Instruction: Danish.

Degrees and Diplomas: Diploma, 3 yrs.

Academic Staff, 1990-91: 8 (c.25).

Student Enrolment, 1990-91: 20.

2283 **DANMARKS JOURNALISTHØJSKOLE**

The Danish School of Journalism
Olof Palmers Allé 11, 8200 Aarhus N
Telephone: (86) 16-11-22
Fax: (86) 16-89-10
Rektor: Peter Kramhøft
Administrator: Mogens Schmidt

Journalism

Founded 1953 as a private institution. Became State institution 1972. Governing body: the Board of Advisors.

Arrangements for co-operation with the School of Journalism, Utrecht.

Academic Year: September to June (September-January; February-June).

Admission Requirements: Entrance examination.

Fees: None.

Language of Instruction: Danish.

Degrees and Diplomas: Diploma in Journalism (Bachelor).

Library: School Library.

Special Facilities (Museums, etc.): Radio and T.V. Studios.

Publications: 'Nu' (International Politics); 'Ogia en Avis'.

Academic Staff, 1990: 29.

Student Enrolment, 1990: 781 (Including 9 foreign students).

2284 **DET KONGELIGE DANSKE KUNSTAKADEMI ARKITEKTSKOLE**

The Royal Danish Academy of Fine Arts, School of Architecture
Kongens Nytorv 1, 1050 København K
Telephone: (33) 12-68-60
Fax: (33) 12-75-98
Rektor: Bente Beedholm (1986-90)
Inspektør: Ebbe Harder

S. of Architecture

Founded 1754 by King Frederik V. Operated under the jurisdiction of the Ministry of Cultural Affairs. Governing body: the Fagrådet (Council).

Academic Year: September to June (September-January; February-June).

Admission Requirements: Secondary school certificate (studentereksamen) or Højere Forberedelseseksamen.

Fees: None.
Language of Instruction: Danish.
Degrees and Diplomas: Diploma in Architecture, 5 ½ yrs. Cand.lic.arch., a further 3 yrs.
Library: 110,170 vols.
Academic Staff, 1990: 34 (158).
Student Enrolment, 1990:

	Men	Women	Total
Of the country	474	416	890
Of other countries	50	38	88
Total	524	454	978

2285 **DET KONGELIGE DANSKE KUNSTAKADEMIS BILLEDKUNSTKOLE**
The Royal Danish Academy of Fine Arts, School of Painting, Sculpture and Graphic Arts
Kongens Nytorv 1, 1050 København K
Telephone: (33) 12-68-60
Fax: (33) 12-75-98
Chancellor: Else Marie Bukdahl (1980-)
Secretary: Else Berenth

S. of Painting
Heads: Ole Sporring; Stig Brøggeer
S. of Graphic Arts
Head: Vibeke Mencke Nielsen
S. of Mural Design
Head: Paul Gernes
S. of Sculpture
Heads: Bjørn Nørgaard; Mogens Møller

Operated under the jurisdiction of the Ministry of Cultural Affairs. Governing body: the Fagrådet (Council).
Academic Year: August to July (October-January; February-May).
Admission Requirements: Art Schools admit on basis of talent.
Fees: None.
Language of Instruction: Danish.
Degrees and Diplomas: Diploma, 5 yrs.
Academic Staff, 1990: 13.
Student Enrolment, 1990: 200.

2286 **NORDJYSK MUSIKKONSERVATORIUM**
North Jutland Academy of Music
Ryesgade 52, 9000 Aalborg
Telephone: (98) 12-77-44
Fax: (98) 11-37-63
Rektor: Erik Bach (1978-90)

Music

Founded 1930 as a private institution. Became a State institution under the jurisdiction of the Ministry of Cultural Affairs 1972. Governing body: the Academic Council, comprising 14 members.

Arrangements for co-operation with: National Academy of Music, Oslo; Birmingham School of Music; Sibelius Academy, Helsinki.
Academic Year: September to June.
Admission Requirements: Entrance examination.
Fees: Tuition, none.
Language of Instruction: Danish.
Degrees and Diplomas: Diplomas, 5 yrs. Teaching qualifications, 4 yrs.
Library: Academy Library.
Academic Staff, 1989-90: 12 (45).
Student Enrolment, 1989-90:

	Men	Women	Total
Of the country	48	51	99

2287 **DET JYSKE MUSIKKONSERVATORIUM**
Royal Academy of Music, Aarhus
Fuglesangs Allé 26, 8210 Aarhus V
Telephone: (86) 15-53-88
Fax: (86) 15-84-76
Principal: Elisabeth Sigurdsson
Administrator: Sander Angelse

Music

Founded 1927 as a private institution. Became a State institution under the jurisdiction of the Ministry of Cultural Affairs 1963. Affiliated to the Royal Academy of Music, Copenhagen.
Academic Year: September to June (September-December; January-June).
Admission Requirements: Entrance examination.
Fees: Tuition, none.
Language of Instruction: Danish.
Degrees and Diplomas: Diplomas, 3 yrs and 6 yrs. Professional qualifications, 6-9 yrs.
Libraries: c. 5400 vols; c. 13,100 vols of music; c. 3800 gramophone records.
Academic Staff: c. 30 (80).
Student Enrolment: c. 200.

2288 **DET FYNSKE MUSIKKONSERVATORIUM**
The Funen Academy of Music
Islandsgade 2, 5000 Odense C
Telephone: (09) 11-06-63
Rektor: Sven Erik Werner (1974-)

Music

Founded 1929. Affiliated to the Royal Danish Academy of Music, Copenhagen.
Academic Year: September to June.
Admission Requirements: Entrance examination.
Fees: Tuition, none.
Language of Instruction: Danish.
Degrees and Diplomas: Diplomas, 3 yrs and 6 yrs.
Academic Staff, 1986-87: 9 (51).
Student Enrolment, 1986-87:

	Men	Women	Total
Of the country	41	41	82
Of other countries	3	2	5
Total	44	43	87

2289 **VESTJYSK MUSIKKONSERVATORIUM**
West Jutland Academy of Music
Islandsgade 50, 6700 Esbjerg
Telephone: (75) 12-61-00
Rektor: Axel Momme (1986-88)

Music

Founded 1946.
Academic Year: September to June.
Admission Requirements: Entrance examination.
Fees: Tuition, none.
Language of Instruction: Danish.
Degrees and Diplomas: Diplomas, 5 yrs. Teaching qualification, 4 yrs.
Academic Staff, 1989-90: 12 (60).
Student Enrolment, 1989-90:

	Men	Women	Total
Of the country	47	32	79
Of other countries	6	2	8
Total	53	34	87

2290 **DET KONGELIGE DANSKE MUSIKKONSERVATORIUM**
The Royal Danish Academy of Music
Niels Brocks Gade 7, 1574 København V
Cables: Musikkonservatoriet
Telephone: (01) 12-42-74

Music

Founded 1867 as a private institution. Became a State institution under the jurisdiction of the Ministry of Cultural Affairs 1949. Governing body: the Konservatorierådet (Council, composed of the Rector and Pro-Rector, 11 members of the academic staff, 10students, and 3 members of the administrative staff.
Academic Year: September to June (September-December; January-June).
Admission Requirements: Entrance examination.
Fees: None.
Language of Instruction: Danish.
Degrees and Diplomas: Diplomas, 5 yrs. Teaching qualifications, 6 yrs. Qualification as soloist, 9 yrs.
Library: c. 50,000 vols.
Academic Staff: c. 60 (90).
Student Enrolment: c. 500.

2291 **DEN SOCIALE HØJSKOLE I ESBJERG**
School of Social Work
Storegade 182, 6705 Esbjerg Ø
Telephone: (05) 13-35-00
Rektor: Grethe Erichsen (1983-)

Social Sciences

Founded 1971. A State institution under the jurisdiction of the Ministry of Education.

Arrangements in co-operation with Whittier College, Los Angeles.

Academic Year: September to June (September-January; February-June).

Admission Requirements: Secondary school certificate (studentereksamen) or Højere Forberedelseseksamen.

Fees: Tuition, none.

Language of Instruction: Danish.

Degrees and Diplomas: Socialrådgiver (socionom), social worker, 3 yrs.

Library: c. 4500 vols.

Academic Staff, 1986-87: 8 (6).

Student Enrolment, 1986-87:

	Men	Women	Total
Of the country	30	128	158
Of other countries	2	–	2
Total	32	128	160

2292 **DEN SOCIALE HØJSKOLE**
School of Social Work
Randersgade 10, 2100 København Ø
Telephone: (01) 42-46-01
Rektor: Erik B. Smith

Social Sciences

Founded 1937. A State institution under the jurisdiction of the Ministry of Education. Governing body: the Uddannelsesrådet with academic staff and student representation.

Academic Year: February to January (February-June; September-January).

Admission Requirements: Secondary school certificate (studentereksamen) or Højere Forberedelseseksamen/Handeseksamen, or foreign equivalent.

Fees: Tuition, none.

Language of Instruction: Danish.

Degrees and Diplomas: Socialrådgiver (socionom), social worker, 3 yrs.

Library: c. 20,000 vols.

Academic Staff, 1986-87: 21 (13).

Student Enrolment, 1986-87: 360.

2293 **DEB SOCIALE HØJSKOLE I ODENSE**
School of Social Work
Campusvej 55, 5230 Odense M

Social Sciences

Admission Requirements: Secondary school certificate (studentereksamen) or Højere Forberedelseseksamen.

Degrees and Diplomas: Socialrådgiver (socionom), social worker, 3 yrs.

2294 **DEN SOCIALE HØJSKOLE AARHUS**
National Danish School of Social Work
Søndervangen 90, 8260 Viby J
Telephone: (86) 14-23-66
Rektor: Ole F. Hermansen (1966-)
Afdelingsleder/Vicerektor: Christen Christensen

Social Sciences (including Social Work)

Founded 1956 and attached to the Copenhagen School of Social Work, became independent 1968. A State institution under the jurisdiction of the Ministry of Education.

Arrangements for co-operation with: Boston University, School of Social Work; Technical College for Social Work, Berlin.

Academic Year: September to June (September-January; February-June).

Admission Requirements: Secondary school certificate (studentereksamen) or Højere Forberedelseseksamen.

Fees: Tuition, none.

Language of Instruction: Danish.

Degrees and Diplomas: Socialrådgiver (socionom), social worker, 3 yrs.

Library: c. 17,000 vols.

Academic Staff, 1990-91: 13 (5).

Student Enrolment, 1990-91:

	Men	Women	Total
Of the country	41	171	212
Of other countries	1	–	1
Total	42	171	213

2295 **AARHUS TANDLÆGEHØJSKOLE**
The Royal Dental College
Vennelyst Boulevard, 8000 Aarhus C
Telephone: (86) 13 25 33
Fax: (86) 19 60 29
Dean: Sven Poulsen
Administration Officer: Rigmor Astrup Andersen

Dentistry

Also 9 Research Institutes.

Founded 1958, the college is a State institution under the jurisdiction of the Ministry of Education.

Academic Year: September to June (September-January; February-June).

Admission Requirements: Secondary school certificate (studentereksamen).

Fees: None.

Language of Instruction: Danish.

Degrees and Diplomas: Candidatus odontologiae, cand.odont. Licentiatus odontologiae, lic.odont. Doctor odontologiae, dr.odont.

Academic Staff, 1989-90: 56 (58).

Student Enrolment, 1989-90: 248.

2296 **KØBENHAVNS TANDLÆGEHØJSKOLE**
The Royal Dental College Copenhagen
Nørre Allé 20, 2200 København N
Telephone: (31)(35 from 25/4/91)37-17-00
Fax: (31) 37-17-43
Rektor: Eigild Møller
Administrator: Anders Secher

Dentistry

Founded 1888, a State institution, financed by the State. Governing bodies: the Konsistorium; the Centralstudienævn.

Participates is the ERASMUS programme.

Academic Year: September to June (September-January; February-June).

Admission Requirements: Secondary school certificate (studentereksamen).

Fees (Kroner): Deposit, 500.

Language of Instruction: Danish.

Degrees and Diplomas: Candidatus odontologiae, cand.odont., 5 yrs. Licentiatus odontologiae, lic.odont., Ph.D., a further 3-5 yrs. Doctor odontologiae, dr.odont.

Library: 23,000 vols.

Academic Staff, 1990: 57 (116).

Student Enrolment, 1990:

	Men	Women	Total
Of the country	112	242	354

2297 **DEN KONGELIGE VETERINÆR-OG LANGBOHØJSKOLE**
The Royal Veterinary and Agricultural University
Bülowsvej 13, 1870 Frederiksberg C
Telephone: (31) 35-17-88
Fax: (31) 37-31-93
Rektor: Bent Schmidt-Nielsen
Administrationschef: Ernst Gravesen

F. of Food and Basic Sciences
Head Ib Skovgaard

F. of Animal Husbandry and Veterinary Science
Head: Jan Hau

F. of Agriculture (including Forestry and Horticulture)
Head: Birger Farestveit

Also 14 departments of the faculties.

Founded 1856 and tracing its history to Veterinary College established 1773. A State institution under the supervision of the Ministry of Education. Governing bodies: the Academic Council; the Board of Teachers.

Arrangements for co-operation with the Universities of: Louvain; Leuven; Gent; London; Nottingham; Reading; Montpeller; Utrecht; Perugia; Lisbon (Technical); Barcelona; Valencia; Göttingen; California, Davis;

Washington State; Wisconsin; Warsaw (Agricultural); Brno (Veterinary Science); Tartu. Royal Veterinary College, London; Institut national agronomique, Paris-Grignon; Ecole nationale supérieure agronomique, Montpellier; Ecole nationale vétérinaire d'Alfort; Landbowhogeschool, Wageningen; Institute of Agriculture, Tirana; Academy of Agriculture, Tartu; Academy of Agriculture, Elgava.

Academic Year: September to August (September-January; February-August).

Admission Requirements: Secondary school certificate (studentereksamen) in appropriate subjects, or equivalent.

Fees: None.

Language of Instruction: Danish.

Degrees and Diplomas: Candidatus–medicinae veterinariae, cand. med.vet., veterinary medicine, 5 ½ yrs; –bromatologiae, cand.brom., 4 ½ yrs; –agronomiae, cand.agro., agriculture; –hortonomiae, cand. hort., landscape architecture and horticulture, 4-5 yrs; –lactonomiae, cand.lact., dairy science, 5 yrs; –silvinomiae, cand.silv., forestry, 6 yrs. Ph.D.,, a further 3 yrs. Also Doctorates–D.V.Sc., Veterinary Science and D.Agr., Agricultural Science, byresearch.

Library: c. 400,000 vols.

Publications: Beretning for Den Kgl. Veterinær-og Landbohǿjskole; Årsskrift.

Academic Staff, 1990:

Rank	Full-time	Part-time
Professorer og Forstander	51	–
Docenter	18	–
Adjunkter	33	1
Amanuenser	17	–
Lektorer	169	27
Total	288	28

Student Enrolment, 1989-90:

	Men	Women	Total
Of the country	1399	1501	2100
Of other countries	62	45	108
Total	1462	1546	3008

2298 **SOCIALPÆDAGOGISK HØJSKOLE**

The Advanced Training School of Social Pedagogues

Kastelsvej 60, 2100 København

= Professional EducationAlso 11 Paramedical Schools and 33 Schools of Nursing

Teacher Training

2300 **DANMARKS LÆRERHØJSKOLE**

The Royal Danish School of Educational Studies

Emdrupvej 101, 2400 København NV

Telephone: (31) 69-66-33

Fax: (39) 66-00-81

Vice-Chancellor: Tom Ploug Olsen (1978-90)

Administrationschef: Kirsten Stenbjerre

Teacher Training (including Education, Psychology, Humanities,and Sciences)

Branches in: Esbjerg; Haderslev; Odense; Skive; Vordingborg; Aalborg; Aarhus.

Founded 1856, acquired present university status 1963. A State institution providing further education and research for teachers from primary schools, teacher training colleges and others of similar professional standing. Under the jurisdiction of the Ministry of Education and financed by the State. There are full-time and part-time courses. Governing body: the Konsistorium. Limited residential facilities for students.

Academic Year: September to June (September-December; January-June).

Admission Requirements: Graduation from teacher training college (lærereksamen) and for students of Education, two years practical experience as a teacher.

Fees: : Tuition, none.

Language of Instruction: Danish.

Degrees and Diplomas: Candidatus Paedagogiae, cand.paed, 3 yrs. Ph.D., 3 yrs. Doctor, Dr.paed.

Library: 450,000 vols.

Academic Staff, 1990:

Rank	Full-time	Part-time
Professorer	20	–
Lektorer	115	–
Adjunkter	10	–
Kandidatstipendiater	18	–
Timelærer	–	c. 500
Total	163	c. 500

Student Enrolment, 1986-87: c. 12,000.

2301 **DANMARKS HØJSKOLE FOR LEGEMSØVELSER**

Danish State Institute of Physical Education

Nǿrre Allé 51, 2200 Kǿbenhavn N

Telephone: (31) 39-25-56

Fax: (31) 35-36-24-14

Principal: Ivar Berg-Sǿrensen

Physical Education

Founded 1911. A State institution under the jurisdiction of the Ministry of Education.

Participates in the ERASMUS programme.

Academic Year: September to June (September-December; February-June).

Admission Requirements: Secondary school certificate (studentereksamen).

Fees: None.

Language of Instruction: Danish.

Degrees and Diplomas: Diploma, 2 yrs. Bachelor, a further 1 yr. Master, 2 yrs following Diploma. Doctor, Ph.D., a further 3 yrs.

Library: c. 20,000 vols.

Academic Staff, 1989-90: c. 18 (18).

Student Enrolment, 1989-90:

	Men	Women	Total
Of the country	123	186	309*

*Also 4 foreign students.

= Teacher TrainingAlso 24 Teacher Training Colleges, 15 Schools of Social Pedagogics, and 25 Pre-school Teacher Training Colleges.

DOMINICAN REPUBLIC

Universities

2303 ***UNIVERSIDAD AUTÓNOMA DE SANTO DOMINGO**

University of Santo Domingo

Avenida Alma Mater, Ciudad Universitaria, Santo Domingo

Cables: Uniausd

Telephone: 533-1694

Rector: José Joaquín Bidó Medina

F. of Humanities (including Philosophy, Education, and Psychology)
F. of Science
F. of Economics and Social Sciences (including Business Administration)
F. of Law (including Political Science)
F. of Engineering and Architecture
F. of Medicine (including Dentistry, Nursing and Pharmacy)
F. of Agriculture and Veterinary Science (including Animal Husbandry)
C. of Basic Studies (for first year students)
Also 3 Regional Centres.

Founded 1538 by Bull of Pope Paul III. Directed by Dominican Order of Preachers until 1802. Closed during French occupation. Became a lay institution in 1815 but again closed 1822-44 during Haitian occupation. Again reopened and reorganized 1865, 1914, and 1937. Following the law on university autonomy of 1961, the university adopted new statutes in 1966. Financially supported by the State. Governing bodies: the Claustro Universitario; the Consejo Universitario.

Academic Year: January to November (January-May; July-November).

Admission Requirements: Secondary school certificate (bachillerato) or recognized foreign equivalent.

Language of Instruction: Spanish.

Degrees and Diplomas: Licenciado in–Sociology, 3 yrs; Philosophy and Letters; History; Letters; Education; Psychology; Information; Languages, 4 yrs; Chemistry; Biology; Physics; Economics; Accountancy; Business Administration; Public Administration; Political Science; Pharmacy, 5 yrs; Law, 6 yrs. Professional titles of–Periodista, journalism; Técnico biólogo; Técnico en Ciencias físicas, physics, 3 yrs; Agrimensor, surveying, 3 ½ yrs; Tecnólogo médico, 4 yrs; Sustanciado económico; Sociógrafo; Ingeniero agrónomo, agriculture, 5 yrs; Ingeniero mecánico electricista; Ingeniero químico; Arquitecto, 6 yrs. Doctor in Dentistry; Veterinary Medicine, 5 yrs; Law; Medicine, 7 yrs. Also lower level teaching and technical qualifications, 2-3 yrs.

Libraries: Central Library, *c.* 252,470 vols; Agriculture *c.* 660; Economics and Social Sciences, *c.* 5130; Humanities, *c.* 2000; Engineering and Architecture, *c.* 1170.

Special Facilities (Museums, etc.): Anthropology Museum.

Publications: El Universitario; Un Año de Labor para el Desarrollo y la Reforma Universitarios; Boletines de la Biblioteca Central; Catálogo General; Ciencia; Derecho y Política; El pequeño universo de la Facultad de Humanidades; Revista dominicana de antropología e Historia; Boletín informativo.

Academic Staff: c. 1180.

Student Enrolment: c. 50,790.

2304 **UNIVERSIDAD CATÓLICA 'MADRE Y MAESTRA'**

Autopista Duarte Km ½, Santiago

Telex: 346-1032

Telephone: 583-0441

Rector: Mgr Agripino Núñez Collado (1970-90)

S. of Engineering
Dean: Nelson Gil; *staff* 37 (43)
S. of Health Sciences (including Medicine, Dentistry, and Nursing)
Dean: Luis José Castillo; *staff* 36 (125)
S. of Science and Humanities (including Architecture and Education)
Dean: Rafael Despradel; *staff* 78 (94)
S. of Social and Administration Sciences (includingLaw, Economics and Social Work)
Dean: Rafael Emilio Yunen; *staff* 28 (109)
S. of Hotel Administration
Head: Claudete Pehna
D. for Lifelong Education
Director: Ramón Pichardo

Founded 1962, as a private, autonomous institution on the initiative of the Bishop of the Dominican Republic. Financed by the State and the business and professional community of Santiago. Governing body: the Board of Directors, comprising 22 members. Some residential facilities for academic staff.

Arrangements for co-operation with the Universities of: Saint Louis; Puerto Rico; Cornell; Florida (International); Simón Bolívar, Caracas; South Carolina; Augsburg; Colorado; Nevada; Nebraska; Sherbrooke; Québec.

Academic Year: August to May (August-December; January-May).

Admission Requirements: Secondary school certificate (bachiller).

Fees (Pesos): 30-75 per credit hour; foreign students, 150.

Language of Instruction: Spanish.

Degrees and Diplomas: Licenciado in–Social Work; Nursing; Education; Philosophy; Hotel Administration, 4 yrs; Law; Economics; Business Administration; Accountancy, 5 yrs. Professional titles in– Engineering, various fields, 5 yrs; Architecture, 5 ½ yrs. Magister in–Agricultural Economics; Applied Economics; Mathematics; Legal Sciences, 1 ½-2 yrs. Doctor in–Dentistry, 5 yrs; Medicine, 6 yrs. Also lower level technical qualifications, 2-2 ½ yrs.

Library: c. 200,000 vols.

Publications: Estudios Dominicanos (bimonthly); Revista de Ciencias Jurídicas (quarterly); Magister (biannually).

Academic Staff, 1986-87:

Rank	Full-time	Part-time
Profesores Titulares	9	–
Profesores Asociados	93	–
Profesores Auxiliares	36	–
Instructores	16	–
Profesores	–	335
Total	154	335

Student Enrolment, 1986-87:

	Men	Women	Total
Of the country	3640	3101	6741
Of other countries	282	146	428
Total	3922	3247	7169

2305 **UNIVERSIDAD 'APEC'**

Avenida Máximo Gómez 72, Santo Domingo

Telephone: 809-687-3181

F. of Administration (including Economics)
F. of Humanities and Science (including Architecture and Computer Sciences)
S. of Languages

Founded 1965 as Instituto de Estudios Superiores by the Acción Pro-Educación y Cultura, Inc. (APEC). Acquired present title 1983. A private institution. Authorized by the government to award degrees 1968. Governing body: the Board of Directors.

Arrangements for co-operation with: Seton Hall University; Boston University; University of New Mexico.

Academic Year: January to December (January-April; May-August; September-December).

Admission Requirements: Secondary school certificate (bachiller) and entrance examination.

Language of Instruction: Spanish.

Degrees and Diplomas: Licenciado, 4 yrs. Magister in Management, a further 2 yrs. Also degree of Associate, 2 yrs.

Library: c. 3000 vols.

Publications: Boletín; Revista Científica.

Press or Publishing House: Imprenta Cenapec.

Academic Staff: c. 50.
Student Enrolment: c. 2530.

2306 **UNIVERSIDAD ADVENTISTA DOMINICANA**
Dominica Adventist University
Apartado postal 770, Sonador, Bonao
Telephone: (525) 3533
Rector: Luis Ant. Sánchez
Vicerrector: Ovidio Morales

D. of Sciences
Head: Cecilio Ureña
D. of Psychology
Head: Miguel Montero
D. of Business Administration
Head: Altagracia Méndez
D. of Theology
Head: Domingo Melenciano
D. of Education
Head: Luis Gregorio
D. of Agronomu
Head: Ralph Wood
D. of Secretarial Studies
Head: Margarita Ramos
Research Ce.
Head: Cecilio Ureña

Founded 1982. Governing body: the Administrative Board. Residential facilities for academic staff and students.

Academic Year: September to May (September-December; January-May).
Admission Requirements: Secondary school certificate (bachillerato).
Fees (Pesos): 3400 per semester.
Language of Instruction: Spanish.
Degrees and Diplomas: Licenciado, 4 yrs.
Library: 15,140 vols.
Academic Staff, 1989-90:

Rank	Full-time	Part-time
Catedráticos Asistentes	5	1
Catedráticos Asociados	1	–
Instructores	9	1
Instructores Asistentes	7	2
Instructores Asociados	10	2
Total	32	6

2307 **UNIVERSIDAD CATÓLICA DE SANTO DOMINGO**
c/ Santo Domingo 3, La Julia, Santo Domingo

D. of Humanities
D. of Social Communication
D. of Theology
D. of Education

Founded 1984.

2308 **UNIVERSIDAD CENTRAL DEL ESTE**
Avenida Circunvalación, San Pedro de Macorís
Telephone: 529-3562
Rector: José E. Hazim F. (1979-)
Secretaria General: Piedad L. Noboa M.

F. of Medicine (including Dentistry)
Dean: Juan A. Silva S.; *staff* 106 (102)
F. of Law and Political Science
Dean: José Ramón González P.; *staff* 12 (93)
F. of Economics and Social Sciences (including Business Administration)
Dean: Rafael Morey; *staff* 4 (90)
F. of Engineering and Architecture (including Agriculture, Veterinary Medicine, Animal Husbandry, Forestry, and Sugar Technology)
Dean: C. Tomás Ramos; *staff* 22 (200)
F. of Humanities (Education)
Dean: José A. Hazim A.; *staff* 2 (130)

Founded 1970. A private institution recognized by the State 1971. Governing body: the Consejo Superior Universitario.

Academic Year: January to December (January-April; May-August; September-December).
Admission Requirements: Secondary school certificate (bachillerato) or equivalent, or recognized foreign equivalent.
Language of Instruction: Spanish.
Degrees and Diplomas: Licenciado in–Social Communication, 3 ½ yrs; Bioanalyses, 4 yrs; Pharmacy; Accountancy; Business Administration; Animal Husbandry, 5 yrs; Education, 4-6 ½ yrs. Professional titles of–Técnico en Piscicultura, 3 yrs; Tecnólogo azucarero, sugar technology, 4 yrs; Zootecnista, 5 yrs; Ingeniero (various fields), 5 ½-6 yrs; Arquitecto, 6 yrs. Doctorado in–Dentistry, 5 ½ yrs; Medicine; Law; Veterinary Medicine, 6 yrs.
Library: Central Library, 600,000 vols.
Special Facilities (Museums, etc.): Anthropology.
Publications: Bulletin (monthly); Medical Journal (monthly).
Academic Staff, 1986-87: c. 150 (620).
Student Enrolment, 1986-87:

	Men	Women	Total
Of the country	7790	6277	14,067
Of other countries	447	213	660
Total	8237	6490	14,727

2309 **UNIVERSIDAD COLEGIO DOMINICANO DE ESTUDIO PROFESIONALES**
Prol. Independencia, Km. 9 ½, Carretera Sánchez, Santo Domingo

F. of Economics and Social Sciences
F. of Humanities
F. of Science and Technology
F. of Juridical Studies
F. of Agriculture (including Veterinary Medicine)
F. of Health Sciences

Founded 1985.

2310 **UNIVERSIDAD DOMINICANA O&M**
Apartado postal 509, Avenida Independencia, Santo Domingo
Founded 1978.

2311 **UNIVERSIDAD EUGENIO MARÍA DE HOSTOS**
Avenida Abraham Lincoln 753, Santo Domingo

F. of Health Sciences
F. of Science and Technology
F. of Economics and Administration
F. of Humanities and Social Sciences

Founded 1984.

2312 **UNIVERSIDAD IBEROMERICANA**
Apartado postal 1600, Avenida Francia 129, Santo Domingo

F. of Architecture and Art
F. of General Studies
F. of Economics
F. of Health Sciences
F. of Agriculture

Founded 1982.

2313 **UNIVERSIDAD INTERAMERICANA**
Dr. Baez 4, Santo Domingo

Communication Studies
Psychology
Public Relations
Statistics
Sociology
Education
Computer Sciences
Tourism
Agricultural Administration
Administration
Secretarial Studies
Business Administration
Law

Founded 1982.

2314 **UNIVERSIDAD NACIONAL EVANGÉLICA**
Avenida Juan Pablo Duarte 110, Santiago
Founded 1986.

2315 **UNIVERSIDAD NACIONAL 'PEDRO HENRÍQUEZ UREÑA'**
Avenida John F. Kennedy, Km. 5 ½, Santo Domingo
Telephone: 565-6651
Rector: Jaime A. Viñas Román

F. of Science
F. of Humanities, Education and Sciences
F. of Health Sciences
F. of Engineering
F. of Architecture and Arts
F. of Agriculture and Veterinary Science
I. of Biomedical Sciences

Founded 1966 as a private institution.

Arrangements for co-operation with the Universities of: Puerto Rico; California State; Ohio State; Haiti; Florida; British Columbia.

Academic Year: August to May (August-December; January-May).

Admission Requirements: Secondary school certificate (bachillerato) and entrance examination.

Language of Instruction: Spanish.

Degrees and Diplomas: Licenciado, 10 sem. Professional title of Técnico, 4-6 sem. Maestría, 3-6 sem.

Library: Central Library.

Publications: Cuadernos Jurídicos; Cuadernos de Filosofía.

Press or Publishing House: Imprenta UNPHU.

Academic Staff: c. 70 (400).

Student Enrolment: c. 8000.

2316 **UNIVERSIDAD NORDESTANA**
P.O. Box 239, San Francisco de Macorís
Telephone: (809) 588-3239; 3505

F. of Medicine
F. of Agriculture
F. of Law
F. of Economics and Social Sciences (including Business Administration)
F. of Engineering
Extension D.

Founded 1978. A private institution recognized by the State. Governing body: the Consejo Superior.

Academic Year: January to December (January-May; August-December).

Admission Requirements: Secondary school certificate (bachillerato).

Language of Instruction: Spanish.

Degrees and Diplomas: Licenciado in–Agriculture, 4 ½ yrs; Accountancy; Business Administration; Law, 5 yrs. Professional titles of–Técnico, 3 yrs; Ingeniero civil, 5 yrs. Doctor in Medicine, 4 yrs 8 months.

Library: c. 10,000 vols.

Academic Staff, 1986-87: 10 (160).

Student Enrolment: c. 1700.

2317 **UNIVERSIDAD ODONTOLÓGICA DOMINICANA**
Prol. 27 de Febrero, Las Caobas, Santo Domingo

Dentistry

Founded 1985.

2318 **UNIVERSIDAD TECNOLÓGICA DEL CIBAO**
Aut. Duarte, Km. 1 ½, Avenida Universitaria, Apartado 401, La Vega
Telephone: (809) 573-3863
Fax: (809) 573-6194
Rector: Juan Ant. Flores

S. of Computer Sciences
Head: Erwin López; *staff* – (11)
S. of Technology
Head: Julio C. Correa; *staff* – (9)
S. of Executive Secretarial Studies
Head: Verónica Núñez; *staff* – (5)
S. of Agriculture (including Veterinary Medicine)
Head: Félix Díaz Tejada; *staff* – (14)
S. of Administration and Accountancy
Head: María Rivas; *staff* – (12)
S. of Engineering and Architecture
Head: Luis Rojas; *staff* – (17)
S. of Education and Humanities
Head: Julián Alvárez; *staff* – (31)
S. of Bioanalysis
Head: María Vicenta de la Cruz; *staff* – (6)

Founded 1983. Governing bodies: the Asamblea General; the Junta Directiva.

Academic Year: January to December (January-May; August-December).

Admission Requirements: Secondary school certificate (bachillerato).

Fees (Pesos): 640,000 per 18 credits, per semester.

Language of Instruction: Spanish.

Degrees and Diplomas: Licenciado in–Business Administration; Accountancy; Law; Education; Nursing, 5 yrs. Professional titles of–Ingeniero agricola; Ingeniero civil; Arquitecto, 5 yrs; Ingeniero industrial, 5 ½ yrs. Doctor in–Medicine;Dentistry; Veterinary Medicine, 5-6 yrs. Also lower level technical qualifications, 2 ½-3 yrs.

Library: Biblioteca Dr. Rubén Alvarez Valencia, 8000 vols.

Academic Staff, 1990: 6 (170)

Student Enrolment, 1990:

	Men	Women	Total
Of the country	845	1188	2033
Of other countries	38	6	44
Total	833	1194	2077

2319 **UNIVERSIDAD TECNOLÓGICA DE SANTIAGO**
Apartado postal 21423, Santiago
Telephone: 582-7156

F. of Economics and Social Sciences
F. of Engineering and Architecture
D. of Secretarial Studies
S. of Languages

Founded 1978.

Academic Staff: c. 100.

Student Enrolment: c. 4000.

2320 **UNIVERSIDAD TECNOLÓGICA DEL SUR**
c/Duarte 46, Azua

Education
Technical Studies
Agricultural Engineering
Accountancy
Administration
Nursing

Founded 1984.

2321 **UNIVERSIDAD ULISES FRANCISCO ESPAILLAT**
c/Rafael A. Sánchez 52, Apartado postal 22432, Ciudad Santo Domingo

F. of Political and Social Sciences

Founded 1986.

2322 **INSTITUTO NACIONAL DE CIENCAS EXACTAS**
Apartado postal 1796, Santo Domingo

Industrial Engineering
Civil Engineering
Architecture
Agriculture

Founded 1974.

2323 **INSTITUTO SUPERIOR DE AGRICULTURA**
Apartado postal 166, Santo Domingo

Business Administration
Philosophy
Economics
Agriculture

Founded 1986.

2324 **INSTITUTO TÉCNICO SUPERIOR**
c/Juan Sánchez Ramírez 23, Ciudad Santo Domingo

Technical Studies
Accountancy
Business Administration

Founded 1987.

2325 **INSTITUTO TECNOLÓGICO DEL CIBAOORIENTAL**
Cotui

F. of Agriculture

F. of Science and Humanities
F. of Engineering
Lifelong Education
Founded 1983.

2326 **INSTITUTO TECNOLÓGICO DE SANTO DOMINGO**
Avenida de los Próceres, Galá, Santo Domingo
Telex: RCA-4184
Telephone: (809) 567-9271
Fax: (809) 566-3200
Rector: Rafael Marion-Landais (1990-93)

F. of Sciences and Humanities (including Education, Linguistics, and Environmental Education)
Dean: César Cuello
F. of Engineering (Civil, Mechanical, Industrial Engineering, Industrial Design, and Computer Sciences)
Dean: Dagoberto Peña
F. of Health Sciences (Medicineand Physical Therapy)
Dean: José Raymunco Jiménez
F. of Social Sciences (including Psychology, Economics, Business Administration, and Accountancy)
Dean: Marcos Villamán
D. of Lifelong Education
Dean: Diómedes Christopher
D. of Research
Director: José Ramón Albaine
D. of Applied Linguistics
Director: Manuel MatosMoquete

Founded 1972. A private and non-profit institution. Authorized by the government to award degrees 1973. Financially supported by tuition fees and a State subsidy. Governing bodies: the Board of Regents, comprising 15 members; the Academic Council, comprising 9 members.

Arrangements for co-operation with the Universities of: Illinois; Valle, Colombia; Cantabria; del Norte, Colombia; Florida State; Wisconsin; Iowa; Santa Catarina, Brazil; Ben-Gurion of the Negev; Brasília; Los Angeles;Georgetown; Valencia.

Academic Year: July to June (July-September; October-December; January-March; April-June).

Admission Requirements: Secondary school certificate (bachillerato).

Language of Instruction: Spanish.

Degrees and Diplomas: Licenciado in–Social Sciences; Economics; Business Administration; Psychology; Accountancy and Finance, 3 ½ yrs. Professional titles in–Civil Engineering; Industrial Engineering; Systems Engineering; Electrical Engineering; Mechanical Engineering; Industrial Design, 3 ½ yrs. Doctor in Medicine, 5 yrs. Maestría, a furtherl ½-2 yrs. Also postgraduate diplomas.

Library: c. 35,000 vols.

Publications: Documentos (annually); Ciencia y Sociedad (quarterly); Boletín (quarterly); Informativo (monthly).

Academic Staff: c. 70 (220).

Student Enrolment, 1990:

	Men	Women	Total
Of the country	1238	807	2045
Of other countries	105	71	176
Total	1343	878	2221

ECUADOR

Universities and Technical Universities

2327 ***UNIVERSIDAD CATÓLICA DE CUENCA**
Catholic University of Cuenca
Calle Bolívar y Benigno Malo, Apartado de Correos 19A, Cuenca
Cables: Unicacue
Telex: 04-8567 UCACUE ED
Telephone: 823040; 830753
Rector: César Cordero Moscoso (1975-)

F. of Law and Political and Social Sciences
F. of Education and Psychology
F. of Medicine and Health Sciences
F. of Economics
F. of Commerce
F. of Chemical and Industrial Engineering
F. of Agriculture and Veterinary Medicine (including Animal Husbandry)
I. of Physical Education
I. of Journalism
S. of Social Work
S. of Secretarial Studies
S. of Teacher Training (elementary level)
U. of Distance Education

Founded 1970. A private institution receiving some financial support from the State. Governing bodies: the Asamblea Universitaria; the Consejo Gubernativo; the Consejo Académico; the Consejo Administrativo.

Academic Year: October to July (October-February; April-July).

Admission Requirements: Secondary school certificate (bachillerato) or recognized foreign equivalent.

Language of Instruction: Spanish.

Degrees and Diplomas: Licenciado in–Law and Social Sciences; Education and Psychology; Social Work; Physical Education; Languages; Secretarial Studies, 4 yrs. Professional titles of–Ingeniero comercial; Ingeniero químico; Ingeniero agrónomo; Ingeniero industrial; Economista; Psicólogo; Veterinario, 5 yrs. Doctorado in–Law and Social Sciences; Education and Psychology, 6 yrs; Medicine. Maestro in Engineering. Also teaching qualification, secondary level.

Library: Central Library, *c.* 6500 vols.

Publications: Colección Panoramas; Colección Ensayos; Colección Documentos.

Academic Staff: c. 130 (310).

Student Enrolment: c. 3400.

2328 **UNIVERSIDAD DE CUENCA**
University of Cuenca
Avenida 12 de Abril, Apartado de Correos 168, Cuenca
Telephone: 824-365

F. of Law
F. of Medicine (including Nursing and Midwifery)
F. of Engineering
F. of Philosophy, Letters, and Education
F. of Chemistry (including Pharmacy and Industrial Chemistry)
F. of Dentistry
F. of Architecture
F. of Economics
A. of Fine Arts
D. of Languages
I. of Physical Education

Founded 1868, the university is an autonomous institution, but receives financial support from the State. Governing body: the Consejo Superior, composed of the Rector, the Vice-Rector, the deans of the faculties, one representative of the academic staff, one representative of the Minister of Education, and one student representative for each faculty.

Academic Year: October to July (October-January; April-July).

Admission Requirements: Secondary school certificate (bachillerato) or recognized foreign equivalent.

Language of Instruction: Spanish.

Degrees and Diplomas: Doctorado in–Philosophy and Letters; Chemistry and Pharmacy; Industrial Chemistry; Dentistry, 5 yrs. Law; Medicine, 6 yrs. Professional titles of–Topógrafo, 2 yrs; Obstetriz, midwifery; Enfermera, nursing; Contador, accountancy; Administrador de Empresas, business administration, 4 yrs; Arquitecto; Economista; Ingeniero civil; Ingeniero eléctrico, 5 yrs.

Libraries: Central Library, *c.* 71780 vols; Engineering, *c.* 2700; Philosophy, *c.* 6830; Economics, *c.* 2810; Medicine, *c.* 21,270; Chemistry, *c.* 1120; Law, *c.* 9850.

Publication: Anales de la Universidad de Cuenca (biannually).

Academic Staff: c. 630.

Student Enrolment: c. 21,600.

2329 ***PONTIFICIA UNIVERSIDAD CATÓLICA DEL ECUADOR**
Pontifical Catholic University of Ecuador
12 de Octubre 1076 y Roca, Apartado 2184, Quito
Telephone: 529-240
Rector: Julio Terán Dutari, S.J. (1985-90)
Secretario General: Manuel Freire Sánchez

F. of Law
Dean: Gonzalo Zambrano; *staff* 1 (52)
F. of Economics
Dean: Manuel Jaramillo; *staff* 23 (29)
F. of Engineering
Dean: Roberto Vallejo; *staff* 10 (43)
F. of Education Sciences
Dean: Hernán Andrade, S.J.; *staff* 3 (18)
F. of Human Sciences
Dean: Marcelo Naranjo; *staff* 16 (33)
F. of Nursing
Dean: Lourdes Carrera; *staff* 21 (14)
F. of Theology and Philosophy Sciences
Dean: José González, S.J.; *staff* 4 (29)
F. of Administration
Dean: José Luis Cagigal; *staff* 4 (75)
F. Exact and Nature Sciences
Dean: Juan Llauger, S.J.; *staff* 20 (22)
F. Linguistic and Literature
Dean: Fernando Miño; *staff* 8 (74)
S. of Social Work
Director: José Ribadeneira, S.J.; *staff* 6 (7)
S. of Psychology
Director: Mercedes Cordero C.; *staff* 1 (23)

Branches at: Cuenca, Esmeraldas, Ibarra, Ambato. Also Research Programmes in: Human and Social Sciences, Biology, Economics, Co-operation Studies, and Linguistics.

Founded 1946 under the Cardinal Archbishop of Quito as Grand Chancellor. Legally recognized as an autonomous institution but partly supported by the State. Other income derived from student fees, from the university's own resources, and from gifts and donations. Governing bodies: the Consejo Superior; the Consejo Académico. Residential facilities for academic staff and students.

Arrangements for co-operation with: Georgetown University; Scripps College, Claremont; Bowlding College.

Academic Year: October to July (October-February; March-July).

Admission Requirements: Secondary school certificate (bachillerato) or recognized foreign equivalent, and entrance examination.

Fees (Sucres): 12,133 per credit per sememster.

Language of Instruction: Spanish.

Degrees and Diplomas: Licenciado in–Science; Social Sciences; Education; Philosophy; Social Work; Nursing; Theology; Psychology; Applied Longuistics; Anthropology; Sociology and Political Science; Accountancy; Biology; History; Human Sciences, 4 yrs; Administration, 4 ½ yrs; Professional titles of–Abogado, law; Economista; Ingeniero civil; Ingeniero comercial; Contador público, accountancy; Tecnólogo médico; Enfermera, nursing, 3-5 ½ yrs, all with dissertaions. Doctorado in–Law; History; Psychology; Economics; Education; Philosophy; Letters; Theology. Also teaching qualifications, secondary level.

Libraries: Central Library, 52,238 vols; Philosophy Documentation Centre, 3000.

Special Facilities (Museums, etc.): Museo 'Jacinto Jijón y Caamaño'.

Publication: Revista (quarterly).

Press or Publishing House: Centro de Publicaciones.

Academic Staff, 1989-90:

Rank	Full-time
Profesores Principales	207
Profesores Agregados	275
Profesores Instructores	47
Total	529

Student Enrolment, 1989-90:

	Men	Women	Total
Of the country	2684	2259	4943
Of other countries	45	70	115
Total	2729	2329	5058

2330 **UNIVERSIDAD CENTRAL DEL ECUADOR**

Central University of Ecuador

Avenida América y Alfredo Pérez Guerrero, Apartado 166, Quito

Telephone: 524714

Rector: Tiberio Jurado

F. of Law

F. of Medicine (including Midwifery and Nursing)

F. of Engineering

F. of Philosophy, Letters and Education

F. of Economics

F. of Administration

F. of Agriculture

F. of Veterinary Medicine and Animal Husbandry

F. of Chemistry and Pharmacy

F. of Dentistry

F. of Architecture and Town Planning

F. of Fine Arts

F. of Psychology

Also departments, institutes and schools attached to the faculties.

Founded 1586 as Universidad de San Fulgencio and 1622 as Universidad de San Gregorio Magno. Replaced 1786 under Don Carlos III by Real Pontificia Universidad de Santo Tomás de Aquino. Title changed to Universidad Central 1897. Granted autonomy 1925. Financed by the State. Some residential facilities for students.

Academic Year: October to July (October-December; January-March; April-June).

Admission Requirements: Secondary school certificate (bachillerato) or equivalent.

Language of Instruction: Spanish.

Degrees and Diplomas: Licenciado in–Social and Political Sciences; International Law; Psychology; Economics; Arts; Education; Administration; Journalism; Nursing; Statistics; Banking, 4 yrs. Professional titles of–Topógrafo, surveying, 2 yrs; Enfermera, nursing, 3 yrs; Obstetriz, midwifery, 4 yrs; Ingeniero civil; Ingeniero químico; Ingeniero en geología y minas; Ingeniero agrónomo; Ingeniero comercial; Administrador supervisor de Educación; Terapistas ocupacionales; Técnicos in Laboratorio clínico e histopatología; Contador público, accountancy; Estadístico; Arquitecto, 5 yrs; Economista; Pintor, painting; Escultor, sculpture; Decorador, design; Abogado, law, 6 yrs. Maestro de música, 3-7 yrs. Doctorate in–Veterinary Medicine; Biochemistry; Industrial Pharmacy; Dentistry, 5 yrs; Law: Political Science; International Studies; Education; Biology; Psychology; Economics; Administration, 6 yrs; Medicine, 7 yrs; Civil Engineering, 10 yrs.

Libraries: Central Library, *c.* 28,470 vols; Faculty libraries; Economics, *c.* 15,000; Agriculture, *c.* 3800; Education, *c.* 2520; Medicine, *c.* 1110; Engineering, *c.* 320; Dentistry, *c.* 500; Law, *c.* 5000; Pharmacy, *c.* 410.

Special Facilities (Museums, etc.): Museums: Ethnography; Natural Sciences.

Publications: Anales; Cuadernos de Arte y Poesía; Revistas de– Economía, Derecho, Derecho Internacional, Derecho Comparado, Medicina, Odontología, Bioquímica; Índice de Precios, Estadísticas Universitarias; Surcos; Tribuna Universitaria; Universidad.

Academic Staff: c. 2500.

Student Enrolment: c. 60,000.

2331 **UNIVERSIDAD CATÓLICA DE SANTIAGO DE GUAYAQUIL**

Catholic University of Guayaquil

Km. 2½ Avenida Carlos Julio Arosemena, Apartado 4671, Guayaquil

Telephone: 202130

Rector: Gustavo Noboa Bejarano (1986-91)

Secretario General: Guillermo Villacres Smith

F. of Architecture

Dean: Hernán Benites; *staff* 5 (4)

F. of Engineering

Dean: Carlos Ordóñez Beltrán; *staff* 3 (4)

F. of Economics

Dean: Eduardo Egas Peña; *staff* 3 (4)

F. of Medicine (including Nursing)

Dean: Fernando Nobao Bejarano; *staff* 5 (4)

F. of Law (including Social Work)

Dean: Ramón Jiménez Carbo; *staff* 5 (8)

F. of Philosophy (including Sociology and Education)

Dean: Cecilia Ansaldo Briones; *staff* 6 (8)

F. of Technology (including Animal Husbandry and Telecommunications)

Dean: Fausto Romero Granda; *staff* 4 (6)

Founded 1962 by the Catholic Church in Ecuador. Legally recognized as an autonomous institution, Governing bodies: the Asamblea Universitaria; the Consejo Universitario.

Arrangements for co-operation with the Universities of: Louvain; Paris VII. Also Universities in North America.

Academic Year: May to February (May-September; October-February).

Admission Requirements: Secondary school certificate (bachillerato), or recognized foreign equivalent, and entrance examination.

Fees (Sucres): 1000-2000.

Language of Instruction: Spanish.

Degrees and Diplomas: Licenciado in–Social Work; Social and Political Sciences; Philosophy; Letters; Education; Law; Nursing; Psychology, 4-5 yrs. Professional titles of–Técnico; Zootecnista, 2 yrs; Trabajadora social, social work; Enfermera, nursing; Decoradora, design, 3-4 yrs; Economista; Ingeniero comercial; Arquitecto; Ingeniero civil en Sistemas Computacionales, 5 yrs; Abogado, law, 6 yrs. Sicólogo. Doctorado in–Law; Medicine; Philosophy; Education; Psychology; Social Service. Also teaching qualifications.

Library: Central Library, *c.* 8000 vols.

Publications: Revista Universidad; Revista de Historia del Derecho (biannually).

Press or Publishing House: Centro de Publicaciones.

Academic Staff, 1986-87: 599.

Student Enrolment, 1986-87:

	Men	Women	Total
Of the country	2000	1550	3550
Of other countries	35	30	65
Total	2035	1585	3615

2332 **UNIVERSIDAD DE GUAYAQUIL**

University of Guayaquil

Calle Chile 900, Apartado 471, Guayaquil

Telex: 4179 UGUAYE-ED

Telephone: 325-432

Rector: Jaime Pólit Alcívar (1984-89)

Secretario General: Alberto Sánchez Balda

F. of Law and Social Sciences

Dean: Claudio Mueckay Arcos; *staff* 81 (46)

F. of Medicine (including Nursing and Midwifery)

Dean: Salomón Quintero Estrada; *staff* 83 (631)

F. of Mathematics and Physics (including Civil Engineering)

Dean: Hugo Avilés; *staff* 53 (78)

F. of Philosophy, Letters and Education (including Library Science)

Dean: Francisco Morán Márquez; *staff* 116 (106)

F. of Agricultural Engineering

Dean: Eduardo Lanata Chapiro; *staff* 32 (46)

F. of Chemistry (including Pharmacy)

Dean: Q.F. Gustavo Villacís; *staff* 35 (60)

F. of Dentistry

Dean: Wenceslao Gallardo Moreno; *staff* 67 (73)

F. of Natural Sciences

Dean: José Cuenca Vargas; *staff* 23 (86)

F. of Economics

Dean: Colón Ramírez M.; *staff* 44 (73)

F. of Architecture
Dean: César Haro; *staff* 91 (26)
F. of Chemical Engineering
Dean: Luis Pactong; *staff* 47 (9)
F. of Social Communication
Dean: Alba Chávez; *staff* 24 (38)
F. of Industrial Engineering
Dean: Osvaldo Navarrete; *staff* 80 (42)
F. of Psychology
Dean: Solón Villavicencio; *staff* 19 (40)
F: of Veterinary Medicine and Animal Husbandry
Dean: Agustín Ribadeneira; *staff* 21 (26)
F. of Administration
Dean: Carlos Cassinelli
I. of Physical Education
Director: Romulo Viteri; *staff* 5 (14)
I. of Diplomatic Studies
Director: Reynaldo Huerta Ortega; *staff* 2 (24)

Founded 1867 as Junta Universitaria, became Universidad del Guayas, then Universidad de Guayaquil 1897. Becameautonomous 1925. Financed mainly by the State, partly by student fees. Governing bodies: the Asamblea Universitaria; the Consejo Universitario.

Arrangements for co-operation with: Patrice Lumumba People's Friendship University, Moscow; University of Havana; Instituto Superior Politécnico 'José Antonio Echeverría', La Habana; Instituto Superior de Ciencias Médicas, La Habana; Instituto Superior de Ciencias Agropecuarias, La Habana; Universidad de Santander; Universidad Nacional de Educación a Distancia, Madrid; Universidad Nacional Mayor de San Marcos, Lima; Universidad Nacional Autónoma de Nicaragua; Tulane University.

Academic Year: April to January.

Admission Requirements: Secondary school certificate (bachillerato) or recognized foreign equivalent, and entrance examination.

Fees (Sucres): 1500.

Language of Instruction: Spanish.

Degrees and Diplomas: Licenciado in–Social and Political Sciences; Sociology; Nursing; Library Science; Social Communication, 4 yrs; Education, 5 yrs. Professional titles of–Asistente en Bibliotecología, 2 yrs; Tecnólogo Médico, 3 yrs; Enfermera, nursing, 4 yrs; Ingeniero (various fields), 5-6 yrs; Sociólogo; Obstetriz, midwifery; Químico farmacéutico; Biólogo; Geólogo, 5 yrs; Economista; Arquitecto, 5 yrs and thesis; Contador público; Psicólogo, 6 yrs. Doctorado in–Education; Chemistry and Pharmacy; Dentistry; Veterinary Medicine and Animal Husbandry; Psychology; Law; Sociology, 5-6 yrs; Medicine, 7 yrs. Also teaching qualifications, secondary level.

Libraries: Central Library, *c.* 15,000 vols; faculty libraries.

Publications: El Universitario (monthly); Revista (quarterly).

Press or Publishing House: Litografía e Imprenta de la Universidad Guayaquil.

Academic Staff, 1986-87: c. 820 (1420).

Student Enrolment, 1986-87: 60,000.

2333 **UNIVERSIDAD LAICA 'ELOY ALFARO' DE MANABÍ**

Via San Mateo Casilla 2732 Manta
Telephone: 610288, 613740
Fax: 614095
Rector: Medardo Mora Solorzano
Secretario General: Carmos San Andrés Cedeño

F. of Education
Dean: José Reyes Cedeño; *staff* 10 (28)
F. of Medicine
Dean: Roddy Mata Moreira; *staff* 10 (50)
F. of Administration
Dan: Rodolfo Menéndez Molina; *staff* 12 (36)
F. of Engineering
Dean: Juan Pelaéz Delgado; *staff* 9 (26)
F. of Dentistry
Dean: Vicente Molina Barcia; *staff* 12 (5)
F. of Law, Social and Political Sciences
Dean: Antonio Hualpa Bello; *staff* 7 (10)
F. of Economics
Dean: Antonio Hualpa Bello; *staff* 7 (10)
F. of Architecture
Dean: Ovidio Moreira; *staff* 7 (13)
F. of Marine Sciences
Dean: Ceferino Castillo; *staff* 6 (18)
S. of Social Work
Dean: Isabel Montero de Alarcón; *staff* 7 (5)
S. of Communication Studies (including Journalism)
Dean: Maurilio Cedeño; *staff* 5 (10)
S. of Accounting and Auditing
Dean: Elizabeth Cañarte de Ruperti; *staff* 7 (12)

Founded 1985.

Academic Year: May to April.

Admission Requirements: Graduation from high school and entranc examination.

Language of Instruction: Spanish.

Degrees and Diplomas: Licencado. Doctorado.

Special Facilities (Museums, etc.): Museo Antropológico.

Academic Staff, 1990: 230.

Student Enrolment, 1990:

	Men	Women	Total
Of the country	2327	3489	5816
Of the country	14	10	24
Total	2341	3490	5840

2334 **UNIVERSIDAD LAICA 'VICENTE ROCAFUERTE'**

Civil University 'Vicente Rocafuerte'
Avenida de las Américas, Apartado 1133, Guayaquil
Telephone: (392-12) 287200
Rector: Elsa Alarcon
Secretary-General: Alfonso Aguilar

F. of Architecture
Dean: Milton Molina Palomeque; *staff* 24
F. of Education
Dean: Gladys Romoleroux: *staff* 22
F. of Economics
Dean: Freddy Delgado; *staff* 28
F. of Administration
Dean: Carlos Espinoza; *staff* 64
F. of Civil Engineering
Dean: Fausto Cabrera Monles; *staff* 23
F. of Law and Social Sciences
Dean: Calos Caicedo Morelra; *staff* 28
F. of Journalism
Dean: Pedro Valverder; *staff* 15
F. of Agricultural Engineering
Dean: Nino Espiniza; *staff* 28
Research Ce.
Dean: Carlos Rojas
Branches at Manta and Portoviejo.

Founded 1963. Governing body: the Consejo Universitario.

Academic Year: April to January (April-August; August-January).

Language of Instruction: Spanish.

Degrees and Diplomas: Licenciado in–Political Science, 4 yrs; Education; Administration; Journalism; Social Service, 5 yrs; Professional title of–Auditor; Decorador, 3 yrs; Trabajador social, 4 yrs; Arquitecto; Economista; Ingeniero civil;Abogado, law, 6 yrs. Also teaching qualifications secondary level.

Special Facilities (Museums, etc.): Observatory.

Publication: The University.

Academic Staff: c. 220.

Student Enrolment: c. 5000.

2335 **UNIVERSIDAD NACIONAL DE LOJA**

National University of Loja
Ciudadila Universitaria 'La Argilia', Loja
Telex: 4135-UNLOJA-ED
Telephone: 960-252
Rector: Guillermo Falconí Espinosa
Secretario General: César Jaramillo Carrió

F. of Jurisprudence
Dean: Luis Cueva Carrión; *staff* 18 (7)
F. of Veterinary Science
Dean: Eduardo Vélez Ruíz; *staff* 17 (2)
F. of Agriculture (including Forestry)
Dean: Alfredo Samaniego; *staff* 23 (8)
F. of Medicine
Dean: Alonso Armijos Luna; *staff* 18 (16)

F. of Administration (including Accountancy)
Dean: Victor Hugo Samaniego; *staff* 16
F. of Philosophy, Letters and Education
Dean: Héctor Silva Vilema; *staff* 88 (1)
F. of Science and Technology
Dean: Duman Rey Trelles; *staff* 17
F. of Arts
I. of Languages
Director: Numa Reinoso; *staff* 10
Popular U.
Director: Galo Pérez; *staff* 8
Also 4 Research Institutes.

Founded 1859 as school of law, acquired present status 1943. The university is an autonomous institution, financed largely by the State. Governing bodies: the Asamblea Universitaria; the Consejo Universitario.

Arrangements for co-operation with: Universidad de Buenos Aires; Universidad Nacional Autónoma de México; Universidad Autónoma de Centro América, San José; Universidad Simón Bolívar, Caracas; Universidad de Aguascalientes; Universidade de Caxias do Sul; Universidad Nacional, Heredia; Universidade Estatal de Ponta Grossa; Universidad Pedagógica Nacional, México; Universidad de Yucatán; Universidad Politécnica, Madrid; Universidad Nacional Experimental del Táchira; Universidad Autónoma de Madrid; University of Stanford; Universidad del Valle; Universidad Nacional de Cajamarca; Universidad de Piura.

Academic Year: October to July (October-December; January-March; April-July).

Admission Requirements: Secondary school certificate (bachillerato).

Fees (Sucres): 12,800-38,400.

Language of Instruction: Spanish.

Degrees and Diplomas: Licenciado in–Social Sciences; Political Sciences; Economics; Social Work; Philosophy; Letters; Education; Nursing; Arts; 4 yrs. Professional titles of–Ingeniero (various fields); Enfermera, nursing; Administrador; Tecnólogo, 5 yrs. Doctorado in–Philosophy; Letters; Education; Arts; Veterinary Medicine; 5-6 yrs. Medicine; 7yrs.

Library: 14 specialized libraries, total, 26,278 vols.

Publications: Monthly publications of the faculties and institutes; Revistas.

Press or Publishing House: Editorial Universitaria.

Academic Staff, 1989: 399.

Student Enrolment, 1989-90:

	Men
Of the country	7730
Of other countries	61
Total	7391

2336 **UNIVERSIDAD TÉCNICA DE AMBATO**
Technical University of Ambato
Ciuddela Ingahurco, Apartado de Correos 334, Ambato
Telephone: 82-21-91
Rector: Luis Aníbal Garcés V. (1980-)

F. of Administration and Management
F. of Accountancy and Auditing
F. of Education and Development
F. of Engineering

Founded 1959 as an Institute of Accountancy, Management and Industrial Technology, became an autonomous institution of higher education 1963 and acquired university status 1969. Governing bodies: the Asamblea Universitaria; the Consejo Universitario.

Academic Year: October to August (October-December; January-March; April-July).

Admission Requirements: Secondary school certificate (bachillerato).

Language of Instruction: Spanish.

Degrees and Diplomas: Licenciado in–Sociology and Co-operatives; Physics and Mathematics; Biology and Chemistry; Accountancy; Administration and Management; Education, 4 yrs. Professional titles of–Contador público, 4 yrs; Ingeniero in–Food Technology; Civil Engineering; Agriculture; Commerce, 5-6 yrs. Doctorado in–Sociology and Co-operatives; Physics and Mathematics; Biology and Chemistry; Accountancy and Auditing. Teaching qualifications, secondary level.

Libraries: Central Library, *c.* 11,780 vols; Administration, *c.* 5620; Accountancy and Auditing, *c.* 4670, Education, *c.* 5050, Engineering, *c.* 3980; Agricultural Engineering, *c.* 2960.

Special Facilities (Museums, etc.): Museo Arqueológico.

Publication: Research publications.

Press or Publishing House: Editorial Universitaria.

Academic Staff: c. 130 (240).

Student Enrolment: c. 10,230.

2337 **UNIVERSIDAD TÉCNICA DE BABAHOYO**
Technical University of Babahoyo
Via Flores, Apartado 66, Babahoyo

F. of Education
F. of Agriculture

Founded 1971.

Degrees and Diplomas: Licenciado in Education, 5 yrs. Professional title of Ingeniero agrónomo, 5 yrs. Teaching qualifications, secondary level.

Academic Staff: c. 400.

Student Enrolment: c. 9800.

2338 **UNIVERSIDAD TÉCNICA DE ESMERALDAS**
Technical University of Esmeraldas
Avenida Nuevo Horizonte, Esmeraldas

F. of Agriculture (including Animal Husbandry and Forestry)
F. of Education (including Social and Exact Sciences)
F. of Administration
I. of Cultural Studies
I. of Scientific Research

Founded 1970. An autonomous State institution.

Degrees and Diplomas: Licenciado in–History and Geography; Political Science and Economics; Literature; Social Work; Sociology; Physical Education; Industrial Engineering; Physics and Mathematics; Chemistry and Biology; Psychology; Vocational Orientation, 4 yrs. Professional titles of–Ingeniero forestal; Ingeniero zootecnista, animal husbandry; Ingeniero comercial; Administrador de Negocios, 5 yrs.

2339 **UNIVERSIDAD TÉCNICA PARTICULAR DE LOJA**
Technical University of Loja
Barrio San Cayetano, Apartado de Correos 608, Loja
Telex: (04) 4533 UNITEL ED
Telephone: (593-4) 961836
Fax: (593-4) 963159 ecuador, loja
Rector: Max Torres Guzmán
Secretary-General: Carlos Ramírez Romero

F. of Civil Engineering
Dean: Luis Sarmiento Salcedo
F. of Agroindustrial Engineering
Dean: Fernando Sararguro Martinez
F. of Economics
Dean: Victor Pucha S.
F. of Architecture
Dean: Juan Flores Cabrera
F. of Computer Sciences
Dean: Martha Schuldis
F. of Mining
Dean: Carlos Salinas Calero
F. of Languages
Dean: Victor Salinas
Open U.
Dean: Leonardo Peñarreta Alvarez
S. of Arts
Dean: Fabián Figueroa
S. of Secretarial Studies
Dean: Edith Bravo
S. of Accountancy and Auditing
Dean: Rosario Moreno
Also 3 Research Institutes.

Founded 1971 by the Marist Brothers of Schools. A private institution financed largely by the State. Governing bodies: the Consejo Gubernativo; comprising 16 members; the Asamblea General.

Arrangements for co-operation with the Technical University of Karlsruhe.

Academic Year: October to August (October-March; April-August).

Admission Requirements: Secondary school certificate (bachillerato) or recognized foreign equivalent, and entrance examination.

Language of Instruction: Spanish.

Degrees and Diplomas: Licenciado in–Science; Arts; Business Administration, 5 yrs.

Library: Central Library, *c.* 30,000 vols.

Publications: Universidad (monthly); Revista (biannually).

Press or Publishing House: Editorial UTPL.

Academic Staff, 1990: 37 (87).
Student Enrolment, 1990:

	Men	Women	Total
Of the country	3400	6700	10100

2340 **UNIVERSIDAD TÉCNICA DE MACHALA**
Technical University of Machala
Calle Tarque entre Sucre y 9 de Octubre, Machala

F. of Agriculture and Veterinary Medicine
F. of Chemistry
F. of Sociology
F. of Administration and Accountancy
F. of Civil Engineering

Founded 1969.

Degrees and Diplomas: Licenciado in–Sociology; 5 yrs; Administration, 5 yrs. Professional titles of–Auditor, 4 yrs; Ingeniero agrónomo; Médico veterinario y Zootécnico; Ingeniero civil; Ingeniero comercial, 5 yrs; Sociólogo, 6 yrs. Doctorado in–Biochemistry and Pharmacy; Industrial Chemistry, 6 yrs.

Academic Staff, 1986-87: 285.
Student Enrolment, 1986-87: 6350.

2341 **UNIVERSIDAD TÉCNICA DE MANABÍ**
Technical University of Manabí
Ciudadela Universitaria, Portoviejo, Prov. de Manabí
Telephone: 652677

F. of Mathematics, Physics, and Chemistry (including Electrical, Mechanical, Civil and Industrial Engineering.)
F. of Agricultural Engineering
F. of Agriculture
F. of Veterinary Medicine (including Animal Husbandry)
F. of Social Sciences and Education (including Psychology and Languages)
F. of Administration and Economics
F. of Nursing

Founded 1952 as a State institution. Governing bodies: the Asamblea General; the Consejo Universitario.

Academic Year: May to January (May-July; August-October; November-January).

Admission Requirements: Secondary school certificate (bachillerato) or foreign equivalent.

Language of Instruction: Spanish.

Degrees and Diplomas: Licenciado in–Psychology; Languages; Chemistry and Biology; Physics and Mathematics; Nursing, 4 yrs. Professional titles of–Ingeniero mecánico; Ingeniero agrícola; Ingeniero agrónomo; Orientador vocacional; Ingeniero industrial; Médico veterinario, 5 yrs; Economista; Ingeniero eléctrico; Ingeniero civil, 6 yrs. Doctorado in–Psychology; Languages; Education, 6 yrs.

Libraries: Central Library, *c.* 4720 vols; specialized library, *c.* 1060.
Academic Staff: c. 380.
Student Enrolment: c. 10,250.

2342 **UNIVERSIDAD TÉCNICA DEL NORTE**
Avenida Pérez Guerrero y Olmedo, Casilla 199, Ibarra
Telephone: 715430

2343 **UNIVERSIDAD TÉCNOLÓGICA EQUINOCCIAL**
Rumipamba y Borgeois 210, Casilla 2764, Quito
Telephone: 442288
Rector: Alvaro Trueba Barahona
Director General Administrativo y Financiero: José Benítez Celi

F. of Applied Administrative Sciences (including Hotel Administration and Tourism)
Dean: Fausto Núnez; *staff* – (90)
F. of Economics
Dean: Marcelo Espinosa A.; *staff* – (108)
F. of Arts
Dean: Agustín Oleas Carrillo; *staff* – (35)
F. of Social Sciences
Dean: José Carrera Rios; *staff* – (55)
F. of Agriculture
Dean: Alfonso Jarrín
F. of Engineering (including Textile, Petroleum, and Civil Engineering)
Dean: Edison Olmedo; *staff* – (73)
Research Ce.
Director: Alfonso Jarrín; *staff* 1 (1)
D. of Languages
Director: Alicia Vanegas; *staff* – (18)

Founded 1986. Governing bodies: the Asamblea Universitaria; the Consejo Universitario.

Arrangements for co-operation with: University of Oklahoma; International University of Florida.

Academic Year: November to August.

Admission Requirements: Secondary school certificate (bachillerato) or recognized foreign equivalent, and entrance examination.

Fees (Sucres): 169,000 per annum.

Language of Instruction: Spanish.

Degrees and Diplomas: Licenciado in–Hotel Administration; Tourism; Co-operatives Administration; Personnel Administration; Business; Foreign Trade; Public Relations; Infant Education; Publicity, 4 yrs. Professional titles of–Tecnólogo (various fields); Ingeniero de Empresas, business; Diseñador de Interiores; Ingeniero textil; Ingeniero del Trabajo, 3-6 yrs.

Library: 8000 vols.
Publication: Campus (bimonthly).
Press or Publishing House: Departamento de Publicaciones de la Universidad Tecnológica Equinoccial.
Academic Staff, 1989-90: –(161)
Student Enrolment, 1989-90:

	Men	Women	TotaL
Of the country	2248	2433	4681

2344 **UNIVERSIDAD TÉCNICA ESTATAL DE QUEVEDO**
Vía a Quito s/n, Casilla 74, Quevedo, Los Rios
Telephone: 751430
Rector: Carlos Cortaza González (1984-89)
Vicerrector: Manuel Haz Alvarez

S. of Forestry Engineering
Director: Guillermo Law Blanco; *staff* 2 (25)
S. of Animal Livestock Engineering
Director: Carlos Aguirre; *staff* 3 (6)
S. of Agro-Business Administration
Director: Joffre Rada Peralta; *staff* 6 (25)
S. of Soils and Water Management Technology
Director: Leonardo Matute; *staff* 2 (8)
S. of Agricultural Mechanization Technology
Director: Leonardo Matude; *staff* (8)
D. of Studies
Director: Rafael Garcés; *staff* 1 (18)
I. of Agricultural Research
Director: Francisco Mite

Also 2 Experimental Farms.

Founded 1984. Governing bodies: the Asamblea Universitaria; the Consejo Universitario.

Academic Year: May to January.

Admission Requirements: Secondary school certificate (bachillerato) and entrance examination.

Fees (Sucres): 1,000,000

Language of Instruction: Spanish.

Degrees and Diplomas: Professional titles, 3-6 yrs.

Library: 1500 vols.
Publication: Boletins Informative UTEQ.
Academic Staff, 1990-91: 22 (32).
Student Enrolment, 1989-90:

	Men	Women	Total
Of the country	667	497	1164

2345 **ESCUELA POLITÉCNICA NACIONAL**
National Institute of Technology
Calle Isabel la Católica y Vientimilla, Apartado Correos 2759, Quito
Telephone: 553699
Rector: J. Rubén Orellana Ricaurte (1974-)

F. of Chemical Engineering
F. of Electrical Engineering
F. of Mechanical Engineering
F. of Civil Engineering
F. of Industrial Engineering
F. of Geology, Mining and Petroleum Engineering
I. of Science

of Social Sciences
of Computer Sciences
of Physical Education
of Technological Research
Observatory

Founded 1870 by President Gabriel García Moreno. Re-established and reorganized 1935. Governing bodies: the Assembly; the Council.

Academic Year: October to July (October-February; March-July).

Admission Requirements: Secondary school certificate (bachillerato) and entrance examination.

Language of Instruction: Spanish.

Degrees and Diplomas: Professional titles of–Tecnólogo en–Electromecánica; Telecomunicaciones; Ingeniero industrial, 3 yrs. Ingeniero-químico; -eléctrico; -electrónica y telecomunicaciones; -mecánico; matemático civil; -geólogo; -petróleos, 5 yrs. Magister.

Library: Central Library, *c.* 7800 vols.

Special Facilities (Museums, etc.): Museums: Geology; Petrology; Vertebrates and Palaeontology.

Publication: Politécnica (weekly).

Academic Staff: c. 900.

Student Enrolment: c. 18,870.

2346 ***ESCUELA SUPERIOR POLITÉCNICA DE CHIMBORAZO**

Institute of Technology of Chimborazo
Kilómetro 1 Panamericana Sur, P.O. Box 4703, Ríobamba
Telephone: 961969
Rector: Rodrigo Jaramillo Garcés (1987-)

F. of Agriculture
F. of Animal Husbandry
F. of Dietetics and Nutrition
F. of Mechanical Engineering
F. of Science
F. of Business Administration
D. of Chemistry
D. of Physical Education
D. of Physics and Mathematics

Founded 1969 as a State institution under the jurisdiction of the Ministry of Education, enjoying some autonomy. Acquired present status as Polytechnic 1973. Governing bodies: the Asamblea; the Consejo.

Academic Year: October to July (October-February; March-July).

Admission Requirements: Secondary school certificate (bachillerato).

Language of Instruction: Spanish.

Degrees and Diplomas: Licenciado in Dietetics and Nutrition, 4-5 yrs. Professional titles of–Tecnólogo; Ingeniero, 5-6 yrs. Also certificate in Technical English, 2 yrs. Doctorado in–Physics and Chemistry, 5 yrs; Mathematics; Physics, 6 yrs.

Library: Central Library, *c.* 11,000 vols.

Publications: La Gaceta Politécnica (annually); Perspectiva (annually).

Press or Publishing House: Departamento de Publicaciones.

Academic Staff: c. 120 (40).

Student Enrolment: c. 5300.

2347 **ESCUELA SUPERIOR POLITÉCNICA DEL LITORAL**

Institute of Technology of the Litoral
Calle Rocafuerte y Loja, Guayaquil
Cables: Espol
Telephone: 303733

D. of Electrical Engineering
D. of Mechanical Engineering
D. of Naval Engineering
D. of Geological, Mining, and Petroleum Engineeering
I. of Physics
I. of Mathematics
I. of Chemistry
I. of General Studies
S. of Nursing
S. of Communications Technology

Founded 1958 as a State institution under the jurisdiction of the Ministry of Education, but enjoys some autonomy.

Academic Year: May to February (May-September; October-February).

Admission Requirements: Secondary school certificate (bachillerato) and entrance examination.

Language of Instruction: Spanish.

Degrees and Diplomas: Licenciado in–Oceanography, 4 yrs. Professional title of Ingeniero in all fields, 6 yrs.

Library: c. 8000 vols.

Academic Staff: c. 80 (50).

Student Enrolment: c. 3000.

EGYPT
(Arab Republic)

Universities

2348 ***AIN SHAMS UNIVERSITY**
Kasr el Zaafran, Abbassia, Cairo
Telex: 94070-U-SHMS-UN
Telephone: 821117
President: Mohamed M. El Hashimy (1983-)

F. of Arts
F. of Law
F. of Commerce
F. of Science
F. of Medicine
F. of Engineering (including Architecture)
F. of Agriculture
F. of Education
F. of Languages
C. for Women (Arts and Science)
I. of Environmental Studies and Research
I. of Nursing
I. of Postgraduate Childhood Studies
Science Education Ce.
Middle East Research Ce.
Computer Ce.
Child-Studies Research Ce.
Research Ce. for the Development of English Language Teaching
Ce. for Papyrological Studies
Business Research Ce.
Information Systems Ce.
Public Service Ce.
Research and Training Ce. on Vectors of Diseases

Founded 1956 as State university and incorporating Abbassia School of Medicine. Formerly known as Ibrahim Pasha University and also as University of Heliopolis. Faculties of Commerce, Education, Agriculture, and Veterinary Medicine at Zagazig detached 1973 to form new University. Governing body: the University Council, composed of the President, 2 Vice-Presidents, deans of the faculties, a representativeof the Ministry of Higher Education, the Secretary-General and two other members. Residential facilities for students.

Academic Year: September to May.

Admission Requirements: Secondary school certificate or equivalent.

Language of Instruction: Arabic.

Degrees and Diplomas: Bachelor of–Arts; Science; Law; Commerce; Agriculture; Civil Engineering; Electrical Engineering; Mechanical Engineering; Arts and Education; Science and Education, 4-5 yrs. Master of–Arts; Arts in Commerce; Science; Engineering; Agriculture; Agricultural Science; Education; Psychology; Medicine, a further 2-3 yrs. Doctorate in–Philosophy (Arts, Science, Agriculture, Education, Commerce); Law; Letters; Architecture; Medicine; MedicalScience. Also Diplomas in–Law, various fields; Home Economics; Education and Psychology.

Libraries: Central Library, *c.* 89,350 vols; faculty libraries, *c.* 3300.

Publications: Annals of the Faculty of Arts; Al-Ulum Al-Kanounia wal Iktisadia (review); Economic and Business Review; Bulletin of Faculty of Engineering; Annals of Agricultural Science.

Press or Publishing House: Ain Shams University Press.

Academic Staff: c. 1870.

Student Enrolment: c. 121,520.

2349 **AL-AZHAR UNIVERSITY**
Cairo
Telephone: 906154; 904051; 706097
President: Mohamed Al-Saadi Farhood

F. of Arab Language
F. of Theology
F. of Law
F. of Islamic Religion
F. of Islamic Daowa (Call)
F. of Islamic Studies
F. of Language and Translation
F. of Commerce
F. of Science
F. of Medicine
F. of Dentistry
F. of Pharmacy
F. of Engineering
F. of Agriculture
F. of Education
F. of Islamic Culture (for girls)
F. of Islamic Language (Assiut)
F. of Theology (Assiut)
F. of Law (Assiut)
F. of Arab Language (Mansoura)
F. of Islamic Religion (Mansoura)
F. of Arab Language (Zagazig)
F. of Islamic Religion (Zagazig)
F. of Arab Language (Menofeiya)
F. of Islamic Religion (Menofeiya)
F. of Law (Tanta)
F. of Islamic Religion (Tanta)
F. of Arab Language (El-Behera)
F. of Law (El Behera)

Founded 970 as a school and developed 1961. Governing body: the University Council.

Academic Year: October to June.

Admission Requirements: Secondary school certificate and entrance examination.

Fees: None.

Language of Instruction: Arabic.

Degrees and Diplomas: Bachelor of–Arts; Science, 4-5 yrs. Master of–Arts; Science, 2-3 yrs after Bachelor. Doctorate in Philosophy, 2-3 yrs after Master.

Library: c. 80,000 vols.

Academic Staff: c. 3600.

Student Enrolment: c. 90,000.

2350 ***ALEXANDRIA UNIVERSITY**
22 Al-Guish Avenue, Chatby, Alexandria
Telex: 54467 UNIVY UN
Telephone: 71675/8
President: Mahmoud Fareed Hassan Mostafa

F. of Arts
F. of Law (including Economics)
F. of Commerce
F. of Science
F. of Medicine
F. of Dentistry
F. of Education
F. of Education (Damanhour)
F. of Veterinary Medicine (Edfina)
F. of Pharmacy
F. of Engineering (including Architecture)
F. of Tourism and Hotel Management
F. of Agriculture (Kafr-el-Sheikh)
I. of Public Health
I. of Medical Research
I. of Nursing
Postgraduate Science Research Ce.
Ce. of Public Services

Founded 1942 as a State university, incorporating former branches of the Faculties of Arts, Law, and Engineering of Fouad I (Cairo) University, and known as Farouk I University until 1953. Faculty of Medicine and Colleges of Education at Tanta detached 1972 to form new University. Governing body: the University Senate. Residential facilities for *c.* 5680 students.

Academic Year: October to June (October-February; March-June).

Admission Requirements: Secondary school certificate or equivalent.

Languages of Instruction: Arabic and English.

Degrees and Diplomas: Bachelor of–Arts; Law; Commerce; Science; Agriculture; Arts and Education; Science and Education; Nursing, 4 yrs; Pharmacy and Pharmaceutical Sciences; Dental Surgery and Medicine; Engineering; Science in Anatomy; Science in Physiology; Veterinary Medicine, 5 yrs; Medicine and Surgery, 6 yrs. Master, a further 1-3 yrs and thesis. Doctorates, 2 yrs after Master and dissertation. Doctor of Science is awarded after doctorate for distinguished contributions to knowledge. Also postgraduate diplomas in applied and professional subjects.

Libraries: Central Library, *c.* 170,000 vols; also faculty and institute libraries, *c.* 40,000.

Special Facilities (Museums, etc.): Museums: Archaeology; Forensic Medical Museum.

Publication: Bulletins.

Academic Staff: c. 3180 (100).

Student Enrolment: c. 96,900 (Also *c.* 28,830 external students).

2351 ***ASSIUT UNIVERSITY**

Assiut

Cables: assiut university-egypt

Telex: 92863 ASUN UN

Telephone: 32 3000

Fax: (20) 88 322564

President: Abd El-Razek Rezk Hassan (1981-)

Secretary-General: Mohamed M. Hefny

F. of Science
Dean: Ahmed F. Rady; *staff* 248

F. of Science (Sohag)
Dean: Mohamed M. El-Sheikh; *staff* 62

F. of Science (Qena)
Dean: Abdel-Hady M. El-Kamel; *staff* 55

F. of Engineering (including Architecture, Civil, Mechanical, Mechanical Electrical Engineering, and Mining and Metallurgy)
Head: Awad I. Saleh; *staff* 113

F. of Medicine
Dean: Mamdouh Mohamed Shaaban; *staff* 278

F. of Agriculture
Dean: Farouk M. Khalil; *staff* 176

F. of Pharmacy
Dean: Nabil Mahmoud Omar; *staff* 70

F. of Veterinary Medicine
Dean: Mohamed H. El-Gindy; *staff* 92

F. of Education
Dean: Moustafa Abdel-Rahman Darwish; *staff* 49

F. of Law
Dean: Abdel-Nasser El-Attar; *staff* 25

F. of Commerce
Dean: Abdel-Hady A. Seweify; *staff* 29

F. of Education (Sohag)
Dean: Ibrahim Bassyouni Emira; *staff* 40

F. of Physical Education
Supervisor: Moustafa A. Darwish *staff* 5

F. of Education (Qena)
Dean: Abdel-Azeem M. Abdel-Mageed; *staff* 16-

F. of Arts (Sohag)
Dean: Asem El-Desouky; *staff* 75

F. of Arts (Qena)
Dean: El-Badrawi M. Zahran; *staff* 12

F. of Commerce (including Political Science) (Sohag)
Dean: Abdel-Hamid Bahgat Fayed; *staff* 13

I. of Nursing
Supervisor: Hammam Mohamed Hammam

F. of Science (Asswan)
Dean: Rifaat El-Sherif; *staff* 55

F. of Education (Asswan)
Dean: Ramadan M. Abdallah; *staff* 20

Founded 1949 by decree, opened 1957. The university is a State institution enjoying administrative autonomy. Faculties of Agriculture, Arts and Education at Minya detached 1976 to form new University. Financed by the State. The University has branches in Sohag, Qena and Asswan. Governing body: the University Council comprising the President as Chairman, four Vice-Presidents, the deans, the Secretary-General, and four other members. Residential facilities for academic staff and for 12,000 students.

Arrangements for co-operation with Arab, Asian, American, and European Universities.

Academic Year: September to May (September-December; January-May).

Admission Requirements: Secondary school certificate or equivalent.

Fees: None.

Languages of Instruction: Arabic and English.

Degrees and Diplomas: Bachelor of–Science, B.Sc., Arts, B.A.; Law, B.Law; Agriculture, B.Agr.; Commerce, B.Com.; Education, B.Ed., 4 yrs; Veterinary Medicine, B.V.Med.; Engineering, B.Eng.; Pharmacy, B.Pharm., 5 yrs; Medicine, M.B.; BCH, 6 yrs. Master in all fields, a further 2-3 yrs and thesis. Doctor of Philosophy, Ph.D., by thesis. Also Diplomas in specialized fields, 2 yrs after Bachelor.

Library: Central Library and faculty libraries, *c.* 320,000 vols.

Special Facilities (Museums, etc.): Geological Museum.

Publication: Faculty Bulletins.

Press or Publishing House: University Printing Press.

Academic Staff, 1989-90:

Rank	Full-time
Professors	401
Associate Professors	366
Lecturers	666
Assistant Lecturers	750
Demonstrators	552
Total	2735

Student Enrolment, 1989-90:

	Men	Women	Total
Of the country	29,848	11,935	41,783

2352 **ASWAN UNIVERSITY**

New Aswan

F. of Science

F. of Education

Founded 1986, incorporating faculties previously forming part of Assiut University. In the process of development.

2353 ***CAIRO UNIVERSITY**

Orman, Giza, Cairo

Telex: 94372 UNCAI UN

Telephone: 727326

President: Maaman M. Salama

Secretary-General: Mokhtar A. El-Shahawa

F. of Arts (including Library Science)
Dean: Hasanane M. Rabea; *staff* 170

F. of Law
Dean: Nooman M. Gomaa; *staff* 67

F. of Economics and Political Science
Dean: Ahmad Abdel Wahab Al-Ghandoor; *staff* 86

F. of Commerce (including Accountancy)
Dean: Shawky Hussein Abd-Allah; *staff* 64

F. of Science (including Astronomy)
Dean: Abd El-Kader Mansour; *staff* 450

F. of Medicine
Dean: Khairey El-Samra; *staff* 864

F. of Dentistry
Dean: Ali Mohamad Sharwy; *staff* 150

F. of Pharmacy
Dean: Abd-El-Kader El-Sayyed; *staff* 121

F. of Engineering (including Architecture)
Dean: Farouk Ismail Ahmad; *staff* 448

F. of Agriculture
Dean: Ahmed Moustageer; *staff* 357

F. of Veterinary Medicine
Dean: Mohammad Said M. Soliman; *staff* 213

F. of Mass Communication
Dean: Jehan Ahmad Rushtey; *staff* 38

F. of Arabic and Islamic Studies (Dar El-Olum)
Dean: Mohamed El-Beltagi; *staff* 79

F. of Archaeology
Dean: Ali Mahmoud Raduan; *staff* 26

F. of Education (El-Fayoum)
Dean: Abd-El-Fattah El-Shershabey; *staff* 57
F. of Engineering (El-Fayoum)
Dean: Mohhamad Azzat Sobeah; *staff* 1 (21)
F. of Social Service (El-Fayoum)
Dean: Abd El-Hameed Abd-El-Mohsen; *staff* (17)
F. of Agriculture (El-Fayoum)
Dean: Saad Nassar; *staff* 64
F. of Commerce (Beni Suef)
Dean: Al-Ghareeb Mohammad Bayyomy; *staff* 10 (13)
F. of Law (Beni Suef)
Dean: Khallaf Abd El-Gaber Khallaf; *staff* 24
F. of Veterinary Medicine (Beni Suef)
Dean: Salah Deeb Aly; *staff* 16
F. of Science (Beni Suef)
Dean: Fayer Mohammad Shaheen; *staff* 13
F. of Arts (Beni Suef)
Dean: Sayyed Hanafy Hasanane; *staff* – (12)
F. of Education
I. of Statistical Study and Research
Dean: Mahmoud Reyad Mahmoud; *staff* 41
I. of African Studies and Research
Dean: Soliman Abd El-Sattar Khater; *staff* 34
I. of Cancer Research
Dean: Mahmoud Nabil El-Balkeeny; *staff* 84
I. of Nursing
Dean: Shahr-Zad Khalid Ghazy; *staff* 20
I. of Physiotherapy
Dean: Khairey El-Sumra; *staff* 26
I. of Town Planning
Dean: Mahmoud Yousry Hassan; *staff* 10
Also 3 Hospitals.

Founded 1908 as a national university, became State university 1925. Known as Fouad I University, 1940 to 1953. A State institution under the supervision of the Ministry of Higher Education. Governing body: the University Council. Residential facilities for *c.* 3200 men students, and *c.* 1800 women students.

Academic Year: October to June.

Admission Requirements: Secondary school certificate or equivalent. University degree for Institutes of Statistical Studies and African Studies.

Languages of Instruction: Arabic, English and French.

Degrees and Diplomas: Bachelor of–Arts (General or Honours); Commerce; Science in Economics; Science in Statistics; Science in Political Science; Agricultural Science (General or Special); Journalism; Arabic and Islamic Studies (General or Special); Science (General or Special); Law, 4 yrs; Veterinary Medicine and Surgery; Pharmaceutical Chemistry, 5 yrs; Dental Surgery, 4 yrs following preparatory yr; Medicine and Surgery, 6 yrs; Civil Engineering; Architecture; Mechanical Engineering; Electrical Engineering; Chemical Engineering; Mining Engineering; Petroleum Engineering, 5 yrs. Master of–Arts; Arabic Language; Islamic Studies; Commerce; Science; Surgery; Journalism; Dental Surgery; Pharmacy; Engineering; Architecture; Agricultural Sciences, a further 2 yrs. Doctorate in–Arts; Law; Commerce; Philosophy; Science; Medicine; Medical Science; Dental Medicine; Pharmacy; Engineering; Architecture; Veterinary Medicine and Surgery; Arabic Language; Islamic Studies, 2 yrs after Master. Diplomas in–Statistics, 2yrs; African Studies.

Library: Central Library and faculty libraries, *c.* 1,000,000 vols.

Special Facilities (Museums, etc.): Museums: Egyptology; Islamic; Entomology; Papyrii and Ancient Coins.

Publication: Faculty Bulletins.

Press or Publishing House: Cairo University Press; Agriculture Faculty Press; Statistical Studies and Research Press.

Academic Staff, 1989-90:

Rank	Full-time
Professors	1160
Assistant Professors	970
Lecturers	1404
Total	3534

Student Enrolment, 1989-90:

	Men	Women	Total
Of the country	46,918	29,964	76,882
Of other countries	1286	656	1942
Total	48,204	30,620	78,824

2354 ***UNIVERSITY OF HELWAN**
96 Ahmed Oraby Street, El-Mohandeseen, Embababa P.O. Cairo
Cables: Helwanuni Cairo
Telex: 21682 HEUNUR
Telephone: (2) 344644
President: M. Kamal El-Etr

F. of Engineering and Technology
F. of Engineering and Technology (Mataria)
F. of Art Education
F. of Fine Arts
F. of Fine Arts (Alexandria)
F. of Applied Arts (Giza)
F. of Music
F. of Agriculture
F. of Commerce and Business Administration
F. of Education
F. of Science
F. of Tourism and Hotel Management
F. of Home Economics
F. of Physical Education (for boys)
F. of Physical Education (for girls)
F. of Physical Education (for boys) (Alexandria)
F. of Physical Education (for girls) (Alexandria)
F. of Cotton Technology (Alexandria)

Founded 1975, incorporating previously existing faculties and institutes of higher education. A State institution under the supervision of the Ministry of Higher Education and financed by the State. Governing body: the University Council, comprising 25 members. Residential facilities for students.

Academic Year: September to June.

Admission Requirements: Secondary school certificate or equivalent.

Fees: None.

Languages of Instruction: Arabic and English.

Degrees and Diplomas: Bachelor of–Science, B.Sc.; Arts, B.A., 4-5 yrs. Master of–Science, M.Sc.; Arts, M.A., a further 2 yrs. Ph.D., 3 yrs after Master. Also Diploma.

Libraries: Central Library, *c.* 600,000 vols; faculty libraries, *c.* 319,000.

Academic Staff: c. 1100.

Student Enrolment: c. 33,300.

2355 ***MANSOURA UNIVERSITY**
P.O. Box 35516, 35516 Mansoura
Telex: 23738 MANSOURA
Telephone: 347054
President: Abdel-Fattah Mohamed Hassan
Secretary-General: Safaa El-Din Arafat

F. of Education
Dean: Emeal Fahmy Hanna Shenouda; *staff* 79 (23)
F. of Science
Dean: Mahmoud Nor El-din Hassan; *staff* 262 (7)
F. of Commerce (including Accountancy, Economics, Statistics, and Business Administration)
Dean: Ibrahim Mohamed Mahdy; *staff* 58 (3)
F. of Engineering
Dean: Said Abdel-Ghany Ashour; *staff* 127 (33)
F. of Agriculture (including Food Science, Horticulture, and Animal Husbandry)
Dean: Ibrahim Tantawy; *staff* 172 (1)
F. of Law
Dean: Abdel-Hady Ali El-Naggar; *staff* 45
F. of Arts (including Arabic, English, and French language, Greece and Latin Studies, History, Geography, Psychology, and Sociology)
Dean: Ali Mohamed Barakat; *staff* 39 (40)
F. of Pharmacy
Dean: Ahmed Fouad Haleem; *staff* 70 (17)
F. of Medicine
Dean: Hamdy Ibrahim El-Aishy; *staff* 33 (1)
F. of Dentistry
Dean: Omar Hassan Mohamed Khashaba; *staff* 30 (47)
F. of Science (Demietta)
Dean: Shakwi Mohamed Hussein; *staff* 47 (27)
F. of Education (Demietta)
Dean: Zaki Mohamed Abdalla; *staff* 27 (5)

Founded 1972, incorporating faculties previously attached to the University of Cairo. A State institution under the authority of the Ministry of Higher Education. Governing bodies: the Board; the Boards of the Faculties. Residential facilities for academic staff and students.

Academic Year: October to June (October-January; March-June).

Admission Requirements: Secondary school certificate or equivalent.

Fees (Pounds): Foreign students, 750-2400 per annum.

Language of Instruction: Arabic.

Degrees and Diplomas: Degree of Bachelor, 4-6 yrs. Degree of Master, a further 2-3 yrs. Ph.D., a further 2-4 yrs.

Libraries: Central Library; faculty libraries.

Special Facilities (Museums, etc.): Pathology Museum; Geology Museum.

Academic Staff, 1989-90:

Rank	Full-time	Part-time
Professors	322	78
Associate Professors	385	34
Assistant Professors	580	94
Total	1287	206

Student Enrolment, 1989-90:

	Men	Women	Total
Of the country	11,016	20,667	31,683
Of other countries	78	508	586
Total	11,094	21,175	32,269

2356 ***MENOUFIA UNIVERSITY**

Gamal Abdel Nasser Street, Shebin El-Kom
Telex: 23832 MUSKE UN
Telephone: 322170
Fax: (2) 777620

President: El Sayed Hassan Hassanein (1989-)
Secretary-General: Mahmoud B. Soultan

F. of Agriculture (including Animal Husbandry)
Dean: Salah Al-Khouli; *staff* 255
F. of Engineering and Technology
Dean: Sayed Hassan; *staff* 260
F. of Electronics (Menouf)
Dean: Ahmed Montaser; *staff* 112
F. of Education
Dean: Hussin Ghareeb; *staff* 45
F. of Science
Dean: Maghawri Shehata; *staff* 180
F. of Commerce (including Business Administration and Economics)
Dean: Mohamed Ibrahim; *staff* 50
F. of Medicine
Dean: Mohamed A. Shoeib; *staff* 189
F. of Arts
Dean: Mohamed A. Bourg; *staff* 76
F. of Law
Dean: Hamdi Abdel Rahman; *staff* 40
F. of Home Economics
Dean: Mohamed S. Al. Dashlouti; *staff* 24
I. of Nursing
Dean: Dalal M. Kholil; *staff* 19
Liver I.
Dean: Mohamed F. Abdel Wahab; *staff* 17

Founded 1976. A State institution under the authority of the Ministry of Higher Education. Governing body: the University Council. Residential facilities for students.

Arrangements for co-operation with the Universities of: Ohio; Illinois; Strathclyde; Glasgow; Warsaw (Technical).

Academic Year: October to May.

Admission Requirements: Secondary school certificate or equivalent.

Fees (Pounds): Foreign students: Registration, 500-800; tuition, 500-800 per annum.

Languages of Instruction: Arabic and English.

Degrees and Diplomas: Bachelor of–Science in Agriculture; Science; Science in Education; Arts in Education; Commerce, 4 yrs; Science in Engineering, 5 yrs. Master, a further 2 yrs. Doctor of Philosophy, Ph.D., 3 yrs after Master. Also Diplomas in–Education; Agriculture.

Libraries: Central Library, *c.* 8970 vols; faculty libraries.

Publications: Menoufia Journal of Agricultural Research; Engineering Research Bulletin; University Guide.

Academic Staff, 1989-90:

Rank	Full-time
Professors	125
Assistant Professors	149
Teachers	339
Assistant Teachers	354
Teaching Assistants	597
Total	1564

Student Enrolment, 1989-90:

	Men	Women	Total
Of the country	13,558	4607	18,165
Of other countries	146	11	157
Total	13,704	4618	18,322

2357 ***MINIA UNIVERSITY**

Minia
Telex: 24000 MNUV
Telephone: (086) 324420

President: Mahmoud K. El-Rayes
Secretary-General: Ahmed Fathy Mohamed Kayed

F. of Agriculture (including Animal Husbandry)
Dean: Mokhtar F. Ouf; *staff* 116 (1)
F. of Arts and Human Sciences
Dean: Abd El-Hady Ahmed El-Gohry; *staff* 68 (20)
F. of Education
Supervisor: Hamed El-Abd
F. of Engineering and Technology
Dean: Maher Abdel-Wahab; *staff* 44 (15)
F. of Science
Dean: Omar A. Kamel; *staff* 61 (37)
F. of Physical Education (for boys)
Dean: Faroul E. Abdel Wahab; *staff* 5 (20)
F. of Medicine
Supervisor: Maher M. Kamel; *staff* 27 (18)
F. of Fine Arts
Supervisor: Mohamed Ahmed Nawar
F. of Arabic Studies
Supervisor: Abdel Hamid Ibrahim; *staff* 11

Founded 1976, incorporating Faculties of Agriculture, Education, Humanities, Science, and Engineering, previously forming part of the University of Assiut. A State institution enjoying administrative autonomy. Financed by the government. Governing bodies: the University Council; the Council for Undergraduate Studies; the Council for Graduate Studies and Research. Residential facilities for *c.* 300 academic staff and *c.* 3000 students.

Arrangements for co-operation with the Universities of: Kassel; Debrecen; Glasgow; Newcastle; Gezira; Missouri-Rolla. University of Agriculture, Debrecen.

Academic Year: October to May (October-January; February-May).

Admission Requirements: Secondary school certificate or equivalent.

Fees (Pounds): 4.5-10.50; foreign students, 500-1500.

Languages of Instruction: Arabic and English.

Degrees and Diplomas: Degree of Bachelor in–Agriculture; Science; Physical Education; Education; Arts, 4 yrs; Engineering, 5 yrs; Surgery, 6 yrs. Master in Art and Education, a further 2 yrs. Doctorate by thesis, 2 yrs after Master. Also Diplomas.

Libraries: Central Library, 7191 vols; libraries of the faculties, 126,278.

Publications: Bulletins; Journal of Agricultural Research.

Academic Staff, 1986-87:

Rank	Full-time	Part-time
Professors	54	37
Associate Professors	117	38
Lecturers	197	40
Total	368	115

Student Enrolment, 1986-87:

	Men	Women	Total
Of the country	9285	4108	13,403
Of other countries	113	12	115
Total	9398	4120	13,518

2358 **SUEZ CANAL UNIVERSITY**

Ek-Shik Zaid, Ismailia
Cables: 63297 scu. fm. um.
Telephone: (64) 24009
Fax: 64225176
President: Ahmed Ismail Khudair
Secretary-General: Mohamed Abdel Rahman El-Kady

F. of Commerce (Port Said)
Dean: Ahmed Mohamed Amer; *staff* 34 (46)
F. of Science
Dean: Ezz-Al Din Mohamed; *staff* 44 (96)
F. of Agriculture (including Animal Husbandry)
Dean: Ahmed Shukry; *staff* 67 (23)
F. of Petroleum and Mining Engineering (Suez)
Dean: Saed Mohamed Abdel-Latif; *staff* 45 (6)
F. of Education
Dean: Ahmed Dwidar; *staff* 9 (24)
F. of Medicine (including Pharmacy)
Dean: Essmat Shehata Ezzat; *staff* 52 (42)
F. of Engineering and Technology (Port Said)
Dean: El Sayed Hussein Higazi; *staff* 56 (32)
F. of Veterinary Science
Dean: Abdel Hamid Shalaby; *staff* 6
Marine Research Station (Sharm El-Shikh)
Head: Ahmed Dwidar El-Basiony
Public Service Ce. (Teaching English)
Head: Abdel Khalek Hephny; *staff* 7 (2)
Fish Research Ce:
Head: Samir Ibrahim Ghonim
Saint Catherine Research Ce. (Ecological Studies of Sinai)
Head: Yaser Ammar; *staff* 3
Medical Research Ce
Head: Essmat Azzat; *staff* 30

Founded 1976. A State institution under the supervision of the Ministry of Higher Education. Governing body: the University Council. Residential facilities for academic staff and students.

Arrangements for co-operation with: University of Boston; Iowa State University; Colorado State University; University of Maryland.

Academic Year: September to June (September-January; February-June).

Admission Requirements: Secondary school certificate or equivalent.

Fees (Pounds): 4.5-7.5 per annum; foreign students, 750-1200.

Language of Instruction: Arabic.

Degrees and Diplomas: Bachelor of–Science; Science in Education; Arts in Education; Science in Agriculture, 4 yrs; Engineering; Commerce; Science in Veterinary Science, 5 yrs; Medicine and Surgery, 6 yrs. Master, a further 1-5 yrs. Doctor of Philosophy, Ph.D in–Education; Engineering; Commerce; Agriculture; Veterinary Science; Science. Also postgraduate diplomas.

Libraries: 3630 vols; faculty libraries, total, 52,100.

Press or Publishing House: Press Unit of University.

Academic Staff, 1989: c. 730.

Student Enrolment, 1989: c. 10,300.

2359 ***TANTA UNIVERSITY**

El-Geish, Tanta
Telex: 23605 UN TNA
Telephone: 327928
President: Rafat Mostafa Issa (1991-94)
Secretary-General: Abdel Rahman Hassan

F. of Education
Dean: Mohamed A. Salama; *staff* 135
F. of Arts (Arabic and French Language, History, Geography, Philosophy, Sociology, and Psychology)
Dean: Fauzi Mekawi; *staff* 136
F. of Science
Dean: Mostafa Ahmad El-Sayed; *staff* 277
F. of Engineering
Head: Mohamed El-Adawi Nasef
F. of Medicine
Dean: Mostafa Fahmy Shamloula
F. of Pharmacy
Dean: Mostafa Kamal Yousef; *staff* 37
F. of Dentistry
Dean: Yahia M. El Baghdady; *staff* 98
F. of Commerce
Dean: Shawky E. Khater; *staff* 79
F. of Law
Dean: Yousr Anwar Ali; *staff* 28
I. of Nursing
Director: Fouad K. Harras; *staff* 11
F. of Agriculture
Dean: Abdel Tawab El Yamany; *staff* 244
F. of Education (Kfar El Shiekh)
Dean: Husny El-Bardie; *staff* 95
Also Teaching Hospital and Study Abroad Programmes.

Founded 1975, incorporating faculties attached to the University of Alexandria. A State institution under the supervision of the Ministry of Higher Education. Governing body: the University Council, comprising 17 members. Residential facilities for academic staff and students.

Arrangements for co-operation with the Universities of: Paris; Missouri; Southern Illinois; Tennessee; Glasgow; Cadi Ayyad, Marrakech; Ankara.

Academic Year: October to June.

Admission Requirements: Secondary school certificate or equivalent.

Fees: None.

Languages of Instruction: Arabic and English.

Degrees and Diplomas: Bachelor of–Arts; Science; Law; Agriculture; Commerce; Science in Education; Arts in Education, 4 yrs; Pharmacy; Dentistry, 5 yrs; Medicine and Surgery, 6 yrs. Master, a further 1-6 yrs. Doctor of–Philosophy; Law; Medicine; Dentistry; Arts. Also Diplomas in–Education; Commerce; Law, 2 yrs.

Libraries: Faculty libraries: 134,213 vols in Arabic; 84,592 in other languages.

Publications: Bulletin (monthly); Tanta University Mirror (quarterly); Annual Report; Commerce and Finance (biannually).

Academic Staff, 1989-90:

Rank	Full-time
Professors	250
Assistant Professors	242
Instructors	474
Assistant Instructors	690
Tutors	386
Total	2042

Student Enrolment, 1989-90: 4560.

2360 ***ZAGAZIG UNIVERSITY**

Zagazig
Telex: 92860 ZU UN
Telephone: 747875
President: Mohamed Abdel-Latif (1983-87)

F. of Commerce
F. of Education
F. of Agriculture
F. of Veterinary Medicine
F. of Arts
F. of Law
F. of Science
F. of Medicine
F. of Pharmacy
F. of Engineering
F. of Physical Education (for boys)
F. of Physical Education (for girls)
F. of Commerce (Benha)
F. of Education (Benha)
F. of Arts (Benha)
F. of Medicine (Benha)
F. of Science (Benha)
F. of Veterinary Medicine (Benha)
F. of Engineering (Shoubra)
F. of Agriculture (Moshtohor)
I. of Production Technology
Computer Ce.

Founded 1974, incorporating faculties previously forming part of Ain Shams University. A State institution under the supervision of the Ministry of Higher Education.

Arrangements for co-operation with the Universities of: California; New York City; Maryland; Connecticut; Halle-Wittenberg; Trieste; Southampton; Saint-Etienne.

Academic Year: October to May (October-January; January-May).

Admission Requirements: Secondary school certificate or equivalent.

Fees: None.

Languages of Instruction: Arabic, English, and French.

Degrees and Diplomas: Bachelor of–Science, B.Sc.; Arts, B.A., 4-6 yrs. Master of–Science, M.Sc.; Arts, M.A., a further 2-4 yrs. Ph.D., 3 yrs after Master. Also Diploma.

Libraries: Central Library; libraries of the faculties.

Special Facilities (Museums, etc.): Museum Tell Basta (Arts).

Publication: Scientific Journals.

Academic Staff: c. 2240.

Student Enrolment: c. 67,870.

2361 ***THE AMERICAN UNIVERSITY IN CAIRO**

113 Sharia Kasr El-Aini, P.O.Box 2511, Cairo
Cables: victorious
Telex: 92224 AUCAI UN
Telephone: (2) 3542964
Fax: 2 355-7565

President: Donald McDonald (1990-)

Vice-President for Academic Affairs: George H. Gibson

D. of Economics, Political Science, and Mass Communication
Chairman: Heba Handoussa; *staff* 22 (18)

D. of English and Comparative Literature
Chairman: Doris Shoukri; *staff* 34 (2)

D. of Sociology, Anthropology and Psychology
Chairman: Soraya Altarki; *staff* 13 (19)

D. of Engineering
Chairman: Adel Aly; *staff* 10 (6)

D. of Science
Chairman: Salah Arafa; *staff* 17 (21)

Ce. of Management Studies
Center Director: Farouk Hitami; *staff* 12 (10)

English Language I.
Director: Salah El-Araby; *staff* 34 (1)

Social Research Ce.
Director: Laila El-Hamamsy; *staff* 12

D. for Commercial and Industrial Training
Director: Robert Younghouse; *staff* 29 (95)

Desert Development Demonstration and Training Ce.
Director: Adli Bishay; *staff* 4 (2)

Ce. for Arabic Studies
Director: Bernard O'Kane; *staff* 12 (12)

Arab Language I.
Director: Aloa El Gibali; *staff* 16 (9)

D. of Computer Sciences
Chairman: Mikhail Mikhail; *staff* 4 (6)

D. of Public Service (Non-degree courses in English, French, German, Communications, Administration, Social Studies, Typing, Shorthand, and Data Processing)
Director: Robert Brown; *staff* – (237)

Founded 1919. Independent of government connections in both Egypt and the U.S.A., although incorporated in Washington D.C. Income from foundations, endowments, gifts, grants, and tuition fees. Governing body: a self-perpetuating American Board of Trustees. Residential facilities for full-time foreign academic staff and for students.

Arrangements for co-operation with the Universities of: California; Pennsylvania (State); Massachussetts; Washington. Duke University; Georgetown University; St. Thomas College; Macalaster College, Minnesota; Cornell University; Brown University; University of the Pacific; Williams College.

Academic Year: September to June (September-January; February-June).

Admission Requirements: Secondary school certificate acceptable to the University.

Fees (US$): 3400 per semester; Summer session, 1700.

Language of Instruction: English.

Degrees and Diplomas: Bachelor of–Arts in–Anthropology; Egyptology; Arabic Studies; Economics; English and Comparative Literature; Mass Communication; Middle Eastern History; Middle East Studies; Political Science; Psychology; Sociology; Business Administration, 4 yrs; Science in–Chemistry; Computer Sciences; Materials Engineering; Mathematics; Physics; Industrial Engineering; Design Engineering; Mechanical Engineering, 5 yrs. Master of–Arts; Science; Business Administration; Public Administration, a further 2 yrs. Also Diplomas and certificates.

Libraries: Central Library, 210,000 vols; K.A.C. Cresswell Collection of Islamic Art and Architecture, 10,000.

Publications: Cairo Papers in Social Science (five times a year); Middle East Management Review (quarterly); ALIF: Journal of Comparative Poetics (annually); Quarterly Newsletter.

Press or Publishing House: American University in Cairo Press.

Academic Staff, 1989-90:

Rank	Full-time	Part-time
Professors	55	–
Associate Professors	42	–
Assistant Professors	34	–
Instructors	124	–
Total	255	156

Student Enrolment, 1989-90:

	Men	Women	Total
Of the country	1173	1271	2444
Of other countries	438	475	913
Total	1611	1746	3357

Other Institutions

Technical Education

2362 **INSTITUTE OF AUTOMOTIVES**

Wadi Hoaf, Cairo

Degrees and Diplomas: Diploma, 2 yrs.

2363 **CHEMICAL INSTITUTE**

Shoubra, Cairo

Degrees and Diplomas: Diploma, 2 yrs.

2364 **INSTITUTE OF CONSTRUCTION**

Mattariya

Degrees and Diplomas: Diploma, 2 yrs.

2365 **INSTITUTE OF ELECTRONICS**

Benha

Degrees and Diplomas: Diploma, 2 yrs.

2366 **INSTITUTE OF INDUSTRIAL STUDIES**

Aswan

Degrees and Diplomas: Diploma, 2 yrs.

2367 **INSTITUTE OF INDUSTRIAL STUDIES**

Sahaffa Street, Cairo

Degrees and Diplomas: Diploma, 2 yrs.

2368 **INSTITUTE OF INDUSTRIAL STUDIES**

Kemb Shizar, Alexandria

Degrees and Diplomas: Diploma, 2 yrs.

2369 **INSTITUTE OF INDUSTRIAL STUDIES**

Kewesna

Degrees and Diplomas: Diploma, 2 yrs.

2370 **INSTITUTE OF INDUSTRIAL STUDIES**

Mattariya

Degrees and Diplomas: Diploma, 2 yrs.

2371 **INSTITUTE OF INDUSTRIAL STUDIES**

Keriesna

2372 **INSTITUTE OF INDUSTRIAL STUDIES**

Port Said

Degrees and Diplomas: Diploma, 2 yrs.

2373 **INSTITUTE OF INDUSTRIAL STUDIES**

Zagazig

Degrees and Diplomas: Diploma, 2 yrs.

2374 **INSTITUTE OF INDUSTRIAL STUDIES**
Naghkamady

2375 **INSTITUTE OF IRRIGATION AND SURVEYING**
Assiut
Degrees and Diplomas: Diploma, 2 yrs.

2376 **INSTITUTE OF IRRIGATION AND SURVEYING**
Gizah, Cairo
Degrees and Diplomas: Diploma, 2 yrs.

2377 **OPTICS INSTITUTE**
Abo - El-Reish, Cairo
Telephone: 847642
Director: Aziz El-Masry Aly
Registrar: Ragab El-Esawy

Optics

Founded 1950. A State institution under the supervision of the Ministry of Higher Education.

Academic Year: October to June.
Admission Requirements: Secondary school certificate.
Fees (Pounds): 12 per annum.
Languages of Instruction: Arabic and English.
Degrees and Diplomas: Diploma, 2 yrs.
Library: Library of Optics Institute, 1500 vols.
Academic Staff, 1989-90: 11 (28).
Student Enrolment, 1989-90:

	Men	Women	Total
Of the country	419	133	552
Of other countries	5	8	13
Total	424	141	565

2378 **TELEVISION TECHNOLOGY INSTITUTE**
Dar El Salam, Cairo
Degrees and Diplomas: Diploma, 2 yrs.

2379 **WOOL TEXTILE AND SPINNING INSTITUTE**
Imbaba, Cairo
Degrees and Diplomas: Diploma, 2 yrs.

Professional Education

2380 **HIGHER INSTITUTE OF CO-OPERATIVES AND AGRICULTURAL GUIDANCE**
Assiut
A private institution.
Degrees and Diplomas: Diploma, 4 yrs.

2381 **INSTITUTE OF AGRICULTURAL CO-OPERATIVE STUDIES**
Shoubra El-Kheima
Degrees and Diplomas: Diploma, 2 yrs.

2382 **HIGHER INSTITUTE OF CINEMA**
Pyramids Road, Gizah, Cairo
A private institution.
Degrees and Diplomas: Diploma, 4 yrs.

2383 **COMMERCIAL TECHNICAL INSTITUTE**
Abbassia
Degrees and Diplomas: Diploma, 2 yrs.

2384 **INSTITUTE OF COMMERCIAL STUDIES**
Alexandria
Degrees and Diplomas: Diploma, 2 yrs.

2385 **INSTITUTE OF COMMERCIAL STUDIES**
Assiut
Degrees and Diplomas: Diploma, 2 yrs.

2386 **INSTITUTE OF COMMERCIAL STUDIES**
Aswan
Degrees and Diplomas: Diploma, 2 yrs.

2387 **INSTITUTE OF COMMERCIAL STUDIES**
Benha
Degrees and Diplomas: Diploma, 2 yrs.

2388 **INSTITUTE OF COMMERCIAL STUDIES**
Beni Sweif
Degrees and Diplomas: Diploma, 2 yrs.

2389 **INSTITUTE OF COMMERCIAL STUDIES**
Damanhour
Degrees and Diplomas: Diploma, 2 yrs.

2390 **INSTITUTE OF COMMERCIAL STUDIES**
Mansoura
Degrees and Diplomas: Diploma, 2 yrs.

2391 **INSTITUTE OF COMMERCIAL STUDIES**
Mattariya
Degrees and Diplomas: Diploma, 2 yrs.

2392 **INSTITUTE OF COMMERCIAL STUDIES**
Port Said
Degrees and Diplomas: Diploma, 2 yrs.

2393 **INSTITUTE OF COMMERCIAL STUDIES**
Roda
Degrees and Diplomas: Diploma, 2 yrs.

2394 **INSTITUTE OF COMMERCIAL STUDIES**
Shebin Al-Kom
Degrees and Diplomas: Diploma, 2 yrs.

2395 **INSTITUTE OF COMMERCIAL STUDIES**
Shoubra
Degrees and Diplomas: Diploma, 2 yrs.

2396 **INSTITUTE OF COMMERCIAL STUDIES**
Sohag

2397 **INSTITUTE OF COMMERCIAL STUDIES**
Sohag
Degrees and Diplomas: Diploma, 2 yrs.

2398 **INSTITUTE OF COMMERCIAL STUDIES**
Tanta
Degrees and Diplomas: Diploma, 2 yrs.

2399 **INSTITUTE OF COMMERCIAL STUDIES**
Zagazig
Degrees and Diplomas: Diploma, 2 yrs.

2400 **HIGHER INSTITUTE OF CO-OPERATIVE AND ADMINISTRATIVE STUDIES**
Mounira, Cairo
A private institution.
Degrees and Diplomas: Diploma, 4 yrs.

2401 **HIGHER INSTITUTE OF DRAMATIC ARTS**
15 El Maahad, El Swissry Street, Zamalek, Cairo
A private institution.
Degrees and Diplomas: Diploma, 4 yrs.

2402 **INSTITUTE FOR HOTEL SERVICE**
Cairo
Degrees and Diplomas: Diploma, 2 yrs.

2403 **INSTITUTE OF SECRETARIAL STUDIES**
Coptic Girls' College, Cairo
Degrees and Diplomas: Diploma, 2 yrs.

2404 **INSTITUTE OF SECRETARIAL STUDIES**
Ramsis Girls' College, Cairo
Degrees and Diplomas: Diploma, 2 yrs.

2405 **INSTITUTE OF MANAGERIAL AND SECRETARIAL STUDIES**
Garden City, Cairo
Branch at Heliopolis
Degrees and Diplomas: Diploma, 2 yrs.

2406 **INSTITUTE FOR MEDICAL ASSISTANTS**
Alexandria
Degrees and Diplomas: Diploma, 2 yrs.

2407 **INSTITUTE FOR MEDICAL ASSISTANTS**
Assiut
Degrees and Diplomas: Diploma, 2 yrs.

2408 **INSTITUTE FOR MEDICAL ASSISTANTS**
Imbaba, Cairo
Degrees and Diplomas: Diploma, 2 yrs.

2409 **INSTITUTE FOR MEDICAL ASSISTANTS**
Mansoura
Degrees and Diplomas: Diploma, 2 yrs.

2410 **INSTITUTE FOR MEDICAL ASSISTANTS**
Tanta
Degrees and Diplomas: Diploma, 2 yrs.

2411 **INSTITUTE FOR MEDICAL ASSISTANTS**
Zagazig
Degrees and Diplomas: Diploma, 2 yrs.

2412 **HIGHER INSTITUTE OF SOCIAL SERVICE**
Alexandria
A private institution.
Degrees and Diplomas: Diploma, 2 yrs.

2413 **INTERMEDIATE INSTITUTE OF SOCIAL SERVICE**
Alexandria
Degrees and Diplomas: Diploma, 2 yrs.

2414 **HIGHER INSTITUTE OF SOCIAL SERVICE**
Aswan
A private institution.
Degrees and Diplomas: Diploma, 4 yrs.

2415 **INTERMEDIATE INSTITUTE OF SOCIAL SERVICE**
Aswan
Degrees and Diplomas: Diploma, 2 yrs.

2416 **INTERMEDIATE INSTITUTE OF SOCIAL SERVICE**
Garden City, Cairo
Degrees and Diplomas: Diploma, 2 yrs.

2417 **HIGHER INSTITUTE OF SOCIAL SERVICE**
Kafr Al Sheikh
Branch at Damanhour
A private institution.
Degrees and Diplomas: Diploma, 4 yrs.

2418 **HIGHER INSTITUTE OF SOCIAL SERVICE**
Cairo
A private institution.
Degrees and Diplomas: Diploma, 4 yrs.

EL SALVADOR

Universities

2419 **UNIVERSIDAD 'ALBERT EINSTEIN'**
Urb. Lomas de San Francisco, Calle Circunvalación, Block L, Lote No. 6, San Salvador
Telephone: 24-3068
Rector: Ricardo Villacorta Benitez

F. of Engineering and Architecture

Founded 1973, first students admitted 1977. A private institution.

Admission Requirements: Secondary school certificate (bachillerato) and entrance examination.

Language of Instruction: Spanish.

Degrees and Diplomas: Professional titles.

2420 **UNIVERSIDAD AMERICANA**
American University of El Salvador
Calle No. 3 Col. La Mascota, Apartado postal (01) 515, San Salvador
Cables: Amschool
Telephone: 23-9691
Rector: Ricardo Gavidia Castro (1982-90)
Secretario General: Rolando Palacios

F. of Sciences and Humanities (including Social Sciences and Education)
Dean: José Mauricio Santamaría; *staff* – (20)

C. of Economics (including Business Administration)
Dean: Genaro Rodas; *staff* – (10)

Founded 1978 as college, acquired present status and title 1982. A private institution recognized by the Ministry of Education and structured as an American university. Governing body: the Board of Directors, comprising 7 members.

Academic Year: August to May (August-December; January-May).

Admission Requirements: Secondary school certificate (bachillerato) and English proficiency examination.

Fees (Colones): 2500 per semester.

Language of Instruction: English.

Degrees and Diplomas: Associate of–Arts; Science, 2 yrs. Bachelor of–Arts; Science, 4 yrs. Licenciado, 5 yrs.

Library: 20,000 vols.

Academic Staff, 1989-90: – (30).

Student Enrolment, 1989-90:

	Men	Women	Total
Of the country	82	39	121
Of other countries	5	8	13
Total	87	47	134

2421 **UNIVERSIDAD AUTÓNOMA DE SANTA ANA**
5a Calle Pte., 28 Santa Ana
Telephone: 40-7023
Rector: Mauricio Abraham Cader
Secretario General: Sergio Amilcar Carranza

F. of Economics
Dean: Federico Calderón Torres; *staff* – (2)

F. of Health Studies
Dean: José Félix Magannña de Paz; *staff* – (27)

F. of Law
Dean: Oscar Armando Aviles Magaña; *staff* – (2)

F. of Science and Humanities
Dean: Martha Eugenia de Guzman; *staff* – (2)

Founded 1982. Governing body: the Consejo Superior Universitario.

Academic Year: February to January (February-July; August-January).

Admission Requirements: Secondary school certificate (bachillerato) and entrance examination.

Fees (Colones): 75 per semester.

Language of Instruction: Spanish.

Degrees and Diplomas: Licenciado in–Business Administration; Law; Psychology; Social Work, 5 yrs. Doctor in–Dental Surgery, 6 yrs;Medicine, 7 yrs. Also teaching qualifications.

Academic Staff, 1990: – (93).

Student Enrolment, 1990:

	Men	Women	Total
Of the country	209	357	566
Of other countries	2	1	3
Total	211	358	569

2422 **UNIVERSIDAD CAP. GENERAL GERARDO BARRIOS**
4a Calle Pte. 207, San Miguel
Telephone: 61-0152
Rector: Dolores Benedicto Saravia

F. of Engineering and Architecture
F. of Economics
F. of Science and Humanities
F. of Law and Social Sciences
F. of Agriculture

Founded 1982.

2423 **UNIVERSIDAD CATÓLICA DE OCCIDENTE**
1a Calle Pte. 32, Santa Ana
Telephone: (503) 41-3217
Fax: (503) 41-2655
Rector: Mons. Marco René Revelo Contreras
Secretario General: Margarito Calderón

F. of Science and Humanities
Dean: Dina del C. Gamero Flores; *staff* 6 (18)

F. of Industrial Engineering
Dean: Mario A. Sánchez; *staff* 1 (6)

F. of Economics
Co-ordinator: Patricia de Ramírez; *staff* 2 (1)

F. of Agricultural Engineering
Co-ordinator: José A. Puig; *staff* 5 (14)

F. of Juridical and Social Sciences
Co-ordinator: Roberto A. Sayes; *staff* – (15)

Human Promotion I.
Director: Mario A. Sánchez; *staff* 1 (6)

Rural Development I.
Director: José A. Puig; *staff* 3 (6)

D. of Distance Education
Director: Castulo A. Hernández; *staff* 1 (10)

Founded 1982 following to the Episcopal Conference of El Salvador agreement. Governing body: the Directive Council.

Arrangements for co-operation with the Universities of: Louisville; Navarra.

Academic Year: February to December (February-June; August-December).

Admission Requirements: Secondary school certificate (bachillerato).

Fees (Colones): 725-975 per semester.

Language of Instruction: Spanish.

Degrees and Diplomas: Licenciado, 5 yrs. Professional titles in Engineering, 5 ½ yrs. Technical Diploma, 3 yrs.

Library: 5000 vols.

Academic Staff, 1990: 14 (96).

Student Enrolment, 1990: 807 (Including 366 Women students).

2424 **UNIVERSIDAD CENTROAMERICANA 'JOSÉ SIMEÓN CAÑAS'**
Apartado postal (01) 168, San Salvador
Cables: Ucasal, Autopista Sur
Telex: 30018 PROCA
Telephone: 24-00-11
Rector:
Secretario General: Mario Cerna Torres

F. of Economics
Dean: Francisco J. Ibisate, S.J.
F. of Industrial Engineering
Dean: Fredy Villalta
F. of Humanities and Natural Sciences
Dean: Armando Oliva

Founded 1965, first students admitted 1966. A private institution. Governing body: the Consejo Superior Universitario.

Arrangements for co-operation with the Universidad Iberoamericana, México.

Academic Year: March to December (March-July; August-December).

Admission Requirements: Secondary school certificate (bachillerato) or equivalent, and entrance examination.

Fees (Colones): Registration, 50; tuition, 250-1000.

Language of Instruction: Spanish.

Degrees and Diplomas: Licenciado in–Philosophy; Letters; Psychology; Sociology; Law; Accountancy; Computer Sciences; Biology and Chemistry; Economics; Business Administration, 5 yrs. Professional titles of–Ténico, 3 yrs; Ingeniero industrial; Ingeniero mecánico; Ingeniero electricista; Ingeniero civil; Ingeniero agronómo; Arquitecto; Químico agrícola, 5 yrs. Maestria in–Business Administration; Theology. Also teaching qualifications.

Library: c. 70,000 vols.

Publications: Revistas: Teología; Ciencias Económicas y Sociales; Administración y Empresas. Boletín.

Press or Publishing House: UCA Imprenta.

Academic Staff, 1986-87: 93 (415).

Student Enrolment, 1986-87:

Men	Women	Total
3345	2529	6074

2425 **UNIVERSIDAD CRISTIANA DE LAS ASAMBLEAS DE DIOS**
27 Calle Ote. 134, San Salvador
Telephone: 25-5046
Rector: Adrián Fernando Archila Morales

F. of Science and Humanities

Founded 1983.

Degrees and Diplomas: Licenciado in Education.

2426 **UNIVERSIDAD DON BOSCO**
3a Avenida Nte. 1403, San Salvador
Telephone: 258878
Rector: Gilberto Aguilar Aviles

F. of Science and Humanities
F. of Engineering

Founded 1983.

2427 **UNIVERSIDAD 'DR. JOSÉ MATÍAS DELGADO'**
Apartado postal 1849, San Salvador
Telex: 20386 UNIDEL SAL
Telephone: 23-4061
Rector: Guillermo Trigueros h. (1982-87)

F. of Law
S. of Liberal and Fine Arts
S. of Applied Arts (including Environmental Design)
S. of Economics
S. of Accountancy
S. of Business Administration and Marketing
S. of Public Administration
S. of Banking Administration
Extension D.

Founded 1977. A private institution. Financed by student fees and private and government grants. Governing bodies: the Board of Trustees; the Consejo de Directores; the Consejo Académico.

Academic Year: January to December (January-June; July-December).

Admission Requirements: Secondary school certificate (bachillerato) or foreign equivalent, and entrance examination. Presentation of original work for School of Applied Arts.

Language of Instruction: Spanish.

Library: Central Library, c. 3500 vols.

Academic Staff: c. 5 (260).

Student Enrolment: c. 2600.

2428 **UNIVERSIDAD DE EDUCACIÓN INTEGRAL**
Avenida España 321, Edificio España, San Salvador

2429 ***UNIVERSIDAD DE EL SALVADOR**
University of El Salvador
Ciudad Universitaria, Final 25 Avenida Norte, San Salvador
Telex: 20794
Telephone: 25-9427
Rector: Juan Tobias
Secretario General: René Mauricio Méndez

F of Medicine (including Nursing)
Dean: Guillermo Rodríguez Pacas; *staff* 714 (678)
F. of Law and Social Sciences
Dean: Oscar de Jesús Zamora; *staff* 26 (31)
F. of Agriculture (including Animal Husbandry)
Dean: Héctor Armando Marroquín Arevalo; *staff* 73 (16)
F. of Science and Humanities (including Education, Psychology, and Library Science)
Dean: Ernesto López Zepeda; *staff* 119 (43)
F. of Engineering (including Architecture)
Dean: Miguel Angel Carballo; *staff* 89 (101)
F. of Chemistry and Pharmacy
Dean: Graciela Chacón Gómez; *staff* 78 (28)
F. of Dentistry
Dean: José Benjamín López Guillén; *staff* 54 (14)
F. of Economics
Dean: María Hortensia Dueñas de García; *staff* 54 (14)
Extension D.
Head: Sandra Rebeca Vásquez de Barraza

Founded 1841, became university 1847. Acquired autonomous status 1950. Governing body: the Asamblea General Universitaria, the Consejo Superior Universitario.

Academic Year: May to March (May-October; October-March).

Admission Requirements: Secondary school certificate (bachillerato) and entrance examination.

Language of Instruction: Spanish.

Degrees and Diplomas: Licenciado in–Laboratory Technology; Dietetics; Health Sciences; Echotechnology; Law and Economics; International Relations; Mathematics; Physics; Chemistry; Engineering (various fields); Accountancy; Biology; Education; Philosophy; Sociology; Psychology; Letters; Journalism; Chemistry and Pharmacy; Economics; Business Administration, 5 yrs. Doctor in–Dentistry; Medicine, 5-7 yrs. Professional titles of–Técnico en Laboratorio clínico; Bibliotecología; Técnico en Diseño de Interiores, 3 yrs; Ingeniero agrónomo zootecnista y fitotecnista; Ingeniero (various fields); Arquitecto, 5 yrs.

Academic Staff, 1986-87: 1148 (821).

Student Enrolment, 1986-87:

	Men	Women	Total
Of the country	9363	22,753	32,122

2430 **UNIVERSIDAD EVANGÉLICA DE EL SALVADOR**
63 Avenida Sur y Pje. 1 No. 138, San Salvador
Telephone: 23-6354
Rector: José Heriberto Alvayero (1987-)
Secretaria: Regina Flores de Pérez Mejia

F. of Medicine
Dean: Hilda Herrera; *staff* 30 (45)
F. of Dentistry
Dean: José Mariano Girón; *staff* 25 (30)
F. of Science and Humanities
Dean: Maragarita Pérez Cruz; *staff* 10 (37)
F. of Engineering (including Architecture)
Dean: Fausto Salvador Anaya; *staff* 3 (25)
F. of Agriculture (including Animal Husbandry)
Dean: Fausto Salvador Anaya; *staff* 2 (27)

Founded 1981. A private, non-profit institution. Governing bodies: the Directorio Ejecutivo, comprising 11 members; the Consejo Académico.

Academic Year: February to November (February-June; August-November).

Admission Requirements: Secondary school certificate (bachillerato) and entrance examination.

Language of Instruction: Spanish.

Degrees and Diplomas: Licenciado in–Education; English Translation and Interpretation; Psychology; Social Work; Nutrition and Dietetics, 4 ½-5 yrs. Professional titles, 5 yrs. Doctor in–Dentistry, 5 yrs; Medicine, 7 yrs. Also teaching qualifications.

Library: Central Library, *c.* 5000 vols.

Publications: Boletín (annually); Revista 'Simiente' (quarterly).

Academic Staff: *c.* 90 (140).

Student Enrolment: *c.* 2040.

2431 **UNIVERSIDAD FRANCISCO GAVIDIA**
Alameda Roosevelt 2937, San Salvador
Telephone: 24-5962
Rector: Adela Cabezas de Rosales

F. of Economics
F. of Social Sciences

Founded 1981.

Admission Requirements: Secondary school certificate (bachillerato) and entrance examination.

Language of Instruction: Spanish.

Degrees and Diplomas: Licenciado in–Business Administration; Economics; Psychology; Education; Social Work; Education; Educational Administration. Teaching qualifications.

2432 **UNIVERSIDAD DE LA PAZ**
9a Calle Ote. y 2a Avenida Norte 618, Edif. San Francisco, San Salvador
Telephone: 22-5980
Rector: José Adalberto Sánchez

In the process of development.

2433 **UNIVERSIDAD LAS AMÉRICAS DE EL SALVADOR**
3a Calle Ote. 111, San Salvador
Telephone: 21-7647
Rector: René Guillermo Mata

F. of Economics
F. of Law and Social Sciences

Founded 1982.

2434 **UNIVERSIDAD LEONARDO DA VINCI**
Avenida Roosevelt 2139, San Salvador
Telephone: 23-6034
Rector: Carlos Benjamin Valiente

F. of Economics

Founded 1981.

Admission Requirements: Secondary school certificate (bachillerato).

Language of Instruction: Spanish.

Degrees and Diplomas: Professional title of Técnico.

2435 **UNIVERSIDAD MODULAR ABIERTA**
3a Calle Pte. 1126, San Salvador
Telephone: 21-9697
Rector: Judith Virginia Mendoza de Draz

F. of Economics
F. of Science and Humanities

Founded 1982. An Open University.

2436 **UNIVERSIDAD NUEVA SAN SALVADOR**
Calle Arce y 23 Av. Sur No. 1243 San Salvado PO BOX. 2596
Telephone: 21-2288
Rector: Rafael Hernan Contreras
Secretario General: José David Grimaldi

F. of Engineering and Architecture
Dean: Oscar Azanudo
F. of Economics
Dean: Enrique Garcia Dubón
F. of Science and Humanities
Dean: Lic. Daniel Alonso Agreda
F. of Law and Social Science
Dean: Ernest Alfredo Parada
F. of Pure and Applied Sciences
Dean: Carlos Rolando Velasquez
F. of Health Sciences
Dean: Jorge Ferrer Denis
F. of Dentistry
Dean: Orlando Ernesto Carpio
F. of Political Science
Dean: Homero Armando Sanchez

Founded 1981.

Academic Year: January to October (January-May; Juin-October).

Admission Requirements: Secondary school certificate (bachillerato) and entrance examination.

Fees (Colones): 125-275 per month.

Language of Instruction: Spanish.

Degrees and Diplomas: Licenciaturas, 5 yrs. Professional title of Técnico, 3 yrs. Doctorado en–Medicine; Dentistry, 5 yrs.

Library: Central Library, 5500 vols.

Publication: Revista Analisis (monthly).

Academic Staff, 1990: 4 (138).

Student Enrolment, 1990:

	Men	Women	Total
Of the country	463	717	1180
Of the countries	8	4	12
Total	471	721	1192

2437 **UNIVERSIDAD OCCIDENTAL DE EL SALVADOR**
6a Avenida Sur 52, Apartado postal 270, Santa Ana
Telephone: 41-0222
Rector: Roberto Molina Castro

F. of Engineering
F. of Economics
F. of Science and Humanities

Founded 1981.

2438 **UNIVERSIDAD DE ORIENTE**
Avenida Gerardo Barrios y 8a C. Pte. 102, San Miguel
Telephone: 61-0542
Rector: Salvador Guerra Hercules

F. of Engineering, Architecture and Agriculture
F. of Science and Humanities
F. of Law and Economics
F. of Health Sciences

Founded 1982.

2439 **UNIVERSIDAD PEDAGÓGICA DE EL SALVADOR**
7a Avenida Nte. 411, San Salvador
Telephone: 22-5052
Rector: Luis A. Aparico
Secretario General: José Antonio Arias Martell

F. of Education
Dean: Etelvina de Palencia; *staff* – (45)

Founded 1982. Governing body: the Junta de Directores.

Academic Year: January to December (January-July; August-December).

Admission Requirements: Secondary school certificate (bachillerato) and entrance examination.

Fees (Colones): Registration, 50; tuition, 20 per class-hour.

Language of Instruction: Spanish.

Degrees and Diplomas: Licenciado in Education, 5 yrs. Teaching qualifications, 3 yrs.

Library: Central Library, 800 vols.

Academic Staff, 1990: – (45).

Student Enrolment, 1990:

	Men	Women	Total
Of the country	277	372	649
Of other countries	–	5	5
Total	277	377	654

2440 **UNIVERSIDAD POLITÉCNICA DE EL SALVADOR**
Boulevard Tutunichapa y 5a Avenida Norte, San Salvador
Telephone: 26-4153
Rector: Romeo Amilcar Rovelo Batres
Secretario General: Carlos Ayala Rodriguez

F. of Engineering and Architecture
Dean: Luis René Villatoro; *staff* 70 (105)
F. of Economics
Dean: José René Cañas; *staff* 20 (62)

Founded 1979. A private institution.

Academic Year: February to December (February-June; August-December).

Admission Requirements: Secondary school certificate (bachillerato) and entrance examination.

Fees (Colones): Registration, 50; tuition, 100 per annum.

Language of Instruction: Spanish.

Degrees and Diplomas: Professional titles, 5 ½ yrs.

Academic Staff, 1986-87: 15 (197).

Student Enrolment, 1986-87:

	Men	Women	Total
Of the country	2950	2300	5250
Of other countries	20	15	35
Total	2970	2315	5285

2441 **UNIVERSIDAD SALVADOREÑA**
Calle San Antonio Abad y Avenida Alvaredo 164, Colonia Buenos Aires, San Salvador
Telephone: 25-8861
Rector: Ricardo Francisco Alfaso Sandoval

F. of Engineering
F. of Economics

Founded 1982.

2442 **UNIVERSIDAD SALVADOREÑA 'ALBERTO MASFERRER' USAM**
19 Avenida Norte, entre 3a Calle Poniente y Alameda Juan Pablo II, San Salvador
Telephone: 21-1136
Fax: 22-8006
Rector: Amilcar Avendaño y Ortíz
Secretaria General: Daysi Carolina M. de Gómez

F. of Medicine and Surgery
Dean: Carlos Uriarte G.; *staff* 10 (50)
F. of Chemistry and Pharmaco-Biology
Dean: Socorro Valdés; *staff* 7 (29)
F. of Dentistry
Dean: José Angel García; *staff* 9 (26)
F. of Veterinary Medicine
Dean: Julio César Castro; *staff* 2 (11)
F. of Law and Social Sciences
Dean: Julio Enrique Acosta; *staff* 7 (29)
I. of Science and Technological Research
Director: Amilcar Avendaño y Ortíz; *staff* 2 (8)
Also 4 Hospitals.

Founded 1979.

Arrangements for co-operation with: Fachhochschule Kempten; Universidad Francisco Marroquín, Guatemala.

Academic Year: February to December (February-June; July-December).

Admission Requirements: Secondary school certificate (bachillerato) and entrance examination.

Fees (Colones): 300 per month; Law and Social Sciences, 125.

Language of Instruction: Spanish.

Degrees and Diplomas: Licenciado, 5-5 ½ yrs. Professional titles, 5 ½-7 ½ yrs.

Library: 4000 vols.

Special Facilities (Museums, etc.): Museo de Anatomía Veterinaria.

Publications: Mammals of El Salvador; Peromyscus Gymnotis (Muridae) from El Salvador; Choeroniscus Godmani; Diaemus Youngi (Phyllostonatidae); In Situ DNA (Hybridization Studies of Rodent and Bat Chromosomes).

Academic Staff, 1989-90:

Rank	Full-time	Part-time
Profesores Titulares	28	143
Profesores Adjuntos	–	2
Instructores	7	–
Total	35	145

Student Enrolment, 1989-90:

	Men	Women	Total
Of the country	793	827	1620
Of other countries	2	–	2
Total	795	827	1622

2443 **UNIVERSIDAD SALVADOREÑA 'BERRY'**
27 Avenida Nte. 1138, San Salvador
Telephone: 25-0854
Rector: Juan Francisco Magaña Abullarade

F. of Economics

Founded 1983.

2444 **UNIVERSIDAD SALVADOREÑA 'ISAAC NEWTON'**
1a Avenida Nte. 838, San Salvador
Telephone: 21-9054
Rector: Francisco Antonio Gómez Benites

F. of Science and Humanities
F. of Economics
F. of Engineering and Architecture

Founded 1982.

2445 **UNIVERSIDAD SANTANECA DE CIENCIA Y TECNOLOGÍA**
2a Planta, Plaza de Vidrio entre 7a y 9a Calle Pte., Santa Ana
Telephone: 41-2399
Rector: Ovidio Antonio Agreda Cardona

F. of Science and Humanities
F. of Economics
F. of Engineering and Architecture

Founded 1982.

2446 **UNIVERSIDAD DE SONSONATE**
2a Avenida Nte. 6-6, Sonsonate
Telephone: 51-0674
Rector: Jesús Adalberto Diaz

F. of Engineering and Natural Sciences
F. of Economics and Social Sciences

Founded 1982.

2447 **UNIVERSIDAD TÉCNICA LATINOAMERICANA**
4a Avenida Norte 2-5, Santa Tecla
Telephone: 28-4775
Rector: Rosen do Mauricio Sermeño Palacios
Secretario General: Francisco A. Carrillo

F. of Engineering
; *staff* – (40)
F. of Economics
; *staff* – (25)
F. of Animal Husbandry
; *staff* – (3)
F. of Social Sciences and Humanities
; *staff* – (15)

Founded 1981.

Academic Year: February to November (February-June; July-November).

Admission Requirements: Secondary school certificate (bachillerato) and entrance examination.

Fees (Colones): 1980 per annum.

Language of Instruction: Spanish.

Degrees and Diplomas: Licenciado, 5 yrs. Professional title of Ingeniero, 5 yrs. Maestría, 2 yrs.

Library: 1800 vols.

Academic Staff, 1990: – (143).
Student Enrolment, 1990:

	Men	Women	Total
Of the country	400	170	570

2448 **UNIVERSIDAD TECNOLÓGICA**

Calle Rubén Darío 1215, Edificio Chaín, San Salvador
Telephone: 22-1173
Rector: Edgar Emilio Zepeda Calderón

D. of Economics
D. of Engineering and Architecture
D. of Humanities and Natural Sciences

Founded 1980. A private institution. Governing body: the Board of Trustees.

Arrangements for co-operation with: University of Notre Dame, Indiana; Francisco Marroquin University, Guatemala.

Academic Year: January to December (January-June; August-December).

Admission Requirements: Secondary school certificate (bachillerato) and entrance examination.

Language of Instruction: Spanish.

Degrees and Diplomas: Licenciado in–Business Administration; Accountancy; Marketing; Insurance; Social Work. Professional titles of–Ingeniería; Arquitectura; Técnico Superior Universitario.

Library: c. 5000 vols.

Academic Staff: c. 25 (130).

Student Enrolment: c. 2820.

2449 **UNIVERSIDAD DEL VENDEDOR SALVADOREÑO**

Boulevard de los Héroes 1421, San Salvador
Telephone: 26-0518
Rector: Alexander Vasquez

In process of development.

Other Institutions

Technical Education

2450 **INSTITUTO TECNOLÓGICO CENTROAMERICANO**

Central American Technical College
Km. 11, Carretera a Santa Tecla, La Libertad
Telephone: 28-06019
Director: Adalberto Díaz Pineda (1981-)

D. of Civil Engineering
D. of Electrical Engineering
D. of Agricultural Engineering
D. of Food Technology
D. of Commerce and Administration
D. of Education
D. of Mechanical Engineering

Founded 1966 under an agreement between the governments of El Salvador and United Kingdom and financially supported by the Ministry of Education. Governing body: the Governing Board.

Academic Year: February to November (February-July; July-November).

Admission Requirements: Secondary school certificate (bachillerato) and entrance examination.

Language of Instruction: Spanish.

Degrees and Diplomas: Diploma, 1 ½-2 yrs.

Library: Central Library, c. 8000 vols.

Academic Staff: c. 60 (40).

Student Enrolment: c. 1850.

2451 **INSTITUTO TECNOLÓGICO DE CHALATENANGO**

Final Calle Morazán, Bo. El Calvario, Chalatenango
Telephone: 35-2126

Agro-Industrial Studies
Business Administration
Health Sciences
Dental Hygiene
Agricultural Engineering
Education

2452 **INSTITUTO TECNOLÓGICO GENERAL FRANCISCO MENÉNDEZ**

29 Calle Ote y 20 Avenida Nte., San Salvador
Telephone: 26-4611

Tourism
Social Work
Architecture Electronics
Industrial Engineering
Mechanical Engineering
Education

2453 **INSTITUTO TECNOLÓGICO DE SAN MIGUEL**

Final 7a Avenida Sur, Bo. San Nicolás, San Miguel
Telephone: 61-316

Business Administration
Agro-Industrial Studies
Hotel Management and Tourism
Social Work
Civil Engineering
Electrical Engineering
Industrial Engineering
Mechanical Engineering
Education
Public Administration
Aquaculture

2454 **INSTITUTO TECNOLÓGICO DE SAN VICENTE**

6a Calle Ote. y 9a Avenida Sur, San Vicente
Telephone: 33-0250

Business Administration
Agricultural Production
Social Work
Education

2455 **INSTITUTO TECNOLÓGICO DE SANTA ANA**

Avenida Santa Ana California y 31 Calle Pte., Santa Ana
Telephone: 41-1132

Business Administration
Social Work
Civil Engineering
Electrical Engineering and Electronics
Industrial Engineering
Mechanical Engineering
Textile Engineering
Education
Public Administration

2456 **INSTITUTO TECNOLÓGICO DE SONSONATE**

25 Calle Pte. y Final Avenida Morazán, Sonsonate
Telephone: 51-0634
Director: Salvador Rafael Morales Meneses

Business Administration
Fishery Production
Health Sciences
Education
Industrial Maintenance
Public Administration
Computer Sciences
Social Work
Electrical Engineering
Agriculture

Founded 1981. Financially supported by the Ministry of Education.

Academic Year: February to November (February-June; July-November).

Admission Requirements: Secondary school certificate (bachillerato) and entrance examination.

Fees (Colones): 325 per semester.

Language of Instruction: Spanish.

Degrees and Diplomas: Professional title of Técnico, 2-3 yrs. Teaching qualification, 3 yrs.

Publication: Producción Agropecuaria (biannually).

Academic Staff, 1990: 8 (35).
Student Enrolment, 1990:

	Men	Women	Total
Of the country	151	164	315

2457 **INSTITUTO TECNOLÓGICO DE USULUTÁN**
Final 7a Calle Ote. y Avenida El Molino, Usulután
Telephone: 62-0406
Director: Juan Bautista Girón (1982-)

D. of Education
Head: Sergio de Jesús Arias
D. of Agricultural Engineering
Head: Cesar Mauricio González
D. of Administration
Head: César Mauricio González

Founded 1982.
Academic Year: February to November (February-June; July-November).
Admission Requirements: Secondary school certificate (bachillerato) and entrance examination.
Fees (Colones): Registration, 70; tuition, 150.
Language of Instruction: Spanish.
Degrees and Diplomas: Professional title of Técnico. Teaching qualifications.
Academic Staff, 1986-87: 419 (200).

2458 **INSTITUTO TECNOLÓGICO DE ZACATECOLUCA**
Calle El Volcán, Zacatecoluca
Telephone: 34-0292

Business Administration
Agricultural Production
Health Sciences
Social Work
Education
Public Administration

ETHIOPIA

Universities

2459 ***ADDIS ABABA UNIVERSITY**
P.O. Box 1176, Addis Ababa
Cables: AA Univ
Telex: 21205
Telephone: 550844
President: Abiy Kifle (1985-)
Academic Vice-President: Mekonnen Dilgassa

F. of Law
Dean: Ato Daniel Haile *staff* 14 (4)
F. of Education
Dean: Seyoum Teferra; *staff* 54 (16)
F. of Medicine (including Pharmacy and Midwifery)
Dean: Asrat Waldeyes; *staff* 82
F. of Science (including Statistics)
Dean: Bisrat Dilnassahu *staff* 134
F. of Technology (including Architecture and Town Planning)
Dean: Negussie Tebeje *staff* 84 (8)
F. of Veterinary Medicine
Dean: Fisseha Tareke; *staff* 36 (10)
C. of Social Sciences (including Political Science and International Relations, Economics, and Administration)
Dean: Tadesse Tamrat; *staff* 101 (10)
Teachers' C.
Dean: Yalew Ingdayehu; *staff* 78
C. of Medicine (Gondar)
Dean: Mallede Maru; *staff* 30
I. of Languages
Dean: Tesfaye Shewaye; *staff* 54 (18)
S. of Pharmacy
Dean: Belachew Desta; *staff* 19
S. of Graduate Studies
Dean: Demissu Gemeda
D. for Lifelong Education
Dean: Abebe Ghedai; *staff* 322 (39)
C. of Agriculture (Awassa)
Dean: Geremew Haile; *staff* 42 (4)
S. of Library Science
Head: Mitiku Ourgay; *staff* 4 (7)
I. of Development Research
Director: Andargachew Tesfaye; *staff* 8 (5)
I. of Ethiopian Studies
Director: Taddese Beyene; *staff* 9
I. of Educational Research
Director: Darge Wole; *staff* 3 (3)

Founded 1961 as Haile Sellassie I University. Incorporating the University College of Addis Ababa, founded 1950; the Imperial College of Engineering, 1953; the Ethio-Swedish Institute of Building Technology, 1954; the Imperial Ethiopian College of Agricultural and Mechanical Arts, 1951; the Public Health College, 1954; and the Theological College of the Holy Trinity, 1960. Present title adopted 1975.

Arrangements for co-operation with the Universities of: Dresden (Technical); Leipzig; Kiev; Vilnius; Michigan State; Warsaw; Strathclyde; Dublin; Stuttgart; Waterloo (Canada); McGill; Khartoum; United Nations, Tokyo.

Academic Year: September to June (September-January; February-June).

Admission Requirements: Secondary school certificate (Ethiopian School Leaving Certificate Examination), or foreign equivalent.

Fees (Birr): 7000; Medicine, 8200.

Language of Instruction: English.

Degrees and Diplomas: Bachelor of–Arts; Science, 4 yrs; Science in Engineering; Law, 5 yrs. Doctor of–Medicine; Veterinary Medicine, 6 yrs.

Library: Total, *c.* 493,000 vols.

Special Facilities (Museums, etc.): Natural Science Museum; Ethiopian Studies Ethnographic Museum.

Publications: Law Journal; Journal of Ethiopian Studies; Ethiopian Journal of Science; Journal of Institute of Development Research; Ethiopian Medical Journal; Journal of Health Development; Journal of Agricultural Science; Journal ofEducation (all biannually).

Press or Publishing House: University Press.

Academic Staff, 1989: c. 900.

Student Enrolment, 1989:

	Men	Women	Total
Of the country	9821	912	10,733
Of other countries	56	9	65
Total	9877	921	10,798

2460 ***ASMARA UNIVERSITY**
P.O. Box 1220, Asmara
Cables: Asmuniv
Telex: 42091
Telephone: (04) 113600/01
President: Tewolde Berhan Gebre Egziabher (1983-)
Registrar: Anna Maria Mariani

F. of Natural Sciences (including Marine Biology)
Dean: Endeshaw Bekele; *staff* 93 (1)
F. of Social Sciences (including Accountancy, Economics, and Management)
Dean: Mebrahtu Negusse; *staff* 72 (9)
F. of Language Studies (English)
Dean: Mohammed Osman Geleway; *staff* 27 (8)
F. of Law
Dean (Acting) Yohannes Behane; *staff* 1 (7)
I. of African Studies
Director: Amanuel Sahle; *staff* 2 (5)
I. of Appropriate Technology
Director: Abraham Amaha; *staff* 2
F. of Arid Zone Agriculture (In process of development)
Extension D.
Co-ordinator: Andeberhan Yemane; *staff* 1 (7)

Founded 1958 as Istituto universitario by the 'Pie Madri della Nigrizia' congregation, became university 1968. Recognized as Catholic university by Holy See 1970. Became a national university under the Commission for Higher Education 1979. Governing body: the University Senate. Residential facilities for academic staff and students from outside Asmara.

Arrangements for co-operation with the Universities of: Rostock; Sassari; Novi Sad.

Academic Year: September to July (September-February; February-July).

Admission Requirements: Secondary school certificate (Ethiopian School Leaving Certificate Examination) or equivalent.

Language of Instruction: English.

Degrees and Diplomas: Bachelor of–Arts in English; Business Administration; Economics; Management; Science in Biology; Science in Mathematics; Science in Chemistry; Science in Physics; Science in Marine Biology; Science in Agriculture, 4 yrs. Also Diploma in–Secretarial Science, 2 yrs; Law, 3 yrs.

Library: c. 67,000 vols.

Publication: Ethiopian Journal of African Studies (biannually).

Academic Staff, 1986-87:

Rank	Full-time	Part-time
Professors	5	–
Associate Professors	10	–
Assistant Professors	18	1
Lecturers	53	45
Assistant Lecturers	98	–
Graduate Assistants	14	–
Sport Instructors	4	–
Total	202	46

Student Enrolment, 1986-87:

	Men	Women	Total
Of the country	1485	147	1632

2461 **ALEMAYA UNIVERSITY OF AGRICULTURE**
P.O. Box 138, Dire Dawa, Harer
Telephone: 05-11-13-99
President: Dejene Makonnen
Academic Vice-President: Asfaw Zelleke

F. of Agriculture
Chairman: Mitiku Haile; *staff* 168
F. of Forestry
hairman: Tesfaye Teshome; *staff* 16
S. of Graduate Studies
Dean: Beyene Chichaibelu
D. of Natural and Social Sciences
Dean: Molla Jemere; *staff* 46
Lifelong Education P.
Co-ordinator: Brook Lemma
Agricultural Research Ce. (Alemaya)
Co-ordinator: Mulat Demeke
Agricultural Research Ce. (Debre Zeit)
Director: Goshu Makonnen
Extension Co-ordination Office
Co-ordinator: Zewdu Kebede
Also research stations and sub-stations at Jijiga, Dire Dawa, Melka Jebdu, Babile, and Akaki.

Founded 1954. Acquired present status 1985. Governing body: the University Senate. Residential facilities for academic staff and students.

Arrangements for co-operation with several universities and international agricultural research centres.

Academic Year: September to July (September-February; February-July).

Admission Requirements: Secondary school certificate (Ethiopian School Leaving Certificate Examination) or equivalent.

Fees (Birr): Foreign students, 7300 per annum.

Language of Instruction: English.

Degrees and Diplomas: Bachelor of Science, B.Sc., 4 yrs. Master of Science, M.Sc., a further 2 yrs. Also Diploma, 2 yrs.

Library: Alemaya University of Agriculture Library.

Publications: Annual Research Reports; Working Papers.

Academic Staff, 1989-90:

Rank	Full-time
Professors	2
Associate Professors	11
Assistant Professors	25
Lecturers	104
Assistant Lecturers	49
Graduate Assistants	12
Technical Assistants	32
Total	235

Student Enrolment, 1989-90:

	Men	Women	Total
of the country	2015	200	2215
of other countries	3	1	4
Total	2018	201	2219

Other Institutions

2462 **AMBO JUNIOR COLLEGE OF AGRICULTURE**
P.O. Box 19, Ambo
Telephone: 59
Dean: Teffera Betru (1986-)

Agriculture

Founded 1931, became Ambo Institute of Agriculture and acquired present status and title 1983. Some residential facilities for academic staff and for all students.

Academic Year: September to July (September-January; February-June).

Admission Requirements: Secondary school certificate (Ethiopian School Leaving Certificate Examination).

Fees: None.

Language of Instruction: English.

Degrees and Diplomas: Diploma, 2 yrs.

Library: 6252 vols.

Academic Staff, 1986-87: 35.

Student Enrolment, 1986-87:

	Men	Women	Total
Of the country	190	10	200

2463 **ARBA MINCH INSTITUTE OF WATER TECHNOLOGY**
P.O. Box 21, Arba Minch

2464 **COLLEGE OF URBAN PLANNING**
P.O. Box 1023, Addis Ababa
Telex: 21 551 NUPI ET
Telephone: (251-1) 55-01-98
Fax: (251-1) 51-05-45
Dean: Gilbert C. Lazar
Administrator: Haïlé Asfaw

Urban Planning
Research Ce.

Founded 1968 with the assistance of the French Technical Co-operation. Under the jurisdiction of the National Urban Planning Institute, Ministry of Urban Development and Housing, as autonomous college since 1985.

Arrangements for co-operation with the Ecole nationale des Travaux publics de l'Etat, Lyon.

Academic Year: October to June (October-January; March-June).

Admission Requirements: Secondary school certificate (Ethiopian School Leaving Certificate Examination).

Fees (US$): Foreign students, 1275-1550 per semester.

Languages of Instruction: French and English.

Degrees and Diplomas: Bachelor, 5 yrs. Diplomas, 3 yrs.

Library: 4000 vols.

Academic Staff, 1989-90: 20 (9)

Student Enrolment, 1989-90:

	Men	Women	Total
Of the country	198	28	226
Of other countries	3	–	3
Total	201	28	229

2465 **DEBRE ZEIT INSTITUTE FOR ANIMAL HEALTH ASSISTANTS**
P.O. Box 34, Debre Zeit
Telephone: 33-84-50
Dean: Fisseha Tareke

D. of Anatomy and Embryology
; *staff* 3
D. of Food Hygiene and Veterinary Public Health
Head: Geressu Birru; *staff* 4
D. of Clinical Studies
Head: Tesfu Kassa; *staff* 8
D. of Pathology and Parasitology
Head: Ketema Shaffo; *staff* 5
D. of Physiology, Biochemistry and Pharmacology
; *staff* 4

D. of Zootechnology
; *staff* 4
Student Enrolment, 1990:

	Men	Women	Total
Of the country	273	20	293

2466 **KOTEBE COLLEGE OF TEACHER EDUCATION**
P.O. Box 31248, Addis Ababa
Dean: Abebe Bezuneh

D. of Ethiopian Language and Literature
Head: Teklu Minas; *staff* 6
D. of English
Head: Derese Edeshaw; *staff* 12
D. of Social Sciences (including Political Science)
Heads: Asnake Ali; Argaw Managdew; Teferi Regassa; *staff* 26
D. of Mathematics
Head: Mezgebu Gezachew
D. of Natural Sciences
Heads: Tilahun Kibret; Bekele Tekola; Biru Tsegaye; *staff* 17
D. of Home Economics
Head: Aziza Abolulahi; *staff* 1 (1)
D. of Physical Education
Head: Sissay Zeleke; *staff* 6
D. of Business Education
Head: Estifanos G. Hawariat; *staff* 3
D. of Production Technology
Heads: Bekele Tezera; Terefe Birke; *staff* 6 (2)
D. of In-Service Education
Head: Amare Bekele; *staff* 1
D. of Instructional Media
Head: Wondimagegnehu Tefera; *staff* 2
D. of Pedagogical Sciences
Head: Abdurahman Mohammed Koram; *staff* 6
D. of Psychology
Head: Redai Birru; *staff* 5 (1)
Ce. for Lifelong Education
Director: Amare Bekele; *staff* 1
Extension D.
Head: Amare Bekele; *staff* 1

Founded 1959 as a section of the Faculty of Education of Addis Ababa University. Detached as separate institution under present title 1969. A State institution under the jurisdiction of the Higher Education Main Department, Ministry of Education. Residential facilities for academic staff and students.

Arrangements for co-operation with Hometon College, Cambridge.

Academic Year: September to June (September-January: January-June).

Admission Requirements: Secondary school certificate (Ethiopian School Leaving Certificate Examination).

Fees (Birr): Foreign students, 5800-7000 per annum.

Language of Instruction: English.

Degrees and Diplomas: Yehuletegna Dereja Temehert Bet Yemastemar Diploma (teaching qualification, secondary level, for grades 7-10),2 yrs; Degree (for grades 11, 12), 4 yrs.

Library: 50,000 vols.

Publications: Newsletter (quarterly); Journal of Kotebe College of Teacher Education (annually).

Academic Staff, 1989-90:

Rank	Full-time	Part-time
Assistant Professors	9	–
Lecturers	59	4
Assistant Lecturers	21	–
Graduate Assistants	10	–
Total	99	4

Student Enrolment, 1989-90:

	Men	Women	Total
Of the country	899	103	1002
Of other countries	2	–	2
Total	901	103	1004*

*Also 1292 external students.

2467 **JUNIOR COLLEGE OF COMMERCE**
P.O. Box 3131, Addis Ababa
Telephone: 51-80-20/21
Dean: Gebre Mariam Gemechu

D. of Commerce
Head: Gebre Marian Gemechu; *staff* 79
D. of Accountancy
Head: Abebe Yitayew; *staff* 12
D. of Secretarial Science and Office Management
Head: Luleseged Zewde; *staff* 17
D. of Purchasing and Supplies Management
Head: Selamawit Ersa; *staff* 10
D. of Banking and Finance
Head: Chemere Emiru; *staff* 8

Founded 1943 as school, acquired present status and title 1978. A State institution under the jurisdiction of the Main Department, Ministry of Education.

Arrangements for co-operation with Saint Lawrence College, Canada.

Academic Year: September to July (September-February; February-July).

Admission Requirements: Secondary school certificate (Ethiopian School Leaving Certificate Examination).

Fees: None.

Language of Instruction: English.

Degrees and Diplomas: Diploma in–Secretarial Sciences; Accountancy; Banking and Finance; Supplies Management, 2 yrs.

Library: c. 15,000 vols.

Publications: Commercial Outlook (annually); Research Bulletin (biannually).

Academic Staff, 1990:

Rank	Full-time
Assistant Professor	2
Lecturers	30
Assistant Lecturers	20
Instructors	8
Graduate Assistants	19
Total	79

Student Enrolment, 1990:

	Men	Women	Total
Of the country	689	389	1078*

*Also 1928 Extension Studies students.

2468 **JIMMA JUNIOR COLLEGE OF AGRICULTURE**
P.O. Box 307, Jimma
Telephone: 110102
Dean: Gashy Habte (1986-)

Agriculture

Founded 1952 as school with American aid, acquired present status and title 1968. A State institution under the jurisdiction of the Commission for Higher Education. Residential facilities for academic staff and students.

Academic Year: September to June (September-January; February-June).

Admission Requirements: Secondary school certificate (Ethiopian School Leaving Certificate Examination).

Language of Instruction: English.

Degrees and Diplomas: Diploma, 2 yrs.

Academic Staff, 1986-87: 28 (5).

Student Enrolment, 1986-87:

	Men	Women	Total
Of the country	256	27	283

2469 **JIMMA HEALTH SCIENCE INSTITUTE**
P.O. Box, Jimma

Medicine

Founded 1983.

2470 **POLYTECHNIC INSTITUTE**
P.O. Box 26, Bahir Dar
Telephone: 200277
Dean: Gebeyehu Ayalew (1986-)
Registrar: Desta Wolde Mariam

D. of Electrical Engineering
Head: Mohammed Adem; *staff* 5
D. of Agricultural Mechanics
Head: Samuel Fikreyesus; *staff* 5

D. of Metallurgy

; *staff* 8

D. of Industrial Chemistry

Head: Ahmed Bushra; *staff* 4

D. of Wood Processing Technology

Head: Abraham Belay; *staff* 4

Founded as school 1963 by the USSR, acquired present status and title 1979. A State institution under the jurisdiction of the Commission for Higher Education.. Residential facilities for academic staff and students.

Academic Year: October to June (October-January; February-June).

Admission Requirements: Secondary school certificate (Ethiopian School Leaving Certificate Examination).

Language of Instruction: English.

Degrees and Diplomas: Diploma, 3 yrs.

Library: 4405 vols.

Academic Staff, 1986-87: 27.

Student Enrolment, 1986-87:

	Men	Women	Total
Of the country	541	28	569

2471 **WONDO GENET FOREST RESEARCH INSTITUTE**

P.O. Box 128, Shashamane

Telephone: 06-100522

Dean: Ato Abera Ashinay

Head of Administration and Finance: Ato Guesh G/Hiwot

D. of Forestry

Head: Sven Sjunnesson

Research and Extension D.

Head: Ato Abraha Loha

Founded 1978 under the jurisdiction of the Ministry of Agriculture. Accredited by the Ministry of Education 1989. Residential facilities for academic staff.

Academic Year: September to July (September-February; March-July).

Admission Requirements: Secondary school certificate (Ethiopian School Leaving Certificate Examination).

Language of Instruction: English.

Degrees and Diplomas: Diploma.

Library: 5000 vols.

Special Facilities (Museums, etc.): Arboretum.

Publication: Acacia Magazine (annually).

Academic Staff, 1989-90: 21.

Student Enrolment, 1989-90:

	Men	Women	Total
Of the country	88	8	96

FINLAND

Universities and University Institutions

2472 ***HELSINGIN YLIOPISTO**

University of Helsinki
Hallituskatu 8, 00100 Helsinki
Telex: 124690 UNIH SF
Telephone: 1911
Fax: 656591
Rehtori: Päiviö Tommila (1988-)
Hallintojohtaja: Timo Esko

F. of Theology
Dean: Eero Huovinen; *staff* 56
F. of Law
Dean: Mikael Hidén; *staff* 81
F. of Medicine (including Dentistry)
Dean: Olli Mäkelä; *staff* 317
F. of Arts
Dean: Arto Mustajoki; *staff* 302
F. of Science (including Pharmacy)
Dean: Antti Siivola; *staff* 475
F. of Education
Dean: Seppo Kontiainen; *staff* 139
F. of Social Sciences (including Economics and Political Science)
Dean: Raimo Väyrynen; *staff* 138
F. of Agriculture and Forestry (including Animal Husbandry)
Dean: Pekka Koivistoinen; *staff* 190
I. of Electron Microscopy
Director: Jorma Wartiovaara; *staff* 12
I. of Seismology
Director: Heikki Korhonen; *staff* 31
I. of Historical Research (Renvall)
Head: Osmo Jussila; *staff* 12
Research I. for Theoretical Physics
Director: Stig Stenholm; *staff* 6
I. of Development Studies
Director: Marja-Liisa Swantz; *staff* 16
I. of Biotechnology
Director: Mart Saarma; *staff* 49
Mathematical Research I.
Head: Olavi Nevanlinna; *staff* 6
Computing Ce.
Director: Lars Backström; *staff* 64
Language Ce.
Director: Eija Ventola; *staff* 75
Ce. for Further Education
Director: Ritva Jakku-Sihvonen *staff* 3
Research and Training Ce. (Lahti)
Head: Seppo Kontiainen; *staff* 93
Further Education I. (Vantaa)
Director: Kauko Hämäläinen; *staff* 21
Ce. for Rural Research and Training (Mikkeli)
Director: Pirjo Siiskonen; *staff* 11
Ce. for Rural Research and Training (Seinäjoki)
Director: Hannu Katajamäki *staff* 13
Also *c.* 200 institutes and departments attached to the different faculties.

Founded 1640 at Turku (Åbo), transferred to Helsinki 1828. An autonomous State institution. The highest official is the Chancellor and the highest governing body the Great Senate (Consistorium Maius), composed of professors holding established chairs. The Small Senate (Consistorium Minus) is composed of the Rector, the two Vice-Rectors and the deans and vice-deans of the faculties. The two bodies are responsible for the general administration of the university which receives the major portion of its income from the State.

Arrangements for co-operation with: Humboldt University of Berlin; Jagiellonian University, Cracow; University of Warsaw; Charles University, Prague; University of Göttingen; University of Sofia; Beijing University; Moscow State University; Academy of Forestry and Wood Technology, Leningrad; University of Forestry and Wood Technology, Sopron; University of Athens; University of Kasetsart, Thailand; University of Copenhagen; La Sapienzia University, Rome; State University of Warsaw.

Academic Year: September to August (September-December; January-May).

Admission Requirements: Secondary school certificate (ylioppilastutkinto) or foreign equivalent.

Fees (Marks): Registration, 12.75.

Languages of Instruction: Finnish and Swedish.

Degrees and Diplomas: First Degrees: Master of–Theology; Laws; Health Care; Arts; Psychology; Science; Science in Pharmacy; Education; Social Sciences; Science in Agriculture and Forestry. Postgraduate Degrees and Doctor: Licenciate in Medecine; Dentistry. Licenciate and Doctor in–Theology; Laws; Medicine; Dentistry; Health Care; Philosophy; Psychology; Pharmacy; Education; Social Sciences; Agriculture and Forestry; Food Sciences.

Libraries: Helsinki University Library, *c.* 2,500,000 vols; Medical library, *c.* 300,000; Agricultural library, *c.* 280,000;Forestry library, *c.* 200,000.

Special Facilities (Museums, etc.): Museums of Zoology, Mineralogy and Botany are parts of Finnish Museum of Natural History; Museums of: Agriculture; Medical History; Coin and Medal Collection; Bird and Mammal Collection.

Publication: Yliopisto. Helsingen yliopiston tiedotuslehti.

Press or Publishing House: University Press.

Academic Staff, 1989:

Rank	Full-time	Part-time
Professori (Professors)	270	–
Apulaisprofessori (Assistant Professors)	177	–
Lehtori (Lecturers)	322	–
Dosentti (Docents)	–	1456
Assistentti (Assistants)	622	
Total	1391	1456

Student Enrolment, 1989:

	Men	Women	Total
Of the country	11,014	15,924	26,938
Of other countries	436	245	681
Total	11,450	16,169	27,619

2473 ***JOENSUUN YLIOPISTO**

University of Joensuu
P.O. Box 111, 80101 Joensuu
Telex: 46223 JOY SF
Telephone: 358-73-1511
Fax: 358-73-151 2050
Electronic mail: savonla@joyl.joensuu.FI; savonla@finujo.EARN; savonla@finujo.BITNET
Rehtori: Paavo Pelkinen (1990-94)
Hallintojohtaja: Matti Halonen

F. of Education
Dean: Simo Seppo; *staff* 107
F. of Arts (including Finnish Language, Literature and Cultural Reaseach, Foreign Languages (English, Swedish, Russian), History, Greek Ortodox Theology)
Dean: Dietrich Assman; *staff* 92
F. of Science (including Mathematics, Biology, Chemistry, Computer Sciences, Geography, and Physics)
Dean: Seppo Pasanen; *staff* 196
F. of Social Sciences (including Economics, Social Policy, Sociology, Psychology, and Regional Planning)
Dean: Mikko A. Salo; *staff* 56
F. of Forestry
Vice-Dean: Kim von Weissenberg; *staff* 69
Savonlinna S. of Translation Studies (English, German, Russian)
Director: Pauli Roinila: *staff* 38

Savonlinna D. of Teacher Education
Director: Kyösti Väänänen; *staff* 80
Language Ce.
Director: Marga Margelin; *staff* 15
Computing Ce.
Director: Laase Katajavuori; *staff* 23
Extension Studies Ce.
Director: Seppo Sivonen *staff* 38
Karelian Research I. (including Ecology, Humanities, and Social Sciences)
Director: Ilkka Savijärvi; *staff* 81
Mekrijärvi Research Station (including Hydrobiology, and Limnology)
Director: Jorma Aho; *staff* 19

Founded 1969. Acquired present status 1984. An autonomous State institution under the supervision of the Ministry of Education. Governing body: the University Senate.

Arrangements for co-operation with: Petrozavodsk State University; Ernst Moritz Arndt University of Greifswald; University of Economics, Berlin; University of Umeå; University of Gothenburg; University of Minnesota, Duluth; Iowa State University; York University

Academic Year: September to May (September-December; January-May).

Admission Requirements: Secondary school certificate or equivalent (ylioppilastutkinto). Knowledge of Finnish or English.

Fees: None.

Languages of Instruction: Finnish and other languages.

Degrees and Diplomas: Master of–Arts; Science; Education; Psychology; Social Sciences; Science in Agriculture and Forestry, 6 yrs. Licenciate, a further 2-3 yrs. Doctor, a further 2-3 yrs. Also teaching diplomas.

Library: University Library, *c.* 600,000 vols (The Kalevala Collection).

Publications: Joensuun yliopisto julkaisuja, Sarja A, Sarja B1, Sarja B11 (University publications, Series A, B1, B11, 2-4 times a year); Sanansaattaja Joensuusta (newsletter).

Press or Publishing House: Joensuun yliopiston monistukeskus

Academic Staff, 1989-90:

Rank	Full-time	Part-time
Professori (Professors)	29	
Apulaisprofessori (Associate Professors)	37	
Dosentti		98
Lehtori (Lecturers)	113	
Yliassistentti	15	
Assistentti (Assistants)	35	
Instructors	86	
Total	315	98

Student Enrolment, 1989-90:

	Men	Women	Total
Of the country	1759	2956	4715
Of other countries	9	7	16
Total	1768	2963	4731*

*Also 313 external students.

2474 ***JYVÄSKYLÄN YLIOPISTO**
University of Jyväskylä
Seminaarinkatu 15, 40100 Jyväskylä
Telex: (LIBRARY): 28219
Telephone: (358 41) 601-211
Fax: (358 41) 601-021
Rehtori: Antti Tanskanen (1988-91)
Hallintojohtaja: Juho Hukkinen

F. of Education (including Teacher Training and Special Education)
Dean: Seppo Hämäläinen; *staff* 124 (40)
F. of Social Sciences (including Sociol Policy, Sociology, Philosophy, Economics, Business Administration, Political Science, Computer Science and Statistics)
Dean: Marjatta Marin; *staff* 90 (43)
F. of Humanities (including Foreign Languages, History, Literature Musicology, Music Education, Music Therapy, Art History, Art Education, Ethnology, Applied Linguistics and Speech Science)
Dean: Jorma Ahvenainen: *staff* 141 (29)
F. of Mathematics and Natural Sciences
Dean: Jorma Korvola: *staff* 117 (19)
F. of Sport and Health Sciences (including Physiotherapy)
Dean: Pauli Vuolle; *staff* 53 (10)
Educational Research I.
Director: Jouko Kari; *staff* 55
Language Ce.
Director: Maisa Martin; *staff* 26
Ce. for Economic Research
Director: Tuomo Nenonen; *staff* 16
Language Ce. for Finnish Universities
Director staff 14
Computer Ce.
Director: Eero Blåfield; *staff* 29
Further Education Ce.
Director: Kari Eklund; *staff* 80

Founded 1863 as a Teacher Training College, became College of Education 1934 and acquired present status and title 1966. An autonomous State institution under the supervision of the Ministry of Education. Governing body: the University Senate, comprising 17 members. Residential facilities for students.

Academic Year: August to July (September-December; January-May; June-July).

Admission Requirements: Secondary school certificate (ylioppilastutkinto) or foreign equivalent, and entrance examination.

Fees: None.

Languages of Instruction: Finnish and Swedish.

Degrees and Diplomas: Maisteri in–Philosophy; Economics; Physical Education; Education; Social Sciences; Psychology, 5-6 yrs. Lisensiaatti in–Education; Social Sciences; Philosophy; Economics; Psychology; Physical Education, 7-8 yrs. Tohtori, Doctorates, in–Education; Social Sciences; Philosophy; Physical Education; Economics; Psychology, by thesis.

Libraries: Central Library, 900,000 vols; department libraries, *c.* 250,000.

Special Facilities (Museums, etc.): University Museum; University Botanical Garden; Konnevesi Biological Research Station.

Publications: Kasvatus (periodical); Studies in: Computer Science, Economics, and Statistics; History; Philology; Education;Psychology and Social Research; Sport, Physical Education and Health; Arts; Biological Research Report.

Press or Publishing House: University Publishing Centre.

Academic Staff, 1989-90:

Rank	Full-time	Part-time
Professori	56	–
Apulaisprofessori	59	–
Dosentti	–	173
Lehtori	170	–
Yliassistentti	35	–
Assistentti	109	–
Päätoiminen tuntiopettaja	69	–
Total	498	173

Student Enrolment, 1989-90:

	Men	Women	Total
Of the country	2685	4899	7584
Of other countries	61	31	92
Total	2746	4930	7676*

*Also 263 external students.

2475 ***KUOPION YLIOPISTO**
University of Kuopio
POB 6, 70211 Kuopio 21
Telex: 42218 KUY SF
Telephone: (971) 162211
Fax: (971) 163410
Electronic mail: Internet, EARN/BITNET, DECnet
Rehtori: Ossi V. Lindqvist (1990-94)
Hallintojohtaja: Tuomo Teittinen

F. of Natural Sciences and Environmental Sciences
Head: Pentti Kalliokoski; *staff* 49
F. of Medicine
Dean: Rauno Mäntyjärvi; *staff* 93
F. of Dentistry
Dean: Heikki Luoma; *staff* 30
F. of Pharmacy
Dean: Petteri Paronen; *staff* 34
F. of Social Sciences (including Nursing)
Dean: Sirkka Sinkkonen; *staff* 22
Public Health Research I.
Head: Jukka T. Salonen
Language Ce.
Head: Maija Metsämäki; *staff* 4

Computer Ce.
Head: Yrjö Jokinen; *staff* 6
Ce. for Training and Development
Head: Saara Lampelo
National L. Animal Ce.
Head: Timo Nevalainen
Veterinary Research Station
Head: Maija Valtonen

Founded 1966. Admitted first students 1972. Acquired present status 1984. An autonomous State institution under the supervision of the Ministry of Education. Governing body: the Hallitus (Administrative Council), comprising 18 members.

Arrangements for co-operation with the Universities of Alaska; California; Minnesota; Craiova; Jena; Ioannina; Pecs; Tartu; Debrecen; Cincinatti. Pedagogic Institute, Tallin; Medical Academy, Moscow; Geological Institute, Estonia; Pavlov Medical Institute, Leningrad; Moscow Stomatological Institute; Institute of Nuclear Chemistry and Technology, Warsaw. Also participates in the NORDPLUS programme with 9 Scandinavian Institutions.

Academic Year: August to July (August-December; January-May).

Admission Requirements: Secondary school certificate (ylioppilastutkinto) and selection according to examination results.

Fees: None.

Language of Instruction: Finnish.

Degrees and Diplomas: Kandidaatti in–Natural Sciences; Social Sciences; Health, Care, 4 yrs., Pharmacy, 5 yrs. Lisensiaatti in–Dentistry, 5 yrs.; Medicine, 6 yrs. Doctorates in–Medicine; Dentistry; Philosophy; Pharmacy; Health Administration; Social Sciences, by thesis. Also Diploma in Pharmacy, 2 ½ yrs.

Library: Central Library, *c.* 150,000 vols.

Special Facilities (Museums, etc.): Botanical Garden

Publications: University publications on: Administration; Community Health; Natural Sciences; Medicine; Social Sciences.

Academic Staff, 1989-90:

Rank	Full-time	Part-time
Professori	48	1
Apulaisprofessori	32	–
Dosentti	–	206
Osastonhammaslääkäri	6	–
Apulaisopettaja	29	–
Lehtori	20	–
Yliassistentti	30	–
Assistentti	66	–
Total	231	207

Student Enrolment, 1989-90:

	Men	Women	Total
Of the country	1155	2093	3194
Of other countries	19	13	32
Total	1174	2052	3226

2476 ***LAPIN KORKEAKOULU**

University of Lapland
Box 122, 96101 Rovaniemi
Telex: 37130 LAPKO SF
Telephone: 960-3241
Fax: 35860-324207
Rehtori: Esko Riepula (1979-93)
Hallintojohtaja: Juhani Lillberg

D. of Law
Head: Ilkka Saraviita; *staff* 37 (3)
D. of Education
Head: Juhani Puro; *staff* 41 (6)
D. of Social Sciences (including Economics and Business Administration)
Head: Teuvo Pohjolainen; *staff* 24 (5)
Language Ce.
Director: Birgitta Vehmas; *staff* 9 (3)
Arctic Ce.
Director: Veijo Ilmavirta; *staff* 10 (3)
D. of Art
Head: Pirkko Seitamaa-Oravala; *staff* 5 (10)
I. for Nordic Law
Head: Terttu Utriainen; *staff* 4 (4)
Ce. for Further Education
Director: Seppo Aho; *staff* 14 (15)

Also teacher training school.

Founded 1979. A State institution. Residential facilities for students.

Arrangements for co-operation with: University of Iceland; University of Miscolo; Lakehead University; University of Stockholm (NORDPLUS).

Academic Year: August to July (August-December; January-May).

Admission Requirements: Secondary school certificate (ylioppilastutkinto) or equivalent.

Languages of Instruction: Finnish and some English.

Degrees and Diplomas: Maisteri in–Education; Administration; Social Sciences, 4-5 yrs; Laws, 5 yrs. Lisensiaatti. Tohtori, Doctorates.

Library: 85,000 vols.

Publications: Faculty Publications; Guides.

Academic Staff, 1989-90:

Rank	Full-time
Professori	17
Apulaisprofessori	11
Lehtori	36
Assistentti	21
Total	95

Student Enrolment, 1989-90: 1466.

2477 ***OULUN YLIOPISTO**

University of Oulu
Kirkkokatu 11A, 90191 Oulu 10
Telex: 32375-OYLIN SF
Telephone: 358-81-222700

F. of Arts
F. of Science
F. of Medicine (including Dentistry)
F. of Technology (including Architecture)
F. of Education
I. of Data Processing
I. of Electron Optics
Research I. of Northern Finland
Language Ce.

Founded 1958. An autonomous State institution under the supervision of the Ministry of Education. Governing bodies: the Consistory; the Administrative Board. Residential facilities for *c.* 2500 students.

Arrangements for co-operation with: University of Ljubljana; Technical University of Gdańsk; Odessa State University.

Academic Year: August to July (September-December; January-May).

Admission Requirements: Secondary school certificate (ylioppilastutkinto) and selection according to examination results.

Language of Instruction: Finnish.

Degrees and Diplomas: Kandidaatti of–Education, KK, 4 yrs; Philosophy, FK; Social Sciences, 5 yrs. Professional title in Architecture, ArKK, 5 yrs. Lisensiaatti in–Dentistry, HLL; Social Sciences; Education, KL; Medicine, LL, 7 yrs; Philosophy, FL; Engineering, TkL, 7-8 yrs. Maisteri in–Science in Engineering, DI, 5-6 yrs. Tohtori, Doctorate in–Philosophy, FT; Technology, TkT; Education, KT; Medicine and Surgery, LKT; Dentistry, HLT, by thesis.

Libraries: Central Library, 537,000 vols; department libraries, 463,000.

Special Facilities (Museums, etc.): Museums: Zoology; Botany; Geology.

Publication: Acta Universitatis Oulunis.

Academic Staff: c. 750 (190).

Student Enrolment: c. 7270.

2478 ***TAMPEREEN YLIOPISTO**

University of Tampere
Kalevantie 4, P.O. Box 607, 33101 Tampere 10
Telex: 22263 TAYKSF
Telephone: 31-156111
Rehtori: Tarmo Pukkila (1987-93)
Hallintojohtaja: Timo Lahti

F. of Social Sciences (including Economics, International Relations, Library and Information Science, Political Science, Psychology, Journalism and Mass Communication)
Dean: Seppo Randell; *staff* 85 (11)
F. of Humanities (including Literature, Folk Tradition, Finnish Language, English and German Philology; Nordic (Swedish) and Slavonic (Russian) Philology, Finnish and General History, English, German and Russian Translation and Interpretation)
Dean: Timo Leisio; *staff* 112 (15)

F. of Economics and Administration (including Business Administration, Computer Science, Municipal Sciences, Philosophy, Private and Public Law, Statistics)
Dean: Portti Järvinen; *staff* 98 (10)
F. of Medicine
Dean: Amos Pasternack; *staff* 104 (15)
F. of Education (including Adult Education)
Dean: Reijo Raivola; *staff* 52 (15)
Sec. for Vocational Studies (Journalism, Public Administration and General Insurance)
Head: Aatto Josiaisluoma; *staff* 29 (3)
Social Sciences Research I.
Director: Ari Ylönen; *staff* 15 (1)
I. of Speech Studies
Director: Timo Leino; *staff* 11 (1)
Computer Ce.
Director: Tauno Kankaanoää; *staff* 20 (1)
Language Teaching Ce.
Director: Liisa Löfman; *staff* 37 (7)
I. of Extension Studies
Director: Matti Parjanen; *staff* 21 (7)

Founded 1925 as private vocational school in Helsinki, became School of Social Sciences 1930 and transferred to Tampere 1960. Formerly known as Yhteiskunnallinen korkeakoulu. Acquired present status and title 1966. An autonomous institution until August 1974, financed by the State 75%, by the city of Tampere 20%, and by students' fees 5%. Subsequently under the supervision of the Ministry of Education and entirely financed by the State. Governing bodies: the Hallitus (University Council); the Valtuusto (Board). Residential facilities for 4500 students.

Arrangements for co-operation with: University of Łódź; Charles University, Prague; Kiev State University; Karl Marx University, Leipzig; Erasmus University, Rotterdam; Martin Luther University, Halle Wittenberg; University of Skopje; University of Havana; Instituto Superior Politecnico 'Jose A. Echeverria', Cuba; University of Porto; Medical University of Szeged; Ahamadu Bello University, Nigeria; United Nations University of Peace; Syracuse University; Tartu University; University of Maryland. Also arrangements for student exchange with the Universities of: West Florida; Manchester; Sheffield; Kent at Canterbury; Oregon; Virginia Polytechnic Institute and State University. Also participates in the COMETT II and NORDPLUS programmes.

Academic Year: August to July (September-December; January-May).

Admission Requirements: Secondary school certificate (ylioppilastutkinto) or foreign equivalent, and entrance examination.

Fees: None.

Languages of Instruction: Finnish and some English.

Degrees and Diplomas: Kandidaatti of–Theater Arts, teatt.tait.kand., 4 yrs.; Education, kasvat.kand; Philosophy, fil.kand; Social Sciences, yht.kand.; Psychology, psyk.kand; Economic Sciences, taloustiet.kand.; Administrative Science, hallintot.kand.; Science, fil.kand.; Health Care, terv.h.kand., 5-7 yrs.Lisensiatti of–Education, kasvat.lis; Philosophy, fil.lis; Social Sciences, yht.lis.; Psychology, psyk.lis; Economic Sciences, taloustiet.lis.; Administrative Science, hallintot.lis.; Science, fil.lis.; Health Care, terv.h.lis., 3-4 yrs. Medicine, Lääket.lis, 6 yrs. Doctorates, Tohtori, in all fields except Theater Arts, 3-4 yrs. Also professional titles in vocational departments.

Library: Total, 1,013,000 vols.

Special Facilities (Museums, etc.): Folk Music Instruments.

Publication: Acta Universitatis Tamperensis (Tampereen yliopiston julkaisusarja).

Press or Publishing House: Tampereen Yliopisto Jäljennepalvelu.

Academic Staff, 1989:

Rank	Full-time	Part-time
Professori	77	–
Apulaisprofessori	65	–
Dosentti	–	319
Yliopettaja/lehtori	165	–
Apulaisopettaja	30	–
Yliassistentti	30	–
Assistentti	99	–
Tuntiopettaja	51	94
Total	523	413

Student Enrolment, 1989:

	Men	Women	Total
Of the country	4203	6644	10,847
Of other countries	67	25	92
Total	4270	6669	10,939*

*Also 3463 external students.

2479 ***TURUN YLIOPISTO**

University of Turku
20500 Turku
Telephone: (921) 633-51
Fax: (921) 633-6220
Rehtori: Arne Rousi (1987-93)
Hallintojohtaja: Esko Välimäki

F. of Arts (including Finnish and General Linguistics, Philology and Translation Studies)
Dean: Kalervo Hovi; *staff* 148
F. of Social Sciences (including Political Studies and Sociology, Economics and Social Policy, Philosophy and Statistics, and Psychology)
Dean: Juhani Pietarinen *staff* 68
F. of Mathematics and Natural Sciences
Dean: Pentti Yli-Jokipii; *staff* 280 (1)
F. of Medicine (including Dentistry and Nursing)
Dean: Pekka Halonen; *staff* 540 (1)
F. of Education
Dean: Erkki Lahdes; *staff* 179
F. of Law
Dean: Olli Mäenpää; *staff* 540 (1)
Wihuri Physical L. (Low Temperature Physics)
Head: Reino Laiho
Archipelago Research I.
Head: Tapani Juusti
Cardiorespiratory Research Ut.
Head: Ilkka Välimäki
Subarctic Research Ce. (Lapland)
Head: Matti Sulkinoja
Ce. for Maritime Studies
Head: Juhani Vainio
Computer Ce.
Head: Heikki Aalto
Satakunta Environmental Research Ce.
Head: Erkki Haukioja
Research Ut. for the Sociology of Education
Director: Osmo Kivinen
Language Ce.
Head: Väqätäjä
Ce. for Extension Studies
Head: Martti Julkunen

Also Turku University Central Hospital and Eastern European Studies Programme.

Founded 1920 as a private institution on the initiative of the Finnish University Society. Inaugurated 1922. Became State institution 1974 under the supervision of the Ministry of Education. Governing bodies: the University Senate, comprising 30 members; the Executive Board, comprising 13 members.

Arrangements for co-operation with: Leningrad State University; University of Gdańsk; József Attila University, Szeged; Albert Szent-Györgyi University, Szeged, University of Rostock; Universities of Aix-Marseille; Tartu University; University of Catania; University of Toronto; USSR Academy of Sciences; Estonian Academy of Sciences; Institute of Experimental Physics, Kosice; Tohoku University. Also participates in the NORDPLUS programme.

Academic Year: September to May (September-December; January-May). Summer school for about 6 weeks June-July.

Admission Requirements: Secondary school certificate (ylioppilastutkinto) or foreign equivalent, and entrance examination.

Fees: None.

Language of Instruction: Finnish.

Degrees and Diplomas: Basic Degrees: Kandidaatti of–Arts, filosofian kand., FK; Sciences, filosofian kand., FK; Health Care, terveydenhulllon kand., THK; Law, oikeustieteen kand, OTK; Social Sciences, valtiotieteen kand., VTK; Psychology, psykologian.kand., PsK; Education, kasvatustieteiden kand., KK, 4-6 yrs. Lisensiaatti of–Medicine, lääketieteen lis., LL; Postgraduate degrees: Lisensiaatti in–Philosophy, filosofian lis., FL; Health Care, terveydenhuollon lis., FL; Law, oikeustieteen lis., OTL; Social Sciences, valtiotiteen.lis., VTL; Psychology, psykologian lis.,PsL. Doctor of–Philosophy, filosofian toh., FT.; Law, oikeustieteen toh., OTT; Medicine, lääketieteen.toh.; Dentistry, hammaslàa4äketieteen toh.,HLT; Health Care; terveydenhuollon toh., THT; Education, kasvatustieteiden toh., KL; Psychology, psykologian.toh., PsT; Law, oikeustieteen toh., OTT; Social Sciences, valtiotieteen toh., VTT.Also diploma in Law, 2-3 yrs.

Library: Central Library, *c.* 1,700,000 vols.

Special Facilities (Museums, etc.): Vanhalinna Museum (Archaeological and Ethnological Collections); Nordic Institute of Folklore; Syntax Archives; Tuorla Obervatory; Botanical Garden; Herbarium; Zoological Museum; Learning Disability Clinic.

Publications: Turun Yliopiston Julkaisuja, Annales Universitatis Turkuensis; Sarja-Ser. AI: Astronomica, Chemica, Physica, Mathematica; Sarja-Ser. AII: Biologica, Geographica-Geologica; Sarja-Ser.B: Humaniora; Sarja-Ser.C: Scripta Lingua Fennica Edita; Sarja-Ser.D: Medica Odontologica; Information Magazine.

Academic Staff, 1989:

Rank	Full-time	Part-time
Professori (Professors)	108	2
Apulaisprofessori (Associate Professors)	101	–
Lehtori (Lecturers)	230	–
Apulaisopettaja (Instructors)	46	–
Assistentti (Assistants)	222	–
Dosentti	–	479
Total	707	481

Student Enrolment, 1989:

	Men	Women	Total
Of the country	4217	6553	10,770
Of other countries	32	8	40
Total	4249	6561	10,810

2480 ***VAASAN KORKEAKOULU**

University of Vaasa

Raastuvankatu 31, P.O. Box 297 65100 Vaasa
Telex: 74262
Telephone: (961) 24-81-11
Fax: (961) 24-82-08

Rehtori: Ilkka Virtanen (1990-94)
Hallintojohtaja: Lars Nyqvist

D. of Accountancy, Business Finance and Methodological Sciences
Head: Timo Sammi; *staff* 17
D. of Administration and Marketing
Head: Vesa Routamaa; *staff* 26
D. of Economics and Law
Head: Juha Tolonen; *staff* 11
D. of Modern Languages (Finnish, Swedish, German, Russian, French and Applied Linguistics)
Head: Andreas F. Kelletat; *staff* 44
D. of Administrative Sciencs (including Public Law)
Head: Ismo Lumijärvi; *staff* 8
Ce. for Lifelong Education
Director: Jouko Havunen; *staff* 107
Western Finland Ce. for Economic Research
Director: Mauri Lehmusto; *staff* 15
Computer Ce.
Director: Matti Taanonen; *staff* 10

Founded 1966 as private School of Economics and Business Studies. Acquired present status and title 1980, under the supervision of the Ministry of Education. Governing bodies: the Council (comprising the Rector, Vice-Rector, 4 professors, 4 other staff and 4 students); the Board of Research and Teaching.

Arrangements for co-operation with the University of Umeå; Tallinn Technical University; University of Greifswald; University of Leipzig. Also participates in the NORDPLUS programme.

Academic Year: September to May (September-December; January-May).

Admission Requirements: Secondary school certificate (ylioppilastutkinto) and certificate of secondary vocational education (opistoasteen tutkinto).

Fees: None.

Languages of Instruction: Finnish and Swedish.

Degrees and Diplomas: Master of–Economics; Business Administration; Arts; Administrative Sciences; 5 yrs. Licentiate in–Economics and Business Administration; Philosophy; Administrative Sciences, a further 3 yrs. Doctor of–Economics and Busines Administration; Philosophy; Administrative Sciences, a further 3 yrs.

Library: *c.*100,000 vols.

Publications: Acta Wasaensia; Proceedings of the University of Vaasa.

Press or Publishing House: University of Vaasa Publishing House.

Academic Staff, 1989-90:

Rank	Full-time
Professori	18
Apulaisprofessori	12
Dosentti	10
Lehtori	36
Yliassistentti	10
Assistentti	20
Tuntipettaja	24
Total	120

Student Enrolment, 1989-90: 2120 (Also 269 external students).

2481 ***ÅBO AKADEMI**

Åbo Akademi University

Domkyrkotorget 3, 20500 Åbo
Telex: 62301 AABIB F
Telephone: (21) 65-43-11
Fax: (21) 51-75-53

Rektor: Bengt Stenlund (1988-91)
Förvaltningsdirektör: Roger Broo

F. of Arts
Dean: Pekka Niemi; *staff* 47
F. of Mathematics and Science (including Pharmacy)
Dean: Johan Reuter; *staff* 168
F. of Economics and Political Science (including Business Administration)
Dean: Guy Bäckman; *staff* 46
F. of Chemical Engineering
Dean: Bruno Lönnberg; *staff* 39
F. of Theology
Dean: Jukka Thurén; *staff* 11
F. of Education
Dean: Helena Hurme; *staff* 48
Language Ce.
Director: Hans Nordström; *staff* 9
Computer Ce.
Director: Stig Göran Lindqvist; *staff* 19
Accelerator L.
Director: Mårten Brenner; *staff* 9
Archipelago I.
Director: Carl Ehlers; *staff* 1
I. of Social Research (concerning Swedish Finland)
Director: Fjalar Finnäs; *staff* 5
I. of Parasitology
Director: Göran Bylund; *staff* 7
I. of Religious and Cultural History
Director: Tore Ahlbäck; *staff* 4
I. for Industrial Pollution Control
Director: Bjarne Holmbom; *staff* 1
External Studies Ce.
Director: Margita Vainio; *staff* 16
I. for Human Rights
Director: Allan Rosas; *staff* 5
I. of Women's Studies
Director: Elianne Riska; *staff* 2
I. of Comparative Nordic Politology and Administration
Director: Kristen Ståhlberg; *staff* 1
I. of Folklore
Director: John Hackman; *staff* 1
Also *c.* 50 departments attached to different faculties.

Founded 1918 as centre of research and higher education for Swedish-speaking minority in Finland. First university established at Åbo, 1640, but was transferred to Helsingfors (Helsinki) in 1827. Incorporated Swedish School of Economics, Åbo 1980. Under the supervision of the Ministry of Education. The highest academic authority is the Chancellor. Governing body: the administrative Council, composed of the Rector, Vice-Rector, the Deans, 8 representatives of the academic staff and 6 representatives of the student body is in charge of general administration and academic matters.

Arrangements for co-operation with the Universities of: Sheffield North Carolina State; Southern Illinois; Warsaw; Ostrava; Leningrad Pädagogische Hochschule Heidelberg; Technische Hochschule Leipzig Florida Institute of Technology at Melbourne. Also participates in the NORDPLUS programme.

Academic Year: August to July (September-December; January-May).

Admission Requirements: Secondary school certificate (studentexamen) or equivalent and, in some cases, entrance examination.

Fees: None.

Language of Instruction: Swedish.

Degrees and Diplomas: Filosofie kandidatexamen, arts or mathematics and natural sciences; Politices kandidatexamen, social science or political science; Diplomingenjörsexamen, chemical engineering; Teologie kandidatexamen, theology, 5-6 yrs. Filosofie licentiatexamen, arts or mathematics and natural sciences; Politices licentiatexamen, social science or political science; Teknologie licentiatexamen, technology; Teologie licentiatexamen, theology, Farmaceutexamen, pharmacology; Farmacie kandidatexamen, pharmacology; Filosofie-, Politices-, Teknologie, and Teologie doktorsgrad (doctorate); Ekonomexamen, business administration; Ekonomie licentiatexamen–och Economie doktorsexamen.

Libraries: Central Library, *c.* 6,000,000 vols; department libraries, *c.* 400,000; Steiner Memorial Library, *c.* 37,000.

Special Facilities (Museums, etc.): Museum of Naval History; Sibelius Museum; Museum 'Ett hem'; Biological Collections; Collection of Cions and Medals.

Publications: Acta Academiae Aboensis (matematik, naturvetenskaper, teknik); Meddelanded från Åbo Akademi (bimonthly during term time).

Press or Publishing House: Abo Academy Press.

Academic Staff, 1989-90:

Rank	Full-time	Part-time
Professorer	62	–
Biträdande professorer	30	–
Lektorer	76	–
Överassistenter/Assistenter	102	–
Docenter	–	146
Total	270	146

Student Enrolment, 1989-90:

	Men	Women	Total
Total	1984	2771	4755*

*Including 110 foreign students. Also *c.* 1300 external students.

2482 ***TEKNILLINEN KORKEAKOULU**

Helsinki University of Technology

Otakaari 1, 02150 Espoo 15

Cables: 12591

Telex: 125161-HTKK SF

Telephone: (358) 0-4511

Fax: (358) 0-465077

Rehtori: Jussi Hyyppä (1985-91)

Hallintojohtaja: Esa Luomala

F. of Information Technology (including Mathematics and System Analysis, Technical Physics, Automation Engineering, Computer Science)

Dean: Heikki Saikkonen; *staff* 134 (115)

F. of Civil Engineering and Surveying (including Structural Engineering and Transportation, and Environmental Engineering)

Dean: Pertti Vakkilainen; *staff* 117 (175)

F. of Mechanical Engineering

Dean: Jorma Pitkänen; *staff* 158 (182)

F. of Electrical Engineering

Dean: Juha Sinkkonen; *staff* 127 (117)

F. of Process Engineering and Materials Science (including Forest Products Technology, Chemical Engineering and Materials Science and Rock Engineering)

Head: Lauri Niinistö; *staff* 217 (132)

F. of Architecture

Dean: Jaakko Laapotti; *staff* 24 (85)

Computing Ce.

Head: Kristel Sarlin; *staff* 29

Low Temperature Physics L.

Head: Olli V. Lounasmaa; *staff* 14

Ce. for Regional and Urban Studies (postgraduate)

Head: Pekka V. Virtanen; *staff* 12

Ce. for Continuing Education

Director: Markku Markkula; *staff* 24

Founded 1849 as technical school, became polytechnic 1879. Acquired present status and title 1908. An autonomous State institution under the supervision of the Ministry of Education. Governing body: the Council of the University.

Arrangements for co-operation with: Aalborg Universitetscenter; Danmarks tekniske hojskole; Norges tekniske hogskole; Chalmers tekniska högskola; Tekniska högskolan vid universitetet i Lund; Tekniska högskolan i Luleå; Kungliga tekniska högskolan; Uppsala universitets tekniska högskola; Häskoli Islands; Högskolesentret i Rogaland; Leeds Polytechnic; Groupe ESC Reims; University of Washington; University of Wisconsin-Madison; Michigan Technological University; Ecole nationale des Ponts et Chaussées; Université de Bordeaux; Technische Universität Dresden; Tallinn Technical University; Warsaw University of Technology; Ingenieurhochschule Zittau; Leningrad Institute of Electrical Engineering; Columbia University in the City of New York; Bergakademie Freiberg; Technical University Košice.

Academic Year: September to August (September-December; January-May).

Admission Requirements: Secondary school certificate (ylioppilastutkinto) or equivalent, and entrance examination.

Fees: None.

Languages of Instruction: Finnish, and some lectures in Swedish. International University Programmes (Pulp and Paper Industry; Architecture) in English.

Degrees and Diplomas: Professional titles of–Diplomi-insinööri, dipl.ins., M.Sc., 5 yrs.; Arkkitehti, Master in Architecture, 6 yrs. Tekniikan lisensiaatti, tekn.lis., Licentiate in Technology, at least a further 2 yrs. Tekniikan tohtori, tekn.tri., Doctor of Technology, by thesis, at least 4 yrs after Diplomi.

Library: Central Library, 3 faculty libraries and 20 departmental libraries, total 1,000,000 vols.

Publications: Research Papers (irregular); Dissertations (irregular); Departmental Report Series.

Academic Staff, 1989-90:

Rank	Full-time	Part-time
Professori	96	–
Apulaisprofessori	58	–
Lehtori	30	–
Yliassistentti	60	–
Assistentti	172	–
Tuntiopettaja	–	1000
Tutkimusassistentti	6	–
Total	422	1000

Student Enrolment, 1989-90:

	Men	Women	Total
Of the country	8250	1822	10,072
Of other countries	168	21	189
Total	8418	1843	10,261

2483 ***LAPPEENRANNAN TEKNILLINEN KORKEAKOULU**

Lappeenranta University of Technology

Skinnarilankatu, 53850 Lappeenranta 85

Telex: 58290

Telephone: (953) 5711

Fax: (953) 571 2350

Rehtori: Juhani Jaakkola (1977-)

Hallintojohtaja: Arto Oikkonen

D. of Information Technology (including Data Processing)

Director: Antti Luukko; *staff* 44 (7)

D. of Mechanical Engineering

Director: Tapani Moisio; *staff* 41 (5)

D. of Energy Technology

Director: Heikki Kalli; *staff* 45 (7)

D. of Industrial Engineering and Management (including International Operations and Marketing, and Logistics)

Director: Veikko Orpana; *staff* 37 (9)

D. of Chemical Technology

Director: Lars Nyström; *staff* 44 (4)

Computer Ce.

Director: Antero Pajari; *staff* 9 (10)

Language Ce. (English, Swedish, German, Spanish, French, Portuguese, Russian, Italian Finnish)

Head: Jukka Taipale; *staff* 19

Ce. for Continuing Education

Director: Seppo Penttinen; *staff* 5

Founded 1969. A State institution under the supervision of the Ministry of Education. Governing bodies: the University Council; the Teaching and Research Council; the Department Councils.

Academic Year: September to May (September-December; January-May).

Admission Requirements: Secondary school certificate (ylioppilastutkinto) or equivalent.

Fees: None.

Language of Instruction: Finnish.

Degrees and Diplomas: Professional title of–Diplomi-insinööri, dipl. ins., 4-5 yrs. Licentiate of Technology, 6-7 yrs. Doctor of Technology, 10 yrs and thesis.

Library: University Library, *c.* 80,000 vols.

Publication: Opetusohjelma.

Academic Staff, 1989:

Rank	Full-time	Part-time
Professori	20	–
Apulaisprofessori	14	–
Dosentti		32
Lehtori	26	–
Yliassistentti	14	–
Assistentti	46	–
Tuntiopettaja	36	
Muu henkilökunta	100	
Total	256	32

Student Enrolment, 1989:

	Men	Women	Total
Of the country	1776	345	2121
Of other countries	4	1	5
Total	1780	346	2126

2484 ***TAMPEREEN TEKNILLINEN KORKEAKOULVU**

Tampere University of Technology

P.O. Box 527, 33101 Tampere

Telex: 22-313 TTKTR-SF

Telephone: (931) 16-21-11

Fax: (931) 16-29-07

Electronic mail: INTERNAT: tlepisto@rapola.tut.fi; BITNET: tlepisto@fintuta

Rehtori: Timo Lepistö (1985-94)

Hallintojohtaja: Seppo Loimio

D. of Electrical Engineering (including Electronics, Physics, Biomedical Engineering, Mathematics, Electrical Metrology, Software Engineering, Signal Processing, Power Systems and High Voltage Engineering, Control Engineering, Power Electronics and Theoretical Electrical Engineering)

Head: Jarl-Thure Eriksson; *staff* 100 (160)

D. of Mechanical Engineering (including Hydraulics and Automation, Machine Design, Production Engineering, Thermal Engineering, Materials Science, Plastics Technology, Engineering Mechanics, Textile Technology, Industrial Economics, and Occupational Safety Engineering)

Head: Antero Aittomaki; *staff* 90 (130)

D. of Civil Engineering (Geodesy and Photogrammetry, Geotechnics, Engineering Geology, Structural Statics, Construction Economics, Buliding Construction, Road and Traffic Engineering, Water and Environmental Engineering)

Head: Jouko Pynnonen; *staff* 40 (70)

D. of Architecture (including Urban Planning)

Head: Jorma Manty; *staff* 30 (20)

Computer Ce.

Director: Erkki Anttila; *staff* 14 (5)

Language Ce.

Director: Pirko Tainio; *staff* 15 (10)

Ce. for Lifelong Education

Director: Tuula Granroth; *staff* 15

Research Ce. for Information Technology

Director: Haanen Taalilida; *staff* 25

Founded 1965 and attached to the Helsinki University of Technology. Acquired independent status 1972. An autonomous State institution under the supervision of the Ministry of Education. Governing body: Hallitus (General Council), comprising the Rector, Vice-Rector, department heads, 3 members of the academic staff, and 3 representatives of the student body. Residential facilities for *c.* 1000 students.

Arrangements for co-operation with all Scandinavian universities of technology, and joint research with over 150 foreign universities or institutes. Member of ISEP (International Student Exchange Programme).

Academic Year: August to July (September-December; January-May).

Admission Requirements: Secondary school certificate (lukion päästötodistus) or equivalent, and entrance examination.

Fees (Marks): International university programmes in Digital Signal Processing and Materials Science, 20,000 per an

Fees: num.

Languages of Instruction: Finnish, and in some courses, English.

Degrees and Diplomas: Professional titles of–Diplomi-insinööri, dipl.ins., 5-6 yrs; Arkkitehti, 5-8 yrs. Tekniikan lisensiaatti, tekn.lis., Licentiate of Technology, at least a further 2 yrs. Tekniikan tohtori, tekn.tri., Doctor of Technology, a further 2 yrs and thesis.

Libraries: Central Library; library of Department of Architecture, total, 120,000 vols.

Academic Staff, 1989-90:

Rank	Full-time	Part-time
Professori	39	–
Apulaisprofessori	34	–
Lehtori	25	–
Yliassistentti	38	–
Assistentti	77	–
Dosentti	–	43
Tuntiopettaja	20	49
Total	233	92

Student Enrolment, 1989-90:

	Men	Women	Total
Of the country	3843	651	4494
Of other countries	78	10	88
Total	3921	661	4582

2485 **HELSINGIN KAUPPAKORKEAKOULU**

Helsinki School of Economics and Business Administration

Runeberginkatu 14-16, 00100 Helsinki

Telex: 122220 ECON SF

Telephone: (358) 0-43131

Fax: (358)) 0-431-3217

Rehtori: Fedi Vaivio (1990-93)

Hallintojohtaja: Matti Sarakontu

D. of Administration and Information Systems (including Applied Psychology)

Head: Risto Tainio; *staff* 22

D. of Accounting (including Finance and Management Economics)

Head: Eero Pitkänen *staff* 19 (1)

D. of Marketing and Production Economy

Head: Reijo Luostarinen; *staff* 21 (1)

D. of Economics

Head: Reijo Helle; *staff* 17 (2)

D. of Law and Social Sciences (including Political Science)

Head: Heikki Niskakangas; *staff* 9 (1)

D. of Systems' Sciences (including Economic Mathematics, Statistics, Philosophy)

Head: Pekka Korhonen; *staff* 9 (1)

D. of Languages

Head: Pirkko Nuolijärvi; *staff* 37 (7)

PRODEC Education Ce. for Developing Countries

Director: Saara Kehusmaa-Pekonen *staff* 21

International Ce.

Head: Veikko Jääskeläinen; *staff* 7 (1)

Ce. for Continuing Education

Head: Jukka Vihersaari; *staff* 8 (1)

Researh D.

Head: Aarni Nyberg

Also Small Business Centre, Mikkeli.

Founded 1904 as college of commerce, became a private School of Economics 1911. Acquired present status as a State institution 1974. Under the supervision of and entirely financed by the Ministry of Education. Governing bodies: the Council, comprising 30 members; the Board of Governors, of 15 members; the Scientific Council. Residential facilities for 365 students.

Arrangements for co-operation with business schools in: Europe; U.S.A.; Canada; USSR.

Academic Year: September to May (September-December; January-May).

Admission Requirements: Secondary school certificate (ylioppilastutkinto) or equivalent, and entrance examination.

Fees: None.

Language of Instruction: Finnish.

Degrees and Diplomas: Degree of Kauppatieteiden maisteri, KTM, 4-5 yrs, followed by Kauppatieteiden lisensiaatti, KTL, 2 ½ yrs, and by Kauppatieteiden tohtori, KTT (doctorate), 4 yrs.

Library: c. 250,000 vols.

Publications: Journal of Business Economics (together with Helsinki Research Institute for Business Economics); Acta Academiae Oeconomicae Helsingiensis.

Academic Staff, 1989:

Rank	Full-time	Part-time
Professori	27	–
Apulaisprofessori	14	–
Yliassistentti	14	–
Lehtori	49	–
Assistentti	32	–
Päätoimiset tuntiopettaja	3	–
Research Assistants	8	60
Total	147	60

Student Enrolment, 1989:

	Men	Women	Total
Of the country	1740	1568	3308

2486 ***SVENSKA HANDELSHÖGSKOLAN**

Swedish School of Economics and Business Administration
Arkadiagatan 22, 0100 Helsinki
Telephone: (358) 0-403-031
Fax: (358) 0-403-03333
Rektor: Alf-Erik Lerviks (1985-93)
Förvaltningsdirektör: Kristina Dufholm

D. of Accounting
Head: Bo-Göran Ekholm; *staff* 12
D. of Business Law
Head: Niklas Bruun; *staff* 5
D. of Economics
Head: Hans Christer Blomqvist; *staff* 7
D. of Entrepreneurship and Management
D. of Finance
Head: Marianne Stenius; *staff* 11
D. of Marketing and Economic Geography
Head: Nils H. Winter; *staff* 14
D. of Modern Languages
Head: Dag Svedstedt; *staff* 21
D. of Organization and Management
Head: Guje Sévon; *staff* 6
D. of Political Science
Head: Ralf Helenius; *staff* 3
D. of Statistics and Computer Sciences
Head: Johan Fellman; *staff* 10
Research I.
Director: Tom Berglund; *staff* 7

Founded 1909. Authorized to grant Master of Science (Econ.) 1927, Doctor 1944, and Licentiate 1953. Unit in Vaasa established 1980. Under the supervision of and entirely financed by the Ministry of Education since 1975. Governing bodies: the University Council comprising 36 members; the Administrative Council, comprising 9 members; the Teaching and Research Council, comprising 24 members. Residential facilities for visiting foreign academic staff.

Arrangements for co-operation with: Stanford University; European Institute of Management Studies, Brussels; Central School of Planning and Statistics, Warsaw. Also participates in the NORDPLUS Programme.

Academic Year: August to July (September-December; January-May).

Admission Requirements: Secondary school certificate (studentexamen) or equivalent, and entrance examination.

Fees: None.

Language of Instruction: Swedish.

Degrees and Diplomas: Ekonomexamen, 4 yrs. Ekonomie licentiatexamen, a further 2 yrs. Ekonomie doktor, by thesis.

Library: 170,000 vols.

Publications: SHH-Aktuell (biannually); Verksamhetsberättelse (Annual Report); Research Catalogue (every 2 years).

Academic Staff, 1989-90:

Rank	Full-time
Professorer	11
Biträdande professorer	14
Lektorer	24
Overassistenter	20
Asistenter	20
Others	11
Total	100

Student Enrolment, 1989-90:

	Men	Women	Total
Of the country	1017	770	1787
Of other countries	33	15	48
Total	1050	785	1835*

*Also 56 external students.

2487 ***TURUN KAUPPAKORKEAKOULU**

The Turku School of Economics and Business Administration
Rehtorinpellonkatu 3, 20500 Turku
Telephone: (921) 512333
Rehtori: Reino Kanerva (1983-)
Hallintojohtaja: Arno Leino

D. of Social Economics
Head: Jaakko Saviranta; *staff* 9 (18)
D. of Business Administration and Marketing
Head: Helena Mäkinen; *staff* 15 (14)
D. of Accountancy
Head: Reino Majala; *staff* 11 (6)
D. of Methodology and Economic Sociology (including Data Processing)
Head: Pentti Malaska; *staff* 9 (14)
D. of Languages
Head: Pertti Widén; *staff* 11 (16)
Computer Ce.
Postgraduate Training Ce.
Director (Acting): Urpo Lehikoinen
Also language laboratories.

Founded 1950 as a private institution. Responsible to the Ministry of Education. Until April 1977, financed 75per cent by the State, by the City of Turku and students' fees. Subsequently entirely financed by the State. Governing bodies: the Board of Governors of 16 members and on which the town of Turku is represented; the Council of Teachers.

Academic Year: August to July (August-December; January-July).

Admission Requirements: Secondary school certificate (ylioppilastutkinto) or equivalent, and entrance examination.

Fees (Marks): 334 per annum.

Language of Instruction: Finnish.

Degrees and Diplomas: Maisteri, *c.* 4 yrs. Lisensiaatti, *c.* 2 ½ yrs. Doctorate, *c.* 1 ½ yrs.

Library: 70,000 vols.

Publications: Turun kauppakorkeakoulu tiedottaa (monthly); Projekti (monthly).

Academic Staff, 1986-87:

Rank	Full-time
Professori	10
Apulaisprofessori	7
Assistentti	12
Lehtori	23
Dosentti	31
Tuntiopettaja	52
Total	135

Student Enrolment, 1986-87:

	Men	Women	Total
Of the country	798	753	1551
Of other countries	4	–	4
Total	802	753	1565

2488 **ELAÄINLÄÄKETIETEELLINEN**

College of Veterinary Medicine
Hämeentie 57 00580 Helsinki
Telephone: (90) 393 141
Fax: (90) 393 1799
Electronic mail: jnet%'hakkinen@finfun'
Rehtori: Jekka Alitalo (1985-)

D. of Basic Veterinary Medicine
Head: Hannu Salonie
D. of Clinical Veterinary Medicine
Head: Matti Alanko
D. of Food and Environmental Hygiene
Head: Timo Pekkanen
Also Farm and Field Station in Hautjärvi and Ambulatory Clinic.

Founded 1945 as a State institution under the supervision of the Ministry of Education. Governing bodies: the Administrative Board; the Rector; the Department Council.

Arrangements for co-operation with: Swedish University of Agricultural Science; Norwegian College of Veterinary Medicine; Royal Veterinary and Agricultural University, Copenhagen. Also Universities of Veterinary Medicinein Hanover, Košiče, Lublin and Tartu.

Academic Year: August to July.

Admission Requirements: Secondary school certificate (ylioppilastutkinto) and entrance examination.

Fees: None.

Languages of Instruction: Finnish and Swedish.

Degrees and Diplomas: Degree of Licentiate in Veterinary Medicine, Eläinääketieteen lisensiaatti, 6 yrs; Doctor of Veterinary Medicine, Eläinääketieteen tohtori, 4 yrs. Specialist degree in Veterinary Medicine, Erikoiseläinlääkärin tutkinto, 4 yrs.

Library: c. 79,000 vols.

Special Facilities (Museums, etc.): Museum of Veterinary History.

Academic Staff, 1990:

Rank	Full-time	Part-time
Professorit	11	–
Apul. Professorit	6	–
Dosentit	–	27
Yliassistentit	22	–
Assistentit	8	–
Tuntiopettajat	–	8
Tutkijat	–	4
Total	47	39

Student Enrolment, 1989-90:

	Men	Women	Total
Of the country	59	248	307
Of other countries	2	–	2
Total	61	248	309

2489 **SIBELIUS-AKATEMIA**

Sibelius Academy
Döbelninkatu 2, 00260 Helsinki
Telephone: (358) 0 405 441
Fax: (358) 0 405 4600
Rehtori: Errki Rautio (1990-)
Hallintojohtaja: Seppo Suihko

D. of Theory of Music and Composition
Head: Matti Saarinen
D. of Solo Performance
Head: Raimo Sariola
D. of Music Education
Head: Roy Asplund
D. of Church Music
Head: Reijo Pajamo
D. of Jazz Music
Head: Jukka-Pekka Uotila
D. of Folk Music
Head: Juhani Näreharju
Music Research I.
Director: Veijo Murtomäki
Continuing Education Ce.
Director: Osmo Palonen
Also Unit at Kuopio, Sibelius-Akatemian kurssikeskus.

Founded 1882 as Helsinki College of Music and a private institution, became Conservatory 1924. Reorganized andpresent title adopted 1939. Acquired present status as State institution 1980. Governing bodies: the Hallitus (Administrative Council), comprising the Rector, 2 Vice-Rectors, and 13 members; the Opetus- ja tutkimusneuvosto (Educational and Research Council). Residential facilities for students.

Academic Year: September to May (September-December; January-May).

Admission Requirements: Secondary school certificate (ylioppilastutkinto).

Fees: None.

Languages of Instruction: Finnish and Swedish.

Degrees and Diplomas: Musiikin kandidaatti, Master of Music, 5-6 yrs. Musiikin lisensiaatti, Licenciate of Music, 2 yrs. minimum. Musiikin tohtori, Doctor of Music, 3 yrs. minimum.

Libraries: c. 7560,000 vols of music; c. 14,000 vols of musical literature, c. 16,500 gramophone records.

Publications: Vuosikertomus (Annual Report); Opinto-opas (annually); Tietoja Sibelius-Akatemiaan pyrkiville (annually).

Academic Staff, 1989-90:

Rank	Full-time	Part-time
Professori	14	–
Apulaisiprofesori	1	–
Yliassistentti	1	–
Assistentti	4	–
Lehtori	131	–
Tuntiopettaja	c.171	c.350
Total	c. 520	c.350

Student Enrolment, 1989-90:

	Men	Wonen	Total
Of the country	531	716	1247
Of other countries	20	16	36
Total	551	732	1283

2490 ***TAIDETEOLLINEN KORKEAKOULU**

University of Industrial Arts
Hämeentie 135c, 00560 Helsinki
Telephone: (358) 0 75 631
Fax: (358) 0 75 63223
Electronic mail: IN %'Taik-sv@cc.helsinki.ff'
Rehtori: Yrjö Sotamaa
Hallintojohtaja: Ilkka Huovio

F. of Art Education
Dean: Antero Salminen; *staff* 11 (20)
F. of Visual Communication
Dean: Jukka Pellinen; *staff* 21 (81)
F. of Industrial and Environmental Design
Dean: Jussi Ahola; *staff* 30 (77)
F. of General Studies
Dean: Severi Parko; *staff* 12 (36)
D. of Graphic Design
Head: Tapani Aartomaa
D. of Stage Design
Head: Paul Suominen
D. of Film and Television
Head: Juha Rosma
D. of Photography
Head: Sakari Sunila
D. of Interior Architecture and Furniture Design
Head: Pekka Heimola
D. of Industrial Design
Head: Raimo Nikkanen
Finnish Design Management I.
Head: Yrjö Sotamaa
I. for Research in Industrial Arts

Founded 1871 as institute. Acquired present status and title 1973. A State institution under the supervision of the Ministry of Education. Governing body: the Board of Trustees.

Arrangements for co-operation with: Academy of Fine Arts, Prague; College of Industrial and Applied Arts, Prague; College of Industrial Design, Halle; Academy of Fine Arts, Cracow; State College of Cinematography, Television and Dramatic Art, Łódź University of the Arts, Belgrade; Hungarian Academy of Fine Arts, Budapest; Tallinn Art Academy; Leeds Polytechnic.

Academic Year: September to May (September-December; January-May).

Academic Year: October to June (October-December; January-March; April-June).

Admission Requirements: Entrance by competition folllowing 2 yrs further study after secondary school certificate (baccalauréat) or following first university qualification (D.U.T. or B.T.S.). Direct entrance to second year by competition following appropriate university degree (Maîtrise).

Language of Instruction: French.

Degrees and Diplomas: Diplôme d'Ingénieur Arts et Métiers, 3 yrs. Diplôme d'études approfondies (D.E.A.), 1 further yr. Doctorat, 2-4 yrs after D.E.A.

Academic Staff: c. 45.

Student Enrolment: c. 275.

2589 **ÉCOLE NATIONALE SUPÉRIEURE DES ARTS ET INDUSTRIES DE STRASBOURG**

24, boulevard de la Victoire, 67084 Strasbourg Cedex
Telephone: 88-35-55-05
Fax: 88-24-14-90
Directeur: Raymond Armbruster
Sous-Directeur: Camille Roth

D. of Architecture (including Town Planning)
Head: Jacques Decoville; *staff* 10 (15)
D. of Civil Engineering
Head: Patrick Frey; *staff* 9 (15)
D. of Mechanical Engineering
Head: Jean-Pierre Freund; *staff* 7 (23)
D. of Electrical and Electronic Engineering
Head: René Roussel; *staff* 5 (27)
D. of Building Services and Energy Engineering
Head: Daniel Marilly; *staff* 4 (25)
D. of Topography
Head: Michel Gruber; *staff* 5 (15)
D. of Plastics Engineering
Head: Pierre Mille; *staff* 5 (20)
Ce. for Energy Utilization and Architectural Design (Habitat)
Head: Alain Régnier; *staff* – (4)
Ce. for Materials Physicochemistry of Surfaces
Head: Alain Cornet; *staff* – (5)
Ce. for Automated Production
Head: Bernard Mutel; *staff* – (5)

Founded 1875, became Ecole nationale supérieure 1966. Residential facilities for students.

Arrangements for student exchanges with: Technische Universität Karlsruhe; Technische Universität Wien; Fachhochschule Lübeck; Syracuse University; Stockholm Royal School fo Engineering.

Academic Year: October to June (October-February; February-June).

Admission Requirements: Entrance by competition following 2 yrs further study after secondary school certificate (baccalauréat) or following first university qualification (D.U.T. or B.T.S.) (for Mechanical Engineering and Electrical and Electronic Engineering).

Language of Instruction: French.

Degrees and Diplomas: Diplôme–d'Ingénieur (with mention of field of specialization); d'Architecte, 4 yrs.

Library: c. 15,000 vols.

Academic Staff, 1989-90:

Rank	Full-time
Professeurs des Universités	7
Maîtres de conférences	10
Professeurs ENSAM	22
Professeurs agrégés et certifiés	12
Chefs de Travaux pratiques ENSAM	13
Total	64

Student Enrolment, 1989-90: 750.

2590 **ÉCOLE NATIONALE SUPÉRIEURE D'ARTS ET MÉTIERS**

Esplanade de l'Université, 33405 Talence
Telephone: 56-80-76-50
Fax: 56-37-90-34

Science and Applied Science
Economics and Law
Humanities

Founded 1806. Attached to the Ecole nationale supérieure d'Arts et Métiers, Paris. Residential facilities for students.

Academic Year: October to June (October-February; March-June).

Admission Requirements: Entrance by competition following 2 yrs further study after secondary school certificate (baccalauréat) or following first university qualification (D.U.T. or B.T.S.).

Language of Instruction: French.

Degrees and Diplomas: Diplôme d'Ingénieur Arts et Métiers, 3 yrs.

Academic Staff: c. 40.

Student Enrolment: c. 300.

2591 **ÉCOLE CENTRALE DE LYON**

36, avenue Guy de Collongue, BP 163 691301 Ecully Cedex
Telex: 310856 ECE LY
Telephone: 78-33-81-27
Fax: 78-43-39-62
Directeur: Jacques Bordet (1988-)
Secrétaire général: C. Lacroix

D. of Fluid Mechanics
Head: Denis Jeandel; *staff* 75
D. of Acoustics
Head: Geneviève Comte-Bellot; *staff* 8
D. of Internal Combustion Engines
Head: Maurice Brun; *staff* 30
D. of Electronical Engineering
Head: Robert Blanchet; *staff* 40
D. of Interface Physical Chemistry
Head: J. Josefh; P. Cléchet; *staff* 31
D. of Electrical Engineering
Head: Philippe Auriol; *staff* 35
D. of Physical Metallurgy and Materials Sciences
Heads: Léo Vincent; P. Guiraldeng; *staff* 20
D. of Surface Technology
Heads: J. Sabot; J.M. Georges; *staff* 35
D. of Computer Sciences and Mathematics Process Control
Heads: B.T. David; J.F. Maître; *staff* 22
D. of Industrial Education
D. of Photocatalysis, Catalysis and Environment Studies
Head: P. Pichot; *staff* 12
Computer Ce.
Ce. for Continuing Education
Head: Michel Futin; *staff* 3

Founded 1857 as a private school, became national school of higher technical learning 1947 and placed under the auspices of the Ministry of Education. Governing body: the Conseil d'administration. Residential facilities for students.

Arrangements for co-operation with: Technical University of Darmstadt; University of Salford; University of Kyoto; Cornell University; University of Indonesia; University College Galway; Free University of Berlin.

Academic Year: September to June.

Admission Requirements: Entrance by competition following 2 yrs further study after secondary school certificate (baccalauréat). Direct entrance by competition following first university qualification (D.U.T. or B.T.S.).

Fees: None.

Language of Instruction: French.

Degrees and Diplomas: Diplôme d'Ingénieur, 3 yrs. Diplôme d'études approfondies (D.E.A.). Doctorat, 2-4 yrs after D.E.A.

Library: 20,000 vols.

Academic Staff, 1989-90: c. 400.

Student Enrolment, 1989-90: c. 1020.

2592 **ÉCOLE NATIONALE SUPÉRIEURE DE CÉRAMIQUE INDUSTRIELLE**

47-73, rue Albert-Thomas, 87065 Limoges Cedex
Telephone: (33) 55-45-22-22
Fax: (33) 55-79-09-98
Directeur: Christian Gault
Secrétaire général: Andrée Grandcoing

Ceramics

Founded 1893 at Sèvres, became Ecole d'Ingénieurs 1926, reorganized 1955 and attained present status 1965.Transferred to Limoges 1979. Governing bodies: the Conseil d'administration; the Conseil de perfectionnement; the Conseil scientifique. Residential facilities for students.

Arrangements for co-operation with the Universities of: Berlin; Hamburg; Leeds; Trieste; Rutgers; Caracas. Tokyo Institute of Technology.

Academic Year: September to June (September-December; January-March; April-June).

Admission Requirements: Entrance by competition following 2 yrs further study after secondary school certificate (baccalauréat) or following first university qualification (D.U.T. or B.T.S.). Direct entrance to second year by competition following appropriate university degree (Maîtrise).

Fees (Francs): 450 per annum.

Language of Instruction: French.

Degrees and Diplomas: Diplôme d'Ingénieur céramiste, 4 yrs. Certificat d'études supérieures de céramique, after Diplôme d'Ingénieur or university degree. Diplôme d'études approfondies (D.E.A.), 1 yr. Doctorat en Sciences des Matériaux, 2-4 yrs after D.E.A.

Library: c. 3000 vols.

Academic Staff: c. 20(20).

Student Enrolment, 1989-90:

	Men	Women	Total
Of the country	104	9	113
Of other countries	1	1	2
Total	105	10	115

2593 **ÉCOLE NATIONALE D'INGÉNIEURS DE BELFORT**

8, rue Anatole France, 90016 Belfort Cedex
Telex: 361526 EMI BEL
Telephone: 84-21-37-00

Engineering

Founded 1962. Residential facilities for students.

Academic Year: September to July.

Admission Requirements: Entrance by competition following 2 yrs further study after secondary school certificate (baccalauréat) or following first university qualification (D.U.T or B.T.S.).

Fees (Francs): 95 per annum.

Language of Instruction: French.

Degrees and Diplomas: Diplôme d'Ingénieur, 4 yrs.

Library: Central Library.

Academic Staff: c. 40.

Student Enrolment: c. 350.

2594 **ÉCOLE NATIONALE D'INGÉNIEURS DE BREST**

Avenue Victor Le Gorgeu, 29283 Brest Cedex
Telephone: 98-03-30-31
Directeur: François Ropars (1985-)

Electronic Engineering

Founded 1961.

Academic Year: October to June (October-February; February-June).

Admission Requirements: Entrance by competition following 2 yrs further study after secondary school certificate (baccalauréat). Direct entrance by competition following first university qualification (D.U.T. or B.T.S.).Entrance by competition following 2 yrs further study after secondary school certificate (baccalauréat). Direct entrance by competition following first university qualification (D.U.T. or B.T.S.).

Fees (Francs): 450 per annum.

Language of Instruction: French.

Degrees and Diplomas: Diplôme d'Ingénieur, 4 yrs.

Academic Staff, 1986-87: 26 (5).

Student Enrolment, 1986-87:

	Men	Women	Total
Of the country	288	4	292
Of other countries	3	–	3
Total	291	4	295

2595 **ÉCOLE NATIONALE D'INGÉNIEURS DE METZ**

Ile du Saulcy, 57045 Metz
Telex: 860217 ENIMETZ
Telephone: 87-32-53-05
Fax: 87-30-39-89

Mechanical Engineering

Founded 1960. Residential facilities at Cité universitaire.

Arrangements for co-operation with Trent Polytechnic.

Academic Year: September to June (September-January; February-June).

Admission Requirements: Entrance by competition following 2 yrs further study after secondary school certificate (baccalauréat). Direct entrance by competition following first university qualification (D.U.T. or B.T.S.).

Language of Instruction: French.

Degrees and Diplomas: Diplôme d'Ingénieur, 4 yrs.

Academic Staff: c. 40.

Student Enrolment: c. 440.

2596 **ÉCOLE NATIONALE D'INGÉNIEURS DE SAINT-ETIENNE**

56, rue Jean-Parot, 42023 Saint-Etienne Cedex 2
Telex: 307125 ENISE
Telephone: 77-25-71-40
Fax: 77-37-55-60
Directeur: Victor Martino

Engineering
Lifelong Education

Founded 1961. Governing bodies: the Conseil d'administration; the Conseil d'établissement and the Conseil scientifique.

Arrangements for co-operation with: Portsmouth Polytechnic; Universität-Gesamthochschule Siegen; University of Patras; North Carolina State University.

Academic Year: October to June (October-February; February-June).

Admission Requirements: Competitive entrance examination following secondary school certificate (baccalauréat). Direct entrance to second year by competition following appropriate university qualification (D.U.T. or B.T.S.).

Fees (Francs): 450 per annum.

Language of Instruction: French.

Degrees and Diplomas: Diplôme d'Ingénieur, 5 yrs.

Library: c. 3500 vols.

Academic Staff: c. 40 (20).

Student Enrolment: c. 350.

2597 **ÉCOLE NATIONALE D'INGÉNIEURS DE TARBES**

Mechanical Engineering School of Tarbes
Chemin d'Azereix, B.P. 1629, 65016 Tarbes Cedex
Telephone: 62-93-98-21
Directeur: Bernard Mugniery (1972-)

Mechanical Engineering

Founded 1963. Attached to the Ministry of Education. Residential facilities for students.

Arrangements for co-operation with: Federal University of Rio de Janeiro; University of Strathclyde; University of Southampton; University of Wales at Cardiff.

Academic Year: September to June (September-January; February-June).

Admission Requirements: Entrance by competition following 2 yrs further study after secondary school certificate (baccalauréat) or following first university qualification (D.U.T. or B.T.S.).

Fees (Francs): 450 per annum.

Language of Instruction: French.

Degrees and Diplomas: Diplôme d'Ingénieur, 5 yrs. Diplôme d'études approfondies (D.E.A.), 6 yrs. Doctorat, 8 yrs.

Library: 5000 vols.

Academic Staff, 1989-90: 51(15).

Student Enrolment, 1989-90:

Men	Women	Total
550	20	570

2598 **ÉCOLE NATIONALE SUPÉRIEURE DE CHIMIE ET DE PHYSIQUE DE BORDEAUX**

351, cours de la Libération, 33405 Talence
Telephone: 56-80-78-93

Chemistry
Chemical Engineering
Physics
Mathematics

Founded 1891, became Ecole nationale supérieure 1953. Attached to the Université de Bordeaux I. Governing body: the Conseil d'administration. Some residential facilities for students.

Academic Year: October to June (October-February; February-June).

Admission Requirements: Entrance by competition following 2 yrs further study after secondary school certificate (baccalauréat) or following first university qualification (D.U.T. or B.T.S.). Direct entrance to second year by competition following appropriate university degree (Maîtrise).

Language of Instruction: French.

Degrees and Diplomas: Diplôme d'Ingénieur chimiste, 3 yrs.

Library: c. 1200 vols.

Academic Staff: c. 10.
Student Enrolment: c. 100.

2599 **ÉCOLE NATIONALE SUPÉRIEURE DE CHIMIE DE CLERMONT-FERRAND**

Ensemble Scientifique des Cézeux, 63174 Aubière Cedex
Telephone: 73-40-71-45
Fax: 73-40-70-95
Directeur: Jacques Gelas (1987-)

D. of Physical Chemistry
Head: Jacques Lemaire
D. of Inorganic Chemical
Head: Jean-Claude Cousseins
D. of Organic Chemistry
Head: Roger Vesiere
D. of Mathematics
Head: Jean-Thierry Lappeste
D. of Chemical Engineering
Head: Claude Richard
I. of Photochemistry
Head: Jacques Lemaire
I. of Carbohydrate Chemistry
Head: Jacques Gelas
I. of Solid State Chemistry
Head: Jean-Claude Cousseins
I. of Organic Synthesis
Head: Roger Vessière

Founded 1908, became Ecole nationale supérieure 1961. Attached to the Université de Clermont-Ferrand II

Academic Year: September to June (September-December; January-March; April-June).

Admission Requirements: Entrance by competition following 2 yrs further study after secondary school certificate (baccalauréat) or following first university qualification (D.U.T. or B.T.S.). Direct entrance to second year by competition following appropriate university degree (Maîtrise).

Fees (Francs): 1250.

Language of Instruction: French.

Degrees and Diplomas: Diplôme d'Ingénieur chimiste, 3 yrs.

Libraries: Central Library (Bibliothèque interuniversitaire); Library of ENSCCF, total, c. 2400 vols.

Academic Staff, 1989-90:

Rank	Full-time	Part-time
Professeurs	6	–
Maîtres de conférences	12	–
Moniteurs (MIES)	1	1
Chargés de cours	–	40
Total	19	41

Student Enrolment, 1989-90:

	Men	Women	Total
Of the country	96	64	160
Of other countries	2	–	2
Total	98	64	162

2600 **ÉCOLE NATIONALE SUPÉRIEURE DE CHIMIE DE LILLE**

Centre Universitaire scientifique, B.P. 40, 59652 Villeneuve-d'Ascq
Telex: 110399/300R EUROR
Telephone: 20-91-00-95

Chemistry
Chemical Engineering

Founded 1894 as institute of applied chemistry, acquired present status 1953. Attached to the Université desSciences et Techniques de Lille. Governing body: the Conseil d'administration.

Academic Year: September to June (September-November; Janu-ary-March; April-June).

Admission Requirements: Entrance by competition following 2 yrs further study after secondary school certificate (baccalauréat) or following first university qualification. Direct entrance to second year by competition following appropriate university degree (Maîtrise).

Language of Instruction: French.

Degrees and Diplomas: Diplôme d'Ingénieur chimiste, 3 yrs. Diplôme d'études approfondies (D.E.A.). Doctorat, 2-4 yrs after D.E.A.

Library: c. 300 vols.
Academic Staff: c. 20 (65).
Student Enrolment: c. 130

2601 **ÉCOLE NATIONALE SUPÉRIEURE DE CHIMIE DE MONTPELLIER**

8, rue de l'Ecole Normale, 34075 Montpellier Cedex
Telephone: 67-63-52-73
Directeur: Patrick Geneste (1982-)
Secrétaire générale: Fernande Aggeri

Chemistry
Chemical Engineering

Founded 1889 as institute and acquired present status 1957. Attached to the Université des Sciences et Techniques du Languedoc (Montpellier II) Governing body: the Conseil d'administration, comprising 24 members. Residential facilities for students.

Partcipates in the ERASMUS ECTS (chemistry) (17 institutions); COMETT (8 institutions), and TEMPUS (3 institutions) programmes.

Academic Year: September to June (September-February; February-June).

Admission Requirements: Entrance by competition following 2 yrs further study after secondary school certificate (baccalauréat) or following first university qualification. Direct entrance to second year by competition following appropriate university degree (Maîtrise).

Fees (Francs): 2000.

Language of Instruction: French.

Degrees and Diplomas: Diplôme d'Ingénieur chimiste, 3 yrs. Diplôme d'études approfondies (D.E.A.), 1 further yr. Doctorat, 2-4 yrs after D.E.A.

Library: 1000 vols.

Publication: Chemia (three times a year).

Academic Staff, 1989-90: c. 90.

Student Enrolment, 1989-90:

	Men	Women	Total
Of the country	189	98	287
Of the countries	41	8	49
Total	230	106	336

2602 **ÉCOLE NATIONALE SUPÉRIEURE DE CHIMIE DE MULHOUSE**

3, rue Alfred Werner, 68019 Mulhouse Cedex
Telephone: 89-42-70-20
Fax: 89-59-98-59
Directeur: Jean-Michel Chezcau (1987-90)
Secrétaire général: Jean-Marie Valder

Chemical Engineering

Founded 1822, acquired status of Ecole nationale supérieure d'Ingénieurs 1948, attached to the Université Louis Pasteur (Strasbourg I) and Université de Haute-Alsace 1976. Acquired present title 1977. Governing body: the Conseil d'administration. Residential facilities for students.

Arrangements for co-operation with: University of Basle; Albert-Ludwigs University of Freiburg in Breisgau; Technical University of Łódź.

Academic Year: September to June (September-December; January-April; April-June).

Admission Requirements: Entrance by competition following 2 yrs further study (Mathematiques supérieurs; Mathematiques spéciales) after secondary school certificate (baccalauréat) or following first university qualification. Direct entrance to second year by competition following appropriate university degree (Maîtrise).

Fees (Francs): 450 per annum.

Language of Instruction: French.

Degrees and Diplomas: Diplôme d'Ingénieur chimiste, 3 yrs. Diplôme d'études approfondies (D.E.A.). Doctorat, 2-4 yrs after D.E.A.

Library: c. 5000 vols.

Special Facilities (Museums, etc.): Museum of Mineralogy.

Academic Staff, 1989-90:

Rank	Full-time	Part-time
Professeurs	11	7
Maîtres de conférences	10	–
Assistants	5	–
Conférenciers	–	6
Total	26	13

Student Enrolment, 1989-90: 270.

2603 **ÉCOLE NATIONALE SUPÉRIEURE DES INDUSTRIES CHIMIQUES DE NANCY**

1, rue de Grandville, 54042 Nancy Cedex
Telex: 961316 F
Telephone: 83-35-21-21

Industrial Chemistry

Founded 1887 as Institut chimique, became Ecole supérieure des industries chimiques 1936, acquired present title 1947. Attached to the Institut national polytechnique de Lorraine. Governing bodies: the Conseil d'administration; the Conseil scientifique.

Arrangements for co-operation with: Technical College, Karlsruhe; University of Bath; Ecole nationale d'Ingénieurs, Gabès.

Academic Year: September to June (September-December; January-March; April-June).

Admission Requirements: Entrance by competition following 2 yrs further study after secondary school certificate (baccalauréat) or following first university qualification.

Fees (Francs): 498 per annum.

Language of Instruction: French.

Degrees and Diplomas: Diplôme d'Ingénieur chimiste, 3 yrs. Diplôme études approfondies (D.E.A.), 1 further yr. Doctorat, 2-4yrs after D.E.A.

Libraries: School Library; Interuniversity library.

Academic Staff, 1986-8:: 47.

Student Enrolment, 1986-87:

	Men	Women	Total
Of the country	173	89	262
Of other countries	9	5	14
Total	182	94	276

2604 **ÉCOLE NATIONALE SUPÉRIEURE DE CHIMIE DE PARIS**

11, rue Pierre-et-Marie-Curie, 75231 Paris Cedex 05
Telex: 270 021 F
Telephone: 44-27-44-27
Fax: 43-25-79-75
Directeur: C. Quivoron
Secrétaire générale: Christine Galinier

Chemistry

Ce. of Material Sciences and Metallurgy
Head: R. Collongues; *staff* 27

Ce. of Molecular Chemistry and Biotechnologies
Head: F. Le Goffic; *staff* 30

Ce. of Energetics and Processes
Head: J. Amouroux; *staff* 27

Founded 1896 as laboratoire de chimie pratique et industrielle de Charles Friedel, became Institut de Chimie 1899 and acquired present title 1948, and status as a public administrative establishment 1986. Attached to theUniversity Pierre et Marie Curie (Paris VI) 1968.

Academic Year: September to June (September-December; January-March; April-June).

Admission Requirements: Entrance by competition following 2 yrs further study after secondary school certificate (baccalauréat) or following first university qualification. Direct entrance to second year by competition following appropriate university degree (Maîtrise).

Language of Instruction: French.

Degrees and Diplomas: Diplôme d'Ingénieur chimiste, 3 yrs. Diplôme d'études approfondies (D.E.A.), 1 further yr. Doctorat, 2-4 yrs after D.E.A.

Academic Staff, 1989-90: 60 (30).

Student Enrolment, 1989-90:

	Men	Women	Total
Of the country	108	66	174
Of other countries	2	3	5
Total	110	69	179

2605 **ÉCOLE NATIONALE SUPÉRIEURE DE CHIMIE DE RENNES**

Avenue du Général Leclerc, 35000 Rennes
Telephone: 99-36-29-95
Directeur: René Dabard (1983-87)

Chemistry
Physics
Mathematics
Mineralogy

Founded 1921 as institute, became Ecole nationale supérieure 1958. Attached to the Université de Rennes I.

Academic Year: November to June (November-January; February-June).

Admission Requirements: Entrance by competition following 2 yrs further study after secondary school certificate (baccalauréat) or following first university qualification (D.U.T. or B.T.S.). Direct entrance to second year by competition following appropriate university degree (Maîtrise).

Fees (Francs): 1160 per annum.

Language of Instruction: French.

Degrees and Diplomas: Diplôme d'Ingénieur chimiste, 3 yrs. Diplôme d'études approfondies (D.E.A.), 1 further year. Doctorat,2-4 yrs after D.E.A.

Academic Staff, 1986-87: 17.

Student Enrolment, 1986-87:

	Men	Women	Total
Of the country	152	115	267
Of other countries	16	122	23
Total	168	122	290

2606 **ÉCOLE NATIONALE SUPÉRIEURE D'INGÉNIEURS DE GÉNIE CHIMIQUE DE TOULOUSE**

Chemin de la Loge, 31078 Toulouse Cedex
Telex: 530-171-211
Telephone: 61-52-92-41
Directeur: H. Angelino (1983-92)
Secrétaire général: C. Balladore

Chemical Engineering

Founded 1949 as institute, became Ecole nationale supérieure 1953 and acquired present title 1985. Attached to the Institut National Polytechnique de Toulouse 1969. Governing bodies: the Conseil d'administration; the Conseil scientifique. Residential facilities for students.

Arrangements for co-operation with the Universities of: Barcelona; Oviedo; Palma de Mallorca; Valencia; Mexico (National Autonomous); Lund; Chulalongkorn; Tunis; Massachusetts, Amherst; Houston; California in Santa Barbara; Seattle Pacific. Royal Institute of Technology, Stockholm; Federal Institute of Technology, Lausanne; Georgia Institute of Technology, Atlanta; Imperial College of Science and Technology, London; Instituto Quimico de Sarriá, Barcelona.

Academic Year: October to June (October-January; February-June).

Admission Requirements: Entrance by competition following 2 yrs further study after secondary school certificate (baccalauréat) or following first university qualification (D.U.T.). Direct entrance to second year by competition following appropriate university degree (Maîtrise).

Fees (Francs): 450 per annum.

Language of Instruction: French.

Degrees and Diplomas: Diplôme d'Ingénieur du Génie chimique, 3 yrs; Diplôme d'Ingénieur de la Section spéciale de Génie chimique de l'Institut National Polytechnique de Toulouse, 1 yr. Diplôme d'études approfondies (D.E.A.),1 further yr. Doctorat, 2-4 yrs after D.E.A.

Library: Central Library, 6500 vols.

Publication: Research Papers.

Academic Staff, 1989-90:

Rank	Full-time
Professeurs	17
Maîtres de conférences	18
Allocataires d'enseignement	5
Professeurs du second degré	2
Total	42

Student Enrolment, 1989-90:

	Men	Women	Total
Of the country	158	65	223
Of other countries	64	11	75
Total	222	76	298

2607 **ÉCOLE NATIONALE SUPÉRIEURE DE CHIMIE DE TOULOUSE**

118, route de Narbonne, 31077 Toulouse Cedex
Telephone: 61-17-56-56
Fax: 61-17-56-00
Directeur: Jean-Jacques Bonnet
Secrétaire générale: Claudette Deweerdt

L. of Agro-Resources Chemistry
Head: Antoine Gaset; *staff* 71 (25)
L. of Materials
Head: Roland Morancho; *staff* 46 (30)
L. of Chemistry of Manufacturing Process
Head: Philippe Kalck; *staff* 16 (24)

Founded 1906 as Institut de chimie, became Ecole nationale supérieure 1953. Forms part of the Institut National Polytechnique de Toulouse since 1971.

Arrangements for co-operation with similar institutions in: Gdańsk, Wrocław, Warsaw, Toruń, Rabat, Sfax, Gabès. Also scientific co-operation agreements with: United States, United Kingdom, Sweden, Brazil, Venezuela, Canada. Participates with 8 other universities in the ERASMUS programme and ECTS, student mobility project.

Academic Year: September to July (September-December; January-March; April-June).

Admission Requirements: Entrance by competition following 2 yrs further study after secondary school certificate (baccalauréat) or following first university qualification.

Fees (Francs): 1320 per annum.

Language of Instruction: French.

Degrees and Diplomas: Diplôme d'Ingénieur chimiste, 3 yrs. Diplôme d'études approfondies (D.E.A.), 1 further yr. Doctorat, 2-4 yrs after D.E.A.

Library: 3000 vols.

Academic Staff: c. 50.

Student Enrolment, 1989-90:

	Men	Women	Total
Of the country	121	70	191
Of other countries	10	2	12
Total	131	72	203

2608 **ÉCOLE NATIONALE SUPÉRIEURE DE L'ÉLECTRONIQUE ET DE SES APPLICATIONS**

Allée des Chênes Pourpres, 95014 Cergy-Pontoise Cedex
Telephone: 30-73-66-66
Fax: 30-73-66-67
Directeur: Jean-Paul Watteau

D. of Industrial Electronic Engineering
Head: Pascal Gourreau
D. of Telecommunications
Head: J.M. Dumas
D. of Electrical Instrumentation Engineering
Head: P. Derethe
D. of Computer Engineering
Head: M. Corneloup
D. of Analysis and Signal Processing
Head: P. Duvaut
D. of Computer and Signal Processing
Head: J.P. Cocquerez
D. of Microwave and Optic Integrated Circuits
Head: D. Pasquet

Founded 1941 as Institut d'Electromécanique, became State institution 1949. Diplôme d'Ingénieur first awarded 1952. Acquired present title 1975. Governing body: the Conseil d'administration, comprising 24 members. Residential facilities for students.

Academic Year: October to June (October-December; January-March; April-June).

Admission Requirements: Entrance by competition following 2 yrs further study after secondary school certificate (baccalauréat) or following first university qualification.

Language of Instruction: French.

Degrees and Diplomas: Diplôme d'Ingénieur, 3 yrs. Diplôme de Docteur-Ingénieur. Diplôme spécialisé en Télécommunications Micro-ondes et optiques.

Library: c. 3000 vols.

Academic Staff, 1989-90:

Rank	Full-time	Part-time
Professeurs d'Université	5	–
Maîtres de conférences	11	–
Professeurs agrégés	25	–
Vacataires industriels	–	30
Total	41	30

Student Enrolment, 1989-90:

	Men	Women	Total
Of the country	410	20	430
Of other countries	12	2	14
Total	422	22	444

2609 **ÉCOLE NATIONALE SUPÉRIEURE D'ÉLECTRONIQUE ET DE RADIOÉLECTRICITÉ DE BORDEAUX**

Faculté des Sciences, 351, cours de la Libération, 33405 Talence
Telephone: 56-80-8469-50
Fax: 56-37-20-23

Electronic Engineering
Radioelectrical Engineering

Founded 1920. Attached to the Université de Bordeaux I. Some residential facilities for students at Cité universitaire.

Academic Year: October to June (October-February; February-June).

Admission Requirements: Entrance by competition following 2 yrs further study after secondary school certificate (baccalauréat) or following first university qualification.

Language of Instruction: French.

Degrees and Diplomas: Maîtrise, 2 yrs. Diplôme d'Ingénieur, 3 yrs.

Academic Staff: c. 10.

Student Enrolment: c. 70.

2610 **ÉCOLE NATIONALE SUPÉRIEURE D'INGÉNIEURS-ÉLECTRICIENS DE GRENOBLE**

Domaine Universitaire, B.P. 46, 38402 Saint-Martin-d'Hères

Electrical Engineering

2611 **ÉCOLE NATIONALE SUPÉRIEURE D'ÉLECTROCHIMIE ET D'ÉLECTROMÉTALLURGIE DE GRENOBLE**

Domaine Universitaire, 38403 Saint-Martin-d'Hères

Chemical Engineering
Metallurgy

2612 **ÉCOLE NATIONALE SUPÉRIEURE D'ÉLECTRONIQUE ET DE RADIOÉLECTRICITÉ DE GRENOBLE**

23, rue des Martyrs, 38031 Grenoble

Electronic Engineering
Radioelectrical Engineering

2613 **ÉCOLE NATIONALE SUPÉRIEURE D'ÉLECTRICITÉ ET DE MÉCANIQUE DE NANCY**

2, rue de la Citadelle, B.P. 850, 54011 Nancy Cedex

Electrical Engineering
Mechanical Engineering

2614 **ÉCOLE NATIONALE SUPÉRIEURE D'ÉLECTROTECHNIQUE, D'ÉLECTRONIQUE, D'INFORMATIQUE ET D'HYDRAULIQUEDE TOULOUSE**

2, rue Charles Camichel, 31071 Toulouse Cedex
Directeur: D. Amoros
Responsable des Services administratifs: L. Verlinde

D. of Electrical Engineering and Automation
Head: B. de Fornel
D. of Electronics and Microelectronics
Head: R. Crampagne
D. of Computer Science and Applied Mathematics
Head: F. Rodríguez
D. of Hydraulics and Fluid Mechanics
Head: C. Thirriot
Also 4 Research Laboratories.

Founded 1907. Attached to the Institut national polytechnique de Toulouse.

Participates in the ERASMUS, ESPRIT, BRITE and PROMETHEUS programmes.

Academic Year: September to June.

Admission Requirements: Entrance by competition following 2 yrs further study after secondary school certificate (baccalauréat). Direct entrance to second year by competition following appropriate university degree (Maîtrise of Diplôme d'Ingénieur).

Fees (Francs): 1000.

Degrees and Diplomas: Diplôme d'Ingénieur, 3 yrs. Doctorate, a further 3 yrs.

Academic Staff, 1989-90: 100.

2615 **INSTITUT FRANÇAIS DU FROID INDUSTRIEL**

French Institute of Refrigeration
Conservatoire national des Arts et Métiers, 292, rue Saint-Martin, 75141 Paris Cedex 03
Telephone: 40-27-21-65
Fax: 42-71-93-29
Directeur: Jean-Jacques Veyssie
Secrétaire générale: Christiane Girard

Refrigeration Engineering

Founded 1942. Attached to the Conservatoire national des Arts et Métiers.

Academic Year: October to July.

Admission Requirements: Diplôme universitaire de Technologie (section B) or Diplôme d'Ingénieur (section A).

Fees (Francs): 5250-5700.

Degrees and Diplomas: Diplôme d'Ingénieur frigoriste, 1 yr. Diplôme de Spécialisation.

Student Enrolment, 1989-90: 101.

2616 **ÉCOLE NATIONALE DES SCIENCES GÉOGRAPHIQUES**

Institut géographique national, 2, avenue Pasteur, 94160 Saint-Mandé
Telex: 210551 IGN SMD F
Telephone: 43-74-12-15

Geography
Surveying
Cartography
Lifelong Education

Founded 1941. Attached to the Institut géographique national. Governing body: the Conseil de perfectionnement.

Academic Year: October to August (October-December; January-April; May-August).

Admission Requirements: (a) Diplôme d'études universitaires générales or Maîtrise ès Sciences and entrance examination; (b) entrance by competition following secondary school certificate (baccalauréat).

Language of Instruction: French.

Degrees and Diplomas: Diplôme–d'Ingénieur civil géographe; d'Ingénieur du Corps des Ingénieurs géographes, 2 yrs. Professional title of Ingénieur diplômé, 3 yrs. Diplôme d'études approfondies (D.E.A.) en études géodésiques. Doctorat en Sciences géodésiques, 2-4 yrs after D.E.A. Brevet, 2 yrs. Also Certificats, 2 yrs.

Library: Central Library.

Academic Staff: c. 35 (40).

Student Enrolment: c. 250.

2617 **ÉCOLE NATIONALE SUPÉRIEURE DE GÉOLOGIE ET DE PROSPECTION MINIÈRE DE NANCY**

94, avenue de Lattre-de-Tassigny, B.P. 452, 54001 Nancy Cedex

Geology
Mining

2618 **ÉCOLE SUPÉRIEURE DE GÉOMÈTRES ET TOPOGRAPHES**

Conservatoire national des Arts et Métiers, 18, allée Jean Rostand, 91000 Evry

Surveying

Founded 1945, reorganized 1947. Attached to the Conservatoire national des Arts et Métiers.

Academic Year: November to July.

Admission Requirements: Entrance by competition following 2 yrs further study after secondary school certificate (baccalauréat) or following first university qualification.

Language of Instruction: French.

Degrees and Diplomas: Diplôme–de Géomètre; de Topographe, 3 yrs, including 1 yr supervised practical experience; d'Ingénieur géomètre; d'Ingénieur topographe, by dissertation.

Academic Staff: c. 50.

Student Enrolment: c. 120.

2619 **ÉCOLE D'APPLICATION DES HAUTS POLYMÈRES DE L'UNIVERSITÉ DE STRASBOURG I**

4, rue Boussingault, 67000 Strasbourg
Telex: ULP 870260 F
Telephone: 88-41-65-00
Fax: 88-61-04-62
Directeur: Jean Brossas
Secrétaire générale: Liliane Neimark

High Polymer Studies

Founded 1963, opened 1965. Attached to the Université Louis-Pasteur (Strasbourg I).

Arrangements for co-operation with McGill University.

Academic Year: October to June (October-December; January-March; April-June).

Admission Requirements: Entrants selected from holders of Diplôme d'Ingénieur or Maîtrise ès Sciences.

Fees (Francs): c. 1000 per annum.

Language of Instruction: French.

Degrees and Diplomas: Diplôme d'Ingénieur, 2 yrs. Diplôme d'études approfondies (D.E.A.), 1 further yr. Doctorat, 2-4 yrs after D.E.A.

Library: 1100 vols.

Academic Staff, 1989-90:

Rank	Full-time
Professeurs	7
Maîtres de conférences	5
Total	12

Student Enrolment, 1988-89:

	Men	Women	Total
Of the country	30	7	37
Of other countries	10	2	12
Total	40	9	49

2620 **ÉCOLE NATIONALE SUPÉRIEURE D'HYDRAULIQUE ET DE MÉCANIQUE DE GRENOBLE**

Domaine Universitaire, B.P. 53, 38400 Saint-Martin-d'Hères Cedex
Telex: 980668 HYMEGRE
Telephone: 76-82-50-00

Hydraulics

Founded 1929. Governing body: the Conseil d'administration, comprising 28 members. Residential facilities for students.

Arrangements for co-operation with: Institut national agronomique et vétérinaire Hassan II, Rabat; Universidad del Zulia.

Academic Year: October to June (October-February; February-June).

Admission Requirements: Entrance by competition following 2 yrs further study after secondary school certificate (baccalauréat) or following first university qualification. Direct entrance to second year by competition following appropriate university degree or diplôme d'Ingénieur.

Language of Instruction: French.

Degrees and Diplomas: Diplôme d'Ingénieur hydraulicien, 3 yrs. Diplôme de spécialisation, a further 2 yrs. Diplôme d'études approfondies (D.E.A.), a further yr. Doctorat, 2-4 yrs after D.E.A.
Library: c. 5000 vols.
Academic Staff: c. 25 (70).
Student Enrolment: c. 200.

2621 INSTITUT INDUSTRIEL DU NORD (IDN)

Domaine Universitaire scientifique de Lille, B.P. 48, 59651 Villeneuve d'Ascq Cedex
Telex: EUNOR 131339 CODE 350
Telephone: (33) 20-91-01-15
Fax: (33) 20-72-74-74
Directeur: Jean-Claude Gentina
Secrétaire général: Patrice Serniclay

Industrial Engineering

Founded 1872, as Ecole impériale de Génie civil. Acquired present status 1975. Governing body: the Conseil d'administration. Residential facilities for students.

Arrangements for co-operation with the Universities of: Manchester; Brunel, London; Zaragoza; Belgrade; Charlottesville; Gdańsk; Casablanca. Munich University of Technology; Institute of Science and Technology, United Kingdom; National Technical University of Athens; Free University of Brussels; Ecole nationale d'Ingénieurs de Tunis.

Academic Year: September to June.
Fees (Francs): 1950 per annum.
Language of Instruction: French.
Degrees and Diplomas: Diplôme d'Ingénieur, 3 yrs. Diplôme d'études approfondies (D.E.A.), a further yr. Doctorat, 2-4 yrs after D.E.A.
Library: Centre de Documentation 'François Laurent', *c.* 8000 vols.
Publication: IDN Entreprises (4 times a year).
Academic Staff, 1990-91:

Rank	Full-time
Professeurs	13
Maîtres de conférences	27
Allocataires d'enseignement	4
Professeurs agrégés	6
Professeurs certifiés	3
Total	53

Student Enrolment, 1990-91:

	Men	Women	Total
Of the country	515	65	580
Of other countries	35	–	35
Total	550	65	615

2622 ÉCOLE NATIONALE SUPÉRIEURE DES TECHNIQUES INDUSTRIELLES ET DES MINES D'ALÈS

6, avenue de Clavières, 30107 Alès
Telex: 490623 F
Telephone: 27-87-16-14

Mining Engineering

Founded 1843. Attached to the Ministry of Science and Industry.
Academic Year: September to July.
Admission Requirements: Entrance by competition following 2 yrs further study after secondary school certificate (baccalauréat) or following first university qualification.
Language of Instruction: French.
Degrees and Diplomas: Diplôme, 4 yrs.

2623 ÉCOLE NATIONALE DES TECHNIQUES INDUSTRIELLES ET DES MINES DE DOUAI

941, rue Charles-Bourseul, 59508 Douai
Telex: 820795 DRINPDE F
Telephone: 27-87-16-14
Fax: 27-88-30-36

Mining Engineering

Founded 1848. Attached to the Ministry of Science and Industry.
Academic Year: September to July.
Admission Requirements: Entrance by competition following 2 yrs further study after secondary school certificate (baccalauréat) or following first university qualification.
Language of Instruction: French.
Degrees and Diplomas: Diplôme, 4 yrs.

2624 CENTRE D'ÉTUDES SUPÉRIEURES DES TECHNIQUES INDUSTRIELLES

3, rue Ferdinand Hainaut, 93407 Saint-Ouen Cedex
Telex: 234125 F
Telephone: 40-11-43-85
Directeur: Henri Veysseyre

Industrial Engineering

Founded 1956.

Arrangements for co-operation with the Universities of: Carnegie Mellon; California-Berkeley; Virginia; Manchester; Leeds; Bangkok; Beijing; Porto; Hanoi.

Academic Year: September to June.
Admission Requirements: Entrance by competition following 2 yrs further study after secondary school certificate (baccalauréat) or following first university qualification.
Fees (Francs): 3000.
Language of Instruction: French.
Degrees and Diplomas: Diplôme d'Ingénieur, 3 yrs.
Academic Staff: c. 20 (150).
Student Enrolment: c. 140.

2625 INSTITUT D'INFORMATIQUE D'ENTREPRISE

Conservatoire national des Arts et Métiers, 18, allée Jean Rostand, 91002 Evry Cedex
Telephone: (1) 60-77-97-40
Fax: (1) 60-77-96-99
Directeur: Alain Cabanes (1985-)
Secrétaire général: Jean-Paul Brutus

Sec. of Computer Sciences
Head: Gérard Berthelot
Sec. of Economics and Management
Head: Christian de Lauzheinghain

Founded 1968 as part of the Conservatoire national des Arts et Métiers, Paris. Transferred to Evry 1984.

Academic Year: October to June (October-December; January-March; April-June).
Admission Requirements: Entrance by competition following 2 yrs further study after secondary school certificate (baccalauréat) or following first university qualification (D.U.T. or B.T.S.). Direct entrance to second year by competition following appropriate university degree (Maîtrise).
Fees (Francs): 1500 per annum.
Language of Instruction: French.
Degrees and Diplomas: Diplôme d'Ingénieur, 3 yrs.
Library: c. 2000 vols.
Academic Staff, 1988-90: 31.
Student Enrolment, 1989-90:

	Men	Women	Total
Of the country	200	54	254
Of other countries	15	2	17
Total	215	56	271

2626 ÉCOLE NATIONALE SUPÉRIEURE D'INFORMATIQUE ET DE MATHÉMATIQUES APPLIQUÉES DE GRENOBLE

(Institut national polytechnique), Domaine Universitaire, B.P. 68, 38400 Saint Martin-d'Hères

Computer Sciences
Applied Mathematics

2627 ÉCOLE DES INGÉNIEURS DE LA VILLE DE PARIS

57, boulevard St. Germain, 75006 Paris
Telephone: 46-34-21-99
Directeur: S. Eyrolls

Engineering

Founded 1959.
Academic Year: September to June (September-December; January-March; March-June).
Admission Requirements: Entrance by competition following 2 yrs further study after secondary school certificate (baccalauréat). Direct entrance by competition following first university qualification (D.U.T.).
Fees (Francs): *c.* 5000 per annum.
Language of Instruction: French.
Degrees and Diplomas: Dilôme d'Ingénieur, 3 yrs.

Academic Staff, 1986-87:: – (69).
Student Enrolment, 1986-87:

	Men	Women	Total
Of the country	44	19	63

2628 **INSTITUT SUPÉRIEUR DES MATÉRIAUX ET DE LA CONSTRUCTION MÉCANIQUE**
Ecole de spécialisation, 3, rue Ferdinand Hainaut, 93407 Saint-Ouen
Telex: 234125 F
Telephone: 46-06-40-85
Directeur: Henri Veysseyre

Materials Technology
Mechanical Construction

Founded 1948. Governing bodies: the Comité de Direction; the Conseil de perfectionnement.

Arrangements for co-operation with the Universities of: Carnegie Mellon; California-Berkeley; Manchester; Leeds; Hanoi; Tsinghua; New Delhi; Porto; Bangkok.

Academic Year: September to June (September-December; January-March; April-June).

Admission Requirements: Diplôme d'Ingénieur or Maîtrise ès Sciences, or recognized foreign equivalent.

Fees (Francs): 3000 per annum.

Language of Instruction: French.

Degrees and Diplomas: Diplôme d'Ingénieur (postgraduate), 1-2 yrs. Diplôme d'études approfondies (D.E.A.).

Publication: Revue Matériaux-Mécanique-Electricité.

Academic Staff, 1986-87:

Rank	Full-time	Part-time
Professeurs	7	
Maîtres de conférences	3	–
Chefs de travaux	9	–
Assistants	1	–
Vacataires	–	200
Total	20	200

Student Enrolment, 1986-87:

	Men	Women	Total
Of the country	250	15	265
Of other countries	35	5	40
Total	285	20	305

2629 **INSTITUT DES SCIENCES DE LA MATIÈRE ET DU RAYONNEMENT**
5, avenue d'Edimbourg, 14032 Caen Cedex
Telephone: 31-93-37-14
Fax: 31-93-39-12
Directeur: Jean-Charles Viénot

S. of Engineering
Head: B. Tamain; *staff* 34 (86)
Atomic Spectroscopy L.
Head: Jean Margerie; *staff* 37
Corpuscular Physics L.
Head: Guy Bizard; *staff* 46
Catalysis and Spectrochemistry L.
Head: Jean-Claude Lavalley; *staff* 36
L. of Composite Thioorganic Chemistry
Head: Jean-Louis Ripoll; *staff* 57
Materials Research L.
Head: Jean-Louis Chermant; *staff* 45
L. of Crystallography and Materials Sciences
Head: Bernard Raveau; *staff* 60
Automation L.
Head: Yves Lecluse; *staff* 9
Robotics L.
Head: Marinette Revenu; *staff* 10

Founded 1987, incorporating 2 schools of Electronics and Chemistry. Residential facilities for students.

Arrangements for co-operation with: Kent University; University of Belfast; Sussex University; University of Constance; Clausthal University.

Academic Year: October to June.

Admission Requirements: Entrance by competition following 2 yrs further study after secondary school certificate (baccalauréat) or following first university qualification.

Fees (Francs): 1500 per annum.

Language of Instruction: French.

Degrees and Diplomas: Diplôme d'Ingénieur, 3 yrs. Doctorat, a further 2 yrs.

Academic Staff, 1989-90: 31.

Student Enrolment, 1989-90: 451.

2630 **ÉCOLE NATIONALE SUPÉRIEURE DE MÉCANIQUE ET DES MICROTECHNIQUES**
La Bouloie, Route de Gray, 25030 Besançon Cedex
Telephone: 81-50-36-55

Industrial Automation and Computer Science
Mechanical Construction
Microelectronics
Microstructure Technology
Physics and Chemistry of Materials

Founded as Institut de Chronométrie et de Mécanique horlogère 1896. Became Ecole nationale supérieure de chronométrie et de micromécanique 1969. Reorganized under the present title 1982, incorporating the Institut de Chimie, Besançon. Attached to the Université de Franche-Comté. Some residential facilities for students at Cité universitaire.

Academic Year: October to July (October-February; February-July).

Admission Requirements: Entrance by competition following 2 yrs further study after secondary school certificate (baccalauréat) or following first university qualification.

Language of Instruction: French.

Degrees and Diplomas: Diplôme d'Ingénieur. Diplôme d'études approfondies (D.E.A.), 1 further yr. Doctorat, 2-4 yrs after D.E.A.

Academic Staff: c. 30.

Student Enrolment: c. 280.

2631 **ÉCOLE NATIONALE SUPÉRIEURE DE MÉCANIQUE**
1, rue de la Noë, 44072 Nantes Cedex 03
Telex: 711716 ENSIMINTE F
Telephone: 40-37-16-00
Fax: 40-74-74-06
Directeur: Pierre Vaussy (1987-92)
Secrétaire général: Christian Palu-Laboureu

Automation L.
Director: M.J. Descusse; *staff* 43
Informatics L.
Director: M. Daubisse; *staff* 12
L. of Marine Hydrodynamics
Director: M. Sulmont; *staff* 26
L. of Turbulence Transfer and Physics Mechanics
Director: C. Rey; *staff* 7
Materials L.
Director: F. Lemaître; *staff* 32
L. of Mechanics and Structures
Director: M. Le Hondic; *staff* 19
L. of Energetics
Director: J.P. Frayret; *staff* 8
Civil Engineering L.
Director: M. Sieffert; *staff* 22

Founded 1919 as Institut polytechnique de l'Ouest. Attached to the Université de Rennes 1927; became Ecole nationale supérieure 1947 and attached to the Université de Nantes. Governing bodies: the Conseil d'administration; the Conseil scientifique.

Arrangements for co-operation with: Brown University; National Taiwan University; Centre Universitaire de Tlemcen, Algeria; Ain Shams University; Universidad de Barcelona; Cairo University; Ecole Polytechnique de Montréal; Ajou University; University of Washington, Seattle; Braunschweig University; University of Newcastle uponTyne; University of Keio; Ecole polytechnique de Masuku, Gabon.

Academic Year: September to June (September-December; January-March; March-June).

Admission Requirements: Entrance by competition following 2 yrs further study after secondary school certificate (baccalauréat) or following first university qualification (D.U.T. or D.E.U.G.). Direct entrance to second year by competition following appropriate university degree (Maîtrise).

Fees (Francs): 900 per annum.

Language of Instruction: French.

Degrees and Diplomas: Diplôme d'Ingénieur, 2-3 yrs. Diplôme d'Ingénieur d'Hydrodynamique, 1 further yr. Diplôme d'étudesapprofondies (D.E.A.), 1 further yr. Doctorat, 2-4 yrs after D.E.A.

Library: 15,000 vols.

Publications: Annales; Gyro (quarterly).

Academic Staff, 1989-90:

Rank	Full-time	Part-time
Professeurs	24	–
Maîtres de conférences	42	–
Assistants	22	–
Autres	12	–
Vacataires	–	120
Total	100	120

Student Enrolment, 1989-90:

	Men	Women	Total
Of the country	712	53	765
Of other countries	111	10	121
Total	823	63	886*

*Also 30 external students.

2632 **ÉCOLE NATIONALE SUPÉRIEURE DE MÉCANIQUE ET D'AÉROTECHNIQUE DE POITIERS**

20, rue Guillaume VII, 86034 Poitiers Cedex
Telephone: 49-88-32-17

Mechanical Engineering

Founded 1948 to train high-level engineers. Attached to the Université de Poitiers. Governing body: the Conseil d'administration. Residential facilities for students.

Academic Year: October to June (October-February; February-June).

Admission Requirements: Entrance by competition following 2 yrs further study after secondary school certificate (baccalauréat) or following first university qualification (D.U.T. or D.E.U.G.). Direct entrance to second year by competition following appropriate university degree (Maîtrise).

Language of Instruction: French.

Degrees and Diplomas: Diplôme d'Ingénieur, 3 yrs. Diplôme d'études approfondies (D.E.A.), 1 further yr. Doctorat, 2-4 yrs after D.E.A.

Academic Staff: c. 50.

Student Enrolment: c. 260.

2633 **ÉCOLE NATIONALE D'INGÉNIEURS DE MÉCANIQUE ET D'ÉNERGÉTIQUE**

Le Mont-Houy, 59326 Valenciennes Cedex
Telephone: 27-41-14-20
Directeur: Roger Torquet

Mechanical Engineering
Energetics

Founded 1979. Attached to the Université de Valenciennes et du Hainaut-Cambrésis. Governing body: the Conseil d' administration. Residential facilities for students.

Arrangements for co-operation with: Faculté polytechnique de Mons; University of Hamburg.

Academic Year: September to June (September-December; January-April; April-June).

Admission Requirements: Entrance by competition following 2 yrs further study after secondary school certificate (baccalauréat). Direct entrance by competition following first university qualification (D.U.T.).

Fees (Francs): 555 per annum.

Language of Instruction: French.

Degrees and Diplomas: Diplôme d'Ingénieur, 3 yrs.

Academic Staff, 1986-87: 15 (22).

Student Enrolment, 1986-87:

	Men	Women	Total
Of the country	100	14	114
Of other countries	19	–	19
Total	119	14	133

2634 **ÉCOLE NATIONALE DE LA MÉTÉOROLOGIE**

Avenue Gustave Cariolis, 31057 Toulouse Cedex
Telex: 521990 MTO JD F
Telephone: 61-07-90-90
Fax: 61-07-96-30

Meteorology
Climatology

Founded 1948. Moved from Paris to Toulouse 1982. Attached to the Ministry of Transport.

Academic Year: September July.

Admission Requirements: Maitrise ès Sciences and competitive entrance examination for course leading to Diplôme d'Ingénieur de la Météorologie; secondary school certificate (baccalauréat) or equivalent, and competitive entrance examination for other courses.

Degrees and Diplomas: Diplôme–d'Ingénieur des Travaux Météorologiques; d'Ingénieur civil de la Météorologie; de Technicien de la Météorologie, 2-3 yrs.

2635 **ÉCOLE SUPÉRIEURE DE MÉTROLOGIE**

941 rue Charles Bourseul, 59508 Douai Cedex
Telephone: 27-87-16-14

Metrology (Weights and Measures)

2636 **ÉCOLE NATIONALE SUPÉRIEURE DES MINES**

Parc de Saurupt, 54042 Nancy Cedex
Telex: 850661 EMIN
Telephone: 83-57-42-32

Metallurgy
Mining

Founded 1919 as Institut métallurgique et minier, became Ecole supérieure in 1921. Acquired present title 1951. Attached to the Institut National Polytechnique de Lorraine 1969. Governing bodies: the Conseil d'administration; the Conseil scientifique. Residential facilities for students.

Arrangements for co-operation with the Massachusetts Institute of Technology.

Academic Year: September to July (September-December; January-April; April-July).

Admission Requirements: Entrance by competition following 2 yrs further study after secondary school certificate (baccalauréat) or following first university qualification (D.U.T. or D.E.U.G.).

Language of Instruction: French.

Degrees and Diplomas: Diplôme d'Ingénieur civil des Mines. Diplôme d'Ingénieur de Spécialisation en Génie des systèmesindustriels. Diplôme d'études approfondies (D.E.A.). Doctorats scientifiques.

Library: 8300 vols.

Academic Staff: c. 30 (100).

Student Enrolment: c. 220.

2637 **ÉCOLE NATIONALE SUPÉRIEURE DES MINES DE PARIS**

Paris School of Mines
60, boulevard Saint-Michel, 75272 Paris Cedex 06
Telex: 600736 MINEFON
Telephone: (1)40-51-90-00
Fax: (1)43-25-94-95
Directeur: Jacques Lévy
Directeur des Etudes: Gilbert Frade

D. of Mathematics and Applied Mathematics
Head: M. Rouchaleau
D. of Physical Sciences
Head: M. Rousset
D. of Earth Sciences
Head: M. de Graciansky
D. of Economics and Social Sciences
Head: M. Callon
D. of Modern Languages
Head: M. Boitier

Also research centres at Fontainebleau, Evry, and Sophia Antipolis covering Earth Sciences and Mining Engineering; Chemical and Mechanical Engineering; Materials Sciences; and Applied Mathematics.

Founded 1783. Attached to the Ministry of Industry. Governing bodies: the Conseil de perfectionnement; the Conseil d'établissement; the Comité d'enseignement; the Comité spécial; the Comité de la Recherche; the Comité scientifique. Residential facilities for students.

Arrangements for co-operation with: Université de Liège; Université catholique de Louvain;, Katholieke Universiteit Leuven; Tsinghua and Wuhan Universities, China; Rheinisch-Westfälische Technische Hochschule Aachen; Universität Berlin; Imperial College of Science and Technology, London; University of Cambridge; University of Manchester; Technische Universiteit, Delft; Universiteit van Amsterdam; Technion of Haifa; Escuela Técnica Superior de Ingenieros de Minas de Madrid; Massachusetts Institute of Technology; University of California at Berkeley; University of Colorado at Boulder; Drexel University; School of Mines, Leningrad.

Academic Year: September to July.

Admission Requirements: Entrance by competition following 2 yrs further study after secondary school certificate (baccalauréat) or following first university qualification (D.U.T. or D.E.U.G.). Direct entrance to second year by competition following appropriate university degree (Maîtrise).

Fees (Francs): 1100 per annum.

Language of Instruction: French.

Degrees and Diplomas: Diplôme–d'Ingénieur du Corps des Mines; d'Ingénieur civil des Mines, 3 yrs. Diplôme d'études approfondies (D.E.A.), 1 further yr. Doctorat, 2-4 yrs after D.E.A. Mastères, 1 yr, postgraduate.

Libraries: School Library, 500,000 vols; Bibliothèque des Sciences de la Terre et Cartothèque, at Fontainebleau.

Special Facilities (Museums, etc.): Museum of Mineralogy.

Academic Staff, 1989-90: 52 (250).

Student Enrolment: c. 650.

2638 ÉCOLE NATIONALE SUPÉRIEURE DES MINES DE PARIS

35, rue St. Honoré, 77305 Fontainebleau

2639 ÉCOLE NATIONALE SUPÉRIEURE DES MINES

158, cours Fauriel, 42023 Saint-Etienne Cedex
Telex: 300923 EMSE
Telephone: 77-42-01-23
Fax: 77-42-00-00
Directeur: M. Saint Raymond (1987-)
Secrétaire général: M. Piatek

D. of Computer Sciences
Director: M. Péroche
D. of Chemical Engineering
Director: M. Lancelot
D. of Materials Science
Director: M. Le Coze
D. of Mining Engineering
Director: M. Davoine
D. of Management Science
Director: M. Mathon
D. of Social Sciences and Economics
Director: M. Coinde
D. of Materials Engineering
Director: M. Verchery
D. of Geology
Director: M. Guy
D. of Mathematics
Director: M. Pla
D. of Physics
Director: M. Lowys

Founded 1816 as Ecole des Mines, became Ecole nationale 1908 and acquired present title and status 1925. Attached to the Ministry of Science and Industry. Governing body: the Conseil de perfectionnement. Residential facilities for students.

Arrangements for co-operation with the Universities of: Bradford; Minnesota; McGill; Berlin; Turin; Madrid; Manchester; Hamburg.

Academic Year: September to July (September-February; February-July).

Admission Requirements: Special one-year engineering degrees in Computer Sciences and Process Automatization: applications open to holders of B.Sc. or M.Sc., or equivalent.

Fees: None.

Language of Instruction: French.

Degrees and Diplomas: Diplôme d'Ingénieur civil des Mines, 3 yrs. Diplôme d'études approfondies (D.E.A.), 1 further yr. Doctorat, 2-4 yrs after D.E.A. Also Diplôme d'Ingénieur; Certificat de la section d'Etudes informatiques; Certificat spécial d'Automatisation des Procédés, 1 yr.

Libraries: Central Library, 8000 vols; Department Libraries, c. 10,000.

Special Facilities (Museums, etc.): Musée de Minéralogie.

Academic Staff, 1989:

Rank	Full-time	Part-time
Professeurs	15	–
Maîtres Assistants	16	–
Directeur et Maîtres de Recherche	–	12
Chargés de Recherche	–	10
Chargés de Mission	–	4
Ingénieurs de Recherche	–	7
Assistants	3	–
Total	34	33

Student Enrolment, 1989:

	Men	Women	Total
Of the country	207	41	248
Of other countries	33	–	33
Total	240	41	281*

*Also 10 external students

2640 INSTITUT NATIONAL DES SCIENCES ET TECHNIQUES NUCLÉAIRES

B.P. 6, 91190 Gif-sur-Yvette
Telephone: 69-08-24-19

Nuclear Sciences

Founded 1956. Governing body: the Conseil de l'enseignement, comprising the Recteur de l'Académie de Paris, the Haut Commissaire à l'Energie Atomique, and 28 other members drawn from important interested public and private bodies.

Academic Year: October to July.

Admission Requirements: By selection. Normal minimum requirement: Maîtrise ès Sciences, Diplôme d'Ingénieur, or professional title in Medicine, Pharmacy, or Veterinary Science.

Language of Instruction: French.

Degrees and Diplomas: Diplôme–d'Ingénieur en Génie atomique; d'Ingénieur en Génie chimique des Industries atomiques, 1 yr. Diplôme d'études approfondies (D.E.A.), 1 further yr. Doctorat, 2-4 yrs after D.E.A.

2641 ÉCOLE NATIONALE SUPÉRIEURE DU PÉTROLE ET DES MOTEURS

4, avenue de Bois-Préau, B.P. 311, 95502 Rueil-Malmaison Cedex
Telex: 203050 IFP AF
Telephone: 47-49-02-14
Fax: 47-49-04-11
Directeur: Jean Limido (1979-88)
Secrétaire général: Daniel Godot

Ce. for Geological and Geophysical Processing
Director: Michel Lavergne; *staff* 14 (88)
Ce. for Drilling and Exploitation of Oil Reserves
Director: Gilbert Sablayrolles; *staff* 12 (56)
Ce. for Chemical Engineering and Refining
Director: Daniel Decroocq; *staff* 8 (76)
Ce. for Motors and Utilization of Petroleum Products
Director: G. Marion; *staff* 7 (60)
Ce. for Petroleum Economics
Director: Jean Masseron; *staff* 13 (106)

Founded 1924, fused with Ecole nationale des Moteurs 1954 to form Ecole nationale supérieure. Responsible tothe Ministries of Industry and of Education. Governing body: the Conseil de perfectionnement. Residential facilities for foreign students.

Arrangements for co-operation with: University of Western Ontario; Université catholique de Louvain; Universidade Técnica de Lisboa; Université de Lausanne; Universidad Politécnica de Barcelona; Ecole Polytechnique de Montréal; University of Caracas.

Academic Year: September to July.

Admission Requirements: Diplôme d'Ingénieur or Maîtrise ès Sciences or recognized foreign equivalent.

Language of Instruction: French.

Degrees and Diplomas: Diplôme d'Ingénieur, 1-2 yrs. Diplôme d'études approfondies (D.E.A.), 1 yr. Doctorat, 2-4 yrs after D.E.A.

Library: 260,000 vols.

Publications: Revue de l'IFP; Cours.

Press or Publishing House: Technip S.A.R.L.
Academic Staff, 1986-87:

Rank	Full-time	Part-time
Professeurs	21	37
Professeurs associés	–	27
Professeurs assistants	6	8
Chargés d'enseignement	10	41
Chargés de conférences	3	276
Total	41	389

Student Enrolment, 1986-87:

	Men	Women	Total
Of the country	143	28	171
Of other countries	44	3	47
Total	187	31	218

Schools of Engineering

2642 **ÉCOLE NATIONALE SUPÉRIEURE DE PHYSIQUE**
Domaine Universitaire, B.P. 46, 38402 Saint-Martin-d'Hyères Cedex
Telephone: 76-82-62-00

2643 **ÉCOLE NATIONALE SUPÉRIEURE DE PHYSIQUE DE MARSEILLE**
Domaine Universitaire de Saint-Jérôme, 13397 Marseille Cedex 4
Telex: 402876 FACST J E
Telephone: 91-28-80-89
Fax: 91-28-80-67
Directeur: Serge J. Huard
Secrétaire générale: Janine Bliek

Applied Physics

Founded 1959, recognized by the State 1963. Attached to the Université d'Aix-Marseille III.

Arrangements for student exchange with: Ecole polytechnique, Montréal; Université de Laval.

Academic Year: September to July.

Admission Requirements: Entrance by competition following 2 yrs further study after secondary school certificate (baccalauréat) or following first university qualification (D.U.T. or D.E.U.G.).

Fees (Francs): 2000 per annum.

Language of Instruction: French.

Degrees and Diplomas: Diplôme d'Ingénieur, 3 yrs. Diplôme d'études approfondies (D.E.A.), 1 yr.

Library: c. 1200 vols.

Publication: Sup Phy Actualités (biannually).

Academic Staff, 1990: 22 (13).

Student Enrolment, 1990:

	Men	Women	Total
Of the country	170	20	190
Of other countries	10	–	10
Total	180	20	200

2644 **ÉCOLE SUPÉRIEURE DE PHYSIQUE ET CHIMIE INDUSTRIELLES DE LA VILLE DE PARIS**
10, rue Vauquelin, 75231 Paris Cedex 05
Telephone: 40-79-44-00
Fax: 43-31-42-22
Directeur: Pierre-Gilles de Gennes

Physics of Liquids and Electrochemistry
Head: Michel Froment; *staff* 7
Polymer Physical Chemistry and Spectroscopy
Dean: Lucien Monnerie; *staff* 27
Electrical Engineering
Dean: J. Lecoiner; *staff* 17
Physical and Applied Mechanics
Director: J.-P. Hulin; *staff* 17
Analytical Chemistry
Heads: Robert Rosset; Denise Bauer; *staff* 57
Electronics
Head: Gérard Dreyfus; *staff* 14
Optics
Head: Albert-Claude Boccara; *staff* 30
Acoustoelectricity
Head: Eugène Dieulesaint; *staff* 10
Ceramics and Inorganic Materials
Head: Philippe Boch; *staff* 10
Inorganic Chemistry
Head: Jacques Simon; *staff* 22
Non-Destructive Testing
Head: D. Fournier; *staff* – (20)
Organic Chemistry
Head: Jean Rigaudy; *staff* 23
Polymer Physical Chemistry
Director: Roland Audebert; *staff* – (19)
Quantum Physics
Head: André-Pierre Legrand; *staff* 29
Solid State Physics
Head: Julien Bok; *staff* 11
Theoretical Physical Chemistry
Director: Jacques Prost; *staff* 10
Thermal Physics
Heads: Pierre Papon; Jacques Leblond; *staff* 13 (3)
Waves and Acoustics
Director: Mathias Fink; *staff* 10
Superconductivity Group
Head: Julien Bok; *staff* 16

Founded 1882 by the City of Paris. Governing body: the Conseil d'administration, comprising 38 members, and presided over by the Mayor of Paris.

Academic Year: September to June (September-December; January-March; April-June).

Admission Requirements: Entrance by competition following 2 yrs further study after secondary school certificate (baccalauréat) or following first university qualification. Direct entrance to third year by to third year by competition following appropriate university degree (Maîtrise or Diplôme d'Ingénieur).

Fees (Francs): 650 per annum.

Language of Instruction: French.

Degrees and Diplomas: Diplôme d'Ingénieur, 4 yrs. Diplôme d'études approfondies (D.E.A.), 1 further yr. Doctorat, 2-4 yrs after D.E.A.

Special Facilities (Museums, etc.): History of Sciences Centre.

Academic Staff: c. 50 (20).

Student Enrolment, 1990: 288.

2645 **ÉCOLE NATIONALE SUPÉRIEURE DE PHYSIQUE DE STRASBOURG**
7, rue de l'Université, 67000 Strasbourg
Telex: 870260 ULP F
Telephone: 88-35-51-50
Directeur: F. Becker

Basic and Applied Mathematics, Physics, Science and Technology, Computer Sciences, Languages, Human Sciences

Also 3 Research Laboratories.

Founded 1981. Affiliated to the Université Louis-Pasteur (Strasbourg I), and enjoys complete autonomy. An institution for training and research. Governing body: the Board of Trustees.

Arrangements for co-operation with: University of Budapest; University of Karlsruhe; University of Munich; Royal Institute of Technology, Sweden.

Academic Year: October to June.

Admission Requirements: Graduation from high school and entrance examination.

Fees (Francs): 1500 per annum.

Language of Instruction: French.

Academic Staff, 1990: 40 (64).

Student Enrolment, 1990:

	Men	Women	Total
Of the country	116	31	147*

*Including 6 foreign students.

2646 **ÉCOLE ET OBSERVATOIRE DE PHYSIQUE DU GLOBE DE STRASBOURG**

5, rue René Descartes, 67084 Strasbourg Cedex
Telex: 870260 ULP F
Telephone: (33) 88-41-63-00
Fax: (33) 88-61-67-47
Directeur: R. Schlich (1980-93)
Directeurs adjoints: M. Cara; Y. Gueguen

Teaching
Research
Observatory

Founded 1919. Attached to the Université Louis-Pasteur (Strasbourg I).

Academic Year: October to June.

Admission Requirements: Entrance by competition following 2 yrs further study after secondary school certificate (baccalauréat) or following first university qualification (D.U.T. or D.E.U.G.).

Language of Instruction: French.

Degrees and Diplomas: Diplôme d'Ingénieur géophysicien, 3 yrs and mémoire.

Academic Staff, 1989-90: 74.

Student Enrolment, 1989-90: 82.

2647 **ÉCOLE POLYTECHNIQUE**

Route de Saclay, 91128 Palaiseau Cedex
Telex: 691596ECOLEX F
Telephone: 69-41-82-00
Fax: 69-41-33-92
Directeur général: Dominique Chavanat (1985-)
Directeur de l'Enseignement et de la Recherche: Maurice Bernard

D. of Mathematics
Head: Alain Guichardet; *staff* 10 (19)
D. of Applied Mathematics
Head: M. Métivier; *staff* 6 (34)
D. of Economics
Head: Thierry de Montbrial; *staff* 1 (23)
D. of Mechanical Engineering
Head: Jean Salençon; *staff* 3 (28)
D. of Physics
Dean: Yves Ouère; *staff* 2 (43)
D. of Chemistry
Head: Marcel Fetizon; *staff* 4 (14)
D. of Humanities and Social Sciences
Head: Jean Doulcier; *staff* 4 (9)
Also 18 associated laboratories and research centres.

Founded in Paris 1794. Transferred to Palaiseau 1976. A State institution under the jurisdiction of the Ministry of Defence. Governing body: the Conseil d'administration, comprising 20 members. Residential facilities for all students.

Academic Year: September to July.

Admission Requirements: Entrance by competition following 2 yrs further study after secondary school certificate (baccalauréat) or following first university qualification.

Fees (Francs): 130,000 for foreign students.

Language of Instruction: French.

Degrees and Diplomas: Diplôme d'Ingénieur de l'Ecole polytechnique, 2 yrs.

Library: c. 300,000 vols.

Academic Staff, 1986-87:

Rank	Full-time	Part-time
Professeurs	11	21
Maîtres de conférences	17	151
Chefs et Attachés de Travaux pratiques	8	19
Total	36	191

Student Enrolment, 1986-87:

	Men	Women	Total
Of the country	614	55	669
Of other countries	49	3	52
Total	663	58	721*

*Also 337 external students.

2648 **ÉCOLE NATIONALE DES PONTS ET CHAUSSÉES**

28, rue des Saints-Pères, 75007 Paris
Telex: 216278 F
Telephone: 42-60-34-13
Fax: 42-60-34-13
Directeur: Bernard Hirsch (1983-88)
Secrétaire général: Paule Neidhart

Civil Engineering
Lifelong Education

Founded 1747 as Bureau des Dessinateurs. A State institution under the jurisdiction of the Ministry of Development, Housing and Transport. The members of the academic staff are selected from among practising engineers, architects, lawyers, and economists. Governing bodies: the Conseil de perfectionnement; the Conseil d'enseignement et de recherche.

Arrangements for co-operation with: University of Colorado; University of Louisiana; University of California-Berkeley; Universidad de Barcelona; University of Qinghua, Beijing; University of Southampton; Université de Tunis; Ecole nationale des Travaux publics, Algérie; Ecole nationale supérieure des Travaux publics, Abidjan; Indian Institute of Technology, Bombay; Politecnico di Milano; Ecole Hassania des Travaux publics, Casablanca; Ecole Polytechnique fédérale de Lausanne; College of Communications and Transport, Hanoi.

Academic Year: September to June (October-December; January-March April-June).

Admission Requirements: Entrance by competition following 2 yrs further study after secondary school certificate (baccalauréat) or following first university qualification (D.U.T. or D.E.U.G.). Direct entrance to second year by competition following appropriate university degree (Maîtrise).

Language of Instruction: French.

Degrees and Diplomas: Diplôme d'Ingénieur civil des Ponts et Chaussées, 3 yrs. Also Certificats d'études supérieures, 1 yr. Diplôme d'études approfondies, 1 yr. Diplômes de Docteur-Ingénieur du Génie civil, 2-4 yrs. Also Diplôme d'Urbaniste de l'Etat; Diplôme d'Ingénieur des Travaux de la Ville de Paris, 1 yr.

Library: Centre pédagogique de documentation et de communication, 170,000 vols.

Publications: Annales (quarterly); Revue française de Géotechnique.

Press or Publishing House: Imprimerie intégrée et Service des Publications.

Academic Staff: c. 375.

Student Enrolment: c. 640.

2649 **INSTITUT NATIONAL DES SCIENCES APPLIQUÉES DE LYON**

20, avenue Albert-Einstein, 69621 Villeurbanne Cedex
Telex: 380856 INSALYN F
Telephone: 78-94-81-25
Directeur: Raymond Hamelin (1974-)
Secrétaire général: Pierre Blanc

D. of Basic Sciences
Head: C. Guillaud; *staff* 140 (14)
D. of Biochemistry
Head: L. Cronenberger; *staff* 21 (13)
D. of Data Processing
Head: R. Arnal; *staff* 37 (38)
D. of Electrical Engineering
Head: H. Kleimann; *staff* 35 (36)
D. of Physical Engineering
Head: J. Robin; *staff* 31 (28)
D. of Civil Engineering and Urbanism
Head: N. Mongereau; *staff* 36 (111)
D. of Mechanical Engineering (Construction)
Head: Claude Marty; *staff* 48 (34)
D. of Mechanical Engineering (Development)
Head: D. Berthe; *staff* 20 (24)
D. of Energetic Engineering
Head: A. Lallemand; *staff* 22 (17)
Ce. for Humanities
Head: J. Bonnefon; *staff* 4 (75)
Extension D.
D. for Lifelong Education
Head: R. Terracher; *staff* – (40)
Also 33 research laboratories.

Founded 1957. Responsible to the Ministry of Education. Governing body: the Conseil d'administration. Residential facilities for foreign academic staff and students at the Cité universitaire.

Arrangements for co-operation with: Free University of Brussel (Bruxelles); University of Sofia; University of Leeds; Delft University of Technology; Université Laval; Ecole polytechnique de Montréal; Université de Sherbrooke; Tufts University; Pennsylvania State University; Illinois Institute of Technology; Washington University, Missouri; University of Central Florida; Louisiana State University; National Polytechnic Institute, Mexico; University of Sydney; New South Wales Institute of Technology, Sydney; Rheinisch-Westfälische Technische Hochschule, Aachen; Universität Karlsruhe; Karl Marx Universität Leipzig; Technische Universität Berlin; Université d'Annaba; Université de Yaoundé; Ecole nationale d'Ingénieurs, Bamako; Mohammed V University, Rabat; Ecole nationale de l'Industrie minérale, Rabat; University of Tunis; Faculté des Sciences de l'Université de Tunis, Monastir; University of Petroleum and Minerals, Dahran; Ain Shams University;Lebanese University; Qinghua University, Beijing; Hefei Plasma Physics Institute, Anhui; East China College of Chemical Engineering, Shanghai; Indian Institute of Technology, New Delhi; University of Campinas; Federal University of Santa Catarina; Federal University of Minas Gerais; National University of Mar del Plata.

Academic Year: September to June (September-February; February-June).

Admission Requirements: Entrance by competition following 2 yrs further study after secondary school certificate (baccalauréat) or following first university qualification (D.U.T. or D.E.U.G.). Direct entrance to second year by competition following appropriate university degree (Maîtrise).

Fees (Francs): 523 per annum.

Language of Instruction: French.

Degrees and Diplomas: Diplôme d'Ingénieur (with mention of field of specialization), 5 yrs. Diplôme d'études approfondies (D.E.A.), 1 further yr. Doctorat in various fields of specialization, 2-4 yrs after D.E.A.

Library: c. 35,000 vols.

Academic Staff, 1986-87:

Rank	Full-time	Part-time
Professeurs	77	24
Maîtres de conférences	156	12
Maîtres-Assistants et Assistants	92	34
Professeurs agrégés	35	12
Professeurs certifiés	17	15
Vacataires	–	279
Divers	44	17
Total	421	393

Student Enrolment, 1986-87:

	Men	Women	Total
Of the country	2888	860	3748
Of other countries	423	55	478
Total	3311	915	4226

2650 INSTITUT NATIONAL DES SCIENCES APPLIQUÉES DE RENNES

20, avenue des Buttes de Coësmes, 35043 Rennes Cedex
Telephone: 99-28-64-00
Fax: 99-63-67-05
Directeur: Claude Chicoix (1983-88)
Secrétaire général: Christian Labelle

D. of Basic Studies
Head: Mme Labaud
D. of Civil Engineering
Head: M. Perrichet
D. of Electrical Engineering
Head: M. Place
D. of Physical Engineering
Head: M. Pelletier
D. of Computer Sciences
Head: M. Camillerapp

Founded 1961, opened 1966 and responsible to the Ministry of Education. Governing body: the Conseil d'administration. Residential facilities for academic staff and students.

Academic Year: September to June (September-February; February-June).

Admission Requirements: Entrance by competition following 2 yrs further study after secondary school certificate (baccalauréat) or following first university qualification (D.U.T. or D.E.U.G.). Direct entrance to second year by competition following appropriate university degree (Maîtrise).

Language of Instruction: French.

Degrees and Diplomas: Diplôme d'Ingénieur (with mention of field of specialization), 5 yrs. Diplôme d'études approfondies (D.E.A.), 1 further yr. Doctorat in various fields of specialization, 2-4 yrs after D.E.A.

Library: c. 7500 vols.

Academic Staff, 1986-87: 94.

Student Enrolment, 1986-87:

	Men	Women	Total
Of the country	650	173	823
Of other countries	49	12	61
Total	699	185	884

2651 INSTITUT NATIONAL DES SCIENCES APPLIQUÉES DE ROUEN

Place Emile Blondel, B.P. 8, 76130 Mont-Saint-Aignan
Telephone: 35-71-29-72

2652 INSTITUT NATIONAL DES SCIENCES APPLIQUÉES DE TOULOUSE

Avenue de Rangueil, 31077 Toulouse Cedex
Telex: 9336152 8123 INSATLSE
Telephone: 61-55-95-13
Fax: 61-55-95-00
Directeur: Armand Sarazin (1976-)
Secrétaire général: Amédée Cini

D. of Civil Engineering and Town Planning
Head: M. Javelas; *staff* 15 (20)
D. of Electrical Engineering (including Computer Sciences)
Head: M. Martinez
D. of Mechanical Engineering
Head: M. Briot
D. of Physics
Head: M. Fert
D. of Biochemical Engineering and Food Technology
L. of Solid State Physics
Director: N. Benazeth
Service in High Magnetic Field Studies
Head: S. Askenazy

Founded 1961. Responsible to the Ministry of Education. Governing body: the Conseil d'administration. Residential facilities for visiting academic staff and students.

Arrangements for co-operation with: Ecole d'Ingénieurs de Tunis et de Gabès; Chulalongkorn University; Instituto Universitario de Tecnología, Caracas; Université du Québec; Bandung Institute of Technology; Xi'an University; Technical University of Lublin; Technical University of Gdańsk; University of Surrey; Universidad de Barcelona; Universités de Louvain et de Liège; Turin Polytechnique.

Academic Year: October to June (October-February; February-June).

Admission Requirements: Entrance by competition following 2 yrs further study after secondary school certificate (baccalauréat) or following first university qualification (D.U.T. or D.E.U.G.). Direct entrance to second year by competition following appropriate university degree (Maîtrise).

Language of Instruction: French.

Degrees and Diplomas: Diplôme d'Ingénieur (with mention of field of specialisation), 5 yrs. Diplôme d'études approfondies (D.E.A.), 1 further yr. Doctorat in various fields of specialization, 2-4 yrs after D.E.A.

Library: Department libraries, 30,500 vols.

Academic Staff, 1989-90:

Rank	Full-time
Professeurs	42
Maîtres de conférences	71
Maîtres-Assistants	1
Assistants	15
Lecteurs	2
Professeurs agrégés et assimilés	8
Professeurs certifiés	7
Adjoints d'enseignement	5
Total	151

Student Enrolment, 1989-90:

	Men	Women	Total
Of the country	937	393	1330
Of other countries	94	24	118
Total	1031	417	1448

2653 **UNIVERSITÉ DE TECHNOLOGIE DE COMPIÈGNE**

Technical University of Compiègne
Rue Roger, 60206 Compiègne Cedex
Telex: UNITECH 150110F
Telephone: 44-20-99-77
Fax: 44-20-43-88
Président: Michel Lavalou (1987-)
Secrétaire général: J.C. Muller

D. of Mechanical Technology
Head: Jean-François Chrétien; *staff* 43
D. of Biological Technology
Head: Georges Chevalier; *staff* 27
D. of Chemical Technology
Head: Roger Ben Aim; *staff* 23
D. of Computer Engineering
Head: Christian Melen; *staff* 30 (1)
D. of Vocational Guidance and Lifelong Education
Head: Nicole Jaffren
Human Sciences and Technology D.
Head: Lilane Vezier; *staff* 21 (1)
D. for Systems and Surface Engineering (Sevenans)
Head: Gilbert Karpman; *staff* 21
D. of Lifelong Education (Industrial Relations)
Director: Michel Cordonnier; *staff* 3
Research Ce.
Information Management I. (Paris)
Director: Gérad Balantzian

Founded 1972, admitted first students 1973. An experimental State institution established under the 1968 law reforming higher education as the first technological university in France, and planned for a student enrolmentof 3000. It combines the characteristics of both a univeristy and a 'Grande Ecole d'Ingénieurs'. Governing body: the Conseil d'Administration of 25 members, 15 appointed by the Minister of Education, and 10 elected members. Residential facilities for students.

Arrangements for co-operation with institutes of higher education in: Belgium, Denmark, Spain, Finland, United Kingdom, Greece, Hungary, Italy, Luxembourg, Netherlands, Portugal, Germany, Sweden, Côte d'Ivoire, Egypt, Morocco, Brazil, Canada, USA, People's Republic of China, Republic of Korea, India, Australia.

Academic Year: September to July (September-January; February-July).

Admission Requirements: Secondary school certificate (baccalauréat) or equivalent, or special entrance examination.

Fees (Francs): 500 per annum.

Languages of Instruction: French and English.

Degrees and Diplomas: Diplôme d'études universitaires technologiques (D.E.U.Tec.), 2 yrs. Diplôme d'Ingénieur in relevant field, 5 yrs; Diplôme d'études approfondies (D.E.A.), 1 yr after Maîtrise; Doctorat, 2-4 yrs after D.E.A.; Diplôme d'études supérieures spécialisées (D.E.S.S.), 1 yr after Maîtrise; Master, 1 yr after Maîtrise.

Library: 55,000 vols.

Special Facilities (Museums, etc.): Movie Studio (Multimedia).

Publication: Info UTC (weekly).

Press or Publishing House: 'Editions Publications'.

Academic Staff, 1989-90: c. 200.

Student Enrolment, 1989-90: c. 2500 (Including 48 foreign students).

2654 **ÉCOLE NATIONALE SUPÉRIEURE DE TECHNIQUES AVANCÉES**

32, boulevard Victor, 75015 Paris
Telephone: (1) 45-52-44-08
Directeur: J.-M. Buscailhon (1982-)

D.of Naval Engineering
Head: Alain Saleur
D. of Chemistry and Physics
Head: Henri Renon
D. of Economics and Administration
Head: Claude Perget
D. of Electrical Engineering, Electronics and Telecommunication
Head: Bogdan Grabowski
D. of Computer Sciences and Automation
Head: Michel Deparis
D. of Materials and Structures
Head: Jacques Kerbrat
D. of Oceanography and Hydrography
Head: André Roubertou
D. of Energetics
Head: Jean-François Roy
D. of Nuclear Technology
Head: Michel Ferry
D. of Mechanics and Vehicles
Head: André Dufoux
D. of Languages
Head: Maurice Gautier
D. of Applied Mathematics
Head: Pierre Bremaud

Founded 1970 and incorporating former Ecole nationale supérieure du Génie maritime, founded 1765 at the Louvre as Ecole des Elèves-Ingénieurs Constructeurs; Ecole d'Application du Service Hydrographique (1814); Ecole nationale supérieure de l'Armement (1936); and Ecole nationale supérieure des Poudres. Responsible tothe Ministry of Defence.

Academic Year: September to July (September-December; January-March; April-July).

Admission Requirements: Entrance by competition following 2 yrs further study after secondary school certificate (baccalauréat).

Fees (Francs): 450 per month.

Language of Instruction: French.

Degrees and Diplomas: Diplôme d'Ingénieur, 2-3 yrs; Diplôme d'études approfondies (D.E.A.), 1 further yr. Doctorat, 2-4 yrs after D.E.A.

Library: 6000 vols.

Press or Publishing House: Service Edition ENSTA.

Academic Staff, 1986-87: – (777).

Student Enrolment, 1986-87:

	Men	Women	Total
Of the country	305	60	365
Of other countries	21	1	22
Total	326	61	387

2655 **ÉCOLE NATIONALE SUPÉRIEURE DES TÉLÉCOMMUNICATIONS DE BRETAGNE**

B.P. 832, 29285 Brest Cedex
Telex: 940729
Telephone: 98-00-11-11
Fax: 98-45-51-33
Directeur: Alain Rousseaux

D. of Electronics and Physics
Head: Serge Toutain; *staff* 35 (80)
D. of Mathematics and Communication Systems
Head: Alain Hillion; *staff* 30 (70)
D. of Computer Sciences
Head: Robert Rannou; *staff* 23 (70)
D. of Networks and Multimedia Systems
Head: Gilbert Martineau; *staff* 5 (40)
D. of Economics
Head: Godefroy Dang N'Guyen; *staff* 4 (40)
D. of Modern Languages
Head: Michel Marc; *staff* 8 (35)
D. of Continuing Education
Head: Jean-Pierre Bonne; *staff* 5 (100)

Founded 1977. Responsible to the Ministry of Posts and Telecommunications. Governing body: the Conseil de perfectionnement. Some residential facilities for students.

Arrangements for student exchange with: Aston University; University College, London; ETSIT, Barcelona; Universidad de Valencia. Joint research projects with: Technische Universität, Munich; Sherbrooke University, Canada.

Academic Year: October to June.

Admission Requirements: Entrance by competition following 2 yrs further study after secondary school certificate (baccalauréat) or first university qualification (D.U.T. or D.E.U.G.). Direct entrance to second year by competition following appropriate university degree (Maîtrise).

Fees (Francs): *c.* 1500 per annum.

Language of Instruction: French.

Degrees and Diplomas: Diplôme d'Ingénieur, 3 yrs. Diplôme d'études approfondies (D.E.A.), 1 further yr; Doctorat, 2-4 yrs after D.E.A. Also certificates.

Library: School Library.

Academic Staff, 1990:

Rank	Full-time
Professeurs	9
Senior Lecturers	31
Lecturers	43
Total	83

Student Enrolment, 1989-90:

	Men	Women	Total
Of the country	315	55	370
Of other countries	35	3	38
Total	350	58	408

2656 **INSTITUT NATIONAL DES TÉLÉCOMMUNICATIONS**

9, rue Charles Fourier, Ilot des Epinettes, 91011 Evry Cedex
Telex: 940729 DIRENSG F
Telephone: 60-77-94-11
Directeur: Jean-Pierre Achouche (1989-)
Secrétaire général: Jean Lecacheux

S. of Engineering
Director: Michel Trelluyer
S. of Management
Director: Jean-Pierre Pecoul
D. of Continuing Education
Director: Michel Le Bricquir

Founded 1979. Responsible to the Ministry of Posts, Telecommunications, and Space. Residential facilities for students.

Academic Year: September to July.

Admission Requirements: Entrance by competition following 2 yrs further study after secondary school certificate (baccalauréat). Direct entrance to second year by competition following appropriate university degree (Maîtrise).

Fees (Francs): 1150.

Language of Instruction: French.

Degrees and Diplomas: Diplôme d'Ingénieur; Diplôme de Gestion des Télécommunications. Also Certificate. Masters.

Press or Publishing House: Intrépide.

Academic Staff, 1989-90: 124 (800).

Student Enrolment, 1989-90: 470 (50).

2657 **ÉCOLE NATIONALE SUPÉRIEURE DES TÉLÉCOMMUNICATIONS**

46, rue Barrault, 75013 Paris
Telex: 200180 SUPTLCM
Telephone: (1) 45-89-77-77
Fax: (1) 45-89-54-42
Directeur: Jean Herr
Secrétaire général: Gérard Corré

Computer Sciences D.
Chairman: Anne Germa; *staff* 24
Humanities D.
Chairman: Yves Jeanneret; *staff* 3
D. of Continuing Education
Director: Pierre Baylet; *staff* – (400)
D. of Aerospace Communications
Chairman: Gérard Maral; *staff* 3
Languages D.
Chairman: Barbara Fietkau; *staff* 4
Signal D.
Chairman: Henri Barral; *staff* 23
Communications D.
Chairman: Philippe Gallion; *staff* 16
Economics D.
Chairman: Laurent Benzoni
Electronics D.
Chairman: Francis Jutand; *staff* 17
Images D.
Chairman: Henri Maître; *staff* 22
Networks D.
Chairman: Samie Tommé; *staff* 12

Also Theseus Institute, Sophia-Antipolis, France.

Founded 1878 as Ecole supérieure de Télégraphie, became Ecole nationale supérieure 1942. Responsible to the Ministry of Posts, Telecommunications, and Space. Governing body: the Conseil de perfectionnement. Residential facilities for students.

Arrangements for co-operation with: University of Stuttgart; University of Ottawa; Texas A & M University; Royal Institute of Technology of Sweden; University of Surrey. Also participates in the ERASMUS and COMETT programmes.

Academic Year: September to June.

Admission Requirements: Entrance by competition following 2 yrs further study after secondary school certificate (baccalauréat). Direct entrance to second year by competition following appropriate university degree (Maîtrise).

Fees (Francs): 1300.

Languages of Instruction: French and English.

Degrees and Diplomas: Diplôme d'Ingénieur civil, 3 yrs; Diplôme d'études approfondies (D.E.A.), 1 further yr. Doctorat, 2-4 yrs after D.E.A. Also Certificate, 1 yr. Mastère, 1 yr; MBA, 1 yr.

Library: Documentation and Information Centre, 18,000 vols.

Special Facilities (Museums, etc.): Movie Studio.

Publications: Collection CNET-ENST; Collection pédagogique de Télécommunication.

Press or Publishing House: Imprimerie de l'Ecole.

Academic Staff, 1989: c. 100.

Student Enrolment, 1989: c. 783.

2658 **ÉCOLE NATIONALE SUPÉRIEURE DES INDUSTRIES TEXTILES**

11, rue Alfred-Werner, 68093 Mulhouse Cedex
Telephone: 89-59-63-20
Fax: 89-59-63-39
Directeur: C. Wolff (1986-91)

D. of Textile Engineering
Head: A. Kirschner; *staff* 17 (19)
D. of Clothing Engineering
Head: B. Durand; *staff* 2 (6)
Textile Physics and Mechanics L.
Head: P. Viallier; *staff* 14 (14)

Founded 1861 as Ecole supérieure de Filature, became Ecole supérieure des Industries textiles 1966. Acquired present title 1977. Attached to the Université de Haute-Alsace. Governing body: the Board of Trustees, comprising 26 members, including 13 representatives of industry.

Arrangements for co-operation with the Universities of: Strathclyde; Wales, Minho; Beira Interior, Covilhã; Łódź; Tunis. Ecole polytechnique de Montréal.

Academic Year: September to July (September-December; January-March; April-June).

Admission Requirements: Entrance by competition following 2 yrs further study after secondary school certificate (baccalauréat) or following first university qualification (D.U.T. or B.T.S.).

Fees (Francs): 450 per annum.

Language of Instruction: French.

Degrees and Diplomas: Diplôme d'Ingénieur, 3 yrs. Diplôme d'études approfondies (D.E.A.), 1 further yr. Doctorat, 2-4 yrs after D.E.A.

Academic Staff, 1990-91:

Rank	Full-time	Part-time
Professeurs	9	1
Maîtres de conférences	6	–
Chefs de travaux ENSAM	6	–
Industriels vacataires	–	17
Professeurs de Langues vivantes	1	7
Total	22	25

Student Enrolment, 1989-90:

	Men	Women	Total
Of the country	120	24	144
Of other countries	15	10	25
Total	135	34	169*

*Also 4 external students.

2659 **ÉCOLE NATIONALE SUPÉRIEURE DES ARTS ET INDUSTRIES TEXTILES DE ROUBAIX**

2, place des Martyrs-de-la-Résistance, 59070 Roubaix Cedex 01
Cables: Ensait
Telephone: (33) 20-25-64-51
Fax: (33) 20-24-84-06,
Electronic mail: minitel 3615 ensait
Directeur: Christian Vasseur
Intendante: Michelle Schryve

D. of Textile Production Management
Head: Christian Vasseur; *staff* 12 (3)
D. of Textile Chemistry
Head: Serge Crutel; *staff* 12 (3)

Founded 1889 as school of industrial arts, became Ecole nationale supérieure 1930. Financed by the State andby industry. Governing body: the Board of Directors.

Participates in Eurotex Vetp (EEC Comett) programme.

Academic Year: October to June (October-February; February-June).

Admission Requirements: Entrance by competition following 2 yrs further study after secondary school certificate (baccalauréat) or following first university qualification (D.U.T. or D.E.U.G.).

Fees: None.

Language of Instruction: French.

Degrees and Diplomas: Diplôme d'Ingénieur, 5 yrs. Mastère, 1 yr.

Library: School Library, *c.* 15,000 vols.

Academic Staff, 1989-90:

Rank	Full-time
Professeurs d'Université	1
Maîtres de conférences	6
Professeurs agrégés	8
Professeurs certifiés	10
Total	25

Student Enrolment, 1989-90:

	Men	Women	Total
Of the country	145	20	165
of other countries	10	5	15
Total	155	25	180

2660 **ÉCOLE TECHNIQUE SUPÉRIEURE DES TRAVAUX IMMOBILIERS ET MARITIMES**

Rue Maurice-Audin, 69120 Vaulx-en-Velin
Telephone: 78-80-62-69

Civil and Maritime Construction

2661 **ÉCOLE NATIONALE DES TRAVAUX PUBLICS DE L'ÉTAT**

Rue Maurice Audin, 69120 Vaulx-en-Velin
Telex: 37 0511 ENTPC F
Telephone: 72-04-70-70
Fax: 72-04-62-54
Directeur: Daniel Sene
Secrétaire général: Jean-Pierre Rossignol

D. of Public Works and Civil Engineering
Head: Henri Lourdaux
D. of Management and Human Sciences
Head: Pierre Robin
D. of Planning and Environment
Head: Patrick Nancy
D. of Mechanics and Computer Sciences
Head: René-Michel Faure
D. of Mathematics
Head: Maurice Pruvost
Geomaterials L.
Head: Hervé di Benedetto; *staff* 20 (1)
L. of Housing Sciences
Head: Gérard Guarracino; *staff* 9 (2)
L. of Environment Engineering and Ecodevelopment
Head: Yvette Bouvet; *staff* 6 (3)
L. of Transportation Economy
Head: Didier Plat; *staff* 8 (2)
Planing, Society, and Territory L.
Head: Josée Jeanneret; *staff* 6
Evaluation of Public Organizations and Policies L.
Head: Eric Monnier; *staff* 7

Founded 1891, became State institution 1953. Responsible to the Ministry of Development, Housing and Transport. Governing body: the Conseil de perfectionnement.

Arrangements for co-operation with: Municipal Technical College, Addis Ababa; Université Libanaise; Technical University of Warsaw; Université Laval; Virginia Polytechnic Institute and State University, University ofCalifornia, Berkeley; MIT.

Academic Year: October to June (October-December; January-March, April-June).

Admission Requirements: Entrance by competition following 2 yrs further study after secondary school certificate (baccalauréat) or following first university qualification (foreign students).

Language of Instruction: French.

Degrees and Diplomas: Diplôme d'Ingénieur des Travaux publics de l'Etat, 3 yrs. Also Certificat d'études supérieures, 1 yr (for foreign students).

Publication: Echanges TPE (quarterly).

Academic Staff, 1989-90: – (500).

Student Enrolment, 1989-90:

	Men	Women	Total
Of the country	241	45	286
Of other countries	130	9	139
Total	371	54	425

Schools of Agriculture and Food Technology

2662 **ÉCOLE SUPÉRIEURE DE FORMATION AGRICOLE**

44, rue Rabelais, 49044 Angers Cedex
Telephone: 41-88-58-12

2663 **ÉCOLE NATIONALE DE FORMATION AGRONOMIQUE**

National Training College of Agronomy
Route de Narbonne, B.P. 87, 31326 Castenet-Tolosan Cedex
Telex: (933) 61-75-03-09 ENFA
Telephone: 61-73-04-25
Directeur: Gilbert F. Bonnes
Secrétarie général: H. George

Agricultural Education

Founded 1961. Responsible to the Ministry of Agriculture. Residential facilities for students.

Arrangements for co-operation with: University of Atlanta; University of Athens.

Academic Year: September to June (September-December; January-March; April-June).

Admission Requirements: Entrance by competition following 2 yrs further study after secondary school certificate (baccalauréat) or following first university qualification (T.S. or D.E.U.G.). For teacher training, Licence.

Fees: None.

Language of Instruction: French.

Degrees and Diplomas: Certificat d'Aptitude à l'enseignement. Brevet de Technicien supérieur, 2 yrs. Diplôme d'Assistant Ingénieur, 1 yr. Diplôme d'études approfondies (D.E.A.).

Library: Centre de Documentation, 12,000 vols.

Academic Staff, 1989-90: 35 (15).
Student Enrolment, 1989-90:

	Total
Of the country	347
Of other countries	21
Total	368

2664 **ÉCOLE NATIONALE D'INGÉNIEURS DES TECHNIQUES AGRICOLES (OPTION HORTICULTURE)**
2, rue Le Nôtre, 49045 Angers Cedex
Telephone: 41-48-36-24
Directeur: Jean-Pierre Bigre (1984-89)
Secrétaire général: Robert Lavigne

Horticulture StudiesČHead: Jacques Boccon-Gibod; *staff* 5
Also 9 Research Laboratories.

Founded 1971. Responsible to the Ministry of Agriculture. Governing bodies: the Conseil général; the Conseil de l'Enseignement et de la Pédagogie; the Conseil intérieur; the Conseil de Discipline; the Conseil des Enseignants; the Conseil scientifique. Residential facilities for students.

Arrangements for co-operation with: University of Bath; Fachhochschule Osnabrück and Weihenstephan; Institute of Architecture, Leningrad. Also participates in the ERASMUS programme.

Academic Year: October to June (October-December; January-March; April-June).

Admission Requirements: Competitive entrance examination following 1 yr further study after secondary school certificate (baccalauréat).

Fees (Francs): 600 per annum; foreign students, 6000.

Language of Instruction: French.

Degrees and Diplomas: Diplôme d'Ingénieur des Techniques de l'Horticulture et du Paysage, 3 yrs.

Library: Centre de Documentation, 9300 vols.

Publication: Résultats d'expérimentations et d'essais (annually).

Academic Staff, 1989-90:

Rank	Full-time
Professeurs	9
Chefs de travaux	11
Ingénieurs	3
Professeurs certifiés	2
Total	25

Student Enrolment, 1986-87:

	Men	Women	Total
Of the country	61	69	131
Of other countries	1	–	1
Total	63	69	132*

*Also 10 external students.

2665 **ÉCOLE NATIONALE D'INGÉNIEURS DES TRAVAUX AGRICOLES DE BORDEAUX**
1, Cours du Général de Gaulle, 33170 Gradignan
Telephone: 56-04-03-03

Agriculture
Animal Husbandry
Mathematics and Statistics
Rural Economics
Chemistry and Technology
Agricultural Mechanization
Agricultural Conservation

Founded 1962. Responsible to the Ministry of Agriculture. Residential facilities for single students.

Academic Year: October to June (October-December; January-Easter; Easter-June).

Admission Requirements: Competitive entrance examination following 1 yr further study after secondary school certificate (baccalauréat or brevet de technicien agricole).

Language of Instruction: French.

Degrees and Diplomas: Diplôme d'Ingénieur des Techniques agricoles, 3 yrs.

Library: c. 6000 vols.

Academic Staff: c. 10 (60).

Student Enrolment: c. 270.

2666 **ÉCOLE NATIONALE D'INGÉNIEURS DES TRAVAUX AGRICOLES DE DIJON**
2, boulevard Olivier de Serres, 21812 Quetigny
Telephone: 80-46-30-01
Directeur: Hervé Lamaury (1984-89)

Agriculture

Founded 1967. Responsible to the Ministry of Agriculture. Residential facilities for students.

Academic Year: October to June (October-December; January-March; April-June).

Admission Requirements: Competitive entrance examination following 1 yr further study after secondary school certificate (baccalauréat or brevet de technicien agricole).

Fees (Francs): 430 per annum.

Language of Instruction: French.

Degrees and Diplomas: Diplôme d'Ingénieur des Travaux agricoles, 3 yrs.

Academic Staff, 1986-87: c. 20.

Student Enrolment, 1986-87:

	Men	Women	Total
Of the country	102	44	146

2667 **ÉCOLE NATIONALE D'INGÉNIEURS DE TRAVAUX AGRICOLES DE MARMILHET**
63370 Lempdes-Clermont-Ferrand
Telephone: 73-92-52-36

2668 **ÉCOLE NATIONALE SUPÉRIEURE DES INDUSTRIES AGRICOLES ET ALIMENTAIRES**
1, avenue des Olympiades, 91305 Massy Cedex
Telex: ENSIA 602174F
Telephone: 69-20-05-23
Directeur: Jean-Michel Clément (1977-87)
Secrétaire général: M.Pienne.

Agricultural Industries
Food Technology (Distilling, Dairying, Brewing, and Sugar Industries) (Douai)

Founded 1893 at Douai. Moved to Paris 1940 and became Ecole nationale supérieure at present site 1961. Responsible to the Ministry of Agriculture. Residential facilities for students at Cité internationale, Paris.

Academic Year: September to June/July (September-December; January-April; April-June).

Admission Requirements: Entrance by competition following 2 yrs further study after secondary school certificate (baccalauréat) or following first university qualification (D.U.T. or D.E.U.G.). Direct entrance to second year by competition following appropriate university degree (Maîtrise) or Diplôme d'Ingénieur.

Language of Instruction: French.

Degrees and Diplomas: Diplôme–d'Ingénieur des Industries agricoles et alimentaires, 3 yrs. Doctorat d'Ingénieur de Science etTechniques de l'Industrie alimentaire.

Library: Service d'Informations scientifiques et techniques, 1000 vols.

Publication: Comptes rendus d'activités des Chaires et Services (annually).

Academic Staff: c. 65.

Student Enrolment: c. 250.

2669 **ÉCOLE NATIONALE SUPÉRIEURE D'AGRONOMIE ET DES INDUSTRIES ALIMENTAIRES DE NANCY**
2, avenue de la Forêt de la Haye, 54500 Vandoeuvre-lès-Nancy
Telephone: 83-59-59-59
Fax: 83-59-59-55
Directeur: Joël Hardy
Secrétaire général: Jean-Yves Rivière

D. of Agriculture
Director: Joël Hardy; *staff* 45 (23o)
D. of Food Technology
Director: Joël Hardy; *staff* 45 (230)
Also 3 Research Laboratories.

Founded 1972, incorporating 3 schools of engineers. Responsible to the Ministry of Education.

Arrangements for co-operation with institutions in: United Kingdom; Belgium; Germany; Spain; Portugal; Denmark; Hong Kong; People's Republic of China; Guinea; Cameroon; Algeria; Morocco; Canada; USA; Brazil; Mexico.

Admission Requirements: Entrance by competition following 2 yrs further study after secondary school certificate (baccalauréat) or first university qualification (D.U.T. or D.E.U.G.). Direct entrance in second year by competition following appropriate university degree (Maîtrise).

Language of Instruction: French.

Degrees and Diplomas: Diplôme of–Ingénieur agronome; Ingénieur des Industries alimentaires, 5 yrs. Diplôme d'études approfondies (D.E.A.); Diplôme d'Etudes supérieures spécialisées (D.E.S.S.). Doctorat.

Library: Bibliothèque de l'ENSAIA.

Academic Staff, 1989-90: 46 (230)

Student Enrolment, 1989-90:

	Men	Women	Total
Of the country	256	235	491
Of other countries	52	69	121
Total	308	304	612

2670 **ÉCOLE NATIONALE D'INGÉNIEURS DES TECHNIQUES DES INDUSTRIES AGRICOLES ET ALIMENTAIRES**

Chemin de la Géraudière, 44072 Nantes Cedex 03
Telephone: 40-40-03-00
Fax: 40-59-63-36
Directeur: Mme Pelekhine
Secrétaire général:M. Le Scornet

S. of Food Technology and Agricultural Engineering

S. of Lifelong Education

Founded 1974 by decree. Responsible to the Ministry of Agriculture. Governing bodies: the Conseil général; the Conseil intérieur.

Academic Year: October to June (October-December; January-March; March-June).

Admission Requirements: Entrance by competition following 2 yrs further study after secondary school certificate (baccalauréat) or following first university qualification (D.U.T. or D.E.U.G.).

Language of Instruction: French.

Degrees and Diplomas: Diplôme d'Ingénieur des Techniques des Industries agricoles et alimentaires, 3 yrs.

Library: School Library.

Academic Staff: c. 20 (20).

Student Enrolment: c. 180.

2671 **ÉCOLE NATIONALE SUPÉRIEURE DES SCIENCES AGRONOMIQUES APPLIQUÉES**

26, boulevard Docteur Petitjean, B.P. 588, 21016 Dijon Cedex
Telephone: 80-66-54-12
Directeur: Jacques Gilot (1983-88)
Attachée d'Administration: Nadine Boussaud

D. of Animal Husbandry
Head: Jean-Louis Tisserand; *staff* 17

D. of Agriculture
Head: Michel Richard; *staff* 12

D. of Economics
Head: Michel Petit; *staff* 8

D. of Applied Social Sciences (Development)
Head: Jean-Baptiste Viallon; *staff* 8

D. of Applied Social Sciences (Teaching)
Head: Joseph Gauter; *staff* 5

D. of Computer Sciences
Head: Dominique Degueurce; *staff* 3

D. for Lifelong Education
Head: Eric Marshall; *staff* 3

Founded 1920, reorganized 1966. Attached to the Institut national agronomique and responsible to the Ministry of Agriculture. Residential facilities for students.

Academic Year: September to June (September-December; January-March; April-June).

Admission Requirements: Diplôme d'agronomie générale from Paris-Grignon, Rennes, Montpellier, Nancy, or Toulouse. Competitive entrance examination for holders of Diplôme d'Ingénieur in horticulture, food production, etc.

Fees (Francs): 3000 per annum.

Language of Instruction: French.

Degrees and Diplomas: Diplôme d'Ingénieur d'agronomie, 2 yrs. Also teaching qualification.

Library: c. 4000 vols.

Academic Staff, 1986-87:

Rank	Full-time
Professeurs	5
Maîtres de conférences	7
Maîtres-Assistants	10
Assistants	4
Ingénieurs	6
Professeur certifié	1
Total	33

Student Enrolment, 1986-87:

	Men
Of the country	33
Of other countries	2
Total	35

2672 **ÉCOLE SUPÉRIEURE D'AGRONOMIE TROPICALE DÉPENDANT DU CENTRE NATIONAL D'ÉTUDES AGRONOMIQUES DESRÉGIONS CHAUDES**

Avenue du Val-de-Montjenaud, 34033 Montpellier Cedex
Telephone: 67-54-55-33

Tropical Agriculture

2673 **ÉCOLE NATIONALE SUPÉRIEURE AGRONOMIQUE**

9, place P. Viala, 34060 Montpellier Cedex
Telex: 490818F
Telephone: 67-61-22-00
Fax: 67-61-25-80

Agriculture

Founded 1872. Responsible to the Ministry of Agriculture.

Academic Year: October to July (October-December; January-Easter; Easter-June).

Admission Requirements: Entrance by competition following 2 yrs further study after secondary school certificate (baccalauréat) or following first university qualification (D.U.T. or D.E.U.G.).

Language of Instruction: French.

Degrees and Diplomas: Diplôme–d'Agronomie générale; d'Agronomie approfondie, 2 yrs; d'Ingénieur agronome, 3 yrs. Diplôme d'études approfondies (D.E.A.), 1 further yr. Doctorat, 2-4 yrs after D.E.A.

Library: 12,000 vols.

Academic Staff: c. 60.

2674 **INSTITUT NATIONAL AGRONOMIQUE PARIS-GRIGNON**

16, rue Claude-Bernard, 75005 Paris
Telex: INAPGN 250985F
Telephone: (1) 45-70-15-50
Directeur: Jacques Delage (1975-88)

Agriculture

I. of Dairying Economics and Technology

Founded 1848, closed 1852. Reopened 1876, attached to the Conservatoire national des Arts et Métiers. Acquired present status 1876. Amalgamated 1972 with Ecole nationale supérieure agronomique, Grignon, founded 1826.A State institution responsible to the Ministry of Agriculture. Governing body: the Conseil général. Residential facilities for students at Cité universitaire.

Arrangements for co-operation for academic staff and student exchange with university institutions in: Morocco; Tunisia; Côte d'Ivoire; Germany; Spain; Canada; Algeria; Senegal. Arrangements for co-operation in research with more than 40 universities and research centres.

Academic Year: September to June (September-December; January-March; April-June).

Admission Requirements: Entrance by competition following 2 yrs further study after secondary school certificate (baccalauréat).

Fees (Francs): 1350 per annum.

Language of Instruction: French.

Degrees and Diplomas: Diplôme d'Agronomie générale, 2 yrs; d'Ingénieur agronome, 3 yrs. Diplôme d'études approfondies (D.E.A.), 3 yrs. Doctorat, 2 yrs after D.E.A.

Library: 40,000 vols.

Academic Staff, 1986-87:

Rank	Full-time
Professeurs	24
Maîtres de conférences	19
Maîtres-Assistants	48
Assistants	34
Total	125

Student Enrolment, 1986-87:

	Men	Women	Total
Of the country	440	335	775
Of other countries	65	10	75
Total	505	345	850

2675 **ÉCOLE NATIONALE SUPÉRIEURE D'AGRONOMIE DE RENNES**

65, rue de Saint-Brieuc, 35042 Rennes Cedex
Telephone: 99-28-50-00
Fax: 99-28-75-10
Directeur: P. Thivend
Secrétaire général: Loïc Rioche

D. of Agriculture (including Animal Husbandry)
Director: P. Thivend; *staff* 5
D. for Lifelong Education
Head: Dupont de Dinechin; *staff* – (2)

Founded 1830 as Institut Agricole de l'Ouest à Grand-Jouan, became Ecole régionale 1848 and Ecole nationale and transferred to Rennes 1896. Acquired present status 1960. Responsible to the Ministry of Agriculture. Governing body: the Conseil général. Residential facilities for students.

Arrangements for co-operation with: University of Reading; University of Rhode Island; Université du Québec à Rimouski.

Academic Year: September to July (September-December; January-March; April-July).

Admission Requirements: Entrance by competition following 2 yrs further study after secondary school certificate (baccalauréat) or following first university qualification (D.U.T. or D.E.U.G.). Direct entrance to second year by competition following appropriate university degree (Maîtrise).

Fees (Francs): 1188 per annum.

Language of Instruction: French.

Degrees and Diplomas: Diplôme–d'Agronomie générale, 2 yrs; d'Agronomie approfondie (2e cycle), 1 further yr; d'Ingénieur agronome, 3 yrs. Doctorat d'Ingénieur, a further 2-3 yrs.

Libraries: Central Library, 20,000 vols; department libraries, *c.* 5000 vols.

Publication: Sciences Agronomiques de Rennes (annually).

Academic Staff, 1990:

Rank	Full-time	Part-time
Professeurs	12	–
Maîtres de conférences	12	–
Maîtres Assistants	21	–
Assistants	12	–
Lecteurs	1	–
Professeurs d'Education physique	1	–
Vacataires	–	200
Total	59	200

Student Enrolment, 1990:

	Men	Women	Total
Of the country	199	150	349
Of other countries	20	5	25
Total	219	155	374

2676 **ÉCOLE NATIONALE SUPÉRIEURE AGRONOMIQUE**

145, avenue de Muret, 31076 Toulouse Cedex
Cables: Ensagro Toulouse
Telephone: 61-42-83-98

Agriculture (including Animal Husbandry)
Lifelong Education

Founded 1947. Attached to the Institut National Polytechnique de Toulouse 1971. Governing body: the Conseil d'administration. Residential facilities for students.

Academic Year: October to July (October-December; January-March; April-July).

Admission Requirements: Entrance by competition following 2 yrs further study after secondary school certificate (baccalauréat) or following first university qualification (D.U.T. or D.E.U.G.).

Language of Instruction: French.

Degrees and Diplomas: Diplôme d'Agronomie générale (D.A.G.), 2 yrs. Diplôme d'Agronomie approfondie (D.A.A.), 3 yrs. Diplôme d'études approfondies (D.E.A.), 1 further yr. Doctorat, 2-4 yrs after D.E.A.

Libraries: Central Library, 1500 vols; department libraries.

Academic Staff: c. 50 (100).

Student Enrolment: c. 300.

2677 **ÉCOLE NATIONALE SUPÉRIEURE AGRONOMIQUE FÉMININE DE RENNES**

65, rue de Saint-Brieuc, 35042 Rennes Cedex
Telephone: 99-59-12-44
Directeur: Camille Moule (1972-87)

Agriculture
Domestic Science

Founded 1964. Responsible to the Ministry of Agriculture. Residential facilities for students.

Academic Year: September to June (September-December; January-March; April-June).

Admission Requirements: Entrance by competition following 2 yrs further study after secondary school certificate (baccalauréat or brevet de technicien agricole). Direct entrance to second year by competition following appropriate university degree (D.E.U.G.).

Fees (Francs): 350 per annum.

Language of Instruction: French.

Degrees and Diplomas: Diplôme, 4 yrs.

Academic Staff, 1986-87: 57.

Student Enrolment, 1986-87:

	Women
Of the country	160
Of other countries	2
Total	162

2678 **ÉCOLE NATIONALE DU GÉNIE RURAL, DES EAUX ET DES FORÊTS**

14, rue Girardet, 54042 Nancy Cedex
Telephone: 83-35-10-20
Directeur: Jean-Pierre Troy (1986-91)
Secrétaire générale: Blanche Mignon

Rural Engineering
Forestry

Founded 1965 replacing former Ecole nationale des Eaux et Forêts, 1825, and Ecole nationale du Génie rural, 1919, and taking over certain functions from the Ecole nationale supérieure des Sciences agronomiques appliquées. Responsible to the Ministry of Agriculture. Governing bodies: the Conseil d'administration; the Conseil de perfectionnement. Residential facilities for students.

Arrangements for co-operation with university institutions in: Cameroon; Burkino Faso; Morocco; Tunisia; Brazil; India; Finland; U.S.A.

Academic Year: September to July (September-Christmas; January-Easter; Easter-July).

Admission Requirements: Diplôme d'Ingénieur from Ecole polytechnique or from Institut national agronomique.

Fees (Francs): 1500.

Language of Instruction: French.

Degrees and Diplomas: Diplôme–d'Ingénieur civil du Génie rural des Eaux et des Forêts; Ingénieur civil des Forêts, 6 yrs after baccalauréat. Diplôme d'études approfondies (D.E.A.).

Library: Forestry.

Publication: Revue Forestière Française.

Academic Staff, 1986-87: 15 (800).

Student Enrolment, 1986-87:

	Men	Women	Total
Of the country	100	39	139
Of other countries	21	2	23
Total	121	41	162

Schools of Agriculture and Food Technology

2679 ÉCOLE NATIONALE DU GÉNIE RURAL, DES EAUX ET DES FORÊTS

19, avenue du Maine, 75732 Paris Cedex 15
Telex: ENGREF 200574F
Telephone: 45-49-88-00
Directeur: Jean-Pierre Troy (1986-91)
Secrétaire générale: Blanche Mignon

Rural Engineering
Forestry

Founded 1965 replacing former Ecole nationale des Eaux et Forêts, 1825, and Ecole nationale du Génie rural 1919, and taking over certain functions from the Ecole nationale supérieure des Sciences agronomiques appliauées. Responsible to the Ministry of Agriculture. Governing bodies: the Conseil d'Administration; the Conseil de perfectionnement.

Arrangements for co-operation with university institutions in: Cameroon; Burkina Faso; Morocco; Tunisia; Brazil; India; Finland; U.S.A.

Academic Year: September to July (September-Christmas; January-Easter; Easter-July).

Admission Requirements: Diplôme d'Ingénieur from Ecole polytechnique or from Institut national agronomique.

Fees (Francs): 1500.

Language of Instruction: French.

Degrees and Diplomas: Diplôme–d'Ingénieur civil du Génie rural des Eaux et des Forêts; Ingénieur civil des Forêts, 6 yrs after baccalauréat. Diplôme d'Études approfondies (D.E.A.).

Libraries: Rural Engineering; Hydraulic Engineering, etc.

Publication: Revue Forestière Française.

Academic Staff, 1986-87: 15 (800).

Student Enrolment, 1986-87:

	Men	Women	Total
Of the country	100	39	139
Of other countries	21	2	23
Total	121	41	162

2680 ÉCOLE NATIONALE D'INGÉNIEURS DES TRAVAUX DES EAUX ET FORÊTS

Domaine des Barres, 45290 Nogent-sur-Vernisson
Telephone: 38-97-60-20
Directeur: Henri Daburon (1979-89)

Forestry
Lifelong Education

Founded 1883 as Ecole secondaire de Sylviculture des Barres, acquired present status and title 1966. Responsible to the Ministry of Agriculture. Governing body: the Conseil d'administration. Residential facilities for academic staff and single students.

Academic Year: September to July (September-December; January-Easter; Easter-July).

Admission Requirements: Entrance by competition following 2 yrs further study after secondary school certificate (baccalauréat) or following first university qualification (D.U.T. or D.E.U.G.). Direct entrance to second year by competition following appropriate university degree (Maîtrise).

Fees (Francs): 700 per annum.

Language of Instruction: French.

Degrees and Diplomas: Diplôme d'Ingénieur des Techniques forestières, 3 yrs.

Library: c. 8000 vols.

Special Facilities (Museums, etc.): Arboretum National des Barres.

Academic Staff, 1986-87: 13 (40).

Student Enrolment, 1986-87:

	Men	Women	Total
Of the country	64	19	83
Of other countries	2	–	2
Total	66	19	85

2681 INSTITUT D'ÉTUDES SUPÉRIEURES D'INDUSTRIES ET D'ÉCONOMIE LAITIÈRES

16, rue Claude-Bernard, 75231 Paris Cedex 05
Telephone: 47-07-16-45

Milk Production and Technology

2682 ÉCOLE NATIONALE DES INGÉNIEURS DES TRAVAUX RURAUX ET DES TECHNIQUES SANITAIRES

National School of Rural and Sanitary Engineering
1, quai Koch, B.P. 1039F, 67070 Strasbourg Cedex
Telex: ENTRTS 890942F
Telephone: 88-25-34-50
Fax: 88-37-04-97 Télétex: 93388354019 = enitrts
Directeur: Pierre Desmartin (1984-90)
Sous-Directeur: René Kersauze

Civil Engineering (Rural)
Public Health Engineering
Lifelong Education

Founded 1960 replacing former Ecole d'Application des Ingénieurs des Travaux ruraux. Responsible to the Ministry of Agriculture. Governing bodies: the Conseil général; the Conseil de l'enseignement et de la pédagogie; the Conseil des enseignants; the Conseil intérieur.

Arrangements for co-operation with: University of Munich; University of Stuttgart; Ecole supérieure des Ingénieurs de l'équipement rural, Medjez El Bab, Tunisia; University of Southampton; Ecole Inter-Etats de l'Equipement rural de Ouagadougou.

Academic Year: September to July.

Admission Requirements: Entrance by competition following 2 yrs further study after secondary school certificate (baccalauréat) or following first university qualification (D.E.U.G.). Direct entrance to second year by competition following appropriate university degree (Licence).

Fees (Francs): 700-30,000 per annum.

Language of Instruction: French.

Degrees and Diplomas: Ingénieur des Techniques de l'Équipement rural, 3 yrs. Certificat d'Études supérieures en Aménagements hydroagricoles; Certificat d'Études supérieures en Equipements d'Hygiène publique, 1 further yr. Mastère en–Aménagements hydroagricoles; Equipements d'Hygiène publique, 1 further yr. Diplôme d'Études approfondies en Sciences et Techniques de l'Eau (D.E.A.), 1 further yr. Doctorat, 2 yrs.

Library: 5000 vols.

Student Enrolment, 1989-90:

	Men	Women	Total
Of the country	82	42	124
Of other countries	26	–	26
Total	108	42	150

2683 ÉCOLE NATIONALE DES HARAS

Le Pin au Haras, 61310 Exmes
Telephone: 33-67-92-79

Horse Breeding

Founded 1840. Responsible to the Ministry of Agriculture. Residential facilities for students.

Academic Year: January to June.

Admission Requirements: Diplôme of the Institut national agronomique, Paris.

Language of Instruction: French.

Degrees and Diplomas: Brevet de Technicien supérieur. Certificat de spécialisation, Sciences hippiques et équitation.

Academic Staff: c. 10.

2684 ÉCOLE NATIONALE SUPÉRIEURE D'HORTICULTURE

4, rue Hardy, 78000 Versailles
Telephone: (3) 49-50-60-87
Directeur: R. Chaux (1975-)
Secrétaire générale: Mme Chabouis

Horticulture
Landscape Gardening
Genetics
Plant Protection
Economics

Lifelong Education

Founded 1874 as Ecole d'Horticulture de Versailles, acquired present status and title 1976. Responsible to theMinistry of Agriculture.Founded 1873.

Arrangements for co-operation with: Ecole supérieure d'Horticulture, Chott Mariem, Tunisie; Institut agronomique et vétérinaire Hassan II, Rabat; Ecole nationale supérieure agronomique, Abidjan.

Academic Year: September to June (September-December; January-March; April-June).

Admission Requirements: Diplôme d'Agronomie générale from the Ecoles nationales supérieures d'Agronomie of Paris-Grignon; Rennes; Montpellier; Nancy; Toulouse. Competitive entrance examination for holders of Maîtrise ès Sciences andforeign students.

Fees (Francs): 1050 per annum; foreign students, 1890.

Language of Instruction: French.

Degrees and Diplomas: Diplôme d'Ingénieur, 2 yrs.

Library: Central Library, *c.* 15,000 vols.

Academic Staff, 1986-87: 10.

Student Enrolment, 1986-87:

	Men	Women	Total
Of the country	34	40	74
Of other countries	4	5	9
Total	38	45	83

2685 **INSTITUT D'OENOLOGIE**

351, cours de la Libération, 33405 Talence Cedex
Telex: IOUBXRF 550415 F
Telephone: 56-84-64-58
Fax: 56-84-64-68
Directeur: Ribéreau-Gayon

Science of Wine

Founded 1957. Reorganized 1964. Attached to the Université de Bordeaux II.

Academic Year: November to September.

Admission Requirements: Diplôme d'Études universitaires générales (D.E.U.G. Sciences).

Language of Instruction: French.

Degrees and Diplomas: Diplôme national d'Oenologue, 2 yrs; Diplôme d'études approfondies (D.E.A.), 1 further yr; Doctorat (œnologie, ampélologie), 2-4 yrs after D.E.A.

Library: c. 3000 vols.

Publications: Connaissance de la Vigne et du Vin (quarterly); Rapport d'Activités de Recherche de l'Institut d'Oenologie (annually).

Academic Staff: c. 10.

Student Enrolment, 1989-90:

	Men	Women	Total
Of the country	102	58	160
Of other countries	28	12	40
Total	130	70	200

2686 **INSTITUT NATIONAL DE PROMOTION SUPÉRIEURE AGRICOLE**

Rue des Champs-Prévois, 21000 Dijon
Telephone: 80-66-72-27
Fax: 80-67-23-43
Directeur: Hervé Lamaury (1987-90)

Agricultural Studies

Head: Paul Broyer

Founded 1966. Responsible to the Ministry of Agriculture.

Academic Year: September to July.

Admission Requirements: Entrance by competition for holders of Licence or foreign recognized equivalent.

Language of Instruction: French.

Degrees and Diplomas: Diplôme d'Ingénieur des Techniques agricoles.

Library: Central Library.

Publication: Etudes et recherches de l'Institut.

Academic Staff: c. 25.

Student Enrolment: c. 70.

2687 **ÉCOLE NATIONALE SUPÉRIEURE DE BIOLOGIE APPLIQUÉE À LA NUTRITION ET À L'ALIMENTATION**

Campus Universitaire Montmuzard, 21100 Dijon
Telephone: 80-39-66-01
Fax: 80-39-66 Teletex: 933 - 80-66-72-65 dijouniv
Directeur: D. Simatos

Applied Biology (Nutrition and Alimentation Technology, and Economics of Agriculture and Food Industries)

Also 4 Research Departments.

Founded 1963 as Institut, acquired present title 1975. Attached to the Université de Dijon. Governing body: the Conseil d'administration, comprising 23 members. Residential facilities for students at Cité universitaire.

Participate in the ERASMUS programme with the University of Leeds.

Academic Year: October to June (October-December; January-March; April-June).

Admission Requirements: Diplôme d'Études universitaires générales (D.E.U.G.), or equivalent, and competitive entrance examination.

Language of Instruction: French.

Degrees and Diplomas: Diplôme d'Ingénieur, 3 yrs. Diplôme d'Études approfondies (D.E.A.), 1 further yr. Thèse de 3e cycle et Doctorat d'Ingénieur, 2 yrs.

Libraries: Central Library; departmental libraries.

Publication: Les Cahiers de l'E.N.S.B.A.N.A. (annually).

Academic Staff, 1989-90: c. 30.

Student Enrolment, 1989-90:

	Men	Women	Total
Of the country	140	130	270

2688 **INSTITUT SCIENTIFIQUE ET TECHNIQUE DE L'ALIMENTATION**

292, rue Saint-Martin, 75003 Paris
Telephone: (1) 48-87-37-38

Food Technology

Founded 1935. Attached to the Conservatoire national des Arts et Métiers.

Academic Year: November to April (November-December; January-April).

Language of Instruction: French.

Degrees and Diplomas: Certificat, 1 yr.

Special Facilities (Museums, etc.): Musée des Sciences et Techniques.

Academic Staff: c. 5.

Student Enrolment: c. 25.

2689 **INSTITUT D'ÉLEVAGE ET DE MÉDECINE VÉTÉRINAIRE DES PAYS TROPICAUX**

10, rue Pierre-Curie, 94704 Maisons-Alfort
Telephone: (1) 43-68-88-73

Tropical Veterinary Medicine and Animal Husbandry

Founded 1920, reorganized in 1948 and 1962. Responsible to the Ministry of Co-operation. Governing bodies: the Conseil d'administration; the Conseil scientifique.

Arrangements for co-operation with a number of laboratories and research centres in Africa.

Academic Year: October to June (October-December; January-March; April-June).

Admission Requirements: French university degrees in veterinary sciences or equivalent.

Language of Instruction: French.

Degrees and Diplomas: Diplôme, 1 yr.

Library: c. 14,500 vols.

Publication: Revue (quarterly).

Academic Staff: c. 5.

Student Enrolment: c. 60.

2690 **ÉCOLE NORMALE SUPÉRIEURE**

45, rue d'Ulm, 75230 Paris Cedex 05
Telephone: (1) 43-29-12-25
Fax: (1) 43-29-73-69
Président (Acting): Josiane Serre
Secrétaire général: Jean-Claude Fonta

D. of French Language and Literature
Head: Michel Charles
D. of Grammar and Linguistics
Head: Jean Lallot
D. of Latin
Head: François Bérard
D. of Greek
Head: Philippe Hoffmann
D. of Philosophy
Head: D. Kambouchner
D. of English and American
Head: P.-Y. Pétillon
D. of Continental Europe Languages
Head: J.-P. Lefebvre
D. of Arabic-Muslim Languages and Civilizations
Head: Daniel Reig
D. of Asian Languages and Civilizations
Head: Anne Sakai
D. of Archaeology
Head: Ch. Peyre
D. of History
Head: J. Verger
D. of Geography
Head: Cl. Bardinet
D. of Music and Musicology
Head: C. Lorent
D. of Social Sciences
Head: Gérard Noiriel
D. of Economic Sciences
Head: F. Bourguignon
D. of Mathematics and Informatics
Head: Michel Broue
D. of Physics
Head: Edouard Brézin
D. of Chemistry
Head: Marc Julia
D. of Geology
Head: Xavier Le Pichon
D. of Biology
Head: Pierre Joliot

Also *c.* 40 Research Laboratories, Centres and Institutes.

Founded 1987 incorporating the Ecole normale supérieure (ex-Ulm) for men, and the Ecole normale supérieure(ex-Sèvres) for women. Governing bodies: the Conseil d'administration; the Conseil de discipline; the Commission des études. Residential facilities for 800 students.

Arrangements for co-operation with the Universities of: California-Berkeley; Stanford; Yale; Columbia; Brandeis; Massachusetts-Amherst; Oxford; Cambridge; Edinburgh; Dublin; Berlin (Free). Scuola Normale Superiore di Pisa; Massachusetts Institute of Technology; King's College, London.

Academic Year: September to July (September-December; January-March; April-July).

Admission Requirements: Competitive entrance examination following 2 yrs study after secondary school certificate (baccalauréat) or equivalent. For admission to graduate studies, students are admitted for 1 yr only if an exchange is organizedbetween their Universities and the Ecole normale supérieure.

Languages of Instruction: French and some English.

Degrees and Diplomas: Students take university degree examinations for a Licence after 1 yr and for a Maîtrise after 1 further yr. They may subsequently take State examinations for Agrégation (teaching qualification, university level). Diplôme d'études approfondies (D.E.A.), in Social Sciences. Doctorat, 2-4 yrs after D.E.A. Magistère in Mathematics, Physics, Chemistry, Biology, and Geology, 3 yrs.

Libraries: *c.* 500,000 vols; Science, 49,500.

Special Facilities (Museums, etc.): Observatory of Nançay.

Publications: Publications des Presses de l'Ecole normale supérieure; Annales scientiques de l'Ecole normale supérieure.

Press or Publishing House: Presses de l'Ecole normale supérieure.

Academic Staff, 1988-89:

Rank	Full-time
Professeurs	16
Maîtres de conférences	50
Agrégés répétiteurs	46
Sous-Directeurs de laboratoire	11
Total	123

Student Enrolment, 1988-89:

	Total
Of the country	886
Of other countries	12
Total	898

2691 **ÉCOLE NORMALE SUPÉRIEURE**

48, boulevard Jourdan, 75690 Paris Cedex 14 (Lettres)and 1, rue Maurice Arnoux 92120 Montrouge (Sciences)
Telephone: (1) 45-89-08-33 (Paris); (1) 46-57-12-86 (Montrouge)

Education and Research

Founded 1881 at Sèvres and attached to the Universités de Paris 1936. Governing body: the Conseil d'administration, comprising 36 members. Residential facilities for students.

Arrangements for co-operation with the Universities of: Yale; Harvard; Princeton; Stanford.

Academic Year: September to June (September-December; January-March; April-June).

Admission Requirements: Competitive entrance examination following 2 yrs further study after secondary school certificate (baccalauréat).

Language of Instruction: French.

Degrees and Diplomas: Preparation in various fields of study for teaching posts in secondary education. Students take university degree examinations for a Licence after 1 yr and for a Maîtrise after 1 further yr. They may subsequently take State examinations for Certificat d'Aptitude au Professorat de l'Enseignement secondaire (C.A.P.E.S.), and for Agrégation (teaching qualification, university level). Diplôme d'études approfondies (D.E.A.). Doctorat, 2-4 yrs after D.E.A. Magistère in Mathematics, Physics and Chemistry, 3 yrs.

Libraries: *c.* 150,000 vols; Sciences, *c.* 12,000.

Academic Staff: *c.* 50 (5).

Student Enrolment: *c.* 420 (Women) (Including 30 foreign students).

2692 **ÉCOLE NORMALE SUPÉRIEURE DE FONTENAY-AUX-ROSES**

31, avenue Lombart, 92260 Fontenay-aux-Roses
Telephone: (1) 47-02-60-50
Directrice: Jacqueline Bonnamour (1975-88)
Secrétaire générale: Chantal Gillette

Education and Research

Founded 1887, acquired present status 1945. Governing body: the Conseil d'administration. Residential facilities for academic staff and students.

Arrangements for co-operation with: University of Heidelberg; University of Oxford; Dartmouth College; Scuola Normale Superiore, Pisa.

Academic Year: October to June (October-December; January-March; March-June).

Admission Requirements: Competitive entrance examination following 2 yrs further study after secondary school certificate (baccalauréat).

Language of Instruction: French.

Degrees and Diplomas: Preparation in various fields of study for teaching posts in secondary education. Students take university degree examinations for a Licence after 1 yr and for a Maîtrise after 1 further yr. They may subsequently take State examinations for Certificat d'Aptitude au Professorat de l'Enseignement secondaire (C.A.P.E.S.) and for Agrégation (teaching qualification, university level). Diplôme d'études approfondies (D.E.A.). Doctorat,2-4 yrs after D.E.A. Magistère in Mathematics, Physics and Chemistry, 3 yrs.

Library: *c.* 60,000 vols.

Publication: Les Cahiers de Fontenay (quarterly).

Academic Staff, 1986-87:

Rank	Full-time
Professeurs	7
Maîtres-Assistants	20
Assistants	3
Agrégés répétiteurs	3
Total	33

Student Enrolment, 1986-87:

Of the country	424
Of other countries	3
Total	427

2693 **ÉCOLE NORMALE SUPÉRIEURE DE SAINT-CLOUD**
Avenue de la Grille d'Honneur, Parc de Saint-Cloud, 92211 Saint-Cloud
Telephone: (1) 47-71-91-11
Fax: 46-02-39-11

Education and Research
Audio-visual Ce.
Ce. of Computer Sciences
Ce. for Lifelong Education

Founded 1882 as teacher training college (primary level), became Ecole normale supérieure 1937. Some residential facilities for students.

Academic Year: October to June (October-December; January-March; April-June).

Admission Requirements: Competitive entrance examination following further study after secondary school certificate (baccalauréat).

Language of Instruction: French.

Degrees and Diplomas: Preparation in various fields of study for teaching posts in secondary education. Students take university degree examinations for a Licence after 1 yr and for a Maîtrise after 1 further yr. Magistère in Mathematics, Physics and Chemistry, 3 yrs. They may subsequently take State examinations for Certificat d'Aptitude au Professorat de l'Enseignement secondaire (C.A.P.E.S.), and for Agrégation (teaching qualification, university level). Diplôme d'études approfondies (D.E.A.). Doctorat, 2-4 yrs after D.E.A.

Library: c. 100,000 vols.

Publications: Annuaire des anciens Elèves; Bulletin; Bilan des Recherches.

Academic Staff: c. 120.

Student Enrolment: c. 470.

2694 **ÉCOLE NORMALE SUPÉRIEURE DE CACHAN**
61, avenue du Président-Wilson, 94235 Cachan Cedex
Telex: ENSET 250948 F
Telephone: (1) 47-40-20-00
Fax: (1) 47-40-20-74
Directeur: Yves Malier (1988-)
Directeur administratif et financier: Eric Bernet

D. of Mathematics
Head: M. Picque; *staff* 8 (8)
D. of Physics
Head: M. Fortunato; *staff* 8 (14)
D. of Chemistry
Head: M. Faure; *staff* 3 (17)
D. of Electrical Engineering
Head: M. Louis; *staff* 7 (26)
D. of Biochemistry
Head: M. Ehrhart; *staff* 6 (17)
D. of Mechanical Engineering
Head: M. Ladevèze; *staff* 30 (23)
D. of Civil Engineering
Head: M. Pailleret; *staff* 8 (15)
D. of Art and Design
Head: M. Grataloup; *staff* 1 (20)
D. of Economics and Management (D1)
Head: M. Peaucelle; *staff* 4 (12)
D. of Economics and Management (D2)
Head: M. Munier; *staff* 6 (10)
D. of Social Sciences (D3)
Head: M. Bitard; *staff* 3 (15)
D. of Practical Language (DLP)
Head: D. Janitza; *staff* 3 (11)
Also *c.* 15 Research Laboratories,

Founded 1912. Became Ecole normale supérieure d'Enseignement technique 1932, and acquired present status andtitle 1985. Governing bodies: the Conseil d'Administration; the Conseil scientifique. Residential facilities for single students.

Arrangements for bilateral agreements with European, Canadian, Russian, and African Universities and Schools. Higher education at undergraduate levels for student exchanges and at postgraduate levels for staff and postgraduate student exchanges and also in research projects. European partnerships with: Technische Universität Braunschweig; Trinity College, Dublin; University of Surrey; Staffordshire Polytechnic; Universidad de Valencia; Università di Bari; Universität Karlsruhe. Also participates in the ERASMUS programme.

Academic Year: September to June (September-October; November-December; January-February; February-March; April-June).

Admission Requirements: Competitive entrance examination following 2 yrs further study after secondary school certificate (baccalauréat) or foreign equivalent. French and foreign students may be admitted principally at postgraduate level (D.E.A. and thesis) in Laboratories on the basis of their previous studies and results.

Fees: None.

Language of Instruction: French.

Degrees and Diplomas: Preparation in various fields of study for teaching posts in secondary education. Students take university degree examinations for a Licence after 1 yr and for a Maîtrise after 1 further yr. They may subsequently take State examinations for Agrégation (teaching qualification, university level). Diplôme d'études approfondies (D.E.A.). Doctorat, 2-4 yrs after D.E.A. After Agrégation, students prepare postgraduate diplomas.

Library: 46,000 vols.

Publications: European Journal of Mechanics; Theory and Decision; Materials and Structures (all monthly).

Academic Staff, 1989-90:

Rank	Full-time	Part-time
Professeurs	26	–
Sous-Directeurs de laboratoire	1	–
Maîtres de conférences	44	–
Assistants	2	–
Professeurs agrégés	27	–
Agrégés préparateurs	7	–
Professeurs certifiés	5	–
Lecteurs	1	–
Vacataires	–	216
Total	114	216

Student Enrolment, 1989-90:

	Men	Women	Total
Of the country	736	295	1031
Of other countries	52	2	54
Total	788	297	1085

2695 **ÉCOLE NORMALE SUPÉRIEURE DE LYON**
46, allée d'Italie, 69364 Lyon Cedex
Telephone: 72-72-80-00
Fax: 72-72-80-80-
Directeur: Guy Aubert
Secrétaire général: Christian Charrel

D. of Mathematics and Computer Sciences
Head: Michel Cosnard
D. of Science of Matter (Physics, Chemistry)
Head: Bernard Bigat
D. of Life and Earth Sciences
Head: Jacques Daillie
Also 6 Research Laboratories.

Founded 1985. Governing body: the Conseil d'administration, comprising 30 members. Residential facilities for students.

Academic Year: September to June.

Admission Requirements: Competitive entrance examination following 2 yrs further study after secondary school certificate (baccalauréat) or equivalent.

Language of Instruction: French.

Degrees and Diplomas: Preparation in various fields of study for teaching posts in secondary education and research. Students take university degree examinations for a Licence after 1 yr and for a Maîtrise after 1 further yr. They may subsequently take State examinations for Certificat d'Aptitude au Professorat de l'Enseignement secondaire (C.A.P.E.S.), and for Agrégation (teaching qualification, university level). Diplôme d'Etudes approfondies (D.E.A.) in Social Sciences. Doctorat, 2-4 yrs after D.E.A.. Magistère in Mathematics, Computer Sciences, Science, Physics, Biology, and Earth Sciences.

Schools of Commerce and Business Administration

2696 **INSTITUT D'ADMINISTRATION DES ENTREPRISES**
29, avenue Robert Schuman, 13617 Aix-en-Provence Cedex
Telephone: 42-59-09-47

Business Administration (Aix and Marseille)
Also centres in Avignon/Arles and Saint-Denis-de-la-Réunion.

Founded 1955. Attached to the Université d'Aix-Marseille III.

Academic Year: October to September.

Admission Requirements: University degree or equivalent.

Language of Instruction: French.

Degrees and Diplomas: Certificat d'Aptitude à l'Administration des Entreprises, 1 yr. Diplôme d'études supérieures spécialisées (D.E.S.S.), 1 yr; Diplôme d'études approfondies (D.E.A.), 1 yr. Doctorat, 2-4 yrs after D.E.A.

Library: 12,000 vols.

Academic Staff: c. 40.

Student Enrolment: c. 300.

2697 **ÉCOLE SUPÉRIEURE DES AFFAIRES DE GRENOBLE**
Domaine Universitaire de Saint-Martin d'Hères, 47X, 38040 Grenoble Cedex
Telephone: 76-82-59-27
Fax: 76-82-59-99
Doyen: Jacques Trahand
Secrétaire générale: Annie Rougier

Management (including International Commerce, Accountancy, Finance, and Marketing)
Head: Jean-Pierre Vicario

Founded 1956 as Centre de Préparation à la Gestion des Entreprises. Acquired present title 1968. Attached to the Université des Sciences sociales (Grenoble II). Governing body: the Conseil d'administration, composed of 5 members of the academic staff, 5 students, 6 members from outside the institute, and a representative of the administrative personnel.

Participates in the ERASMUS programme and ISEP programme.

Academic Year: October to June.

Admission Requirements: University degree (Maîtrise). Graduate degree (D.E.S.S.).

Fees (Francs): 2000-5000.

Language of Instruction: French.

Degrees and Diplomas: Maîtrise, 2 yrs. Magistère, 3 yrs. Diplôme d'études supérieures spécialisées, (D.E.S.S.), 2 yrs;Diplôme d'études approfondies, 2-4 yrs.

Library: Institute Library.

Publication: Cahiers du CERAG (3 times a year).

Academic Staff, 1990:

Rank	Full-time	Part-time
Professeurs	9	–
Professeurs associés	23	220
Assistants	10	–
Total	42	220

Student Enrolment, 1989-90: c. 550.

2698 **INSTITUT D'ADMINISTRATION ET DE GESTION DES ENTREPRISES**
Institute of Business Administration
15, quai Claude Bernard, B.P. 638, 69239 Lyon Cedex 2
Telex: 380311 F
Telephone: (33) 72-72-21-47
Fax: (33) 72-72-20-50
Doyen: Max Crochat

D. of Business Administration
Head: Gilles Guyot
D. of Management Science
Head: Alain Martinet
D. of Accountancy
Head: J.J. Friedrich

D. of Human Resources
Head: Michel Thomas
D. of International Trade
Head: Jacques Fayette
D. of Personal Patrimony Management
Head: Max Crochat
D. of Micro-Computer Sciences Applied to Management
Head: Danielle Boulanger
D. of Enterprise Diagnostics
Head: Alain Marion
Research Ce. in Management Science
Head: Alain Martinet

Founded 1936. Attached to the Université de Lyon III. Governing bodies: the Board of Directors, comprising 9 representatives from business circles and local communities; 10 faculty members; 8 students; and 2 representatives from the administrative staff.

Arrangements for student and academic staff exchanges with Universities in the: USA (14); United Kingdom (4); Ireland (1); Germany (2); Spain (1).

Academic Year: October to June.

Admission Requirements: University degree or equivalent.

Language of Instruction: French.

Degrees and Diplomas: Diplôme d'Etudes universitaires générales (D.E.U.G.), 2 yrs; Licence, 1 further yr; Maîtrise, 1-2 yrs. Diplôme d'Etudes supérieures spécialisées (D.E.S.S.), 1 yr after Maîtrise; Diplôme d'Etudes approfondies (D.E.A.), 1 yr after Maîtrise. Doctorat de Sciences de Gestion, 3 yrs after D.E.A.

Library: Library of Management and Law, 12,000 vols.

Publications: Lexique comptable et financier; Cette Europe dont on parle...LYON; Comptabilité et Gestion des Entreprises; L'Analyse technique : dynamisez la Gestion de votre Portefeuille; Statistique appliquée à la Gestion; Gestion de la Production, Calcul économique; Une Stratégie de Gestion par les Collectivités locales : le Modèle G.C.L.93; Stratégie; Diagnostic stratégique; Lexique de Gestion; Comptabilité privée; Information des Salariés et Stratégies de Communication; Diffusion des nouvelles Technologies; Introduction à l'Analyse économique, Bases méthodologiques et Mécanismes fondamentaux; Lexique d'Economie; Le Budgétaire; Management et Gestion de la Qualité en Europe : Entreprises suisses et italiennes; Qualité et Compétitivité des Entreprises : du Diagnostic aux Actions de Progrès.

Academic Staff, 1989-90:

Rank	Full-time
Professeurs	7
Maîtres de conférences	13
Assistants et Autres	16
Total	36

Student Enrolment, 1989-90: 4500.

2699 **INSTITUT D'ADMINISTRATION DES ENTREPRISES**
Avenue Emile Henriot, 06005 Nice
Telephone: 93-87-14-51

Business Administration

Founded 1966. Attached to the Université de Nice. Governing body: the Conseil d'administration.

Academic Year: September to June (September-December; January-March; April-June).

Admission Requirements: University degree or equivalent.

Language of Instruction: French.

Degrees and Diplomas: Maîtrise, 2 yrs. Diplôme d'études approfondies, D.E.A., 1 further yr. Certificat d'Aptitude à l'Administration des Entreprises, 1 yr after Maîtrise.

Library: c. 5000 vols.

Academic Staff: c. 10 (40).

2700 **INSTITUT D'ADMINISTRATION DES ENTREPRISES**
162, rue Saint-Charles, 75740 Paris Cedex 15
Telephone: (1) 45-54-97-24
Fax: (1) 45-57-33-35
Directeur: Jean-Pierre Helfer

D. of Business Administration
Head: Guy Triolaire; *staff* 16 (350)
D. of Information Systems
Head: Mme Rolland; *staff* 2

D. of Financial Management
Head: Nicolas Hovi; *staff* 1 (30)
D. of Personnel Management
Head: Dimitri Weiss; *staff* 1 (20)
D. of Management Planning and Control
Head: Jean-Pierre Helfer; *staff* 1 (16)

Founded 1956 as Centre. Attached to Université de Paris I. Governing body: the Conseil d'administration.

Academic Year: October to June (October-January; February-April; May-June).

Admission Requirements: University degree or equivalent.

Fees (Francs): 1200.

Language of Instruction: French.

Degrees and Diplomas: Certificat d'Aptitude à l'Administration des Entreprises, 1 yr. Diplôme d'études supérieures spécialisées (D.E.S.S.); Diplôme d'études approfondies (D.E.A.), 1 yr. Doctorat, 2-4 yrs after D.E.A.

Library: c. 3000 vols.

Academic Staff, 1986-87:

Rank	Full-time	Part-time
Professeurs	2	–
Maîtres de conférences	4	–
Maîtres-Assistants	4	–
Assistants	8	–
Vacataires	–	341
Total	18	341

Student Enrolment, 1989-90:

	Men	Women	Total
Of the country	950	425	1375
Of other countries	80	20	100
Total	1030	445	1475

2701 **INSTITUT D'ADMINISTRATION DES ENTREPRISES**
43, place Charles de Gaulle, 86022 Poitiers Cedex
Telephone: 49-88-27-54

Business Administration
Lifelong Education

Founded 1956. Attached to the Université de Poitiers.

Academic Year: October to May (October-December; January-April; April-May).

Admission Requirements: University degree or equivalent.

Fees (Francs): c. 250 per annum.

Language of Instruction: French.

Degrees and Diplomas: Certificat d'Aptitude à l'Administration des Entreprises, 1 yr. Diplôme d'études supérieures spécialisées (D.E.S.S.).

Library: Institute Library.

Publication: Cahiers du Centre d'Etudes de Recherches en Gestion des Entreprises.

Academic Staff: c. 10.

Student Enrolment: c. 130.

2702 **ÉCOLE NATIONALE D'ASSURANCES**
292, rue Saint-Martin, 75003 Paris
Telephone: (1) 42-71-24-14
Directeur général: M. de Vulpillières

Insurance

Founded 1946. Attached to the Conservatoire national des Arts et Métiers. Governing body: the Commission technique.

Academic Year: October to June (October-December; January-March; April-June).

Admission Requirements: Competitive examination following D.E.U.G. or equivalent.

Fees: None.

Language of Instruction: French.

Degrees and Diplomas: Cycle normal: Diplôme d'Études d'Assurances, with specialization, 1 yr. Cycle supérieur: Diplôme d'Études supérieures d'Assurances, 2 yrs.

Academic Staff: c. 70.

Student Enrolment: c. 80.

2703 **INSTITUT TECHNIQUE DE BANQUE**
292, rue Saint-Martin, 75141 Paris Cedex 03
Telephone: (1) 48-87-64-40

Banking Economics and Techniques (evening courses)

Founded 1950. Attached to the Conservatoire national des Arts et Métiers.

Academic Year: October to April.

Admission Requirements: Banking training and admission by selection.

Degrees and Diplomas: Diplôme d'études supérieures de l'Institut, 2 yrs.

2704 **INSTITUT D'ÉTUDES COMMERCIALES**
Domaine Universitaire de Saint-Martin d'Hères, 47X, 38400 Grenoble Cedex
Telex: UNISOG 980910F
Telephone: 76-54-81-78

Commercial Studies

Founded 1912 as institute, adopted present status 1956. Attached to the Université des Sciences sociales (Grenoble II) 1968. Governing body: the Conseil d'administration. Residential facilities for students.

Academic Year: October to July.

Admission Requirements: University degree or equivalent and entrance examination.

Language of Instruction: French.

Degrees and Diplomas: Maîtrise de Sciences et Gestion, M.S.G., 2 yrs. Maîtrise de Sciences et Techniques comptables et financières, M.S.T.C.F., 2 yrs. Diplôme d'Études supérieures spécialisées, (D.E.S.S.), in–Marketing; Fiscal and Financial Management, 1 yr. Diplôme d'Études approfondies (D.E.A.), in Business Law; Management, 1 yr.

Library: c. 8000 vols.

Publications: Lettre d'information (biannually); Papiers de recherche du C.E.R.A.G.

Academic Staff: c. 25 (120).

Student Enrolment: c. 670.

2705 **INSTITUT COMMERCIAL DE NANCY**
4, rue de la Ravinelle, 54000 Nancy
Telephone: 83-35-22-52
Fax: 83-32-47-76
Directeur: Jacques Thévenot
Secrétaire général: Bernard Le Brun

D. of Economics
Chairman: T. Koehl; *staff* 2 (10)
D. of Marketing
Chairman: P. Diou; *staff* 3 (40)
D. of Law
Chairman: G. Venondet; *staff* 2 (5)
D. of Languages
Chairman: G. Dubois; *staff* 3 (25)
D. of Computer Sciences
Chairman: J.C. Brichet; *staff* 3 (26)
D. of Management
Director: C. Bourion; *staff* 2 (18)
D. of International Studies
Director: A. Gogaiz; *staff* 2 (29)

Founded 1905. Attached to the Université de Nancy 1968. Governing body: the Conseil d'administration, comprising 35 members.

Arrangements for co-operation with: Ecole des hautes Etudes commerciales, Liège; Institut catholique des hautes Etudes commerciales de Bruxelles; Copenhagen School of Economics and Business Administration; University of Mannheim; Fachhochschule Nürnberg; University of Trier; University of Aston, Birmingham; City University Business School, London; Heriot-Watt University, Edinburgh; University of Bradford; University of Florence; Universidad de Deusto, Bilbao; Universidad Autónoma de Madrid; University of the Andes, Bogota; Bloomsburg University; Indiana University of Pennsylvania; Eastern Illinois University; Fashion Institute of Technology, New York.

Academic Year: September to June (September-January; January-June).

Admission Requirements: Entrance by competition following 2 yrs further study after secondary school certificate (baccalauréat) or following first university qualification (D.U.T. or D.E.U.G.). Direct entrance to second year by competition following appropriate university degree (Licence) or Diplôme d'Ingénieur.

Fees (Francs): 10,000.

Language of Instruction: French.

Degrees and Diplomas: Diplôme d'Ingénieur commercial, 3 yrs. Maîtrise des Sciences et Techniques comptables et financières. Diplôme de Gestion commerciale des produits (D.E.S.S.). Diplôme international de Management.

Library: 8000 vols.

Publication: ICN Information (weekly).

Academic Staff, 1989-90: 28 (180).

Student Enrolment, 1989-90:

	Men	Women	Total
Of the country	250	250	500
Of other countries	10	40	50
Total	260	290	550

2706 **ÉCOLE DE MANAGEMENT EUROPÉEN**

47, avenue de la Forêt-Noire, 67082 Strasbourg Cedex
Telephone: 88-41-77-40
Fax: 88-41-77-01
Président: Sabine Urban
Secrétaire général: Jean-Pierre Kennel

D. of Commerce
Head: Cr. Croué
D. of Law
Head: G. Michaux
D. of Finance
Head: Serge Vendemini
D. of Strategy
Head: G. Dommange
D. of Statistics and Mathematics
Head: Costas Nanozoulos
D. of Languages
Head: J. Jochum
D. of Human Resources
Head: Ingrid Brunstein
D. of Logistics and Production
Heads: A. Marchal, J. Lionville
Management Sciences Study Ce. (CESAG)
Head: Sabine Urban

Founded 1919 by the Chambre de Commerce de Strasbourg, became university institute 1956. Attached to the Université Robert Schuman (Strasbourg III).

Arrangements for co-operation with 34 European Universities.

Academic Year: October to June (October-February; February-June).

Admission Requirements: Entrance by competition following 2 yrs further study after secondary school certificate (baccalauréat) or following first university qualification (D.U.T. or D.E.U.G.), or HEC selection.

Fees (Francs): 16,000 per annum.

Language of Instruction: French.

Degrees and Diplomas: Diplôme d'Université.

Library: 4000 vols.

Academic Staff: c. 10.

Student Enrolment: c. 50.

2707 **INSTITUT DE TECHNIQUES COMPTABLES**

Domaine Universitaire Littéraire et Juridique, Sac postal 19, 59650 Villeneuve-d'Ascq
Telephone: 20-91-10-26

Accountancy

Attached to the Université du Droit et de la Santé Lille II.

2708 **INSTITUT D'ÉCONOMIE APPLIQUÉE AUX AFFAIRES**

61, avenue des Vosges, 67000 Strasbourg
Telephone: 88-35-03-82

Economics and Business Administration

Founded 1957. Attached to University of Juridical, Political and Social Sciences and of Technology (StrasbourgIII).

Academic Year: October to June (October-December; January-March; April-June).

Admission Requirements: University degree or equivalent.

Language of Instruction: French.

Degrees and Diplomas: Brevet de Capacité en Administration des Entreprises. Certificat d'Aptitude à l'Administration des Entreprises. Also Diplôme.

Library: c. 3200 vols.

Academic Staff: c. 10.

Student Enrolment: c. 100.

2709 **INSTITUT NATIONAL DES TECHNIQUES ÉCONOMIQUES ET COMPTABLES**

292, rue Saint-Martin, 75141 Paris Cedex 03
Telex: 240 247 F
Telephone: 40-27-25-38
Fax: 42-71-70-05
Directeur: Claude Pérochon
Vice-Directeur: P. Hummel

Economic and Accountancy Techniques

Founded 1931 as Institut de Technique Comptable, acquired presen title and status 1952. Attached to the Conservatoire national des Arts e Métiers.

Academic Year: September to May.

Admission Requirements: Secondary school certificate (baccalauréat) o recognized technical or professional qualification.

Fees (Francs): 1400 - 2800 per annum.

Language of Instruction: French.

Degrees and Diplomas: Certificat du ler cycle, 1-2 yrs. D.E.F.C., 2 yrs D.E.S., 1 yr.

Academic Staff, 1989-90: 13 (250).

Student Enrolment, 1989-90: 1800 (Also 8500 students by correspondence).

2710 **INSTITUT D'ÉTUDES ÉCONOMIQUES ET JURIDIQUES APPLIQUÉES À LA CONSTRUCTION ET À L'HABITATION**

2, cours des Arts-et-Métiers, Aix-en-Provence
Telephone: (1) 42-38-13-02

Building Economics and Law

Founded 1960. Attached to the Conservatoire national des Arts e Métiers.

Academic Year: October to June (October-December; January-March April-June).

Admission Requirements: Secondary school certificate (baccalauréat) o equivalent.

Language of Instruction: French.

Degrees and Diplomas: Diplôme de l'Institut, 2 yrs.

Academic Staff: c. 10.

Student Enrolment: c. 600.

2711 **INSTITUT D'ÉTUDES DU DÉVELOPPEMENT ÉCONOMIQUE ET SOCIAL**

58, boulevard Arago, 75013 Paris
Telephone: 43-36-23-55
Directeur: Maxime Haubert

Economic and Social Development Studies

Founded 1957. Attached to the Université de Paris I (Panthéon-Sorbonne) after 1968. Governing bodies: the Conseil; the Consei scientifique.

Academic Year: November to June (November-December; January-Easter; April-June).

Admission Requirements: Maîtrise or equivalent, or foreign equivalent

Fees (Francs): 470 per annum.

Language of Instruction: French.

Degrees and Diplomas: Diplôme d'études supérieures spécialisées (D.E.S.S.); Diplôme d'études approfondies (D.E.A.), 1yr; Doctorat, 2-4 yrs.

Libraries: Institute Library, *c.* 5200 vols; Documentation Centre of IEDES Research Groups.

Publications: Revue Tiers-Monde (quarterly); Collection Tiers-Monde

Academic Staff, 1990: 9 (1).

Student Enrolment, 1990:

Of the country	63
Of other countries	234
Total	297

2712 **INSTITUT DE RECHERCHE ÉCONOMIQUE SUR LA PRODUCTION ET LE DÉVELOPPEMENT**
Domaine Universitaire, 47X, 38400 St.-Martin-d'Hères
Telex: UNISOG 980910 F
Telephone: 76-82-56-92
Fax: 76-82-56-54
Directeur: Amédée Mollard
Secrétaire général: Jean-Claude Guégan

Development Studies, Energy, Industrial Economics, Economics of Labour and Employment
Also 7 Research Centres.

Founded 1988 and incorporating former Institut de Recherche économique et de Planification, founded 1969. Attached to the Université des Sciences sociales de Grenoble (Grenoble II). Governing bodies: the Conseil de Laboratoire; the Comité scientifique interne.

Participates in the ERASMUS programme.

Academic Year: October to June (October-December; January-March; April-June).

Admission Requirements: Diplôme d'Ingénieur, university degree or equivalent.

Language of Instruction: French.

Degrees and Diplomas: Diplôme d'études approfondies (D.E.A.), 1 yr. Doctorat, 2-4 yrs after D.E.A.

Library: 30,000 vols.

Publication: Bulletin du Centre départemental de documentation du Travail (quarterly).

Academic Staff, 1989-90: 19.

Student Enrolment, 1989-90: 101 (Including 46 foreign students).

2713 **INSTITUT TECHNIQUE DE PRÉVISION ÉCONOMIQUE ET SOCIALE**
292, rue Saint-Martin, 75141 ParisDCedex 03
Telephone: (1) 42-71-24-14

Economic and Social Planning

Founded 1962. Attached to the Conservatoire national des Arts et Métiers.

Academic Year: October to June (October-December; January-March; April-June).

Admission Requirements: By selection. Education above the level of secondary school certificate (baccalauréat).

Language of Instruction: French.

Degrees and Diplomas: Diplôme, 2 yrs and mémoire. Diplôme d'études approfondies (D.E.A.), 1 yr. Doctorat, 2-4 yrs after D.E.A.

Library: c. 500 vols.

Academic Staff: c. – (20).

Student Enrolment: c. 90.

2714 **INSTITUT DE SCIENCE FINANCIÈRE ET D'ASSURANCES DE L'UNIVERSITÉ CLAUDE BERNARD**
43, boulevard du 11 Novembre 1918, 69622 Villeurbanne Cedex
Telephone: 78-89-73-38
Directeur: Philippe Picard (1981-)

Finance
Insurance

Founded 1930. Attached to the Université Claude-Bernard (Lyon I). Governing body: the Conseil d'administration.

Arrangements for co-operation with the Université Laval.

Academic Year: September to June (September-February; February-June).

Admission Requirements: Competitive entrance examination following 2 yrs further study after secondary school certificate (baccalauréat).

Fees (Francs): 1000.

Language of Instruction: French.

Degrees and Diplomas: Diplôme d'Actuaire, 3 yrs.

Library: Institute Library 1000 vols.

Academic Staff, 1986-87: 1 (22).

Student Enrolment, 1986-87:

	Men	Women	Total
Of the country	53	17	70
Of other countries	4	1	5
Total	57	18	75

2715 **CENTRE RÉGIONAL DE FORMATION DES PERSONNELS COMMUNAUX**
249, rue Pierre Brossolette Esquerdes, 62380 Lumbres

Local Government Administration

2716 **INSTITUT RÉGIONAL DE GESTION**
35, place Pey-Berland, 33076 Bordeaux Cedex
Telephone: 56-52-99-80
Fax: 56-50-73-38
Directeur: Gérard Hirigoyen
Secrétaire générale: Mme. Barrault

D. of Management Studies
Head: R. Bloch
D. of Human Resources Studies
Head: B. Sire
D. of Management Control and Audit Studies
Head: S. Evraert

Founded 1956. Attached to the Université de Bordeaux I. Governing body: the Conseil de gestion.

Academic Year: October to June (October-February; February-June).

Admission Requirements: Licence in Law or Economics.

Language of Instruction: French.

Degrees and Diplomas: Certificat d'Aptitude à l'Administration des Entreprises, 1 yr. Also Diplôme d'études supérieures spécialisées (D.E.S.S.), and Diplôme d'études approfondies (D.E.A.), 1 yr.

Library: c. 10,000 vols.

Publications: Travaux et Documents; Cahiers de recherche du CIERGO.

Academic Staff, 1989-90: 800.

Student Enrolment: c. 500.

2717 **INSTITUT DE GESTION DE RENNES**
9, rue Jean Macé, 35000 Rennes
Telephone: 99-36-24-57

Business Administration

Founded 1968 as Institut d'Administration des Entreprises. Reorganized 1970. Attached to the Université de Rennes I.

Academic Year: October to June (October-December; January-March; April-June).

Admission Requirements: University degree or equivalent.

Language of Instruction: French.

Degrees and Diplomas: Certificat d'Aptitude à l'Administration des Entreprises, 1 yr. Maîtrise–en Sciences de Gestion; en Sciences et Techniques, 2 yrs. Diplôme d'études supérieures spécialisées (D.E.S.S.), 1 yr. Diplôme d'études approfondies (D.E.A.), 1 yr. Doctorat, 2-4 yrs after D.E.A.

Library: c. 5500 vols.

Academic Staff: c. 30.

Student Enrolment: c. 380.

2718 **INSTITUT DE PRÉPARATION AUX AFFAIRES**
4, boulevard Gabriel, 21000 Dijon
Telephone: 80-65-35-66

Business Administration

Founded 1963. Attached to the Université de Dijon.

Academic Year: October to June (October-December; January-March; April-June).

Admission Requirements: University degree or equivalent.

Language of Instruction: French.

Degrees and Diplomas: Certificat d'Aptitude à l'Administration des Entreprises, 1 yr; Diplôme.

Library: c. 2000 vols.

Academic Staff: c. 20.

Student Enrolment: c. 100.

2719 **INSTITUT DE PRÉPARATION AUX AFFAIRES**
1 bis, rue Georges-Lefèvre, 59000 Lille
Telephone: 20-52-32-56

Business Administration

Founded 1955. Attached to the Université des Sciences et Techniques (Lille I).

Academic Year: October to June.

Admission Requirements: Maîtrise or Diplôme d'Ingénieur.

Language of Instruction: French.

Degrees and Diplomas: Certificat d'Aptitude à l'Administration des Entreprises, 1 yr; Diplôme d'Études supérieures spécialisées (D.E.S.S.) Diplôme d'Études approfondies (D.E.A.) Doctorat.
Library: Centre de documentation.
Publication: Cahiers de Recherche de l'IAE de Lille.
Academic Staff: c. 50.
Student Enrolment: c. 350.

2720 **INSTITUT DE PRÉPARATION AUX AFFAIRES**
Place Eugène-Bataillon, 34060 Montpellier Cedex
Telephone: 67-63-91-44

Business Administration

Attached to the Université des Sciences et Techniques du Languedoc Montpellier II.
Academic Year: October to June.
Admission Requirements: University degree or equivalent.
Language of Instruction: French.
Degrees and Diplomas: Certificat d'Aptitude à l'Administration des Entreprises, 1 yr; Diplôme.

2721 **INSTITUT DE PRÉPARATION AUX AFFAIRES**
2, rue Albert-Lautman, 31070 Toulouse Cedex
Telephone: 61-21-55-18

Business Administration

Founded 1955. Attached to the Université des Sciences Sociales (Toulouse I). Governing body: the Conseil d'administration.
Academic Year: October to June (October-December; January-March; April-June).
Admission Requirements: University degree or equivalent.
Languages of Instruction: French and English.
Degrees and Diplomas: Diplôme universitaire de Gestion, 1 yr. Diplôme d'études supérieures spécialisées (Certificat d'Aptitude à l'Administration des Entreprises), 1 yr.
Library: Library of the Institute.
Publication: Collection: Travaux et Recherches de l'IPA de Toulouse.
Academic Staff: c. 10 (50).
Student Enrolment: c. 720.

2722 **INSTITUT DE STATISTIQUE**
4, place Jussieu, 75230 Paris Cedex 05
Telephone: 43-36-25-25

Statistics

Founded 1920. Attached to the Université Pierre et Marie Curie (Paris 6). Governing body: Comité de direction.
Academic Year: October to July (October-February; February-July).
Admission Requirements: Competitive entrance examination or Maîtrise in Mathematics.
Language of Instruction: French.
Degrees and Diplomas: Certificat supérieur de l'Institut. Diplôme des Actuaires français, 3 yrs. Diplôme d'études approfondies (D.E.A.), 1 yr. Doctorat, 2-4 yrs after D.E.A.
Library: 5000 vols.
Publications: Publications de l'Institut de Statistique (2 issues a year); Revue de Statistique appliquée (4 issues a year); Cahiers du Bureau universitaire de Recherche opérationnelle (2 issues a year); Cahiers de l'Analyse des Données (2 issues a year).
Academic Staff: c. 20 (80).
Student Enrolment: c. 150 (Also c. 900 external students.

2723 **ÉCOLE NATIONALE DE LA STATISTIQUE ET DE L'ADMINISTRATION ÉCONOMIQUE**
3, avenue Pierre Larousse, 92241 Malakoff Cedex
Telephone: 45-40-10-11
Directeur: Jacques Mairesse (1980-)
Secrétaire général: Michel Zampa

D. of Statistics
Directors: M. Grosbras; M. Ladiray
D. of Economics
Directors: M. Cueno; M. Rey

Founded as Ecole d'application 1942, acquired present title 1960. Under the jurisdiction of the Institut national de la Statistique et des Etudes économiques. Governing body: the Conseil de perfectionnement.
Academic Year: September to June (September-December; January-March; April-June).
Admission Requirements: Entrance by competition following 2 yrs further study after secondary school certificate (baccalauréat) or following first university qualification (D.U.T. or D.E.U.G.). Direct entrance to second year by competition following appropriate university degree (Maîtrise).
Fees (Francs): 400-700 per annum.
Language of Instruction: French.
Degrees and Diplomas: Statisticien economiste, 3 yrs. Diplôme de Cadre de Gestion statistique, 2 yrs.
Library: c. 20,000 vols.
Academic Staff, 1986-87: 17 (310).
Student Enrolment, 1986-87:

	Men	Women	Total
Of the country	232	125	357
Of other countries	25	4	29
Total	257	129	386

2724 **INSTITUT D'ÉTUDES SUPÉRIEURES DES TECHNIQUES D'ORGANISATION**
Conservatoire national des Arts et Métiers, 292, rue Saint-Martin, 75141 Paris Cedex 03
Telephone: 42-71-24-14

Organisation technique

Founded 1956. Attached to the Conservatoire national des Arts et Métiers. Financed 85% by student fees.
Academic Year: September to June.
Admission Requirements: Diplôme du Conservatoire national des Arts et Métiers and 3 yrs practical experience or equivalent.
Language of Instruction: French.
Degrees and Diplomas: Diplôme d'études supérieures des Techniques d'Organisation.
Academic Staff: c. – (50).
Student Enrolment: c. 40.

Schools of Political Science and Public Service

2725 **INSTITUT DE PRÉPARATION À L'ADMINISTRATION GÉNÉRALE**
25, rue Gaston de Saporta, 13625 Aix-en-Provence Cedex
Telephone: 42-59-01-15

Administration

2726 **INSTITUT DE PRÉPARATION À L'ADMINISTRATION GÉNÉRALE**
U.E.R. de Droit Esplanade de la Paix, 14032 Caen
Telephone: 31-93-11-78
Director: Etienne Fatome

Administration

2727 **INSTITUT DE PRÉPARATION À L'ADMINISTRATION GÉNÉRALE**
36, Bd. Côte Blain, 63000 Clermont-Ferrand Cedex
Telephone: 73-35-22-88

Administration

2728 **INSTITUT DE PRÉPARATION À L'ADMINISTRATION GÉNÉRALE**
Avenue du Général de Gaulle, 94010 Créteil
Telephone: 48-98-91-44

Administration

2729 **INSTITUT DE PRÉPARATION À L'ADMINISTRATION GÉNÉRALE**
4, boulevard Gabriel, 21000 Dijon
Telephone: 80-39-55-00

Administration

2730 **INSTITUT DE PRÉPARATION À L'ADMINISTRATION GÉNÉRALE**
I.E.P. Domaine Universitaire de Saint-Martin d'Hères, B.P. 17, 38040 Grenoble
Telephone: 76-54-13-54

Administration

2731 **INSTITUT DE PRÉPARATION À L'ADMINISTRATION GÉNÉRALE**
Rue de Lille, B.P. 19, 59653 Villeneuve d'Ascq Cedex
Telephone: 20-91-10-26

Administration

2732 **INSTITUT DE PRÉPARATION À L'ADMINISTRATION GÉNÉRALE**
I.E.P. 1, rue Raulin, 69007 Lyon
Telephone: 78-72-85-63

Administration

2733 **INSTITUT DE PRÉPARATION À L'ADMINISTRATION GÉNÉRALE**
UER de Droit, 39, rue de l'Université, 34000 Montpellier Cedex
Telephone: 67-60-50-66

Administration

2734 **INSTITUT DE PRÉPARATION À L'ADMINISTRATION GÉNÉRALE**
4, rue de la Ravinelle, 54000 Nancy
Telephone: 82-32-05-10
Director (Acting): Paul Jaquet

Administration

2735 **INSTITUT DE PRÉPARATION À L'ADMINISTRATION GÉNÉRALE**
4, rue Danton, 75270 Paris Cedex 06
Telephone: 43-26-94-81
Directeur: Jacques Moreau
Secrétaire générale: Geneviève Depraetère

Administration

2736 **INSTITUT DE PRÉPARATION À L'ADMINISTRATION GÉNÉRALE**
10, rue de l'Université, 86000 Poitiers
Telephone: 49-41-66-38

Administration

2737 **INSTITUT DE PRÉPARATION À L'ADMINISTRATION GÉNÉRALE**
3A, place St. Mélaine, 35000 Rennes
Telephone: 99-38-77-33
Director: Monique Sims

Administration

2738 **INSTITUT DE PRÉPARATION À L'ADMINISTRATION GÉNÉRALE**
61, avenue des Vosges, 67000 Strasbourg Cedex
Telephone: 88-37-07-15
Director: Jacques Groselaude

Administration

2739 **CENTRE DE PRÉPARATION À L'ADMINISTRATION GÉNÉRALE**
Allée Ausone, B.P. 101, 33405 Talence Cedex
Telephone: 56-80-60-57
Directeur: Pierre Sadran
Secrétaire général: Didier Chabault

Administration

2740 **INSTITUT DE PRÉPARATION À L'ADMINISTRATION GÉNÉRALE**
2 ter, rue des Puits Creusés, 31000 Toulouse
Telephone: 61-21-93-10

Administration

2741 **INSTITUT NATIONAL D'ADMINISTRATION PUBLIQUE**
2, avenue de l'Observatoire, 75006 Paris
Cables: insintap
Telephone: (1) 43-20-12-60

Public Administration (for foreign students)

Founded 1966 and replacing former Institut des hautes Etudes d'Outre-Mer. Attached to the Office of the Prime Minister. Governing bodies: the Conseil d'administration under the Chairmanship of the Vice-President of the Council of State, including representatives of major government departments, senior university professors, and other individuals designated for personal competence; a Conseil de perfectionnement for each geographic division (Africa, Latin America, Asia, Mediterranean Middle East), composed of French members and representatives of the foreign governments co-operating directly with the institute. Residential facilities for students in University residences.

Academic Year: September to July (September-December; January-April; April-July).

Admission Requirements: Academic qualification equivalent to Maîtrise or 4 yrs experience in government service.

Language of Instruction: French.

Degrees and Diplomas: Diplôme, 1 yr. Also Certificat at lower level.

Library: c. 80,000 vols.

Publications: Revue française d'Administration publique (quarterly); Encyclopédie administrative et constitutionnelle.

Academic Staff: c. – (150).

Student Enrolment: c. 260.

2742 **ÉCOLE NATIONALE D'ADMINISTRATION**
13, rue de l'Université, 75007 Paris
Telephone: (1) 42-61-55-35
Directeur: Roger Fauroux (1986-)
Secrétaire général: Robert Chelle

Public Administration (including Economics, Finance, International) Relations Science

Founded 1945. Governing body: the Conseil d'administration. Some residential facilities for students.

Academic Year: Duration of studies: 29 months (January-December; January-May).

Admission Requirements: Entrance by competition following university degree or recognized equivalent, or 5 yrs public service.

Language of Instruction: French.

Degrees and Diplomas: Attestation de scolarité, 2 yrs and 5 months.

Library: c. 6000 vols.

2743 **INSTITUT D'ÉTUDES ADMINISTRATIVES ET POLITIQUES**
4, rue de la Ravinelle, 54001 Nancy
Telephone: 83-35-91-13

Business Administration

Founded 1955. Reorganized 1964. Attached to Université de Nancy II.

Academic Year: October to June (October-January; February-June).

Admission Requirements: University degree or equivalent.

Language of Instruction: French.

Degrees and Diplomas: Certificat d'Aptitude à l'Administration des Entreprises, 1 yr.

Academic Staff: c. 10.

Student Enrolment: c. 190.

2744 **INSTITUT RÉGIONAL D'ADMINISTRATION**
B.P. 208, Quai des Martyrs de la Libération, 20200 Bastia, Corse
Telex: 40370
Telephone: 95-32-22-00

Administration

Founded 1979. Responsible to the Office of the Prime Minister.

Academic Year: January to December.

Admission Requirements: Entrance by competition following university degree or recognized equivalent.

Language of Instruction: French.

Degrees and Diplomas: Diplôme d'Administration publique (D.A.P.), 2 yrs.

Library: 4000 vols.

Publication: Revue de Science administrative pour la Méditerranée occidentale.

Academic Staff: c. – (130).

Student Enrolment: c. 120.

2745 **INSTITUT RÉGIONAL D'ADMINISTRATION DE LILLE**

103, rue Barthélemy-Delespaul, 59000 Lille

Administration

2746 **INSTITUT RÉGIONAL D'ADMINISTRATION**

15, avenue de Lyon, 57000 Metz

Telephone: 87-75-44-11

Administration

2747 **INSTITUT RÉGIONAL D'ADMINISTRATION DE NANTES**

6, route de la Jonelière, 44300 Nantes

Cables: I.R.A. Nantes

Telephone: 40-74-34-77

Administration

Lifelong Education

Founded 1972. Responsible to the Office of the Prime Minister. Financially supported by the State. Governing body: the Conseil d'administration, comprising 22 members. Residential facilities for students.

Academic Year: January to December.

Admission Requirements: Entrance by competition following university degree or recognized equivalent.

Language of Instruction: French.

Degrees and Diplomas: Diplôme d'Administration publique (D.A.P.), 2 yrs.

Library: 5,000 vols.

Academic Staff: c. 150.

Student Enrolment: c. 230.

2748 **INSTITUT RÉGIONAL D'ADMINISTRATION**

1, avenue Dutrievoz, B.P. 2016, 69616 Villeurbanne Cedex

Telephone: 78-89-89-41

Administration

Founded 1970. Responsible to the Office of the Prime Minister. Governing body: the Conseil d'administration, comprising 19 members.

Academic Year: January to December (January-August; September-February; March-December).

Admission Requirements: Entrance by competition following university degree or recognized equivalent.

Fees: None.

Language of Instruction: French.

Degrees and Diplomas: Diplôme d'Administration publique (D.A.P.), 2 yrs. Certificat d'Administration publique (foreign students).

Library: 4000 vols.

Academic Staff: c. 130.

Student Enrolment: c. 200.

2749 **ÉCOLE NATIONALE DU CADASTRE**

76, chemin du Calquet, 31081 Toulouse Cedex

Telephone: 61-49-30-87

Directeur: M. Locatelli

Cadastral Surveying

Founded 1948.

Admission Requirements: Entrance by competition following 2 yrs further study after secondary school certificate (baccalauréat) or following first university qualification (D.U.T or B.T.S.) or public service.

Language of Instruction: French.

Degrees and Diplomas: Diplôme d'Inspecteur du Cadastre, 18 months. Diplôme de Contrôleur d'Impôts, 1 yr.

Student Enrolment, 1986-87: 145.

2750 **ÉCOLE DE LA CONCURRENCE ET DE LA CONSOMMATION**

6, rue Saint-Maur, 75011 Paris

Telephone: (1)43-79-41-10

Business Administration

2751 **INSTITUT DE DÉMOGRAPHIE**

Esplanade de la Paix, 14032 Caen Cedex

Telephone: 31-94-59-10

Demographic Studies

Founded 1954 and attached to the Université de Caen.

Academic Year: October to June.

Language of Instruction: French.

Library: Bibliothèque de l'Institut de Démographie, *c.* 1500 vols.

Academic Staff: c. 5.

Student Enrolment: c. 80.

2752 **INSTITUT DE DÉMOGRAPHIE**

13, place Carnot, 54000 Nancy

Cables: Idun-Université Nancy

Telephone: 28-52-21-00

Demographic Studies

Founded 1954 and attached to the Université de Nancy, and to the Institut national d'Etudes démographiques. Governing body: the Conseil d'administration, with the Rector of the university as Chairman.

Academic Year: October to June (October-December; January-March; April-June).

Admission Requirements: Secondary school certificate (baccalauréat).

Language of Instruction: French.

Degrees and Diplomas: Certificat de Démographie.

Academic Staff: c. 10.

Student Enrolment: c. 40.

2753 **INSTITUT DE DÉMOGRAPHIE DE PARIS**

22, rue Vauquelin, 75005 Paris

Telephone: (1) 43-37-48-11

Director: Alfred Dittgen

Demographic Studies

Lifelong Education

Founded 1957. Attached to the Université Panthéon-Sorbonne (Paris I). Governing bodies: the Conseil paritaire, composed of members of academic staff engaged in research and students; the Conseil scientifique.

Arrangements for co-operation with: Université Catholique de Louvain; Université de Yaoundé.

Academic Year: October to June (October-February; February-June).

Admission Requirements: Secondary school certificate (baccalauréat).

Fees (Francs): *c.* 500 per annum

Language of Instruction: French.

Degrees and Diplomas: Certificat d'Aptitude à la Démographie, 1 yr. Diplôme de Démographie générale, 1 further yr. Diplôme d'études supérieures spécialisées d'Expert-Démographe, 2 further yrs. Diplôme d'études approfondies (D.E.A.), 1 yr. Doctorat, 2-3 yrs.

Library: Bibliothèque de l'Institut de Démographie.

Publication: Les Cahiers du CRiDUP.

Academic Staff, 1986-87:

Rank	Full-time	Part-time
Professeurs	2	–
Maîtres de conférences	2	
Maîtres-Assistants	3	
Assistants	2	–
Chargés de cours	–	22
Total	9	22

Student Enrolment, 1986-87:

	Men	Women	Total
Of the country	30	58	88
Of other countries	58	9	67
Total	88	67	155

2754 **INSTITUT NATIONAL DES TECHNIQUES DE LA DOCUMENTATION**
2, rue Conté, 75141 Paris Cedex 03
Telex: 240247F
Telephone: (1) 40-27-25-16
Fax: 42-71-93-29
Directeur: Bruno Delmas
Secrétaire générale: I. Dellatre

Documentation Studies

Founded 1950. Attached to the Conservatoire national des Arts et Métiers.

Academic Year: September to February and October to January

Admission Requirements: Secondary school certificate (baccalauréat) or equivalent and entrance examination.

Fees (Francs): 5600 per semester; 12,000-20,000 per annum according to cycle of study (for Maîtrise and D.E.A.).

Language of Instruction: French.

Degrees and Diplomas: Diplôme technique de documentaliste, 2 ans. Diplôme supérieur de Sciences et Techniques de l' Information et de la Documentation, 1-2 ans. Mastère en Management de l' Information stratégique, 1-2 ans.

Publication: Bulletin bibliographique de l'INTD (mensuel)

Student Enrolment, 1989-90:

	Men	Women	Total
Of the country	18	156	174
Of other countries	–	6	6
Total	18	162	180*

*Also 110 external students.

2755 **ÉCOLE NATIONALE DES DOUANES**
86 Boulevard Orléans, 76037 Rouen
Telephone: (1) 46-24-91-97

Customs and Excise

Founded 1947.

Admission Requirements: Competitive entrance examination following Licence.

Fees: None.

Language of Instruction: French.

Degrees and Diplomas: Diplôme.

Special Facilities (Museums, etc.): Musée historique de la Douane.

Publication: Vie de la Douane–Journal de la Formation professionnelle.

Student Enrolment: c. 250.

2756 **ÉCOLE NATIONALE DES IMPÔTS**
1, rue Ledru, 63033 Clermont-Ferrand Cedex
Telephone: 73-93-88-44

Accountancy
Direct and Indirect Taxation
Law

Founded 1951 in Paris. Transferred to Clermont-Ferrand 1966.

Academic Year: September to April.

Admission Requirements: Licence in Law.

Language of Instruction: French.

Degrees and Diplomas: Professional titles.

Publication: La Feuille de Déclaration.

Academic Staff: c. 50.

Student Enrolment: c. 900.

2757 **ÉCOLE NATIONALE DE LA MAGISTRATURE**
8, rue Chanoinesse, 75004 Paris
Telephone: (1)43-26-22-11

Magisterial Studies

2758 **ÉCOLE NATIONALE SUPÉRIEURE DE POLICE**
8, avenue Gambetta, 69450 St-Cyr-au-Mont-d'Or
Telephone: (1) 78-64-02-88
Directeur: Yves Marchand (1986-)
Secrétaire général: Jean-Claude Philippe

Police Studies

Founded 1941. Attached to the Ministry of the Interior and Decentralization. Residential facilities for some academic staff and all students.

Academic Year: September to June.

Admission Requirements: Entrance by competition following university degree or recognized equivalent.

Language of Instruction: French.

Degrees and Diplomas: Diplôme, 2 yrs.

Library: Central Library, 6000 vols.

Special Facilities (Museums, etc.): Musée de Criminalistique; Musée d'Armement.

Publication: Bulletin (quarterly).

Press or Publishing House: Atelier de reprographie de l'Ecole.

Academic Staff, 1986-87:

Rank	Full-time
Professeurs	8
Adjoints d'enseignement	3
Moniteurs de sport	7
Total	18

Student Enrolment, 1986-87:

	Men	Women	Total
Of the country	75	17	92
Of other countries	16	–	16
Total	91	17	108

2759 **INSTITUT D'ÉTUDES POLITIQUES**
25, rue Gaston de Saporta, Place de l'Université, 13625 Aix-en-Provence Cedex
Telephone: 42-21-06-72
Directeur: Jacques Bourdon (1984-)
Chef des Services administratifs: Colette Fèvre

Political Studies

Founded 1956. Attached to the Université de Droit, d'Economie et des Sciences d'Aix-Marseille (Aix-MarseilleIII). Governing body: the Conseil d'administration, comprising 27 members.

Academic Year: October to June (October-February; February-June).

Admission Requirements: Secondary school certificate (baccalauréat) or equivalent, and entrance examination.

Fees (Francs): 878 per annum

Language of Instruction: French.

Degrees and Diplomas: Diplôme, 3 yrs. Certificat, 1 yr, for foreign students.

Library: c. 5000 vols.

Publication: Annales des pays d'Amérique Centrale et des Caraïbes (biannually).

Press or Publishing House: Presses Universitaires d'Aix-Marseille.

Academic Staff: c. 20 (90).

Student Enrolment: c. 820.

2760 **INSTITUT D'ÉTUDES POLITIQUES**
1, rue Raulin, 69365 Lyon Cedex 2
Telephone: 78-72-85-63

Political History
Politics and Administration
Economics and Industry

Founded 1948. Attached to the Université de Lyon II.

Arrangements for co-operation with: University of Warwick; Leeds Polytechnic; Polytechnic of the South Bank; University of California, Berkeley.

Academic Year: October to June (October-December; January-April; April-June).

Admission Requirements: Secondary school certificate (baccalauréat) and entrance examination.

Fees (Francs): 400 per annum.

Language of Instruction: French.

Degrees and Diplomas: Diplôme, 3 yrs. Diplôme d'études approfondies (D.E.A.), 1 yr.

Library: 14,000 vols.

Publication: Procès (quarterly).

Academic Staff, 1986-87: 22 (100).

Student Enrolment, 1986-87: 1200.

2761 **INSTITUT D'ÉTUDES POLITIQUES DE GRENOBLE**
Domaine Universitaire, B.P. 45, 38402 St. Martin-d'Hères Cedex
Telephone: 76-82-60-
Fax: 76-82-60-70
Directeur François d'Arcy
Secrétaire générale: Catherine Finkel

Political Science
Management
Social Sciences (Including Political Sciences)
Public Administration

Founded 1948. Transformed by decree into a scientific cultural public institution attached to the Universitédes Sciences Sociales (Grenoble II). Governing body: the Conseil d'administration, comprising 30 members

Academic Year: October to June (October-February; February-June).

Admission Requirements: Secondary school certificate (baccalauréat) or equivalent, and entrance examination

Fees (Francs): 1100 per annum.

Language of Instruction: French.

Degrees and Diplomas: Diplôme d'études politiques, 3 yrs; Diplôme d'études approfondies (D.E.A.); Diplôme d'études supérieures spécialisées (D.E.S.S.). Doctorat de Science politique, 2-4 yrs after D.E.A.

Library: Documentation Centre, *c.* 80,000 vols.

Academic Staff, 1989-90:

Rank	Full-time
Professors	11
Maîtres de conférences	16
Assistants	8
Total	35

Student Enrolment, 1989-90:

	Men	Women	Total
Of the country	500	500	1000
Of other countries	30	40	70
Total	530	540	1070

2762 **INSTITUT D'ÉTUDES POLITIQUES**
47, avenue de la Forêt Noire, 67084 Strasbourg Cedex
Telephone: 88-41-77-60
Directeur: Michel Dietsch (1989-)
Secrétaire générale: Francine Berg

Public Administration
Economics and Finance
International Relations
Political Science

Founded 1945. Attached to the Université Robert Schuman (Strasbourg III).

Participates in the ERASMUS programmes with: LSE London; LUISS Rome; Trinity College Dublin; Universität Erlangen-Nürnberg; Universidad de Sevilla.

Academic Year: October to June (October-January; January-May).

Admission Requirements: Secondary school certificate (baccalauréat) or equivalent, and entrance examination.

Fees (Francs): 1000.

Language of Instruction: French.

Degrees and Diplomas: Certificat d'études politiques, 1 yr (for foreign students). Diplôme d'études approfondies de Science politique (D.E.A). Diplôme d'études supérieures spécialisées (D.E.S.S.).

Library: 30,000 vols.

Academic Staff, 1990-91:

Rank	Full-time	Part-time
Professeurs	8	12
Maîtres de conférences	8	10
Assistants	10	–
Total	26	22

Student Enrolment, 1990-91:

	Men	Women	Total
Of the country	305	265	570
Of other countries	34	36	70
Total	339	301	640

2763 **INSTITUT D'ÉTUDES POLITIQUES**
Domaine universitaire AlléeAusone, B.P. 101, 33405 Talence-Pessac Cedex
Telephone: 56-84-42-52, 56-84-42-93
Fax: 56-35-45-37
Directeur: M. Sadran (1986-)
Secrétaire général: M. Chabault

D. of Political Studies
Head: M. Sadran
D. of African Studies
Heads: C. Coulon; J.F. Médard
D. of Canadian Studies
Heads: P. Guillaume; J. Pacard
D. of Administrative Studies
Head: Pierre Sadran
D. of Study of Local Politics
Head: A. Mabileau
Ce. for Lifelong Education
Head: J.M. Peret

Founded 1948. Attached to the Fondation nationale des Sciences politiques. Governing body: the Conseil d'administration.

Arrangements for co-operation with: Université Laval; London University; Universidad de Barcelona. Universities of Colorado and California.Participates in the ERASMUS programme.

Academic Year: September to July.

Admission Requirements: Secondary school certificate (baccalauréat) or foreign equivalent, and entrance examination.

Fees (Francs): 1500.

Language of Instruction: French.

Degrees and Diplomas: Diplôme, 3 yrs. Certificate for foreign students, 1 yr. Diplôme d'études approfondies (D.E.A.) en études africaines and en gouvernement local. Doctorat, 2-4 yrs after D.E.A.

Library: c. 70,000 vols.

Publications: Année africaine; Collection Gouvernment Local; Collection Etudes Africaines; Collection IEP.

Academic Staff, 1989-90:

Rank	Full-time	Part-time
Professeurs	7	25
Maîtres de conférences	18	60
Total	25	85

Student Enrolment, 1989-90:

	Men	Women	Total
Of the country	600	500	1100
Of other countries	60	60	120
Total	660	560	1220

2764 **INSTITUT D'ÉTUDES POLITIQUES**
2 ter, rue des Puits-Creusés, 31000 Toulouse
Telephone: 61-21-93-10

Political Studies
Lifelong Education

Founded 1948. Attached to the Université des Sciences sociales (Toulouse I). Governing body: the Conseil d'administration, comprising 27 members.

Arrangements for co-operation with: University of Lancaster; University of Chicago; Université Hassan II, Casablanca.

Academic Year: October to June (October-December; January-March; April-June).

Admission Requirements: Secondary school certificate (baccalauréat) and entrance examination.

Language of Instruction: French.

Degrees and Diplomas: Diplôme, 3 yrs. Also Certificat d'études supérieures de défense et de sociologie militaire.

Library: General Library, 10,000 vols.

Publication: Revue des Sciences politiques (quarterly).

Press or Publishing House: Presses de l'Institut d'Etudes politiques de Toulouse.

Academic Staff: c. 15 (40).

Student Enrolment: c. 720.

2765 **ÉCOLE NATIONALE DES SERVICES DU TRÉSOR**
Bois de la Grange, Noisiel, 77420 Champs-sur-Marne
Telephone: 60-05-92-04

Public Finance

Founded 1947 by decree of the Minister of Finance to train Treasury Inspectors. Responsible to the Ministry ofEconomy and Finance. Some residential facilities for students

Academic Year: September to August.

Admission Requirements: Entrance by competition for holders of Licence or equivalent. Special admission requirements for civil servants and foreign students.

Language of Instruction: French.

Degrees and Diplomas: Professional Promotion for French students; foreign students, Diplôme.

Library: *c.* 4500 vols.

Press or Publishing House: Imprimerie de l'Ecole.

Academic Staff: *c.* 10 (300).

Student Enrolment: *c.* 450.

Schools of Architecture and Fine Arts

2766 **ÉCOLE D'ARCHITECTURE DE BORDEAUX**
Domaine de Raba, Cours de la Libération, 33405 Talence
Telephone: 56-80-65-44
Fax: 56-37-03-23
Directeur: M. Peyre

Architecture

Founded 1968 as Unité pédagogique d'architecture, acquired present title 1984. Responsible to the Ministryof Development, Housing and Transport. Governing body: the Conseil d'administration.

Academic Year: October to June (October-December; January-March; April-June).

Admission Requirements: Secondary school certificate (baccalauréat) or equivalent.

Language of Instruction: French.

Degrees and Diplomas: Diplôme d'études fondamentales en architecture (D.E.F.A.), 2 yrs; Diplôme d'Architecte, D.P.L.G., a further 3 yrs (State diploma).

Academic Staff: *c.* 40.

Student Enrolment: *c.* 460.

2767 **ANTENNE PÉDAGOGIQUE D'ARCHITECTURE**
B.P. 47, 95000 Cergy Cedex

Architecture

2768 **ÉCOLE D'ARCHITECTURE DE CLERMONT-FERRAND**
71, Boulevard Côte Blatin, 63000 Clermont-Ferrand
Telephone: 73-93-18-55
Directeur: M. Dujardin

Architecture

Founded 1968 as Unité pédagogique d'Architecture, acquired present title 1984. Responsible to the Ministryof Development, Housing and Transport. Governing body: the Conseil d'administration. Residential facilities for students.

Academic Year: October to June.

Admission Requirements: Secondary school certificate (baccalauréat) and entrance examination.

Language of Instruction: French.

Degrees and Diplomas: Diplôme d'études fondamentales en architecture (D.E.F.A.), 2 yrs; Diplôme d'Architecte, D.P.L.G., a further 3 yrs (State diploma).

Library: *c.* 5000 vols.

Academic Staff: *c.* 20.

Student Enrolment: *c.* 200.

2769 **ÉCOLE D'ARCHITECTURE DE GRENOBLE**
10, galerie des Baladins, 38100 Grenoble
Telex: 308658 CRATERE
Telephone: 76-23-31-72
Fax: 76-22-72-56
Directeur: Pierre Mignotte

Architecture

Also 4 Research Laboratories

Founded 1927 as Ecole régionale d'Architecture, became Unité pédagogique d'Architecture 1968 and acquired present title 1984. Responsible to the Ministry of Development, Housing and Transport.

Academic Year: October to June (October-December; January-March; April-June).

Admission Requirements: Secondary school certificate (baccalauréat) or equivalent.

Language of Instruction: French.

Degrees and Diplomas: Diplôme d'études fondamentales en architecture (D.E.F.A.), 2 yrs; Diplôme d'Architecte, D.P.L.G., a further 3 yrs (State diploma). Certificat d'études approfondies en architecture, C.E.A.A., at least 1 yr after D.P.L.G.

Library: Central Library, *c.* 5000 vols.

Academic Staff, 1989-90: 80

Student Enrolment, 1989-90: 855

2770 **ÉCOLE D'ARCHITECTURE DE LILLE**
Rue Verte, Quartier de l'Hôtel de Ville, 59650 Villeneuve-d'Ascq
Telephone: 20-91-26-41

Architecture

Founded 1755 as Ecole régionale d'Architecture, became Unité pédagogique d'Architecture 1968 and acquired present title 1984. Responsible to the Ministry of Development, Housing and Transport. Governing body: the Conseil d'administration.

Academic Year: October to June (October-December; January-March; April-June).

Admission Requirements: Secondary school certificate (baccalauréat), or foreign equivalent.

Language of Instruction: French.

Degrees and Diplomas: Diplôme d'études fondamentales en architecture (D.E.F.A.), 2 yrs. Diplôme d'Architecte, D.P.L.G., a further 3 yrs (State diploma). Diplôme d'études approfondies (D.E.A.), at least 1 yr after D.P.L.G.

Library: Documentation Centre, 5000 vols.

Academic Staff: *c.* 30 (10).

Student Enrolment: *c.* 620 (Including *c.* 70 foreign students).

2771 **ÉCOLE D'ARCHITECTURE DE LYON**
21, rue de Villeneuve, 69130 Ecully
Telephone: 17-33-01-14
Directeur: M. Fraisse

Architecture

Founded 1968 as Unité pédagogique d'Architecture, acquired present title 1984. Responsible to the Ministryof Development, Housing and Transport. Governing body: the Conseil d'administration.

Academic Year: October to June.

Admission Requirements: Secondary school certificate (baccalauréat) or equivalent.

Degrees and Diplomas: Diplôme d'études fondamentales en architecture (D.E.F.A.), 2 yrs; Diplôme d'Architecte, D.P.L.G., a further 3 yrs (State diploma).

Library: *c.* 4600 vols.

Academic Staff, 1986-87: 35 (58).

Student Enrolment, 1986-87:

	Men	Women	Total
Of the country	254	148	402
Of other countries	29	14	43
Total	283	162	445

2772 **ÉCOLE D'ARCHITECTURE DE MARSEILLE-LUMINY**
Route Léon Lechamp, 13288 Marseille-Luminy Cedex 2
Telephone: 91-26-80-80
Directeur: M. Hémy

Applied Arts

Communications (Visual and Audio-Visual)

Art and the Environment

Founded 1752 as Académie de Dessin. Became Unité pédagogique d'Architecture 1968, acquired present title1984. Responsible to the Ministry of Development, Housing and Transport. Residential facilities for students at Cité universitaire.

Arrangements for co-operation with similar institutions in Germany and the United Kingdom.

Academic Year: October to June (October-December; January-March; April-June).

Admission Requirements: Secondary school certificate (baccalauréat) or foreign equivalent.
Language of Instruction: French.
Degrees and Diplomas: Diplôme national supérieur d'Expression plastique (D.N.S.E.P.), 3 yrs. Also Certificat, 2 yrs.
Academic Staff: c. 70.
Student Enrolment: c. 600.

2773 **ÉCOLE D'ARCHITECTURE DU LANGUEDOC-ROUSSILLON**
179, rue de l'Espérance, Plan des 4 Seigneurs, 34000 Montpellier
Telephone: 67-63-34-30
Directeur: Jean Boissonnade

Architecture

Founded 1969 as Unité pédagogique d'Architecture, acquired present title 1984. Responsible to the Ministryof Development, Housing and Transport.
Academic Year: October to June (October-December; January-April; April-June).
Admission Requirements: Secondary school certificate (baccalauréat) and entrance examination, or foreign equivalent.
Language of Instruction: French.
Degrees and Diplomas: Diplôme d'études fondamentales en architecture (D.E.F.A.), 2 yrs; Diplôme d'Architecte, D.P.L.G., a further 3 yrs (State diploma).
Academic Staff: 20 (20).
Student Enrolment: c. 530.

2774 **ÉCOLE D'ARCHITECTURE DE NANCY**
Parc de Rémicourt, 54600 Villers-les-Nancy
Telephone: 83-27-10-77
Fax: 83-27-39-74
Directeur: Rose Meunier (1986-)

Architecture

Founded 1968 as Unité pédagogique d'Architecture, acquired present title 1984. Formerly part of Ecole nationale supérieure des Beaux-Arts. Responsible to the Ministry of Development, Housing and Transport. Governing body: the Conseil d'administration.
Arrangements for co-operation with the Universities of: Venice; Karlsruhe; Newcastle upon Tyne; Porto; Miami; Barcelona; Florence; Delfi.
Academic Year: October to June (October-February; March-June).
Admission Requirements: Secondary school certificate (baccalauréat).
Fees (Francs): 450 per annum.
Language of Instruction: French.
Degrees and Diplomas: Diplôme d'études fondamentales en architecture (D.E.F.A.), 2 yrs; Diplôme d'Architecte, D.P.L.G., a further 3 yrs (State diploma).
Library: c. 10,000 vols.
Academic Staff, 1986-87: 30 (30).
Student Enrolment, 1986-87:

	Men	Women	Total
Of the country	200	90	290
Of other countries	15	5	20
Total	215	95	310

2775 **ÉCOLE D'ARCHITECTURE DE NANTES**
'La Mulotière', rue Massenet, 44300 Nantes
Telephone: 40-76-07-33
Directeur: Jean-Marc Cailleau

Architecture

Founded 1945 as Ecole régionale d'Architecture, became Unité pédagogique d'Architecture 1968 and acquired present title 1984. Responsible to the Ministry of Development, Housing and Transport. Governing body: the Conseil d'administration.
Arrangements for co-operation with: Technical University of Wrocław; Portsmouth Polytechnic; Istituto Universitario di Architettura di Venezia; College of Applied Arts, Vienna.
Academic Year: October to June (October-February; February-June).
Admission Requirements: Secondary school certificate (baccalauréat) or recognized foreign equivalent.
Fees (Francs): 470 per annum.
Language of Instruction: French.
Degrees and Diplomas: Diplôme d'études fondamentales en architecture (D.E.F.A.), 2 yrs; Diplôme d'Architecte, D.P.L.G., a further 3 yrs (State diploma). Certificats d'études approfondies en architecture C.E.A.A., at least 1 yr after D.P.L.G.
Library: Documentation Centre, c. 7700 vols.
Press or Publishing House: Atelier de reprographie de l'Ecole.
Academic Staff, 1986-87: 82.
Student Enrolment, 1986-87:

	Men	Women	Total
Of the country	343	186	529
Of other countries	53	9	62
Total	396	195	591

2776 **ÉCOLE D'ARCHITECTURE DE PARIS-BELLEVILLE**
78-80, rue Rebeval, 75019 Paris
Telephone: (1) 42-41-33-60
Directeur: Claude Cobbi (1972-)

Architecture

Founded 1648 as part of the Ecole nationale des Beaux-Arts, became Unité pédagogique d'Architecture 1968 and acquired present title 1984. Responsible to the Ministry of Development, Housing and Transport. Governing body: the Conseil d'administration.
Arrangements for co-operation with: University of Toronto; University of Stuttgart; Istituto Universitario di Architettura di Venezia; Cooper Union, New York; Technical University of Cataluña, Barcelona; University College, Dublin.
Academic Year: October to June (October-February; February-June).
Admission Requirements: Secondary school certificate (baccalauréat) or equivalent.
Fees (Francs): 450 per annum.
Language of Instruction: French.
Degrees and Diplomas: Diplôme d'études fondamentales en architecture, D.E.F.A., 2 yrs. Diplôme d'Architecte, D.P.L.G., a further 3 yrs (State diploma). Certificats d'études d'architecture approfondies, C.E.A.A., at least 1 yr after D.P.L.G.
Library: Central Library, 10,000 vols.
Academic Staff, 1986-87: 49 (26).
Student Enrolment, 1986-87:

	Men	Women	Total
Of the country	434	275	709
Of other countries	92	29	121
Total	526	304	830

2777 **ÉCOLE D'ARCHITECTURE DE PARIS-CONFLANS**
11, rue du Séminaire de Conflans, 94220 Charenton-le-Pont
Telephone: (1) 43-68-00-55
Director: Jean-Luc Iral (1975-)

Architecture

Academic Year: October to June (October-January; February-June).
Admission Requirements: Secondary school certificate (baccalauréat) or equivalent.
Fees (Francs): 450 per annum.
Language of Instruction: French.
Degrees and Diplomas: Diplôme d'études fondamentales en architecture (D.E.F.A.), 2 yrs; Diplôme d'Architecte, D.P.L.G., a further 3 yrs (State diploma).
Library: 6000 vols.
Academic Staff, 1986-87: 54 (45).
Student Enrolment, 1986-87: 520.

2778 **ÉCOLE D'ARCHITECTURE DE PARIS-LA-DÉFENSE**
58, rue Salvador Allende, 92023 Nanterre Cedex
Telephone: (1) 47-76-01-05
Directeur: Jean-François Roullin (1986-)

Architecture

Founded 1968 as Unité pédagogique d'Architecture. Formerly part of Ecole nationale supérieure des Beaux-Arts, acquired present title 1984. Responsible to the Ministry of Development, Housing and Transport. Governing body: the Conseil d'administration.
Academic Year: October to June.
Admission Requirements: Secondary school certificate (baccalauréat) or equivalent.
Fees (Francs): 450 per annum.
Language of Instruction: French.

Degrees and Diplomas: Diplôme d'études fondamentales en architecture (D.E.F.A.), 2 yrs; Diplôme d'Architecte, D.P.L.G., a further 3 yrs (State diploma).
Library: Documentation Centre, *c.* 4500 vols.
Academic Staff, 1986-87: 53.
Student Enrolment, 1986-87:

	Men	Women	Total
Of the country	157	76	233
Of other countries	71	35	106
Total	228	111	339

2779 **ÉCOLE D'ARCHITECTURE DE PARIS-LA-SEINE**
14, rue Bonaparte, 75006 Paris
Telephone: (1) 42-72-81-11
Directeur: M. Reliquet

Architecture

Founded 1968 as Unité pédagogique d'Architecture. Formerly part of Ecole nationale supérieure des Beaux-Arts, acquired present title 1984. Responsible to the Ministry of Development, Housing and Transport. Governing body: the Conseil d'administration.
Academic Year: October to July (October-December; January-March; April-July).
Admission Requirements: Secondary school certificate (baccalauréat) or equivalent.
Language of Instruction: French.
Degrees and Diplomas: Diplôme d'études fondamentales en architecture (D.E.F.A.), 2 yrs; Diplôme d'Architecte, D.P.L.G., a further 3 yrs (State diploma).
Library: c. 2000 vols.
Academic Staff: c. 80.
Student Enrolment: c. 760.

2780 **ÉCOLE D'ARCHITECTURE DE PARIS-LA-VILLETTE**
144, rue de Flandre, 75019 Paris
Telephone: (1) 42-08-79-70

Architecture
Lifelong Education

Founded 1969 as Unité pédagogique d'Architecture. Formerly part of Ecole nationale supérieure des Beaux-Arts, acquired present title 1984. Responsible to the Ministry of Development, Housing and Transport. Governing body: the Conseil d'administration.
Academic Year: October to June (October-February; February-June).
Admission Requirements: Secondary school certificate (baccalauréat) or equivalent.
Language of Instruction: French.
Degrees and Diplomas: Diplôme d'études fondamentales en architecture (D.E.F.A.), 2 yrs; Diplôme d'Architecte, D.P.L.G., a further 3 yrs (State diploma).
Library: 9000 vols.
Press or Publishing House: Editions de la Villette.
Academic Staff: c. 130.
Student Enrolment: c. 2260.

2781 **ÉCOLE D'ARCHITECTURE DE PARIS-TOLBIAC**
5, rue du Javelot, 75645 Paris Cedex 13
Telephone: (1) 45-84-11-03
Directeur: M. Chevrière

Architecture

Founded 1969 as Unité pédagogique d'Architecture. Formerly part of Ecole nationale supérieure des Beaux-Arts, acquired present title 1984. Responsible to the Ministry of Development, Housing and Transport.
Academic Year: October to June.
Admission Requirements: Secondary school certificate (baccalauréat) and entrance examination.
Language of Instruction: French.
Degrees and Diplomas: Diplôme d'études fondamentales en architecture (D.E.F.A.), 2 yrs; Diplôme d'Architecte, D.P.L.G., a further 3 yrs (State diploma).
Academic Staff: c. 50.
Student Enrolment: c. 630.

2782 **ÉCOLE D'ARCHITECTURE DE PARIS-VILLEMIN**
11, quai Malaquais, 75272 Paris Cedex 06
Telephone: (1) 42-60-34-57
Directeur: S. Clavel

Architecture
Lifelong Education

Founded 1968 as Unité pédagogique d'Architecture. Formerly part of Ecole nationale supérieure des Beaux-Arts, acquired present title 1984. Governing body: the Conseil d'administration. Residential facilities for students on campus.
Arrangements for co-operation with: College of Architecture and Building, Weimar. Universities of Bangkok, Chulalongkorn, Silpakorn, King Mongkut. Ecole d'Architecture, Tunis; College of Architecture, Houston, Texas; Technische Universität Berlin.
Academic Year: October to June (October-February; February-June).
Admission Requirements: Secondary school certificate (baccalauréat) or foreign equivalent, and entrance examination.
Language of Instruction: French.
Degrees and Diplomas: Certificats, 2-4 yrs. Diplôme d'études fondamentales en architecture (D.E.F.A.), 2 yrs; Diplôme d'Architecte, D.P.L.G., a further 3 yrs (State diploma).
Academic Staff, 1990: c. 72 (25).
Student Enrolment, 1990:

	Men	Women	Total
Of the country	429	290	719
Of the countries	155	96	251
Total	584	386	970

2783 **ÉCOLE D'ARCHITECTURE DE BRETAGNE**
44, boulevard de Chézy, 35000 Rennes
Telephone: 99-30-67-67
Fax: 99-30-42-49
Director: M. Guillerm
Secrétaire général: Jean-Patrick Serres

Architecture

Founded 1904, became Unité pédagogique d'Architecture 1968 and acquired present title 1984. Responsible tothe Ministry of Development, Housing and Transport.
Arrangements for student exchange with the Conférence des Recteurs et des Principaux des Universités du Québec.
Academic Year: October to June (October-January; February-June).
Admission Requirements: Secondary school certificate (baccalauréat) or equivalent.
Language of Instruction: French.
Degrees and Diplomas: Diplôme d'études fondamentales en architecture (D.E.F.A.), 2 yrs; Diplôme d'Architecte, D.P.L.G., a further 3 yrs (State diploma).
Library: c. 13,000 vols.
Academic Staff: c. 20.
Student Enrolment, 1989-90:

	Men	Women	Total
Of the country	205	123	328
Of other countries	18	1	19
Total	223	124	347

2784 **ÉCOLE D'ARCHITECTURE DE NORMANDIE**
27, rue Lucien Fromage, 76160 Darnetal
Telephone: 35-08-07-70
Fax: 35-08-38-31
Directeur: M. Maillard
Directeur-adjoint: E. Martinez

Architecture

Founded 1850, became Unité pédagogique d'Architecture 1968 and acquired present title 1984. Responsible tothe Ministry of Development, Housing and Transport.
Arrangements for co-operation with institutions in: Germany; Poland; United Kingdom; Spain; Portugal, etc.
Admission Requirements: Secondary school certificate (baccalauréat) or equivalent.
Fees (Francs): 500 per annum.
Degrees and Diplomas: Diplôme d'études fondamentales en architecture (D.E.F.A.), 2 yrs; Diplôme d'Architecte, D.P.L.G., a further 3 yrs (State diploma).

Library: 8000 vols.
Academic Staff: 22.
Student Enrolment, 1989-90:

	Men	Women	Total
Of the country	451	166	417
Of other countries	42	7	49
Total	293	173	466*

*Also 7 external students.

2785 **ÉCOLE D'ARCHITECTURE DE SAINT-ETIENNE**
1, rue Buisson, 42000 Saint-Etienne
Telephone: 77-32-69-31
Directeur: Etienne de Cointet (1983-)

D. of Architecture
Head: Mario Bonilla
D. of Construction
Head: André Accetta
D. of Plastic Arts
Head: Daniel Vallat
D. of Exact Sciences
Head: Georges Véran
D. of Human Sciences
Head: Christian Eychene

Founded 1971 as Unité pédagogique d'Architecture, acquired present title 1984. Responsible to the Ministryof Development, Housing and Transport. Governing body: the Conseil d'administration.

Arrangements for co-operation with the Universities of: Stuttgart; Berlin; Cambridge.

Academic Year: October to June (October-December; January-March; April-June).

Admission Requirements: Secondary school certificate (baccalauréat) or equivalent.

Fees (Francs): 490 per annum.

Language of Instruction: French.

Degrees and Diplomas: Diplôme d'études fondamentales en architecture (D.E.F.A.), 2 yrs; Diplôme d'Architecte, D.P.L.G., a further 3 yrs (State diploma). Certificats d'études approfondies en architecture C.E.A.A., at least 1 yr after D.P.L.G.

Library: c. 1800 vols.
Academic Staff, 1989-90: c. 60.
Student Enrolment, 1989-90:

Of the country	242
Of other countries	32
Total	274

2786 **ÉCOLE D'ARCHITECTURE DE STRASBOURG**
Grand Garage, 8, boulevard Wilson B.P. 37 67068 Strasbourg Cedex
Telex: 870961 STRARCH
Telephone: 88-32-25-35
Fax: 88-32-82-41
Directeur: M. Ayrault

Architecture (including Town Planning)

Founded 1923 as Ecole régionale d'Architecture, became Unité pédagogique d'Architecture 1968 and acquired present title 1984. Responsible to the Ministry of Development, Housing and Transport.

Arrangements for co-operation with Technical University of Budapest. Participates in the ERASMUS programme with the University of Strathclyde.

Academic Year: October to June.

Admission Requirements: Secondary school certificate (baccalauréat) or equivalent.

Language of Instruction: French.

Degrees and Diplomas: Diplôme d'études fondamentales en Architecture (D.E.F.A.), 2 yrs; Diplôme d'Architecte, D.P.L.G., a further 3 yrs (State diploma).

Library: c. 4500 vols.

Academic Staff: c. – (60).
Student Enrolment, 1990:

	Men	Women	Total
Of the country	336	212	548
Of other countries	66	9	75
Total	402	221	623

2787 **ÉCOLE D'ARCHITECTURE DE TOULOUSE**
83, rue Aristide Maillol, 31100 Toulouse
Telephone: 61-40-47-28
Fax: 61-44-71-21
Directeur: J.L. Bour

Architecture
Also 3 Research Laboratories.

Founded 1968 as Unité pédagogique d'Architecture, acquired present title 1984. Responsible to the Ministryof Development, Housing and Transport.

Academic Year: October to June (October-February; February-June).

Admission Requirements: Secondary school certificate (baccalauréat) or equivalent.

Language of Instruction: French.

Degrees and Diplomas: Diplôme d'études fondamentales en Architecture (D.E.F.A.), 2 yrs; Diplôme d'Architecte, D.P.L.G., a further 3 yrs (State diploma).

Library: c. 9000 vols.
Academic Staff: c. 40.
Student Enrolment: c. 950.

2788 **ÉCOLE D'ARCHITECTURE DE VERSAILLES**
2, avenue de Paris, 78000 Versailles
Telephone: (1) 39-51-52-51
Fax: (1) 39-50-08-51
Directeur: M. Lew

Architecture
Also 2 Research Laboratories.

Founded 1969 as Unité pédagogique d'Architecture. Formerly part of Ecole nationale supérieure des Beaux-Arts, acquired present title 1984. Responsible to the Ministry of Development, Housing and Transport.

Academic Year: October to June.

Admission Requirements: Secondary school certificate (baccalauréat) and entrance examination.

Fees (Francs): Registration 475.

Language of Instruction: French.

Degrees and Diplomas: Diplôme d'études fondamentales en architecture (D.E.F.A.), 2 yrs; Diplôme d'Architecte, D.P.L.G., a further 3 yrs (State diploma).

Library: c. 8000 vols.
Academic Staff: c. 52.
Student Enrolment, 1989-90:

	Men	Women	Total
Of the country	290	211	501
Of other countries	48	15	63
Total	338	226	564

2789 **ÉCOLE NATIONALE SUPÉRIEURE DES ARTS APPLIQUÉS ET DES MÉTIERS D'ART**
63-65, rue Olivier de Serres, 75015 Paris
Telephone: (1) 45-33-72-06

Applied Arts

Founded 1969, incorporating the Ecole des Arts appliqués à l'Industrie and the Ecole des Métiers d'Art.

Academic Year: September to June (September-December; January-March; April-June).

Admission Requirements: Competitive entrance examination following secondary school certificate (baccalauréat).

Language of Instruction: French.

Degrees and Diplomas: Diplôme in various specialities, 3 yrs.

Library: c. 3000 vols.
Academic Staff: c. 80 (20).
Student Enrolment: c. 720.

2790 **ÉCOLE NATIONALE SUPÉRIEURE DES ARTS DÉCORATIFS**
31, rue d'Ulm, 75005 Paris
Telephone: (1) 43-29-86-79
Fax: (1) 40-46-81-54
Directeur: Michel Tourlière (1970-)
Secrétaire générale: Françoise Huault

Decorative Arts

Founded 1766. Acquired present status and title 1927. Responsible to the Ministry of Culture, Communication, and of Great Works, and of the Bicentenary. Studies reorganized in 1987. Governing bodies: the Conseil d'Etablissement; the Conseil scientifique.

Arrangements for co-operation with: Cooper Union, New York; School of Art Institute, Chicago; Georgia Institute of Technology, Atlanta; Royal College of Art, London; Istituto Europeo di Design, Italy; Facultad de Bellas Artes, Barcelona; Hochschule für Gestaltung, Offenbach-am-Main; Hochschule Berlin.

Academic Year: October to June (October-January; February-June).

Admission Requirements: Secondary school certificate (baccalauréat) and competitive entrance examination.

Fees (Francs): 400 per annum.

Language of Instruction: French.

Degrees and Diplomas: Diplôme de l'Ecole nationale supérieure des Arts décoratifs with Certificat de Spécialisation, 4 yrs. Possibility of admission in third degree: production of research.

Library: c. 22,000 vols.

Publications: Autour du Chef-d'oeuvre inconnu de Balzac; Cahier de couleur No. 1; Cahier de couleur No. 2.

Academic Staff, 1990: – (171).

Student Enrolment, 1990:

	Men	Women	Total
Of the country	299	312	611
Of other countries	50	37	87
Total	349	349	698

2791 **ÉCOLE MUNICIPALE DES ARTS DÉCORATIFS DE STRASBOURG**
1, rue de l'Académie, 67000 Strasbourg
Telephone: 88-35-38-58
Directeur: François Cacheux (1959-90)

Decorative Arts
Fine Arts

Founded 1890. Responsible to the Ministry of Culture.

Academic Year: October to June (October-February; February-June).

Admission Requirements: Competitive entrance examination.

Fees (Francs): 800 per annum.

Language of Instruction: French.

Degrees and Diplomas: Diplôme national supérieur d'Expression plastique (D.N.S.E.P.) (Sections: Environment; Art); Diplôme supérieur municipal des Arts décoratifs, 5 yrs.

Academic Staff, 1986-87: 33 (38).

Student Enrolment, 1986-87: 400 (Including c. 50 foreign students).

2792 **CONSERVATOIRE NATIONAL SUPÉRIEUR D'ART DRAMATIQUE**
2 bis, rue du Conservatoire, 75009 Paris
Telephone: (1) 47-70-45-79

Drama

Admission Requirements: Competitive entrance examination.

Degrees and Diplomas: Duration of studies: 3 yrs.

2793 **ÉCOLE NATIONALE DES BEAUX-ARTS ET DES ARTS APPLIQUÉS À L'INDUSTRIE**
7, rue Edouard-Branly, 18000 Bourges
Telephone: 48-70-11-45

Plastic Arts
Ceramics

2794 **ÉCOLE NATIONALE DES BEAUX-ARTS**
3, rue Michelet, 21000 Dijon
Telephone: 80-30-21-27

Fine Arts

Founded 1766. Acquired present status 1864. Responsible to the Ministry of Culture and Communication.

Academic Year: October to June (October-December; January-March; April-June).

Admission Requirements: Secondary school certificate (baccalauréat) or equivalent and competitive entrance tests.

Language of Instruction: French.

Degrees and Diplomas: Certificat d'Initiation plastique. Diplôme national supérieur d'Expression plastique, 5 yrs; Diplôme national d'Arts et Techniques.

Library: c. 4000 vols.

Academic Staff: c. 15 (10).

Student Enrolment: c. 180.

2795 **ÉCOLE NATIONALE DES BEAUX-ARTS**
10, rue Neyret, 69001 Lyon
Telephone: 78-28-13-67
Directeur: Philippe Nanoum

Fine Arts (including Communication and Design)

Founded 1780. Responsible to the Ministry of Culture and Communication, and the City of Lyon.

Participates in the ERASMUS programme with Gloucestershire College of Art and Technology, Cheltenham.

Academic Year: October to June.

Admission Requirements: Secondary school certificate (baccalauréat) and competitive entrance tests.

Fees (Francs): 600-1800.

Language of Instruction: French.

Degrees and Diplomas: Certificat d'Initiation plastique. Diplôme national supérieur d'Expression plastique, ou communication, ouDesign, 5 yrs.

Library: c. 7000 vols.

Academic Staff, 1990-91: c. 29 (11).

Student Enrolment, 1989-90:

	Men	Women	Total
Of the country	166	195	361*

*Including 38 foreign students.

2796 **ÉCOLE NATIONALE DES BEAUX-ARTS**
B.P. 3123, 54013 Nancy Cedex
Telephone: 83-40-16-25
Fax: 83-28-78-60
Directeur: Joël Gauvin
Secrétaire général: Didier Lagrange

D. of Fine Arts
Co-ordinator: Jochen Gerz; *staff* 6 (1)
D. of Design (including Plastic and Technical Industrial Productions)
Co-ordinator: Marc Emery; *staff* 10
D. of Graphic Design
Co-ordinator: Christian Debize; *staff* 10

Founded 1702 as academy of painting and sculpture. Acquired present status 1946. Responsible to the Ministry of Culture and Communication.

Academic Year: October to June (October-December; January-March; April-June).

Admission Requirements: Secondary school certificates (Baccalauréat).

Fees: None.

Language of Instruction: French.

Degrees and Diplomas: Certificat d'études d'Arts plastiques (CEAP), 2 yrs. Diplôme national d'Arts plastiques (DNAP), 3 yrs. Certificat supérieur d'Arts plastiques (CESAP), 4 yrs. Diplõme national supérieur d'Expression plastique (DNSEP), 5 yrs. Also short-term courses (DNAT), 3 yrs.

Library: c. 2000 vols.

Academic Staff: c. 30 (30).

Student Enrolment, 1990: c. 160.

2797 **ÉCOLE NATIONALE SUPÉRIEURE DES BEAUX-ARTS**
17, quai Malaquais, 75272 Paris Cedex 06
Telex: N 30684 EBA +
Telephone: (1) 42-30-64-57
Fax: (1) 42-61-33-57
Directeur: Yves Michaud (1989-)

Painting and Drawing

Sculpture
Multimedia

Founded 1648, moved to present site in 1816. Responsibility for studies in architecture transferred in 1968 toeight teaching establishments in Paris. Under the jurisdiction of the Ministry of Culture and Communication.

Participates in the ERASMUS programme.

Academic Year: September to July.

Admission Requirements: Secondary school certificate (baccalauréat) and competitive entrance tests for Painting and Sculpture.

Fees (Francs): 500.

Language of Instruction: French.

Degrees and Diplomas: Diplôme supérieur d'Arts plastiques, D.S.A.P., 4-5 yrs. Mastère.

Library: c. 130,000 vols.

Publications: Bulletin signalétique, arts plastiques; Cahiers de psychologie de l'Art et de la Culture.

Academic Staff, 1989-90: 72.

Student Enrolment, 1989-90: 1100.

2798 **ÉCOLE RÉGIONALE DES BEAUX-ARTS**

30, rue Hoche, 35000 Rennes
Telephone: 99-30-79-77
Directeur: Jacques Sauvageot

Fine Arts (including Design and Communication)

Founded 1881. Financed by the municipality 95% and the State 5%. Responsible to the Ministry of Culture and Communication. Residential facilities for students.

Arrangements for co-operation with Exeter College of Arts.

Academic Year: October to June (October-December; January-March; April-June).

Admission Requirements: Secondary school certificate (baccalauréat) and entrance examination

Language of Instruction: French.

Degrees and Diplomas: Diplôme national d'Arts plastiques (D.N.A.P.), 3 yrs; Diplôme national d'Arts et Techniques (D.N.A.T.), 3 yrs; Diplôme national supérieur d'Expression plastique, 5 yrs.

Library: c. 1000 vols.

Special Facilities (Museums, etc.): La Galerie du Cloître (art gallery).

Academic Staff, 1989-90: 21 (11).

Student Enrolment, 1989-90:

	Men	Women	Total
Of the country	144	151	295
of other countries	5	8	13
Total	149	159	308

2799 **ÉCOLE DES BEAUX-ARTS ET DES ARTS APPLIQUÉS**

5, quai de la Daurade, 31000 Toulouse
Telephone: (61) 23-25-49
Fax: (61) 22-29-38
Directeur: Albert Pons

Fine Arts (including Communication, Product and Space Design)

Founded 1680. Responsible to the Ministry of Culture and Communication.

Arrangements for co-operation with the Facultés des Beaux-Arts of: Anvers; Rome; Santa Cruz de Tenerife. Participates in the ERASMUS programme.

Academic Year: October to June (October-December; January-March; April-June).

Admission Requirements: Secondary school certificate (baccalauréat) and entrance examination.

Fees (Francs): 500.

Language of Instruction: French.

Degrees and Diplomas: Diplôme national d'Arts plastiques (D.N.A.P.), 3 yrs. Diplôme national supérieur d'Expression plastique (D.N.S.E.P.), 5 yrs.

Library: 11,000 vols.

Special Facilities (Museums, etc.): Palais des Arts.

Student Enrolment, 1989-90:

	Men	Women	Total
Of the country	144	206	350

2800 **INSTITUT DES HAUTES ÉTUDES CINÉMATOGRAPHIQUES**

4, avenue de l'Europe, 94360 Bry-sur-Marne
Telephone: (1) 48-81-39-33

Cinematography and Television

Founded 1943 and responsible to the Ministry of Culture and Communication. Governing body: the Conseil d'administration.

Academic Year: November to June.

Admission Requirements: Competitive entrance examination following secondary school certificate (baccalauréat) or foreign equivalent.

Fees (Francs): 270 per annum.

Language of Instruction: French.

Degrees and Diplomas: Certificat, 3 yrs.

Library: c. 10,000 vols.

Academic Staff: c. – (120).

Student Enrolment: c. 70.

2801 **ÉCOLE NATIONALE LOUIS LUMIÈRE**

7, rue de Vaugirard, B.P. 22 93161 Noisy-le-Grand Cedex
Telephone: (1) 45-92-23-33
Fax: (1) 43-05-63-44
Directeur: Henri Frizet
Directeur des études: Peirre Auffret

Photography
Cinematography
Sound and Videonics

Founded 1926 as Ecole technique de Photographie et de Cinématographie. A State institution.

Academic Year: September to June.

Admission Requirements: Secondary school certificate (baccalauréat) and competitive entrance examination.

Language of Instruction: French.

Degrees and Diplomas: Brevet de Technicien supérieur, 2-3 yrs.

Academic Staff: c. 30 (30).

Student Enrolment, 1990: c. 136 *

*Also 136 external students.

2802 **ÉCOLE DU LOUVRE**

34, quai du Louvre, 75041 Paris Cedex 01
Telephone: (1) 42-60-39-26
Fax: (1) 42-60-40-36
Directeur: Dominique Ponnau
Secrétaire général: Jean Garnero

Archaeology, History of Art, Museology

Founded 1882. Responsible to the Ministry of Culture and Communication.

Academic Year: October to June.

Admission Requirements: Secondary school certificate (baccalauréat) or equivalent.

Fees (Francs): 400-800 per annum.

Language of Instruction: French.

Degrees and Diplomas: Diplômes, 3-7 yrs.

Library: c. 30,000 vols.

Publications: Ecole du Louvre: Notices d'Histoire de l'Art; Actes des Colloques et Rencontres de l'Ecole du Louvre.

Academic Staff, 1989-90: – (111).

Student Enrolment, 1989-90:

Of the country	2550
Of other countries	150
Total	2700

2803 **ÉCOLE NATIONALE DE MUSIQUE ET D'ART DRAMATIQUE**

5, rue de l'Ecole-de-Droit, 21000 Dijon
Telephone: 80-32-83-19

Music
Drama

Responsible to the Ministry of Culture and Communication.

2804 **CONSERVATOIRE NATIONAL SUPÉRIEUR DE MUSIQUE**
14, rue de Madrid, 75008 Paris
Telephone: (1) 42-92-15-20

Music
Founded 1795. Responsible to the Ministry of Culture and Communication.
Academic Year: October to June (October-December; January-March; April-June).
Admission Requirements: Competitive entrance examination.
Degrees and Diplomas: Duration of Studies, 1-4 yrs.
Library: c. 100,000 vols.
Special Facilities (Museums, etc.): Musée Instrumental.
Academic Staff: c. 150 (130).
Student Enrolment: c. 1230.

Institutes of Physical Education

2805 **INSTITUT NATIONAL DU SPORT ET DE L'ÉDUCATION PHYSIQUE**
11, avenue du Tremblay, 75012 Paris
Telephone: (1) 43-74-11-21
Fax: (1) 43-74-54-11
Directeur: Jacques Donzel
Secrétaire général: François Grosjean

D. for High Level Sport
Chief: Robert Poirier
Founded 1975, incorporating the Institut national des Sports and the Ecole normale supérieure d'Education physique, founded 1933. A State institution responsible to the Ministry of Leisure, Youth, and Sport. Governing body: the Management Board.
Arrangements for international exchanges with foreign national institutes for high level sport.
Academic Year: October to June (October-February; February-June).
Admission Requirements: Competitive entrance examination following further study after secondary school certificate (baccalauréat) and possession of teaching qualification in Physical Education (Part 1).
Language of Instruction: French.
Degrees and Diplomas: Certificat d'Aptitude au Professorat d'Education physique (Part 2), 3 yrs. Professorat de Sport, 2 yrs.
Library: c. 60,000 vols.
Publications: Mensuel signalétique (6 times a year); Science et Motricité (quarterly).
Press or Publishing House: Les Éditions de l'INSEP.
Academic Staff: c. 40.
Student Enrolment: c. 240.

2806 **INSTITUT RÉGIONAL D'ÉDUCATION PHYSIQUE**
Place St.-Jacques, 25030 Besançon Cedex

Physical Education

2807 **INSTITUT RÉGIONAL D'ÉDUCATION PHYSIQUE ET SPORTIVE**
3, place de la Victoire, 33076 Bordeaux Cedex
Telephone: 56-91-34-24

Physical Education and Sports
Founded 1928. Attached to the Université de Bordeaux II.
Academic Year: October to June (October-February; March-June).
Admission Requirements: Competitive examination following further study after secondary school certificate (baccalauréat) and possession of teaching qualification in Physical Education (Part 1).
Language of Instruction: French.
Degrees and Diplomas: Certificat d'Aptitude au Professorat d'Education physique (Part 2), 3 yrs.
Academic Staff: c. 10.

2808 **INSTITUT RÉGIONAL D'ÉDUCATION PHYSIQUE**
Campus II, Boulevard Maréchal-Juin, 14032 Caen Cedex

Physical Education

2809 **INSTITUT RÉGIONAL D'ÉDUCATION PHYSIQUE ET SPORTIVE**
Rue Paul Doumer, 63000 Clermont-Ferrand
Telephone: 73-93-93-17

Physical Education and Sport
Founded 1929. Attached to the Université de Clermont-Ferrand II.
Academic Year: November to June.
Admission Requirements: Competitive entrance examination following further study after secondary school certificate (baccalauréat) and possession of teaching qualification in Physical Education (Part 1).
Language of Instruction: French.
Degrees and Diplomas: Certificat d'Aptitude au Professorat d'Education physique (Part 2), 3 yrs.
Academic Staff: c. 5.
Student Enrolment: c. 100.

2810 **CENTRE RÉGIONAL D'ÉDUCATION PHYSIQUE ET SPORTIVE**
Rue des Marettes, 35802 Dinard
Telephone: 99-46-16-23

Physical Education and Sport
Academic Year: October to June.
Admission Requirements: Competitive entrance examination following further study after secondary school certificate (baccalauréat) and possession of teaching qualification in Physical Education (Part 1).
Language of Instruction: French.
Degrees and Diplomas: Certificat d'Aptitude au Professorat d'Education physique (Part 2), 3 yrs.

2811 **CENTRE RÉGIONAL D'ÉDUCATION PHYSIQUE ET SPORTIVE**
Chateau de Mirande, rue Pierre de Coubertin, 21000 Dijon Cedex
Telephone: 80-65-46-12

Physical Education

2812 **INSTITUT RÉGIONAL D'ÉDUCATION PHYSIQUE ET DE CADRES SPORTIFS**
Domaine Universitaire, 38400 St. Martin d'Hères
Telephone: 76-54-45-81

Physical Education and Sport
Attached to the Université scientifique et médicale Grenoble I.
Academic Year: November to June.
Admission Requirements: Competitive entrance examination following further study after secondary school certificate (baccalauréat) and possession of teaching qualification in Physical Education (Part 1).
Language of Instruction: French.
Degrees and Diplomas: Certificat d'Aptitude au Professorat d'Education physique (Part 2), 3 yrs.

2813 **UNITÉ DE FORMATION ET DE RECHERCHE EN SCIENCES ET TECHNIQUES DES ACTIVITÉ PHYSIQUES ET SPORTIVES**
9, chemin Latéral, 59790 Ronchin
Telephone: 20-52-52-85
Directeur: Roland Dhelin
Chef des Services administratifs: Marian Ruszala

Physical Education and Sport
Founded 1928. Attached to the Université du Droit et de la Santé (Lille II).
Academic Year: September to June.
Admission Requirements: Competitive entrance examination following secondary school certificate (baccalauréat) or equivalent.
Language of Instruction: French.
Degrees and Diplomas: Diplôme d'études générales (D.E.U.G.), 2 yrs; Licence, 1 further yr. Maîtrise. Diplôme détudes approfondies (D.E.A.), Diplôme d'études supérieures specialisées (D.E.S.S.). Doctorat.
Library: Bibliothèque de l'UFR STAPS, c. 1300 vols.

Academic Staff: c. 40.
Student Enrolment, 1989-90:

	Men	Women	Total
Of the country	385	298	683
Of other countries	10	5	15
Total	395	303	698

2814 **INSTITUT RÉGIONAL D'ÉDUCATION PHYSIQUE ET SPORTIVE**
15, boulevard du 11-Novembre-1918, 69621 Villeurbanne
Telephone: 78-89-17-53

Physical Education

Founded 1928. Attached to the Université Claude-Bernard (Lyon I).
Academic Year: September to July.
Language of Instruction: French.
Degrees and Diplomas: Teaching qualification in Physical Education. Preparation for Certificat d'études spéciales in Medicine.
Academic Staff: c. 20.

2815 **UNITÉ DE FORMATION ET DE RECHERCHE EN SCIENCES ET TECHNIQUES DES ACTIVITÉS PHYSIQUES ET SPORTIVES**
163, avenue de Luminy, 13288 Marseille Cedex 2
Telephone: 91-26-92-61
Fax: 91-26-92-99
Directeur: M. Laurent
Secrétaire général: M. Traversari

Physical Education (including Psychology, Anatomy and Physiology)
Lifelong Education

Founded 1929. Attached to the Université d'Aix-Marseille II.
Academic Year: October to May (October-January; February-May).
Admission Requirements: Competitive entrance examination following further study after secondary school certificate (baccalauréat) and possession of teaching qualification in Physical Education (Part 1).
Fees (Francs): 650 per annum.
Language of Instruction: French.
Degrees and Diplomas: Licence. Maîtrise. Diplôme d'études appprofondies (D.E.A.). Doctorat.
Academic Staff, 1989-90: 34.
Student Enrolment, 1989-90:

	Men	Women	Total
Of the country	365	321	686
Of other countries	2	2	4
Total	367	323	690

2816 **CENTRE RÉGIONAL D'ÉDUCATION PHYSIQUE ET SPORTIVE**
3 impasse Barnabé, 34000 Montpellier
Telephone: 67-54-16-12

Physical Education

Attached to the Université Montpellier III Paul Valéry.

2817 **CENTRE RÉGIONAL D'ÉDUCATION PHYSIQUE ET SPORTIVE**
1, avenue Foch, 54311 Essey-les-Nancy
Telephone: 83-27-58-51

Physical Education

Founded 1929. Attached to the Université de Nancy I.
Academic Year: October to June.
Admission Requirements: Competitive entrance examination following further study after secondary school certificate (baccalauréat) and possession of teaching qualification in Physical Education (Part 1).
Language of Instruction: French.
Degrees and Diplomas: Certificat d'Aptitude au Professorat d'Education physique (Part 2), 3 yrs.
Library: c. 3000 vols.
Academic Staff: c. 30.
Student Enrolment: c. 70.

2818 **UNITÉ DE FORMATION ET DE RECHERCHE EN SCIENCES ET TECHNIQUES DES ACTIVITÉS PHYSIQUES ET SPORTIVES**
200, avenue de la République, 92001 Nanterre Cedex

Physical Education

2819 **INSTITUT RÉGIONAL D'ÉDUCATION PHYSIQUE**
1, rue Lacretelle, 75015 Paris
Telephone: (1) 48-28-55-62

Physical Education

Founded 1928. Attached to the Université René Descartes (Paris V).
Academic Year: September to July (September-December; January-April; April-July).
Admission Requirements: Competitive entrance examination following further study after secondary school certificate (baccalauréat) and possession of teaching qualification in Physical Education (Part 1).
Language of Instruction: French.
Degrees and Diplomas: Certificat d'Aptitude au Professorat d'Education physique (Part 2), 3 yrs.
Academic Staff: c. 30.
Student Enrolment: c. 340.

2820 **CENTRE RÉGIONAL D'ÉDUCATION PHYSIQUE ET SPORTIVE**
Château de Boivre Vouneuil-sous-Biard 86022 Poitiers
Telephone: 49-53-31-24

Physical Education

2821 **CENTRE RÉGIONAL D'ÉDUCATION PHYSIQUE ET SPORTIVE**
Rue des marettes, 35082 Rennes Cedex
Telephone: 99-46-16-25

Physical Education

2822 **CENTRE RÉGIONAL D'ÉDUCATION PHYSIQUE ET SPORTIVE**
4, Allée du Sommerhof, 67035 Strasbourg Cedex 3
Telephone: 88-30-38-64

Physical Education and Sport

Admission Requirements: Competitive entrance examination following further study after secondary school certificate (baccalauréat) and possession of teaching qualification in Physical Education (Part 1).
Degrees and Diplomas: Certificat d'Aptitude au Professorat d'Education physique (Part 2), 3 yrs.

2823 **UNITÉ DE FORMATION ET DE RECHERCHE EN SCIENCES ET TECHNIQUES DES ACTIVITÉS PHYSIQUES ET SPORTIVES**
118, route de Narbonne, 31062 Toulouse Cedex
Telephone: 61-55-66-32
Fax: 61–55-64-70
Directeur: Michel Jamet

Physical Education

Founded 1929. Attached to the Université Paul Sabatier. Governing body: Arrangements for co-operation with similar institutions in Prague, Barcelona, and Beer-Sheeva.
Academic Year: October to June (October-December; January-March; April-June).
Admission Requirements: Competitive entrance examination following further study after secondary school certificate (baccalauréat).
Fees (Francs): 500 per annum.
Language of Instruction: French.
Degrees and Diplomas: Diplôme d'études génerales (D.E.U.G.), 2 yrs. Licence, 1 further yr. Maîtrise, 1 yr after Licence.
Library: c. 1000 vols.
Academic Staff, 1989-90: c. 40.
Student Enrolment, 1989-90: 695.

Schools of Veterinary Science

2824 **ÉCOLE NATIONALE VÉTÉRINAIRE D'ALFORT**

7, avenue du Général de Gaulle, 94704 Maisons-Alfort Cedex
Telex: ECALFOR 213-863 F
Telephone: (1) 43-96-71-00
Directeur: M. Toma (1984-89)
Secrétaire général: J.P. Elgorriague

Veterinary Science
Animal Husbandry

Founded 1765. Responsible to the Ministry of Agriculture. Governing body: the Conseil d'administration. Residential facilities for students.

Arrangements for co-operation with: Université de Montréal; Free University of Berlin.

Academic Year: September to June (September-December; January-March; April-June).

Admission Requirements: Entrance by competition following 2 yrs further study after secondary school certificate (baccalauréat). Fees (Francs): 2868 per annum.

Language of Instruction: French.

Degrees and Diplomas: Certificat, 4 yrs. Docteur–Vétérinaire, and thesis. Also Maîtrise in Veterinary Science (for foreign students), 2 yrs.

Library: c. 150,000 vols.

Special Facilities (Museums, etc.): Musée de l'Ecole nationale vétérinaire d'Alfort.

Publication: Recueil de médecine vétérinaire de l'Ecole d'Alfort.

Academic Staff, 1986-87: 63 (1).

Student Enrolment, 1986-87:

	Men	Women	Total
Of the country	365	228	593
Of other countries	17	5	22
Total	382	233	615

2825 **ÉCOLE NATIONALE VÉTÉRINAIRE DE LYON**

Avenue Bourgelat, 69752 Charbonnières-les-Bains
Telex: 375 647F
Telephone: 78-87-00-84
Directeur: M. Fontaine

Veterinary Science

Founded 1762 at Lyon. Moved to present site 1977. Responsible to the Ministry of Agriculture. Governing body: the Conseil d'administration. Residential facilities for students.

Arrangements for co-operation with the Universities of: Hanover; Atlanta; Berne; Lublin; Constantine; Curitibá; Cairo.

Academic Year: October to June (October-December; January-April; April-June).

Admission Requirements: Entrance by competition following 2 yrs further study after secondary school certificate (baccalauréat).

Fees (Francs): 3000 per annum.

Language of Instruction: French.

Degrees and Diplomas: Certificat, 4 yrs. Docteur–Vétérinaire, and thesis. Also Maîtrise ès Sciences vétérinaires (foreign students), 2 yrs.

Academic Staff, 1986-87: 62.

Student Enrolment, 1986-87:

	Men	Women	Total
Of the country	362	209	571
Of other countries	14	8	22
Total	376	217	593

2826 **ÉCOLE NATIONALE VÉTÉRINAIRE DE NANTES**

Case Postale 3013, 44087 Nantes Cedex 03
Telex: 376547 ENVL F
Telephone: 40-30-08-40
Fax: 40-25-17-05
Directeur: Jean-Pierre Tillont (1989-94)
Secrétaire général: Serge Chabirand

Veterinary Science
Animal Husbandry

Founded 1979. Responsible to the Ministry of Agriculture. Governing body: the Conseil d'administration.

Arrangements for co-operation with the Universities of: Giessen; Dakar; Niamey. Ecole nationale de Médecine vétérinaire, Sidi Thabet.

Academic Year: October to June (October-January; March-June).

Admission Requirements: Entrance by competition following 2 yrs further study after secondary school certificate (baccalauréat).

Fees (Francs): 2700 per annum.

Language of Instruction: French.

Degrees and Diplomas: Certificat, 4 yrs. Docteur–Vétérinaire, and thesis.

Academic Staff, 1986-87: 56 (3).

Student Enrolment, 1986-87:

	Men	Women	Total
Of the country	366	200	563
Of other countries	18	10	28
Total	384	210	591

2827 **ÉCOLE NATIONALE VÉTÉRINAIRE DE TOULOUSE**

23, chemin des Capelles, 31076 Toulouse Cedex
Telex: ENVTLSE 530724 F
Telephone: 61-49-11-40
Fax: 61-31-00-36
Directeur: Jean Ferney (1984-90)
Secrétaire général: André Chamayou

Veterinary Science (including Animal Husbandry)

Founded 1825, reconstructed 1964. Responsible to the Ministry of Agriculture. Governing body: the Conseil d'administration. Residential facilities for 352 students.

Arrangements for co-operation with: Ecole nationale de médecine vétérinaire de Sidi-Thabet, Tunisia; Institut national agronomique et vétérinaire Hassan II, Rabat; Ecole Inter-Etats des Sciences vétérinaires, Dakar; University of Munich; University of Bonn.

Academic Year: September to June.

Admission Requirements: Entrance by competition following 2 yrs further study after secondary school certificate (baccalauréat).

Fees (Francs): 3402 per annum.

Language of Instruction: French.

Degrees and Diplomas: Certificat, 4 yrs. Docteur–Vétérinaire, and thesis. Also Maîtrise in Veterinary Science (for foreign students), 2 yrs.

Libraries: Central Library, 30,000 vols; departmental libraries.

Special Facilities (Museums, etc.): Botanical Garden.

Publication: Revue de médecine vétérinaire (monthly).

Academic Staff, 1986-87: 63.

Student Enrolment, 1989-90:

	Men	Women	Total
Of the country	316	215	531
Of other countries	5	1	6
Total	321	216	537

Other Specialized Institutions

2828 **ÉCOLE NATIONALE SUPÉRIEURE DES SCIENCES DE L'INFORMATION ET DES BIBLIOTHÈQUES**

17-21, boulevard du 11 Novembre 1918, 69621 Villeurbanne
Telephone: 78-89-64-45

2829 **ÉCOLE NATIONALE SUPÉRIEURE DES SCIENCES DE L'INFORMATION ET DES BIBLIOTHÈQUES**

17/21, boulevard du 11 Novembre 1918, 69621 Villeurbanne
Telephone: 78-89-64-45
Directeur: Jacques Keriguy (1986-)

Library Science

Founded 1963 in Paris as Ecole nationale supérieure de Bibliothèques, acquired present title and transferred to Villeurbanne 1973. Governing body: the Conseil d'administration.

Arrangements for co-operation with similar institutions in: Canada; Senegal.

Academic Year: October to May (October-December; January-March; April-May).

Admission Requirements: Competitive entrance examination following Licence or recognized equivalent.

Fees (Francs): c. 600 per annum.

Language of Instruction: French.

Degrees and Diplomas: Diplôme supérieur de Bibliothécaire (D.S.B.), 1 yr.

Library: c. 25,000 vols.

Academic Staff, 1986-87: 7.
Student Enrolment, 1986-87:

	Men	Women	Total
Of the country	10	14	24
Of other countries	7	5	12
Total	17	19	36

2830 **CENTRE RÉGIONAL DE FORMATION PROFESSIONNELLE DES BIBLIOTHÉCAIRES**
6, place de la République, 67070 Strasbourg Cedex

2831 **INSTITUT DE DROIT CANONIQUE**
9, Place de l'Université, 67084 Strasbourg Cedex
Telephone: 88-25-97-31
Directeur: Jean Schlick
Assesseur Enseignant: Anne Bamberg

Canon Law

Also branches in Montréal and Yaoundé

Founded 1920 as part of the Faculty of Catholic Theology, University of Strasbourg; became Institute attached to the University 1956. Since 1982 the Institute offers degrees in canon law in an international context. The courses are partly on campus (sessions) and partly by correspondence (combined system).

Academic Year: August to June.

Admission Requirements: Direct entrance by competition following appropriate university degree, Diplôme d'Études universitaires générales (D.E.U.G.).

Fees (Francs): 550 per annum.

Language of Instruction: French.

Degrees and Diplomas: Capacité en Droit canonique (university degree), 1-2 yrs. Licence en Droit canonique (national degree with ecclesiastical equivalent, Licentia Iuris Canonici), 1-2 yrs. Diplôme d'Études approfondies (D.E.A.), 1-2 yrs. Doctorat 2-3 yrs.

Library: c. 8,000 vols.

Academic Staff, 1989-90: 9

Student Enrolment, 1989-90:

	Total
Of the country	110
Of other countries	129
Total	239*

*All by correspondence.

2832 **INSTITUT DE DROIT COMPARÉ**
28, rue Saint-Guillaume, 75007 Paris
Telephone: (1) 42-22-35-93
Fax: (1) 42-84-03-27
Directeur: Denis Tallon (1983-)
Secrétaire général: Micheline Van Camelbeke

Comparative Law

Founded 1931 and attached to the Université de Droit, d'Economie et des Sciences sociales de Paris (Paris II) 1971.

Academic Year: October to June (October-December; January-March; April-June).

Admission Requirements: (Diplôme): Diplôme d'études universitaires générales (D.E.U.G.); (Brevet); Registration as a studentor graduate of a French Faculty of Law, or equivalent.

Fees (Francs): 498-845 per annum.

Language of Instruction: French.

Degrees and Diplomas: Diplôme de Droit comparé, 1 yr. Also Brevet in legal terminology and translation.

Library: Institute Library.

Publications: Collections: Travaux et recherches; Les grands systèmes de droit pénal contemporain; Les lois maritimes étrangères; Harmonisation du droit des affaires dans les pays du Marché Commun. Revue de science criminelle et de droit pénal comparé.

Academic Staff, 1990:

Rank	Part-time
Professeurs	10
Maîtres de conférences	1
Chercheurs	5
Maîtres de langue étrangère	2
Avocats	3
Juristes d'entreprise	1
Total	22

Student Enrolment, 1989-90:

	Men	Women	Total
Of the country	109	156	265
Of other countries	30	26	56
Total	139	182	321

2833 **INSTITUT D'ÉTUDES JUDICIAIRES**
Domaine Universitaire Littéraire et Juridique, Sac postal 19, 59650 Villeneuve-d'Ascq
Telephone: 20-91-10-26

Criminal Law

Attached to the Université du Droit et de la Santé Lille II.

2834 **ÉCOLE NATIONALE DE LA MAGISTRATURE**
9, rue du Maréchal Joffre, 33080 Bordeaux Cedex
Telephone: 56-52-05-50
Fax: 56-81-82-63
Directeur: Raymond Exertier (1985-)
Secrétaire général: François Cordier

Magistrature Studies

Founded 1958.

Admission Requirements: Maîtrise and entrance examination.

Language of Instruction: French.

Library: 50,000 vols.

Academic Staff, 1986-87: 19.

Student Enrolment, 1986-87:

	Men	Women	Total
Of the country	201	254	455
Of other countries	28	4	32
Total	229	258	487

2835 **CENTRE EUROPÉEN UNIVERSITAIRE DE NANCY**
15, place Carnot, 54042 Nancy Cedex
Telephone: 83-36-52-84

D. of Law and Political Science

D. of Economics

D. of Contemporary European Studies

Founded 1950 as a private institution, became university institute 1953. Attached to the Université de NancyII. Governing body: the Conseil d'administration, comprising 17 members. Residential facilities for students.

Academic Year: October to May (October-December; January-April; April-May).

Admission Requirements: Maîtrise or recognized foreign equivalent degree or diploma.

Language of Instruction: French.

Degrees and Diplomas: Diplôme d'études supérieures européennes; Diplôme d'études approfondies (D.E.A.), 1 yr; Doctorat, 2-4 yrs after D.E.A.

Library: 7000 vols.

Press or Publishing House: Presses de l'Université de Nancy II (Collection du Centre européen universitaire de Nancy).

Academic Staff: c. 10.

Student Enrolment: c. 75.

2836 **CENTRE DE DOCUMENTATION ET DE RECHERCHES EUROPÉENNES, COMPARATIVES ET INTERNATIONALES**

9, rue Jean Macé, 35000 Rennes
Telephone: 99-38-03-01

European, International, and Comparative Law

Founded 1964 as Institut de Droit comparé. Acquired present title 1981. A centre providing documentation and information on EEC, international, and comparative legislation, attached to the Faculty of Juridical Sciences, University of Rennes I.

Academic Year: October to July.

Admission Requirements: Maîtrise or recognized foreign equivalent.

Library: c. 1500 vols.

2837 **INSTITUT DES HAUTES ÉTUDES EUROPÉENNES**

5, rue Schiller, 67000 Strasbourg Cedex
Telephone: 88-35-02-69

European Studies

Ce. for Germanic Studies

Founded 1951. Attached to the Université des Sciences juridiques, politiques, sociales et de Technologie (Strasbourg III). Governing body: the Conseil, comprising 16 members. Some residential facilities for students.

Academic Year: October to June (October-December; January-March; April-June).

Admission Requirements: Licence or recognized foreign equivalent.

Language of Instruction: French.

Degrees and Diplomas: Certificat d'Études européennes, 1 yr. Diplôme d'Études approfondies (D.E.A.), 1 yr.

Library: Central Library, 15,000 vols.

Publication: Revue d'Allemagne (quarterly).

Academic Staff: c. 5 (10).

Student Enrolment: c. 80.

2838 **INSTITUT D'ÉTUDES FRANÇAISES DE TOURAINE**

1, rue de la Grandière, Boîte postale 2047, 37000 Tours Cedex
Telephone: 47-05-76-83

French Studies (for foreign students)

Founded 1912 and attached to the Université de Poitiers 1921. Now a private institution attached to the Université de Tours. Residential facilities for students.

Arrangements for co-operation with: Bowling Green State University; Michigan State University; University of Michigan; Pine Manor College, Massachusetts; Grinnel College, Iowa; King Alfred College, Bristol; King's College, London; University of Surrey.

Academic Year: October to June (October-December; January-March; April-June); also vacation courses.

Language of Instruction: French.

Degrees and Diplomas: Certificat d'Assiduité. Attestation d'Etudes françaises. Certificat d'Etudes françaises (for advanced students).

Library: 4500 vols.

Publications: Brochures; Publications annuelles.

Academic Staff: c. 20 (60).

Student Enrolment: Men, c. 42%; Women, c. 58%.

2839 **ÉCOLE FRANÇAISE D'EXTRÊME-ORIENT**

22, avenue du Président Wilson, 75116 Paris

2840 **INSTITUT D'ÉTUDES INTERNATIONALES ET DES PAYS EN VOIE DE DÉVELOPPEMENT**

Place Anatole-France, 31070 Toulouse Cedex
Telephone: 61-23-01-45

International Studies and Development

Modern Languages and International Terminology

Economic and Social Aspects of Development

Founded 1959 and attached to the Université des Sciences sociales (Toulouse I).

Academic Year: November to June (November-December; January-March; March-June).

Admission Requirements: 2 yrs university study.

Language of Instruction: French.

Degrees and Diplomas: Diplôme, 1 yr.

Library: c. 3000 vols.

Publications: L'O.N.U. et le développement communautaire des régions retardées (1958; Aspects récents du développement communautaire (1962); Coopération économique et sociale en droit international public (1964); Moyens sociaux du développement économique (1967); Traité de Droit international public–Tome 1 (1966).

Academic Staff: – (c. 10).

Student Enrolment: c. 300.

2841 **ÉCOLE SUPÉRIEURE D'INTERPRÈTES ET DE TRADUCTEURS DE L'UNIVERSITÉ DE PARIS SORBONNE NOUVELLE**

Place du Maréchal-de-Lattre-de-Tassigny, 75116 Paris
Telephone: (1) 45-05-14-10
Fax: (1) 47-04-72-59
Directrice: Marianne Lederer (1990-95)
Secrétaire générale: Bernadette Statien

D. of Interpretation

Head: Christopher Thiery; *staff* 6 (31)

D. of Translation

Head: Florence Herbulot; *staff* 8 (57)

Founded 1957. Attached to the Université de la Sorbonne Nouvelle (Paris III) 1969. Governing body: the Conseil, comprising 14 members.

Arrangements for co-operation with: University of Ottawa; University of Caracas.

Academic Year: November to June.

Admission Requirements: D.E.U.G. or Licence or recognized foreign equivalent, and entrance examination.

Fees (Francs): 3000 per unit per annum.

Degrees and Diplomas: Diplôme de Traducteur, D.E.S.S.; Diplôme d'Interprète de Conférence, D.E.S.S., 2 yrs. Magistère en Interprétation simultanée, 3 yrs. Diplôme d'études approfondies (D.E.A.), 1 yr. Doctorat, a further 2-4yrs.

Library: 500 vols.

Academic Staff, 1989-90:

Rank	Full-time	Part-time
Professeurs	3	–
Maîtres de conférences	13	–
Chargés d'enseignement	–	94
Total	16	94

Student Enrolment, 1989-90: 422.

2842 **INSTITUT DES PROFESSEURS DE FRANÇAIS À L'ÉTRANGER**

46, rue Saint-Jacques, 75005 Paris
Telephone: (1) 43-29-12-13

French Language and Culture

Founded 1920. Formerly Ecole supérieure de préparation et de perfectionnement des professeurs de français à l'Etranger. Acquired present status 1945. Attached to the Université de la Sorbonne Nouvelle (Paris III). The principal purpose of the institute is to provide training facilities for those who will teach French in other countries.

Academic Year: November to June.

Admission Requirements: Secondary school certificate (baccalauréat) or foreign equivalent.

Degrees and Diplomas: Diplôme de–Professeur de français; de culture française contemporaine; de littérature française contemporaine. Also Certificat pratique de Langue française, followed by Diplôme d'études françaises and Diplôme supérieur d'études françaises.

Student Enrolment: c. 1800.

2843 **INSTITUT FRANÇAIS DE PRESSE**

83 bis, rue Notre-Dame-des-Champs, 75006 Paris
Telephone: (1) 45-20-12-24
Directeur: Pierre Albert (1986-)

Press, and Information and Communication Sciences

Founded 1951 as research institute, became Institut d'Université 1957 and attached to the Université de Droit, d'Economie et des Sciences sociales de Paris (Paris II) 1971. Governing bodies: the Conseil scientifique; the Conseil de perfectionnement.

Arrangements for co-operation with: Université Catholique de Louvain; University of São Paulo; Federal University of Minas Gerais; University of Yaoundé; Université de Montréal; University of Navarra; Stanford University; University of Oregon; Boston University; Université de Tunis;

University of Fribourg; Université de Dakar; Institut supérieur de Journalisme, Rabat.

Academic Year: October to July (October-January; January-July).

Admission Requirements: Diplôme de Maîtrise, in another discipline.

Fees (Francs): *c.* 1000 per annum.

Language of Instruction: French.

Degrees and Diplomas: Licence d'information et de communication, 1 yr; Maîtrise, 1 further yr; Diplôme de l'Institut français de Presse, 3 yrs; Diplôme d'études approfondies (D.E.A.), 1 yr after Maîtrise or Diplôme; Diplôme d'études supérieures spécialisées (D.E.S.S.), 1 yr after Maîtrise or Diplôme.

Library: *c.* 4500 vols.

Publications: Les Cahiers de la Communication (bimonthly); Tables du Journal Le Temps; Bulletin de Documentation de l'I.F.P.

Academic Staff, 1989-90:

Rank	Full-time	Part-time
Professeurs	5	3
Maîtres-Assistants	4	7
Assistants	–	2
Extérieurs	–	26
Total	9	38

Student Enrolment, 1989-90: *c.* 915.

2844 **ÉCOLE NATIONALE DE LA MARINE MARCHANDE DU HAVRE**

66, route du Cap, 76310 Sainte-Adresse
Telephone: 35-46-24-63

Marine Engineering
Radio-Electrical Engineering
Thermodynamics
Electronics
Maritime Law
Navigation

Founded 1666. Attached to the Ministry of Development, Housing and Transport. Governing body: the Conseil d'administration, comprising 17 members. Residential facilities for *c.* 200 students.

Academic Year: October to June (October-January; February-June).

Admission Requirements: Competitive entrance examination at the level of secondary school certificate (baccalauréat).

2845 **ÉCOLE NATIONALE DE LA MARINE MARCHANDE**

95, traverse Prat, 13008 Marseille
Telex: 420048 ENMM MA F
Telephone: 91-73-02-98
Directeur: M. Le Rhun (1984-)

Marine Engineering
Radio-Electrical Engineering
Mathematics
Navigation

Founded 1971. Attached to the Ministry of Development, Housing and Transport. Governing body: the Conseil d'administration. Residential facilities for 90 students.

Academic Year: October to July (October-January; January-April; April-July).

Admission Requirements: Competitive entrance examination at the level of secondary school certificate (baccalauréat).

Fees (Francs): 450.

Language of Instruction: French.

Degrees and Diplomas: State diplomas: Diplôme d'Officier de la Marine marchande, 3 yrs. Diplôme d'études supérieures de la Marine Marchande, 1 further yr.

Academic Staff, 1986-87: 28 (8).

Student Enrolment, 1986-87:

	Men	Women	Total
Of the country	136	3	139
Of other countries	3	–	3
Total	139	3	142

2846 **ÉCOLE NATIONALE DE LA MARINE MARCHANDE**

rue Gabriel Péri, 44100 Nantes
Telephone: 40-73-64-80
Fax: 40-69-25-98
Directeur: Henri Le Bas

Marine Engineering
Mathematics
Navigation and Nautical Science
Fishery

Founded 1672 as school of hydrography, present title adopted 1940, became State institution 1959. Attached to the Ministry of Development, Housing and Transport. Governing body: the Conseil d'administration. Residential facilities for students.

Arrangements for regular interchange of students with King's Point, USA.

Academic Year: October to June (October-February; February-June).

Admission Requirements: Competitive entrance examination at the level of secondary school certificate (baccalauréat).

Language of Instruction: French.

Degrees and Diplomas: State diplomas: 1st, 2nd levels, 3 yrs; 3rd level, 1 yr. Fishing, 2 yrs.

Library: *c.* 2300 vols.

Academic Staff, 1989-90: *c.* 45.

Student Enrolment, 1989-90:

	Men	Women	Total
Of the country	212	3	215
Of other countries	15	–	15
Total	227	3	230

2847 **ÉCOLE NATIONALE DE LA MARINE MARCHANDE**

rue Pierre-Loti, 22500 Paimpol
Telephone: 96-20-80-27

Marine Engineering
Radio-Electrical Engineering
Mathematics
Navigation

Founded 1863. Attached to the Ministry of Development, Housing and Transport. Governing body: the Conseil d'administration. Financed by the State.

Academic Year: October to June (October-December; January-March; April-June).

Admission Requirements: Competitive entrance examination at the level of secondary school certificate (baccalauréat).

Language of Instruction: French.

Degrees and Diplomas: State diplomas: Elève au Long Cours; Elève Chef de Quart; Capitaine côtier; Officier mécanicien. Also intermediate qualifications.

Academic Staff: *c.* 30.

Student Enrolment: *c.* 200.

2848 **ÉCOLE NATIONALE DE LA MARINE MARCHANDE**

4, rue de la Victoire, 35412 Saint-Malo Cedex
Telephone: 99-56-68-54
Fax: 99-40-57-63
Directeur: Michel Le Chaffotec
Sous-Directeur: François Sotin

Marine Engineering

Founded 1669 as Ecole royale d'Hydrographie, acquired present status and title 1958. Attached to the Ministry of Development, Housing and Transport. Financed by the State. Governing body: the Conseil d'administration.

Academic Year: October to June (October-January; February-June).

Admission Requirements: Competitive entrance examination at the level of secondary school certificate (baccalauréat).

Fees (Francs): 580 per annum.

Language of Instruction: French.

Degrees and Diplomas: State diplomas: Brevet d'Officier Chef de quart, 1 yr; Brevet d'Officier technicien, 2 yrs; Brevet de Capitaine de 2e classe de la Navigation Maritime, 2 yrs; Brevet de Lieutenant de Pêche, 1 yr; Certificat d'aptitude professionnelle maritime (C.A.P.M.), 3 yrs.

Library: *c.* 3000 vols.

Academic Staff, 1989-90: *c.* 40.

Student Enrolment, 1990: 173 (Including 3 women).

2849 **INSTITUT DE MÉDECINE LÉGALE ET SOCIALE**

Place Théo-Varlet, 59000 Lille
Telephone: 20-56-60-79

Forensic Medicine

Attached to the Université du Droit et de la Santé (Lille II).

2850 **ÉCOLE NATIONALE DE LA SANTÉ PUBLIQUE**

Avenue du Professeur Léon-Bernard, 35043 Rennes Cedex
Telex: ENSP 741465F
Telephone: 99-28-29-30
Fax: 99-28-28-28
Directeur: Christian Rollet (1986-)

Public Health

Founded in Paris 1945, transferred to Rennes 1962. A State institution controlled by the Ministry of Public Health and Social Security. Residential facilities for students.

Academic Year: January to December.

Admission Requirements: University degree or other appropriate professional qualification.

Language of Instruction: French.

Degrees and Diplomas: Diplôme d'Etat de Santé publique, 1 yr for medical doctors. Diplôme de Santé publique, 1 yr for pharmacists, engineers, (or nurses). Certificates for qualified social institution Manager, 2 yrs. Also Diplôme d'études supérieures in Public Health or Social Science, and teaching qualification (to the deaf), 3 yrs.

Library: c. 35,000 vols.

Academic Staff, 1986-87: 47.

Student Enrolment, 1989-90:

	Men	Women	Total
Of the country	130	130	260
Of other countries	–	7	7
Total	130	137	267*

*Also 1700 external students.

2851 **UNITÉ DES SCIENCES ODONTOLOGIQUES**

Bâtiment Universitaire de la Buire, rue Guillaume Paradin, 69008 Lyon
Telephone: 78-74-88-59

Dentistry

Founded 1899 as a private institution, acquired present status 1973. Attached to the Université Claude-Bernard (Lyon I).

Academic Year: October to June (October-December; January-March; April-June).

Admission Requirements: Secondary school certificate (baccalauréat).

Language of Instruction: French.

Degrees and Diplomas: State diploma of Chirurgien-dentiste, 5 yrs.

Library: Specialized Library, *c.* 2000 vols.

Special Facilities (Museums, etc.): Musée d'Anatomie dentaire comparée.

Publication: Annales odonto-stomatologiques.

Academic Staff: c. 50.

Student Enrolment: c. 310.

2852 **INSTITUT DE PSYCHOLOGIE**

Ensemble Universitaire, 69500 Bron-Parilly
Telephone: 78-00-60-10
Directeur: Gérard Broyer (1986-)

Psychology

Founded 1944, acquired present status 1986. Attached to Université Lyon II.

Academic Year: October to June.

Admission Requirements: Entrance by competition following first university degree (D.E.U.G.).

Languages of Instruction: French. Degrees and diplomas: Diplôme d'études supérieures specialisées (D.E.S.S.), 2 yrs.

Academic Staff, 1986-87: 10 (2).

Student Enrolment, 1986-87: 700.

2853 **INSTITUT DE PSYCHOLOGIE APPLIQUÉE**

34, avenue Carnot, 63006 Clermont-Ferrand Cedex
Telephone: 73-92-97-32

Applied Psychology
Social Work

Founded 1947. Attached to the Université de Clermont-Ferrand 1951, reorganized 1964. Governing body: the Conseil de Gestion, comprising 22 members. Residential facilities for students in Résidence universitaire.

Academic Year: November to June (November-February; February-June).

Admission Requirements: 2 yrs university study.

Language of Instruction: French.

Degrees and Diplomas: Diplôme d'études supérieures spécialisées (D.E.S.S.) de Psychologie pratique, 2 yrs after Licence. Diplôme universitaire de Sciences appliquées au Travail social.

Library: c. 200 vols.

Academic Staff: c. 20.

Student Enrolment: c. 150.

2854 **INSTITUT DE PSYCHOPÉDAGOGIE MÉDICO-SOCIALE**

'Mas Prunet', Route de Lavérune, 34000 Montpellier
Telephone: 67-42-46-03

Medico-Social Psycho-Pedagogics
Attached to the Université de Montpellier III.

2855 **INSTITUT DE PSYCHOLOGIE**

1, rue Goethe, 67000 Strasbourg
Telephone: 88-35-59-40

Psychology
Education

Founded 1900. Attached to the Université Louis-Pasteur (Strasbourg I).

Academic Year: October to June (October-February; May-June).

Admission Requirements: Further studies following secondary school certificate (baccalauréat) or equivalent.

Language of Instruction: French.

2856 **INSTITUT DE PSYCHOLOGIE**

4, rue Albert-Lautman, 31070 Toulouse Cedex
Telephone: 61-22-08-31

Psychology
Education

Founded 1959 and attached to the Université de Toulouse. Since 1970 an interuniversity institute.

Academic Year: October to June (October-December; January-Easter; Easter-June).

Admission Requirements: Licence in Psychology.

Language of Instruction: French.

Degrees and Diplomas: Diplôme de–Psychopédagogie; Psychologie industrielle; Psychologie pathologique.

Library: c. 3000 vols.

Academic Staff: c. – (30).

Student Enrolment: c. 100.

2857 **INSTITUT DE PRÉPARATION AUX FONCTIONS SOCIALES ET ÉDUCATIVES SPÉCIALISÉES**

8, rue Joliot-Curie, 51100 Reims
Telephone: 26-06-22-88

2858 **INSTITUT DE FORMATION D'ÉDUCATEURS SPÉCIALISÉS DE L'ENFANCE ET DE L'ADOLESCENCE INADAPTÉES**

Le Château Peynier, 13790 Rousset

Teacher Training for Handicapped Children

2859 **CENTRE DE FORMATION DE CONSEILLERS D'ORIENTATION**

3 bis, rue Jean-Bart, 59000 Lille
Telephone: 20-57-09-29
Directeur: Mme Beuscart (1985-89)
Secrétaire générale: Josiane Ronchin

Vocational Guidance and Counselling

Founded 1959. Attached to the Université des Sciences humaines, Lettres, et Arts (Lille III).

Academic Year: September to June (September-December; January-March; April-June).

Admission Requirements: Entrance by competition following first university qualification (D.E.U.G.) or 4 yrs public service.

Fees (Francs): 500.

Language of Instruction: French.

Degrees and Diplomas: Certificat d'Aptitude aux fonctions de Conseiller d'orientation, 2 yrs.

Student Enrolment, 1986-87:

	Men	Women	Total
Of the country	13	20	33

2860 **INSTITUT NATIONAL D'ÉTUDE DU TRAVAIL ET D'ORIENTATION PROFESSIONNELLE**
41, rue Gay-Lussac, 75005 Paris
Telephone: (1) 43-29-12-23

Labour Study
Professional Orientation

Founded 1928, attached to the Conservatoire National des Arts et Métiers 1941.

Academic Year: October to June (October-December; January-March; April-June).

Admission Requirements: 2 yrs university study.

Language of Instruction: French.

Degrees and Diplomas: Certificat d'Aptitude aux Fonctions de Conseiller d'Orientation, 2 yrs. Diplôme de Médecin d'Orientation scolaire et professionnelle (postgraduate after medical qualification).

Library: c. 14,000 vols.

Publication: L'Orientation Scolaire et Professionnelle (quarterly).

Academic Staff: c. 5 (40).

Student Enrolment: c. 110.

2861 **INSTITUT NATIONAL DU TRAVAIL**
Marcy-l'Etoile, 69260 Charbonnières-les-Bains
Telex: INTLYON 370820 F
Telephone: 78-87-02-44
Fax: 78870118

2862 **INSTITUT UNIVERSITAIRE DE FORMATION CONTINUE**
La Bouloie, Route de Gray, 25030 Besançon Cedex
Telephone: 81-50-32-66

Lifelong Education

Founded 1973.

2863 **SERVICE UNIVERSITAIRE DE FORMATION CONTINUE DE BOURGOGNE, SUFCOB**
6, boulevard Gabriel, B.P. 138, 21000 Dijon Cedex
Telephone: 80-39-51-80
Fax: 80-39-50-69
Directeur: M. De Rosa (1990-)

Adult Education (Accountancy, Staff Management, Languages, Computing, New Technologies, and Health of Social Work)

Founded 1958. Acquired present title 1982. Attached to the Université de Dijon. Governing body: the Conseil d'Administration.

Academic Year: September to June.

Admission Requirements: Levels of secondary school certificate (baccalauréat), and University degrees.

Fees (Francs): 550 per annum.

Language of Instruction: French.

Degrees and Diplomas: Diplôme–interdisciplinaire; d'Aptitude, 1 yr. Certificat d'Aptitude, 2 yrs. Diplôme d'Etudes supérieures spécialisées (D.E.S.S.), 1 yr: Diplôme universitaire de technologie (D.U.T.), 2 yrs.

Publication: Europe, Horizon 2000 (annual).

Academic Staff, 1990: c. – (30).

Student Enrolment, 1990: c. 1290.

2864 **CENTRE UNIVERSITAIRE D'ÉDUCATION ET DE FORMATION DES ADULTES**
Domaine Universitaire, 38400 Saint-Martin-d'Hères
Telephone: 76-54-51-63
Directeur: Y. Brunet (1983-87)
Responsable administrative: Nicole Pellet

Adult Education (Technical) (evening courses)

Founded 1951 as private school; became Ecole de Promotion supérieure du Travail 1959, acquired present title1973. Attached to the Institut Polytechnique de Grenoble. Governing body: the Conseil d'administration.

Academic Year: October to June.

Admission Requirements: Level of secondary school certificate (baccalauréat).

Language of Instruction: French.

Degrees and Diplomas: Diplôme universitaire de technologie (D.U.T.), 2 yrs. Diplôme–Technique; Economique. Diplôme d'études supérieures techniques (D.E.S.T.), 4 yrs; Diplôme d'études supérieures économiques; d'Ingénieur; d'Economiste.

Academic Staff: c. 10.

Student Enrolment: c. 5000.

2865 **CENTRE UNIVERSITÉ ECONOMIE D'ÉDUCATION PERMANENTE**
104, rue Jeanne d'Arc, 59000 Lille
Telephone: 20-52-54-24

Adult Education

Attached to the Université des Sciences et Techniques Lille I.

2866 **CENTRE UNIVERSITAIRE DE FORMATION ET D'ÉDUCATION PERMANENTE**
10, rue de l'Université, 86022 Poitiers
Telephone: 49-41-02-06

Adult Education (Technical)

Founded 1959 and attached to the Université de Poitiers.

Admission Requirements: Level of secondary school certificate (baccalauréat).

Language of Instruction: French.

Degrees and Diplomas: Diplôme d'études supérieures techniques (D.E.S.T.), 4 yrs.

2867 **CENTRE DÉPARTEMENTAL D'ÉDUCATION OUVRIÈRE DU NORD DE LA FRANCE**
Sac postal 19, 59650 Villeneuve d'Ascq

Workers' Adult Education (Economics, Philosophy, Political and Social Sciences)

Founded 1954 under the jurisdiction of the Conseil général du Département du Nord.

Academic Year: November to June.

Admission Requirements: Restricted to workers in the Nord Department.

Language of Instruction: French.

Library: Library of the Centre.

2868 **INSTITUT DE PROMOTION SUPÉRIEURE DU TRAVAIL**
3, place Victor-Hugo, 13331 Marseille Cedex 3
Telephone: 91-95-90-71
Directeur: P. Courbis (1982-)
Secrétaire: J. Deleuze

Adult Education (Technical) (evening courses)

Founded 1958. Attached to the Université de Provence. Recognized by the Conservatoire national des Arts et Métiers 1974. Governing body: the Conseil d'administration.

Academic Year: October to June (October-December; January-March; April-June).

Admission Requirements: Level of secondary school certificate (baccalauréat).

Fees (Francs): 250-450

Language of Instruction: French.

Degrees and Diplomas: Diplôme d'études supérieures techniques (D.E.S.T.), 4-5 yrs. Diplôme d'Ingénieur, a further 2 yrs.

Academic Staff, 1986-87: – (81).

Student Enrolment, 1986-87:

	Men	Women	Total
Of the country	701	50	751
Of other countries	32	8	40
Total	733	58	791

2869 **INSTITUT DE PROMOTION SUPÉRIEURE DU TRAVAIL**
39, allée Jules-Guesde, 31000 Toulouse
Telephone: 61-52-69-70

Adult Education (Technical)

Founded 1958. Recognized by the Conservatoire national des Arts et Métiers 1970 and attached to the InstitutNational Polytechnique de Toulouse 1973. Governing body: the Conseil d'administration. Some residential facilities for students.

Academic Year: October to June (October-December; January-March; April-June).

Admission Requirements: Level of secondary school certificate (baccalauréat).

Language of Instruction: French.

Degrees and Diplomas: Diplôme universitaire de technologie (D.U.T.), 2 yrs. Diplôme–Technique; Economique. Diplôme d'études supérieures techniques (D.E.S.T.), 4 yrs; Diplôme d'études supérieures économiques; d'Ingénieur; d'Economiste.

Academic Staff: c. 10 (300).

Student Enrolment: c. 1260.

2870 **INSTITUT DE PROMOTION SUPÉRIEURE DU TRAVAIL**

39, avenue de la Forêt-Noire, 67000 Strasbourg

Telephone: 88-61-25-21

Adult Education (Technical) (evening courses)

Admission Requirements: Level of secondary school certificate (baccalauréat).

Fees: None.

Degrees and Diplomas: Diplôme d'études supérieures techniques (D.E.S.T.), 4 yrs.

2871 **INSTITUT DES SCIENCES SOCIALES DU TRAVAIL (CENTRE DE FORMATION SUPÉRIEURE)**

37, avenue du Président Franklin-Roosevelt, 92330 Sceaux

Telephone: (1) 47-02-53-73

Social Sciences of Labour

D. for Workers' Education

Founded 1951. Attached to the Université de Paris I (Panthéon-Sorbonne).

Academic Year: November to June (November-December; January-March; April-June).

Admission Requirements: Diplôme d'études juridiques générales; Diplôme d'études économiques générales or equivalent,or entrance examination.

Language of Instruction: French.

Degrees and Diplomas: Brevet des Sciences sociales du Travail; Diplôme de Conseiller du Travail, 1 yr; Diplôme des Sciences sociales du Travail, 3 yrs.

Academic Staff: c. 10.

Student Enrolment: c. 340.

2872 **INSTITUT DES SCIENCES DU TRAVAIL**

Sac postal 19, 59650 Villeneuve-d'Ascq

Telephone: 20-91-10-26

Labour Science

Founded 1950. Attached to the Université du Droit et de la Santé (Lille II).

Academic Year: October to June.

Admission Requirements: Secondary school certificate (baccalauréat).

Language of Instruction: French.

Degrees and Diplomas: Diplôme de l'Institut, by thesis.

2873 **INSTITUT NATIONAL DE FORMATION DES CADRES SUPÉRIEURS DE LA VENTE**

292, rue Saint-Martin, 75141 Paris Cedex 03

Telephone: (1) 42-71-24-14

Directeur: Jean Saurel

Organization of Sales and Distribution

Founded 1957. Attached to the Conservatoire national des Arts et Métiers.

Academic Year: October to June (October-December; January-March; April-June).

Admission Requirements: University degree or corresponding qualification and 3 yrs practical experience.

Language of Instruction: French.

Degrees and Diplomas: Diplôme de l'Institut, 2 yrs.

Library: 900 vols.

Academic Staff, 1986-87: – (35).

Student Enrolment, 1986-87:

	Men	Women	Total
Of the country	35	12	47
Of other countries	16	–	16
Total	51	12	63

2874 **INSTITUT D'ÉTUDES DU TRAVAIL ET DE LA SÉCURITÉ SOCIALE**

1, rue de l'Université, 69224 Lyon Cedex 7

Telephone: 78-69-24-93

Labour and Social Security Studies

Founded 1951. Attached to the Université Jean Moulin (Lyon III).

Academic Year: October to June.

Admission Requirements: University degree–Licence.

Degrees and Diplomas: Diplôme, 1 yr.

Library: c. 800 vols.

Publication: Annales de l'Institut.

Academic Staff: c. – (30).

Student Enrolment: c. 920.

2875 **CENTRE NATIONAL D'ÉTUDES SUPÉRIEURES DE SÉCURITÉ SOCIALE**

27, rue des Docteurs Charcot, 42031 Saint-Etienne Cedex

Telex: CNESS 307102 F

Telephone: 77-81-15-15

Fax: 77-81-15-00

Directeur: Yannick D'Haene

Secrétaire général: Georges Brunet

2876 **INSTITUT FRANÇAIS DE RECHERCHE SCIENTIFIQUE POUR LE DÉVELOPPEMENT EN COOPÉRATION**

213, rue La Fayette, 75010 Paris

Cables: orstrom-Paris

Telex: ORSTOM 214627 F

Telephone: (1) 48-03-77-77

Fax: (1) 48-03-08-29

Directeur général: Gérard Winter

Secrétaire général: Gilbert Morvan

Non-Temperate Zone Techniques and Research

Established by the State to undertake and promote research, chiefly in the biological sciences, and since 1943, to train research workers. Under the supervision of the Ministries of Research and Co-operation. Governing body: the Conseil d'administration of 18 members.

Admission Requirements: Maîtrise ès Sciences, degree in medicine or veterinary medicine, or corresponding qualification in appropriate field of study.

Degrees and Diplomas: Diploma, 2 yrs (of which one is spent abroad).

Academic Staff, 1990: 1500.

Private Establishments

Schools of Engineering

2877 **ÉCOLE SUPÉRIEURE DES TECHNIQUES AEROSPATIALES**

Bâtiment 502 bis, Complexe scientifique d'Orsay, 91405 Orsay

Telephone: 69-28-68-57

2878 **ÉCOLE SUPÉRIEURE DES TECHNIQUES AÉRONAUTIQUES ET DE CONSTRUCTION AUTOMOBILE**

3, rue Pablo Neruda, 92300 Levallois-Perret

Telephone: (1) 47318100

Aeronautical Engineering

Automobile Engineering

Founded 1925.

2879 **INSTITUT CATHOLIQUE D'ARTS ET MÉTIERS DE LILLE**

6, rue Auber, 59046 Lille Cedex
Telephone: 20-93-58-55
Fax: 20-93-14-89
Directeur: Guy Carpier (1981-91)
Directeur des Etudes: Bruno Régent

Engineering (Materials, Mechanical Engineering, Electrical Engineering, Computer Sciences, Fluid Mechanics, Management and Business Studies)
Assistant Head: Jean Gabriel Prieur; *staff* 40 (20)
Economics and Computer Sciences
D. for Lifelong Education
Director: Robert Stahl; *staff* 10 (100)

Founded 1898. A private institution authorized to confer degrees 1935, and recognized by the State 1975. Governing bodies: the Conseil syndical; the Conseil de perfectionnement. Residential facilities for students.

Arrangements for academic staff and student exchange with: Sheffield Polytechnic, Exeter University; Universität Gesamthochschule Essen.

Academic Year: September to June (September-December; January-March; April-June).

Admission Requirements: Entrance by competition following 2 yrs further study after secondary school certificate (baccalauréat) or following first university qualification (B.T.S.).

Fees: Fees (Francs): 7000-16,000 per annum.

Language of Instruction: French.

Degrees and Diplomas: Diplôme d'Ingénieur, 5 yrs.

Library: Institute Library, 25,000 vols.

Academic Staff, 1989-90: c. 80.

Student Enrolment, 1989-90:

	Men	Women	Total
Of the country	432	42	474
Of other countries	4	–	4
Total	436	42	478

2880 **ÉCOLE CATHOLIQUE D'ARTS ET MÉTIERS DE LYON**

40, montée Saint-Barthélémy, 69321 Lyon Cedex 05
Telephone: 78-37-81-81
Directeur général: Jean Guy (1977-)
Secrétaire générale: Suzanne Poilane

Engineering

Founded 1900 at Rheims by the Congrégation des Frères des Ecoles Chrétiennes, moved to Erquelinnes (Belgium) 1914, and to Lyon 1940. Recognized by the State 1962. Became a Fondation 1977. Governing body: the Conseil de la Fondation. Residential facilities for students.

Academic Year: September to June (September-December; January-March; April-June).

Admission Requirements: Entrance by competition following 2 yrs further study after secondary school certificate (baccalauréat) or following first university qualification.

Fees (Francs): 5900-11,000 per annum.

Language of Instruction: French.

Degrees and Diplomas: Diplôme d'Ingénieur, 5 yrs.

Library: 5000 vols.

Academic Staff, 1986-87: 50 (15)

Student Enrolment, 1986-87:

	Men	Women	Total
Of the country	229	16	245
Of other countries	1	–	1
Total	230	16	246

2881 **CENTRE ASSOCIÉ MOSELLAN AU CONSERVATOIRE NATIONAL DES ARTS ET MÉTIERS**

7, rue Androuin-Roucel, 57000 Metz
Telephone: 87-74-17-14

2882 **INSTITUT SUPÉRIEUR DU BÉTON ARMÉ**

28, rue des Electriciens, 13012 Marseille
Telephone: 91-49-91-40

Reinforced Concrete Technology

Founded 1952 and formally recognized by the State 1957. Governing body: the Conseil de perfectionnement, comprising 9 members.

Academic Year: October to June (October-December; January-April; May-June).

Admission Requirements: Diplôme d'Ingénieur.

Language of Instruction: French.

Degrees and Diplomas: Diplôme d'Ingénieur, 1 yr.

Library: Central Library, 2000 vols.

Academic Staff: c. – (15).

Student Enrolment: c. 20.

2883 **ÉCOLE SUPÉRIEURE DU BOIS**

6-8, avenue de Saint-Mandé, 75012 Paris
Telephone: (1) 46-28-09-33

Wood Technology
Forestry

Founded 1935. Under the supervision of the Institut national du Bois and responsible to the Ministries of Education and Agriculture.

Academic Year: October to June (October-December; January-March; April-June).

Admission Requirements: Entrance by competition following 2 yrs further study after secondary school certificate (baccalauréat) or following first university qualification (D.U.T. or D.E.U.G.). Direct entrance to second year by competition following appropriate university degree (Maîtrise).

Language of Instruction: French.

Degrees and Diplomas: Diplôme d'Ingénieur, 3 yrs. Also Brevet de Technicien supérieur, 2 yrs.

Library: Central Library.

Academic Staff: c. 15.

Student Enrolment: c. 170.

2884 **ÉCOLE SUPÉRIEURE DES INDUSTRIES DU CAOUTCHOUC**

60, rue Auber, 94408 Vitry-sur-Seine Cedex
Telephone: (1) 46-71-91-22
Directeur: Jean Curchod (1978-)

Rubber Technology

Founded 1942 by the Institut français du Caoutchouc. Recognized by the State 1943. Acquired present title 1973. Attached to the Institut national de Formation et d'Enseignement professionnel du Caoutchouc. Governing body: the Conseil d'administration.

Academic Year: September to October (14 months).

Admission Requirements: Diplôme d'Ingénieur or Maîtrise ès Sciences, or recognized foreign equivalent.

Admission Requirements: Diplôme d'Ingénieur or Maîtrise ès Sciences or recognized foreign equivalent.

Fees (Francs): None for French students.

Language of Instruction: French.

Degrees and Diplomas: Diplôme d'Ingénieur du Caoutchouc or Certificat, 14 months.

Library: School Library.

Academic Staff, 1986-87: 9 (30).

Student Enrolment, 1986-87:

	Men	Women	Total
Of the country	21	2	23
Of other countries	1	–	1
Total	22	2	24

2885 **ÉCOLE TECHNIQUE SUPÉRIEURE PRIVÉE DE CHIMIE DE L'OUEST**

60, rue Michelet, 49005 Angers Cedex
Telephone: 41-88-98-33

Industrial Chemistry

Founded 1950. Attached to the Facultés Catholiques de l'Ouest.

Academic Year: September to June.

Admission Requirements: Entrance by competition following 2 yrs further study after secondary school certificate (baccalauréat) or following first university qualification (D.U.T. or D.E.U.G.).

Language of Instruction: French.

Degrees and Diplomas: Brevet–de Technicien chimiste; de Technicien supérieur chimiste, 2 yrs.

Academic Staff: c. 10.

2886 **INSTITUT DE CHIMIE ET PHYSIQUE INDUSTRIELLES (ICPI)**

31, place Bellecour, 69288 Lyon Cedex 1
Telephone: 78-37-52-86
Fax: 78-42-39-16
Directeur général: Alexis Dufour
Secrétaire général: A. Favre

D. of Chemistry and Chemical Engineering
Head: M. J. Pont; *staff* 15 (16)
D. of Electronic and Data Processing
Head: M. Jourlin; *staff* 27 (32)
D. of Languages
Head; C. Bourgeois; *staff* 1 (19)
D. for Lifelong Education
Head; M. Vivier; *staff* 2 (2)

Founded 1919, acquired present status and title 1957. Attached to the Facultés Catholiques de Lyon. Governing body: the Conseil d'administration. Some residential facilities for students.

Arrangements for student exchange with the universities of: Birmingham; Newcastle; Nottingham; London; Ulm; Munster; Technion-Haîfa; Barcelona; Madrid; Houston; Oregon; Lausanne.

Academic Year: October to June (October-December; January-February; April-June).

Admission Requirements: Entrance by competition following 2 yrs further study after secondary school certificate (baccalauréat) or following first university qualification (D.U.T. or D.E.U.G.).

Fees (Francs): 20,300 per annum.

Language of Instruction: French.

Degrees and Diplomas: Diplôme–d'Ingénieur chimiste; d'Ingénieur physicien électronicien, 5 yrs.

Library: Scientific library, *c.* 10,000 vols.

Special Facilities (Museums, etc.): Movie Studio.

Publications: Quanta; Proton.

Academic Staff, 1990: c. 48 (53).

Student Enrolment, 1990:

	Men	Women	Total
Of the country	286	96	382
Of other countries	9	–	9
Total	295	96	391

2887 **ÉCOLE NATIONALE SUPÉRIEURE DE SYNTHÈSES, DE PROCÉDÉS ET D'INGÉNIERIE CHIMIQUES D'AIX-MARSEILLE (ENSSPICAM)**

Centre St-Jerôme, Avenue de l'Escadrille Normandie-Nieman, 13397 Marseille Cedex 13
Telephone: 91-28-86-00
Fax: 91-02-77-76
Administrateur: J. Metzger
Secrétaire général: Ph. Lavagne

D. of Chemistry
Head: J. P. Aune; *staff* 11 (5)
D. of Chemical Engineering
Head: J. L. Chevalier; *staff* 4 (9)
D. of Engineering
Head: J. M. Ruiz; *staff* 3 (1)

Founded 1909 incorporating the Ecole supérieure de Chimie de Marseille, founded 1909, and the Ecole supérieure d'Ingénierie, de Pétroléochimie et de Synthèse organique industrielle (1959). Financed by the Chamber of Commerce and the State. Some residential facilities for students at Cité universitaire.

Arrangements for co-operation with: Université du Québec à Trois-Rivières, Canada; Cranfield; Mons; University of York; University of Strathclyde.

Academic Year: September to June.

Admission Requirements: Entrance by competition following 2 yrs further study after secondary school certificate (baccalauréat) or following first university qualification (D.U.T. or D.E.U.G.).

Language of Instruction: French.

Degrees and Diplomas: Diplôme–d'Ingénieur chimiste, 3 yrs; Etudes approfondies (D.E.A.), 1 further yr; Doctor (Ph.D.), a further 3 yrs.

Academic Staff, 1990: c. 25 (7).

Student Enrolment, 1990:

	Men	Women	Total
Of the country	112	36	148
Of other countries	4	2	6
Total	116	38	154

2888 **ÉCOLE SUPÉRIEURE DE CHIMIE ORGANIQUE ET MINÉRALE**

12, rue Cassette, 75006 Paris
Telephone: (1) 45-48-87-43
Fax: (1) 40-49-02-49
Directeur: Yves Guibert

D. of Organic Chemistry
Head: Guy Declercq
D. of Chemical Engineering
Head: Gérard Antonini
D. of Inorganic Chemistry
Head: Marcel Touboul
D. of Analytical Chemistry
Head: Jean-Luc Vialle
D. of Formulation (Tensio-Active Components)
Head: Françoise Brochard

Founded 1957. Recognized by the State 1976. Attached to the Institut Catholique de Paris.

Arrangements for co-operation with universities of: Houston; Ohio; Perude; Yale; North Carolina; Denver; Rodchester; Michigan; McGill.

Academic Year: September to June.

Admission Requirements: Entrance by competition following 2 yrs further study after secondary school certificate (baccalauréat) or following first university qualification (D.E.U.G.). Direct entrance to second year by competition following appropriate university degree (Maîtrise).

Fees (Francs): 10,500-17,500 per annum.

Language of Instruction: French.

Degrees and Diplomas: Diplôme d'Ingénieur chimiste, 5 yrs.

Library: 2000 vols.

Academic Staff, 1989-90: c. 40.

Student Enrolment, 1989-90:

	Men	Women	Total
Of the country	190	192	382
Of other countries	3	2	5
Total	193	194	387

2889 **ÉCOLE SUPÉRIEURE DE CHIMIE INDUSTRIELLE DE LYON**

43, boulevard du 11 novembre 1918, B.P. 2977, 69100 Villeurbanne Cedex
Telephone: 78-89-66-56

Chemistry
Chemical Engineering
Lifelong Education

Founded 1883 as a private institution on the initiative of the Chamber of Commerce and the Université de Lyon. Governing body: the Conseil d'administration, comprising industrial administrators.

Academic Year: October to June (October-December; January-March; April-June).

Admission Requirements: Entrance by competition following 2 yrs further study after secondary school certificate (baccalauréat) or following first university qualification (D.U.T. or D.E.U.G.).

Language of Instruction: French.

Degrees and Diplomas: Diplôme d'Ingénieur chimiste, 3 yrs.

Library: School Library.

Academic Staff: – (70).

Student Enrolment: c. 180.

2890 **LYCÉE TECHNIQUE DU BÂTIMENT**

7, rue St-Lambert, 75015 Paris
Telephone: (1) 45-54-92-32

Building Engineering (Concrete and Metal)

Founded 1957 on the initiative of several national professional bodies.

Governing bodies: the Conseil d'administration; the Conseil de perfectionnement.

Academic Year: October to June (October-December; January-March; April-June).

Admission Requirements: By selection from holders of Diplôme d'Ingénieur or foreign equivalent.

Fees: None.

Language of Instruction: French.

Degrees and Diplomas: Certificat, 1 yr.

Library: c. 400 vols.

Academic Staff: c. – (80).

2891 **ÉCOLE SUPÉRIEURE D'APPLICATION DES CORPS GRAS**

Rue Monge, Parc Industriel de Pessac, 33600 Pessac
Telephone: 56-36-00-44

Technology of Fats

Founded 1942, acquired present status 1955. Governing body: the Conseil d'administration.

Academic Year: October to July (October-December; January-March; April-July).

Admission Requirements: Diplôme d'Ingénieur or Maîtrise ès Sciences.

Fees: None.

Language of Instruction: French.

Degrees and Diplomas: Diplôme d'Ingénieur spécialiste des corps gras, 1 yr.

Library: c. 9000 vols.

Academic Staff: c. – (30).

Student Enrolment: c. 10.

2892 **ÉCOLE SUPÉRIEURE DU CUIR ET DES PEINTURES, ENCRES ET ADHÉSIFS**

181-203, Avenue Jean Jaurès, B.P. 7034, 69342 Lyon Cedex 07
Telephone: 78-72-28-31
Directeur: Philippe Berticat (1982-)

Leather Technology
Paints
Varnish
Adhesives
Lifelong Education

Founded 1899 as Ecole française de Tannerie by the Syndicat Général des Cuirs et Peaux de France. Recognized by the State 1922 and acquired present title 1980. Governing bodies: the Conseil d'administration; the Conseil de perfectionnement. Residential facilities for students.

Academic Year: September to June (September-December; January-March; April-June).

Admission Requirements: Entrance by competition following 2 yrs further study after secondary school certificate (baccalauréat) or following first university qualification (D.U.T., B.T.S., or D.E.U.G.).

Fees (Francs): c. 12,500 per annum.

Language of Instruction: French.

Degrees and Diplomas: Diplôme d'Ingénieur, 3 yrs. Students may simultaneously prepare for university Maîtrise. Also Brevet de Technicien supérieur des Industries du Cuir and Brevet de Technicien supérieur des Peintures, Vernis et Encres d'Imprimerie, 2 yrs.

Academic Staff, 1986-87: 13 (39).

Student Enrolment, 1986-87:

	Men	Women	Total
Of the country	98	61	159
Of other countries	14	2	16
Total	112	63	175

2893 **INSTITUT DES TECHNIQUES ÉCONOMIQUES ET COMPTABLES DE LORRAINE**

46, cours Léopold, 54000 Nancy
Telephone: 83-36-04-25

Economics
Accountancy

Attached to the Université de Nancy II.

2894 **ÉCOLE SUPÉRIEURE D'ÉLECTRICITÉ**

Antenne de Rennes, Avenue de la Boulais, 35510 Cesson Sévigné
Telephone: 99-00-21-00

2895 **ÉCOLE SUPÉRIEURE D'ÉLECTRICITÉ**

Plateau du Moulon, 91190 Gif-sur-Yvette
Telephone: 69-41-80-40
Directeur général: Jean-Loup Delcroix (1978-)
Secrétaire général: André Imbert

Electrical Engineering
Electronic Engineering
Radio Technology
Robotics
Automatic Calculation
Lifelong Education

Also centres at Rennes and Metz.

Founded 1894 by the Société française des Electriciens and attached to the Ministry of Education 1964. Became attached to University of Paris XI 1974. Financed by grants from the Ministries of Education, Defence and Industry. Residential facilities for students.

Academic Year: September to June (September-December; January-Easter; Easter-June).

Admission Requirements: Entrance by competition following 2 yrs further study after secondary school certificate (baccalauréat) or following first university qualification (D.U.T.). Direct entrance to second year by competition following appropriate university degree (Maîtrise or Ingénieur).

Fees (Francs): 470.

Language of Instruction: French.

Degrees and Diplomas: Diplôme d'Ingénieur, 3 yrs. Diplôme de Spécialisation. Mastère spécialisé.

Library: c. 4500 vols.

Academic Staff, 1986-87:

Rank	Full-time	Part-time
Professeurs Chefs de Service	18	–
Ingénieurs enseignants-chercheurs	133	40
Professeurs conférenciers vacataires	–	277
Total	151	317

Student Enrolment, 1986-87:

	Men	Women	Total
Of the country	875	115	990
Of other countries	39	4	43
Total	914	119	1033

2896 **ÉCOLE D'INGÉNIERIE EN GÉNIE DES SYSTÈMES INDUSTRIELS (EIGSI-VIOLET)**

2, rue Braille, 17000 La Rochelle
Telephone: 46-67-87-87
Fax: 46-67-31-01
Directeur général: Max Laulom
Secrétaire général: Jean Dubrulle

Electrical Engineering
Mechanical Engineering
Management

Founded 1990 and replacing the Ecole d'Electricité et Méchanique industrielles (École Violet), founded 1902 in Paris and which ceased its activities 1983. Residential facilities for students.

Arrangements for co-operation with: Birmingham Polytechnic; Université de Liège.

Academic Year: October to June (October-January; January-April; April-June).

Admission Requirements: Entrance examination following secondary school examination (baccalauréat) or following first university degree (D.U.T., B.T.S. or D.E.U.G.) (cycle ingénieur).

Fees (Francs): 19,200 per annum.

Language of Instruction: French.

Degrees and Diplomas: Diplôme d'Ingénieur Electricien-Mécanicien, 4 yrs.

2897 **ÉCOLE SUPÉRIEURE D'ÉLECTRONIQUE, DE L'OUEST**
4, rue Merlet-de-la-Boulaye, 49009 Angers Cedex 01
Telephone: 41-86-67-67
Fax: 41-87-99-27
Directeur: Victor Hamon (1984-)

D. of Electronic Engineering and Computer Sciences
Research Ce.

Founded 1956 as Ecole technique supérieure; achieved present name and status 1962. Attached to the Facultés Catholiques de l'Ouest. An autonomous institution. Research Centre added 1966. Governing bodies: the Conseil d'administration; the Conseil de perfectionnement.

Academic Year: September to June (September-February; March-June).

Admission Requirements: Entrance by competition following 2 yrs further study after secondary school certificate (baccalauréat) or following university degree (Licence or Maîtrise).

Language of Instruction: French.

Degrees and Diplomas: Diplôme d'Ingénieur, 5 yrs. Students may prepare for Diplôme d'études approfondies (D.E.A.).

Library: c. 3000 vols.

Academic Staff, 1989-90: c. 40 (25).

Student Enrolment, 1989-90:

	Men	Women	Total
Of the country	500	70	570

2898 **INSTITUT SUPÉRIEUR D'ÉLECTRONIQUE DU NORD**
41, boulevard Vauban, 59046 Lille Cedex
Telex: 120360
Telephone: 20-30-62-20
Directeur: Gaston Vandecandelaere
Secrétaire général: Paul Astier

Electronic Engineering

Founded 1956. Recognized by the State 1963. Attached to the Fédération Universitaire et Polytechnique de Lille. Governing body: the Conseil d'administration. Residential facilities for students.

Arrangements for co-operation with: King's College, London; Université Catholique de Louvain; State University of Ghent.

Academic Year: September to June (September-December; January-March; April-June).

Admission Requirements: Competitive entrance examination following secondary school certificate (baccalauréat).

Fees (Francs): 6000-14,000 per annum.

Language of Instruction: French.

Degrees and Diplomas: Diplôme d'Ingénieur, 5 yrs.

Library: c. 2500 vols.

Publication: Applica (annually).

Academic Staff, 1986-87: 47 (100).

Student Enrolment, 1986-87:

	Men	Women	Total
Of the country	300	52	352
Of other countries	15	–	15
Total	315	52	367

2899 **INSTITUT SUPÉRIEUR D'ÉLECTRONIQUE DE PARIS**
28, rue Notre-Dame-des-Champs, 75006 Paris
Telephone: (1) 45-54-52-00
Fax: (1) 49-54-52-01
Directeur: François Massot (1986-)
Secrétaire général administratif: Jacques Bloeme

D. of Electronic Engineering
Dean: Jean-Pierre Jourdan; *staff* 50 (150)
Continuing Education Ce.

Founded 1955.

Arrangements for co-operation with the University of Sussex.

Academic Year: September to June (September-December; January-April; April-June).

Admission Requirements: Competitive examination following secondary school certificate (baccalauréat).

Fees (Francs): 8000-18,000 per annum.

Language of Instruction: French.

Degrees and Diplomas: Diplôme d'Ingénieur, 5 yrs.

Special Facilities (Museums, etc.): Branly Museum.

Academic Staff, 1989-90: 22 (150).

Student Enrolment, 1989-90:

	Men	Women	Total
Of the country	426	107	533
Of other countries	5	1	6
Total	431	108	539

2900 **ÉCOLE SUPÉRIEURE DE FONDERIE**
280, avenue Aristide-Briand, 92220 Bagneux
Telephone: (1) 46-64-54-50
Directeur: M. Duflot (1973-)

Foundry Technology

Founded 1924, recognized by the State 1925. Governing body: the Conseil d'administration, composed of six representatives of the profession and six of the Ministry of Education, presided over ex officio by the President of the Syndicat général des Fondeurs de France.

Academic Year: September to July (September-December; January-Easter; Easter-July).

Admission Requirements: Diplôme d'Ingénieur or equivalent, or competitive entrance examination following 2 yrs further study aftersecondary school certificate (baccalauréat).

Fees (Francs): 4325 per annum; 7500 for foreign students.

Language of Instruction: French.

Degrees and Diplomas: Diplôme–d'Ingénieur; de Technicien.

Library: Specialized Library.

Academic Staff, 1986-87: 2 (70).

Student Enrolment, 1986-87: 24.

2901 **CENTRE D'ÉTUDES SUPÉRIEURES INDUSTRIELLES (CESI)**
Tour Europa, 6, boulevard de l'Europe, 91033 Evry Cedex
Telephone: (1) 60-78-12-67
Fax: (1) 60-78-52-04
Directeur: Gérard Leroy

Engineering (Lifelong Education)

Founded 1958. An institution with 20 regional centres throughout France and 1 in Spain.

Academic Year: April to October.

Admission Requirements: Competitive entrance examination following secondary school certificate (baccalauréat) and 2-5 years professional experience.

Fees (Francs): 190,000 per cycle of 2 years.

Language of Instruction: French.

Degrees and Diplomas: Diplôme d'Ingénieur, 2 yrs.

Academic Staff, 1989-90: c. 11 (170).

Student Enrolment, 1989-90:

	Men	Women	Total
Of the country	224	7	231
Of other countries	8	1	9
Total	232	8	240*

Also 30 students by correspondence.

2902 **ÉCOLE DES HAUTES ÉTUDES INDUSTRIELLES**
13, rue de Toul, 59046 Lille Cedex
Telex: 120369
Telephone: 78-33-18-73
Directeur: Michel Vittu
Secrétaire général: Jean Guegen

Engineering

Founded 1885 by the Facultés Catholiques de Lille. Recognized by the State 1968. Since 1967 forms part of the Grandes Ecoles fédérées d'Ingénieurs de la Région Nord. Attached to Fédération Universitaire et Polytechnique de Lille. Governing body: the Conseil d'Administration. Residential facilities for students.

Participates in the ERASMUS Programme.

Academic Year: September to June (September-December; January-March; April-June).

Admission Requirements: Competitive entrance examination following secondary school certificate (baccalauréat) or equivalent.

Fees (Francs): 18,000-20,000 per annum.

Language of Instruction: French.

Degrees and Diplomas: Diplôme d'Ingénieur, 5 yrs.

Library: c. 9000 vols.

Academic Staff, 1989-90: 8 (200).
Student Enrolment, 1989-90:

	Men	Women	Total
Of the country	500	100	600
Of other countries	16	2	18
Total	516	102	618

2903 **ECOLES DES ETUDES ET RECHERCHES EN INFORMATIQUE ET ELECTRONIQUE**
Parc scientifique Georges Besse, 30000 Nîmes
Telephone: 66-29-05-05

2904 **ÉCOLE SUPÉRIEURE D'INFORMATIQUE ÉLECTRONIQUE-AUTOMATIQUE**
9, rue Vésale, 75005 Paris
Telephone: (1) 43-37-78-43
Fax: (1) 43-36-27-02
Président: Amaury Hême de Lacotte

Electronic Engineering
Computer Sciences
Automation

Founded 1958.
Academic Year: September to June (October-December; January-March; April-June).
Admission Requirements: Secondary school certificate (baccalauréat) or equivalent, and entrance examination.
Language of Instruction: French.
Degrees and Diplomas: Diplôme, 5 yrs.
Library: 1000 vols.
Academic Staff: c. 15 (35).
Student Enrolment: c. 750.

Private Establishments

2905 **ÉCOLE FRANÇAISE DE RADIOÉLECTRICITÉ, D'ÉLECTRONIQUE, ET D'INFORMATIQUE**
110, rue Amyot, 75005 Paris
Telephone: (1) 47-07-05-95

Radioelectrical Engineering
Electronic Engineering
Computer Sciences

Founded 1936, recognized by the State 1945.
Academic Year: September to June.
Admission Requirements: Competitive entrance examination at the level of secondary school certificate (baccalauréat).
Language of Instruction: French.
Degrees and Diplomas: Brevet de Technicien électronicien, 3 yrs. Diplôme d'Ingénieur, 4 yrs.
Student Enrolment: c. 240.

Private Establishments

2906 **TECHNOPOLE MARSEILLE PROVENCE**
13451 Marseille Cedex 13

Engineering (Civil, Electrical, Mechanical and Chemical; Physics and Mathematics)
Reinforced Concrete Technology

Student Enrolment: c. 200.

2907 **ÉCOLE SUPÉRIEURE D'INGÉNIEURS EN ÉLECTROTECHNIQUE ET EN ÉLECTRONIQUE**
B.P. 99 Cité Descartes, 93160 Noisy
Telex: 231586 ESIEE F
Telephone: (1) 45-92-65-00
Directeur: Edmund Viviand

Electromechanical Engineering
Electronic Engineering
Ce. for Lifelong Education

Founded 1904 as Ecole d'Ingénieurs Bréguet. Acquired present title 1968. Administered and partly financed (60%) by the Chambre de Commerce et d'Industrie de Paris.
Arrangement for a Tripartite Programme with the Universities of: Karlsruhe; Essex; Southampton. Also student exchange programme with Universities in: USA; United Kingdom; Singapore; Spain.
Academic Year: September to June.
Admission Requirements: Entrance examination following secondary school certificate (baccalauréat).
Fees (Francs): 15,000 per annum.
Language of Instruction: French.
Degrees and Diplomas: Diplôme d'Ingénieur, 5 yrs.
Library: c. 2800 vols.
Academic Staff: c. 50.
Student Enrolment, 1989-90:

	Men
Of other country	600
Of other countries	40
Total	640

2908 **ÉCOLE SUPÉRIEURE D'INGÉNIEURS EN GÉNIE ÉLECTRIQUE (ÉCOLE CHARLIAT)**
58, rue Méridienne, 76100 Rouen

Electrical Engineering

Founded 1901, a private institution recognized by the State.
Academic Year: September to June.
Admission Requirements: Secondary school certificate (baccalauréat) or equivalent, and entrance examination.
Language of Instruction: French.
Degrees and Diplomas: Diplôme d'Ingénieur électricien, 3 yrs.

2909 **ÉCOLE D'INGÉNIEURAT DE TOURS**
L'Auberdière, 37200 Tours
Telephone: 47-38-58-00

2910 **ÉCOLE SPÉCIALE DE MÉCANIQUE ET D'ÉLECTRICITÉ**
4, rue Blaise-Desgoffe, 75006 Paris
Telephone: (1) 45-48-03-70
Fax: (1) 45-44-80-66
Directeur: Jean Doceul (1978-)
Directeur des Etudes Techniques: Hervé Laborne

Mechanical and Electrical Engineering
Electronics
Computer Sciences

Founded 1905, recognized by the State 1922. Governing body: the Conseil de perfectionnement. Residential facilities for students.
Arrangements for co-operation with Plymouth College of Technology; San José University.
Academic Year: October to June (October-December; January-March; April-June).
Admission Requirements: Competitive entrance examination following 1-2 yrs further study after secondary school certificate (baccalauréat) following university degree (D.U.T. or qualification or Maîtrise).
Fees (Francs): 19,000 per annum.
Language of Instruction: French.
Degrees and Diplomas: Diplôme–d'Ingénieur-mécanicien-électricien; d'-Ingénieur-mécanicien-électronicien, 5 yrs.
Library: 1900 vols.
Academic Staff, 1989-90: c. 25 (190).
Student Enrolment, 1989-90:

	Men	Women	Total
Of the country	853	167	1020
Of other countries	107	9	116
Total	960	176	1136

2911 **ÉCOLE NATIONALE SUPÉRIEURE DE MEUNERIE ET DES INDUSTRIES CÉRÉALIÈRES**
16, rue Nicolas-Fortin, 75013 Paris Cedex 06
Telephone: 43-37-42-47

Founded 1924.

2912 **ÉCOLE SUPÉRIEURE D'OPTIQUE**
B.P.43, 91406 Orsay Cedex
Telex: 692166 F
Telephone: (1) 69-07-67-37

2913 **LYCÉE TECHNIQUE PRIVÉ D'OPTOMÉTRIE**
134, route de Chartres, 91440 Bures-sur-Yvette
Telephone: (1) 69-07-67-37
Directeur: Jean-Paul Roosen (1977-)
Directeur des Etudes: Thérèse Thiebaut

Optometry

Founded 1917 as Institut central d'Optique, acquired present title 1954.

Arrangements for co-operation with: University of Cardiff; University of New South Wales.

Academic Year: September to June (September-December; January-March; April-June).

Admission Requirements: Competitive entrance examination following secondary school certificate (baccalauréat).

Fees (Francs): 10,300 per annum.

Language of Instruction: French.

Degrees and Diplomas: Brevet de Technicien supérieur opticien-lunetier, 2 yrs. Licence d'Optique physiologique et d'Optométrie.

Library: 1500 vols.

Publication: L'Optométrie (monthly).

Academic Staff, 1986-87: 21 (12).

Student Enrolment, 1986-87:

	Men	Women	Total
Of the country	78	91	169
Of other countries	1	4	5
Total	79	95	174

2914 **ÉCOLE D'OPTIQUE-LUNETTERIE**
14, rue Nicolas Leblanc, 59000 Lille
Telephone: 20-57-38-52

Optics

2915 **ÉCOLE FRANÇAISE DE PAPETERIE ET DES INDUSTRIES GRAPHIQUES**
B.P. 65, 461, rue de la Papeterie, 38402 St.-Martin-d'Hères
Telephone: 76-82-69-00
Fax: 76-82-69-33
Directeur: Maurice Renaud

D. of Paper Technology
Head: Ch. Voillot
D. of Printing Technology
Head: G. Baudin

Founded 1907, reorganized 1929 with Conseil de perfectionnement composed of academic staff and members of industry. Acquired status of Ecole nationale supérieure d'Ingénieurs 1950. Attached to the Institut National Polytechnique de Grenoble. Residential facilities for students at Cité universitaire.

Academic Year: October to June (October-December; January-March; April-June).

Admission Requirements: Competitive entrance examination following further study after secondary school certificate (baccalauréat).

Language of Instruction: French.

Degrees and Diplomas: Diplôme–d'Ingénieur papetier; d'Ingénieur imprimeur, 3 yrs. Diplôme d'études approfondies (D.E.A.),1 yr. Doctorat, 2-4 yrs after D.E.A.

Library: c. 4000 vols.

Academic Staff, 1989-90: 26 (29).

Student Enrolment, 1989-90:

	Men	Women	Total
Of the country	124	25	149
Of other countries	13	1	14
total	137	26	163

2916 **ÉCOLE POLYTECHNIQUE FÉMININE**
3 bis, rue Lakanal, 92330 Sceaux
Telephone: (1) 46-60-33-31

Technology (including Computer Sciences, Aeronautics, Electronics,) Energetics and Nuclear Energy

Founded 1925. Reorganized by the State 1943. Governing bodies: the Conseil de perfectionnement; the Comité directeur.

Academic Year: September to June (September-December; January-March; April-June).

Admission Requirements: Entrance by competition following secondary school certificate (baccalauréat).

Language of Instruction: French.

Degrees and Diplomas: Diplôme d'Ingénieur, 5 yrs.

Academic Staff: c. 50 (120).

Student Enrolment: c. 700.

2917 **ÉCOLE SUPÉRIEURE DE SOUDAGE ET DE SES APPLICATIONS**
32, boulevard de la Chapelle, 75880 Paris Cedex
Cables: ofisoud
Telex: OFISOUD 210 335F
Telephone: (1) 42-03-94-05

Welding Engineering

Founded 1930. A private institution recognized by the State. Governing body: the Conseil d'administration, comprising 15 members.

Academic Year: September to June (September-December; January-March; April-June).

Admission Requirements: Recognized diploma in Engineering or foreign equivalent.

Language of Instruction: French.

Degrees and Diplomas: Diplôme d'Ingénieur-Soudeur, 1 yr. Certificat de Technicien en Soudure autogène (for non-engineers).

Library: Library of the Institute.

Publications: Soudage et techniques connexes; Souder; Bulletin signalétique 745.

Student Enrolment: c. 20.

2918 **ÉCOLE SUPÉRIEURE DES TECHNIQUES INDUSTRIELLES ET DES TEXTILES**
1, Allée Lakanal, B.P.209, 59654 Villeneuve-d'Asq Cedex
Telex: 120369 GEFIRN F
Telephone: 20-91-35-21
Fax: 20-91-03-18
Directeur: Bertrand Avrin
Secrétaire général: Olivier Descamps

Automation and Computer Sciences
General and Applied Mechanics
Macromolecular Chemistry

Founded 1895 by the Facultés Catholiques de Lille. Since 1967 forms part of the Grandes Ecoles fédérées d'Ingénieurs de la Région Nord. Attached to the Fédération Universitaire et Polytechnique de Lille. Governing bodies: the Assemblée générale; the Conseil d'administration; the Conseil de perfectionnement.

Academic Year: October to June (October-January; February-June).

Admission Requirements: Competitive entrance examination following secondary school certificate (baccalauréat) or foreign equivalent.

Fees (Francs): *c.* 15,000 per annum.

Language of Instruction: French.

Degrees and Diplomas: Diplôme d'Ingénieur, 5 yrs. Also Diplôme de Technicien supérieur, 2 yrs.

Academic Staff, 1989-90: 20 (29).

Student Enrolment, 1989-90: 245.

2919 **ÉCOLE SUPÉRIEURE DES INDUSTRIES TEXTILES D'ÉPINAL**
85, rue d'Alsace, 88000 Epinal
Telex: 960536 F
Telephone: 29-35-50-52
Directeur: Pierre Lecoanet (1978-)

Spinning
Weaving

Founded 1905. Recognized by the State 1922 and authorized to award State Diplôme d'Ingénieur 1962. Administered and partly financed by the Chambre de Commerce et d'Industrie d'Epinal. Governing body: the Conseil de perfectionnement, including members of university institutions and of the textile industry. Residential facilities for students.

Arrangements for co-operation with the Technical College, Coburg.

Academic Year: October to June (September-December; January-March; April-June).

Admission Requirements: Entrance by competition following 2 yrs further study after secondary school certificate (baccalauréat) or following first university qualification (D.U.T. or D.E.U.G.).

Fees (Francs): 5143 per annum; foreign students, 8407.

Language of Instruction: French.

Degrees and Diplomas: Diplôme d'Ingénieur, 3 yrs. Brevets de Technicien supérieur, 2 yrs. Diplôme d'études approfondies, D.E.A. Docteur-Ingénieur.

Library: c. 1500 vols.

Academic Staff, 1986-87: 25 (7).

Student Enrolment, 1986-87:

	Men	Women	Total
Of the country	63	43	106
Of other countries	30	8	38
Total	93	51	144

2920 **ÉCOLE SUPÉRIEURE DES INDUSTRIES TEXTILES DE LYON**

43, cours Général-Giraud, 69201 Lyon Cedex 01
Telephone: (1) 78-27-07-00
Directeur: Philippe Berticat (1984-)

Textile Engineering

Founded 1884 by the City of Lyons, became Ecole supérieure 1942.

Academic Year: September to June (September-February; February-June).

Admission Requirements: Entrance by competition following 2 yrs further study after secondary school certificate (baccalauréat) or following first university qualification (D.U.T. or D.E.U.G.).

Fees (Francs) : 6000 per annum

Language of Instruction: French.

Degrees and Diplomas: Diplôme d'Ingénieur, 3 yrs.

Library: c. 22,000 vols.

Academic Staff, 1986-87: 2 (36).

Student Enrolment, 1986-87:

	Men	Women	Total
Of the country	37	9	46
Of other countries	8	–	8
Total	45	9	54

2921 **ÉCOLE SPÉCIALE DES TRAVAUX PUBLICS, DU BÂTIMENT ET DE L'INDUSTRIE**

57, boulevard Saint-Germain, 75240 Paris Cedex 05
Telex: 203 385
Telephone: (1) 46-34-21-99
Directeur: Serge Eyrolles (1973-)

Public Works
Construction Engineering
Mechanical Engineering
Electrical Engineering
Topography
Lifelong Education

Founded 1891. Recognized by the State 1921. Governing bodies: the Conseil de perfectionnement; the Conseil de direction. Residential facilities for 200 students.

Arrangements for co-operation with: University of Birmingham; Northwestern University, Illinois; University ofMunich.

Academic Year: October to June.

Admission Requirements: Entrance by competition following 2 yrs further study after secondary school certificate (baccalauréat).

Fees (Francs): 15,636-18,192 per annum.

Language of Instruction: French.

Degrees and Diplomas: Diplôme–d'Ingénieur des Travaux publics; d'Ingénieur des Travaux du Bâtiment; d'Ingénieur mécanicien-électricien; d'Ingénieur géomètre, 5-6 yrs. Also Professional titles of Conducteur-technicien des Travaux publics; Conducteur-technicien des Travaux du Bâtiment, 2 yrs.

Library: 5000 vols.

Press or Publishing House: Editions Eyrolles.

Academic Staff, 1986-87:

Rank	Part-time
Professeurs	338
Assistants	208
Total	546

Student Enrolment, 1986-87:

	Men	Women	Total
Of the country	1364	169	1533
Of other countries	185	13	198
Total	1549	182	1731*

*Also 4500 external students.

Schools of Agriculture

2922 **ÉCOLE SUPÉRIEURE D'AGRICULTURE D'ANGERS**

24, rue Auguste-Fonteneau, 49007 Angers Cedex
Telex: 720943
Telephone: 41-88-58-12

Agriculture (including Animal Husbandry)

Founded 1898 by the Jesuits. Under lay supervision since 1970. A private institution recognized by the Ministry of Agriculture.

Academic Year: September to June.

Admission Requirements: Secondary school certificate (baccalauréat) and entrance examination.

Languages of Instruction: French and English.

Degrees and Diplomas: Diplôme of Ingénieur en Agriculture, 4 yrs.

Library: Centre de Documentation, 30,000 vols.

Academic Staff: c. 20 (140).

Student Enrolment: c. 270.

2923 **INSTITUT SUPÉRIEUR D'AGRICULTURE DE BEAUVAIS**

Rue Pierre Waguet, B.P. 313, 60026 Beauvais Cedex
Telephone: 44-45-82-63
Fax: 44-45-30-02
Directeur général: André Blanchard (1984-)

Agriculture (including Afro-Industrial Studies and Food Technology)

Founded 1854. Attached to the Institut Catholique de Paris since 1921. Responsible to the Ministry of Agriculture. Governing body: the Conseil d'administration. Some residential facilities for students.

Arrangements for co-operation with: Technical College, Nürtingen; Royal Agricultural College, Cirencester; Lincolnshire College of Agriculture; also the Universities of: Louvain; Dublin; Valenica.

Academic Year: September to June (September-December; January-April; April-June).

Admission Requirements: Secondary school certificate (baccalauréat) or equivalent.

Fees (Francs): 14,000 per annum.

Languages of Instruction: French and English.

Degrees and Diplomas: Diplôme d'études supérieures agronomiques, économiques et sociales, 4 yrs. Diplôme d'Ingénieur en Agriculture, 1 further yr.

Library: 30,000 vols.

Publication: Technique, Économie, Sociologie en Agriculture (quarterly).

Academic Staff, 1986-87: 22 (164).

Student Enrolment, 1990-91:

	Men	Women	Total
Of the country	340	150	490
Of other countries	3	–	3
Total	343	150	493

2924 **ÉCOLE SUPÉRIEURE D'INGÉNIEURS ET DE TECHNICIENS POUR L'AGRICULTURE**

B.P. 201, 27100 Val De Reuil
Telephone: 32-59-14-59

Agriculture

Founded 1919 in Paris, recognized by the State 1964. Transferred to Le Vaudreuil 1976. Responsible to the Ministry of Agriculture. Governing bodies: the Comité de direction et d'orientation; the Conseil de perfectionnement. Residential facilities for 260 students.

Academic Year: September to June (September-December; January-March; April-June).

Admission Requirements: Secondary school certificate (Baccalauréat) or ‹revet de technicien agricole, and competitive entrance examination.
Language of Instruction: French.
Degrees and Diplomas: Diplôme d'Ingénieur en Agriculture, 5 yrs;)iplôme de Technicien supérieur, 2 yrs.
Academic Staff: c. 200.
Student Enrolment: c. 350 (Also c.100 external students.

925 **INSTITUT SUPÉRIEUR D'AGRICULTURE**
13, rue de Toul, 59046 Lille Cedex
Telex: 120369
Telephone: 20-30-83-14
Fax: 20-42-81-46
Directeur: René Dusautois
Secrétaire général: Jacques Fondeur

Agriculture

Founded 1963, recognized by the State 1967. Attached to the Fédération Universitaire et Polytechnique de Lille. Responsible to the Ministry of Agriculture. Governing body: the Conseil d'administration.

Arrangements for co-operation with: Reading University; Université de Louvain; University of Bonn; Knoxville University; University of Dublin; University of Rome I; University of Bologna; Universities of Valencia; Cordóba; Nijmegen; Delft.

Academic Year: September to June.
Admission Requirements: Secondary school certificate (baccalauréat) and entrance examination.
Fees (Francs): 14,000 per annum.
Language of Instruction: French.
Degrees and Diplomas: Diplôme d'Ingénieur en Agriculture, 5 yrs.
Academic Staff, 1989-90: 50
Student Enrolment, 1989-90:

	Men	Women	Total
Of the country	285	136	421
Of other countries	1	–	1
Total	286	136	422

2926 **INSTITUT SUPÉRIEUR D'AGRICULTURE RHÔNE-ALPES**
31, place Bellecour, 69288 Lyon Cedex 02
Telephone: 78-42-10-78

Agriculture

2927 **ÉCOLE SUPÉRIEURE D'AGRICULTURE DE PURPAN-TOULOUSE**
75, voie du Toec, 31076 Toulouse Cedex
Telex: 532 275 F
Telephone: (61) 49-23-11
Fax: (61) 31-91-48
Président du Groupe Purpan: Dominique Peccoud

D. of Agriculture
Director: Pierre Tapie

Founded 1919. Attached to the Institut catholique de Toulouse. Recognized by the State 1964. Responsible to the Ministry of Agriculture.

Arrangements for co-operation with: California State University, Chico; Kansas State University; Laval University. Universities of: Bologne; Rome I; Dublin; Nimegen. Institute of Agriculture, Chongqing.

Academic Year: November to June.
Admission Requirements: Secondary school certificate (baccalauréat).
Fees (Francs): 14,700 per annum.
Language of Instruction: French.
Degrees and Diplomas: Diplôme d'Ingénieur en Agriculture, 5 yrs.
Libraries: Documentation Centre, 15,000 vols; 859 revues.
Publication: Purpan (quarterly).
Academic Staff, 1989-90: 57 (90).
Student Enrolment, 1989-90:

	Men	Women	Total
Of the country	317	110	427
Of other countries	4	1	5
Total	321	111	432

Schools of Commerce and Business Administration

2928 **ACADÉMIE COMMERCIALE INTERNATIONALE**
43, rue de Tocqueville, 75017 Paris
Telex: 641468 ACCIPEX
Telephone: (1) 47-54-65-00

2929 **INSTITUT EUROPÉEN D'ADMINISTRATION DES AFFAIRES**
THE EUROPEAN INSTITUTE OF BUSINESS ADMINISTRATION
Boulevard de Constance, 77305 Fontainebleau Cedex
Telephone: (1) 60-72-40-00

Business Administration (at the European level)

Founded 1958 on the initiative of the Chambre de Commerce et d'Industrie de Paris, with technical assistance from Harvard Graduate School of Business Administration and the Centre de Perfectionnement dans l'Administration des Affaires. Under the auspices of the European Productivity Agency, the International Chamber of Commerce,and the European League for Economic Co-operation. Governing body: the Conseil d'administration (international in composition). Residential facilities for students.

Special arrangements for co-operation with Harvard Business School and Stanford Business School.

Academic Year: September to June (September-December; January-March; March-June).
Admission Requirements: University degree or equivalent.
Languages of Instruction: French, English and German.
Degrees and Diplomas: Diplôme, 1 yr.
Library: c. 15,000 vols.
Publications: Management Documentation (bimonthly); European Business Review.
Academic Staff: c. 40.
Student Enrolment: c. 200.

2930 **INSTITUT SUPÉRIEUR DES AFFAIRES**
1, rue de la Libération, 78350 Jouy-en-Josas
Telex: 600325 F
Telephone: 39-56-72-41
Fax: 39-56-74-65
Directeur: Nicole Ferry (1989-90)
Directeur administratif, financier et du personnel: Jean-Luc Gulin

Accountancy and Management Control, Business Law and Taxation, Finance and Economics, Languages, Human Resource Management, Marketing, Logistics, and Operations Management, Decision Sciences and Information Systems

Founded 1969. Administered by the Paris Chamber of Commerce and Industry. Residential facilities for students.

Arrangements for co-operation with: McGill University; University of California, Los Angeles; Northwestern University; Instituto de Estudios Superiores de la Empresas, Barcelona; London Business School; Erasmus University; Keio University.

Academic Year: Programme of 16 months, beginning in September.
Admission Requirements: Graduate degree/Diplôme de 2e cycle and professional experience (for 80% of the students).
Fees (Francs): 80,000 per annum.
Languages of Instruction: French and English.
Degrees and Diplomas: Diplôme, 16 months.
Library: 50,000 vols.
Academic Staff, 1989-90: 43 (35).
Student Enrolment, 1989-90: 110.

2931 **ÉCOLE EUROPÉENNE DES AFFAIRES (EAP)**
108, boulevard Malesherbes, 75017 Paris
Telex: EAPFRAN 640611 F
Telephone: (1) 47-54-65-00
Fax: (1) 42-67-46-19
Directeur: Henri Jolles

D. of Business Administration (European Management)
Directeur: Chris Halliburton; *staff* 20 (20)

P. of International Business
Directeur: Farhad Rad-Serecht; *staff* 10 (20)

Ce. for Lifelong Education
Directeur: Patrice Renard; *staff* 5 (10)

Founded 1973 by the Paris Chamber of Commerce and Industry. Branches in Berlin, Oxford, and Madrid. Governing body: the Board of Trustees.

Academic Year: September to June.

Admission Requirements: a) The European Masters in Management Programme: Entrance by competition following 2 yrs further study after secondary school certificate (baccalauréat) or following first university qualification; b) The European M.B.A. in International Business: a First university degree and minimum of 3 yrs with experience in a management position.

Fees (Francs): European Masters in Management programme, 25,000 per annum; European M.B.A. in International Busines

Fees: s, 90,000.

Languages of Instruction: French, English and German or Spanish.

Degrees and Diplomas: Diplôme, 3 yrs. M.B.A. Diplom Kaufmann/Kauffrau.

Publication: European Management Journal (quarterly).

Academic Staff, 1990: 50.

Student Enrolment, 1989-90:

Of the country	190
Of other countries	315
Total	505

2932 **ÉCOLE DU CHEF D'ENTREPRISE ET DES CADRES SUPÉRIEURS**

24, rue Hamelin, 75116 Paris

Telephone: (1) 45-53-31-59

Business Administration

Founded 1944.

Academic Year: October to June.

Admission Requirements: Practical experience in business administration.

Degrees and Diplomas: Diplôme, 1 yr.

Academic Staff: c. 40.

Student Enrolment: c. 260.

2933 **ÉCOLE SUPÉRIEURE DE COMMERCE INTERNATIONAL**

1, rue du Port de Valvins, 77215 Avon-Fontainebleau

Telex: MELU 600767F

Telephone: 60-72-27-37

Fax: 60-72-17-57

Directeur: Claude Saurel

Directeur administratif: Suzanne Chasin Wajntal

D. of International Business Studies

Director: Claude Saurel; *staff* 5 (27)

D. of Communication and Languages (English, German, Spanish, Japanese)

Head: Ann Guigon; *staff* 1 (11)

D. of Computer Science and Data Processing

; *staff* 1 (3)

D. of Export Strategy

Head: M. Baudet; *staff* – (1)

D. of Finance, Accounting and Taxation

; *staff* – (3)

D. of Marketing

Head: Michel Fish; *staff* – (2)

D. of Law

Director: Jacques Hémon; *staff* 1 (1)

D. of Lifelong Education

Founded 1981 by the Chambre de Commerce et d'Industrie de Melun. Governing body: the Commission de la Formation. Residential facilities for students.

Arrangements for co-operation with institutes in: United Kingdom; Denmark; USA, and regular exchange of students with British universities and polytechnics.

Academic Year: September to June (September-December; January-March; April-June).

Admission Requirements: Competitive entrance examination following university qualification (D.U.T., D.E.U.G., D.E.U.S.T., B.T.S.).

Fees (Francs): 17,500 per annum.

Languages of Instruction: French and English.

Degrees and Diplomas: Diplôme, 3 yrs.

Library: Central Library, c. 500 vols.

Publication: Bulletins (quarterly).

Press or Publishing House: Imprimerie de la Chambre de Commerce et d'Industrie de Melun.

Academic Staff, 1989-90: 5 (27).

Student Enrolment, 1989-90: 250.

2934 **GROUPE ÉCOLE SUPÉRIEURE DE COMMERCE DE LYON**

Graduate School of Business

23, avenue Guy de Collongue, B.P. 174 69132 Ecully Cedex

Telex: ESCLYON 400486 F

Telephone: 72-20-25-25

Fax: 78-33-61-69

Electronic mail: EARN BITNET: sdufour@freccl 11

Directeur général: Roger Delay-Termoz

S. of Commerce

Dean: Gordon Shenton

Ce. of Management

Dean: Edith Roesch

Ce. for Lifelong Education

Also research centres for Effective Marketing, Strategic Management Management Development and Entrepreneurial Programmes

Founded 1872 by Rhône-Alpes Industrialists, closely linked with the Lyons Chamber of Commerce and Industry. Recently launched a Europeanization Project for the 1990s. Governing body: the Board of Trustees comprising representatives from the Chamber of Commerce and Industry prominent businessmen and student and alumni representatives. Residential facilities for 200 students.

Arrangements for joint degree programmes with the Universities of Texas at Austin; Connecticut; Southern California; York, Toronto; Lancaster; Manchester Institute of Technology; Saar; Waseda; 'Luigi Bocconi', Milan. Koblenz School of Corporate Management; Netherlands School of Business. Also student exchange with institutions in: Austria, Belgium, Denmark, Italy, Netherlands, Norway, Sweden, Switzerland, USSR.

Academic Year: September to June (September-December; January-March; April-June).

Admission Requirements: Entrance by competition following 2 yrs further study after secondary school certificate (baccalauréat) or following first university qualification (D.U.T., B.T.S. or D.E.U.G.). Direct entrance to second year by competition following appropriate university degree (Licence).

Fees (Francs): 31,500-72,500 per annum.

Languages of Instruction: French and some English.

Degrees and Diplomas: Diplôme, 4-5 yrs. Also Certificat d'études supérieures de Management (CESMA), 1 yr. MS ESC Lyon, 1 yr.

Libraries: 10,000 vols. On-line database, company files on CD ROM; authorized depositary library for EC publications.

Academic Staff, 1990-90: 87 (175).

Student Enrolment, 1990-91:

	Men	Women	Total
Of the country	325	272	597
Of other countries	54	46	100
Total	379	318	697*

*Also 54 students in the 4 MS ESC programmes.

2935 **ECOLE SUPÉRIEURE DE COMMERCE DU CENTRE**

1 rue Leo Delibes, 37005 Tours Cedex

Telephone: 47-27-42-43

2936 **GROUPE ÉCOLE SUPÉRIEURE DE COMMERCE AMIENS-PICARDIE**

18, place Saint-Michel, 80038 Amiens Cedex

Telephone: 22-82-66-00

Fax: 22-92-38-96

Directeur général: Roger Mezin (1981-)

Secrétaire génral: Georges Pouzot

Commerce

I. for Management Assistants (ISAM)

Founded 1942 as municipal institution, recognized by the State 1962 and transferred to Chamber of Commerce andIndustry 1963.

Academic Year: October to June (October-February; February-June).

Admission Requirements: Entrance by competition following 1-2 yrs further study after secondary school certificate (baccalauréat) or following first university qualification (D.U.T. or B.T.S.). Direct entrance to second year by competition following appropriate university degree (Licence).

Fees (Francs): 20,000 per annum.

Language of Instruction: French.

Degrees and Diplomas: Diplôme de l'ISAM, 3 yrs.
Academic Staff: c. 18 (100).
Student Enrolment, 1990-91:

	Men	Women	Total
Of the country	235	220	255
Of other countries	3	1	4
Total	238	221	259

2937 **ÉCOLE SUPÉRIEURE DES SCIENCES COMMERCIALES**
1, rue Lakanal, 49016 Angers Cedex
Telephone: 41-48-30-55

Commerce (including Law, Economics, and Accountancy)

Founded 1909. Recognized by the State. Attached to the Facultés catholiques de l'Ouest. Also administered bythe Chambers of Commerce and Industry of Angers, Cholet, Le Mans, and Saumur. Governing bodies: the Conseil d'administration; the Conseil de perfectionnement.

Academic Year: October to June (October-December; January-March; April-June).

Admission Requirements: Entrance by competition following secondary school certificate (baccalauréat) or following first university qualification (D.U.T., B.T.S. or D.E.U.G.). Direct entrance to third year by competition following appropriateuniversity degree (Licence).

Fees (Francs): 15,600 per annum.
Language of Instruction: French.
Degrees and Diplomas: Diplôme, 4 yrs.
Library: c. 5000 vols.
Academic Staff, 1986-87: 10 (107).
Student Enrolment, 1986-87:

	Men	Women	Total
Of the country	312	189	501
Of other countries	3	–	3
Total	315	189	504

2938 **GROUPE ÉCOLE SUPÉRIEURE DE COMMERCE DE BRETAGNE-BREST**
Graduate Business School of Brest
2, avenue de Provence, B.P. 214, 29272 Brest Cedex
Telephone: 98-34-44-44
Fax: 98-34-44-69
Directeur: Jacques Baguenard

Commerce
Financial Studies, Marketing, Accountancy, International Business Languages, Computer Sciences, Strategic PlanningI. of Agricultural Management

Founded 1962 and recognized by the State. Administered by the Brest Chamber of Commerce and Industry.

Participates in the ERASMUS and Tempus programmes.

Academic Year: October to June (October-February; February-June).

Admission Requirements: Entrance by competition following 1-2 yrs further study after secondary school certificate (baccalauréat) or following first university qualification (D.U.T., B.T.S. or D.E.U.G.). Direct entrance to second year by competition following appropriate university degree (Licence).

Fees (Francs): 18,000 per annum.
Language of Instruction: French.
Degrees and Diplomas: Diplôme d'études supérieures commerciales, administratives et financières, 3 yrs (State diploma).
Library: 500 vols.
Academic Staff, 1990-91: c. 50.
Student Enrolment, 1989-90:

	Men	Women	Total
Of the country	150	180	330*

*Also 35 foreign students

2939 **GROUPE ÉCOLE SUPÉRIEURE DE COMMERCE CLERMONT**
4, boulevard Trudaine, 63037 Clermont-Ferrand
Telex: ESCCLFD 990753
Telephone: 73-92-39-71
Fax: 73-90-26-45
Directeur: Henri Verdier
Secrétaire général: Jean-Louis Besson

Economics, Foreign Languages, Informatics, International Finance, Law, Marketing, Finance and Accountancy, Human Resource ManagementI. of International Trade
Ce. for In-service Training and Consultancy
Research Ce.

Founded 1919. Administered by the Auvergne Regional Chamber of Commerce and Industry.

Special arrangements for international exchange with the Universities of: Kansas; Cornell; Oregon; Georgia Tech; Louisiana State, Baton Rouge. Also arrangements for co-operation with Universities in: United Kingdom, Germany, Italy, Spain, Denmark, Hungary, USSR, Peru.

Academic Year: September to June (September-January; February-June).

Admission Requirements: Entrance by competition following 1-2 yrs further study after secondary school certificate (baccalauréat). Direct entrance to second year by competition following appropriate university degree (Licence, Maîtrise).

Fees (Francs): 20,000 per annum.
Language of Instruction: French.
Degrees and Diplomas: Diplôme d'études supérieures comptables, administratives et financières, DESCAF, 3 yrs (State diploma).
Library: Centre de Documentation, c. 10,000 vols.
Publication: Sup' De Co' Développements (quarterly).
Academic Staff, 1990: c. 21 (110).
Student Enrolment, 1990-91:

	Men	Women	Total
Of the country	209	197	406
Of other countries	6	5	11
Total	215	202	417

2940 **ÉCOLE SUPÉRIEURE DE COMMERCE ET D'ADMINISTRATION DES ENTREPRISES DE BOURGOGNE ET DE FRANCHE COMTÉ**
29, rue Sambin, 21000 Dijon
Telephone: 80-72-12-40

Commerce
Business Administration

Founded 1899 and recognized by the State 1900. Administered by the 11 Chambers of Commerce and Industry of Bourgogne and Franche-Comté. Responsible to the Ministries of Commerce and Industry and Education. Governing body: the Comité d'orientation et de gestion.

Arrangements for co-operation with: Technical College of Business Administration, Pforzheim; Leeds Polytechnic; South Bank Polytechnic; Miami University, Ohio.

Academic Year: September to June.

Admission Requirements: Entrance by competition following 1-2 yrs further study after secondary school certificate (baccalauréat) or following first university qualification. Direct entrance to second year by competition following appropriateuniversity degree.

Language of Instruction: French.
Degrees and Diplomas: Diplôme d'études supérieures commerciales, administratives et financières, 3 yrs (State diploma). AlsoCertificat européen des Affaires.
Library: c. 7300 vols.
Academic Staff: c. 30 (100).
Student Enrolment: c. 340.

2941 **GROUPE ÉCOLE SUPÉRIEURE DE COMMERCE DE GRENOBLE**
7, rue Hoche, 38000 Grenoble
Telex: 320824 F
Telephone: 76-43-02-12
Fax: 76-56-90-52
Electronic mail: t@7el7ematique: 36-15 escg
Doyen: Jean-Paul Leonardi

Marketing, Management, Control and Finance, International Marketing in High Technology, Management of Technology, Information TechnologyLifelong Education

Founded 1984. Administered by the Grenoble Chamber ofCommerce.

Arrangements for co-operation with Institutions in: USA; Canada; United Kingdom; Spain; Germany; Netherlands; Demark; Sweden.

Academic Year: September to June.

Admission Requirements: Entrance by competition following 2 yrs further study after secondary school certificate (baccalauréat) or following first university qualification (D.E.U.G., D.E.U.S.T., or D.U.T.). For Mastère, 5 yrs postsecondary study.

Fees (Francs): 24,000-66,000 per annum.

Languages of Instruction: French, English, German, Italian, Spanish, and Russian.

Degrees and Diplomas: Diplôme, 5 yrs. Mastère, 1 further yr.

Library: Centre de Documentation, 4770 vols.

Academic Staff, 1989-90: 30 (70).

Student Enrolment, 1989-90:

	Men	Women	Total
Of the country	186	202	388
Of other countries	16	16	32
Total	192	218	420

2942 **ÉCOLE DES HAUTES ÉTUDES COMMERCIALES**

Graduate School of Management

1, rue de la Libération, 78530 Jouy-en-Josas

Telex: 697942 F

Telephone: 39-56-70-00

Fax: 39-56-74-40

Directeur: Jean-Louis Scaringella (1989-90)

Directeur administratif, financier et du personnel: Jean-Luc Gulin

D. of Management Control and Planning

Head: Hugues Jordan; *staff* 8

D. of Finance

Head: Joël Bessis; *staff* 10

D. of Marketing

Head: Jean-François Boss; *staff* 6

D. of Entrepreneurship

Head: Robert Papin; *staff* – (250)

D. of Law and Taxation Strategy;

Heads: Philippe Colin; Philippe Corruble; *staff* 8

D. of International Management

Heads: Alain Dumont; Jean Stora; *staff* 8 (10)

D. of Accountancy and Auditing

Head: Dang Pham Huy *staff* 10

Founded 1881. Administered by the Paris Chamber of Commerce and Industry. Residential facilities for students.

Arrangements for co-operation with: University of New York; University of Michigan; University of California, Berkeley; McGill University; University of Cologne; Hitotsubashi University, Tokyo; Stockholm School of Economics; Libera Università di Economia e Commercio 'Luigi Bocconi'; Escola de Administração das Empresas de São Paulo; London Graduate School of Business Studies; Escuela Superior de Administración y Dirección de Empresas, Barcelona; University of British Colombia; University of Business Administration, Vienna; NorwegianCollege of Economics and Business Administration, Bergen.

Academic Year: October to June (October-December; January-March; April-June).

Admission Requirements: Entrance by competition following 1-2 yrs further study after secondary school certificate (baccalauréat). Direct entrance to second year by competition following appropriate university degree, for French or foreign students (HEC International Track; Programme international de Management; CEMS).

Fees (Francs): 13,680 per annum.

Languages of Instruction: French and English.

Degrees and Diplomas: Diplôme, 2-3 yrs. Doctorat. Mastère spécialisé.

Library: 50,000 vols.

Academic Staff, 1989-90: 107 (16).

Student Enrolment, 1989-90:

	Men	Women	Total
Of the country	531	296	827
Of other countries	46	19	65
Total	577	315	892

2943 **ÉCOLE SUPÉRIEURE DE COMMERCE ET D'ADMINISTRATION DES ENTREPRISES**

1, rue Emile Zola, 76000 Le Havre Cedex

Telex: 190091 F

Telephone: 35-21-12-18

Directeur: Michel Poté (1985-)

Commerce

Business Administration

Founded 1871, recognized by the State 1890. Financially supported by the Le Havre Chamber of Commerce and Industry.

Arrangements for co-operation with: Pacific Lutheran University, Tacoma; Leeds Polytechnic; Technical College,Osnabrück; University of Alcala de Henares.

Academic Year: September to June (September-December; January-March; April-June).

Admission Requirements: Entrance by competition following 2 yrs further study after secondary school certificate (baccalauréat) or following first university qualification (D.U.T., B.T.S. or D.E.U.G.). Direct entrance to second year by competition following appropriate university degree (Licence).

Fees (Francs): 12,500 per annum.

Language of Instruction: French.

Degrees and Diplomas: Diplôme d'études supérieures commerciales, administratives et financières, 3 yrs (State diploma).

Library: c. 6000 vols.

Academic Staff, 1986-87: 15 (65).

Student Enrolment, 1986-87:

	Men	Women	Total
Of the country	155	155	310
Of other countries	2	–	2
Total	157	155	312

2944 **ÉCOLE SUPÉRIEURE DE COMMERCE ET D'ADMINISTRATION DES ENTREPRISES**

Lille School of Management

Avenue Gaston-Berger, 59045 Lille Cedex

Telephone: 20-52-67-59

Fax: 20-49-04-56

Directeur général: Jean-Pierre Raman (1989-)

D. of Finance and Auditing;

Head: Jean-Pierre Raman

D. of Human Resources

Head: Rosanne Carlier

D. of Marketing

Head: Gérard François

Industrial Sales S. (Douai)

Service for Lifelong Education

Head: Pierre Pelerin

Also Professional Training and Consulting Services, 2 Research and Developlment Centres, and specialized postgraduate programmes.

Founded 1892. A private institution. Governing body: the Conseil d'administration.

Participates in the ERASMUS programme.

Academic Year: October to June.

Admission Requirements: Entrance by competition following 2 yrs further study after secondary school certificate (baccalauréat) or following first university qualification (D.U.T. or D.E.U.G.). Direct entrance to second year by competition following appropriate university degree (Licence).

Fees (Francs): 19,700 per annum.

Languages of Instruction: French and English.

Degrees and Diplomas: Diplôme d'études supérieures commerciales, administratives et financières, 3 yrs (State diploma).

Library: Centre de Documentation, 18,000 vols.

Publication: Présence (quarterly).

Student Enrolment, 1989-90: 521.

2945 **ÉCOLE DES HAUTES ÉTUDES COMMERCIALES DU NORD**

Graduate School of Management of Northern France

1, rue du Port, 59058 Lille Cedex

Telex: 120369 GEFIRN

Telephone: 20-54-25-34

Fax: 20-30-83-06

Dean: Olivier Oger

Responsable administratif et financier: Marcel Labey

D. of Finance

Head: Ephraïm Clark; *staff* 8 (3)

D. of Marketing

Head: David Lesceux; *staff* 5 (4)

D. of International Business
Head: David Evans; *staff* 8 (3)
D. of Human Resources
Head: Pierre Drelon; *staff* 3 (2)
D. of Strategy
D. of Business Law
D. of International Business
Head: Michel Picavet
D. of Total Quality Management
Head: Elefterios Perrakis; *staff* 3
D. of Insurance Theory
Head: Michel Levasseur

Founded 1921. Acquired present structure 1958. Attached to the Fédération Universitaire et Polytechnique de Lille. Governing bodies: the Conseil d'administration; the Conseil d'orientation et de perfectionnement.

Arrangements for co-operation with Institutions in: United Kingdom; Spain; Germany.

Academic Year: September to June (October-February; February-June).

Admission Requirements: Entrance by competition following 2 yrs further study after secondary school certificate (baccalauréat) or following first university qualification (D.U.T. or D.E.U.G.).

Fees (Francs): 27,000-47,000 per annum.

Language of Instruction: French.

Degrees and Diplomas: Diplôme d'études supérieures commerciales, administratives et financières, 3 yrs. Magistère, 1 further yr. Certificates, 1 yr.

Library: c. 30,000 vols.

Academic Staff: c. 40 (110).

Student Enrolment: c. 750.

2946 **ÉCOLE SUPÉRIEURE DE COMMERCE ET D'ADMINISTRATION DES ENTREPRISES**

Domaine Universitaire de Luminy, Case 911, 13288 Marseille Cedex 09
Telex: 410091F
Telephone: 91-41-01-60
Directeur: Gabriel Murat (1969-83)
Chef de services administratifs: Michel Ponce Commerce Business Administration

Founded 1872. Recognized by the State 1890. Administered since 1935 by the Marseille Chamber of Commerce and Industry. Residential facilities for students.

Academic Year: October to June (October-February; February-June).

Admission Requirements: Entrance by competition following 1-2 yrs further study after secondary school certificate (baccalauréat) orfollowing first university qualification (D.U.T., B.T.S. or D.E.U.G.).

Fees (Francs): 13,800 per annum.

Language of Instruction: French.

Degrees and Diplomas: Diplôme d'études supérieures commerciales, administratives et financières, 3 yrs (State diploma).

Library: Central Library, 15,000 vols.

Academic Staff, 1986-87: 22 (150).

Student Enrolment, 1986-87:

	Men	Women	Total
Of the country	195	203	398
Of other countries	5	2	7
Total	200	205	405

2947 **ÉCOLE SUPÉRIEURE DE COMMERCE DE ROUEN**

Boulevard André Siegfried, B.P. 34, 76130 Mont-Saint-Aignan
Telex: REHANO 770036
Telephone: 35-74-03-00
Fax: 35-76-06-62
Directeur: Pierre-Alain Schieb
Responsable administratif et financier: FabienneBléry

S. of Commerce (including International Environment, Management Control, Computing, English, German, Spanish, Italian, Russian, Marketing, Law, Metholology, Quantitative Marketing, Logistics and International Shipping, International Accountancy, Taxation, Technology and Management Techniques Transfer)
Director: Alain Dulondel; *staff* 25 (120)
Lifelong Education
Head: F. Dorey; *staff* 5 (20)

Founded 1871. Administered by the Rouen Chamber of Commerce and Industry. Residential facilities for students at the Cité universitaire.

Arrangements for co-operation with institutions in: Germany; Netherlands; China; Spain; USA; Finland; Italy; Japan; Norway; United Kingdom; Scandinavia; Senegal.

Academic Year: October to June (October-December; January-March; April-June).

Admission Requirements: Entrance by competition following 2 yrs further study after secondary school certificate (baccalauréat) or following first university qualification (D.U.T. or D.E.U.G.). Direct entrance to second year by competition following appropriate university degree (Licence). For Mastères, D.E.A., D.E.S.S.

Fees (Francs): 24,000-45,000 per annum.

Language of Instruction: French.

Degrees and Diplomas: Diplôme d'Ecole, 4-5 yrs. Diplôme de Mastère.

Library: c. 10,000 vols.

Publication: Magazine (annually).

Academic Staff: c. 10 (130).

Student Enrolment, 1989-90: 850.

2948 **ÉCOLE SUPÉRIEURE DE COMMERCE ET D'ADMINISTRATION DES ENTREPRISES**

2300, avenue des Moulins, 34030 Montpellier Cedex
Telex: 49-00-31 CHAMCO
Telephone: 67-40-42-43
Directeur: Bernard Fabre (1986-)

Commerce
Business Administration

Founded 1897. Administered by the Montpellier Chamber of Commerce. Residential facilities for students.

Arrangements for co-operation with: Kingston Polytechnic, United Kingdom; Technical College Mainz, Worms; Escuela Superior de Marketing, Barcelona.

Academic Year: October to June (October-February; February-June).

Admission Requirements: Entrance by competition following 1-2 yrs further study after secondary school certificate (baccalauréat) or following first university qualification (D.U.T., B.T.S. or D.E.U.G.). Direct entrance to second year by competition following appropriate university degree (Licence).

Fees (Francs): 11,400 per annum.

Language of Instruction: French.

Degrees and Diplomas: Diplôme d'études supérieures commerciales, administratives et financières, 3 yrs (State diploma).

Library: Central Library.

Academic Staff, 1986-87: 12 (40).

Student Enrolment, 1986-87:

Of the country	248
Of other countries	2
Total	250

2949 **GROUPE ÉCOLE DE COMMERCE DE NANTES**

8, route de la Jonelière, 44003 Nantes Cedex
Telephone: 40-29-44-55
Directeur: Jean-Christophe Clerget (1979-)

Commerce
Business Administration
Lifelong Education

Founded 1900. Administered by the City of Nantes and the Nantes Chamber of Commerce. Residential facilities for students at Cité universitaire.

Arrangements for co-operation in student exchange with the Universities of: Ohio State; Bowling Green State; Arizona State; Denver; Laval; Aston; Madrid (Autonomous).

Academic Year: October to June.

Admission Requirements: Entrance by competition following 1-2 yrs further study after secondary school certificate (baccalauréat) orfollowing first university qualification (D.U.T., B.T.S. or D.E.U.G.).

Fees (Francs): 10,000-20,000 per annum.

Language of Instruction: French.

Degrees and Diplomas: Diplôme d'études supérieures commerciales, administratives et financières, 3 yrs (State diploma).

Library: c. 6000 vols.

Academic Staff, 1986-87: c. 50.

Student Enrolment: c. 300.

2950 **ÉCOLE SUPÉRIEURE DE COMMERCE DU CERAM**
Sophia Antipolis, B.P. 20, 06561 Valbonne Cedex
Telex: 461 504F
Telephone: 93-95-45-45
Fax: 93-65-44-01
Directeur: Jacques Lebraty (1985-)

Business Administration
Commerce
Finance
Business Management
Lifelong Education

Founded 1978. Administered by the Nice and Alpes-Maritimes Chamber of Commerce and Industry. Governing body: the Conseil d'administration. Residential facilities for students.

Academic Year: October to June (October-January; February-June).

Admission Requirements: Entrance by competition following 1-2 yrs further study after secondary school certificate (baccalauréat) or following first university qualification (D.U.T. or D.E.U.G.). Direct entrance to second year by competition following appropriate university degree (Licence).

Fees (Francs): 14,000 per annum.

Language of Instruction: French.

Degrees and Diplomas: Diplôme d'études supérieures commerciales, administratives et financières, 3 yrs, (State diploma). Mastère spécialisé, 9 months.

Library: 15,000 vols.

Academic Staff, 1986-87: 20.

Student Enrolment, 1986-87:

	Men	Women	Total
Of the country	136	120	256
Of other countries	7	11	18
Total	143	131	274

2951 **ÉCOLE SUPÉRIEURE DE COMMERCE DE PARIS**
Paris Graduate School of Management
79, avenue de la République, 75543 Paris Cedex 11
Telephone: 43-55-39-08
Fax: 43-55-99-63
Directeur: Véronique de Chantérac

Commerce
Adult Education

Founded 1819. Administered by the Paris Chamber of Commerce and Industry.

Arrangements for co-operation with Institutions in: Austria; Spain; Finland; United Kingdom; Ireland; Italy; Norway; Germany; Sweden; Switzerland; Canada; USA; Peru; People's Republic of China; India; Japan; Thailand.

Academic Year: September to July.

Admission Requirements: Entrance by competition following 1-2 yrs further study after secondary school certificate (baccalauréat) or following first university qualification (D.U.T. or D.E.U.G.). Direct entrance to second year by competition following appropriate university degree (Licence, Maîtrise).

Fees (Francs): 24,000 per annum.

Language of Instruction: French.

Degrees and Diplomas: Diplôme, 3 yrs. Mastère, 1 yr.

Academic Staff, 1990: 58 (24).

Student Enrolment, 1990:

	Men	Women	Total
Of the country	467	365	832
Of other countries	42	24	66
Total	509	389	898

2952 **INSTITUT DE COMMERCE INTERNATIONAL**
5, avenue Pierre Premier de Serbie, 75116 Paris
Telex: CFCEP 611934F
Telephone: (1) 45-05-30-00

International Commerce

Founded 1958. Recognized by the State 1961. Governing body: the Conseil d'administration.

Academic Year: January to December (January-May; April-June; October-December).

Admission Requirements: University degree.

Language of Instruction: French.

Degrees and Diplomas: Diplôme.

Student Enrolment: c. 60.

2953 **GROUPE ÉCOLE SUPÉRIEURE DE COMMERCE ET D'ADMINISTRATION DES ENTREPRISES DE PAU**
3 rue Saint-John Perse, Campus Universitaire, 64000 Pau
Telex: CCI PAU 570 929
Telephone: 59-92-64-64
Fax: 59-92-64-55
Directeur: J.P. Laget (1970-)
Secrétaire général administratif: R. Lanusse

S. of Commerce
I. of Accountancy, Finance and Management (IESCF)
I. of Business Administration (ISMI)

Founded 1970. Administered by the Pau Chamber of Commerce and Industry.

Arrangements for co-operation with: Clemson University, South Carolina; Instituto Católico de Dirección deEmpresas, Madrid; Fachhochschule München.

Academic Year: October to June (October-January; February-June).

Admission Requirements: Entrance by competition following 2 yrs further study after secondary school certificate (baccalauréat) or following first university qualification (D.U.T. or D.E.U.G.).

Fees (Francs): c. 21,000 per annum.

Language of Instruction: French.

Degrees and Diplomas: Diplôme d'études supérieures commerciales, administratives et financières, 3 yrs (State diploma). Diplôme d'études supérieures de Gestion, 3e cycle.

Library: Centrale Documentaire, 5000 vols.

Academic Staff, 1989-90: 12 (55).

Student Enrolment, 1990-91:

	Men	Women	Total
Of the country	194	190	384
Of other countries	8	6	14
Total	202	196	398

2954 **ÉCOLE SUPÉRIEURE DE COMMERCE ET D'ADMINISTRATION DES ENTREPRISES**
11, rue de l'Ancienne Comédie, 86001 Poitiers Cedex
Telex: 793294 ESCPOIT
Telephone: 49-88-25-77
Directeur: M. Rousseau

Commerce
Business Administration

Founded 1961. Administered by the Poitiers and Vienne Chamber of Commerce and Industry. Governing body: the Conseil d'administration.

Academic Year: October to June (October-February; February-June).

Admission Requirements: Entrance by competition following 1-2 yrs further study after secondary school certificate (baccalauréat) or following first university qualification (D.U.T. or D.E.U.G.). Direct entrance to second year by competition following appropriate university degree (Licence).

Fees (Francs): 8925-10,000 per annum.

Language of Instruction: French.

Degrees and Diplomas: Diplôme d'études supérieures commerciales, administratives et financières, 3 yrs (State diploma). Diplôme d'étude comptables supérieures (D.E.C.S.), 9 months.

Library: c. 1500 vols.

Academic Staff: c. 30.

Student Enrolment: c. 190.

2955 **GROUPE ÉCOLE SUPÉRIEURE DE COMMERCE DE REIMS**
B.P. 302, 51061 Reims Cedex
Telex: 890917 F
Telephone: 26-08-06-04
Fax: 26-04-69-63
Directeur: Pierre Lamborelle (1969-)

S. of Commerce
Director: J.C. Bourel

Business Administration

Founded 1929. Administered by the Rheims Chamber of Commerce and Industry. Governing body: the Conseil d'administration and Commission permanente.

Arrangements for joint integrated programmes with institutions in: United Kingdom; Germany; Spain. Also exchange with institutions in: Portugal; USA; Ireland; Canada; United Kingdom; Germany; Finland, Belgium.

Academic Year: October to June (October-February; February-June).

Admission Requirements: Entrance by competition following 1-2 yrs further study after secondary school certificate (baccalauréat), or following first university qualification (D.U.T., B.T.S. or D.E.U.G.). Direct entrance to second year by competition following appropriate university degree (Licence). For Mastère, 4-5 yrs postsecondary study.

Fees (Francs): 25,000-50,000 per annum.

Language of Instruction: French.

Degrees and Diplomas: Diplôme d'études supérieures commerciales, administratives et financières, 3 yrs (State diploma). Mastère, 1 yr.

Library: c. 10,000 vols.

Academic Staff, 1990-91: 30 (100).

Student Enrolment, 1990-91:

Of the country	950
Of other countries	250
Total	1200

2956 **ÉCOLE FRANCO-ALLEMANDE DE COMMERCE ET D'INDUSTRIE**

12, Cours St. Eloi, 75012 Paris
Telephone: (1) 43-44-06-53

2957 **GROUPE ÉCOLE SUPÉRIEURE DE COMMERCE DE BORDEAUX**

Bordeaux Graduate School of Business
Domaine de Raba, Cours de la Libération, 33405 Talence Cedex
Telex: 540549 F
Telephone: 56-80-70-50
Fax: 56-84-44-50
Directeur: Georges Viala (1987-)

S. of Business
Director: Francis Daurat *staff* 5
Multinational S. of Business Administration (EMA)
Director: Leopold Kahn; *staff* 3
I. of Logistics (ISLI)
I. of Organization Management (IMOP)
I. of Risks Management (IMR)
I. of Industrial Purchasing Management (MAI)

Founded 1874. Administered by the Bordeaux Chamber of Commerce and Industry.

Arrangements for co-operation with the Universities of: Aston; Nottingham; Strathclyde; Bayreuth; Hamburg; Trieste; Rotterdam; Deusto; Geneva; Munster Fachhochschule. Escuela Superior de Administración y Dirección de Empresas, Barcelona; Moscow State Institute of International Relations; Institute of National Economy, Moscow.

Academic Year: September to July (September-February; February-July).

Admission Requirements: Entrance by competition following 1-2 yrs further study after secondary school certificate (baccalauréat), or following first university qualification (D.U.T. or D.E.U.G.). Direct entrance to second year by competitionfollowing appropriate university degree (Licence). For Mastère, 5 yrs postsecondary study.

Fees (Francs): 20,000-47,500 per annum.

Language of Instruction: French.

Degrees and Diplomas: Diplôme d'études supérieures commerciales, administratives et financières, 3 yrs. State diploma. Mastères.

Library: 75000 vols.

Academic Staff, 1989-90: 25.

Student Enrolment, 1989-90: 430.

2958 **ÉCOLE SUPÉRIEURE DE COMMERCE DE TOULOUSE**

20, Boulevard Lascrosses, 31068 Toulouse Cedex
Telex: 531877 F
Telephone: 61-29-49-49

Commerce
Business Administration
Lifelong Education

Founded 1903. Administered by the Toulouse Chamber of Commerce and Industry. Reorganized 1980.

Academic Year: September to June (September-January; February-June).

Admission Requirements: Entrance by competition following 2 yrs further study after secondary school certificate (baccalauréat) or following first university qualification (D.U.T. or D.E.U.G.).

Language of Instruction: French.

Degrees and Diplomas: Diplôme d'études supérieures commerciales, administratives et financières, 3 yrs (State diploma).

Publication: Cahiers de recherches.

Academic Staff: 20 (40).

Student Enrolment: c. 350.

2959 **ECOLE SUPÉRIEURE DE COMMERCE DU CENTRE**

Tours Graduate School of Management
1, rue Léo Delibes, 37005 Tours Cedex
Telex: CHAMSOTOURS 750020
Telephone: 47-27-42-43
Fax: 47-27-56-55
Directeur: Philippe Georges Capelle
Directeur administratif et financier: Mireille Lefebure

Commerce
Business Administration
Lifelong Education

Founded 1982 by 6 Chambres de Commerce et d'Industrie.

Arrangements for co-operation with the Universities of: Sofia, Tokyo; Ritsmukeina; Kyoto; Indiana; Northeastern; San Francisco; San Diego; Texas A&M; Siegen; Koblenz. Cranfield Institute of Technology, United Kingdom.

Academic Year: October to June (October-December; January-March; April-June).

Admission Requirements: Entrance by competition following 1-2 yrs further study after secondary school certificate (baccalauréat) or following first university qualification (D.U.T., B.T.S. or D.E.U.G.). Direct entrance to second year by competition following appropriate university degree (Licence).

Fees (Francs): 21,000 per annum.

Language of Instruction: French.

Degrees and Diplomas: Diplôme d'études supérieures commerciales, administratives et financières, 3 yrs (State diploma).

Library: Central Library, 8000 vols.

Academic Staff, 1989-90: 20 (150).

Student Enrolment, 1989-90:

	Men	Women	Total
Of the country	200	180	380
Of other countries	12	8	20
Total	212	188	400

2960 **INSTITUT LIBRE DES HAUTES ÉTUDES ÉCONOMIQUES ET COMMERCIALES**

35, cours Xavier Arnozan, 33000 Bordeaux
Telephone: 56-44-95-97

2961 **ÉCOLE SUPÉRIEURE DES SCIENCES ÉCONOMIQUES ET COMMERCIALES**

Avenue de la Grande Ecole, B.P. 105, 95001 Cergy-Pontoise Cedex
Telephone: (1) 30-30-40-57

Economics
Commerce

Founded 1907.

Admission Requirements: Entrance by competition following 2 yrs further study after secondary school certificate (baccalauréat) or following first university qualification (D.U.T. or D.E.U.G.).

Academic Staff: c. 40 (100).

Student Enrolment: c. 1000.

2962 **INSTITUT D'ÉCONOMIE SCIENTIFIQUE ET DE GESTION**

1, rue François Baës, 59800 Lille
Telephone: 20-54-58-92
Directeur: Christian Bérard (1984-)

Economics

Business Administration (including Law, Computer Sciences and Accountancy)
Founded 1964. Attached to the Catholic University of Lille. Governing body: the Conseil d'administration.
Arrangements for co-operation with: Juniata College, Pennsylvania; Université Catholique de Louvain.
Academic Year: October to June.
Admission Requirements: Competitive entrance examination following secondary school certificate (baccalauréat).
Language of Instruction: French.
Degrees and Diplomas: Diplôme, 5 yrs.
Library: 11,000 vols.
Academic Staff, 1986-87: 7 (42).
Student Enrolment, 1986-87: 309.

2963 **L'INGÉNIEUR MANAGER (IEFSI)**
41, rue du Port, 59046 Lille Cedex
Cables: gefirn
Telex: 120369
Telephone: 20-42-81-46
Directeur: Patrick Verstraete (1972-)

Business Administration
Founded 1961. Recognized by the State 1970. Attached to the Fédération Universitaire et Polytechnique de Lille. Governing body: the Conseil d'administration.
Arrangements for co-operation with: Sheffield Business School; University of Leeds; University of Tennessee, Knoxville.
Academic Year: September to June (September-December; January-March; April-June).
Admission Requirements: By selection from holders of Diplôme d'Ingénieur or foreign equivalent.
Fees (Francs): 48,000 per annum.
Languages of Instruction: French and some English.
Degrees and Diplomas: Diplôme IEFSI (MBA for engineers), 1 yr.
Library: 12,000 vols.
Academic Staff, 1990-91: 2 (40).
Student Enrolment, 1989-90:

	Men	Women	Total
Of the country	49	9	58
Of other countries	8	–	8
Total	57	9	66

2964 **INSTITUT FRANÇAIS DE GESTION**
31320 Castenet Tolosan

Management Studies

2965 **INSTITUT D'EXPERTISE-COMPTABLE**
60, boulevard Vauban, 59000 Lille Cedex
Telephone: 20-93-61-70

Accountancy
Also evening courses.
Founded 1942. Attached to the Fédération Universitaire et Polytechnique de Lille.
Academic Year: October to June.
Admission Requirements: Secondary school certificate (baccalauréat); professional experience for evening courses.
Language of Instruction: French.
Degrees and Diplomas: Brevet professionnel de Comptable; preparatory examination for Diplôme d'Expert-comptable, 2-3 yrs.

2966 **INSTITUT SUPÉRIEUR DES SCIENCES TECHNIQUES ET D'ÉCONOMIE COMMERCIALE**
24, rue Hamelin, 75016 Paris
Telephone: (1) 47-27-88-70

2967 **INSTITUT FRANÇAIS DE GESTION**
31320 Castenet Tolosan
Telephone: 61-53-59-27

2968 **INSTITUT DE GESTION INTERNATIONALE AGRO-ALIMENTAIRE (ÉCOLE SUPÉRIEURE PRIVÉE)**
56 Campus, Avenue du Parc, 95033 Cergy-Pontoise Cedex
Telex: 697789 F
Telephone: (1) 30-73-28-88
Directeur: Bernard Yon (1978-)

Agriculture and Food Technology
Economics and Commerce
Academic Year: October to June (October-December; January-March; April-June).
Admission Requirements: University degree (2e cycle) or 4 yrs professional experience.
Fees (Francs): Registration, 315; tuition, 34,020 per annum.
Languages of Instruction: French and English.
Degrees and Diplomas: Certificat, 12-15 months. Mastère, 1 yr.
Academic Staff, 1986-87: 8 (5).
Student Enrolment, 1986-87:

	Men	Women	Total
Of the country	43	24	67
Of other countries	1	1	2
Total	44	25	69

2969 **INSTITUT SUPÉRIEUR DE GESTION**
45, rue Spontini, 75016 Paris
Telephone: 47-81-21-14

Diplomatic Studies

2970 **CENTRE PARISIEN DE MANAGEMENT**
108, boulevard Malesherbes, 75017 Paris
Telephone: (1) 47-66-51-34

S. of Business Administration
S. of Commerce
C. of Business Management
I. of Personnel Management
Ce. for Lifelong Education
Founded 1973, incorporating previously existing schools and centres. Administered by the Paris Chamber of Commerce and Industry. Residential facilities for students.
Academic Year: October to June.
Admission Requirements: University degree or Diplôme de Grande Ecole. Entrance examination for Commerce and Business Administration.
Language of Instruction: French.
Degrees and Diplomas: Diplôme, 3 yrs.
Library: c. 8000 vols.
Academic Staff: c. 110.
Student Enrolment: c. 870.

2971 **CENTRE D'ENSEIGNEMENT DU MANAGEMENT, COLLÈGE DES SCIENCES SOCIALES ET ÉCONOMIQUES**
3, rue Cassette, 75006 Paris
Telephone: (1) 45-44-38-80

Business Administration
Social Sciences and Economics
Founded 1926, recognized by the State 1957. Incorporated Collège des Sciences sociales et économiques, founded 1968, in 1975. Governing bodies: the Conseil d'administration; the Conseil de perfectionnement.
Academic Year: September to July.
Admission Requirements: Professional experience.
Language of Instruction: French.
Degrees and Diplomas: Certificat.
Library: Specialized Library.
Publication: Management France (bimonthly).
Academic Staff: c. – (c. 220).
Student Enrolment: c. 7000.

Schools of Notarial and Legal Studies

2972 **INSTITUT DE DROIT APPLIQUÉ**
143, avenue de Versailles, 75016 Paris
Telephone: (1) 45-25-56-74

Applied Law

Founded 1946. Receives subventions from the State, from the City of Paris and from industry. Provides evening courses.

Academic Year: October to June (October-December; January-March; April-June).

Admission Requirements: No formal requirements.

Language of Instruction: French.

Degrees and Diplomas: Certificat de technicien, 3 yrs.

Academic Staff: c. – (50).

Student Enrolment: c. 115.

2973 **FACULTÉ LIBRE INTERNATIONALE DE DROIT RURAL ET DES SCIENCES SOCIALES AGRAIRES**
3191, route de Mende, 34000 Montpellier

Rural Law and Social Sciences Applied to Agriculture

2974 **INSTITUT DES HAUTES ÉTUDES DE DROIT RURAL ET D'ÉCONOMIE AGRICOLE**
11, rue Ernest Lacoste, 75012 Paris
Telephone: (1) 46-28-38-96
Directeur: Jean Megret

Rural Law
Agricultural Economics
Agricultural Management and Development

Founded 1950, acquired present status 1961.

Academic Year: October to June (October-December; January-March; April-June).

Admission Requirements: Secondary school certificate (baccalauréat) or equivalent or Brevet de Technicien.

Fees (Francs): 22,500 per annum.

Language of Instruction: French.

Degrees and Diplomas: Diplôme de l'Institut (Diplôme homologué, niveau II), 4 yrs. Also Diplôme d'études supérieures spécialisées (D.E.S.S.) with the Université de Caen.

Library: c. 4000 vols.

Academic Staff, 1986-87: – (140).

Student Enrolment, 1989-90:

	Men	Women	Total
Of the country	244	138	382
Of other countries	3	–	3
Total	247	138	385

2975 **ÉCOLE PRIVÉE DE LÉGISLATION PROFESSIONNELLE**
44, rue Etienne Marcel, 75002 Paris
Telephone: (1) 42-36-32-14

Law of Trades and Professions

Founded 1905. A private institution.

Academic Year: October to May.

Language of Instruction: French.

Degrees and Diplomas: Professional certificates, 2 yrs.

Academic Staff: c. – (20).

Student Enrolment: c. 120.

2976 **ÉCOLE DE NOTARIAT**
3, place Louis-Dewailly, 80000 Amiens
Telephone: 22-91-38-40

Notarial Studies

Recognized by the State. Under the authority of the Ministry of Justice. Attached to the Université de Picardie.

Academic Year: October to June.

Language of Instruction: French.

Degrees and Diplomas: Diplôme, 2 yrs.

2977 **ÉCOLE DE NOTARIAT**
11, rue Chevreuil, 49000 Angers
Telephone: 41-88-72-12

Notarial Studies

Founded 1892, recognized by the State 1905. Under the authority of the Ministry of Justice. Financed by students' fees and subventions from professional bodies.

Academic Year: October to July.

Admission Requirements: Secondary school certificate (baccalauréat) or equivalent or entrance examination.

Language of Instruction: French.

Degrees and Diplomas: Diplôme, 2 yrs.

Academic Staff: c. 10.

Student Enrolment: c. 60.

2978 **ÉCOLE DE NOTARIAT DE CLERMOND-FERRAND**
25, rue de la Rotonde, 63000 Clermont-Ferrand
Telephone: 73-93-81-31

Notarial Studies

Founded 1913, recognized by the State 1915. Under the authority of the Ministry of Justice. Also attached to the Université de Clermont-Ferrand I.

Academic Year: October to June.

Language of Instruction: French.

Degrees and Diplomas: Diplôme, 2 yrs.

Academic Staff: c. – (20).

Student Enrolment: c. 130.

2979 **ÉCOLE DE NOTARIAT**
3, rue du Lycée, 21000 Dijon
Telephone: 80-67-15-71

Notarial Studies

Recognized by the State 1908. Under the authority of the Ministry of Justice. Also attached to the Université de Dijon.

Academic Year: October to June.

Language of Instruction: French.

Degrees and Diplomas: Diplôme, 2 yrs.

2980 **ÉCOLE DE NOTARIAT**
15, quai Claude-Bernard, 69007 Lyon
Telephone: 78-72-80-33

Notarial Studies

Founded 1902. Recognized by the State. Under the authority of the Ministry of Justice. Also attached to the Université de Lyon.

Academic Year: October to June.

Language of Instruction: French.

Degrees and Diplomas: Diplôme, 2 yrs.

2981 **ÉCOLE DE NOTARIAT**
72, Blvd. Périer, 13008 Marseille
Telephone: 91-33-67-13

Notarial Studies

Founded 1902. Recognized by the State. Under the authority of the Ministry of Justice.

Academic Year: October to June (October-December; January-Easter; Easter-June).

Admission Requirements: Secondary school certificate (baccalauréat) or entrance examination.

Language of Instruction: French.

Degrees and Diplomas: Diplôme, 2 yrs.

Library: c. 200 vols.

Academic Staff: c. – (10).

Student Enrolment: c. 100.

2982 **ÉCOLE DE NOTARIAT**
Avenue des Apothicaires, 34000 Montpellier
Telephone: 67-63-22-25

Notarial Studies

Recognized by the State. Under the jurisdiction of the Ministry of Justice. Also attached to the Université de Montpellier I.

Academic Year: October to June.

Language of Instruction: French.

Degrees and Diplomas: Diplôme, 2 yrs.

2983 **ÉCOLE DE NOTARIAT**
119 bis, rue de Coulmiers, 44000 Nantes
Telephone: 40-74-08-76

Notarial Studies

Founded 1905.

Academic Year: October to June (October-December; January-April; April-June).

Admission Requirements: Secondary school certificate (baccalauréat).

Language of Instruction: French.

Degrees and Diplomas: Diplôme, 2 yrs.

Academic Staff: c. – (20).

2984 **ÉCOLE DE NOTARIAT**
15 bis, rue Poulain-Duparc, 35000 Rennes
Telephone: 99-30-36-45

Notarial Studies

Founded 1892. Under the jurisdiction of the Ministry of Justice.

Academic Year: October to June.

Language of Instruction: French.

Degrees and Diplomas: Diplôme, 2 yrs.

2985 **ÉCOLE DE NOTARIAT**
39, rue du Champ-aux-Oiseaux, 76000 Rouen Cedex
Telephone: 35-70-50-41

Notarial Studies

Founded 1893. Under the jurisdiction of the Ministry of Justice.

Academic Year: October to June.

Language of Instruction: French.

Degrees and Diplomas: Diplôme, 2 yrs.

2986 **ÉCOLE DE NOTARIAT**
2, rue des Juifs, 67000 Strasbourg
Telephone: 88-32-10-55

Notarial Studies

Under the jurisdiction of the Ministry of Justice.

Academic Year: October to June.

Language of Instruction: French.

Degrees and Diplomas: Diplôme, 2 yrs.

2987 **ÉCOLE DE NOTARIAT**
2, Rue Albert-Lautman, 31000 Toulouse
Telephone: 61-23-01-45

Notarial Studies

Founded 1898. Recognized by the State. Under the jurisdiction of the Ministry of Justice. Also attached to theUniversité des Sciences sociales (Toulouse I).

Academic Year: October to July.

Language of Instruction: French.

Degrees and Diplomas: Diplôme, 2 yrs.

Library: c. 200 vols.

Academic Staff: c. 10.

Student Enrolment: c. 70.

2988 **ÉCOLE DE NOTARIAT DE PARIS**
9, rue Villaret-de-Joyeuse, 75017 Paris
Telephone: (1) 47-54-01-92

Notarial Studies

Founded 1897. Recognized by the State 1905.

Academic Year: October to June (October-February; February-June).

Language of Instruction: French.

Degrees and Diplomas: Diplôme, 2 yrs.

Academic Staff: c. – (30).

Student Enrolment: c. 240.

2989 **ÉCOLE DE NOTARIAT**
32, rue de Richelieu, 37000 Tours
Telephone: 47-05-60-20

Notarial Studies

Under the jurisdiction of the Ministry of Justice.

Academic Year: October to June.

Language of Instruction: French.

Degrees and Diplomas: Diplôme, 2 yrs.

Other Specialized Institutions

2990 **INSTITUT DES ACTUAIRES FRANÇAIS**
243, rue St. Honoré, 75001 Paris
Telephone: (1) 48-78-46-72

2991 **ÉCOLE D'ANTHROPOLOGIE**
1, place d'Iéna, 75116 Paris
Telephone: (1) 47-93-09-84
Directeur: J.A. Huet

Anthropology

Founded 1876, recognized by the State 1889.

Academic Year: November to June (November-February; February-June).

Admission Requirements: Secondary school certificate (baccalauréat) or foreign equivalent.

Fees (Francs): 800.

Language of Instruction: French.

Degrees and Diplomas: Certificat d'Etudes Anthropologiques, *c.* 1 yr. Diplôme, 2 yrs and thesis.

Student Enrolment, 1986-87: c. 200.

2992 **ÉCOLE SUPÉRIEURE TECHNIQUE DE BIOLOGIE APPLIQUÉE**
56, rue Planchat, 75020 Paris
Telephone: (1) 43-71-47-40

2993 **ÉCOLE DENTAIRE DE PARIS (SOCIÉTÉ DE L'ÉCOLE ET DU DISPENSAIRE DENTAIRES DE PARIS)**
45, rue de la Tour-d'Auvergne, 75009 Paris
Telephone: (1) 48-78-74-86; (1) 45-26-73-94

Dentistry

Founded 1880.

Academic Year: September to June.

Admission Requirements: Secondary school certificate (baccalauréat).

Language of Instruction: French.

Degrees and Diplomas: State diploma of Chirurgien-dentiste; Diplôme de l'Ecole, D.E.D.P. (for French and foreign students), 5 yrs.

Library: c. 10,000 vols.

Special Facilities (Museums, etc.): Musée P. Fauchard.

2994 **INSTITUT INTERNATIONAL SUPÉRIEUR DE FORMATION DES CADRES DE SANTÉ**
162, avenue Lacassagne, 69424 Lyon Cedex 3
Telephone: 78-54-54-12

Founded 1965 as Ecole internationale d'Enseignement infirmier supérieur. Under the supervision of the Hospice civil de Lyon. In the process of reorganization.

2995 **INSTITUT RÉGIONAL DE FORMATION AUX FONCTIONS ÉDUCATIVES**
2, rue Professeur Marion, 21000 Dijon
Telephone: 80-65-23-45
Directeur: Daniel Berchard

Teacher Training for Handicapped Children

Founded 1962.

Academic Year: September to June.

Admission Requirements: Secondary school certificate (baccalauréat).

Fees (Francs): 850 per annum.

Language of Instruction: French.

Student Enrolment, 1989-90: 300.

2996 **INSTITUT OCÉANOGRAPHIQUE**
195, rue Saint-Jacques, 75005 Paris
Telephone: (1) 43-25-63-10

Marine Physiology
Biological Oceanography
Physical Oceanography

Founded 1906 by Prince Albert I of Monaco, the Foundation comprises the Institut océanographique, Paris, andthe Musée océanographique, Monaco. Governing bodies: the Comité scientifique; the Conseil d'administration.

Academic Year: November to May.
Admission Requirements: Courses open to the public.

2997 **CENTRE D'ÉTUDES PRÉPARATOIRES AUX ORGANISATIONS INTERNATIONALES**
16, rue Miollis, 75015 Paris
Telephone: (1) 45-66-97-58

International Studies

Founded 1948 as institute, acquired present title 1975. Responsible to the Ministry of Education.

Academic Year: October to June (October-December; January-April; April-June).

Admission Requirements: Secondary school certificate (baccalauréat) or foreign equivalent.

Language of Instruction: French.

Degrees and Diplomas: Certificat (1e cycle). Brevet (2e cycle). Diplôme 3e cycle d'études universitaires supérieures. Title ofConseiller des Relations internationales by thesis.

Library: Central Library.

Academic Staff: c. – (5).

Student Enrolment: c. 120.

2998 **INSTITUT DE PSYCHANALYSE**
187, rue Saint-Jacques, 75005 Paris
Telephone: (1) 46-33-32-90

Psychoanalysis

2999 **ÉCOLE DE PSYCHOLOGUES PRATICIENS**
21, rue d'Assas, 75270 Paris Cedex 06
Telephone: (1) 45-48-17-75
Directeurs: L. Fanchon; J. Besson

Applied Psychology

Founded 1951. A private institution attached to the Institut Catholique de Paris. Governing body: the Conseil d'administration.

Academic Year: October to June (October-December; January-March; April-June).

Admission Requirements: Competitive entrance examination following at least 1-2 yrs study after secondary school certificate (baccalauréat) or foreign equivalent.

Fees (Francs): 21,000 per annum.

Language of Instruction: French.

Degrees and Diplomas: Diplôme–de Psychologue praticien (spécialisés: Psycho-Pathologie clinique; Psychologie du Travail et des Organisations; Psychologie de l'Éducation et de la Formation).

Library: c. 6000 vols.

Academic Staff, 1990: 40.

Student Enrolment, 1990:

	Men	Women	Total
Of the country	34	240	274
Of other countries	–	4	4
Total	34	244	278

3000 **ÉCOLE DE FORMATION PSYCHO-PÉDAGOGIQUE**
22, rue Cassette, 75006 Paris
Telephone: (1) 45-48-80-46

Applied Psychology
Education
Medical Studies

Founded 1946. Attached to the Institut Catholique de Paris.

Academic Year: October to June.

Admission Requirements: Entrance examination following secondary school certificate (baccalauréat) or equivalent, and minimum 3 months professional experience.

Language of Instruction: French.

Degrees and Diplomas: Diplôme d'Etat d'Educateur spécialisé, 3 yrs.

Academic Staff: c. 15.

3001 **INSTITUT EUROPÉEN DES HAUTES ÉTUDES INTERNATIONALES (IEHEI)**
2229, route des Crêtes, Sophia-Antipolis, 06560 Valbonne
Telex: 460000 IEHEIN-MINITEL
Telephone: 92-94-39-12
Fax: 93-65-31-77
Président: René-Jean Dupuy
Directeur: Claude Nigoul

International Studies
Lifelong Education

Founded 1964 by the International Centre for European Education. An autonomous institution attached to the University of Nice 1968. Moved to Sophia-Antipolis, 1989 within the Centre International de la Communication Avancée. Some residential facilities for students.

Arrangements for co-operation with: University of Bradford; University of Edinburgh; University of Manchester; Leeds Polytechnic; The Polytechnic of North London; Oxford Polytechnic; Portsmouth Polytechnic; King's College, London; Université de Liège.

Academic Year: October to June (October-December; January-March; April-June).

Admission Requirements: University qualification.

Fees (Francs): 1000-26,500 according to diploma.

Language of Instruction: French.

Degrees and Diplomas: Certificat d'études supérieures des Communautés européennes, 1 yr. Diplôme du programme de Civilisation française et européenne contemporaine, 1 yr. Diplôme de l'Institut européen des hautes Etudes internationales, 1 yr. Diplôme Européen d'études générales de la Communication Audiovisuelle (D.E.E.G.),2 yrs. Diplôme Européen d'études supérieures de la Communication Audiovisuelle (D.E.E.S.), 1 yr.

Library: c. 3000 vols.

Academic Staff, 1989-90: 5 (110).

Student Enrolment, 1989-90:

	Men	Women	Total
Of the country	24	57	81
Of other countries	45	57	102
Total	69	114	183

3002 **ÉCOLE INTERNATIONALE DE LANGUE ET DE CIVILISATION FRANÇAISES–ALLIANCE FRANÇAISE**
101, boulevard Raspail, 75270 Paris Cedex 06
Cables: Allfran
Telex: 204941F
Telephone: (1) 45-44-38-28
Fax: (1) 45-44-89-42
Président: Marc Blancpain
Sécretaire général: Jean Harzic

French Language Studies (Business French, Teacher Training, and Refresher Course at all levels)

Founded 1883. Residential facilities for students.

Academic Year: September to August (September-January; February-June; July-August).

Admission Requirements: Written and oral tests. Minimum age, 16 yrs.

Language of Instruction: French.

Degrees and Diplomas: Certificat élémentaire de Français pratique;: Diplôme de Langue française; Diplôme supérieur d'études françaises modernes; Diplôme de hautes Etudes françaises; Brevet d'Aptitude à l'enseignement du français hors de France; Brevet professionnel de Didactique du Français Langue Etrangère.

Library: For academic staff and for students.

Publication: Alliances (every trimester).

Academic Staff, 1989-90: 150 (*c.* 40).

Student Enrolment, 1989-90: 21,000 (Also 750 students by correspondence).

3003 **ÉCOLE SUPÉRIEURE DE JOURNALISME**
50, Rue Gauthier de Chatillon, 59000 Lille
Telex: 120388 ESJULL
Telephone: 20-54-48-21; 20-54-87-64

Journalism

Founded 1924. Attached to the Fédération Universitaire et Polytechnique de Lille. Became independent 1960,recognized by the State 1964. Governing body: the Conseil d'administration.

Academic Year: October to May (October-February; February-May).

Admission Requirements: Competitive entrance examination following 2 yrs further study after secondary school certificate (baccalauréat).
Language of Instruction: French.
Degrees and Diplomas: Diplôme d'Aptitude à la profession de Journaliste, 2 yrs.
Library: c. 6000 vols.
Publication: Trimedia (quarterly).
Academic Staff: c. 5 (40).
Student Enrolment: c. 80.

3004 **ÉCOLE DES HAUTES ÉTUDES INTERNATIONALES**
4, place Saint-Germain-des-Prés, 75006 Paris
Telephone: 42-22-68-06
Fax: 45-44-88-30
Administrateur général: Pascal Chaigneau

Journalism
Founded 1899.
Arrangements for co-operation with: University of Wisconsin; University of Columbia; University of Namibia; Universidad Simón Bolívar, Caracas; University of Seoul; Institute for Strategic Studies, Beijing.
Academic Year: November to June (November-February; March-June).
Admission Requirements: Secondary school certificate (baccalauréat).
Fees (Francs): 8500 per annum.
Language of Instruction: French.
Degrees and Diplomas: Certificat, 1 yr; Diplôme de l'Ecole, 2 yrs; Diplôme de Formation supérieure, 3 yrs, and thesis.
Academic Staff, 1989-90: c. 40.
Student Enrolment, 1989-90:

	Men	Women	Total
Of the country	33	22	55
Of other countries	59	38	97
Total	92	60	152

3005 **ÉCOLE SUPÉRIEURE DE JOURNALISME**
4, place Saint-Germain-des-Prés, 75006 Paris
Telephone: 42-22-68-06
Fax: 45-44-88-30
Administrateur général: Pascal Chaigneau

Journalism
Founded 1899.
Arrangements for co-operation with: University of Wisconsin; University of Columbia; University of Namibia; Universidad Simón Bolívar, Caracas; University of Seoul; Institute for Strategic Studies, Beijing.
Academic Year: November to June (November-February; March-June).
Admission Requirements: Further 2 yrs study following secondary school certificate (baccalauréat).
Fees (Francs): 10,500 per annum.
Language of Instruction: French.
Degrees and Diplomas: Certificat, 1 yr; Diplôme de l'Ecole, 2 yrs; Diplôme de Formation supérieure, 3 yrs, and thesis.
Academic Staff, 1989-90: c. 40.
Student Enrolment, 1989-90:

	Men	Women	Total
Of the country	52	68	120
Of other countries	23	25	48
Total	75	93	168

3006 **FONDATION DES JOURNALISTES DE DEMAIN**
6, rue Ancelle, 92525 Neuilly-sur-Seine
Telephone: (1) 46-24-01-23

3007 **ÉCOLE FRANÇAISE LIBRE DES ATTACHÉS DE PRESSE**
61, rue Pierre-Charron, 75008 Paris
Telephone: (1) 43-59-07-79

Press and Public Relations
Branch at Lyon.
Founded 1961 as a private institution.
Academic Year: October to June (October-January; January-April; April-June).
Admission Requirements: Secondary school certificate (baccalauréat).
Language of Instruction: French.
Degrees and Diplomas: Diplôme, 3 yrs.
Publication: Contact (monthly).
Academic Staff: c. – (350).
Student Enrolment: c. 910 (Also c. 120 external students).

3008 **CENTRE DE FORMATION ET DE PERFECTIONNEMENT DES JOURNALISTES**
33, rue du Louvre, 75002 Paris
Telephone: (1) 45-08-86-71

Journalism
Founded 1946, recognized by the State 1962. Governing body: Conseil d'administration.
Academic Year: September to June (September-December; January-March; April-June).
Admission Requirements: Competitive entrance examination at level of first degree (Licence).
Language of Instruction: French. Knowledge of English obligatory.
Degrees and Diplomas: Certificat–d'Aptitude à la profession de Journaliste; d'études pratiques de Journalisme, 3 yrs.
Library: c. 3000 vols.
Publications: Feuillets du Centre de Formation des Journalistes; Europ (6 times a year).
Academic Staff: c. 10 (160).
Student Enrolment: c. 140.

3009 **ÉCOLE LIBRE DE MARKETING ET DE PUBLICITÉ**
61, rue Pierre Charron, 75008 Paris
Telephone: (1) 43-59-07-79

3010 **INSTITUT SUPÉRIEUR INTERNATIONAL DU PARFUM, DE LA COSMÉTIQUE ET DE L'AROMATIQUE ALIMENTAIRE (ISIPCA)**
International Institute of Perfumery, Cosmetics and Food Flavourings
18, rue Mansart, 78000 Versailles
Telephone: 39-54-85-82
Directeur: Guy Haasser (1984-)

Perfume and Cosmetic Techniques
Food Flavourings
Founded 1969, acquired present status and title 1984. Administered by the Val d'Oise-Yvelines Chamber of Commerce and Industry.
Academic Year: September to July.
Admission Requirements: University degree (D.E.U.G., D.U.T., or B.T.S.), or foreign equivalent.
Fees (Francs): 35,000 per annum.
Language of Instruction: French.
Degrees and Diplomas: Diplôme, 2 yrs.
Academic Staff, 1990: – (53).
Student Enrolment, 1986-87:

	Men	Women	Total
Of the country	11	34	45
Of other countries	5	4	9
Total	16	38	54

3011 **INSTITUT LIBRE D'ÉTUDES SUPÉRIEURES DE LA CÔTE D'AZUR**
37, rue d'Antibes, 06400 Cannes
Telephone: 93-43-43-82

3012 **INSTITUT LIBRE D'ÉTUDES DES RELATIONS INTERNATIONALES**
12, rue des Saints-Pères, 75006 Paris
Telephone: (1) 42-96-51-48

International Studies
Founded 1948 as Institut international d'Etudes et de Recherches diplomatiques, became Institut d'Etudes des Relations internationales contemporaines et de Recherches diplomatiques 1963, present title adopted 1972. Governing bodies: the Conseil d'administration, comprising 19 members; the Comité de direction.
Academic Year: October to June (October-February; February-June).

Admission Requirements: Secondary school certificate (baccalauréat) or equivalent.

Fees (Francs): 15,000 per annum.

Language of Instruction: French.

Degrees and Diplomas: Certificat d'Etudes diplomatiques, 1 yr. Diplôme d'Etudes supérieures, 3 yrs. Diplôme supérieur de Recherche, 1 further yr and thesis.

Academic Staff, 1986-87: – (65).

Student Enrolment, 1986-87: 700.

3013 **ÉCOLE SUPÉRIEURE DES PROFESSIONS IMMOBILIÈRES**

2, Impasse du Mont-Tonnerre, 75015 Paris
Telephone: (1) 47-83-48-75
Fax: (1) 42-73-19-85
Directeurs: MM. Duriez et Baronnie

Estate Agent Studies

Recognized by the State 1985.

Academic Year: October to May (October-June; September-May).

Admission Requirements: Secondary school certificate (baccalauréat) and entrance examination.

Fees (Francs): 21,000 per annum.

Language of Instruction: French.

Degrees and Diplomas: Certificat, 2 yrs.

Academic Staff, 1989-90: 31.

Student Enrolment, 1989-90: c. 200.

3014 **ÉCOLE NOUVELLE D'ORGANISATION ÉCONOMIQUE ET SOCIALE**

62, rue de Miromesnil, 75008 Paris
Telephone: (1) 45-22-53-86
Président: Michel Frybourg
Secrétaire général: Michel Ohayon

D. of Business Administration
Director: Claude Martin; *staff* 2 (40)
D. of Accountancy
Director: Salvador Ballada; *staff* 6 (100)
D. of Transport Services
Director: Jean-Claude Pourteau; *staff* 3 (50)

Founded 1937.

Academic Year: September to June.

Admission Requirements: Secondary school certificate (baccalauréat) or university degree or professional qualifications.

Fees (Francs): 17,250-20,000 per annum.

Degrees and Diplomas: Diplomas, 1-3 yrs.

Student Enrolment, 1989-90: 740 (Also 500 exchange students).

3015 **INSTITUT POLYTECHNIQUE DE SCIENCES APPLIQUÉES**

12, rue Béranger, 75003 Paris
Telephone: (1) 42-72-95-03

3016 **COLLÈGE DES SCIENCES SOCIALES ET ÉCONOMIQUES**

14, rue Monsieur-le-Prince, 75006 Paris
Telephone: (1) 43-29-70-50

3017 **ÉCOLE SUPÉRIEURE POUR LE DÉVELOPPEMENT ÉCONOMIQUE ET SOCIAL (ESDES)**

29, rue du Plat, 69002 Lyon
Telephone: 72-32-50-48
Fax: 72-32-50-19
Directeur: Dominique Moreau
Directeur adjoint: Bernard Rimaud

D. of Financial Management
Heads: Pascale Vergnais; Yves Bouzit
D. of Quantitative Analysis
Head: Hervé Eynard
D. of Economics and Social Sciences
Head: Hélène Mescheriakoff
D. of Human Resources Management
Heads: Fabienne Levy; Henri Lapierre
D. of Marketing
Head: Fabienne Gautrot
D. of Languages and Communication
Heads: Roger Miller; Jean Bianchi; Jean-Jacques Paquette; Dominique Moreau
D. of Adult Education
Director: Bernard Devert

Founded 1987, replacing the Institut de Sciences sociales appliquées. Attached to the Université catholique de Lyon. Residential facilities for students.

Arrangements for co-operation with the Sunderland Polytechnic Business School.

Academic Year: October to June (October-December; January-March; April-June).

Admission Requirements: Secondary school certificate (baccalauréat) or equivalent.

Fees (Francs): 9000-20,000 per annum.

Language of Instruction: French.

Academic Staff: c. 5 (20).

Student Enrolment, 1990-91: c. 175.

3018 **INSTITUT DE SOCIOLOGIE**

25, rue du Plat, 69005 Lyon
Telephone: 78-42-10-30

Sociology

Founded 1953. Attached to the Facultés Catholiques de Lyon.

Academic Year: October to June.

Admission Requirements: Secondary school certificate (baccalauréat).

Language of Instruction: French.

Academic Staff: c. 5 (5).

Student Enrolment: c. 60.

3019 **INSTITUT D'ÉTUDES SOCIALES**

21, rue d'Assas, 75270 Paris Cedex 06
Telephone: (1) 42-22-41-80
Directeur: P. Denis Maugenest, S.J.

Social Studies
Religious Sociology

Founded 1925. Attached to the Institut Catholique de Paris.

Arrangements for co-operation with Université St. Joseph, Beyrouth.

Academic Year: October to June (October-February; February-June).

Admission Requirements: Secondary school certificate (baccalauréat) or equivalent.

Fees (Francs): 3500 per annum.

Language of Instruction: French.

Degrees and Diplomas: Diplôme, 2 yrs. Licence, 3 yrs. Maîtrise, 1 further yr. Doctorat en Sciences Sociales, a further 4 yrs andthesis.

Academic Staff, 1986-87: 3 (41).

Student Enrolment, 1986-87:

Of the country	52
Of other countries	58
Total	110*

*Also 140 external students.

3020 **ÉCOLE DES HAUTES ÉTUDES POLITIQUES ET SOCIALES**

4, place Saint-Germain-des-Prés, 75006 Paris
Telephone: (1) 42-22-68-06
Fax: 45-44-88-30
Administrateur général: Pascal Chaigneau

Social and Political Studies

Founded 1899.

Arrangements for co-operation with: University of Wisconsin; University of Columbia; University of Namibia; Universidad Simón Bolívar, Caracas; University of Seoul; Institute for International Strategic Studies, Beijing.

Academic Year: November to June (November-February; March-June).

Admission Requirements: Secondary school certificate (baccalauréat).

Fees (Francs): 8500 per annum.

Language of Instruction: French.

Degrees and Diplomas: Certificat, 1 yr; Diplôme de l'Ecole, 2 yrs; Diplôme de Formation supérieure, 3 yrs, and thesis.

Academic Staff, 1989-90: c. 40.
Student Enrolment, 1989-90:

	Men	Women	Total
Of the country	37	24	61
Of other countries	41	38	79
Total	78	62	140

3021 **ÉCOLE PRATIQUE DE SERVICE SOCIAL**
139, boulevard du Montparnasse, 75006 Paris
Telephone: (1) 43-22-44-97
Directrice: Antoinette Lang-Crouzet (1979-)

Social Service
Lifelong Education

Founded 1913. A private institution recognized by the State 1921 and responsible to the Ministry of Social Affairs and Solidarity. Governing body: the Conseil d'administration.

Academic Year: September to June (September-December; January-March; April-June).

Admission Requirements: Secondary school certificate (baccalauréat) or equivalent.

Fees (Francs): 620 per annum.

Language of Instruction: French.

Degrees and Diplomas: Diplôme d'Etat d'Assistant(e) de Service social (D.E.A.S.), 3 yrs. Maîtrise en Travail social, 2 yrs. Diplôme supérieur en Travail social.

Academic Staff, 1986-87: 6 (2).
Student Enrolment, 1986-87:

	Men	Women	Total
Of the country	8	180	188
Of other countries	–	2	2
Total	8	182	190

3022 **ÉCOLE NATIONALE DE SERVICE SOCIAL DE LA SÉCURITÉ SOCIALE**
53bis, rue Boussingault, 75013 Paris
Telephone: (1) 45-89-62-49

Social Service

Founded 1947. Administered by the Conseil d'administration de la Fédération Nationale des Organismes de Sécurité sociale.

Academic Year: October to September (October-December; January-March; April-June; July-September).

Admission Requirements: Secondary school certificate (baccalauréat) or equivalent, and entrance examination.

Language of Instruction: French.

Degrees and Diplomas: State diplomas of–Infirmier (Infirmière), 2 yrs; Assistant(e) social(e), 3 yrs.

Academic Staff: c. 40.
Student Enrolment: c. 130.

3023 **ÉCOLE TECHNIQUE DES SURINTENDANTES D'USINES ET DE SERVICES SOCIAUX**
8, villa du Parc Montsouris, 75014 Paris
Telephone: (1) 45-65-00-70
Directrice: E. Leplay (1976-)
Délégué à la gestion: Jean-Claude Lisembard

Industrial Social Service

Founded 1917. Recognized and financially supported by the Ministries of Education and Social Affairs and Employment. Governing body: the Conseil d'administration, comprising 25 members.

Academic Year: September/January to June/December (September/January-December/March; January/April-March/June; April/September-June/December).

Admission Requirements: Secondary school certificate (baccalauréat) or equivalent.

Fees (Francs): 500-10,000.

Language of Instruction: French.

Degrees and Diplomas: Diplôme d'Etat d'Assistant(e) de Service social, 3 yrs; Diplôme de Surintendant(e) d'Usines et de Services sociaux, a further 3 yrs; Diplôme supérieur en Travail social, 3 yrs. Diplôme d'Etat aux Fonctions d'Animation.

Library: c. 5560 vols.

Publication: Bulletin de l'Association des Surintendantes d'Usines et de Services sociaux (annually).

Academic Staff, 1986-87: 2 (110).
Student Enrolment, 1986-87:

Men	Women	Total
34	316	350

3024 **ÉCOLE DE SECRÉTARIAT BILINGUE ET TRILINGUE**
60, boulevard Vauban, 59046 Lille Cedex
Telephone: 20-30-88-27
Directeur: Jean-Marie Dejonghe (1975-)

Bilingual and Trilingual Secretarial Studies
Lifelong Education

Founded 1961. Attached to the Fédération Universitaire Polytechnique de Lille. Governing body: the Conseil d'administration. Residential facilities for students.

Arrangements for co-operation with Heriot-Watt University, Edinburgh.

Academic Year: October to June (October-December; January-March; April-June).

Admission Requirements: Secondary school certificate (baccalauréat), or foreign equivalent.

Fees (Francs): 6300 per annum.

Language of Instruction: French, English, German, Spanish.

Degrees and Diplomas: Title of Secrétaire de Direction bilingue ou trilingue, 3 yrs. Also Brevet de Technicien supérieur (B.T.S.).

Academic Staff, 1986-87: 1 (22).
Student Enrolment, 1986-87:

	Women
Of the country	176
Of other countries	3
Total	179

3025 **ÉCOLE SUPÉRIEURE DE TRADUCTEURS, INTERPRÈTES ET CADRES DU COMMERCE EXTÉRIEUR**
60, boulevard Vauban, 59046 Lille Cedex
Telephone: 20-30-88-27
Directeur: Jean-Marie Dejonghe (1975-)

Translation
Interpretation (English, German, Spanish)
International Commerce

Founded 1961. Attached to the Fédération Universitaire et Polytechnique de Lille. Responsible to the Ministry of Education. Governing body: the Conseil d'administration. Residential facilities for students.

Academic Year: October to May (October-December; January-March; April-May).

Admission Requirements: First university qualification following secondary school certificate (baccalauréat).

Fees (Francs): 7000 per annum.

Languages of Instruction: English, German, Spanish and French.

Degrees and Diplomas: Brevets de–Technicien supérieur; Traducteur commercial (State diploma); Traducteur-Interprète et Cadre duCommerce extérieur (private diploma), 2 yrs; Traducteur-Interprète.

Academic Staff, 1986-87: 1 (14).
Student Enrolment, 1986-87:

	Men	Women	Total
Of the country	6	93	99
Of other countries	8	14	22
Total	14	107	121

3026 **INSTITUT SUPÉRIEUR D'INTERPRÉTATION ET DE TRADUCTION**
21, rue d'Assas, 75270 Paris Cedex 06
Telephone: (1) 42-22-33-16
Directrice: Françoise de Dax (1980-)

Interpretation
Translation (English, German, Spanish)

Founded 1957 and was attached to the Institut Catholique de Paris. Became an autonomous institution 1969. Governing bodies: the Conseil d'administration; the Commission d'orientation. Residential facilities for students.

Academic Year: October to May (October-January; January-May).

Admission Requirements: Competitive entrance examination following secondary school certificate (baccalauréat), or foreign equivalent.

Fees (Francs): 8500-13,100.

Languages of Instruction: English, German, Spanish, and French.

Degrees and Diplomas: Diplôme général de l'Institut, bilingue ou trilingue, 4 yrs. Diplômes de spécialisation. Diplôme spécial d'Interprète de conférences, 1-2 yrs.

Library: Central Library, 2800 vols.

Academic Staff, 1986-87: – (88).

Student Enrolment, 1986-87:

	Men	Women	Total
Of the country	41	463	504
Of other countries	10	71	81
Total	51	534	585*

*Also 27 external students.

FRENCH POLYNESIA

3027 ***UNIVERSITÉ FRANÇAISE DU PACIFIQUE**
B.P. 4635, Papeete, Tahiti
Telephone: (689) 421680
Fax: (689) 410131

D. of Law
Head: Yves Brard; *staff* 7 (10)
D. of Science
Head: Christian Herbaut; *staff* 12 (17)
D. of Languages
Dean: Sylvie André; *staff* 8 (12)

Founded 1987. The University consists of Centres universitaires in Tahiti and Nouméa.

Academic Year: September to July.

Admission Requirements: Secondary school certificate (baccalauréat) and entrance examination.

Fees (Francs C.F.P.): 17,000 per annum.

Language of Instruction: French.

Degrees and Diplomas: Diplôme d'études universitaire générales (D.E.U.G), 2 yrs. Licence, a further 1 yr. Maîtrise, 1 yr after Licence. Diplôme détudes approfondies (D.E.A.), 1 yr after Maîtrise.

Academic Staff, 1989-90: 58 (86).

Student Enrolment, 1989-90: 1125.

GABON

3028 ***UNIVERSITÉ OMAR BONGO**

Boulevard Léon M'ba, B.P. 13.131, Libreville
Telex: UNG 5336 GØ
Telephone: 73-25-06
Recteur: Moïse Oliveira

F. of Law
F. of Letters and Human Sciences (including Sociology)
Ce. for Health Sciences (Medicine)
S. of Education
S. of Forestry and Hydraulics
S. of Technical Teacher Training
S. of Management Studies

Founded 1970 and incorporating institutions previously part of the Fondation de l'Enseignement supérieur en Afrique centrale. Renamed 1978. A State institution enjoying financial autonomy with some aid from France. Residential facilities for academic staff and students.

Arrangements for co-operation with universities in France.

Academic Year: October to June (October-December; January-Easter; Easter-June).

Admission Requirements: Secondary school certificate (baccalauréat) or equivalent, or entrance examination.

Language of Instruction: French.

Degrees and Diplomas: Diplôme universitaire d'études scientifiques (D.U.E.S.); Diplôme universitaire d'études littéraires (D.U.E.L.); Diplôme universitaire d'études économiques (D.U.E.E.); Diplôme universitaire d'études juridiques (D.U.E.J.), 2 yrs. Licence–ès Lettres, 3 yrs; ès Sciences économiques, 4 yrs. Maîtrise ès Lettres, 1 yr after Licence. Doctorat d'Etat en Médecine. Diplôme d'Ingénieur.

Libraries: Central Library, *c.* 12,000 vols; libraries of the faculties and schools.

Publication: Annales.

Academic Staff: c. 300.

Student Enrolment: c. 2400.

3029 **UNIVERSITÉ DES SCIENCES ET TECHNIQUES DE MASUKU**

B.P. 901.913, Franceville
Recteur : Vincent Mintsa-Mi-Eya

F. of Science
S. of Engineering

Founded 1986, incorporating faculty and school of Université Omar Bongo.

Degrees and Diplomas: Diplôme universitaire d'études scientifiques (D.U.E.S.), 2 yrs. Maîtrise en Sciences. Diplôme d'Ingénieur.

Academic Staff: c. 110.

Student Enrolment: c. 550.

GERMANY*
(East)

Universities and Technical Universities

3030 ***HUMBOLDT-UNIVERSITÄT ZU BERLIN**
Humboldt University of Berlin
Unter den Linden 6, 1086 Berlin
Telex: 112-833
Telephone: 20930
Rektor: Henick Finck

Sec. of Marxism-Leninism
Director: Herbert Steininger
Sec. of Theory and Organization of Science
Director: Dieter Schulze
Sec. of Foreign Languages
Director: Helga Wüsteneck
Sec. of Physical Education
Director: Margot Budzisch
Sec. of Mathematics
Director: Herbert Frank
Sec. of Physics
Director: Robert Keiper
Sec. of Chemistry
Director: Dieter Kreysig
Sec. of Biology
Director: Horst Göring
Sec. of Geography
Director: Inge Paulukat
Sec. of Animal Husbandry and Veterinary Medicine
Director: Ernst Lindemann
Sec. of Horticulture
Director: Eberhard Rempel
Sec. of Plant Production
Director: Willi Breunig
Sec. of Psychology
Director: Klaus-Peter Timpe
Sec. of Aesthetics and Arts
Director: Norbert Krenzlin
Sec. of Marxist-Leninist Philosophy
Director: Anneliese Greise
Sec. of History
Director: Adolf Rüger
Sec. of Law
Director: J. Göring
Sec. of Criminology
Director: Ehrenfried Stelzer
Sec. of Economics
Director: Johannes Gurtz
Sec. of Education
Director: Eberhard Mannschatz
Sec. of German Studies
Director: Peter Müller
Sec. of Slavonic Studies
Director: Eduard Bayer
Sec. of English and American Studies
Director: Christopher Müller
Sec. of Romance Studies
Director: Hans-Dieter Paufler
Sec. of Asian Studies
Director: Diethelm Wiedemann
Sec. of Electronics
Director: Henry Langer
Sec. of Theology (Protestant)
Director: Heinrich Fink
Sec. of Rehabilitation and Communications Science
Director: Klaus-Peter Becker
Sec. of Nutrition and Food Technology
Director: Günter Westphal
Control and Computer Ce.
Director: Jan Grabowski
I. of Library Science
Director: Helmut Kubitschek
I. of Marxist-Leninist Sociology
Director: Arthur Meier
D. of Medicine (including Dentistry) (Charité)

Founded 1810 as Friedrich-Wilhelms-Universität. Reorganized 1946 and renamed 1948 Humboldt-Universität zu Berlin. Faculty structure replaced under 1968 reform by series of subject sections. The university is responsible to the Ministry of Higher and Professional Education. Governing bodies: the Konzil; the Gesellschaftliche Rat (Social Council); the Wissenschaftliche Rat (Academic Council) and Senate; and a Rat (Council) for each section. The academic staff, the students and non-academic employees are represented on all governing bodies. The Social Council and the section councils also include representatives of public life. Residential facilities for 7500 students.

Arrangements for co-operation with more than 70 universities including: Moscow State University; Charles University Prague; Universities of Warsaw; Beijing; Athens; Rome; Madrid; 2 American, 7 Japanese, and 7 French universities.

Academic Year: September to July (September-February; February-July).

Admission Requirements: Secondary school certificate (Reifezeugnis) or equivalent.

Fees: None.

Language of Instruction: German.

Degrees and Diplomas: Diplom in various fields, 4 yrs except Medicine, 6 yrs. Doktor, Dr. (Doctorate, first level, in a particular field) by thesis, a further 3-4 yrs. Doktor der Wissenschaften, Dr.sc. (Doctorate, second level) by thesis, 4-5yrs after Doktor, first level.

Libraries: University Library, *c.* 4,100,000 vols; 25 specialized libraries, *c.* 1,700,000.

Special Facilities (Museums, etc.): Natural History Museum.

Publications: Wissenschaftliche Zeitschrift der Humboldt Universität zu Berlin, two series (a) Gesellschafts-und Sprachwissenschaftliche Reihe; (b) Naturwissenschaftliche-Mathematische Reihe; Zeitschrift für Germanistik.

Press or Publishing House: University Publishing House.

Academic Staff, 1986-87: *c.* 5000.

Student Enrolment, 1986-87: 12,000 (Also 7000 external students).

3031 ***ERNST-MORITZ-ARNDT-UNIVERSITÄT GREIFSWALD**
Ernst Moritz Arndt University of Greifswald
Domstrasse 11, 2200 Greifswald
Telex: 031 8336
Telephone: 630
Rektor: Hans Jürgen Zobel (1990-)
Prorektor: Falko H. Hermann

F. of Mathematics and Natural Sciences
Director: Hans-Dietrich Gronau
Sec. of Physics and Electronics
Director: Alfred Rutscher
Sec. of Chemistry
Director: Gerhard Herzog

*Major changes have affected the higher education system of the country and individual institutions during the preparation of this edition. These are reflected as far as they have been communicated to IAU before 30 September 1990.

Sec. of Biology
Director: Dieter Birnbaum
Sec. of Pharmacy
Director: Peter Pflegel
Sec. of Geology
Director: Rolf Langbein
I. of Geography
Director: Jens-Uwe Gerloff
Computer Ce.
Director: Erich Peplow
F. of Philosophy
I. of German Philology
Director: Rolf Bräuer
I. of Music
Director: Lothar Höchel
I. of Arts
Director: Dieter Schwieger
I. of Educational Psychology
Director: Helmut Breuer
I. of Slavonic Studies
Director: Ulf Borgwardt
I. of English and American Studies
Director: Günter Weise
I. of Romance Studies
Director: Thiele Johannes
I. of History
Director: Konrad Fritze
I. of North European Studies
Director: Gregor Putensen
I. of Foreign Languages
Director: Herbert Barten
I. of Philosophy
Director: Hans-Christoph Rauh
I. of Economics
Sec. of Physical Education
Director: Peter Hirtz
F. of Theology
Dean: Berndt Hildebrandt
F. of Medicine (including Dentistry)
Also *c.* 30 clinics, institutes and units of the Faculty of Medicine.

Founded 1456 and confirmed by Papal Bull of Calixtus III. The university came under the control of Sweden in 1648, becoming a Prussian university in 1815. Reorganized 1946. Faculty structure replaced under 1968 reform by series of subject sections. New reforms started 1990. The university is responsible to the Ministry of Higher and Professional Education. Governing bodies: the Senate, comprising 21 members; the Councils of the Faculties, Sections and Institutes. Residential facilities for *c.* 3500 students.

Arrangements for co-operation with university institutions in: USSR; Poland; Czechoslovakia; Hungary; Yugoslavia; Sweden; Finland; France; Denmark; Nigeria.

Academic Year: September to July (September-January; February-July).

Admission Requirements: Secondary school certificate (Reifezeugnis) or equivalent.

Fees: None.

Language of Instruction: German.

Degrees and Diplomas: Diplom in various fields, 4-5 yrs, except Medicine, 6 yrs. Doktor, Dr. (Doctorate, first level, in a particular field) by thesis a further 3-4 yrs. Doktor der Wissenschaften, Dr.sc. (Doctorate, second level) by thesis, 4-5 yrs after Doktor, first level.

Libraries: University Library, *c.* 2,000,000 vols; section libraries, *c.* 700,000.

Special Facilities (Museums, etc.): Geological Collection; Anatomical Museum; Zoological Museum; Exhibition Centre; Arboretum.

Publications: Wissenschaftliche Zeitschrift der Ernst-Moritz-Arndt Universität Greifswald mit Mathematisch-Naturwissenschaftliche Reihe, Gesellschafts-und Sprachwissenschaftliche Reihe, Medizinische Reihe; Greifswalder Universitätsreden.

Academic Staff, 1990:

Rank	Full-time
Ordentliche Professoren (Lehrstuhlprofessoren)	139
Dozenten	130
Wissenschaftliches Personal	1164
Übriges Personal	1335
Total	2768

Student Enrolment, 1986-87: 3500.

3032 ***MARTIN-LUTHER-UNIVERSITÄT HALLE-WITTENBERG**

Martin Luther University of Halle-Wittenberg
Universitätsplatz 10, 4010 Halle Saale
Cables: unihall dd
Telex: 4353
Telephone: 8320
Rektor: Günther Schilling (1990-)

Sec. of History
Director: Hans-Dieter Klein; *staff* 74
Sec. of Philosophy
Director: Günther Schenk; *staff* 45
Sec. of Law
Director: Wolfgang Müller; *staff* 54
Sec. of German Language and Literature and Fine Arts
Director: Dieter Heinemann; *staff* 125 (2)
Sec. of Modern Languages and Literature
Director: Sigrid Hoppe; *staff* 96 (2)
Sec. of Foreign Languages
Director: Gustav-Adolf Krampitz; *staff* 100 (6)
Sec. of Mathematics
Director: Manfred Stern; *staff* 66 (3)
Sec. of Biological Sciences
Director: Erich Ohmann; *staff* 68 (1)
Sec. of Physics
Director: Gunnar Berg; *staff* 70
Sec. of Classical and Oriental Studies
Director: Joachim Ebert; *staff* 44
Sec. of Teacher Training (Polytechnic)
Director: Martin Kleinau
Sec. of Dentistry
Director: Fritz Taege
D. of Medicine
Director: Friedrich-Wilhelm Rath; *staff* 732 (2)
Sec. of Pharmacy
Director: Heinz-Jürgen Hahn; *staff* 49 (1)
Sec. of Agriculture
Director: Theo Wetzel; *staff* 189 (8)
Sec. of Economics
Director: Peter Zwirnmann; *staff* 124 (1)
Sec. of Education
Director: Helmut Herbig; *staff* 53 (2)
Sec. of Chemistry
Director: Karl-Heinz Bergk; *staff* 121 (2)
Sec. of Physical Education
Director: Jürgen Leirich; *staff* 70 (1)
Sec. of Theology
Director: Helmut Obst; *staff* 20
Sec. of Teacher Training
Director: Christian Hein; *staff* 41 (1)
Sec. of Dentistry
Director: Fritz Taege; *staff* 51
Sec. of Geography
Director: Erwin Mücke; *staff* 47
I. of Social Sciences
Director: Ehrenfried Galander; *staff* 70 (2)
I. for Preparation of Students Studying Abroad
Director: Georg Hagena; *staff* 92
Biotechnicum
Director: Rolf Schulze; *staff* 74 (2)
International Research Ce. for European Enlightenment
Director Ulrich Ricken; *staff* 2
Computer Ce.
Head: Johannes Krötenheerdt; *staff* 29 (1)
Also International College Holiday Course.

Universität Wittenberg founded 1502, Universität Halle founded 1694. The two institutions developed independently, but following the Napoleonic occupation Prussia was unable to support two universities, and they were merged to form one institution in 1817. Title changed to Martin-Luther-Universität in 1933. Faculty structure replaced under 1968 reform by series of subject sections. The university is responsible to the Ministry of Education and Science. Governing bodies: the Konzil; the Wissenschaftliche Rat (Academic Council) and Senate; and a Rat (Council) for each section. Theacademic staff, the students and non-academic employees are represented on all governing bodies. Residential facilities for 6429 students.

Arrangements for co-operation with the Universities of: Baghdad; ,Banja Luka; Bitola; Brussels; Coimbra; Grenoble I and II; Helsinki; Kansas; Katowice; Linz; Lille III; Lund; Madagascar; Novi Sad; Osijek; Parix VII; Roskilde; Skopje; Sussex; Stockholm; Uppsala; Zagazig; Al-Azhar University, Cairo; Comenius University, Bratislava; College of Economics, Bratislava; Chalmers Technical College, Göteberg;Academy of Economics, Katowice; Keszthely University of Agriculture; Kings University, Leuven; University Alcala de Henares Madrid; National Autonomous University of Mexico; Mongolia State University; College of Agriculture Nitra; Adam Mickiewicz University, Poznán; Academy of Physical Training, Poznań; Academy of Agriculture, Poznań; Academy of Medicine, Poznán; Academy of Physical Training, Poznán; Medical University of Szeged; Bashkir State University, Ufa; Vorenesh State University.

Academic Year: September to August (September-March; April-August).

Admission Requirements: Secondary school certificate (Reifezeugnis) or equivalent.

Fees: None.

Language of Instruction: German.

Degrees and Diplomas: Diploma in various fields, 5 yrs, except Medicine and Dentistry, 6 yrs. Doktor, Dr. (Doctorate, first level, in a particular field) by thesis, a further 3-4 yrs. Doktor der Wissenschaften, Dr.sc. (Doctorate, second level) by thesis, 4-5 yrs after Doktor, first level.

Libraries: Universitäts-und Landesbibliothek, *c.* 3,910,000 vols; Bibliothek der Deutschen-Morgenländischen-Gesellschaft, *c.* 53,000; Franckesche Stiftungen, library and archives, *c.* 300,610; institute libraries, *c.* 1,410,000.

Special Facilities (Museums, etc.): Archaeological Museum; Museum für mitteldeutsche Erdgeschichte mit Geiseltalsammlung; Zoological Collections; Botanical Garden; Julius-Kühn-Sammlung.

Publications: Wissenschaftle Zeitschrift der Martin-Luther-Universität, two series, (a) Gesellschafts-und Sprachwissenschaftliche Reihe; (b) Mathematisch-Naturwissenschatliche Reihe; Universitätszeitung; Zeitschrift Hercynia; Hallesches Jahrbuch für Geowissenschaften. Wissenschaftliche Beiträge der MLU; Arbeiten aus der Universitäts- une Landesbibliothek Sachsen-Anhalt in Halle a.d. Saale; Mitteilungen aus dem Botanischen Garten der MLU.

Press or Publishing House: Abteilung Wissenschaftspublizistik.

Academic Staff, 1989-90:

Rank	Full-time
Professoren und Dozenten	481
Wissenschaftliche Mitarbeiter	2102
Total	2582

Student Enrolment, 1989-90:

Men	Women	Total
3533	5230	8764*

*Also 666 external students.

3033 ***FRIEDRICH-SCHILLER-UNIVERSITÄT JENA**

Friedrich Schiller University of Jena

Goethe-Allee 1, 6900 Jena

Cables: Uni Jena 588634

Telephone: 820

Rektor: Ernst Schutzer (1990-)

Sec. of Social and Political Sciences
Director: Hans-Jörg Schuster; *staff* 38
Sec. of Physics
Director: Rudolf Müller; *staff* 178 (6)
Sec. of Instrument Technology
Director: Dietrich Hofmann; *staff* 91 (2)
Sec. of Mathematics
Director: Karl-Heinz Fichtner; *staff* 110 (1)
Sec. of Chemistry
Director: Dieter Klemm; *staff* 177 (4)
Sec. of Biology
Director: Siegmund Reissmann; *staff* 98 (4)
Sec. of Philosophy
Director: Dietrich Alexander; *staff* 46
Sec. of Literature and Art
Director: Heinz Hamm; *staff* 76
Sec. of Languages and Philology
Director: Fred Manthey; *staff* 86 (1)
Sec. of Education
Director: Horst Wenge; *staff* 41 (1)
Sec. of Physical Education
Director: Manfred Thiess; *staff* 71
D. of Medicine (including Dentistry)
Dean: Wolfgang Klinger; *staff* 656 (48)
Sec. of History
Director: Detlef Jena; *staff* 42 (1)
Sec. of Psychology
Director: Georg Eckardt; *staff* 25
Sec. of Economics
Director: Karl-Heinz Hoppe; *staff* 70
Sec. of Theology (Protestant)
Dean: Joachim Conrad; *staff* 19
Sec. of Law
Director: Wolfgang Bernet; *staff* 37
Sec. of Classical Studies and Anthropology
Director: Volker Riedel; *staff* 26
D. of Agricultural Science
Head: Wolfram Dorn; *staff* 6 (1)
D. of Comparative History of Conceptions
head: Ludwig Elm; *staff* 12
I. of History of Medicine and Natural Sciences
Director: Rudiger Stolz; *staff* 11 (1)
I. of Languages
Director: Friedrich Beer; *staff* 65 (2)
Computer Ce.
Director: Heinz Scheffel; *staff* 29
Medical Care Training S.
Director: Ulla Rempke; *staff* 67 (3)

Founded 1548 as academy by Kurfürst Johann Friedrich von Sachsen, became university 1558. Faculty structure replaced under 1968 reform by series of subject sections. The university is responsible to the Ministry of Higher and Professional Education. Governing bodies: the Konzil; the Wissenschaftliche Rat (Academic Council) and Senate; and a Rat (Council) for each section. Theacademic staff, the students and non-academic employees are represented on all governing bodies. Residential facilities for academic staff and students.

Arrangements for co-operation with: Bielorussian State University; Tbilisi State University; Jagiellonian University; Eötvös Loránd University; 'Al. I. Cuza' University; University 'Cyril and Methodius', Veliki Tornovo; University of Priština; Semmelweis Medical University, Budapest; University of Nice; University of Aden; University of Mosul; Universidade Eduardo Mondlane, Maputo; Pavel Josef Safarik University of Košice; University of Porto; University of Kent at Canterbury; University of Nankai; University of Erlangen-Nürnberg; University of Tübingen; University of Göttingen.

Academic Year: September to August (September-January; February-July).

Admission Requirements: Secondary school certificate (Reifezeugnis) or equivalent.

Fees: None.

Language of Instruction: German.

Degrees and Diplomas: Diplom in various fields, 5 yrs except Medicine, 6 yrs. Doktor, Dr. (Doctorate, first level in a particular field) by thesis, a further 3-4 yrs. Doktor der Wissenschaften, Dr.sc. (Doctorate, second level) by thesis, 4-5 yrs after Doktor, first level.

Library: 2,637,454 vols.

Special Facilities (Museums, etc.): Phylogenetic Museum; Ernst-Haeckel-Haus (History of Medicine and Natural Science); Botanical Garden with Goethe-Gedenkstätte; Schiller-Gedenkstätte; Herbarium; Observatory.

Publications: Wissenschaftliche Zeitschrift der Friedrich-Schiller-Universität; Jenaer Reden und Schriften; Jenaer Beiträge zur Parteiengeschichte; Georgica; Bibliographische Mitteilungen der Universitätsbibliothek, Jena.

Press or Publishing House: Alma Mater Jenensis.

Academic Staff, 1990:

Rank	
Professoren und Dozenten	361
Wissenschaftliche Mitarbeiter	1925
Total	2286

Student Enrolment, 1989:

Men	Women	Total
2861	3445	6306*

*Also 889 external students.

3034 ***UNIVERSITÄT LEIPZIG**

University of Leipzig
Karl-Marx Platz, PSF 920, 7010 Leipzig
Telex: 051 350
Telephone: 7190
Rektor: Lothar Rathmann (1975-)

Sec. of Marxism-Leninism
Director: Gerhard Wolter
Sec. of Marxist and Leninist Philosophy
Director: Martina Thom
Sec. of Scientific Communism
Director: Jürgen Kübler
Sec. of Economics
Director: Manfred Hentzschel
Sec. of History
Director: Rigoberth Günther
Sec. of Law
Director: Günter Baranowski
Sec. of Education
Director: Helmut Faust
Sec. of Psychology
Director: Harry Schröder
Sec. of Journalism
Director: Gerhard Fuchs
Sec. of German Philology
Director: Klaus Träger
Sec. of Cultural Sciences
Director: Eberhard Lippold
Sec. of Theoretical and Applied Linguistics
Director: Wolfgang Thiele
Sec. of Foreign Languages
Director: Werner Reinecke
Sec. of African and Middle East Studies
Director: Rainer Arnold
Sec. of Mathematics
Director: Horst Shumann
Sec. of Physics
Director: Wolfgang Windsch
Sec. of Chemistry
Director: Ehrenfried Butter
Sec. of Biology
Director: Günther Wagner
Sec. of Animal Husbandry and Veterinary Medicine
Director: Hans-Joachim Schwark
D. of Medicine
Director: Roland Rogos
Sec. of Dentistry
Director: Kurt Birnbaum
Sec. of Theology (Protestant)
Director: Hans Moritz
I. of Teacher Training (basic Marxism-Leninism)
Director: Horst Richter
I. of Teacher Training (Russian Language)
Director: Ulrich Böhme
I. of Interpreter Training
Director: Manfred Schubert
I. of International Studies (Law)
Director: Walter Poeggel
I. of Foreign Studies (German Language Training)
Director: Erhard Hexelschneider
I. of Tropical Agriculture and Veterinary Medicine
Director: Gunther Franke
I. of Physical Education
Director: Werner Kupper
D. for Lifelong Education
Director: Peter Kramer

Founded 1409 when German scholars withdrew from the University of Prague. The establishment of the university was confirmed by Papal Bull. Reorganized 1946. Became Karl-Marx-Universität 1953. Faculty structure replaced under 1968 reform by series of subject sections. The university is responsible to the Ministry of Higher and Professional Education. Governing bodies: the Konzil; the Gesellschaftliche Rat (Social Council); the Wissenschaftliche Rat (Academic Council) and Senate; and a Rat (Council) for each section. The academic staff, the students and non-academic employees are represented on all governing bodies. The Social Council and the section councils also include representatives of public life. Residential facilities for *c.* 8200 students.

Arrangements for co-operation with the Universities of: Kiev State; Leningrad State; Moscow State; Sofia; Olomouc; Wrocław; Ljubljana; Las Villas; Ho Chi-Minh City; Beijing (Foreign Studies); Lyon I, II; Pisa; Salonika; Leeds; Salford; Kent State; Tampere; Nijmegen Catholic; Addis Ababa; Ain Shams; Dar es Salaam; Mexico; INCCA, Colombia; Sana'a. People's University of China.

Academic Year: September to August (September-January; February-July).

Admission Requirements: Secondary school certificate (Reifezeugnis) or equivalent.

Fees: None.

Language of Instruction: German.

Degrees and Diplomas: Diplom in various fields, 4 yrs, except Medicine, Dentistry, Veterinary Medicine, Germanic Studies, and Theology, 5 yrs. Doktor, Dr., or Dr.Ing. (Doctorate, first level, in a particular field) by thesis, a further 3-4 yrs. Doktor der Wissenschaften, Dr.sc. (Doctorate, second level) by thesis, 4-5 yrs after Doktor, first level.

Library: c. 3,340,000 vols.

Special Facilities (Museums, etc.): Museums of: Musical Instruments; Egyptology.

Publications: Wissenschaftliche Zeitschrift; Beiträge zur tropischen Landwirtschaft und Veterinärmedizin (quarterly); Leipziger Universitätsreden-Neue Folge; Schriftenreihe zum Veteranenkolleg der Karl-Marx-Universität Leipzig; Beiträge zum marxistisch-leninistischen Grund-lagenstudium; Linguistische Arbeitsberichte; Theorie und Praxis des sozialistischen Journalismus; Geophysik und Geologie; Deutsch als Fremdsprache; Index seminum; UZ Karl-Marx-Universität.

Academic Staff, 1986-87: c. 4040.

Student Enrolment, 1986-87: c. 13,000 (Including 1150 foreign students).

3035 ***UNIVERSITÄT ROSTOCK**

University of Rostock
Universitätsplatz 1, 2500 Rostock
Cables: Uni rostock
Telex: 31140
Telephone: 3690
Fax: 369666
Rektor: Gerhard Maess (1990-)

Sec. of Biology
Director: L. Spannhof
Sec. of Chemistry
Director: U. Kibbel
Sec. of History
Director: M. Guntau
Sec. of Agricultural Technology
Director: K. Plötner
Sec. of Latin American Studies
Director: K.-Ch. Göthner
Sec. of Land Development and Plant Production
Director: D. Seidel
Sec. of Pedagogics and Psychology
Director: H. Hellfeldt
Sec. of Marine Technology
Director: E. Wiebeck
Sec. of Physics
Director: D. Kremp
Sec. of Socialist Business Administration
Director: H. Gustmann
Sec. of Linguistics and Literature
Director: E.-M. Müller
Sec. of Physical Education
Director: H. Sass
Sec. of Electronic Engineering
Director: S. Thamm

Founded 1419 with faculties of arts, theology, medicine and law. Moved temporarily to Greifswald and Lübeck in 15th century. Became faculty of law and economics 1923. Reorganized and reopened 1946, new faculties added. Faculty structure replaced under 1968 reform by series of subject sections. The university is responsible to the Ministry of Higher and Professional Education. Governing bodies: the Konzil; the Gesellschaftliche Rat (Social Council); the Wissenschaftliche Rat (Academic Council) and Senate; and a Rat (Council) for each section. The academic staff, the students and non-academic employees are represented on all governing bodies. The Social Council and the section councils also include representatives of public life. Residential facilities for *c.* 470 academic staff and students.

Arrangements for co-operation with Universities in: Hungary; USSR; Poland; Czechoslovakia; Yugoslavia; Cuba; Viet Nam; Bulgaria; Peru; UK; Egypt; Iraq; Venezuela; Colombia; Mexico; India; Finland; Ethiopia; Syria; U.S.A.

Academic Year: September to July (September-January; March-July).

Admission Requirements: Secondary school certificate (Reifezeugnis) or equivalent.

Fees: None.

Language of Instruction: German.

Degrees and Diplomas: Diplom in various fields, 4-5 yrs. Doktor, Dr. or Dr.Ing. (Doctorate, first level, in a particular field) by thesis, a further 3-4 yrs. Doktor der Wissenschaften, Dr.sc. (Doctorate, second level) by thesis, 4-5 yrs afterDoctorate, first level.

Libraries: c. 1,641,236 vols; specialized libraries, total, *c.* 127,175.

Publications: Wissenschaftliche Zeitschrift der Universität Rostock; (a) Gesellschaftswissenschaftliche Reihe; (b) Naturwissenschaftliche Reihe; Lateinamerikanische Reihe; Rostocker philosophische Manuskripte; Archiv der Freunde derNaturgeschichte Mecklenburgs; Wissenschaftliche Veröffentlichungen; Rostocker Universitätsreden.

Academic Staff, 1986-87: 1937.

Student Enrolment, 1986-87:

Men	Women	Total
2875	3006	5881

3036 **TECHNISCHE UNIVERSITÄT CHEMNITZ**

Technical University of Chemnitz

Strasse der Nationen 62, Chemnitz 9001

Telex: 75061 233 TU D.D.

Telephone: 6680

Rektor: F. Erfurt (1989-)

Verwaltungsdirektor: H. Kempe

D. of Mathematics
Director: H. Heckendorff; *staff* 110 (4)
D. of Physics and Electronic Engineering
Director: W. Scharff; *staff* 151 (3)
D. of Machine and Component Engineering
Director: H. Bergander; *staff* 77
D. of Metal-Cutting and Industrial Metal Processing Technology
Director: D. Tischendorf; *staff* 150 (7)
D. of Processing Technology
Director: E. Löser; *staff* 94
D. of Textile and Leather Technology
Director: R. Backmann; *staff* 102 (3)
D. of Automation Technology
Director: R. Wächter; *staff* 90
D. of Information Processing
Director: G. Witzschel; *staff* 71
D. of Enterprise Planning and Operation
Director: S. Wirth; *staff* 58
D. of Chemistry and Materials Technology
Director: G. Leonhardt; *staff* 61 (7)
D. of Economics
Director: W. Opitz; *staff* 75 (2)
D. of Philosophy and Social Science
Director: S. Menzel; *staff* 98 (2)
D. of Teacher Training
Director: C. Sachs; *staff* 54
D. of Computer Sciences
Director: K. Mätzel; *staff* 52
D. of Vocational Teacher Training
Director: W. Thomas; *staff* 67 (3)
D. Foreign Languages
Director: G. Fischer; *staff* 81

Founded 1836 as a royal trade school of Chemnitz, became college of engineering 1953 and Technische Hochschule 1963. Renamed Technische Universität 1986. The university is responsible to the Ministry of Ministry of Ecucation and Scinece. Governing bodies: the Konzil; the Gesellschaftliche Rat (Social Council); the Wissenschaftliche Rat (Academic Council) and Senate; and a Rat (Council) for each section. The academic staff, the students and non-academic employees are represented on all governing bodies. The Social Council and the section councils also include representatives of public life. Residential facilities for 5800 students.

Arrangements for co-operation with: Comenius University, Bratislava; Technical University of Bratislava; Technical University of Brno; College of Mechanical and Textile Engineering, Liberec; College of Mechanical and Electronical Engineering, Plzen; Institute for Macro-Molecular Chemistry, Prague; Institute of Physics, Prague; Charles University, Prague; Technical University of Prague; University of Helsinki; University of Patras; Polytechnic Institute of Turin; Kim Chaek University of Technology, Pyongyang; University of Mining and Metallurgy, Leoben; University of Technology, Vienna; Technical University of Czestochowa; Technical University of Cracow; Technical University Łódź; University of Łódź; Technical University of Lublin;Technical University of Szczecin; Technical University of Warsaw; Technical University of Wrocław; University of Aleppo; Institute of Industrial Automation, Madrid; Centre of Nuclear Research, Dubna; Institute for Metal Physics, Kiev; Institute for Physics, Kiev; Kiev Polytechnical Institute; Institute for Materials, Kiev; V.I. Electrical Engineering Institute, Leningrad; Textile and Light Industrial Technology, Leningrad; Institute of Computer Science of the Academy of Science, Leinigrad; Institute of Electronic Technology, Moscow; Institute of Machine Tool Engineering, Moscow; Institute of Physics of the Academy of Science, Moscow; Institute of Printing Technology, Moscow; Institute of Mechanical Engineering, Moscow; State University, Moscow; Institute of Food Technology, Moscow; Institute of Textile Technology, Moscow; Institute of Electrical Engineering, Novosibirsk; Estonian Institute for Cybernetics, Tallin; Tallin Technical University; Tartu State University; Togliatti Polytechnical Institute; Institute of Mechanical and Electrical Electrical Engineering, Sofia;Institute for Physics of Solid Substances, Sofia; Institute of Mechanical and Electrical Engineering, Varna; Central Institute for Cybernetics and Technology, Varna.

Academic Year: October to September (October-February; March-August).

Admission Requirements: Secondary school certificate (Reifezeugnis).

Fees: None.

Language of Instruction: German.

Degrees and Diplomas: Diplom or Diplom-Ingenieur in various fields, Diplom-Mathematiker, Diplom-Physiker, Diplom-Chemiker, Diplom-Kaufmann/Kauffrau, Diplom-Lehrer, diplom-Ingenieurpädagoge, 5 yrs. Doktor, Dr. Ing., Dr. rer. nat., Dr. phil., Dr. oec., Dr. paed. (Doctorate, first level), a further 4 yrs.; Doktor der Wissenschaften, Dr. sc. (Doctorate, second level) by thesis, 4-5 yrs after Doktor, first level.

Library: 700,000 vols.

Publications: Wissenschaftliche Zeitschrift der Technischen Universität Chemnitz (6 times a year); Wissenschaftliche Schriftenreihe (17 times a year); Wissenschaftliche Tagungen (10 times a year); Preprints (30 times a year).

Academic Staff, 1990:

Rank	Full-time	Part-time
Professoren	108	–
Dozenten	152	–
Wissenschaftliche mitarbeiter (Assistenten)	862	28
Lektoren, Lehrer im hochschuldienst	383	14
Total	1505	42

Student Enrolment, 1989:

Men	Women	Total
4760	2405	7165*

*Also 568 external students and students by correspondence.

3037 ***TECHNISCHE UNIVERSITÄT DRESDEN**

Technical University of Dresden

Mommsenstrasse 13, 8027 Dresden

Telex: 2278

Telephone: 463-4312

Fax: 3751 470294

Rektor: Günther Landgraf

F. of Social Sciences
Dean: Franz Pleschak
F. of Natural Sciences and Mathematics
Dean: Winfried Pippel
F. of Electrical Engineering and Electronics
Dean: Heinz Töpfer
F. of Mechanical Engineering
Dean: Werner Lotze
F. of Civil Engineering, Hydraulics, and Forestry
Dean: Hans-Joachim Fiedler
D. of Philosophy and Humanities
Director: Lothar Streibing
D. of Vocational Pedagogics
Director: Alfred Bannwitz
D. of Industrial Economics
Director: Günter Richter

D. of Physics
Director: Walter John
D. of Chemistry
Director: Hermann Scheler
D. of Mathematics
Director: Gerhard Geise
Ce. of Computer Sciences
Director: Horst Tzschoppe
D. of Information Technology
Director: Walter Cimander
D. of Biomedical and Equipment Engineering
Director: Werner Heinrich
D. of Electrical Engineering
Director: Eberhard Paulig
D. of Energy Conversion
Director: Günter Schramm
D. of Fundamentals of Mechanical Engineering
Director: Karl-Heinz Modler
D. of Manufacturing Engineering and Machine Tools
Director: Ludwig Eberlein
D. of Process Engineering
Director: Eberhard Heidenreich
D. of Automotile Engineering, Agricultural Machinery and Materials Handling Equipment
Director: Rudolf Soucek
D. of Civil Engineering
Director: Werner Reichel
D. of Architecture
Director: Eberhard Berndt
D. of Geodesy and Cartography
Director: Hans Werner
D. of Water Sciences
Director: Gerhard Bollrich
D. of Forestry
Director: Klaus Fischer
D. of Labour Studies
Director: Fritjof Mielke
D. of Applied Linguistics
Director: Edgar Baumann
I. of Physical Education
Director: Hartmut Günther
I. of Law in Science and Technology
Director: Lutz Zimmermann
Computer Ce.
Director: Peter Elste

Founded 1828 as a technical college and renamed Polytechnische Schule in 1851. Raised to the rank of Technische Hochschule 1890, renamed Technische Universität 1961. The university is responsible to the Ministry of Education and Science. Governing bodies: the Wissenschaftliche Rat (Academic Council); the Senate. Residential facilities for 10,000 students.

Arrangements for co-operation with: Polytechnical Institute, Leningrad; Institute of Electrical Engineering, Leningrad; Institute of Energetics, Moscow; Institute of Agricultural Engineering, Rostov/Don; College for Mechanical and Electrical Engineering, Sofia; Technical University of Wrocław; College of Economics, Wrocław; Technical University of Warsaw; Czech Technical University, Prague; College of Mechanical and Textile Engineering, Liberec; College of Forestry and Wood Technology, Žvolen; College of Agriculture, Brno; Technical University, Budapest; College for Advanced Technology, Russe; University of Forestry and Wood Technology, Sopron; University of Agriculture, Gödöllö; Tsinghua University, Beijing; College for Advanced Technology, Havana; College for Advanced Technology, Santiago de Cuba; Technical University of Bucharest;University of Belgrade; University of Kragujevac; University of Zagreb; College of Forestry, Hanoi; Technical College, Hanoi; Universidad de Oriente, Santiago; Centro Universitario de Holguin; Centro Universitario de Pinar del Rio; University of Damascus; University of Addis Ababa; Helsinki University of Technology; Institut national polytechnique de Grenoble; University of Technology, Baghdad; University of Technology, Vienna; The Royal Institute of Technology, Stockholm; City University, London; University of Soil Science, Vienna; Indian Institute of Science, Bangalore; University of Khartoum; Autonomous University of Puebla; Technical Middle-East University, Ankara; the Dresden University of Technology. Also participates in the Rectors' Conference of the Universities and Colleges of the two German States and is its partner in co-operation.

Academic Year: September to July (September-January; February-July).

Admission Requirements: Secondary school certificate (Reifezeugnis) or equivalent.

Fees: None.

Language of Instruction: German.

Degrees and Diplomas: Diplom or Diplom-Ingenieur in various fields, 4-5 yrs. Doktor, Dr. or Dr.Ing. (Doctorate, first level, in a particular field) by thesis, a further 3-4 yrs; Doktor der Wissenschaften, Dr.sc. (Doctorate, second level) by thesis, 4-5 yrs after Doktor, first level.

Libraries: Technical Central Library; University Library; and special libraries, total, *c.* 1,300,000 vols.

Special Facilities (Museums, etc.): Forstbotanischer Garten (Tharandt); Internationale Mahn-und Gedenkstätte; Forstliche Jagd-und Lehrschau (Grillenburg); Geologische Sammlung.

Publications: Wissenschaftliche Zeitschrift der Technischen Universität Dresden: Gesellschaftswissenschaften; Sozialistische Betriebswirtschaft; Naturwissenschaften und Mathematik; Datenverarbeitung; Elektrotechnik; Maschinenwesen; Bau- und Wassenwesen; Forstwesen.

Academic Staff, 1990: 2900.

Student Enrolment, 1990:

	Men	Women	Total
Of the country	8500	4000	12,500
Of other countries	850	150	1000
Total	9350	4150	13,500*

Also 1900 external students.

3038 **TECHNISCHE UNIVERSITÄT MAGDEBURG**
Technical University Magdeburg
3010 Magdeburg
Cables: Magdeburg 8214
Telex: 8214
Telephone: 5920
Rektor: Reinhard Probst (1976-)

Sec. of Marxism-Leninism
Director: Wolfgang Brüser
Sec. of Socialist Industrial Economics
Director: Waldo Simmel
Sec. of Computer Sciences
Director: Franz Stuchlik
Sec. of Mathematics
Director: Horst Reichel
Sec. of Physics
Director: Heribert Stroppe
Sec. of Mechanical Engineering
Director: Felix Leistner
Sec. of Metallurgy
Director: Dieter Henring
Sec. of Thermal and Hydraulic Engineering
Director: Eberhard Aepler
Sec. of Automation and Electrical Engineering
Director: Richard Tessmer
Sec. of Chemical Equipment and Plant Construction
Director: Lothar Schuart

Founded 1953 as College of Heavy Mechanical Engineering, became Technical College 1961. Renamed Technische Universität 1987. Faculty structure replaced under 1968 reform by series of subject sections. Governing bodies: the Konzil; the Gesellschaftliche Rat (Social Council); the Wissenschaftliche Rat (Academic Council) and Senate; and a Rat (Council) for each section. The academic staff, the students and non-academic employees are represented on all governing bodies. The Social Council and the section councils also include representatives of public life. The college is responsible to the Ministry of Higher and Professional Education. Residential facilities for 4000 students.

Arrangements for co-operation with: Institute of Mechanical Engineering, Moscow; Polytechnical Institutes of Doneck and Kharkov; University of Heavy Industry, Miskolc; Technical Universities of Bratislava, Brno, Gliwice,Warsaw, Wrocław; Ecole nationale polytechnique, Alger; University of Las Villas.

Academic Year: September to July (September-January; February-July).

Admission Requirements: Secondary school certificate (Reifezeugnis) or graduate from technical college (Ingenieurschule).

Fees: None.

Language of Instruction: German.

Degrees and Diplomas: Diplom or Diplom-Ingenieur (in various fields) 4 yrs. Diplom ingenieur ökonom, 4 yrs. Doktor, Dr. or Dr.Ing. (Doctorate, first level, in a particular field) by thesis a further 3-4 yrs. Doktor der Wissenschaften, Dr.sc. (Doctorate, second level) by thesis, 4-5 yrs after Doktor, first level.

Library: c. 300,000 vols.

Publications: Scientific Journal; Technische Mechanik.

Academic Staff, 1986-87:

Rank	Full-time	Part-time
Professoren und Dozenten	166	–
Assistenten und Wissenschaftliche Mitarbeiter	614	8
Total	780	8

Student Enrolment, 1986-87:

	Men	Women	Total
Of the country	2625	1135	3760
Of other countries	91	7	98
Total	2716	1142	3858*

*Also 547 external students.

3039 **TECHNISCHE HOCHSCHULE LEUNA-MERSEBURG**

Technical University Leuna-Merseburg

Otto-Nuschke Strasse, 4200 Merseburg

Cables: Th Merseburg

Telex: 471320 THIM DD

Telephone: 460

Rektor: E. Fanghänel (1990-)

Verwaltungsdirektor: M. Scharch

D. of Philosophy and Social Sciences
Head: Ingrid Jungblut; *staff* 31
D. of Chemical Engineering
Head: Willi Neumann; *staff* 114
D. of Chemistry
Head: Karl-Heinz Thiele; *staff* 180
D. of Physics
Head: Siegfried Wartewig; *staff* 36
D. of Materials Engineering
Head: Bernd Poltersdorf; *staff* 50
D. of Economics
Head: Dieter Schönknecht; *staff* 110
D. of Mathematics
Head: Alfred Göpfert; *staff* 49
I. for Business Management
Head: Eberhard Sandmann; *staff* 34
D. of Languages
Head: Axel Satzger; *staff* 27
Research Ce. for Industrial Chemical Engineering
Head: Siegfried Weiss; *staff* 35
Computer Ce.
Head: Wolfram Weiss; *staff* 18

Founded 1954. Faculty structure replaced under 1968 reform by series of subject sections. The university is responsible to the Ministry of Education and Science. Governing bodies: the Konzil; the Wissenschaftliche Rat (Academic Council) and Senate; and a Rat (Council) for each section. Theacademic staff, the students and non-academic employees are represented on all governing bodies. Residential facilities for 3260 students.

Arrangements for co-operation with: Institute of Technology, Leningrad; Institute of Chemical Technology, Kazan; Technical University of Bratislava; College of Chemical Technology, Prague; College of Chemical Technology, Pardubice; Technical University of Silesia; Institute of Chemical Technology, Bourgas; Veszprém Technical University of Chemical Engineering; Institute of Chemical Technology, Moscow; University of Homs; Centro Nacional de Investigaciones Cientificas, La Habana.

Academic Year: September to August (September-January; January-August).

Admission Requirements: Secondary school certificate (Reifezeugnis) or graduation from technical college (Ingenieurschule).

Language of Instruction: German.

Degrees and Diplomas: Diplom or Diplom-Ingenieur in various fields, 4-5 yrs. Doktor, Dr. or Dr.Ing. (Doctorate, first level, in a particular field)–Dr.rer.nat., natural sciences; Dr.Ing., engineering; Dr.oec., economics, by thesis, a further 3-4 yrs. Doktor der Wissenschaften, Dr.sc. (Doctorate, second level) by thesis, 4-5 yrs after Doktor, first level.

Library: 206,000 vols.

Publication: Wissenschaftliche Zeitschrift der Technischen Hochschule 'Carl Schorlemmer' Leuna-Merseburg.

Press or Publishing House: University News 'TH-Echo' (14 tägig).

Academic Staff, 1990:

Rank	Full-time
Professoren	78
Dozenten	81
Oberassistenten	125
Lektoren	50
Lehrer im Hochschuldienst	61
Assistenten	265
Total	660

Student Enrolment, 1990:

	Men	Women	Total
Of the country	1170	1470	2640
Of the countries	150	25	175
Total	1320	1495	2815

3040 ***BERGAKADEMIE FREIBERG**

Freiberg Mining Academy

Akademiestrasse 6, 9200 Freiberg

Cables: Akademie Freiberg

Telex: 785035 BAF

Telephone: 510

Fax: 2195

Rektor: Horst Gerhardt (1988-)

Verwaltungsdirektor: Peter Hauk

Sec. of Social Sciences
Head: Herbert Bernhardt; *staff* 31 (1)
Sec. of Mathematics
Head: Dieter König; *staff* 43 (4)
Sec. of Physics
Head: Jochen Monecke; *staff* 54 (14)
Sec. of Chemistry
Head: Horst Holldorf; *staff* 125 (34)
Sec. of Earth Sciences
Head: Roland Wienholz; *staff* 125 (30)
Sec. of Geology and Mining
Head: Armin Krausse; *staff* 145 (19)
Sec. of Processing Technology and Silicate Industry
Head: Wikfgang Schulle; *staff* 162 (30)
Sec. of Metallurgy and Foundry Engineering
Head: Werner Tilch; *staff* 137 (31)
Sec. of Material Sciences
Head: Heinz-Joachim Spies; *staff* 111 (21)
Sec. of Mechanical and Power Engineering
Head: Peter Költzsch; *staff* 148 (15)
Sec. of Economics
Head: Dieter Slaby; *staff* 65 (11)
I. of Enterprise Management
Head: Gerhard Scharf; *staff* 21 (3)
I. of Foreign Languages
Head: Ludwig Dobberitz; *staff* 3 (4)
I. of Sports
Head: Rainer Victor; *staff* 19 (3)
Computer Ce.
Head: Gerhard Bergholz; *staff* 44 (5)
Also Summer School 'German for Foreigners'.

Founded 1765, acquired university status 1905. Reopened 1946, Workers and Peasants Faculty added 1949 and Correspondence Department 1950. Faculty structure replaced under 1968 reform by series of subject sections. The academy is responsible to the Ministry of Education and Science. Governing bodies: the Konzil; the Gesellschaftliche Rat (Social Council); the Wissenschaftliche Rat (Academic Council); and Senate; and a Rat (Council) for each section. The academic staff, the students and non-academic employees are represented on all governing bodies. The Social Council and the section councils also include representatives of public life. Residential facilities for students.

Arrangements for co-operation with universities and colleges in: USSR, Czechoslovakia, Poland, Bulgaria, Hungary, Romania, Yugoslavia, Cuba, Mongolia, Austria, Finland, Sweden, and Bolivia.

Academic Year: September to August (September-January; February-July).

Admission Requirements: Secondary school certificate (Reifezeugnis) or equivalent. Following adoption of the West German University Law (Hochschulrahmengesetz), admission is granted in accordance with this law.

Fees: None.
Language of Instruction: German.
Degrees and Diplomas: Diplom or Diplom-Ingenieur in various fields, 4-5 yrs. Doktor, Dr. or Dr.Ing. (Doctorate, first level, in a particular field). Doktor der Wissenschaften, Dr.sc. (Doctorate, second level)–Dr.sc.techn.; Dr.sc.nat.; Dr.sc.oec., by thesis, 4-5 yrs after Doctorate, first level.
Library: 525,524 vols.
Special Facilities (Museums, etc.): Mineralogical Collection.
Publications: Freiberger Forschungshefte, parts A, B, C, D; Veröffentlichungen der Bergakademie.
Academic Staff, 1990:

Rank	Full-time
Professoren	83
Dozenten	78
Total	161

Student Enrolment, 1989-90:

	Men	Women	Total
Of the country	2135	1192	3327
Of the countries	155	18	173
total	2290	1210	3500*

*Also 111 external students.

3041 **HOCHSCHULE FÜR ARCHITEKTUR UND BAUWESEN WEIMAR**
College of Architecture and Building, Weimar
Geschwister-Scholl-Strasse 8, 5300 Weimar
Telex: 618950
Telephone: 730
Rector: Hans-Ulrich Mönnig (1988-)

Sec. of Architecture
Director: Gerhard Lindner
Sec. of Civil Engineering
Director: Gerhard Burkhardt
Sec. of Material Processing Techniques
Director: Reinhard Schmidt
Sec. of Data Processing and Mathematics
Director: Reinhardt Hübler
Sec. of Town and Regional Planning
Director: Gerold Kind
I. of Town Planning and Architecture
Director: Gerhard Kaspari
D. of Foreign Languages
Director: Wolfgang Kreiter
D. of Physical Education
Director: Werner Dohl
D. of Social Sciences
Director: Christine Weiske
Research Ce. of Industrial and Special Construction
Director: Erhard Hampe

Founded 1860 as academy of fine arts, applied arts added 1907, became college 1926. Applied arts detached 1950. Reorganized 1954 and granted full university status. Faculty structure replaced under 1968 reform by series of subject sections. The college is responsible to the Ministry of Education and Science. Governing bodies: the Konzil; the Senate; and a Rat (Council) for each section. The academic staff, the students and non-academic employees are represented on all governing bodies. The Social Council and the section councils also includerepresentatives of public life. Residential facilities for 2500 students.

Arrangements for co-operation with: Institute of Civil Engineering, Moscow; Institute of Civil Engineering, Vilnius; Institute of Civil Engineering, Kiev; College of Engineering, Zielona Gora; Technical University, Lublin; University of Bratislava; Mihály Pollack College of Engineering, Pécs; University of Havana; University of Venice; University of Aleppo; Tampere University of Technology; Ecole d'Architecture, Paris; Technical University of Graz; Technical University of Prague; College of Building Engineering, Budapest; Moscow Institute of Architecture; Trùong dai Hoc Xay Dung, Hanoi.

Academic Year: September to August (September-January; February-July).
Admission Requirements: Secondary school certificate (Reifezeugnis) or graduation from technical college (Ingenieurschule).
Fees: None.
Language of Instruction: German.
Degrees and Diplomas: Diplom-Ingenieur in various fields, 4 ½-5 yrs. Doctor, Dr. or Dr.Ing. (Doctorate, first level, in a particular field) by thesis, a further 3-4 yrs. Doktor der Wissenschaften, Dr.sc. (Doctorate, second level) by thesis,4-5 yrs after Doktor, first level.
Library: College Library, *c.* 240,000 vols.
Publication: Wissenschaftliche Zeitschrift.
Academic Staff, 1990: 545.
Student Enrolment: *c.* 2500.

3042 **TECHNISCHE HOCHSCHULE LEIPZIG**
Technical University of Leipzig
Karl Liebknecht-Strasse 132, 7030 Leipzig
Cables: Tehael
Telex: 552
Telephone: 39280
Rektor: Wolfgang Altner (1980-)

Sec. of Marxism-Leninism
Director: Heinz Brass
Sec. of Mathematics and Computer Technology
Director: Hans-Jürgen Sebastian
Sec. of Building Technology
Director: Stefan Roehling
Sec. of Constructional Engineering
Director: Wolfgang Wittig
Sec. of Automation (including Cybernetics)
Director: Werner Richter
Sec. of Electrical Engineering Systems
Director: Siegfried Altmann
Sec. of Polygraphic Arts
Director: Thomas Helbig
Sec. of Natural Sciences
Director: Hartmut Baumbach
Sec. of Socialist Factory Management
Director: Roland Hofmann
I. of Socialist Economics
Director: Reimar Hiller
Industrial I.
Director: Wilma Merkel
D. of Foreign Languages
D. of Physical Education

Founded 1977, incorporating Hochschule für Bauwesen, founded 1954 and Ingenieurhochschule Leipzig, founded 1969. The university is responsible to the Ministry of Higher and Professional Education. Governing body: the Wissenschaftliche Rat (Academic Council). Residential facilities for students.

Arrangements for co-operation with similar university institutions in Socialist countries.

Academic Year: September to August (September-January; February-July).
Admission Requirements: Secondary school certificate (Reifezeugnis) or equivalent.
Fees: None.
Language of Instruction: German.
Degrees and Diplomas: Diplom-Ingenieur in various fields, 4-4 ½ yrs. Diplomingenieur ökonom, 4 yrs. Doktor, Dr. or Dr.Ing. (Doctorate, first level, in a particular field) by thesis, a further 3-4 yrs. Doktor der Wissenschaften, Dr.sc. (Doctorate, second level) by thesis, 4-5 yrs after Doktor, first level.
Libraries: Central Library, 100,000 vols; Section libraries, total, 64,500.
Publication: Wissenschaftliche Zeitschrift.
Academic Staff, 1986-87:

Rank	Full-time
Professoren und Dozenten	137
Oberassistenten, Assistenten, Wissenschaftliche Sekretäre, Lektoren, Lehrer	361
Total	498

Student Enrolment: *c.* 2550

3043 **TECHNISCHE HOCHSCHULE ILMENAU**

Technical University of Ilmenau
Postschliessfach 327, 6300 Ilmenau
Cables: TH Ilmenau
Telex: 628 423
Telephone: 740
Rektor: Eberhart Köhler (1990-93)

Sec. of Mathematics, Computer Techniques, and Economic Cybernetics
Director: Frieder Hülsenberg; *staff* 122
Sec. of Technical and Biomedical Cybernetics
Director: Günther Henning; *staff* 75
Sec. of Information Techniques and Theoretical Electrical Engineering
Director: Gert Winkler; *staff* 107
Sec. of Electrical Engineering
Director: Dietrich Stade; *staff* 77
Sec. of Precision Engineering
Director: Peter Wiesner; *staff* 107
Sec. of Physics and Technology of Electronic Devices
Director: Christian Knedlik; *staff* 61
Sec. of Philosophy and Social Sciences
Director: Alfred Kirpal; *staff* 31
I. of Information Science, Patents and Rights
Director: Harald Killenberg; *staff* 18
Polytechnic for Precision Mechanics, Optics and Electronics, (Suhl)
Director: Wolfgang Holle; *staff* 16
D. of Plasma Technology (Meiningen)
Director: Wolfgang Reiss; *staff* 6
D. of Foreign Languages

Founded 1953 as Hochschule für Elektrotechnik, became Technische Hochschule 1963. Faculty structure replaced under 1968 reform by series of subject sections. The university is responsible to the Ministry of Education and Science. Governing bodies: the Konzil; the Wissenschaftliche Rat (Academic Council) and Senate; and a Rat (Council) for each section. Theacademic staff, the students and non-academic employees are represented on all governing bodies. Residential facilities for 90% of the students.

Special arrangements for scientific and technical co-operation with: Institute of Energetics, Moscow; Polytechnical Institute, Minsk; Institute of Mechanical and Electrical Engineering, Sofia; Technical University of Bratislava; University of Niš; Technical University of Budapest; College of Engineering, Zielona Góra; Xi'an Jiaotong University.

Academic Year: September to August (September-January; February-August).

Admission Requirements: Secondary school certificate (Reifezeugnis) or equivalent.

Fees: None.

Language of Instruction: German.

Degrees and Diplomas: Diplom-Ingenieur, 4 ½-5 yrs; Diplom-Mathematiker, 5 yrs; Diplom-Wirtschaftsinformatiker, 4 ½ yrs. Doktor, Dr.rer.nat., Dr. oec. or Dr.-Ing. (Doctorate, first level, in a particular field) by thesis, a further 3-4 yrs. Doktor der Wissenschaften, Dr.sc.techn. or Dr. sc.nat. (Doctorate second level) by thesis, 4-5 yrs after Doktor, first level.

Library: Central Library and Section libraries, 250,000 vols.

Publications: Wissenschaftliche Zeitschrift der Technischen Hochschule Ilmenau (quarterly); Tagungsberichte vom Internationalen Kolloquium über Information und Dokumentation der Technischen Hochschule Ilmenau (biennially); Tagungsbände des Internationalen Wissenschaftlichen Kolloquiums (annually).

Academic Staff, 1989-90:

Rank	Full-time
Professoren und Dozenten	118
Wissenschaftliche Mitarbeiter	515
Total	633

Student Enrolment, 1989-90:

Men	Women	Total
2491	395	2886*

*Also 350 external students.

3044 **HOCHSCHULE FÜR ÖKONOMIE BERLIN**

University of Economic Sciences
Hermann-Duncker-Strasse 8, 1157 Berlin
Cables: 0112850
Telephone: 5040
Rektor: Rolf Sieber

Sec. of Marxism-Leninism
Sec. of Socialist National Economics
Sec. of Foreign Economics
Sec. of Factory Management
Sec. of Management, Data Processing, and Statistics
I. of Commercial Law
I. of Economics of Developing Countries
I. of Socialist Economic Management
I. of Socialist External Economics
I. of Foreign Languages

Founded 1950 as college of economic planning, subsequently joined with colleges of economics and foreign trade to form institution of university rank 1958. Acquired present title 1972. The university is responsible to the Ministry of Higher Education. Governing bodies: the Advisory Social Council; the Scientific Council. Residential facilities for *c.* 1700 students.

Academic Year: September to August (September-January; February-July).

Admission Requirements: Secondary school certificate (Reifezeugnis) or equivalent.

Fees: None.

Language of Instruction: German.

Degrees and Diplomas: Diplomökonom, economics, 5 yrs (by correspondence, 6 yrs). Doktor, Dr. (Doctorate, first level, in a particular field) by thesis, a further 3-4 yrs. Doktor der Wissenschaften, Dr.sc. oec. (Doctorate, second level) by thesis, 4-5 years after Doktor, first level.

Library: *c.* 200,000 vols.

Publications: Wissenschaftliche Zeitschrift der Hochschule für Ökonomie (quarterly); Wissenschaftliche Mitteilungen der Sektionen und Institute.

Academic Staff: *c.* 600.

Student Enrolment: *c.* 2130 (Also *c.* 1350 external students).

3045 **AKADEMIE FÜR STAATS-UND RECHTSWISSENSCHAFT DER DDR**

Academy of Political Science and Law
August-Bebel-Strasse 89, 1502 Potsdam-Babelsberg
Telex: 15508 ASR DD
Telephone: 76701
Rektor: H. Steeger (1984-)
Verwaltungsdirektor: G. Strauss

Sec. of Marxism-Leninism
Sec. of State Law and Management
Sec. of Economic and Administrative Law
Sec. of Agricultural, Civil, Labour, and Penal Law
I. of International Relations
I. of Theory of Law
I. of Administration Studies

Founded 1948. Governing body: the Scientific Council.

Academic Year: September to August (September-December; January-August).

Admission Requirements: Secondary school certificate (Reifezeugnis).

Fees: None.

Language of Instruction: German.

Degrees and Diplomas: Diplom, 4-5 yrs. Doktor, Dr. (Doctorate, first level, in a particular field) by thesis, a further 3-4 yrs. Doktor der Wissenschaften, Dr.sc. (Doctorate, second level) by thesis, 4-5 yrs after Doktor, first level.

Library: *c.* 335,000 vols.

Publications: Staat und Recht; Deutsche Aussenpolitik; Organisation.

Academic Staff: *c.* 440.

Student Enrolment: *c.* 2310.

3046 ***HOCHSCHULE FÜR VERKEHRSWESEN DRESDEN**

College of Transport and Communications
Friedrich-List-Platz 1, 8010 Dresden
Telex: 2444
Telephone: 4620
Rektor: Horst Strobel (1990-)
Verwaltungsdirektor: Peter Bessel

D. of Traffic and Operation Economy
Director: Armin Godau; *staff* 93 (7)
D. of Vehicle Engineering
Director: Wolfgang Trebst; *staff* 81 (3)
D. of Transport Engineering
Director: Klaus Fischer; *staff* 49 (2)

D. of Transport Construction
Director: Werner Voigt; *staff* 70 (2)
D. of Mathematics and Natural Sciences
Director: Hans-Jürgen Grewolls; *staff* 47
D. of Military Transport and Communications
Director: Peter Behnisch; *staff* 40
D. of Telecommunications Engineering
Director: Heinz Stürz; *staff* 44
D. of Process Automation
Director: Wolfgang Fenner; *staff* 37
C. of Traffic
Director: Harald Schmidt; *staff* 128
I. of Trafic Sociology and Ecology
Director: Helga Gantz; *staff* 22
I. of Foreign Languages
Director: Herbert Kullik; *staff* 30
Technology Ce. for Diagnostics and Reliability
Director: Günter Oppermann; *staff* 14
I. of Transport Safety Research
Director: Rolf Ebert; *staff* 51

Founded 1952. Faculty structure replaced under 1968 reform by series of subject sections. The college is responsible to the Ministry of Education and Science. Governing bodies: the Konzil; the Gesellschaftliche Rat (Social Council); the Wissenschaftliche Rat (Academic Council) and Senate; and a Rat (Council) for each section. The academic staff, the students and non-academic employees are represented on all governing bodies. The Social Council and section councils also include representatives of publiclife. Residential facilities for 3500 students.

Arrangements for co-operation with similar institutions worldwide.

Academic Year: September to July (September-January; February-July).

Admission Requirements: Secondary school certificate (Reifezeugnis) or graduation from a technical college (Fachschule), or equivalent.

Fees: None.

Language of Instruction: German.

Degrees and Diplomas: Diplom-Ingenieur in various fields, 4 yrs. Doktor, Dr. (Doctorate, first level, in a particular field) by thesis, a further 3-4 yrs. Doktor der Wissenschaften, Dr.sc. (Doctorate, second level) by thesis, 4-5 yrs after Doktor, first level.

Library: c. 400,000 vols.

Publication: Scientific Journal (5 times a year).

Academic Staff, 1990:

Rank	Full-time	Part-time
Professoren	61	4
Hochschuldozenten	92	10
Oberassistenten/Assistenten	222	–
Lektoren/Lehrer im Hochschuldienst	120	–
Fachschullehrer	128	–
Total	623	14

Student Enrolment, 1990:

	Men	Women	Ttoal
Of the country	3674	1584	5258
Of the countries	151	41	192
total	3825	1625	5450

Other Institutions

3047 **HOCHSCHULE FÜR GRAFIK UND BUCHKUNST LEIPZIG**
College of Graphic Arts and Book Design
Dimitroffstrasse 11, 7010 Leipzig
Telephone: 3913211
Rektor: Arno Rink (1987-)

Sec. of Graphic Arts
Director: Rolf Kuhrt; *staff* 3
Sec. of Book Design
Director: Gert Wunderlich; *staff* 11
Sec. of Photography
Director: Peter Pachnicke; *staff* 10

Founded 1764 as Academy of Drawing, Painting and Architecture, acquired present status and title 1947. A Stateinstitution responsible to the Ministry of Culture. Governing body: the Artistic-Academic Council (Senate).

Academic Year: September to July (September-March; March-July).

Admission Requirements: Secondary school certificate (Reifezeugnis) or certificate from technical school.

Fees: None.

Language of Instruction: German.

Degrees and Diplomas: Diploma in a particular field, 5 yrs.

Library: c. 20,000 vols.

Academic Staff: 50.

Student Enrolment, 1990-91:

Men	Women	Total
73	38	111*

*Also 26 external students.

3048 **HOCHSCHULE FÜR INDUSTRIELLE FORMGESTALTUNG**
College of Industrial Design
Neuwerk 7, 4020 Halle-Burg Giebichenstein
Telex: HIF 4510 DD
Telephone: 8500

Sec. of Marxism-Leninism
Sec. of Basic Design
Sec. of Industrial Design
Sec. of Fine Arts and Crafts
Sec. of Extramural Studies
D. for Further Professional Training

Founded 1915 as school, acquired present status 1958. A State institution responsible to the Ministry of Culture. Residential facilities for students.

Arrangements for co-operation with similar institutions in: Cuba, Czechoslovakia, Hungary, Poland, USSR, and Viet Nam.

Academic Year: September to July (September-February; February-July).

Admission Requirements: Secondary school certificate (Reifezeugnis) or certificate from technical school.

Fees: None.

Language of Instruction: German.

Degrees and Diplomas: Diplom in a particular field, 5 yrs.

Academic Staff: c. 130.

Student Enrolment: c. 400.

3049 **KUNSTHOCHSCHULE BERLIN**
College of Fine and Applied Arts
Strasse 203, 20, 1120 Berlin-Weissensee
Telephone: 56-54-061

Sec. of Architecture
Sec. of Painting
Sec. of Sculpture
Sec. of Industrial Design
Sec. of Graphics
Sec. of Stage Design
Sec. of Fashion Design
Sec. of Textile Design
Sec. of Ceramics
Sec. of Basic Studies
Sec. of Social Sciences
Sec. of Cultural and Art Sciences

Founded 1947. A State institution responsible to the Ministry of Culture. Governing body: the Senate. Residential facilities for *c.* 90 students.

Academic Year: September to July (September-February; March-July).

Admission Requirements: Secondary school certificate (Reifezeugnis).

Fees: None.

Language of Instruction: German.

Degrees and Diplomas: State diploma in relevant field, 5 yrs.

Library: c. 10,000 vols.

Publication: Beiträge.

Academic Staff: c. 80.

Student Enrolment: c. 300.

3050 **HOCHSCHULE FÜR BILDENDE KÜNSTE**
College of Fine Art
Güntzstrasse 34, 8019 Dresden
Telephone: 4590112

Sec. of Painting and Graphics
Sec. of Sculpture
Sec. of Theatrical Design and Costumes
Sec. of Art Restoration
Sec. of Marxism-Leninism

Sec. of Aesthetics
Sec. of Scene Decoration and Theatrical Masks

Founded 1764 as Academy, acquired present status and title 1950. Responsible to the Ministry of Culture. Governing bodies: the Council of Art and Science; the Social Council. Residential facilities for *c.* 80 students.

Academic Year: September to July (September-February; February-July).

Admission Requirements: Secondary school certificate (Reifezeugnis) or equivalent.

Fees: None.

Language of Instruction: German.

Degrees and Diplomas: State diploma in a particular field, 5 yrs.

Library: c. 8000 vols.

Academic Staff: c. 60.

Student Enrolment: c. 1610 (Also *c.* 200 external students).

3051 **HOCHSCHULE FÜR FILM UND FERNSEHEN**

Academy of Film Art and Television
Karl-Marx-Strasse 27, 1591 Potsdam-Babelsberg
Telex: 15547
Telephone: 78981/83

D. of Direction
Head: Wolf-Dieter Panse; *staff* 12 (9)
D. of Camera Technique
Head: Hans-Wolfram Redecker; *staff* 6 (7)
D. of Production
Head: Klaus Eiselt; *staff* 6 (31)
D. of Film and Television Theory
Head: Peter Rabenalt; *staff* 7 (4)
Actors D.
Head: Mattias Härtig; *staff* 7 (18)
Film and Television Technique
Head: Kurt Grusser; *staff* 10 (65)
Audio-visual Research Ce.
Director: Dieter Wiedemann; *staff* 8

Founded 1954. A State institution responsible to the Ministry of Culture. Governing bodies: the Scientific-Artistic Council; the Senate. Residential facilities for all students.

Arrangements for co-operation with similar institutions in several countries.

Academic Year: September to July (September-January; February-July).

Admission Requirements: Secondary school certificate (Reifezeugnis) or equivalent, practical experience, and aptitude tests.

Fees: None.

Language of Instruction: German.

Degrees and Diplomas: Diplom in a particular field, 4-5 yrs. Also certificates, 3 yrs.

Library: Berlin Media Library and Academy Library, 55,000 vols.

Publication: Beiträge zur Film und Fernsehwissenschaft (4 issues a year).

Academic Staff, 1989-90:

Rank	Full-time	Part-time
Professoren	7	3
Dozenten	24	30
Wissenschaftliche Oberassistenten	32	–
Wissenschaftliche Assistenten	7	–
Lehrer im Hochschuldienst	8	–
Total	78	33

Student Enrolment, 1989-90:

	Men	Women	Total
Of the country	118	55	173
Of other countries	15	4	19
Total	133	59	192

3052 **HOCHSCHULE FÜR MUSIK BERLIN**

College of Music, Berlin
Otto-Grotewohlstrasse 19, 1080 Berlin
Cables: Hanns-Eisler-Hochschule
Telephone: 22-02-626

Sec. of Marxism-Leninism
Sec. for String Instruments
Sec. for Wind Instruments
Sec. for Keyboard Instruments
Sec. for Vocal Music
Sec. for Composition
Sec. for Guitar and Accordion Music
Sec. for Conducting
Sec. for Musical Stage Direction
Specialized S. of Music
D. of Evening and Correspondence Courses

Founded 1950. A State institute responsible to the Ministry of Culture. Governing body: the Artistic-Scientific Council. Some residential facilities for students in hostels.

Academic Year: September to July (September-February; February-July).

Admission Requirements: Secondary school certificate (Reifezeugnis) or certificate from a State school of music.

Fees: None.

Language of Instruction: German.

Degrees and Diplomas: State diploma, 4-5 yrs.

Library: c. 42,000 vols.

Academic Staff: c. 100.

Student Enrolment: c. 540.

3053 **HOCHSCHULE FÜR MUSIK, DRESDEN**

College of Music, Dresden
Blochmannstrasse 2-4, 8010 Dresden
Telephone: 45-90-213

Sec. for Singing
Sec. for Piano
Sec. for Orchestral Studies
Sec. for Composition
Sec. for Dance and Light Music
Sec. of Marxism-Leninism
Specialized S. of Music

Founded 1856 as a private school, became a State institution 1945 and acquired present status and title 1952. A State institution responsible to the Ministry of Culture. Residential facilities for students.

Academic Year: September to July (September-January; February-July).

Admission Requirements: Secondary school certificate (Reifezeugnis) or certificate from a State school of music.

Fees: None.

Language of Instruction: German.

Degrees and Diplomas: State diploma, 4-5 yrs.

Libraries: College Library, *c.* 40,000 vols; *c.* 3580 records.

Special Facilities (Museums, etc.): Museum of Musical Instruments.

Publications: Schriftenreihe; Informationsblatt.

Academic Staff: 120 (200).

Student Enrolment: c. 370.

3054 **HOCHSCHULE FÜR MUSIK LEPIZIG**

College of Music, Leipzig
Grassistrasse 8, 7010 Leipzig
Telephone: 31-14-02
Rektor: Werner Felix (1987-90)

Sec. of String Instruments
Head: Klaus Hertel; *staff* 7 (33)
Sec. for Singing
Head: Helga Forner; *staff* 9 (21)
Sec. for Wind Instruments
Head: Werner Seltmann; *staff* 3 (25)
Sec. for Keyboard Instruments
Head: Herbert Sahling; *staff* 15 (20)
Sec. for Composition and Theory
Head: Siegfried Thiele; *staff* 7 (8)
Sec. for Conducting
Head: Günter Blumhagen; *staff* 1 (4)
Sec. for Music Teachers
Dozent: Horst Bohm; *staff* 12 (40)
Sec. for Popular Music
Head: Peter Zwirnmann; *staff* 6 (35)
Sec. for Science
Head: Johannes Forner; *staff* 8 (10)

Also Special School for Music in Halle and Branch in Magdeburg.

Founded 1843 as Conservatory by Felix Mendelssohn-Bartholdy. Acquired present title 1968. A State institution responsible to the Ministry of Culture.

Academic Year: September to July (September-January; February-July).

Admission Requirements: Secondary school certificate (Reifezeugnis).

Fees: None.

Language of Instruction: German.

Degrees and Diplomas: State diploma, 4-5 yrs.
Libraries: College Library, 85,005 vols; 4748 records.
Academic Staff, 1986-87:

Rank	Full-time	Part-time
Professoren	20	15
Dozenten	24	20
Oberassistenten und Assistenten	28	164
Total	72	199

Student Enrolment, 1986-87:

	Men	Women	Total
Of the country	223	204	427
Of the countries	6	1	7
Total	229	205	434*

*Also 85 external students.

3055 **HOCHSCHULE FÜR MUSIK WEIMAR**
College of Music Weimar
Platz der Demokratie 2-3, 5300 Weimar
Telephone: 5241
Rektor: Diethelm Müller-Nilsson (1980-)
Prorektor: Gert Frischmuth

Sec. for Marxism-Leninism
Sec. for Music Education
Sec. for Composition
Sec. for Conducting
Sec. for String Instruments
Sec. for Wind Instruments
Sec. for Keyboard Instruments
Sec. for Vocal Music
Specialized S. of Music
Sec. for Accordion and Guitar Music
Sec. for Dance and Light Music
I. for Folk Music Research

Founded 1872 as school, became State institution 1930. Responsible to the Ministry of Culture. Governing body: the Künstlerisch-Wissenschaftlicher Rat (Artistic-Academic Council). Residential facilities for students.

Academic Year: September to June (September-January; February-June).
Admission Requirements: Secondary school certificate (Reifezeugnis) or equivalent.
Fees: None.
Language of Instruction: German.
Degrees and Diplomas: State diploma, 4-5 yrs.
Library: c. 65,000 vols.
Academic Staff: c. 150.
Student Enrolment: c. 660.

3056 **HOCHSCHULE FÜR SCHAUSPIELKUNST BERLIN**
Schnellerstrasse 104, 1190 Berlin
Telephone: 6352261
Rektor: Kurt Veth
Direktor: Peter Jung

Sec. of Acting
Head: Wolfgang Rodler; *staff* 28
Sec. of Directing
Head: Peter Schroth; *staff* 25
Sec. of Puppetry
Head: Hans-Peter Schreiber; *staff* 16
Sec. of Philosophy and Cultural History
Head: Wolfgang Engler; *staff* 6

Founded 1905, acquired present status and title 1981. Residential facilities for 120 studnets.

Arrangements for co-operation with: Hochschule für Musik und darstellende Kunst 'Mozarteum' Salzburg.

Academic Year: September to August (September-February; February-August).
Admission Requirements: Secondary school certificate (Reifezeugnis) or equivalent.
Fees: None.
Languages of Instruction: German (also English, Russian, and French).
Degrees and Diplomas: Diplomas, 4 yrs.
Library: 30,000 vols.
Academic Staff, 1989: 151.
Student Enrolment, 1989:

Men	Women	Total
127	95	222

3057 **THEATERHOCHSCHULE LEIPZIG**
College of Dramatic Art, Leipzig
Schwägrichenstrasse 3, 7010 Leipzig
Telephone: 32-51-34

Sec. of Acting
Head: Wolfgang Fleischmann
Sec. of Drama
Head: Roland Drebler
Sec. of Choreography
Head: Michail Gawrikow

Founded 1947 as institute in Weimar, became college and moved to Leipzig 1953. A State institution responsibleto the Ministry of Culture. Governing body: the Sachsen. Residential facilities for students.

Academic Year: October to July (October-February April-July).
Admission Requirements: Secondary school certificate (Reifezeugnis) or professional training.
Fees: None.
Language of Instruction: German.
Degrees and Diplomas: Diplomas, 4-5 yrs.
Library: c. 15,000 vols.
Publications: Wissenschaftliche Beiträge der Theaterhochschule 'Hans Otto' Leipzig; Schriften zur Theaterwissenschaft.
Press or Publishing House: College Press.
Academic Staff, 1990:

Rank	Full-time	Part-time
Professoren	3	–
Dozenten	4	–
Assistenten	24	11
Total	31	11

Student Enrolment, 1990-91:

Men	Women	Total
64	59	123

3058 **INSTITUT FÜR LITERATUR LEIPZIG**
Institute of Literature, Leipzig
Karl-Tauchwitz-Strasse 8, 7010 Leipzig
Cables: Litinistitut
Telephone: 310386; 310281

Literature

Founded 1955. A State institution responsible to the Ministry of Culture. Governing bodies: the Academic Council; the Full Council, including also members of the Writers Union of the GDR and members of publishing houses.

Academic Year: September to August (September-January; February-July).
Admission Requirements: Admission on the basis of talent or recommendations.
Fees: None.
Language of Instruction: German.
Degrees and Diplomas: Diploma, 3 yrs.
Library: c. 25,000 vols.
Academic Staff: c. 20.
Student Enrolment: c. 90.

3059 **MEDIZINISCHE AKADEMIE DRESDEN**
Academy of Medicine, Dresden
Fetscherstasse 74, 8019 Dresden
Cables: Medak Dresden
Telex: 2359
Telephone: 4580
Rektor: Joachim Schmidt (1983-89)

Sec. of Medicine (clinical)
Sec. of Dentistry (clinical)

Founded 1954. Faculty structure replaced under 1968 reform by series of subject sections. The academy is responsible to the Ministry of Higher and Professional Education. Governing bodies: the Konzil; the Gesellschaftliche Rat (Social Council); the Wissenschaftliche Rat (Academic Council) and Senate; and a Rat (Council) for each section. The academic staff, the students and non-academic employees are represented on all governing bodies. The Social Council and the section councils also include representatives of public life. Residential facilities for 541 academic staff.

Arrangements for co-operation with: Institute of Medicine, Leningrad; Semmelweis Medical University; Academy of Medicine, Wrocław.

Academic Year: September to August (September-January; February-July).

Admission Requirements: Secondary school certificate (Reifezeugnis) or equivalent, and completed pre-clinical studies.

Fees: None.

Language of Instruction: German.

Degrees and Diplomas: Diplom-Mediziner, Dipl.-Med.; Diplom Stomatologue, dentistry, 5 yrs. Doktor (first level) –Dr.med. or Dr.med.dent. by thesis, a futher 3-4 yrs. Doktor der Wissenschaften (second level)–Dr.sc. by thesis, 4-5 yrs after Doktor, first level.

Library: Central Library, *c.* 96,230 vols.

Publication: Schriften der Medizinischen Akademie Dresden.

Academic Staff, 1986-87:

Rank	Full-time
Professoren	42
Hochschuldozenten	67
Ärzte/Zahnärzte	475
Apotheker	17
Wissenschaftliche Mitarbeiter	221
Total	882

Student Enrolment, 1986-87:

	Men	Women	Total
Of the country	294	512	806

3060 **MEDIZINISCHE AKADEMIE ERFURT**

Academy of Medicine, Erfurt

Nordhäuser Strasse 74, 5010 Erfurt

Cables: Medak

Telex: 61384

Telephone: 500

Rektor: Joachim Knappe (1985-)

Sec. of Medicine (clinical)

Sec. of Dentistry

Founded 1954. Faculty structure replaced under 1968 reform by subject sections. The academy is responsible to the Ministry of Higher and Professional Education. Governing bodies: the Konzil; the Gesellschaftliche Rat (Social Council); the Wissenschaftliche Rat (Academic Council) and Senate; and a Rat (Council) for each section. The academic staff, the students and non-academic employees are represented on all governing bodies. The Social Council and the section councils also include representatives of public life.

Arrangements for co-operation with: Institute of Medicine, Leningrad; University of Vilnius; Medical University of Pécs.

Academic Year: September to August (September-January; February-July).

Admission Requirements: Secondary school certificate (Reifezeugnis) and completed pre-clinical studies.

Fees: None.

Language of Instruction: German.

Degrees and Diplomas: Diplom-Mediziner, Dipl.-Med; Dipl. Stomatologe, dentistry, 5 yrs. Doktor (first level)–Dr.med. by thesis, a further 3-4 yrs. Doktor der Wissenschaften (second level) Dr.sc. by thesis, 4-5 yrs after Doktor, first level.

Libraries: Central Library, *c.* 70,000 vols; clinic and institute libraries.

Publication: Beiträge zur Geschichte der Universität Erfurt (1392-1816).

Academic Staff, 1986-87: 91.

Student Enrolment, 1986-87: 1589.

3061 **MEDIZINISCHE AKADEMIE MAGDEBURG**

Academy of Medicine, Magdeburg

Leipziger Strasse 44, 3090 Magdeburg

Telephone: 670

Rektor: Rolf-Dieter Koch (1979-)

S. of Medicine

S. of Nursing

Also 34 departments and clinics.

Founded 1954. Faculty structure replaced under 1968 reform by subject section. The academy is responsible to the Ministry of Higher and Professional Education. Governing bodies: the Konzil, the Gesellschaftliche Rat (Social Council); the Wissenschaftliche Rat (Academic Council) and Senate; and a Rat (Council) for each section. The academic staff, the students and non-academic employees are represented on all governing bodies. The Social Council and the section council also include representatives of public life. Residential facilities for students.

Arrangements for co-operation with: Pavel Josef Safárik University, Košice; Medical University of Pécs; State Institute of Medicine, Doneck; Charles University, Prague; Instituto Superior de Ciencias Médicas de La Habana.

Academic Year: September to August (September-January; February-July).

Admission Requirements: Secondary school certificate (Reifezeugnis) or equivalent.

Fees: None.

Language of Instruction: German.

Degrees and Diplomas: Diplom-Mediziner, Dipl.-Med., 6 yrs. Doktor (first level)–Dr.med. by thesis, a further 3-4 yrs. Doktor der Wissenschaften (second level)–Dr.sc. by thesis, 4-5 yrs after Doktor, first level.

Library: Central Library, 120,000 vols.

Academic Staff, 1986-87:

Rank	Full-time
Professoren	46
Dozenten	37
Wissenschaftliche Mitarbeiter	161
Oberärzte, Ärzte, Apotheker	415
Total	659

Student Enrolment, 1986-87:

	Men	Women	Total
Of the country	312	483	795

3062 **HOCHSCHULE FÜR LANDWIRTSCHAFT UND NAHRUNGSGÜTERWIRTSCHAFT BERNBURG**

College of Agriculture and Food Technology

Mitschurinstrasse 28, 4351 Bernburg Saale

Cables: 04-8338 HfL

Telephone: 823⅓6

Sec. of Marxism-Leninism

Sec. of Socialist Agricultural Economics and Food Technology

Sec. of Socialist Agricultural Management

Sec. of Agriculture and Animal Husbandry

Computer Ce.

Founded 1953 as institute, became college 1961, and acquired present status 1967. The college is responsible to the Ministry of Agriculture, Forestry and Food Technology. Governing bodies: the Social Council; the Academic Council. Residential facilities for *c.* 560 students.

Academic Year: September to August.

Admission Requirements: Secondary school certificate (Reifezeugnis) or equivalent, and 3-5 yrs practical work.

Fees: None.

Language of Instruction: German.

Degrees and Diplomas: Diplomagraringenieur-ökonom, 2 yrs. Doktor, Dr. (Doctorate, first level, in a particular field), a further 3-4 yrs. Doktor der Wissenschaften, Dr.sc. (Doctorate, second level) by thesis, 4-5 yrs after Doktor, first level.

Library: *c.* 65,000 vols.

Academic Staff: *c.* 140.

Student Enrolment: *c.* 300.

3063 **HOCHSCHULE FÜR LANDWIRTSCHAFTLICHE PRODUKTIONSGENOSSENSCHAFTEN MEISSEN**

College for Agricultural Co-operatives

Freiheit 13, 8250 Meissen

Cables: Hochschule LPG Meissen

Telephone: 8121

Sec. of Marxism-Leninism

Sec. of Economics of Socialist Agriculture

Sec. of Socialist Agricultural Management (including Animal Husbandry)

Agricultural Economics Research I.

Founded 1953. The college is responsible to the Ministry of Agriculture, Forestry and Food Technology. Governing bodies: the Academic Council; the Social Council. Residential facilities for *c.* 480 students.

Academic Year: September to August (September-January; February-July).

Admission Requirements: Graduation from a university institution, professional experience.

Fees: None.
Language of Instruction: German.
Degrees and Diplomas: Diplomagraringenieur, 2 yrs. Doktor, Dr. (Doctorate, first level, in a particular field), a further 3-4 yrs. Doktor der Wissenschaften, Dr.sc. (Doctorate, second level) by thesis, 4-5 yrs after Doktor, first level.
Library: c. 50,000 vols.
Academic Staff: c. 250.
Student Enrolment: c. 1440.

3064 **HANDELSHOCHSCHULE LEIPZIG**
College of Commerce
Markgrafenstrasse 2, 7010 Leipzig
Telex: 51390 CEWA DD
Telephone: 7481
Rektor: Walter Klitzsch (1982-)
Verwaltungsdirektor: Joachim Stenker

Sec. of Marxism-Leninism
Director: Otto Stump
Sec. of Socialist Business Administration
Director: Kurt Leder
Sec. of Socialist Economics
Director: Hans-Joachim Lotze
D. of Merchandise Technology
Director: Günther Grundke
D. of Mathematics and Data Processing
Director: Gerd Goldammer
D. of Catering Economics and Technology
Director: Hans Stündel
I. for Socialist Economic Management
Director: Reinhardt Loos
I. of Commerce
Director: Anneliese Dittloff

Founded 1969. The college is responsible to the Ministry of Higher and Professional Education. Governing bodies: the Konzil; the Gesellschaftliche Rat (Social Council); the Wissenschaftliche Rat (Academic Council); and a Rat (Council) for each section. Residential facilities for c. 1020 students.

Arrangements for co-operation with: Latvian State University; Institute of Commerce, Kiev; College of Economics, Bratislava; Academy of Economics, Poznań; 'Karl Marx' Institute of Economics, Sofia; Prague College of Economics.

Academic Year: September to August (September-January; February-July).
Admission Requirements: Secondary school certificate (Reifezeugnis) or equivalent.
Fees: None.
Language of Instruction: German.
Degrees and Diplomas: Diplomwirtschaftler, Dipl.oec., 4 yrs. Doktor–Dr.oec. (first level); Doktor–Dr.sc.oec. (second level).
Library: c. 60,000 vols.
Publications: Warenkundliche Berichte; Wissenschaftliche Zeitschrift.
Academic Staff, 1986-87:

Rank	Full-time
Professoren	28
Dozenten	65
Oberassistenten	68
Lehrer im Hochschuldienst	44
Unbefristete Assistenten	68
Befristete Assistenten	42
Total	315

Student Enrolment, 1986-87:

Men	Women	Total
301	1242	1543*

*Also 268 external students.

3065 **INGENIEURHOCHSCHULE BERLIN-WARTENBERG**
College of Engineering
Dorfstrasse, PF 56 1120 Berlin-Wartenberg
Cables: IH 1120 berlin
Telex: 114792
Telephone: 48150
Rektor: Dietmar Rössel (1987-)
Prorektor: Reinhard Werner

Sec. of Agricultural Machinery Maintenance
Director: Hans Gäse; *staff* 34
Sec. of Mathematics, Natural Science, and Technical Basic Studies
Director: Helmut Bausch
Sec. of Land Technology
Director: Klaus Queitsch
I. of Economics and Social Science
Director: Rudolf Schoob
D. for Lifelong Education
Prorektor: Anneliese Schütze

Founded 1953 as Ingenieurschule; acquired present status 1969. The college is responsible to the Ministry of Higher and Professional Education. Governing bodies: the Gesellschaftliche Rat (Social Council); the Wissenschaftliche Rat (Academic Council). Residential facilities for 90% of the students.

Arrangements for co-operation with: Institute of Agriculture, Volgograd; College of Agriculture, Olsztyn-Kortowo; College of Agriculture, Prague; University of Agriculture, Warsaw; University of Agriculture, Debrecen.

Academic Year: September to August (September-February; March-August).
Admission Requirements: Technical training and secondary school certificate (Reifezeugnis).
Language of Instruction: German.
Degrees and Diplomas: Diplomingenieur, in a particular field, 4 yrs. Doktor-Ingenieur, Dr.Ing. Dr.sc.techn.
Library: c. 60,000 vols.
Publication: Wissenschaftliche Beiträge.
Academic Staff, 1989-90:

Rank	Full-time
Professoren	14
Dozenten	29
Assistenten	80
Lehrer	28
Oberassistenten	34
Wissenschaftliche Sekretäre	18
Total	203

Student Enrolment, 1990:

Men	Women	Total
740	80	820*

*Also 90 external students.

3066 **INGENIEURHOCHSCHULE COTTBUS**
College of Engineering
Karl-Marx-Strasse 17, 7500 Cottbus
Telephone: 690
Rektor: H. Prässler (1969-)

Building Technology

Founded 1969. The college is responsible to the Ministry of Higher and Professional Education. Governing bodies: the Gesellschaftliche Rat (Social Council); the Wissenschaftliche Rat (Academic Council). Residential facilities for all students.

Arrangements for co-operation with: Institute of Civil Engineering, Kharkov; Pollack Mihály College of Engineering, Pécs; College of Engineering, Zielona Góra.

Academic Year: September to July (September-January; February-July).
Admission Requirements: Technical training and secondary school certificate (Reifezeugnis).
Fees: None.
Language of Instruction: German.
Degrees and Diplomas: Diplomingenieur, 4 yrs.
Library: c. 200,000 vols.
Academic Staff, 1986-87: 321.
Student Enrolment, 1986-87:

Men	Women	Total
1005	580	1585

3067 **INGENIEURHOCHSCHULE KÖTHEN**
College of Engineering
Bernburger-Strasse 52-57, 4370 Köthen
Telex: 04 7720
Telephone: 670
Rektor: Kurt Gramlich (1986-)
Verwaltungsdirektor: Günter Holstein

Sec. of Plant Construction (including Food Technology)
Director: Fritz Koch
Sec. of Chemical Engineering
Director: Herbert Rödicker
Sec. of Socialist Industrial Management
Director: H. Engels
D. of Mathematics and Computer Sciences
Director: Claus Richter
I. of Marxism-Leninism
Director: Roland Eberhardt
Ce. for Lifelong Education
Director: Udo Franz

Founded 1891 as industrial academy. Became Ingenieurschule 1948 and acquired present status 1969. The college is responsible to the Ministry of Higher and Professional Education. Residential facilities for students.

Arrangements for co-operation with: Institute of Chemical Technology, Moscow; Institute of Food Technology, Odessa; Technical University of Budapest; Veszprém Technical University of Chemical Engineering; Technical University of Bratislava; College of Chemical Technology, Prague; Technical University of Gdansk.

Academic Year: September to August (September-February; March-July).

Admission Requirements: Technical training and secondary school certificate (Reifezeugnis).

Fees: None.

Language of Instruction: German.

Degrees and Diplomas: Diplomingenieur; Diplomingenieurökonom, 4 yrs. Doktor-Ingenieur, Dr.Ing. Habilitation (teaching qualification), Dr.Ing.habil., by thesis.

Library: 98,920 vols.

Publication: Wissenschaftliche Beiträge (annually).

Academic Staff, 1986-87:

Rank	Full-time	Part-time
Professoren und Dozenten	64	10
Wissenschaftliche Mitarbeiter	265	116
Total	329	126

Student Enrolment, 1986-87:

	Men	Women	Total
Of the country	712	631	1343
Of other countries	48	11	59
Total	760	642	1402

3068 **INGENIEURHOCHSCHULE MITTWEIDA**

College of Engineering

Platz der Deutsch-Sowjetischen Freundschaft 17, 9250 Mittweida
Telex: 77520 IHSMIT
Telephone: 580
Rektor: Gerhard Zscherpe (1981-87)
Verwaltungsdirektor: Rudi Kusch

Sec. of Electronic Technology
Director: Horst Boden
Sec. of Data Processing Technology
Director: Ludwig Rettelbusch
Ce. for Electronic Instruments
Director: Hans-Holger Arndt
I. of Marxism-Leninism
Director: Dietmar Fischer

Founded 1969. The college is responsible to the Ministry of Higher and Professional Education. Residential facilities for students.

Arrangements for co-operation with: Institute of Telecommunications, Moscow; Institute of Precision and Optical Engineering, Leningrad; Institute of Mechanical and Electrical Engineering, Gabrovo; College of Transport Engineering, Žilina; Technical University of Kielce; Technical University of Wrocław; Technical University of Budapest.

Academic Year: September to August (September-January; February-July).

Admission Requirements: Technical training and secondary school certificate (Reifezeugnis).

Fees: None.

Language of Instruction: German.

Degrees and Diplomas: Diplomingenieur, 4 yrs. Doktor-Ingenieur, Dr.Ing.

Library: 6300 vols.

Academic Staff, 1986-87:

Rank	Full-time
Professoren	17
Dozenten	24
Oberassistenten und unbefristete Assistenten	92
Lektoren/Lehrer im Hochschuldienst	27
Total	160

Student Enrolment, 1986-87:

Men	Women	Total
561	93	654

3069 **INGENIEURHOCHSCHULE ZWICKAU**

College of Engineering

Dr.-Friedrichs-Ring 2A, 9540 Zwickau
Cables: 77038 ihzrz
Telephone: 8230
Rektor: Franz Meissner (1984-87)

Sec. of Metal Processing Industries
Director: Manfred Auerswald
Sec. of Automobile Engineering
Director: Volkmar Küntscher
Sec. of Automation Technology
Director: Klaus Gola
Sec. of Socialist Industrial Management
Director: Wolfgang Opitz
I. of Marxism-Leninism
Head: Siegfried Schumann

Founded 1969. The college is responsible to Ministry of Higher and Professional Education. Governing bodies: the Gesellschaftliche Rat (Social Council); the Wissenschaftliche Rat (Academic Council). Residential facilities for 1300 students.

Special arrangements for co-operation with: Technical University of Košice; L'vov Polytechnical Institute; Technical University of Rzeszów; College of Transport and Telecommunications, Györ.

Academic Year: September to July (September-January; February-July).

Admission Requirements: Technical training and secondary school certificate (Reifezeugnis).

Fees: None.

Language of Instruction: German.

Degrees and Diplomas: Diplomingenieur; Diplomingenieurökonom, 4 yrs. Doktor, Dr.Ing., (Doctorate, first level), a further 3 yrs. Doktor der Wissenschaften, Dr.sc. (Doctorate, second level)–Dr.sc.techn.

Library: c. 105,000 vols.

Publication: Scientific Publications.

Academic Staff, 1986-87: 397.

Student Enrolment, 1986-87:

Men	Women	Total
987	510	1497

3070 **HOCHSCHULE FÜR SEEFAHRT WARNEMÜNDE/WUSTROW**

Maritime Academy Warnemünde/Wustrow

Richard-Wagner-Strasse, 2530 Rostock-Warnemünde
Telex: 31338 IHSWM DD
Telephone: 570
Rektor: J. Lüsch (1990-)
Prorektor: B. Gless

D. of Navigation (including Fishery Technology)
Director: F. Weber; *staff* 70
D. of Marine Engineering
Director: H. Strickert; *staff* 72
D. of Shipbuilding
Director: S. Brandstädter; *staff* 55
D. of Basic Education
Director: U.-D. Hünicke; *staff* 46
D. of Shipping Economics
Director: A. Stoehr; *staff* 28
I. of Philosophy and Time History
Director: M. Rothbarth; *staff* 26
D. of Data Processing
Director: H. Mennenga; *staff* 15
D. of Ship Security
Director: J. Hahne; *staff* 27

D. of Foreign Languages
Director: G. Traenkner; *staff* 16
D. of Training Vessels
Director: D. Kehrsandt; *staff* 37

Founded 1969, as Ingenieurhochschule für Seefahrt, incorporating School of Navigation, Wustrow (1864), and Marine Engineering School Warnemünde (1948). Acquired present status and title 1989. Governing body: the Wissenschaftliche Rat (Scientific Council).

Arrangements for co-operation with: College of Navigation, Szczecin; College of Navigation, Gdynia; College of Navigation, Odessa; College of Marine Engineering, Leningrad; Institute of Mechanical and Electrical Engineering, Varna, Arab Maritime Transport Academy, Alexandria; World Maritime University, Malmö.

Academic Year: September to August (September-February; February-August).

Admission Requirements: Technical training and school leaving certificate (Reifezeugnis).

Fees: None.

Language of Instruction: German.

Degrees and Diplomas: Diplomingenieur (Master) 4-4 ½ yrs. Doktor-Ingenieur, a further 3-4 yrs.

Library: 100,000 vols.

Special Facilities (Museums, etc.): Training Vessel 'Störtebeker'

Publication: Scientific Periodical (quarterly).

Academic Staff, 1989-90:

Rank	Full-time
Professoren und Dozenten	48
Wissenschaftliche Mitarbeiter	249
Total	297

Student Enrolment, 1989-90:

Men	Women	Total
1011	74	1085

Teacher Training

3071 **DEUTSCHE HOCHSCHULE FÜR KÖRPERKULTUR**
German College of Physical Education
Friedrich-Ludwig-Jahn-Allee 59, 7010 Leipzig
Cables: DHfK-Leipzig
Telephone: 49740
Rektor: Hans-Georg Herrmann (1978-87)
Verwaltungsdirektor: Herbert Gross

Physical Education and Sport
Research I.
I. of Medicine (Sports)
I. of Marxism-Leninism

Founded 1950, achieved full university rank 1965. Governing bodies: the Academic Council; the Social Council. Residential facilities for students.

Arrangements for co-operation with: Central Institute of Physical Culture, Moscow; Institute of Physical Education and Sport, Charles University, Prague; Academy of Physical Education, Warsaw; College of Physical Education, Budapest; Institute of Physical Culture, Sofia; Higher Institutes of Physical Education, Cairo and Alexandria; School of Physical Education, Havana.

Academic Year: September to August (September-January; February-July).

Admission Requirements: Secondary school certificate (Reifezeugnis) and aptitude test.

Fees: None.

Language of Instruction: German.

Degrees and Diplomas: Diplomsportlehrer, in various sections, 4 yrs. Doktor, Dr. (Doctorate, first level, in a particular field); by thesis, a further 3-4 yrs. Doktor der Wissenschaften, Dr.sc. (Doctorate, second level) by thesis, 4-5 yrs after Doktor, first level. Also qualifications for foreign students: Diploma of Trainer; Diploma of Merit in Coaching, 8 months. Magister Diplom, 3 sem postgraduate study.

Library: College Library, 116,000 vols.

Publication: Wissenschaftliche Zeitschrift.

Academic Staff, 1986-87:

Rank	Full-time
Professoren und Dozenten	66
Wissenschaftliche Mitarbeiter	411
Total	477

Student Enrolment, 1986-87:

Men	Women	Total
1264	534	1798

3072 **PÄDAGOGISCHE HOCHSCHULE DRESDEN**
College of Education, Dresden
Wigardstrasse 17, 8060 Dresden
Telephone: 59900
Rektor: Werner Jokubeit (1990-93)

I. of Education and Psychology
Head: Hans-Joachim Schille; *staff* 47
I. of Mathematics and Didactics
Head: Hans-Dietrich Hecker; *staff* 47
I. of Physics and Didactics
Head: Christian Blochwitz; *staff* 34
I. of Foreign Languages and Didactics
Head: Günther Böhme; *staff* 66
I. of German
Head: Wilfried Bock; *staff* 37
I. of History and Didactics
Head: Volker Ruhland; *staff* 29
I. of Geography and Didactics
Head: Wolfgang KaulfuB; *staff* 49
I. of Art Education
Head: Roland Unger; *staff* 27
I. of Information and Didactics
Head: Immo Kerner; *staff* 16
I. of Cultural Education
Head: Rainer Schütz; *staff* 28
Ce. of Audio-visual Techniques
Head: Christian Miesch; *staff* 27
D. of Physical Education
Head: Annerose Zwicker; *staff* 12

Founded 1953 as institute, acquired present status and title 1967. The college is responsible to the Ministry of Training and Science. Residential facilities for foreign academic staff and for 85% of the students.

Arrangements for co-operation with similar institutions in different countries.

Academic Year: October to September (October-April; May-September).

Admission Requirements: Secondary school certificate (Reifezeugnis) or equivalent.

Fees: None.

Language of Instruction: German.

Degrees and Diplomas: State diploma, 5 yrs. Doctorates.

Library: c. 72,000 vols.

Publication: Wissenschaftliche Zeitschrift.

Academic Staff, 1990:

Rank	Full-time
Hochschullehrer (Professoren, Dozenten)	100
Oberassistenten, Assistenten	92
Lektoren, Lehrer im Hochschuldienst	138
Total	330

Student Enrolment, 1990:

	Men	Women	Total
Of the country	435	1524	1959
Of the countries	10	7	17
Total	445	1531	1976

3073 **PÄDAGOGISCHE HOCHSCHULE ERFURT/MÜHLHAUSEN**
College of Education, Erfurt/Mühlhausen
Nordhäuser Strasse 63, 5080 Erfurt/Mühlhausen
Telephone: 5360

Sec. of Marxism-Leninism
Sec. of Education and Psychology
Sec. of Mathematics and Physics
Sec. of Chemistry and Biology
Sec. of Philology, Literature, and Aesthetics

Sec. of Basic Studies
Polytechnic Sec.
I. of Didactics
Research Ce.

Founded 1953 as institute, acquired present status and title 1969. The college is responsible to the Ministry of Education. Governing bodies: the Gesellschaftliche Rat (Social Council); the Wissenschaftliche Rat (Academic Council).

Academic Year: September to June (September-January; February-June).

Admission Requirements: Secondary school certificate (Reifezeugnis).

Fees: None.

Language of Instruction: German.

Degrees and Diplomas: State diploma, 4 yrs. Doktor, Dr. (Doctorate, first level, in a particular field) by thesis, a further 3-4 yrs.

Library: Central Library, *c.* 112,000 vols.

Publication: Wissenschaftliche Zeitschrift des Pädagogischen Instituts Erfurt.

Academic Staff: c. 500.

Student Enrolment: c. 2290.

3074 **PÄDAGOGISCHE HOCHSCHULE GÜSTROW**

Pedagogical University, Güstrow
Goldbergerstrasse 12, 2600 Güstrow
Telex: 328587
Telephone: 360
Rektor: Rainer Tichatschke (1990-93)
Kanzler: Klaus Helling

I. of Mathematics
Director: R. Strecker; *staff* 35
I. of Physics
Director: K. Henneberger; *staff* 35
I. of Biology
Director: R. Buschbeck; *staff* 23
I. of Chemistry
Director: H. Dehne; *staff* 27
I. of Technical Education
Director: R. Kastl; *staff* 38
I. of Pedagogical and Social Sciences
Director: W. Naumann; *staff* 76
Also 5 Research Groups.

Founded 1949 as institute, acquired present status and title 1972. Teaching and research is concentrated in the areas of mathematics, natural sciences, technical education, and pedagogics. Responsible to the Ministry of Education. Residential facilities for 1200 students.

Academic Year: September to July (September-February; March-July).

Admission Requirements: Secondary school certificate (Reifezeugnis).

Fees (Marks): Foreign students, 10,000 per annum.

Language of Instruction: German.

Degrees and Diplomas: State certificate of education (Staatsexamen), 4 yrs. Diploma of education (Diplomlehrer), 1 further yr. Doktor, Dr. (Doctorate, first level, in a particular field) by thesis, a further 3-4 yrs. Doktor der Wissenschaften, Dr.sc. (Doctorate, second level) by thesis, 4-5 yrs after Doktor, first level.

Library: Central Library, *c.* 130,000 vols.

Special Facilities (Museums, etc.): Centre of Marine Biology (Boiensdorf).

Publications: Wissenschaftliche Zeitschrift der Pädagogischen Hochschule Güstrow (6 times a year); Güstrower Beiträge (biannually).

Academic Staff, 1990:

Rank	Full-time
Professoren	22
Dozenten	27
Lektoren	35
Oberassistenten, Assistenten	95
Lehrer im Hochschuldienst	77
Total	256

Student Enrolment, 1990:

	Men	Women	Total
Of the country	403	741	1144
Of the countries	46	10	56
total	449	751	1200

3075 **PÄDAGOGISCHE HOCHSCHULE HALLE**

College of Education, Halle
Kröllwitzer Strasse 44, 4050 Halle
Telephone: 30288
Rektor: Fritz Bauer (1990-)

Sec. of Education and Psychology
Director: Christine Krätzschmar; *staff* 43 (7)
Sec. of Mathematics
Director: Horst Kretzschlar; *staff* 46 (9)
Sec. of Biology
Director: Ingo Zelmer; *staff* 40 (8)
Technical Sec.
Director: Margret Kempe; *staff* 25 (4)
I. of Teacher Training
Director: Hans-Joachim Schwier; *staff* 92 (9)
I. of Physics
Director: Otto Simmich; *staff* 29 (3)
I. of Chemistry
Director: Wieland Schäfer; *staff* 56 (11)
I. for Training and In-service Training (pre-school level)
Director: Franz Rudolph; *staff* 19 (1)
D. of International Pedagogical Co-operation
Director: Hans-Joachim Wichmann; *staff* 17

Founded 1953 as institute. Acquired present status and title 1972. The college is responsible to the Ministry of Education. Governing bodies: the Wissenschaftliche Rat (Academic Council); the Senate. Residential facilities for *c.* 1040 students.

Arrangements for co-operation with Colleges of Education: in Moscow, Ufa, Kursk, Blagoievgrad, Olomouc, Ceske Budejovice, Białystok, Kielce, Slupsk, Zanka, Baja, Pyongyang, Karlsruhe.

Academic Year: September to August (September-January; February-July).

Admission Requirements: Secondary school certificate (Reifezeugnis) or equivalent.

Fees: None.

Language of Instruction: German.

Degrees and Diplomas: State diploma, 5 yrs. Doktor, Dr. (Doctorate, first level, in a particular field) by thesis, a further 3-4 yrs. Dr.sc. (Doctorate, second level in pedagogics), by thesis.

Library: c. 120,000 vols.

Publication: Wissenschaftliche Zeitschrift.

Academic Staff, 1990:

Rank	Full-time	Part-time
Professoren	44	–
Hochschuldozenten	38	–
Assistenten	187	57
Lektoren/Lehrer i. Hochschuldienst	183	–
Total	452	57

Student Enrolment, 1990:

	Men	Women	Total
Of the country	495	1402	1897
Of the countries	26	3	29
Total	521	1405	1926*

*Also 38 external students.

3076 **INSTITUT KÖTHEN DER PÄDAGOGISCHEN HOCHSCHULE HALLE-KÖTHEN**

Institute Köthen of College of Education, Halle-Köthen
Lohmannstrasse 23, 4370 Köthen
Telephone: 690
Direktor: H. J. Schwier (1990-)

D. of Pedagogics
Head: E. Klinger
D. of Psychology
Head: M. Baumann
D. of Mathematics and Mathematic Didactics
Head: W. Jungk
D. of German Language and Literature and Didactics
Head: N. Schulz
D. of Art and Artistic and Technical Manual Instruction
Head: L. Gräser
D. of Music and Music Didactics
Head: E. Wolf

D. of Sport and Didactics
Head: R. Schützke
D. of Environmental Studies
Head: H.-J. Schwier
D. of General Education
Head: M. Laumann

Founded 1950 as institute, acquired present status and title 1988. The college is responsible to the Ministry of Education. Governing bodies: the Senate; the Academic Council. Residential facilities for students.

Arrangements for co-operation with similar institutions in: Germany, USSR, Poland, Hungaria, Czechoslovakia.

Academic Year: September to July (September-January; February-July).

Admission Requirements: Secondary school certificate (Reifezeugnis) or equivalent.

Fees: None.

Language of Instruction: German.

Degrees and Diplomas: State examination, 5 yrs. Doktor, Dr. (Doctorate, first level, in a particular field) by thesis, a further 3-4yrs.

Library: Central Library.

Special Facilities (Museums, etc.): Botanical Gardens, Video Studio.

Academic Staff: c. 270.

	Men	Women	Total
Of the country	56	612	668

3077 **PÄDAGOGISCHE HOCHSCHULE LEIPZIG**
College of Education, Leipzig
Karl-Heine-Strasse 22b, 7031 Leipzig
Telephone: 4 9770

Sec. of German and Russian
Sec. of Marxism-Leninism (including Civics)
Sec. of History
Sec. of Education and Psychology
D. of General Education

Founded 1953 as institute, acquired present status and title 1972. The college is responsible to the Ministry of Education. Governing bodies: the Academic Council; the Social Council. Residential facilities for students.

Academic Year: September to August (September-January; February-July).

Admission Requirements: Secondary school certificate (Reifezeugnis).

Fees: None.

Language of Instruction: German.

Degrees and Diplomas: State diploma, 5 yrs. Doktor, Dr. (Doctorate, first level, in a particular field) by thesis, a further 3-4 yrs.

Publication: Wissenschaftliche Zeitschrift (Scientific Journal).

Academic Staff: c. 240.

Student Enrolment: c. 1310.

3078 **PÄDAGOGISCHE HOCHSCHULE MAGDEBURG**
College of Education, Magdeburg
Brandenburger Strasse 9, 3040 Magdeburg
Telephone: 3-36-66
Rektor: Winfried Baudisch

Sec. of History
Sec. of Physical Education
Sec. of Pedagogics and Psychology
Sec. of Germanic Philology
Sec. of Special Pedagogics
Sec. of Philosophy and Social Sciences
Sec. of Foreign Philologies
D. of History of Pre-bourgeois Revolutions
Head: H. Asmus; *staff* 6
D. of Pedagogical Rehabilitation of the Handicapped
Head: H. Baudisch; *staff* 12
D. of Sports for Handicapped and Chronically Ill Children
Head: H. Giebel; *staff* 6

Founded 1962 as institute, acquired present status and title 1972. The college is responsible to the Ministry of Education. Governing body: the Senate, the Council, the Academic Council. Residential facilities for c. 1200 students.

Arrangements for co-operation with similar institutions in: Poland, Hungary, USSR, Bulgaria, Czechoslovakia.

Academic Year: October to July (October-January; February-July).

Admission Requirements: Secondary school certificate (Reifezeugnis) or equivalent.

Fees: None.

Languages of Instruction: German, English and Russian.

Degrees and Diplomas: State diploma, 4 yrs. Doktor, Dr.–Dr.paed., Dr.phil., Dr.sc.paed., Dr.sc.phil., by thesis, a further 3-4 yrs.

Library: 110,000 vols.

Publications: Scientific Journal of the College; Journal 'Magdeburger Blätter'.

Academic Staff: c. 150.

Student Enrolment: c. 2400 (Also 75 external students).

3079 **PÄDAGOGISCHE HOCHSCHULE POTSDAM**
College of Education, Potsdam
Am Neuen Palais, 1500 Potsdam-Sanssouci
Telephone: 9100

Sec. of Marxism-Leninism
Sec. of Education and Psychology
Sec. of Mathematics and Physics
Sec. of Chemistry and Biology
Polytechnic Sec.
Sec. of History, German, and Music
Sec. of Slav and English Studies
Sec. of Education and Physical Education
I. of Languages
I. of Audio-and Tele-Education
Ce. for Scientific Studies
D. of Cultural Education

Founded 1948. Acquired present title 1972. The college is responsible to the Ministry of Education. Governing bodies: the Gesellschaftliche Rat (Social Council); the Wissenschaftliche Rat (Academic Council); the Senate. Residential facilities for c. 2080 students.

Arrangements for co-operation with similar institutions in: USSR; Poland; Hungary; Czechoslovakia.

Academic Year: September to July (September-January; February-July).

Admission Requirements: Secondary school certificate (Reifezeugnis) or equivalent.

Fees: None.

Language of Instruction: German.

Degrees and Diplomas: State diploma, 4 yrs. Doktor, Dr. (Doctorate, first level, in a particular field) by thesis, a further 3-4 yrs. Doktor der Wissenschaften, Dr.sc. (Doctorate, second level) by thesis, 4-5 yrs after Doktor, first level.

Library: Total, c. 267,000 vols.

Publications: Potsdamer Forschungen; Wissenschaftliche Zeitschrift.

Academic Staff: c. 580.

Student Enrolment: c. 2040.

3080 **PÄDAGOGISCHE HOCHSCHULE ZWICKAU**
College of Education, Zwickau
Scheffelstrasse 39, 9500 Zwickau
Telephone: 7480

Sec. of Education and Psychology
Sec. of Marxism and Leninism (including Civics)
Sec. of German and Music
Sec. of Physical Education

Founded 1965 as institute, acquired present status and title 1973. The college is responsible to the Ministry of Education. Governing bodies: the Senate; the Academic Council. Residential facilities for c. 900 students.

Academic Year: September to August (September-January; February-July).

Admission Requirements: Secondary school certificate (Reifezeugnis).

Fees: None.

Language of Instruction: German.

Degrees and Diplomas: State diploma, 4 yrs. Doktor, Dr., (Doctorate first level, in a particular field) by thesis, a further 3-4 yrs.

Library: c. 49,580 vols.

Publication: Scientific Journal.

Academic Staff: c. 180.

Student Enrolment: c. 1110.

GERMANY
(West)

Universities and University Institutions

3081 ***RHEINISCH-WESTFÄLISCHE TECHNISCHE HOCHSCHULE**

Rhenish-Westphalian Technical University
Templergraben 55, 5100 Aachen
Cables: 08/32704 thac d
Telephone: (241) 801
Rektor: Klaus Habetha
Kanzler: Burkhart Müller

F. of Mathematics and Natural Sciences
Dean: D. Schmitz; *staff* 643 (194)
F. of Architecture
Dean: W. Schöfl; *staff* 106 (26)
F. of Civil Engineering
Dean: W. Wittke; *staff* 302 (33)
F. of Mechanical Engineering
Dean: U. Renz; *staff* 1157 (64)
F. of Mining and Metallurgy
Dean: H. Hoberg; *staff* 494 (113)
F. of Philosophy
Dean: L. Jäger; *staff* 203 (25)
F. of Economics
Dean: H. Vormbaum; *staff* 70 (14)
F. of Electrical Engineering
Dean: W. Ameling; *staff* 412 (42)
F. of Medicine
Dean: H. Beier; *staff* 3375 (407)
F. of Education
Dean: B. Gilles; *staff* 195 (32)
I. of Plastic Technology
Head: Georg Menges
Wool Research I.
Director: Helmut Zahn
Rationalization Research I.
Director: Rolf Hackstein
I. of Biomedical Technology
Directors: Günter Rau; Sven Effert
Pre-University Course for Foreign Students
Head: Karl Büttgenbach
House of Technology (Essen)
Director: Eberhard Steinmetz
Technical A. (Wuppertal-Elberfeld)
Director: Werner Holste
Experimental Station for Inland Shipbuilding (Duisburg)
Director: Hans H. Heuser
Research Ce. for Technical and Economic Structures of the Steel Industry
Head: Herman Schenck
Interdisciplinary Ce. for Environmental Protection
Director: H.J. Einbrodt
Research I. for Hydrotechnology
Director: B. Böhnke
Research I. for Laser Technology
Head: Gerd Herziger
Research I. for Production Technology
Head: Wilfried König

Also *c.* 150 institutions, seminars, laboratories, and clinics of the different faculties.

Founded 1870 as Polytechnikum, became Technische Hochschule in 1880 and acquired present title and status in 1948, reorganized 1970. The institution falls under the jurisdiction of and is financed by the State of North Rhine-Westphalia. Governing bodies: the Senat; the Grosse Rat. Residential facilities for academic staff and students.

Arrangements for co-operation with: University of Rheims; Institut national des Sciences appliquées, Lyon-Villeurbanne; Ecole supérieure d'Electricité, Malakoff; State University of Liège; University of Salford; Queen's University, Belfast; Sheffield City Polytechnic; Imperial College, London; Keio University, Tokyo; Indian Institute of Technology, Madras; Florida Atlantic University; Columbia University, New York; Space Institute, University of Tennessee; Osmania University; University of Skopje; National Cheng Kung University, Tainan; Technical University of Madrid; Universities of Cairo and Suez; University of Helsinki; Dong-A University, Busan; Oinghua (Tsinghoua) University, Beijing; Technical University of Warsaw; University of Trondheim (Institute of Technology); Institute of Iron and Steel, Beijing (Peking); Federal University of Santa Catarina.

Academic Year: October to September (October-March; April-September).

Admission Requirements: Secondary school certificate (Reifezeugnis) or equivalent.

Fees: : Tuition, none.

Language of Instruction: German.

Degrees and Diplomas: State Examinations–Prüfung für das Lehramt an höheren Schulen und an berufsbildenden Schulen (teaching qualification, secondary level and vocational schools), 4 yrs; Ärztliche Prüfung, medicine, 5 ½ yrs. Diplomas–Diplom-Ingenieur in–Architecture; Civil Engineering; Mining Engineering; Electrical Engineering; Metallurgy; Mine Surveying; Fuel Technology; Mechanical Engineering. Diplom-Chemiker, chemistry; -Geologe, geology; -Mathematiker, mathematics; -Mineraloge, mineralogy; -Physiker, physics, 4 yrs; -Wirtschaftsingenieur, industrial engineering, 2 yrs. Magister Artium, arts, 4 yrs. Doctorates–Dr.rer.nat.; Dr.phil.; Dr. Ing., 3-4 yrs after diploma. Habilitation (teaching qualification, university level), at least 3 yrs after doctorate.

Libraries: Central Library, *c.* 570,000 vols; institute libraries.

Publication: Alma Mater Aquensis (Annual Report).

Academic Staff, 1986-87:

Rank	Full-time	Part-time
Hochschullehrer	472	–
Wissenschaftliche Mitarbeiter	2351	334
Nichtwissenschaftliche Mitarbeiter	5122	616
Total	7945	950

Student Enrolment, 1986-87:

	Men	Women	Total
Of the country	23,279	8213	31,492
Of other countries	3004	734	3738
Total	26,283	8947	35,230

3082 ***UNIVERSITÄT AUGSBURG**

University of Augsburg
Universitätsstrasse 2, 8900 Augsburg
Telex: 53830
Telephone: (821) 5981
Fax: (821) 598-5505
Präsident: Josef Becker (1987-91)
Kanzler: Dieter Köhler

F. of Economics and Social Sciences
Dean: Richard Stehle; *staff* 105
F. of Law
Dean: Wilfried Bottke; *staff* 48
F. of Catholic Theology
Dean: Joachim Piegsa; *staff* 35
F. of Mathematical and Natural Sciences
Dean: Jürgen Ritter; *staff* 99
F. of Philosophy I (Human Sciences and Education)
Dean: Godwin Lammermann; *staff* 93

F. of Philosophy II (Modern Languages)
Dean: Norbert Oettinger; *staff* 101
D. for Professional Further Training
Head: Michael Kochs
D. for Sports
Head: Helmut Altenberger *staff* 11
Also professional further training in Neu-Ulm, München, Ingolstadt and Chemnitz.

Founded 1970. An autonomous institution financially supported by the State of Bavaria and under the jurisdiction of the Ministry of Education. Governing bodies: the Versammlung; the Senat. Residential facilities for 1200 students

Special arrangements for co-operation with: University of Osijek; University of Pittsburgh. Also arrangements for co-operation with: Universidad Católica Andrés Bello, Caracas; University of the Republic, Montevideo; University of Chile; National University of Córdoba; Pontifical Catholic University of Ecuador; Universidad Católica 'Nuestra Señora de la Asunción'; Universidad Católica 'Madre y Maestra', Santiago; Emory University; Waseda University; Université Laval; Instituto Caro y Cuervo, Bogotá; Université d'Avignon; University of Shandong, Jinan; Universidad de Costa Rica; University of British Columbia; Academia de Ciencias dela República de Cuba; Libera Università degli Studi, Trento.

Academic Year: October to September (October-March; April-September).

Admission Requirements: Secondary school certificate (Reifezeugnis) or equivalent.

Fees: None.

Language of Instruction: German.

Degrees and Diplomas: State Examinations–Juristische Staatsprüfung, law; Prüfung für das Lehramt (teaching qualifications, primary and secondary levels). Diplomas–Diplom-Ökonom, economics; -Mathematiker; -Geograph; -Wirtschaftsmathematiker; -Pädagoge, 4 yrs; -Theologie, 5 yrs. Magister Artium, 4 yrs. Doctorate, Dr., in all fields. Habilitation (teaching qualification, university level), at least 3 yrs after doctorate.

Library: Central Library, 1,570,815 vols.

Press or Publishing House: Pressestelle.

Academic Staff, 1989-90:

Rank	Full-time
Professoren	133
Wissenschaftliche Mitarbeiter	358
Total	491

Student Enrolment, 1989-90:

	Men	Women	Total
Of the country	5538	5160	10,698
Of other countries	303	228	531
Total	5841	5388	11,229*

*Also 868 external students.

3083 ***OTTO-FRIEDRICH-UNIVERSITÄT BAMBERG**

University of Bamberg
Kapuzinerstrasse 16, 8600 Bamberg
Telephone: (951) 863-1
Fax: (951) 863-301
Präsident: Siegfried Oppolzer (1976-92)
Kanzler: Alfred Hemmerlein

F. of Catholic Theology
Dean: Ernst L. Grasmück; *staff* 23 (5)
F. of Education, Philosophy, and Psychology
Dean: Lothar Laux; *staff* 66 (48)
F. of Languages and Literatures (German, English and American, French, Italian, Spanish, Turkish, Arabic, Persian and Urdu/Indian)
Dean: Annegret Bollée; *staff* 56 (26)
F. of History and Geography
Dean: Adrim Hubel; *staff* 43 (18)
F. of Economics, Business Administration, and Social Sciences (including Political Sciences, Business Studies, Economics, Sociology, Demography and Computer Applications to Business Studies)
Dean: Ulrich Meyer; *staff* 74 (12)
S. of Social Work
Head: Hans Günther Essing; *staff* 19 (21)
Computer Ce.
Director: Friedrich Vogel
I. of Physical Education
Ce. for Lifelong Education
Head: Werner Faber
Sociological Research Ce.
Head: Laszlo Vaskovics; *staff* 5
Ce. of Research in the History of the German Language
Head: Rolf Bergmann; *staff* 4
Ce. of Research in Islamic Art
Head: Klaus Krüser; *staff* 6

Founded 1972 as a Gesamthochschule, a new type of university designed to integrate all forms of postsecondary education within a single framework. Incorporating School of Theology, formerly part of 18th century University of Bamberg, and a College of Education established in 1958. An autonomous institution under the jurisdictionof and financially supported by the State of Bavaria. Acquired present title 1979. Governing body: the Senat, comprising 14 members. Limited residential facilities for students.

Arrangements for student exchange with: Brown University; University of South Carolina; University College, Galway; Université de La Réunion; Aston University at Birmingham, UK; University College of Swansea; Budapest University of Economic Sciences; Université de Paris X, Nanterre; Universidad de Deusto, Bilbao; University of Toruń; University of Poznań; Åarhus Universitet; Universtaire Instelling, Antwerp; Université de l'Etat, Liège.

Academic Year: October to September (November-February; May-July).

Admission Requirements: Secondary school certificate (Reifezeugnis).

Fees: None.

Language of Instruction: German.

Degrees and Diplomas: State Examination–Prüfung für das Lehramt an Öffentlichenschulen (teaching qualification, primary and secondary level), 4-5 yrs. Diplomas, Diplom-Theologe; -Pädagoge; -Germanist; -Geograph; -Orientalist; -Historiker; -Soziologe; -Kaufmann; -Volkswirt; -Politologe, 4-5 yrs. Lizentiat in Theology, 5 yrs. Magister Artium, 4-5 yrs. Doctorates–Dr.theol.; Dr.-phil; Dr.rer.pol. Habilitation (teaching qualification, university level).

Library: Central Library, 1,000,000 vols.

Publications: Forschungsbericht (irregular); Bamberger Universitätszeitung, 'Dialog' (7 per year).

Academic Staff, 1989-90:

Rank	Full-time	Part-time
Professoren	130	–
Hauptberuflichtätige	181	–
Lehrbeauftragte Mitarbeiter	30	145
Total	341	145

Student Enrolment, 1989-90:

Of the country	6300
Of other countries	250
Total	6550

3084 ***UNIVERSITÄT BAYREUTH**

University of Bayreuth
Universitätstrasse 30, 8580 Bayreuth
Telex: (17) 92184 UBT
Telephone: (921) 608-1; 55-1
Fax: (921) 55-2208
Electronic mail: x.400: S = siller; P = uni bayreuth; A = dbp; C = de
Präsident: Klaus Dieter Wolff (1973-91)
Kanzler: Wolf-Peter Hentschel

F. of Mathematics and Physics
Dean: Wolf von Wahl; *staff* 140 (90)
F. of Biology, Chemistry, and Earth Sciences
Dean: Hans-Ludwig Krauss; *staff* 350 (246)
F. of Law and Economics
Dean: Egon Görgens; *staff* 135 (40)
F. of Languages and Literature (German, English, Romance, African, Arabic, Islamic, Slav and Comparative Theatre Sciences)
Dean: Werner Röcke; *staff* 60 (20)
F. of Cultural Sciences (Education, Theology, Philosophy, Psychology, Sociology, Ethnology, Political Science, Sport, History and Musical Science)
Dean: Michael Zöller; *staff* 80 (20)
Music and Drama Research I.
Director: Sieghart Döhring; *staff* 8 (2)
Computer Ce.
Head: Friedrich Siller; *staff* 17

Ce. for African Culture
Head: Ulli Beier; *staff* 3 (1)
Language Ce.
Head: Walter Breu; *staff* 15 (2)
Research I. for Experimental Geochemistry and Geophysics
Head: Friedrich Seifert; *staff* 33 (3)
I. for Macromolecular Research
Director: Markus Schwoerer; *staff* 10
I. for African Studies
Director: Helmut Ruppert; *staff* 25 (7)
I. for Materials Science
Director: Claus Eisenbach; *staff* 12
Economic Research Ce.
President: Heymo Böhler; *staff* 15

Founded 1972. Formally opened 1975. Incorporating department of education formerly attached to University of Erlangen-Nuremberg. An autonomous institution financially supported by the State of Bavaria, and under the jurisdiction of its Ministry of Education. Governing bodies: the Versammlung (Assembly), comprising the President, 2 Vice-Presidents, Kanzler, 18 members of the academic staff, 6 scientific employees, 6 representatives of the student body, and 3 members of the non-scientific staff; the Senat. Residential facilities for students in Studentewohnheime.

Arrangements for co-operation with: University of Pécs; University of Dakar; National University of the Côte d'Ivoire; Université du Bénin, Lomé; Université nationale du Bénin, Cotonou; University of Maribor; Université de Perpignan; Université de Paris VII; Indiana University; Shanghai Foreign Language Institute; Aston University, Birmingham; University of Nairobi, Universidad Iberoamericana, Mexico; Université de Picardie, Amiens; Indiana University; University of Delaware; University of Gent; Universidad de la Frontera Temuco, Chile; Université de Montpellier; University of Aalborg; University of Poznań; University of Tel Aviv; University of Durham; University of St. Andrews; Universidad de la Serena, Chile; Gakushuin University, Tokyo; Ecole supérieure de Commerce, Nantes.

Academic Year: October to September (October-March; April-September).

Admission Requirements: Secondary school certificate (Reifezeugnis).

Fees: None.

Language of Instruction: German.

Degrees and Diplomas: State examination–Prüfung für das Lehramt (teaching qualifications, primary and secondary levels). Diplomas–Diplom-Volkswirt; -Kaufmann, 4 yrs; -Mathematiker; -Physiker; -Physiker in Technischer Physik; -Biologie; -Chemiker; -Geograph; -Geoökologe; -Biochemiker; -Sportökonom, 5 yrs; Volljurist; Assessor, 7 yrs. Degrees of Magister Artium. Doctorates–Dr., in all fields. Habilitation (teaching qualification, university level), at least 3 yrs after doctorate. Also Certificates of postgraduate studies: African Sciences, 2 yrs; Sport Law and Sport Administration, 1 yr.

Library: Total, *c.* 980,000 vols.

Special Facilities (Museums, etc.): Ökologisch-Botanischer Garten.

Publications: Thurnauer Schriften zum Musiktheater; Bayreuther Beiträge zur Sprachwissenschaft; Bayreuther Geowissenschaftliche Arbeiten; Bayreuther Beiträge zur Literaturwissenschaft; Spektrum, komparatistische Hefte; Bayreuther Mathematische Schriften; Jahres Bericht; Forschungsbericht (every 3 yrs). Betriebswirtschaftliche Forschungsergebnisse; Schriften zur Gesundheitskonomie; Bayreuther African Studies Series.

Academic Staff, 1989-90:

Rank	Full-time	Part-time
Professoren	162	–
Wissenschaftliche Assistenten	96	1
Akademische Räte und Studienräte	41	-
Wissenschaftliche Hilfskräfte	70	103
Lehrbeauftragte	–	125
Total	369	229

Student Enrolment, 1990:

	Men	Women	Total
Of the country	4332	2454	6786
Of other countries	165	56	221
Total	4497	2510	7007

3085 ***FREIE UNIVERSITÄT BERLIN**
Free University of Berlin
Altensteinstrasse 40, 1000 Berlin 33
Telex: 184019 FUBLN-D
Telephone: (30) 838-1
Präsident: Dieter Heckelmann (1983-92)
Kanzler: Kurt Hammer

D. of Medicine
Dean: Friedrich Körber
D. of Clinical Medicine (Steglitz)
Dean: Hans Weitzel
D. of Clinical Medicine (Charlottenburg)
Dean: Dieter Scheffner
D. of Dentistry
Dean: Karl Eichner
D. of Veterinary Medicine
Dean: Franz Hoerchner
D. of Law
Dean: Georg Thielmann
D. of Economics and Business Administration
Dean: Peter T. Wilrich
D. of Philosophy and Social Sciences I (Psychology, Philosophy, and Sociology)
Dean: Dietrich Boehler
D. of Philosophy and Social Sciences II (Theology, Islamic Studies, Iranian Studies, East Asian Studies, and Ethnology)
Dean: Günter Gobrecht
D. of Communication Sciences
Dean: Axel Zerdick
D. of Education
Dean: Bernard Schwenk
D. of History
Dean: Dietrich Kurze
D. of Classical Studies and Archaeology
Dean: Adalbert Gail
D. of Political Science
Dean: Friedemann Buettner
D. of German Philology
Head: Bernd Balzer
D. of Modern Languages and Literature
Dean: Winfried Engler
D. of Mathematics
Dean: Martin Aigner
D. of Physics
Dean: Helmut Gabriel
D. of Chemistry
Dean: Jürgen Fuhrhop
D. of Pharmacy
Dean: Hans-Dieter Hoeltje
D. of Biology
Dean: Ingolf Lamprecht
D. of Earth Sciences
Dean: Karin Labitzke
I. of Social Science Research
Head: Nils Diederich
Eastern Europe I. (Slav Studies)
Head: Siegfried Baskse
I. of Latin American Studies
Head: Reinhart Liehr
I. of North American Studies
Head: Willi Paul Adams
D. of Physical Education
Director: Harald Binnewies
I. of Data Processing
Director: Alexander Giedke
I. for Didactics and Curricula Research
Head: Andreas Fritsch
Language L.
Director: Wolfgang Mackiewicz

Founded 1948 in response to the demand for the creation of a university in West Berlin. Reorganized and faculty structure replaced 1970. The university is an independent body financially supported by the City of Berlin and the federal government. Governing bodies: the Board of Trustees, including 5 Senators, 3 members of the Abgeordnetenhaus von Berlin (House of Deputies), 9 representatives each of the academic staff and scientific employees, 4 representatives of the employees' organizations or trade unions, and 2 representatives of the student body; the University Council; the Academic Senate. Limited residential facilities for students.

Arrangements for student exchange with the following Universities: Ankara; Istanbul; Leningrad; London; Edinburgh; East Anglia; Cornell; Duke; Indiana; Minnesota; Stanford; Texas; Wake Forest; Maryland; Tulane; Vanderbilt; Washington; Western Michigan; Wisconsin; Laval; York; Kon-Kuk; Nihon; Kyoto; Beijing; Pará (Federal); Copenhagen; Athens; La Paz; Uppsala; Bénin, Togo; Khon-Kaen; Mahidol; Kossuth Lajos, Debrecen; Salta (Nacional); Pelotas (Federal); Lanzhou; Hebrew, Jerusalem; Ohio State; New York at Albany.

Academic Year: October to July (October-February; April-July).

Admission Requirements: Secondary school certificate (Reifezeugnis) or equivalent.

Fees: None.

Language of Instruction: German.

Degrees and Diplomas: State Examinations–Medizinische Staats-prüfung, medicine; Zahnärztliche–, dentistry; Tierärztliche–, veterinary medicine; Juristische–, law; Pharmazeutische–, pharmacy; Pädagogische–; Prüfung für das Lehramt an höheren Schulen (teaching qualification, secondary level, all fields), 4-6 yrs. Diplomas–Diplom-Biologe, biology; -Chemiker, chemistry; -Geologe, geology; -Pädagoge, education; -Kaufmann, business administration; -Mathematiker, mathematics; -Meteorologe, meteorology; -Physiker, physics; -Politologe, political science; -Soziologe, social sciences; -Volkswirt, economics; Library Science, 4-6 yrs. Magister Artium, arts, 4-6 yrs. Doctorates–Dr. in all fields, 1-6 yrs. Zahnärztliche Staatsprüfung and Dr.med.dent., 10 sem; Medizinische Staatsprüfung and Dr.med., 12 sem. Habilitation (teaching qualification, university level), at least 3 yrs after doctorate.

Libraries: Central Library, 1,550,000 vols; libraries of the departments and Central Institute.

Publications: Mitteilungen für Dozenten und Studenten; FU-Dokumentation; Pressedienst Wissenschaft, FU Info; Statistics (biannually).

Academic Staff, 1990:

Rank	Full-time
Professoren	949
Oberassistenten	26
Wissenschaftliche Assistent	266
Wissenschaftliche Mitarbeiter	2616
Total	3857

Student Enrolment, 1990:

	Men	Women	Total
Of the country	26,478	26,687	53,165
Of other countries	2574	2258	4832
Total	29,052	28,845	57,997

3086 **TECHNISCHE UNIVERSITÄT BERLIN**

Technical University of Berlin

Strasse des 17. Juni 135, 1000 Berlin 12

Telex: 184 262 TUBLN D

Telephone: (30) 314-1

Fax: 314-23222

Präsident: Manfred Fricke (1985-)

D. of Communications and Historical Sciences
D. of Social and Planning Sciences
D. of Mathematics
D. of Physics
D. of Synthetic and Analytical Chemistry
D. of Physical and Applied Chemistry
D. of Building Construction and Surveying
D. of Architecture
D. of Mechanics and Thermodynamics
D. of Processing Technology
D. of Construction and Manufacturing
D. of Transport
D. of Food Technology and Biotechnology
D. of Agriculture
D. of International Rural Development
D. of Mining and Earth Sciences
D. of Materials Technology
D. of Economics
D. of Electrical Engineering
D. of Computer Sciences
D. of Environmental Studies
D. of Educational Sciences
I. of Turbulence Research

Founded 1799 as Bauakademie (building academy), became Technische Hoschschule 1879. The Bergakademie (mining academy), founded 1770, was incorporated in 1916. Reopened as Technische Universität in 1946. Reorganized 1969 and faculties replaced by series of Fachbereiche (departments). An autonomous institution financed by West Berlin municipal authorities. Governing bodies: the Academic Senate, composed of 13 professors, 5 members of the academic staff, 4 students, 2 other employees and, without vote, the President as Chairman, the Vice-President, the Chairman of Standing Commissions, the Chancellor, and a representative of the non-academic staff council; the Kuratorium, consisting of the two Senators, the President and 4 members of the House of Parliament of Berlin, 5 members appointed by the Konzil, 4 members appointed by the Academic Senate, 2 employees and 2 representatives of the trade union.

Arrangements for co-operation with the Universities of: Assiut; Cairo; San Andrés, La Paz; Ouru (Technical); North, Antofagasta; Shanghai Jiaotong; Zhejiang; Zheijian (Agricultural); Huazhong; Helsinki (Technical); Paris VI; Toulon; Hasanuddin, Ujung Pandang; Negev; Jerusalem (Hebrew); Keio; Cracow (Technical); Warsaw (Technical); Nova, Lisbon; Istanbul; Istanbul (Technical); Michigan; California, Berkeley; Oklahoma; North Carolina at Chapel Hill. Centre Universitaire, Batna; Beijing Institute of Technology; China Institute of Mining, Xuzhou; Ecole national supérieure de l'Electronique et de ses Applications, Cergy; University College, London; Surabaya Institute of Technology; Weizmann Institute of Science; Technion-Israel Institute of Technology; University of Education and Technology of Columbia, Tanja; Bodø College of Education; Technical University for Heavy Industry, Miskolc; Institute of Machine Tool Engineering, Moscow; Institute of Civil Engineering, Moscow; Massachusetts Institute of Technology.

Academic Year: October to September (October-March; April-September).

Admission Requirements: Secondary school certificate (Reifezeugnis) or equivalent.

Fees: Tuition, none.

Language of Instruction: German.

Degrees and Diplomas: Diplomas–Diplom-Psychologe, psychology; -Mathematiker, mathematics; -Landwirt, agriculture; -Volkswirt, economics; -Geologe, geology; -Mineraloge, mineralogy; -Ingenieur in Mathematics; Physics; Chemistry; Architecture; Civil Engineering; Surveying; Mechanics; Marine Engineering; Aeronautics; Agriculture (including brewery techniques); Mining; Metallurgy; Industrial Engineering; Electrical Engineering. Degree of Magister Artium. Prüfung für das Lehramt an höheren Schulen in den technisch-wissenschaftlichen Fächern (teaching qualification, secondary level, technical sciences). Doctorates–Dr. or Dr.Ing. Habilitation (teaching qualification, university level), at least 3 yrs after doctorate.

Library: University Library, *c.* 1m. vols.

Publications: Vorlesungsverzeichnis der Technischen Universität Berlin (each semester); Universitätsverzeichnis (annually); TU-Journal (monthly); Magazin Wissenschaft (2-3 times a year); TUB Dokumentation; TUB Dokumentation (Lehreund Studium; Kongresse und Tagungen; Weiterbildung); TU-Trends der Wissenschaft.

Academic Staff, 1986-87: c. 2000.

Student Enrolment, 1986-87:

	Men	Women	Total
Of the country	*c.* 16,000	6505	22,505
Of other countries	3630	853	4483
Total	19,630	7358	26,988

3087 ***UNIVERSITÄT BIELEFELD**

University of Bielefeld

Universitätsstrasse 25, 4800 Bielefeld 1

Telex: 932 362 UNIBI

Telephone: (521) 106-1

Fax: (521) 1065844

Rektor: Karl Peter Grotemeyer (1970-92)

Kanzler: Karl Hermann Huvendick

F. of History and Philosophy
Dean: Elizabeth Harder-Gersdorff; *staff* 49 (2)

F. of Linguistics and Literature
Dean: Peter Finke; *staff* 93 (2)

F. of Mathematics
Dean: Ludwig Elsner; *staff* 56 (2)

F. of Education
Dean: Dieter Timmermann; *staff* 48 (8)

F. of Physics
Dean: Dieter Beck; *staff* 44 (12)
F. of Law
Dean: Otto Backes; *staff* 50 (12)
F. of Sociology
Dean: Helmut Willke; *staff* 68
F. of Biology
Dean: Holk Cruse; *staff* 55 (14)
F. of Chemistry
Dean: Thomas Dorfmüller; *staff* 37 (48)
F. of Economics
Dean: Walter Trockel; *staff* 45
F. of Psychology and Physical Education
Dean: Rainer Dollase; *staff* 55 (14)
F. of Theology, Geography, Music and Art
Dean: Ulrich Mai; *staff* 17 (2)
F. of Technology
Dean: Jürgen Lehmann; *staff* 24
Interdisciplinary Research Ce.
Director: Peter Weingart; *staff* 5
I. for the Didactics of Mathematics
Director: Heinrich Bauersfeld; *staff* 17
I. for Mathematical Economics
Director: Joachim Rosenmüller; *staff* 8
Ce. for Teacher Training
Head: Volke Möhle; *staff* 9 (1)
Ce. for Science Studies
Director: Günter Küppers; *staff* 3
Ce. for Science Transfer
Director: Peter Stichel; *staff* 2
I. for Population Research and Social Policy
Director: F.X. Kaufmann; *staff* 4
Ce. for Women's Studies
Director: Marlene Stein-Hilbers; *staff* 3.5
Also 5 Research Centres and 2 experimental schools (Laborschule/Oberstufenkolleg).

Founded in 1969 in response to the demand for the creation of a university in east Westphalia. An autonomous institution financially supported by the State of North Rhine-Westphalia under the jurisdiction of its Ministryof Science and Research. Governing bodies: the Rektorat; the Senat; the Konvent. Residential facilities for students.

Arrangements for co-operation with: Tokyo University of Foreign Studies; Ecole des hautes Etudes en Sciences sociales, Paris; University of Aix-Marseilles; Cairo University; University of Perugia; University of Turin; University of Lyons II; University of Madagascar; University of Warsaw; Chulalongkorn University; University of Groningen; East China Normal University, Shanghai; Ben-Gurion University of the Negev; Academy for Science, Budapest; Academy of Science, Warsaw; Erasmus-University, Rotterdam; The Johns Hopkins University, Baltimore; Reitaku University, Japan; University of Alicante; Wuhan Institute of Physical Education; University of Strasburg; University of Alexandria; California State University, Long Beach.

Academic Year: October to July (October-February; April-July).

Admission Requirements: Secondary school certificate (Reifezeugnis) or equivalent.

Fees: None.

Language of Instruction: German.

Degrees and Diplomas: State Examinations–Diplomas–Diplom-Biologe, biology; -Chemiker, chemistry; -Mathematiker, mathematics; -Betriebswirt, business management; -Physiker, physics; -Pädagoge, education; -Psychologe, psychology; -Soziologe, sociology; -Volkswirt, economics; -Informatiker, computer sciences; Gesundheitswissenschaftler, public health; Sportwissenschaftler, sports; -Referendar, law, 4 yrs. Magister Artium, 4 yrs. Doctorates, Dr., in all fields, 4 yrs. Habilitation (teaching qualification, university level), at least 3 yrs after doctorate. Master's degre: English, French, German, German as a foreign language, History, Latin, Linguistics, Literary Studies, Philosophy, Russian, Spanish/Latin America Studies.

Library: 1,500,000 vols.

Special Facilities (Museums, etc.): Pädagogisches Museum; Kunstgalerie.

Publications: Schriften zum Aufbau einer Universität; Schriftenreihe Wissenschaft (Forschungsbericht der Universität) (annually); Materialien zur Planung; Vorlesungsverzeichnis; Forschungsmagazin (bimonthly).

Academic Staff, 1990:

Rank	Full-time	Part-time
Professoren	272	–
Wissenschaftliche Assistenten	160	–
Wissenschaftliche Mitarbeiter	341	–
Laborschule/Oberstufenkolleg Lehrbeauftragte	148	–
Wissenschaftliche Hilfskräfte	–	210
Total	921	210

Student Enrolment, 1989-90:

	Men	Women	Total
Of the country	6781	6342	12,123
Of other countries	419	360	779
Total	7200	6702	13,902

3088 ***RUHR-UNIVERSITÄT BOCHUM**
University of the Ruhr
Universitätsstrasse 150, 4630 Bochum 1
Telex: 825860
Telephone: 700-1
Rektor: Knut Ipsen
Kanzler: Bernhard Wiebel

F. of Protestant Theology
Dean: Dieter Vetter; *staff* 41
F. of Catholic Theology
Dean: Heribert Smolinsky; *staff* 32
F. of Philosophy, Education, and Journalism
Dean: Detlev Müller; *staff* 83
F. of History (including History of Arts, Archaeology, and Musicology)
Dean: Bernd Bonwetsch; *staff* 85
F. of Languages and Literature
Dean: Harro Müller-Michaels; *staff* 220
F. of Law
Dean: Wolfgang Loschelder; *staff* 114
F. of Economics
Dean: Walther Busse von Colbe; *staff* 95
F. of Social Sciences
Dean: Franz Lehner; *staff* 76
F. of Mechanical Engineering
Dean: Hans Berns; *staff* 237
F. of Civil Engineering
Dean: Klaus Krass; *staff* 187
F. of Electrical Engineering
Dean: Jürgen Mentel; *staff* 170
F. of Mathematics
Dean: Hartmut Ehlich; *staff* 62
F. of Physics and Astronomy
Dean: Manfred Bormann; *staff* 143
F. of Geosciences
Dean: Jürgen Dodt; *staff* 93
F. of Chemistry
Dean: Gerhard M. Schneider; *staff* 134
F. of Biology
Dean: Ulrich Winkler; *staff* 102
F. of Psychology
Dean: Bernhard Zimolong; *staff* 48
F. of Medicine
Dean: Peter Scheide; *staff* 676
F. of Physical Education
Dean: Dieter Voigt; *staff* 46

Founded in 1961 in response to the demand for the creation of a university in the Ruhr area. Formally opened June 1965. Governing bodies: the Versammlung; the Senat. An autonomous institution financially supported by the State of North Rhine-Westphalia, and under the jurisdiction of its Ministry of Education. Some residential facilities for students.

Arrangements for co-operation with the Universities of: Kabul; Cracow; Hyderabad; Mohammed V, Rabat; Orléans; Oviedo; Niš; Sussex; Texas A&M; Tongji, Shanghai; Tokyo; Tours; Bucharest; Keimyung; Utrecht; Sheffield.

Academic Year: October to July (October-February; April-July).

Admission Requirements: Secondary school certificate (Reifezeugnis) or equivalent.

Fees: None.

Language of Instruction: German.

Degrees and Diplomas: State Examinations–Juristische Staatsprüfung, law, 7 sem. Prüfung für das Lehramt an höheren Schulen (teaching qualification, secondary level, all fields), 8 sem. Magister Artium, arts, 8 sem. Diplomas–Diplom-Psychologe, psychology; -Mathematiker, mathematics; -Geophysiker, geophysics; -Pädagogik, education; -Physiker, physics; -Biochemiker, biochemistry; -Ökonom, economics; -Geologe, geology; -Chemiker, chemistry; -Soziologe, social sciences; -Geograph, geography; -Biologe, biology; -Ingenieur, engineering, 8 sem. Doctorates, Dr., approximately 8 sem. Habilitation (teaching qualification, university level), at least 3 yrs after doctorate.

Libraries: University Library, *c.* 700,000 vols; libraries of the faculties and institutes.

Publications: Forschungsbericht; Rechenschaftsbericht des Rektors; Jahrbuch; RUB-aktuell.

Academic Staff, 1986-87:

Rank	Full-time
Professoren	459
Hochschulassistenten	87
Akademische Räte	156
Oberassistenten	3
Studienräte	88
Sonstige beamtete Hilfskräfte	27
Lektoren/Sportlehrer	33
Lehrbeauftragte	263
Wissenschaftliche Assistenten/Wissenschaftliche Mitarbeiter	586
Total	1702

Student Enrolment, 1986:

	Men	Women	Total
Of the country	17,603	10,593	28,196
Of other countries	1202	483	1685
Total	18,805	11,076	29,881

3089 *RHEINISCHE FRIEDRICH-WILHELMS-UNIVERSITÄT BONN

Rhenish Friedrich-Wilhelm University of Bonn
Regina-Pacis-Weg 3, 5300 Bonn 1
Cables: 88 6657 Unibo
Telephone: (228) 731
Rektor: Franz Böckle (1983-)

F. of Protestant Theology
F. of Catholic Theology
F. of Law and Political Science (including Economics)
F. of Medicine (including Dentistry)
F. of Philosophy (including Liberal Arts, Psychology, Political Science, and Musicology)
F. of Mathematics and Natural Sciences (including Pharmacy)
F. of Agriculture (including Surveying)
F. of Education I. of River and Water Jurisprudence
I. of Orthodox Theology
Oriental Languages Seminar
I. of French Culture
I. of Radioastronomy
I. of Bank and Credit Finance
I. of Mathematics
C. for Foreign Students

Also *c.* 190 institutes, seminars, and clinics of the different faculties, and 6 paramedical schools.

Founded 1777 by the Electoral Archbishop of Cologne, raised to university rank 1786, dissolved 1794 during the French occupation. Refounded 1818 by William III of Prussia. Academy of agriculture incorporated 1934. Most buildings destroyed during the Second World War, but since restored. An autonomous institution financially supported by the State of North Rhine-Westphalia, and under the jurisdiction of its Ministry of Education. Governing body: the Senat, composed of the Rector, the Pro-Rektor, 8 deans of faculties, 11 professors, 3 assistants, and 3 students. Residential facilities for some academic staff and *c.* 5000 students.

Arrangements for co-operation with: University of Toulouse; University of Warsaw; Waseda University, Tokyo.

Academic Year: October to September (October-February; April-July).

Admission Requirements: Secondary school certificate (Reifezeugnis) or equivalent.

Fees: None.

Language of Instruction: German.

Degrees and Diplomas: State Examinations–Juristische Staatsprüfung, law; Medizinische–, medicine; Zahnärztliche–, dentistry; Pharmazeutische–, pharmacy; Lebensmitteltechnische–, food technology; Prüfung für das Lehramt an höheren Schulen (teaching qualification, secondary level, all fields); Magisterprüfung, arts. Diplomas– Diplom-Biologe, biology; -Chemiker, chemistry; -Geologe, geology; -Landwirt, agriculture; -Mathematiker, mathematics; -Mineraloge, mineralogy; -Physiker, physics; -Psychologe, psychology; -Vermessungsingenieur, surveying; -Volkswirt, economics. Doctorates–Dr. or Dr.Ing., approximately 8 sem, except Dr.med.dent. and Zahnärztliche Staatsprüfung, 10 sem; Dr.med. and Medizinische Staatsprüfung, 11 sem. Habilitation (teaching qualification, university level), at least 3 yrs after doctorate.

Library: University Library, *c.* 1,500,000 vols.

Special Facilities (Museums, etc.): Akademisches Kunstmuseum (Classical Art); Collection of Mineralogy.

Publications: Politeia; Bonner Akademische Reden; Alma Mater; Bonner Universitäts-Nachrichten.

Academic Staff: c. 720.

Student Enrolment: c. 38,500 (Including *c.* 1500 foreign students).

3090 *TECHNISCHE UNIVERSITÄT CAROLO-WILHELMINA ZU BRAUNSCHWEIG

Carolo-Wilhelmina Technical University of Brunswick
Pockelsstrasse 14 (Forum), 3300 Braunschweig
Telex: 0952526
Telephone: (531) 391-0
Fax: (531)391-4587
Präsident: Bernd Rebe (1983-87)
Kanzler: Harald Wagner

D. of Philosophy and Social Sciences (including Education)
Dean: Ernst Burgschmidt; *staff* 57 (4)
F. of Natural Sciences
Dean: Wolfgang Gey; *staff* 275 (162)
D. of Mathematics, Computer Sciences and Economics
Dean: Helmut Brass; *staff* 81 (30)
D. of Chemistry, Pharmacy, and Biological Sciences (including Psychology)
Dean: Gottfried Galling; *staff* 124 (103)
D. of Physics and Earth Sciences
Dean: Horst Wachendorf; *staff* 70 (29)
D. of Architecture
Dean: Peter Färber; *staff* 33 (38)
D. of Construction Engineering
Dean: Joachim Scheer; *staff* 171 (13)
F. of Mechanical and Electrical Engineering
Dean: Werner Oldekop; *staff* 335 (36)
D. of Mechanical Engineering
Dean: Manfred Mitschke; *staff* 335 (36)
D. of Electrical Engineering
Dean: Manfred Lindmayer; *staff* 139 (12)
D. of Educational Sciences
Dean: Erhard Forndran; *staff* 73 (1)
Wood Research I.
Director: Gert Kossatz
I. of Physical Education
Head: Martin Sklorz
I. of Agricultural Technology and Sugar Manufacturing
Director: E. Reinefeld
Computer Ce.
Head: Georg Bayer
Ce. for Lifelong Education

Founded 1745 as Collegium Carolinum and divided into faculties of arts, commerce, and technology 1835. Reorganized 1862, became Technische Hochschule 1877, and Technische Universität 1968. Severely damaged by bombing in 1944, since reconstructed and enlarged. The Braunschweig branch of the College of Education, Lower Saxony, incorporated 1978. An autonomous institution under the jurisdiction of and financed by the State of Lower Saxony. Governing bodies: the Konzil; the Senat. Some residential facilities for students.

Arrangements for co-operation with: Northwestern Polytechnical University, Xi'an; Tongji University, Shanghai; Chongqing Institute of Architecture and Engineering; East China Technical University of Water Resources, Nanjing; Bandung Institute of Technology; State University of New York; State University of Nebraska; University of Sofia; University of Hull.

Academic Year: October to September (April-September; October-March).

Admission Requirements: Secondary school certificate (Reifezeugnis) or equivalent.

Fees: None.

Language of Instruction: German.

Degrees and Diplomas: Prüfung für das Lehramt an höheren Schulen, naturwissenschaftliche Fächer (teaching qualification, secondary level, natural sciences). Magister Artium, 8 sem. Diplomas– Diplom-Architekt, architecture; -Bauingenieur, civil engineering; -Chemiker, chemistry; -Elektroingenieur, electrical engineering; -Geologe, geology; -Informatiker, data processing; -Mineralogie; -Leibeserziehung, physical education; -Maschinenbauingenieur, mechanical engineering; -Mathematiker, mathematics; -Physiker, physics; -Psychologe, psychology; -Pharmazie; -Geographie; -Biologie; -Pädagogik, 7-10 sem. Doctorates–Dr.rer.nat.; Dr.phil.; Dr.rer.pol.; Dr.Ing., approximately 8 sem. Habilitation (teaching qualification, university level), at least 3 yrs after doctorate.

Library: University Library, *c.* 770,000 vols.

Special Facilities (Museums, etc.): Botanical Gardens.

Publications: Personal-und Vorlesungsverzeichnis; Mitteilungen der Technischen Universität Carolo-Wilhelmina zu Braunschweig; TU aktuell.

Academic Staff, 1986-87:

Rank	Full-time	Part-time
Professoren	276	3
Honorar-Professoren	–	34
Ausserplanmässige Professoren	9	32
Hochschulassistenten	29	–
Akademische Räte/Oberräte	142	–
Lehrbeauftragte und Lektoren	2	137
Privatdozenten	10	19
Total	468	225

Student Enrolment, 1986-87:

Of the country	14,285
Of other countries	618
Total	14,903

3091 **UNIVERSITÄT BREMEN**

University of Bremen

Bibliotheksstrasse, 2800 Bremen 33

Telex: UNI 245811

Telephone: (421) 2181

Rektor: Jürgen Timm (1982-92)

D. of Physics and Electrical Engineering

Speaker: Stefan von Aufschnaiter

D. of Chemistry and Biology

Speaker: Karl Schauz

D. of Mathematics and Computer Sciences

Speaker: Jürgen Friedrich

D. of Mechanical and Process Engineering

Speaker: Klaus Genthner

D. of Geology

Speaker: Gerold Wefer

D. of Law

Speaker: Christian Joerges

D. of Economics

Speaker: Gerhard Leithäuser

D. of Geography, History and Social Sciences

Speaker: Rüdiger Lautmann

D. of Religion, Psychology, and Political and Social Sciences (II)

Speaker: Jörg Berndt

D. of Languages, Art, and Music

Speaker: Françoise Pourardier Duteil

D. of Sport, and Labour and Cultural Sciences

Speaker: Reiner Drechsel

D. of Educational Sciences

Speaker: Wiltrud Drechsel

Founded 1971 as an autonomous institution under the jurisdiction of and financed by the State of Bremen. Previously existing College of Education (1947) incorporated 1973. Governing bodies: the Konvent, composed of 20 professors, 10 assistants, 10 other employees, and 20 representatives of the student body; the Senat, comprising 15 members. Residential facilities for *c.* 1000 students.

Arrangements for co-operation with the Universities of: Paris VIII; Bogotá; Bratislava; Gdansk; Essex; London; Maryland; Poona; Riga; Rostock; Birzeit, Jordan; Nankai; Aarhus. Dickinson College, Carlisle, U.S.A.; Portsmouth Polytechnic; Graduate Faculty of the New School for Social Research, New York; East China Normal University, Shanghai.

Academic Year: October to September (October-March; April-September).

Admission Requirements: Secondary school certificate (Reifezeugnis) or equivalent.

Fees: None.

Language of Instruction: German.

Degrees and Diplomas: State teaching qualifications, secondary level, 4 yrs. Juristische Staatsprüfung, law, 5 yrs. Diplomas–Diplom-Physiker; -Mathematiker; -Informatiker; -Berufspädoge ; -Geograph; -Geologe; Politologe; Soziologe. -Psychologe; -Sozialwissenschaftler; -Ökonom; -Sozialpädagoge; -Pädagoge; -Ingenieur; Magister der -Anglistik;-Romanistik; -deutschen Sprach- und Literaturwissenschaft; -Geschichte; -Kulturgeschichte Osteuropas; -Kulturwissenschaft; -Linguistik; -Philosophie, 4 yrs. -Biologe; -Chemiker, 5 yrs. Doctorates-Dr.phil.; Dr.rer.pol.; Dr.jur.; Dr.Ing.; Dr.rer.nat., 5-6 yrs.

Library: University Library, *c.* 1,200,000 vols.

Publications: Research Reports and Papers; Universitätszeitung. Forschungseitung.

Academic Staff, 1989-90: 800.

Student Enrolment, 1989-90:

Of the country	12,297
Of other countries	881
Total	13,178

3092 **TECHNISCHE UNIVERSITÄT CLAUSTHAL**

Technical University of Clausthal

Adolph-Roeer-Strasse 2A, 3392 Clausthal-Zellerfeld

Telex: 09-53828 TUCLX D

Telephone: (5323) 72-1

Fax: (5323)723 500

Rektor: Georg Müller (1990-92)

Kanzler: Peter Kickartz

F. of Natural Sciences and Humanities

Dean: Heinz-Dietrich Doebner

F. of Mining, Metallurgy, and Mechanical Engineering

Dean: Peter Dietz

D. of Mathematics and Computer Sciences

Director: Hans-Heinrich Kairies

D. of Physics

Director: Heinz-Dietrich Doebner

D. of Chemistry

Director: Eberhard Stumpp

D. of Geology

Director: Peter Halbach

D. of Mining and Raw Materials

Director: Klaus Schönert

D. of Material Sciences and Metallurgy

Director: Hans-Joachim Bunge

D. of Mechanical and Process Engineering

Director: Ulrich Draugelates

Non-metallic Inorganic Materials Testing L.

Head: I. Odler

Computer Ce.

Director: Julius Albrecht

O. for Technology Transfer and Continuous Education

Head: Erhard Schumann

German Petroleum I.

Director: Dagobert Kessel

Founded 1775, became 'Bergakademie Clausthal' 1864, acquired university status 1912. Present title conferred 1968. The university is an autonomous institution under the jurisdiction of and financially supported by the State of Lower Saxony. Governing bodies: the Konzil; the Senat, including representatives of academic and non-academic staff and students. Some residential facilities for academic staff and 900 students.

Arrangements for co-operation with: National University of Salta; National University of Catamarca; University of Mining and Metallurgy, Leoben; University of Ljubljana; Academy of Mining and Metallurgy, Cracow; Federal University of Ouro Prêto; University of Caen; University of Metz; University of Belgrade; University of Rennes; School of Mining, Fuxin; Xiangtan Mining Institute; East China University of Chemical Technology; University of Illinois; Autonomous University of Nuevo Léon; Hunan University, Changsha.

Academic Year: October to September (October-March; April-September).
Admission Requirements: Reifezeugnis (Abitur) or equivalent.
Fees: None.
Language of Instruction: German.
Degrees and Diplomas: Diplomas–Diplom-Bergingenieur, mining engineering; -Chemiker, chemistry; -Geologe, geology; -Geophysiker, geophysics; -Hütteningenieur, metallurgy; -Markscheider, mine surveying; -Maschinenbauingenieur, mechanical engineering; -Mathematiker, mathematics; -Metallkunde, science of metals; -Mineraloge, mineralogy; -Physiker, physics; -Informatiker, computer sciences; -Steine und Erden, ceramics and clay minerals, 8-10 sem. Prüfung für das Lehramt an höheren Schulen in den naturwissenschaftlichen Fächern (teaching qualification, secondary level, natural sciences). Doctorates–Dr.rer.nat.; Dr.Ing. Habilitation (teaching qualification, university level), at least 3 yrs after doctorate.
Libraries: University Library, 271,000 vols; Calvörsche Bibliothek, 4400 (literature).
Special Facilities (Museums, etc.): Musuem of Mineralogy.
Publications: Mitteilungsblatt der TU Clausthal; Informationen der TU Clausthal.
Academic Staff, 1989-90: 1130.
Student Enrolment, 1989-90:

	Men	Women	Total
Of the country	2892	540	3432
Of other countries	310	49	359
Total	3202	589	3791

3093 ***TECHNISCHE HOCHSCHULE DARMSTADT**
University of Darmstadt
Karolinenplatz 5, 6100 Darmstadt
Cables: TH Darmstadt
Telex: 419579 TH D
Telephone: (6151) 161
Fax: (6151) 165 489
Präsident: Helmut Böhme (1971-95)
Kanzler: Hans Seidler

D. of Law and Economics
Dean: Ekkehart Schlicht; *staff* 62
D. of Social Sciences and History
Dean: Gernot Böhme; *staff* 45
D. of Education and Psychology
Dean: Helmut Digel; *staff* 38
D. of Mathematics
Dean: Benno Artmann; *staff* 76
D. of Physics
Dean: Panagiotis Manakos; *staff* 102
D. of Mechanics
Dean: Gerhard Manier; *staff* 33
D. of Chemistry
Dean: Klaus-Heinrich Homann; *staff* 104
D. of Biology
Dean: Kathryn Nixdorff; *staff* 42
D. of Earth Sciences and Geography
Dean: Dietrich Schumann; *staff* 26
D. of Surveying
Dean: Hansdieter Grosse; *staff* 18
D. of Hydraulic and Transport Engineering
Dean: Wolfgang Schröder; *staff* 40
D. of Construction Engineering
Dean: Gert König; *staff* 45
D. of Architecture
Dean: Heiner Kell; *staff* 75
D. of Machine Engineering
Dean: Wolfgang Kubbat; *staff* 156
D. of Electrical Power Engineering
Dean: Jürgen Stenzel; *staff* 48
D. of Radio-Electronics
Dean: Gerhard Sessler; *staff* 49
D. of Electronic Control and Data Processing
Dean: Manfred Glesner; *staff* 53
D. of Computer Sciences
Dean: Gerhard Lustig; *staff* 54
D. of Material Science
Dean: Hans Hartnagel; *staff* 16
I. for Physical Education
Language Ce.
Ce. for Interdisciplinary Studies on Technolgy
Ce. for Applied Mathematics
State Material-Testing I.

Founded 1836 as Höhere Gewerbeschule, became Technische Hochschule in 1877 and acquired university status in 1895. An autonomous institution under the jurisdiction of the State of Hesse. Faculties replaced by a series of departments 1971. Governing bodies: the Konvent; the Senat, including representatives of academic and non-academic staff, and students. Residential facilities for *c.* 1800 students.

Arrangements for co-operation with: Veszprém Technical University of Chemical Engineering; Ecole centrale de Lyon; State University of New York at Buffalo; Tongji University, Shanghai; Technical University of Warsaw; Ben Gurion University of the Negev; Middle East Technical University, Ankara; State University of Campinas; New University of Lisbon; University of Bordeaux II; University of Birmingham; University of East Anglia, Norwich; University of Surrey; Autonomous University of Nuevo León; Cornell University; Technical Institute of Bucharest; University of Graz; University of Florence; University of Compiègne; University of Iceland; University of Illinois; Université catholique de Louvain; Czech Technical University, Prague; Tongji University, Shanghai; Institut national polytechnique de Grenoble; Université d'Orléans;University of Bagdad; University of Sussex; Trinity College, Dublin; Politecnico di Torino; Instituto superior Técnico, Lisboa; Universidade de Coimbra; National Cheng Kung University, Taiwan; University of Technology, Eindhoven; Royal Institute of Technology, Stockholm; Imperial College, London.
Academic Year: October to September (November-February; April-July).
Admission Requirements: Secondary school certificate (Reifezeugnis) or equivalent.
Fees: None.
Language of Instruction: German.
Degrees and Diplomas: State teaching qualifications, secondary and technical levels, 9-11 sem. Diplomas–Diplom-Ingenieur, engineering; -Informatiker, computer sciences; -Chemiker, chemistry; -Biologe, biology; -Geologe, geology; -Mineraloge, mineralogy; -Mathematiker, mathematics; -Physiker, physics; -Meteorologe, meteorology; -Wirtschaftsingenieur, industrial engineering, 10-13 sem. Degrees of Magister Artium, M.A. in–History; Literature and Language (German Studies); Political Science; Sports Studies; Educational Theory; Geography, 9-12 sem. Doctorates–Dr. or Dr.-Ing., a further 2-3 yrs. Habilitation (teaching qualification, university level), at least 3 yrs after doctorate.
Library: Land (State) and University Library, *c.* 900,000 vols.
Special Facilities (Museums, etc.): Botanical Garden.
Publications: Die Hochschule (every 2 weeks); Personal-und Studienplanverzeichnis (annually); Jahrbuch (annually); Rechenschaftsbericht des Präsidenten (annually); Forschungsbericht (biannually); THD-Intern (every 3 weekws).
Academic Staff, 1990:

Rank	Full-time
Professoren	330
Hochschulassistenten	28
Wissenschaftliche Mitarbeiter	823
Total	1181

Student Enrolment, 1990:

	Men	Women	Total
Of the country	11,886	2882	14,768
Of other countries	1107	285	1392
Total	12,993	3167	16,160

3094 ***UNIVERSITÄT DORTMUND**
University of Dortmund
August-Schmidt-Strasse, 4600 Dortmund 50
Telex: 822465
Telephone: (231) 755-1
Rektor: Detlef Müller-Böling
Kanzler: Klaus Anderbrügge

D. of Mathematics
Dean: Manfred Reimer; *staff* 76
D. of Physics
Dean: Dieter Nachtigall; *staff* 132
D. of Chemistry
Dean: Herbert Jacobs; *staff* 151
D. of Chemical Engineering
Dean: Karl Strauss; *staff* 165

D. of Computer Sciences
Dean: Herbert Weber; *staff* 98
D. of Mechanical and Industrial Engineering
Dean: Ludolf Cronjäger; *staff* 129
D. of Electrical Engineering
Dean: Edmund Handschin; *staff* 116
D. of Urban and Regional Planning
Dean: GWalburga Rödding; *staff* 94
D. of Economics and Social Sciences
Dean: Karl Kurbel; *staff* 76
D. of Statistics
Dean: Götz Trenkler; *staff* 23
D. of Construction Engineering (including Architecture)
Dean: Gernot Nalbach; *staff* 90
D. of Education and Biology
Dean: Hand Günther Rolff; *staff* 70
D. of Special Education and Rehabilitation of the Handicapped
Dean: Dietmar Schmetz; *staff* 58
D. of Human Sciences (including Theology, Political Science, Psychology and Home Economics)
Dean: Klaus Bräuer; *staff* 63
D. of Language and Literature (including Journalism and History)
Dean: Albert Klein; *staff* 78
D. of Music, Arts, Sport, and Geography
Dean: Stephan Starischka; *staff* 62
I. of Occupational Health
Head: H.M. Boldt
I. of Spectrochemistry
Director: Günther Tölg
I. of Environmental Studies
Head: Hans-Jürgen Karpe
Ce. for Didactics
Head: Sigrid Metz-Göckel
I. for Transport Technology
Head: R. Jünemann
I. of Robotics Research
Head: E. Freund
Computer Ce.
Ce. for Lifelong Education
Director: Werner Habel

Founded 1965, opened 1968. An autonomous institution financially supported by the State of North Rhine-Westphalia and under the jurisdiction of its Ministry of Science and Research. College of Education of the Ruhr incorporated 1980. Governing bodies: the Convocation, which elects the Rector; the Senat, comprising members of the professional staff, other members of academic staff and students; the Kuratorium, composed of lay members appointed by the Minister of Education on the recommendation of the Rector. Residential facilities for academic staff and 1777 students.

Arrangements for co-operation with: Université de Picardie; Technische Hogeschool, Twente; University of Pisa; University of Sheffield; Liverpool Polytechnic; State University of New York at Buffalo; Istituto Universitario di Architettura, Venezia; Technical University of Szczecin; Beijing University of Iron and Steel Technology; University of Science and Technology, Kumasi; University of Agriculture, Gödöllö; Institut national de Sciences appliquées, Rouen.

Academic Year: October to July (October-February; April-July).

Admission Requirements: Secondary school certificate (Reifezeugnis) or equivalent.

Fees: None.

Language of Instruction: German.

Degrees and Diplomas: State Examinations–Prüfung für das Lehramt an höheren Schulen und an berufsbildenden Schulen (teaching qualification, secondary and vocational schools), 3-4 yrs. Diplom-Ingenieur, in various fields; -Mathematiker; -Physiker; -Chemiker; -Statistiker; -Informatiker, computing; -Volkswirt, economics; -Pädagoge; -Journalist; -Kaufmann; -Sozialoekonom, 4-5 yrs. Doctorates–Dr.Ing.; Dr.rer.nat.; Dr.rer.pol., economics; Dr.oec.; Dr. phil.; Dr.paed., 3-4 yrs after Diploma. Habilitation (teaching qualification, university level), at least 3 yrsafter doctorate.

Libraries: University Library, 728,000 vols; libraries of the departments and institutes, *c.* 468,000

Publications: Forschungsbericht (every 3 yrs); Amtliche Mitteilungen; Vorlesungsverzeichnis; Uni-Report (biannually).

Press or Publishing House: Presse-und Informationsstelle der Universität Dortmund.

Academic Staff, 1989-90: c. 1014.

Student Enrolment, 1989-90: c. 17,760.

3095 ***HEINRICH-HEINE-UNIVERSITÄT DÜSSELDORF**

University of Düsseldorf
Universitätsstrasse 1, 4000 Düsseldorf 1
Telex: 8587 348 UNI D
Telephone: (211) 31-11
Fax: (211)342-2229 Electronic Mail: BITNET: kaiserđ0rud81
Rektor: Gert Kaiser (1983-)
Kanzler: Carl Friedrich Curtius

F. of Medicine (including Dentistry)
Dean: Peter Pfitzer; *staff* 775 (72)
F. of Mathematics and Natural Sciences (including Pharmacy and Psychology)
Dean: Detlev Riesner; *staff* 283 (248)
F. of Philosophy
Dean: Wilhelm Busse; *staff* 191 (33)
F. of Economics (in preparation)
Diabetic Research I.
Director: Hans Reinauer; *staff* 37
I. of Dietetics and Nutrition
Director: Hans Reinauer; *staff* 37
Air Pollution and Silicosis Research I.
Director: Hans Schlipköter; *staff* 48
Ce. for Neurological Therapy
Dean: V. Hömberg; *staff* 2
Also *c.* 50 institutes and clinics of the faculties.

Founded 1907 as an Academy for practical medicine, acquired university status 1923. Became university 1965 and acquired present title 1989. Under the jurisdiction of and financially supported by the State of North Rhine-Westphalia. Governing body: the Senat. Residential facilities for academic staff and students.

Arrangements for co-operation with: University of Nantes; University of Naples; University of Beijing; University of Alicante; University of Reading

Academic Year: October to September (October-February; April-July).

Admission Requirements: Secondary school certificate (Reifezeugnis) or equivalent.

Fees: None.

Language of Instruction: German.

Degrees and Diplomas: State Examinations–Ärztliche Staatsprüfung, medicine; Zahnärztliche–, dentistry; Pharmazeutische–, pharmacy, 3 ½-6 yrs. Prüfung für das Lehramt an höheren Schulen (teaching qualification, secondary level). Magisterprüfung, arts, 4 yrs. Diplomas–Diplom-Mathematiker, mathematics; -Physiker, physics; -Biologe, biology; -Psychologe, psychology; -Chemiker, chemistry; -Erziehungswissenschaft, education, 4 yrs. Doctorates–Dr. in all fields, 6 yrs.

Libraries: Central Library, *c.* 2.2m vols; specialized libraries, *c.* 540,000; Medicine, *c.* 440,000.

Special Facilities (Museums, etc.): Botanical Institute; Botanical Garden.

Publications: Calendar (biannually); Yearbook (biennially).

Academic Staff, 1990:

Rank	Full-time	Part-time
Professoren	336	–
Ausserplanmässige Professoren und Privatdozenten	–	353
Wissenschaftliche Mitarbeiter und Hochschulassistenten	913	–
Total	1249	353

Student Enrolment, 1990:

	Men	Women	Total
Of the country	7518	7539	15,057
Of other countries	726	731	1457
Total	8244	8270	16,514

3096 ***UNIVERSITÄT GESAMTHOCHSCHULE-DUISBURG**

University of Duisburg
Lotharstrasse 65, 4100 Duisburg 1
Telex: 855793 UNIDUD
Telephone: (203) 3790
Fax: (203) 379-3333
Rektor: Gernot Born (1986-90)
Kanzler: Rudolf Baumanns

D. of Philosophy, Theology, and Social Sciences
Dean: Dankwart Danckwerts; *staff* 75 (54)
D. of Education, Psychology, and Physical Education
Dean: Manfred Bayer; *staff* 42 (23)
D. of German and Romance Languages and Literature
Dean: Herbert Kaiser; *staff* 60 (53)
D. of Fine and Applied Arts
Dean: Norbert Linke; *staff* 11 (54)
D. of Economics
Dean: Manfried Tietzel; *staff* 74 (15)
D. of Biology, Chemistry, and Geography
Dean: Robert Kosfeld; *staff* 11 (54)
D. of Mechanical, Industrial and Marine Engineering
Dean: Manfred Hiller; *staff* 13 (9)
D. of Mining Engineering, Foundry and Glass Technology, Ceramics
Dean: Rüdiger Zeihe; *staff* 14 (5)
D. of Electrical Engineering
Dean: Heinz Fissan; *staff* 124 (8)
D. of Physics and Technology
Dean: Roland Feder; *staff* 69 (14)
D. of Mathematics
Dean: Hans-Joachim Arnold; *staff* 42 (1)

Founded 1972 as a Gesamthochschule, a new type of university designed to integrate all forms of postsecondary education within a single framework. Incorporating the Duisburg branch of the College of Education of the Ruhr and the Technical College, Duisburg. An autonomous institution under the jurisdiction of and financially supported by the State of North Rhine-Westphalia. Residential facilities for students.

Special arrangements for co-operation with: Universidade Federal de Minas Gerais; University of Minnesota. Also co-operation with: University of Washington; Portsmouth Polytechnic; Louis Pasteur University, Strasbourg; Central School of Planning and Statistics, Warsaw; Dokkyo University; University of Kyoto; University of Durham; Huazhong University of Science and Technology, Wuhan; Wuhan University.

Academic Year: October to September (October-March; April-September).

Admission Requirements: Secondary school certificate (Reifezeugnis). Fachhochschulreife (technical secondary school education) for certain courses.

Fees: None.

Language of Instruction: German.

Degrees and Diplomas: State Examinations–Prüfung für das Lehramt (teaching qualification, secondary level), 4 yrs. Diplomas, 3 yrs. Doctorates, Dr. Habilitation (teaching qualification, university level).

Libraries: University Library, *c.* 650,500 vols; department libraries.

Publications: Vorlesungsverzeichnis; Amtliche Mitteilungen; Uni-Report (University newspaper).

Academic Staff, 1989-90:

Rank	Full-time	Part-time
Professoren	252	–
Wissenschaftliche Personal	432	71
Assistenten	72	–
Lehrbeauftragte	–	230
Total	756	301

Student Enrolment, 1989-90:

	Men	Women	Total
Of the country	8319	3871	12,190
Of other countries	623	226	849
Total	8942	4097	13,039

3097 ***KATHOLISCHE UNIVERSITÄT EICHSTÄTT**

Catholic University of Eichstätt
Ostenstrasse 26, 8078 Eichstätt
Cables: Uni Eichstätt
Telex: 55941 LRAED
Telephone: (8421) 201
Fax: (8421) 20474
Präsident: Nikolaus Lobkowicz (1984-96)
Kanzler: Carl Heinz Jacob

F. of Catholic Theology
Dean: Bernhard Mayer; *staff* 31 (5)
F. of Education and Philosophy
Dean: Reto Fetz; *staff* 37 (34)
F. of Modern Languages and Literature (German, English, Romance, American; Journalism, Classical Philosophy (including Medieval Latin) and Archaeology)
Dean: Otto Winkelmann; *staff* 58 (8)
F. of History and Social Sciences (including Political Science, Sociology and Ethnology)
Dean: Hans Maul; *staff* 24 (1)
F. of Mathematics and Geography
Dean: Hans-Peter Blatt; *staff* 34 (10)
F. of Business Administration
Dean: Eduard Gangler; *staff* 25
F. of Religious Education
Dean: Walentin Hertle; *staff* 12 (75)
F. of Social Service
Dean: Peter Erath; *staff* 13 (17)
I. of Latin American Studies
Director: Karl Kohut; *staff* 6
Special Collaborative P. with University of Würzburg (transmission of knowledge in late Middle Ages)
Director: Georg Steer; *staff* 10 (5)
Research Ce. for Ethnology of Old European Languages
Director: Alfred Baummesberger; *staff* 5

Also Summer Courses in German for Foreign Students; Introduction to German Language and Culture (one year programme).

Founded 1972 as Gesamthochschule, incorporating College of Education, founded 1958 and College of Philosophy and Theology, established 1924 and tracing its origins to the Collegium Willibaldinum, founded 1564. A new type of university designed to integrate all forms of postsecondary education within a single framework. Became university 1980. An autonomous institution financially supported by the State of Bavaria 90% and the seven Bavarian Dioceses (10%). Governing bodies: the Senat, comprising 15 members; the Versammlung (Assembly), comprising 36 members. Residential facilities for students.

Arrangements for co-operation with: Catholic University of America; University of Aberdeen; University of São Paulo; Catholic University of Lublin.

Academic Year: October to September (November-February; May-July).

Admission Requirements: Secondary school certificate (Reifezeugnis).

Fees: None.

Language of Instruction: German.

Degrees and Diplomas: Diplomas–Diplom-Religionspädagoge; Sozialpädagoge, 4 yrs; -Geograph, -Journalist, -Kaufmann, -Mathematiker, -Pädagoge, -Psychologe, 4 ½ yrs. Lizentiat in Theology. Degree of Magister Artium, 4 yrs. Prüfung für das Lehramt an höheren Schulen (teaching qualification, secondary level, all fields). Doctorates–Dr. theol.; Dr.phil.; Dr.rer.nat. Habilitation (teaching qualification, university level), at least 3 yrs after doctorate.

Library: Central Library, *c.* 1,200,000 vols.

Special Facilities (Museums, etc.): T.V. and Broadcasting Studio; Computer Centre; German Language Training Centre.

Publications: Eichstätter Theologische Studien; Eichstätter Hochschulreden; Eichstätter Beiträge; Eichstätter Materialien.

Academic Staff, 1989-90:

Rank	Full-time	Part-time
Professoren	115	2
Wissenschaftliche und künstlerische Mitarbeiter	170	6
Lektoren	–	172
Total	285	280

Student Enrolment, 1990:

	Men	Women	Total
Of the country	1039	1448	2487*

*Also 143 foreign students.

3098 ***FRIEDRICH-ALEXANDER-UNIVERSITÄT ERLANGEN-NÜRNBERG**

Friedrich Alexander University of Erlangen-Nuremberg
Schlossplatz 4, 8520 Erlangen
Telex: 06-29 830 UNIER D

Telephone: (9131) 851
Fax: (9131)85-2131
Rektor: Gothard Jasper (1990-)
Kanzler: Thomas A. H. Shörk

F. of Theology
Dean: A.I.C. Hevon
F. of Law
Dean: C. Link
F. of Medicine (including Dentistry)
Dean: E. Lungershausen
F. of Philosophy I (Philosophy, History and Social Sciences)
Dean: E. Olbrich
F. of Philosophy II (Languages and Literature)
Dean: T. Heydenreidn
F. of Natural Sciences I (Mathematics and Physics)
Dean: P. Plaumann
F. of Natural Sciences II (Biology and Chemistry)
Dean: H. Kersten
F. of Natural Sciences III (Earth Sciences)
Dean: U. Treter
F. of Economics and Social Sciences
Dean: W. Pfeiffer
F. of Technology
Dean: A. Kuhn
F. of Education
Dean: W. Einsiedler
Astrophysics Ce. (Bamberg)
Director: I. Bues
I. of Biomedical Technology
Director: Max Schaldach
Social Science Research Ce.
Director: U. Schlottmann
Computer Ce.
Head: F. Wolf
Physical Education Ce.
Head: E. Wahl

Founded 1743 by Friedrich of Bayreuth. In the 19th century the university occupied the Castle of Erlangen, presented to it by Friedrich Wilhelm III of Prussia. The former Hochschule für Wirtschafts-und Sozialwissenschaften, Nürnberg, was formally incorporated as a faculty of the university in 1961, and the name Nürnberg was added to its title. College of Education, Nuremberg incorporated 1972. Reorganized 1974. An autonomous institution, financially supported by the State of Bavaria and under the jurisdiction of its Ministry of Education. Governing bodies: the Versammlung; the Senat. Residential facilities for academic staff and students in several hotels.

Arrangements for co-operation with: Universities of Rennes I, II; Ain-Shams University; University of Cracow; University of St. Andrews, Scotland.

Academic Year: October to September (October-March; April-September).

Admission Requirements: Secondary school certificate (Reifezeugnis) or equivalent.

Fees: None.

Language of Instruction: German.

Degrees and Diplomas: State Examinations–Juristische Staatsprüfung, law; Pharmazeutische–, pharmacy; Lebensmittelchemie–, food chemistry; Medizinische–, medicine; Zahnärztliche–, dentistry, 3-6 yrs. Prüfung für das Lehramt an höheren Schulen (teaching qualification, secondary level, all fields). Diplomas–Diplom-Chemiker, chemistry; -Biologe, biology; -Mineraloge, mineralogy; -Betriebswirt, business management; -Sozialwirt; -Ingenieur, engineering, several fields; -Geologe, geology; -Handelslehrer (commercial teaching qualification); -Mathematiker, mathematics; -Physiker, physics; -Psychologe, psychology; -Volkswirt, economics. Degree of Magister Artium, 4 yrs. Doctorates–Dr. or Dr.-Ing. Habilitation (teaching qualification, university level), at least 3 yrs after doctorate.

Libraries: University Library, *c.* 3,456,000 vols; Faculty of Econo-mics and Social Sciences, *c.* 164,000; Engineering, *c.* 70,000; Education, *c.* 68,000.

Publications: Erlanger Forschungen; Erlanger Universitätsreden; Jahrbuch der Fränkischen Landesforschung.

Academic Staff, 1987-88: c. 2030.
Student Enrolment, 1988-89:

Men	Women	Total
17,095	10,404	27,499*

*Including 1164 foreign students.

3099 ***UNIVERSITÄT-GESAMTHOCHSCHULE-ESSEN**

University of Essen
Universitätsstrasse 2, 4300 Essen 1
Telex: 08-579091 UNIE D
Telephone: (201) 183-1
Fax: (201)183-2151
Rektor: Christian Streffer (1988-92)
Kanzler: Dieter Leuze

D. of Philosophy, Religious Studies, and Social Sciences
Dean: Günter Schmitt
D. of Education, Psychology, and Physical Education
Dean: Tassilo Knauf
D. of Languages and Literature
Dean: Jochen Vogt
D. of Fine and Applied Arts
Dean: Paul Schüllner
D. of Economics
Dean: Joachim Zentes
D. of Mathematics
Dean: Wilfried Schwirtz
D. of Physics
Dean: Volker Buck
D. of Chemistry
Dean: Paul Rademacher
D. of Architecture and Bio-Geosciences
Dean: Guido Benno Feige
D. of Construction Engineering
Dean: Ewald Bubner
D. of Surveying
Dean: Friedrich-Wilhelm Ehrich
D. of Mechanical Engineering
Dean: Wolfgang Merzkirch
D. of Energetics, Processing Engineering, and Electronics
Dean: Rudolf Pruschek
D. of Medicine
Dean: Wolfgang Fischer

Founded 1972 as a Gesamthochschule, a new type of university designed to integrate all forms of postsecondary education within a single framework. Incorporating former Departments of Theoretical and Practical Medicine of the University of the Ruhr, the Essen branch of the College of Education of the Ruhr, and the Technical College. An autonomous institution under the jurisdiction of and financially supported by the State of North Rhine-Westphalia. Residential facilities for *c.* 1600 students.

Arrangements for co-operation with: Beijing Medical University; Tongji Medical University, Wuhan; Tianjin University; Ain Shams University; University of Alexandria; University of Braşov; Academy of Medicine, Sofia; National Research Centre, Cairo; University of Queensland; University of Porto; University of Pisa; Tampere University of Technology; University College of North Wales, Bangor; University College, Dublin; Centre universitaire de Luxembourg; California State University of Long Beach.

Academic Year: October to September (October-March; April-September).

Admission Requirements: Secondary school certificate (Reifezeugnis), or Fachhochschulreife (technical secondary education) for certain courses, or special examination to qualify for studies at university level (Einstufungsprüfung) if over 24 yrs of age and following at least 5 yrs vocational experience.

Fees: None.

Language of Instruction: German.

Degrees and Diplomas: State Examinations–Ärztliche Prüfung, medicine. Prüfung für das Lehramt (teaching qualifications, primary and secondary level), 3-4 yrs. Diplomas–Diplom-Mathematiker; -Physiker; -Chemiker; -Kaufmann, business administration; -Volkswirt, economics; -Ingenieur, engineering, several fields; -Designer; -Pädagoge; -Ökologe, 4 yrs. Degree of Magister Artium, 4 yrs. Doctorates–Dr.; Dr.med., *c.* 4 yrs after diploma. Habilitation (teaching qualification, university level), at least 3 yrs after doctorate.

Library: Central Library, *c.* 810,000 vols.

Publications: Rechenschaftsbericht des Rektorats; Forschungsberichts; Essener Universitätsberichte; Informationsheft fürStudienbewerber; Schriften und Berichte.

Academic Staff, 1990:

Rank	Full-time
Universitätsprofessoren, Professoren, Honorarprofessoren	*c.* 361
Hochschuldozenten/Oberassistenten/Oberingenieure	*c.* 30
Wissenschaftliche Assistenten	*c.* 107
Wissenschaftliche Mitarbeiter/Hilfskräfte	*c.* 235
Lehrbeauftrage	*c.* 271
Total	*c.*1850

Student Enrolment, 1990:

	Men	Women	Total
Of the country	9086	6627	15,713
Of other countries	658	322	980
Total	9744	6949	16,693

3100 **NORDISCHE UNIVERSITÄT**

Speicherlinie 34a, 2390 Flensburg

F. of Economics

F. of Agriculture (in process of development)

F. of Engineering (in process of development)

Founded 1985.

3101 **PÄDAGOGISCHE HOCHSCHULE FLENSBURG**

College of Education

Mürwikerstrasse 77, 2390 Flensburg

Telephone: (461) 35052

Fax: (461) 38543

Rector: W. Schmid (1989-92)

Kanzler: Dieter Hass

Education

Also 23 disciplines including didactics for primary and secondary teacher education.

Founded 1946. Reorganized 1973. Financially supported by the State of Schleswig-Holstein. Governing bodies: the Konsistorium, comprising 48 members; the Senat, comprising 15 members. Residential facilities for 90 students.

Arrangements for co-operation with: University of Salford; Penn State University; California State University,Sacramento; Teacher Training College, Silkeborg.

Academic Year: October to September (October-March; April-September).

Admission Requirements: Secondary school certificate (Reifezeugnis) or equivalent.

Fees: None.

Language of Instruction: German.

Degrees and Diplomas: Erste Staatsprüfung für das Lehramt, for primary education, 3 yrs; for lower secondary education, 3 ½ yrs. Diplompädagoge, 4 yrs. Doctorate, Dr.sc.päd.

Library: 120,000 vols.

Academic Staff, 1990:

Rank	Full-time	Part-time
Professoren	41	–
Wissenschaftliche Mitarbeiter	40	–
Lehrbeanfragte	–	80
Total	81	80

Student Enrolment, 1990:

	Men	Women	Total
Of the country	235	501	736
Of other countries	11	3	14
Total	246	504	750

3102 **JOHANN WOLFGANG GOETHE-UNIVERSITÄT FRANKFURT**

Johann Wolfgang Goethe University of Frankfurt

Senckenberganlage 31, 6000 Frankfurt am Main 11

Telex: 413932 UNIF D

Telephone: (69) 798-1

Präsident: Klaus Ring (1986-94)

Kanzler: Wolfgang Busch

D. of Law

Dean: Hans Meyer; *staff* 73

D. of Medicine (including Dentistry)

Dean: Hans Joachim Müller; *staff* 585

D. of Philosophy

Dean: Norbert Altwicker *staff* 22

D. of Economics

Dean: Ulrich Ritter *staff* 113

D. of Educational Sciences

Dean: Helga Deppe; *staff* 160

D. of Psychology

Dean: Peter Kutter; *staff* 45

D. of Theology

Dean: Josef Hainz; *staff* 68

D. of Social Sciences

Dean: Alfred Lorenzer; *staff* 121

D. of History

Dean: Johannes Fried; *staff* 59

D. of Classical Philology and Fine Arts

Dean: Hadwig Hörner; *staff* 112

D. of Philology (Germanic and Romance)

Dean: Olaf Hansen; *staff* 191

D. of Eastern and Non-European Languages and Culture

Dean: Bodo Zelinsky; *staff* 48

D. of Mathematics

Dean: Jürgen Wolfart; *staff* 40

D. of Physics

Dean: Wolfgang Pohlit; *staff* 97

D. of Chemistry

Dean: Walter Sterzel; *staff* 47

D. of Biochemistry and Pharmacy (including Food Technology)

Dean: Hugo Fasold; *staff* 47

D. of Biology

Dean: Christian Winter *staff* 76

D. of Earth Sciences

Dean: Hans Barth; *staff* 67

D of Geography

Dean: Wilhelm Lutz; *staff* 26

D. of Labour Studies and Physical Education

Dean: Dieter Böhme; *staff* 50

D. of Computer Sciences

Dean: Mario Dal Cin; *staff* 12

Also 119 institutes, seminars, and clinics.

Founded 1914 by public subscription and with the support of the City of Frankfurt. As a result of inflation in the 1920s the university lost most of its capital. Financial responsibility accepted by the Prussian State and City of Frankfurt 1923. Title of Johann Wolfgang Goethe adopted 1932. It is now an autonomous institution financed by the State of Hesse. Governing bodies: the Konvent; the Senat.

Arrangements for co-operation with: Universities of Lyons; Trenton State College, New Jersey; Hebrew University of Jerusalem; University of Tel Aviv; University of Turin; University of Pisa; Vilnius State University; Eastern Illinois University; University of Wisconsin, Milwaukee; University of Southampton.

Academic Year: October to September (October-March; April-September).

Admission Requirements: Secondary school certificate (Reifezeugnis) or equivalent.

Fees: None.

Language of Instruction: German.

Degrees and Diplomas: State Examinations–Juristische Staatsprüfung, law; Lebensmittel-chemische–, food chemistry; Medizinische–, medicine; Zahnärztliche–, dentistry; Pharmazeutische–, pharmacy; Prüfung für das Lehramt an Schulen (teaching qualifications, elementary, primary or secondary level, or for the education of handicapped, all fields). Diplomas–Diplom-Chemiker, chemistry; -Geologe, geology; -Geophysiker, geophysics; -Handelslehrer (commercial teaching qualification); -Kaufmann, business administration; -Informatiker, computer sciences; -Theologe (Kath.); -Sportswissenschaftlicher, physical education; -Mathematiker, mathematics; -Meteorologe, meteorology; -Pädagoge; -Biologe; -Geographe; -Mineraloge, mineralogy; -Physiker, physics; -Psychologe, psychology; -Soziologe, sociology; -Volkswirt, economics. Degree of Magister Artium, 8 sem. Doctorates–Dr. in all fields, approximately 8 sem, except Dr.med.dent. and Zahnärztliche Staatsprüfung, 10 sem; Dr.med. and Medizinische Staatsprüfung, 13 sem.Habilitation (teaching qualification, university level), at least 3 yrs after doctorate.

Libraries: Municipal and University Library, *c.* 2,400,000 vols; Senckenberg Library *c.* 930,000; libraries of the departments and institutes *c.* 2,000,000.

Special Facilities (Museums, etc.): Senckenberg-Museum.

Publications: Rechenschaftsbericht (annually); Forschungsbericht (biennially); Studienführer (annually); Personalverzeichnis (annually); Vorlesungsverzeichnis (biannually); Jahresbibliographie (triennially).

Academic Staff, 1986-87:

Rank	Full-time
Emeritierte und pensionierte Professoren	129
Universitätsprofessoren	588
Hochschulassistenten	58
Honorarprofessoren	234
Privatdozenten	187
Lehrbeauftragte	775
Oberstudienräte und Studienräte i.H.	25
Akademische Direktoren, Akademische Oberräte und Räte mit Unterrichtsaufgaben	8
Lektoren	22
Aussesplanmässige Professoren	21
Gastprofessor	1
Professorenstellenvertreter	12
Total	2060

Student Enrolment, 1986-87:

	Men	Women	Total
Of the country	14,563	12,363	26,926
Of other countries	1359	1107	2446
Total	15,922	13,450	29,372

3103 ***ALBERT-LUDWIGS-UNIVERSITÄT FREIBURG IM BREISGAU**

Albert Ludwig University of Freiburg
Heinrich-von-Stephan-Strasse 25, 7800 Freiburg im Breisgau
Telex: 772740-60 UFD
Telephone: (761) 2031
Rektor: Christoph Rüchardt (1987-91)
Kanzler: Friedrich-Wilhelm Siburg

F. of Theology (Catholic)
Dean: Lothar Ruppert; *staff* 23 (21)
F. of Law
Dean: Albin Eser; *staff* 31 (26)
F. of Economics
Dean: Dietrich Lüdecke; *staff* 16 (11)
F. of Medicine
Dean: Klaus Starke; *staff* 664 (119)
F. of Philosophy
I (Fine Arts)
Dean: Uwe Koch; *staff* 32 (26)
II (Foreign Languages and Literature)
Dean: Eckard Lèfevre; *staff* 27 (34)
III (Germanic and English Studies)
Dean: Bernhard Greiner; *staff* 30 (29)
IV (History, Political and Social Sciences)
Dean: Christian Strahm; *staff* 29 (42)
F. of Mathematics
Dean: Otto H. Kegel; *staff* 15 (10)
F. of Physics
Dean: Josef Honerkamp; *staff* 23 (14)
F. of Chemistry and Pharmacy
Dean: Kurt-Heinz Bauer; *staff* 33 (11)
F. of Biology
Dean: Rudolf Hausmann; *staff* 41 (8)
F. of Earth Sciences
Dean: Hugo Ganser; *staff* 27 (31)
F. of Forestry
Dean: Michel Becker; *staff* 21 (20)

Founded 1457 by Archduke Albrecht of Austria and confirmed by the Emperor and the Pope. Brought into strongly dependent relationship to the State in the 18th century. Now academically autonomous but financially supported by the State of Baden-Württemberg and under the jurisdiction of its Ministry of Science and Art. Teaching staff employed by the State (Land), independent in teaching and research, responsible to the above mentioned Ministry. No legal relationship with municipal authorities. The status of the university is guaranteed by the Constitution of the State (Land). Governing bodies: the Grosser Senat; the Senat. Senior and junior members of academic staff, students, and non-academic employees are members of both bodies. Some residential facilities for students.

Special arrangements for co-operation with the Universities of: Strasbourg (I,II,III); Grenoble (II and III); Sussex; Massachusetts; Texas (Austin); Glasgow; Wayne State; Michigan; Michigan State. Also arrangements with: 'Al. I. Cuza' University, Iaşi; University of Innsbruck; Hebrew University, Jerusalem; Universidad Complutense de Madrid; University of Padua; Institute of European Studies, Chicago.

Academic Year: October to July (October-February; April-July).

Admission Requirements: Secondary school certificate (Reifezeugnis) or equivalent.

Fees: None.

Language of Instruction: German.

Degrees and Diplomas: State Examination–Juristische Staatsprüfung, law; Medizinische–, medicine; Zahnärztliche–, dentistry; Pharmazeutische–, pharmacy; Prüfung für das Lehramt an höheren Schulen (teaching qualification, secondary level, all fields). Diplomas– Diplom-Chemiker, chemistry; -Forstwirt, forestry; -Geologe, geology; -Mathematiker, mathematics; -Mineraloge, mineralogy; -Physiker, physics; -Psychologe, psychology; -Volkswirt, -Betriebswirt, economics. Magister Artium, arts, 8 sem. Doctorates–Dr., in all fields, approximately 8 sem, except Dr.med. and Medizinische Staatsprüfung, 11 sem. Habilitation (teaching qualification, university level), at least 3 yrs after doctorate.

Library: University Library, 2m. vols.

Publications: Freiburger Universitätsblätter; Uni-Aktuell.

Academic Staff, 1986-87:

Rank	Full-time
Professoren	448
Honorarprofessoren	47
Ausserplanmässige Professoren,Privatedozenten	279
Hochschulassistenten	70
Wissenschaftliches Personal	1582
Total	2426

Student Enrolment, 1986-87:

	Men	Women	Total
Of the country	13,150	8957	22,107
Of other countries	830	843	1673
Total	13,980	9800	23,780

3104 ***JUSTUS LIEBIG-UNIVERSITÄT GIESSEN**

Justus Liebig University of Giessen
Ludwigstrasse 23, 6300 Giessen
Telex: 04-82956
Telephone: (641) 702-1
Fax: 702-2099
Präsident: Heinz Bauer
Kanzler: Ludwig Wolf

D. of Law
D. of Economics
D. of Social Sciences
D. of Education
D. of Physical Education and Fine Arts
D. of Psychology
D. of Theology
D. of History
D. of German Language and Literature
D. of English and Anglo-American Literature
D. of Mediterranean and East European Languages and Literature
D. of Mathematics
D. of Physics
D. of Chemistry
D. of Biology
D. of Applied Biology (Agriculture and Environment Conservation)
D. of Veterinary Medicine
D. of Nutrition and Home Economics

D. of Food Technology
D. of Earth Sciences and Geography
D. of Medicine (including Pharmacy and Dentistry)
Ce. for Data Processing
Radiation Ce. (including Nuclear Physics and Radiation Protection)
Continental Agricultural and Economic Research Ce.
Ce. for Basic Philosophy of Science
Teacher Training Ce.
Ce. for Regional Development Research
I. of Tropical Studies
Also *c.* 120 affiliated institutions of the departments.

Founded 1607 as university. Became the Justus Liebig-Hochschule (academy) in 1946. Full university status restored 1957. An autonomous institution financially supported by the State of Hesse, and under the jurisdiction of its Ministry of Education. Governing bodies: the Konvent, comprising 40 representatives of the academic staff, 10 research-auxiliary personnel, 10 technical and other personnel; and 30 representatives of the student body; the Senat. Some residential facilities for students.

Special arrangements for co-operation with: Kansas State University (student exchange); Universidad de los Andes, Bogotá; University of Wisconsin, Milwaukee and Madison; University of Agriculture Gödöllö; Université de Limoges; University of Łódź; Universidade Federal do Paraná; Northwest China College of Agriculture, Wugong; Ege Üniversitesi, Izmir; Institute of Agriculture, Bucharest; Institute of Agriculture, Iaşi; Kasetsart University; Ecole nationale vétérinaire de Nantes; University of Warwick; University of Naples; Kazan State University.

Academic Year: October to September (October-February; April-July).

Admission Requirements: Secondary school certificate (Reifezeugnis) or equivalent.

Fees: None.

Language of Instruction: German.

Degrees and Diplomas: State Examinations–Juristische Staatsprüfung, law; Medizinische–, medicine. Diplomas–Diplom-Biologe, biology; -Chemiker, chemistry; -Geologe, geology; -geograph, geography; -Landwirt, agriculture; -Mathematiker, mathematics; -Mineraloge, mineralogy; -Betriebswirt, economics; -Psychologie, psychology; -Physiker, physics; -Wirtschaftslehre des Haushalts, home economics, 4-6 yrs. Degree of Magister Artium, 4 yrs. Doctorates–Dr., in all fields, 8-14 sem. Habilitation (teaching qualification, university level), at least 3 yrs after doctorate.

Library: University Library, *c.* 450,000 vols.

Special Facilities (Museums, etc.): Biological Garden.

Publications: Personal- und Vorlesungsverzeichnis der Justus-Liebig-Universität; Uni-Forum; Spiegel der Forschung.

Academic Staff, 1989-90: c. 985.

Student Enrolment, 1989-90:

	Men	Women	Total
Of the country	9491	9936	19,427
Of other countries	584	431	1015
Total	10,075	10,367	20,442

3105 ***GEORG-AUGUST-UNIVERSITÄT GÖTTINGEN**
Georg August University of Göttingen
Wilhelmsplatz 1, 3400 Göttingen
Telex: 96703
Telephone: (551) 39-4311/12
Fax: (551) 399612
Präsident: Norbert Kamp
Kanzler: Klaus Volle

F. of Theology (Protestant)
F. of Law
F. of Medicine (including Dentistry)
F. of History and Philosophy
F. of Mathematics
F. of Physics
F. of Chemistry
F. of Earth Sciences
F. of Biology
F. of Forestry
F. of Agriculture
F. of Economics
F. of Social Sciences
F. of Education
Also 150 institutes, seminars, and clinics of the different faculties.

Founded 1737 by George II, Prince Elector of Hanover and King of England, and was the first modern university foundation in Germany. An autonomous institution financially supported by the State of Lower Saxony, and underthe jurisdiction of its Ministry of Science and Arts. Governing bodies: the Senat; the Konzil, comprising 130 members. Some residential facilities for students.

Arrangements for co-operation with Universities in: China, Japan, Mexico, U.S.A., Hungary, Netherlands, and several European countries.

Academic Year: April to March (April-September; October-March).

Admission Requirements: Secondary school certificate (Reifezeugnis) or equivalent.

Fees: None.

Language of Instruction: German.

Degrees and Diplomas: State Examinations–Juristische Staatsprüfung, law; Medizinische–, medicine, 2 sem; Prüfung für das Lehramt an Gymnasien, teaching qualification, secondary level, all fields; Zahnärztliche–, dentistry, 10 sem. Diplomas–Diplom-Theologe, theology; -Mathematiker, mathematics; -Wirtschaftsmathematiker, economic mathematics; -Physiker, physics; -Geophysiker, geophysics; -Chemiker, chemistry; -Geograph, geography; -Geologe, geology; Mineraloge, mineralogy; -Biologe, biology; Psychologe, psychology; -Forstwirt, forestry; -Agraringenieur, agricultural engineering; -Kaufmann, business management; -Volkswirt, economics; -Handelslehrer, commercial teaching qualification; -Sozialwirt, social sciences; -Pädagoge, education; Degree of Magister Artium in–History; Philology and Social Sciences, 4-5 yrs. Doctorates-Dr., in all fields. Period of study approximately 9 sem, resp. 4-5 yrs, except Lehramt an Gymnasien, 10 sem, Medizinische Staatsprüfung, 12 sem, Zahnmedizinische Staatsprüfung, 10 sem. Habilitation (teaching qualification, uiversity level) at least 3 yrs after doctorate.

Library: University and State Library of Lower Saxony, *c.* 3m. vols.

Special Facilities (Museums, etc.): Art Gallery; Ethnological Museum; Zoological Museum; Chemical Museum; Archaeological Museum; Musical Instruments; Physical Instruments; Geological Museum; Biological Garden; Movie Studio.

Publications: Personal-und Vorlesungsverzeichnis; Georgia-Augusta, Nachrichten aus der Universität Göttingen.

Academic Staff, 1990:

Rank	Full-time	Part-time
Professoren	557	10
Assistenten	1611	792
Total	2168	802

Student Enrolment, 1990:

	Men	Women	Total
Of the country	16,236	12,252	28,488
Of other countries	1035	709	1744
Total	17,271	12,961	30,232

3106 ***FERNUNIVERSITÄT-GESAMTHOCHSCHULE**
Open University
Feithstrasse 152, 5800 Hagen 1
Cables: feuni d
Telex: 823137
Telephone: (2331) 804-1
Fax: (2331) 804-313
Rektor: Ulrich Battis (1984-94)
Kanzler: Ralf Bartz

F. of Economics
Dean: A. Kuss; *staff* 50 (139)
F. of Law
Dean: D. Tsatsos; *staff* 24 (34)
F. of Mathematics and Computer Sciences
Dean: W. Schneeweiss; *staff* 76 (75)
F. of Electronics
Dean: H. Wupper; *staff* 33 (20)
F. of Social Sciences and Education
Dean: K. Röttgers; *staff* 55 (64)
I. of Distance Study Research
Director: Börje Holmberg; *staff* 9 (1)
Ce. for Distance Study Development
Director: J. Wurster; *staff* 22 (4)
Computer Ce.
Director: Klaus Sternberger; *staff* 12 (7)
Study centres in: Berlin (1); Bremen (1); Hessen (3); Lower Saxony (3); North Rhine-Westphalia (29); Austria (3); Bavaria (1); Hamburg (1).

Founded 1974 by decision of the Government of North Rhine-Westphalia as an integrated Gesamthochschule to provide distance education for both full-time and part-time students. Instruction is given by correspondence courses, cassettes, and video-cassettes and the University has set up a network of study and advisory centres. Governing bodies: the Kuratorium; the Konvent; the Senat, composed of the Rector, the Pro-Rector, 8 professors, 3 other members of the academic staff, 3 students, and 2 members of non-academic staff, together with the Chancellor, ex officio.

Arrangements for co-operation with: Université de Paris X; Université de Grenoble; Universidad del Valle Cali, Colombia; Universidad Estatal a Distancia, San José, Costa Rica; Open Universiteit, Heerlen, Netherlands; Technical University, Brno, Czechoslovakia; Universidad Nacional de Educación a Distancia, Madrid.

Academic Year: Winter and Summer semesters corresponding to a year of 28 weeks full-time study.

Admission Requirements: Secondary school certificate (Hochschulreife or Fachhochschulreife) or recognized equivalent.

Fees (Marks): 250 per semester; part-time, 150.

Language of Instruction: German.

Degrees and Diplomas: Diplom in various fields, 3 1/2-5 yrs. Magister Artium. Doctorates. Habilitation (teaching qualification, university level).

Library: 460,000 vols (including study and advisory centres).

Special Facilities (Museums, etc.): Sound Stage; Movie Studio.

Publications: Transparent (monthly staff journal); Contacte; Fernuniversität - Die Hagener Hochschulzeitung.

Academic Staff, 1989-90: 270 (300).

Student Enrolment, 1989-90:

Of the country	39,355
Of other countries	1849
Total	41,204*

*All students by correspondence.

3107 ***UNIVERSITÄT HAMBURG**

University of Hamburg

Edmund-Siemens-Allee 1, 2000 Hamburg 13

Cables: uni hh

Telex: 214732

Telephone: (40) 4123-4475

Fax: (40) 4123-2449

Präsident: Peter Fischer-Appelt (1970-91)

Leitender Verwaltungsbeamter: Hugbert Flitner

D. of Theology (Protestant)
Dean: Henning Paulsen; *staff* 27 (37)

D. of Law I
Dean: Michael Köhler; *staff* 111 (34)

D. of Law II
Dean: Peter Behrens; *staff* 44 (29)

D. of Economics (including Data Processing)
Dean: Dieter Pressmar; *staff* 192 (40)

D. of Medicine (including Dentistry)
Dean: Karl Heinz Hölzer; *staff* 1034 (29)

D. of Philosophy and Social Sciences
Dean: Heinz J. Kleinsteuber; *staff* 85 (31)

D. of Education
Dean: Wolfgang Schulz; *staff* 186 (228)

D. of Languages
Dean: Heimo Reinitzer; *staff* 187 (169)

D. of History (including Classical Philology)
Dean: Arnold Sywottek; *staff* 55 (27)

D. of Fine Arts (including Archaeology and Ethnology)
Dean: Hermann Hipp; *staff* 47 (45)

D. of Oriental Studies
Dean: Jutta Rall-Niu; *staff* 57 (35)

D. of Mathematics
Dean: Claus Peter Ortlieb; *staff* 65 (14)

D. of Physics (including Astronomy)
Dean: Heinrich J. Wendker; *staff* 205 (30)

D. of Chemistry (including Pharmacy)
Dean: Heindirk tom Diek; *staff* 306 (35)

D. of Biology (including Wood Economics)
Dean: Eckart Zeiske; *staff* 239 (47)

D. of Earth Sciences
Dean: Martin Dunst; *staff* 177 (38)

D. of Psychology
Dean: Detlef Rhenius; *staff* 53 (78)

D. of Computer Sciences
Dean: Christopher Habel; *staff* 88 (21)

D. of Physical Education
Dean: Claus Tiedemann; *staff* 22 (78)

I. for Shipbuilding
Director: Harald Keil; *staff* 22 (4)

I. for Radio and Television
Director: Wolfgang Hoffmann-Riem; *staff* 8

I. for Peace Research and Security
Director: Egon Bahr; *staff* 8

I. for Integration Research
Director: Eberhard Grabitz; *staff* 5

Computer Ce.
Director: Karl Kaiser; *staff* 18 (1)

Interdisciplinary Ce. for University Didactics
Director: Gerhard Portele; *staff* 13

International Tax I.
Director: Gerold Krause-Junk; *staff* 8

Theatre I. for Drama
Director: Johannes Krogoll; *staff* 5

Also 126 institutes and seminars.

Founded 1919 with four faculties created through the incorporation of a number of existing institutions. Reorganized under a presidential constitution 1969 and faculties replaced by 19 Fachbereiche (departments) and several central institutes. The university is an autonomous institution in which all academic staff and students take part in the tasks of self-government. Financially supported by the State of Hamburg and under the jurisdiction of its Ministry of Science and Research. Governing bodies: the Academic Senate, including the President, Vice-President, 11 professors, 1 lecturer, 3 assistants, 4 students, and 2 members of the administrative staff; the Council, including the Vice-President, 15 professors, 5 lecturers, 11 assistants, 16 members of the non-academic staff, and 16 students; the Councils of the departments. Residential facilities for *c.* 3800 students.

Special arrangements for co-operation with: Technical University of Dresden; College of Transport and Communications, Dresden; Academy of Medicine, Dresden; College of Education, Dresden; Leningrad State University; Institute of Shipbuilding, Leningrad; Technical University of Gdańsk; University of Warsaw; Charles University, Prague; Prague College of Economics; Eötvös Loránd University, Budapest; University of Economics, Budapest; University of Forestry and Wood Sciences, Sopron; University of Zagreb; University of Belgrade; University of Bucharest; University of Sofia; Aegean University, Izmir; Dokuz Eylül University, Izmir; Hebrew University of Jerusalem; University of Tel Aviv; University of Bordeaux III; University of Southampton; University of Bradford; University of East Anglia, Norwich; Jordanhill College of Education, Glasgow; The Johns Hopkins University, Baltimore; Temple University, Philadelphia; Smith College, Northampton; Cornell University, Ithaca; Ohio State University, Columbus; Indiana University, Bloomington; Purdue University, West Lafayette; Tulane University, New Orleans; Autonomous University of Nuevo León, Monterrey; University of Guadalajara; University of Khartoum; Beijing University of Foreign Studies; Tongji University, Shanghai; Shanghai Second Medical University. Also participates in the ERASMUS programme.

Academic Year: October to September (October-February; April-July).

Admission Requirements: Secondary school certificate (Reifezeugnis) or equivalent.

Fees: None.

Language of Instruction: German.

Degrees and Diplomas: State Examinations–Juristische Staatsprüfung, law; Lebensmittelchemische–, food chemistry; Medizinische–, medicine; Zahnärztliche–, dentistry; Pharmazeutische–, pharmacy, 3-6 yrs. Prüfung für das Lehramt an höheren Schulen (teaching qualification, secondary level, all fields). Diplomas, Diplom, in–Shipbuilding, 3-5 yrs; Insurance, 3 1/2 yrs; Economics; Business Administration; Philosophy and Social Science; Education; Wood Economics; Psychology; Computer Sciences; Music and Theatre; Economic Engineering, 4 yrs; Physics, Chemistry, 4 1/2 yrs; Earth Sciences, 4-5 yrs; Mathematics, 5 yrs. Magister–Mag.theol.; Mag.phil., 4 yrs. Doctorates–Dr., in all fields, 4-5 yrs, except Dr.med.; Ärztliche Prüfung, 6 yrs. Habilitation (research qualification), at least 3 yrs after doctorate. Lehrbefugnis als Privatdozent (teaching qualification, university level) after Habilitation.

Libraries: State and University Library, 2,000,000 vols; Hamburg Research Centre and Archives of World Economics, 850,000.

Special Facilities (Museums, etc.): Museums of: Mineralogy; Zoology; Geology; Applied Botany. Botanical Garden.

Publications: uni hh Berichte und Meinungen; uni hh Reform; uni hh Forschung; uni hh Planung; Informationen zum Studium in Hamburg; Wegweiser durch die Universität; Informationen für ausländische Studenten; Jahresbericht des Präsidenten.

Academic Staff, 1988:

Rank	Full-time	Part-time
Professoren	1022	–
Assistenten	571	–
Sonstiges wissenschaftliche Personal	938	–
Lehrbeauftragte	–	1066
Total	2531	1066

Student Enrolment, 1988-89;

	Men	Women	Total
Of the country	21,690	17,890	39,580
Of other countries	1085	935	2020
Total	22,775	18,825	41,600*

*Also 1290 external students.

3108 **TECHNISCHE UNIVERSITÄT HAMBURG-HARBURG**

Technical University Hamburg-Harburg
Schlossmühlendamm 30, 2100 Hamburg
Telephone: (40) 77-18-1
Fax: (40) 77-18-2288
Präsident: Heinrich Mecking (1987-93)
Leitender Verwaltungsbeamter: Justus Woydt

D. of Mechanical Engineering
D. of Electrical and Electronical Engineering
D. of Industrial Process Engineering and Chemical Engineering
D. of Construction Engineering
Research Area of City and Environment Technology
Research Area of Systems Engineering
Research Area of Construction and Marine Technologies
Research Area of Information and Communication Technologies
Research Area of Materials, Design, and Manufacturing
Research Area of Processing Technology and Energy Systems

Founded 1978. Admitted first students 1982. Divided unto 4 teaching departments and 6 research areas. Under the jurisdiction of the State of Hamburg. Governing body: the Konzil.

Arrangements for co-operation with: Technical University, Prague; Ege Ùniversitesi, Izmir; Iowa State University; University of Notre Dame; University of Toulouse; University of Science and Technology, Shanghai; Université Aix-Marseille II; Ecole de Mines de Saint-Etienne; University of Lublin; Technical University of Luleå.

Academic Year: October to September (April-July; October-February).

Admission Requirements: Secondary school certificate (Abitur).

Fees: None.

Language of Instruction: German.

Degrees and Diplomas: Title of Diplom-Ingenieur, Dipl.Ing., 4 1/2 yrs. Doktor-Ingenieur, *c.* 3 yrs.

Library: University Library, *c.* 220,000 vols.

Academic Staff, 1990: c. 420.

Student Enrolment, 1990:

	Men	Women	Total
Of the country	972	138	1110
Of other countries	117	20	137
Total	1089	158	1247

3109 **MEDIZINISCHE HOCHSCHULE HANNOVER**

Hanover Medical School
Konstanty-Gutschow-Strasse 8 3000 Hannover 61
Telex: 922044
Telephone: (511) 5321
Fax: (511) 532-3852
Rektor: Heinz Hundeshagen (1989-91)
Leiterin des Rektorats: Almuth Plumeier

Medicine
Dentistry
Biochemistry
Pharmacy
Public Health Medical Technology and Informatics
Training Ce. (for Technicians and Nurses)

Founded 1963. Admitted first students 1965. An autonomous institution under the jurisdiction of and financially supported by the State of Lower Saxony. Governing bodies: the Rektor; the Senat; the Konzil. Residential facilities for students.

Arrangements for co-operation with Jinan University; Hiroshima University.

Academic Year: October to September (October-March; April-September).

Admission Requirements: Secondary school certificate (Reifezeugnis) or equivalent.

Fees: None.

Language of Instruction: German.

Degrees and Diplomas: Staatsexamen, State Examination in–Dentistry, 11 sem; Medicine, 12 sem. Dr.med.dent.; Dr.med; Dr.biol.hum. Habilitation (teaching qualification, university level), at least 3 yrs after doctorate.

Library: c. 212,000 vols.

Publication: Mitteilungen der Medizinischen Hochschule Hannover (research projects, published every 2 yrs).

Academic Staff, 1989-90: 1000.

Student Enrolment, 1989-90:

	Men	Women	Total
Of the country	1940	1551	3491
Of other countries	100	80	180
Total	2040	1631	3671

3110 ***UNIVERSITÄT HANNOVER**

University of Hanover
Welfengarten 1, 3000 Hannover 1
Telex: 923868 UNIHN D
Telephone: (511) 762-0
Fax: (511) 762-2768
Präsident: Hinrich Seidel (1979-91)
Kanzler: Jan Gehlsen

D. of Mathematics
Dean: K. Kopfermann; *staff* 83
D. of Physics
Dean: H. Welling; *staff* 92
D. of Chemistry
Dean: G. Meyer; *staff* 139
D. of Earth Sciences
Dean: L. Schätzl; *staff* 68
D. of Biology
Dean: R. Pott; *staff* 56
D. of Architecture
Dean: G. Harder; *staff* 100
D. of Civil Engineering and Surveying
Dean: R. Mull; *staff* 220
D. of Mechanical Engineering
Dean: H. Haferkamp; *staff* 243
D. of Electrical Engineering
Dean: J. Graul; *staff* 167
D. of Horticulture
Dean: J. Grunewaldt; *staff* 193
D. of Soil Conservation
Dean: K. Selle; *staff* 47
D. of Literature and Languages
Dean: D. Hoeges; *staff* 51
D. of History, Philosophy, and Social Sciences
Dean: O. Mickler; *staff* 71
D. of Education Sciences II
Dean: K. Rüttersr *staff* 6871
D. of Law
Dean: F.-J. Peine; *staff* 78
D. of Economics
Dean: U. Schreiber; *staff* 157
D. of Educational Sciences I (Teacher Training)
Dean: R. Narr; *staff* 157

Also 6 Research Areas, including Marine Engineering, Chemical Research.

Founded 1831 as Höhere Gewerbeschule (secondary vocational school), became Polytechnische Hochschule 1847 and Königliche Technische Hochschule 1879. Accorded university status 1880. Reorganized 1922 and became Technische Universität 1968 and Universität 1978. An autonomous institution under the jurisdiction of and financed by the State of Lower Saxony. Governing body: the Senat, comprising 7 professors, 2 scientific collaborators, 2 representatives of the student body, and 2 representatives of the non-academic staff.

Arrangement for cooperation with: Rijksuniversiteit, Gent; Universidade Federal do Rio Grande do Sul, Porto Alegre; Polytechnika Poznanzka; Université de haute Normandie, Rouen; University of Nebraska; Kalinin Polytechnikum, Leningrad; Kyushu University, Fukuoka. Also arrangements for student exchange with: Michigan Technological University; Purdue University; University of Nebraska. Participates in the ERASMUS and LINGUA programmes.

Academic Year: October to September (October-March; April-September).

Admission Requirements: Secondary school certificate (Reifezeugnis) or foreign equivalent.

Fees: None.

Language of Instruction: German.

Degrees and Diplomas: State Examinations–Juristische Staatsprüfung, law; Prüfung für das Lehramt an Grund-und Hauptschulen, Realschulen, Gymnasien, Berufsbildende schulen, Sonderschulen (teaching qualifications). Diplomas–Diplom-Mathematiker, mathematics; -Geologe, geology; -Sozialwissenschaftlicher, Social Sciences; -Architekt, architecture; -Geograph, geography; -Physiker, physics; -Chemiker, chemistry; -Ingenieur, engineering; -Pädagoge; -Meteorologe; -Ökologe, 4-5 yrs. Degree of Magister Artium, 4 yrs. Doctorate–Dr. or Dr.Ing. Habilitation (teachingqualification, university level), at least 3 yrs after doctorate.

Libraries: University Library, 3,440,000 vols; State Library of Lower Saxony (including department libraries of University of Hanover), *c.* 1,700,000.

Publication: Zeitschriften der Universität Hannover (Präsident der Universität Hannover, Bericht der Präsidenten/Zahlenspiegel and Forschungsbericht).

Academic Staff, 1989-90:

Rank	Full-time
Professoren	407
Wissenschaftliche Mitarbeiter	848
Total	1255

Student Enrolment, 1989-90:

	Men	Women	Total
Of the country	17,058	10,060	27,118
Of other countries	870	434	1,304
Total	17,928	10,494	28,422

3111 **TIERÄRZTLICHE HOCHSCHULE HANNOVER**

Hanover School of Veterinary Medicine

Bischofsholer Damm 15, 3000 Hannover 1

Telex: 9 22034 TIHO D

Telephone: (511) 856-6

Fax: (511) 856-7685

Rektor: Michel Rommel (1989-91)

Kanzler: Hans Linnemann

Veterinary Medicine (including Food Technology)

Founded 1778 as school, acquired university status 1887. Residential facilities for students.

Arrangements for co-operation with: Universidad Austral de Chile; University of Bristol; Universidade Federal do Rio Grande do Sul; Universidade Federal de Minas Gerais; Universidade Federal de Santa Maria; Universidade Rural de Pernambuco; Universidade Federal da Bahia; Universidade de São Paulo; University of Veterinary Sciences, Budapest; University of Ankara; Ecole nationale vétérinaire, Lyon; University of Khartoum; Warsaw Agricultural University; Universidad de Córdoba; College of Veterinary Medicine, Helsinki; Nanjing Agricultural University; Kujushu-University, Fukuoka; Cornell University, Ithaca; University of Leipzig.

Academic Year: October to July (October-February; April-July).

Admission Requirements: Secondary school certificate (Abitur) or equivalent.

Fees: None.

Language of Instruction: German.

Degrees and Diplomas: State Examination–Tierärztliche Staatsprüfung, veterinary medicine, 5 yrs. Doctorate–Dr.med.vet., by thesis. Habilitation, Privatdozent, venia legendi (teaching qualification, university level), at least 3 yrs after doctorate.

Library: Central Library, *c.* 69,000 vols.

Special Facilities (Museums, etc.): Veterinärmedizinhistorisches Museum.

Publication: TiHo-Anzeiger (8 times a year).

Academic Staff, 1989:

Rank	Full-time
Professoren	67
Wissenschaftliche Mitarbeiter	278
Technische/Verwaltliche Mitarbeiter	678
Total	1023

Student Enrolment, 1989:

	Men	Women	Total
Of the country	700	1127	1827
Of other countries	73	59	132
Total	773	1186	1959

3112 ***RUPRECHT-KARLS-UNIVERSITÄT HEIDELBERG**

Rupert Charles University of Heidelberg

Grabengasse 1, Postfach 105760, 6900 Heidelberg

Telex: 46 15 15

Telephone: (6221) 541

Fax: (6221) 542618

Rektor: Volker Sellin (1987-91)

Kanzler: Siegfried Kraft

F. of Theology (Protestant)
Dean: Theo Sündermeier; *staff* 43
F. of Law
Dean: Thomas Hillenkamp; *staff* 48
F. of Basic Medical Sciences
Dean: Hartmut Kirchheim; *staff* 65
F. of Theoretical Medicine
Dean: Friedrich Vogel; *staff* 136
F. of Clinical Medicine I
Dean: Christian Herfarth; *staff* 425
F. of Clinical Medicine II (including Dentistry)
Dean: Werner Hacke; *staff* 257
F. of Clinical Medicine (Mannheim)
Dean: Uwe Ganzer; *staff* 71
F. of Philosophy and History
Dean: Hermann Jakobs
F. of Oriental Studies and Antiquities
Dean: Harald Hauptmann
F. of Modern Languages
Dean: Norbert Greiner
F. of Economics (including Physical Education)
Dean: Oskar Gans
F. of Social and Behavioural Sciences
Dean: Wolfgang Schluchter
F. of Mathematics
Dean: Friedrich Tomi
F. of Chemistry
Dean: Dieter Hellwinkel
F. of Physics and Astronomy
Dean: Roland Wielen
F. of Biology
Dean: Konrad Beyreuther
F. of Earth Sciences
Dean: Reinhard O. Greiling
F. of Pharmacy
Dean: Eberhard Hackenthal
South Asia I.
Director: Dietmar Rothermund; *staff* 50
Ce. of Molecular Biology
Director: Hermann Bujard
Ce. of Scientific Calculation
Director: Willi Jäger

Founded 1386 by Rupert I, Elector of the Palatinate. The character of the university was profoundly affected by the Renaissance and the Reformation. It was reorganized as an independent institution by the Grand Duke Charles Frederick of Baden in 1803 and is now an autonomous university financially supported by the State of Baden-Württemberg, and under the jurisdiction of its Ministry of Science and Art. Governing bodies: the Grosse Senat; the Senat; the Verwaltungsrat (Council of Administration). Some residential facilities for a foreign academic staff and for *c.* 2500 students.

Arrangements for co-operation with: University of Budapest; Semmelweis Medical University, Budapest; University of Montpellier; Hebrew University of Jerusalem; Beijing Foreign Languages Institute; Shanghai

Institute of Foreign Languages; University of Cambridge; Tongji Medical University; Nankai University; Cornell University; University of Kentucky; Bucknell University; University of Sussex; Moscow State Institute of Foreign Languages; Louisiana State University; Ecole normale supérieure de Fontenay-aux-Roses; University of Pisa; University of Salamanca; California State University; Wesleyan University; University of Massachusetts; University of Oregon; Randolph-Macon Woman's College, Lynchburg; Sweet Briar College; Arizona State University; University of Miami; University of New Mexico; University of Kansas; University of Utah; Heidelberg College, Ohio; Pace University, New York; University of Illinois; Jagiellonian University, Cracow; Charles University, Prague; Federal University of Rio Grande do Sul, Porto Alegre.

Academic Year: October to September (October-March; April-September).

Admission Requirements: Secondary school certificate (Reifezeugnis) or equivalent.

Fees: None.

Language of Instruction: German.

Degrees and Diplomas: State Examinations–Juristische Staatsprüfung, law; Medizinische–, medicine; Zahnärztliche–, dentistry; Prü fung für das Lehramt an höheren Schulen (teaching qualification, secondary level, all fields); Magister der Theologie, theology, 4 yrs. Magister Artium, 4 yrs. Diplomas–Diplom-Chemiker, chemistry; -Dolmetscher, interpretation; -Geologe, geology; -Mathematiker, mathematics; -Physiker, physics; -Biologe, biology; -Mineraloge, mineralogy; -Psychologe, psychology; -Publizist, journalism; -Übersetzer, translation; -Volkswirt, economics. Doctorates–Dr., in all fields, approximately 8 sem, except Dr.med.dent. and Zahnärztliche Staatsprüfung, 10 sem, and Dr.med. and Medizinische Staatsprüfung, 12 sem. Habilitation (teaching qualification, university level), at least 3 yrs after doctorate.

Libraries: University Library, *c.* 2,316,000 vols; libraries of the institutes and seminars.

Special Facilities (Museums, etc.): Museum of Antiquities; Museum of Egyptology; Zoology Museum; Geology and Palaeontology Museum; Mineralogy Collection; Botanical Garden; Prehistory Collection; Archaeological Collection of Plaster Casts; Collection of Historical Instruments.

Publications: Heidelberger Jahrbücher (annually); Ruperto Carola.

Academic Staff, 1989-90:

Rank	Full-time	Part-time
Professoren	524	–
Wissenschaftliche Assistenten/Hochschulassistenten	93	–
Akademische Räte/Oberräte/Direktoren	175	–
Wissenschaftliche Angestellte	1027	363
Lektoren	53	19
Lehrbeauftragte	–	*c.* 200
Total	1872	*c.* 582

Student Enrolment, 1989-90:

	Men	Women	Total
Of the country	13,402	12,209	25,611
Of other countries	1338	1386	2724
Total	14,740	13,595	28,335

3113 **HOCHSCHULE FÜR JÜDISCHE STUDIEN**

College for Jewish Studies
Friedrichstrasse 9, 6900 Heidelberg
Telephone: (6221) 22576
Rector: Julius Carlebach (1989-)
Rector's Assistant: Irene Rosenberg

Jewish Studies

Founded 1979, recognized by the State of Baden-Württemberg 1981. An institution of the Zentralrat der Juden in Deutschland and associated with the University of Heidelberg. Governing bodies: the Kuratorium; the Senat.

Arrangements for co-operation with: Hebrew University of Jerusalem; Oxford Centre for Postgraduate Hebrew Studies.

Academic Year: October to July (October-February; April-July).

Admission Requirements: Secondary school certificate (Abitur).

Language of Instruction: German.

Degrees and Diplomas: Magister Artium, 9 sem.

Library: 30,000 vols.

Academic Staff, 1989-90:

Rank	Full-time	Part-time
Professoren	6	–
Lektoren	5	–
Wissenschaftliche Mitarbeiter	–	7
Total	11	7

Student Enrolment, 1989-90:

	Men	Women	Total
Of the country	34	60	94
Of other countries	3	3	6
Total	37	63	100

3114 **UNIVERSITÄT HILDESHEIM**

University of Hildesheim
Marienburger Platz 22, 3200 Hildesheim
Telephone: (5121) 883-0
Fax: (5121) 8675-58
Rektor: Ernst Cloer (1989-91)
Kanzler: Wolf-D. von Fircks

D. of Educational Sciences
Dean: Dieter Lüttge; *staff* 45 (4)

D. of Social Work and Cultural Education
Dean: Wolfgang Menzel; *staff* 23 (5)

D. for Languages
Dean: Reiner Arntz; *staff* 27 (4)

D. of Mathematics, Computer Sciences, and Natural Sciences
Dean: Heinz-Wilhelm Alten; *staff* 25 (6)

Computer Ce.
Head: Franz Hagenberg; *staff* 4

Ce. for Lifelong Education and Distance Study
Head: Erwin Wagner; *staff* 5

Founded 1978. An autonomous institution financially supported by the state of Lower Saxony, and under the jurisdiction of its Ministry of Science. Governing bodies: the Konzil; the Senat.

Arrangements for co-operation with: Dublin City University; University of Manchester, Institute of Science and Technology; Aston University, Birmingham; Liverpool Polytechnic; Université de Haute-Alsace; Université de Pau et des Pays de l'Adour; Université de Clermont-Ferrand II; Université de l'Etat à Mons; Universidad Autónoma de Barcelona; Universidad de Granada; Universidad Politécnica de Las Palmas; Universidad de Oviedo; Minia University; Beijing Agricultural Engineering University.

Academic Year: October to September (October-March; April-September).

Admission Requirements: Secondary school certificate (Reifezeugnis) or equivalent.

Fees: None.

Language of Instruction: German.

Degrees and Diplomas: Erste Prüfung für das Lehramt (teaching qualifications, primary and secondary level), 3-4 yrs. Diplomas in–Education; Cultural Education; Technical Translation; Social Studies in Education; Computer Sciences, 3 ½-4 ½ yrs. Doctorates–Dr.phil., Dr.rer.nat., natural sciences. Habilitation (teaching qualification, university level), at least 3 yrs after Doctorate.

Library: Central Library, *c.* 2500,000 vols.

Publication: 'aktuell' (quarterly).

Academic Staff, 1986-87:

Rank	Full-time	Part-time
Professoren	542	–
Akademische Räte	59	–
Wissenschaftliche Angestellte	44	12
Total	157	12

Student Enrolment, 1986-87:

	Men	Women	Total
Of the country	867	1666	2533
Of other countries	34	53	87
Total	901	1719	2620*

*Also 1900 external students.

3115 ***UNIVERSITÄT HOHENHEIM**

University of Hohenheim
Postfach 7005 62,B7000 Stuttgart 70 (Hohenheim)
Telex: 7022959 UNIHO-D
Telephone: (711) 459-0
Präsident: E. Reisch (1986-90)
Kanzler: Konrad Stahlecker

F. of General and Applied Natural Sciences
Dean: H. Seiler; *staff* 108 (37)
F. of Biology
Dean: C.-U. Hesemann; *staff* 91 (37)
F. of Agriculture I (Plant Production and Landscape Ecology)
Dean: W. Koch; *staff* 208 (50)
F. of Agriculture II (Agricultural Economics, Agricultural Engineering, Animal Husbandry)
Dean: W. Grosskopf, *staff* 202 (72)
F. of Economics and Social Sciences
Dean: G. Scherhorn; *staff* 56 (37)
I. of Agricultural Chemistry (Research)
Director: R. Seibold
I. of Seed Cultivation (Research)
Director: W. Schmütz; *staff* 45 (11)
I. of Agricultural Mechanics and Construction (Research)
Director: Th. Bischoff; *staff* 3 (2)
I. of Apiculture (Research)
Director: G. Vorwohl; *staff* 10
Also 31 institutes of the faculties.

Founded 1818, became Hochschule 1904 and acquired university status 1919. Acquired present title 1967. An autonomous institution under the jurisdiction of and financed by the State of Baden-Württemberg. Governing bodies: the Grosse Senat, comprising 38 members; the Senat; the Verwaltungsrat. Residential facilities for *c.* 550 students.

Arrangements for co-operation with: Çukurova University; Universities in Oregon; Beijing University of Agriculture; Warsaw Agricultural University; Konkook University; University of Georgia; University of California, Los Angeles; State University of Massachusetts; University of Rhode Island; Agricultural University, Wageningen; Ecole supérieure de Commerce de Paris; University of Nebraska; Hebrew University of Jerusalem.

Academic Year: October to September (October-February; April-July).

Admission Requirements: Secondary school certificate (Reifezeugnis) or equivalent.

Fees: Tuition, none.

Language of Instruction: German.

Degrees and Diplomas: State Examinations–Prüfung für das Lehramt an Gymnasien (teaching qualification, secondary level, in Biology, Chemistry, Physics). Diplomas–Diplom -Journalist; -Agraringenieur, Dipl.Ing.agr., agricultural engineering; -Lebensmittel-ingenieur, food technology; -Ernährungswissenschaftler, nutrition; Ökonom, economics, Dipl.oec.; -Haushaltsökonom, home economics; -Biologe, biology; -Agrarbiologe, agricultural biology, 5-6 yrs. Doctorates, Dr. in all fields, 6 yrs.

Library: c. 327,000 vols.

Special Facilities (Museums, etc.): Landwirtschaftsmuseum; Zoology and Veterinary Medicine.

Publications: Arbeiten der Universität Hohenheim; Amtliche Mitteilungen; Rechenschaftsbericht; Daten und Dokumente zum Umwelt-schutz; Forschungsbericht (Scientific Reports).

Academic Staff, 1986-87: 280 (67).

Student Enrolment, 1986-87:

	Men	Women	Total
Of the country	3044	2138	5182
Of other countries	230	107	337
Total	3274	2245	5519

3116 **UNIVERSITÄT KAISERSLAUTERN**

University of Kaiserslautern
Erwin-Schrödinger Strasse, Postfach 3049, 6750 Kaiserslautern
Telex: 04-5627 UNIKL D
Telephone: (631) 205-1
Präsident: Klaus Landfried (1987-93)
Administrator: Hermann Fahse

F. of Mathematics and Physics
Dean: Joachim Wick
F. of Chemistry and Food Technology
Dean: Otto Scherer
F. of Biology
Dean: Roland Plapp
F. of Mechanical Engineering
Dean: Fritz Ebert
F. of Electrical Engineering
Dean: Jochen Beister
F. of Architecture, Planning, Environmental Studies, and Education
Dean: Heinrich Eissler
F. of Economics and Social Sciences
F. of Computer Sciences
Dean: Gerhard Zimmermann

Founded 1970 with divisions in Kaiserslautern and Trier which were detached 1975 to form separate universities. An autonomous institution under the jurisdiction of and financially supported by the State of Rheinland-Pfalz. Governing body: the Senat. Residential facilities for students.

Arrangements for co-operation with the Universities of: Australian National; Louvain; Liège; Rio de Janeiro (Federal); Campinas (State); Montréal; Laval; Humboldt, Berlin; Magdeburg; Aston, Birmingham; Edinburgh; Essex; Manchester; Oxford; Grenoble; Paris; Montpellier II; Rennes; Gujarat, Ahmedabad; Calcutta; Panjab; Dublin (Trinity College); Haifa (Technion); Genoa; Florence; Milan; Rome; Kyoto; Kyushu; Shinshu; Jutendo, Tokyo; Banjaluci; Wellington; Utrecht; Leiden; Innsbruck; Mining and Metallurgy, Leoben; Linz; Salzburg; Vienna (Technology); Gdańsk; Warsaw; Łódź Technical; Bucharest; Prague; Duke; Louisiana State; California, Berkeley; Michigan; Utah; Vanderbilt; Harvard; Missouri; Wisconsin; Temple; Philadelphia; Nebraska; Northeastern, Boston; New York State at Stony Brook; Washington State; Kansas; Connecticut; Rockefeller, New York; Carnegie-Mellon; Texas at Austin; Pennsylvania State; Southern Methodist; Arizona State; Lehigh; Texas A&M; Illinois. NanjingInstitute of Posts and Telecommunications; Imperial College, London; Twente University of Technology; Swiss Federal Institute of Technology; Middle East Technical University, Ankara; Massachusetts Institute of Technology; Polytechnic Institute of Milan; Polytechnic Institute of Turin.

Academic Year: October to September (October-March; April-September).

Admission Requirements: Secondary school certificate (Reifezeugnis).

Fees: None.

Language of Instruction: German.

Degrees and Diplomas: State Examinations–Prüfung für das Lehramt an Realschulen und Gymnasien (teaching qualification, secondary level), 4-6 yrs. Diplomas–Diplom-Mathematiker, mathematics; -Physiker, physics; -Chemiker, chemistry; -Biologe, biology; -Informatiker, computer sciences; -Wirtschaftsingenieur, industrial engineering; -Ingenieur, engineering, 4-6 yrs. Degree of Magister Artium. Doctorates–Dr.rer.nat., natural sciences; Dr.rer.pol., economics; Dr.phil; Dr.-Ing., engineering. Habilitation (teaching qualification, university level), at least 3 yrs after doctorate.

Library: c. 270,000 vols.

Press or Publishing House: Uni-Pressestelle.

Academic Staff: c. 50

Student Enrolment: c. 7560.

3117 ***UNIVERSITÄT FRIDERICIANA KARLSRUHE (TECHNISCHE HOCHSCHULE)**

University of Karlsruhe
Kaiserstrasse 12, 7500 Karlsruhe 1
Telex: 07 826 521
Telephone: (721) 608-0
Fax: (721) 608-4290
Rektor: Heinz Kunle (1983-87)
Kanzler: Gerhard Selmayr

F. of Mathematics
Dean: Wilhelm Niethammer; *staff* 98
F. of Physics (including Meteorology)
Dean: Friedhold Baumann; *staff* 119 (31)
F. of Chemistry
Dean: Ulrich Schindewolf; *staff* 80 (55)
F. of Biological and Earth Sciences
Dean: Wilfried Hanke; *staff* 69 (33)
F. of Social Sciences and Humanities
Dean: Bernhard Schäfers; *staff* 38 (4)
F. of Architecture
Dean: Ulrich Schnitzer; *staff* 57 (24)
F. of Civil Engineering and Surveying
Dean: Ernst-Ulrich Hiersche; *staff* 257 (10)

F. of Mechanical Engineering
Dean: Georg Jungbluth; *staff* 248 (2)
F. of Chemical Engineering
Dean: Werner Stahl; *staff* 129 (15)
F. of Electrical Engineering
Dean: Hans-Martin Lipp; *staff* 134 (5)
F. of Computer Sciences
Dean: Ulrich Rembold; *staff* 123 (1)
F. of Economics
Dean: Frank Stehling; *staff* 87 (6)
I. of Regional Planning
Head: Claus Heidemann; *staff* 5
I. for Applied Computer Sciences
Head: Hans-Martin Staudenmaier
Computer Ce.
Head: Adolf Schreiner
Also *c.* 90 institutes and seminars of the different faculties.

Founded 1825 as Polytechnische Schule on the model of the Ecole polytechnique, Paris. Accorded university status 1865. Became Technische Hochschule Fridericiana 1902, acquired present title 1967. An autonomous institution under the jurisdiction of and financed by the State of Baden-Württemberg. Governing body: the Senat. Residential facilities for academic staff and *c.* 1700 students.

Arrangements for co-operation with: University of Nancy; Institut national des Sciences appliquées de Lyon, Villeurbanne; Technical University of Budapest; University of Reykjavik; University of California at Berkeley; Technion Haifa; Technical University, Gdańsk; Kyoto University; Ecole supérieure d'Ingénieurs en Electrotechnique et en Electronique, Paris; Kunming Institute of Technology; Beijing Institute of Technology.

Academic Year: October to September (October-February, April-July).

Admission Requirements: Secondary school certificate (Reifezeugnis) or equivalent.

Fees: Tuition, none.

Language of Instruction: German.

Degrees and Diplomas: State Examinations–Lebensmittelchimie, food chemistry; Prüfung für das Lehramt an höheren Schulen (teaching qualifications, secondary and vocational levels). Diplomas–Diplom-Ingenieur, engineering; -Chemiker, chemistry; -Informatiker, computer sciences; -Mathematiker, mathematics; -Physiker, physics; -Meteorologe, meteorology; -Geophysiker, earth sciences; -Geologe, geology; -Mineraloge, mineralogy; -Wirtschaftsingenieur, industrial engineering; -Volkswirt, economics; -Biologe, biology, 4-5 yrs. Licentiate, Lic.rer. reg., a further 2 yrs. Degree of Magister Artium, 4 yrs. Doctorates– Dr.rer.nat., natural sciences; Dr.phil.; Dr.rer.pol.; Dr.-Ing., 2-4 yrs. Habilitation (teaching qualification, university level), at least 3 yrs after doctorate.

Libraries: University Library, *c.* 650,000 vols; faculty and institute libraries.

Publications: Fridericiana; Uni-Informationen Karlsruhe.

Press or Publishing House: Pressestelle.

Academic Staff, 1986-87:

Rank	Full-time	Part-time
Professoren	274	–
Wissenschaftliche Mitarbeiter	717	92
Ausserplanmässige Professoren	–	59
Lehrbeauftragte	–	182
Total	991	333

Student Enrolment, 1986-87:

	Men	Women	Total
Of the country	14,325	2598	16,923
Of other countries	1104	228	1332
Total	15,429	2826	18,255

3118 ***GESAMTHOCHSCHULE KASSEL**

University of Kassel
Mönchebergstrasse 19, 3500 Kassel
Telex: 99572 GHKKS D
Telephone: (561) 804-1
Präsident: Franz Neumann (1981-89)
Kanzler: Hubert Sauer

D. of Humanities and Education
Dean: Ben Bachmair; *staff* 30 (25)
D. of Ergonomics and Vocational Education
Dean: Eckehard Frieling; *staff* 41
D. of Psychology, Physical Education, and Music
Dean: Helmut Rösing; *staff* 31 (42)
D. of Social and Political Sciences
Dean: Johannes Weiss; *staff* 37
D. of Applied Social Sciences and Law
Dean: Michael Kittner; *staff* 33
D. of Economics and Business Administration
Dean: Kurt Reding; *staff* 46 (12)
D. of Romance and English Languages
Dean: Manfred Raupach; *staff* 30 (5)
D. of German
Dean: Hans Otto Spillmann; *staff* 20
D. of Art
Dean: Heiner Georgsdorf; *staff* 30
D. of Graphic Art and Industrial Design
Dean: Horst Sommerlatte; *staff* 16
D. of Architecture
Dean: Jochem Jourdan; *staff* 29 (3)
D. of Town Planning and Landscape Architecture
Dean: Detlev Ipsen; *staff* 38 (19)
D. of Civil Engineering
Dean: Helmut Körner; *staff* 49 (16)
D. of Mechanical Engineering
Dean: Gunnar Johannsen; *staff* 76 (12)
D. of Electrical Engineering
Dean: Günter Kompa; *staff* 51 (12)
D. of Mathematics
Dean: Werner Blum; *staff* 36 (6)
D. of Physics
Dean: Kay Spreckelsen; *staff* 40 (7)
D. of Chemistry and Biology
Dean: Jörg-Peter Ewert; *staff* 47 (5)
D. of Agriculture
Dean: Franz Lieber; *staff* 32 (19)
D. of International Agricultural Studies
Dean: Carl Hoeppe; *staff* 26 (6)
D. of Social Studies
Dean: Heide Andres-Müller; *staff* 50 (34)
D. of Visual Communication
Dean: Gerhard Mathias; *staff* 15

Founded 1970 as a Gesamthochschule, a new type of university designed to integrate all forms of postsecondary education within a single framework. An autonomous institution financially supported by the State of Hesse andunder the jurisdiction of its Ministry of Education. Residential facilities for students.

Arrangements for co-operation with: University of Angers; University of Reading; University of Wisconsin; King Mongkut's Institute of Technology; Minya University; Marie Curie-Skłodowska University, Lublin; Riga Polytechnical Institute; University of Delaware.

Academic Year: October to September (October-February; April-July).

Admission Requirements: Secondary school certificate (Reifezeugnis). Fachhochschulreife (technical secondary education) for certain courses.

Fees: Tuition, none.

Language of Instruction: German.

Degrees and Diplomas: State Examination–Prüfung für das Lehramt in höheren Schulen (teaching qualification, secondary level, all fields), 4-5 yrs. Graduierung in various fields, 3 yrs. Diplomas–Diplom-Ingenieur; -Architekt; -Volkswirt, economics; -Handelslehrer (commercial teaching qualification); -Bauplaner; -Stadtplaner; -Landschaftsplaner; -Bauingenieur; -Maschinenbauingenieur; -Biologe; -Sozial-pädagoge; -Sozialarbeiter, social work; -Mathematiker; -Physiker; -Anglist; -Romanist, 3-5 yrs. Magister Artium, arts. Doctorates, Dr. in Human, Social and Natural Sciences; Engineering. Habilitation (teaching qualification, university level) at least 3 yrs after doctorate.

Library: Central Library, 1m. vols.

Publications: Prisma (biannually); Schriftenreihe zur Psychoanalyse (quarterly); Preciosa Casselana und Studia Casselana.

Academic Staff, 1986-87: 805 (209).

Student Enrolment, 1986-87:

	Men	Women	Total
Of the country	5672	3535	9207
Of other countries	605	189	794
Total	6277	3724	10,001

3119 ***CHRISTIAN-ALBRECHTS-UNIVERSITÄT ZU KIEL**

Christian Albrecht University of Kiel
Olshausenstrasse 40, 2300 Kiel
Telex: 292656 CAUKI D
Telephone: (431) 880-00
Fax: (431) 880-2072
Rektor: Michael Müller-Wille (1989-92)
Kanzler: Horst Neumann

F. of Theology (Evangelical)
Dean: Reiner Preul; *staff* 24 (6)
F. of Law
Dean: Franz J. Säcker; *staff* 49 (6)
F. of Economics and Social Sciences
Dean: Jürgen Hauschildt; *staff* 71 (7)
F. of Medicine (including Dentistry)
Dean: Werner Grote; *staff* 719 (9)
F. of Philosophy (including Liberal Arts, Pedagogy, Psychology, History, History of East European Countries, Pre-History, Archaeology, History of Art, Science of Music, Philologies of Modern Languages, General and Indogermanic Linguistics, Phonetics of Digital Linguistics)
Dean: Ernst R. Schwinge; *staff* 233 (102)
F. of Mathematics and Natural Sciences
Dean: Dieter Adelung; *staff* 432 (30)
F. of Agriculture (including Ecotrophology (Dietetics))
Dean: Ulrich Köster; *staff* 88 (28)
I. of World Economics
President: Horst Siebert; *staff* 235 (79)
I. of Marine Sciences
Director: Jan C. Duinker; *staff* 182 (65)
Research Ce. for Maritime Earth Sciences (GEOMAR)
Director: Jörn Miede; *staff* 60 (70)
I. of Science Education
Director: Heinrich Stork; *staff* 88
Also *c.* 130 institutes, seminars, and clinics of the different faculties.

Founded 1665 by Christian Albrecht, Duke of Holstein-Gottorf. Became the Landes-Universität (provincial university) for the State of Schleswig-Holstein 1773. Incorporated as a Prussian University in 1867 and re-established as the Landesuniversität in 1945. The university is an autonomous institution financially supported by the State of Schleswig-Holstein, and under the jurisdiction of its Ministry of Education and Sciences. Governing bodies: the Senat, composed of 25 members of the academic, 2 members of the non-academic staff, and 4 students; the Konsistorium, comprising 71 members. Residential facilities for *c.* 1500 students in Studentenwohnheime.

Arrangements for co-operation with the Universities of: Greifswald; Rostock; Copenhagen; Tampere; Brest; Lyon III; Aberdeen; Hull; Queens, Belfast; Sussex; Surrey; Dublin; Oslo; Poznań; Warsaw (Agricultural); Szczecin; Linköping; Vaxjö; Stockholm; Lund; Uppsala; Santiago, Chile; Shanghai; Hangzhou; Zhejiang (Medical); Zhejiang (Agricultural); Brown; Indiana; Kansas; Utah; Wisconsin; Pennsylvania; Minnesota; Hawai; Tartu; Kiev. Academy of Medicine, Poznań; Academy of Physical Education, Gdańsk; Central School of Planning and Statistics, Warsaw; Helsinki School of Economics and Business Administration.

Academic Year: October to September (October-March; April-September).

Admission Requirements: Secondary school certificate (Abitur) or equivalent.

Fees: None.

Language of Instruction: German.

Degrees and Diplomas: State Examinations–Juristische Staatsprüfung, law; Pharmazie–, 4 yrs; Zahnärztliche–, 5 yrs; Medizinische–, 6 yrs. Prüfung für das Lehramt an Realschulen und Gymnasien (teaching qualification, secondary level, all fields), 5 yrs. Diplomas–Diplom-Mathematiker, mathematics; -Chemiker, chemistry; -Physiker, physics; -Volkswirt, Betriebswirt, economics; -Handelslehrer, commercial teaching qualification; -Sozialökomomie, social economics; -Psychologe, psychology; -Biologe, biology; -Mineraloge, mineralogy; -Ozeanograph, oceanography ; -Geologe, geology; -Geograph, geography; -Informatiker, data processing; -Agrarokönomie; -Agrarwissenschaft; -Ozeanograph; -Meteorologe; -Ökotrophologie, 4-5 yrs. Degree of Magister Artium, arts, 4 yrs. Doctorates–Dr., in all fields, 3-5 yrs. Habilitation (teaching qualification, university level) at least 3 yrs after doctorate. Also Kirchlich-Theologische Examen.

Libraries: University Library, *c.* 1.4m vols; Institute of World Economics Library, *c.* 1.6m.

Special Facilities (Museums, etc.): Zoologisches Museum; Mineralogisch-Petrographisches Museum; Geologische-Paläontologisches Museum; Theatergeschichtliche Sammlung und Hebbelsammlung; Wanderndes Museum; Kunsthalle; Archäologisches Landesmuseum und Wikinger-museum Haithabu.

Academic Staff, 1989-90:

Rank	Full-time	Part-time
Ordentliche Professoren	233	–
Professoren	167	–
Wissenschaftliche Assistenten/Wiss. Angestellte	871	–
Dozenten/Oberärzte/Oberassistenten	206	–
Wissenschaftliche Räte	114	–
Studienräte/Lektoren	56	–
Lehrbeauftragte	–	189
Total	1647	189

Student Enrolment, 1989-90:

	Men	Women	Total
Of the country	9715	7498	17,213
Of other countries	522	364	886
Total	10,237	7862	18,099

3120 **PÄDAGOGISCHE HOCHSCHULE KIEL**

College of Education, Kiel
Ohlshausenstrasse 75, 2300 Kiel
Telephone: (431) 54331
Präsident: Helmut Dahncke (1981-87)
Kanzler: Werner Fiesel

Education
Psychology
Philosophy
Sociology
Also 17 disciplines including didactics for primary and secondary teacher education.

Founded 1781 as Seminar, acquired present status and title 1946. Under the jurisdiction of and financially supported by the State of Schleswig-Holstein. Governing bodies: the Senat, comprising 17 members; the Konsistorium, comprising 36 members. Residential facilities for students in Studentenwohnheime.

Academic Year: October to September (October-March; April-September).

Admission Requirements: Secondary school certificate (Reifezeugnis) or aptitude test.

Fees: None.

Language of Instruction: German.

Degrees and Diplomas: Staatsprüfung für das Lehramt, for primary education, 3 yrs; for lower secondary education; for special schools, 4 yrs. Diplompädagoge, 4 yrs. Doctorate–Dr.sc.päd., 4 yrs.

Library: College Library, *c.* 250,000 vols.

Publications: Jahresbericht; Forschungsbericht (annually); Vorlesungsverzeichnis.

Academic Staff, 1986-87:

Rank	Full-time	Part-time
Professoren	64	–
Hochschulassistenten	3	–
Akademischer Räte/Direktoren	4	–
Studienräte/Direktoren	13	–
Lektoren	2	–
Angestellte	3	–
Lehrbeauftragte/Abgeordnete Lehrkräfte	–	114
Total	89	114

Student Enrolment, 1986-87:

	Men	Women	Total
Of the country	395	982	1377
Of other countries	5	11	16
Total	400	993	1393

3121 **UNIVERSITÄT KOBLENZ-LANDAU**

Rheinau 3-4, 5400 Koblenz Im Fort 7, 6740 Landau
Telephone: Koblenz: (261) 91190; Landau: (6341) 2800
Fax: Koblenz: (261) 37524; Landau: (6341) 280101
Präsident: Hermann Saterdag (1988-94)
Kanzler: Reiner Wanner

F. of Educational Science
F. of Philology
F. of Natural Science
F. of Computer Sciences (Koblenz)
F. of Psychology (Landau)
I. for Media Didactics (Koblenz)
Head: Wolfgang Fraunholz
I. for Educational Research (Landau)
Head: Reinhold Jäger
Research Ce. for Sex Sciences and Education (Landau)
Head: Norbert Kluge
I. of Computer Sciences (Koblenz)
Head: Klaus Troitzsch
Branches in Koblenz and Landau.

Founded 1949 as academy, became college 1964 and University of Educational Sciences 1969. Acquired present status and title 1990. Under the jurisdiction of and financially supported by the State of Rheinland-Pfalz. Governing bodies: the Versammlung (Assembly); the Senat.

Academic Year: October to September (October-March; April-September).

Admission Requirements: Secondary school certificate (Reifezeugnis).

Fees: None.

Language of Instruction: German.

Degrees and Diplomas: Staatsprüfung für das Lehramt, for primary education, 3 yrs; for lower secondary education, 4 yrs. Degree of Magister Artium. Diplom Pädagoge; Diplom Psychologe; Diplom-Informatiker, 4 yrs. Musikschullehrer; Privatmusiklehrer, 3 yrs. Doctorates, Dr.phil.; Dr.rer.nat. Habilitation (teaching qualification, university level).

Libraries: Koblenz, *c.* 170,000; Landau, *c.* 210,000.

Special Facilities (Museums, etc.): Biologisch-Ökologische Station (Betzenfeld/Koblenz); Movie Studio (Landau).

Publications: Vorlesungsverzeichnis; Jahresbericht des Präsidenten; Forschungs- und Veröffentlichungsdokumentation; Universitätszeitschrift; Eigene Jahresberichte der Institute

Press or Publishing House: University Press

Academic Staff, 1989-90:

Rank	Full-time
Professoren	115
Akademische Mitarbeiter	102
Total	217

Student Enrolment, 1989-90:

Men	Women	Total
1418	2070	3488

3122 **WISSENSCHAFTLICHE HOCHSCHULE FÜR UNTERNEHMENSFÜHRUNG KOBLENZ**
Koblenz School of Corporate Management
Haus d'Ester Heerstrasse 52, 5414 Vallendar
Cables: Whuk
Telephone: (261) 6509-0
Fax: (261) 65909-111
Electronic mail: geonet whu.koblenz
Rektor: Wilhelm Pfähler (1989-)
Geschäftsführer der Stiftung: Jürgen Büring

Triad Ce. for Comparative Management
Director: Horst Albach; *staff* 3
Ce. for Financial Management
Director: Adolf-Friedrich Jacob; *staff* 4 (1)
Area for Marketing Management
Head: Hans H. Bauer; *staff* 6 (1)
Area for Management Information Systems
Head: Wolfgang König; *staff* 12
Area for Accountancy and Control
Head: Jürgen Weber; *staff* 6 (3)
Area for Economics

Founded 1984 under the auspices of the Chamber of Industry and Commerce. A private institution recognized by the Ministry of Cultural Affairs. Governing body: the Senat.

Arrangements for co-operation with: Helsinki School of Economics and Business; Centre d'Enseignement et de Recherche appliqués au Management, Valbonne/Nice; Centre des hautes Etudes commerciales, Jouy-en-Josas/Paris; Ecole des hautes Etudes commerciales du Nord, Lille; Ecole supérieure de Commerce de Grenoble; Ecole supérieure de Commerce de Reims; Ecole supérieure de Commerce de Rouen, Mont-Saint-Aignan; Ecole supérieure de Commerce du Centre, Tours; University Aix-Marseilles, Aix-en-Provence; Libera Università Internazionale degli Studi Sociali, Rome; Universidad de Alcalá de Henares, Madrid; Escuela Superior de Administración y Dirección de Empresas, Barcelona; Plekhanov Institute of National Economy, Moscow; Cranfield Institute of Technology; University of Bath; University of Lancaster; University of Manchester; Queen's University at Kingston, Ontario; Universit de Montréal; University of Western Ontario; Brandeis University; Carnegie-Mellon University; Northwestern University; Pennsylvania State University; Texas A&M University; University of Southern California, Los Angeles; University of Texas; Universidad Adolfo Ibañez, Valparaiso; Keio University, Yokohama; Kobe University.

Academic Year: September to May (September-December; January-May).

Admission Requirements: Secondary school certificate (Reifezeugnis), practical experience and proficiency in German, good knowledge ofEnglish, and working knowledge of French.

Fees (Marks): 5500 per semester.

Languages of Instruction: German and English.

Degrees and Diplomas: Vordiplom, 3 sem. Diplom-Kaufmann, 8 sem. Doctorate, Dr.rer.pol. Habilitation (teaching qualification, university level), at least 3 yrs after Doctorate.

Library: 12,000 vols.

Publication: Hochschulnachrichten aus der Wissenschaftlichen Hochschule für Unternehmensführung.

Academic Staff, 1989-90:

Rank	Full-time	Part-time
Professoren	6	13
Dozenten	–	12
Assistenten	25	–
Total	31	25

Student Enrolment, 1989-90:

	Men	Women	Total
Of the country	167	41	208

3123 **UNIVERSITÄT ZU KÖLN**
University of Cologne
Albertus-Magnus-Platz, 5000 Köln 41
Telex: 08882291 (UNIKD)
Telephone: (221) 470-1
Fax: (221) 470-5151
Rektor: Bernhard König

F. of Economics and Social Sciences (including Business Administration and Political Science)
Dean: Udo Koppelmann
F. of Law
Dean: Georg Brunner
F. of Medicine (including Experimental Surgery)
Dean: Wolf Isselhard
F. of Philosophy
Dean: Jürgen Lenerz
F. of Mathematics and Natural Sciences
Dean: Achim Bachem
F. of Education
Dean: Werner Weiser
F. of Education for the Handicapped
Dean: Hans-Günther Richter
Also *c.* 170 institutes, seminars, and clinics of the different faculties.

Founded 1388 as a municipal university. Closed from 1798 under the French occupation. Cologne again became a university city at the beginning of the 20th century with the establishment of a college of commerce, a medical academy and a college of social administration. These formed the basis for the re-establishment of the university in 1919. The Rheinland College of Education incorporated 1980. An autonomous institution financially supported by the State of North Rhine-Westphalia, and under the jurisdiction of its Ministry of Education since 1953. Since 1970, under the jurisdiction of its Ministry of Science and Research. Governing bodies: the Senat, comprising 22 members; the Konvent; the Kuratorium.

Special arrangements for co-operation with: Universities of Clermont-Ferrand I and II; National University of Córdoba; University of California; Keio University; University of Kabul; Pennsylvania State University; University of Sofia.

Academic Year: October to September (October-March; April-September).

Admission Requirements: Secondary school certificate (Reifezeugnis) or equivalent.

Fees: None.

Language of Instruction: German.

Degrees and Diplomas: State Examinations–Juristische Staatsprüfung, law; Ärztliche–, medicine; Zahnärztliche–, dentistry; Prüfung für das Lehramt an Schulen (teaching qualification, primary or secondary level, or for education of handicapped). Diplomas–Diplom-Chemiker, chemistry; -Geologe, geology; -Geophysiker, geophysics (only pre-examination); -Handelslehrer (commercial teaching qualifica-tion); -Kaufmann, business administration; -Mathematiker, mathematics; -Pädagoge, education; -Biologe, biology; -Physiker, physics; -Geograph; -Meteorologe; -Mineraloge; -Psychologe, psychology; -Volkswirt, economics, all 8 sem, except physics and chemistry, 10 sem. Magister Artium, arts, 8 sem. Doctorates–Dr., in all fields, *c.* 8 sem, except Juristische Staatsprüfung, Dr.iur., 7 sem; Dr.rer.pol.; Dr.med. dent.; Zahnärztliche Staatsprüfung, 10 sem; Dr.med. and Ärztliche Staatsprüfung, 11 sem. Habilitation (teaching qualification, university level), at least 3 yrs after doctorate.

Libraries: University and City Library, *c.* 2.2m vols; Library of Medicine, *c.* 600,000.

Special Facilities (Museums, etc.): Theatermuseum; Museum of Papyrus; Musical Instruments; Biology.

Publications: Vorlesungsverzeichnis; Universitätsreden; Universitätsführer; Jahrbuch der Universität; Veröffentlichungen einzelner Institute.

Academic Staff: c. 1870.

Student Enrolment, 1990:

	Men	Women	Total
Of the country	24,291	22,969	47,260
Of other countries	2153	1777	3930
Total	26,444	24,746	51,190

3124 **DEUTSCHE SPORTHOCHSCHULE KÖLN**

Carl-Diem-Weg, 5000 Köln 41
Telephone: (221) 4982-1
Fax: (221) 4971-782
Rektor: Christiane Stang-Voss (1987-91)
Kanzler: Eike Reschke

Physical Education

Founded 1947 and tracing its origins to the former Deutsche Hochschule für Leibesübungen Berlin, founded 1920. Acquired university status 1970. Under the jurisdiction of and financially supported by the State of North Rhine-Westphalia. Governing bodies: the Konvent; the Senat. Residential facilities for students.

Arrangements for co-operation with: Beijing Institute of Physical Culture; Deutsche Hochschule fáur Körperkultur, Leipzig; Forschungsinstitut für Körperkultur und Sport, Leipzig; Japan College of Physical Education, Tokyo; State University of New York, College at Cortland; Universidad del Valle, Cali; Academy of Physical Education, Warsaw; Universidade Federal do Rio Grande do Sul; Universidade de São Paulo; Trent Polytechnic; Nottingham Polytechnic; University of Illinois at Urbana; Instituto Nacional de Educacíñ Física de Buenos Aires 'Dr. Enrique Romero Best'; Institute of Physical Culture, Sofia; Univerzita Karlova, Prague; Wingate Institute for Physical Education and Sport, Israel; Universidade do Porto.

Academic Year: April to March (April-September; October-March).

Admission Requirements: Secondary school certificate (Reifezeugnis).

Fees: None.

Language of Instruction: German.

Degrees and Diplomas: Diplomsportlehrer, 7 sem. Staatsexamen, State Examinations-Prüfung für das Lehramt an Schulen (teaching qualifications, primary or secondary level), 8 sem. Doktor der Sportwissenschaften.

Libraries: 196,000 vols; Specialized libraries of the institutes, 69,000.

Academic Staff, 1990:

Rank	Full-time	Part-time
Professoren	31	–
Wissenschaftliche Mitarbeiter	112	2
Wissenschaftliche Hilfskräfte	–	36
Total	143	38

Student Enrolment, 1990:

	Men	Women	Total
Of the country	3193	2315	5508
Of other countries	317	106	423
Total	3510	2421	5931

3125 ***UNIVERSITÄT KONSTANZ**

University of Constance
Universitätsstrasse 10, 7750 Konstanz
Cables: Postfach 5560
Telex: 0733359 UNIV. D.
Telephone: (7531) 881
Fax: (7531) 88-3688,Teletex: Bitnet
Rektor: Horst Sund (1987-91)
Kanzler: Jürgen Hess

F. of Mathematics
Dean: Dieter Hoffmann; *staff* 27 (3)

F. of Physics
Dean: Rudolf Klein; *staff* 48 (40)

F. of Chemistry
Dean: Ewald Daltrozzo; *staff* 28 (58)

F. of Biology
Dean: Rolf Knippers; *staff* 76 (27)

F. of Social Sciences
Dean: Detlef Kantowsky; *staff* 27 (3)

F. of Economics and Statistics
Dean: Siegfried Heiler; *staff* 39 (6)

F. of Law
Dean: Bertram Schulin; *staff* 35 (12)

F. of Philosophy and History
Dean: Werner Lehfeldt; *staff* 86 (10)

Founded 1966. The university is an autonomous State institution financially supported by the State of Baden-Württemberg. Governing bodies the Grosser Senat; the Senat.

Special arrangements for co-operation with: University of Lusaka University of Dakar; University of Warsaw; Jiao Tong University; Fudan University; University of Tel Aviv; Université Cadi Ayyad, Marrakech Academy of Economics, Poznań; Università degli Studi di Pavia; Université de Grenoble I; University College, Cork; Université de Grenoble II University of Pittsburg; Universidade de Coimbra; University of Dublin University of Economics, Kiev; York University, Toronto. Co-operation between faculties with: Ecole supérieure de Commerce, Marseille; University of Okayama. Regular interchange of students with: St. Olaf College Minnesota; Oregon State University; University of Oregon; Portland State University; Arizona State University; University of Massachusetts; Susquehanna University, Pennsylvania; Wellesley College; University of Sussex; University of Bristol; University of Bath; Kingston Polytechnic Université de Lyon II; Rutgers University, New Jersey.

Academic Year: October to September (October-February; April-July).

Admission Requirements: Secondary school certificate (Reifezeugnis) or equivalent.

Fees: None.

Language of Instruction: German.

Degrees and Diplomas: Staatsexamen, State Examinations–Prüfung für das Lehramt an Gymnasien (teaching qualification, secondary level), 4-5 yrs; Juristische Staatsprüfung I, II, law, 6 ½ yrs. Diplom, 4 yrs. Degree of Magister Artium, 4 yrs. Licentiates, a further 2 yrs. Doctorates. Habilitation (teaching qualification, university level), at least 2 yrs after doctorate.

Library: Central Library, 1.4 m vols.

Publications: Personal-u. Veranstaltungsverzeichnis; Konstanzer Blätter für Hochschulfragen; Konstanzer Universitätszeitung und Hochschulnachrichten.

Press or Publishing House: Uni-info der Universität Konstanz.

Academic Staff, 1989-90:

Rank	Full-time	Part-time
Professoren	180	–
Akademische Räte	47	1
Wissenschaftliche Angestellte	234	248
Assistenten	45	2
Total	506	251

Student Enrolment, 1989-90:

	Men	Women	Total
Of the country	4735	3369	8104
Of other countries	340	307	647
Total	5075	3676	8751

3126 **MEDIZINISCHE UNIVERSITÄT ZU LÜBECK**

Lübeck Medical University

Ratzeburger Allee 160, 2400 Lübeck

Telex: 26 492 MHL

Telephone: (451) 50 00

Fax: (451) 500-3016

Rektor: Wolfgang Henkel

Kanzler: Wolf-Dieter von Detmering

F. of Pre-clinical and Natural Medicine

Dean: Alfred X. Trautwein

F. of Medicine

Dean: Horst Dilling

Founded 1964 as academy and faculty of Christian Albrecht University of Kiel. Became independent and acquired present title and status 1973. Governing bodies: the Konsistorium; the Senat. Residential facilities for students.

Arrangements for co-operation with: University of Bergen; University of Tartu; Medical University of Zhejiang,Hangzhou; University of Rostock; Semmelweis-University, Budapest.

Academic Year: October to September (October-March; April-September).

Admission Requirements: Secondary school certificate (Reifezeugnis) or equivalent.

Fees: None.

Language of Instruction: German.

Degrees and Diplomas: Staatsexamen, Ärztliche Prüfung, 8 yrs. Dr.med.dent.; Dr.med.; Dr.rer.nat. Habilitation (teaching qualification, university level).

Library: c. 90,000 vols.

Publication: FOCUS MHL, Zeitschrift für Wissenschaft, Forschung und Lehre an der Medizinischen Universität zu Lübeck (quarterly).

Academic Staff: c. 140.

Student Enrolment: c. 1300.

3127 **UNIVERSITÄT LÜNEBURG, WISSENSCHAFTLICHE HOCHSCHULE DES LANDES NIEDERSACHSEN**

Lüneburg University

Wilschenbrucher Weg 84, 2120 Lüneburg

Telex: 02 182 112

Telephone: (4131) 714-1

Fax: (4131) 714-428

Rektor: Hartwig Donner (1989-91)

Kanzler: Hans-Georg Schultz-Gerstein

D. of Educational Sciences

Dean: Otfried Hoppe; *staff* 40

D. of Economics and Social Sciences (including Law and Political Science)

Dean: Egbert Kahle; *staff* 55

D. of Applied Cultural Studies

Dean: Theodor Klimek; *staff* 35

C. for Lifelong Education

Head: Johann-G. Wellendorf; *staff* 4 (6)

Founded 1946 as teachers' training college. Acquired present status and title 1978. Reorganized into three divisions, 1988. Under the jurisdiction of and financially supported by the State of Lower Saxony. Governing bodies: the Konzil; the Senat. Residential facilities for 330 students.

Arrangements for co-operation with: Colorado College; Loughborough College; University of North Texas; Lancashire Polytechnic; Universidad de Córdoba; University of Göteborg.

Academic Year: October to July (October-February; April-July).

Admission Requirements: Secondary school certificate (Reifezeugnis) or equivalent.

Fees: None.

Language of Instruction: German.

Degrees and Diplomas: Staatsprüfung für das Lehramt (teaching qualifications, primary and secondary levels), 3 yrs. Diplom-Pädagoge; -Sozialpädagoge; -Sozialökonom, 4 ½ yrs; -Kaufmann, 4 yrs. Magister Artium, 4 yrs. Doctorates –Dr.phil.; Dr.rer.pol., economics. Habilitation (teaching qualification, university level), at least 3 yrs afterdoctorate.

Library: c. 190,000 vols.

Academic Staff, 1989-90:

Rank	Full-time
Professoren	5
Lehrbeauftragte	93
Akademische Räte, Oberäte, Direktoren	40
Wissenschaftliche Angestellte	53
Hochschulassistenten	6
Lehrkräfte/Lektoren	93
Total	259

Student Enrolment, 1989-90:

	Men	Women	Total
Of the country	1562	2212	3774
Of other countries	30	36	66
Total	1592	2248	3840

3128 ***JOHANNES GUTENBERG-UNIVERSITÄT MAINZ**

Johannes Gutenberg University of Mainz

Saarstrasse 21, Postfach 3980, 6500 Mainz

Telex: 4187 476

Telephone: (6131) 391

Fax: (6131) 39-33-82

Präsident: Klaus Beyermann (1984-89)

Kanzler: Dieter Vogel-Arnoldi

D. of Theology (Catholic)

Dean: Isard Frank; *staff* 38 (6)

D. of Theology (Protestant)

Dean: Gerhard May; *staff* 34 (5)

D. of Law and Economics

Dean: W. Zohlnhöfer; *staff* 125 (28)

D. of Medicine (including Dentistry)

Dean: Jörg Michaelis; *staff* 729 (17)

D. of Philosophy and Education

Dean: Franz Hamburger; *staff* 59 (43)

D. of Social Sciences

Dean: Hellmuth Benesch; *staff* 76 (47)

D. of Philology I (German)

Dean: Wolfgang Düsing; *staff* 40 (7)

D. of Philology II (English)

Dean: Peter Erlebach; *staff* 35 (9)

D. of Philology III (Romance, Slav, Classical, History of Art, Indology, Egyptology, Oriental Studies)

Dean: Eberhard Reissner; *staff* 78 (16)

D. of History

Dean: Christoph H. Mahling; *staff* 46 (12)

D. of Mathematics

Dean: Wolfgang Börsch-Supan; *staff* 61 (2)

D. of Physics

Dean: Peter Beckmann; *staff* 110 (12)

D. of Chemistry and Pharmacy

Dean: Christian Schulz; *staff* 154 (18)

D. of Biology

Dean: Ferdinand Radler; *staff* 89 (9)

D. of Earth Sciences

Dean: Wendelin Klaer; *staff* 50 (11)

D. of Applied Linguistics (Germersheim)

Dean: Karl-Heinz Stoll; *staff* 94 (45)

D. of Fine Arts

Dean: Gregor Lambert; *staff* 19 (17)

D. of Music

Dean: Eduard Wollitz; *staff* 28 (69)

D. of Sport

Dean: Willi Petter; *staff* 32 (6)

Sec. for Lifelong Education (Philosophy)
Head: F. Pfurtscheller; *staff* 2
Also *c.* 100 institutes, seminars, and clinics of the different departments.

Founded 1477 by the Archbishop of Mainz. Closed 1816 although the faculty of Catholic theology continued as a seminary. Re-established 1946. An autonomous institution financially supported by the State of Rhineland-Palatinate, and under the jurisdiction of its Ministry of Education. Governing bodies: the Konzil; the Senat. Residential facilities for students.

Arrangements for co-operation with: University of Dijon; Nihon University; University of Zagreb; University of the Andes; University of Valencia; University of Haifa; Dankook University; National University of Rwanda; University of Paris III.

Academic Year: October to September (October-February; April-July).

Admission Requirements: Secondary school certificate (Reifezeugnis) or equivalent.

Fees: Tuition, none.

Language of Instruction: German.

Degrees and Diplomas: State Examinations–Juristische Staatsprüfung; law; Medizinische–, medicine; Zahnärztliche–, dentistry; Prüfung für das Lehramt an höheren Schulen (teaching qualification, secondary level, all fields). Diplomas–Diplom-Psychologe, psychology; -Biologe, biology; -Volkswirt; -Theologe; -Chemiker, chemistry; -Geologe, geology; -Mathematiker, mathematics; -Meteorologe, meteorology; -Mineraloge, mineralogy; -Physiker, physics; -Dolmetscher, interpretation; -Übersetzer, translation. Degree of Magister Artium, 8 sem. Doctorates–Dr., all fields, 8 sem, except Dr.med.dent. and Zahnärztliche Staatsprüfung, 10 sem; Dr.med. and Medizinische Staatsprüfung, 11 sem. Habilitation (teaching qualification, university level), at least 3 yrs after doctorate.

Library: University Library, *c.* 1,018,100 vols.

Publications: Annual Reports; Scientific Reports.

Academic Staff, 1986-87: 1904 (298).

Student Enrolment, 1986-87:

	Men	Women	Total
Of the country	12,235	11,802	24,037
Of other countries	796	759	1555
Total	13,041	12,561	25,592

3129 ***UNIVERSITÄT MANNHEIM**

University of Mannheim
Schloss, Postfach 103462, 6800 Mannheim
Telex: 462588 UNIMA D
Telephone: (621) 292-0
Fax: (621) 292-2587
Rektor: Otto H. Jacobs (1988-91)
Kanzler: Dietmar Ertmann

F. of Law
Dean: Wolfgang Frisch; *staff* 50 (22)
F. of Industrial Management Studies
Dean: Erwin Dichtl; *staff* 94 (30)
F. of Economics and Statistics
Dean: Eberhard Wille; *staff* 44 (4)
F. of Social Sciences (including Political Science)
Dean: Klaus Schönhoven; *staff* 37 (24)
F. of Philosophy, Psychology, and Educational Sciences
Dean: Lothar Michel; *staff* 32 (21)
F. of Languages and Literature
Dean: Meinhard Winkgens; *staff* 56 (24)
F. of History and Geography (including Archaeology)
Dean: Peter Frankenberg; *staff* 18 (19)
F. of Mathematics and Data Processing
Dean: Herbert Popp; *staff* 23 (2)
Computer Ce.
Head: Hans W. Meuer

Founded 1907 as Städtische Handelshochschule, attached to University of Heidelberg 1933, became Wirtschaftshochschule 1946. Title of university conferred 1967. Governing bodies: the Grosse Senat; the Senat. Residential facilities for *c.* 730 students in Studentenwohnheime.

Arrangements for co-operation with the Universities of: Toulon et du Var; Sarajevo; Wales; New York State at Stony Brook; Waterloo, Canada; Kyoto; Grenoble III; Franche-Comté, Besançon; Tel-Aviv; Warsaw; Georgetown, Washington.

Academic Year: October to September (April-September; October-March).

Admission Requirements: Secondary school certificate (Reifezeugnis) or recognized equivalent.

Fees: None.

Language of Instruction: German.

Degrees and Diplomas: State Examination–Juristische Staatsprüfung law. Diplomas–Diplom-Kaufmann, business administration; -Wirtschaftinformatik, computer sciences; -Wirtschafts pädagogik; -Geograph; -Handelslehrer (commerce, teaching qualification); -Volkswirt, economics; -Soziologe, sociology, 8 sem; -Mathematiker, mathematics, 9 sem; -Psychologe, psychology, 10 sem. Magister Artium, 8 sem. Doctorates–Dr.iur., law Dr.rer.pol., political science; Dr.phil. Habilitation (teaching qualification university level), at least 3 yrs after doctorate.

Library: Total, *c.* 1.6 m vols.

Publications: Veröffentlichungen der Universität Mannheim; Amtliche Mitteilungen; Mannheimer Berichte.

Academic Staff, 1990:

Rank	Full-time	Part-time
Professoren	140	27
Assistenten	37	–
Akademische Räte, Oberräte, Direktoren	25	–
Wissenschaftliche Mitarbeiter	179	–
Lehrbeauftragte	–	97
Total	381	124

Student Enrolment, 1989-90:

	Men	Women	Total
Of the country	7474	4232	11,706
Of other countries	526	350	876
Total	8000	4582	12,582

3130 ***PHILIPPS-UNIVERSITÄT MARBURG**

University of Marburg
Biegenstrasse 10, 3550 Marburg/Lahn
Telex: 482372
Telephone: (6421) 281
Fax: 282500
Präsident: Dietrich Simon
Kanzler: Bernd Höhmann

D. of Law
Dean: Eibe Riedel
D. of Economics
Dean: Hans-Günter Krüsselberg
D. of Social Sciences and Philosophy (including Education)
Dean: Hans-Joachim Giegel
D. of Psychology
Dean: Frank Rösler
D. of Theology (Protestant)
Dean: Horst Schwebel
D. of History
Dean: Hermann-Josef Rupieper
D. of Classical Studies (including Archaeology)
Dean: Hans Lauter
D. of General and Germanic Linguistics and Philology
Dean: Monika Rössing-Hager
D. of Modern German Literature and Arts
Dean: Wolfgang Kemp
D. of Modern Languages and Literaure
Dean: Hans-Joachim Lope
D. of Non-European Languages and Literature
Dean: Michael Hahn
D. of Mathematics
Dean: Walter Miesner
D. of Physics
Dean: Christian Wissel
D. of Physical Chemistry
Dean: Paul Patzelt
D. of Chemistry
Dean: Kurt Dehnicke
D. of Pharmacy and Chemistry of Foods
Dean: Klaus Kuschinsky
D. of Biology
Dean: Albrecht Klein
D. of Earth Sciences
Dean: Rudolf Allmann
D. of Geography
Dean: Ekkehard Buchhofer

D. of Medicine (including Dentistry)
Dean: Hans-Jürgen Hering
D. of Education (including Physical Education)
Dean: Wolfgang Klafki
Also *c.* 120 institutes, seminars, and clinics of the different departments.

Founded 1527 by Philip the Generous of Hesse as a Protestant State university. An autonomous institution financially supported by the State of Hesse under the jurisdiction of its Ministry of Science and Art. Governing body: the Konvent. Residential facilities for students.

Arrangements for exchange of students with: University of Poitiers; University of Maribor; Cairo University; University of Moscow; Syracuse University; Wilfrid Laurier University; Linköping University; University of Canterbury; London School of Economics; University of Venere; University of Illinois at Urbana Champaign; University of Tokyo; University of Tirana; University of the Extremadura, Spain.

Academic Year: October to July (October-February; April-July).

Admission Requirements: Secondary school certificate (Reifezeugnis) or equivalent.

Fees: None.

Language of Instruction: German.

Degrees and Diplomas: State Examinations–Juristische Staatsprüfung, law, 7 sem; Medizinische–, medicine, 12 sem; Zahnärztliche–, dentistry, 10 sem; Pharmazeutische–, pharmacy, 7 sem; Prüfung für das Lehramt an höheren Schulen (teaching qualification, secondary level, all fields). Diplomas–Diplom-Chemiker, chemistry; -Geologe, geology; -Mathematiker, mathematics; -Physiker, physics; -Psychologe, psychology; -Volkswirt, economics. Degree of Magister Artium, 8 sem. Doctorates–Dr., in all fields, approximately 8 sem, except Dr.med. dent. and Zahnärztliche Staatsprüfung, 10 sem; Dr.med. and Medizinische Staatsprüfung, 12 sem. Habilitation (teaching qualification, university level), at least 3 yrs after doctorate.

Libraries: University Library, *c.* 1,000,000 vols; libraries of the institutes and departments.

Special Facilities (Museums, etc.): Museum of Art and Cultural History; Collection of Religious Art and Ceremonial Utensils; Museum of Mineralogy.

Academic Staff: c. 650.

Student Enrolment, 1990:

	Men	Women	Total
Of the country	7920	7054	14,974
Of other countries	630	429	1059
Total	8550	7483	16,033

3131 ***LUDWIG-MAXIMILIANS-UNIVERSITÄT MÜNCHEN**
University of Munich
Geschwister Scholl-Platz 1, 8000 München 22
Telex: (5) 29860
Telephone: (89) 2180-1
Fax: (89) 260-4212
Rektor: Wulf Steinmann (1982-94)
Kanzler: Hendrik Rust

F. of Theology (Catholic)
Dean: Peter Neuner; *staff* 57
F. of Theology (Protestant)
Dean: Ferdinand Hahn; *staff* 35
F. of Law
Dean: Klaus Volk; *staff* 108
F. of Industrial Economics
Dean: Hermann Meyer zu Selhausen; *staff* 86
F. of Political Economics
Dean: Friedrich Haffner; *staff* 56
F. of Forestry
Dean: Hans-Dietrich Löffler; *staff* 52
F. of Medicine (including Dentistry)
Dean: Klaus Peter; *staff* 1497
F. of Veterinary Medicine
Dean: Jürgen Unshelm; *staff* 197
F. of History and Fine Arts (including Musicology)
Dean: Walter Koch; *staff* 91
F. of Philosophy, Theory of Science, and Statistics
Dean: Peter Hinst; *staff* 65
F. of Psychology and Pedagogics
Dean: Rolf Oerter; *staff* 114
F. of Antiquities and Cultural Sciences (Archaeology, Eastern Language, Ethnology)
Dean: Peter Rehder; *staff* 90
F. of Languages and Literature I (Indogerman, Indology and Iranistics, Greek, Latin, English, Romance Languages)
Dean: Walter Gabler; *staff* 126
F. of Languages and Literature II (Phonetics, Nordic Philology, German)
Dean: Gerhard Neumann; *staff* 106
F. of Social and Behavioural Sciences
Dean: Heinz Laufer; *staff* 779
F. of Mathematics
Dean: Otto Forsterg; *staff* 73
F. of Physics
Dean: Joseph Egger; *staff* 146
F. of Chemistry and Pharmacy
Dean: Theodor Severin; *staff* 205
F. of Biology
Dean: Charles N. David; *staff* 92
F. of Earth Sciences
Dean: Hubert Miller; *staff* 72
Also *c.* 180 constituent institutes and clinics.

Founded 1472 at Ingolstadt by Ludwig, Duke of Upper and Lower Bavaria, transferred to Landshut 1800 by King Maximilian I, and to Munich 1826 by King Ludwig I. An autonomous institution financially supported by the State of Bavaria, and under the jurisdiction of its Ministry of Sciences and Arts. Governing bodies: the Versammlung (Assembly), comprising 36 professors, 12 assistants, 5 students, 3 members of the non-professional staff, and 1 Universitätsfrauenbeauftragte; the Senat, comprising 12 professors, 4 assistants, 2 students, 2 members of the non-academic staff, and 1 Universitätsfrauen beauftragte; the Rektoratskollegium, comprising the Rektor, 3 Prorektoren, Kanzler. Some residential facilities for students.

Arrangements for co-operation with: Kliment-Ochridski University, Sofia; University of Leipzig; University of Paris VII; University of Athens; University of Manchester; University of Kent, Canterbury; University of Sussex, Brighton; University College of Swansea; Sunderland Polytechnic; Università degli Studi di Padova; Scuola Normale Superiore, Pisa; University of Zagreb; Bołesaw-Bierut University, Wrocław; University of Istanbul; Université du Bénin, Lomé; Universidad Nacional de Tucuman; Universidad Austral de Chile; Universidad de Concepción; Wayne State University; University of Minnesota; Kansas State University; Washington University St. Louis; Beijing University; Tel Aviv University; Hokkaido University; Kokushikan University; Sung Kyun Kwan University, Seoul; Yeungnam University, Taegu, Seoul; Yonsei University, Seoul; National Chengchi University, Taipei; Tamkang University, Taipei; Tamsui University.

Academic Year: November to July (November-February; May-July).

Admission Requirements: Secondary school certificate (Reifezeugnis) or equivalent.

Fees: None.

Language of Instruction: German.

Degrees and Diplomas: State Examinations–Juristische Staatsprüfung, law; Medizinische–, medicine; Zahnärztliche–, dentistry; Pharmazeutische–, pharmacy; Tierärztliche–, veterinary medicine; Lebensmitteltechnische–, food technology; Prüfung für das Lehramt an höheren Schulen (teaching qualification, all fields). Diplomas–Diplom-Biologe, biology; -Chemiker, chemistry; -Forstwirt, forestry; -Geologe, geology; -Mineraloge, mineralogy; -Geograph, geography; -Geophysiker, geophysics; -Handelslehrer (commercial teaching qualification); -Kaufmann, industrial economics; -Mathematiker, mathematics; -Meteorologe, meteorology; -Physiker, physics; -Psychologe, psychology; -Volkswirt, political economics; -Soziologe, sociology; -Statistiker, statistics. Lizentiat der Theologie, theology. Degree of Magister Artium. Doctorates, Dr.theol. (Cath. and Prot.); Dr.jur.can.; Dr.jur.; Dr.rer.pol.; Dr.eco.publ.; Dr.rer.silv.; Dr.med.; Dr.med.dent.; Dr.rer.biol.; Dr.med.vet.; Dr.phil.; Dr.rer.nat. Habilitation (teaching qualification, university level), at least 3 yrs after doctorate.

Libraries: University Library, *c.* 2.15m. vols; faculty libraries, *c.* 3m.

Special Facilities (Museums, etc.): Beschleuniger Laboratorium; Laboratorium für Molekulare Biologie; Zentrum für Informations- und Sprachverarbeitung; Sonnenobservatorium Wendelstein; Geophysikalisches Observatorium; Anatomische Staatssammlung; Anthropologische Staatssammlung; Staatliche Sammlung Ägyptischer Kunst; Botanische Staatssammlung und Botanischer Garten; Geologische Staatssammlung; Mineralogische-, Paläontologische-, Abdrucksammlung Klassischer Bildwerke.

Publications: Münchener Universitätsschriften (Monograph Series); Zeitschrift für Politik (monthly); Berichte aus der Forschung; Chronic; Münchner Uni-Magazin.

Press or Publishing House: Pressereferat.

Academic Staff, 1990:

Rank	Full-time
Professoren	807
Akademische Räte auf Zeit/Wissenschaftliche Ober-/Assistenten	1829
Akademische Räte/Studienräte auf Lebenzeit	488
Wissenschaftliche Angestellte (Stellen)	301
Total	3425

Student Enrolment, 1989-90:

	Men	Women	Total
Of the country	28,541	29,734	58,275
Of other countries	1858	2009	3867
Total	30,399	31,743	62,142

3132 ***TECHNISCHE UNIVERSITÄT MÜNCHEN**

Technical University of Munich

Arcisstrasse 21, 8000 München 2

Telex: 522854 TUMUE D

Telephone: (89) 21051

Präsident: Otto Meitinger

D. of Mathematics and Computer Sciences
Dean: Christopher Zenger
D. of Physics
Dean: Edgar Lüscher
D. of Chemistry, Biology, and Earth Sciences
Dean: Karl-Heinz Schleifer
D. of Economics and Social Sciences
Dean: Franz Holzheu
D. of Construction Engineering and Surveying
Dean: Hermann Schröder
D. of Architecture
Dean: Hermann Schröder
D. of Mechanical Engineering
Dean: Klaus Erlenspiel
D. of Electrical Engineering
Dean: Wolfgang Harth
D. of Agriculture and Horticulture (Weinhenstephan)
Dean: Wolfgang Horn
D. of Brewing, Food Technology and Dairy Science (Weinhenstephan)
Dean: Rudolf Krüger
D. of Medicine
Dean: Hans Werner Pabst
I. of Environmental Planning and Research
Ce. for Physical Education

Founded 1827 as Polytechnische Zentralschule, became Polytechnische Schule in 1868 and Technische Hochschule in 1877 and Universität 1970. Buildings severely damaged by bombing in 1945, since reconstructed and enlarged. An autonomous institution under the jurisdiction of the State of Bavaria. Governing body: the Senat, composed of the President, Vice-Presidents, the deans, and other members of the academic staff.

Arrangements for co-operation with: University of Illinois; University of Tokyo; Wuhan University; Ecole spéciale des Travaux publics, du Bâtiment et de l'Industrie, Paris.

Academic Year: October to September (October-March; April-September).

Admission Requirements: Secondary school certificate (Reifezeugnis) or equivalent.

Fees: Tuition, none.

Language of Instruction: German.

Degrees and Diplomas: State Examinations–Lebensmittelchemike Staatsprüfung, food chemistry, 4-5 yrs; Medizinische–, 6 yrs. Diplomas–Diplom-Braumeister, brewing, 2 yrs; -Ingenieur in: Physics, Civil Engineering, Surveying, Agricultural Engineering, Horticulture, Mechanical Engineering, Electrical Engineering; Brewing; -Mathematiker, mathematics; -Informatiker, computer sciences; -Physiker, physics; -Chemiker, chemistry; -Biologe, biology; -Geologe, geology; -Mineraloge, mineralogy; -Geograph, geography; -Landespfleger, landscape cultivation; -Ökotrophologe, ocotrophology; -Lebensmitteltechnologe, food technology; -Architekt; -Landwirt, agriculture; -Sportlehrer, physical education, 4-5 yrs. State Examinations–Prüfung für das Lehramt an Gymnasien und für das höhere Lehramt an beruflichen Schulen (teaching qualification for secondary level schools). Doctorates–Dr.-Ing.; Dr.rer.pol.; Dr.phil.; Dr.med.; Dr.med.dent., at least 2 yrs after end of studies.Habilitation (teaching qualification university level), at least 2 yrs of scientific research after doctorate.

Library: University Library, *c.* 1,250,000 vols.

Publications: Jahrbuch der Technischen Hochschule; TUM–Mitteilungen (monthly).

Academic Staff: c. 7330.

Student Enrolment: c. 21,750 (Also *c.* 780 external students).

3133 **WESTFÄLISCHE WILHELMS-UNIVERSITÄT MÜNSTER**

University of Münster

Schlossplatz 2, 4400 Münster

Telex: 892529 UNIMS D

Telephone: (251) 83-1

Fax: (251) 83-2090

Rektor: Maria Wasna (1990-94)

Kanzler: Klaus Triebold

F. of Theology (Protestant)
Dean: Manfred Jacobs
F. of Theology (Catholic)
Dean: Adel-Theodor Khoury
F. of Law
Dean: Rolf Stober
F. of Economics and Social Sciences
Dean: Manfred Steiner
F. of Medicine (including Dentistry)
Dean: Ute Witting
F. of Philosophy (including Liberal Arts, Psychology, Musicology, and Education)
Dean: Dietmar Krafft
F. of Mathematics and Natural Sciences (including Pharmacy)
Dean: Elisabeth Peveling
D. of Social Sciences
Dean: Josef Lingnau
D. of Philosophy
Dean: Klaus Hortschansky
D. of Psychology
Dean: Renate de Jong-Meyer
D. of Education, Sociology, and Communications
Dean: Hubert Steinhaus
D. of History
Dean: Heinz Buchhardt
D. of Germanic Studies
Dean: Ludwig Völker
D. of English Studies
Dean: Klaus Ostheeren
D. of Romance and Slav Studies
Dean: Gerhard Ressel
D. of Classical and Non-European Studies
Dean: Albrecht Jockenhövrel
D. of Earth Sciences
Dean: Peter Weber
D. of Mathematics
Dean: Wolfram Pohlers
D. of Physics
Dean: Helmut Mehrer
D. of Chemistry
Dean: Harald Züchner
D. of Biology
Dean: Dieter J. von Willert
D. of Physical Education
Dean: Ulrich Garske
D. of German Language and Literature, Arts (Teacher Training)
Dean: Josef Billen
Ce. for Mature Students
Pro-Rector: Volkmar Leite

Also *c.* 140 institutes, seminars, and clinics of the different faculties and departments.

Founded 1780 as a university but in 1818 became an academy of philosophy and theology. The institution was then restored to university status in 1902 and received its present title in 1907. An autonomous institution financially supported by the State of North Rhine-Westphalia, and under the jurisdiction of its Ministry of Education. Governing body: the Senat. Residential facilities for students.

Arrangements for co-operation with: University of Lille; University of Lima; Catholic Universities of Louvain/Leuven; Universidad Católica Boliviana, La Paz; Twente University of Technology; Pontifical Catholic University of Ecuador; Centre Universitaire de Luxembourg; National University of Tucumán; Universidad Santo Tomas, Bogotá; Catholic University of Nijmegen; California State University, Fresno; Academy of Economics, Wrocław; Trinity and All Saints College, Horsforth, Leeds; Federal University of Rio Grande do Sul; Federal University of Santa Catarina; Pontifical Catholic University of São Paulo; University of Lund.

Academic Year: October to September (October-March; April-September).

Admission Requirements: Secondary school certificate (Reifezeugnis) or equivalent.

Fees: Tuition, none.

Language of Instruction: German.

Degrees and Diplomas: State Examinations–Juristische Staatsprüfung, law; Medizinische–, medicine; Zahnärztliche–, dentistry; Lebensmitteltechnische–, food technology; Pharmazeutische–, pharmacy; Prüfung für das Lehramt an höheren Schulen (teaching qualification, secondary level, all fields). Diplomas–Diplom-Chemiker, chemistry; -Geograph, geography; -Geologe, geology; -Kaufmann, business administration; -Mathematiker, mathematics; -Mineraloge, mineralogy; -Pädagoge, education; -Physiker, physics; -Psychologe, psychology; -Publizist, journalism; -Volkswirt, economics. Degrees in Catholic and Protestant Theology. Degree of Magister Artium, 8 sem. Doctorates, Dr. in all fields, 6-10 sem. Habilitation (teaching qualification, university level), at least 3 yrs after doctorate.

Libraries: University Library, *c.* 1,655,000 vols; institute and seminar libraries.

Special Facilities (Museums, etc.): Geological Museum; Mineralogical Museum; Archaeological Museum.

Academic Staff, 1989-90:

Rank	Full-time	Part-time
Professoren	644	–
Wissenschaftliche Mitarbeiter	2050	–
Lehrbeauftragte	–	537
Total	2694	537

Student Enrolment, 1990:

	Men	Women	Total
Of the country	21,828	19,661	41,489
Of other countries	1224	739	1963
Total	23,052	20,400	43,452

3134 **UNIVERSITÄT OLDENBURG**
University of Oldenburg
Ammerländer Heerstrasse 67-69, 2900 Oldenburg
Telex: 2-56-55
Telephone: (441) 798-0
Fax: (441) 789-3000
Präsident: Michael Daxner
Kanzler: Jürgen Lüthje

D. of Education
; *staff* 48
D. of Modern Languages and Fine Arts
; *staff* 20
F. of Social Sciences
; *staff* 68
F. of Economics and Law
; *staff* 57
F. of Philosophy, Psychology, and Physical Education
; *staff* 34
D. of Mathematics and Computer Sciences
; *staff* 24
F. of Biology
; *staff* 42
F. of Chemistry
; *staff* 40
D. of Physics
; *staff* 32
D. of Computer Sciences
; *staff* 35
D. of Foreign Languages and Literature
; *staff* 49

Founded 1970. Teaching started 1974 with incorporation of the Oldenburg branch of the College of Education, Niedersachsen. An autonomous institution financially supported by the State of Lower Saxony, and under the jurisdiction of its Ministry of Education. Governing bodies: the Konzil, comprising 91 members; the Senat, comprising 13 members. The members of both bodies are represented in the ratio of 7 professors, 2 students, 2 members of the academic staff, and 2 members of the non-academicstaff. Residential facilities for students.

Arrangements for co-operation with: University of Lancaster; University of Newcastle upon Tyne; Sunderland andManchester Polytechnics; University of Groningen; University of Toruń; University of South Dakota.

Academic Year: October to September (October-March; April-September).

Admission Requirements: Secondary school certificate (Reifezeugnis) or recognized equivalent. Fachhochschulreife (technical secondary education) for certain courses.

Fees: Tuition, none.

Language of Instruction: German.

Degrees and Diplomas: Staatsprüfung für das Lehramt (teaching qualifications, primary and secondary levels). Diplomas–Diplom-Ingenieur; -Psychologe; -Pädagoge; -Mathematiker; -Chemiker; -Physiker; -Ökonom; -Sozialwissenschaftler, social sciences; -Biologe, 5-6 yrs. Doctorates–Dr.phil.; Dr.rer.pol.; Dr.rer.nat. Habilitation (teaching qualification, university level), at least 3 yrs after doctorate.

Library: Total, *c.* 700,000 vols.

Academic Staff: c. 370 (40).

Student Enrolment: c. 9400.

3135 **UNIVERSITÄT OSNABRÜCK**
University of Osnabrück
Schloss/Neuer Graben, 4500 Osnabrück
Cables: unios d 944850
Telephone: (541) 6081

D. of Social Sciences (including Sociology and Political Sciences)
D. of Social Sciences (including Philosophy, Geography, and History)
D. of Social Sciences (including Education, Psychology, Music, Protestant Theology, and Physical Education)
D. of Natural Sciences (Experimental Physics)
D. of Natural Sciences (Biology and Chemistry)
D. of Natural Sciences (Mathematics)
D. of Communication Studies and Aesthetics
D. of Psychology
D. of Economics
D. of Law
D. of Catholic Theology (Vechta)
D. of Education (Vechta)
D. of Communication Studies and Aesthetics (Vechta)
D. of Natural Sciences (Vechta)
D. of Social Sciences (Vechta)
Computer Ce.
Education Ce.
Extramural Ce.

Founded 1970. Teaching started 1974. Previously a branch of the College of Education, Lower Saxony. An autonomous institution financially supported by the State of Lower Saxony.

Academic Year: October to September (October-March; April-September).

Admission Requirements: Secondary school certificate (Reifezeugnis).

Fees: None.

Language of Instruction: German.

Academic Staff: c. 500.

Student Enrolment: c. 5000.

3136 ***UNIVERSITÄT-GESAMTHOCHSCHULE-PADERBORN**
University of Paderborn
Warburger Strasse 100, 4790 Paderborn
Telex: 936776 UNIPB D
Telephone: (5251) 60-1
Fax: (5251) 60-2519
Electronic mail: eunet/usenet
Rektor: Hans-Dieter Rinkens (1987-)
Kanzler: Ulrich Hintze

D. of Philosophy, and Religious and Social Sciences (including Political Sciences)
Dean: Norbert Mette; *staff* 48 (19)

D. of Education, Psychology, and Physical Education
Dean: Wilhelm Hagemann; *staff* 54 (13)
D. of Languages and Literature
Dean: Rolf Breuer; *staff* 63 (21)
D. of Fine Arts and Music
Dean: Wilfried Fischer; *staff* 21
D. of Economics and Business Studies
Dean: Winfried Reiss; *staff* 61 (7)
D. of Physics
Dean: Harald Overhof; *staff* 67
D. of Chemistry and Chemical Engineering
Dean: Hans-Josef Altenbach; *staff* 60 (32)
D. of Landscape Architecture
Dean: Udo Schmidt; *staff* 21 (6)
D. of Environmental Protection Technology
Dean: Horst Wardemann; *staff* 5
D. of Agriculture (Soest)
Dean: Heinrich Schulte-Sienbeck; *staff* 13 (3)
D. of Mechanical Engineering I
Dean: Hans Albert Richard; *staff* 96 (3)
D. of Mechanical Engineering II (Meschede)
Dean: Siegfried Geipel; *staff* 11 (6)
D. of Mechanical Engineering III (Soest)
Dean: Günter Havenstein; *staff* 11 (6)
D. of Electrical Engineering and Electronics
Dean: Jürgen Voss; *staff* 79 (7)
D. of Telecommunication Technology (Meschede)
Dean: Hans-Dieter Meierling; *staff* 20 (1)
D. of Electrical Power Engineering (Soest)
Dean: Jürgen Grüneberg; *staff* 13 (9)
D. of Mathematics and Computer Sciences
Dean: Uwe Kastens; *staff* 100 (7)
Computer-Aided Design L.
Head: Thomas Lengauer; *staff* 10

Founded 1972 as a Gesamthochschule, a new type of university designed to integrate all forms of postsecondary education within a single framework. Incorporating former Colleges of Education and of Engineering. An autonomous institution financially supported by the State of North Rhine-Westphalia. Governing bodies: the Senat; the Konvent; the Kuratorium. Residential facilities for *c.* 530 students.

Arrangements for co-operation with: Université du Maine; Nottingham Polytechnic; Saint Olaf College, Northfield; Illinois State University; University of Illinois; Howard University; Lock Haven University; Universidad de Alcalá de Henares; Universidad de Santiago de Compostela; Catholic University of Nijmegen; Eötvös Loránd University; Guangzhou Institute of Foreign Languages; Universidad de Zaragoza; Dublin City University; Université Louis Pasteur, Strasbourg I; Stockholms Universitet; Athens School of Economics and Business Science; Academy of Economics, Poznań; University of Kansas; Western Michigan University; University of Waterloo;Xi'an Jiaotong University; Zhejiang University; King Mongkut's Institute of Technology, North Bangkok.

Academic Year: October to September (October-March; April-September).

Admission Requirements: Secondary school certificate (Reifezeugnis) or equivalent.

Fees: Tuition, none.

Language of Instruction: German.

Degrees and Diplomas: Diplomas–Diplom-Chemiker; -Ökonom; -Chemieingenieur; -Physiker; -Mathematiker; -Kaufmann, business administration; -Volkswirt, economics; -Pädagoge; -Ingenieur; -Informatiker, 7-10 sem. Degree of Magister Artium, 9 sem. Prüfung für das Lehramt (teaching qualification primary and secondary levels). Doctorates–Dr.-ing.; Dr.phil.; Dr.paed.; Dr.rer.pol., economics; Dr. rer.nat. Habilitation (teaching qualification, university level).

Library: Central Library, *c.* 800,000 vols.

Publications: Hausmitteilung; Schriften der Universität; Paderborner Universitätszeitung (PUZ).

Academic Staff, 1988:

Rank	Full-time	Part-time
Professoren	357	–
Wissenschaftliche Mitarbeiter	369	150
Total	726	150

Student Enrolment, 1988-89:

Of the country	12,500
Of other countries	600
Total	13,100

3137 ***UNIVERSITÄT PASSAU**
University of Passau
Dr.-Hans-Kapfinger-Str. 22, 8390 Passau
Telephone: (851) 5090
Fax: (851) 509 130
Präsident: Karl-Heinz Pollok (1988-94)
Kanzler: Karl August Friedrichs

F. of Catholic Theology
Dean: Ehrenfried Schulz; *staff* 13
F. of Law
Dean: Michael Schweitzer; *staff* 16
F. of Economics
Dean: Rolf Bühner; *staff* 14
F. of Mathematics and Data Processing
Dean: Klaus Donner; *staff* 15
F. of Philosophy
Dean: Hans-Werner Eroms; *staff* 39
I. East Bavaria Home Research
Head: August Leidl; *staff* 1 (1)
I. of New Psychology History
; *staff* 1 (4)
I. of Agricultural Law
Head: Hans-Joachim Musielak; *staff* 4
I. of International and Foreign Law
Director: Klaus Schurig; *staff* 6

Founded 1973. Teaching started 1978. An autonomous institution financially supported by the State of Bavaria. Governing bodies: the Versammlung (Assembly); the Senat. Residential facilities for students.

Arrangements for co-operation with: Charles University, Prague; King's College of University of London; Université d'Angers; Université de Tours; University College of North Wales Bangor; University of South Alabama Mobile; University of Puget Sound Tacoma; Università degli Studi di Pavia; Aston University, Birmingham; University of Edinburgh; Universidad de Barcelona; Universidad de Málaga; Zhongshan University; Chiang Mai University; Universidad de Santiago de Compostela; Université de Toulouse I; Catholic University of Lisbon and Porto; Lisbon Technical University; Western Michigan University; University of Ankara; Università degli Studi di Verona; Mohammed V University, Rabat; Wales College of Cardiff; University of Amsterdam; University of East Anglia Norwich; Università degli Studi di Siena; Karl Marx University of Economic Sciences, Budapest; Università degli Studi di Parma; University of Ivanovo; University College of Dublin.

Academic Year: October to September (October-March; April-September).

Admission Requirements: Secondary school certificate (Reifezeugnis).

Fees: None.

Language of Instruction: German.

Degrees and Diplomas: State Examination–Juristische Staatsprüfung, law; Prüfung für das Lehramt. Diplomas–Diplom-Theologe; -Kaufmann; -Volkswirt; -Mathematiker; -Informatiker, data processing, 4 yrs. Lizentiat in Theology, 4 yrs. Degree of Magister Artium, 4 yrs. Doctorates. Habilitation (teaching qualification, university level), at least 3 yrs after doctorate.

Library: 1.100,000 vols.

Publications: Schriften der Universität Passau; Nachrichten und Berichte.

Press or Publishing House: Passavia Universitätsverlag und -Druck GmbH.

Academic Staff, 1989-90:

Rank	Full-time
Professoren	97
Wissenschaftliche Mitarbeiter	205
Lehrbeauftragte	91
Total	393

Student Enrolment, 1989-90:

	Men	Women	Total
Of the country	3501	2945	6446
Of other countries	143	117	260
Total	3644	3062	6706

3138 ***UNIVERSITÄT REGENSBURG**

University of Regensburg
Universitätsstrasse 31, 8400 Regensburg
Telex: 065658 UNIRE D
Telephone: (941) 9431
Fax: (941) 943 2305
Rektor: Helmut Altner (1989-)
Kanzler: Hans-Hagen Zorger

F. of Theology (Catholic)
Dean: Karl Hausberger; *staff* 53
F. of Law
Dean: Udo Steiner; *staff* n9
F. of Economics
Dean: Gerhard Niemeyer: *staff* 85
F. of Medicine (including Dentistry)
Dean: U.-G. Tammoscheit; *staff* 176
F. of Philosophy, Physical Education and the Fine Arts
Dean: Heinz Lutter: *staff* 42
F. of Education and Psychology
Dean: Alf Zimmer; *staff* 67
F. of History, Social Sciences, and Geography
Dean: Klaus Köhle; *staff* 81
F. of Languages and Literature
Dean: Hans Gärtner; *staff* 122
F. of Mathematics
Dean: Günter Tamme; *staff* 48
F. of Physics
Dean: K.F. Reuk; *staff* 128
F. of Pre-Clinical Medicine and Biology
Dean: Dietrich Burkhardt; *staff* 213
F. of Chemistry and Pharmacy
Dean: Helmut Schönenberger; *staff* 204

Founded 1962. Admitted first students 1967. An autonomous institution financially supported by the State of Bavaria. Governing bodies: the Versammlung; the Senat. Residential facilities for students in Studentenwohnheime.

Arrangements for co-operation with: University of Colorado; Vanderbilt University; University of Ljubljana; University of Novi Sad; University of Trieste; University of Szeged; Dongguk University, Seoul; University of Brno; University of Odessa.

Academic Year: October to September (April-September; October-March).

Admission Requirements: Secondary school certificate (Reifezeugnis).

Fees: Tuition, none.

Languages of Instruction: German and English in some cases.

Degrees and Diplomas: State Examinations–Juristische Staatsprüfung, law; Pharmazeutische–; Prüfung für das Lehramt an öffentlichen Schulen (teaching qualification, various fields). Diplomas–Diplom-Theologe, theology; -Kaufmann, business administration; -Psychologe, psychology; -Pädagoge, education; -Soziologe, sociology; -Geograph; -Mathematiker, mathematics; -Physiker; -Biologe; -Chemiker, 4-6 yrs. Magisterprüfung der philosophischen Fachgebiete, philosophy, 4-5 yrs. Doctorates, 2-4 yrs. Habilitation (teaching qualifications, university level), at least 3 yrs after doctorate.

Library: c. 2,393,000 vols.

Special Facilities (Museums, etc.): Botanical Garden with Pharmaceutical Section.

Publications: Universitätszeitung (monthly); Forschungsbericht (every 3 years); Schriftenreihe; Jahresbericht (annual report).

Academic Staff, 1988-89:

Rank	Full-time	Part-time
Professoren	253	–
Wissenschaftliche Mitarbeiter/Studienräte	594	–
Wissenschaftliche Hilfskräfte	–	250
Total	847	250

Student Enrolment, 1989-90:

	Men	Women	Total
Of the country	6951	6149	13,070
Of other countries	324	293	577
Total	7245	6402	13,647

3139 **UNIVERSITÄT DES SAARLANDES**

University of the Saar
Im Stadtwald, 6600 Saarbrücken
Telex: 4428851
Telephone: (681) 302-1
Fax: (681)302-3900
Präsident: Richard Johannes Meiser (1983-)
Kanzler: Hartwig Cremers

F. of Law and Economics (including Political Science and European Studies)
Dean: Jürgen Domes; *staff* 190
F. of Medicine (including Dentistry) (Homburg)
Dean: Paul Fritsche; *staff* 216
F. of Philosophy (including Social Studies, Theology, and Modern Languages)
Dean: Dietrich Fliedner; *staff* 313
F. of Mathematics and Natural Sciences (including Computer Sciences)
Dean: Gerd Schmidt; *staff* 335
I. of Physical Education

Also *c.* 70 institutes, seminars, and clinics of the different faculties.

Founded 1947 as Saarländisches Hochschulinstitut, became university 1948. Became an autonomous university 1957 financially supported by the State of the Saar, and under the jurisdiction of its Ministry of Education. Governing bodies: the Senat, comprising 20 representatives of the academic staff, 4 representatives of the non-academic staff, and 4 students; the Konzil, comprising 80 representatives of the academic staff, 10 representatives of the non-academic staff, and 20 students. Residential facilities for academic staff and 1525 students.

Arrangements for co-operation with the Universities of: Paris I, III; Strasbourg II, Nancy I, II; Haute-Alsace, Mulhouse; Maryland; Michigan, Ann Arbor; Yokohama; Lomé; Dakar; Warsaw; Sofia; Exeter; Los Angeles; Columbia; Tbilissi. Institut national polytechnique de Lorraine, Nancy; Ecole supérieure de Commerce, Lyon; Centre Universitaire de Luxembourg; Academy of Medicine, Poznań; Hyogo Medical College; University College of Wales, Cardiff; Federal University of Rio Grande do Sul.

Academic Year: October to September (October-March; April-September).

Admission Requirements: Secondary school certificate (Reifezeugnis) or equivalent.

Fees: Tuition, none.

Languages of Instruction: German. (French at Centre for French Legal Studies and Institute of French Studies.)

Degrees and Diplomas: State Examinations–Juristische Staatsprüfung, law; Medizinische–, medicine; Pharmazeutische–, Zahnärztliche–, Prüfung für das Lehramt an höheren Schulen (teaching qualification, secondary level, all fields). Diplomas–Diplom-Chemiker, chemistry; -Dolmetscher, interpretation; -Geograph, geography; -Geologe, geology; -Handelslehrer, commercial teaching qualification; -Ingenieur der Fachrichtung Metallkunde, metallurgy; -Kaufmann, business administration; -Biologe, biology; -Bauingenieur, civil engineering; -Mathematiker, mathematics; -Mineraloge, mineralogy; -Physiker, physics; -Psychologe, psychology; -Soziologe, sociology; -Übersetzer, translation; -Volkswirt, economics. Lizentiat der Rechte. Magister Artium, arts. Doctorates–Dr., in all fields, approximately 8 sem, except Dr.rer.pol. and Dolmetscher and Diplom-Übersetzer, 6 sem; Dr.med.dent., 10 sem; Dr.med. and Medizinische Staatsprüfung, 11 sem. Habilitation (teaching qualification, university level), at least 3 yrss after doctorate. Also Certificate and Diploma in European Studies.

Libraries: University Library, *c.*1,118,000 vols; Medicine (Homburg), 191,000; institute libraries, *c.* 1m.

Publications: Forschungsbericht; Annales Universitatis Saraviensis; Serie Rechts-und Wirtschaftswissenschaften; Serie Medizin; Serie Philosophie; Serie Naturwissenschaften; Campus.

Academic Staff, 1986-87:

Rank	Full-time
Professoren	304
Akademische Mitarbeiter	247
Wissenschaftliche Mitarbeiter	470
Wissenschaftliche Hilfskräfte	76
Total	1097

Student Enrolment, 1986-87:

	Men	Women	Total
Of the country	9511	7426	16,937
Of other countries	704	551	1255
Total	10,215	7977	18,192

3140 ***UNIVERSITÄT-GESAMTHOCHSCHULE-SIEGEN**

University of Siegen

Am Herrengarten 3, 5900 Siegen
Telex: 87 2337 GHSGND
Telephone: (271) 740-1
Fax: (271) 740-2310 Teletex: 211383
Rektor: Klaus Sturm (1989-93)
Kanzler: Hans-Joachim Herrmann

D. of Philosophy, History, Geography, and Religious and Social Sciences
Dean: Rainer Albertz; *staff* 78 (51)
D. of Education, Psychology, and Physical Education
Dean: Karin Weber; *staff* 35 (6)
D. of Languages and Literature
Dean: Hans Hoppe ; *staff* 61 (26)
D. of Fine Arts and Music
Dean: Daniel Hees; *staff* 17 (36)
D. of Economics and Business Administration
Dean: Hans-E. Loef; *staff* 68 (5)
D. of Mathematics
Dean: Wolfgang Hein; *staff* 47
D. of Physics
Dean: Torsten Fliessbach; *staff* 36
D. of Chemistry and Biology
Dean: W. H. E. Schwarz; *staff* 51 (4)
D. of Architecture and Town Planning
Dean: Rolf Becker; *staff* 13 (6)
D. of Civil Engineering
Dean: Heinz Mellmann; *staff* 23 (4)
D. of Mechanical Engineering
Dean: Manfred Köhne; *staff* 65 (2)
D. of Electrical Engineering
Dean: Werner Köller; *staff* 64 (4)
Graduate Ce. in Humanities
Research I. for Humanities and Social Sciences
I. for Empirical Literature and Media Research
Research Project on Aesthetics, Pragmatism and History of German Television
Research Ce. for Monetary Macroeconomics
Ce. for Sensor Systems
I. for Language in Industry, Business and Other Vocational Areas
L. for Surface Technology
Computer Ce.
I. for European Regional Research

Founded 1972 as a Gesamthochschule, a new type of university designed to integrate all forms of postsecondary education within a single framework. Incorporating former Technical College, Siegen-Gummersbach and branch of College of Education, Westfalen-Lippe. Became University 1980. An autonomous institution under the jurisdiction of and financially supported by the State of North Rhine-Westphalia. Residential facilities for *c.* 800 students.

Arrangements for co-operation with: University of Houston; Portsmouth Polytechnic; University of British Columbia; Université d'Orléans; Ecole nationale d'Ingénieurs de Saint-Etienne; Universidad de los Andes; University of Missouri; Shanghai Institute of Mechanical Engineering; Ecole polytechnique, Palaiseau; Universidad de Deusto; Beijing Polytechnic University; Shanghai Institute of Railway Technology; Northern Jiaotung University; Leningrad Institute of Fine Mechanics and Optics; University of Ulster.

Academic Year: October to September (October-March; April-September).

Admission Requirements: Secondary school certificate (Reifezeugnis). Fachhochschulreife (technical secondary education) for certain courses.

Fees: None.

Language of Instruction: German.

Degrees and Diplomas: State Examinations–Prüfung für das Lehramt (teaching qualifications), 3-4 yrs. Integrated courses: Diplomas–Diplom–Ingenieur (Mechanical, Electrical, and Computer Science Engineering); -Physikingenieur; -Laborchemiker; -Kaufmann, business administration, 3 ½ yrs; -Ingenieur (Mechanical, International Project, Electrical, Computer Science/Engineering); -Mathematiker; -Kaufmann; -Volkswirt, economics; -Wirtschaftsingenieur, industrial engineering; -Medienwirt, Media Science, 4 ½ yrs; -Physiker, 5 yrs; -Sozialarbeiter; -Sozialpädagoge, educational social work; Pädagoge, 5 ½ yrs (consecutive model). Also 2 ½ yrs postgraduate degree in–Mechanical and Electrical Engineering, and Chemistry. Diplom-Ingenieur (Architecture, Civil Engineering), 3 ½ yrs as basis for 5 ½ yr degree integrated course. Degree of Magister Artium, arts in–Germanistik; Anglistik/Amerikanistik; Romanistik; Allgemeine Literaturwissenschaft; Philosophie; Politikwissenschaft; Soziologie, 4 ½ yrs. Doctorates–Dr.-Ing.; Dr.rer.pol.; Dr.rer.nat.; Dr.phil.; Dr.paed. Habilitation (teaching qualification, university level).

Library: Central Library, 900,000 vols.

Special Facilities (Museums, etc.): Audio-Visual Media Centre.

Publications: Reihe Siegen; Forschungsbericht (Research Report); Amtliche Mitteilungen; Muk (Massenmedien und Kommunikation); Siegener Pädagogische Studien; SPIEL (Siegener Periodicum zur International Empirischen Literaturwissenschaften); Lumis-Schriften; HiMon-Diskussionsbeiträge.

Academic Staff, 1989-90:

Rank	Full-time	Part-time
Professoren	310	–
Wissenschaftliche Mitarbeiter	370	70
Lehrbeauftragte	–	136
Total	680	206

Student Enrolment, 1989-90:

	Men	Women	Total
Of the country	6714	2703	9417
Of other countries	495	170	665
Total	7209	2873	10,082

3141 **HOCHSCHULE FÜR VERWALTUNGSWISSENSCHAFTEN SPEYER**

School of Administrative Sciences

Freiherr-vom-Stein-Strasse 2, 6720 Speyer
Telephone: (6232) 910-1
Rektor: Carl Böhret (1989-91)
Oberregierungsrat: Alfons Schnabel

Administrative Sciences (including Municipal Law, Political Science, Economics, Sociology and Constitutional Law;) *staff* 106 (34)
Public Administration Research I.
Director: Willi Blümel; *staff* 21 (3)

Founded 1947 as Staatliche Akademie, acquired present status and title 1950. A postgraduate institution financed by the State of Rheinland-Pfalz, the Federal Government and other State governments. Governing bodies: the Senat; the Verwaltungsrat. Residential facilities for students.

Arrangements for co-operation with: Wuhan University, Beijing; Beijing University; Dongguk University.

Academic Year: October to September (November-January; May-July).

Admission Requirements: University degree in Law, Economics, or Social Sciences.

Fees: None.

Language of Instruction: German.

Degrees and Diplomas: Degree of Magister. Doktor der Verwaltungswissenschaften (doctor rerum publicarum), 2-3 yrs. Habilitation (teaching qualification, university level).

Library: Central Library, 190,000 vols.

Publications: Schriftenreihe der Hochschule Speyer; Speyerer Arbeitshefte; Speyer Forschungsberichte, Speyerer Vorträge.

Academic Staff, 1989-90:

Rank	Full-time	Part-time
Professoren	18	–
Wissenschaftliche Beamte	8	–
Wissenschaftliche Angestellte	31	1
Nichtwissenschaftliche Beamte	8	–
Nichtwissenschaftliche Angestellte	32	29
Arbeiter	9	4
Total	106	34

Student Enrolment, 1990:

	Men	Women	Total
Of the country	305	173	478
Of other countries	13	2	15
Total	318	175	493

3142 ***UNIVERSITÄT STUTTGART**

University of Stuttgart
Keplerstrasse 7, 7000 Stuttgart 1
Telex: 72-17-03
Telephone: (711) 20731
Fax: (711)121-3500
Rektor: Franz Effenberger

F. of Civil Engineering and Surveying
Dean: E. Ramm
F. of Architecture and Town Planning
Dean: K. Humpert
F. of Chemistry
Dean: B. Predel
F. of Electrical Engineering
Dean: A. Boehringer
F. of Energetics (including Nuclear Technology, Internal and External Combustion, and Hydraulic Engineering)
F. of Production Technology
Dean: G. Lechner
F. of Earth and Biological Sciences
F. of History and Social and Economic Sciences
Dean: P. Horváth
F. of Aeronautics and Space Technology
Dean: A. Frohn
F. of Mathematics and Computer Sciences
Dean: Walter Knödel
F. of Philosophy
F. of Physics
Dean: Hermann Haken
F. of Processing Technology
Dean: Richard Eppler
Computer Ce.
Director: K.-G. Reinsch
Language Ce.
Director: G. Nickel
Ce. for Infrastructure Planning
Director: Jürgen Giesecke
I. of Biomedical Technology
Director: Uwe Faust
I. for Computer Applications
Director: John H. Argyris
I. for Textile Research
Also 7 affiliated institutes.

Founded 1829 as a grammar and vocational school, became Polytechnische Schule 1840, Technische Hochschule 1890. Present title conferred 1967. An autonomous institution under the jurisdiction of and financed by the State of Baden-Württemberg. Governing bodies: the Grosse Senat; the Senat. Residential facilities for *c.* 100 academic staff and *c.* 2000 students.

Arrangements for co-operation with the Universities of: Oregon State; Arizona; Arizona State; Colorado, Boulder; Kansas; Massachusetts; George Washington; Northwestern; Cincinnati; Wisconsin; Missouri; Washington; Michigan Technological; Adelaide; Addis Ababa; Rio Grande do Sul (State); Paraíba (Federal); Hefei (Technical); Shenyang Polytechnic; Jiaotong, Shanghai; Tsinghua; Brunel, Uxbridge; Manchester; Tehran (Technical); Kyoto; Tokyo; Wrocław (Technical); Aegean, Izmir. Georgia Institute of Tecnology; Rose-Hulman Institute of Technology, Indiana; Shanghai Institute of Mechanical Engineering; Ecoles d'Architecture, Paris-Conflans, Lyon; Ecole nationale supérieure des Télécommunications, Paris; Ecole europėene des hautes Etudes des Industries chimiques de Strasbourg; Polytechnic of the South Bank, London; East China University of Chemical Technology, Shanghai.

Academic Year: October to September (October-March; April-September).

Admission Requirements: Secondary school certificate (Reifezeugnis) or equivalent.

Fees: Tuition, none.

Language of Instruction: German.

Degrees and Diplomas: State Examinations–Prüfung für das Lehramt an höheren Schulen, und an berufsbildenden Schulen (teaching qualifications, secondary level, and vocational schools), 4-5 yrs. Diplomas–Diplom-Architekt, architecture; -Bauingenieur, civil engineering; -Biologe, biology; -Geograph, geography; -Informatiker, data processing; -Chemiker, chemistry; -Elektroingenieur, electrical engineering; -Technische Kybernetik; -Verfahrenstechnik, chemical engineering; -Mineraloge; -Geologe, geology; -Luft-und Raumfahrtingenieur, aeronautical engineering; -Maschinenbauingenieur, mechanical engineering; -Mathematiker, mathematics; -Physiker, physics; -Vermessungsingenieur, surveying, 4-5 yrs. Degree of Magister Artium, 4-5 yrs. Master of Infrastructure Planning, 2 yrs. Doctorates–Dr.-Ing.; Dr.rer.nat.; Dr.phil.; Dr.rer.pol., a further 3-5 yrs. Habilitation (teaching qualification, university level), at least 3 yrs after doctorate.

Libraries: University Library, *c.* 700,000 vols; institute libraries.

Publications: Vorlesungsverzeichnis; Stuttgarter Uni-Kurier (Zeitung der Universität Stuttgart); Wechselwirkungen (Aus Lehre und Forschung der Universität Stuttgart-Jahrbuch); Forschungsbericht.

Academic Staff: c. 3620.

Student Enrolment: c. 16,630.

3143 **UNIVERSITÄT TRIER**

University of Trier
Postfach 3825, 5500 Trier
Telex: 472680 UNITR
Telephone: (651) 201-1
Fax: (651) 300519
Electronic mail: btx*920285
Präsident: Jörg Hasler (1986-91)
Kanzler: Ignaz Bender

D. of Education, Philosophy, and Psychology
Dean: Peter Schwenkmezger
D. of Languages and Literature
Dean: Hartmut Reinhardt
D. of History, Political Science, Classical Archaeology, Egyptology, Art History, and Papyrology
Dean: Günter Grimm
D. of Management Economics, Sociology, Political Economy, Mathematics, and Ethnology
Dean: Roland Eckert
D. of Law
Dean: Peter-Christian Müller-Graff
D. of Geography/Geosciences
Dean: Gerold Richter
I. for Cusanus Studies
Director: Rudolf Haubst
I. for Labour Legislation and Labour Relations in the European Community
Directors: Rolf Birk; Dieter Sadowski

Founded 1970 with divisions in Kaiserslautern and Trier which were detached 1975 to form separate universities. An autonomous institution under the jurisdiction of and financially supported by the State of Rheinland-Pfalz. Governing bodies: the Versammlung, comprising 40 members; the Senat, comprising 16 members. Residential facilities for students.

Arrangements for co-operation with: University of Nancy; University of Stirling; Clark University, Worcester, Massachusetts; Universidad de Santiago de Compostela; University of Katowice; University of Manitoba; Wuhan University; University of Hitotsubashi; Academy of Economics, Katowice.

Academic Year: October to September (October-March; April-September).

Admission Requirements: Secondary school certificate (Reifezeugnis).

Fees: Tuition, none.

Language of Instruction: German.

Degrees and Diplomas: State Examinations–Prüfung für das Lehramt an Realschulen und Gymnasien (teaching qualifications, secondary level), 4-5 yrs. Juristische Staatsprüfung, law, 6 yrs. Diplomas, 5 yrs. Degree of Magister Artium, 5 yrs. Doctorates–Dr.phil.; Dr.rer.pol.; Dr.jur. Habilitation (teaching qualification, university level), at least3 yrs after doctorate.

Library: Central Library, 900,000 vols.

Publications: Unijournal; Trierer Beiträge; Forschungsbericht; Trierer Universitätsreden.

Academic Staff, 1990:

Rank	Full-time
Professoren	129
Wissenschaftliche Mitarbeiter	412
Total	541

Student Enrolment, 1989-90:

	Men	Women	Total
Of the country	3945	3972	7917
Of other countries	443	382	825
Total	4388	4354	8742

3144 ***EBERHARD-KARLS-UNIVERSITÄT TÜBINGEN**

Eberhard Karl University of Tübingen

Wilhelmstrasse 7, 7400 Tübingen 1

Cables: Uni Tuebingen

Telex: 7262867 UTZV D

Telephone: (7071) 291

Fax: (7071)29-5990

Präsident: Adolf Theis (1972-96)

Kanzler: Georg Sandberger

F. of Protestant Theology
Dean: Joachim Mehlhausen; *staff* 49 (5)

F. of Catholic Theology
Dean: Georg Wieland; *staff* 33 (3)

F. of Law
Dean: Ferdinand Kirchhof; *staff* 72 (5)

F. of Economics and Business Administration
Dean: Ralph Berndt; *staff* 57 (9)

F. of Theoretical Medicine
Dean: Eberhard Betz; *staff* 77 (8)

F. of Clinical Medicine (including Dentistry)
Dean: Wolfgang Küsswetter; *staff* 695 (34)

F. of Philosophy
Dean: Klaus Hartmann; *staff* 16 (4)

F. of Social and Behavioural Sciences (including Political Science and Education)
Dean: Günter L. Huber; *staff* 122 (28)

F. of Modern Languages
Dean: Rolf-Dieter Kluge; *staff* 132 (14)

F. of History
Dean: Frank Kolb; *staff* 37 (6)

F. of Antiquities and Cultural Sciences
Dean: Jürgen Paul; *staff* 84 (10)

F. of Mathematics
Dean: Wolfgang Knapp; *staff* 46

F. of Physics
Dean: Friedemann Rex; *staff* 102 (62)

F. of Chemistry and Pharmacy
Dean: Heinz Oberhammer; *staff* 130 (129)

F. of Biology
Dean: Wolfgang Maier; *staff* 99 (36)

F. of Earth Sciences and Geography
Dean: Adolf Karger; *staff* 60 (13)

German I. for Distance Studies
Director: Heinz Mandl

Data Processing Ce.
Director: Dietmar Kaletta

I. for Special Pedagogics (Reutlingen)
Director: Werner Dittmann

Also *c.* 130 institutes, seminars, and clinics of the different departments.

Founded 1477 by Count Eberhard the Bearded, and in 1863 was the first German university to establish a faculty of natural sciences. An autonomous institution financially supported by the State of Baden-Württemberg, andunder the jurisdiction of its Ministry of Arts and Sciences. Governing bodies: the Grosse Senat, comprising the President, 3 Vice-Presidents, 16 deans ex officio, 21 professors, 7 other members of the academic staff, 7 representatives of the student body, and 7 members of the non-academic staff; the Senat, comprising the President, 3 Vice-Presidents, 16 deans ex officio, 9 professors, 3 members of the academic staff, 3 representatives of the student body, and 3 members of the non-academic staff. Residential facilities for foreign academic staff and *c.* 3500 students.

Arrangements for co-operation with: University of Provence; University of Law, Economics and Science, Aix-Marseille; University of Bordeaux II; University of Human Sciences, Strasbourg; State University of Ghent; Trinity College, University of Dublin; University of Durham; University of Leeds; University College of North Wales, Bangor; University of Warsaw; Hiroshima University; University of Florida; University of Kansas; University of Michigan; State University of New York at Stony Brook; Tufts University; University of Washington, Seattle; Washington University, St. Louis; Antioch College, Yellow Springs; University of California, Berkeley; California State University; University of Denver; University of Maryland; University of Oregon; Oregon State University; Arizona State University; University of Colorado; Université de Fribourg; Georgetown University, Washington; Louisiana State University; McMaster University, Hamilton; Medical University of Pecs; University of Perugia; Pontifical Catholic University of Rio Grande do Sul; Rikkyo University, Tokyo; Temple University; Texas A & M University; University of Virginia; University of North Carolina; Federal University of Fluminense; University of São Paulo; Yarmouk University; Brown University, Providence; College of Mining, Ostrava; Tel-Aviv University; University of Nanjing; University of Queensland, St. Lucia; National Chung-Hsing University, Taichung; Heilongjiang University, Harbin; University of Copenhagen; Université des Sciences Sociales, Grenoble; Université Jean Moulin, Lyon; University of Edinburgh; Scuola Normale Superiore, Pisa; Università degli Studi di Roma, Rome; Tsukuba University, Ibaraki-ken; Tokyo University; Hanyang University, Seoul; Universidad de Guadalajara; University of Amsterdam; University of Oslo; University of Coimbra; Janus Pannonius University of Pécs; Northern Arizona University, Flagstaff; University of Arizona, Tucson; University of Miami, Coral Gables; Valparaiso University, Indiana; University of Missouri; Portland State University, Oregon; Reed College, Portland; Rhodes College, Memphis.

Academic Year: October to July (October-February; April-July).

Admission Requirements: Secondary school certificate (Reifezeugnis) or equivalent.

Fees: Tuition, none.

Language of Instruction: German.

Degrees and Diplomas: State Examinations–Erste Juristische Staatsprüfung, law; Ärztliche–, medicine; Zahnärztliche–, dentistry; Pharmazeutische–, pharmacy, 4-6 yrs. Wissenschaftliche Prüfung für das Lehramt an Gymnasien (Kleine facultas) (teaching qualifications, secondary level), 4 yrs. Diplomas–Diplom-Chemiker, chemistry; -Geologe, geology; -Mathematiker, mathematics; -Mineraloge, mineralogy; -Physiker, physics; -Volkswirt, economics; -Psychologe, psychology; -Biologe; -Geograph; -Pädagoge; -Theologe; Diplom der Physiologischen Chemie und der Biochemie, physiological chemistry and biochemistry, 4-4 ½ yrs. Degree of Magister Artium, 4 yrs. Doctorates, Dr., in all fields, approximately 8 sem, except Dr.med. dent. and Zahnärztliche Staatsprüfung, 10 sem; Dr.med. and Medizinische Staatsprüfung, 11 sem. Habilitation (teaching qualification, university level), at least 3 yrs after doctorate.

Libraries: University Library, *c.* 2,200,000 vols; 100 institute libraries, *c.* 2,500,000.

Special Facilities (Museums, etc.): Museums: Archaeology; Egyptology; Geology and Palaeontology; Zoology. Botanical Gardens.

Publications: Attempto (annually); Vorlesungsverzeichnis (biannually); Studienführer, Tübinger Universitätszeitung; Amtliche Mitteilungen.

Press or Publishing House: Tübingen University Press.

Academic Staff, 1989-90:

Rank	Full-time	Part-time
Professoren	455	–
Akademische Räte	187	1
Assistenten	1140	366
Lektoren	26	–
Lehrbeauftragte	–	138
Privatdozenten, Honorarprofessoren	–	297
Total	1808	802

Student Enrolment, 1989-90:

	Men	Women	Total
Of the country	12,950	10,214	23,164
Of other countries	765	769	1534
Total	13,715	10,983	24,698

3145 **UNIVERSITÄT ULM**
University of Ulm
Oberer Eselsberg, Postfach 4066, 7900 Ulm-Donau
Telex: 7212 567 UNIULD
Telephone: (731) 1761-1
Fax: (731) 176-2038
Präsident: T.M. Fliedner (1983-91)
Kanzler: D. Eberhardt

F. of Clinical Medicine (including Dentistry)
Dean: R. Hartmann; *staff* 50
F. of Theoretical Medicine (including Dentistry)
Dean: G. Klotz; *staff* 37
F. of Natural Sciences and Mathematics
Dean: B. Walther; *staff* 67
F. of Mathematics and Economics
Dean: H. Fiedler
F. of Engineering
Dean: E.P. Hofer
F. of Computer Sciences
Dean: P. Schulthess

Founded 1967. Financially supported by the State of Baden-Württemberg. Governing bodies: the Grosse Senat; the Senat. Residential facilities for students.

Arrangements for co-operation with: Universidade Federal do Rio Grande do Sul; University of Western Ontario; University of Colorado; Ben Gurion University of the Negev; Universities of Medicine, Debrecen and Szeged; Texas A & M University; Mahidol University; Chulalongkorn University; University of Cairo; Tufts University Boston; University of Jordan; University of North Carolina at Chapel Hill; University of Massachusetts; Boston University; University of California Medical School, San Francisco; Oregon State University; State University, San Diego; Syracuse University, New York; University of Wisconsin; University of Southern California; University of Illinois; Worcester Polytechnic Institute Massachusetts; University of California Berkeley; Universidad de Costa Rica, San José; Universidad de San Carlos, Guatemala City; Academy of Medicine, Poznań; Tongji Medical University, Wuhan.

Academic Year: October to July (October-February; April-July).

Admission Requirements: Secondary school certificate (Reifezeugnis).

Fees: Tuition, none.

Language of Instruction: German.

Degrees and Diplomas: State Examinations–Prüfung für das Lehramt an Gymnasien (teaching qualification, secondary level). Diplomas–Diplom-Physiker, physics; -Mathematiker, mathematics; -Chemiker, chemistry; -Biologe, biology; -Wirtschaftsmathematiker. Doctorates, Dr.med.; Dr.rer.nat. Dr. Habilitation (teaching qualification, university level), at least 3 yrs after doctorate.

Library: c. 550,000 vols.

Publication: Forschungsbericht (biennially).

Press or Publishing House: Universitätsverlag Ulm.

Academic Staff, 1986-87:

Rank	Full-time
Ordinarien	62
Universitätsprofessoren	61
Professoren	26
Hochschulassistenten	5
Total	154

Student Enrolment, 1986-87:

	Men	Women	Total
Of the country	3049	1587	4636
Of other countries	73	57	130
Total	3122	1644	4766

3146 **UNIVERSITÄT WITTEN/HERDECKE**
University of Witten/Herdecke
Ruhrstrasse 70, 5810 Witten
Telephone: (2302) 5706⅔

F. of Medicine
F. of Business Administration
F. of Dentistry
F. of Oriental Studies

Founded 1983 as the first private university in the Federal Republic of Germany. Financed by donations and grants stipulated for specific research programmes. Governing body: the Senat.

Academic Year: May to June.

Admission Requirements: Secondary school certificate (Abitur).

Fees: None.

Language of Instruction: German.

Academic Staff: c. 40.

Student Enrolment: c. 100.

3147 ***BAYERISCHE JULIUS-MAXIMILIANS-UNIVERSITÄT WÜRZBURG**
University of Würzburg
Sanderring 2, 8700 Würzburg
Cables: uniwbg d
Telex: 068671
Telephone: (931) 31-1
Präsident: Theodor Berchem (1975-90)
Kanzler: Reinhard Günther

F. of Theology (Catholic)
Dean: Klaus Wittstadt *staff* 34
F. of Law
Dean: Günter Grasmann; *staff* 41
F. of Medicine (including Dentistry)
Dean: Kurt Kochsiek; *staff* 719
F. of Arts I (Archaeology, Philology, Music, Prehistory, Oriental Studies)
Dean: Erika Simon; *staff* 35
F. of Arts II (Philology, History, History of Art)
Dean: Werner Habicht; *staff* 73
F. of Arts III (Education, Philosophy, Social Sciences)
Dean: Paul-Ludwig Weinacht; *staff* 91
F. of Biology
Dean: Martin Heisenberg; *staff* 67
F. of Chemistry and Pharmacy (including Food Technology)
Dean: Waldemar Adam; *staff* 53
F. of Earth Sciences
Dean: Dieter Böhn; *staff* 37
F. of Mathematics
Dean: Hermann Heineken; *staff* 48
F. of Astronomy and Physics
Dean: Max Scheer; *staff* 51
F. of Economics
Dean: Rainer Thome; *staff* 34
S. of Medical Technology
Director: Jürgen Heesemann; *staff* 46
S. of Physiotherapy
Director: Kurt Kochsiek; *staff* 16
S. of Physical Rehabilitation
Director: Ernst Kern; *staff* 24
S. of Midwifery
Director: Karl-Heinrich Wulf; *staff* 10
S. of Nursing
Director: Edgar Brugger; *staff* 42
S. of Dietetics
Director: Heinrich Kasper; *staff* 13
S. of Child Care
Director: Helmut Bartels; *staff* 19

Also institutes and 16 clinics of the different faculties.

Founded 1402 by the Prince Bishop Johann von Egloffstein, refounded 1582 by Julius Echter von Mesprelbrunn, Duke of Franconia, the university is an autonomous institution financially supported by the State of Bavaria andunder the jurisdiction of its Ministry of Education. Governing bodies: the Versammlung; the Senat; the Präsidialkollegium. Residential facilities for foreign academic staff and for students.

Special arrangements for co-operation and exchanges of students and graduates with: University of Caen; University of Padua; State University of New York at Oneonta, Buffalo, and Albany; University of Hull; University of Lisbon; Federal University of Maranhão; University of Umeå; University of Salamanca; Academy of Medicine, Cracow; Pontifical Catholic University of Chili; University of Nigeria; Hankuk University of Foreign Studies,Seoul; University of Niamey; Davidson College, North Carolina; University of Zhejiang; University of Urbino.

Academic Year: October to September (November-February; May-July).

Admission Requirements: Secondary school certificate (Reifezeugnis) or equivalent.

Fees: Tuition, none.

Language of Instruction: German.

Degrees and Diplomas: State Examinations–Juristische Staatsprüfung, law; Medizinische–, medicine; Zahnärztliche–, dentistry; Pharmazeutische–, pharmacy; Lebensmitteltechnische–, food technology, 4-6 yrs;

Prüfung für das Lehramt an öffentlichen Schulen (teaching qualification, all fields). Diplomas–Diplom-Chemiker, chemistry; -Geologe, geology; -Geograph, geography; -Kaufmann, business administration; -Mathematiker, mathematics; -Pädagoge; -Theologe; -Physiker, physics; -Psychologe, psychology; -Volkswirt, economics; -Mineraloge, mineralogy; -Biologe, biology, 4-5 yrs. Lizentiat in Theology, 4-5 yrs. Degree of Magister Artium, 4 yrs. Doctorates, Dr. in all fields, approximately 4 yrs, except Dr.med.dent., 5 ½ yrs; Dr.med., 5 ½ sem; Dr.theol., 6 yrs. Habilitation (teaching qualification, university level), at least 3 yrs after doctorate.

Libraries: University Library, *c.* 1m. vols; institute libraries, *c.* 1.4m.

Special Facilities (Museums, etc.): Martin-von-Wagner Museum; Mineralogisches Museum.

Publications: Würzburg-heute; Jahresbericht; Vorlesungsverzeichnis; Informationsblatt.

Academic Staff, 1989-90:

Rank	
Professoren	353
Honorarprofessoren	27
Ausserplanmässige Professoren, Universitätsdozenten und Privatdozenten	276
Entpflichtete Professoren und Professoren im Ruhestand	93
Studienräte, Oberstudienräte, Studiendirektoren, Oberstudiendirektoren	53
Akademische Räte, Oberräte und Direktoren	135
Lehrbeauftragte	259
Wissenschaftliche Mitarbeiter und Hochschulassistenten	996
Lektoren	13
Total	2195

Student Enrolment, 1989-90:

	Men	Women	Total
Of the country	9271	8204	17,475
Of other countries	542	525	1067
Total	9813	8729	18,542

3148 ***BERGISCHE UNIVERSITÄT GESAMTHOCHSCHULE-WUPPERTAL**

University of Wuppertal

Gaussstrasse 20, 5600 Wuppertal 1

Telex: 8592262

Telephone: (202) 439-1

Fax: (202) 439-2901

Rektor: Siegfried Maser (1987-)

Kanzler: Klaus Peters

D. of Social Sciences (including Law and Political Science)
Dean: Dieter Beckmann; *staff* 41

D. of Philosophy and Theology, and History
Dean: Günter Wohlfahrt; *staff* 17

D. of Education (including Psychology and Physical Education)
Dean: Doris Küpper; *staff* 47

D. of Languages and Literature
Dean: Jürgen Jacobs; *staff* 56

D. of Economics
Dean: Günter Schiller; *staff* 50

D. of Mathematics
Dean: Klas Diederich; *staff* 49

D. of Architecture
Dean: W.D. Weigert; *staff* 15

D. of Art, Design, Music, and Printing Technology
Dean: Jürgen Bazon Brock; *staff* 56

D. of Natural Sciences I (Physics)
Dean: Klaus Schilling; *staff* 51

D. of Natural Sciences II (Chemistry and Biology)
Dean: Günter Vogel; *staff* 57

D. of Construction Engineering
Dean: Hans Kaldenhoff; *staff* 46

D. of Mechanical Engineering
Dean: Siegfried Stendorf; *staff* 24

D. of Electrical Engineering
; *staff* 58

D. of Security Technology
Dean: Wolfgang Krüger; *staff* 42

Computer Ce.
Director: Hans-Georg Hilpert

Also *c.* 30 institutes and laboratories of the departments.

Founded 1972 as a Gesamthochschule, a new type of university designed to integrate all forms of postsecondary education within a single framework. Incorporating a branch of Rheinland College of Education, Köln and Technical College. Acquired present title 1975. An autonomous institution under the jurisdiction of and financially supported by the State of North Rhine-Westphalia. Governing body: the Senat. Some residential facilities for *c.* 2000 students.

Arrangements for co-operation with: Catholic University of Louvain; University of Saint-Etienne; Pavel Josef Safárik University, Košice; Ben Gurion University of the Negev.

Academic Year: October to September (October-March; April-September).

Admission Requirements: Secondary school certificate (Reifezeugnis). Fachhochschulreife (Technical secondary education) for certain courses.

Fees: Tuition, none.

Language of Instruction: German.

Degrees and Diplomas: State Examination–Prüfung für das Lehramt (teaching qualification, primary and secondary levels), 3-4 yrs. Diplomas–Diplom-Sozialwissenschaftler; -Pädagoge; -Psychologe; -Designer; -Ökonom; -Mathematiker, mathematics; -Physiker, physics; -Physikingenieur; -Lebensmittelchemiker, food chemistry; -Chemiker, chemistry; -Ingenieur; -Bauingenieur; -Architekt/Innenarchitekt; -Sicherheitsingenieur, security; -Elektroingenieur; -Maschinenbauingenieur, 7-10 sem. Degree of Magister Artium, 8 sem. Doctorates, Dr. Habilitation (teaching qualification, university level).

Libraries: Central Library, *c.* 770,000 vols; department libraries.

Academic Staff, 1989-90:

Rank	Full-time
Professoren	326
Wissenschaftliche Mitarbeiter	306
Lehrkräfte für besondere Aufgaben	13
Nichtwissenschaftliche Mitarbeiter	635
Total	1280

Student Enrolment, 1989-90:

	Men	Women	Total
Of the country	10,583	4966	15549*

*Also 1271 foreign students.

Schools of Education

3149 **PÄDAGOGISCHE HOCHSCHULE FREIBURG IM BREISGAU**

College of Education

Kunzenweg 21, 7800 Freiburg im Breisgau

Telephone: (761) 682-1

Fax: (761) 682-402

Rektor: Rudolf Denk

Education (including Psychology, Languages and Human Sciences, Natureal Sciences, Art, Music, and Physical Education)

Founded 1962. Acquired present status 1971. Under the jurisdiction of and financially supported by the State of Baden-Württemberg. Governing bodies: the Grosse Senat; the Kleine Senat. Residential facilities for students.

Academic Year: April to March (April-September; October-March).

Admission Requirements: Secondary school certificate (Reifezeugnis) or equivalent.

Fees: None.

Languages of Instruction: German, English, and French.

Degrees and Diplomas: Erste Staatsprüfung für das Lehramt, for primary education, or for lower secondary education, 3 yrs. Diplompädagoge, 4 yrs.

Library: c. 120,000 vols.

Academic Staff, 1990: 153 (9).

Student Enrolment, 1990:

	Men	Women	Total
Of the country	625	1613	2238

3150 **PÄDAGOGISCHE HOCHSCHULE HEIDELBERG**

College of Education
Keplerstrasse 87, 6900 Heidelberg 1
Telephone: (6221) 4770
Rektor: Michael Schallies (1990-94)
Leitender Verwaltungsbeamter: Jürgen Frommer

Education (including Philosophy, Psychology, Languages and Natural Sciences)
I. for Further Education
Director: Willi Wölfing; *staff* 2
I. for Computer Sciences
Principals: Hartmut Göhner, Reinhard Mauve; *staff* 3
Research Ce. for Applied Linguistics in the Rehabilitation of the Handicapped
Principal: Klaus Schulte

Founded 1962. Governing body: the Senat, comprising 22 members.

Arrangements for co-operation with: Ecole normale de Montpellier; Ecole normale mixte de la Marne; Coventry Polytechnic; Charlotte Mason College Ambleside; Abo Akademi Vasa; University of Uppsala; Universidad del Estado de Morelos; West-Virginia University; Michigan State University; University of Zagreb; Foreign Language Institute of Science Xian; Weizman Institute of Science; Institut Keguruan dan Ilmu Pendidikan; Hacettepe University, Ankara; Universidad Santo Tómas, Bogotá.

Academic Year: October to September (October-March; April-September).

Admission Requirements: Secondary school certificate (Reifezeugnis).

Fees: None.

Language of Instruction: German.

Degrees and Diplomas: Staatsprüfung für das Lehramt, for primary education; for lower secondary education; or for special education. Diplompädagoge, 4 yrs. Dr.päd., 2 yrs after Diplom.

Library: 140,000 vols.

Publication: Schriftenreihe (irregulary).

Academic Staff, 1989-90:

Rank	Full-time	Part-time
Professoren	102	–
Akademische Räte, usw./Lehrkräfte für besondere Aufgaben	40	–
Wissenschaftliche Angestellte	6	6
Lehrbeauftragte	–	63
Total	148	69

Student Enrolment, 1989:

	Men	Women	Total
Of the country	442	1612	2054*

*Also 22 foreign students.

3151 **PÄDAGOGISCHE HOCHSCHULE KARLSRUHE**

College of Education
Bismarckstrasse 10, 7500 Karlsruhe 1
Telephone: (721) 23991

Education

Founded 1768 as Schul-Seminarium, became college 1962.

Academic Year: April to February (April-July; October-February).

Admission Requirements: Secondary school certificate (Reifezeugnis).

Fees: None.

Languages of Instruction: German, English and French.

Degrees and Diplomas: Staatsprüfung für das Lehramt, for primary education, 3 yrs; for lower secondary education, 4 yrs. Diplom in Educational Sciences, 5-6 yrs. Dr.päd., 6 yrs.

Library: c. 70,000 vols.

Academic Staff: c. 110.

Student Enrolment: c. 1300.

3152 **PÄDAGOGISCHE HOCHSCHULE LUDWIGSBURG**

College of Education
Reuteallee 46, 7140 Ludwigsburg
Cables: PH Ludwigsburg
Telephone: (7141) 140/1

Education

Founded 1962 in Stuttgart, transferred to present site 1966. Acquired present status 1971. Under the jurisdiction of and financially supported by the State of Baden-Württemberg. Governing body: the Senat. Residential facilities for c. 480 students.

Academic Year: April to March (April-September; October-March).

Admission Requirements: Secondary school certificate (Reifezeugnis).

Fees: None.

Language of Instruction: German.

Degrees and Diplomas: Erste Staatsprüfung für das Lehramt, for primary or for lower secondary education, 3 yrs. Diplompädagoge, 5 yrs. Dr.päd., 2 yrs after Diplom.

Library: c. 124,000 vols.

Academic Staff: c. 140.

Student Enrolment: c. 1840.

3153 **PÄDAGOGISCHE HOCHSCHULE SCHWÄBISCH GMÜND**

University of Education
Oberbettringer Strasse 200, 7070 Schwäbisch Gmünd
Telephone: (7171) 606-346
Fax: (7171) 606-212
Rektor: Albert Heller (1990-94)
Oberregierungsrat: Hartmut Kies

F. of Educational Sciences (including Philosophy and Psychology)
Head: H. Kolb; *staff* 16
F. of Languages
Head: H. Leuschner; *staff* 14
F. of Mathematics and Natural Sciences
Head: H. Werner; *staff* 20
F. of Social Sciences and Theology
Head: H. Traut
F. of Arts and Crafts
Head: H. Schmid; *staff* 20
D. of Lifelong Education
D. of Media Education
Head: H. Kolb; *staff* 3 (1)
D. of Multicultural Education
Head: Coburna Staelge; *staff* – (1)

Also Summer Academy for students from Portland State University, and Continuing Education for Senior Citizens.

Founded 1825 as University College with the right to award doctorate since 1977. Became institute 1947 and college 1962. Under the jurisdiction of and financially supported by the State of Baden-Württemberg. Governing body: the Senat. Some residential facilities for students in Studentenwohnheime.

Arrangements for co-operation with: City of Birmingham Polytechnic; Institut d'Enseignement Supérieur pédagogique de Liège; Pädagogische Hochschule 'Clara Zetlein', Leipzig.

Academic Year: October to September (April-September; October-March).

Admission Requirements: Secondary school certificate (Reifezeugnis) or aptitude test.

Fees: Tuition, none.

Language of Instruction: German.

Degrees and Diplomas: Staatsprüfung für das Lehramt, for primary education, 3 yrs; for lower secondary education, 4 yrs. Diplomain–Multicultural Education; Computer Education; Educational sciences, 4 yrs. Dr.päd., 2 yrs after Diploma.

Library: c. 160,000 vols.

Publication: Gmünder Hochschulreihe (G.H.R.) 1987 (2 vols).

Press or Publishing House: Gmünder Press

Academic Staff, 1989-90:

Rank	Full-time
Professors	57
Lecturers	22
Research Assistants	8
Total	87

Student Enrolment, 1989-90:

	Men	Women	Total
Of the country	232	467	699
Other countries	4	6	10
Total	236	473	709

3154 **PÄDAGOGISCHE HOCHSCHULE WEINGARTEN**
College of Education
Kirchplatz 2, 7987 Weingarten
Telephone: (751) 44081/5

Education

Founded 1949 as institute, became college 1962. acquired present status 1971. Under the jurisdiction of and financially supported by the State of Baden-Württemberg. Governing bodies: the Grosse Senat; the Senat, comprising 21 members of the academic staff and 3 representatives of the student body. Residential facilities for students in three residences.

Academic Year: April to February (April-July; October-February).

Admission Requirements: Secondary school certificate (Reifezeugnis) or aptitude test.

Fees: None.

Language of Instruction: German.

Degrees and Diplomas: Staatsprüfung für das Lehramt, for primary education, 3 yrs; for lower secondary education, 4 yrs. Diplompädagoge. Dr.päd., 2 yrs after Diplom.

Library: c. 6500 vols.

Academic Staff: c. 100 (20).

Student Enrolment: c. 890.

Professional Education

3155 **FACHHOCHSCHULE AACHEN**
Kurbrunnenstrasse 22, 5100 Aachen
Telephone: (241) 66075

D. of Architecture
D. of Construction Engineering
D. of Chemistry
D. of Design
D. of Electrical Engineering
D. of Aircraft Engineering
D. of Mechanical Engineering
D. of Economics
D. of Chemistry (Jülich)
D. of Electrical Engineering (Jülich)
D. of Nuclear Technology (Jülich)
D. of Physical Technology (Jülich)

Founded 1971, incorporating 3 previously existing institutions founded *c.* 1900. Under the jurisdiction of and financially supported by the State of North Rhine-Westphalia.

Academic Year: September to August (September-February; March-August).

Admission Requirements: Technical school certificate (Fachhochschulreife) or secondary school certificate (Abitur).

Fees: None.

Language of Instruction: German.

Degrees and Diplomas: Titles of–Diplom-Ingenieur; -Designer; -Betriebswirt, 6 sem.

Library: c. 92,700 vols.

Publications: Jahrbuch der Fachhochschule Aachen; FH-Texte; FH-Mitteilungen.

Academic Staff: c. 190 (200).

Student Enrolment: c. 5120.

3156 **FACHHOCHSCHULE AALEN**
Beethovenstrasse 1, Postfach 1728, 7080 Aalen
Telephone: (7361) 5760
Fax: (7361) 576-250
Rektor: Helmut Rosswag (1989-93)
Leitender Verwaltungsbeamter: Heinz Kistner

D. of Optics
Head (Acting): H. Diepes; *staff* 6
D. of Chemistry
Head: G. Dehoust; *staff* 11
D. of Electronics
Head: D. Schäffer; *staff* 10
D. of Precision Technology
Head: M. Reichert; *staff* 9
D. of Production Engineering
Head: B. Biegert; *staff* 10
D. of Synthetic Materials Technology
Head: P. Wippenbeck; *staff* 9
D. of Mechanical Engineering
Head: D. Maute; *staff* 10
D. of Surface and Materials Science
Head: P. Kunz; *staff* 10
D. of Industrial Engineering
Head: E. Zwilling; *staff* 9

Founded 1962 as school of engineering, acquired present status and title 1971. Under the jurisdiction of and financially supported by the State of Baden-Württemberg. Governing bodies: the Senat; the Erweiterter Senat. Residential facilities for students.

Arrangements for co-operation with: Teesside Polytechnic; Institut Universitaire de Technologie (I.U.T.), Strasbourg.

Academic Year: September to August (October-February; March-July).

Admission Requirements: Technical school certificate (fachhochschulreife) or secondary school certificate (Abitur).

Fees: None.

Language of Instruction: German.

Degrees and Diplomas: Diplom-Ingenieur; -Wirtschaftsingenieur, 8 sem.

Library: Central Library.

Publication: FH-Info

Academic Staff, 1989-90:

Rank	Full-time	Part-time
Professoren	87	–
Lehrbeauftragte	–	80
Assistenten	6	–
Laboringenieure	6	–
Total	193	158

Student Enrolment, 1989-90:

Men	Women	Total
2003	282	2285

3157 **FACHHOCHSCHULE AUGSBURG**
Baumgartnerstrasse 16, 8900 Augsburg
Telephone: (821) 5586-1
Präsident: Hans Benedikt (1988-94)
Kanzler: Ernst Mayer

D. of General Science (Computer Sciences)
Head: M. Lutz; *staff* 14 (22)
D. of Architecture and Construction Engineering
Head: K. Koberling; *staff* 20 (27)
D. of Electrical Engineering
Head: H. Tempich; *staff* 24 (33)
D. of Mechanical Engineering
Head: F. Fischer; *staff* 20 (29)
D. of Business Administration
Head: B. Höng; *staff* 19 (28)
D. of Graphic Arts and Design
Head: H.J. Palm; *staff* 13 (19)

Founded 1710 as academy, acquired present status and title 1971. Under the jurisdiction of and financially supported by the State of Bavaria. Governing bodies: the Versammlung; the Senat. Residential facilities for students.

Academic Year: October to September (October-March; March-September).

Admission Requirements: Technical school certificate (Fachhochschulreife) or secondary school certificate (Abitur). Also aptitude testfor Graphic Arts and Design.

Fees: Tuition, none.

Language of Instruction: German.

Degrees and Diplomas: Titles of–Diplom-Ingenieur; -Betriebswirt; -Designer; -Informatiker, 8 sem.

Library: c. 38,223 vols.

Publication: Fachhochschul Nachrichten und Berichte (twice a semester).

Academic Staff, 1989-90: 119 (160).

Student Enrolment, 1989-90:

Of the country	3400
Of other countries	160
Total	3560

3158 **TECHNISCHE FACHHOCHSCHULE BERLIN**

Luxembourger Strasse 10, 1000 Berlin 65
Telephone: (30) 4504-1

D. of Humanities and Economics for Engineers
Head: H. Lohe; *staff* 24 (68)
D. of Mathematics and Physics
Head: G. Ackermann; *staff* 46 (108)
D. of Chemistry and Biotechnology
Head: A. Ernsberger; *staff* 20 (34)
D. of Architecture
Head: E. Hirschfelder
D. of Civil Engineering
Head: M. Haase; *staff* 16 (25)
D. of Utility Supply and Energy Engineering
Head: E. Meerwald; *staff* 13 (27)
D. of Surveying and Cartography
Head: G. Kramer; *staff* 11 (11)
D. of Processing Technology and Environmental Technology
; *staff* 15 (18)
D. of Mechanical Engineering
Head: W. Budich; *staff* 32 (91)
D. of Precision Technology
Head: H. Müller; *staff* 14 (38)
D. of Landscape Gardening and Horticulture
Head: H.E. Pawlowsky; *staff* 14 (24)
D. of Electrotechnics
Head: S. Hecht; *staff* 36 (57)
D. of Computer Science
Head: G. Christaller; *staff* 29 (70)
D. of Food Technology
Head: D. Gelbrich; *staff* 15 (21)
I. for Distance Study
Head: H.-J. Bargel

Founded 1971. Under the jurisdiction of and financially supported by the City of Berlin. Governing bodies: the Senat; the Konzil. Residential facilities for academic staff and students.

Academic Year: October to September (October-March; April-September).

Admission Requirements: Technical school certificate (Fachhochschulreife) or secondary school certificate (Abitur).

Fees: Tuition, none.

Language of Instruction: German.

Degrees and Diplomas: Titles of–Diplom-Wirtschaftsingenieur; -Mathematiker; -Ingenieur, 4 yrs.

Library: Five college libraries.

Publications: TFH-Presse (every 2 months); Amtliche Mitteilungen; Forschungsberichte (annually).

Press or Publishing House: Presse-und Informationsamt.

Academic Staff, 1990: 302 (626).

Student Enrolment, 1989-90:

	Men	Women	Total
Of the country	4894	1011	5905
Of other countries	683	106	789
Total	5577	1117	6654

3159 **FACHHOCHSCHULE FÜR WIRTSCHAFT BERLIN**

Badensche Strasse 50/51, 1000 Berlin 62
Telephone: (30) 867-8244
Fax: (30) 867-8270
Rektor: Edgar Uherek (1971-)
Verwaltungsleiter: Norbert Nerlich

D. of Business Administration

Also teaching and Research Units for: Labour and Production; Financing and Investment; Market and Consume Studies; Personnel and Management; Macro-Economic and Economic Policy; Corporation Taxes and Public Finance; Accounting; Politics and Society; Economics and Languages; Administrative Economic Analysis; Economic Law; EconomicInformation Science.

Founded 1971. Under the jurisdiction of and financially supported by the City of Berlin.

Arrangements for co-operation with: Anglican Higher Education College, Cambridge; Institut of Finanace and Economics, Leningrad.

Academic Year: April to March (April-September; Octoberr-March).

Admission Requirements: Technical school certificate (Fachhochschulreife) or secondary school certificate (Abitur).

Fees: None.

Language of Instruction: German.

Degrees and Diplomas: Title of Diplom-Wirtschaft, 6 sem.

Publications: F.H.W.-Forschung; F.H.W.-Report (both biannually).

Student Enrolment, 1990: 42 (120).

Student Enrolment, 1990:

Men	Women	Total
1041	735	1776*

*Also 124 foreign students.

3160 **FACHHOCHSCHULE FÜR SOZIALARBEIT UND SOZIALPÄDAGOGIK BERLIN**

Karl-Schrader-Strasse 6, 1000 Berlin 31
Telephone: (30)2105-1
Fax: (30) 216-6411
Rektor: Reinhart Wolff (1990-)
Verwaltungsleiter: Klaus Johannssen

Social Work and Education

Founded 1971, incorporating 4 previously existing schools for social work. Under the jurisdiction of and financially supported by the City of Berlin. Governing bodies: the Senat, comprising 16 members; the Konzil, comprising 25 members.

Arrangements for co-operation with: Manchester Polytechnic; Ulster Polytechnic, Belfast; Academy of Social Sciences, Ankara; University of Paris XIII; University of Barcelona; Longwood College, Virginia; New York State University, Stony Brook.

Academic Year: April to March (April-September; October-March).

Admission Requirements: Technical school certificate (Fachhochschulreife) or secondary school certificate (Abitur).

Fees: None.

Language of Instruction: German.

Degrees and Diplomas: Titles of–Diplom-Sozialarbeiter; -Sozialpädagoge, 3 ½ yrs.

Library: c. 24,400 vols.

Academic Staff, 1990:

Rank	Full-time	Part-time
Professoren	40	–
Fachdozenten	2	–
Lehrbeauftragte	–	86
Tutoren	–	10
Total	42	96

Student Enrolment, 1989-90:

	Men	Women	Total
Of the country	240	552	792
Of other countries	28	22	50
Total	268	574	842

3161 **EVANGELISCHE FACHHOCHSCHULE**

Reinerzstrasse 40/41, 1000 Berlin 33
Telephone: (30) 8264051

D. of Social Work and Education

Admission Requirements: Technical school certificate (Fachhochschulreife) or secondary school certificate (Abitur).

Language of Instruction: German.

Degrees and Diplomas: Titles of–Diplom-Sozialarbeiter; -Sozialpädagoge, 6 sem.

Student Enrolment: c. 500.

3162 **FACHHOCHSCHULE BERLIN DER DEUTSCHEN BUNDESPOST TELEKOM**

Ringbahnstrasse 130, 1000 Berlin 42
Cables: FH der DBP Berlin
Telex: 1-83-660 FHBLND
Telephone: (30) 758-4700
Fax: (30) 7522070
Rektor: Helmut Schmidt (1988-)
Verwaltungsdirektor: Winfrid Homann

Telecommunications Engineering

Founded 1954 as engineering school, acquired present status and title 1972. Under the jurisdiction of and financially supported by the Federal German Post Office. Governing bodies: the Senat, comprising 15 members; the Konzil, comprising 36 members.

Academic Year: March to February (March-August; September-February).
Admission Requirements: Technical school certificate (Fachhochschulreife) or secondary school certificate (Abitur).
Fees: None.
Language of Instruction: German.
Degrees and Diplomas: Title of Diplom-Ingenieur, 3 ½ yrs.
Library: 19,000 vols.
Publication: Information (monthly).
Academic Staff, 1989-90: 35 (1).
Student Enrolment, 1989-90:

	Men	Women	Total
Of the country	528	47	575
Of other countries	11	–	11
Total	539	47	586

3163 **FACHHOCHSCHULE BIBERACH AN DER RISS**
Karlstrasse 9/11, 7950 Biberach/Riss
Telephone: (7351) 7991

D. of Architecture
D. of Construction Engineering

Under the jurisdiction of and financially supported by the State of Baden-Württemberg.
Admission Requirements: Technical school certificate (Fachhochschulreife) or secondary school certificate (Abitur).
Language of Instruction: German.
Degrees and Diplomas: Title of Diplom-Ingenieur, 6 sem.
Student Enrolment: c. 400.

3164 **FACHHOCHSCHULE BIELEFELD**
Kurt-Schumacherstrasse 6, 4800 Bielefeld 1
Telephone: (521) 1061

D. of Design
D.of Electrical Engineering
D. of Mechanical Engineering
D. of Social Studies
D. of Economics

Under the jurisdiction of and financially supported by the State of North Rhine-Westphalia.
Admission Requirements: Technical school certificate (Fachhochschulereife) or secondary school certificate (Abitur).
Language of Instruction: German.
Degrees and Diplomas: Title of Diplom-Ingenieur, 6 sem.
Student Enrolment: c. 4000.

3165 **FACHHOCHSCHULE BOCHUM**
Universitätsstrasse 150, 4630 Bochum 1
Telex: 825860
Telephone: (234) 700-7831
Rektor: Wolfgang Rüdiger (1980-88)
Kanzler: Wolfgang Rudloff

D. of Architecture (Recklinghausen)
Dean: Bodo Boden; *staff* 13
D. of Construction Engineering (Recklinghausen)
Dean: G. Krumm; *staff* 15
D. of Electrical Engineering and Electronics
Dean: F. Schneeberger; *staff* 19
D. of Electrical Engineering and Electronics (Gelsenkirchen)
Dean: H. Pass; *staff* 17
D. of Mechanical Engineering
Dean: E.-O. Dessel; *staff* 17
D. of Mechanical Engineering (Gelsenkirchen)
Dean: W. Beckmann; *staff* 22
D. of Surveying
Dean: R. Puruckherr; *staff* 14
D. of Business Studies and Economics
Dean: K.-H. Ernst; *staff* 33 (1)

Founded 1951 as school, acquired present status and title 1971. Under the jurisdiction of and financially supported by the State of North Rhine-Westphalia. Governing bodies: the Konvent; the Senat. Residential facilities for academic staff and students.
Academic Year: September to August (September-February; March-August).
Admission Requirements: Technical school certificate (Fachhochschulreife) or secondary school certificate (Abitur).
Language of Instruction: German.
Degrees and Diplomas: Titles of–Diplom-Ingenieur; -Betriebswirt; -Wirtschaftsingenieur, 6 sem.
Library: Central Library, c. 68,000 vols.
Academic Staff, 1986-87: 337 (15).
Student Enrolment, 1986-87:

	Men	Women	Total
Of the country	5260	666	5926
Of other countries	292	37	329
Total	5552	703	6255

3166 **FACHHOCHSCHULE BERGBAU BOCHUM**
Herner Strasse 45, 4630 Bochum
Telex: 825701 WBKD
Telephone: (234) 625-381

D. of Mining
D. of Mechanical Engineering and Process Technology
D. of Electrical Engineering

Founded 1816 as school, acquired present status and title 1971. Under the jurisdiction of and financially supported by the State of North Rhine-Westphalia. Governing bodies: the Konvent; the Senat. Residential facilities for students.
Academic Year: September to August (September-February; March-August).
Admission Requirements: Technical school certificate (Fachhochschulreife) or secondary school certificate (Abitur).
Fees: None.
Language of Instruction: German.
Degrees and Diplomas: Title of Diplom-Ingenieur, 7 sem.
Academic Staff: c. 30 (40).
Student Enrolment: c. 2000.

3167 **FACHHOCHSCHULE FÜR DAS ÖFFENTLICHE BIBLIOTHEKSWESEN BONN**
Wittelsbacherring 9, 5300 Bonn

Public Library Science

3168 **FACHHOCHSCHULE BRAUNSCHWEIG-WOLFENBÜTTEL**
Salzdahlumer Strasse 46/48, 3340 Wolfenbüttel
Telephone: (5331) 301-0
Fax: (5331) 301-153
Rektor: Wolf-Rüdiger Umhach
Kanzler: Wilfried Kroll

D. of Mechanical Engineering
Dean: Karl Bruns; *staff* 26 (19)
D. of Electrical Engineering
Dean: Winfried Rogalla; *staff* 23 (36)
D. of Social Services
Dean: K. H. Pesch; *staff* 33 (28)
D. of Supply Technologies
Dean: Martin Fock; *staff* 23 (16)
I. for Automotive Engineering
Head: Gerhart Rinne

Founded 1928 as a private engineering school, acquired present status and title 1972. Under the jurisdiction of and financially supported by the State of Lower Saxony. Governing body: the Senat. Residential facilities for 100 students.
Arrangements for co-operation with: Institut Universitaire de Technologie de Montpellier-Nimes; Universidad Central del Ecuador; Universidad Técnica de Ambato; Shanghai University of Engineering Science; Technische Hochschule Zwickau; Birmingham Polytechnic; Coventry Polytechnic.
Academic Year: March to January (March-July; September-January).
Admission Requirements: Technical school certificate (Fachhochschulreife) or secondary school certificate (Abitur).
Fees: None.
Language of Instruction: German.
Degrees and Diplomas: Titles of–Diplom-Ingenieur; -Sozialarbeiter; -Sozialpädagoge, 8 sem.
Library: c. 40,000 vols.

Publication: Hochschulreihe der Fachhochschule Braunschweig/Wolfenbüttel (annually).

Academic Staff, 1990: 150 (65).

Student Enrolment, 1990:

	Men	Women	Total
Of the country	2172	606	2778
Of other countries	111	21	132
Total	2283	627	2910

3169 **HOCHSCHULE FÜR GESTALTENDE KUNST UND MUSIK**

Academy of Arts and Music

Am Wandrahm 23, 2800 Bremen 1

Telephone: (421) 31-00-51

D. of Graphic Design
D. of Architecture
D. of Painting
D. of Fashion Design
D. of Plastic Arts
D. of Music

Founded 1873 as School of Handicrafts, acquired present status and title 1979, incorporating the Conservatory of Music Bremen. Under the jurisdiction of and financially supported by the State of Bremen. Governing bodies: the Senat, comprising 15 members; the Konvent, comprising 30 members.

Academic Year: September to August (September-February; March-August).

Admission Requirements: Technical school certificate (Fachhochschulreife) or secondary school certificate (Abitur).

Language of Instruction: German.

Degrees and Diplomas: Titles of–Diplom-Ingenieur; -Designer, 3 yrs. Professional titles in Music.

Library: c. 22,500 vols.

Academic Staff: c. 50 (90).

Student Enrolment: c. 720.

3170 **HOCHSCHULE BREMEN**

Langemarckstrasse 116, 2800 Bremen 1

Telephone: (421) 5905-1

Rektor: Ronald Mönch (1982-)

Kanzler: Jürgen-Peter Henckel

D. of Architecture
Head: Karsten Schwerdtfeger; *staff* 16
D. of Construction Engineering
Head: Klaus Steffens; *staff* 11
D. of Electrical Engineering
Head: Hartmut Greger; *staff* 35
D. of Mechanical Engineering
Head: Ulrich Schulte; *staff* 33
D. of Shipbuilding
Head: Horst Petermann; *staff* 8
D. of Marine Navigation
Head: Christof Marcus; *staff* 21

Founded 1982, incorporating colleges founded between 1799 and 1963. Under the jurisdiction and financially supported by the State of Bremen. Governing bodies: the Senat; the Konvent. Residential facilities for 663 students.

Arrangements for co-operation with: Ecole supérieure de Commerce et d'Administration d'Entreprise, Toulouse; Leeds, Plymouth and South Bank Polytechnics; University of Osijek; University of Rijeka; University of Alcalá de Henares; Institute of River and Maritime Transport, Leningrad; University of South Florida; University of Gdańsk; Marine Engineering College, Gdyńia; Technical University of Gdańsk.

Academic Year: September to August (September-February; March-August).

Admission Requirements: Technical school certificate (Fachhochschulreife) or secondary school certificate (Abitur).

Language of Instruction: German.

Degrees and Diplomas: Titles of–Diplom-Ingenieur; -Sozialpädagoge; -Betriebswirt, 3-4 yrs.

Publication: Publications of the Departments.

Academic Staff, 1986-87:

Rank	Full-time
Professoren	200
Wissenschaftliche Mitarbeiter	6
Lehrkräfte für besondere Aufgaben	1
Lehrbeauftragte	36
Total	243

Student Enrolment, 1986-87:

	Men	Women	Total
Of the country	2744	1095	3839
Of other countries	252	35	287
Total	2996	1130	4126

3171 **HOCHSCHULE BREMERHAVEN**

An der Karlstadt 8, 2850 Bremerhaven

Telephone: (471) 48230

Fax: (471) 4823-1155

Rektor: W. Arlt (1986-91)

Kanzler: Renate Bitter

D. of Marine Engineering
Dean: H. Könecke; *staff* 27
D. of Transport Technology and Systems Analysis
Dean: H. Haugen; *staff* 23 (15)
D. of Food Technology
Dean: H. Kurzhals; *staff* 8 (3)
D. of Processing Technology
Dean: W. Arlt; *staff* 10
D. of Operation and Supply Engineering
Dean: H. Könecke
Transfer Ce.

Also 6 Institutes of the Transfer Centre, including Environmental Protection, Food Technology, Organization and Software (BIOS), Air Transport, Energy and Systems Technology.

Founded 1884, acquired present status and title 1975. Under the jurisdiction of and financially supported by the State of Bremen. Residential facilities for c. 120 students.

Arrangements for co-operation with the College of Navigation, Gdynia.

Academic Year: September to August (September-February; March-August).

Admission Requirements: Technical school certificate (Fachhochschulreife) or secondary school certificate (Abitur).

Fees: None.

Language of Instruction: German.

Degrees and Diplomas: Title of Diplom-Ingenieur, 6 sem.

Special Facilities (Museums, etc.): Deutsches Schiffahrtsmuseum; Alfred Wegener Institut für Polarforschung.

Academic Staff, 1990-91: 54.

Student Enrolment, 1990-91:

	Men	Women	Total
Of the country	950	217	1167
Of other countries	21	10	31
Total	971	227	1198

3172 **FACHHOCHSCHULE COBURG**

Friedrich-Streib-Strasse 2, 8630 Coburg

Telephone: (9561) 317-109

Fax: (9561) 317 275

Rektor: Ekkehard Stiller (1988-)

Vewaltungsleiter: Klaus Schubert

D. of Architecture
Head: Hanfried Slawik; *staff* 13 (34)
D. of Civil Engineering
Head: Günter Wolf; *staff* 9
D. of Electrical Engineering
Head: Georg Seidel; *staff* 14 (10)
D. of Mechanical Engineering
Head: Eckardt Piltz; *staff* 17 (5)
D. of General Sciences, Business Administration, and Social Studies
Head: Gerhard Fehn; *staff* 27 (34)
D. of Textile Technology and Design (Münchberg)
Head: Arnulf Bührle; *staff* 13 (22)
C. of Foreign Students
Head: Klaus Rupinski; *staff* 5 (5)

Branch in Münchberg. Also 60 laboratories.

Founded 1971 under the jurisdiction of and financially supported by the State of Bavaria. Residential facilities for academic staff and 380 students.

Admission Requirements: Technical school certificate (Fachhochschulreife) or secondary school certificate (Abitur).

Fees: None.

Language of Instruction: German.

Degrees and Diplomas: Titles of–Diplom-Ingenieur, F.H.; -Betriebswirt, F.H.; Designer, F.H.; -Sozialpädagoge, F.H., 6 semester.

Library: Central Library, 42,000 vols.

Academic Staff, 1990: c. 90.

Student Enrolment, 1990:

Men	Women	Total
2058	962	3020

3173 **FACHHOCHSCHULE DARMSTADT**

Schöfferstrasse 3, 6100 Darmstadt
Telephone: (6151) 16-0
Fax: (6151) 16-8900
Rektor: Manfred Kremer (1984-92)
Kanzler: Reinhard Krieger

D. of Architecture
Head: H.J. Portmann; *staff* 19 (16)
D. of Construction Engineering
Head: D. Knauf; *staff* 21 (5)
D. of Chemical Technology
Head: R. Kruse; *staff* 15 (10)
D. of Electrical Engineering
Head: P. v.d. Hagen; *staff* 33 (18)
D. of Design
Head: G. Schweizer; *staff* 17 (7)
D. of Computer Sciences
Head: U. Bleimann; *staff* 16 (16)
D. of Information and Documentation
Head: J. Kind; *staff* 5 (1)
D. of Synthetic Technology
Head: H. Hulek; *staff* 13
D. of Mechanical Engineering
Head: R. Baumann *staff* 20 (8)
D. of Mathematics and Natural Sciences
Head: M. Gubitz; *staff* 28 (4)
D. of Social Education
Head: W. Burgheim; *staff* 17 (15)
D. of Social and Cultural Sciences
Head: D. Harke; *staff* 13 (20)

Founded 1971. Under the jurisdiction of and financially supported by the State of Hesse. Governing bodies: the Konvent; the Rat. Some residential facilities for students.

Arrangements for co-operation with: Hogeschool Alkmaar; Instituts Universitaires de Technologie (I.U.T.) of Orsay, Troyes, Ville d'Avray; Birmingham Polytechnic; Brighton Polytechnic; North China University, Beijing.

Academic Year: September to July (September-January; March-July).

Admission Requirements: Technical school certificate (Fachhochschulreife) or secondary school certificate (Abitur).

Fees: None.

Language of Instruction: German.

Degrees and Diplomas: Titles of–Diplom-Ingenieur; -Designer; -Informatiker; -Mathematiker; -Sozialpädagoge, 3-4 yrs.

Library: c. 123,000 vols.

Publication: Vorlesungs-und Personalverzeichnis (biannually).

Academic Staff, 1990-91: 437.

Student Enrolment, 1989-90:

	Men	Women	Total
Of the country	6346	1908	8254
Of other countries	485	128	613
Total	6831	2036	8867

3174 **EVANGELISCHE FACHHOCHSCHULE DARMSTADT**

Zweifalltorweg 12, 6100 Darmstadt
Telephone: (6151) 8798-0
Rektor: Thomas Dell-George (1990-94)
Kanzler: Gustav Fetzer

D. of Social Work
Dean: Hans-Georg Trescher; *staff* 9 (29)
D. of Social Education
Dean: Gertrud Nolterieke; *staff* 12 (23)
D. of Pastoral Work
Dean: Horst Seibert; *staff* 9 (14)
Ce. for Lifelong Education
Head: Rolf Bick; *staff* 3 (38)

Founded 1971, incorporating previously existing departments founded by the Diakonieverein and Elisabethenstift Darmstadt in 1927. Responsible to the Ministry of Education of the State of Hessen and financially supported by the State and the Evangelical Church in Hessen and Nassau. Governing body: the Kuratorium. Residential facilities for 4 single members of the academic staff and for *c.* 30 students.

Academic Year: September to July (September-January; March-July).

Admission Requirements: Technical school certificate (Fachhochschulreife) or secondary school certificate (Abitur).

Fees: None.

Language of Instruction: German.

Degrees and Diplomas: Titles of–Diplom-Sozialarbeiter; -Sozialpädagoge;-Religionspädagoge, 7 sem.

Library: 31,150 vols.

Publications: Studium und Praxis; Hochschulbrief (annually); Schritte...

Academic Staff, 1990: 33.

Student Enrolment, 1990:

	Men	Women	Total
Of the country	184	444	628

3175 **DEUTSCHE BUNDESPOST TELEKOM FACHHOCHSCHULE DIEBURG**

Max-Planck-Strasse 2, 6110 Dieburg 2
Telex: 4191840
Telephone: (6071) 28-0
Fax: (6071) 282752
Rektor: Eberhard Mathée (1982-90)
Verwaltungsdirektor: Ralf Siegbert Blum

Electrical Engineering

Founded 1968 as engineering academy, acquired present status and title 1971. Under the jurisdiction of and financially supported by the Federal German Post Office. Governing bodies: the Rat; the Konvent. Residential facilities for all students.

Academic Year: September to August (September-February; March-August).

Admission Requirements: Technical school certificate (Fachhochschulreife) or secondary school certificate (Abitur) and practical experience.

Fees: None.

Language of Instruction: German.

Degrees and Diplomas: Title of Diplom-Ingenieur, 7 sem.

Library: Central Library, 55,000 vols.

Academic Staff, 1990: 82.

Student Enrolment, 1990:

	Men	Women	Total
Of the country	808	78	886
Of other countries	8	–	8
Total	816	78	894

3176 **FACHHOCHSCHULE DORTMUND**

Sonnenstrasse 96/100, 4600 Dortmund 1
Telephone: (231) 1391-0
Fax: (231) 100309
Rektor: Jürgen Kottmann (1989-)

D. of Architecture
Dean: Wolfgang Richter; *staff* 20 (19)
D. of Design
Dean: Klaus Kirschner; *staff* 30 (35)
D. of Electrical Engineering and Energetics
Dean: Wolfram Peperle; *staff* 14 (11)
D. of Computer Sciences
Dean: Roland Schneider; *staff* 22 (10)
D. of Mechanical Engineering
Dean: Gerfried Ehlert; *staff* 34 (24)
D. of Communications Technology
Dean: Rudolf Hefner; *staff* 24 (16)

D. of Social Work
Dean: Gerhard Naegele; *staff* 23 (44)
D. of Social Education
Dean: Klaus Neumann; *staff* 26 (28)
D. of Economics
Dean: Michael Popp; *staff* 42 (36)
C. for Foreign Students

Founded 1971, incorporating colleges founded between 1890 and 1949. Under the jurisdiction of and financially supported by the State of North Rhine-Westphalia.

Arrangements for co-operation with: Leeds Polytechnic; Plymouth Polytechnic; Ecole des Praticiens du Commerce international (EPSCI), Cergy-Pontoise; Institut Universitaire de Technologie (IUT), Amiens; Hogere Economische School, Amsterdam; State University College, Buffalo; University of Ljubljana; Szczecin University; College of Engineering, Zwickau.

Academic Year: September to August (September-February; March-August).

Admission Requirements: Technical school certificate (Fachhochschulreife) or secondary school certificate (Abitur) and practical experience.

Fees: None.

Language of Instruction: German.

Degrees and Diplomas: Titles of–Diplom-Ingenieur; -Wirtschaftsinformatiker; -Informatiker; -Sozialarbeiter; -Sozialpädagoge; -Betriebswirt, 7 sem.; -Betriebswirt (Bachelor of Arts International Business); -Designer, 8 sem; -Wirtschaftsingenieur, a further 4 sem.

Library: c. 90,000 vols.

Academic Staff, 1989-90:

Rank	Full-time	Part-time
Professoren	209	–
Lehrkräfte für besondere Aufgaben	26	–
Lehrbeauftragte	–	223
Total	235	223

Student Enrolment, 1989-90:

Men	Women	Total
6433	2469	8902*

*Including 571 foreign students.

3177 **FACHHOCHSCHULE DÜSSELDORF**
Universitätsstrasse, 4000 Düsseldorf
Telephone: (211) 3111-3355
Rektor: Klaus-W. Bosak (1984-88)
Kanzler: Harald Lutter

D. of Architecture
; *staff* 24 (29)
D. of Design
; *staff* 18 (36)
D. of Electrical Engineering
; *staff* 34 (44)
D. of Mechanical Engineering and Processing Technology
; *staff* 30 (22)
D. of Social Work
; *staff* 22 (16)
D. of Social Education
; *staff* 25 (5)
D. of Economics
; *staff* 19 (26)

Founded 1971. Under the jurisdiction of and financially supported by the State of North Rhine-Westphalia. Governing bodies: the Senat; the Konvent.

Arrangements for co-operation with: School of Architecture, Canterbury, United Kingdom; Ecole d'Architecture, Nanterre; Academy of Mining and Metallurgy, Cracow; University of Cracow.

Academic Year: September to August (September-February; March-July).

Admission Requirements: Technical school certificate (Fachhochschulreife) or secondary school certificate (Abitur).

Language of Instruction: German.

Degrees and Diplomas: Titles of–Diplom-Ingenieur; -Designer; -Sozialarbeiter; -Sozialpädagoge; -Betriebswirt, 3-4 yrs.

Library: c. 100,000 vols.

Publications: Journal (quarterly); OETZ (Design) (biannually); ad (Architecture).

Press or Publishing House: Pressestelle der Fachhochschule Düsseldorf.

Academic Staff, 1986-87: 329.

Student Enrolment, 1986-87:

Of the country	6611
Of other countries	398
Total	7009

3178 **FACHHOCHSCHULE FÜR TECHNIK ESSLINGEN**
Kanalstrasse 33, 7300 Esslingen-am-Neckar
Telephone: (711) 3511-1
Rektor: Dieter Birkle (1985-89)
Amtsrat: Klaus Bandl

D. of Electrical Engergy Technology
Head: H. Grünberger
D. of Data Processing
Head: H.Lörcher
D. of Precision Technology
Head: H. Hang
D. of Mechanical Engineering and Energetics
Head: H. Hermann
D. of Vehicular Transport Technology
Head: H. Walliser
D. of Production Technology
Head: H. Feiler
D. of Maintenance Technology
Head: H. Seng
D. of Industrial Economics
Head: H. Schmid
D. of Communications Technology
Head: H. Aubele
D. of Basic Studies
Head: H. Martin

Founded 1868, acquired present status and title 1971. Under the jurisdiction of and financially supported by the State of Baden-Württemberg.

Admission Requirements: Technical school certificate (Fachhochschulreife) or secondary school certificate (Abitur).

Language of Instruction: German.

Degrees and Diplomas: Titles of–Diplom-Ingenieur; -Wirtschaftsingenieur, 8 sem.

Academic Staff, 1986-87: 126.

Student Enrolment, 1986-87: 2832.

3179 **FACHHOCHSCHULE FÜR SOZIALWESEN ESSLINGEN**
Flandernstrasse 101, 73 Esslingen
Telephone: (711) 394-1

D. of Social Education
D. of Social Work

Founded 1917, acquired present title 1971. Under the jurisdiction of and financially supported by the State ofBaden-Württemberg. Governing body: the Senat.

Academic Year: September to July (October-February; March-July).

Admission Requirements: Technical school certificate (Fachhochschulreife) or secondary school certificate (Abitur).

Language of Instruction: German.

Degrees and Diplomas: Titles of–Diplom-Sozialpädagoge; -Sozialarbeiter, 4 yrs. Also a certificate in Supervision.

Library: College Library, c. 80,000 vols.

Academic Staff: c. 30 (80).

Student Enrolment: c. 620.

3180 **FACHHOCHSCHULE FLENSBURG**
Kanzleistrasse 91/93, 2392 Flensburg
Telephone: (461) 8051

Marine Navigation Engineering
Mechanical Engineering (Munketoft)
Electrical Energy Technology
Technical Computer Sciences

Founded 1866 as Marine Engineering School, acquired present status and title 1965. Under the jurisdiction of and financially supported by the State of Schleswig-Holstein. Governing bodies: the Konsistorium; the Senat. Residential facilities for c. 100 students.

Academic Year: September to July (September-January; March-July).

Admission Requirements: Technical school certificate (Fachhochschulreife) or secondary school certificate (Abitur), or equivalent.

Language of Instruction: German.

Degrees and Diplomas: Title of Diplom-Ingenieur, 6 sem and 2 sem practical work.

Publications: Studienführer und Vorlesungsverzeichnis (biannually); Schiffsbetriebstechnik (annually); Mitteilungsblatt.

Academic Staff: c. 60.

Student Enrolment: c. 830.

3181 **FACHHOCHSCHULE FRANKFURT-AM-MAIN**

Nibelungenplatz 1, 6000 Frankfurt-am-Main 1
Telephone: (69) 1533-0
Fax: (69) 1533-2400
Rektor: Johann Schneider
Kanzler: Peter Gussmann

D. of Architecture
Dean: J. Riegert; *staff* 19 (32)
D. of Construction Engineering
Dean: J. Speck; *staff* 18 (6)
D. of Surveying
Dean: J. Uthoff; *staff* 11 (3)
D. of Electrical Engineering
Dean: G. Schnell; *staff* 22 (19)
D. of Precision Technology
Dean: D. Wacker; *staff* 16 (25)
D. of Mechanical Engineering
Dean: M. Banfel; *staff* 14 (10)
D. of Processing Technology
Dean: K. Friedrich; *staff* 11 (14)
D. of Social Work (including Economics and Society, Law and the Institutions)
Dean: W. Münch; *staff* 36 (66)
D. of Social Education
Dean: B. Naumann; *staff* 29 (65)
D. of Economics
Dean: Th. Scherer; *staff* 31 (50)
D. of Social and Cultural Sciences
; *staff* 6 (23)
D. of Mathematics, Natural Sciences, and Data Processing
Dean: U. Timm; *staff* 16 (19)

Founded 1970. Under the jurisdiction of and financially supported by the State of Hesse. Governing bodies: the Konvent; the Rat. Residential facilities for *c.* 310 students.

Arrangements for co-operation with: University of Coimbra; Technical University of Prague; Polytechnic University of Madrid; University of Aix-Marseilles II; University of Hull; University of Stockholm/Socialhögskolan.

Academic Year: March to January (March-June; September-January).

Admission Requirements: Technical school certificate (Fachhochschulreife) or secondary school certificate (Abitur) and practical experience.

Fees: None.

Language of Instruction: German.

Degrees and Diplomas: Titles of–Diplom-Ingenieur; -Betriebswirt; -Sozialarbeiter; -Sozialpädagoge, 6 sem.

Library: c. 100,000 vols.

Publication: Volksungs- und Personalverzeichnis (biannually).

Academic Staff, 1989-90: 225 (318).

Student Enrolment, 1989-90:

	Men	Women	Total
Of the country	5119	1810	6929
Of other countries	845	189	1034
Total	5964	1999	7963

3182 **KATHOLISCHE FACHHOCHSCHULE FÜR SOZIALWESEN UND RELIGIONSPÄDAGOGIK**

Wölflinstrasse 4, 7800 Freiburg
Telephone: (0761) 42241

D. of Social Work
D. of Social Education
D. of Religious Education
D. of Therapeutic Education

Founded 1971 incorporating two Colleges of Social Work (for men and for women), founded 1920 by the Deutsche Caritasverband. Under the jurisdiction of and financially supported by the State of Baden-Württemberg. Also receives financial support from the Deutsche Caritasverband. Governing body: the Senat.

Academic Year: September to August (September-February; March-August).

Admission Requirements: Technical school certificate (Fachhochschulreife) or secondary school certificate (Abitur).

Language of Instruction: German.

Degrees and Diplomas: Title of Diplom, 6 sem.

Libraries: Deutscher Caritasverband, *c.* 130,000 vols; Dozenten Bibliothek, *c.* 700.

Academic Staff: c. 30 (100).

Student Enrolment: c. 700.

3183 **FACHHOCHSCHULE FÜR SOZIALWESEN, RELIGIONSPÄDAGOGIK UND GEMEINDEDIAKONIE IN FREIBURG**

Bugginger Strasse 38, 78 Freiburg im Breisgau
Telephone: (761) 47812-0
Fax: (761) 47812-30
Rektor: Hans Ulrich Nübel (1984-92)
Kanzler: Dieter Maertins

D. of Social Work
Dean: Joachim Walter; *staff* 1
D. of Cultural Education
Dean: Bernd Seibel; *staff* 1
D. of Religious Education and Pastoral Care
Dean: Rudolf Mack; *staff* 1
Advanced Training Ce.
Dean: Werner Balsam; *staff* – (1)

Founded 1918 as school, acquired present status and title 1971. Responsible to the Ministry of Culture of the State of Baden-Württemberg and financially supported by the State and the Evangelical Church of Baden. Governing body: the Senat, comprising 12 members. Residential facilities for students.

Academic Year: September to August (October-January; March-July).

Admission Requirements: Technical school certificate (Fachhochschulreife) or secondary school certificate (Abitur) and practical experience.

Language of Instruction: German.

Degrees and Diplomas: Titles of–Diplom-Sozialarbeiter; -Sozialpädagoge;-Religionspädagoge, 4 yrs.

Library: Central Library, 30,000 vols.

Publication: Fachhochschulbrief (annual).

Academic Staff, 1990: 21.

Student Enrolment, 1990:

	Men	Women	Total
Of the country	202	391	593
Of other countries	–	2	2
Total	202	393	595

3184 **FACHHOCHSCHULE FULDA**

Marquardstrasse 35, 6400 Fulda
Telephone: (661) 60080
Fax: (661) 6008199
Rektor: Joseph Dehler
Kanzler: Erwin Jacobs

D. of Social Work and Social Education (including Pedagogic Integration of the Handicapped, Tourism, and Leisure-time Science)
Dean: Gerd Schirrmacher; *staff* 34
D. of Economics
Dean: Günter Jacobi; *staff* 20
D. of Social and Cultural Sciences (including Political Science, Philosophy, Sociology, Economics, Languages and Physical Education)
Dean: Rainer Gamp; *staff* 8 (15)
D. of Applied Informatics and Mathematics
Dean: Timm Grams; *staff* 23 (1)
D. of Domestic Science and Nutrition
Dean: Werner Merkle; *staff* 12 (2)
D. of Food Technology
Dean: Siegfried Ripperger; *staff* 9

Founded 1974. Under the jurisdiction of and financially supported by the State of Hesse. Governing bodies: the Rat, comprising 15 members; the Konvent, comprising 54 members. Residential facilities for students.

Arrangements for co-operation with: Polytechnics of Sheffield and Portsmouth; National Technical University ofAthens; Dorset Institute, United Kingdom; State University of California.

Academic Year: September to August (September-February; March-August).

Admission Requirements: Technical school certificate (Fachhochschulreife) or secondary school certificate (Abitur).

Fees: None.

Language of Instruction: German.

Degrees and Diplomas: Titles of–Diplom-Sozialarbeiter; -Sozialpädagoge, 7 sem; -Betriebswirt; -Informatiker; -Ökotrophologe; -Ingenieur, 8 sem.

Library: c. 120,000 vols.

Academic Staff, 1990: 100 (c.100).

Student Enrolment, 1989-90:

Of the country	2716
Of other countries	85
Total	2801

3185 **FACHHOCHSCHULE FURTWANGEN**

Gerwigstrasse 11, 7743 Furtwangen
Telex: (17) 772315
Telephone: (7723) 6560
Fax: (7723) 1656610 Teletex: 656630
Rektor: Walter Zahradnik (1987-91)
Leitender Verwaltungsbeamter: Karl-Ewald Rombach

D. of Precision Mechanical Engineering
Head: K. Agne; *staff* 17 (5)
D. of Electronics
Head: W. Karger; *staff* 20 (5)
D. of Computer Sciences (General)
Head: H. V. Niemeier; *staff* 12 (12)
D. of Business Application of Computer Sciences
Head: H. Kemler; *staff* 9 (9)
D. of Product Engineering
Head: W. Bornholdt; *staff* 14 (13)
D. of Basic Subjects
Head: Th. Rami; *staff* 17 (22)
D. of Computer Engineering
Head: H. Nielinger; *staff* 20 (2)
D. of Media Informatics
Head: F. Steimer; *staff* 4 (3)
D. of Microelectronics
Head: K. Schmidt; *staff* 7
D. of Materials and Surface Engineering (Villiger-Schwerningen)
Head: J. Vogt; *staff* 11 (7)
I. for Innovation and Transfer
Director: A. Stoffel

Founded 1850 as School for Watchmaking, reorganized as School of Engineering 1947 and acquired present status and title 1971. Under the jurisdiction of and financially supported by the State of Baden-Württemberg. Governing body: the Grosse Senat. Residential facilities for students.

Arrangements for co-operation with: Leicester Polytechnic; Eastern Michigan University; Kandó Kálmán College of Electrical Engineering.

Academic Year: October to July (October-February; March-July).

Admission Requirements: Technical school certificate (Fachhochschulreife) or secondary school certificate (Abitur).

Language of Instruction: German.

Degrees and Diplomas: Titles of–Diplom-Ingenieur; -Informatiker, 8 sem.

Library: Central Library, 36,000 vols.

Special Facilities (Museums, etc.): Deutsches Uhrenmuseum.

Publications: Studienführer (1 per semester); Rechenschaftsbereicht (annually).

Academic Staff, 1990: 99 (86).

Student Enrolment, 1990:

	Men	Women	Total
Of the country	1457	159	1616
Of other countries	59	6	65
Total	1516	165	1681

3186 **FACHHOCHSCHULE GIESSEN-FRIEDBERG**

Wiesenstrasse 14, 6300 Giessen 1
Telephone: (641) 3091
Fax: (641) 309417
Rektor: Hans-Jörg Kollmar (1989-93)
Kanzler: Arno Martin

D. of Construction Engineering
Dean: Ernst Schuster; *staff* 12 (19)
D. of Mechanical Engineering
Dean: H. Schwalbe; *staff* 13 (26)
D. of Electrical Engineering I
Dean: H. Grieb
D. of Electrical Engineering II (Friedberg)
Dean: H. Held
D. of Economy Engineering and Production
Dean: H. Langhans; *staff* 21
D. of Foundry Mechanical Engineering and Materials Technology
Dean: H. Messer; *staff* 7
D. of Energy and Heating Engineering
Dean: H. Engelhorn; *staff* 14
D. of Health Technology
Dean: H. Neumann; *staff* 18
D. of Business Administration
Dean: H. Folkmann; *staff* 17
D. of Mathematics, Natural Sciences, and Computer Sciences
Dean: H. Boergens; *staff* 46
D. of Computer Sciences
Dean: H. Pieper

Founded 1970. Under the jurisdiction of and financially supported by the State of Hesse. Governing bodies: the Rat; the Konvent.

Arrangements for co-operation with University of Nanchang.

Academic Year: January to December (March-July; September-January).

Admission Requirements: Technical school certificate (Fachhochschulreife) or secondary school certificate (Abitur).

Fees: None.

Language of Instruction: German.

Degrees and Diplomas: Titles of–Diplom-Ingenieur; -Mathematiker; -Informatiker; -Wirtschaftsingenieur; -Betriebswirt, 3 ½-4 yrs.

Library: c. 80,000 vols.

Academic Staff, 1990: c. 215.

Student Enrolment, 1989-90:

Of the country	7790
Of other countries	453
Total	8243

3187 **FACHHOCHSCHULE HAMBURG**

Winterhuder Weg 29, 2000 Hamburg 76
Telephone: (40) 29188-1
Präsident: Roff Dalheimer (1975-87)
Leitender Verwaltungsbeamter: Heinrich Göring

D. of Mechanical and Chemical Engineering
Speaker: Erhard Wiebe; *staff* 62
D. of Electrical Engineering and Electronics
Speaker: Bruno Giesl; *staff* 62
D. of Transport Technology
Speaker: Heinz Krisch; *staff* 39
D. of Marine and Plant Engineering
Speaker: Gerd Peters; *staff* 26
D. of Architecture
Speaker: Friedhelm Grundmann; *staff* 27
D. of Civil Engineering
Speaker: Hellmuth Schulz; *staff* 27
D. of Surveying
Speaker: Jürgen Zastrou; *staff* 21
D. of Applied Biology, Production and Processing Technology
Speaker: Hans-Dieter Cargill; *staff* 43
D. of Navigation
Speaker: Werner Huth; *staff* 22
D. of Social Studies
Speaker: Dieter Neumann; *staff* 17
D. of Library Science
Speaker: Gerhard Kay Birkner; *staff* 17
D. of Art and Design
Speaker: Manfred Schmidt; *staff* 44

D. of Nutrition and Home Economics
Speaker: Henning Reimer Edens; *staff* 16
Inter-F. D. of Industrial Management Engineering
Inter-F. D. of Naval Architecture
Ce. for Lifelong Education
Head: Berend Brouër

Founded 1970, incorporating 10 previously existing engineering and technical institutions. Under the jurisdiction of and financially supported by the State of Hamburg. Governing body: the Senat, comprising 23 members. Residential facilities for students.

Arrangements for co-operation with: Portsmouth Polytechnic; Iowa State University; Shanghai Institute of Mechanical Technology.

Academic Year: March to February (March-July; October-February).

Admission Requirements: Technical school certificate (Fachhochschulreife) or secondary school certificate (Abitur), or equivalent.

Fees: None.

Language of Instruction: German.

Degrees and Diplomas: Titles of–Diplom-Wirtschaftsingenieur; -Sozialpädagoge, -Designer; -Oekotrophologe; -Bibliothekar, library science; -Ingenieur, 6-8 sem.

Library: 185,000 vols.

Publications: 'fh'; info 1-4; Berichte.

Academic Staff, 1986-87: 546 (c. 300).

Student Enrolment, 1986-87:

Of the country	11,720
Of other countries	965
Total	12,685

3188 **EVANGELISCHE FACHHOCHSCHULE FÜR SOZIALPÄDAGOGIK DER DIAKONENANSTALT DES RAUHEN HAUSES HAMBURG**
Horner Weg 170, 2000 Hamburg 74
Telephone: (40) 65591-180
Rektor: Wolfgang Braun

D. of Social Education

Founded 1971.

Academic Year: March to February.

Admission Requirements: Technical school certificate (Fachhochschulreife) or secondary school certificate (Abitur).

Fees: None.

Language of Instruction: German.

Degrees and Diplomas: Title of Diplom-Sozialpädagoge und Diakon.

Library: c. 14,000 vols.

Academic Staff, 1990: 9.

Student Enrolment, 1989-90:

	Men	Women	Total
Of the country	40	110	150

3189 **FACHHOCHSCHULE HANNOVER**
Ricklinger Stadtweg 120, 3000 Hannover 91
Telephone: (511) 444201

D. of Architecture
D. of Construction Engineering
D. of Electrical Engineering
D. of Mechanical Engineering
D. of Dairy Technology
D. of Design
D. of Library and Information Sciences

Founded 1971, incorporating 6 formerly independent departments. Department of Library and Information Sciencesadded 1979. Under the jurisdiction of and financially supported by the State of Lower Saxony.Founded 1971, incorporating 6 formerly independent departments. Department of Library and Information Sciences added 1979. Under the jurisdiction of and financially supported by the State of Lower Saxony. Some residential facilities for students. Some residential facilities for students.

Academic Year: September to August (September-February; March-August).

Admission Requirements: Secondary school certificate (Reifezeugnis).

Fees: None.

Language of Instruction: German.

Degrees and Diplomas: Titles of–Diplom-Ingenieur in–Architecture; Civil Engineering; Electrical Engineering; Mechanical Engineering; Dairy Technology; Diplom-Designer; -Bibliothekar; -Dokumentar.

Library: c. 30,000 vols.

Academic Staff: c. 150 (40).

Student Enrolment: c. 2350.

3190 **EVANGELISCHE FACHHOCHSCHULE HANNOVER**
Blumhardtstrasse 2, 3000 Hannover 61
Telephone: (511) 5301-0
Fax: (511) 5301-195
Rektor: Manfred Bergs (1987-)
Kanzler: Günter Schulz Falten

D. of Social Studies (including Psychology, Law and Administration, Pedagogics, Social Medicine, Ethics and Aesthetic Communication)
Dean: Jan Tillmann; *staff* 69 (34)
D. of Religious Education and Pastoral Work
Dean: Georg Bruno Herrmann; *staff* 11 (35)

Founded 1971. A private institution under the jurisdiction of and financially supported by the Evangelical-Lutheran Church of Hannover. Governing bodies: the Senat, comprising 12 members; the Konzil, comprising 12 members; Board of Trustees, comprising 7 members. Some residential facilities for students.

Arrangements for co-operation with the University of Ankara.

Academic Year: October-July (October-February; April-July).

Admission Requirements: Technical school certificate (Fachhochschulreife) or secondary school certificate (Abitur).

Fees: None.

Language of Instruction: German.

Degrees and Diplomas: Titles of–Diplom-Sozialarbeiter; -Sozialpädagoge (F), -Religionspädagoge (FH), 4 yrs.

Library: c. 47,000 vols.

Academic Staff: c. 50.

Student Enrolment: c. 830.

3191 **FACHHOCHSCHULE DER STIFTUNG REHABILITATION HEIDELBERG**
Bonhoefferstrasse, 6900 Heidelberg 1
Telephone: (6221) 882258

Architecture
Business Administration
Electronics
Computer Sciences
Mechanical Engineering
Social Work
Social Education

3192 **FACHHOCHSCHULE HEILBRONN**
Max-Planck-Strasse 39, 7100 Heilbronn
Telephone: (7131) 5040
Fax: (7131) 52470
Rektor: Otto Grandi
Verwaltungsleiter: Eberhard Harst

D. of Mechanical Engineering
Head: H. Fleischmann; *staff* 9 (8)
D. of Physical Technology
Head: H. Pruckner; *staff* 9 (7)
D. of Precision Technology
Head: H. Beck; *staff* 10 (11)
D. of Production Technology
Head: K. Sinn; *staff* 11 (5)
D. of Transport Management
Head: H. Pilzecker; *staff* 10 (12)
D. of Medical Data Processing
Head: H. Frey; *staff* 10 (32)
D. of Basic Sciences
Head: H. Bolz; *staff* 9 (2)
D. of Production Management
Head: H. Haberlandt; *staff* 11 (9)
D. of Electrical Technology
Head: K. Blecken; *staff* 4 (4)
D of Wine Manufacturing and Marketing
Head: H. Bernkopf; *staff* 4 (6)
D. of Electronics
Head: H. Dorsch; *staff* 9 (15)
D. of Tourism Management
Head: H. Barg; *staff* 13 (14)

Technical A.
Head D. Schmidt
Transfer Ce.
Head H. Horsch
Computer Ce.

Founded 1971. Under the jurisdiction of and financially supported by the State of Baden-Württemberg. Governing body: the Senat. Residential facilities for 226 students.

Arrangement for co-operation with: Ancona University; Newcastle upon Tyne Polytechnic; University of the Savoie; Dorset Institute, United Kingdom.

Admission Requirements: Technical school certificate (Fachhochschulreife) or secondary school certificate (Abitur).

Fees: None.

Language of Instruction: German.

Degrees and Diplomas: Titles of–Diplom-Ingenieur; -Betriebswirt, 4 yrs; -Informatiker der Medizin, 5 yrs.

Library: 70,000 vols.

Publication: Heilbronner Hochschul-Informationen (twice a year).

Academic Staff, 1989-90: 114 (285).

Student Enrolment, 1989-90:

	Men	Women	Total
Of the country	2385	708	3113
Of other countries	98	18	116
Total	2483	726	3229

3193 **FACHHOCHSCHULE HILDESHEIM/HOLZMINDEN**
Hohnsen 3, 3200 Hildesheim
Telephone: (5121) 81012/14

D. of Architecture
D. of Construction Engineering
D. of Communications
D. of Production Design
D. of Social Work
D. of Architecture (Holzminden)
D. of Construction Engineering (Holzminden)
D. of Forestry (Göttingen)

Founded 1972, incorporating previously existing colleges in Holzminden (1831) and Hildesheim(1900). Under the jurisdiction of and financially supported by the State of Lower Saxony. Governing bodies: the Senat; the Konzil.

Academic Year: March to February (March-August; September-February).

Admission Requirements: Technical school certificate (Fachhochschulreife) or secondary school certificate (Abitur).

Fees: None.

Language of Instruction: German.

Degrees and Diplomas: Titles of–Diplom-Ingenieur; -Sozialarbeiter; -Sozialpädagoge, 6 sem; -Designer, 8 sem.

Library: c. 34,680 vols.

Academic Staff: c. 150 (70).

Student Enrolment: c. 2170.

3194 **FACHHOCHSCHULE ISERLOHN**
Frauenstuhlweg 31, 5860 Iserlohn

3195 **NATURWISSENSCHAFTLICH-TECHNISCHE AKADEMIE PROF. DR. GRÜBLER**
Seidenstrasse 12-35, 7972 Isny
Telephone: (7562) 2427

Chemistry
Physics

3196 **FACHHOCHSCHULE KARLSRUHE**
Moltkestrasse 4, 7500 Karlsruhe
Telephone: (721) 169-1
Fax: (721) 169-200
Rektor: Werner Fischer (1990-94)
Kanzler: Udo Bitter

D. of Architecture
Dean: Gert Peter; *staff* 8 (29)
D. of Civil Engineering
Dean: Paul Brunner; *staff* 11 (30)
D. of Precision Engineering
Dean: Jochen Köhler; *staff* 11 (14)
D. of Surveying/Cartography
Dean: Rainer Hanauer; *staff* 19 (40)
D. of Mechanical Engineering
Dean: Klaus Jäger; *staff* 20 (20)
D. of Electrical Power Engineering
Dean: Hans-Werner Schwarz; *staff* 10 (16)
D. of Construction Management (including Civil Engineering)
Dean: Winfried Pfefferle; *staff* 9 (31)
D. of Computer Sciences
Dean: Dieter Exner; *staff* 10 (11)
D. of Business Computer Science
Dean: Peter Goldberg; *staff* 9 (10)
D. of Communications Engineering
Dean: Peter Schlenning; *staff* 14 (11)
D. of Business Engineering
Dean: Valentin Merger; *staff* 10 (16)
D. of Natural Sciences
Dean: Gunther Krieg; *staff* 22 (2)
D. of Humanities and Economics
Dean: Martha Samsel Lerch; *staff* 3 (21)
I. for Innovation and Transfer
Dean: J. Schäfer; *staff* 1 (5)
I. for Programmetry and Cartography
Dean: G. Hell; *staff* 2 (8)
I. for the Rational Use of Energy
Dean: H.-W.Schwarz; (8)

Founded 1878 as Grand Duchy's College of Building, acquired present status and title 1971. Under the jurisdiction of and financially supported by the State of Baden-Württemberg. Governing body: the Senat. Residential facilities for *c.* 140 students.

Special arrangements for co-operation with Polytechnics in the United Kingdom. Arrangements for student and academic staff exchange with institutions in China, France, Israel, USSR and the United Kingdom.

Academic Year: March to February (March-July; October-February).

Admission Requirements: Technical school certificate (Fachhochschulreife) or secondary school certificate (Abitur), and practical experience.

Fees: None.

Language of Instruction: German.

Degrees and Diplomas: Titles of–Diplom-Ingenieur; -Wirtschaftsingenieur; -Informatiker, 8 sem.

Library: c. 230,000 vols.

Special Facilities (Museums, etc.): Öffentliche Banstoffprüfstelle; DIN - Prufstelle für Wäkmepumpers und Kältetechnik.

Publication: FH Magazin (1 per semester).

Press or Publishing House: FH Karlsruhe.

Academic Staff, 1990: 143 (218).

Student Enrolment, 1990:

	Men	Women	Total
Of the country	3244	506	3750
Of other countries	189	25	214
Total	3433	531	3964

3197 **FACHHOCHSCHULE KEMPTEN**
Immenstädter Strasse 69, 8960 Kempten/Allgäu
Telephone: (831) 2523-0
Fax: (831) 2523-104
Rektor: Hanns Ott (1984-90)
Kanzler: Volker Büchner

F. of Humanities, Economics, Business Administration and Management
Dean: Paul Krupp; *staff* 16 (60)
D. of Mechanical Engineering
Dean: Gerhard Wenzel; *staff* 18 (5)
D. of Electrical and Electronic Engineering
Dean: Johannes Steinbrunn; *staff* 17 (7)
I. for Medium-Sized Entreprises
Head: Richard Geml; *staff* 2 (2)
Ce. for Microelectronics and New Technologies
Head: Heinz Scherz; *staff* 2 (10)

Founded 1977. Under the jurisdiction of and financially supported by the State of Bavaria and the Federal Government. Residential facilities for students.

Student echange programmes with: University of Ulster; Lancashire Polytechnic; Regional Technical College Sligo, Ireland; Manchester Polytechnic; College of Home Trade, Budapest; Instituts universitaires de Technologie Montpellier and Valenciennes.

Academic Year: October to July (October-March; March-July).

Admission Requirements: Technical school certificate (Fachhochschulreife) or secondary school certificate (Abitur).

Fees: None.

Language of Instruction: German.

Degrees and Diplomas: Titles of–Diplom-Ingenieur; -Betriebswirt, 4 yrs.

Library: mod 11x

Academic Staff, 1989-90: 106 (78).

Student Enrolment, 1989-90:

	Men	Women	Total
Of the country	1569	498	2067
Of other countries	41	21	62
Total	1610	519	2129

3198 **FACHHOCHSCHULE KIEL**

Breiter Weg 10, 2300 Kiel
Telex: 2627-431752 FHKIEL
Telephone: (431) 5709-0
Fax: (431) 570918
Rektor: udo Lampe (1987-93)
Kanzler: Dietmar Wabbel

D. of Civil Engineering (including Architecture)
Head: Christian Luther; *staff* 27 (22)
D. of Social Work
Head: Eckhard Hümme; *staff* 22 (74)
D. of Technology
Head: H. Mix; *staff* 72 (83)
D. of Design
Head: Bernhard Schwichterberg; *staff* 25 (61)
D. of Agriculture
Head: Hans-Heinrich Kohnke; *staff* 13 (12)
D. of Economics
Head: Dieter Kaerger; *staff* 26 (48)

Founded 1969. Under the jurisdiction of and financially supported by the State of Schleswig-Holstein.

Arrangements for co-operation with: Sunderland Polytechnic; Tallin Polytechnical Institute.

Academic Year: February to January (February-July; August-January).

Admission Requirements: Technical school certificate (Fachhochschulreife) or secondary school certificate (Abitur).

Language of Instruction: German.

Degrees and Diplomas: Titles of–Diplom-Ingenieur; -Betriebswirt; -Sozialpädagoge, 6 sem; -Designer; -Frei bildende Kunst, 8 sem; -Wirtschaftsingenieur, 3 sem.

Academic Staff, 1989-90: 185

Student Enrolment, 1989-90:

	Men	Women	Total
Of the country	3536	1520	5056
Of other countries	187	34	221
Total	3723	1554	5277

3199 **FACHHOCHSCHULE KÖLN**

Claudiusstrasse 1, 5000 Köln
Telex: 8873330 FHSK D
Telephone: (221) 8275-1
Fax: (221) 8275-3131
Rektor: Joachim Metzner
Kanzler: Karlfriedrich Lange von Stocmeier

D. of Architecture
Dean: Jürgen Hartmann; *staff* 24
D. of Vehicle Engineering
Dean: Siegfried Stepanek; *staff* 17
D. of Construction Engineering
Dean: Günter Siebert; *staff* 14
D. of Electrical Energy Technology
Dean: Karl-Heinz Clemens; *staff* 15
D. of Agricultural Engineering
Dean: Lothar Nolte; *staff* 8
D. of Communications Engineering
Dean: Gerhard Wencker; *staff* 22
D. of Photographic Engineering
Dean: Jaroslav Poncar; *staff* 11
D. of Production Engineering
Dean: Wolfram Kortendieck; *staff* 12
D. of Social Work
Dean: Wolfgang Piepenstock; *staff* 16
D. of Social Education
Dean: Maria Mies; *staff* 21
D. of Modern Languages
Dean: Lother Cerny; *staff* 12
D. of Economics
Dean: Hubert Severin; *staff* 34
D. of Insurance Economics
Dean: Werner Greb; *staff* 14
D. of Art
Dean: Renate Lewandowski; *staff* 12
D. of Design
Dean: Hubert Schaffmeister; *staff* 8
D. of Supply Systems Engineering
Dean: Herbert Bley; *staff* 15
D. of Informatics
Dean: Peter Schwanenberg; *staff* 18
D. of Mechanical Engineering and Technology
Dean: Ernst Ulrich Roth; *staff* 18
D. of Electrical Engineering
Dean: Martin Ulrich Reissland; *staff* 14
I. of Technology in the Tropics
Head: Hartmut Gaese; *staff* 3
D. of Plant and Process Engineering
Head: Klaus Plassmeier; *staff* 12
D. of Civil Engineering
Head: Manfred André; *staff* 20
D. of Art and Culture Restoration and Preservation
Head: Karl Ludwig Dasser; *staff* 6

Founded 1971. Under the jurisdiction of and financially supported by the State of North Rhine-Westphalia. Governing bodies: the Konvent, comprising 102 members; the Senat, comprising 17 members.

Arrangements for co-operation with: the Université de Provence (Aix-Marseille I); Université de Haute-Normandie, Le Havre; Institut industriel du Nord, Villeneuve d'Ascq; King Mongkut's Institute of Technology, Bangkok; Université de Burundi; Ecole nationale des Ingenieurs de Sfax; Politechnika Warszawska; Uniwersytet Mikolaja Kopernika, Torún; Universidade Federal do Ceará; Universidade do Fortaleza; Hochschule für bildendeKünste, Dresden.

Academic Year: March to February (March-July; October-February).

Admission Requirements: Technical school certificate (Fachhochschulreife) or secondary school certificate (Abitur), and 6 months practical experience.

Fees: None.

Language of Instruction: German.

Degrees and Diplomas: Title of Diplom-Ingenieur, 7 sem.

Libraries: Central Library; specialized libraries.

Publications: FH-Intern; Pressespiegel.

Academic Staff: c. 370 (280).

Student Enrolment, 1989:

	Men	Women	Total
Of the country	12,700	4950	17,650
Of other countries	1120	730	1850
Total	13,820	5680	19,500

3200 **FACHHOCHSCHULE FÜR BIBLIOTHEKS- UND DOKUMENTATIONSWESEN IN KÖLN**

Claudiusstrasse 1, 5000 Köln 1
Telephone: (221) 8275-3374
Rektor: Engelbert Plassmann (1986-90)
Kanzlerin: Brigitte Husmann

Library Science and Documentation

Founded 1928. Acquired present status and title 1981. Under the jurisdiction of and financially supported by the State of North Rhine-Westphalia.

Academic Year: October-July (October-February; April-July).

Admission Requirements: Technical school certificate (Fachhochschulreife) or secondary school certificate (Abitur).

Fees: None.

Degrees and Diplomas: Title of Diplom–Bibliothekar; Dokümentar, 3 yrs.

Library: 43,000 vols.
Publications: Vorlesungsverzeichnis; Jahresbericht; Kölner Arbeiten zum Bibliotheks- und Dokumentationswesen (13 vols since 1981).
Academic Staff, 1990: 22 (23).
Student Enrolment, 1989-90:

	Men	Women	Title
Of the country	110	545	655
Of other countries	1	4	5
Total	111	549	660

3201 **RHEINISCHE FACHHOCHSCHULE KÖLN**
Hohenstaufenring 16/18, 5000 Köln 1
Telex: 8882425 VFHS D
Telephone: (221) 20-30-20

D. of Electrical Engineering
D. of Mechanical Engineering
D. of Production Technology
Founded 1959 as school, acquired present status and title 1971. Under the jurisdiction of and financially supported by the State of North Rhine-Westphalia.
Academic Year: March to February (March-August; September-February).
Admission Requirements: Technical school certificate (Fachhochschulreife) or secondary school certificate (Abitur).
Fees: None.
Language of Instruction: German.
Degrees and Diplomas: Title of Diplom-Ingenieur, 6 sem.
Library: c. 11,000 vols.
Academic Staff: c. 40 (20).
Student Enrolment: c. 810.

3202 **FACHHOCHSCHULE KONSTANZ**
Brauneggerstrasse 55, 7750 Konstanz
Telex: 733355 FUKN D
Telephone: (7531) 2060
Fax: (7531) 206400
Rektor: Olaf Harder (1980-90)
Amtsrat: Axel Schuler

D. of Architecture
Head: Fritz Wilhelm; *staff* 12 (7)
D. of Civil Engineering
Head: Hans-G. Kempfert; *staff* 12 (12)
D. of Power Engineering
Head: Hovatin Mikolčič; *staff* 10 (4)
D. of Communications Engineering
Head: Lothar Zwick; *staff* 12 (5)
D. of Computer Sciences (Economic)
Head: Manfred Knoll; *staff* 16 (16)
D. of Mechanical and Production Engineering
Head: Frowald Weis; *staff* 11 (13)
D. of Mechanical and Construction Engineering
Head: Arunef Schneider; *staff* 11 (3)
D. of Basic Sciences
Head: Wolfgang Pistor; *staff* 9 (3)
D. of Social Sciences
Head: Anneliese Fearns; *staff* 9 (3)
C. for Foreign Students
Head: Dieter Vormstein; *staff* – (23)
Founded 1906 as a private college, acquired present title and status 1971. Under the jurisdiction of and financially supported by the State of Baden-Württemberg. Governing bodies: the Senat, comprising 23 members; the Grosse Senat. Residential facilities for students.
Arrangements for co-operation with: Shanghai Jiang-Tong University; Nanjing Institute of Mechanical Engineering; Coventry Polytechnic.
Academic Year: September to June (September-February; March-June).
Admission Requirements: Technical school certificate (Fachhochschulreife) or secondary school certificate (Abitur).
Fees: None.
Language of Instruction: German.
Degrees and Diplomas: Titles of Diplom-Ingenieur; -Informatiker, 4 yrs.
Library: c. 40,000 vols.
Academic Staff, 1989-90: 102 (79).
Student Enrolment, 1989-90:

	Men	Women	Total
Of the country	1982	216	2198
Of other countries	169	9	178
Total	2151	225	2376

3203 **INSTITUT FÜR KOMMUNIKATIONSDESIGN A. D. FH KONSTANZ (STAATLICH ANERKANNTE FAHHOCHSCHULE)**
Seestrasse 33, 7750 Konstanz

Communication Design

3204 **FACHHOCHSCHULE LANDSHUT**
Am Lurzenhof 4, 8300 Landshut
Telephone: (871) 506-0
Fax: (871) 51315
Präsident: H.-J. Fischer
Kanzler: Hansgeorg Falterer

D of Business Administration
Dean: H. Windl
D. of Social Sciences
Dean: H. Eikelmann
D. of Mechanical Engineering
Dean: H. Kohlberger
D. of Electrical Engineering
Dean: H. Kohlberger
Founded 1978.
Arrangement for co-operation with: Université Robert Schumann, Strasbourg; Ecole Supérieure de Commerce, Compiègne; Ulster University; Essex Institute of Higher Education, U.K.
Academic Year: October-September (October-March; March-September).
Admission Requirements: Technical school certificate (Fachhochschulreife) or secondary school certificate (Abitur).
Language of Instruction: German.
Degrees and Diplomas: Titles of–Diplom-Ingenieur; -Betriebswirt; -Sozialpädagoge, 4 yrs.

3205 **FACHHOCHSCHULE LIPPE**
Liebigstrasse 87, 4920 Lemgo 1
Telex: 935 411 FHL D
Telephone: (5621) 702-1
Rektor: Dietrich Lehmann (1984-88)
Kanzler: Helmuth Hoffstetter

D. of Architecture and Interior Design
Dean: H. Schultz; *staff* 30 (30)
D. of Construction Engineering
Dean: H. Buth; *staff* 21
D. of Electrical Engineering
Dean: H. Heidemanns; *staff* 18 (3)
D. of Food Technology
Dean: H. Baumgart; *staff* 21 (14)
D. of Mechanical Engineering
Dean: H. Schotte; *staff* 11
D. of Production and Processing Technology
Dean: H. Pätzold; *staff* 14 (2)
Founded 1971 with sections in Detmold and Lemgo. Under the jurisdiction of and financially supported by the State of North Rhine-Westphalia. Residential facilities for students.
Arrangements for co-operation with: Université de Nancy; Medical Junior College, Taejon.
Academic Year: September to August (September-February; March-August).
Admission Requirements: Technical school certificate (Fachhochschulreife) or secondary school certificate (Abitur).
Fees: None.
Language of Instruction: German.
Degrees and Diplomas: Title of Diplom-Ingenieur, 8-9 sem.
Library: c. 70,000 vols.

Academic Staff, 1986-87: 115.
Student Enrolment, 1986-87:

	Men	Women	Total
Of the country	2812	1091	3903
Of other countries	90	26	116
Total	2902	1117	4019

3206 **FACHHOCHSCHULE LÜBECK**

Stephensonstrasse 3, 2400 Lübeck 2
Telephone: (451) 500-5001
Präsident: Heiko Ukens (1984-87)
Kanzler: Horst Drewello

D. of Natural Sciences
Dean: Christian Jentsch; *staff* 20 (5)
D. of Architecture and Construction Engineering
Dean: Peter Eymann; *staff* 20 (10)
D. of Electrical and Mechanical Engineering
Dean: Herbert Noppe; *staff* 40 (20)

Founded 1969, incorporating previously existing institutions. Under the jurisdiction of and financially supported by the State of Schleswig-Holstein.Founded 1969, incorporating previously existing institutions. Under the jurisdiction of and financially supported by the State of Schleswig-Holstein. Residential facilities for students. Residential facilities for students.

Academic Year: February to January (February-July; August-January).

Admission Requirements: Technical school certificate (Fachhochschulreife) or secondary school certificate (Abitur).

Fees: None.

Language of Instruction: German.

Degrees and Diplomas: Title of Diplom-Ingenieur, 6-8 sem.

Library: c. 92,300 vols.

Academic Staff, 1986-87: 110 (35).

Student Enrolment, 1986-87:

	Men	Women	Total
Of the country	1770	100	1870
Of other countries	125	5	130
Total	1895	105	2000

3207 **EVANGELISCHE FACHHOCHSCHULE FÜR SOZIALWESEN**

Maxstrasse 29, 6700 Ludwigshafen
Telephone: (621) 518007
Rektor: Dieter Wittmann
Kanzler: Wilfried Kramer

D. of Social Work
Head: Raimund Hassemer; *staff* 7
D. of Social Pedagogy
Head: Kurt Witterstätter; *staff* 7
I. of Advanced Training

Founded 1948 as Evangelische Schule für Kirchlichen und sozialen Dienst. Acquired present status and title 1971. Governing body: the Rat.

Academic Year: September to August (September-February; March-August).

Admission Requirements: Technical school certificate (Fachhochschulreife) or secondary school certificate (Abitur).

Fees: None.

Language of Instruction: German.

Degrees and Diplomas: Titles of–Diplom-Sozialarbeiter; -Sozialpädagoge, 6 sem.

Library: 30,000 vols.

Academic Staff, 1989-90:

Rank	Full-time
Professors	11
Fachhochschullehrer	3
Assistant	2
Total	16

Student Enrolment, 1989-90:

	Men	Women	Total
Of the country	93	219	312

3208 **KATHOLISCHE FACHHOCHSCHULE FÜR SOZIALARBEIT, SOZIALPÄDAGOGIK UND PRAKTISCHE THEOLOGIE**

Saarstrasse 2, 6500 Mainz
Telephone: (6131) 3703½4
Rektor: Hans Zeimentz (1985-87)
Verwaltungsleiter: Clemens Bendowski

D. of Social Work
Head: Wolfgang Schnabel; *staff* 8
D. of Social Education
Head: Heinz Rommel; *staff* 7
D. of Pastoral Work
Head: Hanneliese Steichele; *staff* 9

Founded 1972 by the six bishoprics within the State. The college enjoys academic autonomy and is under the supervision of and financially supported by the State of Rheinland-Pfalz. Governing bodies: the Senat; the Versammlung.

Academic Year: October to September (October-March; April-September).

Admission Requirements: Technical school certificate (Fachhochschulreife) or secondary school certificate (Abitur).

Fees: None.

Language of Instruction: German.

Degrees and Diplomas: Titles of–Diplom-Sozialarbeiter; -Sozialpädagoge; -Religionspädagoge, 6 sem.

Library: 25,000 vols.

Academic Staff, 1986-87:

Rank	Full-time
Professoren im Kirchendienst	20
Lehrende Sozialarbeiter	3
Assistenten	3
Total	26

Student Enrolment, 1986-87:

	Men	Women	Total
Of the country	163	345	508
Of other countries	2	5	7
Total	165	350	515

3209 **FACHHOCHSCHULE FÜR TECHNIK MANNHEIM**

Speyererstrasse 4, 6800 Mannheim 1
Telephone: (621) 292-6369
Fax: (621) 292-6420
Electronic mail: Teletex: zaoo@dnafht1
Rektor: D. von Hoyningen-Huene
Prorektoren: O. Becker; A. Hampel

D. of Mechanical Engineering
Head: W. Paetzold; *staff* 12 (5)
D. of Chemical Processing Engineering
Head: R. Stahl; *staff* 13 (7)
D. of Chemical Engineering
Head: W. Leuchte; *staff* 14 (4)
D. of Electrical Engineering
Head: A. Schmied; *staff* 12 (6)
D. of Telecommunications Engineering and Electronics
Head: F. Unger; *staff* 16 (7)
D. of Computer Science
Head: H. Schnitzspan; *staff* 10 (4)
D. of Business Education
Head: E. Scharff; *staff* 6 (4)
D. of Basic Natural Sciences
Head: O. Schott; *staff* 13 (5)
I. for Innovation and Transfer
Head: H. Hassenpflug; *staff* 3 (5)
Transfer Ce. for Chemical, Biochemical and Environmental Engineering
Head: J. Hagen; *staff* 3 (6)
Transfer Ce. for Microelectronics and Sensoric Engineering
Head: K. Abel; *staff* 4 (7)
Computer Ce.
Head: K. Rädle; *staff* 4 (5)

Founded 1898 as a private school of engineering. Acquired present status and title 1971. Under the jurisdiction and financially supported by the State of Baden-Württemberg. Governing bodies: the Senat; the Kuratorium. Residential facilities for students.

Arrangements for co-operation with institutions of higher education in: Toulon; Montpellier; Grenoble; Strasbourg; Metz; Nancy; Heerlan; Hengelo; Winterthur; Sarajevo; Swansea; London; Middlesbrough; Moscow; Connecticut; Maryland; Melbourne; Adelaide; Singapore.

Academic Year: September-August (September-February; March-August).

Admission Requirements: Technical school certificate (Fachhochschulreife) or secondary school certificate (Abitur).

Fees: None.

Language of Instruction: German.

Degrees and Diplomas: Titles of–Diplom-Ingenieur; -Informatiker; Wirtschaftsingenieur, 4 yrs.

Library: 45,000 vols. Several specialized libraries of the institutes.

Special Facilities (Museums, etc.): Museum of Technology Mannheim.

Publications: Profil (Report on Research, annually); Studienführer (annually).

Academic Staff, 1990: 90 (65).

Student Enrolment, 1990:

	Men	Women	Total
Of the country	2143	292	2435
Of other countries	107	15	122
Total	2250	307	2557

3210 **FACHHOCHSCHULE FÜR SOZIALWESEN MANNHEIM**

Pettenkoferstrasse 24-30, 6800 Mannheim
Telephone: (621) 333033
Rektor: Joachim Auer (1983-)
Kanzler: Giselher Rupp

D. of Social Work
Head: Carsten Otte; *staff* 8 (15)
D. of Social Education
Head: Franz Kemper; *staff* 9 (16)

Founded 1972. Under the jurisdiction of and financially supported by the State of Baden-Württemberg.

Academic Year: October to September.

Admission Requirements: Technical school certificate (Fachhochschulreife) or secondary school certificate (Abitur).

Language of Instruction: German.

Degrees and Diplomas: Titles of–Diplom-Sozialarbeiter; -Sozialpädagoge, 6 sem, including practical work, 2 sem.

Library: Fachhochschulbibliothek.

Academic Staff: c. 20 (30).

Student Enrolment: c. 500.

3211 **STÄDTLICHE FACHHOCHSCHULE FÜR GESTALTUNG MANNHEIM**

E3. 16, 6800 Mannheim 1
Telephone: (1621) 293-2774

Graphic Design

Founded 1964. Under the jurisdiction of and financially supported by the City of Mannheim.

Academic Year: March to February (March-September; October-February).

Admission Requirements: Technical school certificate (Fachhochschulreife) or secondary school certificate (Abitur).

Language of Instruction: German.

Degrees and Diplomas: Title of Diplom-Designer, 6 sem.

Library: c. 700 vols.

Academic Staff: c. 20.

Student Enrolment: c. 160.

3212 **FACHHOCHSCHULE MÜNCHEN**

Lothstrasse 34, 8000 München 2
Telephone: (89) 12071

D. of Architecture
D. of Construction Engineering
D. of Mechanical and Transport Engineering
D. of Electrical Engineering
D. of Environmental Technology
D. of Precision Technology
D. of Data Processing and Mathematics
D. of Surveying
D. of Engineering Economics
D. of Business Administration (including Tourism)
D. of Social Sciences
D. of Design
D. of Basic Sciences

Founded 1971. Under the jurisdiction of and financially supported by the State of Bavaria. Governing body: the Senat.

Academic Year: October to July (October-February; March-July).

Admission Requirements: Technical school certificate (Fachhochschulreife) or secondary school certificate (Abitur).

Fees: None.

Language of Instruction: German.

Degrees and Diplomas: Titles of–Diplom-Ingenieur; -Informatiker; -Wirtschaftsingenieur; -Betriebswirt; -Designer; -Sozialwesen; -Sozialpädagoge, 8 sem.

Library: Central Library, c. 22,500 vols.

Publications: Baudokumentation; Dokumentation der Tagungen der Fachhochschule München und der Evangelischen Akademie Tutzing.

Academic Staff: c. 340 (350).

Student Enrolment: c. 10,000.

3213 **KATHOLISCHE STIFTUNGSFACHHOCHSCHULE MÜNCHEN**

Preysingstrasse 83, 8000 München 80
Telephone: (89) 48092-271
Präsident: Karljörg Schäflein (1986-94)
Verwaltungsleiter: Peter Obermaier-van Deun

Social Studies (Social Work and Social Education)

Founded 1971 incorporating four colleges and schools of social work founded between 1909 and 1967. Under the jurisdiction of and financially supported by the State of Bavaria. Also receives financial support from the Catholic Church. Residential facilities for women students.

Academic Year: October to July (October-February; March-July).

Admission Requirements: Technical school certificate (Fachhochschulreife) or secondary school certificate (Abitur).

Fees: None.

Language of Instruction: German.

Degrees and Diplomas: Titles of–Diplom-Sozialarbeiter; -Sozialpädagoge.

Library: c. 15,000 vols.

Publication: Informationsdienst (annually).

Press or Publishing House: Schriftenreihe der Katholischen Stiftungsfachhochschule München (6 vols. edited).

Academic Staff, 1990: c. 44 (192).

Student Enrolment, 1990:

	Men	Women	Total
Of the country	384	956	1340

3214 **FACHHOCHSCHULE MÜNSTER**

Hüfferstrasse 27, 4400 Münster
Cables: unims d
Telex: 08-92 529
Telephone: (251) 83-4283
Fax: (251) 83-9739
Rektor: Peter Schulte (1984-90)
Kanzler: Hans Michatsch

D. of Architecture
Dean: Herbert Bühler; *staff* 20
D. of Construction Engineering
Dean: Hermann Kintrup; *staff* 16
D. of Design
Dean: Marjan Vojska; *staff* 18
D. of Nutrition and Home Economics
Dean: Margarete Sobotka; *staff* 15
D. of Economics
Dean: Henner Hentze; *staff* 33
D. of Social Sciences
Dean: Gernot Alterhoff; *staff* 36
D. of Chemical Engineering (Steinfurt)
Dean: Anton Janssen; *staff* 16
D. of Electrical Engineering (Steinfurt)
Dean: Reiner Diehl; *staff* 15
D. of Mechanical Engineering (Steinfurt)
Dean: Karl-Heinz Illgner; *staff* 17
D. of Environmental Technology (Steinfurt)
Dean: Erich Schwager; *staff* 21

I. of Informatics
Head: Reinhard Volmer; *staff* 1

Founded 1878 as school, acquired present status and title 1971. Under the jurisdiction of and financially supported by the State of North Rhine-Westphalia. Governing body: the Senat. Residential facilities for students.

Special arrangements for co-operation in International Courses in European Studies with: Ecole multinationale des Affaires, Bordeaux; Humberside College of Higher Education, Hull; Centro Europeo de Gestion de Empresas, Madrid. Also co-operation with: Hogeschool Alkmaar, Netherlands; Akademia Ekonomiczna, Krakow; Politechnika Krakowska, Krakow; State University of New York College at Cortland; Universidad Metropolitana, Caracas.

Academic Year: March to February (March-August; September-February).

Admission Requirements: Technical school certificate (Fachhochschulreife) or secondary school certificate (Abitur).

Fees: None.

Language of Instruction: German.

Degrees and Diplomas: Titles of–Diplom-Ingenieur; -Betriebswirt; -Designer; -Oekotrophologe; -Sozialarbeiter; -Sozialpädagoge, 7-8 sem.

Library: Central Library.

Publication: FH - Report.

Academic Staff, 1989-90:

Rank	Full-time	Part-time
Professoren	235	–
Lehrkräfte für besondere Aufgaben	15	–
Lehrbeauftragte	–	164
Total	250	164

Student Enrolment, 1989-90:

	Men	Women	Total
Of the country	5773	3439	9212
Of other countries	276	122	398
Total	6049	3561	9610

3215 **FACHHOCHSCHULE NIEDERRHEIN**
Reinarzstrasse 49, 4150 Krefeld 1
Telephone: (2151) 8220
Fax: (2151) 822153
Rektor: Heinrich Broermann
Kanzler: Wilhelm Josef Thelen

D. of Chemistry
Head: Peter Sroka; *staff* 24 (26)
D. of Design
Head: Peter Wörgel; *staff* 17 (16)
D. of Electrical Engineering
Head: Albert Kolnsberg; *staff* 32 (19)
D. of Mechanical and Process Engineering
Head: Hermann Ostendorf; *staff* 30 (15)
D. of Nutrition and Home Economics (Mönchengladbach)
Head: Hans-Joachim Isken; *staff* 24 (24)
D. of Social Sciences (Mönchengladbach)
Head; Wilhelm Klüsche; *staff* 27 (11)
D. of Textile and Clothing Technology (Mönchengladbach)
Head: Rolf Klinke; *staff* 31 (41)
D. of Economics (Mönchengladbach)
Head: Werner Fussing; *staff* 34 (17)

Acquired present status and title 1971. Under the jurisdiction of and financially supported by the State of North Rhine-Westphalia. The present college dates back to thirteen former institutions, the oldest being founded1855 as school. Governing bodies: the Konvent, comprising the Rector, Pro-Rector, Kanzler, 47 professors, 10 other members of the academic staff, and 30 students; the Senat, comprising the Rector, Pro-Rector, Kanzler, 6 professors, 2 other members of theacademic staff, and 6 students. Residential facilities for students.

Arrangements for co-operation with: Western Michigan University; Loughborough University of Technology; Rockhurst College Kansas; Université de Lille, Roubaix.

Academic Year: September to July (September-February; March-July).

Admission Requirements: Technical school certificate (Fachhochschulreife) or secondary school certificate (Abitur).

Fees: : None.

Language of Instruction: German.

Degrees and Diplomas: Titles of–Diplom-Ingenieur; -Oekotrophologe; -Betriebswirt, -Sozialarbeit; -Sozialpadagoge, 6 sem; -Designer,8 sem.

Libraries: Central Library; department libraries, total, 153,000 vols.

Publications: FH-Report (2-3 times per year); Forschungsbericht (every 2 years).

Academic Staff, 1988:

Rank	Full-time
Professoren	219
Fachlehrer	16
Verwaltungspersonal	83
Bibliothekspersonal	17
Technisches Personal	87
Verwaltungsarbeiter	39
Auszubildende	27
Technischer Betriebsdienst	20
Total	508

Student Enrolment, 1988:

Of the country	9213
Of other countries	661
Total	9874

3216 **FACHHOCHSCHULE NORDOSTNIEDERSACHSEN**
Munstermannskamp 1, 2120 Lüneburg
Telephone: (4131) 706-0
Fax: (4131) 706-111
Rektor: R. Dietrich Fornaschon (1989-91)
Kanzler: Roland Schmidt

D. of Architecture (Buxtehude)
Dean: A. Hiller; *staff* 12 (4)
D. of Social Studies
Dean: K. Bader; *staff* 21 (31)
D. of Economics and Business Computing (Buxtehude)
Dean: G. Weinrich; *staff* 29 (17)
D. of Civil Engineering (Water Management and Drainage Engineering) (Suderburg)
Dean: H.-J. Lemke; *staff* 19 (36)
D. of Civil Engineering
Dean: H. Hoins; *staff* 12 (22)

Founded 1971. Under the jurisdiction of and financially supported by the State of Lower Saxony. Residential facilities for students.

Arrangements for co-operation with: East China Jiaoting University; North East London Polytechnic; University of Paris XIII; Ecole Supérieure de Commerce de Compiègne; Institut Universitaire de Technologie (IUT) de l'Université de Rouen-Haute Normandie, Le Havre; The Polytechnic of Wolverhampton; University of Kent, Canterbury; Université des Sciences Sociales de Grenoble (II); Institut de Travail social, Montrouge; Escuola Superiore Regionale di Servizio Sociale, Trento; Escuola Superiore di Servicio Social, Coimbra.

Academic Year: September to July (September-January; March-July).

Admission Requirements: Technical school certificate (Fachhochschulreife) or secondary school certificate (Abitur).

Fees: None.

Language of Instruction: German.

Degrees and Diplomas: Titles of–Diplom-Ingenieur; -Kaufmann; -Wirtschaftsinformatiker; -Sozialarbeiter; -Sozialpädagoge, 6 sem.

Library: Central Library, 75,000 vols.

Academic Staff, 1990:

Rank	Full-time	Part-time
Professoren	85	–
Lehrbeauftragte	–	89
Lehrkräfte	8	21
Total	93	110

Student Enrolment, 1990:

	Men	Women	Total
Of the country	1630	737	2367
Of other countries	97	23	120
Total	1727	760	2487

3217 **KATHOLISCHE FACHHOCHSCHULE NORDRHEIN-WESTFALEN**
Wörthstrasse 10, 5000 Köln 1
Telephone: (221) 7757-0
Fax: (221) 7757-180
Rektor: Joachim Baltes (1980-88)
Kanzler: Erhard Fries

D. of Social Studies
D. of Therapeutic Education
D. of Religious Education
Sections in: Aachen, Köln, Münster, and Paderborn.

Founded 1971 by the five dioceses within the State. Under the supervision of and financially supported by the State of North Rhine-Westphalia. Governing body: the Senat.

Academic Year: September to August (September-February; March-August).

Admission Requirements: Technical school certificate (Fachhochschulreife) or secondary school certificate (Abitur).

Fees: None.

Language of Instruction: German.

Degrees and Diplomas: Titles of–Diplom-Sozialpädagoge; -Sozialarbeiter; -Heilpädagoge, therapy; -Religionspädagoge, 7 sem.

Library: 108,500 vols.

Publication: Forum KFH NW (annually).

Academic Staff, 1989-90: 95 (1).

Student Enrolment, 1989-90:

Men	Women	Total
688	1932	2620*

*Including 34 foreign students.

3218 **GEORG-SIMON-OHM FACHHOCHSCHULE NÜRNBERG**
Kesslerplatz 12, 8500 Nürnberg 21
Telephone: (911) 5880-0
Fax: (911) 5880-309
Rektor: Helmut Stahl
Kanzler: Henning Hofmeister

D. of General Sciences and Computer Sciences
Dean: Werner Neft; *staff* 31 (1)
D. of Architecture
Dean: Jürgen Göttler; *staff* 14
D. of Construction Engineering
Dean: Günter Steuzel; *staff* 15 (1)
D. of Business Administration
Dean: Adalbert Rüschel; *staff* 41 (1)
D. of Communication Design
Dean: Ethelbert Hörmann; *staff* 13 (2)
D. of Electrical Engineering
Dean: Adolf Böhm; *staff* 19 (3)
D. of Communications and Precision Technology
Dean: Robert Schimke; *staff* 48
D. of Mechanical Engineering
Dean: Helmut Bär; *staff* 48
D. of Social Science
Dean: Klaus-Frieder Zauder; *staff* 31
D. of Chemical Engineering
Dean: Albrecht Hoffmann; *staff* 21 (7)
D. of Material Science
Dean: Wolfgang Kraft; *staff* 9 (1)
D. of Process Engineering
Dean: Manfred Körner; *staff* 13 (1)
Ce. for Applied Micro-Electronics and New Technologies
Head: Helmut Stahl; *staff* 12 (58)
Computer Ce.

Founded 1823 as school, acquired present status and title 1971. Under the jurisdiction of and financially supported by the State of Bavaria.

Arrangements for co-operation with: Ecole supérieure de Commerce de Toulouse; Ecole nationale supérieure de Céramique industrielle, Limoges; Ecole supérieure de Commerce de Compiègne; Institut commercial de Nancy; Ben-Gurion University Ben-Sheva; Shanghai Light Industry College.

Academic Year: October to July (October-March; March-July).

Admission Requirements: Technical school certificate (Fachhochschulreife) or secondary school certificate (Abitur).

Fees: None.

Language of Instruction: German.

Degrees and Diplomas: Titles of–Diplom-Ingenieur; -Betriebswirt; -Sozialpädagoge; -Designer; -Informatiker, 8 sem.

Library: Central Library, *c.* 100,000 vols.

Publications: FH Nachrichten (quarterly); FHN-Fahresbericht (annually).

Academic Staff, 1989-90:

Rank	Full-time	Part-time
Professoren	216	2
Lektoren	–	330
Total	216	332

Student Enrolment, 1989-90:

	Men	Women	Total
Of the country	6160	2124	8284
Of other countries	160	56	216
Total	6380	2180	8500

3219 **EVANGELISCHE STIFTUNGSFACHHOCHSCHULE NÜRNBERG - FACHRICHTUNG SOZIALWESEN**
Burgschmietstrasse 10, 8500 Nürnberg 90
Telephone: (911) 331019

Social Studies

Founded 1928 as technical academy, acquired present status and title 1971. Under the jurisdiction of and financially supported by the State of Bavaria. Governing bodies: the Senat; the Versammlung.

Academic Year: October to September (October-February; March-July).

Admission Requirements: Technical school certificate (Fachhochschulreife) and secondary school certificate (Abitur).

Fees: None.

Language of Instruction: German.

Degrees and Diplomas: Title of Diplom-Sozialpädagoge, 4 yrs.

Library: School Library.

Academic Staff: c. 20 (70).

Student Enrolment: c. 510.

3220 **FACHHOCHSCHULE FÜR KUNSTTHERAPIE D. FREIEN KUNSTSCHULE NÜRTINGEN**
Villa Melchior, Neckarstrasse 13a, 7440 Nürtingen

Art Therapy

3221 **FACHHOCHSCHULE NÜRTINGEN**
Neckarsteige 6-10, 7440 Nürtingen
Telephone: (7022) 701-l
Fax: (7022) 701-303
Rektor: E. Mändle
Prorektor: Th. Müller

D. of Agriculture
Head: R. Mohn; *staff* 16 (26)
D. of Landscape Ecology
Head: W. Schreiber; *staff* 13 (40)
D. of Business Studies (2)
Agricultural Teaching and Research D.
Head: G. Knecht; *staff* 9
Land Cultivation Teaching and Research Experimental Ut.
Directors H. Weller; H. Knecht; *staff* 12
I. for Computer Studies
Head E. Mändle; *staff* 1 (5)
I. for Co-operative Studies
Head: E. Mändle *staff* 1 (5)
I. for Banking
Head: H. Gumpert; *staff* 2 (4)
I. for Controlling
Head: G. Ebert
I. for Plant Growing and Cultivation
Head: J. Sneyd
I. for Innovation and Transfer
Head: K.J. Durwen
I. for Systems Innovation in Work
Head: H. Hub

Founded 1952 as agricultural college, acquired present status and title 1972. Under the jurisdiction of and financially supported by the Ministry of Science and Arts of Baden-Württemberg. Governing body: the Senat.

Arrangements for co-operation with: West Glamorgan Institute for Higher Education; Manchester Polytechnic; Polytechnic of East London;

Instituts universitaires de Technologie (Metz, Grenoble, Colmar); Ecole de Commerce, Troyes; Royal Agricultural College, Cirencester.

Academic Year: March to February (March-July; October-February).

Admission Requirements: Technical school certificate (Fachhochschulreife) or secondary school certificate (Abitur).

Language of Instruction: German.

Degrees and Diplomas: Titles of–Diplom-Betriebswirt; -Ingenieur Fachrichtung Landwirtschaft; -Ingenieur Fachrichtung Landespflege, 8 sem.

Library: Total, *c.* 40,000 vols.

Special Facilities (Museums, etc.): Landwirtschaftliches Versuchsgelände Tachenhausen.

Academic Staff, 1990: 57 (122).

Student Enrolment, 1990:

	men	Women	Total
Of the country	1374	587	1961*

*Also 95 foreign students.

3222 **EUROPEAN BUSINESS SCHOOL**

Schloss Reichartshausen, 6227 Oestrich-Winkel
Telex: 42138 EBS D
Telephone: (6723) 69-0
Fax: (6723) 3064
Präsident: Klaus Evard (1971-)

Business Administration (at the European level)
Dean: Ulrich Grimm
Computer Sciences
Dean: Günther Schmidt
I. for Marketing Research
Head: Manfred Bruhn
I. for Ecology and Environmental Management
Head: Ulrich Steger
I. for Finance Management
Head: Karl-Werner Schulte
International I. for Law and Business Administration
Head: Jürgen Bunge
I. for Multilingual Business Communications
Head: Anthony Lee
I. for Research and Consulting in System Development
Head: Peter Sokolowsy
I. for Research in International Economics and Management
Head: Rolf Caspers

European Business School, London; Paris Business School; European Business School, Prague; European Business School; Parma.

Founded 1971. A private university authorized by the government to award degrees.

Arrangements for co-operation with: American Graduate School of International Management, Phoenix, Arizona; San Diego State University; Gonji University, Shanghai; Universidad Argentina de la Empresa, Buenos Aires; Carnegie-Mellon University, Pittsburgh.

Academic Year: October to July (October-February; March-July).

Admission Requirements: Secondary school certificate (Abitur) and entrance examination (two languages).

Fees (Marks): 5350 per semester.

Languages of Instruction: German, English, French, Spanish, Italian and Chinese.

Degrees and Diplomas: Titles of Diplom-Betriebswirt; -Informatiker; -Kaufmann.

Library: 15,000 vols.

Academic Staff, 1989-90: 12 (120).

Student Enrolment, 1989-90:

	Men	Women	Total
Of the country	402	235	637
Of other countries	40	30	70
Total	442	265	707

3223 **FACHHOCHSCHULE OFFENBURG**

Badstrasse 24, 7600 Offenburg
Telephone: (781) 2050
Fax: (781) 205214
Rektor: Fritz Peter Adam (1989-93)
Verwaltungsdirektor: Werner Lutz

D. of Electrical Engineering
Head: H. Kirstein; *staff* 18 (10)
D. of Industrial Economics
Head: H. Oesterlee; *staff* 8 (9)
D. of Mechanical Engineering
Head: H. Klingenschmidt; *staff* 18 (15)
D. of Business Management
Head: H. Fuhl; *staff* 10 (10)
D. of Transport and Environment
Head: H. Indruch; *staff* 11 (7)
I. for Innovation and Transfer
Director: H. Kern; *staff* 3 (5)

Founded 1964 as school, acquired present status and title 1971. Under the jurisdiction of and financially supported by the State of Baden-Württemberg.

Arrangements for co-operation with: University of Strasbourg I; University of Grenoble; University of the Savoie, Chambery; Ecole catholique d'Arts et Metiers, Lyon; Ecole Superieure de Commerce de Compiègne; Hatfield Polytechnic.

Academic Year: March to February (March-August; September-February).

Admission Requirements: Technical school certificate (Fachhochschulreife) or secondary school certificate (Abitur).

Language of Instruction: German.

Degrees and Diplomas: Titles of–Diplom-Ingenieur; -Wirtschaftsingenieur; -Betriebswirt, 8 sem.

Library: Central Library, *c.* 35,000 vols.

Publication: Berichte (biannually).

Academic Staff, 1990: 49 (54).

Student Enrolment, 1990: c. 1300.

3224 **FACHHOCHSCHULE OLDENBURG**

Ofener Strasse 16, 2900 Oldenburg
Telephone: (441) 71086
Fax: (441) 73227
Rektor: Karl-Heinz Jung
Kanzler: Helmut Heine

D. of Architecture
Dean: Ekkehard Reiss; *staff* 14
D. of Engineering
Dean: Werner Heckler; *staff* 17
D. of Surveying
Dean: Jörg Mucke; *staff* 17
D. of Navigation (Elsfleth)
Dean: Manfred Dornieden; *staff* 12
Research I. for Radar Simulation (Elsfleth)
Head: Jürgen Rahn; *staff* 1 (4)
Research I. for Pipelines, Mains and Sewers
Head: Joachim Lenz; *staff* 1 (3)

Under the jurisdiction of and financially supported by the State of Lower Saxony.

Arrangements for co-operation with: Copernicus University, Toruń; Technical University, Szczecin; Marine Engineering College, Szczecin. Participates in the ERASMUS programme.

Academic Year: March to February (March-August; September-February).

Admission Requirements: Technical school certificate (Fachhochschulreife) or secondary school certificate (Abitur).

Fees: None.

Language of Instruction: German.

Degrees and Diplomas: Title of Diplom-Ingenieur (FH), 6 sem.

Library: 38,000 vols.

Academic Staff, 1990: 60.

Student Enrolment, 1990:

	Men	Women	Total
Of the country	706	200	906
Of other countries	14	5	19
Total	720	205	925

3225 **FACHHOCHSCHULE OSNABRÜCK**

Albrechtstrasse 30, 4500 Osnabrück
Telephone: (541) 608-1
Fax: (541) 608-2041
Rektor: E. Mielenhausen
Kanzler: H. Eickhorst

D. of Electrical Engineering
Dean: P. Kästner; *staff* 25 (10)
D. of Agriculture (including Home Economics and Nutrition)
Dean: B. Marquering; *staff* 17 (9)
D. of Mechanical Engineering
Dean: K. H. Werner; *staff* 27 (14)
D. of Materials Technology
Dean: R. Reichel; *staff* 12 (4)
D. of Economics (including European Business Studies)
Dean: S. Streckel; *staff* 34 (42)
D. of Horticulture
Dean: L. Mayr; *staff* 15 (11)
D. of Soil Conservation
Dean: D. Schmidt; *staff* 21 (9)

Founded 1971. Under the jurisdiction of and financially supported by the State of Lower Saxony. Governing bodies: the Senat; the Konzil. Residential facilities for students.

Arrangements for co-operation with: Ecole supérieure de Commerce et Administration des Entreprises, Clermont-Ferrand; Ecole supérieure de Commerce, Le Havre-Caen; University of Deusto; Coventry (Lanchester) Polytechnic; University of Salerno; University of Catania; International University of Social Studies, Rome; Athens School of Economics and Business Science; University of Reading; Cranfield Institute of Technology.

Academic Year: March to February (March-July; August-February).

Admission Requirements: Technical school certificate (Fachhochschulreife) or secondary school certificate (Abitur).

Fees: None.

Language of Instruction: German.

Degrees and Diplomas: Titles of Diplom-Ingenieur; -Kaufmann, 6 sem.

Library: 100,000 vols.

Academic Staff, 1990:

Rank	Full-time	Part-time
Professoren	162	–
Lehrkräfte für besondere Aufgaben	10	–
Lehrgeauftragte	–	99
Total	172	99

Student Enrolment, 1990:

	Men	Women	Total
Of the country	3050	842	3892
Of other countries	57	21	78
Total	3107	863	3970

3226 **KATHOLISCHE FACHHOCHSCHULE NORDDEUTSCHLAND**

Detmarstrasse 2, 4500 Osnabrück Driverstrasse 23, 2848 Vechta
Telephone: (541) 27378
Telephone: (4441) 3208
Rektor: Jochen Windheuser
Kurator: Hanns Huning

Social Studies (Nursing) (for teaching and leading positions)

Founded 1971. Under the jurisdiction of and financially supported by the State of Lower Saxony.

Academic Year: October to September.

Admission Requirements: Technical school certificate (Fachhochschulreife) or secondary school certificate (Abitur).

Fees: None.

Language of Instruction: German.

Degrees and Diplomas: Titles of–Diplom-Sozialarbeiter; -Sozialpädagoge.

Student Enrolment, 1990:

	Men	Women	Total
Of the country	150	340	490
Of other countries	1	2	3
Total	151	342	493

3227 **FACHHOCHSCHULE OSTFRIESLAND**

Constantiaplatz 4, 2970 Emden
Telephone: (4921) 807-0
Fax: (4921) 807-201
Rektor: Harro Ohlenburg
Kanzler: Peter Reissaus

D. of Electrical Engineering
Dean: Ewald Matull; *staff* 10
D. of Mechanical Engineering
Dean: Ernst Rüdiger Koch; *staff* 11
D. of Natural Sciences
Dean: Ernst Schmitt; *staff* 16
D. of Navigation
Dean: Rüdiger Böhlhoff; *staff* 6
D. of Social Studies
Dean: Gregor Terbuyken; *staff* 22
D. of Economics
Dean: Helmut Kind; *staff* 6

Founded 1973. Under the jurisdiction of and financially supported by the State of Niedersachsen. Governing body: the Senat.

Arrangements for co-operation with: University of Hefei; Technical College of Hangzhou; Leicester Polytechnic;Ingenieurhochschule Mittweida; Rijks Hoogeschool Groningen.

Academic Year: September to August (March-August; September-February).

Admission Requirements: Technical school certificate (Fachhochschulreife) and 6 months practical experience.

Fees: None.

Language of Instruction: German.

Degrees and Diplomas: Titles of–Diplom-Ingenieur; -Informatiker; -Kaufmann; -Sozialpädagoge/Sozialarbeiter; -Kauffrau; -Wirtschafts-Ingenieur; -Wirtschafts-Ingenieur für den Seeverkehr, 6 sem.

Library: c. 60,000 vols.

Academic Staff, 1989-90: 88.

Student Enrolment, 1989-90:

	Men	Women	Total
Of the country	1864	642	2506
Of other countries	35	7	42
Total	1899	649	2548

3228 **FREIE KUNST-STUDIENSTÄTTE**

Am Wiestebruch 66-68, 2802 Ottersburg 1

3229 **FACHHOCHSCHULE FÜR GESTALTUNG PFORZHEIM**

Holzgartenstrasse 36, 7530 Pforzheim
Telephone: (7231) 63258
Rektor: Klaus Limberg (1985-89)

D. of Jewellery and Fashion Design
D. of Graphic Arts
D. of Industrial Design
D. of Basic Studies

Founded 1877 as school, acquired present status and title 1971. Under the jurisdiction of and financially supported by the State of Baden-Württemberg. Governing body: the Senat.

Arrangements for student exchange with Nova Scotia College of Art and Design, Halifax.

Academic Year: October to July (October-February; March-July).

Admission Requirements: Technical school certificate (Fachhochschulreife) or secondary school certificate (Abitur), 6-12 months' practical experience, and entrance examination.

Language of Instruction: German.

Degrees and Diplomas: Title of Diplom-Designer, 4 yrs.

Library: c. 11,000 vols.

Academic Staff: c. 30 (40).

Student Enrolment: c. 340.

3230 **FACHHOCHSCHULE FÜR WIRTSCHAFT PFORZHEIM**

Tiefenbronner Strasse 65, 7530 Pforzheim
Telephone: (7231) 603-0
Rektor: Rupert Huth (1973-)

D. of Business Administration
Head: H. Schroter; *staff* 10 (14)
D. of Economics
Head: H. Löffler; *staff* 9 (3)
D. of Law and Social Sciences
Head: H. Quittnat; *staff* 9 (1)
D. of Marketing
Head: H. Kreuz; *staff* 4 (2)
D. of Purchasing and Logistics
Head: H. Dörsch; *staff* 4 (2)
D. of Publicity
Head: H. Pflaum; *staff* 4 (2)

D. of Market and Opinion Research
Head: H. Müller; *staff* 4 (2)

Founded 1967, acquired present title and status 1972. Under the jurisdiction of and financially supported by the State of Baden-Württemberg. Governing body: the Senat. Residential facilities for *c.* 400 students.

Arrangements for co-operation with more than 30 institutions in nearly 20 different countries.

Academic Year: September to August (September-February; March-August).

Admission Requirements: Technical school certificate (Fachhochschulreife) or secondary school certificate (Abitur).

Fees: None.

Language of Instruction: German.

Degrees and Diplomas: Titles of–Diplom-Betriebswirt, European Business Certificate (graduate programme), 4 yrs; -Wirtschaftsingenieur, 2 yrs following Diplom-Ingenieur; General Business Certificate (undergraduate programme), 1 yr. abroad.

Library: c. 90,000 vols.

Academic Staff, 1989-90: c. 70.

Student Enrolment, 1989-90: c. 2750.

3231 **FACHHOCHSCHULE RAVENSBURG-WEINGARTEN**
Doggenriedstrasse, 7987 Weingarten
Telephone: (751) 5011
Fax: (751) 49240
Rektor: G. Zibold (1990-)
Oberamtsrat: P. Höllander

D. of Mechanical Engineering (including Production Technology)
Head: H.-P. Langer; *staff* 11
D. of Physical Technology
Head: J. Vogt; *staff* 10
D. of Electrical Engineering
Head: P. Scheuffelen; *staff* 15
D. of Social Sciences
Head: W. Zipp; *staff* 8

Founded 1964 as school, acquired present status and title of Fachhochschule Ravensburg 1971. Acquired present title 1982. Under the jurisdiction of and financially supported by the State of Baden-Württemberg. Governing body: the Senat.

Arrangements for co-operation with : Sunderland Polytechnic; IUT, Université Claude Bernard, Lyon; IUT, Université Jean Monnet, Saint-Etienne.

Academic Year: October to July (October-February; March-July).

Admission Requirements: Technical school certificate (Fachhochschulreife) or secondary school certificate (Abitur).

Fees: None.

Language of Instruction: German.

Degrees and Diplomas: Titles of–Diplom-Ingenieur; -Sozialarbeiter, 4 yrs.

Library: Central Library.

Academic Staff, 1989-90: 44 (72).

Student Enrolment, 1989-90:

Of the country	1374
Of other countries	31
Total	1405

3232 **FACHHOCHSCHULE REGENSBURG**
Prüfeningerstrasse 58, 8400 Regensburg
Telephone: (941) 23091
President: Rudolf Vogt (1970-90)
Kanzler: Maximilian Roth

D. of Architecture
Dean: H. Arnold; *staff* 12 (20)
D. of Construction Engineering
Dean: H. Bulenda; *staff* 12 (7)
D. of Electrical Engineering
Dean: H. Gröhn; *staff* 30 (29)
D of Mathematics and Computer Sciences
Dean: H. Wagner; *staff* 31 (15)
D. of Business Administration
Dean: H. Huber; *staff* 24 (12)
D. of Mechanical Engineering
Dean: H. Sander; *staff* 25 (12)
D. of Social Sciences
Dean: H. Steinbach; *staff* 14 (12)

Founded 1898 as school, acquired present title and status 1971. Under the jurisdiction of and financially supported by the State of Bavaria. Governing body: the Senat. Residential facilities for students.

Academic Year: October to July (October-February; March-July).

Admission Requirements: Technical school certificate (Fachhochschulreife) or secondary school certificate (Abitur).

Fees: None.

Language of Instruction: German.

Degrees and Diplomas: Titles of–Diplom-Ingenieur; -Informatiker; -Mathematiker; -Betriebswirt; -Sozialpädagoge, 4 yrs.

Library: Central Library, 50,000 vols.

Academic Staff, 1989-90: c. 130 (130).

Student Enrolment, 1989-90: c. 4490.

3233 **HOCHSCHULE FÜR BERUFSTÄTIGE**
Adolf-Steckel-Strasse 17, 2370 Rendsburg

3234 **FACHHOCHSCHULE FÜR TECHNIK UND WIRTSCHAFT REUTLINGEN**
Alteburgstrasse 150, 7410 Reutlingen 1
Telex: 729794 EABWD
Telephone: (7121) 271-1
Fax: (7121) 271-224
Rektor: Georg Obieglo (1981-)
Leitender Verwaltungsbeamter: Winfried Hermanutz

D. of Textile Technology
Head: Wolfgang Schäch; *staff* 9
D. of Chemistry
Head: Johannes Rau; *staff* 10
D. of Mechanical Engineering
Head: Helmut Seitz; *staff* 7
D. of Production Management and Economics
Head: Klaus-Dieter Kern; *staff* 7
D. of External Trade (Foreign Trade)
Head: Jean-Claude Marandon; *staff* 10
D. of European Business Administration
Dean: Eva Maria Haberfellner; *staff* 12
D. of Automation Technology
Head: Werner Eissler; *staff* 10
D. of Business Computer Science
Head: Fritz Laux; *staff* 5
D. of Electronics
Head: Wolfgang Steimle; *staff* 5
Transfer Ce. for the Use of Raw Materials
Head: Jörg Wurster
Ce. for Applied and Environmental Chemistry
Head: Dietrich Frahne
Ce. for Sensors
Head: Werner Eissler
Ce. for Erosion Processes
Head: Karl Schekulin

Founded 1855 as Textile College, acquired present status and title 1971. Under the jurisdiction of and financially supported by the State of Baden-Württemberg. Governing body: the Senat. Some residential facilities for students.

Arrangements for co-operation with: Middlesex Polytechnic; Ecole supérieure de Commerce et d'Administration des Entreprises, Reims; Pontifical University, Comillas. Also student and staff exchange with: Wolverhampton Polytechnic; Ecole supérieure de Commerce, Angers; Valparaiso University, Indiana; Université de Savoie, Chambéry; Institut de Textile et de Chimie de Lyon; Leicester Polytechnic; Portsmouth Polytechnic; Regional Technical College, Galway; University of Exeter.

Academic Year: March to February (March-July; September-January).

Admission Requirements: Technical school certificate (Fachhochschulreife) or secondary school certificate (Abitur).

Fees: None.

Language of Instruction: German.

Degrees and Diplomas: Titles of–Diplom-Ingenieur; -Betriebswirt, business administration; -Informatiker; -Exportwirt, 4 yrs.

Library: Total, 40,000 vols.

Special Facilities (Museums, etc.): Textile Gewebesammlung (Collection of textiles).

Publication: Tex (biannually).

Academic Staff, 1990: 120 (180).
Student Enrolment, 1990:

Of the country	2740
Of other countries	247
Total	2987

3235 **EVANGELISCHE FACHHOCHSCHULE FÜR SOZIALWESEN REUTLINGEN**
Ringelbachstrasse 221, 7410 Reutlingen
Telephone: (7121) 2414-0
Rektor: Gottfried Hermann
Prorektor: Wolfgang Liegle

Social Work
Social Education

Founded 1954 as school, acquired present status and title 1970. A private institution financially supported bythe Evangelische Landeskirche Württemberg (50%) and the State of Baden-Württemberg (50%).

Academic Year: October to July (October-February; March-July).
Admission Requirements: Technical school certificate (Fachhochschulreife) or secondary school certificate (Abitur).
Fees: None.
Language of Instruction: German.
Degrees and Diplomas: Diplom–Sozialpädagoge; -Sozialarbeiter, 4 yrs.
Library: c. 15,000 vols.
Academic Staff, 1990: c. 18 (42).
Student Enrolment, 1990: c. 390.

3236 **FACHHOCHSCHULE RHEINLAND-PFALZ**
Seppel-Glückert-Passage 10, 6500 Mainz
Telephone: (6131) 2392-0
Fax: (6131) 239212
Präsident: Dieter Wilmes (1988-94)
Kanzler: Dieter Eckert

Architecture
Construction Engineering
Business Administration (8 Divisions)
Electrical Engineering
Domestic and Food Sciences
Information Systems (General and Business)
Interior Design
Ceramics
Communication Design
Agriculture
Agriculture and Environmental Conservation
Mechanical Engineering
Fashion Design
Social Work
Social Teacher Training
Textile Science
Process Technology
Technical Engineering

Sections in Bingen, Kaiserslautern, Koblenz, Ludwigshafen/Worms, Mainz(2) and Trier.

Founded 1971. Under the jurisdiction of and financially supported by the State of Rheinland-Pfalz.

Arrangements for co-operation with Polytechnics in: France; Italy; Israel; Poland; Sweden; Netherlands; UnitedKingdom; Spain; United States of America; Luxemburg.

Academic Year: October to July (October-January; March-July).
Admission Requirements: Graduation from high school and entrance examination.
Fees: None.
Language of Instruction: German.
Degrees and Diplomas: Titles of–Diplom-Ingenieur; -Betriebswirt; -Wirtschaftsingenieur; -Designer; -Sozialarbeiter; -Sozialpädagoge, 6-9 sem.
Library: Total c. 272,000 vols.
Publication: FH-Journal (biannually).
Academic Staff, 1988-89:

Rank	Full-time	Part-time
Professoren	586	10
Assistenten	123	20
Soustige Lehrende	12	–
total	721	30

Student Enrolment, 1988-89:

	Men	Women	Total
Of the country	10,408	4345	14,753
Of other countries	432	160	592
Total	10,840	4505	15,345

3237 **EVANGELISCHE FACHHOCHSCHULE RHEINLAND-WESTFALEN-LIPPE**
Immanuel-Kant-Strasse 18-20, 4630 Bochum 1
Telephone: (234) 369-010
Fax: (2324) 369-0124
Rektor: Gottfried Schmidt
Kanzler: Klaus Meinert

D. of Social Work
Dean: E.U. Huster; *staff* 17 (27)
D. of Social Education
Dean: M. Bellermann; *staff* 19 (33)
D. of Health Education
Dean: M. Hellmann; *staff* 12 (12)
D. of Religious Education
Dean: F. Bargheer; *staff* 4 (5)

Founded 1977 by the Evangelische Kirche im Rheinland, Evangelische Kirche von Westfalen, Lippische Landeskirche.

Academic Year: March to February (March-July; September-February).
Admission Requirements: Secondary school certificate.
Fees: None.
Language of Instruction: German.
Degrees and Diplomas: Diplom–Sozialarbeiter; –Sozialpädagoge; –Heilpädagoge, 3 ½ yrs. Diplom–Religionspädagoge, a further 2 yrs.
Library: 73,000 vols.
Publication: Denken und Handeln, 2-3 times annually.
Student Enrolment, 1990:

Men	Women	Total
470	985	1455

3238 **FACHHOCHSCHULE ROSENHEIM**
Marienberger Strasse 26, 8200 Rosenheim
Telephone: (8031) 805-0
Fax: (8031) 805105
Präsident: Hans Zang (1986-90)
Kanzler: Helmut Hanika

D. of General Sciences
Dean: H. Hermkes; *staff* 18
D. of Business Administration
Dean: H. Cyron; *staff* 10
D. of Wood Technology
Dean: H. Dusil; *staff* 22
D. of Computer Science
Head: H. Feindor; *staff* 2 (2)
D. of Interior Architecture
Dean: H. Leder; *staff* 25
D. of Synthetics Technology
Dean: H. Wetter; *staff* 8
D. of Production Engineering
Head: H. Förster; *staff* 8
D. of Engineering Economics
Head: H. Wenzel; *staff* 4

Founded 1925 as school, acquired present status and title 1971. Under the jurisdiction of and financially supported by the State of Bavaria. Governing bodies: the Versammlung; the Senat. Residential facilities for c. 400 students.

Arrangements for co-operation with: The Hatfield Polytechnic; Thames Polytechnic; The Polytechnic of Wales; University of Lowell.

Academic Year: October to September (October-March; March-September).
Admission Requirements: Technical school certificate (Fachhochschulreife) or secondary school certificate (Abitur).

Language of Instruction: German.
Degrees and Diplomas: Titles of–Diplom-Ingenieur; -Betriebswirt; -Informatiker; -Wirtschaftsingenieur, 4 yrs.
Academic Staff, 1990: 94 (98).
Student Enrolment, 1990:

	Men	Women	Total
Of the country	2495	832	3327
Of other countries	69	28	97
Total	2564	860	3424

3239 **FACHHOCHSCHULE DES SAARLANDES**
Goebenstrasse 40, 6600 Saarbrücken 1
Telephone: (681) 5867-0
Fax: (681) 56013
Rektor: Herbert Frisch (1988-)
Verwaltungsdirektor: Guido Arbeck

D. of Architecture
Head: H. Grund; *staff* 8 (14)
D. of Construction Engineering
Head: C. Hinrichs; *staff* 10 (7)
D. of Business Administration
Head: H. Schmidt; *staff* 20 (15)
D. of Electrical Engineering
Head: D. Knuth; *staff* 12 (10)
D. of Engineering Economics
Head: H. Hütter; *staff* 11 (13)
D. of Mechanical Engineering
Head: H. Altjohann; *staff* 20 (17)
D. of Computer Sciences
Head: H. Schurich; *staff* 15 (3)
I. for Environmental Informatics
Head: Helmut Groh
I. for Technology Transfer
Head: H. Frisch
German/French I. for Engineering and Economics
Director: Rainer Reisel

Founded 1971, incorporating 3 previously existing schools. Under the jurisdiction of and financially supportedby the State of Saarland. Governing bodies: the Senat; the Konzil.

Arrangements for co-operation with: Manchester Polytechnic; Leicester Polytechnic; Muhlenberg College; Georgian Polytechnical Institute, Tbilisi; Ecole supérieure de Commerce, Chambéry; Institut de Gestion sociale (IGS), Paris.

Academic Year: October to July (October-February; April-July).
Admission Requirements: Technical school certificate (Fachhochschulreife) or secondary school certificate (Abitur), or equivalent.
Fees: None.
Language of Instruction: German.
Degrees and Diplomas: Titles of–Diplom-Betriebswirt; -Informatiker; -Ingenieur; Wirtschaftsingenieur, 3-4 yrs.
Library: Total, 29,270 vols.
Academic Staff, 1990: 96.
Student Enrolment, 1989-90:

	Men	Women	Total
Of the country	2523	645	3168*

*Including 264 foreign students.

3240 **KATHOLISCHE FACHHOCHSCHULE FÜR SOZIALWESEN SAARBRÜCKEN**
Rastpfuhl 12a, 6600 Saarbrücken
Telephone: (681) 72031
Rektor: Arnold Pütz (1986-)

D. of Social Studies

Founded 1964 as school, acquired present status and title 1971. Under the jurisdiction of the Bishopric of Trier.

Academic Year: October to September (October-March; April-September).
Admission Requirements: Technical school certificate (Fachhochschulreife) or secondary school certificate (Abitur).
Language of Instruction: German.
Degrees and Diplomas: Titles of–Diplom-Sozialarbeiter; -Sozialpädagoge,6 sem.
Student Enrolment: c. 50.

3241 **FACHHOCHSCHULE FÜR GESTALTUNG SCHWÄBISCH GMÜND**
Rektor-Klaus-Strasse 100, 7070 Schwäbisch Gmünd
Telephone: (7171) 602-600
Fax: (7171) 692-59
Rektor: Wilfried Reinke (1979-)
Amtsrat: Franz Reif

D. of Graphic Design
Head: M. Klar; *staff* 4 (20)
D. of Industrial Design
Head: R. Michel; *staff* 3 (10)
D. of Jewellery Design
Head: P. Schlevogt; *staff* 3 (10)
D. of Basic Design
Head: H. Stetzer; *staff* 5 (3)
I. for Innovation and Transfer
Director: G. Hörmann

Founded 1907 as school for precious metals, acquired present status and title 1971. Under the jurisdiction of and financially supported by the State of Baden-Württemberg.

Arrangements for co-operation with: Ravensbourne College of Art and Design, U.K.; Leicester Polytechnic; Central St. Martins School of Art & Design, U.K.; Middlesex Polytechnic.

Academic Year: October to July (October-February; March-July).
Admission Requirements: Technical school certificate (Fachhochschulreife) or secondary school certificate (Abitur).
Language of Instruction: German.
Degrees and Diplomas: Title of Diplom-Designer, 8 sem.
Library: c. 13,000 vols.
Academic Staff, 1990: c. 60.
Student Enrolment, 1990:

	Men	Women	Total
Of the country	154	138	292
Of other countries	6	6	12
Total	160	144	304

3242 **FACHHOCHSCHULE FÜR TECHNIK SIGMARINGEN**
Anton-Günther Strasse 41, 7480 Sigmaringen 1
Telephone: (07571) 4076/7

D. of Clothing Technology
D. of Home Economics and Nutrition

Founded 1971. Under the jurisdiction of and financially supported by the State of Baden-Württemberg. Governing bodies: the Grosse Senat; the Senat. Residential facilities for c. 50 students.

Academic Year: October to July (October-February; March-July).
Admission Requirements: Technical school certificate (Fachhochschulreife) or secondary school certificate (Abitur).
Fees: None.
Language of Instruction: German.
Degrees and Diplomas: Titles of Diplom, 6-8 sem.
Academic Staff: c. 20 (20).
Student Enrolment: c. 430.

3243 **FACHHOCHSCHULE FÜR BIBLIOTHEKSWESEN STUTTGART**
Feuerbacher Heide 38-42, 7000 Stuttgart 1
Cables: FHB Stuttgart
Telephone: (711) 227420
Fax: (711) 22742-33
Rektor: Peter Vodosek (1990-94)
Oberamtsrat: Adolf Fleischmann

D. of Library Science (Public Libraries)
Head: Franz Bienert; *staff* 11 (8)
D. of Basic Studies
Head: Agnes Jülkenbeck; *staff* 10 (6)
D. of Library Science (Research Libraries and Information Science)
Head: Hellmut Pozeler; *staff* 10 (14)
D. of Music Library Science
Head: Wolfgang Krueger; *staff* – (2)

Founded 1942 as Süddeutsche Büchereischule, acquired present status and title 1972. Under the jurisdictionof and financially supported by the State of Baden-Württemberg. Governing body: the Senat.

Arrangements for co-operation with the Royal School of Library Science, Copenhagen; Boras College, Sweden.

Academic Year: October to July (October-February; April-July).
Admission Requirements: Secondary school certificate (Abitur) or equivalent.
Fees: None.
Language of Instruction: German.
Degrees and Diplomas: Title of–Diplom-Bibliothekar, 6 sem; -Dokumentar, 7 sem. Also Zusatzdiplom für Musikbibliothekare.
Library: 60,000 vols.
Academic Staff, 1989-90:

Rank	Full-time	Part-time
Professoren	29	30
Others	2	–
Total	31	30

Student Enrolment, 1989-90:

	Men	Women	Total
Of the country	87	517	604
Of other countries	1	7	8
Total	88	524	612

3244 **FACHHOCHSCHULE FÜR DRUCK STUTTGART**
Nobelstrasse 10, 7000 Stuttgart 80
Telephone: (711) 6852805

D. of Printing Technology
D. of Industrial Economics
D. of Colour Technology
D. of Basic Sciences

Founded 1972. Under the jurisdiction of and financially supported by the State of Baden-Württemberg.
Academic Year: September to August (September-February; March-August).
Admission Requirements: Technical school certificate (Fachhochschulreife) or secondary school certificate (Abitur).
Fees: None.
Language of Instruction: German.
Degrees and Diplomas: Titles of–Diplom-Ingenieur; -Wirtschaftsingenieur, 6sem.
Library: c. 20,000 vols.
Academic Staff: c. 60 (40).

3245 **FACHHOCHSCHULE FÜR TECHNIK STUTTGART**
Willi-Bleicher-Strasse 29, 7000 Stuttgart 1
Telephone: (711) 121-2660
Fax: (711) 2666
Rektor: Klaus-Jürgen Zabel (1984-93)

D. of Architecture
Head: H. Zinsmeister; *staff* 25 (54)
D. of Construction Engineering
Head: H. Schilp; *staff* 18 (32)
D. of Construction Physics
Head: H. Stohrer; *staff* 11 (28)
D. of Mathematics
Head: H. Steinbrunn; *staff* 15 (26)
D. of Surveying
Head: H. Johannsen; *staff* 13 (31)
I. for Construction Technology
Head: H. Natzschka; *staff* – (6)

Founded 1832 as school, acquired present status and title 1971. Under the jurisdiction of and financially supported by the State of Baden-Württemberg. Residential facilities for students.
Arrangements for co-operation with: Leicester Polytechnic; Middlesex Polytechnic; Polytechnic of Wales, Pontypridd; Technical University, Delft; Université de Nancy I; Technical University, Wrocław; Academy of Economics, Wrocław; Politecnico di Milano; Università degli Studi di Brescia; University of Southampton.
Academic Year: October to July (October-February; April-July).
Admission Requirements: Technical school certificate (Fachhochschulreife) or secondary school certificate (Abitur).
Language of Instruction: German.
Degrees and Diplomas: Titles of Diplom-Ingenieur; -Mathematiker, 4 yrs.
Library: c. 25,000 vols.
Academic Staff, 1989: 86 (140).
Student Enrolment, 1989:

Of the country	1950
Of other countries	50
Total	2000

3246 **MERZ-AKADEMIE**
Gänsheidestrasse 119, 7000 Stuttgart 1
Telephone: (771) 21034-56
Fax: (771) 21034-61
Rektor: Markus Merz

D. of Graphic Design
Head: Jorgen Hoffmann; *staff* 4 (5)
D. of Electronic Design
Head: Markus Merz; Detlev Langer; *staff* 2 (2)
D. of Foundation Studies
Head: Julio Rondo; *staff* 3 (2)

Founded 1918. Since 1985 the only state-recognized Art College in Germany entitled to give out Diploma in Graphic Design.
Arrangements for co-operation with: Nova Scotia College of Art and Design; Ravensbourne College of Art, U.K.
Academic Year: April to February (April-July; October-February).
Admission Requirements: Technical school certificate (Fachhochschulreife) or secondary school certificate (Abitur).
Fees (Marks): 450.
Language of Instruction: German.
Degrees and Diplomas: Title of Diplom–in Graphic Design.
Academic Staff, 1990: 9 (11).

3247 **FACHHOCHSCHULE ULM**
Prittwitzstrasse 10, Postfach 3860, 7900 Ulm/Donau
Telephone: (731) 20530
Fax: (731) 2053-270
Rektor: Günter Hentschel (1989-93)
Regierungsamtmann: Herbert Jarosch

D. of Precision Technology
Head: Gerhard Schaub; *staff* 10 (3)
D. of Light Metal Construction
Head: Engelbert Schlipf; *staff* 8 (9)
D. of Mechanical Engineering
Head: Paul Gotterbarm; *staff* 11 (3)
D. of Communications Technology
Head: Dieter Gwisdalla; *staff* 12 (10)
D. of Production Technology
Head: Bernhard Dienstdorf; *staff* 7 (9)
D. of Technical Computer Sciences
Head: Otto Künzel; *staff* 8
D. for Basic Studies
Head: Heiner Fränkel; *staff* 20 (26)

Founded 1960 as school, acquired present status and title 1971. Under the jurisdiction of and financially supported by the State of Baden-Württemberg. Governing body: the Senat. Residential facilities for students.
Arrangements for co-operation with: Plymouth Polytechnic; Hubei Automotive Industries Institute.
Academic Year: September to August (September-February; March-August).
Admission Requirements: Technical school certificate (Fachhochschulreife) or secondary school certificate (Abitur), or equivalent.
Fees: None.
Language of Instruction: German.
Degrees and Diplomas: Title of Diplom-Ingenieur, 8 sem, including 2 sem ofpractical experience.
Library: c. 33,200 units.
Special Facilities (Museums, etc.): Museum of Radios.
Publication: Mitteilungen der Fachhochschule Ulm.
Academic Staff, 1990: 90 (125).
Student Enrolment, 1990:

	Men	Women	Total
Of the country	1980	128	2108
Of other countries	59	–	59
Total	2039	128	2167

3248 **FACHHOCHSCHULE WEDEL**
Feldstrasse 143, 2000 Wedel/Holstein
Telephone: (4103) 82008

Physical Technology
Computer Science

3249 **FACHHOCHSCHULE WEIHENSTEPHAN**
8050 Freising 12
Telephone: (8161) 71-3339
Fax: (8161) 71-4207
Präsident: Josef Herz (1989-93)

D. of Horticulture
Dean: Georg Ohmayer *staff* 13
D. of Forestry
Dean: Anton Moser; *staff* 11
D. of Landscape Planning
Dean: Stephan Königer *staff* 19
D. of Agriculture
Dean: Karl Oppitz; *staff* 17
D. of Biotechnology
Dean: Reinhold Moser; *staff* 7
D. of Agriculture II
Dean: Henning Willeke; *staff* 13

Founded 1971. Under the jurisdiction of and financially supported by the State of Bavaria, Ministry of Scienceand Arts. Residential facilities for students.

Arrangements for co-operation with: University of Warsaw; University College, Dublin; Agravische Hogeschool, Delft; Ecole nationale d'Ingénieurs de Travaux agricoles, Angers.

Academic Year: October to July (October-March; March-July).

Admission Requirements: Technical school certificate (Fachhochschulreife) or secondary school certificate (Abitur).

Language of Instruction: German.

Degrees and Diplomas: Title of Diplom-Ingenieur, 4 yrs.

Academic Staff, 1989-90: 80.

Student Enrolment, 1989-90:

Of the country	2250
Of other countries	50
Total	2300*

*Also 296 external students.

3250 **FACHHOCHSCHULE WIESBADEN**
Kurt-Schumacher-Ring 18, 6200 Wiesbaden
Telephone: (6121) 4940
Fax: (6121) 444696
Rektor: Clemens Klockner
Kanzler: Peter Mertens

D. of Architecture (Idstein)
Dean: Alfram R.E. von Hössle; *staff* 10 (9)
D. of Construction Engineering (Idstein)
Dean: Klaus Fiedler; *staff* 12
D. of Mechanical Engineering (Rüsselsheim)
Dean: Jürgen Bauer; *staff* 24 (45)
D. of Electrical Engineering (Rüsselsheim)
Dean: Dietrich Schulz; *staff* 23 (23)
D. of Physical Technology (Rüsselsheim)
Dean: Wilfried Bernhard; *staff* 13 (13)
D. of Design
Dean: Olga Schulisch; *staff* 16 (21)
D. of Social Studies
Dean: Monika Simmel-Joachim; *staff* 20 (28)
D. of Economics
Dean: Dieter Fladung; *staff* 15 (14)
D. of Viticulture (Geisenheim)
Dean: Karl Bayer; *staff* 4 (33)
D. of Horticulture and Soil Conservation (Geisenheim)
Dean: Wolfgang Prollius; *staff* 5 (39)
D. of Mathematics, Natural Sciences, and Data Processing
Dean: Heinrich Rackel; *staff* 22 (17)
D. of Social and Cultural Sciences
Dean: Peter Bergen; *staff* 9 (35)
D. of Computer Sciences
Dean: Detlef Richter *staff* 5

Founded 1971 incorporating 4 formerly independent schools. Under the jurisdiction of and financially supportedby the State of Hesse. Governing bodies: the Konvent, comprising 26 members of the academic staff, 10 members of the non-academic staff, and 18 students; the Rat, comprising the Rector, Pro-Rector, 16 members of the academic staff, 2 members of the non-academicstaff, and 10 students.

Arrangements for co-operation with: University of Technology, Sydney; Universidad de El Salvador; PolitechnikaWrocławska.

Academic Year: September to August (October-January; March-July).

Admission Requirements: Technical school certificate (Fachhochschulreife) or secondary school certificate (Abitur).

Language of Instruction: German.

Degrees and Diplomas: Titles of–Diplom-Ingenieur; -Sozialpädagoge; -Designer; -Betriebswirt, business administration; -Informatiker.

Library: 130,000 vols.

Publications: Rechenschaftsbericht des Rektors; Fachhochschul-Pressespiegel; Fachhochschul-Journal; Schriftenreihe; Veröffentlichungslehre; angewandte Forschung und Weiterbildung.

Academic Staff, 1989-90: 160 (240).

Student Enrolment, 1989-90:

	Men	Women	Total
Of the country	4875	1679	6554
Of other countries	372	97	469
Total	5247	1776	7023

3251 **FACHHOCHSCHULE FRESENIUS WIESBADEN**
Dambachtal 20, 6200 Wiesbaden
Telephone: (6121) 522054

Chemistry

3252 **FACHHOCHSCHULE WILHELMSHAVEN**
Friedrich-Paffrath-Strasse 101, 2940 Wilhelmshaven
Telephone: (4421) 804 200
Fax: (4421) 81950
Rektor: Dr. Godel

D. of Electrical Engineering
D. of Precision Technology
D. of Mechanical Engineering
D. of Economics
D. of Industrial Economics

Academic Year: September to July (September-February; March-July).

Admission Requirements: Technical school certificate (Fachhochschulreife) or secondary school certificate (Abitur).

Language of Instruction: German.

Degrees and Diplomas: Title of Diplom-Ingenieur, 4 yrs.

Student Enrolment, 1990:

	Men	Women	Total
Of the country	2197	338	2535
Of other countries	59	8	67
Total	2256	346	2602

3253 **FACHHOCHSCHULE WÜRZBURG-SCHWEINFURT**
Sanderring 8, 8700 Würzburg
Telephone: (931) 13048

D. of General Sciences (Schweinfurt)
D. of Business Administration
D. of Architecture and Construction Engineering
D. of Social Studies
D. of Design
D. of Synthetics Technology, Surveying, and Data Processing
D. of Electrical Engineering (Schweinfurt)
D. of Mechanical Engineering and Industrial Economics (Schweinfurt)

Under the jurisdiction of the Ministry of Education and Culture of the State of Bavaria.

Admission Requirements: Technical school certificate (Fachhochschulreife) or secondary school certificate (Abitur).

Language of Instruction: German.

Degrees and Diplomas: Title of Diplom, 6 sem.

Student Enrolment: c. 2300.

Schools of Fine Arts and Music

3254 **HOCHSCHULE DER KÜNSTE BERLIN**
Ernst-Reuter-Platz 10, 1000 Berlin 12
Telex: 17308066
Telephone: (30) 3185-0
Präsident: Ulrich Roloff (1977-88)

D. of Fine Arts
D. of Architecture
D. of Design
D. of Visual Communications
D. of Advertising
D. of Art Education
D. of Music
D. of Musical Education
D. of Performing Arts
D. of Educational and Social Sciences
D. of Aesthetics

Founded 1696 as academy, acquired present status and title 1975. Governing bodies: the Senat; the Konzil.

Academic Year: October to July (October-February; April-July).

Admission Requirements: Entrance examination.

Fees: None.

Language of Instruction: German.

Degrees and Diplomas: Diplomas, 6-10 sem. Title of Diplom-Ingenieur. Staatsexam in Music and Art Education.

Libraries: Central Library, *c.* 175,640 vols; libraries of the departments, *c.* 357,800.

Publication: Information (monthly).

Academic Staff: c. 940.

Student Enrolment: c. 4000.

3255 **HOCHSCHULE FÜR BILDENDE KÜNSTE BRAUNSCHWEIG**
College of Fine Arts
Johannes-Selenka-Platz 1, 3300 Braunschweig
Telephone: (531) 391-0

D. of Painting
D. of Graphics and Printing
D. of Plastic Arts
D. of Theatre Design
D. of Photography
D. of Cinema and Video
D. of Architecture and Town Planning
D. of Graphics and Design
D. of Industrial Design
D. of Art Education
D. of Industrial Education
D. of Advertising

Founded 1853 as technical school. Acquired present status and title 1972. Under the jurisdiction of and financially supported by the State of Lower Saxony.

Arrangements for co-operation with; Art Institute of Chicago; San Francisco State University; University of Baroda; University of Barcelona; Bandung Institute of Technology.

Academic Year: October to July (October-February; April-July).

Admission Requirements: Entrance examination.

Fees: None.

Language of Instruction: German.

Degrees and Diplomas: State examination–Prüfung für das Lehramt (teaching qualification), 6 yrs. Title of Diplom-Designer, 5 yrs. Degree of Magister Artium, 2 yrs. Doctorates. Habilitation (teaching qualification, university level), at least 3 yrs after doctorate.

Library: c. 25,600 vols.

Publications: Vorlesungsverzeichnis (biannually); HBK Schrifttausch; HBK-Materialien; Ausstellungskataloge.

Academic Staff: c. 50 (45).

Student Enrolment: c. 1020.

3256 **STAATLICHE KUNSTAKADEMIE DÜSSELDORF**
Academy of Fine and Applied Arts
Eiskellerstrasse 1, 4000 Düsseldorf 1
Telephone: (211) 329334

Free Arts (Painting, Construction, Graphics, Photography)
Art Education
Science of Arts

Founded 1773. Under the jurisdiction of and financially supported by the State of North Rhine-Westphalia. Governing body: the Senat.

Academic Year: April to March (April-July; October-February).

Admission Requirements: Entrance examination.

Fees: None.

Language of Instruction: German.

Degrees and Diplomas: State examination–Prüfung für das Lehramt (teaching qualification). Professional titles, 5 yrs.

Libraries: c. 55,000 vols; *c.* 47,000 slides.

Special Facilities (Museums, etc.): Archives and Art Collection.

Academic Staff: c. 70.

Student Enrolment: c. 1070.

3257 **STAATLICHE HOCHSCHULE FÜR BILDENDE KÜNSTE (STÄDELSCHULE)**
College of Fine Arts
Dürerstrasse 10, 6000 Frankfurt am Main 70
Telephone: (69) 621091

D. of Architecture
D. of Painting and Theory of Art
D. of Painting and Graphics (2)
D. of Plastic Arts
D. of Technology of Sculpture
D. of Cinematographic Art
D. of Printing

Founded 1817 as art school, acquired present status and title 1942. Under the jurisdiction of and financially supported by the State of Hesse.

Academic Year: October to September (October-March; April-September).

Admission Requirements: Entrance examination.

Fees: None.

Language of Instruction: German.

Degrees and Diplomas: Diplom (planned).

Library: c. 12,000 vols.

Academic Staff: c. 10 (20).

Student Enrolment: c. 130.

3258 **HOCHSCHULE FÜR BILDENDE KÜNSTE HAMBURG**
College of Fine Arts
Lerchenfeld 2, 2000 Hamburg 76
Telephone: (40) 29188

D. of Art
D. of Art Education
D. of Architecture
D. of Industrial Design
D. of Visual Communications

Founded 1767 as school, became institute 1905 and acquired present status and title 1972.

Admission Requirements: Entrance examination.

Student Enrolment: c. 1300.

3259 **STAATLICHE AKADEMIE DER BILDENDEN KÜNSTE KARLSRUHE**
Academy of Fine Arts
Reinhold-Frank-Strasse 81/83, 7500 Karlsruhe 1
Telephone: (721) 843038
Fax: (721) 848150
Rektor: Andreas Franzke (1988-)

D. of Art Education
D. of Painting and Graphics
D. of Sculpture

Founded 1854. Under the jurisdiction of and financially supported by the State of Baden-Württemberg.

Regular interchange of students with Norwich School of Art, UK.

Academic Year: October to September (October-March; April-September).

Admission Requirements: Entrance examination.

Language of Instruction: German.

Degrees and Diplomas: State Examination–Prüfung für das Lehramt an Gymnasien (teaching qualification), 8 sem. Diplom, 8 sem.

Library: c. 20,000 vols.

Academic Staff, 1990: 18.
Student Enrolment, 1990:

	Men	Women	Total
Of the country	91	88	179
Of other countries	8	6	14
Total	99	94	193

3260 **AKADEMIE DER BILDENDEN KÜNSTE IN MÜNCHEN**
Academy of Fine Arts
Akademiestrasse 2, 8000 München 40
Telephone: (89) 3852-0
Präsident: Wieland Schmied

D. of Painting and Graphics
D. of Sculpture
D. of Interior Decoration
D. of Theatre Design
D. for Goldsmiths
D. of Art Education
D. of Ceramics
D. of Applied Graphics
D. of Architecture

Founded 1808. Under the jurisdiction of and financially supported by the State of Bavaria. Governing body: the Senat.
Academic Year: November to October (November-February; May-July).
Admission Requirements: Entrance examination.
Fees: None.
Language of Instruction: German.
Degrees and Diplomas: State Examination–Prüfung für das Lehramt an Gymnasien (teaching qualification), 8 sem. Diplom, 8 sem.
Library: c. 70,000 vols.
Special Facilities (Museums, etc.): Art Gallery.
Academic Staff, 1989-90: 38 (17)
Student Enrolment, 1989-90:

	Men	Women	Total
Of the country	276	339	615
Of other countries	46	33	79
Total	322	372	694

3261 **KUNSTAKADEMIE MÜNSTER**
Academy of Arts
Scheibenstrasse 109, 4400 Münster

3262 **AKADEMIE DER BILDENDEN KÜNSTE IN NÜRNBERG**
Academy of Fine Arts
Bingstrasse 60, 8500 Nürnberg 30
Telephone: (911) 40-5061
Präsident: Rainer Beck (1987-93)
Leitender Verwaltungsleiter: Herbert Fürstenhöfer

D. of Painting
D. of Sculpture
D. of Graphics and Design
Head: Heinz Schillinger
D. of Art Education
Head: Günter Dollhopf
D. of History of Art
Head: Hans-Pieter Reuter
D. of Textile Design
Head: Hans Herpich
D. of Metall Design (Gold and Silver)
Head: Erhard Hössle
D. of Interior Architecture
Head: Helmut Magg

Founded 1662, acquired present title and status 1940. Under the jurisdiction of and financially supported by the State of Bavaria.
Academic Year: October to September (October-March; April-September).
Admission Requirements: Secondary school certificate (Abitur) and entrance examination.
Fees: None.
Language of Instruction: German.
Degrees and Diplomas: State Examination–Prüfung für das Lehramt an Gymnasien Fachrichtung Kunsterziehung (teaching qualification), 3-4 yrs. Diplom-Ingenieur Fachrichtung Innenarchitektur, 9 sem.
Library: c. 14,000.
Academic Staff, 1990-91:

Rank	Full-time	Part-time
Professoren	14	–
Assistenten	1	6
Studiendirektoren	3	–
Studienräte	1	–
Fachlehrer	10	–
Lehrbeauftragte	–	9
Total	29	15

Student Enrolment, 1990-91:

	Men	Women	Total
Of the country	128	175	290
Of other countries	6	14	20
Total	134	189	317

3263 **HOCHSCHULE FÜR GESTALTUNG OFFENBACH AM MAIN**
College of Arts
Schlossstrasse 31, 6050 Offenbach am Main
Telephone: (69) 800590
Fax: (69) 880791
Rektor: Kurt Steinel (1974-)
Kanzlerin: Vera Sponheimer-Bram

D. of Visual Communication
Dean: Adam Jankowski
D. of Product Design
Dean: Richard Fischer

Founded 1832 as school, acquired present status and title 1970. Under the jurisdiction of and financially supported by the State of Hessen.
Academic Year: October to September (October-February; April-July).
Admission Requirements: Secondary school certificate (Abitur) or equivalent and proficiency in the arts.
Fees: None.
Language of Instruction: German.
Degrees and Diplomas: Title of Diplom-Designer. Also postgraduate Certificate.
Library: College Library.
Publications: Forum (biannually); Studien und Materialien (annually).
Academic Staff, 1990:

Rank	Full-time	Part-time
Professoren	21	–
Lehrkräfte für besondere Aufgaben	12	–
Lehrbeauftragte	–	26
Total	33	26

Student Enrolment, 1990:

	Men	Women	Total
Of the country	241	210	451
Of other countries	20	4	24
Total	261	214	475

3264 **STAATLICHE ACADEMIE DER BILDENDEN KÜNSTE**
Academy of Fine Arts
Am Weissenhof 1, 7000 Stuttgart 1
Telephone: (711) 251061

D. of Art Education
D. of Applied Graphics
D. of Sculpture
D. of Theatre Design
D. of Interior Architecture
D. of Ceramics
D. of Painting
D. of Textile Design

Founded 1761.
Admission Requirements: Entrance examination.
Student Enrolment: c. 30.

3265 **HOCHSCHULE FÜR MUSIK UND DARSTELLENDE KUNSTE FRANKFURT AM MAIN**
College of Music and Dramatic Art
Eschersheimer Landstrasse 29-33, 6000 Frankfurt am Main 1
Telephone: (611) 550826/28

D. of Music Education
D. of Performing Arts
D. of Professional Training
D. of Church Music

Founded 1938. Under the jurisdiction of and financially supported by the State of Hessen.

Academic Year: April to March (April-September; October-March).
Admission Requirements: Entrance examination.
Fees: None.
Language of Instruction: German.
Degrees and Diplomas: Diploma, 4-5 yrs. Staatsprüfung für das Lehramt an Gymnasien (teaching qualification), 4 yrs. Staatliche Prüfung für–Musiklehrer, 3-4 yrs; Organisten und Chorleiter, 4 yrs. Konzertexamen, 5-6 yrs.
Library: c. 20,000 vols.
Academic Staff: c. 60 (110).
Student Enrolment: c. 610.

3266 **HOCHSCHULE FÜR MUSIK FREIBURG**
College of Music
Schwarzwaldstrasse 41, 7800 Freiburg im Breisgau
Telephone: (761) 3603$^{2}/_{3}$4
Fax: (761) 3191542

D. of Composition
Head: Brian Ferneyhough; *staff* 8 (8)
D. of Stringed Instruments
Head: Marcel Cervera; *staff* 11 (7)
D. of Wind Instruments
Head: Hans Elharst; *staff* 12 (16)
D. of Song and Opera
Head: Ramon Walter; *staff* 12 (18)
D. of Conducting
Head: Klaus Hövelmann; *staff* 3 (6)
D. of Keyboard Instruments
Head; James Avery; *staff* 17 (16)
D. of Church Music
Head: Hans Musch; *staff* 3 (6)
D. of Musicology and Music Pedagogics
Head: Hannsdieter Wohlfarth; *staff* 3 (4)

Founded 1946. Under the jurisdiction of the State of Baden-Württemberg.

Arrangements for co-operation with Eastman School of Music, Rochester, New York.

Academic Year: October to July (October-February; April-July).
Admission Requirements: Secondary school certificate (Reifezeugnis) and entrance examination.
Degrees and Diplomas: Diplomas with corresponding professional titles, 5-6 yrs.
Student Enrolment, 1989-90:

	Men	Women	Total
Of the country	236	231	467
Of other countries	41	77	118
Total	277	308	585

3267 **HOCHSCHULE FÜR MUSIK UND DARSTELLENDE KUNST HAMBURG**
College of Music and Dramatic Art
Harvestehuder Weg 12, 2000 Hamburg 13
Telephone: (40) 44-19-51
Präsident: Hermann Rauhe (1976-90)

D. of Music Theory
D. of Instrumental Music
D. of Performing Arts
D. of Music Education
D. of Church Music

Founded 1950. Became an autonomous public institution 1967. Under the jurisdiction of and financially supported by the State of Hamburg. Governing body: the Konzil. Residential facilities for students.

Academic Year: April to March (April-September; October-March).
Admission Requirements: Entrance examination.
Fees: None.
Language of Instruction: German.
Degrees and Diplomas: Diploma, 4-6 yrs. Staatsexamen in Music Education, 4 yrs. Diploma in Church Music, 5 yrs.
Libraries: c. 9390 vols; c. 1890 records.
Academic Staff: c.90 (140).
Student Enrolment: c. 810.

3268 **HOCHSCHULE FÜR MUSIK UND THEATER HANNOVER**
College of Music and Drama
Emmichplatz 1, 3000 Hannover
Telephone: (511) 3100-22$^{3}/_{4}$

D. of Professional Training
D. of School Music
D. of Music Education
D. of Church Music
D. of Opera
D. of Drama
D. of Dancing

Founded 1911 as Städtisches Konservatorium, became Landesmusikschule 1943 and acquired present status 1950.

Academic Year: October to July (October-March; April-July).
Admission Requirements: Entrance examination.
Fees: None.
Language of Instruction: German.
Degrees and Diplomas: Diplomas with corresponding professional titles.
Academic Staff: c. 100.
Student Enrolment: c. 540.

3269 **STAATLICHE HOCHSCHULE FÜR MUSIK HEIDELBERG-MANNHEIM**
College of Music
L 15, 16, 6800 Mannheim 1
Telephone: (621) 292-3511

D. of School Music
D. of Music Education
D. of Professional Training
D. of Dancing
D. of Orchestral Music

Founded 1971, incorporating previously existing colleges of music and drama in Heidelberg. Under the jurisdiction of and financially supported by the State of Baden-Württemberg. Governing body: the Senat. Residential facilities for students in Studentenwohnheime.

Academic Year: October to September (October-March; April-September).
Admission Requirements: Entrance examination.
Fees: None.
Language of Instruction: German.
Degrees and Diplomas: Diplomas with corresponding professional titles.
Libraries: Central Library, c. 6000 vols; c. 2000 records; c. 50,000 sheet music.
Academic Staff: c. 40 (110).
Student Enrolment: c. 570.

3270 **STAATLICHE HOCHSCHULE FÜR MUSIK KARLSRUHE**
College of Music
Weberstrasse 8, 7500 Karlsruhe 1
Telephone: (721) 135-3294

D. of Music (School Music, Music Education, Orchestral Music, Church Music, Conducting, Composition, Arts)

Founded 1929. Under the jurisdiction of and financially supported by the State of Baden-Württemberg.

Academic Year: October to July (October-February; April-July).
Admission Requirements: Entrance examination.
Fees: None.
Language of Instruction: German.
Degrees and Diplomas: Diplomas with corresponding professional titles; teaching qualifications.
Academic Staff: c. 30 (80).
Student Enrolment: c. 400.

3271 **HOCHSCHULE FÜR MUSIK KÖLN**
College of Music
Dagobertstrasse 38, 5000 Köln 1
Telephone: (221) 12-40-33
Leiter: Franz Müller-Heuser (1989-92)
Kanzler: Isabel Pfeiffer-Poensgen

F. 1 (Composition, Music Theory, Conducting, Keyboard Instruments)
Dean: Manfred Reiter; *staff* 44 (44)
F. 2 (Instrumental)
Dean: Christoph Caskel *staff* 26 (49)
F. 3 (Singing, Music Theatre, Rhythm, Dance)
Dean: Lieselotte Hammes; *staff* 17 (39)
F. 4 (Music Education, Musicology)
Dean: Siegmund Helms; *staff* 8 (18)
F. 5 (Music Theory, Structure, Conducting, Instruments, Singing, Music Education) (Aachen)
Dean: Hans-Jochem Münstermann; *staff* 13 (45)
F. 6 (Music Theory, Conducting, Instruments, Singing, Music Education) (Wuppertal)
Dean: Karl-Heinz Zarius; *staff* 15 (47)

Founded 1825. Incorporated Staatliche Hochschule für Musik Rheinland 1987. Under the jurisdiction of and financially supported by the State of North Rhine-Westphalia. Governing body: the Senat.

Academic Year: September to August (October-March; April-September).

Admission Requirements: Entrance examination.

Fees: None.

Language of Instruction: German.

Degrees and Diplomas: Diplomas with corresponding professional titles, 8-12 sem.

Libraries: Total, *c.* 130,000 vols; 6000 records.

Publication: Journal-Zeitschrift der Hochschule (biannually).

Academic Staff, 1990: 123 (242).

Student Enrolment, 1989-90:

	Men	Women	Total
Of the country	859	784	1643
Of other countries	129	150	279
Total	988	934	1922

3272 **MUSIKHOCHSCHULE LÜBECK**
College of Music
Gr. Petersgrube 17-29, 2400 Lübeck
Telephone: (451) 3208⅔

D. of Professional Training
D. of Singing
D. of Music Education
D. of Church Music
D. of School Music

Founded 1933 as Conservatory, acquired present status and title 1973. Under the jurisdiction of the State of Schleswig-Holstein.

Admission Requirements: Entrance examination.

Degrees and Diplomas: Diplomas with corresponding professional titles; teaching qualifications.

Student Enrolment: c. 240.

3273 **HOCHSCHULE FÜR MUSIK IN MÜNCHEN**
College of Music
Arcisstrasse 12, 8000 München 2
Telephone: (89) 55-91-⅔2

Music

Founded 1867 as Royal School of Music financed by Ludwig II. Acquired present status and title 1924. Under thejurisdiction of and financially supported by the State of Bavaria. Governing bodies: the Versammlung; the Senat.

Academic Year: October to July.

Admission Requirements: Entrance examination.

Fees: None.

Language of Instruction: German.

Degrees and Diplomas: Diplomas with corresponding professional titles; teaching qualifications.

Academic Staff: c. 70 (100).

Student Enrolment: c. 650.

3274 **MUSIKHOCHSCHULE DES SAARLANDES**
College of Music
Bismarckstrasse 1, 6600 Saarbrücken 3
Telephone: (681) 62408/9

D. of Vocal Music
D. of Instrumental Music
D. of Theory of Music

Founded 1947 as Conservatory, became college 1957. Under the jurisdiction of and financially supported by the Ministry of Culture of the State of the Saar.

Academic Year: October to September (October-March; April-September).

Admission Requirements: Entrance examination.

Fees: None.

Languages of Instruction: German. Also some French and English.

Degrees and Diplomas: Diplomas, 3-6 yrs.

Library: c. 39,600 vols.

Academic Staff: c. 35 (40).

Student Enrolment: c. 330.

3275 **STAATLICHE HOCHSCHULE FÜR MUSIK UND DARSTELLENDE KUNST STUTTGART**
College of Music and Dramatic Art
Urbanplatz 2, 7000 Stuttgart 1
Telephone: (711) 21248 40/48 72

D. of Professional Training
D. of Private Music
D. of School Music
D. of Rhythmic Education
D. of Church Music (Protestant)
D. of Church Music (Catholic)
S. of Opera
D. of Drama
D. of Speech Education
D. of Modern Music

Founded 1922.

Admission Requirements: Entrance examination.

Degrees and Diplomas: Diplomas with corresponding professional titles.

Student Enrolment: c. 630.

3276 **STAATLICHE HOCHSCHULE FÜR MUSIK TROSSINGEN**
College of Music
Schultheiss-Koch-Platz 3, 7218 Trossingen 1
Telephone: (7425) 6057

Music

3277 **STAATLICHE HOCHSCHULE FÜR MUSIK WESTFALEN-LIPPE**
College of Music
Nordwestdeutsche Musikakademie Detmold, Allee 22, 4930 Detmold
Telephone: (5231) 26945

D. of School Music
D. of Church Music
D. of Conducting
D. of Music Education

Founded 1947 as academy, acquired present status and title 1972 with institutes in Dortmund and Münster. Under the jurisdiction of and financially supported by the State of North Rhine-Westphalia. Residential facilities for students.

Academic Year: October to July (October-February; April-July).

Admission Requirements: Entrance examination.

Degrees and Diplomas: Diplomas with corresponding professional titles, 8 sem.

Academic Staff: c. 100 (140).

Student Enrolment: c. 1400.

3278 **ROBERT-SCHUMANN-HOCHSCHULE DÜSSELDORF**
College of Music
Fischerstrasse 110, 4000 Düsseldorf

3279 **FOLKWANG-HOCHSCHULE ESSEN FÜR MUSIK, THEATER, TANZ**
College of Music, Drama and Dance
Abtei, 4300 Essen 16
Telephone: (201) 49030
Fax: (201) 4903288
Rektor: Wolfgang Hufschmidt
Kanzler: Eberhard Raaf

D. of Music
D. of Drama
D. of Dance

Founded 1927 as Folkwangschule für Musik, Tanz und Sprechen, acquired present status and title 1972. Under the jurisdiction of and financially supported by the State of North Rhine-Westphalia.

Arrangements for co-operation with: Academy of Fine Arts, Tirana.

Academic Year: October to September (October-March; April-September).

Admission Requirements: Secondary school certificate (Abitur) and entrance examination.

Fees: None.

Language of Instruction: German.

Degrees and Diplomas: Diploma, 4-5 yrs. Staatsexamen, 4 yrs. Konzertexamen, 1-2 yrs.

Library: c. 80,000 vols.

Academic Staff, 1990: 85 (141).

Student Enrolment, 1989-90:

	Men	Women	Total
Of the country	481	317	798
Of other countries	39	91	130
Total	520	408	928

3280 **HOCHSCHULE FÜR MUSIK**
College of Music
Hofstallstrasse 6-8, 8700 Würzburg
Telephone: (931) 50641/43
Präsident: Bertold Hummel (1979-87)
Kanzler: Erich Lurz

Composition
Music Theory
Conducting
Church Music (Catholic and Protestant)
Singing
Ancient Instruments

Founded 1804. Acquired present status and title 1973. Under the jurisdiction of and financially supported by the State of Bavaria. Governing body: the Senat, comprising 14 members.

Academic Year: November to July (November-March; April-July).

Admission Requirements: Entrance examination.

Fees: None.

Language of Instruction: German.

Degrees and Diplomas: Diplomas with corresponding professional titles, 3-10 sem. Staatsprüfung für das Lehramt (teaching qualification). Meister Klassendiplom, a further 2-4 sem.

Library: c. 30,000 vols.

Academic Staff, 1986-87: 46 (93).

Student Enrolment, 1986-87:

	Men	Women	Total
Of the country	253	238	491
Of other countries	24	27	51
Total	277	265	542

Theological Schools

3281 **PHILOSOPHISCH-THEOLOGISCHE HOCHSCHULE DER SALESIANER DON BOSCOS**
Don Boscos Strasse 1, 8174 Benediktbeuern
Telephone: (8857) 88-215
Fax: (8857) 88376
Rektor: Otto Wahl (1988-91)
Verwaltungsleiter: P. Oskar Falk

I. of Theology (Catholic)
Head: Horacio E. Lona; *staff* 12 (7)
I. of Philosophy
Head: Josef Privoznik; *staff* 5 (5)
I. of Religious Education
Head: Michael Spitz; *staff* 3 (7)
I. of Spiritual Studies
Head: Josef Weber; *staff* 1 (1)

Founded 1931. Affiliated to the Università Pontificia Salesiana, Rome 1970. Recognized by the State as institution of university status 1981.

Academic Year: October to July (October-January; March-July).

Admission Requirements: Secondary school certificate (Abitur).

Fees: None.

Language of Instruction: German.

Degrees and Diplomas: Baccalaureat in–Philosophy, 2 yrs; Theology, 5 yrs. Diplom-Theologe, 5 yrs.

Library: 24500,000 vols.

Academic Staff, 1986-87:

Rank	Full-time	Part-time
Professoren	13	–
Dozenten	6	1
Gastprofessoren	–	21
Lehrbeauftrafte	–	6
Total	19	28

Student Enrolment, 1989-90:

	Men	Women	Total
Of the country	147	147	294
Of other countries	11	1	12
Total	158	148	306*

*Also 49 external students.

3282 **KIRCHLICHE HOCHSCHULE BERLIN**
Teltower Damm 120-122, 1000 Berlin 37
Telephone: (30)8160050
Fax: (30) 81600570
Rektor: Peter Welten (1989-90)
Kurator: Uwe Jessen

Theology (Protestant)

Founded 1935. Recognized by the State as institution of university status. Residential facilities for students.

Academic Year: October to July (October-February; April-July).

Admission Requirements: Secondary school certificate (Abitur).

Fees: None.

Language of Instruction: German.

Degrees and Diplomas: Diplom Theologe, 5-6 yrs. Magister, 6-7 yrs. Doctor.

Library: 200,000 vols.

Academic Staff, 1986-87: 17.

Student Enrolment: c. 770.

3283 **KIRCHLICHE HOCHSCHULE BETHEL**
Remterweg 45, 4800 Bielefeld 13

Theology (Protestant)

3284 **PHILOSOPHISCH-THEOLOGISCHE HOCHSCHULE ST. GEORGEN**
Offenbacher Landstrasse 224, 6000 Frankfurt-am-Main 70
Telephone: (69) 6061-0
Rektor: Werner Löser S.J.

Theology (Catholic)

Language of Instruction: German.

3285 **PHILOSOPHISCH-THEOLOGISCHE HOCHSCHULE (PÄPSTLICH THEOLOGISCHE FAKULTÄT)**
Domplatz 2, 6400 Fulda

Theology (Catholic)

3286 **PHILOSOPHISCH-THEOLOGISCHE HOCHSCHULE DER REDEMPTORISTEN**

Waldstrasse 9, 5202 Hennef/Sieg.
Rektor: Josef Schmitz
Prorektor: Heinz Giesen

Theology (Catholic)

Founded 1861, acquired present status and title 1983.
Academic Year: October to September (October-February; March-September).
Admission Requirements: Secondary school certificate (Abitur).
Fees: None.
Language of Instruction: German.
Degrees and Diplomas: Diplom, 5 yrs.
Library: Library, *c.* 360,000 vols.
Academic Staff, 1989-90: 13 (2)
Student Enrolment, 1989-90:

	Men	women	Total
Of the country	34	6	40
Of other countries	14	–	14
Total	48	6	54

3287 **PHILOSOPHISCH-THEOLOGISCHE HOCHSCHULE DER FRANZISKANER UND KAPUZINER**

Hörster Platz, 4400 Münster
Telephone: (251) 57677
Rektor: Eckehard Krahl
Sekretär: Ildefons Vanderheyden

Theology (Catholic)

Founded 1971.
Academic Year: October to July (October-February; April-July).
Admission Requirements: Secondary school certificate (Abitur).
Language of Instruction: German.
Degrees and Diplomas: Diplom, 5 yrs.
Academic Staff: 15 (15).
Student Enrolment, 1990:

	Men	Women	Total
Of the country	45	10	55
Of other countries	29	1	30
Total	74	11	85

3288 **HOCHSCHULE FÜR PHILOSOPHIE (PHILOSOPHISCHE FAKULTÄT, S.J.)**

Kaulbachstrasse 33, 8000 München
Telephone: (89) 2386-312
Rektor: Peter Ehlen (1988-94)
Kanzler: Karl Frings

Philosophy

Founded 1926, acquired present title 1971. Supervised by the Society of Jesus, and recognized by the State as institution of university status.
Academic Year: October to September (October-March; April-September).
Admission Requirements: Secondary school certificate (Abitur).
Fees: None.
Language of Instruction: German.
Degrees and Diplomas: Baccalaureat in Philosophy, 2 yrs. Magister Artium. Doctorat, Dr.Phil.
Library: 150,000 vols.
Academic Staff, 1990-91: 25 (26).
Student Enrolment, 1990-91:

	Men	Women	Total
Of the country	197	104	301
Of other countries	28	5	33
Total	225	109	334*

*Also 276 external students.

3289 **AUGUSTANA HOCHSCHULE NEUENDETTELSAU**

8806 Neuendettelsau
Telephone: (9874) 744
Rektor: H. Schneider (1985-87)
Verwaltungsleiter: H. Dieter

Theology (Protestant)

Founded 1947. Supervised by the Evangelical-Lutheran Church of Bavaria, and recognized by the State as institution of university status. Residential facilities for academic staff and 131 students.
Academic Year: September to July (September-February; May-July).
Admission Requirements: Secondary school certificate (Abitur).
Fees: None.
Language of Instruction: German.
Degrees and Diplomas: Diploma, 4 yrs. Doctor.
Library: 80,000 vols.
Academic Staff, 1986-87: 14 (9).
Student Enrolment, 1986-87:

	Men	Women	Total
Of the country	127	63	190
Of other countries	3	2	5
Total	130	65	195

3290 **LUTHERISCHE THEOLOGISCHE HOCHSCHULE OBERURSEL**

Altkönigstrasse 150, 6370 Oberursel (Taunus)
Telephone: (6171) 24340
Rektor: Gottfried Hoffmann

Theology (Protestant)

Academic Year: September to August (September-March; April-August).
Admission Requirements: Secondary scholl certificate (Abitur).
Language of Instruction: German.
Degrees and Diplomas: Diplom, 6 yrs.
Academic Staff: 5
Student Enrolment, 1989-90:

	Men	Women	Total
Of the country	61	3	64
Of other countries	4	–	4
Total	65	3	68

3291 **THEOLOGISCHE FAKULTÄT PADERBORN**

Kamp 6, 4790 Paderborn

Theology (Catholic)

3292 **PHILOSOPHISCH-THEOLOGISCHE HOCHSCHULE SVD ST. AUGUSTIN**

Arnold-Janssen-Strasse 30, 5205 Sankt Augustin 1
Rektor:

Theology (Catholic)

Academic Year: October to March.
Admission Requirements: Secondary school certificate (Reifezeugnis).
Language of Instruction: German.
Degrees and Diplomas: Diplom in Theology. Lizenziat. Doktor.
Library: 95,000 vols.
Special Facilities (Museums, etc.): Haus Völker und Kulturen.
Academic Staff: 88
Student Enrolment, 1989:

	Men
Of the country	68
Of other countries	14
Total	82

3293 **THEOLOGISCHE FAKULTÄT TRIER**

Jesuitenstrasse 13, 5500 Trier
Telephone: (651) 7191-22
Rektor: Jost Eckert (1987-91)

Theology (Catholic)

Founded 1950.
Arrangements for co-operation with the University of Winnipeg.
Academic Year: Secondary school certificate (Abitur).
Language of Instruction: German.
Degrees and Diplomas: Diplom Theologe, 5 yrs; Lizenziat in Theology, a further 1-2 yrs. Doktorat in Theology, Dr.theol., a further 2-4 yrs. Habilitation, Dr.theol.habil.
Press or Publishing House: Paulinus-Verlag.

Academic Staff, 1990: 18 (6)
Student Enrolment, 1990:

	Men	Women	Total
Of the country	159	71	230
Of other countries	20	3	23
Total	179	74	253*

*Also 76 external students.

3294 **THEOLOGISCHE HOCHSCHULE VALLENDER DER GESELLSCHAFT DES KATHOLISCHEN APOSTOLATES (PALLOTTINER)**
Pallottistrasse 3, 5414 Vallendar
Telephone: (261) 6402-1
Fax: (261) 6402-290
Rektor: Manfred Probst (1986-)
Studiensekretär: Heribert Niederschlag

Theology (Catholic)

Founded 1896. Recognized by the State as institution of university status 1979. Governing body: the Rat.

Arrangements for co-operation with Salesian Pontifical University, Rome.

Academic Year: October to July (October-February; April-July).

Admission Requirements: Secondary school certificate (Abitur).

Fees: None.

Language of Instruction: German.

Degrees and Diplomas: Diplom Theologe, 5 yrs; Lizenziat in Theology, Lic.theol., a further 1-2 yrs. Doktorat in Theology, dr.theol.,a further 2-4 yrs. Habilitation, Dr.theol.habil.

Library: c. 85,000 vols.

Academic Staff, 1990: 13 (15)

Student Enrolment, 1990:

	Men	Women	Total
Of the country	57	47	104
Of other countries	7	–	7
Total	64	47	111*

*Also 50 external students.

3295 **KIRCHLICHE HOCHSCHULE WUPPERTAL**
Missionsstrasse 9-17, 5600 Wuppertal 2
Telephone: (202) 85005
Rektor: Lothar Schreiner (1986-)
Ephorus: Siegward Kunath

Theology (Protestant)

Founded 1935. Recognized by the State as institution of university status. Residential facilities for academic staff and *c.* 110 students.

Academic Year: October to August (October-February; April-July).

Admission Requirements: Secondary school certificate (Abitur).

Fees: None.

Language of Instruction: German.

Degrees and Diplomas: Magister der Theologie, 5-6 yrs. Doctor.

Library: 70,000 vols.

Academic Staff, 1986-87: 14 (7).

Student Enrolment, 1986-87:

	Men	Women	Total
Of the country	236	215	551
Of other countries	3	1	4
Total	239	216	555

Other Institutions

3296 **HOCHSCHULE FÜR WIRTSCHAFT UND POLITIK HAMBURG**
Von-Melle-Park 9, 2000 Hamburg 13
Telephone: 41232198

Sociology
Economics

Founded 1966.

3297 **UNIVERSITÄT DER BUNDESWEHR HAMBURG**
University of the Armed Forces
Holstenhof Weg 85, 2000 Hamburg 70
Telex: 02-14 952 BW D
Telephone: (040) 651-41-1

D. of Electrical Engineering
D. of Mechanical Engineering
D. of Economic and Administrative Sciences
Ce. for Didactics
Language Ce.

Founded 1973.

3298 **UNIVERSITÄT DER BUNDESWEHR MÜNCHEN**
University of the Federal Armed Forces Munich
Werner-Heisenberg-Weg 39, 8014 Neubiberg
Cables: RGF LMO
Telex: 5215800
Telephone: (89) 6004-1
Fax: (89) 6004-3560
Präsident: Jürgen Freiherr von Kruechener
Kanzler: Albrecht Anders

F. of Construction Engineering and Surveying
Dean: W. Welsch; *staff* 59 (4)
F. of Electrical Engineering
Dean: H.-R. Traukler; *staff* 85 (3)
F. of Computer Sciences
Dean: R. Auenhaus; *staff* 45 (2)
F. of Air and Space Technology
Dean: K. Marti; *staff* 97 (6)
F. of Education
Dean: A. Hoffmann; *staff* 36 (2)
F. of Social Sciences
Dean: J. Brandt; *staff* 34 (2)
F. of Economics and Organizational Sciences
Dean: K. Wilde; *staff* 43

Founded 1973 by decision of the Federal Government. Authorized 1973 by the Bavarian Ministry for Education and Culture. Responsible to the Bavarian Ministry of Education and Culture and to the Federal Ministry of Defence. Governing bodies: the Senat, composed of 10 professors, 4 other members of the academic staff, 1 member of the non-academic staff, and 3 students; the Kuratorium, composed of up to 18 members nominated by the Minister of Defence of whom 3are proposed by the Bavarian Ministry of Education and Culture. Residential facilities for academic staff and *c.* 2400 students.

Academic Year: October to June (October-December; January-March; April-June).

Admission Requirements: Secondary school certificate (Reifezeugnis) or equivalent. Students must have passed the Armed Forces officersexamination and have accepted a 12 yr engagement.

Fees: None.

Language of Instruction: German.

Degrees and Diplomas: Titles of–Diplom-Ingenieur; -Kaufmann; -Informatiker; -Wissenschaftlicher, 3-4 yrs. Doctorates in various fields.

Library: 600,000 vols.

Publication: Hochschulkurier.

Academic Staff, 1990: 425 (105)

Student Enrolment, 1990:

	Men
Of the country	2471
Of other countries	38
Total	2509

3299 **HOCHSCHULE FÜR FERNSEHEN UND FILM MÜNCHEN**
College of Television and Cinema Technology
Ohmstrasse 11, 8000 München 40
Telephone: (089) 2-38-04-0

D. of Communications Sciences
D. of Film Techniques
D. of Cinema and Television Programmes
D. of Documentary Films and Television Advertising

Founded 1967.

Academic Year: October to July (October-February; May-July).

Admission Requirements: Secondary school certificate (Abitur).

Language of Instruction: German.
Library: c. 24,000 vols.

Academic Staff: c. 20.
Student Enrolment: c. 120.

GREECE

Universities and Technical Universities

3300 ***ETHNIKON KAI KAPODISTRIAKON PANEPISTIMION ATHINON**

National and Capodistrian University of Athens
Odos Panepistimiou 30, 10679 Athinai
Telex: 223815/UNIV. GR.
Telephone: 36-14-301
Fax: 36-02145
Prytanis (Rector): Michael P. Stathopoulos (1983-91)

F. of Theology
Dean: Ilias Economou
D. of Theology
President: Konstantinos Skouteris
D. of Pastoral Theology
President: Ilias Economou; *staff* 19 (12)
F. of Law, Economics, and Political Science
Dean: George Krimpas
D. of Law
President: Ioannis Spyridakis; *staff* 83 (55)
D. of Economics
President: Konstantinos Vaitsos; *staff* 41 (13)
D. of Political Sciences and Public Administration
President: Anastasios-Ioannis Metaxos; *staff* 29 (4)
F. of Health Sciences
Dean: Konstantinos Dimopoulos
D. of Medicine
President: Constantinos Dimopoulos; *staff* 605 (16)
D. of Dentistry
President: Sotiris Sykaras *staff* 119 (26)
D. of Pharmacy
President: Evangelos Kostakis; *staff* 33
D. of Nursing
President: Loucas Sparros; *staff* 22 (3)
F. of Humanities
Dean: Ioannis Paraskevopoulos
D. of Literature
President: Panagiotis Mastrodimitris; *staff* 49 (18)
D. of History and Archaeology
President: Emmanuel Mikroyiannakis; *staff* 40 (26)
D. of Philosophy, Education, and Psychology
President: Antonios Danassis-Afendakis; *staff* 48 (19)
D. of English Language and Literature
President: Constantinos Evangelides; *staff* 27 (7)
D. of French Language and Literature
President: Ioanna Konstandoulaki-Hantzai *staff* 18 (8)
D. of German Language and Literature
President: William Benning; *staff* 6 (11)
F. of Applied Sciences
Dean: Nikolaos Simeonidis
D. of Physics
President: Pavlos Laskaridis; *staff* 102 (56)
D. of Chemistry
President Dimitrios Galanos *staff* 77 (37)
D. of Mathematics
President: Eustratios Kounias; *staff* 62 (37)
D. of Biology
President: Loucas Margaritis; *staff* 54 (21)
D. of Geology
President: Grigorios Marakis; *staff* 56 (21)
D. of Physical Education and Sport
President: Antonios Danassis-Afendakis; *staff* 33 (18)
D. of Teacher Training
President: Theodoros Exarchakos; *staff* 15 (9)
D. of Teacher Training (Nursing)
President Ioannis Papacostas *staff* 10
D. of Informatics
President: George Phylokyprou; *staff* 21

Also 2 University Hospitals and Summer Course in Modern Greek Studies.

Founded 1837 by King Otto. Became an autonomous State institution under the jurisdiction of the Ministry of Education 1932. Reorganized 1982. Governing body: the Senate. Residential facilities for 1350 students.

Arrangements for co-operation with the Universities of: Nankai; Munich; Brussels (Free); Tirana; Warsaw; Paris 6; Helsinki; Cracow; Prague; Essex; Trieste; Gent; Malta; Gröningen; Belgrade; Sofia; Moscow; Berlin (Humboldt); Seoul; Beijing; Damascus. Universidad Nacional de Educación a Distancia, Madrid.

Academic Year: September to August (September-January; February-June).

Admission Requirements: Secondary school certificate (Apolytirion Lykiou) or foreign equivalent, and entrance examination.

Fees: None.

Language of Instruction: Greek.

Degrees and Diplomas: Ptychion, Diploma, in–Theology; Law; Political Science; Economics; Literature; Philosophy, Education and Psychology; Physical Education; History and Archaeology; Byzantine and Modern Greek Studies; English; French; German; Mathematics; Physics; Chemistry; Geology; Nursing; Pharmacy; Biology, 4 yrs; Dentistry, 5 yrs; Medicine, 6yrs. Doctorates by thesis.

Library: Department libraries.

Special Facilities (Museums, etc.): Anatomical Museum; Botanical Museum; Museums of: Geology and Palaeontology; Zoology; Ore-deposits and Petrology; Criminology; Anthropology; Hygienics; Archaeology and History of Art. Museum of the History of the University. Botanical Garden; Observatory.

Academic Staff, 1989-90:

Rank	Full-time	Part-time
Kathigites (Professors)	218	–
Anaplirotes Kathigites (Associatre Professors)	152	–
Epikouri Kathigites (Assistant Professors)	712	–
Lektores (Lecturers)	499	–
Others	–	456
Total	1581	456

Student Enrolment, 1989-90:

Of the country	63011
Of other countries	460
Total	63,471

3301 ***ETHNIKON METSOVION POLYTECHNEION ATHINON**

National Technical University of Athens
Odos 28 Octovriou 42, Athinai 10682
Telex: NTUA 221682
Telephone: 36169, 36911
Fax: 3626792
Prytanis (Rector): George Noutsopoulos
Genikos Grammateus (Secretay-General): Vasilis Tzevelekas

D. of Civil Engineering
Chairman: [illegible] Efremidis; *staff* 120 (12)
D. of Mechanical Engineeering
Chairman: N. Papageorgiou; *staff* 55

D. of Electrical Engineering
Chairman: N. Ouzounoglou; *staff* 61
D. of Architecture (including Town Planning)
Chairman: D. Zivas; *staff* 110
D. of Chemical Engineering
Chairman: Th. Skoulikidis; *staff* 91
D. of Rural Surveying and Engineering
Chairman: C. Koutsopoulos; *staff* 57
D. of Mining and Metallurgical Engineering
Chairman: G. Papadimitriou; *staff* 42 (1)
D. of Naval Architecture and Marine Engineering
Chairman: I. Ioannidis
D. of General Science
Chairman: E. Aggelopoulos; *staff* 143
Computer Ce.
Head: Kiriakos Spiropoulos

Founded 1836 by decree as technical school, became technical college 1887 and university in 1929. Reorganized 1982. An autonomous institution under the supervision of the Ministry of Education. Governing body: the Senate, comprising 37 members. Residential facilities for *c.* 600 students.

Academic Year: September to August (September-February; February-June).

Admission Requirements: Secondary school certificate (Apolytirion Lykiou) or foreign equivalent, and entrance examination.

Fees: None.

Language of Instruction: Greek.

Degrees and Diplomas: Ptychion, Diploma, in Engineering, 5 yrs. Doctorate in Engineering, by thesis.

Libraries: Central Library, *c.* 150,000 vols; libraries of the departments.

Academic Staff: c. 700.

Student Enrolment: c. 5500.

3302 **PANEPISTIMION KRITIS**

University of Crete
Rethymnon and Iraklion
Telephone: (0831) 240-69

S. of Philosophy (Rethymnon)
S. of Science (Iraklion)
S. of Health Sciences (Iraklion)
D. of Education

Founded 1973. A State institution under the jurisdiction of the Ministry of Education. Governing body: the Executive Committee, composed of professors from the Universities of Athens (3), Thessa-lonika (1), Ioannina (1).

Academic Year: October to June (October-February; February-June).

Admission Requirements: Secondary school certificate.

Fees: None.

Language of Instruction: Greek.

Library: c. 125,000 vols.

Academic Staff: c. 110.

Student Enrolment: c. 1040.

3303 **POLYTECHNION KRITIS**

Technical University of Crete
P.O. Box 49, Chania 73101
Telex: 291211 TUC (CHANIA); 223029 TUC (ATHINAI)
Telephone: (01) 3604087; (0821) 58089/92
President: Thales Argyropoulos (1982-)

D. of Mechanical Engineering
D. of Chemical Engineering
D. of Electronics
D. of Mineral Resources Engineering
D. of Production and Management Engineering

Founded 1977. Admitted first students 1984. An autonomous institution under the supervision of the Ministry of Education.

Academic Year: September to August (September-January; February-June).

Admission Requirements: Secondary school certificate (Apolytirion Lykiou) or foreign equivalent, and entrance examination.

Fees: None.

Language of Instruction: Greek.

Degrees and Diplomas: Ptychion, Diploma, in Engineering, 5 yrs. Doctorate in Engineering, by thesis.

Library: Central Library, 6000 vols.

Academic Staff, 1986-87:

Rank	Full-time	Part-time
Professors	6	–
Associate Professors	4	–
Assistant Professors	3	–
Visiting Professors	–	14
Teaching Associates	3	–
Total	16	14

Student Enrolment, 1986-87:

	Men	Women	Total
Of the country	249	60	309
Of other countries	5	–	5
Total	254	60	314

3304 **PANEPISTIMION IOANNINON**

University of Ioannina
odos Domboli 30, Ioannina 45110
Telex: 6322160 PNPS
Telephone: (651) 25915
Fax: (651) 74112
Electronic mail: BITNET: pubrel@grioanun
Prytanis (Rector): Dimitris Glaros (1988-91)
Secretary-General: Lucas Papaloukas

S. of Philosophy (Literature, History and Archaeology, Philosophy, Education and Psychology)
Dean: Maria Nistazopoulou-Pelekidou; *staff* 112 (30)
S. of Science (Physics, Mathematics, Chemistry, Informatics)
Dean: Christos Philos; *staff* 132 (43)
S. of Medicine
Dean: Kostantinos Psilas; *staff* 96 (21)
D. of Teacher Training (elementary level)
Chairman: Michael Damanakis; *staff* 5 (4)
D. of Teacher Training (pre-school level)
Chairman : Georgios Ploumidis; *staff* 4
Ce. for Aquatic Biology Research
Chairman: Panayiotis Asimacopoulos
Computer Ce.
President: Thomas Bakas
Also 2 Hospitals.

Founded 1964 as a section of the Aristoteleion University of Thessalonika, acquired present status and title 1970. Reorganized 1982. A State institution of the Epirus Region. Governing bodies: the Senate, comprising 26 members; the Rector's Council comprising 5 members; the Technical Council, comprising 5 members. Some residential facilities for 470 students.

Arrangements for co-operation with the Universities of: Leeds; 'Cyril and Methodius', Veliko Turnovo; Bologna;Padova; Kuopio; Birmingham; Boston.

Academic Year: September to June (September-January; February-June).

Admission Requirements: Secondary school certificate (Apolytirion Lykiou) and entrance examination.

Fees: None.

Language of Instruction: Greek.

Degrees and Diplomas: Ptychion, Diploma, 4 yrs; Medicine, 6 yrs. Doctor of–Philosophy, Ph.D.; Science, Sc.D.

Library: Total, 280,000 vols.

Special Facilities (Museums, etc.): Folklore Museum; Ancient Greek and Byzantine Casts and Copies Museum; Observatory; Video Studio; Photography Unit; Bookshop.

Publication: Dodoni (annually) and Technical Reports.

Press or Publishing House: University of Ioannina Press.

Academic Staff, 1989-90:

Rank	Full-time	Part-time
Kathigites (Professors)	65	–
Anaplirotes Kathigites (Associate Professors)	39	–
Epikouriki Kathigites (Assistant Professors)	167	–
Lektores (Lectures)	111	–
Ediki Epistimones (Special Scientists)	–	16
Ediko Ekpedeftiko Prosopiki (Technical Staff)	102	–
Epistimoniki Synergates (Scientific Collaborators)	–	29
Total	493	45

Student Enrolment, 1989-90:

Of the country	8000
Of other countries	25
Total	8025

3305 ***UNIVERSITY OF MACEDONIA**
45 Odos Tsimiski, Thessaloniki 546 23
Telephone: (031) 279-339
Prytanis (Rector): Demetrios Papadopoulos
Genikos Grammateus (Secretary-General): Michalis Eleftheriadis

Sec. of Economics
President: Maria Negreponti-Delivanis; *staff* 35 (2)
Sec. of Business Administration (including Political Science and Computer Sciences)
President: Dimitrios Xouris; *staff* 29 (3)

Founded 1948, reorganized 1958. Previously the Graduate Industrial School of Thessaloniki. Governing bodies: the Council; the Senate.

Academic Year: September to August (September-January; February-June).

Admission Requirements: Secondary school certificate (Apolytirion Lykiou) and entrance examination.

Fees: None.

Language of Instruction: Greek.

Degrees and Diplomas: Ptychion, Diploma, 4 yrs. Doctorate by thesis.

Library: c. 20,000 vols.

Academic Staff, 1986-87:

Rank	Full-time	Part-time
Kathigites	12	–
Anaplirotes Kathigites	2	–
Epikouri Kathigites	4	–
Lektores	6	–
Voïthi Kathigiton	15	–
Epistimoniki Synergates	23	–
Idiki Epistimones	1	–
Epimelites	1	–
Episkeptes Kathigites	–	5
Total	64	5

Student Enrolment, 1986-87:

	Men	Women	Total
Of the country	1456	1295	2751
Of other countries	102	40	142
Total	1558	1335	2893

3306 ***PANEPISTIMION PATRON**
University of Patras
Patrai 261 10Spilios Papathanassopoulos
Telex: 312447 UNPA GR
Telephone: (61) 991-822
Fax: (61) 991-996
Prytanis (Rector): Alexios Lycourghiotis (1988-91)
Genikos Grammateus (Acting Secretary-General): Spilios Papathanassopoulos

S. of Natural Sciences
Dean: Ch. Zagouras; *staff* 220
S. of Engineering (Civil, Chemical, Electrical, Electronic, Mechanical; and Informatics)
Dean: Th. Kermanides; *staff* 185
S. of Health Sciences (Medicine and Pharmacy)
Dean: E. Kouvelas; *staff* 113
S. of Humanities and Social Sciences
Dean: G. Polydorides-Kontogiannopoulou; *staff* 35
D. of Economics
Chairman: N. Vernardakis; *staff* 9
I. of Computer Technology
Director: Th. Papatheodorou
I. of Chemical Engineering and High Temperature Process
Director: Xenophon Verykios; *staff* 10 (30)

Founded 1964. Reorganized 1982. An autonomous institution under the supervision of the Ministry of Education. Governing body: the Senate. Residential facilities for c. 550 students.

Arrangements for co-operation with: Université de Saint-Etienne; Ecole nationale d'Ingénieurs, Saint-Etienne; Uppsala University. Also participate in the Santander Group, and ERASMUS programme.

Academic Year: September to June (September-February; February-June).

Admission Requirements: Secondary school certificate (Apolytirion Lykiou).

Fees: None.

Language of Instruction: Greek.

Degrees and Diplomas: Ptychion, Diploma, in–Mathematics; Geology; Physics; Chemistry; Biology; Pharmacy; Education; Economics, 4 yrs; Engineering (Electrical, Chemical, Electronics, Mechanical, and Civil); Theatrical Studies, 5 yrs; Medicine, 6 yrs. Doctorates, Ph.D.

Libraries: Central Library, c. 15,000 vols; Departmental Libraries c. 120,000.

Special Facilities (Museums, etc.): Zoological Museum; Botanical Museum.

Publication: Bulletin (annually).

Academic Staff, 1989-90:

Rank	Full-time
Kathigites	121
Anaplirotes Kathigites	52
Epikouri Kathigites	143
Lektores	110
Voithi	21
Epistimoniki Synergates	72
Idiki Epistimones	25
Others	18
Total	562

Student Enrolment, 1989-90:

	Men	Women	Total
Of the country	6232	2016	8248
Of other countries	219	20	239
Total	6451	2036	8487

3307 ***PANEPISTIMIO PIREOS**
University of Piraeus
40 Karaoli and Dimitriou, Piraeus 18532
Telex: 241321
Telephone: (1) 4173159
Fax: (1) 4179064
Prytanis (Rector): Theodor Gamaletsos
Proistamenos Grammatias (Secretary-General): A. Gotsis

D. of Economics
Chairman: Styl. Sarandidis; *staff* 39 (1)
D. of Business Administration
Chairman: Charal. Kanellopoulos; *staff* 41
D. of Statistics and Actuarial Science (including Computer Sciences)
Chairman: Dim. Athanasopoulos; *staff* 27
D. of Banking and Financial Management
Chairman: P.J. Athanasopoulos; *staff* 7
D. of Maritime Studies
Chairman: Vas. Metaxas; *staff* 9
D. of Industrial and Operations Management
Chairman: Nik Blesseos; *staff* 6

Founded 1938 as private school. An autonomous State institution under the supervision of the Ministry of Education. Governing body: the Senate.

Academic Year: September to July (September-January; February-July).

Admission Requirements: Graduation from high school and entrance examination.

Fees: None.

Language of Instruction: Greek.

Degrees and Diplomas: Ptychion, Diploma, in–Economics; Statistics and Quantitative Studies; Business Administration, 4 yrs. Doctorate by thesis.

Library: c. 50,000 vols.

Publication: Spoudai (studies) (quarterly).

Academic Staff, 1989-90:

Rank	Full-time
Professors	25
Associate Professors	8
Assistant Professors	21
Lecturers	13
Teaching and Research Assistants	56
Total	123

Student Enrolment, 1989-90:

Of the country	10,629
Of other countries	24
Total	10,653

3308 ***ARISTOTELEION PANEPISTIMION THESSALONIKIS**

Aristoteleion University of Thessalonika

Thessaloniki

Telex: 0412181 AUTH GR

Telephone: (31) 99-1666, 99-1612

Fax: (31)206 138

Prytanis (Rector): Antonios Trakatellis (1988-91)

F. of Theology
Dean: B. Gioulzis
F. of Philosophy
Dean: D. Pantermalis
F. of Sciences (including Physics, Mathematics, and Pharmacy)
Dean: P.-Ch. Vassiliou
F. of Law and Economics
Dean: A. Manitakis
F. of Geotechnical Sciences (including Agriculture, Forestry, Veterinary Medicine)
F. of Health Sciences (Medicine, Dentistry, Pharmacy)
F. of Technology
Dean: M. Pappadopoulos
F. of Fine Arts
Dean: D. Giannou
S. of Physical Education and Athletics
President: I. Mouratidis
S. of Teacher Training (pre-school level)
President: C. Erangos
Also 4 Hospitals, Central Hospital and Courses for Foreign Students (Modern Greek).

Founded 1925. The university is an autonomous institution under the supervision of the Ministry of Education. Financed by the State. Governing bodies: the Academic Senate; the Rectors Council. Residential facilities for students.

Arrangements for co-oparetion with institutions in: Bulgaria, Canada, Germany, United Kingdom, France, Iraq, Poland, USA, USSR. Also participates in the Coimbra Group.

Academic Year: September to June (September-January; February-June).

Admission Requirements: Secondary school certificate (Apolytirion Lykiou) or recognized foreign equivalent, and entrance examination.

Fees (Drachmas): Foreign students, 54,000-72,000 per annum.

Language of Instruction: Greek.

Degrees and Diplomas: Diplomas and doctorates in all faculties.

Library: Central Library, 2,000,000 vols.

Special Facilities (Museums, etc.): 'Telloglou' Foundation Museum; Art Gallery; Education Centre.

Publication: Academic reports of each faculty (annually).

Academic Staff, 1989:

Rank	Full-time
Professores	335
Associate Professors	243
Assistant Professors	662
Lecturers	465
Total	1735

Student Enrolment: c. 62,000.

3309 **DIMOKRITION PANEPISTIMION THRAKIS**

Democritus University of Thrace

Komotini 69100

Telex: 462205 DUTH GR

Telephone: (10531) 26-111

Fax: (0531) 26-660

Prytanis (Rector): Evangelos Galoussis (1988-91)

Proïstamenos Grammateus (Secretary-General): Stephanos Mourouzis

F. of Law
President: Krateros Ioannou; *staff* 38 (3)
F. of Engineering (Xanthi)
Dean: Vassilios Stephanis; *staff* 55
D. of Civil Engineering
President: Konstantinos Sideris; *staff* 33
D. of Electrical Engineering
President: Ioannis Yakinthos; *staff* 35
F. of Medicine (Alexandroupolis)
President: Konstantinos Simopoulos; *staff* 47
D. of Physical Education and Sport
President: Yannis Panoussis; *staff* 8 (5)
D. of Educational Sciences (primary level)
President: Dim. Panagiotakopoulos; *staff* 4
D. of Educational Sciences (pre-school level)
President: Georgios Kartalis; *staff* 3
Also General Hospital in Alexandroupoli.

Founded 1974. An autonomous institution under the supervision of the Ministry of Education. Governing bodies: the Senate; the Rectorial Council. Residential facililties for students.

Participates in the ERASMUS programme.

Academic Year: September to August (October-January; February-May).

Admission Requirements: Secondary school certificate (Apolytirion Lykiou).

Fees: None.

Language of Instruction: Greek.

Degrees and Diplomas: Ptychion, Diploma, in–Law; Physical Education and Sprt; Primary and Infant School Education, 4 yrs; Engineering, 5 yrs; Medicine, 6 yrs.

Library: Faculty libraries, 113,950 vols.

Press or Publishing House: Printing Office of the University.

Academic Staff, 1989-90:

Rank	Full-time
Kathigites	48
Anaplirotes Kathigites	16
Epikouri Kathigites	40
Lektores	64
Total	168

Student Enrolment, 1989-90:

	Men	Women	Total
Of the country	3782	3032	6814

3310 **PANTEION UNIVERSITY OF SOCIAL AND POLITICAL SCIENCES**

Leoforos A. Syngrou 136, Athinai 17671

Telex: 224296 PSPE

Telephone: 92-20-100

Fax: 92-23-100

Prytanis (Rector): George Contogeorgis (1987-90)

Proistamene Grammateus (Secretary-General): Maria Varella

D. of Political Science and International Studies
President: D. Constas
D. of Public Administration
President: G. Stamatis
D. of Sociology
President: D. Tsaousis
D. of Communication and Mass Media Studies
Chairman: G. Contogeorgis
D. of Urban and Regional Development
President: N. Consolas
D. of Social Anthropology, Geography and Politics
Chairman: D. Tsaousis
General D. of Law
President: D. Spinellis
D. of Psychology
I. of Regional Development
President: N. Consolas

I. of International Relations
President: D. Constas
Ce. for Political Research
Ce. for International Affairs
Ce. for Social Morphology and Social Politics
Ce. for Criminology
Ce. for Research of Greek Modern Society
Ce. for the Study of Ancient Greek and Hellenistic Law
Ce. for Research of State Politics

Founded 1930 as private school, acquired present status 1937 as a State institution. Reorganized 1983 and acquired 5 new departments and present title 1989. Governing bodies: the Senate; the General Assembly. Residential facilities for students.

Arrangements in co-operation with: Free University of Brussels; Catholic University of Louvain-la-Neuve.

Participates in the ERASMUS programme.

Academic Year: September to August (September-January; February-June).

Admission Requirements: Secondary school certificate (Apolytirion Lykiou) and entrance examination.

Language of Instruction: Greek.

Degrees and Diplomas: Diplomas in–Political Science and International Studies; Sociology; Public Administration, 4 yrs. Diplomas, 4yrs. Doctorate, by thesis.

Library: Central Library, 40,000 vols.

Publication: University Newspaper.

Academic Staff, 1989-90:

Rank	Full-time
Kathigites	25
Anaplirotes Kathigites	21
Epikouri Kathigites	42
Lektores	34
Voithi	41
Scientific Collaborators	10
Scientists	3
Total	176

Student Enrolment, 1989-90:

	Men	Women	Total
Of the country	2750	3738	6488

3311 **IKONOMIKON PANEPISTIMION ATHINON (ASOEE)**
Athens University of Economics and Business (ASOEE)
Odos Patission 76, Athinai 10434
Telex: 2253 63 ASOE GR
Telephone: (1) 8211-124
Fax: (1) 8226-204
Prytanis (Rector): Andreas A. Kintis (1989-92)
Genikos Grammateus (Secretary-General): Sotiris Benos

D. of Economics
Chairman: Kaprianos Prodromidis; *staff* 17 (2)
D. of Business Administration
Chairman: Athanasios Stathopoulos; *staff* 22 (2)
D. of Statistics
Chairwoman: Evdokia Xekalaki; *staff* 8
D. of International and European Economic Studies
Chairman: Theodore Georgakopoulos; *staff* 3
D. of Management and Marketing
Chairman: Gregory Prastacos; *staff* 9 (2)
D. of Informatics
Chairman: Panayiotis Miliotis; *staff* 18 (11)
Ce. of Economic Research
Chairman: Athanasios Skouras

Founded 1920. A State institution under the supervision of the Ministry of Education. Governing body: the Rector's Council.

Arrangements in co-operation with: University of Aston-in-Birmingham; European Business School in Strasbourg; Fachhochschule Osnabruck. Participates in the ERASMUS programme.

Academic Year: September to May (September-January; February-June including the exams).

Admission Requirements: Secondary school certificate (Apolytirion Lykiou) and entrance examination.

Fees: None.

Language of Instruction: Greek.

Degrees and Diplomas: Ptychion, Diploma, in–Business Administration; Economics, Informatics, 4 yrs. Metaptychiako Diploma, Master in–Business Administration; Economics, a further 2 yrs. Didaktoriko, Doctorate by research.

Library: c. 60,000 vols.

Academic Staff, 1989-90:

Rank	Full-time
Kathigites (Professors)	39
Anaplirotes Kathigites (Associate Professors)	6
Epikouri Kathigites (Assistant Professors)	21
Lektores (Lecturers)	15
Episkeptes Kathigites (Visiting Professors)	2
Total	83

Student Enrolment, 1989-90: 9650.

Other Institutions

Professional Education

3312 **ANOTATI GEOPONIKI SCHOLI ATHINON**
Agricultural College of Athens
Iero Odos 75, Votanikos, Athinai 301
Telephone: (01) 3461-944

Agriculture

Founded 1920. Under the jurisdiction of the Ministry of Education. Financed by the State.

Academic Year: September to August (October-January; February-June).

Admission Requirements: Secondary school certificate and entrance examination.

Fees: None.

Language of Instruction: Greek.

Degrees and Diplomas: Ptychion, Diploma, 5 yrs. Doctorate by thesis.

Library: c. 11,000 vols.

Academic Staff: c. 200.

Student Enrolment: c. 990.

3313 **ANOTATI SCHOLI KALON TECHNON**
School of Fine Art
Patission 42, Athinai 106 82
Telephone: 3616930
Fax: 3601 098
Prytanis (Rector): Panayotis Tetsis (1989-91)
Genikos Grammateus (Secretary-General): Helen Fostiropoulou

Fine Arts (including Theoretical Studies of Art)

Founded 1836, acquired present status 1930. Under the jurisdiction of the Ministry of Education. Annexes at Hydra, Mykonos, Delphi, and Lesbos. Some residential facilities for students.

Participates in the ERASMUS programme.

Academic Year: September to June.

Admission Requirements: Secondary school certificate (Apolytirion Lykiou).

Fees (Drachmas): foreign students, 54,000-108,000 per annum.

Language of Instruction: Greek.

Degrees and Diplomas: Diploma in–Painting; Sculpture; Engraving, 5 yrs.

Library: 15,000 vols.

Academic Staff, 1989-90:

Rank	Full-time	Part-time
Kathigites	11	1
Anaplirotes Kathigites	5	–
Epikouri Kathigites	4	–
Lektores	5	–
Idiki Epistimones	–	22
Idiki Technites	–	10
Total	25	33

Student Enrolment, 1989-90:

	Men	Women	Total
Of the country	166	243	409*

*Also 14 foreign students.

GUADELOUPE

3314 **UNIVERSITÉ DES ANTILLES ET DE LA GUYANE**
Boulevard Légitimus, B.P. 771, 97173 Pointe-à-Pitre Cedex
Telex: UNIVAG 919739 GLV
Telephone: 82-38-22
Président: Philippe Saint-Cyr (1982-87)
Secrétaire général: Raphaël Bourdy

Ut. of Letters and Human Sciences (Martinique)
Ut. of Exact and Natural Sciences
Ut. of Law and Economics
Ut. of Medicine
Ut. of Law and Economics (Martinique)
Science Research Ce.
Criminology Research Ce.
Regional Economic Research Ce.
Creole Studies Research Ce.
Ibero-American Research Ce.

Founded 1970 as Centre Universitaire, incorporating previously existing university centres in Guadeloupe and Martinique. Became university 1982. Attached to the Académie de Bordeaux. Financially supported by the Ministry of Education. Governing body: the Conseil d'administration. Residential facilities for students.

Academic Year: October to June (October-December; January-March; April-June).

Admission Requirements: Secondary school certificate (baccalauréat) or foreign equivalent, or special entrance examination.

Language of Instruction: French.

Degrees and Diplomas: Capacité en Droit, 2 yrs. Diplôme d'études universitaires générales (D.E.U.G.) in–Law, Economics, Science, Letters and Human Sciences, 2 yrs; Licence–en Droit, law; ès Sciences économiques, 1 yr after D.E.U.G.; Diplôme d'études universitaires scientifiques et techniques (D.E.U.S.T.) in Gestion Informatique, 2 yrs. Maîtrise, 1 yr after Licence. Diplôme d'études approfondies (D.E.A.) in–Anthropology; Pathology; Diplôme d'études supérieures spécialisées (D.E.S.S.) in Foreign Trade, 1-2 yrs after Maîtrise. Also Diplôme universitaire de 2e cycle de Développement agricole Caraïbe, 2 yrs.

Library: c. 9500 vols.

Publications: Bulletin d'Information (monthly); Bulletin de liaison des chercheurs.

Academic Staff: c. 130.

GUATEMALA

3315 **UNIVERSIDAD FRANCISCO MARROQUÍN**

6 Calle Final, Zona 10, Guatemala City
Cables: ufama guatemala
Telephone: (502-2) 346886
Fax: (502-2) 346896
Rector: Fernando Monterroso
Secretario-General: Juan F. Bendfeldt

S. of Economics and Business Administration
Dean: Fritz Thomas; *staff* 3 (15)
S. of Law
Dean: Eduardo Mayora A.; *staff* 1 (24)
S. of Architecture
Dean: Augusto de León; *staff* 3 (20)
S. of Medicine
Dean: Rodolfo Herrera Llerandi; *staff* 24 (33)
S. of Dentistry
Dean: Ramiro Alfaro; *staff* 1 (33)
D. of Education, History and Communication
Director: F. Felix Serrano; *staff* – (34)
S. of Systems Engineering and Computer Sciences
Dean: Eduardo Suger; *staff* 9 (29)
I. of Public Accounting and Auditing
Director: Taufic Aranky; *staff* 1 (27)
Graduate S. of Economics and Business Administration
Dean: Ricardo Alvarado; *staff* 2 (14)
D. of Psychology
Director: Luis A. Recinos; *staff* 2 (25)
Graduate S. of Social Sciences
Director: Armando de la Torre; *staff* 1 (4)
D. of Theology
Dean: Felix Serrano; *staff* 1 (7)
D. of Philosophy
Director: Enrique Morales; *staff* 1 (16)
Extension D.
Director: Salvador Aguado-Andreut; *staff* 1 (2)
D. of Teacher Training (secondary level)
Director: Salvador Aguado-Andreut; *staff* 1 (17)
D. of Political Studies
Director: Jesús Amurrio; *staff* 3 (15)
I. of Art and P. in Scientific Extension
Director: Geraldina Baca; *staff* – (3)
D. of Religious Science
Director: F. Eduardo Aguirre O.; *staff* – (25)
History of Art D.
Director: Josefina A. Rodríguez; *staff* – (3)
Also Teaching Hospital.

Founded 1971. A private institution financed by tuition fees and donations. Governing bodies: the Board of Trustees, comprising 50 members; the Academic Council.

Arrangements for co-operation with: Texas A&M University; Baylor College of Medicine, Houston; University of Florida, Gainesville.

Academic Year: January to November (January-May; July-November).

Admission Requirements: Secondary school certificate (bachillerato) or foreign equivalent, and entrance examination.

Language of Instruction: Spanish.

Degrees and Diplomas: Licenciado in–Economics; Business Administration; Psychology; Theology, 4 yrs; Law, 5 yrs. Professional titles of–Arquitecto; Abogado y Notario, law, 5 yrs; Médico; Cirujano Dentista, 7 yrs. Degree of Magister Artium in–Psychology; Economics; Business Administration; Social Sciences; Family Medicine, a further 2 yrs. Doctorate in Psychology, 2 yrs after Magister Artium. Also teaching qualification, secondary level, 3 yrs.

Libraries: Central Library, *c.* 25,000 vols; Theology, *c.* 50,000.

Special Facilities (Museums, etc.): Museo Popol-Vuh (Mayan and Pre-Columbian pieces; Spanish Colonial Art; Folklore).

Academic Staff, 1990: 63 (286).

Student Enrolment, 1990:

Men	Women	Total
2472	2030	4502*

*Including 316 foreign students. Also 605 external students.

3316 **UNIVERSIDAD 'MARIANO GÁLVEZ'**

'Mariano Gálvez' University
3a Avenida 9-00, Zona 2, Apartado 1811, Guatemala
Telephone: 53-43-39
Rector: Rolando Torres Moss
Secretario General: Adalberto Santizo Román

F. of Economics (including Business Administration and Accountancy)
Dean: René A. Orellano
F. of Law and Social Sciences
Dean: Fernando A. Bonilla Martínez

Founded 1966. A private institution recognized by the State. Governing body: the Consejo Directivo.

Academic Year: February to November (February-June; July-November).

Admission Requirements: Secondary school certificate (bachillerato) or foreign equivalent.

Fees (Quetzales): 50-70 per semester.

Language of Instruction: Spanish.

Degrees and Diplomas: Licenciado in–Law and Social Sciences; Economics; Business Administration, 5-6 yrs. Professional title of Ingeniería civil, 6 yrs. Teaching qualification, secondary level, in Plastic Arts, 4 yrs. Also technical diplomas, 2 yrs.

Library: 12,000 vols.

Academic Staff, 1986-87: 1 (155).

Student Enrolment, 1986-87:

	Men	Women	Total
Of the country	3000	1000	4000

3317 **UNIVERSIDAD RAFAEL LANDÍVAR**

Vista Hermosa 111, Zona 16, Guatemala
Cables: Uniland
Telephone: 69215/3
Rector: Luis Manresa Formosa (1981-87)

F. of Economics (including Business Administration)
F. of Humanities (including Education, Social Work, and Tourism)
F. of Law and Social Sciences
F. of Industrial Engineering
F. of Architecture
F. of Agriculture
I. of Political and Social Sciences
S. of Teacher Training (secondary level)
I. of Psychology
Ce. for Social Development

Founded 1961, a private catholic institution recognized by the State. Achieved status of independent university 1966. Governing bodies: the Consejo Directivo, comprising 15 members; the Consejo Superior Universitario.

Arrangements for co-operation with the University of Tulane.

Fees (Quetzales): Registration, 20; tuition, *c.* 80 per month.

Language of Instruction: Spanish.

Degrees and Diplomas: Licenciado, 5 yrs. Professional title of Técnico in various fields, 3 yrs. Degree of Maestría, 2 yrs. Doctorado, 2 yrs. Teaching qualification, secondary level, 4 yrs.

Library: *c.* 42,980 vols.

Publication: Revistas.

Academic Staff: *c.* 20 (870).

Student Enrolment: *c.* 7560.

3318 ***UNIVERSIDAD DE SAN CARLOS DE GUATEMALA**

University of San Carlos of Guatemala
Ciudad Universitaria, Zona 12, Guatemala
Telephone: 760790/4
Rector: Roderico Segura Trujillo (1986-90)
Secretario General: Hector Adolfo Cifuentes Mendoza

F. of Agriculture
Dean: Anibal Bartolomé Martínez; *staff* 74 (33)
F. of Economics (including Business Administration and Accountancy)
Dean: Gilberto Batres Paz; *staff* 22 (676)
F. of Architecture
Dean: Francisco Chavarria Smeaton; *staff* 33 (138)
F. of Law and Social Sciences
Dean: Cipriano Soto Tobar; *staff* 22 (207)
F. of Medicine
Dean: Humberto Aguilar Staackmann; *staff* 136 (214)
F. of Chemistry and Pharmacy
Dean: Clemencia Galvez de Avila; *staff* 61 (112)
F. of Humanities
Dean: Eleazar A. Monroy Mejia; *staff* 51 (66)
F. of Engineering
Dean: Jorge Mario Morales Gonzáles; *staff* 24 (481)
F. of Medicine and Animal Husbandry
Dean: Juan Pablo Morataya Cuevas; *staff* 60 (32)
F. of Dentistry
Dean: Norman Aquino Estebán; *staff* 65 (37)
Also Regional Centres in : Cobán, Chiquimula, Escuintla, Mazatenango, Jalapa, San Marcos, Santa Elena, Monterrico, Huehuetenango, and Izabal.

Founded 1676 by royal decree of Charles II of Spain. Became an autonomous institution 1945. Governing body: the Consejo Superior Universitario, comprising members of academic staff, students, and members of non-academic staff.

Academic Year: January to December (January-June; July-December).

Admission Requirements: Secondary school certificate (bachillerato) or recognized foreign equivalent.

Fees (Quetzales): 60 per annum; foreign students, 800-2700.

Language of Instruction: Spanish

Degrees and Diplomas: Licenciado in–Philosophy; Classical Languages and Literature; Spanish Language and Literature; Education; Library Science; Sociology; International Relations; Applied Mathematics; Physics; Law; Social Sciences; Journalism; History; Anthropology; Archaeology, 5 yrs. Degree of Maestro, a further 1-2 yrs. Professional titles of–Bibliotecario, library science; Periodista profesional, journalism; Trabajador social, social work; Técnico (various fields), 3 yrs; Nutricionista, 4 yrs; Arquitecto; Contador público y Auditor, accountancy; Economista; Administrador de Empresas, business administration; Politicólogo; Químico; Químico Farmacéutico; Químico Biólogo; Biólogo, 5 yrs; Psicólogo; Médico y Cirujano, 6 yrs. Doctorado. Also teaching qualifications, secondary level, 3 ½ yrs.

Library: Central Library, *c.* 235,000 vols.

Special Facilities (Museums, etc.): Jardín Botánico; Historia Natural.

Academic Staff, 1990: 3539.

Student Enrolment, 1990: 64,435.

3319 **UNIVERSIDAD DEL VALLE DE GUATEMALA**

Apartado postal 82, Guatemala
Cables: Uvalle Guatemala
Telephone: 692563
Rector: Miguel Angel Canga-Argüelles (1985-)
Secretario General: Daniel Contreras

F. of Science and Humanities
Dean: Jorge Antillón; *staff* 11 (110)
F. of Social Sciences (including Psychology)
Dean: Daniel Contreras; *staff* 1 (21)
F. of Education
Dean: Gloria J. Aguilar; *staff* 2 (60)
I. of Educational Research
Dean: Jorge Arias de Blois; *staff* 11 (18)
Also 1 university college.

Founded 1961 as a private institution under the patronage of Asociación del Colegio Americano de Guatemala. Formally recognized 1966. Governing bodies: the Consejo Fiduciarios; the Consejo Administrativo.

Academic Year: January to November (January-May; June-July; August-November).

Admission Requirements: Secondary school certificate (bachillerato) or foreign equivalent, and entrance examination.

Fees (Quetzales): 60 per annum; foreign students, 800-2700

Language of Instruction: Spanish.

Degrees and Diplomas: Licenciado, 5-6 yrs. Maestría, a further 1-2 yrs. Doctorate, Dr., a further 1-2 yrs and thesis. Teaching qualifications, 4 yrs.

Library: 26,300 vols.

Academic Staff, 1986-87:

Rank	Full-time	Part-time
Profesores	26	160
Profesores Auxiliares	–	76
Correctores	–	26
Total	26	262

Student Enrolment, 1986-87:

	Men	Women	Total
Of the country	520	780	1300
Of other countries	64	17	81
Total	584	797	1381

GUINEA

3320 **UNIVERSITÉ DE CONAKRY**
B.P. 1147, Conakry
Telephone: 46-16-65
Recteur: Abou Sompаré
Secrétaire: Aly Oulare

F. of Biology
Dean: Paul M. Conde; *staff* 61
F. of Chemistry
Dean: Sekou A. Conde; *staff* 29
F. of Law and Economics
Dean: Ansoumane Camara; *staff* 20
F. of Electrical Engineering (including Electronics and Radio)
Dean: Aboulaye Diakite; *staff* 33
F. of Civil Engineering
Dean: Mamady Touré; *staff* 18
F. of Mechanical Engineering
Dean: Alpha Lamine Sylla; *staff* 18
F. of Medicine
Dean: Madigbe Fofana; *staff* 48
F. of Pharmacy
Dean: Almamy Soumah; *staff* 25
F. of Natural Sciences
Dean: Sayon Oularé; *staff* 75
F. of Social Sciences
Dean: Abdoul Goudoussi Diallo; *staff* 58

Founded 1962 as Institut Polytechnique, acquired present status and title 1984. A State institution under the supervision of the Ministry of Education.

Arrangements for co-operation with: Institute of Electrical Engineering, Leningrad; Institute of Technology, Leningrad; University of Leningrad; Institute of Civil Engineering, Leningrad; University of Cologne; University of Lille I; University of Bordeaux III.

Academic Year: October to June (October-January; February-June).

Admission Requirements: Competitive examination following secondary school certificate (baccalauréat).

Fees: None.

Language of Instruction: French.

Degrees and Diplomas: Licence. Diplôme d'études supérieures. Maîtrise.

Library: Central Library.

Publications: Problèmes actuels de la Médecine en Guinée (annually); Electron (quarterly).

Academic Staff, 1986-87: 393.

Student Enrolment, 1986-87:

	Men	Women	Total
Of the country	3727	661	4388
Of other countries	10	7	17
Total	3737	668	4405

3321 **UNIVERSITÉ DE KANKAN**
B.P. 203, Kankan
Telephone: 20-93
Recteur: Sekou Konaté (1985-)
Secrétaire: Ouo-Ouo Pivi

F. of Social Sciences
Dean: Aboubacar Cissé; *staff* 25
F. of Natural Sciences
Dean: Aboubacar Thiam; *staff* 44

Founded 1963 as school, became Institut polytechnique 1967 and acquired present status and title 1984. A Stateinstitution under the supervision of the Ministry of Education. Residential facilities for students.

Academic Year: October to June (October-December; January-March; April-June).

Admission Requirements: Competitive entrance examination following secondary school certificate (baccalauréat).

Fees: None.

Language of Instruction: French.

Degrees and Diplomas: Diplôme d'études supérieures.

Academic Staff, 1986-87: 61 (8).

Student Enrolment, 1986-87:

	Men	Women	Total
Of the country	892	59	951

3322 **INSTITUT DES SCIENCES AGRO-ZOOTECHNIQUES 'VALÉRY GISCARD D'ESTAING'**
Faranah
Telephone: 81-08-59
Directeur général: Bourah Camara (1979-)
Secrétaire: Abdoul Gadiri Diallo

Agriculture and Animal Husbandry (including Veterinary Medicine,) Forestry, and Rural Engineering

Founded 1978. A State institution under the supervision of the Ministry of Education. Residential facilities for academic staff and students.

Academic Year: October to June (October-December; January-March; April-June).

Admission Requirements: Competitive examination following secondary school certificate (baccalauréat).

Fees: None.

Language of Instruction: French.

Degrees and Diplomas: Diplôme d'Ingénieur, 5 yrs.

Library: 1816 vols.

Academic Staff, 1986-87: 88 (10).

Student Enrolment, 1986-87:

	Men	Women	Total
Of the country	244	24	268

3323 **ÉCOLE NATIONALE D'AGRICULTURE DE MACENTA**
Macenta

Agriculture

3324 **ECOLE NATIONALE D'AGRICULTURE DE TOLO**
B.P. 29, Mamou
Directeur: Alpaba Bayo (1983-)

Agriculture (including Animal Husbandry)

Founded 1932, acquired present status and title 1974. Residential facilities for academic staff and 450 students.

Academic Year: October to June (October-January; January-June).

Admission Requirements: Secondary school certificate (baccalauréat) and entrance examination.

Fees: None.

Language of Instruction: French.

Degrees and Diplomas: Diplôme, 3 yrs.

Library: School Library

Academic Staff, 1989-90: 48.

Student Enrolment, 1986-87:

	Men	Women	Total
Of the country	277	23	300

3325 **ÉCOLE NATIONALE FORESTIÈRE DE SÉRÉDOU**
Macenta

Forestry

Founded 1971.

3326 **ÉCOLE NATIONALE DES POSTES ET TÉLÉCOMMUNICATIONS**
Conakry

Telecommunication Engineering

Founded 1970.

3327 **ÉCOLE NATIONALE DE LA SANTÉ**
Kindia

Health Sciences
Founded 1966.

3328 **ÉCOLE NATIONAL DE LA SANTÉ**
Labé

3329 **ÉCOLE NATIONALE VÉTÉRINAIRE**
Mamou

Veterinary Medicine
Founded 1972.

3330 **ÉCOLE NORMALE SUPÉRIEURE DE MANÉAH**
B.P. 795, Conakry
Directeur: Amadou Tidjane Diallo (1984-)
Secrétaire: Mohamed Lamine Sanoh

Teacher Training
Founded 1979. A State institution under the supervision of the Ministry of Education. Residential facilities for academic staff and students.

Arrangements for co-operation with: University of Paris X; University of Rennes II; University of Montreal; Ecoles normales supérieures, Meknès and Takaddoum-Rabat.

Academic Year: October to July (October-January; February-July).

Admission Requirements: Competitive entrance examination following secondary school certificate (baccalauréat).

Fees: None.

Language of Instruction: French.

Degrees and Diplomas: Maîtrise–ès Sciences; ès Lettres; ès Sciences sociales, 5 yrs.

Library: c. 5000 vols.

Academic Staff, 1986-87: 57 (9).

Student Enrolment, 1986-87:

	Men	Women	Total
Of the country	230	24	254
Of other countries	2	–	2
Total	232	24	256

3331 **ÉCOLE NORMALE SUPÉRIEURE D'ENSEIGNEMENT TECHNIQUE**
B.P. 592, Conakry
Directeur: Taliby Kaba (1986-)

Teacher Training (Technical)
Founded 1980 as Institut de Formation des Professeurs d'Enseignement technique, acquired present status and title 1984.

Academic Year: October to June (October-December; January-March; April-June).

Language of Instruction: French.

Degrees and Diplomas: Diplôme, 3 yrs.

Library: 2259 vols.

Academic Staff, 1986-87: 41 (1).

Student Enrolment, 1986-87:

	Men	Women	Total
Of the country	296	12	308

HAITI

Universities

3332 **UNIVERSITÉ D'ÉTAT D'HAÏTI**
State University of Haïti
25-35, rue Bonne Foi, Boite postale 2279, Port-au-Prince
Telephone: 2-3210; 2-1146

F. of Law and Economics
F. of Sciences
F. of Humanities
Co-ordinator: Lucien Jn-Bernard; *staff* – (60)
F. of Dentistry
Dean: André Cantave; *staff* – (31)
F. of Medicine and Pharmacy
Dean: Gérard Charlier
F. of Agriculture and Veterinary Science
Dean: Fritz Michel; *staff* – (73)
F. of Ethnology
Co-ordinator: Chavannes Douyon *staff* – (30)
Teacher Training S.
I. of Business Administration and International Studies
Director: Herntz Larsen
I. of African Research and Studies
Dean: Charles P. Romain; *staff* – (12)
Ce. for Applied Linguistics
Director: Pierre Vernet; *staff* – (12)

Founded 1944 by decree incorporating or affiliating existing institutions of higher education. Individual faculties and schools are responsible to the relevant Ministries and Government Departments. Confirmed as State institution by decree 1960. Financed by the State.

Academic Year: October to July.

Admission Requirements: Secondary school certificate (baccalauréat), and competitive entrance examination.

Fees (Gourdes): 200-500.

Language of Instruction: French.

Degrees and Diplomas: Licence–ès Sciences sociales et administratives; ès Sciences anthropologiques, 3 yrs; Licence–en Linguistique; en Etudes des Recherches africaines, afro-américaine et Caraibéenne, 3yrs;en Droit, law; en Lettres; ès Sciences naturelles; en Histoire; en Géographie; en Mathématiques; en Gestion; en Diplomatie; en Sciences comptables, accountancy, 5 yrs. Licence et Maîtrise–en Psychologie; en Sociologie; en Communications; en Anthropologie, 4yrs. Diplôme–d'Ingénieur en Agronomie; d'Ingénieur civil, 5 yrs; d'Ingénieur architecte, 3 yrs, plus 1 yr practical work.

Library: University Library, *c.* 7000 vols.

Publications: Université d'Haïti Bulletin; INAGHEI actuel.

Student Enrolment, 1990: 6269.

Other Institutions

Public Establishments

3333 **FACULTÉ DE DROIT DU CAP-HAÏTIEN**
Cap-Haïtien

Law

Founded 1867 as Ecole libre de Droit, recognized by the State 1947, acquired present title, attached to the Université d'Etat d'Haïti 1969. Operated under the supervision of the Department of Education and the State University, but enjoying autonomy in the appointment of academic staff and in financial matters.

Academic Year: October to July (October-February; February-July).

Admission Requirements: Secondary school certificate (baccalauréat).

Language of Instruction: French.

Degrees and Diplomas: Licence en Droit, 4 yrs.

Academic Staff: c. – (10).

Student Enrolment: c. 30.

3334 **ÉCOLE DE DROIT DES CAYES**
Cayes

Law

Founded 1894 as Ecole libre de Droit. Acquired present title 1969. A private institution under the supervisionof the Department of Educa-tion and the State University.

Academic Year: October to July (October-January; March-April).

Admission Requirements: Secondary school certificate (baccalauréat).

Fees: None.

Language of Instruction: French.

Degrees and Diplomas: Licence en Droit, 4 yrs.

Library: c. 150 vols.

Academic Staff: c. 10.

Student Enrolment: c. 20.

3335 **ÉCOLE DE DROIT DE GONAÏVES**
Gonaïves

Law

Founded 1922 as Ecole libre de Droit. Closed between 1929 and 1947. Acquired present title 1969. A private institution under the supervision of the Department of Education and the State University.

Academic Year: October to July (October-February; March-July).

Admission Requirements: Secondary school certificate (baccalauréat).

Language of Instruction: French.

Degrees and Diplomas: Licence en Droit, 4 yrs.

Library: c. 200 vols.

Academic Staff: c. 10.

Student Enrolment: c. 50.

3336 **ÉCOLE DE DROIT DE JACMEL**
Rue Seymour Pradel 23, Port-au-Prince
Telephone: (509) 88-2090
Directeur: Louis A. Lafontant
Secrétaire: Jean Massénat

Law

Founded 1981. A private institution under the direct supervision of the Ministry of Justice, the State University, and the National Education Departement. Governing body: the Board of Trustees.

Academic Year: October to July (October-December; January-March; April-July).

Admission Requirements: Secondary school certificate (baccalauréat).

Fees (Gourdes): 450 per ammum.

Language of Instruction: French.

Degrees and Diplomas: Licence, 4 yrs.

3337 **ÉCOLE D'INFIRMIÈRES DU CAP-HAÏTIEN**
Hôpital Justinien, Cap-Haïtien

Nursing

Founded 1952 and attached to the Université d'Etat d'Haïti. Under the jurisdiction of the Department of Public Health. Financed by the State.

Academic Year: October to July (October-December; January-March; April-July).

Admission Requirements: Secondary school certificate.

Language of Instruction: French.

Degrees and Diplomas: Diplôme d'Infirmière licenciée, 3 yrs.

Academic Staff: c. 5 (20).

Student Enrolment: c. 50.

3338 **ÉCOLE D'INFIRMIÈRES S.O.D. DES CAYES**
Cayes

Nursing

Founded 1958 and attached to the Université d'Etat d'Haïti. Under the jurisdiction of the Department of Public Health. Financed by the State.

Academic Year: October to July (October-December; January-March; April-July).

Admission Requirements: Secondary school certificate.

Language of Instruction: French.

Degrees and Diplomas: Diplôme d'Infirmière licenciée, 3 yrs.

Library: c. 500 vols.

Academic Staff: c. 20.

Student Enrolment: c. 50.

3339 **ÉCOLE NATIONALE D'INFIRMIÈRES SIMONE O. DUVALIER**

Port-au-Prince

Nursing

Attached to the Université d'Etat d'Haïti.

Academic Year: October to July (October-December; January-March; April-July).

Admission Requirements: Secondary school certificate.

Language of Instruction: French.

Degrees and Diplomas: Diplôme d'Infirmière licenciée, 3 yrs.

Private Establishments

3340 **INSTITUT DES HAUTES ÉTUDES ÉCONOMIQUES ET COMMERCIALES**

P.O. Box T, Port-au-Prince
Cables: Ihece
Telephone: 5-4581

Commerce
Economics

Founded 1961.

Academic Year: October to June (October-December; January-March; April-June).

Admission Requirements: Secondary school certificate (baccalauréat).

Language of Instruction: French.

Degrees and Diplomas: Licence ès Sciences commerciales et économiques, 4 yrs.

Library: c. 1000 vols.

Publication: Bulletin.

Academic Staff: c. 20.

Student Enrolment: c. 100 (Also c. 30 external students).

3341 **INSTITUT INTERNATIONAL D'ÉTUDES UNIVERSITAIRES**

c/o Fondation Haïtienne de Développement, 106 avenue Christophe, Port-au-Prince

3342 **INSTITUT POLYTECHNIQUE**

61, Ruelle Nazon, Port-au-Prince

3343 **INSTITUT SUPÉRIEUR DES SCIENCES ÉCONOMIQUES ET POLITIQUES**

Port-au-Prince

Economics
Political Science

3344 **INSTITUT SUPÉRIEUR TECHNIQUE D'HAÏTI**

24, avenue du Chili, P.O. Box 992, Port-au-Prince
Cables: insutec
Telephone: 245-87

Civil Engineering, Architecture, Surveying

Founded 1962 as Ecole privée de Génie. Reorganized and adopted present title 1963. Recognized by the State1965. Degrees and diplomas officially recognized 1966.

Academic Year: October to July (October-March; March-July).

Admission Requirements: Secondary school certificate (baccalauréat).

Language of Instruction: French.

Degrees and Diplomas: Diplôme–d'Ingénieur civil; d'Ingénieur-Architecte, 4 yrs. Diplôme–de Topographe; de Technicien en Réfrigération; Dessinateur en Bâtiment, 1 yr. Diplôme de Technicien en Electronique, 2 yrs.

Library: c. 500 vols.

Academic Staff: c. 20.

Student Enrolment: c. 450.

3345 **INSTITUT DE TECHNOLOGIE ÉLECTRONIQUE D'HAÏTI**

159, rue de l'Enterrement, Port-au-Prince
Telex: 203-0001
Telephone: 2-2932

Electronic Technology

Founded 1977. A private institution recognized by the State.

Arrangements for co-operation with Florida International University.

Academic Year: October to June (October-February; February-June.

Admission Requirements: Secondary school certificate (baccalauréat).

Languages of Instruction: French–Creole and English.

Degrees and Diplomas: Associate of Science, 2 yrs. Bachelor of Science, 4 yrs.

Library: c. 200 vols.

Academic Staff: c. 20.

Student Enrolment: c. 240.

3346 **INSTITUT UNIVERSITAIRE ROI HENRI CHRISTOPHE**

B.P. 98, Cap-Haïtien

HOLY SEE

Universities

3347 ***PONTIFICIA UNIVERSITÀ GREGORIANA**
Pontifical Gregorian University
Piazza della Pilotta 4, 00187 Roma
Cables: Pugi Roma
Telephone: (06) 67011
Rettore: Gilles Pelland, S.J. (1986-92)
Segretario Generale: John R. Crocker, S.J.

F. of Theology
Dean: Gerald O'Collins, S.J.; *staff* 48 (58)
F. of Canon Law
Dean: Urbano Navarrete, S.J.; *staff* 7 (17)
F. of Philosophy
Dean: Salvino Biolo, S.J.; *staff* 20 (15)
F. of Ecclesiastical History
Dean: Paulius Rabikauskas, S.J.; *staff* 16 (2)
F. of Missiology
Dean: Jesus Lopez-Gay, S.J.; *staff* 6 (11)
F. of Social Sciences
Dean: Sergio Bernal Restrepo, S.J.; *staff* 10 (15)
I. of Spiritual Theology
President: Charles A. Bernard, S.J.; *staff* 16 (14)
I. of Psychology
President: Bartholomew Kiely, S.J.; *staff* 7 (8)
I. of Religious Sciences
President: Giovanni Magnani, S.J.; *staff* 1 (17)
S. of Latin Language and Literature
Director: Urbano Navarrette, S.J.; *staff* – (2)
Interdisciplinary Ce. for Social Communication
Director: Peter Henrici, S.J.; *staff* – (8)
Biblical I. (see below)
Oriental I. (see below)

Founded 1551 as 'Collegium Romanum' by Ignatius of Loyola and Francis Borgia. Constituted as a university by Pope Julius III, 1552. The institution developed considerably under Pope Gregory XIII, who is considered to be 'founder and father' of the university which now bears his name. The university depends directly on the Holy See and its administration is entrusted to the Society of Jesus. The Grand Chancellor is the Cardinal Prefect of the Sacred Congregation of Studies and the Vice-Grand Chancellor the Superior-General of the Society of Jesus. Juridical recognition is accorded to the university by the government of Italy. Governing body: the Academic Senate. Residential facilities for academic staff.

Academic Year: October to September (October-January; February-May).

Admission Requirements: Completed classical secondary education and, where necessary, additional preparatory studies to meet faculty requirements.

Fees (Lire): 1,400,000-1,870,000 per annum.

Languages of Instruction: Italian. Also some teaching in English, French, German and Spanish.

Degrees and Diplomas: Baccalaureatus in–Philosophy; Missiology; Social Sciences; Psychology, 2 yrs; Theology, 3 yrs. Master of Arts in–Theology; Religious Sciences, 4 yrs. Licentia in–Canon Law; Spiritual Theology, 2 yrs; Church History; Social Sciences; Missiology; Psychology, 3 yrs; Philosophy, 4 yrs; Theology, 5 yrs. Doctor in– Canon Law; Spiritual Theology, 4 yrs; Church History; Social Sciences; Missiology; Psychology, 5 yrs; Philosophy, 6 yrs; Theology, 7 yrs. Diplomas in–Spiritual Theology; Latin Language, 2 yrs; Higher Religious Culture, 3 yrs.

Library: University Library, *c.* 1,000,000 vols.

Publications: Gregorianum; Periodica de re morali, canonica, liturgica; Archivum Historiae Pontificiae; Studia Missionalia; Docu-menta Missionalia.

Press or Publishing House: Editrice della Pontificia Universitas Gregoriana.

Academic Staff, 1989-90:

Rank	Full-time	Part-time
Emeriti	–	45
Ordinari	57	–
Straordinari	12	–
Aggiunti	21	–
Assistenti	–	34
Incaricati	–	64
Invitati	–	61
Total	90	204

Student Enrolment, 1989-90:

	Men	Women	Total
Of the country	2238	645	2853

3348 **PONTIFICIA UNIVERSITÀ LATERANENSE**
Pontifical Lateran University
Piazza S. Giovanni in Laterano 4, 00184 Roma
Cables: 3318 vaticano
Telex: 2024 DIRIGENTEL VA
Telephone: 698/6401
Fax: 698/6103
Rettore: Mons. Pietro Rossano
Segretario Generale: Americo Ciani

F. of Theology
Dean: Ignazio Sanna
F. of Canon Law
Dean: Reginaldo Pizzorni
F. of Civil Law
Dean: Franco Biffi
F. of Philosophy
Dean: Marcello Sánchez Sorondo
I. of Pastoral Studies
President: Francesco Marinelli
I. of Patristic Studies
President: Vittorino Grossi
I. of Moral Theology
President: Sean Cannon
I. of Education
I. of Religious Sciences
President: Pino Scabini
I. of Family Studies
President: Mons. Carlo Caffarra
I. of Theology (by correspondence)
I. of Religious Life
President: José Rovira Arumi

Also 5 affiliated institutes in Jerusalem, Chelmno, Rome, Chieti, Assisi, Verona, Ferlo-Fano, and Montreal.

Founded 1773 by Pope Clement XIV as Collegio Romano. Moved to the Lateran 1913 and became Pontificio Ateneo Lateranense and Pontificia Universitas Lateranensis 1959. Under the jurisdiction of the Sacred Congregation of Studies.

Academic Year: October to June (October-February; February-June).

Admission Requirements: Secondary school certificate.

Fees (Lire): Registration, 325,000; tuition, 325,000-480,000 per annum.

Language of Instruction: Italian

Degrees and Diplomas: Baccalaureatus and Licentia in all fields, 2-3 yrs. Laurea, Doctor, in–Philosophy; Theology; Canon Law; CivilLaw; Civil and Canon Law (Laurea a utroque iure). Diplomas of postgraduate specialization.

Libraries: Central Library, *c.* 500,000 vols; Institute of Pastoral Studies, *c.* 5000.

Publications: Studia et Documenta Historiae et Iuris (1880-); Lateranum; Aquinas; Apollinaris.

Press or Publishing House: Ed. Pontificia Università Lateranense.

Academic Staff, 1990:

Rank	Full-time	Part-time
Ordinari	34	–
Straordinari	10	–
Incaricati	26	–
Invitati	24	50
Total	94	50

Student Enrolment, 1990:

	Men	Women	Total
Of the country	750	158	908
Of other countries	208	168	218
Total	958	168	1126

3349 **PONTIFICIA UNIVERSITAS URBANIANA**
Via Urbano VIII 16, 00165 Roma
Cables: Urban University–Vatican
Telephone: (06) 655-992
Rettore: Daniel Acharuparambil (1988-)
Segretario Generale: Germana Mantese

F. of Philosophy
F. of Philosophy
Dean: G. Battista Mondin
F. of Theology
Dean: Erich Schmid
F. of Canon Law
Dean: Che Chen-Tao
F. of Missiology
Dean: Juan Esquerda Bifet
I. for Missionary Catechesis
Director: J. Dinh Duc Dao
I. for the Study of Atheism
Director: Luis Clavell
Also 47 affiliated institutes throughout the world.

Founded 1627 as college by Pope Urban VIII, became Pontifical University 1962. Directed by the Society for thePropagation of the Faith. Governing bodies: the Academic Council; the Faculty Councils.

Academic Year: October to June (October-February; February-June).

Admission Requirements: Secondary school certificate.

Language of Instruction: Italian.

Degrees and Diplomas: Baccalaureatus in–Canon Law, 1 yr; Philosophy; Missiology, 2 yrs; Theology, 3 yrs. Licentia in–Philosophy; Theology, a further 4-5 yrs. Laurea, Doctor, in–Philosophy; Theology; Canon Law; Missiology, at least 2 yrs after Licentia.

Library: 150,000 vols.

Publications: Euntes Docete; Annales; Bibliografia Missionalia.

Press or Publishing House: Urbaniana University Press.

Academic Staff, 1989-90:

Rank	
Ordinari	12
Straordinari	8
Incaricati	35
Invitati	48
Assistenti	1
Total	104

Student Enrolment, 1989-90:

Of the country	184
Of other countries	1072
Total	1256

3350 ***PONTIFICIA STUDIORUM UNIVERSITAS A S. THOMA AQUINATE IN URBE**
Pontifical University of St. Thomas Aquinas in Rome
Largo Angelicum 1, 00184 Roma
Telephone: 670-21
Rector: José F. Castaño, O.P. (1985-89)
Segretario Generale: Giorgio Marcato

F. of Theology
Dean: John Zerafa; *staff* 82
F. of Canon Law
Dean: Mark Said; *staff* 12
F. of Philosophy
Dean: Abelardo Lobato; *staff* 21
F. of Social Sciences
Dean: Raimundo Spiazzi; *staff* 23
I. of Spiritual Studies
President: Emeterio de Cea; *staff* 22
I. of Religious Sciences
President: Angelo Urru; *staff* 25
I. of Theology

Founded 1580 as College of St. Thomas for students of the Dominical Order. Faculty of philosophy added 1882 by Apostolic Decree of Pope Leo XIII, faculty of Canon Law added 1896. Became Pontifical University 1906. Present title adopted 1963. Residential facilities for *c.* 70 academic staff and 70 students.

Academic Year: October to June (October-January; February-May).

Admission Requirements: Completed classical secondary education. Fees (Lire): 955,000 per annum.

Languages of Instruction: Italian and English (Theology); Latin (Canon Law); Italian (Philosophy and Social Sciences).

Degrees and Diplomas: Baccalaureatus in–Theology; Canon Law; Philosophy; Social Sciences, 2-3 yrs. Licentia in–Theology; Canon Law; Philosophy; Social Sciences, a further 2 yrs. Laurea, Doctorat, 2 yrs after Licentia.

Library: University Library, 277,553 vols.

Publication: Angelicum (annually).

Academic Staff, 1986-87: 136.

Student Enrolment, 1986-87:

	Men	Women	Total
Of the country	149	18	167
Of other countries	740	120	860
Total	889	138	1027

3351 **UNIVERSITÀ PONTIFICIA SALESIANA**
Salesian Pontifical University
Piazza Ateneo Salesiano 1, 00139 Roma
Telephone: (6) 881-20-41
Fax: (6) 881-20-57
Rettore: Tarcisio Bertone (1989-92)
Segretario Generale: Mario Morra

F. of Theology
Dean: Juan Picca; *staff* 25 (9)
F. of Canon Law
Dean: Piero Giorgio Marcuzzi; *staff* 5 (4)
F. of Philosophy
Dean: Adriano Alessi *staff* 11 (1)
F. of Education
Dean: Emilio Alberich Sotomayor *staff* 29 (16)
I. of Classical Studies (Latin and Greek)
Dean: Sergio Felici *staff* 5 (5)
I. of Religious Sciences
Dean: Juan Picca
I. of Social Communication Sciences
Dean: Roberto Gianinatelli; *staff* 15 (6)
Also associated institutions in: Bangalore, Barcelona, Benediktbeuern, Cremisán, Guatemala, Madrid, Messina,São Paulo, Shillong, Los Teques, Bahía Blanca, Nave, Nashik, Yercaud, India, Santiago, Manila, Caracas.

Founded 1904 as institute, became Athenaeum 1940 and university 1973. Faculties which were previously in Turin transferred to Rome 1965. Under the jurisdiction of the Congregation for Catholic Education and of the Salesian Order, which also finances the university. Governing bodies: the Senato Accademico; the Consiglio, comprising the Rector, Vice-Rector, 5 deans, 2 professors from each faculty, and 1 student from each faculty. Residential facilities for academic staff and students.

Academic Year: October to June (October-January; February-May).

Admission Requirements: Secondary school certificate acceptable for university admission in the country of award.

Fees (Lire): 500,000-650,000 per annum.

Language of Instruction: Italian.

Degrees and Diplomas: Baccalaureato in–Theology, 3 yrs; Education; Classical Studies; Philosophy, 2 yrs; Canon Law, 1 yr. Licenza in–Theology; Philosophy; Canon Law; Education; Pastoral Studies, a further 2 yrs. Magistero in Religious Sciences, 4 yrs. Dottorato, at least 2 yrs after Licenza, and thesis.

Libraries: 600,000 vols; 14 institute libraries, *c.* 200,000.

Publications: Salesianum; Orientamenti Pedagogici; Osservatorio della Condizione Giovanile.

Press or Publishing House: Libreria Ateneo Salesiano.

Academic Staff, 1989-90:

Rank	Full-time	Part-time
Docenti ordinari	36	–
Docenti straordinari	24	–
Docenti aggiunti	34	–
Docenti invitati	–	73
Total	94	73

Student Enrolment, 1989-90:

	Men	Women	Total
Of the country	269	248	517
Of other countries	360	132	692
Total	629	380	1009

Other Institutions

352 **PONTIFICIO ISTITUTO BIBLICO**
Pontifical Biblical Institute
Via della Pilotta 25, 00187 Roma
Telephone: (06) 679-6453
Fax: (06) 6701-6151
Rettore: Klemens Stock, S.J. (1990-93)
Segretario Generale: John R. Crocker, S.J.

F. of Biblical Studies
; *staff* 21 (9)
F. of Ancient Oriental Studies
Dean: Werner Mayer, S.J.; *staff* 5 (3)

Founded 1909 by Pope Pius X, the institute is a centre of higher studies in Sacred Scripture and allies disciplines. The administration is entrusted to the Society of Jesus. Empowered to award degrees 1928. Attached to the Pontificia Universitas Gregoriana and to the Pontificium Institutum Orientalium Studiorum. Governing bodies: the Senato Accademico; the Consiglio Accademico; the Consiglio di Facoltà.

Academic Year: October to June (October-January; February-June).

Admission Requirements: Completed classical secondary education; baccalaureatus in Theology for Faculty of Biblical Studies.

Fees (Lire): Registration, 275,000; tuition, 183,000 per course.

Languages of Instruction: Latin and other languages.

Degrees and Diplomas: Licentia–Biblical Studies; Oriental Studies, 3-4 yrs. Candidatus ad doctoratum, Biblical Studies, 1 yr after Licentia. Laurea, Doctorate, in–Biblical Studies, Oriental Studies, 3 yrs after Licentia.

Library: c. 150,000 vols.

Publications: Biblica (quarterly); Orientalia (quarterly); Elenchus Bibliographicus Biblicus (annually).

Press or Publishing House: Biblical Institute Press.

Academic Staff, 1989-90:

Rank	Full-time	Part-time
Professori emeriti	6	–
Professori ordinarii	14	–
Professori straordinarii	5	–
Professori lectores	7	–
Professori assistentes	2	1
Professori invitati	–	14
Total	34	15

Student Enrolment, 1989-90:

Men	Women	Total
288	29	317

353 **PONTIFICIUM INSTITUTUM ORIENTALE**
Pontifical Oriental Institute
Piazza S. Maria Maggiore 7, 00185 Roma
Telephone: (06) 731-22-54/55
Rettore: Clarence Gallagher, S.J. (1990-)
Segretario Generale: James Kulič, S.J.

F. of Oriental Ecclesiastical Studies (including Patristic Theology)
Dean: Vincent Poggi, S.J.; *staff* 11 (30)
F. of Oriental Canon Law (including Interpretation and Commentary on the Canonical Collections)
Dean: Clarence Gallagher, S.J.; *staff* 4 (10)

Founded 1917 by Pope Benedict XV. Attached to the Pontificia Universitas Gregoriana and to the Pontificio Istituto Biblico 1928. Governing bodies: the Senatus Academicus; the Consilium Academicum; the Consilium Facultatis.

Academic Year: October to June (October-February; February-June).

Admission Requirements: Completed classical secondary education.

Language of Instruction: Italian.

Degrees and Diplomas: Licentiatus, 2-3 yrs. Doctoratus, 3 yrs.

Library: c. 150,000 vols. Specialized library for study of Eastern Churches.

Publication: Orientalia Christiana Periodica.

Academic Staff, 1990: c. 15 (40).

Student Enrolment, 1990: c. 260 (from 42 different countries).

3354 **PONTIFICIO ATENEO S. ANSELMO**
Piazza Cavalieri di Malta 5, 00153 Roma
Cables: santanselmo aventino roma
Telephone: (6) 578-22-74
Rettore: Pius-Ramon Tragan (1990-94)
Segretario Generale: Vincent Tobin

F. of Philosphy
Dean: Elmar Salmann; *staff* 7 (5)
F. of Theology
Dean: Pius Engelbert; *staff* 15 (16)
Liturgical F.
Presidente: Ildebrando Scicolone: *staff* 17 (13)
F. of Philosophy

Founded as a theological college 1687 by Pope Innocent XI. Closed 1837. Reopened 1887 as university by Pope Leo XIII and raised to the rank of pontifical institution 1933. The university is directed by the Benedictine Order. Degrees awarded by the university are recognized by the Italian Government. Governing bodies: the Benedictine Confederation of Monasteries; the Commission for S. Anselmo. Residential facilities for academic staff and students of the Benedictine Order.

Academic Year: October to June (October-February; February-June).

Admission Requirements: Completed classical secondary education and, where necessary, additional preparatory studies to meet faculty requirements.

Language of Instruction: Italian.

Degrees and Diplomas: Baccalaureatus in–Philosophy, Ph.B., Theology, S. Th.Lic., 2 yrs. Licenza in Sacred Liturgy, 2 yrs. Magisterium in Theology, 1 yr. Dottorato in–Sacred Liturgy; Theology, S. Th.D.; Theology, with specialization in Liturgy, 2 yrs after Licentia.

Library: c. 70,000 vols.

Publications: Studia Anselmiana; Rerum Ecclesiasticarum Documenta (Series Major and Minor); Anamnesis (Marietti).

Press or Publishing House: Editrice Anselmiana; Ecclesia Orans.

Academic Staff, 1989-90:

Rank	Full-time	Part-time
Professori ordinari	6	–
Professori straordinari	5	–
Professori consociati	10	–
Professori lettori	–	13
Professori invitati	–	33
Total	21	46

Student Enrolment, 1989-90:

	Men	Women	Total
Of the country	65	14	79
Of other countries	145	19	164
Total	210	33	243*

*Also 65 external students and students by correspondence.

3355 **PONTIFICIO ATENEO 'ANTONIANUM'**
Via Merulana 124, 00185 Roma
Telephone: 757-4551
Rettore: Martino Conti, OFM
Segretario Generale: Valentino Natalini, OFM

F. of Theology
Dean: Vincenkzo Battaglia, OFM; *staff* 32 (12)
F. of Canon Law
Dean: Andrea Boni, OFM; *staff* 8
F. of Philosophy
Dean: José Antonio Merino; *staff* 10 (1)
I. of Biblical Studies (Jerusalem)
Pro-Dean: Alviero Niccacci, OFM

I. of Spiritual Theology
President: Luigi Padovese, OFM; *staff* 12 (5)
I. of Religious Sciences
President: Andrea Mercatali, OFM; *staff* 9 (5)
S. of Medieval Franciscan Studies
Moderator: Leonardo Sileo, OFM; *staff* 5
Also affiliated institutes in: Bari, Bologna, Milan, Venice, Verona, and Benevento.

Founded 1890, became Pontifical University 1933. Under the jurisdiction of the Sacred Congregation of Studies. Degrees awarded by the University are recognized by the government of Italy and of some other countries. Financed and directed by the Franciscan Order. Residential facilities for clerical staff and students.

Academic Year: October to June (October-January; February-June).

Admission Requirements: Completed classical secondary education.

Fees (Lire): 450,000.

Language of Instruction: Italian.

Degrees and Diplomas: Baccalaureatus in–Canon Law, 1 yr; Philosophy, 2 yrs; Theology, 3 yrs. Licentia in–Canon Law; Philosophy, a further 2 yrs. Theology, a further 5 yrs. Doctorate by thesis in–Canon Law; Philosophy, 3 yrs after Licentia; Theology, 6 yrs after Licentia. Diploma in Education.

Libraries: Central Library, *c.* 220,000 vols; libraries of the Institutes, *c.* 17,000.

Publication: Rivista Antonianum (quarterly).

Press or Publishing House: Antonianum Casa Editrice.

Academic Staff, 1989-90: 91 (22).

Student Enrolment, 1989-90:

Men	Women	Total
312	232	544*

*Including 317 foreign students.

3356 **PONTIFICIO ISTITUTO DI MUSICA SACRA**
Via di Torre Rossa 21, 00165 Roma
Telephone: 62-01-73
Preside: Johannes Overath (1982-87)

Sacred Music

Founded 1910 as school, became Pontifical Institute 1931. Some residential facilities for academic staff and students.

Academic Year: October to June (October-February; February-June).

Admission Requirements: Entrance examination.

Fees (Lire): 220,000 per annum.

Language of Instruction: Italian.

Degrees and Diplomas: Baccalaureato, 1 yr; Licenza, 2 yrs; Magistero, 3 yrs; Dottorato, at least 2 yrs after Licenza.

Library: 45,000 vols.

Academic Staff, 1986-87: 9 (3).

Student Enrolment, 1986-87:

	Men	Women	Total
Of the country	22	18	40
Of other countries	22	9	31
Total	44	27	71

3357 **PONTIFICIO ISTITUTO DI ARCHEOLOGIA CRISTIANA**
Via Napoleone III 1, 00185 Roma
Telephone: (06) 735824
Rettore: Victor Saxer
Segretario Generale: Albrecht Weiland

Archaeology

Founded 1925 by Pope Pius XI.

Academic Year: November to June (November-December; January-Easter; Easter-June).

Admission Requirements: Completed theological studies or degree (Laurea) in law or letters.

Fees (Lire): Registration, 100,000; tuition, 150,000.

Language of Instruction: Italian.

Degrees and Diplomas: Baccalaureato, 1 yr. Licenza, 2 yrs. Laurea, Doctor, 3 yrs.

Library: c. 35,000 vols.

Publications: Rivista di Archeologia Cristiana; Monumenti dell'Antichità Cristiana; Roma Sotterranea Cristiana; Inscriptiones Christianae; Studi di Antichità Cristiana; Sussidi allo Studio delle Antichià Cristiane.

Press or Publishing House: Publishing House of the Institute.

Academic Staff, 1989-90:

Rank	Full-time	Part-time
Professores ordinarii	4	–
Professores straordinarii	2	–
Professore incaricato	–	1
Assistente	–	1
Total	6	2

Student Enrolment, 1989-90:

	Men	Women	Total
Of the country	5	30	35
Of other countries	11	5	16
Total	16	35	51

3358 **PONTIFICIA FACULTÀ TEOLOGICA 'SAN BONAVENTURA'**
Via del Serafico 1, 00142 Roma
Telephone: (06) 5192-007
Fax: (06) 5192-067
Preside: Giovanni Iammarrone (1986-89)
Segretario Generale: Julian ZambaninPasquale Magro

Theology (including Philosophy and Franciscan Studies)
Franciscan Ce. for Environmental Studies
Director: Bernard Przewozny; *staff* 2 (1)

Founded 1587 and became Pontifical Faculty 1935. Residential facilitie for students.

Academic Year: October to June (October-January; February-June).

Admission Requirements: Completed classical secondary education.

Language of Instruction: Italian, English, Latin.

Degrees and Diplomas: Baccalaureate in Theology, S.T.B., 5 yrs. Licentiate in Theology, S.T.L., 2 yrs. Doctorate, S.T.D., a further2 yrs.

Library: 150,000 vols.

Publication: Miscellanea Francescana (quarterly).

Press or Publishing House: Casa Editrice 'Miscellanea Francescana'.

Academic Staff, 1989-90:

Rank	Full-time	Part-time
Ordinario	7	1
Straordinio	3	–
Incaricato	2	–
Invitato	–	17
Aggiunto	2	–
Assistente	–	3
Emerito	3	1
Total	17	22

Student Enrolment, 1989-90:

	Men	Women	Total
Of the country	44	17	61
Of other countries	51	–	51
Total	95	17	112*

*Also 10 external students.

3359 **PONTIFICIA FACULTÀ TEOLOGICA SS. 'TERESIANUM'**
Piazza S. Pancrazio 5a, 00152 Roma
Telephone: (06) 582-362

Theology

Founded 1935, became Pontifical Faculty 1963. Under the juris-dictio of the Sacred Congregation of studies. Governing bodies: the Consigli delle Facoltà; the Commissiones.

Academic Year: October to June (October-January; February-June).

Admission Requirements: Completed classical secondary education.

Language of Instruction: Italian.

Degrees and Diplomas: Baccalaureato, 3 yrs. Licenza, a further 2 yrs Dottore.

Library: c. 140,000 vols.

Special Facilities (Museums, etc.): Museo Carmelitano.

Publications: Bibliografia internationalis Spiritualitatis (annually); Archivium Bibliographicum Carmelitanun (annually); Ephemerides Carmeliticae (biannually); Rivista di Vita spirituale (bimonthly); Collana: 'Biblioteca Carmelitica'.

Academic Staff: c. 20.

Student Enrolment: c. 330.

3360 **PONTIFICIA FACOLTÀ TEOLOGICA 'MARIANUM'**
Viale Trenta April 6, 00153 Roma
Telephone: (6) 58-90-441/44
Fax: (6) 58-80-292
Preside: Salvatore M. Meo, O.S.M. (1986-89)
Segretario: Tiziano Civiero, O.S.M.

Marian and Theological Studies

Founded 1950. Directed by the Ordine dei Servi di Maria and under the jurisdiction of the Congregation for Catholic Education.

Academic Year: October to June (October-February; February-June).

Admission Requirements: Completed classical secondary education.

Fees (Lire): 500,000.

Language of Instruction: Italian.

Degrees and Diplomas: Baccalaureato in Theology, 3 yrs. Licenza, a further 2 yrs. Dottorato, 2 yrs after Licenza. Diploma in–Religious Sciences; Marian Studies.

Library: Total, 165,000 vols.

Publications: Rivista 'Marianum'–Ephemerides Mariologiae (weekly); Scripta Pontificia Facultatis Theologicae 'Marianum'.

Academic Staff, 1989-90:

Rank	Full-time	Part-time
Ordinari	6	–
Straordinari	3	–
Associati	1	–
Incaricati	25	–
Invitati	–	3
Total	35	3

Student Enrolment, 1989-90:

	Men	Women	Total
Of the country	60	83	143
Of other countries	74	159	233
Total	134	242	376

3361 **PONTIFICIO ISTITUTO DI STUDI ARABI E D'ISLAMISTICA**
Pontifical Institute of Arabic and Islamic Studies
Viale di Trastevere 89, 00153 Roma
Telephone: (06) 686-11-31
Vice-Chancellor: Etienne Renaud, m.afr
Rector: Michel Gagnon, m.afr

Arabic Studies (including Classical and Modern Arabic, and Islamic Theology)

Founded 1949 as Séminaire d'Etudes Orientales des Pères Blancs in La Manouba, Tunisia. Transferred to Rome 1964 and recognized by the Sacred Congregation of Seminaries and Universities as a Pontifical Institute of Oriental Studies 1960. Acquired present title 1980. The Grand Chancellor is the Cardinal Prefect of the Sacred Congregation of Seminaries and Universities and the Vice-Grand Chancellor is the Superior of the White Fathers.Partly financed by the Holy See. Governing body: the Council of the Institute. Residential facilities for academic staff.

Academic Year: October to June (October-December; January-Easter; Easter-June).

Admission Requirements: Completed classical secondary education.

Fees (Lire): 1300,000.

Languages of Instruction: French, English, Italian and Arabic.

Degrees and Diplomas: Diploma in Arabic Studies, 2 yrs. Licence in Arabic and Islamic Studies, 3 yrs. Doctor, at least 2 yrs after Licence.

Library: c. 17,000 vols.(One-third in Arabic).

Publications: Bulletin d'Etudes arabes (3 times a year); Islamochristiana (annually); Encounter (Christian-Muslim Understanding) (10 times a year).

Academic Staff, 1989-90: 8 (9).

Student Enrolment, 1989-90:

	Men	Women	Total
Of the country	3	8	11
Ofother countries	19	8	27
Total	22	16	38

3362 **PONTIFICIA FACOLTÀ DI SCIENZE DELL'EDUCAZIONE 'AUXILIUM'**
Via Cremolino 141, 00166 Roma
Telephone: (6) 68-90-790
Fax: (6-) 69-64-640
Preside: Enrica Rosanna (1989-95)
Segretaria: Carla Sartorio

Educational Sciences

Founded 1954 as institute in Turin, reorganized 1970 as branch of the Salesian Pontifical University. Moved toRome 1978. Under the jurisdiction of the Congregation for Catholic Education.

Academic Year: October to June (October-February; February-June).

Admission Requirements: Secondary school certificate acceptable for university admission in the country of award.

Language of Instruction: Italian.

Degrees and Diplomas: Baccellierato, 3 yrs. Licenza, 2 further yrs. Dottorato, at least 1 yr after Licenza.

Library: c. 30,000 vols.

Publication: Rivista di Scienze dell'Educazione (quarterly).

Academic Staff, 1989-90:

Rank	Full-time	Part-time
Professori stabili	11	–
Professori aggiunti	12	–
Professori invitati	3	6
Professori incaricati	–	4
Professori emeriti	1	–
Total	27	10

Student Enrolment, 1989-90:

	Women
Of the country	63
Of other countries	107
Total	170

HONDURAS

3363 ***UNIVERSIDAD NACIONAL AUTÓNOMA DE HONDURAS**

National Autonomous University of Honduras
Ciudad Universitaria, Tegucigalpa D.C.
Telephone: 32-22-08
Rector: Oswaldo Ramos Samos Soto (1982-)

F. of Law and Social Sciences
F. of Medicine (including Nursing)
F. of Engineering (Civil, Mechanical, Electrical, and Chemical)
F. of Economics (including Business Administration and Accountancy)
F. of Dentistry
F. of Chemistry and Pharmacy
Ce. for General Studies
Ce. for General Studies (San Pedro Sula)
Ce. for General Studies (Agriculture and Forestry) (La Ceiba)
I. of Economic Research
Ce. for Industrial Studies
Extension D.

Founded 1845 as academy, came under State control 1847. Became autonomous institution 1957. Governing bodies: the Claustro Pleno (Plenary Assembly); the Consejo Universitario (University Council), comprising 12 members of the professional staff and 12 students.

Academic Year: February to December (February-June; July-December).

Admission Requirements: Secondary school certificate (bachillerato) or equivalent.

Language of Instruction: Spanish.

Degrees and Diplomas: Bachiller in Social Work. Licenciado in–Nursing; Microbiology and Chemistry, 4 yrs; Economics; Education; Business Administration; Public Administration; Accountancy and Auditing; Journalism; Mathematics and Natural Sciences, 5 yrs. Professional titles of–Técnico en Lab. Clínico, laboratory technology, 1 ½ yrs; Técnico en Dibujo, design; Topógrafo, surveying, 3 yrs; Ingeniero (Chemical, Mechanical, Electrical, or in Agriculture or Forestry), 5 yrs; Ingeniero civil, 6 yrs; Pedagogía. Doctorates in–Dental Surgery; Chemistry and Pharmacy, 6 yrs; Medicine, 7 yrs.

Libraries: Central Library; specialized libraries, total *c.* 105,000 vols.

Publications: Revista de la Universidad (monthly); Memoria Anual de la Universidad; Revista Economía Política (monthly);Presencia; Boletín del Instituto de Ciencias Económicas (monthly); Boletín Estadístico (annually).

Academic Staff: c. 630 (380).

Student Enrolment: c. 27,110.

3364 **UNIVERSIDAD DE SAN PEDRO SULA**

18 Avenida, 6 calle, N.O., San Pedro Sula, Cortés

3365 **UNIVERSIDAD JOSÉ CECILIO DEL VALLE**

Apartado postal 917, Tegucigalpa
Telephone: 011-504-22-8961; 22-8963

Engineering
Administration and Accountancy

Founded 1978. A private autonomous institution financially supported by tuition fees and donations.

Arrangements for co-operation with: Instituto Tecnológico de Monterrey; Universidad Católica de Chile.

Academic Year: January to December (January-March; April-June; July-September; October-December).

Admission Requirements: Secondary school certificate (bachillerato).

Language of Instruction: Spanish.

Degrees and Diplomas: Bachiller, 4 yrs. Licenciado, 5 yrs.

Library: c. 5,000 vols.

Academic Staff: c. 60.

3366 **UNIVERSIDAD PEDAGÓGICA NACIONAL 'FRANCISCO MORAZÁN'**

Boulevard Miraflores, Apartado Postal 3394, Tegucigalpa, D.C.
Telephone: 32-7417
Rector: Roque Ramos Motiño (1990-)
Secretario General: Adulvín Díaz Bonilla

I. of Science and Technology
Head: Gonzalo Cruz C.; *staff* 1
D. of Natural Sciences
Head: Julia Angélica Solis de Zelaya; *staff* 13 (1)
D. of Business Education
Head: Jorge Alberto Urquía; *staff* 6 (1)
D. of Technical Industry Education
Head: Amílcar Antonio Cruz; *staff* 10 (2)
D. of Mathematics
Head: Rolando Baltazar Núñez; *staff* 14
D. of Home Economics Education
Head: Julia Isabel de Morales; *staff* 7
S. of Human Sciences
Head: Ramón Ulises Salgado; *staff* 1
D. of Education
Head: Régulo de Jesús Mancía; *staff* 22
D. of Social Sciences
Head: Modesto Sánchez Cordero; *staff* 8 (3)
D. of Languages and Literature
Head: José Dagoberto Martínez B.; *staff* 12 (1)
D. of Physical Education
Head: René Cardona; *staff* 5
D. of Plastic Arts
Head: Virgilio Guardiola; *staff* 1
University Ce.
Head: Oscar Celán Martínez; *staff* 32 (12)

Also Regional University Centre at San Pedro Sula.

Founded 1990. Financed by the central government. Under the jurisdiction of the Consejo de Educación Superior and the government. Governing bodies: the Consejo Superior Universitario; the Consejo Directivo.

Arrangements for co-operation with: State University at Las Cruces, New México.

Academic Year: February to November (February-June; July-November).

Admission Requirements: Secondary school certificate (bachillerato).

Fees (Lempiras): 15 per semester.

Language of Instruction: Spanish.

Degrees and Diplomas: Teaching qualification (secondary level), 4 yrs; pre-primary level, primary level, and special education, 2 yrs.

Library: 20,000 vols.

Academic Staff, 1989-90: 161 (20).

Student Enrolment, 1989-90: 5803 (Also 2460 external students).

3367 **ESCUELA AGRÍCOLA PANAMERICANA**

Panamerican Agricultural School
P.O. Box 93, Tegucigalpa
Telex: 1567 EAPZAM-HO
Telephone: 332717
Fax: 328543
Rector: Simón E. Malo (1979-)
Dean: Jorge Román

Tropical Agriculture (including Animal Science and Horticulture)

Founded 1942. A private international institution offering intensive studies in tropical agriculture. Governing body: the Board of Trustees, comprising 22 members from different countries. Residential facilities for academic staff and students.

Arrangements for co-operation with the Universities of: Florida; Texas A&M; Kansas State; Mississippi State; Iowa State; Colorado State; Cornell; Auburn.

Academic Year: January to November (January-April; April-August; August-November).

Admission Requirements: Secondary school certificate (bachillerato) or equivalent, and entrance examination in Spanish.

Fees (US$): 6500 per annum.

Languages of Instruction: Spanish and English.

Degrees and Diplomas: Degree of Agrónomo, 33 months. Title of Ingeniero agrónomo, a further 11 months. (A total of 288 credit hours).

Library: 12,000 vols.

Publication: Ceiba.

Academic Staff, 1990: 114.

Student Enrolment, 1990:

	Men	Women	Total
Of the country	280	20	300
Of other countries	350	45	395
Total	630	65	695

HUNGARY*

Universities and Technical Universities

3368 ***EÖTVÖS LORÁND TUDOMÁNYEGYETEM**

Eötvös Loránd University
Egyetem tér 1/3, 1364 Budapest
Telex: 22-5467 ELTE H
Telephone: 180-820
Rektor: Lajos Vekas
Főtitkár (Secretary-General): Gyula Kisfaludy

F. of Law and Political Science
Dean: Tamás Földesi; *staff* 107 (38)
F. of Arts (including Education)
Dean: Ferenc Pölöskei; *staff* 478 (35)
F. of Science
Dean: Kálmán Medzihradszky; *staff* 482 (54)
Ce. for Foreign Languages
Director: Győző Sipőczy; *staff* 43
I. of Sociology
Director: Tibor Huszár; *staff* 21
Postgraduate I. of Law and Political Science
Director: Rezsob Hársfalvi; *staff* 2
Computer Ce.
Director: Imre Kátai
Biological Experimental Plant (Göd)
Director: János Gergely
Also 131 departments of the different faculties and 3 secondary/primary training schools.

Founded 1561 as Jesuit college and established as a university at Nagyszombat 1635 by Archbishop Péter Pázmány. Became secular institution 1773. Transferred to Buda 1777, and to Pest 1784. Present title adopted 1950. Faculty of Medicine detached and re-established as separate Medical University 1949. The university is under the jurisdiction of the Ministry of Culture and Education and is financed by the State. Governing body: the Council. Residential facilities for students in three hostels.

Special arrangements for co-operation with: Erevan State University; Leningrad State University; 'Babeş-Bolyai' University, Cluj Napoca; University of Bucharest; Humboldt University, Berlin; Friedrich Schiller University of Jena; Martin Luther University, Halle-Wittenberg; University of Paris I; University of Padua; Charles University, Prague; University of Sofia; University of Chile; University of Havana; Comenius University, Bratislava; University of Belgrade; University of Priština; University of Zagreb; University of Stockholm; University of Venice; Central University of Venezuela; University of Vienna; University of Heidelberg; University of Hamburg; University of Paderborn; University of Cracow; University of California, Santa Barbara; University of Rome; University of Paris VI.

Academic Year: September to June (September-January; February-June).

Admission Requirements: Secondary school certificate and entrance examination.

Fees (Forints): 100-1300 per semester, according to academic record and parents' income.

Language of Instruction: Hungarian.

Degrees and Diplomas: Doctor iuris et rerum politicarum, dr.iur. et rer.pol., law and political science, 4 1/2 yrs. Professional qualifications in–Archaeology; Biology; Chemistry; Ethnography; Geography; Geology; Geophysics; History; History of Art; Library Science; Literature; Mathematics; Meteorology; Philology; Philosophy; Physics; Psychology, 5 yrs. Doctor philosophiae, dr.phil., or Doctor rerum naturalum dr. rer.nat., science, after one of the above, by thesis and examination. Teaching qualification, secondary level, 5 yrs.

Libraries: Central Library, *c.* 1,300,000 vols; faculty and department libraries, *c.* 1,000,000.

Publications: Annales Universitatis de Rolando Eötvös nominatae (15 sections); Acta Facultatis Politico-Iuridicae; Opuscula Zoologica, Dissertationes Archeologicae; Bulletin of the Eötvös Loránd University.

Academic Staff, 1986-87:

Rank	Full-time	Part-time
Egyetemi tanár (Professors)	151	29
Docens (Associate Professors)	307	36
Adjunktus (Assistant Lecturers)	471	117
Tanársegéd (Assistant Lecturers)	158	17
Total	1087	189

Student Enrolment, 1986-87:

	Men	Women	Total
Of the country	2155	3416	5571
Of other countries	121	87	308
Total	2276	3503	5879*

*Also 2603 external students.

3369 **BUDAPESTI MŰSZAKI EGYETEM**

Technical University of Budapest
Műegyetem rakpart 3, 1111 Budapest XI
Telex: 225931 MÜEGY
Telephone: (1) 664-011
Fax: (1) 66-6808
Rektor: Lajos Fodor (1987-92)
Főtitkár (Secretary-General): József Györgyi

F. of Civil Engineering
Dean: Ákos Detrekői; *staff* 187 (82)
F. of Mechanical Engineering
Dean: István Artinger; *staff* 267 (85)
F. of Architecture
Dean: Miklós Hofer; *staff* 162 (39)
F. of Chemical Engineering
Dean: Sándor Gál; *staff* 223 (48)
F. of Electrical Engineering
Dean: László Zombory; *staff* 327 (124)
F. of Engineering Transportation
Dean: Pál Michelberger; *staff* 146 (75)
F. of Natural and Social Sciences (Physics, Economics, Education, Pedagogy, Sociology, Languages, Physical Education)
Dean: György Kerékgyártó; *staff* 222 (64)
International Ce. for Engineering Ps.
Director: Géza Gordos
I. of Postgraduate Engineering Courses
Director: Attila Horváth
University Information Ce.
Director: István Szüts
Also correspondence courses.

Founded 1782 as Institutum Geometricum Hydrotechnicum, acquired university rank 1872 and present title 1949; incorporating former Technical University of Building and Transport Engineering, founded 1952. The university is under the jurisdiction of the Ministry of Education and financed by the State. Governing body: the Senat, under the chairmanship of the Rector. Residential facilities for 50% of the students.

Arrangements for co-operation with similar institutions in: Austria; Bulgaria; Cuba; Czechoslovakia; Finland; Germany; Poland; United Kingdom; USSR; Yugoslavia; Belgium; France; Greece; Netherlands; Japan; Canada; Democratic People's Republic of Korea; Italy; Switzerland; Turkey; USA.

Academic Year: September to June (September-January; February-June).

Admission Requirements: Secondary school certificate and entrance examination.

*Major changes have affected the higher education system of the country and individual institutions during the preparation of this edition. These are reflected as far as they have been communicated to IAU before 30 September 1990.

Fees (Forints): 500-2000 per semester, according to academic record; foreign students, US$ 600-2500.
Languages of Instruction: Hungarian and English.
Degrees and Diplomas: Diploma in Production Engineering (B.Sc.), 3 yrs. Diploma of Engineering (M.Sc.) in various fields, 5 yrs. Doctorate (Dr.Univ.), a further 2-3 yrs., and special examinations and thesis.
Library: Central Library, 395,206 vols.
Publications: Periodica Polytechnica (quarterly, 6 series); Newsletter (quarterly).
Academic Staff, 1988-89:

Rank	Full-time	Part-time
Egyetemi tanár (Professors)	132	18
Docens (Associate Professors)	326	28
Adjunktus (Assistant Professors)	771	61
Tanársegéd (Assistants)	176	22
Nyelvtanár (Language Teachers)	127	3
Tesknevelö tanár (Physical Education Teachers)	23	1
Total	1555	133

Student Enrolment, 1988-89:

	Men	Women	Total
Of the country	6789	1408	8197
Of other countries	435	90	1275
Total	7224	1498	9472*

*Also 869 external students.

3370 **KOSSUTH LAJOS TUDOMÁNYEGYETEM**
Kossuth Lajos University
Egytem tér 1-3, 4010 Debrecen
Telephone: 16-666

F. of Arts (including Education)
F. of Science
I. of Marxism-Leninism
Also demonstration grammar and elementary schools for teachers.
Founded 1912, incorporating the faculties of the Reformed College of Debrecen, founded 1538. Of the original four faculties two, Medicine and Theology, became separate institutions in 1949 and one, Law, has been discontinued. Faculty of Mathematics and Natural Sciences added 1949. Governing body: the University Council, under the chairmanship of the Rector. The university is under the jurisidiction of theMinistry of Education and is financed by the State. Residential facilities for *c.* 50% of the students.
Academic Year: September to June (September-December; February-May).
Admission Requirements: Secondary school certificate.
Fees (Forints): According to academic record.
Language of Instruction: Hungarian.
Degrees and Diplomas: Professional qualifications in–Chemistry; Physics; Mathematics; Biology; Psychology; Education Administration; Finno-Ugrian linguistics; Ethnography, 3-5 yrs. Doctorates by thesis. Teaching qualifications, secondary level.
Libraries: University Library, *c.* 1,600,000 vols; institute libraries.
Publications: Acta Marxistica et Leninistica; Nevelés, Müvelödés; Studia Litteraria; Magyar Nyelvjárások; Magyar Történelmi Tanulmányok; Egyetemes Történeti Tanulmányok; Hungarian Studies in English; Studia Romanica; Német Filológiai Tanulmányok; Slavica; Acta Classica; Müvéltség és Hagyomány; Publicationes Mathematicae; Acta Physica et Chimica; Acta Biologica; Acta Geonomica; Könvy és Könvytár; Diákköri Füzetek; KLTE Evkönyve.
Academic Staff: c. 400.
Student Enrolment: c. 1880 (Also *c.* 400 external students).

3371 ***MISKOLCI EGYETEM**
University of Miskolc
3515 Miskolc-Egyetemváros
Telex: 62223 NMEMIS H
Telephone: (46) 65-111
Fax: (46) 69-554
Rektor: Ferenc Kovács (1986-91)
Főtitkár (Secretary-General): Béla Mang

F. of Mining
Dean: Zsolt Somosvári; *staff* 65 (9)
F. of Metallurgical Engineering
Dean: Attila Biró; *staff* 71 (2)
F. of Mechanical Engineering
Dean: István Páczelt; *staff* 243 (19)
F. of Legal and Political Sciences
Dean: Tibor Horváth; *staff* 49 (24)
I. of Metallurgical Technology (Dunaujváros)
Director: Bertalan Gábor; *staff* 85 (3)
F. of Economics
Dean: János Czabán; *staff* 17 (6)
Computer Ce.
Director: László Balla; *staff* 18 (4)
Also correspondence courses and courses for studentsin English.
Founded 1735 as school of mining, became academy 1770. German replaced by Hungarian as language of instruction 1867. Reorganized at Sopron 1919, became Technical University of Heavy Industry and transferred to Miskolc 1949. Acquired present title 1990. Under the jurisdiction of the Ministry of Culture and financed by the State. Governing body: the Council. Residential facilities for 82% of the students.
Arrangements for co-operation with: Technical University of Berlin; Institute of Steel and Alloys Technology, Moscow; Institute of Petroleum and Gas Technology, Moscow; Institute of Mining, Moscow; Kharkov Polytechnical Institute; Institute of Metallurgy, Ždanov; Otto von Guericke Technical College, Magdeburg; Freiberg Mining Academy; Technical University of Košice; College of Mining, Ostrava; Institute of Mining and Geology, Sofia; Centro Universitario de Holguin; University of Mining and Metallurgy, Leoben; Ryerson Polytechnical Institute, Toronto; Academy of Mining and Metallurgy, Cracow; Technische Universität Clausthal; Universität Dortmund; University of Trieste; Imperial College, London.
Academic Year: September to May (September-December; February-May).
Admission Requirements: Secondary school certificate and entrance examination.
Fees (Forints): Up to 1300 per semester, according to academic record and parents' income; for foreign students, 14
Fees: 00.
Languages of Instruction: Hungarian and English.
Degrees and Diplomas: Diploma of–Okleveles üzemmérnök, production engineering; üzemgazdász, business administration, 3 yrs; Okleveles bányamérnök, mining engineer; Okleveles kohomérnök, metallurgical engineer; Okleveles gépészmérnök, mechanical engineer; Közgazdász, economics, 5 yrs. Müszaki doktor, Dr.techn., by thesis, a further 2-3 yrs. Allam és jogtudományok doktora, Doctor of Laws.
Libraries: c. 640,000 vols; Selmec Museum library, 30,000.
Special Facilities (Museums, etc.): Selmec Museum.
Publications: Nehézipari Muszaki Egyetem Közleményei (Bulletin); Nehézipari Muszaki Egyetem Idegen Nyelvu Kozleményei (Foreign Language Bulletin); Évkönyv (Yearbook).
Academic Staff, 1989-90:

Rank	Full-time	Part-time
Tanár (Professors)	42	4
Docens (Lecturers)	83	6
Adjunktus (First Assistants)	243	18
Tanársegéd (Assistants)	60	22
Others	17	10
Total	445	60

Student Enrolment, 1989-90:

	Men	Women	Total
Of the country	2204	685	2289
Of other countries	138	2	140
Total	2342	687	3029*

*Also 868 students by correspondence.

3372 **PÉCSI JANUS PANNONIUS TUDOMÁNYEGYETEM**
Janus Pannonius University of Pécs
Rákóczi út 80, 7601 Pécs
Telex: 12301
Telephone: (72) 11-443
Fax: (72) 14-027
Rektor: Mária Ormos (1987-92)
Főtitkár (Secretary-General): János Gáspár

F. of Law and Political Science
Dean: János Bruhács; *staff* 65 (11)
F. of Economics (including Business Administration)
Dean: Jósef Vörös; *staff* 96 (6)

F.of Teacher Training
Dean: Attila Borhidi; *staff* 309 (40)
Also practice schools, summer semesters for foreign students, and American Study Programme.

Founded 1921, formerly academy of law established 1785, and succeeding University of Pécs founded by King Louis I in 1367. Faculties of theology and medicine detached and re-established as separate institutions 1949 and 1951. Faculty of Teacher Training incorporated and acquired present title 1982. The university is under the jurisdiction of the Ministry of Education and is financed by the State. Governing body: the Council. Residential facilities for students.

Arrangements for co-operation with: Jagiellonian University, Cracow; Comenius University, Bratislava; Martin Luther University of Halle-Wittenberg; University of Osijek; College of Economics, Bratislava; University of Graz; University of Vienna; Philipps University of Marburg; University of Bayreuth; University of Jena; University of Novi Sad; University of Warsaw; University of Leipzig; Pedagogická Fakulta, Plzeň.

Academic Year: September to June (September-December; February-May).

Admission Requirements: Secondary school certificate or equivalent, and entrance examination.

Fees: None.

Language of Instruction: Hungarian.

Degrees and Diplomas: State examination and Doctor iuris, law, 4 yrs. Licence ès Sciences économiques, 8 sem. Doctorate, by thesis, 4 ½ yrs. Also teaching qualifications, 8-10 sem.

Library: Central Library, *c.* 700,000 vols.

Special Facilities (Museums, etc.): Biological Garden; Movie Studio.

Publications: Studia Iuridica Auctoritate Universitatis Pécs Publicata; Studia Oeconomica Auctoritate Universitatis Pécs; Studia Philosophica et Sociologica Auctoritate Universitatis Pécs Publicata; Studia Paedogogia AuctoritateUniversitatis Pécs Publicata.

Academic Staff, 1990:

Egyetemi tanár	21	13
Egyetemi docens	79	17
Egyetemi adjunktus	170	20
Egyuetemi tanársegéd	109	6
Főskolai tanár	5	–
Főskolai adjunktus	17	–
Főskolai tanársegéd	1	–
Tudományos munkatárs	7	–
Lektor	5	–
Nyelvtanár	25	–
Testnevelő tanár	4	–
Total	471	58

Student Enrolment, 1990:

	Men	Women	Total
Of the country	969	1642	2611
Of other countries	12	12	24
Total	981	1654	2635

3373 **JÓZSEF ATTILA TUDOMÁNYEGYETEM**
József Attila University
Dugonics tér 13, 6701 Szeged
Telex: 82 4OL JATE H
Telephone: (62) 24-022
Fax: (62) 11-998
Rektor: Béla Csákány
Főtitkar (Secretary-General): Károly Tóth

F. of Law and Political Science
Dean: Ottó Czucz; *staff* 44 (14)
F. of Arts (including Education, Psychology, Hungarian Language and Literature, Ancient Studies, History, Foreign Languages)
Dean: Tibor Mikola; *staff* 201 (23)
F. of Science
Dean: Ferenc Gécseg; *staff* 281 (6)
Ds. of Political Theory
Head: András Koksondi; *staff* 46 (2)
L. of Cybernetics
Head: Árpad Makay

Founded 1921 in succession to the former Hungarian Franz-Joseph University of Kolozsvar (1872); known as Franz-Joseph University until 1940. Reorganized and became Szeged University 1945, acquired present title 1962. Faculty of Medicine detached and re-established as separate Medical University 1951. The university is under the jurisdiction of the Ministry of Education and is financed by the State. Governing body: the Senate. Residential facilities for some academic staff and for most students.

Arrangements for co-operation with the Universities of: Regensburg; Göttingen; Greifswald, Leipzig; Udine; Turku; Leningrad, Odessa; Łódź, Brno, Novi Sad, Skopje, Plovdiv, Timisoara.

Academic Year: September to June (September-December; February-June).

Admission Requirements: Secondary school certificate and entrance examination.

Fees: According to academic record.

Language of Instruction: Hungarian.

Degrees and Diplomas: Doctor iuris, law, 8 sem. Doctorate in all other faculties, 10 sem and thesis.

Library: Central Library, *c.* 600,000 vols.

Publications: Acta Universitatis Szegediensis de Attila József Nominatae; Acta Antiqua et Archeologica; Acta Bibliothecaria; Acta Biologica; Acta Climatologica; Dissertationes Salavicae; Sectio Ethnographica et Linguistica; Acta Geographica; Acta Historica; Acta Iuvenum; Sectio Philologica et Historica; Acta Juridica et Politica; Acta Historiae Litterarum Hungaricarum; Acta Mineralogica-Petrographica; Sectio Oeconomico-Politica; Sectio Paedagogica et Psychologica; Sectio Scientiarum Philologiae Germanicae; Sectio Philosophica; Acta Physica et Chemica; Acta Romanica; Sectio Scientiae Socialismi; Acta Scientiarum Mathematicarum; Acta Uralo-Altaica; Fontes Rerum Scolasticarum; Dissertationes ex Bibliotheca Universitatis Attila Jósef Nominate; Könyvtártörténeti Füzetek; Lymbus Müvelődéstörténeti Tár; Adattár XVI-XVIII, századi szellemi mozgalmaink történetéhez.

Press or Publishing House: Attila Jósef University Press, Szeged.

Academic Staff, 1989-90:

Rank	Full-time	Part-time
Egyetemi tanánar (Professors)	57	3
Docens (Associate Professors)	162	10
Adjunktus (Assistant Professors)	213	28
Tanársegéd (Assistants)	122	5
Nyelvtanár (Language Teachers)	38	–
Total	592	46

Student Enrolment, 1989-90:

	Men	Women	Total
Of the country	1267	1578	2845
Of other countries	–	33	87
Total	1267	1611	2932*

*Also 971 external students.

3374 **VESZPRÉMI VEGYIPARI EGYETEM**
Veszprém Technical University of Chemical Engineering
Schönherz Zoltán út 10, 8201 Veszprém
Cables: egyetem veszprém
Telex: 32397
Telephone: (80) 125-50
Rektor: Bálint Heil (1984-89)
Főtikár (Secretary-General): Zoltán Csapo

Heavy Chemical Engineering (including Inorganic Chemistry, Technology, Technology of Mineral Oil and Coal, Silicate, Chemistry, Radiochemistry, Chemistry Process Control, and Automation)
Also evening and correspondence courses.

Founded 1949 as faculty of the Technical University of Budapest, detached and re-established as separate institution 1951. The university is under the jurisdiction of the Ministry of Education and Culture. Governing body: the Senate. Some residential facilities for academic staff and for *c.* 600 students.

Arrangements for regular exchange of students with: Technical University of Silesia; College of Chemical Technology, Pardubice; 'Carl Schorlemmer' Technical University Leuna-Merseburg; Otto von Guericke Technical College of Magdeburg; Technical University of Silesia, Gliwice; Institute of Technology, Leningrad; Institute of Chemical Technology, Moscow; Institute of Chemical Technology, Bourgas. Arrangements for co-operation in research with: Technical University of Graz; University of Nancy; University of the Ruhr, Bochum; Technical University of Darmstadt; University of Surrey; University of Georgia; Pennsylvania State University; University of Ferrara; Institute of Chemical Technology, Bourgas; Institute of Technology, Leningrad; Otto von Guericke Technical College of Magdeburg; Technical University of Leuna-Merseburg; Institute of Chemical Technology, Moscow.

Academic Year: September to June (September-January; February-June).

Admission Requirements: Secondary school certificate and entrance examination.

Fees (Forints): 100-1300, according to academic record and parents' income.

Language of Instruction: Hungarian. English in postgraduate courses.

Degrees and Diplomas: Professional titles of–Üzemi vegyészmérnök, production engineer; Production Management Engineer, 3 yrs; Okleveles vegyészmérnök, chemical engineer, 5 yrs. Doctorate–Müszaki doktor, Dr.techn., by thesis and final examination.

Libraries: Central Library 128,000 vols; also specialized libraries of the departments.

Publications: A Veszprémi Vegyipari Egyetem Közlemények (Yearbook); Hungarian Journal of Industrial Chemistry (quarterly).

Academic Staff, 1986-87:

Rank	Full-time	Part-time
Egyetemi tanár (Professors)	15	2
Docens (Assistant Professors)	45	–
Adjunktus (Assistant Lecturers)	102	–
Tanársegéd (Assistants)	26	–
Nyelvtanár (Language Teachers)	9	–
Testnevelö tanár (Physical Education Teachers)	4	–
Total	201	2

Student Enrolment, 1986-87:

	Men	Women	Total
Of the country	264	197	461
Of other countries	18	12	30
Total	282	209	491*

*Also 138 external students.

3375 **AGRÁRTUDOMÁNYI EGYETEM**

University of Agriculture

Böszörményi út 138, 4015 Debrecen

Telex: 72-2111 H

Telephone: 17-888

Fax: 13-385

Rektor: András Kozma (1989-92)

Fõtitkár (Secretary-General): György Nádas

F. of Agricultural Sciences

Dean: György Supp

F. of Agricultural and Water and Ecological Management

Director: Sándor Hodossi

F. of Animal Husbandry (Hódmezobvásárhely)

Director: Imre Mucsi

I. of Production Development

Director: Imre Lovas

Land Research I. (Karcag)

Director: László Nyiri

Extension D.

Head: István Szabó

Also 31 institutes and departments of the faculties.

Founded 1868. Reorganized 1953 and became university 1970. The institution is under the jurisdiction of the Ministry of Food and Agriculture and is financed by the State. Governing body: the University Council. Residential facilities for students.

Academic Year: September to June (September-December; February-May).

Admission Requirements: Secondary school certificate and entrance examination.

Fees (Forints): 100-1300, according to academic record.

Language of Instruction: Hungarian.

Degrees and Diplomas: Diplomas of Engineer in Agriculture, 3-5 yrs. Doctorates. Also postgraduate diploma.

Library: Total, *c.* 153,360 vols.

Publication: Scientific Publications.

Academic Staff, 1989-90:

Rank	Full-time	Part-time
Egyetemi tanár (Professors)	37	–
Egyetemi docens (Associate Professors)	38	–
Adjunktus (First Assistants)	81	–
Tanársegéd (Assistants)	33	–
Others	58	1
Total	247	1

Student Enrolment, 1989-90:

	Men	Women	Total
Of the country	777	176	953
Of other countries	9	1	10
Total	786	177	963*

*Also 160 external students.

3376 ***GÖDÖLLÖ AGRÁRTUDOMÁNYI EGYETEM**

Gödöllö University of Agriculture

Páter Károly út 1, 2103 Gödöllö

Telex: 224892

Telephone: 28-10-200; 28-20-20

Fax: 28-10-804

Rektor: Károly Kocsis (1990-)

Fõtitkár (Secretary-General): Guth László

F. of Agricultural Sciences (including Horticulture and Animal Husbandry)

Dean: Mihály Sajgó; *staff* 402 (5)

F. of Agricultural Mechanical Engineering

Dean: Péter Szendró; *staff* 307 (9)

C. of Agricultural Mechanical Engineering (Mezötur)

General Director: István Patkás; *staff* 55

C. of Farm Management (Gyöngyös)

General Director: Sándor Magda; *staff* 56

F. of Agricultural Mechanical Engineering (correspondence course)

Assistant Dean: Zoltán Jeszensky

F. of Agricultural Sciences (postgraduate correspondence courses)

Assistant Dean: Zoltán Barcsák

Teacher Training I.

Director: Pál Vólgyesy; *staff* 21

I. of Agricultural Mechanization

Director: Péter Szendrö; *staff* 17 (1)

I. of Labour Studies

Director: László Udvari; *staff* 19

I. of Mathematics and Computer Sciences

Director: András Kósa; *staff* 9

Research I. (Kompolt)

Director: Alajos Fehér; *staff* 87

Also 43 departments of the faculties, 4 demonstration schools, and 4 special agricultural secondary schools.

Founded 1945 in Budapest with faculties of veterinary medicine, forestry, horticulture and viticulture, and agriculture. Transferred to Gödöllö 1950. The university is under the jurisdiction of the Ministry of Foodand Agriculture and is financed by the State. Governing body: the University Council. Residential facilities for academic staff and 80% of the students.

Special arrangements for co-operation with: Humboldt University of Berlin; Technical University of Dresden; University of Leipzig; Academy of Agriculture and Technology, Olsztyn-Kortowo; College of Agriculture, Brno; College of Agriculture, Nitra; Academy of Agriculture, Moscow; University of Agriculture, Warsaw; College of Agriculture, Prague; University of Novi Sad; Justus Liebig University of Giessen; Institute of Agriculture, Plovdiv; University of Dortmund; Agricultural University, Wageningen; Institute of Hydrology, Moscow; College of Engineerinig, Wismar; Agricultural University, Vienna; University of Stuttgart; Institute of Agriculture, Paris-Grignon; Purdue University, West Lafayette; Minnesota State University, St. Paul; Cornell University; University of Guelph; Mcgill University; State Faculty of Agricultural Science, Gembloux; Catholic University, Leuven; University of Aleppo; Agricultural College, Ciego de Avila; University of Agriculture and Forestry, Ho Chi Minh City; Ankara University.

Academic Year: September to June (September-January; February-June).

Admission Requirements: Secondary school certificate and entrance examination.

Fees (Forints): Up to 200-1300 per semester, according to academic record.

Language of Instruction: Hungarian.

Degrees and Diplomas: Diploma in Farm Administration, 3 yrs. Diplomas of Engineer in–Agriculture; Agricultural Engineering; Farm Management, 5 yrs. Doctorate in–Agriculture, Dr.agr.; Agricultural Technology, Dr.agr.techn., by thesis. Also postgraduate diplomas.

Libraries: Central Library, 302,851 vols; College of Agriculture (Gyöngyös), 32,725; College of Agricultural Mechanical Engineering 18,000; (Mezötur) Research Institute, 7850. Libraries of the departments.

Publications: Tudományos Értesitobje (Scientific Bulletin); Közleményei (Proceedings); Évkönyv (Yearbook); Library publications.

Academic Staff, 1989-90:

Rank	Full-time	Part-time
Egyetemi tanár (Professors)	53	2
Egyetemi docens (Associate Professors)	72	3
Egyetemi adjunktus (Assistant Professors)	140	5
Egyetemi tanársegéd (Instructors)	47	–
Főiskolai tanár (College Professors)	4	2
Főiskolai docens	13	–
Főiskolai adjunktus	18	–
Főiskolai tanársegéd	4	–
Nyelvtanár (Language Teachers)	29	1
Testnevelő tanár (Physical Education Teachers)	11	–
Tudományos gyakornok (Graduate Assistants)	9	–
Total	391	13

Student Enrolment, 1989-90:

	Men	Women	Total
Of the country	1348	402	1750
Of other countries	183	27	210
Total	1531	429	1360*

*Also 1070 external students and 1269 in demonstration schools.

3377 **AGRÁRTUDOMÁNYI EGYETEM**

University of Agriculture

Deák Ferenc út 16, 8360 Keszthely

Telephone: 123-30

F. of Agriculture (Mosonmagyaróvár)

F. of Animal Husbandry (Kaposvár)

Director: Peter Horn

Founded 1797. Reorganized 1906, acquired university rank 1942 and present status 1962. Reorganized as university 1970, incorporating former college at Mosonmagyaróvár. College of Agriculture at Kaposvár incorporated 1986. Financed by the Ministry of Food and Agriculture. Governing body: the Council. Residential facilities for students.

Arrangements for co-operation with Martin Luther University of Halle-Wittenberg.

Academic Year: September to June (September-January; February-June).

Admission Requirements: Secondary school certificate and entrance examination

Fees (Forints): According to academic record.

Language of Instruction: Hungarian.

Degrees and Diplomas: Diplomas of–Production Engineering, 3 yrs; Engineer of Agriculture, 5 yrs. Doctorate.

Library: c. 40,000 vols.

Publications: Georgikon; Reports, Articles and Scientific Mémoires published annually.

Academic Staff: c. 240.

Student Enrolment: c. 2000.

3378 ***BUDAPEST UNIVERSITY OF ECONOMIC SCIENCES**

Fövám tér 8, 1828 Budapest

Telex: 22-4186

Telephone: 117-6268

Fax: 117-8883

Rektor: Csaba Csáki

Főtitkár (Secretary-General): Hedvig Huszar

F. of Economics (including Political Economy, Micro Planning and Modelling, Mathematics and Computer Sciences, Economic Geography and Environmental Economics, History of Economic Thought and Statistics)

Dean: Lajos Zelko

F. of Business Administration

Dean: Tamas Mészaros

F. of Socio-Political Studies (including International Relations, Philosophy, Sociology, Economic History, Business Law, Physical Education and Foreign Languages)

Dean: Ildikó Hrubos

F. of Postgraduate Studies

Dean: Balázs Hamori

D. of C. Training

Dean: Sandor Kovacs

D. of Basic Studies

Dean: Györgyné Kerékgyártó

Also part-time studies for students coming from foreign partner universities. An Undergraduate English Degree Programme to begin September 1991. MBA and Ph.D. programmes planned.

Founded 1920, as Faculty of Economics of the Royal Hungarian University of Budapest. Became part of the Hungarian University of Economics from 1948. Academic programme divided into three faculties in 1952. A new system of instruction established 1988. Acquired present title 1990. Governing body: the University Council. Residential facilities for students.

Arrangements for co-operation with major universities worldwide.

Academic Year: September to June (September-December; February-June)

Admission Requirements: Secondary school certificate and entrance examination.

Language of Instruction: Hungarian.

Degrees and Diplomas: Professional titles, 3-5 yrs. Doctorate. Postgraduate Diploma courses 2 yrs (part-time).

Library: Central Library, *c.* 600,000 vols.

Publications: Közgazdász (bi-weekly) Egyetemi Szemle (quarterly); Tájákoztató a küföldi közgazdasági irodalomról (periodical); Hungarian Bibliography of Economics and Statistics.

Academic Staff, 1990:

Rank	Full-time
Egyetemi tanár/professzor (Professors)	51
Docens (Associate Professors)	79
Adjunktus (Assistant Professors)	114
Tanársegéd (Research Assistants)	193
Total	437

Student Enrolment, 1990: 2500 (Also 500 part-time students).

3379 **ERDÉSZETI ÉS FAIPARI EGYETEM**

University of Forestry and Wood Sciences

Bajcsy-Zsilinszky út 4, 9400 Sopron

Telex: 249126

Telephone: (99) 11-100

Fax: (99) 12-240

Rektor: András Winkler (1989-)

Főtitkár (Secretary-General): Szabolcs Varga

F. of Forestry

Dean: Miklos Kosztra; *staff* 70

F. of Wood Technology

Dean: Zsolt Kovacs; *staff* 48

C. for Surveying and County Planning

Director: István Joö; *staff* 38

I. of Paper and Wood Technology

Director: József Cziraky; *staff* 13

Founded in 1808 as a School of Forestry, became an academy in 1846. Moved to Sopron 1919 and reorganized and acquired present status in 1962. Governing bodies: University Council; the Faculty Councils. The university is under the jurisdiction of the Ministry of Agriculture. Residential facilities for students.

Arrangements for co-operation with: Institute of Forestry, Moscow; Institute of Forestry, Lwow; Academy of Agriculture, Warsaw; Academy of Agriculture, Poznań; Technical University, Dresden; College of Agriculture, Zvolen; College of Agriculture, Brno; University of Helsinki; University of Freiburg; University of Göttingen; University of Hamburg; Technical University Graz; University of Brasov; University of Vienna; University of British Columbia, Vancouver.

Academic Year: September to July (September-December; February-May).

Admission Requirements: Secondary school certificate and entrance examination.

Fees: None.

Language of Instruction: Hungarian.

Degrees and Diplomas: Diplomas of Engineer in–Forestry; Wood Technology, 5 yrs. Doctorate, Dr.techn., by thesis. Also Certificates in–Wood Technology; Surveying; Landscape Planning, 3 yrs. Also diplomas of specialization.

Library: 310,000 vols.

Special Facilities (Museums, etc.): Botanical Garden.

Publications: Scientific Publications (of Forestry and Timber Industry); Acta Facultatis Forestalis and Acta Facultatis Ligniensis (annuals).

Press or Publishing House: Press and Multiplying Office.

Academic Staff, 1989-90:

Rank	Full-time
Tanár (Professors)	14
Docens (Associate Professors)	36
Adjunktus (Assistant Professors)	65
Tanársegéd (Assistant Lecturers)	18
Kutató (Researchers)	22
Nyelvtanár (Language Teachers)	11
Testnevelőtanár (Physical Education Teachers)	3
Total	169

Student Enrolment, 1989-90:

	Men	Women	Total
Of the country	484	56	540
Of other countries	7	4	11
Total	491	60	551

3380 **KERTÉSZETI ÉS ÉLELMISZERIPARI EGYETEM**

University of Horticulture and Food Technology

Villányi út 35-43, 1118 Budapest

Telex: 226011

Telephone: (1) 850-666

Electronic mail: 512zal@ella.uucp

Rektor: István Tamássy (1986-92)

Főtitkár (Secretary-General): Tibor Kovacs

F. of Horticulture

Dean: János Papp

F. of Viticulture

F. of Food Industry

Dean: Tibor Deák

Also 2 Research Institutes at Kecskemét and Pécs, and Experimental Farm.

Founded 1853 as school of horticulture, became faculty of horticulture and viticulture of the University of Agriculture 1943. Acquired present status as university 1968 and present title 1986. Under the jurisdiction of the Ministry of Agriculture and financed by the State. Governing body: the Senate. Residential facilities for students.

Arrangements for co-operation with similar institutions in: Bulgaria; Czechoslovakia; Egypt; Germany; Netherlands; Poland; United Kingdom; Switzerland; USSR; Yugoslavia, USA.

Academic Year: September to June (September-December; January-June)

Admission Requirements: Secondary school certificate and entrance examination.

Fees (Forints): Up to 2000 per semester, according to parents' income and academic record.

Language of Instruction: Hungarian.

Degrees and Diplomas: Professional title of–Kertész-uzemmérnok, horticultural production engineer; Elelmiszeripari uzemmérnok, food industrial engineer, 3 yrs; Kertészmérnőki oklevél, horticultural engineer; Táj-és Kertépitész mérnok, landscape architect, 5 yrs. Doctorate by thesis.

Libraries: Central Library, 278,000 vols; department libraries.

Special Facilities (Museums, etc.): Botanical Garden. Arboretum of the Institute of Environmental Management.

Publication: Publicationes universitas Horticulturae.

Press or Publishing House: University Press.

Academic Staff, 1990:

Rank	Full-time
Tanár (Professors)	39
Docens (Lecturers)	63
Adjunktus (Assistant Professors)	119
Tanársegéd (Assistant Lecturers)	39
Research Workers	147
Total	407

Student Enrolment, 1989-90:

	Men
Of the country	1512
Of other countries	64
Total	1576*

*Also 209 students by correspondence.

3381 **SEMMELWEIS ORVOSTUDOMÁNYI EGYETEM**

Semmelweis Medical University

Üllobi út 26, 1085 Budapest VII

Telex: 226720

Telephone: (361) 134-610

Rector: Endre Somogyi (1985-88)

Secretary-General: Pál Blahó

F. of Medicine

Dean: A. Fonyó

F. of Dentistry

Dean: J. Dénes

F. of Pharmacy

Dean: Károly Zalai

Also 48 clinics, institutes, and departments.

Founded 1769 as faculty of medicine of the Eötvös Loránd University, detached and re-established as separate institution 1951. Under the jurisdiction of the Ministry of Health. Governing body: the University Council. Residential facilities for 1070 students.

Arrangements for co-operation with: the Universities of: Bari; Freiburg im Breisgau; Parma; Liège; Brussels; Indianopolis; Tashkent; Ulm. The Stockholm Institute of Medicine and Dentistry; Humboldt University of Berlin; Institute of Medicine, Moscow; Friedrich Schiller University of Jena; Academy of Medicine, Dresden; Academy of Medicine, Erfurt; Academy of Medicine, Sofia; Charles University, Prague; Jana Ev. Purkyně University, Brno; Comenius University, Bratislava; Instituto Superiori de Ciencias Médicas de Santiago de Cuba; Universityof Heidelberg.

Academic Year: September to June (September-January; February-June).

Admission Requirements: Secondary school certificate and entrance examination.

Fees: None.

Language of Instruction: Hungarian.

Degrees and Diplomas: Mag.pharm., Ph.M., pharmacy, 9 sem. Dr. med.dent., M.D.D., dentistry, 10 sem. Dr.med.univ., M.D., medicine, 12sem.

Libraries: Central Library, *c.* 200,000 vols; department libraries, *c.* 220,000.

Publication: Orvosegyetem (every two weeks).

Academic Staff, 1986-87:

Rank	Full-time
Tanszekvezető egyetemi tanár	52
Egyetemi tanár	48
Egyetemi Docens	87
Egyetemi Adjunktus	273
Egyetemi tanársegéd	539
Tudományos főmunkatárs	38
Tudományos munkatárs	93
Tudományos segédmunkatárs	22
Tudományos tanácsadő	12
Total	1164

Student Enrolment, 1986-87:

	Men	Women	Total
Of the country	1215	1776	2991
Of other countries	215	138	353
Total	1430	1914	3344

3382 **DEBRECENI ORVOSTUDOMÁNYI EGYETEM**

University of Medicine Debrecen
P.O.B. 15, 4012 Debrecen
Telex: 72411 H
Telephone: 17-571
Rektor: A. Leövey
Registrar: F. Uzvölgyi

Medicine and Dentistry

Also 13 teaching hospitals.

Founded 1912 as faculty of medicine of the Kossuth Lajos University, and commenced teaching 1918. Detached and re-established as separate institution 1951. A State institution under the jurisdiction of the Ministry of Health. Governing body: the University Council. Some residential facilities for academic staff and for 706 students.

Arrangement for co-operation with: Medical Academy, Kaunas; Medical Academy, Kiev; Institute of Stomatology, Moscow; Medical Academy, Riga; Medical Academy, Plovdiv; University of Brno; Pavel Josef Safárik University, Košice; Wilhelm Pieck University, Rostock; Medical Academy, Magdeburg; University of Liège.

Academic Year: September to August (September-December; February-May; July-August).

Admission Requirements: Secondary school certificate and entrance examination.

Fees (Forints): Up to 4000 per annum, according to academic record and parents' income. Foreign students, US$ 4500.

Languages of Instruction: Hungarian and English.

Degrees and Diplomas: Doctor of–Medicine; Dentistry, 5-6 yrs.

Library: Total, 138,000 vols.

Publications: Calendar; Annual.

Press or Publishing House: Printing Office.

Academic Staff, 1989-90:

Rank	Full-time	Part-time
Tanár (Professors)	54	9
Docens (Assistent Professors)	59	1
Adjunktus (Senior Assistants)	159	2
Tanársegéd (Assistants)	330	–
Nyelvtanár (Language Teachers)	16	–
Testnevelő (Physical Education Teachers)	5	–
Egyéb diplomás (Others)	99	–
Total	722	12

Student Enrolment, 1989-90:

	Men	Women	Total
Of the country	675	645	1320
Of other countries	165	51	216
Total	840	696	1536

3383 **PÉCSI ORVOSTUDOMÁNYI EGYETEM**

Medical University of Pécs
Szigeti-út 12, 7643 Pécs
Telex: 12311 POTE H
Telephone: (72) 24-122
Fax: (72) 26-244
Rektor: Miklós Bauer (1985-91)
Főtitkár (Secretary-General): József Hajnal

Medicine

Dentistry

Computer Ce.

Also 2 Research Laboratories and Teaching Hospitals.

Founded 1923 as faculty of medicine of the University of Pécs, detached and re-established as separate institution 1951. A State institution under the jurisdiction of the Ministry of Health. Governing body: the University Council. Residential facilities for 650 students.

Arrangements for co-operation with: Academy of Medicine, Erfurt; L'vov State University; Comenius University, Bratislava; University of Kuopio; University of Tübingen.

Academic Year: September to June (September-January; February-June).

Admission Requirements: Secondary school certificate and entrance examination.

Fees: None.

Languages of Instruction: Hungarian and English for foreign students.

Degrees and Diplomas: Professional qualifications in–Dentistry, 5 yrs; Medicine, 6 yrs.

Library: University Library, 208,610 vols.

Academic Staff, 1989-90:

Rank	Full-time
Egyetemi tanár (Professors)	36
Docens (Lecturers)	38
Adjunktus (First Assistants)	127
Tanársegéd (Assistants)	182
Others	112
Total	495

Student Enrolment, 1989-90:

	Men	Women	Total
Of the country	620	581	1201
Of other countries	178	66	244
Total	798	647	1445

3384 **SZENT-GYÖRGYI ALBERT ORVOSTUDOMÁNYI EGYETEM**

Albert Szent-Györgyi Medical University
Dugonics tér 13, 6722 Szeged
Telex: 82-441
Telephone: (62) 12-729
Fax: (62) 26-444
Rektor: János Szilárd (1986-)
Főtitkár: István Takáts

F. of Medicine and Dentistry
Dean: Gyula Telegdy

F. of Pharmacy
Dean: Béla Selmeczi

S. of Nursing
Director: Éva Szél

I. of Social Sciences
Director: Ferenc Bárány

I. of Foreign Languages
Head: József Torma

Medical Education Ce.
Head: Tamás Zoltán Örrs

Computer Ce.
Director: István Győri

Also *c.* 40 preclinical and clinical departments of the faculties.

Founded 1872 as a faculty of medicine of the former Franz-Joseph University of Kolozsvár, became faculty of University of Szeged 1921, detached and re-established as separate institution 1951. A State institution underthe jurisdiction of the Ministry of Health. Governing body: the University Council. Residential facilities for students.

Arrangements for co-operation with: Martin Luther University, Halle-Witttenberg; University of Ulm; University of Göttingen; Ernst Moritz Arndt University, Greifswald; Comenius University, Bratislava; Institute of Medicine, Odessa; Institute of Medicine, Varna; Palacky University, Olomouc; Turku University.

Academic Year: September to July (September-February; February-July).

Admission Requirements: Secondary school certificate and entrance examination.

Fees (US$): 300-500 per month.

Languages of Instruction: Hungarian and English.

Degrees and Diplomas: Gyógyszerészi oklevél, Diploma in Pharmacy, 5 yrs. Fogorvosdoktori diploma, Doctorate of Dental Medicine, 5 yrs; Orvosdoktori diploma; Doctorate of Medicine, 6 yrs.

Library: Central Library, *c.* 137,360 vols.

Publications: Studia Medica Szegedinensia; Yearbook; Scientific Publications.

Academic Staff, 1990-91:

Rank	Full-time
Professors	60
Associate Professors	76
Assistant and Principal Professors and Assistants	719
Total	855

Student Enrolment, 1989-90:

Men	Women	Total
2606	1230	3836*

*Including 2533 English language students. Also 124 foreign students.

3385 **ÁLLATORVOSTUDOMÁNYI EGYETEM**

University of Veterinary Science
Landler Jenö u. 2, P.O. Box 2, 1400 Budapest
Telex: 224439
Telephone: (1) 122-2260
Fax: (1) 142-6518
Rektor: Ferenc Kovacs (1984-92)
Főtitkár (Secretary-General): Tibor Jankovits

Veterinary Science

Also 17 Departments, and undergraduate training in German for foreign students.

Founded 1787 as Veterinary Institute of the University of Pest, became independent 1851, incorporated in University of Engineering and Economics 1934 and in University of Agriculture 1945. Became separate institution of university rank 1952 and acquired present status and title 1962. A state institution under the jurisdiction ofthe Ministry of Agriculture and Food. Governing bodies: the Academic Board; the University Council. Residential facilities for 250 students.

Arrangements for co-operation with similar institutions in: Germany (Berlin, Hanover, Leipzig); Czechoslovakia(Brno, Košice); USSR (Moscow); Netherlands (Utrecht); Poland (Warsaw); Austria (Vienna).

Academic Year: September to May (September-December; February-May).

Admission Requirements: Secondary school certificate and entrance examination.

Fees (Forints): 1000-2000 per term, according to academic record and parents' income.

Language of Instruction: Hungarian.

Degrees and Diplomas: Diploma of Doctor of Veterinary Medicine, 5 yrs. Postgraduate Veterinary Specialist, a further 2 yrs.

Library: Central Library, 130,000 vols.

Special Facilities (Museums, etc.): Museums of Veterinary History and of Departments of Surgery, Anatomy, and Pathological Anatomy.

Academic Staff, 1989-90:

Rank	Full-time
Tanár	20
Docens	15
Egyetemi adjunktu	40
Egyetemi tanársegéd	12
Tudományos főmunkatárs	4
Tudományos munkatárs	21
Tudományos tanácsadó	1
Others	9
Total	112

Student Enrolment, 1989-90:

	Men	Women	Total
Of the country	446	108	554
Of other countries	37	9	46
Total	483	117	600

3386 **MAGYAR TESTNEVELÉSI EGYETEM**

Hungarian University of Physical Education
Alkotás ú. 44, 1123 Budapest XII
Telephone: (1) 156-63-37
Fax: (1) 156-44-44
Rektor: Csaba Istvánfi (1989-93)
Főtitkár (Secretary-General): Márta Makkár

Physical Education and Sport

Founded 1925, four-year courses instituted 1929. Became university 1975. Acquired present title 1989. A State institution under the jurisdiction of the National Bureau of Physical Education and Sports, the Ministry of Education, and the Hungarian Academy of Sciences. Governing bodies: the Senate, comprising 29 members; the University Council, comprising 41 members; the Rector's Council comprising 17 members. Residential facilities for academic staff and students.

Arrangements for co-operation with: College of Physical Education, Leningrad; Academy of Physical Education, Warsaw; Institute of Physical Culture, Sofia; Comenius University; Slippery Rock University; Istituto Superiore Statale di Educazione Fisica di Roma. Also similar institutions in: Moscow; Leipzig; Bratislava; Bucharest; Paris.

Academic Year: September to June (September-January; February-June).

Admission Requirements: Secondary school certificate or foreign equivalent, and entrance examination.

Fees (Forints): According to academic record and parents' income. Foreign students, US$ 300 per month.

Language of Instruction: Hungarian.

Degrees and Diplomas: Teaching diploma, 4 yrs. Doctorate. Also trainer's certificate, 3 yrs.

Library: c. 70,000 vols.

Special Facilities (Museums, etc.): Video Studio.

Publications: A Magyar Testnevelési Egyetem Közleményei (Communiqué of the Hungarian University of Physical Education); Szakirodalmi Tájékoztató (Bulletin of Special Literature), monthly. Review of the Hungarian University of Physical Education (annually in English).

Academic Staff, 1989-90: 133 (17).

Student Enrolment, 1989-90:

	Men	Women	Total
Of the country	219	195	414
Of other countries	6	3	9
Total	225	198	423*

*Also 598 students by correspondence.

Other University Institutions

3387 **MAGYAR IPARMŰVÉSZETI FŐISKOLA**

Hungarian Academy of Crafts and Design
Zugligeti u. 1½5, 1121 Budapest XII
Telephone: (1) 761-722
Rektor: István Gergely (1982-)
Főtitkár (Secretary-General): Ferenc Müller

I. of Basic Studies

Director: József Scherer; *staff* 21 (1)

I. of Design

Director: József Gollob; *staff* 31 (23)

I. of Art and Design Management

Director: Ferenc Müller

Teachers Training I.

Director: Imre Bak; *staff* 17 (14)

Also International Ceramic Studio of Kecskemét

Founded 1880 as school, became college 1949. Under the jurisdiction of the Ministry of Culture and financed bythe State. Governing bodies: the Rector's Council; the University Council. Residential facilities for students.

Participates in the CITE-TEMPUS programme.

Academic Year: September to July (September-January; February-July).

Admission Requirements: Secondary school certificate.

Fees (Forints): According to academic record and parents' income. Foreign students, US$ 350 per month.

Language of Instruction: Hungarian.

Degrees and Diplomas: Bachelor of Arts in Industrial Design, 4 yrs. Master of Arts in–Industrial Design and Crafts, an additional 3sem; Pedagogy, 5 yrs.

Library: Central Library, *c.* 30,000 vols.

Special Facilities (Museums, etc.): Tölgyfa Gallery; International Ceramic Studio.

Academic Staff, 1989:

Rank	Full-time	Part-time
Professors	1	2
Docens (Assistant Professors)	26	14
Adjunktus (Assistant Lecturers)	34	27
Tanársegéd (Assistants)	20	10
Szakoktató (Special Teachers)	22	5
Nyelvtanár (Language Teachers)	8	–
Total	111	58

Student Enrolment, 1989:

	Men	Women	Total
Of the country	167	221	388

3388 **MAGYAR KÉPZŐMŰVÉSZETI FŐISKOLA**

Hungarian Academy of Fine Arts
Népköztársaság u. 69/71, 1389 Budapest VI
Telephone: (36-11) 428-556
Rector: Lajos Sváby
Secretary-General: István Szñyi

Fine Arts (Painting, Murals, Sculpture, Environment Design, Graphic Art, Graphic Design, Stage and Constume Design, Restoration)
Sec. of Art Theory (2)
I. of Foreign Languages

Founded 1871 as school, reorganized 1949 and acquired university status 1971.

Arrangements for interchange of students and graduates. Guest students admitted for two semesters.

Academic Year: October to June (October-January; February-June).

Admission Requirements: Secondary school certificate and presentation of original work.

Fees (US$): 300 per month.

Languages of Instruction: Hungarian and English.

Degrees and Diplomas: Master of Arts, 5 yrs. Ph.D., a further 1-2 yrs.

Library: Libraries of the Academys of Fine and Applied Arts.

Academic Staff, 1990-91:

Rank	Full-time	Part-time
Egyetemi tanár (Professors)	26	1
Egyetemi docens (Lecturers)	19	–
Egyetemi adjunktus (Assistant Professors)	21	8
Egyetemi tanársegéd (Assistant Lecturers)	13	–
Total	79	9

Student Enrolment, 1990-91: 320 (Also 50 external students).

3389 **LISZT FERENC ZENEMŰBVÉSZETI FŐISKOLA**

Franz Liszt Academy of Music
Liszt Ferenc tér 8, 1391 Budapest
Telephone: (1) 214-407
Rektor: József Sopron
Registrar: Franciska Ispán Puskás

Music

Branches in Debrecen, Györ, Miskolc, Pécs, and Szeged.

Founded 1875 by Franz Liszt. Acquired university status 1971. The academy is under the jurisdiction of the Ministry of Culture. Governing body: the Council, comprising 26 members. Residential facilities for students.

Arrangements for co-operation with College of Music and Dramatic Art, Stuttgart and Vienna.

Academic Year: September to June (September-January; February-June).

Admission Requirements: Secondary school certificate and adequate musical knowledge.

Fees (Forints): According to academic record.

Language of Instruction: Hungarian.

Degrees and Diplomas: Teaching qualification, 4-5 yrs. Performing qualification, 5-7 yrs.

Libraries: c. 120,000 vols; *c.* 80,000 musical works.

Special Facilities (Museums, etc.): Franz Liszt Commemorative Museum.

Academic Staff, 1989-90:

Rank	Full-time	Part-time
Professors	30	–
Assistant Professors	62	–
Assistant Lecturers	74	–
Language Teachers	8	–
Instrumental Teachers	–	82
Total	174	82

Student Enrolment, 1989-90:

	Men
Of the country	512
Of other countries	160
Total	672

3390 **SZINHÁZ-ÉS FILMMŰVÉSZETI FŐISKOLA**

College of Drama and Cinematography
Vas u. 2/c, 1088 Budapest VIII

Drama
Cinematography

Founded 1865.

3391 **ORVOSTOVÁBBKÉZŐ EGYETEM**

University of Graduate Medical Studies
Szabolcs u. 33/34, 1398 Budapest

Medicine (Graduate Level)

Other Institutions

3392 **APÁCZAI CSERE JÁNOS TANITÓKÉOZŐ FŐISKOLA**

Teachers' Training College
Liszt Ferenc u. 42, 9200 Györ
Telephone: 96-13655
Director-General: Ernö Molnár
Főtitkás (Secretary-General): Mrs. Somogyl

D. of Educational Theory
Head: Irén Feher
D. of Foreign Languages
Head: Klara Zaker
D. of General Education
Head: József Gesitesi
D. of Hungarian Literature and Language
Head: Marianna Hegri
D. of Music
Head: Zoltan Barothy
D. of Natural Sciences
Head: Istvan Juhász
D. of Physical Education
Head: Göncröl László
D. of Visual Education
Head: László Barakas

Founded in 18th century, aquired present status 1959. A State institution under the jurisdiction of the Ministry of Education. Residential facilities for students.

Academic Year: September to June (September-January; February-June).

Admission Requirements: Secondary school certificate.

Fees: None.

Language of Instruction: Hungarian.

Degrees and Diplomas: Teaching qualifications, 3 yrs.

Library: 40,665 vols.

Academic Staff, 1989-90: 68.

Student Enrolment, 1989-90:

	Men	Women	Total
Of the country	48	504	552

3393 **MAGYAR TÁNCMÜVÉSZETI FŐISKOLA**

Hungarian Dance Academy
Andrássy út 25, 1061 Budapest VI
Telephone: (1) 1224-044
Föigazgató (General-Director): Imre Dózsa (1989-90)
Főtitkár (Secretary-General): Györgyné Kovács

Dance (including Classical and Folk Dance, and Musicology)

Also primary and secondary schools.

Founded 1950 as State Institute of Ballet. Acquired present status and title 1983. Under the jurisdiction of the Ministry of Cultural and General Education. Governing body: the Academy Council. Some residential facilities for students.

Academic Year: September to June (September-January; February-June).

Admission Requirements: Dance teacher training. Secondary school certificate. Folk dancing: elementary education. Ballet: no preliminary training needed, general education given at the Academy. Students over the age of 10 accepted.

Fees (US$): 250 a month.

Languages of Instruction: Hungarian and English.

Academic Staff, 1989-90:

Rank	Full-time	Part-time
Professors	7	2
Assistant Professors	4	4
Assistant Lecturers	15	5
Professor's Assistants	11	11
School-teachers	49	8
Total	86	30

Student Enrolment, 1989-90:

	Men	Women	Total
Of the country	58	194	252
Of other countries	2	6	8
Total	60	200	260

3394 **BÁNKI DONÁT GÉPIPARI MŰSZAKI FŐISKOLA**

Bánki Donát Technical College for Mechanical Engineering
Népszinház u. 8, 1081 Budapest VIII
Telex: 226803 MFISK
Telephone: (1) 1134-000
Fax: (1) 1338-183
Főigazgató (Director): Lajos Pomázi
Főtitkár (Secretary-General): József Gáti

D. of Production
Director: Béla Angyal; *staff* 50 (15)
D. of Engineering and Production Planning
Director: Lajos Pomázi; *staff* 42 (2)
D. of Computer Science and Business Administration
Director: Imre Rudas; *staff* 30 (1)
Technical Teachers' Training D.
Director: Gyula Csanádi; *staff* 28 (2)

Founded 1963 in succession to industrial institute founded 1879. Acquired present status 1969. Under the jurisdiction of the Ministry of Culture. Governing body: the Council.

Arrangements for co-operation with similar institutions in: Germany; Yugloslavia; Netherlands; Finland.

Academic Year: September to June (September-January; February-June).

Admission Requirements: Secondary school certificate and entrance examination.

Fees (Forints): According to academic record and parents' income. Foreign students, US$ 1200 per annum.

Languages of Instruction: Hungarian and English.

Degrees and Diplomas: Diploma in–Mechanical Engineering; Factory Organization, 3 yrs; Mechanical Engineering and Teaching, 4 yrs.

Library: c.31,000 vols.

Publications: Bulletin (biennially); College News.

Academic Staff, 1989-90: 123 (3).

Student Enrolment, 1989-90:

	Men	Women	Total
Of the country	482	44	526
Of other countries	7	–	7
Total	489	44	533*

*Also 236 students by correspondence and 417 at evening courses.

3395 **BÁRCZI GUSZTÁV GYÓGYPEDAGÓGIAI TANÁRKÉPZŐ FŐISKOLA**

Gusztáv Bárczi Training College for Teachers of the Handicapped
Bethlen tér 2, 1071 Budapest
Telephone: 226-494
Főigazgató (Director): Sándor Illyés
Főtitkár (Secretary-General): Vilmos Hanos

Special Education

Founded 1900. A State institution under the jurisdiction of the Ministry of Education.

Academic Year: September to June (September-January; February-June).

Admission Requirements: Secondary school certificate.

Fees: None.

Language of Instruction: Hungarian.

Degrees and Diplomas: Diplomas in Teaching of Handicapped Children, 4 yrs.

Library: c. 40,000 vols.

Special Facilities (Museums, etc.): College Museum.

Publications: Bulletin (quarterly); Gyópedagógia (every 2 months); Scientific works.

Academic Staff, 1990:

Rank	Full-time	Part-time
Főiskolai Tanár (Professors)	12	4
Docens (Lecturers)	16	2
Adjunktus (Associate Professors)	38	7
Tanársegéd (Assistant Professors)	10	6
Total	76	19

Student Enrolment, 1990:

	Men
Of the country	431
Of other countries	12
Total	443*

*Also 1040 external students.

3396 **BERZSENYI DÁNIEL TANÁRKÉPZŐ FŐISKOLA**

Teachers' Training College
Szabadság tér 4, 9701 Szombathely
Telex: 37-241 TANFSZ.H.
Telephone: (94) 12-248
Főigazgató (Acting Director): János Iker (1987-)
Főtitkár (Secretary-General): József Bokor

D. of Arts
Head: János Horváth; *staff* 6
D. of Biology (Botany)
Head: Attila Szabó; *staff* 5
D. of Biology (Zoology)
Head: János Izsák; *staff* 3
D. of Chemistry
Head: Sándor Lorencz; *staff* 6
D. of Community Culture
Head: Arpád Szabó; *staff* 7
D. of Education Science
Head: Károly Molnár; *staff* 9
D. of Teacher Training (elementary level)
Head: László Sulyok; *staff* 5
D. of English Language and Literature
Head: István Kecskés; *staff* 3
D. of History
Head: Péter Varsányi; *staff* 8
D. of Geography
Head (Acting): Márton Varess; *staff* 6
D. of German Language and Literature
Head: Eajos Szalai; *staff* 6
D. of Hungarian Language and Literature
Head: Gusztáv Láng; *staff* 7
D. of Hungarian Linguistics
Head: Géza Szabó; *staff* 8
D. of Librarianship
Head: Gyula Tóth; *staff* 10
D. of Mathematics
Head: Jenő Horváth; *staff* 14
D. of Music
Head: Csaba Szabó
D. of Physical Education
Head: László Gál; *staff* 18
D. of Physics
Head: László Kovács; *staff* 6
D. of Russian Language and Literature
Head: Mihály Erdei; *staff* 7
D. of Slovenian Language and Literature
Head: Károly Gadányi; *staff* 4
D. of Social Sciences
Head: József Gutter; *staff* 12
D. of Technology
Head: István Bajsz; *staff* 7
I. of Foreign Languages
Head: Mária Barota; *staff* 15
Ut. of Educational Technology
Head: Zoltán Király; *staff* 4

Founded 1959 as Institute for Primary Teachers Training. Acquired present status 1971. Under the jurisdiction of the Ministry of Education. Governing body: the College Council. Residential facilities for students.

Arrangements for co-operation with: Teachers' Training College, Tallin; University of Maribor.

Academic Year: September to June (September-January; February-June).
Admission Requirements: Secondary school certificate.
Fees: None.
Language of Instruction: Hungarian.
Degrees and Diplomas: Teachers qualifications, 3-4 yrs. Diploma in–Library Science; Community Culture, 4 yrs.
Library: 150,000 vols.
Publication: Scientific publications.
Press or Publishing House: BDTF Nyomdája.
Academic Staff, 1989-90:

Rank	Full-time
Főiskolai tanár (Professors)	14
Főiskoai docens (Associate Professors)	42
Főiskolai adjunktus (Assistant Professors)	148
Nyelvtanár (Language Teachers)	15
Testnevelő tanár (Physical Education Teacher)	1
Lektor	2
Total	224

Student Enrolment, 1989-90:

	Men	Women	Total
Of the country	655	845	1500
Of other countries	–	5	5
Total	655	850	1505*

*Also 755 external students.

3397 **BESSENYEI GYÖRGY TANÁRKÉPZŐ FŐISKOLA**
Teachers' Training College
Pf. 166, 4401 Nyiregyháza
Telex: 73380 TKFOE H
Telephone: 11788; 11874

Teacher Training

Founded 1962. A State institution under the jurisdiction of the Ministry of Education. Residential facilities for students.

Arrangements for co-operation with universities or colleges in: Rzeszów; Ustí nad Labem; Zwickau; Jena; Erfurt; USSR.

Academic Year: September to July (September-January; February-June).
Admission Requirements: Secondary school certificate.
Fees (Forints): According to parents' income.
Language of Instruction: Hungarian.
Degrees and Diplomas: Teaching qualifications, 2-4 yrs.
Libraries: Central Library, *c.* 145,000 vols; libraries of the departments, *c.* 175,000.
Academic Staff: c. 250.
Student Enrolment: c. 1930 (Also *c.* 750 external students).

3398 **BUDAPESTI TANITÓKÉPZŐ FŐISKOLA**
Teachers' Training College
Kiss János altábornagy u. 40, 1531 Budapest

3399 **COMENIUS TANITÓKÉPZŐ FŐISKOLA**
Teachers' Training College
Eötvös u. 7, 3950 Sárospatak
Telex: 62-787
Telephone: 11-211
Főigazgató (Director): Főldy Ferenc
Irodavezető (Secretary-General): Debreczeni Gézáné

D. of Education
Head: Főldy Ferenc; *staff* 11
D. of Linguistics, Literature and Languages (English, Russian, German, Italian, Esperanto)
Head: Komáromy Sándor; *staff* 14
D. of Social Sciences
Head: Balázsi Károly; *staff* 10
D. of Natural Sciences
Head: Szilágyi Sándor; *staff* 14
D. of Physical Education
Head: Csajka Imre; *staff* 4 (1)

Founded 1531. Acquired present status 1959. Under the jurisdiction of the Ministry of Education. Residential facilities for students.

Arrangements for co-operation with Katowice University.

Academic Year: September to June.
Admission Requirements: Secondary school certificate and entrance examination.
Language of Instruction: Hungarian.
Degrees and Diplomas: Teaching qualification, 3 yrs.
Library: 70,000 vols.
Special Facilities (Museums, etc.): Exhibition of the Comenius Society.
Academic Staff, 1989-90:

Rank	Full-time
Tanár	4
Docens	16
Adjunktus	30
Nyelvtanár	1
Tanársegéd	8
Total	59

Student Enrolment, 1990:

	Men	Women	Total
Of the country	48	353	401*

*Also 306 external students.

3400 **DEBRECENI TANÍTÓKÉPZŐ FŐISKOLA**
Teachers' Training College
Péterfia u. 1/7, 4001 Debrecen

3401 **EÖTVÖS JÓZSEF TANÍTÓKÉPZŐ FŐISKOLA**
Teachers' Training College
Szegedi u. 2, 6501 Baja

3402 **VITÉZ JÁNOS TANÍTÓKÉPZŐ FŐISKOLA**
Vitéz János Teachers' Training College
Majer István u. 1-3, 2501 Esztergom
Telephone: (33) 13-699
Főigazgató (Director): Endre Kaposi (1989-94)
Főtitkár (Secretary-General): Arató Albert

Teacher Training (elementary and pre-school levels)

Founded 1842, acquired present status and title 1976. A State institution under the jurisdiction of the Ministry of Education. Governing body: the College Council.

Arrangements for co-operation with similar institutions in: Germany (Passau); Czechoslovakia (Nitra); USSR (Odessa).

Academic Year: September to June (September-December; January-May).
Admission Requirements: Secondary school certificate.
Fees (Forints): 400-3000, according to academic record.
Languages of Instruction: Hungarian and Slovakian.
Degrees and Diplomas: Teaching qualifications, 3-4 yrs. Also Diplomas in–Social Work; Public Education; Pre-school Education; German Minority Education; Slovakian Minority Education, 3-4 yrs.
Library: 75,000 vols.
Special Facilities (Museums, etc.): Movie Studio; Art Gallery.
Academic Staff, 1989-90:

Rank	Full-time
Főiskola tanár (Professors)	9
Főiskola docens (Assistant Professors)	17
Főiskola adjunktus (Assistant Lecturers)	30
Főiskola tanársegéd (Assistants)	10
Total	66

Student Enrolment, 1989-90:

	Men	Women	Total
Of the country	52	327	379*

*Also 177 external students.

3403 **GÉPIPARI ÉS AUTOMATIZÁLÁSI MŰSZAKI FŐISKOLA**
College of Mechanical Engineering and Automation
Izsáki út. 10, 6000 Kecskemét
Telex: 26-328
Telephone: 76-21-611
Főigazgató (Director): Béla Kulcsár (1985-88)
Főtitkár: Béla Szabó

Mechanical Engineering
Automation

Founded 1969. A State institution under the jurisdiction of the Ministry of Education. Residential facilities for academic staff and 300 students in hostels.

Arrangements for co-operation with: Technical University, Brno; Technical University of Cracow; University of Novi Sad.

Academic Year: September to June (September-January; February-June).

Admission Requirements: Secondary school certificate.

Fees (Forints): 100-1300, according to academic record and parents' income.

Language of Instruction: Hungarian.

Degrees and Diplomas: Diploma of Production Engineer, 3 yrs.

Library: 58,300 vols.

Academic Staff, 1986-87:

Rank	Full-time
Főiskola tanár (Professors)	11
Főiskola docens (Assistant Professors)	15
Főiskola adjunktus (Assistant Lecturers)	37
Főiskola tanársegéd (Assistants)	10
Nyelvtanár (Language Teachers)	
Testnevelö (Physical Education Taches)	11
Total	84

Student Enrolment, 1986-87:

	Men	Women	Total
Of the country	360	20	380

3404 **HO-SHI-MINH TANÁRKÉPZŐ FŐISKOLA**

Teachers' Training College

Szabadság tér 2, 3301 Eger

Telex: 63-309

Telephone: 10-466

Teacher Training

Founded 1948. The college is under the jurisdiction of the Ministry of Education and is financed by the State.Residential facilities for students in 3 hostels.

Arrangements for co-operation with: Pedagogická Fakulta, Banská Bystrica; College of Education, Erfurt; Vinh Institute of Education; College of Education, Zielona-Góra; University of Exeter; Institutes of Educationin the USSR.

Academic Year: September to June (September-December; February-June).

Admission Requirements: Secondary school certificate.

Fees (Forints): According to academic record.

Language of Instruction: Hungarian.

Degrees and Diplomas: Teaching qualification, 4 yrs.

Library: c. 220,000 vols.

Publication: Scientific Publications.

Academic Staff: c. 200 (30).

Student Enrolment: c. 1420 (Also c. 860 external students).

3405 **TANITÓKÉPZŐ FŐISKOLA**

Teachers' Training College

Rákóczi u. 53, 5102 Jászberény

Telex: 23-705

Telephone: (57) 12-155

Főigazgató (Director): József Nagy

Főtitkár (Secretary-General): Ilona Kertész

D. of Hungarian Language and Literature

Head: József Nagy; *staff* 7

D. of Foreign Languages

Head: Odőn Horgosi; *staff* 9

D. of Music and Art

Head: György Máté; *staff* 7

D. of Physical Education

Head: György Andrási; *staff* 5

D. of Science

Head: László Gedon; *staff* 11

D. of General Education (Library Science, Sociology, History of Civilization)

Head: Mária Harmath; *staff* 4 (6)

D. of Philosophy

Head: Pál Kalmár; *staff* 5

D. of Pedagogy

Head: Lajos Gledura; *staff* 6 (5)

Founded as secondary school 1917, became college 1959. Under the jurisdiction of the Ministry of Education. Governing body: the College Council. Residential facilities for students.

Academic Year: September to May (September-December; February-May).

Admission Requirements: Secondary school certificate.

Fees: None.

Languages of Instruction: Hungarian. Also English, German, and Russian.

Degrees and Diplomas: Teaching qualifications, 3 yrs. Diploma in Library Science, 4 yrs.

Library: Central Library, 70,000 vols.

Academic Staff, 1989-90:

Rank	Full-time	Part-time
Főiskolai tanár	5	–
Főiskolai docens	12	1
Főiskolai adjunktus	30	–
Főiskolai tanársegéd	5	–
Lektor	1	–
Total	53	1

Student Enrolment, 1989-90:

	Men	Women	Total
Of the country	30	310	340*

*Also 250 students by correspondence.

3406 **JUHÁSZ GYULA TANÁRKÉPZŐ FŐISKOLA**

Teachers' Training College

Április 4 út 6, 6701 Szeged

Cables: 6701 Pf.: 396

Telephone: 10-495; 10-244

Teacher Training

Founded 1873, acquired present status 1947, and title of Teacher Training College 1962. A State institution under the jurisdiction of the Ministry of Education. Governing body: the Council.

Academic Year: September to May (September-December; February-May).

Admission Requirements: Secondary school certificate.

Fees (Forints): According to academic record.

Language of Instruction: Hungarian.

Degrees and Diplomas: Teaching qualification, 4 yrs.

Libraries: Central Library, c. 131,850 vols; specialized libraries, total, c. 85,550.

Publications: Tudományos Közlemények (annually); Módszertani Közlemények (five times a year).

Academic Staff: c. 190.

Student Enrolment: c. 1450 (Also c. 1030 external students).

3407 **KANDÓ KÁLMÁN VILLAMOSIPARI MÜSZAKI FŐISKOLA**

Kandó Kálmán College of Electrical Engineering

Tavaszmező u. 17, 1084 Budapest VIII

Telex: 224897

Telephone: (1) 335-530

Fax: (1) 1342-132

Rektor: István Vágó

Főtitkár (Secretary-General): Győző Diószeghy

I. of Heavy Current Automation and Equipment

Director: György Fehér; *staff* 29 (5)

I. of Power Engineering

Director: János Orosz; *staff* 30

I. of Mathematics and Computer Sciences

Director: Dezső Sima; *staff* 25

I. of Electronic Components Technology

Director: József Korom; *staff* 27 (2)

I. of Instrumentation and Control Engineering

Director: Elek Horváth; *staff* 27 (2)

I. of Telecommunications

Director: István Kerpán; *staff* 27 (3)

I. of Computer Production

Director: Mihály Tóth; *staff* 30 (10)

I. of Education and Languages

Director: János Sallai; *staff* 31 (2)

I. of Social Sciences

Director: András Medve; *staff* 23

Founded as school 1898, became college 1969. Reorganized 1979. Under the jurisdiction of the Ministry of Culture and Education and financed by the State. Governing body: the College Council. Residential facilities for students.

Arrangements for co-operation with: Mohawk College, Canada; Hochschule Bremen; Université d'Angers; Technical University Varna; Technische Hochschule Leipzig; Višs technička škola Subotica; Fachhochschule Furtwangen; Fachhochschule Wilhelmshaven.

Academic Year: September to July (September-December; February-May).

Admission Requirements: Secondary school certificate.

Fees (Forints): According to academic record.

Language of Instruction: Hungarian.

Degrees and Diplomas: Diploma, 6-8 sem. Diploma in–Production Engineering, 6 sem; Engineering and Teaching, 8 sem.

Library: c. 75,000 vols.

Publication: Tudományos Közlemények (annually).

Academic Staff, 1989-90:

Rank	Full-time	Part-time
Főiskolai tanár	26	4
Docens	63	2
Adjunktus	111	16
Tanársegéd	18	–
Uzemmérnök	60	–
Total	278	22

Student Enrolment, 1989-90:

	Men	Women	Total
Of the country	1473	52	1525
Of other countries	25	–	25
Total	1498	52	1550*

*Also 261 external students.

3408 **CSOKONAI VITÉZ MIHÁLY TANITÓKÉPZŐ FŐISKOLA**

Teachers' Training College

Bajcsy Zsilinszky u. 10, 7401 Kaposvár

Telex: 13209

Telephone: (82) 13552

Fax: (82) 12432

Főigazgató (Director-General): Leitner Sándor

Főtitkar (Secretary-General): Kálmán Katalin

Teacher Training (pre-school and primary levels)

Founded 1950. A State institution under the jurisdictiion of the Ministry of Education. Residential facilities for students.

Arrangments for co-operation with institutes in: Poland (Olsztyn); Austria (Linz); USSR (Odessa); United Kingdom (Bath).

Academic Year: September to May (September-December; February-May).

Admission Requirements: Secondary school certificate and entrance examination.

Fees (Forints): 1000-1500, according to academic record.

Language of Instruction: Hungarian.

Degrees and Diplomas: Teaching qualifications, 3 yrs.

Library: College Library, 100,573 vols.

Press or Publishing House: College Press.

Academic Staff, 1990:

Rank	Full-time
Tanár	8
Docens	15
Adjunktus	32
Tanársegéd	22
Gyakorlatvezető	4
Nyelvtanar	3
Total	84

Student Enrolment, 1990:

	Men	Women	Total
Of the country	57	502	559*

*Also 280 external students.

3409 **KECSKEMÉTI TANITÓKÉPZŐ FŐISKOLA**

Teachers' Training College

Kaszap u. 6/14, 6001 Kecskemét

Telex: 26-478

Telephone: (76) 21-444

Fögazgató (Director): Dovala Márta

Főtitkár (Secretary-General): Szombathy Zoltán

Teacher Training

Founded 1959. Acquired present status 1983. A State institution under the jurisdiction of the Ministry of Education. Residential facilities for students.

Academic Year: September to May (September-December; February-May).

Admission Requirements: Secondary school certificate.

Fees (Forints): 1000-3000, according to academic record.

Language of Instruction: Hungarian.

Degrees and Diplomas: Teaching qualifications, 3 yrs.

Library: c. 50,000 vols.

Press or Publishing House: College Press.

Academic Staff, 1989-90:

Rank	Full-time	Part-time
Főiskolai tanár	7	–
Főiskolai docens	13	–
Főiskolai adjunktus	24	–
Főiskolai tanársegéd	8	2
Total	52	2

Student Enrolment, 1989-90:

	Men	Women	Total
Of the country	35	364	399*

*Also 288 external students.

3410 **KÖNNYÜIPARI MÜSZAKI FŐISKOLA**

College of Light Industrial Technology

Doberdó út 6, 1034 Budapest

Telephone: 1803-333

Főigazgató (Director): Gyula Kanczler

Főtitkár (Secretary-General): Béláné Huppán

Sec. for Clothing Industry

Head: Béla Bődi; *staff* 20 (3)

Sec. for Textile Technology

Head: Sándor Téti; *staff* 23 (4)

Sec. for Leather Industry

Head: János Beke; *staff* 15 (4)

Sec. for Printing Technology

Head: Miklós Gara; *staff* 30 (3)

Sec. for Paper Technology

Head: József Erdélyi; *staff* 15 (2)

D. of Basic Sciences

Head: Viktor Scharnitzky; *staff* 8

D. of Mechanical Engineering

Head: József Bódi; *staff* 10 (2)

D. of Data Processing

Head: Ilona Beck; *staff* 10

D. of Management

Head: András Berey; *staff* 5

Founded 1963 as technical school, acquired present status and title 1972. Under the jurisdiction of the Ministry of Education. Governing body: the College Council. Residential facilities for students.

Arrangements for co-operation with institutes in: Kiev; Moscow; Dresden.

Academic Year: September to May (September-December; January-May).

Admission Requirements: Secondary school certificate.

Fees (Forints): 500-2500 per sem.

Language of Instruction: Hungarian.

Degrees and Diplomas: Diploma of Production Engineer, 3 yrs; 4 yrs for external and correspondence students.

Library: Central Library, *c.* 42,000 vols.

Publication: Scientific Works (annually).
Academic Staff, 1990:

Rank	Full-time	Part-time
Tanár	9	–
Docens	8	2
Adjunktus	40	5
Tanársegéd	25	8
Total	82	15

Student Enrolment, 1990:

	Men	Women	Total
Of the country	130	302	432
Of other countries	6	13	19
Total	136	315	451*

*Also 180 external students.

3411 **KÜLKERESKEDELMI FŐISKOLA**
College of Foreign Trade
Ecseri út 3, Budapest 1097
Telephone: 573-166

Foreign Trade

Founded 1962. Under the jurisdiction of the Ministry of Education. Financed by the Ministry of Foreign Trade. Governing body: the Council. Some residential facilities for students in hostels.

Arrangements for co-operation with similar institutions in Austria, Czechoslovakia, Finland, German DemocraticRepublic, Poland, USSR.

Academic Year: September to June (September-January; February-May).

Admission Requirements: Secondary school certificate and entrance examination.

Fees (Forints): According to academic record.

Language of Instruction: Hungarian.

Degrees and Diplomas: Diplomas of–Business Administration for Foreign Trade, 3-4 yrs; Foreign Language Correspondent for Foreign Trade, 3 yrs.

Library: c. 30,000 vols.

Academic Staff: c. 170.

Student Enrolment: c. 890 (Also c. 460 external students).

3412 **PÉNZÜGYI ÉS SZÁMVITELI FŐISKOLA**
College of Finance and Accountancy
Buzogány út. 10, 1149 Budapest
Telex: 226868 PSZFB
Telephone: (361) 252-1444
Főgazgató (Director-General): Lajos Kállai (1985-93)
Főtitkár (Secretary-General): István Németh

D. of Finance
Head: Géza Ambrózy; *staff* 15 (2)
D. of Accountancy
; *staff* 15 (14)
D. of Mathematics and Statistics
Head: László Csernyk; *staff* 9 (2)
D. of Foreign Languages
Head: Tamás Radványi; *staff* 18 (2)
D. of Information Management
Head: Pál Bodnár; *staff* 13 (6)
D. of Social Sciences
Head: Károlyné Marjenek; *staff* 6 (4)
I. of Computer Sciences
D. of Physical Education
Branches in: Zalaegerszeg and Salgótargán

Founded 1964. A State institution under the jurisdiction of the Ministry of Education. Governing body: the College Council. Residential facilities for students.

Arrangements for co-operation with: State University of Kiev; Institute of Finance and Economics, Svichtov; Karl Marx University of Leipzig; Academy of Economics, Wrocław; Institut supérieur de Gestion, Paris.

Academic Year: September to June (September-December; February-May).

Admission Requirements: Secondary school certificate and entrance examination.

Fees (Forints): 1000-2500 per semester, according to academic record.

Language of Instruction: Hungarian.

Degrees and Diplomas: Diploma in various fields, 3 yrs.

Library: Central Library, 50,000 vols.
Academic Staff, 1989-90:

Rank	Full-time	Part-time
Főiskola tanár (Professors)	17	6
Főiskola docens (Assistant Professors)	30	9
Főiskola adjunktus (Assistant Lecturers)	58	16
Főiskola tanársegéd (Assistants)	44	5
Testnevelö (Physical Education Teachers)	8	–
Kollegiumi tanár	4	–
Total	161	36

Student Enrolment, 1989-90:

	Men	Women	Total
Of the country	385	1134	1419
Of other countries	1	–	1
Total	386	1034	1420*

*Also 1601 external students.

3413 **POLLACK MIHÁLY MÜSZAKI FŐISKOLA**
Pollack Mihály Technical College
Boszorkány út 2, 7624 Pécs
Telex: 12501
Telephone: (72) 24-277
Fobigazgató (Director): Zotán Nagy (1985-88)
Fobigazgatói hivatalvezetob: Gyula Radics

I. of Architecture
Director: József Biró; *staff* 26 (1)
I. of Civil Engineering
Director: Medvetzky Antalné; *staff* 38 (5)
I. of Sanitary Engineering
Director: László Tornai; *staff* 38 (5)
I. of Chemical-Silicate Engineering
Director: Gyula Kucsera; *staff* 23 (3)
I. of Irrigation and Hydrology (Baia)
I. of Mathematics and Computer Sciences
Director: László Müller; *staff* 17
I. of Education
Director: Elemér Kiss; *staff* 23
I. of Marxism-Leninism
Director: József Komanovics; *staff* 12
I. of Water Management (Baja)
Director: László Vaskó; *staff* 41

Founded 1971. A State institution under the jurisdiction of the Ministry of Education. Some residential facilities for students.

Arrangements for co-operation with: Technical University of Bratislava; College of Engineering, Cottbus; College of Architecture and Building, Weimar; Technical University of Wrocław; Institute of Civil Engineering, Vilnius.

Academic Year: September to July (September-December; January-May).

Admission Requirements: Secondary school certificate.

Fees (Forints): 100-800, according to academic record and parents' income.

Language of Instruction: Hungarian.

Degrees and Diplomas: Diploma of Production Engineer, 3 yrs. Also technical teaching qualification, 4 yrs.

Library: Central Library, 73,138 vols.

Publications: Acta Academiae Polytechnicae; A Pollack Mihaly Múszaki Fobiskola Tudományos Közlemények.

Press or Publishing House: College Press.

Academic Staff, 1986-87:

Rank	Full-time	Part-time
Főiskolai tanár (Professors)	20	1
Főiskolai docens (Associate Professors)	38	3
Főiskolai adjunktus (Assistant Professors)	93	7
Főiskolai tanársegéd (Assistant Lecturers)	37	1
Total	188	12

Student Enrolment, 1986-87:

	Men	Women	Total
Of the country	927	177	1104
Of other countries	14	–	14
Total	941	177	1118*

*Also 417 external students.

3414 **SZÉCHENYI ISTVÁN MÜSZAKI FŐISKOLA**

Széchenyi István' College of Technology
Ságvári Endre út. 3, 9026 Győr
Telex: 24-267
Telephone: (96)-29-722
Fax: (96) 29-263
Főigazgató (Director-General): Tamás Szekeres (1989-)
Főtitkár (Secretary-General): Károly Horráth

S. of Civil Engineering
Director: Csaba Koren; *staff* 42
S. of Mechanical Engineering
Director: Tibor Kázmér; *staff* 68
S. of Transport and Postal Management
Director: Bálint Hirkó; *staff* 29
S. of Telecommunications and Automation
Director: József Kuti; *staff* 28
D. of Teacher Training
Head: Zsuzsa Vásárhelyi; *staff* 9

Founded 1968. Other colleges founded 1962-3 incorporated 1971. A State institution under the jurisdiction of the Ministry of Education. Residential facilities for 1050 students.

Arrangements for co-operation with: Hochschule für Verkehrswesen 'Friedrich Liszt', Dresden; College of Engineering, Zwickau; Otto von Guericke Technical University of Magdeburg; Cracow Technical University; Technical College Radom; Hatfield Polytechnic.

Academic Year: September to June (September-December; February-June).

Admission Requirements: Secondary school certificate and entrance examination.

Fees: Fees (Forints): Up to 1300, according to academic record and parents' income.

Language of Instruction: Hungarian.

Degrees and Diplomas: Diploma, 3 yrs. Technical teaching qualification, 4 yrs. Postgraduate diploma, a further 2 yrs.

Library: 112,000 vols.

Publication: Scientific Publications (2-3 times a year).

Academic Staff, 1990:

Rank	Full-time	Part-time
Fobiskola tanár (Professors)	13	–
Fobiskola docens (Assistant Professors)	64	–
Fobiskola adjunktus (Assistant Lecturers)	106	2
Fobiskola tanársegéd (Assistants)	30	1
Nyelvtanár (Language Teachers)	13	–
Testnevelö (Physical Education Teachers)	6	–
Total	232	3

Student Enrolment, 1989-90: 1293 (Also 707 external and 412 postgraduate students).

3415 **ZSÁMBÉKI TANITÓKÉPZŐ FŐISKOLA**

Zsambéki Teachers' Training College
Lenin tér 3, 2072 ambék
Telephone: 26-42-122
Főigazgató (Director): Albert Tóth (1985-)
Hivatalvezetob: Kázmér Domokos

Teacher Training (elementary and kindergarten levels)

Founded 1977. A State institution under the jurisdiction of the Ministry of Culture and Education. Residential facilities for academic staff and students.

Academic Year: September to May (September-December; February-May).

Admission Requirements: Secondary school certificate.

Language of Instruction: Hungarian.

Degrees and Diplomas: Teaching qualifications, 2-3 yrs.

Library: 31,000 vols.

Academic Staff, 1986-87:

Rank	Full-time	Part-time
Főiskola tanár (Professors)	3	–
Főiskola docens (Assistant Professors)	8	–
Főiskola adjunktus (Assistant Lecturers)	31	7
Főiskola tanársegéd (Assistants)	15	–
Total	57	7

Student Enrolment, 1986-87:

	Men	Women	Total
Of the country	19	139	158*

*Also 198 external students.

3416 **YBL MIKLÓS ÉPITŐIPARI MÜSZAKI FŐISKOLA**

Polytechnic 'Ybl Miklós'
Thököly út 74, 1146 Budapest
Telex: 224699
Telephone: 229-602; 426-315
Főigazgató (Director): Lajos Pozsgai (1985-88)

Building Engineering
Lifelong Education

Founded as separate schools (1879 Budapest, 1965 Debrecen), reorganized with present status and title 1972. A State institution under the jurisdiction of the Ministry of Culture and Education. Governing body: the Council.

Arrangements for co-operation with: Institute of Civil Engineering, Moscow; Institute of Civil Engineering, Leningrad; Institute of Architecture and Civil Engineering, Sofia; Technical University of Leipzig; College of Architecture and Building, Weimar; University of Novi Sad.

Academic Year: September to June (September-December; February-June).

Admission Requirements: Secondary school certificate.

Fees (Forints): According to academic record.

Language of Instruction: Hungarian.

Degrees and Diplomas: Diploma of Production Engineer, 3 yrs. Also diplomas of specialization.

Library: Technical libraries at Budapest and Debrecen.

Publication: Scientific Papers (2 times a year).

Academic Staff, 1986-87:

Rank	Full-time	Part-time
Főiskolai tanár (Professors)	20	1
Readers	44	3
Főiskolai docens (Lecturers)	77	3
Főiskolai tanársegéd (Assistants)	14	–
Total	151	7

Student Enrolment, 1986-87:

	Men	Women	Total
Of the country	1192	378	1570
Of other countries	8	–	8
Total	1200	378	1578*

*Also 215 external students.

3417 **KERESKEDELMI ÉS VENDÉGLÁTÓIPARI FŐISKOLA**

College of Commerce, Catering, Hotel Management and Tourism
Alkotmány 9/11, 1054 Budapest V
Telephone: 327-150
Fax: (1) 1315-720
Principal: M. Horn (1985-)
Vice-Principal: T. Szüts

F. of Commerce
F. of Catering and Hotel Management
F. of Tourism and Hotel Management
D. of Social Sciences
D. of Foreign Languages
D. of Pedagogy
D. of Statistic and Accounting
D. of Hospitality Management
D. of Management of Commerce
D. of Management of Tourism

Branch in Szolnok (Commerce, Catering and Hotel Management).

Founded 1962 as Institute, acquired present status and title 1968. Branch in Szolnok founded 1979. Under the jurisdiction of the Ministry of Trade. Resdiential facilities for *c.* 350 students.

Academic Year: September to June (September-December; January-May).

Admission Requirements: Secondary school certificate and entrance examination.

Language of Instruction: Hungarian.

Degrees and Diplomas: Professional title of Business Administrator in–Commerce; Hotel Management, 3-3 ½ yrs. Master, a further 2 yrs.

Library: c. 46,000 vols.

Academic Staff, 1989-90:

Rank	Full-time	Part-time
Főiskolai tanàr	15	–
Docens	21	–
Adjunktus	45	
Tanársegéd	28	70
Total	109	70

Student Enrolment, 1989-90:

	Men	Women	Total
Of the country	430	840	1270
Of other countries	–	–	18
Total	430	840	1288

3418 **MEZŐGAZDASÁGI FŐISKOLA**

College of Agriculture

Rákóczi-u. 69, 4400 Nyíregyháza 4401

Telex: 73209

Telephone: 06-42-15-034

Főigazgató (Director): János Bánházi (1983-91)

Főigazatói hivatalvezetob: Iván Kökéndy

I. of Agricultural Engineering
Director: István Rukóber; *staff* 27

I. of Aviation Production Engineering
Director: Dyula Szabó; *staff* 14

D. of Lifelong Education

Founded 1961, acquired present status and title 1971. A State institution under the jurisdiction of the Ministry of Agriculture and Food. Governing body: the Council. Residential facilities for students.

Academic Year: September to June (September-December; February-June).

Admission Requirements: Secondary school certificate and entrance examination.

Fees (Forints): 1000-1300, according to academic record and parents' income.

Language of Instruction: Hungarian.

Degrees and Diplomas: Diploma of Production Engineer, 3 yrs.

Library: 40,000 vols.

Publication: Scientific Research Papers (annually).

Academic Staff: c. 60.

Student Enrolment, 1986-87:

	Men	Women	Total
Of the country	260	1	261*

*Also 78 external students.

3419 **ÁLLAMIGAZGATÁSI FŐISKOLA**

School of Public Administration

Ménesi út 5, 1118 Budapest XI

Telex: 22 5229

Telephone: 185-2122

Főigazgató (Director): Lajos Lőrincz (1989-90)

Főtitkár (Secretary-General): Klára Ispán

D. of Public Administration
Head: Gyula Németh; *staff* 8 (5)

D. of General Social Theory
Head: Vilmos Rahnai; *staff* 7 (4)

D. of Languages and Physical Training
Head: Ottó Czifra; *staff* 10 (9)

D. of Law
Head: László Papp; *staff* 9 (5)

D. of Management Studies
Head: Sádor Kiss; *staff* 12 (3)

D. of Financial and Economic Theory
Head: Árpád Nagy; *staff* 9 (5)

I. of Postgraduate Studies
Head: Gábor Máthé; *staff* – (21)

D. for Correspondence Courses
Head: János Kovács; *staff* 8 (7)

Founded 1952 as academy, acquired present status and title 1977. A State instution under the jurisdiction of the Ministry of Interior. Governing body: the Council. Residential facilities for *c.* 330 students.

Academic Year: September to June (September-December; February-June).

Admission Requirements: Secondary school certificate.

Fees (Forints): According to academic record and parents' income.

Language of Instruction: Hungarian.

Degrees and Diplomas: Diploma, 2-4 yrs.

Library: 41,000 vols.

Publication: Acta Academiae Administrationis Dei Publicae.

Press or Publishing House: School Press.

Academic Staff, 1989-90:

Rank	Full-time	Part-time
Főiskolai tanár (Professors)	7	6
Főiskolai docens (Assistant Professors)	14	5
Főiskolai adjunktus (Assistant Lecturers)	26	3
Főiskolai tanársegéd (Assistants)	6	–
Others	10	44
Total	63	58

Student Enrolment, 1989-90:

	Men	Women	Total
Of the country	130	415	545*

*Also 526 external students.

ICELAND

3420 ***HÁSKÓLI ÍSLANDS**
University of Iceland
1101 Reykjavik
Telephone: 354-1-694300
Rektor: Sigmundur Gudbjarnason
Háskólaritari: Stefán Sörensson

F. of Theology
Dean: Jón Sveinbjörnsson
F. of Medicine
Dean: Asmundur Brekkan
F. of Law
Dean: Jónatan Thórmundsson
F. of Economics
Dean: Thórir Einarsson
F. of Philosophy (including Liberal Arts)
Dean: Páll Skúlason
F. of Engineering
Dean: Vladimar K. Jàonsson
F. of Science
Dean: Sveinbjörn Björnsson
F. of Dentistry
Dean: Gudjón Axelsson
F. of Social Sciences
Dean: Thórrólfur Thórlindsson
F. of Nursing
F. of Physiotherapy

Founded 1911 by merging existing theological seminary, medical college, and school of law, and adding faculty of philosophy. A State institution, financed by the Treasury. University matters are dealt with by the Senate, composed of the Rector, who is elected by the professors, and the deans of the faculties. The university is responsible to the Ministry of Education. Residential facilities for students.

Academic Year: September to June (September-January; February-June).

Admission Requirements: Secondary school certificate.

Fees: None.

Languages of Instruction: Icelandic.

Degrees and Diplomas: Cand.theol., theology; Cand.med.etchir., medicine; Cand.med.dent., dentistry; Cand.jur., law; Cand.oecon., economics; Cand.mag., B.A., arts. B.S., engineering; science; social sciences; nursing; physiotherapy.

Library: University Library. *c.* 250,000 vols.

Publication: Arbók Háskóla Islands.

Academic Staff, 1986-87: c. 450.

Student Enrolment, 1986-87: c. 4500.

3421 **HÁSKÓLINN Á AKUREYRI**
University of Akureyri
P.O. Box 875, 602 Akureyri

F. of Economics
F. of Nursing

Founded 1987. A State institution.

Academic Year: September to June (September-December; January-June).

Admission Requirements: Secondary school certificate.

Languages of Instruction: Icelandic.

3422 **TÆKNISKÓLI ÍSLANDS**
Technical College of Iceland
Höfoabakka 9, 112 Reykjavik
Telephone: 91-84833
Rektor: Bjarni Kristjánsson (1966-)

D. of Electrical Engineering
Head: Halldór Arnórsson; *staff* 2 (6)
D. of Mechanical Engineering
Head: Helgi Gunnarsson; *staff* 2 (6)
D. of Construction
Head: Guobrandur Steinbórsson; *staff* 4 (24)
D. of Management
Head: Aage Steinsson; *staff* 1 (18)
D. of Medical Technology
Head: Guorún Yngvadóttir; *staff* 2 (32)

Founded 1964. A State institution.

Arrangements for co-operation with Odense Teknikum.

Academic Year: September to June (September-December; January-June).

Admission Requirements: Secondary school certificate.

Languages of Instruction: Icelandic.

Degrees and Diplomas: Associate degree, 1 ½ yrs. Bachelor, 3 ½ yrs.

Academic Staff, 1986-87: c. 100.

Student Enrolment, 1986-87:

	Men	Women	Total
Of the country	380	60	440

3423 **KENNARAHÁSKÓLI ÍSLANDS**
University College of Education, Iceland
v. Stakkahlid, 105 Reykjavik
Telephone: 91-688700
Fax: (354-1) 688837
Rektor: Jónas Pálsson (1983-91)
Sigurjón Mýrdal Kennslustjori (Dean of Academic Affairs): Hjalti Hugason

D. of Pre-service Education
D. of In-service Education
Head: Ólafur H. Jóhannsson
Experimental S.
Head: Steinunn H. Lárusdóttir

Founded 1908 as school, became university college 1971. A State institution.

Academic Year: August to July (August-December; January-May; June-July).

Admission Requirements: Secondary school certificate or equivalent.

Languages of Instruction: Icelandic.

Degrees and Diplomas: Bachelor of–Education, B.Ed., Arts, B.A., 3 yrs; Bachelor of Arts in Special Education, 1-2 yrs. Also postgraduate diploma.

Library: College Library, *c.* 50,000 vols.

Publication: Hradberg, newsletter (biannually).

Academic Staff, 1989-90:

Rank	Full-time
Professors	4
Associate Professors	13
Assistant Professors	25
Sessionals	12
Total	54

Student Enrolment, 1989-90:

	Men	Women	Total
Of the country	131	875	1006*

*Also 419 external students.

INDONESIA

Universities

State Institutions

3424 **UNIVERSITAS AIRLANGGA**
Airlangga University
Jalan Airlangga 4-6, Surabaya
Cables: unair
Telex: 31138
Telephone: (31) 41348/470983
Rektor: Soedarso Djojonegoro (1989-92)
Pembantu Rektor: Soedoko Sidohoetomo

S. of Medicine
Dean: Gde Ranuh; *staff* 476 (61)
S. of Dentistry
Dean: Rai Thandri S. Rahman; *staff* 192 (68)
S. of Law
Dean: R. Djoko Soemadijo; *staff* 89 (41)
S. of Economics
Dean: Soedjono Abipraja; *staff* 100 (38)
S. of Pharmacy
Dean: Soemadi; *staff* 80 (123)
S. of Social and Political Sciences
Dean: J. Dwi Narwoko; *staff* 111 (37)
S. of Mathematics and Natural Sciences
Dean: Ami Soewandi J S *staff* 80 (46)
S. of Veterinary Medicine
Dean: Soehartojo Hardjoparnjoto; *staff* 132 (101)
Graduate S.
Dean: Soetarjadi; *staff* – (301)
C. of Health Sciences
Dean: R. Hariadi; *staff* 49 (230)
Research Ce. for Nutrition
Head: Eddy Pranowo Soedibjo
Research Ce. for Traditional Medicine
Head: Sedatono
Research Ce. for Enviromental Health
Head: Hermien Hadiati Koeswadji
Research Ce. for Regional Development
Head: Moedjio Slamet
Research Ce. for Law Development
Head: Rudhi Prasetya

Founded 1954 as State university by merger of faculties of law and medicine, formerly faculties of Gadja Mada University and of the University of Indonesia, and the Teachers' College at Malang. Some residential facilities for academic staff and for women students.

Academic Year: July to June (July-December; January-June).

Admission Requirements: Secondary school certificate (Sekolah Menengah Tingkat Atas, S.M.T.A.) and entrance examination.

Fees (Rupiahs): 120,000 per semester; Graduate School, 600,000.

Language of Instruction: Indonesian.

Degrees and Diplomas: Sarjana, 4 yrs. Dokter med., medicine, 6 yrs; Dokter Gigi, dentistry, 5 yrs; Apotheker, pharmacy, 5 yrs. Diplomas II and III, 2-3 yrs. Dokter hewan, veterinary medicine, 5 yrs. Magister Sains, a further 2 yrs. Also Doctorates by thesis. Also postgraduate Diplomas, 2-3 yrs.

Library: Central Library, 258,086 vols.

Publications: Majalah Kedokteran (Medicine); Majalah Kedokteran Gigi (Dentistry); Majalah Yuridika (Law); Majalah MasyarakatKebudayaan dan Politik (Social and Political Sciences).

Press or Publishing House: Airlangga University Press.

Academic Staff, 1989-90:

Rank	Full-time	Part-time
Guru Besar (Professors)	49	
Lektor Kepala (Associate Professors)	198	
Lektor (Assistant Professors)	178	
Lektor Muda (Lecturers)	444	
Asisten Madya (Assistant Lecturers)	440	
Total	1309	1046

Student Enrolment, 1989-90:

	Men	Women	Total
Of the country	5474	5053	10,527

3425 **UNIVERSITAS ANDALAS**
Andalas University
Perintis Kemerdekaan Jalan 77, Padang, West Sumatra
Cables: unand
Telephone: 21535; 21565

F. of Medicine
F. of Law
F. of Letters
F. of Economics (including Business Administration)
F. of Agriculture
F. of Animal Husbandry
F. of Science

Founded 1956. A State institution under the administration of the Department of Education and Culture. Some residential facilities.

Academic Year: January to December (January-June; August-December).

Admission Requirements: Secondary school certificate (Sekolah Menengah Atas, S.M.A.).

Fees: None.

Language of Instruction: Indonesian.

Degrees and Diplomas: Insinjur, Ir., in Agriculture, 5-6 yrs. Doctorandus, Drs., in–Animal Husbandry; Economics; Science and Mathematics, 5-6 yrs. Sarjana Hukum, S.H., in Law and Social Sciences, 5 yrs. Dokter, medicine, 6-7 yrs.

Library: c. 22,930 vols.

Publications: Majalah Universitas Andalas; Mediterna.

Academic Staff: c. 520 (90).

Student Enrolment: c. 6090.

3426 **UNIVERSITAS BENGKULU**
Jalan Raya Kandang Limun, Bengkulu

F. of Law
F. of Economics
F. of Social and Political Sciences
F. of Agriculture
F. of Education (Teacher Training)

Founded 1982.

3427 **UNIVERSITAS BRAWIJAJA**
Brawijaja University
Mayor Jendral Haryono 169, Malang
Telephone: 7376
Fax: 51993
Rector: Z.A. Achmady
Pembantu Rektor: M. Kafrawi

F. of Engineering (Mechanical and Civil)
Dean: Aziz Husein; *staff* 147 (45)
F. of Agriculture
Dean: Bambang Guritno; *staff* 159 (34)
F. of Animal Husbandry
Dean: Widji Widodo; *staff* 92 (43)
F. of Administration
Dean: Chalim Chalil Yusuf; *staff* 98 (32)

F. of Economics
Dean: Ubud Salim; *staff* 130 (21)
F. of Law
Dean: A. Mukti Fadjar; *staff* 98 (29)
F. of Fishery
Dean: H.M.Rudhi; *staff* 76 (17)
F. of Medicine
Dean: Achmad Hidayat; *staff* 136 (59)
Research Ce.
Head: Iksan Semaoen; *staff* 10 (4)

Founded 1957 by municipal authorities as a private university, became State university 1963.

Academic Year: January to December (January-July; August-December).

Admission Requirements: Secondary school certificate (Sekolah Menengah Atas, S.M.A.).

Fees (Rupiahs): 12,000 per semester.

Language of Instruction: Indonesian.

Degrees and Diplomas: Sarjana Hukum, S.H., in law, 5 yrs. Doctorandus, Drs., in–Economics; Administration, 5 yrs. Professional title of–Insinjur in Agriculture and Engineering, 5 yrs. Dokter, medicine, 4 yrs (S1 programme). Magister Seins (S2 programme) (Under the credit earnings programme with Gajah Mada University, Yogyakarta).

Library: 74,610 vols.

Publications: Journal; Agrivira; Jaya.

Academic Staff, 1989-90: 1160.

Student Enrolment, 1989-90:

	Men	Women	Total
Total	8065	4801	12,866

3428 **UNIVERSITAS CENDERAWASIH**
Cenderawasih University
Jalan Pendidikan, Abepura, Irian Barat
Cables: ucen japura
Telephone: Abe-151

F. of Law
F. of Agriculture
F. of Teacher Training
F. of Education
F. of Social and Political Sciences
I. of Anthropology
I. of Educational Research
I. of Public Administration Development

Founded 1962. A State university under the jurisdiction of the Department of Education and Culture.

Academic Year: January to November.

Admission Requirements: Secondary school certificate (Sekolah Menengah Atas, S.M.A.) or equivalent.

Fees: None.

Language of Instruction: Indonesian.

Degrees and Diplomas: Sarjana Muda, 3 yrs, following which students proceed to other universities.

Library: Central Library, *c.* 40,000 vols.

Special Facilities (Museums, etc.): Anthropology.

Publications: Majalah Universitas Centrawasih (quarterly); Pustaka Jurusan Geography; Seri Anthropologi.

Academic Staff: c. 80.

Student Enrolment: c. 1500.

3429 **UNIVERSITAS DIPENEGORO**
Diponegoro University
Jalan Imam Barjo, SH 1-3, P.O. Box 270, Semarang
Telex: 22315 UNDIP SM
Telephone: 311520

F. of Law
F. of Economics
F. of Engineering (including Architecture)
F. of Medicine
F. of Social and Political Sciences (including Business Administration)
F. of Letters and Education
F. of Animal Husbandry and Fishery
Coastal Area Development L. (Jepara)
Ce. for Educational Systems and Development
D. of Biology
Computer Ce. and Data Processing

Founded 1956 as Universitas Semarang, a private institution. Became State institution and acquired present name 1961. Under the jurisdiction of the Department of Education and Culture and financed by the central government. Some residential facilities for academic staff.

Academic Year: January to December (January-June; July-December).

Admission Requirements: Secondary school certificate (Sekolah Menengah Atas, S.M.A.) and entrance examination.

Language of Instruction: Indonesian.

Degrees and Diplomas: Sarjana Hukum, S.H., in law, 5 yrs; Doctorandus, Drs., in various fields, 5 yrs; Insinjur, Ir., in various fields, 5 yrs. Dokter, Medicine, 7 yrs.

Libraries: Central Library. *c.* 13,000 vols; faculty libraries.

Publications: Bulletins of the faculties; Manunggal (monthly).

Press or Publishing House: Diponegoro University Press Board.

Academic Staff: c. 2200.

Student Enrolment: c. 12,350.

3430 **UNIVERSITAS GADJAH MADA**
Gadjah Mada University
Bulaksumur, Yogyakarta 55281
Cables: ungam
Telex: 25135
Telephone: (274) 88688
Fax: (274) 88974
Rektor: Mochamad Adnan (1990-94)
Pembatu Rektor II: Bambang Riyanto

F. of Biology
Dean: Judup Subahyo; *staff* 58 (117)
F. of Economics
Dean: Dibyo Prabowo; *staff* 104 (15)
F. of Pharmacy
Dean: Mohammad Anief; *staff* 77
F. of Philosophy
Dean: Soejadi, S.H.; *staff* 55
F. of Geography
Dean: Karmono Mangunsukardjo; *staff* 72
F. of Law
Dean: Emmy P. Simanjuntak; *staff* 81
F. of Social and Political Sciences
Dean: Ichlasul Amal; *staff* 88
F. of Medicine
Dean: Radjiman; *staff* 285
F. of Dentistry
Dean: Soebagjo Hardjowijoto; *staff* 112
F. of Veterinary Medicine
Dean: Busono; *staff* 80
F. of Forestry
Dean: Achmad Sumitro; *staff* 65
F. of Mathematics and Natural Sciences
Dean: Prajoto; *staff* 122
F. of Agriculture
Dean: Jutono; *staff* 153
F. of Animal Husbandry
Dean: Sunaryo Keman; *staff* 69
F. of Psychology
Dean: Sri Mulyani Martanian; *staff* 77
F. of Letters
Dean: T. Ibrahim Alfian; *staff* 132
F. of Engineering
Dean: Pragnjono Mardjikoen; *staff* 246
F. of Agricultural Technology
Dean: Zuheid Noor; *staff* 88
F. of Postgraduate Studies
Dean: Sunardi Prawirohatmodjo; *staff* – (344)
Ce. for Population Studies
Head: Sofian Effendi
Ce. for Rural and Regional Development
Head: Mubyarto
Ce. for Culture
Head: Umar Kayam
Ce. for National Planning and Development
Head: Sumiarto
Ce. for Japanese Studies
Head: Yahya Muhaimin

Ce. for Environmental Studies
Head: Sugeng Martopo
Ce. for Traditional Medicine
Head: Suwidjijo Pramono

Founded 1949 by merger of six existing faculties. A State university under the jurisdiction of the Department of Education and Culture. Governing bodies: the Board of Curators; the Senate. Residential facilities for academic staff and students.

Academic Year: July to June (July-December; January-June).

Admission Requirements: Secondary school certificate (Sekolah Menengah Atas, S.M.A.) and entrance examination.

Fees (Rupiahs): 180,000-210,000 per annum.

Language of Instruction: Indonesian.

Degrees and Diplomas: Strata 1 (S1), 4 yrs. Diploma III. S2, a further 2 yrs. S3, by thesis.

Library: Central Library, *c.* 209,540 vols.

Special Facilities (Museums, etc.): Biological Museum; Paleoanthropology Museum. Forest Station; Agricultural Experiment Station.

Publications: Economics; Medicine; Anatomy (all in Indonesian).

Press or Publishing House: Gadjah Mada University Press.

Academic Staff, 1989-90:

Rank	Full-time
Guru Besar (Professors)	63
Lektor Kepala (Senior Lecturers)	303
Lektor (Lecturers)	929
Asisten Ahli Madya (Instructors)	705
Total	2000

Student Enrolment, 1989-90:

	Men	Women	Total
Of the country	19,346	9561	28,907
Of other countries	47	–	47
Total	19,393	9561	28,954

3431 **UNIVERSITAS HALUOLEO**
Haluoleo University
Jalan Mayjen S. Parmen, Kenaraya, Kendari 93121, Sulawesi Tenggara
Telephone: 21834; 21503
Rektor: Soleh Solahuddin

F. of Education
Dean: H. Ahmad Sarita
F. of Economics
Dean: H. Usman D. Masiki
F. of Social and Political Sciences
Dean: M. Nur Rakhman
F. of Agriculture
Dean: Suleman
I. of Social Research
Director: M. Gazali
I. of Community Sercice
Director: Tumbo Saranani
Ce. for Ecological Studies
Director: Suleman
Ce. for Population Studies
Director: Abd. Azis Rassake
Ce. for Computer Science and Information Systems
Director: Faad Maonde
Rural Areas Development Studies Ce.
Director: Abdurrauf Tarimana
Open U.
Director: H. Usman D. Masiki

Founded 1964 as private institution. Acquired present status 1981. A State institution under the jurisdiction of the Department of Education and Culture. Residential facilities for married academic staff.

Arrangements for co-operation with Washington State University.

Academic Year: July to June (July-December; January-June).

Admission Requirements: Secondary school certificate (Sekolah Lanjutan Tingkat Atas, S.L.T.A.).

Fees (Rupiahs): 37,500-39,900 per annum.

Language of Instruction: Indonesian.

Degrees and Diplomas: Sarjana, 4 yrs. Diplomas I, II, and III.

Library: c. 20,000 vols.

Publications: Research Journal (biannually); Untukmu Indonesiaku Bulletin (every two months); Science Magazine.

Academic Staff: c. 266.

Student Enrolment: c. 5819.

3432 **UNIVERSITAS HASANUDDIN**
Hasanuddin University
55 Jalan Mesjid Raya, Ujung Pandang
Cables: unhas
Telephone: 5335; 6343

F. of Economics
F. of Law
F. of Medicine (including Dentistry)
F. of Engineering (Marine, Civil, Electrical and Architecture)
F. of Public Health
F. of Dentistry
F. of Letters
F. of Social and Political Sciences
F. of Agriculture (including Forestry and Fishery)
F. of Animal Husbandry
F. of Mathematics and Natural Sciences

Also 5 research departments attached to the faculties.

Founded 1949 as faculties of economics and law attached to the University of Indonesia, became State university 1965, under the jurisdiction of the Department of Education and Culture. Some residential facilities for academic staff.

Academic Year: January to December (January-June; July-December).

Admission Requirements: Secondary school certificate (Sekolah Lanjutan Atas, S.L.A.), and entrance examination.

Language of Instruction: Indonesian.

Degrees and Diplomas: Doctorandus, Drs., in–Social and Political Sciences; Mathematics and Physical Sciences; Literature; Economics, 5 yrs. Professional title of Insinjur in–Engineering; Agriculture; Animal Husbandry, 5 yrs. Sarjana Hukum, law, 5 yrs. Dokter Hewan, animal husbandry, 5 yrs. Dokter, medicine, 6 yrs. Doctorate in–Economics; Social and Political Sciences; Medicine, by thesis.

Libraries: Central Library, *c.* 66,800 vols; faculty libraries.

Publication: Majalah Universitas Hasanuddin (three times a year).

Academic Staff: c. 690.

Student Enrolment: c. 7900.

3433 ***UNIVERSITAS INDONESIA**
University of Indonesia
Jalan Salemba Raya 4, Jakarta Pusat 10430
Cables: univ
Telex: 45680 UI JKT-IA
Telephone: (21) 330335
Fax: (21) 7270017
Rektor: M. Sujudi (1986-94)
Pembantu Rektor II (Administrative): M. Legowo

F. of Medicine
Dean: Asri Rasad; *staff* 606 (135)
F. of Dentistry
Dean: Herwati Djoharmans; *staff* 160 (76)
F. of Mathematics and Sciences
Dean: G. Parangtopo; *staff* 196 (78)
F. of Engineering
Dean: Indradjid Subardjo; *staff* 218 (34)
F. of Law
Dean: Charles Himawan; *staff* 155 (42)
F. of Economics
Dean: M. Arsjad Anwar; *staff* 232 (6)
F. of Letters
Dean: Achdiati A. Ikram; *staff* 269 (55)
F. of Psychology
Dean: Soesmalijah Soewondo; *staff* 106 (16)
F. of Political and Social Sciences
Dean: Juwono Sudarsono; *staff* 201 (93)
F. of Public Health
Dean: Fahmi D. Saifuddin; *staff* 69 (72)
F. of Postgraduate Studies
Dean: Iskandar Wahidijat; *staff* 4
Polytechnic F.
Dean: Poerwoto Soeratomodjo; *staff* 170
Research I.
Chairman: Kartomo Wirosuhardjo

Ce. for Institutional Development Research
Chairman: Rozy Munir
Ce. for Health Research
Chairman: Budi Utomo
Ce. for Social and Cultural
Chairman: Edi Sediawati
Ce. for Research of Human Resources and Environment
Chairman: M. Soerjani
Ce. for Research of Sciences and Technology
Chairman: Suwito
I. for Social Services
Chairman: Tapi Omas Ihromi
Ce. for Education and Social Services
Chairman: Istiqomah Wibowo
Ce. for Regional Development
Chairman: Firman Lubis
Ce. for Services on Social Communication
Chairman: Harsono Soewardi
Ce. for Justice and the Role of Law
Chairman: Mardjono Reksodiputro
Also 8 institutes and centres of the faculties.

Founded 1950, incorporating the Balai Perguruan Tinggi Republik Indonesia (Institution of Higher Learning of the Republic of Indonesia), 1945, and the Universiteit van Indonesia, re-established 1945 and tracing its origins to an engineering college 1920, a law college 1924, and a medical college 1927. Faculties in Bandung, Surabaya, and Makassar have since been incorporated in newly established State universities. The university is a State institution responsible to the Department of Education and Culture. Governing body: the Senate. Some residential facilities for academic staff and students.

Academic Year: August to July (August-January; February-July).

Admission Requirements: Secondary school certificate (Sekolah Lanjutan Atas, S.L.A.) and entrance examination.

Fees (Rupiahs): 360,000 per annum.

Language of Instruction: Indonesian.

Degrees and Diplomas: Doctorandus, Drs., in–Science; Social Sciences; Psychology. Sarjana-Hukum, law; -Ekonomi; -Sastra, letters; -Kesehatan Masyarakat. Insinjur, 5 yrs; Dokter Gigi, dentistry, 5 yrs; Dokter, medicine, 6 yrs. Magister. Doctorates by thesis.

Library: Faculty libraries, total, *c.* 459,822 vols.

Special Facilities (Museums, etc.): Pathological Museum.

Publications: Majalah Hukum dan Pembangunan (bimonthly); Ekonomi dan Keuangan Indonesia (quarterly); Majalah Demografi Indonesia (biannually); Management dan Usahawan (quarterly); Majalah Ilmu Ilmu Sastra Indonesia (biannually); Berita Antropologi (quarterly); Majalah Arkeologi (quarterly).

Press or Publishing House: University of Indonesia Press.

Academic Staff, 1989-90: 2477.

Student Enrolment, 1989-90:

	Men	Women	Total
Of the country	12,064	7963	20,027
Of other countries	40	12	52
Total	12,104	7975	20,079

3434 **UNIVERSITAS JAMBI**
University of Jambi
Jln.Prof.Dr.Sri. Soedewi Masjchun Sofwan, SH Jambi.
Telephone: 23198
Rektor: S.B. Samad (1963-)
Registrar: A.R. Kasim

F. of Law
Dean: Fuad Bafadhal; *staff* 68 (18)
F. of Economics
Dean: A. Hakim Lubis; *staff* 63 (12)
F. of Agriculture
Dean: Bakry Wahab; *staff* 102 (17)
F. of Animal Husbandry
Dean: Mohd. Toha; *staff* 79 (27)
F. of Education
Dean: Idris Djakfar; *staff* 94 (27)
F. of Teacher Training
Computer Ce.
Research Ce.

Founded 1963. A State institution under the jurisdiction of the Ministry of Education and Culture. Residential facilities for academic staff.

Arrangements for co-operation with the University of Kentucky.

Academic Year: August to July (August-December; January-July).

Admission Requirements: Secondary school certificate (Sekolah Menengah, S.M.A.).

Fees (Rupiahs): 80,000 per annum.

Language of Instruction: Indonesian.

Degrees and Diplomas: Sarjana, 5 yrs. Also diplomas, 2-3 yrs.

Library: University Library, *c.* 30,408 vols.

Publications: Berita Universitas Jambi (magazine); Journal Penelitian Universitas Jambi (journal).

Academic Staff, 1989-90:

Rank	Full-time	Part-time
Guru Beaar Madya (Associate Professors)	1	–
Lektor Kepala (Senior Lecturers)	8	–
Lektor Kepala Madya	10	–
Lektor (Lecturers)	13	–
Lektor Madya (Junior Lecturers)	19	–
Lektor Muda (Assistant Lecturers)	21	53
Asisten Ahli (Senior Assistants)	53	69
Asisten Ahli Madya (Instructors)	94	166
Total	219	288

Student Enrolment, 1989-90:

	Men	Women	Total
Of the country	3565	2032	5597

3435 **UNIVERSITAS JEMBER**
Jember University
Jalan Veteran 3, Jember, East Java
Telephone: (0331) 21270; 41500
Rektor: Simannadi Widyaprakosa (1986-90)
Registrar: Made Pedungan Sardha

F. of Law
Dean: Sorhztdono; *staff* 78 (26)
F. of Social and Political Sciences (including Business Administration)
Dean: Soenarjo; *staff* 91 (58)
F. of Agriculture
Dean: Susijohadi; *staff* 141 (23325)
F. of Teachers Training and Educational Sciences
Dean: Ida Bagus Alit Anna; *staff* 137 (27)
F. of Letters
Dean: Soedardi; *staff* 65 (21)
F. of Economics
Dean: Sugiharto; *staff* 76 (15)
Agricultural Polytechnic
Director: Sutrisno Widjaja; *staff* 43 (25)
Computer Ce.
Director: Kaswali
Research Ce.
Director: Wagito; *staff* 10 (30)

Founded 1957 as a private university, affiliated to Brawijaja University 1963, acquired present status and title November 1964. A State institution responsible to the Department of Education and Culture. Some residential facilities for academic staff and students.

Arrangements for co-operation with Australian Universities.

Academic Year: July to June (July-December; January-June).

Admission Requirements: Secondary school certificate (Sekolah Menengah Tingkat Atas, S.M.T.A.) or equivalent, and extrance examination.

Fees (Rupiahs): 180,000-216,000 per annum.

Language of Instruction: Indonesian.

Degrees and Diplomas: Sarjana, 4-6 yrs. Diplomas I, II, III, 2-3 yrs.

Library: Central Library, 69,503 vols.

Press or Publishing House: Jember University Press.

Academic Staff, 1989-90: 631 (505).

Student Enrolment, 1989-90:

	Men	Women	Total
Of the country	6637	4509	11,146

3436 **UNIVERSITAS JENDERAL SOEDIRMAN**
General Soedirman University
Kampus Unsoed, Grendeng P.O. Box 15, Purwokerto, Central Java
Telephone: 292; 804/5

F. of Law
F. of Agriculture
F. of Biology

F. of Animal Husbandry
F. of Economics

Founded 1963 as college of agriculture, attached to Universitas Diponegoro, became State university 1963. Governing body: the Board of Regents; the Senate; the Faculty Councils. Some residential facilities for academic staff.

Academic Year: January to December (January-June; August-December).

Admission Requirements: Secondary school certificate (Sekolah Menengah Atas, S.M.A.) and entrance examination.

Language of Instruction: Indonesian.

Degrees and Diplomas: Sarjana Hukum, law; Doctorandus, Drs., in Faculties of Biology and Economics. Insinjur, Ir., in Faculties of Agriculture and Animal Husbandry, 5 yrs. Doctorates by thesis.

Libraries: Central Library, *c.* 3500 vols; faculty libraries.

Academic Staff: c. 290.

Student Enrolment: c. 2150.

3437 **UNIVERSITAS LAMBUNG MANGKURAT**

Lambung Mangkurat University

Jalan Kayu Tangi, P.O. Box 219, Banjarmasin

Cables: unlam banjarmasin

Telephone: (0511) 4177; 4195

F. of Law
F. of Economics
F. of Social and Political Sciences
F. of Agriculture (including Horticulture)
F. of Teacher Training and Education
F. of Forestry
F. of Fishery
F. of Civil Engineering
Ce. for Environmental Study

Founded 1958 by the Lambung Mangkurat Foundation, became State university 1960. Responsible to the Department of Education and Culture. Some residential facilities for academic staff and students.

Academic Year: July to June (July-December; January-June).

Admission Requirements: Secondary school certificate (Sekolah Menengah Atas, S.M.A.) and entrance examination.

Language of Instruction: Indonesian.

Degrees and Diplomas: Sarjana in various fields, 4-5 yrs. Diplomas I, II and III, 1-3 yrs.

Library: Central Library, *c.* 14,820 vols.

Publications: Faculty publications; Kalimantan Scientie.

Academic Staff: c. 350 (100).

Student Enrolment: c. 8000.

3438 **UNIVERSITAS LAMPUNG**

University of Lampung

Kampus Unila, Gedung Meneng, Kedaton, Bander Lampung

Cables: unila

Telephone: 52673

F. of Economics
F. of Law
F. of Education
F. of Teacher Training
F. of Agriculture

Founded 1961 as branch to Sriwijaya University, acquired present status 1965. A State institution responsible to the Department of Education and Culture. Governing body: the Senate. Some residential facilities for academic staff.

Academic Year: August to July (February-August; August-December).

Admission Requirements: Secondary school certificate (Sekolah Lanjutan Tingkat Atas (S.L.T.A.).

Language of Instruction: Indonesian.

Degrees and Diplomas: Sarjana Muda in various fields, 3 yrs. Doctorandus, Drs., in Economics or Sarjana Hukum, law, or Professional title of Insinjur in Agriculture, a further 2 yrs.

Libraries: Central Library, *c.* 3260 vols; branch libraries, *c.* 11,190.

Publications: Varia UNILA (monthly); Bulletin Ilmiah UNILA (quarterly).

Academic Staff: c. 200.

Student Enrolment: c. 4720.

3439 **UNIVERSITAS MATARAM**

Mataram University

Jalan Pendidikan 37, Mataram

Telephone: 21166; 23007

Rektor: M. Qazuini (1984-88)

Head of Administration: Muhid Ramli

F. of Economics
; *staff* 48 (13)

F. of Law
; *staff* 58 (22)

F. of Agriculture
; *staff* 55 (31)

F. of Animal Husbandry
; *staff* 80 (24)

Founded 1962 with faculty of economics. Faculties of agriculture and law added 1967 and faculty of animal husbandry 1968. A State institution responsible to the Department of Education and Culture. Governing bodies: the Senate; the Board of Counsellors. Some residential facilities for academic staff.

Academic Year: January to December (January-June; July-December).

Admission Requirements: Secondary school certificate (Sekolah Lanjutan Atas, S.L.A.) and entrance examination.

Fees (Rupiahs): 31,500-90,000 per semester.

Language of Instruction: Indonesian.

Degrees and Diplomas: Strata 1 (S1), 4 yrs. Diplomas I, II, and III 1-3 yrs.

Library: Central Library, *c.* 32,320 vols.

Academic Staff, 1986-87: 305 (121).

Student Enrolment, 1986-87:

	Men	Women	Total
Of the country	4774	1644	6418

3440 **UNIVERSITAS MULAWARMAN**

Mulawarman University

Jalan Pulau Flores 7, P.O. Box 7, Samarinda, Kalimantan Timor

Cables: unmul samarinda

Telephone: (0541) 21118

Rektor: Soetrisno Hadi (1980-88)

F. of Social and Political Sciences
F. of Economics
F. of Agriculture
F. of Forestry
F. of Teacher Training
F. of Education
Forestry Research I.

Founded 1962. A State institution under the jurisdiction of the Department of Education and Culture. Governing body: the Board of Advisors.

Academic Year: January to December (January-June; July-December).

Admission Requirements: Secondary school certificate (Sekolah Menengah Atas, S.M.A.) and entrance examination.

Language of Instruction: Indonesian.

Degrees and Diplomas: Doctorandus, Drs., 4-7 yrs. Professional title of Insinjur. Diploma in Education.

Libraries: Central Library, *c.* 17,500 vols; faculty libraries, *c.* 15,580.

Publications: Frontir; Berita Unmul; Research Reports.

Academic Staff: c. 210.

Student Enrolment: c. 4620.

3441 **UNIVERSITAS NUSA CENDANA**

Nusa Cendana University

Jalan Jenderal Suharto 72, Kupang, Timor

Cables: undana

Telephone: 290

Rektor: Mozes R. Toelihare

Pembantu Rektor (Administrative): G.H.C. Hattu

F. of Administration
Dean: Paulus Isliko

F. of Education and Teacher Training
Dean: A.M. Fangyidal

F. of Education (including School Administration)

F. of Law
Dean: S.H. Klaas

F. of Agriculture
Dean: S. Bartiman

F. of Animal Husbandry
Dean: U. Ginting
Research Ce
Head: A.S. Benu
Environmental Life Study Ce.
Head: H. Ataupah
Population Study Ce.
Head: D.J. Kallau
Ce. for the Assessment and Development of Dry Land Farming
Head: S. Benu
Ce. for the Assessment and Development of the Province
Head: A. Zoh
Social Service Ce
Head: Lukas B. Bora

Founded 1962. A State institution under the jurisdiction of the Department of Education and Culture. Governing body: the Senate. Some residential facilities for senior academic staff.

Academic Year: January to November (January-June; July-November).

Admission Requirements: Secondary school certificate (Sekolah Menengah Atas, S.M.A.).

Language of Instruction: Indonesian.

Degrees and Diplomas: Sarjana Muda, 3 yrs. Doctorandus, Drs., a further 2 yrs.

Library: c. 65,400 vols.

Special Facilities (Museums, etc.): Museums of Palaeontology and Ethnology.

Academic Staff, 1988: 567.

Student Enrolment, 1989-90: 5767.

3442 **UNIVERSITAS PADJADJARAN**

Padjadjaran University
Jalan Dipati Ukur 35, Bandung
Cables: unpad
Telephone: 8327178

F. of Law
F. of Social and Political Sciences (including Public Administration)
F. of Economics (including Accountancy)
F. of Letters
F. of Psychology
F. of Medicine
F. of Dentistry
F. of Agriculture (including Fishery)
F. of Animal Husbandry
F. of Natural Sciences (including Pharmacy and Mathematics)
F. of Communication Studies (including Journalism)
I. of Parasitology
I. of Natural Sciences
I. of Ecology
I. of Religious Studies
I. of Social Research
I. of Cultural Studies
D. of Extramural Studies

Founded 1952 as Independence University, a private institution with faculties of law and economics. Amalgamated with State Teacher Training College, founded 1954, to become Padjadjaran State University 1957, and faculty of medicine added. Faculties of science added 1958, dentistry and agriculture 1959, political science and arts1960, psychology 1961. Governing bodies: the Senate; the Board of Curators. Some residential facilities for academic staff and students.

Academic Year: February to November (February-June; July-November).

Admission Requirements: Secondary school certificate (Sekolah Menengah Atas, S.M.A.) and entrance examination.

Language of Instruction: Indonesian.

Degrees and Diplomas: Sarjana, 5 yrs. Dokter, medicine; Dokter Gigi, dentistry; Dokter Apotheker, pharmacy; Dokter Notaris, public notary, a further 1-2 yrs. Doctorates by thesis.

Library: Central Library and faculty libraries, c. 110,000 vols.

Publications: Tridharma (monthly); Padjadjaran (quarterly); Sastra dan Budaya; Agrikultura, Mediciana; Economica, Pembina.

Academic Staff: c. 1330.

Student Enrolment: c. 11,959 (Also c. 800 external students).

3443 **UNIVERSITAS PALANGKA RAYA**

University of Palangka Raya
Jalan Yos Sudarso BII-5, Tanjung Nyaho, Palangka Raya
Cables: unpar palangka raya
Telephone: 21722

F. of Teacher Training
F. of Economics
F. of Education
F. of Agriculture

Founded 1963. A State institution under the jurisdiction of the Department of Education and Culture. Some residential facilities for academic staff and for c. 40 students.

Academic Year: July to June (July-December; January-June).

Admission Requirements: Secondary school certificate (Sekolah Menengah Atas, S.M.A.) and entrance examination.

Fees: According to parents' income.

Language of Instruction: Indonesian.

Degrees and Diplomas: Sarjana, in various fields, 3 yrs. Doctorandus, Drs., a futher 2 yrs. Diplomas I, II, and III in all fields except Economics, 1-3 yrs.

Library: Central Library.

Publication: The Heavenly Voice (monthly).

Academic Staff: c. 110 (150).

Student Enrolment: c. 2750.

3444 **UNIVERSITAS PATTIMURA**

Jalan Jr. M. Putuhenan Kampus Unpatti Poka-Ambon, Ambon
Cables: kotak pos 95
Telex: 73139
Telephone: 3053; 2189; 2551
Rektor: Jan Laurens Nanere (1973-)
Pembantu Rektor (Administrative): P.J. Siwabessy

F. of Law
Head: C.M. Pattiruhu; *staff* 42 (12)
F. of Social and Political Sciences
Head: M. Renur; *staff* 62 (14)
F. of Agriculture and Forestry
Head: J. Tuhumury; *staff* 114 (16)
F. of Animal Husbandry and Fishery
Head: J.M. Nanlohy; *staff* 66 (13)
F. of Economics
Head: R. Manikalo; *staff* 50 (9)
F. of Teacher Training
Head: T.J.A. Uneputty; *staff* 107 (25)
F. of Education
Head: P.J. Siwabessy; *staff* 46 (5)
F. of Technology (including Marine Sciences)
Head: A.F. Salamony; *staff* 60 (18)
Ce. of Research
Head: P. Sitaniapessy; *staff* 15 (5)
Ce. of Public Service
Head: M. Huliselan; *staff* 20 (5)

Founded 1956 as college, acquired present status 1963. A State institution under the jurisdiction of the Department of Education and Culture. Residential facilities for academic staff and students.

Academic Year: August to July (August-January; February-July).

Admission Requirements: Secondary school certificate (Sekolah Lanjutan Atas, S.L.T.A.) and entrance examination.

Fees: According to parents' income.

Language of Instruction: Indonesian.

Degrees and Diplomas: Sarjana, 5-6 yrs.

Library: Central Library, c. 9010 vols.

Publications: Bulletin (monthly); 'Majalah Ilmiah' (Research Paper 1976); Marine Sciences and Ocean Engineering (Seminar 1977); Annual Reports; Field Study Reports

Academic Staff: c. 240.

Student Enrolment, 1990:

	Men	Women	Total
Of the country	4584	2414	6998

3445 **UNIVERSITAS RIAU**
University of Riau
Jalan Pattimura 9, Pekanbaru, Riau
Telephone: (0761) 21341
Rektor: Muchtar Lutfi (1980-88)

F. of Mathematics and Natural Sciences
F. of Economics
F. of Social and Political Sciences
F. of Fishery
F. of Education
F. of Engineering (non-degree)

Founded 1962. A State institution under the jurisdiction of the Department of Education and Culture. Limited residential facilities for academic staff.

Arrangements for co-operation with the University of Kentucky.

Academic Year: July to June (July-December; January-June).

Admission Requirements: Secondary school certificate (Sekolah Lanjutan Tingkat Atas, S.L.T.A.) and entrance examination.

Language of Instruction: Indonesian.

Degrees and Diplomas: Doctorandus, Drs., 4 yrs. Professional title of Insinjur, 4 yrs. Also Diploma I, II, and III, 1-3 yrs.

Library: c. 22,770 vols.

Academic Staff: c. 320 (180).

Student Enrolment: c. 5520.

3446 **UNIVERSITAS SAM RATULANGI**
Sam Ratulangi University
Kampus Unsrat, Kleak, Manado
Telephone: 3586/7

F. of Medicine
F. of Agriculture
F. of Animal Husbandry
F. of Law
F. of Economics
F. of Social and Political Sciences
F. of Engineering
F. of Letters
F. of Fishery
F. of Education
F. of Teacher Training

Also 14 institutes of the faculties.

Founded 1965. A State institution under the jurisdiction of the Department of Education and Culture. Residential facilities for academic staff and students.

Academic Year: January to December (January-June; July-December).

Admission Requirements: Secondary school certificate (Sekolah Lanjutan Atas, S.L.A.).

Language of Instruction: Indonesian.

Degrees and Diplomas: Sarjana, 5 yrs.

Libraries: Central Library, c. 14,000 vols; 9 faculty libraries, c. 2000 each faculty.

Publications: Kalawarta Unscrat; Majalah Sam Ratulangi; Dedikasi.

Academic Staff: c. 310 (640).

Student Enrolment: c. 2930.

3447 **UNIVERSITAS SEBELAS MARET**
University of Sebelas Maret
Jalan Ir. Soetami 36A, Kentingan, Surakarta
Telephone: 36633
Rektor: Koento Wibisono Siswomihardjo (1976-)

F. of Education
F. of Teacher Training and Education
Head: Sukiyo; *staff* 368 (102)
F. of Letters
Head: Suwito; *staff* 133 (37)
F. of Social and Political Sciences
Head: Hainudin; *staff* 85 (17)
F. of Law
Head: Amik Sumindriyatmi; *staff* 83 (25)
F. of Economics
Head: Bahtiar Effendi; *staff* 89 (28)
F. of Medicine
Head: Soetiipto; *staff* 205 (223)
F. of Agriculture
Head: Toeranto Sugivatmo; *staff* 113 (105)
F. of Engineering (including Architecture)
Head: Rembang Suseno; *staff* 119 (84)
Ce. of Educational Systems Development
D. of English
Head: Sri Samiati Taryana; *staff* 19 (2)

Also 2 Research Centres.

Founded 1976, incorporating nine existing institutions. A State institution under the jurisdiction of the Department of Education and Culture. Residential facilities for academic staff and students.

Participates in the International Development Programme (IDP), Australia.

Academic Year: January to December (January-June; July-December).

Admission Requirements: Secondary school certificate (Sekolah Menengah Atas, S.M.A.).

Language of Instruction: Indonesian.

Degrees and Diplomas: Sarjana, 5 yrs. Dokter med., medicine, 7 yrs.

Library: Central Library, c. 95,000 vols.

Publication: Widya Bawana (quarterly).

Press or Publishing House: University Press of Sebelas Maret.

Academic Staff, 1990: 1197.

Student Enrolment, 1990: 16,694

3448 **UNIVERSITAS SRIWIJAYA**
Sriwijaya University
Jalan Arif Rachman Hakim, Palembang
Cables: rektor unseri
Telephone: 26388

F. of Economics (including Accountancy and Business Administration)
F. of Law
F. of Engineering
F. of Medicine
F. of Agriculture
F. of Teacher Training
F. of Education

Founded 1953 as faculty of economics and faculty of law, acquired present status 1960. A State institution under the jurisdiction of the Department of Education and Culture. Governing bodies: the Board of Regents; the Senate. Some residential facilities for academic staff and students.

Academic Year: July to May (July-December; January-June).

Admission Requirements: Secondary school certificate (Sekolah Menengah Atas, S.M.A.) and entrance examination.

Language of Instruction: Indonesian.

Degrees and Diplomas: Doctorandus, Drs., in various fields, 5 yrs. Dokter, medicine, 7 yrs. Professional title of Insinjur, 5 yrs.

Library: University Library, c. 12,000 vols.

Publication: University and faculty magazines.

Press or Publishing House: University Publishing House.

Academic Staff: c. 540 (620).

Student Enrolment: c. 8430.

3449 **UNIVERSITAS SUMATERIA UTARA**
University of North Sumatra
Jalan Universitas 9, Medan
Telex: 51753
Telephone: (061) 23210

F. of Agriculture
F. of Medicine
F. of Law
F. of Engineering
F. of Economics
F. of Mathematics and Natural Sciences
F. of Letters
F. of Dentistry

Founded 1957. A State institution. Residential facilities for academic staff and students.

Academic Year: January to December (January-June; August-December).

Admission Requirements: Secondary school certificate (Sekolah Menengah Atas, S.M.A. or Sekolah Lanjutan Tingkat Atas, S.L.A.).

Language of Instruction: Indonesian.

Degrees and Diplomas: Bakalaureus in Business Administration, 3 yrs. Professional titles of–Insinjur in–Engineering; Agriculture; Sarjana Hukum, law, 5-6 yrs. Doctorandus, Drs., in–Economics; Dentistry; Letters, Science; Social Science, 5-6 yrs. Dokter Gigi, dentistry, 5-6 yrs; Dokter, Medicine, 7-8 yrs.

Library: c. 200,000 vols.

Academic Staff: c. 990.
Student Enrolment: c. 13,850.

3450 **UNIVERSITAS SYIAH KUALA**
Syiah Kuala University
Darussalam, Banda Aceh
Cables: unsyiah
Telex: USK BNA 54153
Telephone: 22721; 23408
Rektor: Abdullah Ali (1982-90)
Pembantu Rektor (Academic): Ali Basyah Amin

F. of Economics
Dean: Zulkifli Husin
F. of Law
Dean: Abdullah Ahmed
F. of Veterinary Medicine and Animal Husbandry
Dean (Acting): Ahmad Damhuri
F. of Engineering (including Architecture)
Dean: Buchari RA
F. of Agriculture
Dean: Zainal Abidin Pian
F. of Teacher Training and Education
Dean: Idris Ibrahim
F. of Medicine
Dean (Acting): Ridwan Ibrahim
Language Ce.
Head: Idris Ibrahim
Open University
Resident Director: Utju Alibasya
Ce. for Public Service
Head: Bahrein T. Sugihen

Founded 1959 as faculty of economics attached to Universitas Sumatera Utara, Medan. Became State university 1961. Governing body: the Board of Trustees. Residential facilities for academic staff and 600 students.

Academic Year: February to December (February-May; June-December).

Admission Requirements: Secondary school certificate (Sekolah Menengah Atas, S.M.A.) and entrance examination.

Fees (Rupiahs): Social Sciences, 42,000 per annum; Science, 120,000.

Language of Instruction: Indonesian.

Degrees and Diplomas: Strata 1 (S1), 4 yrs. Diplomas, 2-3 yrs.

Library: Syiah Kuala University Library System, 150,000 vols.

Publication: Warta Unsyiah (monthly).

Press or Publishing House: Badan Penerbitan dan Percetakan Unsyiah (Syiah Kuala University Press).

Academic Staff, 1990:

Rank	Full-time
Professors	5
Associate Professors	21
Assistant Professors	129
Research Assistants	209
Teaching Assistants	456
Total	820

Student Enrolment, 1990:

	Men	Women	Total
Of the country	8201	7220	15,421

3451 **UNIVERSITAS TADULAKO**
Kampus Bumi Bahari, Palu

F. of Law
F. of Social and Political Sciences
F. of Agriculture
F. of Education
F. of Teacher Training

Founded 1981.

3452 **UNIVERSITAS TANJUNGPURA**
Tanjungpura University
Jalan Imam Bonjol, Pontianak, Kalimantan Barat
Telephone: 4399

F. of Law
F. of Economics
F. of Agriculture
F. of Engineering
F. of Social and Political Sciences
F. of Teacher Training
F. of Education

Founded 1965.

Academic Year: July to June (July-December; January-June).

Admission Requirements: Secondary school certificate (Sekolah Menengah Atas, S.M.A.).

Language of Instruction: Indonesian.

Degrees and Diplomas: Sarjana, 4-7 yrs. Diplomas I, II, III, 1-3 yrs.

Academic Staff: c. 130 (520).

Student Enrolment: c. 4450.

3453 **UNIVERSITAS TERBUIKA**
Open University
Jalan Terbang Layang, Pondok Cabe, Ciputat

Education and Teacher Training
Economics
Social and Political Sciences
Mathematics and National Sciences

Founded 1984.

3454 **UNIVERSITAS UDAYANA**
Udayana State University
Jalan Panglima, Sudirman, Denpasar, Bali
Telephone: 23791

F. of Letters
F. of Medicine
F. of Animal Husbandry
F. of Law and Social Sciences
F. of Engineering (including Architecture)
F. of Agriculture
F. of Economics
F. of Education
F. of Teacher Training

Founded 1962 incorporating former faculty of letters, founded 1950 and attached to Airlangga University. A State institution under the jurisdiction of the Department of Education and Culture. Governing body: the Senate. Some residential facilities for academic staff and students.

Academic Year: February to November (February-June; July-November).

Admission Requirements: Secondary school certificate (Sekolah Menengah Atas, S.M.A.).

Language of Instruction: Indonesian.

Degrees and Diplomas: Sarjana, 5 yrs. Doctorandus, Drs., in various fields, 5 yrs. Insinjur, 5 yrs. Dokter, medicine, 7 yrs.

Libraries: Central Library; faculty libraries, c. 25,450 vols.

Publication: Majalah Ilmiah Universitas Udayana (Scientific Publication).

Academic Staff: c. 280 (290).

Student Enrolment: c. 3110.

Private Institutions

3455 **UNIVERSITAS AMIR HAMZAH**
Jalan HM Joni 22, Medan

Law
Economics

Founded 1981. A private institution under the supervision of the Department of Education and Culture.

3456 **UNIVERSITAS ADVENT INDONESIA**
Indonesia Adventist University
Pos Cipaganti, Bandung
Rektor: Richard A. Hutagaol (1983-88)
Panitera (Registrar): Joseph E. Muskita

D. of Theology
Dean: John H. Rantung; *staff* 7
D. of Education
Dean: Raja A. Nainggolan; *staff* 14
D. of Business Administration (including Accountancy, and Secretarial Studies)
Dean: Henry L. Foster; *staff* 14
D. of Biology
Dean: Canadian Z. Panjaitan; *staff* 5

C. of Nursing
Dean: Theodoro Djagia; *staff* 6 (12)
Founded 1948 as Seminary by the Indonesian Union Mission of Seventh-Day Adventists, became college 1962 and acquired present status and title 1982. A private institution under the supervision of the Department of Education and Culture. Residential facilities for academic staff and students.
Academic Year: August to May (August-December; January-May).
Admission Requirements: Secondary school certificate (Surat Tanda Tamat Belajar).
Fees (Rupiahs): 595,000 per semester.
Language of Instruction: Indonesian.
Degrees and Diplomas: Strata 1 (S1) in–Theology; Arts, 4 yrs. Diploma III, 3 yrs.
Library: 26,827 vols.
Academic Staff, 1986-87:

Rank	Full-time	Part-time
Guru Besar (Professors)	3	–
Lektor Kepala (Associate Professor)	1	–
Lektor (Assistant Professors)	27	–
Asisten Ahli Madya (Instructors)	17	12
Total	48	12

Student Enrolment, 1986-87:

	Men	Women	Total
Of the country	426	276	702
Of other countries	4	7	11
Total	430	283	713

3457 **UNIVERSITAS ATMAJAYA**
Jalan Demangan Baru 29, Yogyakarta

Law
Economics
Engineering
Founded 1965. A private institution under the supervision of the Department of Education and Culture.

3458 **UNIVERSITAS ATMAJAYA**
Atma Jaya University of Ujung Pandang
Jalan Tanjung Alang 23 (Kampus Tanjung Bunga), Ujung Pandang 90134
Telephone: (411) 81038; 81733
Rektor: Lucas Paliling (1990-93)
Pembantu Rektor II (Administrative): Olga Limarno

F. of Economics
Dean: Julia Ullfah Toar; *staff* 13 (30)
F. of Law
Dean: Anita Tungadi; *staff* 14 (44)
F. of Technicology
Dean: Paul A. Harrianta; *staff* 11 (22)
Agrarian Law Study and Research Ce.
Head: Agnes M. Toar; *staff* 4
Founded 1981. A private institution under the supervision of the Department of Education and Culture. It was founded by lay-Catholic people in collaboration with the local Catholic Church (Archdiocese of Ujung Pandang). Governing body: the Board of Trustees.
Academic Year: September to July (September-February; March-July).
Admission Requirements: Secondary school certificate (Sekolah Menengah Atas, S.M.A.) or foreign equivalent.
Fees (Rupiahs): 300,000-375,000 per annum.
Language of Instruction: Indonesian.
Degrees and Diplomas: Strat 1 (S1) Ekonomi, 4 yrs. Sarjana Hukum, law, 4 yrs. Insinjur, Ir., 4 yrs.
Library: University Library, *c.* 5000 vols.
Academic Staff, 1989-90: 38 (96).
Student Enrolment, 1989-90:

	Men	Women	Total
Of the country	780	407	1187

3459 **UNIVERSITAS BOJONEGORO**
Jalan Jenderal Basuki Rakhmat 23 A, Bojonegoro

Law
Social and Political Sciences
Agriculture
Founded 1981. A private institution under the supervision of the Department of Education and Culture.

3460 **UNIVERSITAS BUNG HATTA**
Bung Hatta University
Jalan Sumatera, Ulak Karang, Padang, Sumatra Barat
Telephone: 24439
Rektor: Adrin Kahar (1985-)
Registrar: Rohana

F. of Economics (including Business Administration and Economics)
Dean: Sjafrizal; *staff* 7 (55)
F. of Law
Dean: Azmi Djamarin; *staff* 12 (44)
F. of Teacher Training and Education
Dean: Syahwin Nikelas; *staff* 15 (61)
F. of Letters
Dean: Yusuf Gandor; *staff* 3 (31)
F. of Engineering (including Architecture)
Dean: Syamsul Asri; *staff* 9 (92)
F. of Fisheries
Dean: Zoeslim Zay; *staff* 14 (29)
Founded 1981. A private institution under the supervision of the Department of Education and Culture. Governing body: the Senate. Residential facilities for academic staff.
Arrangements for co-operation with: Technical University, Braunschweig; Technical College, Hildesheim/Holzminden.
Academic Year: September to August (September-February; March-August).
Admission Requirements: Secondary school certificate (Sekolah Lanjutan Atas, S.L.T.A.).
Fees (Rupiahs): 137,500-171,500 per semester,
Language of Instruction: Indonesian.
Degrees and Diplomas: Sarjana, 4-4 ½ yrs.
Library: 36,000 vols.
Special Facilities (Museums, etc.): Laboratory of Biology, Chemistry, Physics and Electronics.
Academic Staff, 1989-90:

Rank	Full-time	Part-time
Guru Besar (Professors)	–	5
Lektor Madya (Senior Lecturers)	2	164
Lektor Muda (Lecturers)	4	86
Asisten Ahli Madya (Instructors)	78	110
Total	84	365

Student Enrolment, 1989-90:

	Men	Women	Total
Of the country	3562	2297	5859

3461 **UNIVERSITAS DARMA AGUNG**
Jalan Bantam 21, Medan

Law
Social and Political Science
Economics
Education and Teacher Training
Engineering
Agriculture
Industrial and Textile Engineering
Letters
Founded 1957. A private institution under the supervision of the Department of Education and Culture.

3462 **UNIVERSITAS DARUL'ULUM**
Jalan Merdeka 29A, Jombang

Law
Social and Political Sciences
Education Engineering
Economics
Founded 1965. A private institution under the supervision of the Department of Education and Culture.

3463 **UNIVERSITAS DR. SOETOMO SURABAYA**
Jalan Semolowaru, Surabaya

Administration

Fishery
Education
A private institution under the supervision of the Department of Education and Culture.

3464 **UNIVERSITAS GRESIK**
Jalan Jaksa Agung Suprapto 1, Gresik

Engineering
Education
Law Economics
Founded 1981. A private institution under the supervision of the Department of Education and Culture.

3465 **UNIVERSITAS HKBP NOMMENSEN**
Nommensen University
Jalan Dr. Soetomo 4A, Medan 20234, Sumatera Utara
Telex: 51577 NOM MON
Telephone: 511426; 522922
Rektor: Biliater Napitupulu

F. of Economics
Dean: Juliana Lumbantobing; *staff* 44 (14)
F. of Public and Business Administration
Dean: Adelaide Pardede; *staff* 18 (25)
F. of Education and Teacher Training
Dean: M.A. Hutahaean; *staff* 45
F. of Engineering
Dean: Farel Napitupulu; *staff* 36 (30)
F. of Animal Husbandry
Head: M. Panjaitan; *staff* 18 (3)
F. of Law
Dean: Issanuddin; *staff* 18 (17)
F. of Arts
Head: Biliater Napitupulu; *staff* 2 (15)
F. of Agriculture
Dean: Ponten Naibaho; *staff* – (21)
Research D.
Director: Purba Ohs
D. of Batak Studies
Head: B. Simanjuntak

Founded 1954. A private institution under the supervision of the Department of Education and Culture. Residential facilities for academic staff and students.

Academic Year: August to June (August-January; February-June).

Admission Requirements: Secondary school certificate (Sekolah Lanjutan Atas, S.L.A.).

Fees (Rupiahs): 275,000-475,000.

Language of Instruction: Indonesian.

Degrees and Diplomas: Sarjana, 5 yrs. Also Diploma in Secretarial Studies, 3 yrs.

Libraries: Nommensen University Library; Batak Studies Library.

Special Facilities (Museums, etc.): Simalingkar.

Publications: Warta Nommensen; Visi.

Academic Staff: c. 160 (215).

Student Enrolment: c. 11,560.

3466 **UNIVERSITAS IBNU CHALDUN**
IBN Khaldun University
Jalan Pemuda 1 Kav. 97, Rawamangun, Jakarta Timur
Telephone: 4880599
Rektor: Haji Amura (1981-88)
Secretary-General: Muhsin Soleiman

F. of Journalism and Mass Communication
Dean: Abbas Abdullah; *staff* 7 (15)
F. of Social and Political Sciences
Dean: Djohan Makmur; *staff* 9 (17)
F. of Law
Dean: Hardjito Notopuro; *staff* 11 (28)
F. of Agriculture
Dean: Affendi Anwar; *staff* 5 (18)
F. of Economics
Dean: Soekadi Mulyo Putro; *staff* 8 (27)
F. of Islamic Studies
Dean: Imam Syihrowardi Bustomi; *staff* 6 (16)
F. of Shari'a (Islamic Law)
Dean: Abdul Cholik Nur Ali; *staff* 5 (11)

Founded 1956 as institute, became university 1960. A private institution under the supervision of the Department of Education and Culture.

Arrangements for co-operation with: Thammasat University, Bangkok; Chulalongkorn University, Bangkok.

Academic Year: September to July (September-January; February-June).

Admission Requirements: Secondary school certificate (Sekolah Lanjutan Atas, S.L.A.).

Fees (Rupiahs): 400,000 per annum.

Language of Instruction: Indonesian.

Degrees and Diplomas: Strata 1 (S1), 4-7 yrs. Stratas 2 and 3 (in preparation).

Library: Total, c. 4160 vols.

Publication: Bulletin.

Academic Staff, 1986-87:

Rank	Full-time	Part-time
Guru Besar (Professors)	3	2
Lektor Kepala (Associate Professors)	7	15
Lektor (Assistant Professors)	10	17
Lektor Madya (Senior Lecturers)	10	15
Lektor Muda (Lecturers)	7	10
Asisten Lektor	5	7
Total	42	66

Student Enrolment, 1986-87:

	Men	Women	Total
Of the country	1250	350	1600
Of other countries	4	–	4
Total	1254	350	1604

3467 **UNIVERSITAS IBNU CHALDUN BOGOR**
Ibn Khaldun University Bogor
Jalan R.E. Martadinata 2-4, Bogor
Telephone: (0251) 21112-28203
Rektor: Rais Ahmad (1985-89)

F. of Economics (including Business Administration)
Dean: Mas Soeryanata; *staff* 2 (2)
F. of Law
Dean: Benny Sofyan; *staff* 2 (2)
F. of Islamic Law
Dean: Didin Hafidhuddin; *staff* – (2)
F. of Engineering
Dean: Soepomo; *staff* 1 (3)
F. of Islamic Theology
Dean: Yusaf Iskandar; *staff* – (2)
F. Education
Dean: Adoeng Soempana; *staff* 3 (1)
F. of Islamic Education
Dean: Hassanuddin; *staff* 1 (1)

Founded 1961. A private institution under the supervision of the Department of Education and Culture. Residential facilities for academic staff and students.

Arrangements for co-operation with King Adbul Aziz University.

Academic Year: March to February (March-August; October-February).

Admission Requirements: Secondary school certificate (Surat Menengah Atas S.M.A.).

Language of Instruction: Indonesian.

Degrees and Diplomas: Strata 1 (S1), 4 yrs. Strata 2 (S2), a further 2 yrs.

Library: c. 7080 vols.

Academic Staff, 1986-87: 33 (232).

Student Enrolment, 1986-87:

	Men	Women	Total
Of the country	2488	718	3306

3468 **UNIVERSITAS INDONESIA MUDA**
Jalan Letjen Suprapto 22, Jakarta

Engineering
Law
Founded 1965. A private institution under the supervision of the Department of Education and Culture.

3469 **UNIVERSITAS ISLAM BANDUNG**
Bandung Islamic University
Jalan Tamansari 1, Bandung 40116
Telephone: (022) 50368
Rektor: H. Achmad Tirtosudiro
Pembantu Rektor (Academic): Mansur Mulyakusumah

F. of Law
; *staff* 43 (38)
F. of Psychology
; *staff* 23 (33)
F. of Engineering
Dean: Bambang Pranggono; *staff* 28 (144)
F. of Economics
Dean: Soelaeman Baehaki; *staff* 34 (43)
F. of Mathematics and Natural Sciences
Dean: Lukman Wiriakinata; *staff* 20 (21)
F. of Communication (Journalism, Information and Public Relations)
Dean: Iir Syair; *staff* 20 (20)
F. of Islamic Law (Syariah)
Dean: H. Abdurrachman; *staff* 15 (8)
F. of Islamic Theology
Dean: Abdullah Yusuf; *staff* 18 (8)
F. of Islamic Education
Dean: Sanusi Uwes; *staff* 17 (11)
I. for Research and Extension
Director: Saefullah

Founded 1959. A private institution under the auspices of the Islamic Education Foundation and under the supervision of the Department of Education and Culture and Religious Affairs.

Academic Year: September to August (September-February; March-August).

Admission Requirements: Secondary school certificate (Sekolah Lanjutan Atas, S.L.A.) and entrance examination.

Fees (Rupiahs): 450,000 per annum.

Language of Instruction: Indonesian.

Degrees and Diplomas: Sarjana, 4 ½ yrs.

Library: University Library, 15,446 vols.

Publication: Mimbar (quarterly).

Academic Staff, 1989:

Rank	Full-time	Part-time
Guru Besar (Professors)	1	10
Lektor Kepala (Associate Professors)	9	17
Lektor Kepala Madya	5	36
Lektor (Assistant Professors)	15	50
Lektor Madya (Senior Lecturers)	6	58
Lektor Muda (Lecturers)	14	51
Assisten Ahli (Senior Assistants)	40	40
Assisten Ahli Madya (Instuctors)	128	64
Total	218	326

Student Enrolment, 1989:

	Men	Women	Total
Of the country	3240	2253	5493

3470 **UNIVERSITAS ISLAM INDONESIA**
Islamic University of Indonesia
Jalan Cik Ditiro 1, Yogyakarta
Telephone: 3091

F. of Economics
F. of Law
F. of Civil Engineering
F. of Textile Technology

Founded 1945 and officially recognized under present title 1951. A private institution under the supervision of the Department of Education and Culture.

Academic Year: July to June (July-December; January-June).

Admission Requirements: Secondary school certificate (Sekolah Menengah Atas, S.M.A.).

Language of Instruction: Indonesian.

Degrees and Diplomas: Sarjana, 3 yrs. Professional title of Insinjur. Dokter, by thesis.

Library: Central Libary *c.* 31,680 vols.

Publications: Majallah UNISIA (quarterly scientific periodical); Detente.

Academic Staff: c. 500.

Student Enrolment: c. 7720.

3471 **UNIVERSITAS ISLAM JAKARTA**
Islamic University of Jakarta
Jalan Nanas II, Utan Kayu, Jakarta
Telephone: 45286

F. of Law
F. of Economics

Founded 1951. A private institution under the supervision of the Department of Education and Culture.

3472 **UNIVERSITAS ISLAM MALANG**
Jalan Mayjen Haryono 193, Malang

Law
Agriculture
Economics
Engineering
Education and Teacher Training

Founded 1981. A private institution under the supervision of the Department of Education and Culture.

3473 **UNIVERSITAS ISLAM NUSANTARA**
Jalan Sukarno Hatta, Jalan Taman Halimun 37, Bandung

Economics
Law
Education

Founded 1959. A private institution under the supervision of the Department of Education and Culture.

3474 **UNIVERSITAS ISLAM RIAU**
Islamic University of Riau
Jalan Prof. Mohd. Yamin 69, Pekanbaru, Riau
Telephone: 21016
Rektor: H. Rawi Kunin (1984-88)
Pembantu Rektor (Academic): Muchtar Ahmad

F. of Law
Dean: H. Rawi Kunin; *staff* 12 (33)
F. of Theology
Dean: Muchtaruddin S.; *staff* 6 (28)
F. of Engineering
Dean: Zulkifli Saleh; *staff* 8 (39)
F. of Agriculture (including Fishery and Aquaculture)
Dean: Tengku Dahril; *staff* 9 (36)
F. of Economics
Dean: Yulifar; *staff* 9 (35)
F. of Social and Political Sciences
Dean: H.S. Balia; *staff* 6 (37)
F. of Education
Dean: Zainal Zein; *staff* 6 (74)
I. of Legal Aid Studies
Director: Rawi Kunin; *staff* 5
Ce. for Rural Development Studies
Director: Tengku Dahril; *staff* 3 (3)
Management Development Ce.
Director: Muchtar Ahmad; *staff* 4 (4)

Founded 1962. A private institution under the supervision of the Department of Education and Culture. Residential facilities for academic staff and 24 women students.

Academic Year: July to June (July-December; January-June).

Admission Requirements: Secondary school certificate (Sekolah Menengah Atas, S.M.A.).

Fees (Rupiahs): Registration, 150,000 per semester; tuition, 5000 per unit/credit.

Language of Instruction: Indonesian.

Degrees and Diplomas: Sarjana, 4 yrs. Diplomas II and III, 2-3 yrs.

Library: 6000 vols.

Publications: Bulletin of Rural Development (annually, in Indonesian); Assalam (bimonthly).

Press or Publishing House: University Press.

Academic Staff, 1986-87:

Rank	Full-time	Part-time
Guru Besar (Professors)	–	8
Lektor Kepala (Assistant Professors)	5	28
Lektor (Lecturers)	17	39
Docents	29	234
Asisten	17	10
Total	68	319

Student Enrolment, 1986-87:

	Men	Women	Total
Of the country	3417	1990	5407
Of other countries	2	–	2
Total	3419	1990	5409

3475 **UNIVERSITAS ISLAM 'SYEKH-YUSUF' TANGERANG**

Islamic University of 'Syekh-Yusuf'

Jalan Harapan II, Babakan Tangerang, Jawa Herat

Telephone: 22340

Rektor: Barli Djajadikarga (1985-89)

Secretary: Alfonsvuri Lintou

F. of Social and Political Sciences
Dean: Lande M. Suruhi; *staff* 9 (20)
F. of Law
Dean: Siti Fatimah; *staff* 8 (18)
F. of Theology (Islam)
Dean: Mahmudi; *staff* 2 (15)
F. of Engineering
Dean: Soesarno; *staff* 5 (28)
F. of Education
Dean: Yusuf Budiana Tanu; *staff* 7 (28)

Founded 1966 as branch of Islamic University of Jakarta, became independent 1975. A private institution under the supervision of the Department of Education and Culture.

Academic Year: September to August (September-January; February-August).

Admission Requirements: Secondary school certificates (Sekolah Menengah Tingkat Atas S.M.T.A.) and entrance examination.

Fees (Rupiahs): 300,000-450,000 per annum.

Language of Instruction: Indonesian.

Degrees and Diplomas: Doktorandus in Social and Political Sciences; Sarjana Hukum in Law; Insinjur, 4 yrs.

Library: 4000 vols.

Academic Staff, 1986-87:

Rank	Full-time	Part-time
Guru Besar (Professors)	1	1
Lektor Kepala (Senior Lecturers)	1	2
Lektor (Lecturers)	4	5
Lektor Madya (Junior Lecturers)	1	4
Lektor Muda (Assistant Lecturers)	3	23
Asisten Ahli (Senior Assistants)	6	34
Asisten Ahli Madya (Instructors)	6	68
Asisten Madya	–	15
Total	22	151

Student Enrolment, 1986-87:

	Men	Women	Total
Of the country	1179	213	1392

3476 **UNIVERSITAS ISLAM SYEKH YUSUF**

Jalan Harapan II, Babakan, Tangerang

Social and Political Sciences
Law
Textile Technology
Education

Founded 1975. A private institution under the supervision of the Department of Education and Culture.

3477 **UNIVERSITAS ISLAM SUMATERA UTARA**

Islamic University of North Sumatera

Jalan Sisingamangaraja, Teladan, Medan 20217

Telephone: 24382

Rektor: Mustafa Majnu

Pembantu Rektor: Sanwani Nasution

F. of Law
Dean: Saiful Anwar
F. of Letters
Dean: Jumino Suhadi
F. of Economics
Dean: A. Chazali
F. of Education and Teacher Training
Dean: M. Yamin Lubis
F. of Social and Political Science
Dean: Amru Nasution
F. of Agriculture
Dean: Usman Nasution
F. of Medicine
Dean: Mochtar Tarigan
F. of Engineering
Dean: Soryan Siregar
F. of Islamic Law (Syariah)
Dean: Hamdan Abbas
F. of Islamic Teaching
Dean: Ahmad Ashari
F. of Islamic Communication
Dean: Nuh Nasution

Also 4 Research Centres for Law, Economics, Agriculture and Engineering.

Founded 1952. A private institution under the supervision of the Department of Education and Culture for non-Islamic studies and under the Department of Religion for Islamic Studies.

Academic Year: July to July (July-January; January-July).

Admission Requirements: Secondary school certificate (Sekolah Menengah Atas, S.M.A.) or recognized foreign equivalent.

Fees (Rupiahs): 250,000-700,000 per annum.

Language of Instruction: Indonesian.

Degrees and Diplomas: Sarjana, 5 yrs. Professional titles of–Insinjur, 5 yrs; Medical Doctor (MBBS), 6 ½ yrs.

Library: Libraries for each faculty.

Publication: Bulletin Pertamian (3 times a year).

Academic Staff, 1989-90:

Rank	Full-time	Part-time
Guru Besar (Professors)	–	15
Lektor Kepala (Senior Lecturers)	15	115
Lektor Kepala (Junior Lecturers)	175	442
Total	190	572

Student Enrolment, 1989-90:

	Men	Women	Total
Of the country	4601	3203	7804
Of the countries	10	5	15
Total	4611	3208	7819

3478 **UNIVERSITAS ISLAM SULTAN AGUNG**

Islamic University of Sultan Agung

Jalan Raya Kaligawe, Semarang

Cables: unissula

Telephone: 2844; 2534

F. of Law
F. of Economics
F. of Engineering
F. of Medicine

Founded 1962. A private institution under the supervision of the Department of Education and Culture.

Academic Year: January to December (April-May; November-December).

Admission Requirements: Secondary school certificate (Sekolah Menengah Atas, S.M.A.).

Language of Instruction: Indonesian.

Degrees and Diplomas: Sarjana, 5 yrs.

Academic Staff: c. 260.

Student Enrolment: c. 950.

3479 **UNIVERSITAS JAKARTA**

Jalan Pulo Mas Barat, Jakarta

Engineering
Law

Public and Business Administration

Founded 1965. A private institution under the supervision of the Department of Education and Culture.

3480 **UNIVERSITAS JANABADRA**

Jalan KHA Dahlan 1, Yogyakarta

F. of Law

Founded 1958. A private institution under the supervision of the Department of Education and Culture.

3481 **UNIVERSITAS JAJABAYA**

Jajabaya University

Jalan A. Yani, Jakarta

Telephone: 414771

Rektor: Taher Moeslim (1962-)

F. of Economics

Dean: Ali Rachmat; *staff* 23 (57)

F. of Law

Dean: Wiryawan Piet; *staff* 18 (35)

F. of Political and Social Sciences

Dean: Atmowasito Soetedjo; *staff* 16 (30)

F. of Engineering

Dean: Anwar Syamsu; *staff* 12 (36)

Founded 1958. A private institution under the supervision of the Department of Education and Culture. Governing body: the Board of Trustees. Residential facilities for academic staff.

Academic Year: September to July (September-February; March-July).

Admission Requirements: Secondary school certificate (Sekolah Menengah Atas, S.M.A.).

Fees (Rupiahs): *c.* 900,000-1,300,000 per annum.

Language of Instruction: Indonesian.

Degrees and Diplomas: Sarjana, 4-7 yrs. Diploma III, 3-4 yrs.

Library: 13,000 vols.

Academic Staff, 1986-87:

Rank	Full-time	Part-time
Guru Besar (Professors)	2	6
Lektor Kepala (Senior Lecturers)	5	22
Lektor (Lecturers)	10	52
Asisten	52	78
Total	69	158

Student Enrolment, 1986-87:

	Men	Women	Total
Of the country	8476	3129	11,605

3482 **UNIVERSITAS KATOLIK INDONESIA ATMA JAYA**

Atma Jaya Catholic University of Indonesia

Jalan Jendral Sudirman 49A, Jakarta Selatan

Cables: unikatolik

Telephone: 586491/94

Rektor: Mariana Setiadarma (1987-)

F. of Economics (including Business Administration and Accountancy)

F. of Social and Political Sciences

F. of Education and Teacher Training

F. of Engineering

F. of Law

F. of Medicine

Founded 1960. A private institution under the supervision of the Department of Education and Culture.

Academic Year: September to May (September-December; February-May).

Admission Requirements: Secondary school certificate (Sekolah Menengah Atas, S.M.A.) or equivalent.

Language of Instruction: Indonesian.

Degrees and Diplomas: Doctorandus, Drs., in–Economics; Social Sciences; Education, 5 yrs. Sarjana Hukum, law, 5 yrs. Professional title of Insinjur, 5 yrs. Dokter, medicine, 6 yrs.

Libraries: Central Library, *c.* 22,730 vols; Research Centre, *c.* 16,000; Language Institute, *c.* 1910.

Publications: Linguistic Studies in Indonesian and Languages in Indonesian (2-3 times a year); Philosophy Series.

Academic Staff: c. 130 (320).

Student Enrolment: c. 4860.

3483 **UNIVERSITAS KEDIRI**

Jalan Sodanco Supriadi 3, Kediri

Law

Social and Political Science

Agriculture

Economics

Engineering

Founded 1980. A private institution under the supervision of the Department of Education and Culture.

3484 **UNIVERSITAS KATOLIK PARAHYANGAN**

Parahyangan Catholic University

Jalan Merdeka 30, Bandung

Cables: unpar, bandung

Telephone: 52090; 8369½

Rektor: A. Koesdarminta (1983-86)

Pembantu Rektor II (Administrative): F. Vermeulen

F. of Economics

F. of Law

F. of Engineering

Founded 1955 as Academy of Commerce, reorganized 1958 and acquired present title and status 1962. A private institution under the supervision of the Department of Education and Culture.

Academic Year: January to December (January-June; July-December).

Admission Requirements: Secondary school certificate (Sekolah Menengah Atas, S.M.A.).

Language of Instruction: Indonesian.

Degrees and Diplomas: Doctorandus, Drs.; Sarjana Hukum, law; Insinjur, 5 yrs.

Library: University Library, *c.* 15,000 vols.

Publications: Profil; Bina; ETSHA; Bina Ekonomi; Socio; Investasi (all monthly); Melintas (biannually); Pengayoman (quarterly); Journal (monthly); Pedoman UNPAR (annual catalogue).

Academic Staff: c. 110 (440).

Student Enrolment: c. 7280.

3485 **UNIVERSITAS KATHOLIK SOEGIJAPRANATA**

Soegijapranata Catholic University

Jalan Pandanaran 100, Semarang 50241, Central Java

Telephone: (24) 411480

Rektor: M. Sastrapratedja

F. of Economics

Dean: Leo Gunawan; *staff* 14 (52)

F. of Engineering (including Architecture)

Dean: A.M.S. Darmawan; *staff* 35 (188)

F. of Law

Dean: Supratignja; *staff* 16 (62)

F. of Psychology

Dean: M.L. Oetomo; *staff* 15 (30)

I. of English Language Training

Director: Andre Purba; *staff* 7 (10)

I. of Applied Research

Director: A. Sidharta; *staff* 5

Research Ce.

Director: Alex Emyll; *staff* 4

Founded 1966. A private institution under the supervision of the Department of Education and Culture. Governing bodies: the Sandjojo Foundation; the Board of Trustees.

Academic Year: August to July (August-January; February-July).

Admission Requirements: Secondary school certificate (Sekolah Menengah Atas, S.M.A.) and entrance examination.

Fees (Rupiahs): 500,000 per annum.

Language of Instruction: Indonesian.

Degrees and Diplomas: Strata 1 (S1), 4 yrs.

Library: 30,000 vols.

Publication: PRANATA (scientific magazine).

Academic Staff, 1990:

Rank	Full-time	Part-time
Guru Besar (Professors)	2	10
Lektor (Assistant Professors)	5	75
Lektor Muda (Lecturers)	19	104
Asisten Lektor (Assistant Lecturers)	64	143
Total	90	332

Student Enrolment, 1990:

	Men	Women	Total
Of the country	1521	1094	2615

3486 **UNIVERSITAS KATHOLIK WIDYA KARYA**

Jalan Bondowoso 2, Malang

Economics
Agriculture
Engineering

Founded 1982. A private institution under the supervision of the Department of Education and Culture.

3487 **UNIVERSITAS KATHOLIK WIDYA MANADALA**

Jalan Dinoyo 42-44, Surabaya 60265
Telephone: 684478
Rektor: M.P. Soetrisno (1987-90)

F. of Education and Teacher Training
Dean: Soeharto; *staff* 27 (71)
F. of Pharmacy
Dean: Soewandhy Widjaja; *staff* 26 (61)
F. of Economics
Dean: Mustadjab; *staff* 22 (77)
F. of Engineering
Dean: V.W. Prasetyo; *staff* 14 (84)
F. of Agricultural Technology
Dean: J.H. Arisasmita; *staff* 9 (48)
Ce for Applied Research
Director: Adrianta

Founded 1960. A private institution under the supervision of the Department of Education and Culture.

Academic Year: February to January (February-July; August-January).

Admission Requirements: Secondary school certificate (Sekolah Menengah Atas, S.M.A.).

Languages of Instruction: Indonesian and English.

Degrees and Diplomas: Diploma, 3 yrs. Master, 4 yrs.

Library: 36,747 vols.

Academic Staff, 1989-90:

Rank	Full-time	Part-time
Guru Besar (Professors)	1	6
Lektor Kepala (Associate Professors)	–	22
Lektor Kepala Madya (Assistant Professors)	3	33
Lektor (Lecturers)	8	52
Lektor Madya (Junior Lecturers)	8	52
Lektor Muda (Assistant Lecturers)	18	29
Asisten Ahli (Senior Assistants)	16	59
Asisten Ahli Madya (Instructors)	57	106
Total	113	359

Student Enrolment, 1990:

	Men	Women	Total
Of the country	1109	2180	3289

3488 **UNIVERSITAS KHAIRUN**

Jalan Hasan Esa, Ternate

Law
Economics
Education

Founded 1964. A private institution under the supervision of the Department of Education and Culture.

3489 **UNIVERSITAS KLABAT**

Mount Klabat University
Airmadidi-Manado, Sulawesi Utara
Cables: adventist manado
Telephone: (431) 51430
President: D. Min (1987-91)

D. of Agriculture
Head: Paul Raubun; *staff* 21 (6)
D. of Business Administration
Head: S. Nangoy; *staff* 21 (4)
D. of Secretarial Studies
Head: Anna Kalangi; *staff* 19 (4)
D. of Theology
Head: Hendrik Sumendap; *staff* 21
D. of Education
Head: Agus Wahongan; *staff* 21

Founded 1965. A private institution operated by the Seventh-Day Adventist Church of East Indonesia and under the supervision of the Department of Education and Culture.

Academic Year: August to May (August-December; January-May).

Admission Requirements: Secondary school certificate (Sekolah Menegah Atas, S.M.A.).

Fees (Rupiahs): 180,000 per semester.

Language of Instruction: Indonesian.

Degrees and Diplomas: Strata 1 (S1), 4 yrs. Diplomas II and III, 2-3 yrs.

Academic Staff, 1986-87:

Rank	Full-time	Part-time
Guru Besar (Professors)	3	–
Lektor Kepala (Associate Professors)	4	–
Lektor (Assistant Professors)	12	–
Asisten Ahli Madya (Instructors)	24	2
Total	43	2

Student Enrolment, 1988-90:

	Men	Women	Total
Of the country	388	286	674

3490 **UNIVERSITAS KRISNADWIPAYANA**

Jatiwaringin, Jakarta

Engineering
Public and Business Administration
Law
Economics

Founded 1952. A private institution under the supervision of the Department of Education and Culture.

3491 **UNIVERSITAS KRISTEN INDONESIA**

Jalan Diponegoro 86, Jakarta

Engineering
Letters
Medicine
Law
Economics
Education and Teacher Training

Founded 1953. A private institution under the supervision of the Department of Education and Culture.

3492 **UNIVERSITAS KRISTEN INDONESIA PAULUS**

Jalan Cenderawasih 65, Ujung Pandang

Engineering
Law
Economics
Letters

Founded 1965. A private institution under the supervision of the Department of Education and Culture.

3493 **UNIVERSITAS KRISTEN INDONESIA TOMOHON**

Indonesian Christian University of Tomohon
Jalan Kakaskasen III, Tomohon 95362 (North Sulawesi)
Telephone: 169
Rektor: E.A. Worang
Pembantu Rektor (Administrator): Kelly Rondo

F. of Theology
Dean: William Langi; *staff* 53 (22)

F. of Education and Teacher Training
Dean: Mrs. R. Montolalu-Sumarauw; *staff* 19 (41)
F. of Psychology
Dean: Joseph Sinolungan; *staff* 10 (21)
F. of Mathematical and Natural Sciences
Dean: R. Rompas; *staff* 9 (27)
F. of Law
Dean: G.M.A. Ingkiriwang; *staff* 10 (35)
F. of Veterinary Medicine
Dean: L.A. Lantang; *staff* 7 (5)
F. of Public Health
Dean: S.A. Tandaju; *staff* – (37)
F. of Technical Engineering
Dean: W.A. Malingkas; *staff* 9 (18)
F. of Agricultural Technology
Dean: W.A. Najoan; *staff* 6 (27)
Research and Development Ce.
Director: Soetiman

Founded 1965. Private Christian University under the supervision of the Minahasa Christian Evangelical Church. Governing bodies: the Senate; the Advisory Council. Residential facilities for limited academic staff and for theological students.

Admission Requirements: Secondary school certificate (Sekolah Menengah Atas, S.M.A.) and entrance examination.

Fees (Rupiahs): 90,000-120,000 per semester.

Degrees and Diplomas: Sarjana in–Theology; Law, 4 yrs. Doktorandus in–Education; Mathematics and Natural Sciences; Psychology; Public Health, 4 yrs. Insinyur, 4 yrs. Dokter Hewan in Veterinary Medicine, 4 yrs.

Library: 12,465 vols.

Special Facilities (Museums, etc.): Experimental Farm Station.

Publication: Inspirasi (quarterly).

Academic Staff, 1989-90.:

Rank	Full-time	Part-time
Guru Besar (Professors	3	–
Guru Besar Madya	3	12
Lektor Kepala	2	17
Lektor Kepala Madya	1	29
Lektor	6	33
Lektor Madya	4	24
Lektor Muda	6	22
Asisten Ahli	6	26
Asisten Ahli Madya	99	53
Total	128	216

Student Enrolment, 1989-90: 3074.

3494 **UNIVERSITAS KRISTEN DJAYA**
Djaya Christian University
Jalan Tanjung Duren Raya 4, Jakarta 11470
Telephone: 599601
Rektor: O.E. Engelen (1974-87)

F. of Medicine
Dean: Toebe Makaminan; *staff* 34 (61)
F. of Engineering
Dean: P.J. Simeon; *staff* 10 (72)
F. of Economics
Dean: R.L. Lokollo; *staff* 6 (61)
I. for Social Welfare
Also a research institute.

Founded 1967 by the Synod of the Church of Indonesia in West Java. A private institution under the supervisionof the Department of Education and Culture.

Academic Year: September to August (September-January; February-July).

Admission Requirements: Secondary school certificate (Sekolah Menengah Atas, S.M.A.).

Fees (Rupiahs): 350,000-450,000 per semester.

Language of Instruction: Indonesian.

Degrees and Diplomas: Sarjana, 6-7 yrs.

Library: 5794 vols.

Academic Staff, 1986-87:

Rank	Full-time	Part-time
Guru Besar (Professors)	–	3
Lektor Kepala (Associate Professors)	–	24
Lektor (Assistant Professors)	2	49
Lektor Madya (Senior Lecturers)	1	36
Lektor Muda (Lecturers)	–	25
Asisten Ahli (Senior Assistants)	5	24
Asisten Ahli Madya (Assistant Lecturers)	42	29
Asisten Muda (Junior Assistant Lecturers)	–	4
Total	50	194

Student Enrolment, 1986-87:

	Men	Women	Total
Of the country	328	145	473

3495 **UNIVERSITAS KRISTEN MARANATHA**
Jalan Cihampelas 169, Bandung

Medicine
Engineering
Psychology
Letters

Founded 1965. A private institution under the supervision of the Department of Education and Culture.

3496 **UNIVERSITAS KRISTEN PETRA**
Petra Christian University
Siwalankerto 121-131, Tromolpos 5304, Surabaya 60002
Telephone: 813040
Rektor: Wasis (1988-92)
Kepala Biro Administrasi (Registrar): Guana Tandjung

F. of Letters
Dean: Josefa Juniorti; *staff* 17 (19)
F. of Engineering (including Architecture)
Dean: Oentoeng; *staff* 103 (213)
F. of Economics (including Management)
Dean: Yan Pandi; *staff* 12 (40)

Founded 1961 by the 'Petra' Association for Christian Education and Instruction. A private institution under the supervision of the Department of Education and Culture. Governing bodies: the Foundation; the Senate. Some residential facilities for students.

Academic Year: August to June (August-December; February-June).

Admission Requirements: Secondary school certificate (Sekolah Menengah Atas, S.M.A.) and entrance examination.

Fees (Rupiahs): 228,000 per semester; 10,000 per credit.

Language of Instruction: Indonesian.

Degrees and Diplomas: Sarjana, 9 sem. Diplomas, 6 sem.

Library: Central Library, 35,000 vols.

Publications: Madjalah 'Genta' (quarterly); Dimensi (quarterly).

Press or Publishing House: University Press.

Academic Staff, 1989-90:

Rank	Full-time	Part-time
Guru Besar (Professors)	4	1
Lektor Kepala (Assistant Professors)	15	18
Lektor (Lecturers)	15	22
Lektor Madya (Junior Lecturers)	17	21
Lektor Muda (Assistant Lecturers)	26	28
Asisten Ahli (Senior Assistants)	27	18
Asisten Ahli Madya (Instructors)	30	107
Asisten	–	11
Asisten Muda	–	46
Total	134	272

Student Enrolment, 1989-90: 3326.

3497 **UNIVERSITAS KRISTEN SATYA WACANA**
Satya Wacana Christian University
Jalan Diponegoro 52-60, Salatiga 50711, Central Java
Telex: 22364 UKSWSA
Telephone: (298) 81362/4
Fax: (298) 81420
Vice-Chancellor: Willi Toisuta (1983-93)
Registrar: Hot Pasaribu

F. of Law
Dean: Budi Lazarusli; *staff* 25

F. of Economics (including Management and Accountancy)
Dean: Hendrawan Supratikno; *staff* 32
F. of Theology
Dean: Meno Subagyo; *staff* 7
F. of Agriculture
Dean: O. Tjahjakartana; *staff* 19
F. of Biology
Dean: Kris Timotius; *staff* 21
F. of Electronics (including Computer Sciences)
Dean: Herman Kanalebe; *staff* 21
F. of Teacher Training and Education (including Languages)
Dean: Made Markus; *staff* 104
D. of Natural Sciences and Mathematics
Head: Jimmy Hendarto; *staff* 8
D. of General Studies
Head: Sunarso; *staff* 19 (20)
Language Ce.
Head: Urip Sutiyono; *staff* 4
Computer Ce.
Director: Danny manongga; *staff* 10
Ce. for the Advancement of Teaching
Director: Towapala Hamakonda; *staff* 6
University Research I.
Director: Nico L. Kana; *staff* 10
Ce. for Research in Science and Technology
Head: Kris Timotius
Community Service I.
Director: R. Gultom; *staff* 8

Founded 1956 as private Christian Teacher Training College, became University and Teacher Training Institute 1962 and acquired present status and title 1977. A private institution under the supervision of the Department of Education and Culture. Governing body: the Board of Trustees. Residential facilities for academic staff and 400 students.

Arrangements for co-operation with the Universities of: Sydney; Kwansei; Amsterdam; Payap, Thailand; Pennsylvania State; Charles Sturt, Australia; Perth College, Australia; St. Olaf College, USA.

Academic Year: September to June (September-January; March-June).

Admission Requirements: Secondary school certificate (Sekolah Lanjutan Atas, S.L.A.) or equivalent, and entrance examination.

Fees (Rupiahs): 200,000 per semester, according to credits taken.

Languages of Instruction: Indonesian and English (for special programmes).

Degrees and Diplomas: Strata 1 (S1), 4 yrs. Diplomas II and III, 2-3 yrs. Strata 2 (S2), a further 2 yrs.

Library: Central Library, 87,000 vols.

Publications: Warta Satya Wacana (monthly); Kritis (quarterly).

Press or Publishing House: Percetakan Satya Wacana.

Academic Staff, 1989-90:

Rank	Full-time
Guru Besar/Guru Besar Madya	6
Lektor Kepala/Lektor Kepala Madya	19
Lektor (Lecturers)	10
Lektor Madya/Lektor Muda	56
Asisten Ahli/Asisten Ahli Madya	101
Total	192

Student Enrolment, 1989-90:

	Men	Women	Total
Of the country	3041	3023	6064

3498 **UNIVERSITAS MADURA**

Jalan Slamet Riyadi 2, Pamekasan

Law
Economics
Social and Political Science
Education

Founded 1978. A private institution under the supervision of the Department of Education and Culture.

3499 **UNIVERSITAS MAHASARASWATI**

Mahasaraswati University Denpasar
Jalan Kembodja, Denpasar
Telephone: 27019
Rektor: I. Gusti Made Tamba (1963-)

F. of Agriculture
Dean: Alit Wiswasta; *staff* 22 (58)
F. of Law
Dean: Istri Ramaswati; *staff* 30 (30)
F. of Economics
Dean: Anak Agung Pt. Agung; *staff* 15 (28)
F. of Education and Teacher Training
Dean: Made Legana; *staff* 13 (31)
F. of Engineering
Dean: Winasa Kesama; *staff* 19 (52)
Research Ce.
Principal: Wayan Cipta; *staff* 2

Founded 1962. A private institution under the supervision of the Department of Education and Culture.

Admission Requirements: Seconda;ry school certificate (Sekolah Menengah Atas, S.M.A.) or equivalent, and entrance examination.

Fees (Rupiahs): 16,000-24,500 per month.

Languages of Instruction: Indonesian and English.

Degrees and Diplomas: Bachelor, 4 yrs.

Library: Central Library, 2647 vols.

Publication: Mahawidya (quarterly).

Academic Staff, 1989-90:

Rank	Full-time	Part-time
Guru Besar	–	4
Lektor Kepala	–	10
Lektor Kepala Muda	–	25
Lektor	1	50
Lektor Madya	1	40
Lektor Muda	20	60
Asisten Ahli	17	5
Asisten Ahli Madya	84	–
Total	131	194

Student Enrolment, 1989-90:

	Men	Women	Total
Of the country	1433	1008	2441
Of other countries	1	–	1
Total	1434	1008	2442

3500 **UNIVERSITAS MARHAEN**

Jalan Ken Arok 5, Denpasar

Social and Political Sciences
Law

Founded 1963. A private institution under the supervision of the Department of Education and Culture.

3501 **UNIVERSITAS MERDEKA MADIUN**

Jalan Pahlawan 25, Madiun

Law
Economics
Social and Political Sciences
Engineering

Founded 1979. A private institution under the supervision of the Department of Education and Culture.

3502 **UNIVERSITAS MERDEKA PUSAT**

Jalan Bandung 1, Malang
Telephone: 2893

F. of Law
F. of Economics
F. of Political and Social Sciences
F. of Engineering

Founded 1964. Hanura University, Surabaya incorporated 1972. A private institution under the supervision of the Department of Education and Culture.

Academic Year: June to June (June-October; November-June).

Admission Requirements: Secondary school certificate (Sekolah Menengah Atas, S.M.A.).

Language of Instruction: Indonesian.

Degrees and Diplomas: Sarjana, 5 yrs.
Library: c. 2230 vols.
Academic Staff: c. 30 (150).
Student Enrolment: c. 850.

3503 **UNIVERSITAS METHODIST INDONESIA**
Jalan Hang Tuah 8, Medan

Letters
Medicine
Agriculture

Founded 1965. A private institution under the supervision of the Department of Education and Culture.

3504 **UNIVERSITAS MUHAMMADIJAH JAKARTA**
Jalan Limau I, II, III, Keb, Baru, Jakarta

F. of Engineering
F. of Law
F. of Social and Political Sciences
F. of Economics

Founded 1955. A private institution under the supervision of the Department of Education and Culture.

3505 **UNIVERSITAS MUHAMMADIYAH JEMBER**
Muhammadiyah University of Jember
Jalan Karimata, 43, Jember 68121 (East Java)
Telephone: 21640
Rektor: Mohammed Ionak (1981-)

F. of Agriculture
Dean: Hartadi; *staff* 11 (14)
F. of Law
Dean: Irawan Soerodjo; *staff* 10 (30)
F. of Education and Teacher Training
Dean: Rachman Tawil; *staff* 24 (15)
F. of Economics
Dean: Sri Muljati; *staff* 10 (23)
F. of Social and Political Sciences
Dean: Rosyidah Khusyairi; *staff* 11 (15)
F. of Technology
Dean: Rusgianto; *staff* 6 (10)
Research and Social Development I.
Head: Tjuk Sugiarto; *staff* 4 (3)

Founded 1981. A private institution under the supervision of the Department of Education and Culture.

Academic Year: January to July.

Language of Instruction: Indoniesian.

Library: 16,597 vols.

Special Facilities (Museums, etc.): Biological Garden; Movie Studio; English Laboratorium; Technology Laboratorium.

Publication: IQRO Magazine (every 3 months).

Academic Staff, 1989-90: 90 (1).

Student Enrolment, 1989-90:

	Men	Women	Total
Of the country	1700	1800	3500

3506 **UNIVERSITAS MUHAMMADIYAH MAGELANG**
Jalan Tidar 21, Magelang

Economics
Law
Education

Founded 1964. A private institution under the supervision of the Department of Education and Culture.

3507 **UNIVERSITAS MUHAMMADIYAH MALANG**
Jalan Bandung 1, Malang

Education and Teacher Training
Social and Political Sciences
Law
Economics
Engineering
Agriculture

Founded 1965. A private institution under the supervision of the Department of Education and Culture.

3508 **UNIVERSITAS MUHAMMADIYAH MATARAM**
Mataram Muhammadiyah University
Jalan K.H.A. Dahlan, Pagesangan Mataram
Telephone: 23723
Rektor: Abdul Karim Sahidu (1986-90)
Kepala Baak: H. Sumadi

F. of Social and Political Sciences (including Business Administration)
Dean: Ki Agus Azhar; *staff* 2 (67)
F. of Education
Dean: Suraba; *staff* 14 (56)
F. of Civil Engineering
Dean: Zaini Basri; *staff* 2 (33)
F. of Agriculture
Dean: Soeharto Tjitrohardjono; *staff* 12 (32)

Founded 1980. A private institution under the supervision of the Department of Education and Culture.

Academic Year: August to July (August-February; March-July).

Admission Requirements: Secondary school certificate (Sekolah Menengah Atas, S.M.A.).

Fees (Rupiahs): 300,000-370,000.

Language of Instruction: Indonesian.

Degrees and Diplomas: Sarjana.

Library: 25,000 vols.

Publication: Ulul Albab (quarterly).

Academic Staff, 1989-90:

Rank	Full-time	Part-time
Guru Besar Madya	–	1
Lektor Kepala	–	9
Lektor	–	6
Lektor Madya	–	12
Lektor Muda	2	22
Asisten Ahli	3	38
Asisten Ahli Madya	30	149
Total	35	137

Student Enrolment, 1989-90:

	Men	Women	Total
Of the country	1490	650	2141

3509 **UNIVERSITAS MUHAMMADIYAH SUMATERA UTARA**
Jalan Gedung Arca 53, Medan

Education
Sociology
Economics
Agriculture

Founded 1957. A private institution under the supervision of the Department of Education and Culture.

3510 **UNIVERSITAS MUHAMMADIYAH UJUNG PANDANG**
Jalan Kanggang 7, Ujung Pandang

Education and Teacher Training
Social Work
Social and Political Sciences
Economics

Founded 1963. A private institution under the supervision of the Department of Education and Culture.

3511 **UNIVERSITAS MUHAMMADIYAH SURAKARTA**
Jalan Dr. Rajiman 78, Surakarta

Education and Teacher Training

Founded 1958. A private institution under the supervision of the Department of Education and Culture.

3512 **UNIVERSITAS MUHAMMAD SEROEDJI**
Jalan Bromo 89, Jember

Social and Political Sciences
Education
Economics
Engineering
Law

Founded 1981. A private institution under the supervision of the Department of Education and Culture.

3513 **UNIVERSITAS MURIA KUDUS**
Jalan Sunan Muria I/Bawah, Kudus

Economics
Law
Education and Teacher Training

Founded 1980. A private institution under the supervision of the Department of Education and Culture.

3514 **UNIVERSITAS MUSLIM INDONESIA**
Jalan Kakatua 27, Ujung Pandang

Economics
Law
Engineering

Founded 1954. A private institution under the supervision of the Department of Education and Culture.

3515 **UNIVERSITAS NAROTAMA**
Jalan Pahlawan 30, Surabaya

Economics
Law
Engineering

Founded 1981. A private institution under the supervision of the Department of Education and Culture.

3516 **UNIVERSITAS NASIONAL**
National University
Jalan Sawo Manila, Pejaten, Pasar Minggu, Jakarta 12760
Telephone: 782700; 782462
Rektor: S.T. Alisjahbana (1968-87)
Administratur: Umar Said

F. of Political Science
Dean: Muchlis Dasuki
F. of Biology
Dean: Salim Usman
F. of Law
Dean: Soedjono Hardjosoediro
F. of Economics
Dean: Sugeng Sumarjono
F. of Language and Literature
Dean: N. Sulaiman
F. of Mathematics and Physics
Dean: Bambang Permadi
F. of Engineering
Dean: Sriati Djafrie
F. of Agriculture
Dean: Satta Wigenasantana
Ce. for Islamic Studies
Director: Deliar Noer
Ce. for Japanese Studies
Director: Arifin Bey

Founded 1949, acquired present status and title 1953. A private institution under the supervision of the Department of Education and Culture. Receives some financial support from the central and municipal governments.

Arrangements for co-operation with: Tenri University; Griffith University, Brisbane; Ryuku University; University of Utrecht.

Academic Year: September to August (September-March; March-August).

Admission Requirements: Secondary school certificate (Sekolah Menengah Atas, S.M.A.) or equivalent.

Languages of Instruction: Indonesian, English, and Japanese.

Degrees and Diplomas: Strata 1 (S1), 4 yrs. Strata 2 (S2), a further 2 yrs. Strata 3 (S3), a further 3-4 yrs.

Library: 23,000 vols.

Publications: Ilmu dan Budaya (monthly); Berita Universitas Nasional (monthly); Biologica; Politika.

Academic Staff, 1986-87:

Rank	Full-time	Part-time
Guru Besar (Professors)	11	8
Lektor Kepala (Associate Professors)	23	31
Lektor (Assistant Professors)	17	52
Lektor Madya (Senior Lecturers)	12	40
Lektor Muda (Lecturers)	26	36
Asisten Ahli (Senior Assistants)	35	34
Asisten Madya (Assistant Lecturers)	118	102
Total	242	301

Student Enrolment, 1986-87:

	Men	Women	Total
Of the country	2852	1785	4637
Of other countries	2	1	3
Total	2854	1786	4640

3517 **UNIVERSITAS NGURAH RAI**
Jalan Patih Jelantik 9, Denpasar, Bali

Law
Economics
Social and Political Sciences
Engineering

Founded 1979. A private institution under the supervision of the Department of Education and Culture.

3518 **UNIVERSITAS PAKUAN**
Pakuan University
Jalan Pakuan, P.O. Box 353, Bogor T
Telephone: 312206
Rektor: Rubini Atmawidjaja
Pembantu Rektor (Administrative): Hidir Sastraatmadja

F. of Law (including Sociology and Public Administration)
Dean: Subandi Almarsudi; *staff* 22 (47)
F. of Economics (including Business Administration)
Dean: Hari Gursida; *staff* 22 (47)
F. of Education and Teacher Training
Dean: Sumardi; *staff* 28 (40)
F. of Letters
Dean: Ade Natawiria; *staff* 7 (24)
F. of Technology
Dean: B. Sunarwan; *staff* 19 (83)
F. of Mathematics and Natural Sciences
Dean: D. Suherman; *staff* 25 (51)
I. of Research and Development
Head: Poernomo; *staff* 7
I. of Academic Services to the Community
Head: Y. Senawat; *staff* 2
Computer L.
Head: Sutrisno
Language L.
Head: T. Parijati

Founded 1961 as Universitas Bogor, merged 1977 with other private colleges in Bogor, renamed Universitas Pakuan 1980. A private institution under the supervision of the Department of Education and Culture. Governing body: the Kartika Siliwangi Foundation.

Academic Year: September to July (September-January; March-July).

Admission Requirements: Secondary school certificate (Sekolah Lanjutan Tingkat Atas, S.L.T.A.).

Fees (Rupiahs): 200,000 per semeter.

Language of Instruction: Indonesian.

Degrees and Diplomas: Sarjana Hukum, Law. Doktorandus.

Libraries: Central Library, 5624 vols; faculties libraries, total, 6360.

Academic Staff, 1989-90:

Rank	Full-time	Part-time
Professors	2	15
Assistant Professors	8	45
Junior Lecturers	106	223
Total	116	283

Student Enrolment, 1989-90:

	Men	Women	Total
Of the country	509	261	770

3519 **UNIVERSITAS PANCASILA**

Pancasila University

Srengseng Sawah, Pasar Minggu 12640, Jakarta (Selatan)

Telephone: 7270086

Rektor: Awaloedin Djamin

Registrar: R. Soegijono

F. of Law

Dean: Sutarso; *staff* 27 (103)

F. of Economics

Dean: H. Sutanto; *staff* 38 (184)

F. of Pharmacy

Dean: R. B. Sutrismo; *staff* 32 (52)

F. of Engineering (including Architecture)

Dean: C. Soenhadji; *staff* 15 (249)

Founded 1966. A private institution under the supervision of the Department of Education and Culture.

Academic Year: September to August (September-January; February-August).

Admission Requirements: Secondary school certificate (Sekolah Menengah Atas, S.M.A.).

Fees (Rupiahs): 550,000.

Language of Instruction: Indonesian.

Degrees and Diplomas: Sarjana, 4-7 yrs.

Library: Faculty libraries, total, 17,212 vols.

Publications: Media Humas University Periodical; Journal Fakultas Teknik; Bulletin Fakultas Farmasi; Suara Ekonomi; RetirikaFakultas Hukum (all monthly).

Press or Publishing House: Pancasila Press.

Academic Staff, 1989-90:

Rank	Full-time
Guru Besar (Professors)	5
Lektor Kepala (Associate Professors)	38
Lektor Muda (Lecturers)	75
Asisten Madya (Assistant Lecturers)	203
Total	321

Student Enrolment, 1989-90:

	Men	Women	Total
Of the country	7152	2884	10,036

3520 **UNIVERSITAS PANCASILA TEGAL**

Pancasila University Tegal

Jalan Pancasila 2, Tegal

F. of Social and Political Sciences

F. of Fishery

F. of Teacher Training

Founded 1979.

Academic Year: September to July (September-December; February-August).

Admission Requirements: Secondary school certificate (Sekolah Menengah Atas, S.M.A.).

Language of Instruction: Indonesian.

Degrees and Diplomas: Sarjana. Magister.

3521 **UNIVERSITAS PASUNDAN**

Jalan Tamansari 8, Bandung

Law

Economics

Engineering

Education and Teacher Training

Founded 1960. A private institution under the supervision of the Department of Education and Culture.

3522 **UNIVERSITAS PEKALONGAN**

Jalan Garuda 49, Pekalongan

Economics

Law

Fishery

Founded 1981. A private institution under the supervision of the Department of Education and Culture.

3523 **UNIVERSITAS PEMBANGUNAN PANCA BUDI**

Jalan Jenderal Gatot Subroto, Medan 20122

Telephone: 519571

Rektor: Kadirun Yahya.

Secretary-General: Abdul Khalik Fajduani

F. of Law

Dean: Syahril Sofyan; *staff* 4 (4)

F. of Philosophy

Dean: Abdul Khalik F.; *staff* 4 (4)

F. of Economics

Dean: T. Ezmel; *staff* 6 (2)

F. of Agriculture

Dean: Djamil Ritongo; *staff* 5 (3)

F. of Architecture

F. of Technology

Dean: Dien S. Halim; *staff* 5 (2)

Founded 1961. A private institution under the supervision of the Department of Education and Culture. Residential facilities for academic staff and students.

Academic Year: September to June (September-January; February-June).

Admission Requirements: Secondary school certificate (Sekolah Lanjutan Tingkat Atas, S.L.T.A.).

Fees (Rupiahs): 150,00-350,000 per annum.

Language of Instruction: Indonesian.

Degrees and Diplomas: Sarjana Hukum, Law; Doktorandus, Insinyur, 5 yrs.

Library: 9374 vols.

Special Facilities (Museums, etc.): Biological Garden; Movie Studio.

Publications: Pelantikan Sarjana; Pengabdian Masyarakat; Kuliah Umum; /emelitian.

Academic Staff, 1989-90: 47 (36).

Student Enrolment, 1988-89:

	Men	Women	Total
Of the country	970	343	1313

3524 **UNIVERSITAS PEPABRI UJUNG PANDANG**

Jalan Syarif Alqadri 32A, Ujung Pandang

Social and Political Sciences

Engineering

Administration

3525 **UNIVERSITAS PROF. DR. R. MUSTOPO**

Jalan Hanglekir 1/8 Blok, H. Kebayoran Baru, Jakarta

Telephone: 70269

F. of Dentistry

F. of Social and Political Science

F. of Economics

F. of Communication Studies

Founded 1958 as School of Dentistry, became a university 1962. A private institution under the supervision of the Department of Education and Culture. Governing body: the Prof. Dr. Moestopo Foundation. Residential facilities for students.

Academic Year: February to December (February-June; July-December).

Admission Requirements: Secondary school certificate (Sekolah Menengah Atas, S.M.A.).

Language of Instruction: Indonesian.

Degrees and Diplomas: Sarjana, 5 yrs. Postgraduate certificate in Dentistry.

Publications: Coronia; Fax–Economica.

Academic Staff: c. 110.

Student Enrolment: c. 800.

3526 **UNIVERSITAS PROKLAMASI**

Jalan Dagen 129, Yogyakarta

F. of Law

F. of Economics

F. of Social and Political Sciences

Founded 1964. A private institution under the supervision of the Department of Education and Culture.

3527 **UNIVERSITAS SARJANA WIYATA TAMAN SISWA**

Jalan Kusumanegara 95, Yogyakarta

F. of Education and Teacher Training

F. of Economics
Founded 1955.

3528 **UNIVERSITAS SILIWANGI**
Siliwangi University
Jalan Siliwangi, Tasikmalaya 46115, West Java
Telephone: 21634
Rektor: H. Mashudi (1984-89)

F. of Teacher Training and Education
Dean: Sujono Azhara; *staff* 51 (111)
F. of Economics
Dean: Soelaeman Baehaki; *staff* 10 (36)
F. of Agriculture
Dean: Syamsudin; *staff* 17 (22)
F. of Engineering
Dean: Djuanda; *staff* 5 (42)

Founded as branch of Institute of Teacher Training and Education, Bandung. Acquired present status and title 1979. A private institution under the supervision of the Department of Education and Culture.

Academic Year: August to July (August-December; February-June).

Admission Requirements: Secondary school certificate (Sekolah Lanjutan Tingkat Atas, S.L.T.A.).

Fees (Rupiahs): 219,000-380,000 per annum.

Language of Instruction: Indonesian.

Degrees and Diplomas: Doktorandus. Insinjur.

Libraries: Central Library; libraries for the faculties.

Academic Staff, 1986-87:

Rank	Full-time	Part-time
Guru Besar (Professors)	–	5
Lektor Kepala (Senior Lecturers)	–	11
Lektor (Lecturers)	5	34
Lektor Madya (Junior Lecturers)	12	47
Lektor Muda (Assistant Lecturers)	3	63
Asisten Ahli (Senior Assistants)	18	24
Asisten Ahli Madya (Instructors)	45	18
Asisten	–	9
Total	83	211

Student Enrolment, 1986-87:

	Men	Women	Total
Of the country	2183	1345	3528

3529 **UNIVERSITAS SIMALUNGUN**
Jalan Sisingamangaraja Barat, Pematang Siantar
Telephone: 24719
Rektor: Urbanus S. Napitu
Secretary: Jasman Purba

F. of Economics
Dean: Iden Purba; *staff* 10 (20)
F. of Agriculture
Dean: Alimin Sipayung; *staff* 17 (9)
F. of Law
Dean: Sakiben Saragih; *staff* 27 (17)
F. of Engineering
Dean: Djabat Rajagukguk; *staff* 13 (10)
F. of Education and Teacher Training
Dean: Janiapoh Purba; *staff* 34 (22)

Founded 1966. A private institution under the supervision of the Department of Education and Culture. Governing body: the Simalungun University Foundation. Residential facilities for academic staff.

Academic Year: August to June (August-January; March-June).

Admission Requirements: Secondary school certificate (Sekolah Menengah Atas, S.M.A.).

Fees (Rupiahs): 400,000 per annum.

Language of Instruction: Indonesia.

Degrees and Diplomas: Sarjana, 4-7 yrs.

Academic Staff, 1989-90: c. 400.

Student Enrolment, 1989-90: c. 2600.

3530 **UNIVERSITAS SLAMET RIYADI SURAKARTA**
Jalan Sumpah Permuda, Surakarta, Central Java
Telephone: 7839
Rektor: Ananto Soekarno (1983-87)

F. of Law
Dean: Radjijo; *staff* 27 (26)
F. of Economics
Dean: Sutantya; *staff* 11 (24)
F. of Agriculture
Dean: Djiwandi; *staff* 23 (40)
F. of Social and Political Sciences
Dean: Sulastri; *staff* 15 (47)
F. of Teacher Training and Education
Dean: Suhardi; *staff* 16 (22)
Ce. of Research and Community Service
Head: Y. Slamet; *staff* 3 (3)

Founded 1980. A private institution under the supervision of Directorate General of High Education, Departmentof Education and Culture. Residential facilities for students.

Academic Year: July to June (July-December; January-June).

Admission Requirements: Secondary school certificate (Sekolah Menengah Atas, S.M.A.) and entrance examination.

Fees (Rupiahs): 280,000-320,000 per annum.

Language of Instruction: Indonesian.

Degrees and Diplomas: Sarjana, Drs., Ir., SH., SE., 4-7 yrs.

Library: Central Library, 6860 vols.

Publication: JOGLO (Science Magazine).

Academic Staff, 1989-90:

Rank	Full-time
Guru Besar Madya	1
Lektor Kepala Madya	1
Lektor	4
Lektor Madya	2
Lektor Muda	8
Asisten Ahli	22
Asisten Ahli Mada	55
Total	93

Student Enrolment, 1989-90:

	Men	Women	Total
Of the country	2831	1441	4272

3531 **UNIVERSITAS SOERJO**
Jalan Jurusan Ngawi Cepu, Ngawi

Law
Social and Political Science
Agriculture

Founded 1981. A private institution under the supervision of the Department of Education and Culture.

3532 **UNIVERSITAS SUNAN GIRI**
Jalan Citarum 1, Surabaya

Engineering
Economics
Social and Political Science
Law

Founded 1976. A private institution under the supervision of the Department of Education and Culture.

3533 **UNIVERSITAS SURABAYA**
University of Surabaya
Jalan Ngageljaya Selatan 169, Surabaya
Telephone: 60866
Rektor: Soebijono Tjitrowinoto (1984-89)

F. of Pharmacy
Dean: H. Ma'mur; *staff* 21 (41)
F. of Law
Dean: Eko Sugitario; *staff* 29 (23)
F. of Economics
Dean: Wibisono Hardjopranoto; *staff* 26 (42)
F. of Psychology
Dean: Hari K. Lasmono; *staff* 11 (27)
F. of Engineering
Dean: Darmo Handoyo; *staff* 14 (10)

Founded 1966. A private institution governed by a Foundation and under the supervision of the Department of Education and Culture.

Academic Year: September to August (September-February; March-August).

Admission Requirements: Secondary school certificate (Sekolah Menengah Atas, S.M.A.) and entrance examination.

Fees (Rupiahs): 235,000-410,000 per annum.

Language of Instruction: Indonesian.

Degrees and Diplomas: Sarjana, 4-7 yrs. Doktorandus Apoteker, 5 yrs. Insinjur, 5 yrs.

Library: Faculty libraries, total, 20,684 vols.

Publication: Anima (Psychology).

Academic Staff, 1986-87:

Rank	Full-time	Part-time
Guru Bedar (Professors)	3	5
Lektor Kepala (Associate Professors)	3	17
Lektor (Assistant Professors)	3	24
Lektor Madya (Senior Lecturers)	2	20
Lektor Muda (Lecturers)	24	19
Asisten Ahli (Senior Assistants)	26	16
Asisten Ahli Madya (Assistant Lecturers)	44	29
Asisten Muda (Junior Assistant Lecturers)	–	2
Total	105	132

Student Enrolment, 1986-87:

	Men	Women	Total
Of the country	2724	3602	6326
Of other countries	93	187	280
Total	2817	3789	6606

3534 **UNIVERSITAS SWADAYA GUNUNG JATI**

Jalan Dr. Ciptomangun Kusumo, Cirebon

Law

Economics

Education and Teacher Training

Founded 1960. A private institution under the supervision of the Department of Education and Culture.

3535 **UNIVERSITAS TAMANSISWA**

University of Tamansiswa

Jalan Kusumanegara 95, Yogyakarta

Telephone: 87265

Rektor: Iman Soedijat (1984-88)

F. of Teacher Training and Education

Dean: Fudyar Tanta; *staff* 74 (10)

F. of Agriculture

Dean: Th. Darini; *staff* 11 (18)

F. of Economics

Dean: Goentoer Soedarsono; *staff* 12 (7)

Founded 1955. A private institution under the supervision of the Department of Education and Culture.

Academic Year: August to June (August-January; March-June).

Admission Requirements: Secondary school certificate (Sekolah Menengah Atas, S.M.A.).

Fees (Rupiahs): 140,000-240,000 per annum.

Languages of Instruction: Indonesian and English.

Degrees and Diplomas: Sarjana Muda, 3-5 yrs. Sarjana, 4-7 yrs. Diplomas II and III, 2-3 yrs.

Academic Staff, 1986-87: 97 (135).

Student Enrolment, 1986-87:

	Men	Women	Total
Of the country	2751	2855	5606

3536 **UNIVERSITAS TARUMANAGARA**

Tarumanagara University

Jalan Letjen S Parman 1, Jakarta 11440

Telephone: 591747

Rektor: D. Khumarga (1983-87)

F. of Medicine

Dean: W.A.F.J. Tumbelaka; *staff* 70 (136)

F. of Engineering (including Architecture)

Dean: Kuntjoro Jakti; *staff* 40 (312)

F. of Law

Dean: Ismail Hasan; *staff* 22 (65)

F. of Economics

Dean: Syahruddin A. Hadi; *staff* 5 (220)

Founded 1962. A private institution under the supervision of the Department of Education and Culture.

Academic Year: September to August (September-January; February-August).

Admission Requirements: Secondary school certificate (Sekolah Menengah Atas, S.M.A.) and entrance examination.

Fees (Rupiahs): 250,000-500,000 per semester.

Language of Instruction: Indonesian.

Academic Staff, 1986-87: 944.

Student Enrolment, 1986-87: 8484.

3537 **UNIVERSITAS TIDAR MAGELANG**

Jalan Kapten Suparman, Magelang

Telephone: 2438, 4113

Rektor: A. Gambiro

Pembantu Rektor: Jojok Tarunawijaya

F. of Economics

Dean: M.A. Purba; *staff* 9 (15)

F. of Education and Teacher Training

Dean: Dulchori Arief; *staff* 13 (9)

F. of Agriculture

Dean: Suryo Sodo Adisewoyo; *staff* 10 (20)

F. of Social and Political Sciences

Dean: Haryono; *staff* 9 (7)

F. of Engineering

Dean: Bambang Surendro

Research I.

Head: Kuntjoro Wibowo; *staff* 2

Founded 1979. A private institution under the supervision of the Department of Education and Culture and the Municipal Authorities.

Academic Year: August to July (August-January; February-July).

Admission Requirements: Secondary school certificate (Sekolah Lanjutan Tinagkat Atas S.L.T.A.).

Language of Instruction: Indonesian.

Degrees and Diplomas: Sarjana, 4-7 yrs. Doktorandus. Insinjur.

Publication: Idea (every 2 months).

Academic Staff, 1990: 54 (104).

Student Enrolment, 1990:

	Men	Women	Total
Of the country	1361	758	2119

3538 **UNIVERSITAS TRI DHARAM**

Jalan Kapten Tendean 26, Balkipapan

Law

Engineering

Education and Teacher Training

Founded 1978. A private institution under the supervision of the Department of Education and Culture.

3539 **UNIVERSITAS TRISAKTI**

Trisakti University

Jalan Kiyai Tapa, Grogol, Jakarta 11440

Telephone: 591356

Rektor: Mulyatno Sindhudarmoko (1990-94)

Pembantu Rektor I (Academic): Suwarto

F. of Medicine

Dean: Moedanton Moertedjo; *staff* 97 (41)

F. of Dentistry

Dean: Hamilah Djoeana K.; *staff* 101 (37)

F. of Law

Dean: E. Suherman; *staff* 45 (47)

F. of Economics

Dean: Yuswar Zainul Basri; *staff* 67 (154)

F. of Landscape Architecture (including Environment Technology)

Dean: Wahyudi Wisaksono; *staff* 48 (28)

F. of Civil Engineering and Planning

Dean: E. Suherman; *staff* 121 (271)

F. of Industrial Technology

Dean: Semiawan; *staff* 121 (76)

F. of Mineral Technology

Dean: Ismet Akil; *staff* 74 (65)

Insurance A.

Director: I.K. Suprakto

A. of Tourism

Director: Mulyatno Sindhudarmoko; *staff* 18 (54)

A. of Accountancy

Director: Winarsa; *staff* 33 (40)

A. of Graphic Technology

Director: C.B. Hardjowijono

C. of Transportation Management
Director: Bambang Sumarsono; *staff* 25 (46)
Research I.
Director: Ishak Sadrach
Also 2 Teaching Hospitals and Study Abroad Programmes.
Founded 1965. A private institution under the supervision of the Department of Education and Culture. Governing body: the Trisakti Foundation.
Academic Year: September to August.
Admission Requirements: Secondary school certificate (Surat Tanda Tamat Belajar).
Fees (Rupiahs): 724,000-1424,000 per annum.
Language of Instruction: Indonesian.
Degrees and Diplomas: Professional title of Insinjur, 4 ½-7 yrs. Sarjana, 5-7 yrs. Dokter, medicine, 7 yrs. Dokter Gigi, dentistry, 4-8 yrs.
Library: Central Library, *c.* 7560 vols.
Publications: Tri Dharma Magazine (quarterly); Trisakti Magazine (monthly); Maristi (weekly); The Journal of Law.
Press or Publishing House: Instalasi Percetakan Trisakti.
Academic Staff, 1989-90:

Rank	Full-time	Part-time
Guru Besar	10	–
Guru Besar Madya	7	22
Lektor Kepala	26	31
Lektor Kepala Madya	30	37
Lektor	146	141
Lektor Madya	62	127
Lektor Muda	73	129
Asisten Ahli	117	89
Asisten Ahli Madya	205	204
Total	676	780

Student Enrolment, 1989-90: c. 14,319.

3540 **UNIVERSITAS 17 AGUSTUS 1945**
University of 17 August 1945
Jalan Adi Sucipto 26, Banyuwangi, East Java
Telephone: (0333) 41980
Rektor: Moenaris (1985-)

F. of Economics
Dean: Bambang Basuki
F. of Social and Political Sciences
Dean: Suhardji
F. of Law
Dean: Mrs. Zubaidah
F. of Agriculture
Dean: Eko Soekartono
F. of Teacher Training and Education
Dean: Gede Ari Subrata
Founded 1980 by the 17 August 1945 National Education Foundation. A private institution under the supervision of the Department of Education and Culture.
Academic Year: September to August (September-February; March-August).
Admission Requirements: Secondary school certificate (Sekolah Lanjutan Atas, S.L.A.).
Fees (Rupiahs): 110,000-150,000 per semester.
Language of Instruction: Indonesian.
Degrees and Diplomas: Sarjana, 4 yrs.
Academic Staff, 1986-87: 42 (38).
Student Enrolment, 1986-87:

	Men	Women	Total
Of the country	1314	322	1636

3541 **UNIVERSITAS 17 AGUSTUS 1945 CIREBON**
Jalan Siliwanga 94, Cirebon

Public and Business Administration
Law
Founded 1964 by the 17 August 1945 National Education Foundation. A private institution under the supervision of the Department of Education and Culture.

3542 **UNIVERSITAS 17 AGUSTUS 1945**
University of 17 August 1945
Jalan Teuku Cik Ditiro 46, Jakarta
Telephone: 345610

F. of Social and Political Sciences
F. of Law
F. of Public and Business Administration
F. of Engineering
F. of Pharmacy
F. of Economics
Founded 1952 by the 17 August 1945 National Education Foundation. A private institution under the supervision of the Department of Education and Culture.
Academic Year: January to December (January-July; August-December).
Admission Requirements: Secondary school certificate (Sekolah Lanjutan Atas, S.L.A.).
Languages of Instruction: Indonesian and some English.
Degrees and Diplomas: Sarjana, 4 yrs.
Library: c. 5790 vols.
Publication: Bulletin (monthly).
Academic Staff: c. 170.
Student Enrolment: c. 860.

3543 **UNIVERSITAS 17 AGUSTUS 1945 SAMARINDA**
Jalan Ir. H. Juanda, Samarinda

Law
Social and Political Sciences
Economics
Engineering
Founded 1965 by the 17 August 1945 National Education Foundation. A private institution under the supervision of the Department of Education and Culture.

3544 **UNIVERSITAS 17 AGUSTUS 1945 SEMARANG**
Jalan Seteran Dalam 9, Semarang 50134
Telephone: (024) 318 202
Rektor: Hari Soeharno

F. of Law
Dean: Sarsintorini; *staff* 144 (75)
F. of Social and Political Sciences
Dean: Soekirno; *staff* 47 (54)
F. of Economics
Dean: Siti Sulastri; *staff* 50 (44)
F. of Engineering
Dean: Soejanto; *staff* 31 (129)
I. of Research and Development
Head: Bawadiman; *staff* 12
Founded 1963 by the 17 August 1945 National Education Foundation. A private institution under the supervision of the Department of Education and Culture. Residential facilities for academic staff.
Academic Year: September to July (September-January; February-July).
Admission Requirements: Secondary school certificate (Sekolah Lanjutan Atas, S.L.A.) and entrance examination.
Fees (Rupiahs): Registration, 25,000; 300,000 per annum.
Language of Instruction: Indonisian.
Degrees and Diplomas: Strata 1 (S1), 5 yrs.
Library: Total, 21,148 vols.
Student Enrolment, 1990:

	Men	Women	Total
Of the country	6590	3881	10,471

3545 **UNIVERSITAS 17 AGUSTUS 1945 SURABAYA**
Jalan Semolowara 45, Surabaya

Public and Business Administration
Economics
Law
Industrial Technology
Founded 1964 by the 17 August 1945 National Education Foundation. A private institution under the supervision of the Department of Education and Culture.

3546 **UNIVERSITAS TUNAS PEMBANGUNAN**
Jalan Irian 22, Surakarta

Engineering

Economics
Agriculture
Education
Founded 1980. A private institution under the supervision of the Department of Education and Culture.

3547 **UNIVERSITAS VETERAN RI**
Jalan G. Bawekaraeng 72, Ujung Pendang
Education and Teacher Training
Social and Political Sciences
Engineering
Founded 1961. A private institution under the supervision of the Department of Education and Culture.

3548 **UNIVERSITAS WIJAYAKUSUMA**
Kampus UNWIKU Karangsalam, P.O. Box 85, Purwokerto Jawa Tengah
Telephone: (281) 21889
Rektor: R. Djanuar
F of Law
Dean: Iswanto; *staff* 38 (45)
F. of Social and Political Sciences
Dean: Soeyatno Wongsokenongo; *staff* 23 (34)
F. of Economics
Dean: Suyitno; *staff* 28 (39)
F. of Engineering
Dean: Indrayana Gandadinata; *staff* 21 (31)
F. of Animal Husbandry
Dean: R. Djanuar; *staff* 12 (9)
Research I.
Director: Kasirun Hendro Bintoro; *staff* 7
Founded 1980. A private institution under the supervision of the Department of Education and Culture. Residential facilities for academic staff.
Academic Year: September to August (September-February; March-August).
Admission Requirements: Secondary school certificate (Sekolah Menengah Atas, S.M.A.) and entrance examination.
Fees (Rupiahs): 350,000-400,000 per annum.
Degrees and Diplomas: Strata 1 (S1), 4 yrs.
Publication: Biological Garden.
Academic Staff, 1989-90: 69 (202).
Student Enrolment, 1989-90:

	Men	Women	Total
Of the country	1532	744	2276

3549 **UNIVERSITAS WIJAYAKUSUMA SURABAYA**
Jalan Dukuh Kupang XXV, 60225 Surabaya
Telephone: (31) 67577
Rektor: H.R.M. Soejoenoes
F. of Engineering
Dean: Achmad Ashari; *staff* 5 (24)
F. of Agriculture
Dean: Pribadi; *staff* 15 (37)
F. of Law
Dean: Dyatmiko Soemodihardjo; *staff* 11 (36)
F. of Economics
Dean: Oemar Said; *staff* 6 (44)
F. of Social and Political Sciences
Dean: Kartini Mochtar; *staff* 6 (27)
F. of Education and Teacher Training
Dean: Aekanu Akbar; *staff* 11 (55)
F. of Medicine
Dean: H.R.M. Soejoenoes; *staff* 18 (151)
F. of Veterinary Medicine
Dean: A. Silitonga; *staff* 4 (36)
I. for Research and Public Services
Head: A.W. Batara Goa; *staff* 1
Founded 1980. A private institution under the supervision of the Department of Education and Culture. Governing body: the Board of Trustees.
Academic Year: August to July (August-January; February-July).
Admission Requirements: Secondary school certificate (Sekolah Menengah Tingkat Atas, S.M.T.A.) and entrance examination.
Fees (Rupiahs): 360,000 per annum; Medicus, 1,200,000.
Degrees and Diplomas: Strata 1 (S1) 4 yrs. Dokter, medicine, 6 yrs.
Academic Staff, 1990:

Rank	Full-time	Part-time
Guru Besar/Guru Besar Madya (Professors)	3	14
Lektor Kepala/Lektor (Associate Professors/Assistant Professors)	5	155
Lektor Madya/Lektor Muda (Senior Lecturers/Lecturers)	5	129
Asisten Ahli/Asisten Ahli Madya (Senior Assistants)	70	67
Lain-lain	–	45
Total	83	410

Student Enrolment, 1990:

	Men	Women	Total
Of the country	3779	2900	6679

3550 **UNIVERSITAS WISNU WARDHANA**
Jalan Raya Dieng 1, Malang
Law
Economics
Agriculture
Education and Teacher Training
Founded 1981. A private institution under the supervision of the Department of Education and Culture.

Other Institutions

Technical Education

3551 **INSTITUT PELAYARAN NIAGA**
Jalan Kebun Nanas, Jakarta
F. of Marine Technology
F. of Marine Management
Founded 1981. A private institution.

3552 **INSTITUT PERTANIAN BOGOR**
Bogor University of Agriculture
Jalan Raya Pajajaran, Bogor 16143
Telephone: (251) 23081
Fax: (251) 311868
Rektor: Sitanala Arsyad
Pembantu Rektor (Administrative): Anwar Nur
F. of Agriculture
Dean: Soleh Solahuddin; *staff* 265 (15)
F. of Veterinary Medicine
Dean: Singgih Harsoyo Sigit; *staff* 133 (10)
F. of Forestry
Head: Dudung Darusman; *staff* 99 (15)
F. of Animal Husbandry
Dean: Lily Amalia Sofyan; *staff* 90 (20)
F. of Fisheries
Dean: Ismudi Muchsin; *staff* 123 (10)
F. of Agricultural Engineering and Technology
Dean: Aman Wirakartakusumah; *staff* 133 (10)
F. of Science and Mathematics
Dean: Barizi; *staff* 133 (20)
Polytechnic F.
Dean: Yuyu Mahyu; *staff* 26 (75)
Graduate S.
Dean: Edi Suhardja; *staff* – (260)
Research I.
Chairman: Lutfi I. Nasoetion; *staff* – (20)
Ce. for Food Technology Development
Head: Rizal Sjarief Sjaifulnazli; *staff* – (10)
Ce. for Tropical Biology Research
Head: Siti Soetami Tjitrosomo; *staff* – (20)
Ce. for Development Studies
Head: Sajogyo; *staff* – (10)
Ce. for Environmental Study
Head: Soeratno Partoatmodjo *staff* – (10)

Ce. for Food and Nutrition Policy Study
Head: Suhardjo; *staff* – (10)
Public Service I.
Head: Sjafri Mangkuprawira; *staff* – (15)
Ce. for Community Education
Head: Aida Vitayala Syafri; *staff* – (8)
Ce. for Community Service
Head: Abdul Gani Amri Siregar; *staff* – (8)
Ce. for Rural and Regional Development
Head: Kuntjoro; *staff* – (8)
Ce. for Management of Student Service Study
Head: Surdiding Ruhendi; *staff* – (10)
Also Experimental Farm Unit and Language Laboratory.

Founded 1941, closed and reopened 1948 as faculties of agriculture and veterinary medicine of University of Indonesia. Became separate State agricultural university 1963, under the Department of Education and Culture of the Republic of Indonesia. Governing body: the University Senate. Residential facilities for *c.* one-half of academic staff and limited facilities for students.

Arrangements for co-operation with: University of Philippines at Los Banos; Kasetsart University, Thailand; University of Tokyo; Kyoto University; Georg-August University of Göttingen.

Academic Year: August to June (August-January; January-June).

Admission Requirements: Secondary school certificate (Sekolah Menengah Atas, S.M.A.) or foreign equivalent.

Fees (Rupiahs): 750,000-1,500,000 per semester.

Language of Instruction: Indonesian.

Degrees and Diplomas: Sarjana, 4 yrs. Diplomas I, II and III, 1-3 yrs. Doctor of Veterinary Medicine (DVM), a further yr. Magister Sains, a further 2 yrs. Doctor, 2-3 yrs following Magister Sains.

Library: 117,830 vols.

Publications: Indonesian Journal of Tropical Agriculture; Forum Pasca Sarjana; Media Peternakan; Media Veteriner; Communicationess Agriculturae; Buletin Makanan ternak; Buletin Agronomi; Buletin Hama dan Penyakit Tumbuhan; Gema Penelitian; Media Konservasi; Buletin Ilmu Tanah; Teknolog.

Press or Publishing House: Penerbit IPB (IPB Press).

Academic Staff, 1990: 1002 (564).

Student Enrolment, 1990:

	Men	Women	Total
Of the country	6095	4782	10,877

3553 **INSTITUT TEKNOLOGI BANDUNG**
Bandung Institute of Technology
Jalan Tamansari 64, Bandung
Telephone: 830 47/8

F. of Mathematics and Natural Sciences (including Pharmacy)
F. of Civil Engineering and Town Planning
F. of Industrial Engineering
F. of Mineral Engineering
F. of Arts and Design
Bureau for General Studies
Development Technology Ce.

Founded 1920, became faculty of the University of Indonesia 1949. Detached and re-established as separate State institution 1959. Governing body: the Board of Trustees. Residential facilities for academic staff and for *c.* 500 students.

Academic Year: September to June (September-January; February-June).

Admission Requirements: Secondary school certificate (Sekolah Menengah Atas, S.M.A.) and entrance examination.

Language of Instruction: Indonesian.

Degrees and Diplomas: Sarjana, 3 ½ to 7 yrs. Doctor of–Science; Engineering.

Libraries: Central Library, *c.* 45,000 vols; department libraries, *c.* 130,000.

Publications: Proceedings (quarterly); Campus (monthly); Scientiae (monthly); Berita (daily).

Academic Staff: *c.* 740.

Student Enrolment: *c.* 7820.

3554 **INSTITUT TEKNOLOGI NASIONAL MALANG**
The National Institute of Technology of Malang
Jalan Bendungan Sigura-gura 2, Malang East Java 65145
Rektor: R. Iswandi Kartasentana (1989-1993)

F. of Industrial Technology
Dean: Nasir Kaban;E80 (56)
F. of Civil Engineering and Planning
Dean: H.M. Liliek Dumairi; *staff* 64 (41)
Research and Community Service D.
Head: Pranjoto; *staff* 3 (2)

Founded 1962. A private institution. Governing bodies: the Advisory Council; the Senate.

Academic Year: August to July (August-January; February-July).

Admission Requirements: Secondary school certificate (Sekolah Lanjutan Atas S.L.A.).

Fees (Rupiahs): 360,000 per annum.

Degrees and Diplomas: Strata 1 (S1), 4 yrs.

Library: 22,678 vols.

Academic Staff, 1988-89: 116 (163).

Student Enrolment, 1988-89:

	Men	Women	Total
Of the country	781	300	1081

3555 **INSTITUT TEKNOLOGI PEMBANGUNAN**
Jalan Manyar Tirtomoyo VIII/I, Surabaya

F. of Engineering
F. of Planning Engineering
F. of Industrial Engineering

Founded 1980. A private institution.

3556 **INSTITUT TEKNOLOGI SEPULAN NOPEMBER**
Sepulah Nopember Institute of Technology
Kampus ITS, Keputih, Sukolilo, Surabaya
Telephone: 60651/54
Rektor: Oedjoe Djoeriaman (1982-87)

F. of Mathematics and Natural Sciences
Dean: Achmad Subyanto; *staff* 78 (58)
F. of Industrial Technology
Dean: Adi Suryanto; *staff* 152 (210)
F. of Civil Engineering and Town Planning
Dean: Harwijono Dirdjosukarto; *staff* 124 (69)
F. of Marine Engineering
Dean: Soegiono; *staff* 41 (66)

Founded 1957 with faculties of civil and mechanical engineering. Became a State institution with new faculties1960. Responsible to the Department of Education and Culture. Residential facilities for 149 academic staff and *c.* 300 students.

Arrangements for co-operation with the Universities of: Tokyo; Leuven; Delft; Osaka.

Academic Year: January to December (January-June; July-December).

Admission Requirements: Secondary school certificate (Sekolah Menengah Atas, S.M.A.) and entrance examination.

Fees (Rupiahs): 240,000 per annum.

Language of Instruction: Indonesian.

Degrees and Diplomas: Sarjana, 4-7 ys.

Library: Central Library. *c.* 20,000 vols.

Publications: Berita (Bulletin); Media (monthly newspaper).

Academic Staff, 1986-87:

Rank	Full-time
Guru Besar (Professors)	2
Lektor Madya (Senior Lecturers)	25
Lektor Muda (Lecturers)	136
Asisten Madya (Assistant Lecturers)	285
Total	448

Student Enrolment, 1986-87:

	Men	Women	Total
Of the country	6427	872	7299

Professional Education

3557 **INSTITUT KESENIAN JAKARTA**
Jakarta Institute of the Arts
Jalan Cikini Raya 73, Jakarta-Pusat 10330
Telephone: 324807
Rektor: Slamet Danusudirdjo (1987-90)
Pambantu Rektor I.: Ayatrohaedi

F. of Visual Arts
Dean: Yulianti Parani; *staff* – (2)

F. of Art and Design
Dean: Wagiona Soenarto; *staff* – (2)
F. of Film and Television
Dean: Soetomo Gandasoebrata; *staff* – (2)
Research Ce.
Head: Wiyoso Yudoseputro; *staff* – (1)

Founded 1970. A private institution. Responsible of the Department of Education and Culture.

Academic Year: September to July (September-February; March-July).

Admission Requirements: Secondary school certificate (Sekolah Menengah Atas, S.L.A.).

Fees (Rupiahs): Total, 700,000 per semester.

Language of Instruction: Indonesian.

Degrees and Diplomas: Bachelor, 6 sem. Master, 10 sem.

Library: 5500 vols.

Special Facilities (Museums, etc.): Art Galery; Movie Studio.

Academic Staff, 1990-91: 21 (17).

Student Enrolment, 1990-91:

Of the country	452
Of the countries	6
Total	458

3558 **INSTITUT MANAJEMEN KOPERASI INDONESIA**
Indonesian Institute for Co-operative Management
Jalan Raya Bandung, Sumedang Km. 20,5, Bandung
Rektor: Herman Soewardi (1982-87)

F. of Finance
Dean: Faisal Afiff; *staff* 7 (3)
F. of Human Resource Management
Dean: Kudus Danasasmita; *staff* 7 (38)
F. of Production and Marketing
Dean: Tuhpawana Priatna Sendjaja; *staff* 8 (29)

Founded 1964 by the Co-operatives Movement, acquired present status and title 1982. A State institution supported by the Ministry of Co-operatives and under the supervision of the Ministry of Education and Culture. Residential facilities for academic staff and students.

Arrangements for co-operation with the Universities of: Ghent State; Marburg.

Academic Year: August to June (August-January; February-June).

Admission Requirements: Secondary school certificate (Sekolah Menengah Atas, S.M.A.) and entrance examination.

Fees (Rupiahs): 350,000 per annum.

Language of Instruction: Indonesian.

Degrees and Diplomas: Licence, 9 sem.

Library: 2600 vols.

Academic Staff, 1986-87: 46 (109).

Student Enrolment, 1986-87:

	Men	Women	Total
Of the country	2523	764	3287

Teacher Training

3559 **INSTITUT KEGURUAN DAN ILMU PENDIDIKAN**
Institute of Teacher Training and Education
Jalan Dr. Setyabudhi 229 (Km 8), Bandung, Jawa Barat
Telephone: 83162; 83651
Rektor: Muhammad Numan Somantri (1979-87)

F. of Education
F. of Social Sciences
F. of Mathematics and Natural Sciences
F. of Languages and Arts
F. of Technical and Vocational Education
F. of Physical Education
Ce. for Educational Research
Population Education Research Ce.
Language Ce.

Founded 1954 as college and acquired present status and title 1963. A State institution under the jurisdictionof the Department of Education and Culture. Receives some co-operation from the West Java government. Residential facilities for academic staff and students.

Arrangements for co-operation with: University of South Alabama; Hiroshima University; University of Houston.

Academic Year: August to June (August-November; January-June).

Admission Requirements: Secondary school certificate (Sekolah Menengah Tingkat Atas, S.M.T.A.) or foreign equivalent, and entrance examination.

Language of Instruction: Indonesian.

Degrees and Diplomas: Sarjana, 4 yrs. Diplomas I, II, III, 1-3 yrs.

Library: Central Library, *c.* 33,030 vols.

Special Facilities (Museums, etc.): Wira Yudha Batara.

Publications: Mimbar Pendidikan (Educational Forum, quarterly); Berita (News, monthly); Warta Pendidikan.

Academic Staff: c. 750.

Student Enrolment: c. 12,250.

3560 **INSTITUT KEGURUAN DAN ILMU PENDIDIKAN**
Institute of Teacher Training and Education
Kompleks IKIP-Jakarta Rawamangun, Jakarta Timur 13220
Telephone: 4897927
Fax: 4893854
Rektor: Conny R. Semiawan (1984-92)
Registrar: Minarma Hutajulu

D. of Education
Dean: Suhaenah Suparno; *staff* 155 (20)
D. of Languages and Arts
Dean: Djunaedi; *staff* 162 (26)
D. of Social Sciences
Dean: Mohammad Hasan; *staff* 174 (12)
D. of Mathematics and Natural Sciences
Dean: Rukiah Asikin S. Djanegara; *staff* 88 (11)
D. of Technical and Vocational Education
Dean: Koesno Sastromihardjo; *staff* 127 (35)
D. of Physical Education
Dean: Sutardiono; *staff* 67 (28)
D. of Post Graduate Studies
Dean: Situmorang; *staff* 5 (46)
Also Laboratory School (kindergarten, elementary, junior and senior high schools).

Founded 1963. A State institution. Governing bodies: the Board of Trustees; the Senate. Some residential facilities for academic staff and students.

Arrangements for co-operation with: Victoria College, Sydney; Institut national de Langues et de Civilisationsorientales, Paris.

Academic Year: January to December (January-June; July-December).

Admission Requirements: Secondary school certificate (Sekolah Menengah Atas, S.M.A.) or equivalent, and entrance examination.

Fees (Rupiahs): 100,000 per semester.

Language of Instruction: Indonesian.

Degrees and Diplomas: Sarjana, 4 yrs. Diplomas II, III, 2-3 yrs.

Library: College Library (Perpustakaan IKIP Jakarta), 42,863 vols.

Special Facilities (Museums, etc.): Biological Garden.

Publication: Parameter: Communications Media and Research Information (ISSN 0216-261X).

Press or Publishing House: Percetakan IKIP-Jakarta.

Academic Staff, 1989-90:

Rank	Full-time	Part-time
Guru Besar	10	–
Guru Besar Ladya	3	–
Lektor Kepala	57	35
Lektor Kepala Madya	84	28
Lektor	145	26
Lektor Madya	66	20
Lektor Muda	108	12
Asisten Ahli	114	11
Asisten Ahli Madya	186	–
Total	773	132

Student Enrolment, 1989-90:

	Men	Women	Total
Of the country	4136	4210	8346
Of other countries	4	3	7
Total	4140	4213	8353*

*Also 250 external students.

3561 **INSTITUT KEGURUAN DAN ILMU PENDIDIKAN MUHAMMADIYAH**
Institute of Teacher Training and Education Muhammadiyah
Jalan Limau II, Jakarta 12130
Telephone: 773177
Rektor: Agustiar (1979-)
Pembantu Rektor II: Anwar Abbas

F. of Education
Dean: Dimyati Safari; *staff* 59
F. of Languages and Arts
Dean: Yasin; *staff* 59
F. of Mathematics and Natural Sciences
Dean: Djam'an Sakeh; *staff* 40
F. of Social Sciences
Dean: Agusaiar (Acting); *staff* 47
Ce. for Educational Resarch
Head: Abdul Hamid; *staff* 5
Public Service Ce.
Head: Habib Chirzin; *staff* 5

Founded 1957. A private institution accredited by Coordination Board of Private Schools and Colleges.

Academic Year: August to June (August-November; January-June).

Admission Requirements: Secondary school certificate (Sekolah Menengah Tingkat Atas, S.M.T.A.) and entrance examination.

Fees (Rupiahs): 730,000 per annum.

Languages of Instruction: Indonesian and English.

Degrees and Diplomas: Doktorandus, 4 yrs.

Library: 6349 vols.

Academic Staff, 1989-90: 10.

Student Enrolment, 1989-90:

	Men	Women	Total
Of the country	2500	3456	5956

3562 **INSTITUT KEGURUAN DAN ILMU PENDIDIKAN MUHAMMADIYAN**
Institute of Teacher Training and Education Muhammadiyah
Jalan Komplek Pendidikan, Karanganyar

F. of Education

Founded 1969. A private institution.

3563 **INSTITUT KEGURUAN DAN ILMU PENDIDIKAN**
Institute of Teacher Training and Education
Jalan Bendogantungan, Klaten

F. of Languages and Arts
F. of Social Sciences

Founded 1965. A private institution.

3564 **INSTITUT KEGURUAN DAN ILMU PENDIDIKAN**
Institute of Teacher Training and Education
Jalan Surebaya 6, Malang 65114
Telephone: 51312/13
Rektor: Achmad Icksan (1982-86)
Pembantu Rektor I: Mas Hadi Soeparto

F. of Education
Dean: P. A. Sahertian; *staff* 126 (21)
F. of Mathematics and Natural Sciences
Dean: Herman Hudojo; *staff* 123 (30)
F. of Social Sciences (including Business Administration)
Dean: Suharto; *staff* 141 (35)
F. of Languages and Arts
Dean: Imam Hasan; *staff* 119 (24)
F. of Technical and Vocational Education
Dean: Rinanto Roesman; *staff* 92 (15)

Founded 1954 as college, became faculty of Airlangga University 1958, and acquired present status and title 1964. A State institution responsible to the Department of Education and Culture. Residential facilities for the academic staff and students.

Arrangements for co-operation with the Universities of: Ball State; Ohio State; Cornell.

Academic Year: July to May (July-November; January-May).

Admission Requirements: Secondary school certificate (Sekolah Lanjutan Tingkat Atas, S.L.T.A.) and entrance examination.

Fees (Rupiahs): 90,000 per semester.

Language of Instruction: Indonesian.

Degrees and Diplomas: Strata 1 (S1), 4 yrs. Diplomas II, III, 2-3 yrs. Strata 2 (S2), a further 2 yrs. Strata 3 (S3), a further 3 yrs.

Library: Total, 106,069 vols.

Publications: Scientific Writings (annually); News and Reports (monthly); Scientific News (quarterly); Faculty publications.

Academic Staff, 1986-87: 609 (125).

Student Enrolment, 1986-87:

	Men	Women	Total
Of the country	3678	4964	8642
Of other countries	1	1	2
Total	3679	4965	8644

3565 **INSTITUT KEGURUAN DAN ILMU PENDIDIKAN**
Institute of Teacher Training and Education
Kampus Unsrat, Kliak, Manado
Telex: 71409
Telephone: 51193; 51241
Rektor: A. E. Sinolungan (1983-)

F. of Technical and Vocational Education
Dean: D. Wantasen; *staff* 22 (40)
F. of Education
Dean: S. Pamantung
F. of Social Sciences
Dean: Max Waney
F. of Languages and Arts
Dean: F. Rogi-Warouw
F. of Physical Education
Dean: E. Rorintulus
F. of Mathematics and Natural Sciences
Dean: Ibrahim Antou

Founded 1955. Acquired present status 1965. A State institution responsible to the Department of Education andCulture. Limited residential facilities for academic staff and students.

Academic Year: July to June (July-December; January-June).

Admission Requirements: Secondary school certificate (Sekolah Lanjutan Tingkat Atas, S.L.T.A.) and entrance examination.

Fees (Rupiahs): 180,000 per annum.

Language of Instruction: Indonesian.

Degrees and Diplomas: Sarjana, 4 yrs. Diplomas I, II, and III, 1-3 yrs.

Library: Central and faculty libraries.

Publication: Academic Journal (biannually).

Press or Publishing House: Percetakan IKIP Manado.

Academic Staff, 1986-87:

Rank	Full-time
Guru Besar (Professors)	12
Lektor Kepala (Senior Lecturers)	118
Lektor (Lecturers)	595
Total	725

Student Enrolment, 1986-87:

	Men	Women	Total
Of the country	2280	2748	5028

3566 **INSTITUT KEGURUAN DAN ILMU PENDIDIKAN**
Institute of Teacher Training and Education
Jalan Pemuda, Mataram

F. of Education
F. of Languages and Arts
F. of Mathematics and Natural Sciences
F. of Physical Education

Founded 1967. A private institution.

3567 **INSTITUT KEGURUAN DAN ILMY PENDIDIKAN**
Institute of Teacher Training and Education
38a Jalan Merbau, Medan
Telephone: 327704; 324402

F. of Education
F. of Social Sciences
F. of Languages and Arts
F. of Mathematics and Natural Sciences
F. of Technology
F. of Physical Education

Founded 1955 as a college, became a faculty of Islamic University of North Sumatra 1957, and acquired present status and title 1965. A State institution responsible to the Department of Education and Culture.Founded 1955 as a college, became a faculty of Islamic University of North Sumatra 1957, and acquired present status and title 1965. A State institution responsible to the Department of Education and Culture. Some residential facilities for academic staff and students.

Academic Year: January to December (February-June; June-November).

Admission Requirements: Secondary school certificate (Sekolah Lanjutan Tingkat Atas, S.L.T.A.) or graduation from teacher training college, and entrance examination.

Language of Instruction: Indonesian.

Degrees and Diplomas: Sarjana, 4 yrs. Diplomas I, II, III, 1-3 yrs.

Library: Central Library, *c.* 30,220 vols.

Publications: Educandum; Gema Alma Mater.

Academic Staff: c. 540 (210).

Student Enrolment: c. 6050.

3568 **INSTITUT KERGURUAN DAN ILMU PENDIDIKAN ASWASLIYAH**

Institute of Teacher Training and Education Aswasliyah

Jalan Sisingamangaraja, Medan

F. of Education

F. of Mathematics and Natural Sciences

F. of Social Sciences

F. of Languages and Art

Founded 1963. A private institution.

3569 **INSTITUT KERGURUAN DAN ILMY PENDIDIKAN GUNUNG SITOLI**

Institute of Teacher Training and Education Gunung Sitoli

Jalan Labuhan Angin, Nias

F. of Education

F. of Mathematics and Natural Sciences

F. of Social Sciences

Founded 1965. A private institution.

3570 **INSTITUT KEGURUAN DAN ILMU PENDIDIKAN**

Institute of Teacher Training and Education

Air Tawar, Padang, Sumatera Barat

Cables: ikip padang

Telephone: 21260

F. of Education

F. of Mathematics and Natural Sciences

F. of Social Sciences

F. of Languages and Arts

F. of Technical and Vocational Education

F. of Physical Education

Laboratory S.

Founded 1954, acquired present status and title 1965. Under the jurisdiction of and financially supported by the Department of Education and Culture.Founded 1954, acquired present status and title 1965. Under the jurisdiction of and financially supported by the Department of Education and Culture. Residential facilities for *c.* 20% of the academic staff.

Academic Year: February to November (February-June; August-December).

Admission Requirements: Secondary school certificate (Sekolah Lanjutan Tingkat Atas, S.L.T.A.) and entrance examination.

Languages of Instruction: Indonesian and English.

Degrees and Diplomas: Sarjana, 4 yrs. Diplomas I, II, III, 1-3 yrs.

Library: Central Library, *c.* 55,280 vols.

Publications: Bulletin (bimonthly); Forum Pendidikan (quarterly).

Academic Staff: c. 440 (50).

Student Enrolment: c. 5720.

3571 **INSTITUT KERGURUAN DAN ILMY PENDIDIKAN MUHAMMADIYAH**

Institute of Teacher Training and Education Muhammadiyah

Jalan dr. Angka 1, Purwokerto

F. of Education

F. of Social Sciences

Founded 1965. A private institution.

3572 **INSTITUT KEGURUAN DAN ILMU PENDIDIKAN**

Institute of Teacher Training and Education

Jalan Kelud Utara III, Semarang

Cables: ikip

Telephone: (024) 311501; 311510

C. of Languages and Arts

C. of Education

C. of Mathematics and Natural Sciences

C. of Social Sciences

C. of Technical and Vocational Education

C. of Physical Education

Founded 1950 as a college, became a faculty of Diponegoro University 1960, and acquired present status 1965. AState institution operated under the jurisdiction of the Department of Education and Culture. Governing body: the Board of Trustees. Some residential facilities for academic staff and students. Some residential facilities for academic staff and students.

Academic Year: September to May (September-December; January-May).

Admission Requirements: Secondary school certificate (Sekolah Lanjutan Tingkat Atas, S.L.T.A.) or equivalent, and entrance examination.

Language of Instruction: Indonesian.

Degrees and Diplomas: Sarjana, 4 yrs. Diplomas I, II, III, 1-3 yrs.

Library: Central Library, *c.* 36,500 vols.

Publications: Lembaran Ilmu Pengetahuan (quarterly); College publications (biannually).

Press or Publishing House: IKIP Semarang Press.

Academic Staff: c. 500.

Student Enrolment: c. 6920.

3573 **INSTITUT KERGURUAN DAN ILMU PENDIDIKAN VETERAN JAWA TENGAH**

Institute of Teacher Training and Education Veteran Jawa Tengah

Jalan Pemuda 138, Semarang

F. of Education

F. of Social Sciences

F. of Technical Education

Founded 1962. A private institution.

3574 **INSTITUT KERGURUAN DAN ILMU PENDIDIKAN**

Institute of Teacher Training and Education

Jalan dr. Muwardi, Sukoharjo

F. of Education

F. of Social Sciences

F. of Languages and Arts

Founded 1968. A private institution.

3575 **INSTITUT KEGURUAN DAN ILMU PENDIDIKAN**

Institute of Teacher Training and Education

Kampus Ketintang Surabaya Surabaya

Telephone: 815654

Rektor: Soerono Martorahardjo (1989-90)

F. of Education

Head: Suwarno; *staff* 5

F. of Languages and Arts

Head: Suwadji; *staff* 5

F. of Mathematics and Natural Sciences

Head: Kuspono; *staff* 5

F. of Social Sciences

Head: Pramono; *staff* 5

F. of Technical and Vocational Education

Head: Sardjio; *staff* 5

F. of Physical Education

Research Ce.

Head: Sunarto; *staff* 31

Founded 1965. A State institution.

Academic Year: January to December (January-June; July-December).

Admission Requirements: Secondary school certificate (Sekolah Lanjutan Tingkat Atas, S.L.T.A.) and entrance examination.

Language of Instruction: Indonesian.

Degrees and Diplomas: Sarjana, 4 yrs. Diploma I, II, III, 1-3 yrs.

Academic Staff, 1989-90:

Rank	Full-time
Professors	6
Lektor Kepala (Associate Professors)	109
Lektor (Lecturers)	303
Asisten Ahli (Assistant Lecturers)	238
Total	659

Student Enrolment, 1989-90:

	Men	Women	Total
Of the country	8839	4529	13,368

3576 **INSTITUT KERGURUAN DAN ILMU PENDIDIKAN MUHAMMADIYAH**

Institute of Teacher Training and Education Muhammadiyah
Jalan Kapasan 73-75, Surabaya

F. of Education
F. of Mathematics and Natural Sciences
F. of Social Sciences
F. of Languages and Arts
Founded 1980. A private institution.

3577 **INSTITUT KERGURUAN DAN ILMU PENDIDIKAN PGRI**

Institute of Teacher Training and Education PGRI
Jalan Ngagel Dadi IIIB, Surabaya

F. of Education
F. of Social Sciences
F. of Languages and Arts
F. of Mathematics and Natural Sciences
Founded 1971. A private institution.

3578 **INSTITUT KERGURUAN DAN ILMU PENDIDIKAN SARASWATI**

Institute of Teacher Training and Education Saraswati
Jalan Pahlawan, Tabanan

F. of Social Sciences
Founded 1965. A private institution.

3579 **INSTITUT KERGURUAN DAN ILMU PENDIDIKAN**

Institute of Teacher Training and Education
Andi Pangerang Pettarani, Gunungsari Baru, Ujung Pandung, 90222
South Sulawesi
Telex: 71173
Telephone: 83930
Rektor: Paturungi Parawansa (1982-90)
Pembantu Rektor (Administration): Kadir Suma

F. of Education
Dean: Tawani Rahamma; *staff* 94 (18)
F. of Social Sciences
Dean: Muh. Abduh; *staff* 140 (21)
F. of Languages and Arts
Dean: Zainuddiin Taha; *staff* 106 (43)
F. of Mathematics and Natural Sciences
Dean: Baharuddin; *staff* 110 (54)
F. of Technical and Vocational Education
Dean: Muhammad Yunus; *staff* 126 (27)
F. of Physical Education
Dean: M. Anwar Pasau; *staff* 56 (55)
Community Service Ce.
Principal: M.A. Timbamg; *staff* 6
Computer Ut.
Principal: Mannangkasi; *staff* 10
Research Ce.
Principal: Sahabuddin Tuppu; *staff* 6
Teaching Practice Ut.
Principal: Taha' Rangginia; *staff* 7

Founded 1962 as faculty of Hasanuddin University, acquired present status and title 1965. A State institution under the supervision of the Department of Education and Culture. Limited residential facilities for academic staff and 111 students.

Academic Year: January to December (January-June; July-December).

Admission Requirements: Secondary school certificate (Sekolah Menengah Atas, S.M.A.) and entrance examination.

Fees (Rupiahs): 135,000-157,500 per annum.

Language of Instruction: Indonesian.

Degrees and Diplomas: Strata 1 (S1), 4 yrs.

Library: 109,514 vols.

Publication: Berita IKIP (monthly).

Academic Staff, 1989-90: 623.

Student Enrolment, 1989-90:

	Men	Women	Total
Of the country	5572	4011	9582
Of other countries	1	–	1
Total	5573	4011	9583

3580 **INSTITUT KERGURUAN DAN ILMU PENDIDIKAN**

Institute of Teacher Training and Education
Kampus IKIP, Karang Malang, Yogyakarta
Telephone: 3262; 3561; 2192

F. of Education
F. of Mathematics and Natural Sciences
F. of Social Sciences
F. of Technical and Vocational Education
F. of Languages and Arts
Ce. for Educational Research

Founded 1964. A State institution, incorporating former faculties of Gadjah Mada University. Receives 80% financial aid from the Department of Education and Culture. Some residential facilities for academic staff.

Academic Year: January to December (January-June; July-December).

Admission Requirements: Secondary school certificate (Sekolah Lanjuton Tingkat Atas, S.L.T.A.) or foreign equivalent, and entrance examination.

Language of Instruction: Indonesian or Javanese.

Degrees and Diplomas: Sarjana, 4 yrs. Diplomas I, II, III, 1-3 yrs.

Library: Central Library, *c.* 38,390 vols.

Publication: Departmental publications.

Academic Staff: *c.* 280 (870).

Student Enrolment: *c.* 4420.

3581 **INSTITUT KERGURUAN DAN ILMU PENDIDIKAN PGRI**

Institute of Teacher Training and Education PGRI
Jalan Stasiun 1, Wates

F. of Education
F. of Social Sciences
Founded 1969. A private institution.

3582 **INSTITUT KERGURUAN DAN ILMU PENDIDIKAN PGRI**

Institute of Teacher Training and Education PGRI
Jalan Wates 147, Yogykarta

F. of Education
F. of Social Sciences
Founded 1962. A private institution.

3583 **INSTITUT KERGURUAN DAN ILMU PENDIDIKAN SANATA DHARMA**

Institute of Teacher Training and Education Sanata Dharma
Mrican, Yogykarta

F. of Education
F. of Mathematics and Natural Sciences
F. of Social Sciences
F. of Languages and Arts
Founded 1955. A private institution.

3584 **INSTITUT KERGURUAN DAN ILMU PENDIDIKAN MUHAMMADIYAH**

Institute of Teacher Training and Education Muhammadiyah
Jalan Kapas 6, Yogykarta

F. of Education
F. of Languages and Arts
F. of Mathematics and Natural Sciences
Founded 1960. A private institution.

3585 **INSTITUT KERGURUAN DAN ILMU PENDIDIKAN VETERAN**
Institute of Teacher Training and Education Veteran
Jalan Mantrigawen Lor 38, Yogykarta

F. of Social Sciences
Founded 1967. A private institution.

Also 3 Universities and 42 Academies, Schools and Institutes of professional training attached to relevant Ministries (Government Departments), and 316 private professional Academies and Schools.

IRAN

Universities and University Complexes

3587 ***ALLMEH TABATABAI UNIVERSITY**
Karimkhan Zand Avenue, North Aban, Tehran
President: Mohsen Khalidji

F. of Economics
F. of Management and Accountancy
F. of Social Sciences
F. of Psychology and Education
F. of Persian and Foreign Languages

Founded 1984, incorporating 22 previously existing universities, faculties, colleges, and institutes.

Academic Year: October to June.

Admission Requirements: Secondary school certificate and entrance examination.

Language of Instruction: Persian.

Degrees and Diplomas: Bachelor of Arts. Master. Doctor.

Libraries: Central Library, 48,000 vols; libraries of the faculties.

Academic Staff, 1989-90: 270 (180).

Student Enrolment, 1989-90: 11,283.

3588 **AMIR KABIR UNIVERSITY OF TECHNOLOGY**
Hafez Avenue, Tehran

3589 **AVICENNA UNIVERSITY**
Mahdieh Avenue, Tehran
Telephone: 99050

F. of Health and Medical Sciences
F. of Environmental Sciences
F. of Natural Resources

Founded 1974.

3590 **AZZAHRA UNIVERSITY**
Vanak Avenue, Tehran
Telephone: (021) 684051/5

F. of Science
F. of Accountancy and Management
F. of Letters
F. of Social Sciences
F. of Arts
I. of Islamic Studies (Social Sciences)
I. for Women's Studies

Founded 1964 as Iran Girl's College. Acquired present status and title 1975. The only university for women in the country. Residential facilities for students.

Academic Year: September to July (September-February; February-July).

Admission Requirements: Secondary school certificate and entrance examination.

Fees: None.

Language of Instruction: Persian.

Degrees and Diplomas: Bachelor of Science in all fields.

Library: Central Library, 52,600 vols.

Academic Staff: *c.* 80 (160).

Student Enrolment: *c.* 2810 (Women).

3591 **UNIVERSITY OF ENGINEERING AND TECHNOLOGY**
412 Shahin Alley, Seyed Khandan, Tehran

Founded 1967

Academic Year: October to June (October-January; February-June).

Admission Requirements: Secondary school certificate and entrance examination.

Language of Instruction: Persian.

Degrees and Diplomas: Bachelor of Science, 4 yrs. Also Associate of Science, 2 yrs.

3592 ***UNIVERSITY OF ESFAHAN**
Esfahan
Telex: 312295 IREU IR
Telephone: (031) 71071/79, 430390/9
Chancellor: Hassan Razmjoo
Vice-Chancellor (Finance and Administration): Reza Enshaie

F. of Administrative Sciences and Economics
Dean: Abdul Hussein Sassan
F. of Educational Sciences
Dean: Abdul Ali Ghera'ati
F. of Foreign Languages
Dean: Reza Hadizadeh
F. of Letters and Humanities
Dean: Mohammad Ali Ejeii
F. of Pure Science
Dean: Sayid Mohammad Hasan Feiz
F. of Engineering
Dean: Mohammad Taghi Fallahi

Founded 1936 as college, became a State university 1958. Faculty of Medicine detached 1986 to form separate University. Responsible to the Ministry of Culture and Higher Education. Residential facilities for some academic staff and students.

Academic Year: September to August (September-January; January-June; July-August).

Admission Requirements: Secondary school certificate and competitive entrance examination.

Fees: None.

Language of Instruction: Persian.

Degrees and Diplomas: Licentiate, 4 yrs. Master, a further 2-3 yrs.

Libraries: Central Library; faculty libraries and department libraries, total, 283,000 vols (in Persian, Arabic, English,French, German, Armenian, etc.).

Academic Staff: 350.

Student Enrolment: 10,200.

3593 **ESFAHAN UNIVERSITY OF TECHNOLOGY**
Esfahan
Telephone: (031) 38043
President: Mohammad Shahedi

C. of Electrical Engineering
Head: A. Doost Hosseini; *staff* 35
C. of Mechanical Engineering
Head: E. Shirani; *staff* 40
C. of Civil Engineering
Head: A.M. Keynia; *staff* 25
C. of Materials Technology (including Metallurgy)
Head: A.A. Ziaee; *staff* 18 (4)
C. of Chemical Engineering
Head: M. Morshed; *staff* 20
C. of Industrial Engineering and Operations Research
Head: H. Zokae Ashtiani; *staff* 15
C. of Agricultural Engineering
Head: A. Ahomanesh; *staff* 71
C. of Textile Engineering
Head: M. Moradi; *staff* 4
C. of Science
Also 2 junior colleges.

Founded 1977. A State institution responsible to the Ministry of Culture and Higher Education. Residential facilities for academic staff and students.

Academic Year: October to July (October-January; February-June).

Admission Requirements: Secondary school certificate and entrance examination.

Fees: None.

Language of Instruction: Persian.

Degrees and Diplomas: Bachelor of Science in–Engineering, several fields; Physics; Chemistry; Mathematics, 5 yrs. Master, a further2 yrs.

Library: Central Library, 451,000 vols.
Publication: Independence (biannually).
Academic Staff, 1986-87:

Rank	Full-time
Daneshyar (Associate Professors)	5
Ostadyar (Assistant Professors)	111
Morabbi (Instructors)	124
Total	240

Student Enrolment, 1986-87:

	Men	Women	Total
Of the country	4163	314	4477

3594 **FERDOWSI UNIVERSITY OF MASHHAD**
Mashhad
Telephone: (051) 31031/5
Chancellor: H. Eshtiagh-Hosseini
Vice-Chancellor for Administration: Hassan-Ali-Azarnoush

S. of Letters and Human Sciences
Dean: Mohammad-Kazem Khajavian; *staff* 51
S. of Science
Dean: Ali Jabari Azad; *staff* 96
S. of Theology and Islamic Studies
Dean: Mohammad Reza Mashshaei; *staff* 16
S. of Education
Dean: Hossien-Ali-Koohestani; *staff* 15
S. of Agriculture
Dean: Ebrahim-Bazari; *staff* 30
S. of Engineering
Dean: Ali-Haerian; *staff* 48

Founded 1937 as State school of hygiene, became faculty of medicine 1949, and university 1956. School of Medicine detached 1986 to form separate University. A State institution responsible to the Ministry of Culture and Higher Education. Residential facilities for academic staff and students.

Academic Year: September to June (September-February; February-June).

Admission Requirements: Secondary school certificate and entrance examination.

Language of Instruction: Persian.

Degrees and Diplomas: Licentiate in–Letters; Science; Theology, 4 yrs. Master, M.Sc. Also diploma in Persian Language and Literature, 2 yrs.

Libraries: Letters and Human Sciences, 65,003 vols; Education, 26,296; Agriculture, 10,600; Engineering, 14,038.

Special Facilities (Museums, etc.): Zoology Museum and Herbarium.

Academic Staff, 1986-87:

Rank	Full-time
Professors	7
Associate Professors	18
Assistant Professors	131
Lecturers	114
Total	270

Student Enrolment, 1986-87:

Men	Women	Total
6287	2166	8453

3595 **GILAN UNIVERSITY**
P.O. Box 401, Rasht
Telex: 232100
Telephone: 35035

F. of Science
F. of Agriculture
F. of Technology
F. of Humanities

Founded 1977.

3596 **IMAM SADEGH UNIVERSITY**
Martyr Chamran Park Way, Farahzad Road, Tehran

1983

3597 **IRAN UNIVERSITY OF SCIENCE AND TECHNOLOGY**
Narmak, Tehran 16844
Telex: 212965 IR
Telephone: 792991/5
Chancellor: A. Taeb

C. of Civil Engineering
Head: H. Behbahani; *staff* 25 (8)
C. of Mechanical Engineering
Head: Mohammad Haghpanahi; *staff* 24 (7)
C. of Chemical Engineering
Head: Hojatollah Karimpour; *staff* 30 (15)
C. of Electrical Engineering and Electronics
Head: Karim Mohammadi; *staff* 30 (15)
C. of Industrial Engineering
Head: S.G. Jalali-Naini; *staff* 36 (8)
C. of Architecture and Urban Planning
Head: Hamid Nouhi; *staff* 22 (35)
C. of Science
Head: Akbar Hassani; *staff* 34
Ce. of Computer Engineering
Head: Mehdi Mirshamsi
Graduate S.
Head: S.M. Seyed-Hosseini; *staff* 56 (70)

Founded 1928 as technical school, acquired present status and title 1977. A State institution responsible to the Ministry of Culture and Higher Education. Limited residential facilities for students.

Academic Year: September to June (September-January; February-June).

Admission Requirements: Secondary school certificate and entrance examination.

Fees: None.

Language of Instruction: Persian.

Degrees and Diplomas: Bachelor of Science. Master of Science.

Library: Central Library, *c.* 20,000 vols.

Academic Staff, 1988:

Rank	Full-time	Part-time
Professors	5	–
Associate Professors	9	10
Assistant Professors	61	33
Instructors	83	18
Total	158	61

Student Enrolment, 1988: c. 6000.

3598 **MARTYR BAHONAR UNIVERSITY**
Islamic Republic Boulevard, Kerman
Telephone: 24637

C. of Agriculture
C. of Letters and Human Sciences
C. of Science
C. of Technology

Founded 1975.

3599 **MARTYR BEHESHTI UNIVERSITY**
Evin, Tehran
Telephone: 214111

C. of Law
C. of Economics and Political Science
C. of Architecture (including Town Planning)
C. of Education and Psychology
C. of Letters and Human Sciences
C. of Science
C. of Dentistry
C. of Accountancy and Management

Founded 1959. School of Medicine detached 1986 to form separate University.

Academic Year: September to June (September-January; February-May).

Admission Requirements: Secondary school certificate and entrance examination.

Language of Instruction: Persian.

Degrees and Diplomas: Licentiate in–Letters and Humanities; Law; Economics and Political Science; Architecture, 4 yrs. Master of Arts in–Law; Economics and Political Science; Architecture, a further 2 yrs. Doctor in Dentistry. Diplomas in Dental Hygiene and Dental Prosthetics.

Libraries: Central Library, *c.* 55,000 vols; Science, *c.* 700; Dentistry, *c.* 900; Letters and Humanities, *c.* 4000; Architecture, *c.* 800; Law, *c.* 2500; Economics, *c.* 770.

Publications: Bulletin of the National University of Iran; Journals of the Colleges of Dentistry; Law.

Academic Staff: c. 350 (130).

Student Enrolment: c. 8410.

3600 **MARTYR CHAMRAN UNIVERSITY**
Ahwaz
Telephone: 30012

C. of Science
C. of Agriculture
C. of Engineering
C. of Basic Medical Sciences
C. of Medical Technology
C. of Letters and Foreign Languages
C. of Education and Psychology
C. of Economics and Social Sciences
C. of Physical Education
C. of Theology and Islamic Studies
C. of Agriculture (including Food Technology) (Mollasani)
C. of Veterinary Medicine
Branches at Khoramshahr, Dezful, and Lorestan.

Founded 1955 on a campus site dating back to 241 and 272 A.D. College of Medicine detached 1986 to form separate University. Responsible to the Ministry of Culture and Higher Education. Some residential facilities for academic staff and for women students.

Academic Year: September to June (September-January; January-June).

Admission Requirements: Secondary school certificate and entrance examination.

Language of Instruction: Persian

Degrees and Diplomas: Bachelor of–Arts; Science, 4 yrs. Master of Science, a further 3 yrs.

Publications: Journal (biannually); Journal of Scientific Agriculture (biannually).

Academic Staff: c. 500.

Student Enrolment: c. 3800.

3601 ***MAZANDARAN UNIVERSITY**
P.O. Box 444, Bobolsar
Telephone: 02491-4093

S. of Economics and Social Science
F. of Natural Resources (Forestry, Fishery, Environmental Science)
F. of Teacher Training (Technical)
I. of Chemistry
C. of Agriculture
F. of Medicine

Founded 1980 incorporating previously existing institutions in the Province. Faculty of Medicine detached 1986 to form separate University. A State institution responsible to the Ministry of Culture and Higher Education.Residential facilities for academic staff and students.

Academic Year: September to June (September-February; February-June).

Admission Requirements: Secondary school certificate and entrance examination.

Fees: None.

Language of Instruction: Persian.

Degrees and Diplomas: Bachelor of Science in–Forestry; Wood Science; Fishery and Environmental Science; Economics; Accountancy, 4 yrs. Master of Science in Chemistry, a further 2 yrs. Also Degree in–Engineering; Agriculture, 2 yrs.

Libraries: Central Library, *c.* 7000 vols; libraries of the school and faculties, *c.* 55,000.

Academic Staff: c. 130 (20).

Student Enrolment: c. 1350.

3602 **RAZI UNIVERSITY**
Azadi Square, Bakhtaran
Telephone: (0431) 28046/48

C. of Science
C. of Animal Husbandry (Ilam)
C. of Teacher Training (Sanandaj)

Founded 1972. School of Medicine detached 1986 to form separate University. A State institution responsible tothe Ministry of Culture and Higher Education.

Academic Year: September to June (September-January; February-June).

Admission Requirements: Secondary school certificate and entrance examination.

Language of Instruction: Persian.

Degrees and Diplomas: Bachelor of–Arts; Science, 4 yrs.

Library: Central Library, *c.* 10,000 vols.

3603 **SHARIF UNIVERSITY OF TECHNOLOGY**
Azadï Avenue, Tehran
Telephone: 972001/9

C. of Construction Engineering
C. of Industrial Engineering
C. of Mathematics and Computer Sciences
C. of Chemistry
C. of Physics
C. of Electrical Engineering
C. of Chemical Engineering
C. of Metallurgy
C. of Mechanical Engineering
Water and Energy Research I.
Materials and Energy Research I.
Biochemical Engineering Research I.

Founded 1965. Acquired present title 1979. A State institution responsible to the Ministry of Culture and Higher Education. Governing body: the Board of Trustees. Residential facilities for students.

Academic Year: September to June (September-January; January-June).

Admission Requirements: Secondary school certificate and entrance examination.

Language of Instruction: Persian.

Degrees and Diplomas: Bachelor of Science, B.Sc., 4 yrs. Master of Science, M.Sc., in–Construction Engineering; Mathematics and Computer Sciences; Chemistry; Physics; Electrical Engineering, a further 2 yrs.

Libraries: Central Library, *c.* 50,000 vols; department libraries.

Academic Staff: 300.

Student Enrolment: c. 3000.

3604 ***SHIRAZ UNIVERSITY**
Zand Avenue, Shiraz
Telephone: 3211½

C. of Education
C. of Letters and Science
C. of Dentistry
C. of Veterinary Medicine
C. of Engineering
C. of Agriculture (including Animal Husbandry)
C. of Electronics
Also high school.

Founded 1962. College of Medicine detached 1986 to form separate University. Residential facilities for students.

Academic Year: September to June (September-January; February-June; June-August).

Admission Requirements: Secondary school certificate and competitive entrance examination.

Languages of Instruction: Persian and English.

Degrees and Diplomas: Bachelor of–Arts; Science; Science in Agriculture; Science in Nursing, 4 yrs; Science in Engineering, 5 yrs. Master of Science in–Agriculture; Engineering; Mathematics; Physics; Chemistry; Biology; Biochemistry; Microbiology. Master of Arts in–English; Economics. Doctor of–Veterinary Medicine; Dentistry, 6 yrs.

Libraries: Central Library, *c.* 120,000 vols (in English), *c.* 30,000 (in Persian); College libraries.

Publications: Iranian Journal of Science and Technology; Iranian Agricultural Journal; Bulletin of Institute of Asian Studies; Economics.

Academic Staff: c. 520.

Student Enrolment: c. 4610.

3605 **UNIVERSITY OF SISTAN AND BALUCHISTAN**
P.O. Box 161-98135, Khash Road, Zahedan
Cables: Dasibal
Telephone: 25981-6
Chancellor: Ataollah Koohian (1985-)
Registrar: Mahdi Khalili

F. of Science
Dean: A.A. Noura; *staff* 13
F. of Electrical Engineering
Dean: Jaleel Rashed Mohassel; *staff* 7
F. of Mechanical Engineering
Dean: M. Jafarian; *staff* 5
F. of Civil Engineering
Dean: Ismail Nezhad; *staff* 16
C. of Marine Science (Chah-Bahar)
Dean: Hossain Langroodi *staff* 6
F. of Chemical Engineering
Dean: Koochak Hossain Atashi; *staff* 8
C. of Agriculture (Zabol)
Dean: Jafar Vali-Zadeh; *staff* 6

Founded 1975. A State institution responsible to the Ministry of Culture and Higher Education. Residential facilities for academic staff and students.

Academic Year: September to July (September-February; February-July).

Admission Requirements: Secondary school certificate and entrance examination.

Fees: None.

Language of Instruction: Persian.

Degrees and Diplomas: Bachelor, 4 yrs. Diploma, 2 yrs.

Libraries: 11,725 vols (in Persian, Urdu, Arabic); 7673 (in English).

Academic Staff, 1986-87: 75.

Student Enrolment, 1986-87:

	Men	Women	Total
Of the country	2276	53	2329

3606 ***UNIVERSITY OF TABRIZ**
29th of Bahman Boulevard, Tabriz
Telex: 412045 TBUN
Telephone: (41) 31 300
Fax: (41)34 013
Chancellor: Seyed Mehdi Golabi (1989-)
Secretary-General: M. E. Kaghazchi

F. of Agriculture (including Animal Husbandry)
Dean: Cyrus Massiha; *staff* 51
Higher Education Complex (Agriculture) (Ardabil)
Dean: Gadir Nouri; *staff* 15
F. of Education and Psychology
Dean: Parviz Sarandi; *staff* 20
F. of Engineering
Dean: Jawad Faiz; *staff* 57
F. of Persian Literature and Foreign Languages
Dean: Reza Irandoust; *staff* 31
F. of Science
Dean: Mohammed Hossein Pour-Faizi; *staff* 131
F. of Human and Social Science
Dean: Abdelhamid Rajai-Asl; *staff* 31
I. of Chemistry
; *staff* 27
C. of Agriculture (Maragheh)
Dean: Ali Nazemieh; *staff* 12
I. for Urban Research
Director: Abdelhamid Rajai-Asl
I. of Persian History and Culture
Director: N. Magsoodi Magsoodlou
Ce. for Astronomical Research and Observatory
Head: M. Adjabshirizadeh

Also Teaching and Research Centre of the Faculty of Agriculture (Khalat-Poushan).

Founded 1946 as Tabriz University, became University of Azarabadegan 1975 and resumed first title 1979. Faculty of Medicine and Pharmacy detached 1986 to form separate University. A State institution responsible to the Ministry of Culture and Higher Education. Residential facilities for *c.* 100 academic staff and 4000 single and 210 married students.

Arrangement for co-operation with the International Centre for Theoretical Physics, Trieste.

Academic Year: September to June (September-January; February-June).

Admission Requirements: Secondary school certificate and competitive entrance examination.

Fees: None.

Language of Instruction: Persian.

Degrees and Diplomas: Lesans, Bachelor, of–Arts, B.A.; Science, B.Sc., 4 yrs. Foq Lesans, Master, of–Arts, M.A.; Science, M.Sc., afurther 2 yrs. Doctor of Literature.

Libraries: Central Library, 81,769 vols; faculty libraries, total, *c.* 145,165.

Special Facilities (Museums, etc.): Khadjeh Nassir-Aldin Observatory and Planetarium.

Publication: Pazhoohesh (Research publication, annually).

Press or Publishing House: Printing Office.

Academic Staff, 1989-90:

Rank	Full-time
Ostad (Professors)	4
Daneshyar (Associate Professors)	41
Ostadyar (Assistant Professors/Readers)	131
Morabbi (Lecturers)	134
Others	26
Total	336

Student Enrolment, 1989-90:

	Men	Women	Total
Of the country	7717	1852	9569*

*Also 7 foreign students.

3607 **UNIVERSITY FOR TEACHER EDUCATION**
49 Mobarezan Avenue, Tehran
Telephone: 825012/15

C. of Education
C. of Science
C. of Letters and Humanities

Branches at Zahedan, Arak, Yazd, Kashan.

Founded 1930 as a Teacher Training College. Acquired present status and title 1976. A State institution responsible to the Ministry of Culture and Higher Education. Residential facilities for students.

Academic Year: September to June (September-January; February-June).

Admission Requirements: Secondary school certificate and entrance examination.

Language of Instruction: Persian.

Degrees and Diplomas: Bachelor of–Arts, B.A.; Science, B.Sc., 4 yrs. Master, a further 2 yrs.

Libraries: Central Library, 31,243 vols (in Persian), 26,843 (in foreign languages); Mathematics, 5751 (in foreign languages); Literature 671 (in Persian), 1300 (in foreign languages); Research Institute, 2000 and 4000.

Press or Publishing House: University Press.

Academic Staff: c. 170.

Student Enrolment: c. 3740.

3608 ***UNIVERSITY OF TEHRAN**
Avenue Enghelab, Tehran
Telex: 213944 IR IBB
Telephone: (0021) 6111
President: Mohammad Rahimian (1987-)
Vice-Chancellor: S. Jalaleddin Hashemi

F of Letters and Humanities
Dean: Jalaleddin Mojtabavi; *staff* 184 (2)
F. of Fine Arts
Dean: M.K. Seyfian; *staff* 127
F. of Science
Dean: M. Ghandi; *staff* 300 (1)
F. of Engineering
Dean: A. Mir-Ghaderi; *staff* 284 (7)
F. of Agriculture (including Animal Husbandry)
Dean: H. Fardad; *staff* 643
F. of Natural Sciences (including Forestry)
Dean: Hassan Ahmadi; *staff* 99
F. of Law and Political Science
Dean: S.M. Safaei; *staff* 91 (1)
F. of Education
Dean: K. Dorrani; *staff* 112
F. of Islamic Theology and Culture
Dean: S. Aboulfazl Mirmohammadi; *staff* 74
F. of Social Sciences
Dean: Gholamabas Tavasoli; *staff* 133

F. of Economics
Dean: J. Ebadi; *staff* 81
F. of Management and Business Administration
Dean: A. Rezaeyan *staff* 55
F. of Veterinary Medicine
Dean: S.M. Kjaei; *staff* 217
I. of Geophysics
Supervisor: A. Javaherian; *staff* 104
I. for the Dehkhoda Encyclopedias
Supervisor: Jafar Shaheidi; *staff* 14
I. of Geography
Supervisor: F. Mahmoodi; *staff* 13
I. of Comparative Law
Supervisor: H. Safaei; *staff* 4
I. of Biochemistry and Biophysics
Supervisor: M. N. Sarboloki; *staff* 53
Desert Studies Ce.
Supervisor: N. Khorasani; *staff* 21
Ce. for Environmental Studies
Supervisor: H. Bahraini *staff* 8
Ce. for International Studies
Supervisor: H. Safaei; *staff* 16
Foreign Language F.
Supervisor: A. Afghami Aghda; *staff* 16
Also Educational Complex at Abooreihan

Founded 1934 as an autonomous institution, responsible to the Ministry of Culture and Higher Education. Received Charter of Independence 1941. Faculty of Medicine detached 1986 to form separate University. Residential facilities for students.

Academic Year: September to July (September-February; February-July).

Admission Requirements: Secondary school certificate and competitive entrance examination.

Language of Instruction: Persian.

Degrees and Diplomas: Bachelor of–Arts; Science, 4-6 yrs. Master, a further 2 ½-4 ½ yrs. Doctorates.

Library: Central Library, *c.* 450,000 vols.

Special Facilities (Museums, etc.): Museum of Zoology and Entomology.

Publication: Faculty publications.

Press or Publishing House: Tehran University Press.

Academic Staff, 1989-90:

Rank	Full-time
Professors	111
Associate Professors	172
Assistant Professors	368
Lecturers	387
Total	1038

Student Enrolment, 1989-90:

	Men	Women	Total
Of the country	16,467	5471	21,938*

*Also 50 external students.

3609 **UNIVERSITY OF URMIA**

P.O. Box 165, Urmia, West Azarbeyjan 57135
Telex: 442081 URMU IR
Telephone: (441) 48131-33
Chancellor: M. Razavi-Routani (1986-)

S. of Agriculture (including Animal Husbandry)
Dean: Komari Zadeh; *staff* 44 (6)
S. of Science
Dean: M. Baradarani; *staff* 63 (12)
S. of Veterinary Medicine
Dean: M. Sadrkhanloo; *staff* 23
I. of Technology and Engineering
Dean: M. Ghaffari; *staff* 23 (21)
S. of Literature and Social Science (including Economics and Business Administration)
Dean: M. Talei; *staff* 13 (10)
S. of Agriculture (Miandoab)
S. of Veterinary Medicine (Khoy)

Founded 1964 as college, became university 1976. School of Medicine detached 1986 to form separate University. Governing body: the University Board. Residential facilities for *c.* 100 academic staff and *c.* 2000 students.

Academic Year: September to July (September-February; February-July).

Admission Requirements: Secondary school certificate and entrance examination.

Fees: None.

Language of Instruction: Persian.

Degrees and Diplomas: Bachelor of Science, 4 yrs. Doctor of–Veterinary Medicine, 6 ½ yrs. Also diplomas, 2-2 ½ yrs.

Library: Total, 30,000 vols.

Special Facilities (Museums, etc.): Entomology Museum; Collection of Plant Diseases.

Academic Staff, 1989-90: 145 (63).

Student Enrolment, 1989-90:

	Men	Women	Total
Of the country	2097	372	2469

3610 **UNIVERSITY FACULTY TRAINING CENTRE**

North Karegar Avenue, Tehran

Founded 1981.

3611 **MEDICAL SCIENCES UNIVERSITY OF IRAN**

Gandhi Avenue, Tehran
Telephone: 688191
Chancellor: A. Khosravi (1980-)
Vice-Chancellor: A. Mussavi

Medicine (including Nursing and Midwifery)

Founded 1974. A State institution responsible to the Ministry of Health, Medical Care and Education. Residential facilities for 1800 students.

Academic Year: September to July (September-February; March-July).

Admission Requirements: Secondary school certificate and entrance examination.

Language of Instruction: Persian.

Degrees and Diplomas: Doctor of Medicine, 7 yrs.

Library: Total, *c.* 30,000 vols.

Academic Staff, 1986-87:

Rank	Full-time	Part-time
Professors	–	2
Associate Professors	10	8
Assistant Professors	92	30
Instructors	121	30
Total	223	70

Student Enrolment, 1986-87:

Men	Women	Total
3200	2800	6000

3612 **UNIVERSITY OF MEDICAL SCIENCES MARTYR CHAMRAN**

Golestan Road, Ahwaz

Medicine

Founded 1986. Previously part of the University of Shahid Chamran.

3613 **BAKHTARAN UNIVERSITY OF MEDICAL SCIENCES**

Martyr Behesti Boulevard, Bahktaran
Telephone: 8239
Fax: 708093
President: Masoum Ali Masoumi (1987-)

S. of Medicine
Dean: Ali Reza Janbakhsh; *staff* 67
Nursing, Midwifery and Para-Medical Studies
Dean (Acting): Soheila Astanegi; *staff* 25

Founded 1986. Previously part of the University of Razi. Responsible to the Ministry of Health and Medical Education. Residential facilities for academic staff and 820 students.

Academic Year: September to June (Septembre-January; January-June).

Admission Requirements: Secondary school certificate and competitive entrance examination.

Fees: None.

Language of Instruction: Persian.

Degrees and Diplomas: Bachelor of–Nursing, Midwifery, 4 yrs. Doctor of Medicine, 6 yrs. Also Diploma of Technician, 2 yrs.

Library: 20,000 vols.

Academic Staff, 1990: 92 (40).

Student Enrolment, 1990:

	Men	Women	Total
Of the country	685	544	1221

3614 **UNIVERSITY OF MEDICAL SCIENCES OF MAZANDARAN**
Gang Afrooz, Babol

Medicine

Founded 1986. Previously part of the University of Mazandaran.

3615 **ESFAHAN UNIVERSITY OF MEDICAL SCIENCES**
Shiraz Gate University Avenue, Esfahan
Telex: 212308 EMSU IR
Telephone: 71071-9
President: Ebrahim Esfandiari
Vice-President for Admission and Education: Ali Ghafoori

F. of Medicine
Dean: Massoud Pourmoghadass; *staff* 196 (13)
F. of Pharmacy
Dean: Soleiman Afsharipoor; *staff* 36
F. of Dentistry
Dean: Behrooz Moosavi; *staff* 49 (4)
F. of Health and Nutrition
Dean: Abas-Ali Javadi; *staff* 18 (8)
F. of Nursing and Gynaecology
Dean: Asghar Khalifeh-Zadeh; *staff* 60 (1)
F. of Medicine (Kashan)
Nutrition Research I.
Head: Abdolrahim Emami; *staff* 6

Founded 1986. Previously part of the University of Esfahan. Responsible to the Ministry of Health and MedicalEducation. Some residential facilities for academic staff and students.

Academic Year: September to June.

Admission Requirements: Secondary school certificate and competitive entrance examination.

Fees: None.

Language of Instruction: Persian.

Degrees and Diplomas: Bachelor, 4 yrs. Master, a further 1-2 yrs. Doctor of–Dentistry, Pharmacy, 5 yrs; Medicine 6 yrs. Residency, a further 3-5 yrs.

Library: Central library, 64,264 vols.

Publication: Journal.

Academic Staff, 1990-91: 365 (25).

Student Enrolment, 1990:

	Men	Women	Total
Of the country	3575	2549	6124
Of other countries	25	16	41
Total	3600	2565	6165

3616 **UNIVERSITY OF MEDICAL SCIENCES**
Ayattollah Kashani Boulevard, Hamedan

Medicine

Founded 1986. Previously part of the University of Boalisina.

3617 **UNIVERSITY OF MEDICAL SCIENCES**
I.R.I. Boulevard, Kerman

Medicine

Founded 1986. Previously part of the University of Shahid Bahonar.

3618 **UNIVERSITY OF MEDICAL SCIENCES**
University Avenue, Mashhad

Medicine
Pharmacy

Founded 1986. Previously part of the University of Mashhad.

3619 **UNIVERSITY OF MEDICAL SCIENCES OF GILAN**
Saadi Avenue, Resht

Medicine

Founded 1986. Previously part of the University of Gilan.

3620 **UNIVERSITY OF MEDICAL SCIENCES**
Ghods Square, Shiraz

Medicine

Founded 1986. Previously part of the University of Shiraz.

3621 **UNIVERSITY OF MEDICAL SCIENCES**
29th Bahman Avenue, Poorsina, Tabriz

Medicine
Pharmacy

Founded 1986. Previously part of the University of Tabriz.

3622 **SHAHEED BEHESHTI UNIVERSITY OF MEDICAL SCIENCES**
P.O. Box 19395, Tehran
Telephone: 214111
Chancellor: Fereidoun Azizi
Vice-Chancellor of Administration and Finance: M. Nobakht

S. of Medicine
Dean: M. Noorisafa *staff* 396
S. of Dentistry
Dean: M. Dahlaie *staff* 91
S. of Nutrition and Food Science
Dean: M. Balaghi *staff* 25
S. of Pharmacy
Dean: M. Fanaie; *staff* 7
S. of Nursing and Midwifery
Dean: Mrs. Ghaem-maghami; *staff* 18
S. of Allied Health
Dean: M. Sharafi; *staff* 44
Also teaching hospitals.

Founded 1960 as Iran National University. Acquired present status and title 1986. Responsible to the Ministry of Health and Medical Education. Governing body: the Supreme Council of Higher Education. Residential facilities for students.

Academic Year: September to June (September-January; February-June).

Admission Requirements: Secondary school certificate and entrance examination.

Language of Instruction: Persian.

Degrees and Diplomas: Bachelor, 4 yrs. Master, a further 3 yrs. Doctor of–Philosophy, Ph.D., a further 3 yrs; Medicine, 7 yrs. Residency, 3 yrs after Doctor of Medicine.

Libraries: School libraries, total, *c.* 40,000 vols; teaching hospitals, 25,000 vols.

Publication: Journal of the Faculty of Medicine

Academic Staff, 1990:

Rank	Full-time
Instructors	191
Assistant Professors	348
Associate Professors	45
Professors	36
Total	620

Student Enrolment, 1990:

	Men	Women	Total
Of the country	5162	4452	9614

3623 **UNIVERSITY OF MEDICAL SCIENCES**
Martyr Beheshti, Urmia

Medicine

Founded 1986. Previously part of the University of Urmia.

3624 **UNIVERSITY OF MEDICAL SCIENCES**
Bafgh Road, Safaeeyeh, Yazd

3625 **UNIVERSITY OF MEDICAL SCIENCES OF SISTAN AND BALUCHESTAN**
Goorband Road, Zaneden

Medicine

Founded 1986. Previously part of the University of Sistan and Baluchstan.

Other Institutions

3626 **UNIVERSITY COMPLEX OF ART**
499 Vali Asr Street, Tehran
Telephone: 641-202; 644-409

Art (including Textile and Graphic Design, Cinema and Television,) Drama, Scenography, and Interior Design

Founded 1960 as college. Acquired present status and title 1980. A State institution responsible to the Ministry of Culture and Higher Education. Residential facilities for students.

Academic Year: October to June (October-February; February-June).

Admission Requirements: Secondary school certificate and entrance examination.

Fees: None.

Language of Instruction: Persian.

Degrees and Diplomas: Bachelor of Arts. Master.

Library: Central Library.

Academic Staff: c. 50 (50).

Student Enrolment: c. 630.

3627 **BIRJAND COMPLEX CENTRE**
Birjand

Founded 1975.

3628 **DEH-KHODA HIGHER EDUCATIONAL COMPLEX**
University Avenue, Ghazvin

3629 **LORESTAN HIGHER EDUCATIONAL COMPLEX**
Enghelab Avenue, Khorramn Abad

3630 **ZANJAN HIGHER EDUCATIONAL COMPLEX**
6th Kilometer of Tabriz Road, Zanjan

Founded 1975.

3631 **ARAK HIGHER EDUCATIONAL RESEARCH COMPLEX**
Martyr Shiroodi Avenue, Arak

Founded 1986.

3632 **BUSHEHR HIGHER EDUCATIONAL RESEARCH COMPLEX**
Bushehr

Founded 1986.

3633 **HORMOZGAN HIGHER EDUCATIONAL RESEARCH COMPLEX**
Iman Khomeini Boulevard, Bandar Abbas

Founded 1983.

3634 **LORESTAN HIGHER EDUCATIONAL RESEARCH COMPLEX**
Enghelab Avenue, Khorram Abad

Founded 1983.

3635 **SANANDAJ HIGHER EDUCATIONAL RESEARCH COMPLEX**
Towheed Hospital, Sanandaj

Founded 1978.

3636 **SEMNAN HIGHER EDUCATIONAL RESEARCH COMPLEX**
17th of Shahrivar Avenue, Semnan

3637 **SHAHROOD HIGHER EDUCATIONAL RESEARCH COMPLEX**
Railway Road, Shahrood

Founded 1975.

3638 **ZANJAN HIGHER EDUCATIONAL RESEARCH COMPLEX**
Parvin Etesami, Zanjan

Founded 1986.

3639 **COLLEGE OF INTERNATIONAL RELATIONS**
North of Ostad Nejatollahi Avenue, Rahbar Alley, Tehran

Founded 1982.

3640 **COLLEGE OF I.R.I.B.**
Martyr Khaled Eslamboli Avenie, I. Alley, Tehran

3641 **COLLEGE OF JUDICIAL LAW AND ADMINISTRATIVE SERVICES**
Enghelab Avenue/Khark, Tehran

Founded 1981.

3642 **ABADAN COLLEGE OF PETROLEUM**
National Islamic Republic of Iral Oil Company, Abadan

Petroleum Engineering

3643 **SCHOOL OF CIVIL AVIATION**
Mehr-Abad Airport, Meraj Avenue, Tehran

Founded 1961.

3644 **SCHOOL OF INDUSTRIAL SAFETY AND OCCUPATIONAL HEALTH**
Vali-Asr Avenue, Esteghlal Hotel Avenue, Tehran

Occupational Safety of Techniques

Founded 1975. Responsible to the Ministry of Culture and Higher Education and Labour and Social Affairs.

Academic Year: September to June (September-January; January-June).

Admission Requirements: Secondary school certificate.

Fees: None.

Language of Instruction: Persian.

Degrees and Diplomas: Diploma, 2 yrs.

Library: c. 10,000 vols.

Publication: Journal (quarterly).

Academic Staff: c. 20 (20).

Student Enrolment: c. 170.

3645 **SCHOOL OF JUDICIAL LAW**
Salariyeh, Ghom

Founded 1984.

3646 **SCHOOL OF MARTYR MOTAHARI**
Bahrestan Square, Tehran

Founded 1981.

3647 **SCHOOL OF MINING**
Shahroud
Telephone: (02731) 6000;

Mining

Founded 1974. Residential facilities for academic staff and students.

Academic Year: September to June (September-January; February-June).

Admission Requirements: Secondary school certificate and entrance examination.

Fees: None.

Language of Instruction: Persian.

Degrees and Diplomas: Diplomas, 2 yrs.

Library: c. 1000 vols.

Academic Staff: c. 5 (20).

Student Enrolment: c. 70 (Men).

3648 **NATIONAL BANK OF IRAN SCHOOL OF NURSING**
Ferdowsi Avenue, National Bank Building, Tehran
Telephone: 323980; 311361/8
Director: Fatemeh Zaimi

Nursing

Founded 1974.

Degrees and Diplomas: Bachelor of Science in Nursing, 4 yrs.
Academic Staff, 1986-87: 13 (20).
Student Enrolment, 1986-87: 140 (Women).

3649 **INSTITUTE OF PSYCHIC MEDICINE**
Taleghani Avenue, Jahan Alley, Tehran

Founded 1977.

3650 **SCHOOL OF TECHNOLOGY**
17th of Shahrivar Boulevard, Semnan

Founded 1973.

3651 **AHWAZ TECHNICAL SCHOOL**
20th Kianpars Avenue, Ahwaz

Founded 1967.

3652 **BAKTARAN TECHNICAL SCHOOL**
Martyr Jafari Avenue, Bakhtaran

Founded 1976.

3653 **ESFAHAN TECHNICAL SCHOOL**
Shiraz Gate, Esfahan

Founded 1973.

3654 **HAMMEDAN TECHNICAL SCHOOL**
2nd Kilometer of Shorin Road, Hammedan

Founded 1978.

3655 **KASHAN TECHNICAL SCHOOL**
6th Kilometer of Ravand Road, Kashan

Founded 1975.

3656 **KERMAN TECHNICAL SCHOOL**
Shahab Avenue, Kerman

Founded 1975.

3657 **MASHHAD TECHNICAL SCHOOL**
Reza City, Taleghani Road, Mashhad

Founded 1967.

3658 **RASHT TECHNICAL SCHOOL**
Rooman Road, Rasht

Founded 1986.

3659 **SANANDAJ TECHNICAL SCHOOL**
Pasdaran Avenue, Sanandaj

Founded 1974.

3660 **SARI TECHNICAL SCHOOL**
Khazar Abad Boulevard, Tabarestan Alley, Sari

Founded 1975.

3661 **SHIRAZ TECHNICAL SCHOOL**
Horr Avenue, Shiraz

Founded 1967.

3662 **TABRIZ TECHNICAL SCHOOL**
Tabriz

Founded 1979.

3663 **TEHRAN TECHNICAL SCHOOL NO. 1**
Ray Avenue, Tehran

Founded 1976.

3664 **TEHRAN TECHNICAL SCHOOL NO. 2**
Vanak Square, Brazil Avenue, Tehran

Founded 1975.

3665 **TEHRAN TECHNICAL SCHOOL NO. 3**
Pasdaran Avenue, Sokhandan Avenue, Tehran

Founded 1967.

3666 **TEHRAN TECHNICAL SCHOOL FOR WOMEN**
Damavand Avenue, Tehran

Founded 1983.

3667 **TOWHEED TECHNICAL SCHOOL**
45th Kilometer of Esfahan Road, Shahre Kord, Esfahan

Founded 1986.

3668 **URMIA TECHNICAL SCHOOL**
Sarve Road, Urmia

Founded 1970.

3669 **YAZD TECHNICAL SCHOOL**
Students' Boulevard, Yazd

Founded 1973.

3670 **ZAHEDAN TECHNICAL SCHOOL**
Goorhand 1st Boulevard, Zahedan
Telephone: 0541-4920

Civil Engineering
Electrical Engineering

Founded 1978. A State institution responsible to the Ministry of Culture and Higher Education. Residential facilities for students.

Academic Year: September to June (September-February; February-June).

Admission Requirements: Secondary school certificate and entrance examination.

Fees: None.

Language of Instruction: Persian.

Degrees and Diplomas: Associate. Diploma, 2 yrs.

Library: c. 2000 vols.

Academic Staff: c. 10 (20).

Student Enrolment: c. 140 (Men).

IRAQ

Universities

3671 **UNIVERSITY OF AL-ANBAR**
Al-Anbar

C. of Education
C. of Education (for girls)
C. of Science
C. of Medicine

Founded 1988.

Academic Year: September to June (September-January; February-June).

Admission Requirements: Secondary school certificate or equivalent.

3672 ***AL-JAMI'AT AL-MUSTANSIRIYAH**
Al-Mustansiriyah University
Waziriyah, Baghdad
Telex: 2066
Telephone: 4168511
President: Riadh Hamid Al-Dabbagh (1982-)

C. of Arts (including Modern Languages, Library Science, and Psychology)
Dean: Hammed Macklif El Heeti
C. of Science
Dean: Adel Shakir Al Tai
C. of Administration and Economics (including Tourism)
Dean: Muthana Taka Eeeedeen Al-Houri
C. of Medicine (including Pharmacy)
Dean: Dawood Ahmen Al Iani
C. of Education
Dean: Salman Ahmen Salman Al Jenabi
C. of Medicine (Kufa)
Dean: Thafir Daoud Salman
C. of Islamic Law
Dean: Adnan Ali Al Bakoa
I. of National and Socialist Studies
Director: Nasar Abdel Latif Al-Hadithi
A. of Fine Arts
Director: Abd Al Rahman Al Gailani
I. of Asian and African Studies
Director: Sabah Mahmoud Mohamed
C. of Engineering (including Architecture)
Dean: Mohamed Ali Abd Al Razzaq Al Aws

Founded 1963 by the Republic of Iraq Teachers' Union. Merged by government decree with Al-Sha'ab University 1964 to form University College and became part of University of Baghdad. Accorded independent status as a private university by the government 1965. Became a State university 1974. Financed by the government. Residential facilities for students.

Arrangements for co-operation with the Universities of: Cairo; United Arab Emirates; Rennes II; Kuwait.

Academic Year: September to June (September-January; February-June).

Admission Requirements: Secondary school certificate or equivalent.

Fees: None.

Languages of Instruction: Arabic and English.

Degrees and Diplomas: Bachelor of–Arts; Science, 4 yrs. Master of–Arts; Science, 1 ½-3 yrs after Bachelor. Also postgraduate Diplomas, 2 yrs.

Libraries: Central Library, *c.* 120,000 vols; libraries of the colleges and institutes.

Publications: College of Arts Magazine; College of Business Administration and Economics Magazine (both monthly).

Academic Staff: c. 430.

Student Enrolment: c. 11,000.

3673 **UNIVERSITY OF AL-QADISIYA**
P.O. Box 381, Diwania, Al-Qadisiya
Telex: 216500 UNQAD
Telephone: (366) 28066
President: J.M. Al-Aubaidi

C. of Education
Dean: Sattam H. Al-Jebori; *staff* 49 (1)
C. of Administration and Economics
Dean: Kh. K. Hmood; *staff* 25 (1)
C. of Art
Dean: Mohsen Al-Mudhaffar; *staff* 16 (1)

Founded 1988. An autonomous state institution under central supervision of the Ministry of Higher Education and Scientific Research. Governing body: the University Council. Residential facilities for academic staff and students (planned).

Academic Year: September to June (September-January; February-June).

Admission Requirements: Secondary school certificate or equivalent.

Fees: None.

Languages of Instruction: Arabic and English.

Degrees and Diplomas: Bachelor, 4 yrs.

Library: Central library, 27,604 vols.

Special Facilities (Museums, etc.): Geographical Museum; Geological Museum; Historical Museum.

Academic Staff, 1989-90: 86.

Student Enrolment, 1989-90:

	Men	Women	Total
Of the country	655	350	1005
Of other countries	14	–	14
Total	669	350	1019

3674 ***JAMI'AT BAGHDAD**
University of Baghdad
Jadyriya, Baghdad
Telephone: 93091
President: Taha T. Al-Naimi

C. of Law and Political Science
C. of Arts (including Sociology, Psychology, Languages, Islamic Studies, Archaeology and Journalism)
C. of Education
C. of Agriculture
C. of Science
C. of Medicine
C. of Pharmacy
C. of Dentistry
C. of Veterinary Medicine
C. of Alsharea' (Islamic Law and Sciences)
C. of Nursing
C. of Administration and Economics
C. of Physical Education
C. of Engineering (including Architecture)
A. of Fine Arts
Ce. of Psychiatry
Research Ce. for Palestinian Studies
Ce. of Psychology and Educational Research
Ce. of Natural History Research
Arab-Scientific Research Ce.
Ce. for Urban and Regional Planning
Administration and Economics Research Ce.
Medical Research Ce.
Dental Research Ce.
Computer Ce.

Founded 1958 as a State university incorporating existing colleges established between 1908 and 1952. Branches in Mosul and Basrah detached to form separate universities 1967. Reorganized 1969 when ten colleges were merged to form four new colleges of Law and Political Science, Administration and Economics, Arts, and Agriculture and Veterinary Medicine. In

1970 placed under the authority of the Ministry of Higher Education and Scientific Research. Financed by the government. Governing body: the University Council. Some residential facilities for students.

Academic Year: September to May (September-January; February-May).

Admission Requirements: Secondary school certificate or equivalent.

Fees: None.

Languages of Instruction: Arabic and English.

Degrees and Diplomas: Bachelor of Arts, B.A., 4 yrs; Bachelor of Sciences, B.Sc., 4-6 yrs. Master of Arts, M.A.; Master of Science, M.Sc., 2 yrs after Bachelor. Doctor of Medicine, 6 yrs.

Libraries: Central Library, *c.* 270,000 vols; libraries of the colleges and institutes.

Special Facilities (Museums, etc.): Natural History.

Publication: College Bulletins.

Press or Publishing House: University Press.

Academic Staff: *c.* 1990.

Student Enrolment: *c.* 35,300.

3675 **JAMI'AT AL-BASRAH**

University of Basrah
Garmat Ali, Basrah
Telex: 207025 IK
Telephone: 417 951

President: Dakhil Hassan Jerew (1985-)
Assistant to the President: Mohamed A. Al-Najim

C. of Science (including Computer Sciences)
Dean: Gorgis A.A. Adam; *staff* 158
C. of Engineering
Dean: Qais Baqir Merzah
C. of Medicine (including Pharmacy)
Dean: Khalil A. Maki; *staff* 92
C. of Agriculture (including Animal Husbandry and Food Technology)
Dean: Nazar A. Shukri; *staff* 139
C. of Economics and Administration
Dean: Abdul Sattar M. Al-Ali; *staff* 66
C. of Arts (including Arab and English Languages, and Library Science)
Dean: Kahtan A. Al-Hudethi; *staff* 74
C. of Education
Dean: Reyadh S. Naom; *staff* 176
C. of Physical Education
Dean: Raysan K. Majeed; *staff* 29
C. of Law
Dean: Fakhri R. Al-Mehana; *staff* 10
Ce. for Arab Gulf Studies
Head: Kahtan S. Al-Nassiri
Computer Ce.
Head: Sabah Abdul Azeez Ali
Ce. for Marine Sciences
Director: Najah A. Hussein

Founded 1964, comprising colleges forming part of the University of Baghdad. Became independent university 1967. Under the jurisdiction of the Ministry of Higher Education and Scientific Research and financed by the government. Governing body: the University Council. Residential facilities for *c.* 4550 students.

Arrangements for co-operation with: University of Rostock; Technical University of Gdańsk; University Paul-Sabatier, Toulouse; University of Zagreb; University of Wrocław.

Academic Year: September to June (September-January; February-June).

Admission Requirements: Secondary school certificate or equivalent.

Fees: None.

Languages of Instruction: Arabic and English.

Degrees and Diplomas: Bachelor of–Arts, B.A.; Science, B.Sc., 4 yrs; Veterinary Medicine and Surgery, B.V.M.S., 5 yrs; Medicine and Surgery, M.B., Ch.B., 6 yrs. Master of–Arts, M.A.; Science, M.Sc., 2-4 further yrs. Doctorate, Ph.D. in–Science; Arts. Also higher diploma in Engineering, 1 yr.

Libraries: Central Library, 123,000 vols; 10 specialized libraries, *c.* 594,000.

Special Facilities (Museums, etc.): Natural History Museum..

Publications: Centre for Arab Gulf Studies Journal; Iraqi Journal of Marine Science; Iranian Studies.

Press or Publishing House: Publishing House of Basrah University.

Academic Staff, 1986-87:

Rank	Full-time
Ustaz (Professors)	6
Associate Professors	4
Ustaz Musaeed (Assistant Professors)	77
Mudarees (Lecturers)	324
Mudarees Musaeed (Assistant Lecturers)	259
Total	670

Student Enrolment, 1986-87:

	Men	Women	Total
Of the country	2211	1274	3485
Of other countries	55	8	63
Total	2266	1282	3548

3676 **UNIVERSITY OF KUFA**

P.O. Box 21, Kufa
Telex: 216304 KF UNI IK
Telephone: 346 109
Fax: 346 049

President: Yehya Taufik Al Rawi
Director, Student Affairs: Hadi Mohammed Abd Al Rawi

C. of Education (for girls)
Dean: Bassiem Kathem Habbeeib; *staff* 34 (8)
C. of Fine Arts Education
Dean: Nusaief Jasem Al Delamy; *staff* 43 (8)
C. of Alfikih
Dean: Abd Al Ammeer Al Aasam; *staff* 19 (8)
C. of Art
Dean: Malik Ebrageem Al Delamy; *staff* 16
C. of Science
Dean: Fuozy Shnawah Al Zubaidy; *staff* 35
C. of Engineering
Dean: Fadiel Mohammad Hasson
C. of Law
Dean: Ali Khalieb Al Aany; *staff* 11 (5)
C. of Medicine
Dean: Thafeer Dawood Salman; *staff* 83
Ce. for Ancient Law Studies
Dean: Ali Khalieb Al Aanny; *staff* 2
Saddam Ce. for Embryology and Infertility Research and Treatment
Dean: Munthir Barazanji; *staff* 5
Ut. for Lifelong Education

Founded 1988. Governing body: the University Council.

Academic Year: September to June (September-January; February-June).

Admission Requirements: Secondary school certificate or equivalent.

Fees: None.

Languages of Instruction: Arabic and English.

Degrees and Diplomas: Bachelor, 4 yrs. Master, a further 2 yrs. Also higher diploma, 1-2 yrs.

Publications: Journal (annually); Kufa Medical Journal (biannually).

Academic Staff, 1989:

Rank	Full-time
Professors	12
Assistant Professors	33
Lecturers	107
Assistant Lecturers	111
Total	263

Student Enrolment, 1989-90:

	Men	Women	Total
Of the country	2164	1054	3218
Of other countries	42	10	52
Total	2206	1064	3270

3677 ***JAMI'AT AL-MOSUL**

University of Mosul
Mosul
Telex: 8015 ENGCOLMO

President: Mohammed Majeed Al-Sa'eed (1978-)

C. of Medicine (including Pharmacy)
C. of Engineering
C. of Science
C. of Agriculture and Forestry

C. of Arts
C. of Administration and Economics
C. of Education
C. of Veterinary Medicine
C. of Physical Education
C. of Dentistry
C. of Law
Computer Ce.

Founded 1967, comprising colleges formerly part of the University of Baghdad. A State institution financed by the government. Governing body: the University Council. Some residential facilities for academic staff and students.

Academic Year: September to June (September-January; February-June).

Admission Requirements: Secondary school certificate or equivalent.

Fees: None

Languages of Instruction: Arabic, English, and French.

Degrees and Diplomas: Bachelor of–Arts, B.A.; Sciences, B.Sc., 4-6 yrs. Master of–Arts, M.A.; Science, M.Sc., 2 yrs after Bachelor. Doctorate, Ph-D. in Agriculture and Forestry (Field Crops).

Libraries: Central Library, *c.* 250,000 vols; libraries of the colleges.

Special Facilities (Museums, etc.): Museums: Science History; Folklore; Fine Arts.

Publications: Abstracts of Science; Journal of Tannilat Al-Rafidian.

Academic Staff: c. 1200.

Student Enrolment: c. 22,000.

3678 **JAMI'AT AL-SALAHADDIN**

University of Salahaddin
Erbil
Cables: Zanco
Telex: 218510
Telephone: (566) 21422
President: Khusrow Ghani Shali (1980-)

C. of Science
C. of Engineering
C. of Agriculture (including Animal Husbandry)
C. of Arts (including Arabic and Kurdish Languages, and Social Science)
C. of Administration
C. of Education
C. of Medicine

Founded 1968 as an independent State institution financed by the government. Formerly titled University of Sulaymaniyah. Governing body: the University Council. Some residential facilities for academic staff and students.

Arrangements for co-operation with the Universities of: Yarmouk; Cracow; Mohammed V, Rabat; Ljubljana.

Academic Year: September to June (September-February; February-June).

Admission Requirements: Secondary school certificate or equivalent.

Fees: None.

Languages of Instruction: Arabic and English.

Degrees and Diplomas: Bachelor of–Arts; Science in–Agriculture; Science; Engineering; Education; Administration; Social Sciences; Geology; Kurdish Studies, 4 yrs. Master of Science, 2 yrs after Bachelor.

Libraries: Central Library, *c.* 100,000 vols; libraries of the colleges.

Publications: University of Salahaddin–Statistical Abstract; Bulletin; Zanco-Scientific Journal (annually); Humanities.

Press or Publishing House: University Press.

Academic Staff: c. 540 (20).

Student Enrolment: c. 5850.

3679 **AL-JAMI'AT AL-TECHNOLOGIA**

University of Technology
P.O. Box 35010, Baghdad
Cables: Unitech
Telex: 2149
Telephone: 719 60 21
President: Ahmed Bashir Al Naib (1981-)

S. of Mechanical Engineering
Head: Hesham Tawfiq; *staff* 58 (6)
S. of Electrical Engineering
Head: Sahib R. Alwash; *staff* 24 (28)
S. of Building and Construction Engineering
Head: Ilham Al Nouri; *staff* 48 (5)
S. of Applied Sciences
Head: Alae Al Naimi; *staff* 40 (12)
S. of Technical Education
Head: Ramzi B. Abdul-Ahad; *staff* 80 (29)
S. of Production Engineering and Metallurgy
Head: Dhia Shanshal; *staff* 34 (12)
S. of Control and Systems Technology (including Computer Sciences)
Head: Tarik Hameed S. Al Baldawi; *staff* 31 (24)
S. of Chemical Engineering
Head: Mohammed Salah Hameed; *staff* 32 (6)
S. of Architecture
Head: Muamm al A. Ibrahim; *staff* 22 (12)
Ce. for Lifelong Education
Head: M.S. Nasralla; *staff* 1 (120)
D. of Computer Sciences
Head: Khalid Jirjis Aldhaimi; *staff* 11

Founded 1960, and attached to the University of Baghdad 1969 as College of Engineering, became independent university with present title and status 1975. A State institution financed by the government. Governing body: the Council. Residential facilities for students.

Arrangements for co-operation with the Universities of: McGill; Dresden; Compiègne; São Paulo.

Academic Year: September to July (September-January; February-July).

Admission Requirements: Secondary school certificate.

Fees: None.

Languages of Instruction: Arabic and English.

Degrees and Diplomas: Bachelor of Science, B.Sc., 4-5 yrs. Master of Science, M.Sc., 2 yrs after Bachelor.

Library: c. 30,000 vols.

Publication: Engineering and Technology.

Press or Publishing House: University Press.

Academic Staff, 1987:

Rank	Full-time	Part-time
Professors	5	–
Assistant Professors	35	–
Lecturers	140	60
Assistant Lecturers	200	50
Total	385	110

Student Enrolment, 1988:

	Men	Women	Total
Of the country	5670	1680	7350
Of other countries	300	50	350
Total	5970	1730	7700

3680 **UNIVERSITY OF TIKRIT**

Tikrit

C. of Engineering
C. of Education (for girls)
C. of Medicine

Founded 1988.

Academic Year: September to June (September-January; February-June).

Admission Requirements: Secondary school certificate or equivalent.

Other Institutions

3681 **INSTITUTE OF ADMINISTRATION**

Al-Risafa, Baghdad

Administration

Founded 1969. A State institution attached to the Foundation of Technical Institutes. Governing body: the Council. Residential facilities for students.

Academic Year: September to June (September-January; February-May).

Admission Requirements: Secondary school certificate.

Fees: None.

Languages of Instruction: Arabic and English.

Degrees and Diplomas: Diploma, 2 yrs.

Academic Staff: c. 100.

Student Enrolment: c. 1300.

3682 **INSTITUTE OF APPLIED ARTS**

Baghdad

Applied Arts
Founded 1969. A State institution attached to the Foundation of Technical Institutes. Governing body: the Council. Residential facilities for students.
Academic Year: September to June (September-January; February-May).
Admission Requirements: Secondary school certificate.
Fees: None.
Languages of Instruction: Arabic and English.
Degrees and Diplomas: Diploma, 2 yrs.
Academic Staff: c. 50.
Student Enrolment: c. 100.

3683 **INSTITUTE OF TECHNICAL TRAINERS**
Baghdad
Founded 1986.
Academic Year: September to June (September-January; February-May).
Admission Requirements: Secondary school certificate.

3684 **INSTITUTE OF TECHNOLOGY**
Zafarania, Baghdad
Telephone: 7731491
D. of Industrial Chemistry
D. of Surveyancy
D. of Mechanical Engineering
D. of Electrical Engineering
D. of Civil Engineering
D. of Teacher Training (Technical)
Founded 1969. A State institution attached to the Foundation of Technical Institutes. Governing body: the Council. Residential facilities for *c.* 1090 students.
Academic Year: September to June (September-January; February-June).
Admission Requirements: Secondary school certificate.
Fees: None.
Languages of Instruction: Arabic and English.
Degrees and Diplomas: Diplomas, 2 yrs.
Library: c. 42,450 vols.
Academic Staff: c. 190.
Student Enrolment: c. 3280.

3685 **TECHNICAL INSTITUTE OF ADMINISTRATION**
Al-Karkh, Baghdad
Administration
Founded 1976. A State institution attached to the Foundation of Technical Institutes. Governing body: the Council. Residential facilities for students.
Academic Year: September to June (September-January; February-May).
Admission Requirements: Secondary school certificate.
Fees: None.
Languages of Instruction: Arabic and English.
Degrees and Diplomas: Diploma, 2 yrs.
Academic Staff: c. 30.
Student Enrolment: c. 200.

3686 **TECHNICAL INSTITUTE**
Al-Huwayja
D. of Technology
Founded 1980.

3687 **TECHNICAL INSTITUTE**
Al-Kufa
D. of Technology
Founded 1988.

3688 **TECHNICAL INSTITUTE**
Al-Misayab, Babylon
Agriculture (including Animal Husbandry and Horticulture)
Founded 1979.

3689 **TECHNICAL INSTITUTE**
P.O. Box 3, Kufah, Al Najaf
Cables: Techman
Telephone: 20938 (Ext. 0334)
D. of Office Management
D. of Accountancy
D. of Mechanical Engineering
D. of Electrical Engineering
D. of Civil Engineering
Founded 1978. A State institution attached to the Foundation of Technical Institutes. Governing body: the Council. Residential facilities for academic staff and students.
Academic Year: September to June (September-January; February-June).
Admission Requirements: Secondary school certificate.
Fees: None.
Languages of Instruction: Arabic and English.
Degrees and Diplomas: Diplomas, 2 yrs.
Library: c. 9000 vols.
Academic Staff: c. 50 (20).
Student Enrolment: c. 910.

3690 **TECHNICAL INSTITUTE**
Baghdad Street, Al-Nassirya
Telephone: 042-231315
D. of Technology
D. of Management (including Accountancy)
Founded 1980. A State institution attached to the Foundation of Technical Institutes. Residential facilities for academic staff and students.
Academic Year: September to June (September-January; February-June).
Admission Requirements: Secondary school certificate.
Fees: None.
Languages of Instruction: Arabic and English.
Degrees and Diplomas: Diplomas, 2 yrs.
Academic Staff: c. 20.
Student Enrolment: c. 40.

3691 **TECHNICAL INSTITUTE**
Al-Ramadi
D. of Technology
D. of Office Management (including Accountancy)
Founded 1978. A State institution attached to the Foundation of Technical Institutes. Governing body: the Council. Residential facilities for students.
Academic Year: September to June (September-January; February-May).
Admission Requirements: Secondary school certificate.
Fees: None.
Languages of Instruction: Arabic and English.
Degrees and Diplomas: Diplomas, 2 yrs.
Academic Staff: c. 40.
Student Enrolment: c. 300.

3692 **TECHNICAL INSTITUTE**
Al-Shabra, Thikar
Agriculture (including Animal Husbandry and Horticulture)
Founded 1979.

3693 **TECHNICAL INSTITUTE**
Al-Taamim
D. of Technology
Founded 1976.

3694 **TECHNICAL INSTITUTE**
Basrah
D. of Electrical Engineering
D. of Civil Engineering
D. of Mechanical Engineering
D. of Industrial Chemistry
D. of Management
D. of Accountancy
Founded 1973 as Institute of Technology. Acquired present title 1977. A State institution attached to the Foundation of Technical Institutes. Governing body: the Council. Residential facilities for students.
Academic Year: September to June (September-January; February-May).

Admission Requirements: Secondary school certificate.
Fees: None.
Languages of Instruction: Arabic and English.
Degrees and Diplomas: Diplomas, 2 yrs.
Academic Staff: *c.* 90.
Student Enrolment: *c.* 800.

3695 **TECHNICAL INSTITUTE**
Hilla

D. of Office Management
D. of Accountancy
D. of Technology
Founded 1976. A State institution attached to the Foundation of Technical Institutes. Governing body: the Council. Residential facilities for students.
Academic Year: September to June (September-February; March-June).
Admission Requirements: Secondary school certificate.
Fees: None.
Languages of Instruction: Arabic and English.
Degrees and Diplomas: Diplomas, 2 yrs.
Academic Staff: *c.* 100.
Student Enrolment: *c.* 1100.

3696 **TECHNICAL INSTITUTE**
Misan

D. of Technology
Founded 1979.

3697 **TECHNICAL INSTITUTE**
Mosul
Telex: 5603
Telephone: 81891

D. of Civil Engineering
D. of Electrical Engineering
D. of Mechanical Engineering
D. of Industrial Chemistry
D. of Office Management
D. of Store Management
D. of Accountancy
D. of Clinical Pathology
Founded 1976. A State institution attached to the Foundation of Technical Institutes. Governing body: the Council. Residential facilities for academic staff and *c.* 1000 students.
Academic Year: September to June (September-January; February-June).
Admission Requirements: Secondary school certificate.
Fees: None.
Languages of Instruction: Arabic and English.
Degrees and Diplomas: Diplomas, 2 yrs.
Library: *c.* 22,000 vols.
Academic Staff: *c.* 160.
Student Enrolment: *c.* 1600.

3698 **TECHNICAL INSTITUTE**
Namrood, Naynawa

Agriculture (including Animal Husbandry and Horticulture)
Founded 1980.

3699 **TECHNICAL INSTITUTE**
Wasit

Agriculture (including Animal Husbandry and Horticulture)
Founded 1980.

3700 **TECHNICAL INSTITUTE OF MEDICINE**
Baghdad
Telephone: 888-5153-4

Medicine
Dentistry
Nursing
Founded 1967. A State institution attached to the Foundation of Technical Institutes. Residential facilities for students.
Academic Year: September to June (September-January; February-May).
Admission Requirements: Secondary school certificate.
Fees: None.
Languages of Instruction: Arabic and English.
Degrees and Diplomas: Diploma, 2 yrs.
Library: *c.* 4900 vols.
Academic Staff: *c.* 330.
Student Enrolment: *c.* 780.

IRELAND

Universities and University Colleges

3701 ***THE UNIVERSITY OF DUBLIN, TRINITY COLLEGE**
Dublin 2
Cables: Trinity, Dublin
Telex: DUBLIN 93782 TCD EI
Telephone: 772 941
Fax: 772 694
Provost: William Arthur Watts (1981-91)

F. of Arts (Humanities)
Dean: Patrick Hyde Kelly; *staff* 65
D. of Arts (Letters)
Dean: Barbara Wright; *staff* 61
F. of Business, Economic and Social Studies
Dean: Brian Torode; *staff* 41
F. of Engineering and Systems Sciences
Dean: Simon Herbert Perry; *staff* 65
F. of Health Science (Medicine and Dentistry)
Dean: Ian Jesse Temperley; *staff* 79
F. of Science
Dean: Denis Lawrence Weaire; *staff* 128
F. of Graduate Studies
Dean: Helga Herta Wilhelmine Robinson Hammerstein
Graduate S. of Engineering Studies (evening courses)
Director: Bernard Corbally
Irish S. of Ecumenics
Director: John D'Arcy May; *staff* 3 (4)
Church of Ireland Theological C.
Principal: John Raymond Bartlett; *staff* 4
Irish Management I.
Director-General: Maurice O'Grady *staff* 28
I. of Public Administration
Director-General: John Gallagher; *staff* 33
Dublin C. of Music
Principal: Frank Henegan; *staff* 44 (96)
Royal Irish A. of Music
Director: Lindsay Armstrong; *staff* 22 (13)
Also 4 Teacher Training Colleges.

Founded and incorporated 1592 by royal charter as 'mater universitatis'. As no other college has been founded, University of Dublin and Trinity College are interchangeable terms. Financially supported by the Department of Education. Governing bodies: the Board, responsible for general government of the college; the University Council, responsible for academic matters. Membership of both bodies is drawn from the academic and senior administrative staff. There are alsostudent observers. Residential facilities for academic staff and students.

Arrangements for co-operation for joint research with other universities including collaboration with industry. Special arrangements with universities in North America and Europe. Also participates in the ERASMUS programme with most of the E.C. countries.

Academic Year: September to July (September-December; January-March; March-July).

Admission Requirements: Irish Leaving Certificate with matriculation, or equivalent.

Fees (Pounds): Registration, 145; tuition, 1262-1564 (E.C.); 4200-10,500 (non E.C.) according to field of study.

Language of Instruction: English.

Degrees and Diplomas: Bachelor in–Education (pass), B.Ed.(pass); Theology (pass), B.Th.(pass), 3 yrs; Arts (honors), B.A.(honors); Education (honors), B.Ed.(honors); Education (Home Economics), B.Ed.(Home Econ.); Music Education, B.Mus.Ed.; Laws, LL.B.; Theology (honors), B.Th.(honors); Business Studies, B.B.S.; Social Studies, B.S.S.; Computer Science, B.Sc.(Comp.) (evening course); Engineering, B.A.I.; Clinical Speech and Language Studies, B.Sc. (Clin.Lang.); Occupational Therapy, B.Sc.(Cur.Occ.); Physiotherapy, B.Sc.(Physio.); Human Nutrition and Dietetics, B.Sc.(Hum.Nut.); Pharmacy, B.Sc.(Pharm.), 4 yrs. Dental Science, B.Dent.Sc., 5 yrs and 1 term. Medicine, Surgery, Obstetrics, M.B., B.Ch., B.A.O., 5-6 yrs. Master in Arts, M.A., 3 yrs after Bachelor of Arts, without further examination. (Not an additional academic qualification but confers seniority). Postgraduate degrees: Bachelor in Divinity, B.D., by examination and dissertation. Master in–Letters, M.Litt., 2 yrs, by research and thesis; Philosophy, M.Phil., (in Anglo-Irish Literature, Applied Linguistics, Reformation and Enlightenment, Textual and Visual Studies, Women's Studies); Philosophy (Ecumenics), M.Phil.(Ecum.); Philosophy (Peace Studies), M.Phil.(Peace Studies); Busines Administration, M.B.A., 1 yr. Education, M.Ed., 2 yrs; Engineering, M.A.I., by research and thesis or by course work with examination and dissertation; Science, M.Sc., 1 yr by research and thesis or by course work with examination and dissertation. Community Health; Counselling Psychology; Engineering; Environmental Science; Management Science; Statistics; Theoretical Physics; Molecular Genetics, 1 yr; Physical Sciences in Medicine, 3 yrs (part-time) Economics, M.Sc.(Econ.) (in Policy Studies); Management, M.Sc.(Mgmt.) (in Business Administration, Management Practics, Organization Behaviour, Strategic Management), 2 yrs part-time; Clinical Biochemistry, 3 yrs; Dental Science, M.Dent. Sc.; Obstetrics, M.A.O.; Surgery, M.Ch.; all by research and thesis. Doctor in–Philosophy, Ph.D., 2-5 yrs; Medicine, M.D. by research and Science, Sc.D.; Letters, Litt.D.; Laws, LL.D.; Divinity, D.D.; Music, Mus.D. Also undergraduate and postgraduate Diplomas in various fields.

Library: Trinity College Library, *c.* 3,000,000 vols.

Special Facilities (Museums, etc.): Weingreen Museum of Biblical Antiquities; Anatomy Museum; Geology Museum; Zoology Museum.

Publications: An introduction to Trinity College; Hermathena (literary and scientific papers) (biannually); The University of Dublin Calendar.

Academic Staff, 1989-90:

Rank	Full-time
Professors	64
Associate Professors	41
Senior Lecturers	129
Lecturers	205
Total	439

Student Enrolment, 1989-90:

	Men	Women	Total
Of the country	3927	4073	8000
Of other countries	337	271	608
Total	4264	4344	8608

3702 ***OLLSCOIL NA HÉIREANN**
NATIONAL UNIVERSITY OF IRELAND
49 Merrion Square, Dublin 2
Cables: Natuniv, Dublin
Telephone: 767246/7
Chancellor: T.K. Whitaker
Vice-Chancellor: Michael P. Mortell

F. of Arts
F. of Philosophy and Sociology
F. of Celtic Studies
F. of Law
F. of Science
F. of Medicine (including Dentistry)
F. of Engineering and Architecture
F. of Commerce
F. of Agriculture
F. of Dairy Science
F. of Veterinary Medicine

Founded 1908, and incorporating existing colleges in Dublin, Cork, and Galway, as constituent Colleges. The university is essentially an examining body and classes are held in the constituent Colleges, in College of St Patrick, Maynooth, and in 4 Colleges of Education. Governing body: the Senate. For further information see following entries.

Degrees and Diplomas: Bachelor of–Arts, B.A. (general or honours); Social Science, B.Soc.Sc.; Music, B.Mus.; Civil Law, B.C.L.; Science, B.Sc.;

Commerce, B.Comm., 3 yrs; Science (honours), B.Sc.hons.; Dairy Science, B.Sc.Dairying, Science (Dairy Science), B.Sc.; Nursing, B.N., B.N.S.; Physiotherapy, B.Physio.; Radiography, B.Radiog.; Engineering, B.E.; Technology, B.Tech.; Agricultural Science, B.Agr.Sc.; Public Administration, B.P.A., 4 yrs; Dental Surgery, B.D.S.; Architecture, B.Arch.; Veterinary Medicine, M.V.B., 5 yrs; Medicine, Surgery, Obstetrics, M.B., B.Ch., B.A.O., 6 yrs. Postgraduate Degrees: Bachelor of Law, LL.B., 2-3 yrs. Master of–Arts, M.A.; Social Science, M.Soc.Sc.; Commerce, M.Econ.Sc., M.Comm., M.B.A.; Science, M.Sc.; Dairy Science, M.Sc. Dairying; Science (Dairy Science), M.Sc.; Engineering, M.Eng.Sc., M.E., M.Eng.Design; Laws, LL.M.; Library and Information Studies,M.L.I.S.; Psychological Science, M.Psych.Sc.; Counselling, M.Couns.; Management Science, M.Mangt.Sc.;Applied Science, M.Appl.Sc.; Business Studies, M.B.S.; Architectural Science, M.Arch.Sc.; Agricultural Science, M.Agr.Sc.; Science (Agriculture), M.Sc.(Agr.); Veterinary Medicine, M.V.M.; Animal Science, M.An.Sc.; Education, M.Ed.; Philosophy, M.Phil. (in Medieval or Irish Studies); Public Administration, M.P.A.; Industrial Engineering, M.Ind.Eng.; Regional and Urban Planning, M.R.U.P., M.U.B.C.; Obstetrics, M.A.O.; Surgery, M.Ch.; Public Health, M.P.H.; Medical Science, M.Med.Sc., Dentistry, M.D.S.; Architecture, M.Arch., Rural Development, M.R.D., 1-5 yrs. Doctor of–Philosophy, Ph.D., 2-5 yrs and thesis; also Literature, D.Litt.; Laws, LL.D.; Science, D.Sc.; Medicine, M.D.; Music, D.Mus.; Economic Science, D.Econ.Sc., 3-5 yrs after Bachelor. Also undergraduate and postgraduate Diplomas in various fields.

3703 **COLAISTE NA HOLLSCOILE, CORCAIGH**
UNIVERSITY COLLEGE, CORK

Cork
Cables: U.C.C. Ireland
Telex: 26050
Telephone: (021) 26871
President: Michael P. Martell (1989-99)

F. of Arts (including Mathematics, Social Sciences, and Education)
Dean: T.J. Dunne
F. of Celtic Studies
Dean: S. Ó Coileáin
F. of Commerce
Dean: E.P. Cahill
F. of Science
Dean: N.S. Murphy
F. of Law
Dean: J.F. O'Connor
F. of Dairy Science
Dean: C. Daly
F. of Engineering
Dean: D.P. Ó Cinnéide
F. of Medicine (including Dentistry)
Dean: C.T. Doyle
C. of Education (Limerick)
D. for Lifelong Education

Founded 1849 as Queen's College Cork, became College of Royal University of Ireland 1880. Incorporated by charter as constituent College of National University of Ireland 1908. Governing bodies: the Governing Body, comprising the President (ex officio), 3 members appointed by the government, 2 members appointed by the Senate of the National University of Ireland, 6 professors elected by the Academic Council, 4 graduates, 3 ex-officio members (Lord Mayor of Cork, Mayors of Limerick and Waterford), 5 members of Munster County Councils, and 4 co-opted members; the Academic Council.

Arrangements for co-operation with the Universities of: Boston; Maine; Rome; Padua; Rennes; Constance.

Academic Year: October to September (October-December; January-March; April-May).

Admission Requirements: Irish Leaving Certificate with matriculation, or equivalent. Students must be 17 years of age or over.

Fees (Pounds): Undergraduate, 1198-2346; postgraduate, 175-2474.

Language of Instruction: English. Additional lectures in Irish where required.

Degrees and Diplomas: See National University of Ireland.

Libraries: College Library, *c.* 350,000 vols; Boole Library, *c.* 480,000 vols.

Publications: Undergraduate Prospectus (annually); Postgraduate Prospectus (every 3-4 years); Calendar (annually).

Press or Publishing House: Cork University Press.

Academic Staff, 1989-90: c. 273 (103).

Student Enrolment: c. 6000.

3704 **UNIVERSITY COLLEGE DUBLIN**

Belfield, Dublin 4
Telex: 32693 EI
Telephone: 693244
President: Patrick Masterson (1986-96)
Registrar: John J. Kelly

F. of Arts
Dean: Donald McQuillan
F. of Law
Dean: James C. Brady
F. of Commerce
Dean: Harold Harrison
F. of Science
Dean: David Brown
F. of Medicine
Dean: Geoffrey Bourke
F. of Engineering and Architecture
Dean: Vincent McCabe
F. of Agriculture (including Horticulture and Forestry)
Dean: Patrick Leo Curran
F. of Veterinary Medicine
Dean: John Hannan
D. of Extramural Studies
Director: Vincent F.J. Kelly

Founded 1851 as Catholic University of Ireland, became college of Royal University of Ireland 1879. Incorporated by charter as constituent College of the National University of Ireland 1908. Governing bodies: the Council, comprising the President (ex officio), 4 members appointed by the government, 3 members appointed by the Senate of the National University of Ireland, 6 members elected by the Academic Council, 6 graduates, the Lord Mayor of the City of Dublin (ex officio), 1 nominee of Dublin City Council, 8 members elected by General Council of County Councils, and 4 co-opted members; the Academic Council.

Arrangements for co-operation with the Universities of: Erlangen; Wuppertal; West Florida; Missouri at Rolla; Stonehill College, Massachusetts; University of Jordan; the Universities of: London; Bristol; Cambridge; Glasgow; Edinburgh; Liverpool; Newcastle-upon-Tyne; Khartoum.

Academic Year: October to May (October-December; January-March; April-May).

Admission Requirements: Irish Leaving Certificate with matriculation, or equivalent. Students must be 17 years of age or over.

Fees (Pounds): 960-1415 per annum, according to field of study. Double for foreign students, except from EC countri

Fees: es.

Language of Instruction: English.

Degrees and Diplomas: See National University of Ireland.

Library: Main Library, *c.* 600,000 vols.

Academic Staff, 1985::

Rank	Full-time	Part-time
Professors	92	13
Associate Professors	32	–
Statutory Lecturers	144	
College Lecturers	278	46
Assistant Lecturers	49	
Other teaching staff	19	–
Folklorists	3	–
Demonstrators, Tutors, etc.	2	146
Total	629	205

Student Enrolment, 1986-87:

	Men	Women	Total
Of the country	5501	4722	10,223
Of other countries	238	149	387
Total	5739	4871	10,610

3705 **COLÁISTE NA HOLLSCOILE, GAILLIMH**
UNIVERSITY COLLEGE, GALWAY

Galway
Telex: 50023
Telephone: (091) 24411
President: Colm Ó hEocha (1975-)
Registrar: P.F. Fottrell

F. of Arts
Dean: G. MacNiocaill; *staff* 80

F. of Celtic Studies
Dean: B. Ó Madaǵain
F. of Commerce
Dean: W.A.K. Warnock; *staff* 19
F. of Engineering
Dean: James H. Calderwood; *staff* 30 (1)
F. of Law
Dean: Dennis J. Driscoll; *staff* 5 (1)
F. of Medicine (including Pharmacy)
Dean: J. Flynn; *staff* 13 (30)
F. of Science (including Agriculture)
Dean: A. Ó Rodaighe; *staff* 74
Board of Extramural Studies

Founded 1845 as Queen's College, Galway, incorporated by charter as constituent College of National Universityof Ireland 1908. Governing body: the Academic Council, comprising the President ex officio, 4 members appointed by the Senate of the National University of Ireland, 4 professors elected by the Academic Council, 4 graduates, 7 representatives of the local authorities, 3 members nominated by the government, and 3 co-opted members.

Academic Year: September to June (September-December; January-March; April-June).

Admission Requirements: Irish Leaving Certificate with matriculation, or equivalent. Students must be 17 years of age or over.

Fees (Pounds): 882-1554, according to field of study. Double for foreign students, except from EEC countries.

Language of Instruction: English.

Degrees and Diplomas: See National University of Ireland.

Library: James Hardiman Library, *c.* 200,000 vols.

Special Facilities (Museums, etc.): James Mitchell Geology Museum.

Press or Publishing House: Galway University Press.

Academic Staff, 1986-87:

Rank	Full-time	Part-time
Professors	44	9
Associate Professors	11	1
Lecturers	99	21
Junior Lecturers	55	–
Others	11	1
Total	220	32

Student Enrolment, 1985-86:

	Men	Women	Total
Of the country	2364	2427	4791
Of other countries	99	61	160
Total	2463	2488	4951*

*Also 1222 external students.

3706 **SAINT PATRICK'S COLLEGE**
Maynooth, County Kildare
Telephone: (01) 285-222
President: Miceal Ledwith (1985-)
Registrar: Peter Carr

F. of Theology
Dean: P.J. McGoldrick; *staff* 21 (3)
F. of Philosophy
Dean: Matthew O'Donnell; *staff* 5
F. of Arts
Dean: Barbara Hayley; *staff* 45 (24)
F. of Science
; *staff* 21 (17)
F. of Celtic Studies
; *staff* 6 (3)

Founded 1795, became Pontifical university 1895 and incorporated by charter as college of the National University of Ireland 1908. Residential facilities for 50 academic staff and 390 students.

Arrangements for co-operation with: University of Ulster. Universities in the U.S.A.

Academic Year: October to June (October-December; January-Easter; Easter-June).

Admission Requirements: Irish Leaving Certificate with matriculation. Fees (Pounds): 850-1000 per annum.

Languages of Instruction: Irish and English.

Degrees and Diplomas: See National University of Ireland.

Library: Total, *c.* 250,000 vols.

Special Facilities (Museums, etc.): Museum of Ecclesiastical Affairs.

Academic Staff, 1986-87:

Rank	Full-time	Part-time
Professors	23	–
Senior Lecturers	12	–
Lecturers	54	33
Junior Lecturers	5	–
Total	94	33

Student Enrolment, 1986-87: 2100.

3707 ***DUBLIN CITY UNIVERSITY**
Glasnevin, Dublin 9
Telex: 30690 DCU EI
Telephone: (353 1) 370-077
Fax: (353 1) 360-830
Director: Daniel O'Hare (1977-)
Registrar: Michael Gleeson

S. of Business (Accountancy and Finance)
Head: D. Keating; *staff* 13 (6)
S. of Business (Management)
Head: P. Chisnall; *staff* 14 (13)
S. of Applied Languages (French, German, Spanish, Japanese, English as a Foreign Language)
Head: Robert Leslie Davis; *staff* 16 (22)
S. of Communication Studies
Head: F. Corcoran; *staff* 13 (7)
S. of Biological Sciences
Head (Acting): R. O'Kennedy; *staff* 11 (44)
S. of Chemical Sciences
Head: A. C. Pratt; *staff* 9F16
S. of Physical Sciences
Head: Eugene T. Kennedy; *staff* 20 (25)
S. of Electronics
Head: Charles McCorkell; *staff* 12 (18)
S. of Computer Applications
Head: M. Ryan; *staff* 13 (11)
S. of Mathematical Sciences
Head: Alastair D. Wood; *staff* 8 (10)
S. of Mechanical and Manufacturing Engineering
Head: S. Hashmi; *staff* 2 (4)
National Ce. for Distance Learning
Head: Chris Curran; *staff* 13 (1)
Ce. for New Technologies in Education
Director: P. McKenna; *staff* 5
National Information Technology in Education Ce.
Director: P. McKenna; *staff* 2
National Cell and Tissue Culture Ce. and National Bioprocessing Ut.
Director: Martin Clynes; *staff* 15
Eurotra - Ireland (Terminology, Sub-languages, Machine Translation)
Director: J. Pearson; *staff* 6

Founded 1975 National Institute for Higher Education, Dublin. First students admitted 1980. Became Dublin City University through legislation enacted June 1989. Receives financial support from the Government. Governing body: the Governing Body, comprising 25 members appointed by the Minister for Education and representatives of higher education institutions, business, industry, staff and students of the university.

Arrangements for co-operation with the Universities of: Graz; Innsbruck; Mons; Laval; Waterloo, Ontario; Concepción, Chile; Aarhus; Paris V; Lyons III; Clermont-Ferrand II; Haute Alsace, Mulhouse; Compiègne; Dortmund; Cologne; Paderborn; Berlin; Hildesheim; Bayreuth; Mainz; Hagen; Trier; Saarbrucken; Bologna; Crete; Anshan (Science and Technology), China; Aveiro; Lisboa; Porto; Lisboa (Open); Alcalá de Henares, Madrid; Barcelona (Autonomous); Madrid (Autonomous); Extremadura; Oviedo; Valencia; Tunghai, Taiwan; Dar es Salaam; Brunel; Salford; Heriot-Watt; Sussex; Texas. Institut supérieur de l'Etat de Traducteurs et Interprètes, Bruxelles; Abo Academy, Turku; Ecole supérieure des Sciences commerciales, Angers; Ecole supérieure de Commerce, Reims; Ecole normale supérieure, Cachan; Open Universiteit, Heerlen; Universidad Nacional de Educación a Distancia, Madrid; Staffordshire Polytechnic; Middlesex Polytechnic; Sunderland Polytechnic; Open University, Madrid;Rollins College, Florida.

Academic Year: October to June (October-December; January-March; April-June).

Admission Requirements: Irish Leaving Certificate with matriculation or approved equivalent, and aptitude test.

Fees (Pounds): 1405-1603 per annum.

Language of Instruction: English.

Degrees and Diplomas: Bachelor of–Business Studies; Arts; Accounting and Finance; Science; Engineering; Communication Studies, 3-4 yrs. Master of–Arts; Science; Engineering; Business Administration, 1-2 yrs. Doctor of Philosophy, 3-4 yrs. Graduat Diploma, 1 yr. following Bachelor.

Library: Main Library, 54,000 vols.

Publications: Occasional Research Papers; Journal of Higher Education Studies (3 times a year); Newslink (3 times a year).

Academic Staff, 1989:

Rank	Full-time
Professors (Principal Lecturers)	8
Principal Lecturers (Head of School)	3
Senior Lecturers	27
Lecturers	52
Assistant Lecturers	48
Total	138

Student Enrolment, 1989-90:

	Men	Women	Total
Of the country	1708	1191	2899
Of other countries	79	90	169
Total	1787	1281	3068*

*Also 2080 external students.

3708 ***UNIVERSITY OF LIMERICK**

Plassey Technological Park, Limerick
Telex: 500-26959
Telephone: (61) 333-644
Fax: (61) 330-316
Electronic mail: HEANET, JANET, BITNET
President: Edward M. Walsh (1970-)
Registrar: P. Leo Colgan

C. of Business
Dean: Noel Whelan; *staff* 50 (3)
C. of Engineering and Science
Dean: Noel Mulcahy; *staff* 64 (10)
C. of Humanities
Dean: Patrick F. Doran; *staff* 37 (18)
D. of Business Studies
Head: Donal A. Dinen; *staff* 33 (2)
D. of Management Systems
Head: Kevin Ryan; *staff* 16 (1)
D. of Electronic and Computer Engineering
Head: Cyril J. Burkley; *staff* 22 (5)
D. of Materials Engineering and Industrial Chemistry
Head: Evan R. Petty; *staff* 13 (2)
D. of Mathematics
Head: Frank Hodnett; *staff* 10 (2)
D. of Mechanical and Production Engineering
Head: Kenneth Wylie; *staff* 17 (1)
D. of European Integration and Administration
Head: Henry Ellis; *staff* 15 (4)
D. of Languages and Applied Social Studies
Head: Joyce O'Connor; *staff* 21 (14)
Graduate Ce. of Business
Director: Stephen Dewar; *staff* 2 (1)
Advanced Manufcturing Technology Ut.
Director: Mark Owen; *staff* 9 (1)
Lightwave Technology Research Ce.
Director: Conleth Hussey; *staff* 6
National Microelectronics Applications Ce.
Director: J.J. O'Flaherty; *staff* 10
Social Research Ce.
Director: Joyce O'Connor; *staff* 4 (9)

Founded 1972 as National Institute for Higher Education, Limerick. Became University of Limerick through legislation enacted June 1989. Receives financial support from the Government. Governing body: the Governing Body, comprising 25 members appointed by the Minister of Education. Residential facilities for 300 students.

Special arrangements for co-operation with: Université Catholique du Louvain; University of Leeds; University of Helsinki; Ecole nationale supérieure de Chimie, Paris; Technische Hochschule, Darmstadt; Ben-Gurion University of the Negev; Queen's University, Belfast; Worcester Polytechnic Institute; Iona College; Eindhoven University of Technology; Twente University of Technology; Instituto Superior Técnico, Lisboa. Universities of: Cornell; Tulsa; New York (State); New Mexico; Dallas; Northeastern, Boston.

Academic Year: September to June (September-December; January-March; March-June).

Admission Requirements: Irish Leaving Certificate or approved equivalent.

Fees (Pounds): 1154-1615 (E.C.students); 3366-4626 (non E.C. students) per annum.

Language of Instruction: English.

Degrees and Diplomas: Bachelor of–Arts; Business Studies; Engineering; Science; Technology, 4 yrs. Master, a further 1-2 yrs. Doctor, Ph.D., a further 2-3 yrs following Bachelor.

Library: Information Systems Division incorporating Campus Library, 115,000 vols.

Special Facilities (Museums, etc.): Hunt Museum; National Self-Portrait Collection.

Press or Publishing House: Prospectus (biennially); Undergraduate Degree Courses (annually); President's Report (annually).

Academic Staff, 1989-90:

Rank	Full-time	Part-time
Professors	12	–
Associate Professors	11	2
Senior Lecturers	34	–
Lecturers	67	2
Assistant Lecturers	43	12
Teaching Assistants	6	55
Research Staff	31	–
Total	204	71

Student Enrolment, 1989-90:

	Men	Women	Total
Of the country	2058	971	3029
Of other countries	48	7	55
Total	2106	978	3084*

*Also 1503 external students.

Other Institutions

Technological and Technical Education

3709 **DUBLIN INSTITUTE OF TECHNOLOGY**

14 Mount Street, Upper, Dublin 1
Telephone: 611 133
Fax: 726 608
Director: M. O'Donnell (1982-)
Registrar: T. Duff

C. of Technology (2)
Principals: M. O'Dónnell, F.M. Brennan; *staff* 425
C. of Music
Principal: F. Heneghan; *staff* 41
C. of Commerce
Principal: J.S. Hickey; *staff* 74
C. of Marketing and Design
Principal: T. Madden; *staff* 64
C. of Catering
Principal: R.J. Lawlor; *staff* 69

Founded 1978, incorporating six established colleges under the aegis of the City of Dublin. Courses are offered at Professional, Technical and Craft level leading to Diploma awards of the Institute or in some cases of the National Council for Education Awards. Through a partnership agreement with the University of Dublin (Trinity College), degrees are awarded in parallel to graduates of certain professional-level courses. Governing body: the Governing Body, comprising 12 members.

Academic Year: September to June.

Academic Staff, 1989-90: 1500.

Student Enrolment, 1989-90: 22,000.

3710 **DUBLIN COLLEGE OF CATERING**
Cathal Brugha Street, Dublin 1
Telephone: 747-886
Fax: 743-634
Principal: R.J. Lawlor
Registrar: B. Keyes

Hotel and Catering Administration
Home and Social Sciences
Food Science and Environmental Health

Founded 1941. A constituent college of Dublin Institute of Technology.

3711 **COLLEGE OF COMMERCE**
Rathmines, Dublin 6
Telephone: 970-666
Fax: 965-088
Principal: J.S. Hickey
Registrar: C.G. Lynch

Accountancy and Business Studies
Management Studies
Professional and Social Studies

Founded 1902. A constituent college of Dublin Institute of Technology.

3712 **COLLEGE OF MARKETING AND DESIGN**
Mountjoy Square, Dublin 1
Telephone: 363-000
Principal: T.P. Madden
Registrar: D. Gallenagh

Art and Design
Business and Management

A constituent college of Dublin Institute of Technology.

3713 **COLLEGE OF MUSIC**
Chatham Row, Dublin 2
Telephone: 778-903
Principal: Frank Heneghan (1973-)

Music and Drama

Founded 1894 as school, acquired present status and title 1965. A constituent college of Dublin Institute of Technology.

Academic Year: September to June (September-January; January-June).

Admission Requirements: Irish Leaving Certificate or equivalent.

Fees (Pounds): 96-1050.

Languages of Instruction: English and Irish.

Degrees and Diplomas: Bachelor of Education in Music, 4 yrs. Advanced Diploma in Music.

Academic Staff, 1986-87: 43 (75).

Student Enrolment, 1986-87:

Men	Women	Total
700	1450	2150

3714 **COLLEGE OF TECHNOLOGY**
Bolton Street, Dublin 1
Telephone: 727-177
Fax: 727-879
Principal: M. O'Donnell
Registrar: M. Marname

Architecture and Town Planning
Building Technology and Surveying
Engineering
Science
Mathematics and General Studies
Printing

Founded 1911. A constituent college of Dublin Institute of Technology.

3715 **COLLEGE OF TECHNOLOGY**
Kevin Street, Dublin 8
Telephone: (353 1) 757-741
Fax: (353 1) 780-282
Principal: F.M. Brennan
Secretary: D.C.Spring

D. of Electronics and Communications Engineering
Head: B.J. O'Connor; *staff* 31 (50)
D. of Control Systems and Electrical Engineering
Had: J.C. Fisker; *staff* 20 (20)
D. of Chemistry
Head: E.J. Rothery; *staff* 20 (20)
D. of Physics
Head: M. Hussey; *staff* 30 (30)
D. of Biological Sciences
Head: B.A. Ryan; *staff* 26 (80)
D. of Mathematics, Statistics and Computer Science
Head: B. Goldsmith; *staff* 26 (15)
D. of Electrical Installation
Head: J.T. O'Donnell; *staff* 30 (5)
D. of Languages and Industrial Studies
Head: K.M. Tierney; *staff* 21 (8)
D. of Bakery Technology
Head: D. O'Brien; *staff* 5 (6)

Founded 1887. A constituent college of Dublin Institute of Technology.

Arrangements for co-operation with: Fachhochschule Köln; Université de Provence; Institut Pierre et Marie Curie; University of Messina; Universität Essen; University of St. Andrews; University of Valencia.

Academic Year: September to June.

Admission Requirements: Irish Leaving Certificate or equivalent.

Fees (Pounds): 800.

Language of Instruction: English.

Degrees and Diplomas: Bachelor, 4 yrs. Master, a further 2 yrs. Doctor, Ph.D., 3-3 ½ yrs after Bachelor. Diploma of Technician, 3yrs.

Special Facilities (Museums, etc.): National Photographic Archives.

Academic Staff, 1989-90: 208 (300).

Student Enrolment, 1989-90:

	Men	Women	Total
Of the country	2600	2000	4600
Of other countries	10	10	20
Total	2610	2010	4620

3716 **CRAWFORD MUNICIPAL SCHOOL OF ART**
Sharman Crawford Street, Cork
Telephone: (21) 966777

Visual Education
Fine Art

Founded 1850 as school of design, acquired present status and title 1884. Financed by the Department of Education through the City of Cork Vocational Education Committee. Governing bodies: the Board of Management; the Academic Board.

Academic Year: October to June (October-December; January-April; April-June).

Admission Requirements: Irish Leaving Certificate with Matriculation or equivalent.

Language of Instruction: English.

Degrees and Diplomas: Certificate in Visual Education, 1 yr. Diploma in Art, a further 3 yrs. Also teaching diploma, 1 further yr.

Libraries: c. 4000 vols; c. 6000 slides.

Academic Staff: c. 20 (20).

Student Enrolment: c. 210.

3717 **DUNLAOGHAIRE SCHOOL OF ART AND DESIGN**
Carriglea Park, Kill Avenue, Dun Laoghaire, Co. Dublin

3718 **LIMERICK COLLEGE OF ART, COMMERCE AND TECHNOLOGY**
Moylish Park, Limerick
Telephone: (61) 51344
Fax: (61) 51717
Principal: James Patrick MacDonash
Senior Staff Officer: Mary Costello

S. of Art and Design:
Head: James Dennison; *staff* 25 (8)
S. of Professional and Management Studies
Head: George Fleming *staff* 12 (7)
S. of Engineering
Head: Edward Hayes; *staff* 92 (24)

Founded 1852 as School of Arts and Crafts, acquired p

Arrangements for co-operation with: Heriot-Watt Unive

Academic Year: September to June.

Admission Requirements: Irish Leaving Certificate with Matriculation.

Fees (Pounds): 420-6990.

Language of Instruction: English.

Degrees and Diplomas: Diplomas in Art and Design, 1-3 yrs. National Certificates and Diplomas in Engineering, 1-2 yrs. Titles in–Certified Accountancy; Industrial Engineering/Training Management; Marketing Management, 3-4 yrs.

Library: 16,000 vols.

Academic Staff, 1990: 129 (39).

Student Enrolment, 1990:

	Men	Women	Total
Of the country	1046	747	1793
Of other countries	2	3	5
Total	1048	750	1798

3719 **NATIONAL COLLEGE OF ART AND DESIGN**

100 Thomas Street, Dublin 8
Telephone: (01) 711377
Fax: (01) 711748
Director: John Turpin (1989-)
Registrar: Mealla C. Gibbons

F. of Design
Head: Margaret Walsh; *staff* 16 (9)
F. of Fine Art
Head: Theo McNab; *staff* 12 (3)
F. of Education
Head: Iseult McCarthy: *staff* 5 (3)
F. of History of Art and Design
Head: Frances Ruane; *staff* 6 (3)

Founded 1746. Acquired present status 1971.

Academic Year: October to June.

Admission Requirements: Irish Leaving Certificate with Matriculation.

Fees (Pounds): 1135.

Language of Instruction: English.

Degrees and Diplomas: Bachelor, 4 yrs. Master, a further 2 yrs.

Library: 30,000 vols. 300,000 slides.

Academic Staff, 1990: 47 (15).

Student Enrolment, 1990:

Men	Women	Total
218	401	619

= Technological and Technical EducationAlso Regional Technical Colleges at: Athlone; Carlow; Cork; Dundalk; Galway; Letterkenny; Sligo; Tralee; Waterford.

Professional Education

3721 **NATIONAL COLLEGE OF INDUSTRIAL RELATIONS**

Sandford Road, Ranelagh, Dublin 2
Telephone: (01) 972 917
Fax: (01) 972 200
Executive Director: Joyce O'Connor (1990-)
Registrar: Andrew F. Ryan

Industrial Relations
Trade Union Studies
Personnel and Human Resource Management
Supervisory Management Studies
Management and Industrial Relations

Founded 1951. An independent institution receiving financial support from the government. Governing body: the Board of Management.

Academic Year: September to June (September-December; January-April; April-May).

Admission Requirements: Irish Leaving Certificate (National Diploma courses); Vocational experience (other courses).

Fees (Pounds): 60-748 per annum.

Language of Instruction: English.

Degrees and Diplomas: College Diploma, 2-3 yrs. National Diploma, 4 yrs. Degree, 5 yrs. All part-time, evening.

Library: 8000 vols.

Academic Staff, 1989-90: c. 20.

Student Enrolment, 1989-90:

	Men	Women	Total
Of the country	393	314	707

3722 **COLLEGE OF HOTEL MANAGEMENT**

Shannon Free Airport, Co. Claire
Telephone: (61) 61 444
Fax: (61) 61 982
Director: Phillip J. Smyth (1989-)

Hotel Management and Administration

Founded 1952. First Hotel Management College in Ireland. A private institution under the auspices of Aer Rianta, the Airport Authority. Awards own Diploma validated by the International Hotel Association. Governing body: the College Board. Residential facilities for 80 students.

Academic Year: September to May (September-December; December-May).

Admission Requirements: Irish Leaving Certificate or foreign equivalent.

Fees (Pounds): 4200; foreign students, 5560.

Language of Instruction: English.

Degrees and Diplomas: Shannon Diploma in Hotel Management, 4 yrs.

Library: Steve Foley Memorial Library, *c.* 1240 vols.

Academic Staff, 1990: 7 (20).

Student Enrolment, 1990:

Men	Women	Total
80	80	160

3723 **DUBLIN INSTITUTE FOR ADVANCED STUDIES**

8-10 Burlington Road, Dublin 4

S. of Celtic Studies
S. of Theoretical Physics
S. of Cosmic Physics

Founded 1940.

3724 **ROYAL COLLEGE OF PHYSICIANS OF IRELAND**

6 Kildare Street, Dublin 2
Telephone: 616 677
Fax: 616 677

Medicine

Founded 1667.

3725 **ROYAL COLLEGE OF SURGEONS**

123 St. Stephen's Green, Dublin 2

Surgery

Founded 1784. Recognized by the National University of Ireland.

Teacher Training

3726 **CHURCH OF IRELAND COLLEGE OF EDUCATION**

Upper Rathmines Road, Dublin 6
Telephone: 970033
Principal: S. Blain

Teacher Training (Primary level)

Founded 1811. An Associated College of Trinity College, Dublin.

Admission Requirements: Irish Leaving Certificate with Matriculation.

Degrees and Diplomas: Bachelor in Education, 3 yrs.

Special Facilities (Museums, etc.): Plunket Museum of Irish Education.

3727 **FROEBEL COLLEGE OF EDUCATION**

Sion Hill, Blackrock, Co. Dublin
Principal: Sister M. Duggan

Teacher Training (Primary level)

Founded 1943. An Associated College of Trinity College, Dublin.

3728 **COLÁISTE MHUIRE GAN SMÁL, LUIMNEACH**
MARY IMMACULATE COLLEGE, LIMERICK

South Circular Road, Limerick
Telephone: (061) 314923
Uachtaran (President): Sister Cabrini Ní Mhaoldomnaigh (1979-88)
Cláraitheoir (Registrar): Seán A. Bromell

Teacher Training (Primary level)

Founded 1898. An Associated College of University College, Cork and recognized by the National University of Ireland. Governing body: the Governing Body, comprising not more than 20 members. Residential facilities for 120 students.

Academic Year: September to June (September-December; January-Easter; Easter-June).

Admission Requirements: Irish Leaving Certificate with Matriculation.

Fees (Pounds): *c.* 900 per annum.

Languages of Instruction: English and Irish.

Degrees and Diplomas: Bachelor of Education. Diploma in–Religious Education; Philosophy.

Libraries: c. 100,000 vols; Audio-visual and closed circuit T.V. units.

Academic Staff, 1986-87: –(3).

Student Enrolment, 1986-87:

	Men	Women	Total
Of the country	100	456	556

3729 **MATER DEI INSTITUTE OF EDUCATION**

Clonliffe Road, Dublin 3

President: Eileen Randles

Director: Dermot Lane

Teacher Training

Religious Education

Founded 1966 by the Archbishop of Dublin.

Academic Year: September to May.

Admission Requirements: Irish Leaving Certificate with Matriculation.

Fees (Pounds): 1400-2000.

Language of Instruction: English.

Degrees and Diplomas: Bachelor of–Religious Science, 4 yrs. Master, a further, 2 yrs. Diploma in Theology and Spirituality. Post-graduate Diploma in Chaplaincy Studies.

Academic Staff, 1990: 30 (50).

Student Enrolment, 1990:

	Men	Women	Total
Of the country	30	200	230
Of other countries	2	4	6
Total	32	204	236

3730 **ST. ANGELA'S COLLEGE OF EDUCATION FOR HOME ECONOMICS**

Lough Gill, Sligo

Telephone: (071) 43580

President: Sr. Marianne O'Connor (1983-)

Registrar: Maura Fox

D. of Teacher Education

Head: Michael Hanley; *staff* 3 (5)

D. of Home Economics

; *staff* 5 (4)

Founded 1950, became a recognized College of the National University of Ireland 1978. Governing body: the Board of Governors. Residential facilities for 1st and 2nd year students.

Academic Year: September to June (September-December; January-April; April-June).

Admission Requirements: Matriculation of the National University of Ireland and entrance examination.

Fees (Pounds): Tuition, 1160 per annum.

Language of Instruction: English.

Degrees and Diplomas: Bachelor of Education (Home Economics), 4 yrs.

Library: College Library, *c.* 15,000 vols.

Publication: Irish Home Economics Research Journal (biannually).

Academic Staff, 1989-90: 12 (4).

Student Enrolment, 1989-90: 112 (Women).

3731 **ST. CATHERINE'S COLLEGE OF HOME ECONOMICS**

Sion Hill, Blackrock, Co. Dublin

Principal: Sister H. McGing

D. of Teacher Training (Secondary level)

Head: Paul McElwee

D. of Home Economics

Head: Marion Gallagher

Academic Year: October to June.

Admission Requirements: Irish Leaving Certificate with Matriculation.

Fees (Pounds): 1160.

Language of Instruction: English.

Degrees and Diplomas: Bachelor of Education (Home Economics), 4 yrs.

Academic Staff, 1990: 14 (19).

Student Enrolment, 1990: 144 (Women).

3732 **ST. MARY'S COLLEGE OF EDUCATION**

Marino, Dublin 9

Principal: Brother J.P. Nolan

Teacher Training (Primary level)

3733 **ST. PATRICK'S COLLEGE**

Drumcondra, Dublin 9

Telephone: 376191

President: Simon Clyne, C.M.

Registrar: Stiofan Ó hAnnrachain

Teacher Training (including Education, Psychology, Philosophy, History of Education, Irish Literature, Irish Language, English, French, History, Geography, Mathematics, Music, Biology, Divinity and Catechitics)

Educational Research Ce.

Director: Thomas Kellaghan; *staff* 13 (2)

Special Education D.

Director: Patrick McGee; *staff* 3; (35)

Founded 1875 for the education of teachers for primary schools. Recognized as college of the National University of Ireland 1975. Residential facilities for students.

Arrangements for co-operation with Chico University, California.

Academic Year: September to July (September-December; January-April; April-July).

Admission Requirements: Irish Leaving Certificate with minimum Grade C in 3 subjects at higher level, competence in English and oral examination in Irish and music test.

Fees (Pounds): Tuition, 1206 per annum.

Languages of Instruction: Irish and English.

Degrees and Diplomas: Bachelor of Education, 3 yrs. Diploma in Special Education; Remedial Reading and Language, 1 yr. In-Service degree course, 2 yrs. Course for Confined Recognized Teachers, 2 yrs.

Library: College Library, 75,000 vols.

Publications: Studia Hibernica; Irish Journal of Education (both annually).

Academic Staff, 1989-90: 57.

Student Enrolment, 1989-90:

	Men	Women	Total
Of the country	151	544	695

3734 **COLÁISTE OIDEACHAIS THUAMHUMHAN, LUIMNEACH**

THOMOND COLLEGE OF EDUCATION, LIMERICK

Plassey Park, Castletroy, Limerick

Telex: 26959 EI

Telephone: (061) 334 488

Fax: (061)331 499

Director: James Christian (1976-91)

Registrar (Acting): Hugh O'Donnell

Teacher Education (Physical Education, Wood and Building Technology, Metal and Engineering Technology, General and Rural Science, Business Education, In-Service Education, Recreation Management)

Founded 1973 as college of physical education. Acquired present status and title 1976. Governing body: the Governing Body, comprising 25 members.

Arrangements for co-operation with: Slippery Rock University; Central State University, Connecticut.

Academic Year: October to May (October-December; January-March; March-May).

Admission Requirements: Irish Leaving Certificate with passes in six approved subjects, competence in English and oral examination in Irish. Students must be 17 years of age or over.

Fees (Pounds): 1180 (E.C. students), 2690 (non E.C. students.

Languages of Instruction: English and Irish.

Degrees and Diplomas: Bachelor of–Arts in Physical Education; Science (Education); Technology (Education), 4 yrs. Master of–Arts; Science. Graduate Diploma in–Education (Business Studies); Computer Studies; Recreation Management; Office Technology; Drama, 1 yr. Also Certificate in Equestrian Studies.

Libraries: Plassey Campus Library, 42,000 vols; Teaching Resource centre, 12,000 vols.

Special Facilities (Museums, etc.): National Coaching and Training Centre; Plassey Woodtech (wood processing technology and design centre); Schools Information Centre on the Irish Chemical Industry; Thomond Videotex/Petra Videotex; Daghdha Dance Company.

Publications: Prospectus; Calendar (both annually); Thomond College News (per semester).

Academic Staff, 1990-91:

Rank	Full-time
Senior Lecturers	1
Lecturers	44
Assistant Lecturers	7
Total	61

Student Enrolment, 1990-91:

	Men	Women	Total
Of the country	361	195	556
Of other countries	4	1	5
Total	365	196	561*

*Also 46 external students.

ISRAEL

Universities and Technical Universities

3735 **UNIVERSITAT BEN GURION BA-NEGEV**

Ben Gurion University of the Negev
P.O. Box 653, Beer-Sheva 84105
Telex: 5253 UNASI IL
Telephone: (57) 461111
Fax: (57) 39949
President: Avishay Braverman (1990-)
Rector: Dow Bahat
Director-General: Uri Laor

F. of Humanities and Social Sciences (Bible and Ancient East, Hebrew Language and Literature, Geography, History, Education, Philosophy, Economics, Foreign Languages and Literatures, Behavioural Sciences, Social Work)
Dean: Gerald Blidstein; *staff* 172 (5)
F. of Natural Sciences (including Computer Sciences)
Dean: Noun Shavit; *staff* 114 (1)
F. of Engineering (including Industrial Engineering and Management, Nuclear Engineering)
Dean: Nachum Finger; *staff* 93
F. of Health Sciences (Medicine, Physiotherapy, Nursing)
Dean: Shimon Moses; *staff* 35 (2)
Desert Research I.
Director: Amos Richmond; *staff* 31
Applied Research I. (Chemistry and Chemical Technology, Agriculture and Applied Biology, Biotechnology)
Director: Arnon Shani
David Ben-Gurion Research I.
Director: Meir Avizohar; *staff* 8
S. for Lifelong Education
Director: Mordechai Cogan

Founded 1964 as Institute for Higher Education, recognized as a university 1969 and acquired present title 1973. Receives some financial support from the government. Governing bodies: the Board of Governors, comprising 94 public and academic personalities from Israel and abroad; the UniversitySenate. Residential facilities for 1200 students.

Arrangements for co-operation with the Universities of: Udine; Arizona; New York (City); New York (State); California, Los Angeles; North Carolina; Utah; California State; Pennsylvania; Southern Illinois; Texas Tech; New Mexico (State); Maryland; Alagoas (Federal); Pernambuco (Federal); San carlos, Guatemala; Berlin (Technical); Wuppertal; Ulm; Heidelberg; Bayreuth; Orange Free State; Witwatersrand, Johannesburg; Rand Afrikans; Central, Caracas; Sonora, Hermosillo; Puerto Rico; Chile (Catholic); Bogota; Tecnológica de Santiago, Dominican Republic ;Industrial de Santanda-Bucaramanga Montpellier III; Paris I; Paris V; Paris VI; Valencia; Alicante; Konkook, Seoul; Concordia, Montreal; Winnipeg; Alberta; Québec à Trois Riviřes. Universidad National Autonoma, Honduras; Universidad Nacional Experimental de los Llanos Centrales, San Juan de los Morros; Technical College of Darmstadt.

Academic Year: October to June (October-January; February-June).

Admission Requirements: Secondary school certificate (Teudat Bagrut) or recognized foreign equivalent and entrance examination for Science and Engineering.

Fees (Shekels): 3400 per annum.

Language of Instruction: Hebrew.

Degrees and Diplomas: Bachelor of–Arts, B.A., 3 yrs; Science, B.Sc., 3-4 yrs; Nursing, B.N.,; Physiotherapy, B.P.T., 4 yrs. Master of–Arts, M.A.; Science, M.Sc.; Medical Science, M.Med.Sc., a further 2 yrs. Doctor of–Philosophy, Ph.D., 4 yrs; Medicine, M.D., 7 yrs. Joint programme with Boston University for Master of Science in Management, 3 sem. Also teaching certificate, 2 yrs.

Library: Central Library, *c.* 400,000 vols.

Special Facilities (Museums, etc.): Baron Art Gallery

Publications: Israel Social Science Research (biannually); Geographical Research Forum (biannually).

Press or Publishing House: Ben Gurion University of the Negev Press

Academic Staff, 1989-90:

Rank	Full-time
Professors	102
Assistant Professors	126
Senior Lecturers/Lecturers	224
Total	452

Student Enrolment, 1989-90:

Men	Women	Total
2784	3016	5800

3736 **UNIVERSITAT HAIFA**

University of Haifa
Mt. Carmel, Haifa 31999
Telex: 46660 UNIHA IL
Telephone: (04) 240111
President: Ephraim Evron (1986-89)
Director-General: Naftali Weitman
Rector: Gabriel Ben Don

F. of Humanities
Dean: Avraham Ronen; *staff* 130 (120)
F. of Social Sciences and Mathematics (including Economics, Computer Sciences, and Political Science)
Dean: Arnon Sofer; *staff* 87 (49)
S. of Education
Head: Pearla Nesher; *staff* 23 (20)
S. of Education (Oranim)
S. of Social Work
Head: Yehzkiel Taler; *staff* 21 (13)
S. of Graduate Studies
Dean: Aryeh Grabois; *staff* 3 (2)
Arab-Jewish Ce.
Ce. for Psychological Stress Studies
Ce. for Holocaust Studies
Ce. for Marine Studies
Ce. for Rehabilitation and Human Development
Ce. for Study of the Kibbutz and Co-operative Idea
I. for French Culture and Civilization
I. for German Culture and History
I. for Archaeological and Marine Studies
I. of Evolutionary Biology
D. of Extramural Studies

Founded 1963 as University Institute of Haifa under an agreement between the municipal authorities of Haifa and the Hebrew University, Jerusalem. Became an autonomous institution 1972. Receives financial support from thegovernment. Governing bodies: the Senate, the Board of Governors; the Executive Committee. Residential facilities for students.

Arrangements for co-operation with: Johannes Gutenberg University of Mainz; University of Nice; Temple University, Philadelphia.

Academic Year: November to July (November-March; March-July).

Admission Requirements: Secondary school certificate (Teudat Bagrut) or equivalent, and entrance examination.

Fees (Shekels): 2000 per annum.

Language of Instruction: Hebrew.

Degrees and Diplomas: Bachelor of Arts, B.A., 3-4 yrs. Master of Arts, M.A., a further 2-3 yrs. Doctorate, Ph.D. Also diploma in Librarianship and Teaching Diploma, 2 yrs.

Library: Central Library, *c.* 600,000 vols.

Special Facilities (Museums, etc.): Edith and Reuven Hecht Museum of Archaeology; Ghez Holocaust Art Collection.

Publications: Asian and African Studies; Approaches (biannually); Occasional Papers and Monograph Service on the Middle East.

Press or Publishing House: Haifa University Press.

Academic Staff: c. 350.
Student Enrolment, 1986-87:

	Men	Women	Total
Of the country	2353	4060	6413*

*Also 4200 external students.

3737 ***TECHNION-MACHON TECHNOLOGI LE'ISRAEL**
Technion-Israel Institute of Technology
Technion City, Haifa 32000
Cables: Technion Haifa
Telex: 46406
Telephone: (04) 292111
President: Max W. Reis (1986-90)
Vice-President for Administration and Finance: Michael Schussheim

F. of Civil Engineering
Dean: Gedaliahu Shelef; *staff* 64 (88)
F. of Architecture and Town Planning
Dean: D. Havkin; *staff* 49 (55)
F. of Mechanical Engineering
Dean: Ehud Lenz; *staff* 41 (79)
F. of Electrical Engineering
Dean: Gideon Inbar; *staff* 48 (164)
F. of Chemistry
Dean: Asher Mandelbaum; *staff* 36 (43)
F. of Chemical Engineering
Dean: Eliezer Kehat; *staff* 17 (20)
F. of Physics
Dean: Yacov Eckstein; *staff* 52 (51)
F. of Mathematics
Dean: Moshe Marcus; *staff* 51 (32)
F. of Agricultural Engineering
Dean: Ido Seginer; *staff* 23 (31)
F. of Aeronautical Engineering
Dean: Daniel Weihs; *staff* 36 (44)
F. of Industrial Engineering and Management
Dean: Ury Passy; *staff* 44 (108)
F. of Medicine (including Pharmacy)
Dean: David Gutman; *staff* 126 (66)
F. of Computer Science
Dean: Shimon Even; *staff* 26 (25)
D. of Materials Engineering
Head: Moshe Ron; *staff* 18 (32)
D. of Food Technology and Biotechnology
Head: I. Kopelman; *staff* 12 (16)
D. of Nuclear Engineering
Head: N.H. Shafrir; *staff* 9 (22)
D. of Education (Science and Technology)
Head: Azriel Evyater; *staff* 11 (7)
D. of Biology
Head: David Gershon; *staff* 17 (28)
D. of Biomedical Engineering
Head: Uri Dinnar; *staff* 37 (11)
Transport Research I.
Head: Daniel Shefer; *staff* 12 (20)
I. for Advanced Studies in Science and Technology
Director: Zeher Tadmor
I. for Medical Research
Director: Yoram Palti
Solid State I.
Head: Rafael Kalish; *staff* 22 (5)
D. of General Studies
Head: Michael Mor; *staff* 27 (63)
Research and Development Foundation
Director: Yehuda Dvir; *staff* 351 (91)
Computer Ce.
Director: Nathanel Frankel; *staff* 46
Extension D.
Director: Arnan Seginer
Ce. for Pre-Academic Studies (courses for new immigrants)
Director: Yoram Zuirin; *staff* 10 (50)
Also junior technical college, vocational high school, and school for senior technicians.

Founded 1912, opened 1924. Independent institution administered by the Board of Governors, comprising members from Israel and abroad including representatives of the government, and representatives of students and academic staff. The supreme academic authority is the Senate. The government meets 75% of the operational costs and provides 50% of the budget for building and development. Residential facilities for junior academic staff and 1641 students.

Arrangements for co-operation with Universities in Europe, and North and South America.

Academic Year: October to July (October-February; March-July).

Admission Requirements: Secondary school certificate (Teudat Bagrut) or equivalent, and entrance examination.

Language of Instruction: Hebrew.

Degrees and Diplomas: Bachelor of–Arts, B.A., in–Physics; Chemistry; Mathematics and Biology, 3 yrs; Science, B.Sc., 4-5 yrs. Master of–Science, M.Sc., 2 yrs after Bachelor. Doctor of Science, D.Sc.; Doctor of Philosophy, Ph.D.; Doctor of Science in Technology, D.Sc.Tech., 2-3 yrs after Master. Doctor of Medicine, M.D., 7 yrs. Also diploma in Engineering, 4 yrs and thesis, and teaching certificate in science (secondary level).

Libraries: Central Library, c. 375,000 vols; faculty libraries.

Special Facilities (Museums, etc.): Museum for Science and Development of Technology.

Publications: The Joseph Wunsch Lectures (annually); Synopses of D.Sc., Ph.D., and M.Sc. theses (annually); Technion (bimonthly); Research Reports (biannually); Bulletin (weekly); Israel Journal of Technology.

Press or Publishing House: Technion Printing Department.

Academic Staff, 1986-87:

Rank	Full-time	Part-time
Professors	170	–
Associate Professors	219	–
Senior Lecturers	228	–
Lecturers	70	–
Adjuncts	–	80
Assistants and Instructors	–	111
Total	687	191

Student Enrolment, 1986-87: 7462.

3738 ***HA'UNIVERSITA HA'IVRIT BI'YERUSHALAYIM**
The Hebrew University of Jerusalem
Mount Scopus, Jerusalem 91905
Cables: Scopus
Telex: 26458 SCOPM IL
Telephone: (02) 882111
Rector and Acting President: Amnon Pazy
Director-General: Yoash Vaadia

F. of Humanities (including Jewish, Asian, and African Studies, Archaeology, and Education)
Dean: Yochanan Friedmann; *staff* 288
F. of Social Sciences (including Economics, Political Science, and Business Administration)
Dean: Michael Inbar; *staff* 170
F. of Law
Dean: Yitzhak Englard; *staff* 28
F. of Mathematics and Natural Sciences
Dean: Eliahu Friedman; *staff* 258
F. of Agriculture (including Horticulture and Animal Husbandry)
Dean: Ilan Chet; *staff* 99
F. of Medicine
Dean: R. Rahaminoff; *staff* 433
F. of Dentistry
Dean: A. Garfunkel; *staff* 20
S. of Pharmacy
Associate Dean: Avraham Kreiser
S. of Education
Director: Z. Klein
S. of Veterinary Medicine
Director: K. Perk
S. of Applied Science and Technology
Director: N. Ben-Yosef
S. of Social Work
Director: A. Rosen
S. of Library and Archive Studies
Director: D. Schidorsky
S. for Overseas Students
Provost: A. Shiloah
S. of Business Administration
Director: A. Friedman
S. of Domestic Science and Nutrition
Director: N. Trostler

S. of Occupational Therapy
Chairman: B. Efrati
S. of Nursing
Associate Dean (Acting): H. Kurtzman
S. of Public Health and Community Medicine
Director: Ch. Greenblatt
Middle East Research I.
I. of Advanced Studies
Chairman: M. Ya'ari
Research I. for the Advancement of Peace
Chairman: H.Z. Schiffrin
Ce. for Jewish Education in the Diaspora
Adult Education I.
Head: Rivka Bar Yosef

Founded 1918 and opened on Mount Scopus 1925. Transferred to Jerusalem 1948 when Mount Scopus was cut off from Jewish section of the city. Contruction of Givat Ram campus started 1954, completed 1958. Mount Scopus campusreopened 1967. A private institution financially supported by the government, tuition fees and donations. Governing bodies: the Board of Governors, of 150 members and composed of representatives of Jewish communities in all parts of the world; the Executive Committee, comprising 36 members; the Senate, the supreme academic body of the university. Residential facilities for *c.* 6000 students.

Many arrangements for co-operation with universities in other countries.

Academic Year: October to June (November-December; January-March; April-June).

Admission Requirements: Secondary school certificate (Behinat Bagrut) or recognized foreign equivalent, and entrance examination for many fields.

Fees (Shekels): 2000 per annum.

Language of Instruction: Hebrew.

Degrees and Diplomas: Bachelor of–Arts, B.A.; Science, B.Sc.; Medical Science, B.Med.Sc.; Pharmacy, B.Pharm.; Social Work, B.S.W.; Occupational Therapy, B.O.T.; Nursing, B.N.; Domestic Science and Nutrition, 3 yrs; Science in Agriculture, B.Sc.Agr., 3 ½ yrs; Laws, LL.B., 4 yrs. Master of–Arts, M.A.; Social Sciences, M.Soc.Sc.; Social Work, M.S.W.; Laws, LL.M.; Library Science, M.L.S., a further 2 yrs; Science, M.Sc.; Public Health, M.P.H.; Science in Agriculture, M.Sc.Agr., an additional 3-4 semesters. Doctor of–Philosophy, Ph.D. in–Humanities; Social Sciences; Science; Agriculture; Laws, Dr.Jur., at least 2 yrs after Master; Medicine, M.D.; Dental Medicine, D.M.D., 6 yrs. Diploma in–Librarianship; Business Administration; Criminology, 2 yrs after Bachelor. Also teaching certificates.

Libraries: Jewish National and University Library, *c.* 2,000,000 vols; Agricultural Library, *c.* 80,000; National Medical Library, *c.* 250,000; specialized libraries.

Publications: Research (annually); Kiryat Sefer (quarterly); Tarbiz (quarterly); Israel Law Review (quarterly); Scripta Hierosolymitana (annually); Scopus (annually).

Press or Publishing House: The Magnes Press.

Academic Staff, 1986-87:

Rank	Full-time	Part-time
Professor (Professors)	373	–
Professor Haver (Associate Professors)	296	–
Martze Bahir (Senior Lecturers)	241	–
Martze (Lecturers)	164	–
Assistant and Madrich (Assistants and Instructors)	–	300
Language Teachers, etc.	–	200
Total	1074	500

Student Enrolment, 1986-87: 17,000.

3739 ***BAR-ILAN UNIVERSITY**
Ramat-Gan 52100
Cables: Unibarilan
Telex: 361311
Telephone: (03) 718111
President: Michael Albeck (1986-)
Director-General: David Altman
Rector: Ernest Krausz

F. of Jewish Studies
Dean: Daniel Sperber; *staff* 117 (38)
F. of Humanities
Dean: Benjamin Gross; *staff* 93 (32)
F. of Social Sciences
Dean: Harvey Babkoff; *staff* 197 (51)
F. of Natural Sciences (including Mathematics and Computer Science)
Dean: Abraham Mayefsky; *staff* 120 (24)
F. of Law
Dean: Sinai Deutsch; *staff* 11 (4)

Also 23 institutes of advanced studies and research. Extramural departments at Ashkelon, Safed, Zemach.

Founded 1955. The university combines secular and religious studies and is recognized by the Ministry of Education. The State provides 60% of the budget. Governing bodies: the Senate; the Global Board of Trustees, composed mainly of members from the U.S.A., but also from Israel, Canada, and the United Kingdom; the Executive Council. Some residential facilities for academic staff and students.

Arrangements for co-operation with: City University of New York; University of Pennsylvania; State University of New York; Concordia University; University of Berne; University of Paris-Sorbonne.

Academic Year: November to June (November-February; March-June).

Admission Requirements: Secondary school certificate (Teudat Bagrut) or equivalent, and entrance examination.

Language of Instruction: Hebrew.

Degrees and Diplomas: Bachelor of–Arts, B.A.; Science, B.Sc.; Law, LL.B., 3-4 yrs. Master of–Arts, M.A.; Science, M.Sc., 1-2 yrs after Bachelor. Doctorate, Ph.D., a further 2-3 yrs. Also Diplomas in–Criminology; Social Sciences; Local Government; Interpretation and Translation; Librarianship.

Libraries: Wurzweiler Library, *c.* 250,000 vols; department libraries, *c.* 63,000.

Publications: Bar-Ilan Annual; Catalogue (annually, in Hebrew and English); Philosophia (quarterly); Da'at (biannually); Hebrew Computational Linguistics; Criticism and Interpretation; Crime and Social Deviance; Alei Sefer (quarterly).

Academic Staff, 1986-87:

Rank	Full-time	Part-time
Professor (Professors)	62	9
Professor Haver (Associate Professors)	88	2
Martze Bahir (Senior Lecturers)	180	21
Martze (Lecturers)	111	34
Madrich (Instructors)	58	51
Assistants	15	27
Teaching Assistants	26	14
Total	540	158

Student Enrolment, 1986-87:

	Men	Women	Total
Of the country	4256	6384	10,640
Of other countries	104	156	260
Total	4360	6540	10,900

3740 ***MAKHON WEIZMANN LEMADA**
Weizmann Institute of Science
P.O. Box 26, Rehovot 76100
Cables: Weizinst
Telex: 361900
Telephone: (8) 343-111
Fax: (8) 466-966
President: Haim Harari (1989-94)
Vice-President (Finance and Administration): Gideon Elrom

F. of Mathematics
Dean: Z. Artstein; *staff* 32
F. of Physics (including Nuclear Physics)
Dean: Z. Fraenkel; *staff* 51
F. of Chemistry
Dean: I. Procaccia; *staff* 62
F. of Biophysics and Biochemistry
Dean: M. Avron; *staff* 71
F. of Biology
Dean: E. Galun; *staff* 76
D. of Science Teaching
Head; U. Ganiel
Computer Ce.
Director: J. Finkel

Graduate S.
Dean: B. Geiger; *staff* 5

Founded 1934 as Daniel Sieff Research Institute, renamed 1949. A private institution, operated under the supervision of the Council for Higher Education. Financially supported by the government, the Jewish Agency, research grants and contracts, gifts, and bequests. Governing bodies: the Board of Governors, of international membership; the Scientific Council, comprising professors, associate professors, and representatives of the scientific staff. Residential facilities for scientific academic staff and students.

Arrangements for co-operation with: University of Wisconsin; University of Pennsylvania; Swiss Federal Institute of Technology; University of Paris V; University of Strasbourg I; University of Cambridge; Imperial College, London.

Academic Year: October to June (October-February; March-June).

Admission Requirements: For Master of Science, a good B.Sc. from an accredited university in Israel, or its equivalent; for Doctor of Philosophy, a good M.Sc. from an accredited university in Israel, or its equivalent.

Fees: None.

Languages of Instruction: Hebrew and English.

Degrees and Diplomas: Master of Science, M.Sc., 2 yrs. Doctor of Philosophy, Ph.D., a further 4 ½ yrs.

Library: Total, 205,000 vols.

Special Facilities (Museums, etc.): The Weizmann House; The Weizmann Archives; Ullman Gallery.

Publications: Rehovot (annually); Interface (quarterly); Research (quarterly); Scientific Activities (annually); Annual Report.

Academic Staff, 1989-90:

Rank	
Professors	114
Associate Professors	93
Senior Scientists	63
Scientists	26
Total	296

Student Enrolment, 1989-90:

	Men	Women	Total
Of the country	314	199	513
Of other countries	87	40	127
Total	401	239	640

3741 ***UNIVERSITAT TEL AVIV**

Tel Aviv University
P.O. Box 39040, Ramat-Aviv 69978
Cables: Versity TA
Telex: 342171 VERSY IL
Telephone: (03) 420111
Chancellor: George S. Wise
Rector: Yehuda Ben-Shaul
President: Moshe Many
Director-General: N. Gur

F. of Visual and Performing Arts
Dean: A. Zuckerman; *staff* 66 (143)
F. of Social Sciences
Dean: E. Yaar; *staff* 72 (80)
F. of Exact Sciences
Dean: D. Amir; *staff* 175 (27)
F. of Humanities (including Jewish Studies, Archaeology, and Education)
Dean: M. Gil; *staff* 356 (167)
F. of Management
Dean: S. Neuman; *staff* 61 (70)
F. of Law
Dean: U. Reichman; *staff* 31 (44)
F. of Life Sciences
Dean: Iafa Keydar; *staff* 108
F. of Engineering
Dean: Ady Seidman; *staff* 66 (72)
F. of Medicine (including Dentistry and Nursing)
Dean: Hayim Boichis; *staff* 127 (562)
S. of Social Work
Head: D. Schnit; *staff* 18
S. of Jewish Studies
S. of Languages and Literature
A. of Music
S. of Education
Head: M. Chen
S. of Continuing Medical Education
S. of Dentistry
Head: Amos Buchner
S. of Communication Disorders
Ut. of Extramural Studies
Also 50 research institutes.

Founded 1953 as a municipal institution, incorporating the former School of Law and Economics, established 1935, the Institute of Natural Sciences, and the Institute of Jewish Studies. Became university 1956. An autonomous institution with independent organizational status. 70% of income provided by the government. Governing bodies: the Board of Governors; the Executive Council; the Academic Senate, the supreme academic body of the university. Residential facilities for 1000 students.

Arrangements for co-operation with Universities in Europe, and North and South America.

Academic Year: October to June (October-January; March-June).

Admission Requirements: Secondary school certificate (Teudat Bagrut) or recognized foreign equivalent, and entrance examination.

Fees (Shekels): 1195 per annum.

Language of Instruction: Hebrew.

Degrees and Diplomas: Bachelor of–Arts, B.A.; Science, B.Sc.; Law, LL.B.; Social Work, B.S.W.; Fine Arts, B.F.A.; Music, B.Mus., Physical Therapy, B.P.T.; Communication Disorders, 3-4 yrs. Master of–Arts; M.A.; Science, M.Sc.; Communication Disorders; Social Work; Business Administration, M.B.A.; Science in Management Sciences, M.S.M.; Fine Arts, M.F.A.; Music; Law, LL.M.; Jewish Law, M.A. (Jewish Law), a further 1-2 yrs. Doctor of–Medicine, 7 yrs. Doctorof Philosophy, Ph.D., in all disciplines. Doctor of Law.

Libraries: Central Library, *c.* 700,000 vols; Exact Sciences and Engineering, *c.* 130,000; Life Sciences and Medicine, *c.* 155,000; Social Sciences and Management, *c.* 140,000; Law, *c.* 70,000; Jewish Studies, *c.* 115,000.

Special Facilities (Museums, etc.): Zoology Museum. Experimental Zoological and Botanical Garden.

Publications: Hasifrut (quarterly); Middle East Record (annually); Iunei Mishpat (monthly); Middle East Contemporary Survey (annually).

Academic Staff, 1986-87:

Rank	Full-time	Part-time
Professor Min-Ha Minyan (Professors)	230	51
Professor Chaver (Associate Professors)	275	138
Martze Bachir (Senior Lecturers)	274	153
Moreh Bachir (Senior Teachers)	67	–
Martze (Lecturers)	173	220
Moreh (Teachers)	31	–
Madrich (Instructors)/Assistants	304	–
Total	1354	562

Student Enrolment, 1985-86:

Men	Women	Total
9210	9098	18,308*

*Also 650 foreign students.

3742 **HA'UNIVERSITA HA'PETUHA**

Everyman's Open University
16 Klausner Street, P.O. Box 3928, Tel-Aviv 61-392
Telephone: (03) 422511

Humanities
Behavioural Sciences
Mathematics
Natural and Life Sciences
Economics and Managements
Education
Jewish Studies
Ce. for Adult Education

Founded 1974 to provide distance education. Instruction is given by correspondence courses, and through television and radio, and the University has set up over 25 Study Centres throughout the country. Governing bodies: the Council; the Academic Committee.

Special arrangements for co-operation with The Open University, Milton Keynes.

Academic Year: Two 18-week semesters, in the autumn and in the spring.

Admission Requirements: Secondary school certificate (Teudat Bagrut).

Degrees and Diplomas: Degree of Bachelor of Arts.

Student Enrolment: *c.* 12,000.

Other Institutions

Professional Education

3743 **COLLEGE OF ADMINISTRATION**
13 Persits Street, Kiryat Hachinuch, Tel-Aviv 61480
Telephone: (03) 429297
Dean: Haim N. Kretsch (1984-)

Business Administration (including Accountancy) (evening studies)

Founded 1970. Under the supervision of the Ministry of Education. Governing body: the Board of Trustees.

Academic Year: November to July (November-February; March-June).

Admission Requirements: Secondary school certificate (Teudat Bagrut).

Fees (Shekels): 2000 per annum.

Language of Instruction: Hebrew.

Degrees and Diplomas: Diploma, 4 yrs.

Academic Staff, 1986-87: 19 (19).

Student Enrolment, 1986-87:

	Men	Women	Total
Of the country	428	137	565

3744 **MIDRASHET RUPPIN**
Ruppin College of Agriculture
Emek Hefer 60960

Agriculture

3745 **BEZALEL ACADEMY OF ARTS AND DESIGN**
1 Bezalel Street, Jerusalem 94591
Telex: IL-26452 BEZAL
Telephone: (02) 225-116
Fax: (2) 247-738
Head: Ran Shechori (1979-91)

D. of Graphic Design
Head: Avi Eisenstein; *staff* 2 (17)
D. of Ceramics Design
Head: Lidia Zavadsky; *staff* 3 (16)
D. of Environmental Design
Head: Saadi Mandl; *staff* 7 (16)
D. of Industrial Design
Head: Shmuel Kaplan; *staff* 2 (16)
D. of Gold- and Silversmith Studies
Head: Alex Ward; *staff* 4 (16)
D. of Fine Arts
Head: Ryoram Merose; *staff* 6 (13)
D. of Photography
Head: Hanan Laskin

Founded 1906 as school, acquired present status and title 1970. A private institution receiving financial support (62%) from the government. Governing bodies: the Board of Governors; the Board of Directors; the Senate.

Arrangements for co-operation with: Parsons School of Design, New York; Cooper Union, New York; School of Visual Arts, New York; Royal College of Arts, London.

Academic Year: November to July (November-January; January-April; April-July).

Admission Requirements: Secondary school certificate (Teudat Bagrut) or equivalent, and entrance examination.

Fees (Shekels): 3700 per annum.

Language of Instruction: Hebrew.

Degrees and Diplomas: Bachelor of–Design; Fine Arts, 4 yrs.

Library: Central Library, *c.* 30,000 vols.

Publication: Periodical News Bulletin, Bezalel in Brief.

Press or Publishing House: Bezalel Academy of Arts and Design Publishing House.

Academic Staff, 1989-90:

Rank	Full-time	Part-time
Professors	8	–
Senior Lecturers	20	100
Total	28	100

Student Enrolment, 1989-90:

Of the country	620
Of other countries	55
Total	675

3746 **HA'ACADEMIA LEMUSIKA ULEMAHOL BIYERUSHAKAYIM AL'SHEM RUBIN**
The Jerusalem Rubin Academy of Music and Dance
7 Peretz Smolenskin Street, Jerusalem 92101
Telephone: 02-635271

Music and Dance

Founded 1947, accredited by the Council of Higher Education 1971. Governing bodies: the Board of Governors; the Board of Directors. Some residential facilities for students.

Academic Year: October to June (October-December; January-March; April-June).

Admission Requirements: Secondary school certificate (Teudat Bagrut) or equivalent and entrance examination.

Language of Instruction: Hebrew.

Degrees and Diplomas: Bachelor of–Music; Music Education; Arts in Music, 4 yrs. Postgraduate Artist Diploma, 2 yrs.

Library: c. 60,000 vols.

Special Facilities (Museums, etc.): Museum of Musical Instruments.

Publications: Periodicals; Music in Time (annually).

Academic Staff: c. 40 (40).

Student Enrolment: c. 1500.

3747 **BEIT SEFER GAVOAH LETECHNOLOGIA**
Jerusalem College of Technology
Havaad Haleumi 21, Jerusalem 91160
Telex: JERTEC
Telephone: (02) 423131

D. of Physics and Electro-Optics
D. of Computer Sciences
D. of Electronics
D. of Advanced Science Teacher Training
S. of Industrial Management
D. of Jewish Studies

Founded 1969. Recognized by the Council for Higher Education 1974. An independent institution financially supported by the government, tuition fees, and donations. Governing bodies: the Board of Governors; the Academic Council. Residential facilities for students.

Academic Year: September to June.

Admission Requirements: Secondary school certificate (Bagrut).

Language of Instruction: Hebrew.

Degrees and Diplomas: Associate in Engineering, Ass.Eng., 3 yrs. Bachelor of Science, B.Sc., in Applied Science and Technology, 4 yrs. Also teaching certificate.

Libraries: Technical, *c.* 10,000 vols; Jewish Studies library, *c.* 2000.

Academic Staff: c. 10.

Student Enrolment: c. 200 (Men).

3748 **SHENKAR-BEIT HASHEFER HAGAVOHA L'MADAEI HATEXTILE ULEOFFNA**
Shenkar College of Textile and Fashion
24, Anna Frank Street, Ramat-Gan 52526
Telex: 341118 BTVIL EXT. 5790
Telephone: (03) 7521133/37
President (Acting): Alec Lerner (1986-)
General Director: Michael Nir

D. of Textile Technology
Head: Yeshayahu Armon; *staff* 8 (16)
D. of Textile Chemistry
Head: Amotz Wienberg; *staff* 4 (11)
D. of Industrial Management
Head: Yacov Gargir; *staff* 3 (22)
D. of Fashion and Textile Design
Head: Terence Kavanagh; *staff* 8 (41)

Extension D.

Head: Dvora Cohen; *staff* 1 (2)

Founded 1970, on the initiative of the 1968 Jerusalem Economic Conference. An independent institution recognized by the Council of Higher Education and sponsored and supported by Industry and the Ministries of Education,Commerce and Industry, Labour and Finance. Financially supported by the Levy Fund and tuition fees. Governing bodies: the Board of Governors, comprising 120 members from all parts of the world; the Executive Council of 40 members; the Academic Council.

Academic Year: November to June (November-February; March-June).

Admission Requirements: Secondary school certificate (Teudat Bagrut) or foreign equivalent. Examination for Design.

Fees (Shekels): *c.* 3500 per annum.

Language of Instruction: Hebrew.

Degrees and Diplomas: Bachelor of–Design; Technology, 4 yrs. Diploma in Practical Engineering, 2 yrs.

Library: 170,000 vols.

Academic Staff, 1986-87: 23 (4).

Student Enrolment, 1986-87:

Men	Women	Total
99	232	331

Teacher Training

3749 **MIHLELET BEIT-BERL**

Beit-Berl Teachers' Training College

Beit-Berl Post, Tzofit 44925

Teacher Training

3750 **HAMICHLALA LEHINUCH GUFANI AL'SHEM ZINMAN**

The Zinman College of Physical Education

Wingate Institute, Netanya 42902

Telephone: (53) 29222

Fax: (53) 650960

Rector: David Eldar

Assistant Rector (Adminstration and Development): Zvi Artzi

D. of Education

Head: Nevat Ephram

D. of Life Sciences

Head: Michael Sagiv

D. of Sports

Head: Micha Kanitz

D. of Biomechanics

Head: Alberto Avalon

D. of Special Education

Head: Atara Sherman

D. of Dance

Head: Haya Halperin

D. of Recreation

Head: Shlomo Zidkiyahu

Founded 1944 as seminary for physical education. Became affiliated with Tel-Aviv University 1970 and acquired present status 1984. Residential facilities for students.

Arrangements for co-operation with: Adelphi University; Boston University.

Academic Year: October to June (October-January; February-June).

Admission Requirements: Secondary school certificate (Teudat Bagrut).

Fees (Shekels): 240 per annum.

Language of Instruction: Hebrew.

Degrees and Diplomas: Bachelor of Education, 4 yrs. Teaching Diploma, 3 yrs. Also Diplomas of specialization, 2 yrs.

Library: Wingate Library, *c.* 52,000 vols.

Publication: Agid–Readings in the Science of Physical Education and Sport (annually).

Academic Staff: c. 60 (105).

*Student Enrolment, 1990: c.*2000.

3751 **HAMICHLALA LEHINUCH AL'SHEM DAVID YELLIN**

The David Yellin Teachers College

P.O. Box 3578, 89 Herzl Boulevard, Beit Hakerem, Jerusalem 91035

Telephone: (2) 533-111

Fax: (2) 521-548

Dean: Itay Zimran (1988-)

Registrar: Margalit Matityahu

Teacher Education (Early Childhood, Elementary, Special, Junior High, Remedial)

I. for Arab-Jewish Co-existence

Co-ordinator: Hadar Keich

I. for Developing an Israel-Jewish Identity

Co-ordinator: Yair Shifman

Preparatory P. for New Immigrants

Co-ordinator: Lea Skiva

Founded 1913. An independent institution financially supported by the Ministry of Education, tuition fees, the Israel Society and donations (Friends of the David Yellin Teachers' College).

Arrangements for co-operation with the University of North Carolina.

Academic Year: September to June (September-January; February-June).

Admission Requirements: Secondary school certificate (Bagrut) or foreign equivalent, and entrance examination.

Fees (Shekels): 3125.

Languages of Instruction: Hebrew, English, Arabic and French.

Degrees and Diplomas: Bachelor of Education, 4 yrs. Also teaching certificates, 3-4 yrs.

Library: 150,000 vols.

Publications: English Newsletters, Update (bimonthly); College Voice (biannually).

Academic Staff, 1990-91: 52 (155).

Student Enrolment, 1989-90:

	Men	Women	Total
Of the country	154	1060	1214

3752 **HAMICHLALA LECHINUCH AL'SHEM LEVINSKY**

Levinsky Teachers' College

15 Persitz Street, P.O. Box 48130, Tel-Aviv 61480

Telephone: (3) 642-6162

Fax: (3) 417-146

Head: Avraham Rocheli

Administrator: Moshe Shalev

Teacher Education (including Early Childhood, Elementary, Special, Junior High, Music, In-Service training)

Founded 1913 as school, acquired present status and title 1983. Under the supervision of the Ministry of Education and recognized by the Council of Higher Education. Governing body: the Board of Trustees.

Arrangements for co-operation with: University Complutense, Madrid; City University of New York.

Academic Year: October to July.

Admission Requirements: Secondary school certificate (Teudat Bagrut) and entrance examination.

Fees (Shekels): 3600.

Language of Instruction: Hebrew.

Degrees and Diplomas: Bachelor of Education, 4 yrs. Also teaching certificate, 3 yrs.

Library: c. 100,000 vols.

Publication: Mahalachin (biannually).

Press or Publishing House: Levinsky Publishing Department

Academic Staff, 1989-90: 111 (247).

Student Enrolment, 1989-90:

	Men	Women	Total
Of the country	38	1998	2036

3753 **MICHLALAH YERUSHALAYIM LEBANOT**

Michlalah-Jerusalem College for Women

P.O. Box 16078, Bayit Vegan, Jerusalem 91160

Telephone: (2) 422 481

Fax: (2)422 483

Rector: Rabbi Yehudah Copperman (1964-)

Director-General: Rabbi Martin Louis Applbaum

Teacher Training

Founded 1964. Under the supervision of the Ministry of Education, Department of Teacher Training and recognized by the Council of Higher Education. Governing body: the Academic Council. Residential facilities for students.

Arrangements for co-operation with a number of American Universities.

Academic Year: September to June (September-January; February-June).

Admission Requirements: Secondary school certificate (Teudat Bagrut) and entrance examination.

Language of Instruction: Hebrew.

Degrees and Diplomas: Bachelor of Education, 4 yrs. Teaching Certificate (junior high school), 3 yrs. Postgraduate diploma in JewishStudies.

Library: Joseph & Faye Tanenbaum Central Library, *c.* 40,000 vols.

Publication: Publications in Hebraica and Judaica.

Press or Publishing House: Michlalah Press.

Academic Staff, 1988-89: 47 (182).

Student Enrolment, 1988-89:

	Women
Of the country	650
Of other countries	150
Total	800

ITALY

Universities and Technical Universities

3754 **UNIVERSITÀ DEGLI STUDI DI ANCONA**
University of Ancona
Piazza Roma 23, 60100 Ancona
Telephone: (39) 71-28212
Rettore: Paoli Bruni

F. of Engineering
F. of Medicine and Surgery
F. of Economics and Commerce

Founded 1969 as a private university, became a State institution enjoying administrative autonomy 1970. Governing bodies: the Senato Accademico; the Consiglio di Amministrazione.

Academic Year: November to October.

Admission Requirements: Secondary school certificate (maturità).

Language of Instruction: Italian.

Degrees and Diplomas: Laurea, Doctor, in–Economics and Commerce; Civil, Mechanical and Electrical Engineering, 4-5 yrs; Medicine and Surgery, 6 yrs.

Library: Faculty libraries.

Academic Staff: c. 250.

Student Enrolment: c. 6500.

3755 **UNIVERSITÀ DELL'AQUILA**
University of Aquila
Piazza dell'Annunziata 1, 67100 L'Aquila
Telephone: (39) 862-6461
Rettore: Giovanni Schippa

F. of Magistero (Teacher Training)
F. of Mathematics, Physics, and Natural Sciences
F. of Engineering
F. of Medicine and Surgery

Founded 1952. A State institution enjoying administrative autonomy.

Academic Year: November to October.

Admission Requirements: Secondary school certificate (maturità).

Language of Instruction: Italian.

Degrees and Diplomas: Laurea, Doctor in–Mathematics; Physics; Biological Sciences, 4 yrs; Engineering, 5 yrs.

Library: c. 35,000 vols.

Academic Staff: c. 130.

Student Enrolment: c. 5300.

3756 ***UNIVERSITÀ DEGLI STUDI DI BARI**
University of Bari
Piazza Umberto I, 70100 Bari
Telex: 810598 UNIVBA I
Telephone: (39) 80-314111
Rettore: Attilo Alto (1986-)
Dirigente Amministrativo: Mario Natale

F. of Law
Dean: Gaetano Piepoli
F. of Economics and Commerce
Dean: Giuseppe Chiassino
F. of Medicine and Surgery
Dean: Vincenzo Mitolo
F. of Pharmacy
Dean: Vincenzo Tortorella
F. of Agriculture
Dean: Emilio Bellitti
F. of Letters and Philosophy
Dean: Francesco Tateo
F. of Mathematics, Physics, and Natural Science
Dean: Aldo Cossu
F. of Engineering
Dean: Attilio Alto
F. of Veterinary Medicine
Dean: Giuseppe Onofrio Marcotrigiano
F. of Magistero (Teacher Training)
Dean: Michele Dell'Aquila
F. of Foreign Languages and Literature
Dean: Vitilio Masiello

Also 117 institutes of the different faculties and c. 50 schools for specialized study.

Founded 1924 with faculty of medicine. A State institution enjoying administrative autonomy. Governing bodies: the Senato Accademico; the Consiglio di Amministrazione. Residential facilities for students.

Arrangements for co-operation with: University of Titograd; Semmelweis University of Medicine.

Academic Year: November to October.

Admission Requirements: Secondary school certificate (classical, scientific or technical high school), or qualification as primary school teacher.

Language of Instruction: Italian.

Degrees and Diplomas: Laurea, Doctor, in–Law; Political Science; Economics and Commerce; Foreign Languages; Letters; Philosophy; Literature; Forestry; Education; Mathematics; Physics; Natural Sciences; Biology; Geology; Pharmacy; Pharmaceutical Chemistry and Technology; Information Science, 4 yrs; Agriculture; Chemistry; Civil Engineering; Electrotechnical Engineering; Mechanical Engineering; Dentistry; Veterinary Medicine, 5 yrs; Medicine and Surgery, 6 yrs. Diploma in Statistics, 2 yrs. Diploma of School Inspector, 3 yrs.

Libraries: Libraries of faculties and institutes including Law, c. 120,000 vols; Economics and Commerce, c. 60,000; Letters and Philosophy, c. 35,000; Agriculture, c. 8000; Science, c. 18,000; Medicine and Surgery, c. 5000; Engineering, c. 12,000.

Special Facilities (Museums, etc.): Archaeology Museum.

Publications: Official Bulletin; Annals of the Faculty of Law; Annals of the Faculty of Economics and Commerce; Annals of the Faculty of Foreign Languages and Literature; Annals of the Faculty of Letters and Philosophy; Annals of the Faculty of Agriculture; Annals of the Faculty of Engineering.

Academic Staff: c. 570 (240).

Student Enrolment: c. 55,000.

3757 **UNIVERSITÀ LIBERA DI BERGAMO**
University of Bergamo
Via Salvecchio 19, 24100 Bergamo
Telephone: (39) 35-217111
Fax: (39) 35-243054
Rector: Pietro Enrico Ferri (1984-93)
Direttore Amministrativo: Domenico Danisi

F. of Foreign Languages and Literature
Head: Nina Kaucisvili
F. of Economic and Commerce
Head: Antonio Amaduzzi
D. of Economic Business
Director: Mario Masini
D. of Economic Sciences
Director: Luigi Filippini
D. of Law
Director: Giorgio Saceerdoti
D. of Mathematics
Director: Emilio Spedicato
D. of Comparative Language and Literature
Director: Alberto Castoldi
D. of Neo-Latin Language and Literature
Director: Giorgio Mirandola

Founded 1968. A free institution financially supported by the local government. Governing body: the Administration Board, comprising teachers, students and local government representatives.

Arrangements for co-operation with: New York University. Participates in the ERASMUS programme.

Academic Year: Foreign Languages and Literature, November to May; Economics and Commerce, (October-March; March-May).
Admission Requirements: Secondary school certificate (maturità).
Fees: According to family's income.
Language of Instruction: Italian.
Academic Staff, 1989-90: 111 (11).
Student Enrolment, 1989-90: 5000.

3758 ***UNIVERSITÀ DEGLI STUDI DI BOLOGNA**
University of Bologna
Via Zamboni 33, 40126 Bologna
Telephone: (39) 51-220980
Rettore: Fabio Roversi Monaco (1985-88)
Direttore Amministrativo: Francesco Stumpo

F. of Law
Dean: Roberto Bonini; *staff* 11 (26)
F. of Political Science
Dean: Augusto Balloni; *staff* 23 (7)
F. of Economics and Commerce
Dean: Giancarlo Barbiroli; *staff* 31 (12)
F. of Statistics, Demography, and Actuarial Sciences
Dean: Scardovi Italo
F. of Letters and Philosophy
Dean: Giancarlo Susini; *staff* 66 (2)
F. of Magister (Teacher Training)
Dean: Mario Pazzaglia; *staff* 41
F. of Medicine and Surgery
Dean: Gianpaolo Salvioli; *staff* 43 (53)
F. of Mathematics, Physics, and Natural Sciences
Dean: Sergio Focardi; *staff* 75 (3)
F. of Industrial Chemistry
Dean: Paolo Edgardo Todesco; *staff* 19
F. of Pharmacy
Dean: Sergio Ferri; *staff* 14
F. of Engineering (including Architecture)
Dean: Leonardo Marchetti; *staff* 80 (27)
F. of Agriculture (including Forestry and Zoology)
Dean: Gabriele Goidanich; *staff* 42 (2)
F. of Veterinary Medicine
Dean: Giuseppe Gentile; *staff* 25
I. of Music and Drama
Language Ce.
Research Ce. for Medieval Texts
Also 10 postgraduate schools and courses of the different faculties.

Founded 11th century with faculties of law and arts. Faculty of science developed in 17th century. Acquired present status 1802. A State institution enjoying administrative autonomy. Financially supported by the State and by other bodies. Governing bodies: the Consiglio di Amministrazione (Administrative Board); the Senato Accademico (Academic Senate). Residential facilities for 1004 students.

Arrangements for co-operation with the Universities of: Montpellier; Łódź.

Academic Year: November to October (November-June).
Admission Requirements: Secondary school certificate (maturità) or recognized foreign equivalent.
Language of Instruction: Italian.
Degrees and Diplomas: Laurea, Doctor, in–Law; Political Science; Economics and Commerce; Letters; Philosophy; Modern Languages and Literature; Education; Mathematics; Physics; Mathematics and Physics; Natural Sciences; Biology; Geology; Pharmacy; Agriculture; Veterinary Medicine, 4 yrs; Chemistry; Industrial Chemistry; Civil Engineering; Mechanical Engineering; Electrical Engineering; Chemical Engineering; Mining Engineering; Nuclear Engineering, 5 yrs; Medicine, 6 yrs. Diploma in Statistics, 2 yrs. Also postgraduate diplomas of specialization.
Libraries: Central Library, *c.* 660,000 vols; faculty libraries.
Special Facilities (Museums, etc.): Museums: History; Naval; Zoology; Geology and Palaeontology; Astronomy.
Publication: Bollettino ufficiale (quarterly).

Academic Staff, 1986-87:

Rank	Full-time	Part-time
Professori ordinari e straordinari	535	133
Professori associati	802	127
Total	1337	260

Student Enrolment, 1986-87:

	Men	Women	Total
Of the country	31,070	26,487	57,557
Of other countries	1664	547	2211
Total	32,734	27,034	59,768

3759 **UNIVERSITÀ DEGLI STUDI DI BRESCIA**
University of Brescia
Piazza Mercato 15, 25121 Brescia
Telex: 304116 UNIVBS I
Telephone: (39-30) 29881
Fax: (39-30) 2988329
Rettore: Augusto Preti
Direttore Amministrativo: Franco Quarantelli

F. of Medicine and Surgery
Dean: Pier Franco Spano; *staff* 34 (27)
F. of Engineering (including Mathematics, Chemistry, Physics, Electronics, Mechanics, Materials Science related to Civil Engineering, Building Restoration)
Dean: Antonio Bugini; *staff* 25 (14)
F. of Economics and Commerce (including Business Adinistration, Civil and Labour Law, Social Sciences, Mathematics and Statistics)
Dean: Vincenzo Allegri; *staff* 27 (13)
Also 15 departments of the different faculties.

Founded 1982. A State institution enjoying administrative autonomy. Governing bodies: the Consiglio di Amministrazione; the Senato Accademico.

Arrangements for co-operation with the Polytecnic of East London.

Academic Year: October to June (October-February; March-June).
Admission Requirements: Secondary school certificate (maturità) or recognized foreign equivalent.
Fees (Lire): 284,000-441,000 per annum.
Language of Instruction: Italian.
Degrees and Diplomas: Laurea, 4-5 yrs; Medicine and Surgery, 6 yrs. Diploma of Technician for Biomedical Laboratories, 2 yrs.
Libraries: Total, *c.* 37,500 vols. Engineering, *c.* 8500; Medicine and Surgery, *c.* 8000; Economics and Commerce, *c.* 21,000.
Publication: Notiziario dell'Università degli Studi di Brescia (quarterly review).

Academic Staff, 1989-90:

Rank	Full-time	Part-time
Full Professors	39	27
Associate Professors	47	27
Researchers	83	3
Total	169	57

Student Enrolment, 1989-90:

	Men	Women	Total
Of the country	4567	2351	6918
Of the countries	125	32	157
Total	4692	2383	7075

3760 ***UNIVERSITÀ DEGLI STUDI DI CAGLIARI**
University of Cagliari
Via Università 40, 09100 Cagliari, Sardinia
Telephone: (39) 70-662493
Rettore: Dulio Casula

F. of Law
F. of Political Science
F. of Economics and Commerce
F. of Letters and Philosophy
F. of Magistero (Teacher Training)
F. of Medicine and Surgery
F. of Mathematics, Physics, and Natural Sciences
F. of Pharmacy
F. of Engineering (Hydraulic, Mechanical, Transport, Construction and Architecture)
Also 24 postgraduate schools and courses of the different faculties.

Founded 1606 by Bull of Pope Paul V, confirmed by Philip III of Spain in 1620. A State institution enjoying administrative and academic autonomy. Financed by the State. Governing bodies: the Consiglio di Amministrazione, composed of government representatives and members of the academic staff nominated by the deans; the Senato Accademico. Some residential facilities.

Academic Year: November to October (November-May).

Admission Requirements: Secondary school certificate (maturità).

Language of Instruction: Italian.

Degrees and Diplomas: Laurea, Doctor, in all fields, 4 yrs, except Engineering, 5 yrs, and Medicine and Surgery, 6 yrs. Diploma of School Inspector, 3 yrs. Diplomas of postgraduate specialization.

Library: Faculty libraries.

Special Facilities (Museums, etc.): Museums: Anthropology; Geology; Natural Sciences.

Publications: Studi Sardi; Rendiconti Seminario Scienze; Studi Economico-giuridici; Annali Facoltà di Lettere e Filosofia;Annali Facoltà Economia e Commercio; Rassegna Medica Sarda.

Academic Staff: c. 1280.

Student Enrolment: c. 18,250.

3761 **UNIVERSITÀ DEGLI STUDI DELLA CALABRIA**

University of Calabria

Via Giacomo Matteotti, 87100 Calabria (Cosenza)

Telephone: (39) 984-861961

Rettore: Rosario Aiello (1987-90)

F. of Letters and Philosophy

F. of Mathematics, Physics, and Natural Sciences

F. of Engineering

F. of Economics and Social Sciences

Founded 1972.

Academic Staff: c. 500.

Student Enrolment: c. 6000.

3762 ***UNIVERSITÀ DEGLI STUDI DI CAMERINO**

University of Camerino

Via del Bastione, 62032 Camerino, C.A.P.

Telex: 560024 UNICAM

Telephone: (737) 4011

Fax: (737) 40289

Rettore: Mario Giannella (1989-92)

Direttore Amministrativo: Mario Rosario Cavliere

F. of Law (including Political Science)

President: Ignazio Buti

F. of Mathematics, Physics, and Natural Sciences

President: Giovanni Materazzi

F. of Pharmacy

President: Mario Grifantini

Also 2 postgraduate schools, and 6 departments and 7 institutes of the different faculties.

Founded as Collegio dei Dottori 1336 by Bull of Pope Benedetto XII, formally recognized as university 1727 by Bull of Pope Benedetto XIII, and 1753 by Charter of Emperor Francis I of Lorraine who conferred on the Rector the title of Count (which is still used). Closed except for chair of Law by Napoleon. Re-established by Pope Pius VII 1816, and finally reorganized by Bull of Pope Leo XII. Recognized as a free university by decree 1861,confirmed 1923. Became a State institution 1958, enjoying administrative autonomy. Governing bodies: the Senato Accademico; the Consiglio di Amministrazione. Residential facilities for academic staff and students.

Arrangements for co-operation with the Universities of: Moscow; Ljubljana; Warsaw; Nice; Besançon; Maryland;Boston; Leeds. Technical University of Gdańsk.

Academic Year: November to October.

Admission Requirements: Secondary school certificate (maturità) (classical or scientific), or in some fields, technical secondary certificate.

Language of Instruction: Italian.

Degrees and Diplomas: Laurea, Doctor, in–Law; Political Science; Mathematics; Geology; Biology; Natural Sciences; Pharmacy, 4 yrs; Chemistry; Pharmaceutical Chemistry and Technology, 5 yrs. Also postgraduate diplomas of specialization.

Libraries: Law, *c.* 192,000 vols; libraries of the Departments and Institutes.

Publications: Annuario; Notiziario dell'Università degli Studi di Camerino; Medicina Legale–Quaderni Camerti; Studi geologici camerti.

Press or Publishing House: Centro Stampa.

Academic Staff, 1989-90:

Rank	Full-time	Part-time
Ordinari	47	3
Associati	92	13
Assistenti	3	–
Total	142	16

Student Enrolment, 1989-90: 5000.

3763 **UNIVERSITÀ DEGLI STUDI DI CASSINO**

University of Cassino

Via Marconi, 03043 Cassino (Frosinone)

Telephone: (39) 776-26633

Rettore: Piergiorgio Parroni

F. of Magistero (Teacher Training)

F. of Economics and Commerce

F. of Mechanical Engineering

Founded 1979. A State institution enjoying administrative autonomy.

Academic Year: November to October.

Admission Requirements: Secondary school certificate (maturità).

Language of Instruction: Italian.

Degrees and Diplomas: Doctor, 4-5 yrs.

3764 ***UNIVERSITÀ DEGLI STUDI DI CATANIA**

University of Catania

2 Piazza dell'Università, 95129 Catania

Telephone: (39) 95-311022

Rettore: Gaspare Rodolico (1974-)

F. of Law

F. of Political Science

F. of Economics and Commerce

F. of Letters and Philosophy

F. of Medicine and Surgery

F. of Mathematics, Physics and Natural Sciences

F. of Pharmacy

F. of Agriculture

F. of Engineering

Also 14 schools for specialized studies and schools of nursing and midwifery.

Founded 1434 as Siciliae Studium Generale by decree of King Alfonso of Aragon. The university is under the jurisdiction of the Ministry of Public Instruction, but enjoys administrative autonomy. Governing bodies: the Consiglio di Amministrazione; the Senato Accademico. Residential facilities for students.

Academic Year: November to October (November-January; February-March; June-October).

Admission Requirements: Secondary school certificate (maturità). Qualifications from appropriate technical or industrial schools also recognized for admission to faculties of Economics and Commerce and Agriculture.

Language of Instruction: Italian.

Degrees and Diplomas: Laurea, Doctor, in–Law; Political Science; Economics and Commerce; Letters; Philosophy; Foreign Languages and Literature; Physics; Mathematics; Engineering; Natural Sciences; Geology; Biology; Pharmacy; Agriculture, 4 yrs; Medicine and Surgery, 6 yrs.

Library: Faculty libraries.

Special Facilities (Museums, etc.): Zoology Museum.

Publications: Rivista di Diritto romano e antico 'Jura'; Annali del Seminario giuridico; Siculorum Gymnasium; Le Matematiche; La Pediatria; Nuova Didascaleion; Orpheus.

Academic Staff: c. 860.

Student Enrolment: c. 32,380.

3765 **UNIVERSITÀ ABRUZZESE DEGLI STUDI 'GABRIELE D'ANNUNZIO'**

Via dei Vestini, 66013 Chieti

Telephone: (39) 871-586141

Rettore: Aldo Bernadini

F. of Law (Teramo)

F. of Political Science (Teramo)

F. of Economics and Commerce (Pescara)

F. of Foreign Languages and Literature (Pescara)

F. of Letters and Philosophy

F. of Architecture (Pescara)

F. of Medicine and Surgery
Also 26 institutes of the different faculties.

Founded as a private institution 1961 with the support of various local and municipal authorities. Received State recognition 1965. Under the supervision of the Ministry of Education. Financed by an Inter-provincial Consortium consisting of the local and municipal authorities of Pescara, Chieti, and Teramo.

Academic Year: November to October.

Admission Requirements: Secondary school certificate (maturità) or foreign equivalent.

Language of Instruction: Italian.

Degrees and Diplomas: Laurea, Doctor, in–Law; Political Science; Economics and Commerce; Foreign Languages and Literature; Letters;Philosophy, 4 yrs; Architecture, 5 yrs; Medicine and Surgery, 6 yrs.

Publication: Collections of the Faculties of Medicine and Law.

Academic Staff: c. 600.

Student Enrolment: c. 16,000.

3766 **UNIVERSITÀ DEGLI STUDI DI FERRARA**

University of Ferrara
Via Savonarola 9, 44100 Ferrara
Telephone: (39) 532-39181
Rettore: Antonio Rossi (1974-)

F. of Law
F. of Medicine and Surgery
F. of Mathematics, Physics, and Natural Sciences
F. of Pharmacy
F. of Magistero (Teacher Training)

Founded 1391 as Studium Generale by Bull of Pope Boniface IX with faculties of law, arts, and theology. Suppressed in 1394, the institution was re-established in 1402. Became Università dello Stato Pontificio 1598. Reformed 1771 by Pope Clement XIV. Became an independent institution 1860. A private university, became a national university 1942. Some residential facilities for students.

Academic Year: November to October (November-May).

Admission Requirements: Secondary school certificate (maturità).

Language of Instruction: Italian.

Degrees and Diplomas: Laurea, Doctor, in–Law; Mathematics; Physics; Natural Sciences; Biology; Geology; Pharmacy, 4 yrs; Chemistry,5 yrs; Medicine and Surgery, 6 yrs.

Special Facilities (Museums, etc.): Natural History Museum; Mineralogy and Geology Museum.

Publication: Annali della Università di Ferrara.

Academic Staff: c. 260.

Student Enrolment: c. 6000.

3767 **UNIVERSITÀ DEGLI STUDI DI FIRENZE**

University of Florence
Piazza San Marco 4, 50121 Firenze
Telex: 572400 UNIFI
Telephone: (39) 55-27571
Rettore: Franco Scaramuzzi (1979-)

F. of Law
Dean: Francesco Onida
F. of Political and Social Sciences
Dean: Luigi Lotti
F. of Economics and Commerce
Dean: Gianni Galli
F. of Letters and Philosophy
Dean: Guido Clemente
F. of Magistero (Teacher Training)
Dean: Mario Citroni
F. of Medicine and Surgery
Dean: Ugo Teodori
F. of Pharmacy
Dean: Giuseppe Colosi
F. of Architecture
Dean: Mario Guido Cusmano
F. of Agriculture
Dean: Ugo Sorbi
F. of Mathematics, Physics, and Natural Sciences
Dean: Mario Primicelio
F. of Engineering
Dean: Giuliano Augusti
Also 17 institutes, 2 laboratories, 22 schools and courses for specialized studies, and 32 schools of the Faculty of Medicine.

Founded 1321 as Studium Generale by the Republic of Florence. Recognized by Bull of Pope Clement VII 1349 and by Royal Decree of Charles IV 1364. Transferred to Pisa 1472 but law and medicine continued to be taught in Florence. Reorganized as Istituto di Studi Superiori Pratici e di Perfezionamento 1859. The institution became autonomous 1872 and was granted full university status 1924. The university is under the jurisdiction of the Ministry of Public Instruction and is financially supported by the State. Governing bodies: the Consiglio di Amministrazione; the Senato Accademico.

Arrangements for co-operation with: The Johns Hopkins University; Rutgers University; Cornell University; Virginia Polytechnic Institute; University of Paris III; University of Rheims; Institut d'Etudes politiques, Paris; University of Nanking; Kiev State University; University of the Punjab.

Academic Year: November to May.

Admission Requirements: Secondary school certificate (maturità). Qualifications from appropriate technical or industrial schools also recognized for admission to faculties of Economics and Commerce, and Agriculture.

Language of Instruction: Italian.

Degrees and Diplomas: Laurea, Doctor, in–Agriculture; Forestry; Economics and Commerce; Pharmacy; Law; Letters; Philosophy; Modern Languages and Literature; Education; Foreign Languages and Literature (F. of Magistero); Physics; Mathematics; Natural Sciences; Statistics; Education; Biology; Geology; Political Science, 4 yrs; Engineering, 5 yrs; Medicine and Surgery, 6 yrs. Diploma of School Inspector (elementary level). Post-Laurea certificates and courses of specialization in all faculties.

Library: Faculty libraries: *c.* 280,000 vols.

Special Facilities (Museums, etc.): Museums: Anthropology; Botany; Geology and Palaeontology; Mineralogy.

Publications: Monitore Zootecnico Italiano; Webbia; Caryologo (Botanical); Ortoflorofrutticoltura; Lo Sperimentale.

Academic Staff: c. 810 (560).

Student Enrolment: c. 42,700.

3768 ***UNIVERSITÀ DEGLI STUDI DI GENOVA**

University of Genoa
Via Balbi 5, 16126 Genova
Telex: 271114
Telephone: (39-10) 2099
Fax: (39-10) 2099227
Rettore: Enrico Beltrametti
Direttore Amministrativo: Domenico Pellitteri

F. of Law
Dean: Franca de Marini
F. of Political Science
Dean: Adriano Giovannelli
F. of Economics and Commerce
Dean: Vittorio Sirotti
F. of Letters and Philosophy
F. of Magistero (Teacher Training)
Dean: Adriana Della Casa Puccioni
F. of Medicine and Surgery
Dean: Sandro Pontremoli
F. of Mathematics, and Physical and Natural Sciences
Dean: Riccardo Ferro
F. of Pharmacy
Dean: Gaetano Bignardi
F. of Engineering
Dean: Orestino Acton
F. of Architecture
Dean: Edoardo Benvenuto
Also 12 schools of specialization and 52 schools of the Faculty of Medecine.

Founded 1471 by Bull of Pope Sixtus IV, recognized by Emperor Maximilian. Acquired university status and reorganized 1773. The university is under the jurisdiction of the Ministry of Public Instruction, but enjoys administrative autonomy. Financially supported by the State. Governing bodies: Consiglio di Amministrazione; the Senato Accademico; the Direttore Amministrativo; the Consiglio di Facoltà. Some residential facilities for students.

Arrangements for co-operation with the Universities of: Pecs; Ohio; Paris X; Bordeaux; Cantabri; Innsbruck. Participates in the ERASMUS, COMETT, BRITE, Science programmes.

Academic Year: November to October (November-May).
Admission Requirements: Secondary school certificate (maturità) or equivalent.
Fees (Lira): 177,000-384,000 per annum.
Language of Instruction: Italian.
Degrees and Diplomas: Laurea, Doctor, in–Geography; Political Science; Law; Economics and Commerce; Letters; Education; Philosophy; Foreign Languages and Literature; Modern Languages and Literature; History; Pharmacy; Chemistry; Physics; Mathematics; Natural Sciences; Geology; Biology; Industrial Chemistry, 4 yrs; Civil Engineering; Mechanical Engineering; Electrical Engineering; Chemical Engineering; Naval Engineering; Electronic Engineering; Pharmaceutical Technology and Chemistry; Architecture, 5 yrs; Medicine and Surgery, 6 yrs. Diploma in Optometry. Diploma of School Inspector (elementary level), 3 yrs. Also Post-Laurea certificates and courses of specialization in various faculties.
Libraries: Central Library; faculty libraries.
Special Facilities (Museums, etc.): Orto Botanico.
Publications: Annali della Facoltà di Giurisprudenza; Annali della Facoltà di Scienze Politiche; Lo Stato della Ricerca (annually).
Academic Staff, 1989-90: 1316 (370).
Student Enrolment, 1989-90: 38,767 (Also 464 foreign students).

3769 **UNIVERSITÀ DEGLI STUDI DI LECCE**
University of Lecce
Viale Taranto 2, 73100 Lecce
Telex: 860830 UNSTLE I
Telephone: (39) 0832-4711
Rettore: Donato Valli (1983-89)
Direttore Amministrativo: Claudio Mellina

F. of Letters and Philosophy
Dean: Mario Marti; *staff* 72
F. of Magistero (Teacher Training)
Dean: O. Bianco; *staff* 130
F. of Mathematics, Physics, and Natural Sciences
Dean: S. Mongelli; *staff* 95
F. of Economics and Banking

Founded 1966. Under the jurisdiction of the Ministry of Public Instruction but enjoys administrative autonomy. Governing bodies: Consiglio di Amministrazione; the Senato Accademico. Residential facilities for students.
Arrangements for co-operation with the Universities of: Lublin; Amsterdam; Warsaw.
Academic Year: November to October.
Admission Requirements: Secondary school certificate (maturità).
Language of Instruction: Italian.
Degrees and Diplomas: Laurea, Doctor, in–Letters; Philosophy; Education; Languages; Mathematics; Physics; Biology; Diploma of School Inspector (elementary level).
Library: Central Library, *c.* 90,000 vols.
Publications: Publications of the institutes and departments; Bollettino di Storia della Filosofia.
Academic Staff, 1986-87 350.:
Student Enrolment, 1986-87:

	Men
Of the country	6800
Of other countries	200
Total	7000

3770 ***UNIVERSITÀ DEGLI STUDI DI MACERATA**
University of Macerata
Piaggia dell'Università 2, 62100 Macerata
Telephone: (39-733) 44181
Fax: (39-733) 232639
Rettore: Giovanni Ferretti (1988-91)
Direttore Amministrativo: Tito Morelli

F. of Law
Dean: Alberto Febbrajo
F. of Letters and Philosophy
Dean: Ferdinando Montuschi
F. of Political Science
Dean: Alberto Massera
Also 22 institutes, departments and schools of specialization of the different faculties.

Founded 1290 as a school of law. Recognized as a university, Studium Generale, by the Bull of Pope Paul III 1540. Governing bodies: the Senato Accademico; the Consiglio di Amministrazione. Residential facilities for students.
Arrangements for co-operation with: University of Abidjan; University of Alicante; University of Łódź. Participates in the ERASMUS programme.
Academic Year: November to October.
Admission Requirements: Secondary school certificate (maturità).
Fees (Lira): Registration, 50,000; tuition, 120,000.
Language of Instruction: Italian.
Degrees and Diplomas: Laurea, Doctor, in–Law; Letters; Philosophy; Political Science; Foreign Languages; Letters, 4 yrs. Diploma ofpostgraduate specialization in Syndicate Law, 2 yrs. Also Diploma in Musicology and Music Pedagogy, 2 yrs.
Libraries: Central Library, 20,000 vols; institute libraries, 220,000.
Publications: Annali e Pubblicazioni della Facoltà di Giurisprudenza; Annali e Pubblicazioni della Facoltà di Lettere e Filosofia.
Academic Staff, 1989-90:

Rank	Full-time	Part-time
Professori ordinari	37	2
Professori associati	52	5
Professori incaricati	3	–
Assistenti	11	4
Ricercatori	49	3
Total	152	14

Student Enrolment, 1989-90:

	Men	Women	Total
Of the country	2277	308	6085
Of other countries	95	61	156
Total	2372	3869	6241

3771 **UNIVERSITÀ DEGLI STUDI DI MESSINA**
University of Messina
Via Tommaso Cannizzaro, 98100 Messina
Telephone: (39) 90-711022
Rettore: Guglielmo Stagno d'Alcontres

F. of Law
F. of Political Science
F. of Economics and Commerce
F. of Letters and Philosophy (including Archaeology)
F. of Magistero (Teacher Training)
F. of Medicine and Surgery
F. of Veterinary Medicine
F. of Pharmacy
F. of Mathematics, Physics, and Natural Sciences

Founded 1548 and recognized by Bull of Pope Paul III. Suppressed by the Spanish 1678, restored 1838. A State institution under the jurisdiction of the Ministry of Public Instruction. Governing bodies: the Consiglio di Amministrazione; the Senato Accademico; Consiglio di Facoltà. Some residential facilities for students.
Academic Year: November to October (November-May).
Admission Requirements: Secondary school certificate (maturità).
Language of Instruction: Italian.
Degrees and Diplomas: Laurea, Doctor, in–Law; Political Science; Economics and Commerce; Letters; Philosophy; Foreign Languages; Literature; Education; Veterinary Medicine; Mathematics; Physics; Natural Sciences; Biology; Pharmacy, 4 yrs; Chemistry, 5 yrs; Medicine and Surgery, 6 yrs. Postgraduate diploma of specialization. Diploma of School Inspector (elementary level), 3 yrs.
Academic Staff: *c.* 150.
Student Enrolment: *c.* 15,000.

3772 ***UNIVERSITÀ DEGLI STUDI DI MILANO**
University of Milan
Via Festa del Perdono 7, 20122 Milano
Telex: 320484
Telephone: (39-2) 88461
Fax: (39-2) 58304482
Rettore: Paolo Mantegazza (1987-93)
Direttore Amministrativo: Piero Cassani

F. of Law
Dean: Antonio Schioppa; *staff* 16 (25)

F. of Political Science
Dean: Alberto Martinelli; *staff* 17 (14)
F. of Letters and Philosophy
Dean: Enrico Decleva; *staff* 61 (2)
F. of Medicine and Surgery (including Dentistry)
Dean: Antonio Scala; *staff* 18 (97)
F. of Pharmacy
Dean: Rodolfo Paoletti; *staff* 28 (1)
F. of Mathematics, Physics, and Natural Sciences
Dean: Marcello Fontanesi; *staff* 149 (10)
F. of Agriculture
Dean: Dario Casati; *staff* 38 (4)
F. of Veterinary Medicine
Dean: Giuseppe Rognoni; *staff* 30 (1)
Ce. for Lifelong Education
Also 139 institutes and departments of the faculties and 94 schools of specialized studies, and 55 research centres. Also 10 schools for short-term courses.

Founded 1924. The university is under the jurisdiction of the Ministry of University and Scientific Technological Research but enjoys administrative autonomy. Governing bodies: the Consiglio di Amministrazione; the Senato Accademico. Some residential facilities for academic staff and students.

Arrangements for co-operation with the Universities of: São Paulo; Renè Descartes (Paris V); Buenos Aires; Düsseldorf; Pennsylvania; Bahia; Pittsburg; Ljubljana; San Diego; California; Chicago; Santiago di Compostela; City of Dublin; Colorado (Health Sciences Centre); Pierre et Marie Curie (Paris VI); Institute of Chemical Technology, Moscow; Católica di Nuestra Senora de la Asunción, (Paraguay); Bordeaux I; Louvain; Novosibirsk; Valencia; Zagreb; Pettsburgh; Rosario, Argentina. 2nd Medical College of Shanghai; Royal Postgraduate Medical School of London; Georgia Institute of Medicine, USSR; Academy of Science, Kiev; Academy of Political Science, Poznán.

Academic Year: November to October (October-February; March-July).

Admission Requirements: Secondary school certificate (maturità) in appropriate subjects, or in some fields, technical school certificate.

Fees (Lira): 473,000-668,000.

Language of Instruction: Italian.

Degrees and Diplomas: Laurea, Doctor, in–Law; Letters; Philosophy; Political Science; History; Information Sciences; Modern Languages and Literature; Physics; Mathematics; Natural Sciences; Biology; Geology; Pharmacy; 4 yrs; Chemistry; Pharmaceutical Technology; Agriculture; Nutrition; Veterinary Medicine; Dentistry; Industrial Chemistry; Animal Husbandry, 5 yrs; Medicine and Surgery, 6 yrs. Diploma of postgraduate specialization. Dottorato di ricerca, Doctorate of Research.

Libraries: Faculty of Agriculture, 61,240 vols; Faculty of Veterinary Medicine, *c.* 31,420; Law, Letters and Philosophy, *c.* 637,860; Political Science, *c.* 46,179; Medicine, *c.* 79,233; Sciences, *c.* 103,850; Pharmacy *c.* 13,730.

Special Facilities (Museums, etc.): Zoology Museum; Observatory.

Publications: Guida alle Scuole di specializzazione (annually); Scientific Publications; Educazione Permanente (monthly).

Academic Staff, 1988-89:

Rank	Full-time	Part-time
Professori ordinori i straordinari	417	154
Professori associati	609	219
Assistenti	32	29
Ricercatori	471	96
Total	1519	498

Student Enrolment, 1988-89: 83,098 (Also 914 externel students).

3773 *UNIVERSITÀ CATTOLICA DEL SACRO CUORE

Catholic University of the Sacred Heart
Largo Agostino Gemelli I, 20123 Milano
Cables: universcatmi
Telex: 321033 UCATMI
Telephone: (39-2) 8856
Fax: (39-2) 8856-508
Rettore: Adriano Bausola (1989-92)
Direttore Amministrativo: Domenico Lofrese

F. of Law
Dean: Giorgio Pastori; *staff* 21 (19)
F. of Political Science
Dean: Alberto Quadrio Curzio; *staff* 31 (6)
F. of Economics and Commerce
Dean: Sergio Zaninelli; *staff* 25 (25)
F. of Letters and Philosophy
Dean: Giovanni Tarditi; *staff* 112 (2)
F. of Magistero (Teacher Training) (Milan and Brescia)
Dean: Enzo Noè Girardi; *staff* 94 (8)
F. of Agriculture (including Forestry and Viticulture) (Piacenza)
Dean: Gianfranco Piva; *staff* 76 (1)
F. of Medicine and Surgery (including Dentistry) (Rome)
Dean: Ermanno Manni; *staff* 426 (159)
F. of Mathematics, Physical and Natural Sciences (Brescia)
Dean: Carlo Banfi; *staff* 12
Also 39 institutes, and 36 clinics and schools of the Faculty of Medicine.

Founded 1920 by decree of the Sacred Congregation of Studies and recognized by the Italian Government 1924. The degrees and diplomas awarded by the university are formally recognized by the State. Governing bodies: the Consiglio di Amministrazione; the Senato Accademico. Residential facilities for academic staff and students.

Arrangements for co-operation with: the Catholic Universities of Louvain; Catholic University of Lublin.

Academic Year: November to October.

Admission Requirements: Secondary school certificate (maturità), teacher's diploma or technical school diploma, or foreign equivalent.

Language of Instruction: Italian.

Degrees and Diplomas: Laurea, Doctor, in–Law; Political Science; Economics and Commerce; Economics and Banking; Mathematics; Philosophy; Modern European Languages and Literature; Foreign Languages and Literature, Letters; Education, 4 yrs; Agriculture; Dentistry, 5 yrs; Medicine and Surgery, 6 yrs. Diploma in Statistics, 2 yrs. Diploma of School Inspector (elementary level), 3 yrs. Also Diploma of postgraduate specialization.

Libraries: University Library, *c.* 1,296,500 vols; Rome, *c.* 226,700.

Publications: Acta Medica Romana (quarterly); Studi di Sociologia (quarterly); Aevum (every four months); Archivio di Psicologia, Neurologia e Psichiatria (quarterly); Rivista Internazionale di Scienze Sociali (quarterly); Aegyptus (biannually); Rivista di Filosofia Neoscolastica (quarterly); Vita e Pensiero (monthly); Annali della Facoltà di Agraria (biannually); Rivista del Clero Italiano (monthly); Bollettino dell'Archivo per la Storia del Presenza (quarterly); Giovani amici (monthly). JUS Rivista di Scienze Giruediche; Comunicazioni Sociali; Rivista Internazionale dei Diritti dell'Uomo.

Press or Publishing House: Editrice 'Vita e Pensiero'.

Academic Staff, 1989-90:

Rank	Full-time	Part-time
Professori ordinari	112	43
Professori associati	208	105
Ricercatori universitari	496	56
Professori a contratto	–	204
Assistenti ordinari	29	20
Total	845	428

Student Enrolment, 1989-90:

	Men	Women	Total
Of the country	11,873	15,210	27,083
Of other countries	62	105	167
Total	11,945	15,315	27,250

3774 UNIVERSITÀ COMMERCIALE 'LUIGI BOCCONI'

Via R. Sarfatti 25, N20136 Milano
Telex: UNIBOCI 316003
Telephone: (39) 2-5836.1
Fax: (39) 2-5836.2000
Rettore: Mario Monti (1989-)
Direttore Amministrativo: Enrico Resti

D. of Business Administration (including Civil and Public Law, Corporate Law, Mathematics Sociology, Statistics, Business Policy, Management of Commercial Companies, Banking, Management of Industrial Companies, Cost Accounting and Management Control Systems, Organizational Analysis, Economic Policy and Public Finance)
Director: Tancredi Bianchi
D. of Economics
Director: Adalberto Predetti
I. of Business Administration (including Accounting and Control, Management of the Public Administration)
Director: Carlo Masini

I. of Industrial and Commercial Companies Management
Director: Luigi Guatri
I. of Financial Intermediaries
Director: Paulo Mottura
I. of Economics (including Industrial and Labour Economics, International Economics, Monetary and Financial Economics)
Director: Mario Monti
I. of Quantitative Methods
Director: Donato Michele Cifarelli
I. of Economic History
Director: Aldo De Madalena
I. of Comparative Law
Director: Ariberto Mignoli
Computer Ce.
Director: Giorgio Faini
Also *c.* 20 Research Centres and Institutes.

Founded 1902, an autonomous institution recognized by the State. Governing bodies: the University Board; the Faculty Council. Residential facilities for academic staff and students.

Arrangements for co-operation with: ESADE, Barcelona; Ecole des hautes Etudes commerciales, Paris; Universität zu Köln; Erasmus Universiteit, Rotterdam; Université catholique de Louvain; Leningrad International Management Institute. Participates in the Programme of International Management (P.I.M.).

Academic Year: October to June (October-February; March-June).

Admission Requirements: Secondary school certificate (maturità) or foreign equivalent.

Fees (Lira): 800,000-6,000,000 according to family income.

Language of Instruction: Italian.

Degrees and Diplomas: Bachelor, 3-5 yrs. Master in Business Administration, 15 months.

Library: Central Library, 480,000 vols.

Publications: Giornale degli Economisti e Annali di Economia; Rivista Internazionale delle Scienze Economiche e Commerciali; Economia Internazionale delle Fonti di Energia; Commercio, Finanza Marketing e Produzione; Economia e Management; Economia e Politica Industriale; Sviluppo e Organizzazione; Bocconi Notizia (newsletter, monthly).

Press or Publishing House: EGEA Spa.

Academic Staff, 1989-90:

Rank	Full-time	Part-time
Professori ordinari	14	22
Professori associati	7	17
Ricercatori	8	11
Professori a contratto	–	194
Assistenti ordinari	2	1
Assistenti interni	1	–
Esercitatori	–	160
Contrattisti	–	52
Borsisti	–	115
Total	32	572

Student Enrolment, 1989-90: 10,600.

3775 **UNIVERSITÀ DEGLI STUDI DI MODENA**
University of Modena
Via Università 4, 41100 DModena
Telephone: (39) 59-329111
Rettore: Mario Vellani (1984-87)
Direttore Amministrativo: Placido Raffa

F. of Law
Dean: Luisa Galantino; *staff* 44 (9)
F. of Medicine and Surgery (including Dentistry)
Dean: Georgio Mattioli; *staff* 184 (50)
F. of Mathematics, Physics, and Natural Sciences
Dean: Paoli Fazzini
F. of Pharmacy
Dean: Maria Di Bella; *staff* 37
F. of Economics and Commerce
Dean: Marco Lippe; *staff* 51 (18)
F. of Science
Dean: Piero Vivarelli; *staff* 196 (10)
Computing Ce.
Electron-Microscopy Ce.
Marine Biology Ce. (Livorno)
Also 40 schools of specialized studies in medicine and 28 departments and institutes of the faculties.

Founded 1175 as a school of law. A State institution enjoying administrative autonomy. Governing bodies: the Consiglio di Amministrazione; the Senato Accademico. Some residential facilities for students.

Arrangements for co-operation with the University of Lublin.

Academic Year: November to October.

Admission Requirements: Secondary school certificate (maturità) or in some fields, technical school diploma.

Language of Instruction: Italian.

Degrees and Diplomas: Laurea, Doctor, in–Economics and Commerce; Law; Mathematics; Physics; Biology; Geology; Natural Sciences; Pharmacy, 4 yrs; Chemistry; Pharmaceutical Chemistry and Technology; Dentistry, 5 yrs; Medicine and Surgery, 6 yrs. Dottorato. Also postgraduate diplomas of specialization.

Libraries: Faculty libraries: Economics and Commerce, *c.* 23,000 vols; Law, *c.* 60,800; Institute of Mathematics, *c.* 8900.

Special Facilities (Museums, etc.): Museums: Anatomy; Zoology; Mineralogy.

Academic Staff, 1986-87:

Rank	Full-time	Part-time
Professori 1 fascia	106	30
Professori 2 fascia	231	57
Assistenti	27	–
Ricercatori	148	–
Incaricati	22	–
Supplenti	60	–
Total	594	87

Student Enrolment, 1986-87:

	Men	Women	Total
Of the country	4097	3176	7273
Of other countries	123	49	172
Total	4220	3225	7445

3776 **UNIVERSITÀ DEGLI STUDI DEL MOLISE**
Piazza G. Pepe, 86100 Campobasso
Telephone: (0874) 63045

F. of Economics and Social Sciences
F. of Agriculture

Founded 1982. In process of development.

3777 **UNIVERSITÀ DEGLI STUDI DI NAPOLI**
University of Naples
Corso Umberto 1, 80138 Napoli
Telephone: (39) 81-7819111
Rettore: Biagio de Giovanni

F. of Agriculture
F. of Architecture
F. of Economics and Commerce
F. of Pharmacy
F. of Law
F. of Letters and Philosophy
F. of Engineering
F. of Medicine and Surgery I
F. of Medicine and Surgery II
F. of Veterinary Medicine
F. of Mathematics, Physics and Natural Sciences
F. of Political Science
Also *c.* 110 schools for specialized studies.

Founded 1224 as Studium Generale by Frederick II. Dissolved 1229 and re-established 1234. Transferred to Salerno 1252 but returned to Naples 1258. The university is a State institution enjoying administrative autonomy. Governing bodies: the Consiglio di Amministrazione; the Senato Accademico.

Academic Year: November to October (November-May).

Admission Requirements: Secondary school certificate (maturità) or in certain fields, abilitazione tecnica.

Language of Instruction: Italian.

Degrees and Diplomas: Laurea, Doctor, in–Law; Political Science; Economics and Commerce; Letters; Philosophy; Modern Languages and Literature; Physics; Mathematics; Natural Sciences; Biology; Geology; Pharmacy; Agriculture, 4 yrs; Chemistry; Industrial Chemistry; Veterinary Medicine; Architecture; Civil Engineering; Constructional Engineering; Transport Engineering; Hydraulic Engineering; Mechanical Engineering; Chemical Engineering; Electrical Engineering; Aeronautical Engineering;

Electronic Engineering; Naval and Mechanical Engineering, 5 yrs; Medicine and Surgery, 6 yrs. Postgraduate diplomas of specialization.

Library: Faculty and institute libraries, *c.* 290,000.

Special Facilities (Museums, etc.): Museums: Zoology; Palaeontology; Geology and Earth Sciences; Mineralogy. Erbario.

Publications: Annuario; Statuto (every three years); Faculty publications.

Academic Staff: c. 3430.

Student Enrolment: c. 128,520.

3778 ***UNIVERSITÀ DEGLI STUDI DI PADOVA**

University of Padua

Via VIII Febbraio 2, 35122 Padova

Telex: UNPADU 430176

Telephone: (39-49) 8283111

Fax: (39-49) 8283099

Rettore: Mario Bonsembiante (1987-90)

Direttore Amministrativo: Dino Artmann

F. of Law

Dean: Gentile Francesco

F. of Political Science

Dean: Dino Fiorot

F. of Statistical, Demographic, and Actuarial Sciences

Dean: Lorenzo Bernardi

F. of Letters and Philosophy

Dean: Vincenzo Milanesi

F. of Magistero (Teacher Training)

Dean: Giovanni Vicario

F. of Medicine and Surgery (including Dentistry)

Dean: Carolo Gregolin

F. of Mathematics, Physics and Natural Sciences

Dean: Vincenzo Albergoni

F. of Pharmacy

Dean: Sebastiao Marciani Magno

F. of Engineering

Dean: Luigi Mariani

F. of Agriculture

Dean: Arturo Zamorani

National I. of Nuclear Physics (I.N.F.N.)

Director: Antonio Cantele

Also 108 institutes and departments of the different faculties and 53 schools for short-term courses.

Founded 1222. A State institution enjoying administrative autonomy. Governing bodies: the Consiglio di Amministrazione; the Senato Accademico. Some residential facilities for students.

Arrangements for co-operation with: Eötvös Loránd University; Charles University, Prague; University of Warsaw; Copernicus University, Toruń; Jagiellonian University, Cracow. Universities of:Innsbruck; California, Santa Barbara; Würzburg; Zagreb; Boston; Paris VI, VII, and XI; Melbourne; Munich; Caxias do Sul; Salamanca; California, Berkeley; Cuyo do Mandoza; Münster; Nice; Minnesota; Pennsylvania; Fluminense, Niteroi. FukuiInstitute of Technology; Boston School of Medicine.

Academic Year: November to October (November-May).

Admission Requirements: Secondary school certificate (maturità) or equivalent.

Fees (Lira): 300,000 per annum.

Language of Instruction: Italian.

Degrees and Diplomas: Laurea, Doctor, in–Law; Political Science; Arts and Literature; Philosophy; Education; Physics; Mathematics; Biology; Psychology; Economics; Commerce; Astronomy; Geology; Languages; Statistics; Natural Sciences; Forestry; Pharmacy; Agriculture, 4 yrs; Chemistry; Industrial Chemistry; Engineering; Dentistry, 5 yrs; Medicine and Surgery, 6 yrs. Diploma in Statistics, 2 yrs. Diploma of School Inspector (elementary level). Postgraduate diplomas of specialization, 2 yrs after degree.

Libraries: Central Library; American Library; faculty libraries.

Special Facilities (Museums, etc.): Museums of Anthropology and Ethnology.

Publications: Scienza e Cultura; Giano Pannonio.

Academic Staff, 1989-90:

Rank	Full-time
Professori ordinari	541
Professori associati	778
Researchers	568
Total	1887

Student Enrolment, 1989-90:

	Men	Women	Total
Of the country	25,648	26,661	52,309
Of other countries	550	356	906
Total	26,198	27,017	53,215

3779 **UNIVERSITÀ DEGLI STUDI DI PALERMO**

University of Palermo

Piazza Marina 61, 90100 Palermo

Telephone: (39) 91-283041

Rettore: Ignazio Melisanda Giambertoni

F. of Law

F. of Letters and Philosophy

F. of Economics and Commerce

F. of Medicine and Surgery

F. of Mathematics, Physics, and Natural Sciences

F. of Engineering

F. of Architecture

F. of Agriculture

F. of Pharmacy

F. of Magistero (Teacher Training)

Founded 1779 as academy, became university by Royal Decree 1806. A State institution enjoying administrative autonomy. Governing bodies: the Consiglio di Amministrazione; the Senato Accademico.

Arrangements for co-operation with: National University of San Agustin, Arequipa; Huazhong Normal University; Moscow State University.

Academic Year: November to October (November-May).

Admission Requirements: Secondary school certificate (maturità) or recognized equivalent.

Fees (Lira): Registration, 50,000; tuition, 120,000.

Language of Instruction: Italian.

Degrees and Diplomas: Laurea, Doctor, in–Law; Political Science; Economics and Commerce; Letters; Philosophy; Physics; Mathematics; Natural Sciences; Biology; Geology; Agriculture; Literature; Education; Foreign Languages and Literature; Pharmacy, 4 yrs; Chemistry; Architecture; Engineering, 5 yrs; Medicine and Surgery, 6 yrs. Dottorato di ricerca, Doctorate of Research.

Library: Faculty libraries, total, 470,780 vols.

Special Facilities (Museums, etc.): Museo de Paleontologia.

Academic Staff, 1986-87:

Rank	Full-time	Part-time
Professori ordinari	252	89
Professori associati	462	184
Assistenti ordinari	142	–
Total	756	273

Student Enrolment, 1986-87:

	Men	Women	Total
Of the country	17,354	15,188	32,542
Of other countries	395	114	509
Total	17,749	15,302	33,051

3780 ***UNIVERSITÀ DEGLI STUDI DI PARMA**

University of Parma

Via Università 12, 43100 Parma

Telex: 530327

Telephone: (521) 2041

Fax: (521) 207521

Rettore: Nicola C. Occhiocupo (1989-92)

Dirigente Superiore: Gian Paolo Usberti

F. of Law

Dean: A. Albisetti; *staff* 46 (28)

F. of Arts (including Letters and Philosophy)

Dean: Arturo Carlo Quintavalle; *staff* 114 (12)

F. of Economics and Commerce
Dean: G. Bonilini; *staff* 54 (24)
F. of Pharmacy
Dean: Tullio Vitali; *staff* 37
F. of Medicine and Surgery
Dean: A. Novarini; *staff* 2032 (57)
F. of Veterinary Medicine
Dean: G. Ballarini; *staff* 54 (3)
F. of Mathematics, Physics, and Natural Sciences
Dean: Franco Conterio; *staff* 242 (2)
F. of Engineering
Dean: G. Albanese; *staff* 36 (5)
S. of Midwifery
Director: Francesco Coppola
S. of Optometry
Director: Mario Maione
S. of Social Work
Director: Guglielmo Masotti
S. of Physiotherapy
Director: A. Lechi
S. of Audiometrics
Director: Carlo Zini
S. of Health Physics
Director: I. Ortalli
S. Of Business Management (IFOA)
Director: G.P. Lugli
S. of Informatics
Director: U. Emiliani
Also *c.* 120 institutes and departments, 34 schools for specialized medical studies, and 3 for law, 2 for sciences, 3 for pharmacy, and 1 for veterinary medicine.

Founded 1064 but traces origin to schools of medicine and law established in the 8th century. A State institution enjoying administrative autonomy. Governing bodies: the Consiglio di Amministrazione; the Senato Accademico; Consigli di Facoltà. Residential facilities for *c.* 640 students.

Arrangements for co-operation with: University of Poitiers; University of Erlangen-Nürnberg; University of Mainz; University of Twente; Université Claude Bernard-Lyon I; University of Passau; Université de Bretagne occidentale; Université de Lille II; Université de Robert Schumann, Strasbourg; University of Wales; College of Cardiff.

Academic Year: November to October (November-May).

Admission Requirements: Secondary school certificate (maturità) or equivalent.

Fees (Lire): 408,000-524,000 per annum, according to Faculty.

Language of Instruction: Italian.

Degrees and Diplomas: Laurea, Doctor, in–Law; Economics and Commerce; Mathematics; Physics; Natural Sciences; Geology; Pharmacy; Arts; Philosopy; Modern Foreign Languages and Literature; Arts, 4 yrs; Dentistry; Chemical and Pharmaceutical Technology; Biology; Engineering; Chemistry; Industrial Chemistry; Veterinary Medicine, 5 yrs; Medicine and Surgery, 6 yrs. Postgraduate diplomas of specialization, 2 yrs after Laurea. Also Diploma in–Midwifery; Business Management; Informatics; Health Physics, 2 yrs; Social Work; Optometry; Physiotherapy; Audiometrics, 3 yrs. Dottorato di ricerca, Doctorate of Research.

Libraries: Faculty libraries: Medicine, *c.* 45,000 vols; Economics and Commerce, *c.* 60,000; Law, *c.* 57,000; Teacher Training, *c.* 35,000; Veterinary Medicine, *c.* 25,000; Science and Pharmacy, *c.* 50,000; Historical Library of Medicine, *c.* 8070.

Special Facilities (Museums, etc.): Museum of Natural Sciences; Centro Studi Archivio della Comunicazione (CSAC).

Publications: Annali di Economia e Commercio; Annali di Magistero; Annali dell'Istituto di Lingue e Letterature Germaniche; Rassegna di Storia della Filosofia; Quaderni di Storia dell'Arte; Rivista di Chimica; Rivista di Matematica; L'Ateneo Parmense (Act Biomedica) (Acta Naturalia); Rivista di Sociologia.

Academic Staff, 1989-90:

Rank	Full-time	Part-time
Professori ordinari i straordinari	202	33
Professori associati	300	45
Assistenti	33	8
Ricercatori	251	18
Lettori	–	16
Total	786	131

Student Enrolment, 1989-90:

	Men	Women	Total
Of the country	9359	9461	18,820
Of other countries			237
Total			19,057

3781 ***UNIVERSITÀ DEGLI STUDI DI PAVIA**

University of Pavia

Strada Nuova 65, 27100 Pavia
Telex: 312841 UNISAV I
Telephone: (39-382) 3871
Fax: (39-382) 21389
Electronic mail: BITNET:maint + @*pvccn ttention of*
Rettore: Roberto Schmid (1988-91)
Direttore Amministrativo: Gesuino Piga

F. of Law
Dean: Ferdinando Bona; *staff* 29 (18)
F. of Political Sciences
Dean: Pasquale Scaramozzino; *staff* 51 (10)
F. of Economics and Commerce
Dean: Piero Mella; *staff* 36 (22)
F. of Letters and Philosophy
Dean: Giorgetto Georgi; *staff* 122 (14)
F. of Medicine and Surgery
Dean: Egidio Romero; *staff* 165 (134)
F. of Mathematics, Physics, and Natural Sciences
Dean: Giuseppe Gerzeli; *staff* 247 (24)
F. of Pharmacy
Dean: Cesare Sinistri; *staff* 46 (9)
F. of Engineering (including Architecture, and Civil, Chemical, Electronic and Electrotechnical Engineering)
Dean: Vito Svelto; *staff* 79 (39)
Also 35 research institutes, 18 laboratories centres, and 30 departments of the different faculties.

Founded 825 as school of law, recognized as university, Studium Generale, 1361 by Emperor Charles IV. A State institution enjoying administrative autonomy. Governing bodies: the Senate; the Administrative Board; the Faculty Boards. Residential facilities for students, including twelve colleges, two of them dating from the 15th century.

Arrangements for co-operation with the Universities of: Fudan; Saint-Etienne; Dublin, Trinity College; Łódź (Technical); Besançon; Missouri; Hull; Strathclyde; Passau; Tianjin; Yunnan; Konstanz; Toulouse; Fourier, Grenoble; Vilnius. Participates in the ERASMUS programme, Coimbra Group, and PRIUS programme.

Academic Year: October to June (October-January; March-June).

Admission Requirements: Secondary school certificate (maturità) or equivalent.

Fees (Lire): 800,000-1,100,000 per annum, according to faculty.

Language of Instruction: Italian.

Degrees and Diplomas: Laurea, Doctor, in–Law; Political Sciences; Economics and Commerce; Letters; Philosophy; Foreign and Modern Languages and Literature; Mathematics; Physics; Natural Sciences; Geology; Pharmacy; Musicology, 4 yrs; Dentistry; Pharmaceutical Chemistry and Technology; Engineering; Chemistry; Biological Sciences, 5 yrs; Medicine and Surgery, 6 yrs. Doctorates in all fields. Also first level diplomas, postgraduate diplomas of specialization, and doctorate.

Libraries: Central University, *c.* 480,000 vols; libraries of the faculties departments and Humanities, *c.* 210,000; Economics, *c.* 30,000; Medicine, *c.* 60,000; Chemistry, *c.* 30,000; Mathematics, *c.* 25,000; Physics, *c.* 13,000; Engineering, *c.* 8500; Musicology, *c.* 10,000; Law, *c.* 90,000; Political Sciences, *c.* 10,000; Botany, *c.* 45,000.

Special Facilities (Museums, etc.): Museums: University History; Archaeology; Anatomy; Zoology; Mineralogy; Geology. Botanical Garden.

Publications: Atheneum (biannually); Autografo (every 4 months); Avocetta (biannually); Atti Istituto Botanico e Laboratorio Crittogamico (annually); Atti Ticinensi di Scienze della Terra (annually); Basic and applied Histochemistry (quarterly); Diritto Finanziario e Scienza delle Finanze (quarterly); Epidemiologia e Scienze Sanitarie Applicate (biannually); haematologica (monthly); Il Confronto Letterario (biannually); Microbiologica (annually); Il Politico (quarterly); Selecta Paediatrica (annually).

Academic Staff, 1986-87:

Rank	Full-time	Part-time
Professori ordinari	241	81
Professori associati	275	144
Ricercatori	275	45
Total	791	270

Student Enrolment, 1986-87:

	Men	Women	Total
Of the country	13,582	11,904	23,486
Of other countries	553	313	866
Total	14,135	12,217	26,352

3782 **UNIVERSITÀ DEGLI STUDI DI PERUGIA**

University of Perugia

Piazza della Università, 06100 Perugia

Telex: 662078

Telephone: (39) 75-4691

Rettore: Giancarlo Dozza (1976-)

Direttore Amministrativo: Carmelo Saetta

F. of Law
Dean: Severino Caprioli; *staff* 19 (2)
F. of Political Science
Dean: Franco Crespi; *staff* 11
F. of Letters and Philosophy
Dean: Antonio Pieretti; *staff* 21
F. of Magistero (Teacher Training)
Dean: Edoardo Mirri; *staff* 13
F. of Medicine and Surgery
Dean: Francesco Bistoni; *staff* 31 (23)
F. of Mathematics, Physics and Natural Sciences
Dean: Gian Gualberto Volpi; *staff* 51
F. of Pharmacy
Dean: Giuseppina Scassellati Sforzolini; *staff* 14
F. of Agriculture
Dean: Franco Lorenzetti; *staff* 31 (3)
F. of Veterinary Medicine
Dean: Guido Avellini; *staff* 19 (1)
F. of Economics and Commerce
Dean: Giuseppe Calzoni; *staff* 14 (2)
F. of Engineering
Dean: Calogero Vinti; *staff* 9 (2)
Also 105 institutes and departments of the different faculties, 4 research centres, and 32 schools of specialization.

Founded 1200, recognized as university, Studium Generale, by Pope Clement V 1308. A State institution. Governing bodies: the Consiglio di Amministrazione; the Senato Accademico. Some residential facilities for students.

Arrangements for co-operation with the Universities of: Tübingen; Bielefeld; Salzburg; Florida State; Santiago de Compostela; Campinas; Mississippi State; Granada; Newcastle-upon-Tyne; Copenhagen; Bratislava; Alicante;Southampton; Aix-Marseille II; Buenos Aires; Paris I. Wrocław Academy of Economics.

Academic Year: November to October (November-May).

Admission Requirements: Secondary school certificate (maturità) or foreign equivalent.

Fees (Lire): Registration, 50,000; tuition, 120,000-240,000, per annum.

Language of Instruction: Italian.

Degrees and Diplomas: Laurea, Doctor, in–Law; Letters and Philosophy; Education; Political Science; Economics and Commerce; Veterinary Medicine and Surgery; Agriculture; Pharmacy; Mathematics; Geology; Physics; Biology; Natural Sciences, 4 yrs; Medicine and Surgery, 6 yrs. Dottorato di ricerca, Doctorate of Research, 3-4 yrs. Also postgraduate diplomas of specialization in Faculty of Medicine and Surgery.

Libraries: Central Library, 150,000 vols; libraries of the faculties, 230,500; Classical Studies, 22,500.

Publications: Annali della Facoltà di–Giurisprudenza; Lettere e Filosofia; Medicina e Chirurgia; Scienze agrare; Medicina veterinaria; Scienze politiche; Economia e Commercio. La Salute Umana; Annali Italiani di Dermatologia e Clinica Sperimentale; Rivista di Idrobiologia; L'Università; Prosopon.

Academic Staff, 1989-90:

Rank	Full-time	Part-time
Professori 1 fascia	195	54
Professori 2 fascia	424	70
Professori incaricati	22	–
Assistenti di ruolo	42	–
Ricercatori universitari	280	–
Total	963	124

Student Enrolment, 1989-90:

	Men	Women	Total
Of the country	9819	10,658	20,477
Of other countries	477	436	913
Total	10,296	11,094	21,390

3783 **UNIVERSITÀ DEGLI STUDI DI PISA**

University of Pisa

Lungarno Pacinotti 43, 56100 Pisa

Telex: UNIVPI 590035

Telephone: (50) 590000

Fax: (50) 40834

Rettore: Gianfranco Elia (1989-92)

Direttore Amministrativo: Giorgio Coluccini

F. of Law
Dean: Eugenio Ripepe; *staff* 54 (16)
F. of Economics and Commerce
Dean: Alberto Cambini; *staff* 15 (2)
F. of Letters and Philosophy
Dean: Carlo Da Pozzo; *staff* 44 (11)
F. of Political Science
Dean: Agostino Palazzo; *staff* 58 (3)
F. of Foreign Languages and Literature
Dean: Guido Paduano; *staff* 39
F. of Medicine and Surgery
Dean: Francesco Squartini; *staff* 225 (71)
F. of Mathematics, Physics and Natural Sciences (including Computer Sciences)
Dean: Piero Maestrini
F. of Pharmacy
Dean: Bruno Macchia; *staff* 31
F. of Engineering (including Civil, Mechanical, Aeronautic, Electronic, and Nuclear Engineering)
Dean: Enrico Maria Latrofa; *staff* 117 (12)
F. of Agriculture (including Animal Husbandry)
Dean: Luciano Iacoponi; *staff* 44 (1)
F. of Veterinary Medicine
Dean: Aldo Romagnoli; *staff* 20 (1)
S. of Social Service
Director: Aldo Toscano
S. of Computer Sciences
Director: Franceso Romani
S. for Technicians of Audiometry and Phonologopaedics
Director: Franco Piragine
Also 35 departments of the different faculties and 24 institutes of the Faculty of Medicine and Surgery.

Founded 1343 as Studium Generale by decree by Pope Clement VI. A State institution enjoying administrative autonomy. Financially supported by the State. Governing bodies: the Consiglio di Amministrazione; the Senato Accademico. Residential facilities for 697 students.

Arrangements for co-operation with the Universities of: Angers; Syracuse; Dortmund; Frankfurt/Main; Leipzig. Sheffield City Polytechnic; Washington State; Campinas; Caracas; Groningen; Lublin; Paris VI.

Academic Year: November to October.

Admission Requirements: Secondary school certificate (maturità).

Fees (Lire): 150,000-200,000 per semester.

Language of Instruction: Italian.

Degrees and Diplomas: Laurea, Doctor, in–Law; Political Sciences; Economics and Commerce; Foreign Languages and Literature; Letters; Philosophy; Agricultural Science; Physics; Mathematics; Natural Sciences; Business Economics; Pharmacology; History; Biological Sciences; Geological Sciences; Computer Sciences; Science of Animal Production, 4 yrs; Chemistry; Industrial Chemistry; Civil Engineering; Mechanical Engineering; Electrotechnic Engineering; Chemical Engineering; Electronic Engineering; Nuclear Engineering; Veterinary Science; Chemistry and

Pharmaceutical Technology; Aeronautic Engineering; Dentistry and Dental Prothesis, 5 yrs. Medicine and Surgery, 6 yrs. Dottoratodi ricerca, Doctorate of Research, 3-4 yrs. Also postgraduate diplomas of specialization, 3 yrs.

Libraries: University libraries, 600,000 vols; Bibliographic patrimony belonging to the University, *c.* 900,000.

Special Facilities (Museums, etc.): Museum of Natural and Territorial Sciences; Collection of Drawings and Prints in the History of Art Department; Anatomical Collections (Istituto di Anatomia Umana Normale); Museum and Institute of Morbid Anatomy; Botanical Museum and Gardens; Archaeological Antiquarium; Egyptological Collection; Departmental Centre for the Preservation and Study of Scientific Instruments.

Publications: Notiziario (monthly); Pubblicazioni scientifiche (annually); Annuario.

Press or Publishing House: University Lithography Department; Giardini Editori e Stampatori in Pisa.

Academic Staff, 1989-90:

Rank	Full-time	Part-time
Professori ordinari e straordinari (including Fuori ruolo)	402	55
Professori associati	602	70
Professori incaricati	5	–
Assistenti	77	–
Ricercatori	530	–
Total	1616	125

Student Enrolment, 1989-90:

	Men	Women	Total
Of the country	18,439	15,181	33,620
Of other countries	177	147	324
Total	18,616	15,328	33,944

3784 **UNIVERSITÀ DEGLI STUDI DELLA BASILICATA**

Via Nazario, Sauro, 85, 85100 Potenza
Telex: 812492 UNSTBA I
Telephone: (39-971) 474111
Fax: (39-971) 54847
Rettore: Cosimo Damiano Fonseca
Dirigente Amministrativo: Innocenzo Santoro

F. of Mathematics, Physics, and Natural Sciences
Dean: Antonio Mario Tamburro; *staff* 44 (1)
F. of Engineering
Dean: Gianfranco Boari; *staff* 19 (17)
F. of Agriculture
Dean: Francesco Basso; *staff* 56 (6)
F. of Letters and Philosophy
Dean: Piero Innocenti; *staff* 28
Southern Italy Neutrino and Gamma Observatory (S.I.N.G.A.O.)
President: Cosimo Damiano Fonseca
I. for Special Materials Study (CNR)
Head: Anna Giardini Guidoni
I. for Advanced Methodology and Environmental Analysis (CNR)
Head: Vincenzo Cuomo
Industrial Horticulture I. (CNR)
Head: Gian Tommaso Scarascia Mugnozza
Clay Research I.
Head: Giuseppe Piccarreta
International I. 'di Studi Federiciani' (CNR)
Head: Cosimo Damiano Fonseca

Founded 1982. Governing body: the Senato Academico. Some residential facilities for students.

Arrangements for co-operation with the Universities of: St. Andrews, Scotland; Seville; Barcelona; Berlin; Heidelberg; Saar; Trier.

Academic Year: November to October.

Admission Requirements: Secondary school certificate (maturità).

Fees (Lire): 271,000-301,000 per annum, according to faculty.

Language of Instruction: Italian.

Degrees and Diplomas: Laurea, Doctor, in–Languages; Mathematics, 4 yrs; Engineering; Agriculture; Chemistry, 5 yrs.

Library: Interfaculty Library, 65,000 vols.

Special Facilities (Museums, etc.): Serre della Facoltà di Agraria.

Publications: Basilicata Università (quarterly); L'Universitá Italiana; Annali della Facoltà di Lettere e Filosifia (annually); Collana 'Atti e Memorie'; Collana 'Strumenti e Materiali'.

Academic Staff, 1989-90:

Rank	Full-time	Part-time
Professori ordinari e straordinari	52	35
Professori associati	66	18
Ricercatori	88	–
Total	206	53

Student Enrolment, 1989-90:

	Men	Women	Total
Of the country	1329	1194	2523

3785 **UNIVERSITÀ DEGLI STUDI DI REGGIO CALABRIA**

Via dei Correttori 8, 88100 Reggio Calabria
Telephone: (39) 33051-27091
Rettore: Antonio Quistelli

F. of Architecture
F. of Agriculture
F. of Engineering
F. of Law (Catanzaro)
F. of Medicine and Surgery (Catanzaro)

Founded 1982. In process of development.

3786 ***UNIVERSITÀ DEGLI STUDI DI ROMA 'LA SAPIENZA'**

University of Rome 'La Sapienza'
Piazzale Aldo Moro 5, 00185 Roma
Telex: 620564 UNISAP
Telephone: (39) 6-4991
Rettore: Giuseppe Talamo (1987-90)
Direttore Amministrativo: Savino Strippoli

F. of Law
Dean: Mario Talamanca
F. of Political Science
Dean: Mario d'Addio
F. of Economics and Commerce
Dean: Ernesto Chiacchierini
F. of Statistics, Demography, and Actuarial Science
Dean: Antonio Golini
F. of Letters and Philosophy (including Archaeology)
Dean: Achille Tartaro
F. of Magistero (Teacher Training)
Dean: Giuseppe Talamo
F. of Mathematics, Physics, and Natural Sciences
Dean: Giorgio Tecce
F. of Engineering
Dean: Paolo Piga
F. of Architecture
Dean: Ciro Cicconcelli
F. of Medicine and Surgery (including Dentistry)
Dean: Carlo De Marco
F. of Pharmacy
Dean: Romano Cipollini
S. of Aerospatial Engineering
Director: Luigi Broglio
S. for Archivists and Librarians
Director: Arnaldo D'Addario
National I. of Higher Mathematics

Also 200 institutes, departments, and clinics of the different faculties.

Founded 1303 by Pope Boniface VIII. Acquired present status 1935. A State institution enjoying administrative autonomy. Financially supported by the State. Governing bodies: the Consiglio di Amministrazione; the Senato Accademico.

Arrangements for co-operation with the Universities of: Alagoas (Federal); Beijing; Berlin (Humboldt); Besançon; Bonn; Bordeaux I; Brandeis; Budapest; New York; Campinas (State); Colombia, Bogotá; Cornell; Cracow; Hofei; Istanbul; Liverpool; Madrid; Maranhão (Federal); Mexico; Montreal; Olomouc; Paris VI, VII, IX; Pittsburgh; Priština; Reading; Rio de Janeiro; São Paulo; Sofia; Sydney; Tirana; Tübingen; Tunis; Virginia; Warsaw; Waseda; Washington; Wrocław; Xi'an. University College, Cork; Technical University of Gdańsk; New YorkInstitute of Technology; Jefferson Medical College, Philadelphia.

Academic Year: November to October (November-July).

Admission Requirements: Secondary school certificate (maturità) or foreign equivalent.
Fees (Lire): Registration, 50,000; tuition, 120,000.
Language of Instruction: Italian.
Degrees and Diplomas: Laurea, Doctor, in–Library Science; Aerospatial Engineering, 2 yrs; Law; Political Science; Economics and Commerce; Statistics; Actuarial Science; Demography; Letters; Foreign Languages and Literature; Education; Philosophy; Sociology; Psychology; Physics; Mathematics; Natural Sciences; Biology; Geology; Pharmacy, 4 yrs; Chemistry; Industrial Chemistry; Pharmaceutical Technology; Chemical Engineering; Civil Engineering; Electronic Engineering; Electrical Engineering, Mechanical Engineering; Mining Engineering; Nuclear Engineering; Architecture; Dentistry, 5 yrs; Medicine and Surgery, 6 yrs. Dottorato di ricerca, Doctorate of Research, 3-4 yrs. Diploma of School Inspector (elementary level), 3 yrs. Diploma in–Statistics, 2 yrs. Also postgraduate diplomas of specialization.
Libraries: Biblioteca Alessandrina, *c.* 1,000,000 vols; libraries of the faculties.
Special Facilities (Museums, etc.): Museums: Mineralogy; Geology; Palaeontology; Physics; Anthropology; Classic Art; Zoology; History of Medicine.Museums of the Institutes.
Publications: Annuario; Notiziario (monthly); Quaderni di Informazione; publications of the departments and institutes.
Academic Staff, 1986-87: *c.* 4060 (1050).
Student Enrolment, 1986-87:

	Men	Women	Total
Of the country	83,786	78,021	161,807
Of other countries	3258	1236	4494
Total	87,044	79,257	166,301

3787 **UNIVERSITÀ DEGLI STUDI DI ROMA II 'TOR VERGATA'**
Via Orazio Raimondo, 00173 Roma
Telephone: (39) 6-79791
Rettore: Enrico Garaci

F. of Law
F. of Letters and Philosophy
F. of Medicine and Surgery
F. of Mathematics, Physics, and Natural Sciences
F. of Engineering

3788 **LIBERA UNIVERSITÀ INTERNAZIONALE DEGLI STUDI SOCIALI**
International University of Social Studies
Viale Pola 12, 00198 Roma
Telephone: (39) 6-841051
Presidente: Guido Carli (1984-87)
Direttore Amministrativo: Giovanni Nocco
Rettore: Carlo Scognamiglio

F. of Political Science
F. of Economics and Commerce
Dean: Mario Di Lazzaro
F. of Law
Dean: Natalino Irti
Computer Ce.
S. of Journalism and Mass Communication
Founded 1945 as school of mass communications media. A private institution operated and financed by the Associazione Internazionale Pro Deo, recognized by the State 1965 and became university 1966. Governing bodies: the Consiglio di Amministrazione; the Consiglio di Facoltà. Residential facilities for students.
Academic Year: November to October (November-May).
Admission Requirements: Secondary school certificate (maturità) or foreign equivalent.
Fees (Lira): 900,000-6,000,000 according to income.
Language of Instruction: Italian.
Degrees and Diplomas: Degrees and Diplomas (recognized by the State): Laurea, Doctor, in–Political Science; Economics and Commerce;Law, 4 yrs. Postgraduate diploma in Journalism and Mass Communication, 2 yrs.
Libraries: Central Library, *c.* 43,000 vols; institute libraries.
Publication: Collana di pubblicazioni della Libera Università Internazionale degli Studi Sociali.

Academic Staff: *c.* 130.
Student Enrolment, 1986-87: *c.* 3000.

3789 **UNIVERSITÀ DEGLI STUDI DI SALERNO**
University of Salerno
Via Urbano II, 84100 Salerno
Telephone: (39) 89-613111
Rettore: Vincenzo Buonocore

F. of Law
F. of Economics and Commerce
F. of Letters and Philosophy
F. of Magistero (Teacher Training)
F. of Mathematics, Physics, and Natural Sciences
Founded 1970.

3790 ***UNIVERSITÀ DEGLI STUDI DI SASSARI**
University of Sassari
Piazza Università, 21, 07100 Sassari, Sardinia
Telex: 790299 SACER I
Telephone: (79) 211211
Fax: (79) 211410
Rettore: Antonio Milella (1988-91)
Direttore Amministrativo: Orazio Nicotra

F. of Law (including Political Science)
Dean: Paolo Fois; *staff* 71 (24)
F. of Medicine and Surgery
Dean: Egidio Miele; *staff* 87 (45)
F. of Pharmacy
Dean: Gerolamo Pirisino; *staff* 29 (7)
F. of Veterinary Medicine
Dean: Antonio Marongiu; *staff* 32 (5)
F. of Agriculture
Dean: Pietro Bullitta; *staff* 66 (1)
F. of Mathematics, Physics, and Natural Sciences
Dean: Giovanni Fadda; *staff* 73 (1)
F. of Magistero (Teacher Training)
Dean: Mario Manca; *staff* 71 (1)
D. of Economics
Head: Virgilio Mura; *staff* 27 (4)
D. of History
Head: Guido Melis; *staff* 25
D. of Chemistry
Head: Giovanni Minghetti; *staff* 30
Also 76 institutes, 9 centres, 28 schools of specialization, and 11 schools for short-term courses.
Founded 1562 as Studium Generale and recognized by Bull of Pope Paul V. Established as university 1617, reorganized 1766. A State institution enjoying administrative autonomy. Governing bodies: the Consiglio di Amministrazione; the Senato Accademico. Residential facilities for students.
Arrangements for co-operation with Autonomous University of Madrid; Université de Cort; Corsica. Participates in the ERASMUS programme.
Academic Year: November to October (November-May).
Admission Requirements: Secondary school certificate (maturità) or for some fields, technical school diploma.
Language of Instruction: Italian.
Degrees and Diplomas: Laurea, Doctor, in–Law; Pharmacy; Letters; Education; Foreign Languages and Literature; Agriculture; Biology, 4 yrs; Veterinary Medicine, 5 yrs; Medicine, 6 yrs. Diploma for school inspection (elementary level), 3 yrs. Diploma of specialization in medical sciences, 2-4 yrs after Laurea.
Libraries: Law, *c.* 30,000 vols; Teacher Training, *c.* 40,000.
Special Facilities (Museums, etc.): Orto Botanico.
Publications: Annuario; Bollettino Ufficiale; Bilancio di previsione; Conto Consuntivo.

Academic Staff, 1990:

Rank	Full-time	Part-time
Ordinari	108	22
Associati	170	29
Ricercatori	106	16
Assistenti	26	10
Incaricati e Stabilizzati	15	–
Total	425	77

Student Enrolment, 1986-87:

	Men	Women	Total
Of the country	3977	6135	10,072
Of other countries	71	13	84
Total	4048	6148	10,156

3791 **UNIVERSITÀ DEGLI STUDI DI SIENA**
University of Siena
Via Banchi di Sotto 55, 53100 Siena
Telex: 572459
Telephone: (39-577) 298000
Fax: (39-577) 298367
Rettore: Luigi Berlinguer (1988-91)
Direttore Amministrativo: Jolanda Semplici

F. of Law (including Political Science)
Dean: Remo Martini; *staff* 31 (10)
F. of Medicine and Surgery (including Dentistry)
Dean: Piero Tosi; *staff* 61 (62)
F. of Pharmacy (including Chemistry, and Pharmaceutical Technology)
Dean: Cesare Pellerano; *staff* 30 (1)
F. of Economics and Banking
Dean: Giancarlo Rolla; *staff* 46 (11)
F. of Mathematics, Physics, and Natural Sciences
Dean: Romano Dallai; *staff* 77 (2)
F. of Magistero (Teacher Training)
Dean: Domenico Conci; *staff* 43 (1)
F. of Letters and Philosophy
Dean: Maurizio Bettini; *staff* 58 (2)
Also 32 schools of specialization, and 17 departments and 56 institutes of the different faculties.

Founded 1240 but tracing its history to a school of Roman Law, 1056. Recognized as Studium Generale, confirmed by Frederick II 1248, and Pope Innocent IV 1252. Became a State institution 1859. A State institution enjoying administrative autonomy. Financially supported by the State, the Municipality and Province of Siena, and other bodies. Governing bodies: the Consiglio di Amministrazione; the Senato Accademico. Some residential facilities for students.

Arrangements for co-operation with the Universities of: Toronto; Aix-Marseille I; Kinshasa; New York; Sussex; Massachusetts; Cracow; Kyoto; Georgetown; Columbia; Bridgeport; Prague; Paris VII; Amsterdam; Gröningen; La Plata; Tucuma; Kaza; Wuhan; Nankai; Yuman; Barcelona; Tasmania. King's College, Cambridge; Polytechnic of Central London; State University of New York at Buffalo; London School of Economics; Monclair State College; City University, New York.

Academic Year: November to October.

Admission Requirements: Secondary school certificate (maturità).

Fees (Lire): Registration, 85,000; tuition, 165,000 per annum.

Language of Instruction: Italian.

Degrees and Diplomas: Laurea, Doctor, in–Law; Political Sciences; Pharmacy; Economics and Banking; Economics; Economics and Statistics; Biology; Natural Sciences; Geology; Mathematics; Letters; Education; Foreign Languages and Literature; History; Philosophy, 4 yrs; Chemistry and Pharmaceutical Technology; Dentistry, 5 yrs; Medicine and Surgery, 6 yrs. Diplomas of specialization in medicine, 3 yrs after Laurea. Also Diploma for school inspection (elementarylevel) and in Social Work, 3 yrs.

Libraries: Central Libraries of the Faculties, *c.* 143,590 vols; Libraries of the Institutes, *c.* 223,230.

Special Facilities (Museums, etc.): Accademia dei Fisiocritici.

Publications: Annuario Accademico; Bollettino.

Academic Staff, 1989-90: 396 (70).

Student Enrolment, 1989-90:

	Total
Of the country	13,975
Of other countries	387
Total	14,362

3792 **UNIVERSITÀ DEGLI STUDI DI TORINO**
University of Turin
Via Giuseppe Verdi 8, 10124 Torino
Telephone: (39) 11-88021
Rettore: Mario Umberto Dianzani

F. of Agriculture
F. of Economics and Commerce
F. of Pharmacy
F. of Law
F. of Letters and Philosophy
F. of Magistero (Teacher Training)
F. of Medicine and Surgery
F. of Veterinary Medicine
F. of Mathematics, Physics, and Natural Sciences
F. of of Political Science
S. of Business Administration
S. of Audiometrics and Phonology
Also 158 institutes and centres of the faculties and 49 schools for specialized studies.

Founded 1404 by Benedetto XIII. Reorganized and re-established 1713. A State institution enjoying administrative autonomy. Financially supported by the State and local public funds. Governing bodies: the Consiglio di Amministrazione; the Senato Accademico. Some residential facilities for students.

Academic Year: November to October (November-May).

Admission Requirements: Secondary school certificate (maturità) or equivalent.

Language of Instruction: Italian.

Degrees and Diplomas: Laurea, Doctor, in–Law; Political Science; Economics and Commerce; Letters; Philosophy; Foreign Languages and Letters; Education; Mathematics; Physics; Natural Sciences; Biology; Geology; Pharmacy; Veterinary Medicine; Agriculture, 4 yrs; Chemistry; Industrial Chemistry, 5 yrs; Medicine and Surgery, 6 yrs. Diploma in Education (elementary level).

Libraries: Libraries of the Faculties; Agriculture; Economics and Commerce; Letters and Philosophy; Veterinary Medicine.

Special Facilities (Museums, etc.): Museums: Anthropology; Geology; Zoology; Criminal Anthropology.

Academic Staff: c. 2000.

Student Enrolment: c. 42,000.

3793 **UNIVERSITÀ DEGLI STUDI DI TRENTO**
University of Trento
Via Belenzani 12, 38100 Trento
Telex: UNIVIN 400674
Telephone: (39-461) 881111
Fax: (39-461) 881299
Rettore: Fabio Ferrari (1978-90)
Direttore Amministrativo: Vitaliano Agostini

F. of Sociology
Dean: Antonio De Lillo
F. of Mathematics, Physics, and Natural Sciences
Dean: Luigi Salvadori
F. of Economics and Commerce
Dean: Mario Fedrizzi
F. of Law
Dean: Fulvio Zuelli
F. of Letters and Philosophy
Dean: Giuseppe Beschin
F. of Engineering
Dean: Roberto Contro
I. of Statistics and Operative Research
Director: Silvano Montanari
I. of Informatics
Director: Mario Fedrizzi
I. of Business Studies
Director: Valentino Gandolfi

I. of Chemical Studies
Director: Francesco Pietra
Also 11 departments of the different faculties.

Founded 1962 as private Istituto superiore di Scienze Sociali by the Istituto Trentino di Cultura. Recognized by the State 1966 and became Libera Università 1972. Acquired present status and title 1982. A State institution enjoying administrative autonomy. Governing bodies: the Consiglio di Amministrazione; the Senato Accademico. Residential facilities for academic staff and students.

Academic Year: November to October (November-February; March-June).

Admission Requirements: Secondary school certificate (maturità) or recognized foreign equivalent.

Language of Instruction: Italian.

Degrees and Diplomas: Laurea, Doctor, in–Sociology; Mathematics; Physics; Biology; Political Economics; Economics and Commerce; Law; Letters; Foreign Languages and Literature, 4 yrs; Civil, Materials, and Forestry Engineering, 5 yrs. Diploma in Statistics, 2 yrs. Postgraduate diplomas of specialization, 2 yrs after Laurea. Dr. in–Statistics; Sociology, 3 yrs.

Library: Biblioteca Marcello Boldrini, *c.* 200,000 vols.

Academic Staff: c. 200 (60).

Student Enrolment, 1989-90:

	Men	Women	Total
Of the country	4285	3473	7759

3794 ***UNIVERSITÀ DEGLI STUDI DI TRIESTE**

University of Trieste
Piazzale Europa 1, 34100 Trieste
Telex: 460865 UNIVTS
Telephone: (39-40) 56038
Fax: (39-40) 5603176
Rettore: Giacomo Borruso (1990-93)
Direttore Amministrativo: Maria Dobran

F. of Law
Dean: Georgio Conetti; *staff* 21 (11)
F. of Political Sciences
Dean: Domenico Coccopalmerio; *staff* 38 (4)
F. of Economics and Commerce
; *staff* 77 (6)
F. of Letters and Philosophy
Dean: Silva Monti; *staff* 132
F. of Magistero (Teacher Training)
Dean: Luciano Lago; *staff* 42
F. of Medicine and Surgery (including Dentistry)
Dean: Andrea Bosatra; *staff* 69 (77)
F. of Mathematics, Physics, and Natural Sciences
Dean: Giacomo Costa; *staff* 172 (10)
F. of Pharmacy
Dean: Paolo Linda; *staff* 38 (1)
F. of Engineering
Dean: Lucio Delcaro; *staff* 121 (13)
S. of Translation and Interpretation
Dean: Franco Crevatin; *staff* 39 (1)
Also 20 departments, 59 institutes, and 54 schools of specialization.

Founded 1877 by private initiative as college of commerce. Transformed by Italian Government into Institute of Economics and Commerce 1920, raised to university rank 1924. Faculty of Law established 1936. Faculty of Engineering authorized by decree 1942, but not established until 1945. Faculty of Letters and Philosophy created 1943 on the initiative of the academic staff and subsequently granted formal recognition. The university is a State institution enjoying administrative and didactic autonomy under the supervision of the Ministry of PublicEducation. Governing bodies: the Consiglio di Amministrazione; the Senato Accademico. Some residential facilities for students.

Arrangements for co-operation with the Universities of: Rijeka; Campinas; Trujillo; Cuzco (National); Tacna; Stanford; Emory; Wisconsin; Poznań; Paris VI; Louvain; Veszprém; Columbia (National); Los Andes; Rosario (National); Regensburg; Graz; Alabama; Ife; Western Ontario; Ljubljana; Zagreb; Vienna; Regensburg; Wrocław; Split; Belgrade; Bochum; Tours; Zaragoza; Athens; Malta; Miskolc; Semmelweis, Budapest; Economics, Budapest; Grodno; Jordan; New York; Ohio State; The John Hopkins; San Francisco; West Virginia; California; Maryland; Indiana; Nacional Colombiana; Antioquia; São Paulo. University of Technology, Vienna; Polytechnic Institute, New York; Institute of Technology of the Litoral, Guayaquil; Weizmann Institute of Science; Moscow State Institute of Foreign Languages; Universidad Peruana 'Cayetano Heredia'; Universidad Particular Inca Garcilaso de la Vega, Lima. Participates in ERASMUS programme.

Academic Year: November to October (November-May).

Admission Requirements: Secondary school certificate (maturità) or foreign equivalent.

Fees (Lire): 250,000-500,000 per annum.

Language of Instruction: Italian.

Degrees and Diplomas: Laurea, Doctor, in–Law; Political Sciences; International and Diplomatic Science; History; Economics; Statistics and Actuarial Science; Philosophy; Literature; Modern Languages and Literature; Literary Studies; Pedagogy; Foreign Languages and Literature, 4 yrs; Dentistry; Chemistry; Physics; Mathematics; Biology; Geology; Natural Sciences; Pharmacy; Chemistry and Pharmaceutical Technology; Chemical Engineering; Civil Engineering; Electronic Engineering; Electrical Engineering; Mechanical Engineering, 5 yrs; Medicine and Surgery, 6 yrs. Diplomas–School Inspection (primary level), 3 yrs; Translation and Interpretation, 4 yrs; Translation, 2 yrs. Dottorato di ricerca, Doctorate of Science, 3-4 yrs. Also postgraduate diploma of specialization, 2 yrs.

Libraries: Central Library, 163,234 vols; Medicine, Engineering, Letters and Philosophy, Teacher Training; 90 libraries of the institutes, total, *c.* 880,000 vols.

Special Facilities (Museums, etc.): Museum of Mineralogy and Petrography.

Press or Publishing House: University Press.

Academic Staff, 1989-90:

Rank	Full-time	Part-time
Professors	200	34
Associate Professors	373	47
Researchers	146	12
Assistant Professors	46	–
Language Assistants	39	–
Others	312	–
Total	1116	93

Student Enrolment, 1989-90:

	Total
Of the country	16,715
Of other countries	680
Total	17,395

3795 **UNIVERSITÀ DEGLI STUDI DELLA TUSCIA**

Viterbo State University
Via San Giovanni Decollato 1, 01100 Viterbo
Telex: 614076 TUSVIT I
Telephone: (39-761) 2571
Fax: (39-761) 225785
Rettore: Gian Tommaso Scarascia Mugnozza
Direttore Amministrativo: Franco Fracassa

F. of Agriculture (including Forestry)
Dean: Ervedo Giordano
F. of Modern Foreign Languages and Literature
Dean: Massimo Miglio
F. of Physics and Natural Sciences
Dean: Angelo Rambelli
F. for the Conservation of Cultural Property
Also 11 institutes and 2 departments of the different faculties.

Founded 1979. A State institution enjoying administrative autonomy. Financially supported by the State. Governing bodies: the Senato Academico; the Consiglio Amministrativo. Residential facilities for students.

Participates in the ERASMUS and COMMETT programmes.

Academic Year: November to October.

Admission Requirements: Secondary school certificate (maturità).

Fees (Lire): 349,000-378,000 per annum.

Language of Instruction: Italian.

Degrees and Diplomas: Laurea, Doctor, 4-5 yrs.

Library: Libraries of the Faculties of Agriculture and Foreign Languages and Literature.

Academic Staff, 1990: c. 200.
Student Enrolment, 1989-90:

	Men	Women	Total
Of the country	1000	1087	2097
Of other countries	31	11	42
Total	1031	1108	2139

3796 ***UNIVERSITÀ DEGLI STUDI DI UDINE**
University of Udine
Via Antonini 8, 33100 Udine
Telex: 450412
Telephone: (39) 432-297105
Rettore: Franco Frilli (1983-89)
Direttore Amministrativo: Aldo Baldini

F. of Agriculture (including Animal Husbandry)
Dean: Cesare Gottardo; *staff* 129
F. of Engineering
Dean: Giuliano Dolcetti; *staff* 81 (10)
F. of Mathematics, Physics, and Natural Sciences (including Information Sciences)
Dean: Flavio Waldner; *staff* 40 (1)
F. of Letters and Philosophy
Dean: Giuseppe M. Pilo; *staff* 66
F. of Foreign Languages and Literature
Dean: Guido Barbina; *staff* 78
F. of Medicine and Surgery
Dean: Francesco S. Ambesi Impiombato; *staff* 11
F. of Economics and Banking
Dean: Feliciano Benvenuti; *staff* 14
Computer Ce.
Audiovisual Language Ce.

Founded 1978, incorporating faculties previously attached to the University of Trieste. A State institution enjoying administrative autonomy. Financially supported by the State. Governing bodies: the Consiglio di Amministrazione; the Senato Accademico. Residential facilities for 264 students.

Arrangements for co-operation with the Universities of: Klagenfurt (Educational Sciences); Bratislava; Szeged;Cracow; Ljubljana. Ben Gurion University of the Negev.

Academic Year: November to October (November-May).

Admission Requirements: Secondary school certificate (maturità).

Fees (Lire): Registration, 310,500-385,500; subsequent years, 254,-500-329,500.

Language of Instruction: Italian.

Degrees and Diplomas: Laurea, Doctor, in–Foreign Languages and Literature; Economics and Banking; Information Sciences; Agriculture; Animal Husbandry, 4 yrs; Engineering; Food Technology, 5 yrs; Medicine and Surgery, 6 yrs.

Libraries: Faculty Libraries, c. 65,630 vols; libraries of the institutes.

Publications: Incontri Linguistici; Filologia Moderna.

Academic Staff, 1986-87:

Rank	Full-time	Part-time
Professori ordinari e straordinari	87	6
Professori associati	46	6
Professori incaricati	7	–
Assistenti	30	–
Supplenti	73	–
A contratto	90	–
Ricercatori	58	–
Lettori	27	–
Total	418	12

Student Enrolment, 1986-87:

	Men	Women	Total
Of the country	2212	2123	4335
Of other countries	31	13	44
Total	2243	2136	4379

3797 **UNIVERSITÀ DEGLI STUDI DI URBINO (LIBERA)**
University of Urbino
Via Saffi 2, 61029 Urbino
Telephone: (39) 722-4141
Rettore: Carlo Bo (1980-87)

F. of Law
F. of Economics and Commerce
F. of Letters and Philosophy
F. of Teacher Training (Magistero)
F. of Pharmacy
F. of Mathematics, Physics, and Natural Sciences
S. for Laboratory Technicians
S. of Graphology
I. of Religious Studies
S. of Journalism
International L. for Architecture and Urban Design
International Ce. for Semiotics and Linguistics
Ce. for Marche Cultural Studies
Observatory

Also 7 schools for specialized studies and 46 institutes of the faculties.

Founded 1506 as college of law by Guidobaldo I of Montefeltro, Duke of Urbino. Recognized by Bull of Pope Julius II 1507 and authorized to award the title of doctor 1566. Formally recognized as a university by the Sacred Congregation of Studies 1826, and by Royal decree 1862. Recognized as Libera Università 1923. A State institution enjoying administrative autonomy under the supervision of the Ministry of Public Education. Financiallysupported by the State and provincial subventions, and tuition fees. Governing bodies: the Consiglio di Amministrazione; the Senato Accademico. Residential facilities for c. 60 academic staff and c. 1130 students.

Academic Year: November to October.

Admission Requirements: Secondary school certificate (maturità) or equivalent.

Language of Instruction: Italian.

Degrees and Diplomas: Laurea, Doctor, in–Law; Economics and Commerce; Foreign Languages and Literature; Education; Sociology; Geology; Biology; Pharmacy; Letters; Philosophy; Natural Sciences; Teacher Training, 4 yrs. Diploma of School Inspector (elementary level), 3 yrs. Also postgraduate diploma of specialization, 2-3 yrs.

Libraries: Central Library, c. 46,000 vols; Law, c. 85,000; Economics and Commerce, c. 40,000.

Publications: Rivista Studi Urbinati, series A Law and Economics; Series B History, Philosophy and Literature; series C Pharmacy; Quaderni Urbiniti di Cultura classica (every 4 months).

Press or Publishing House: University Press.

Academic Staff: c. 590.

Student Enrolment: c. 13,310.

3798 ***UNIVERSITÀ DEGLI STUDI DI VENEZIA**
University of Venice
Ca' Foscari, Dorsoduro 3246, 30123 Venezia
Telex: 410638
Telephone: (39) 41-5285420
Rettore: Giovanni Castellani (1985-88)
Direttore Amministrativo: Augusto Toselli

F. of Economics
Dean: Maurizio Rispoli
F. of Foreign Languages and Literature
Dean: Umberto Corsini
F. of Letters and Philosophy
Dean: Luigi Ruggiu
F. of Industrial Chemistry
Dean: Gian Antonio Mazzochin
S. of Philology
Director: Giorgio Padoan
Inter-F. Ce. of Linguistics
Director: Andrea Csyllaghi
Ce. for Statistics
Head: Giuseppe Volpato
Computer Ce.
Head: Elio Castellani

Founded 1868 as Istituto universitario di Economia e Commercio e di Lingue e Letterature straniere. Became university 1968. A State institution enjoying administrative autonomy. Financially supported by the State. Governing bodies: the Senato Accademico; the Consiglio di Amministrazione.

Arrangements for co-operation with the Universities of: Marburg; California; Columbia (Barnard College); Göttingen; Warwick; Ljubljana; Budapest.

Academic Year: November to October (October-February; February-June).

Admission Requirements: Secondary school certificate (maturità) or qualifications from appropriate technical, commercial, industrial, agricultural or nautical institutes (Economics and Commerce), or recognized foreign equivalent.

Language of Instruction: Italian.

Degrees and Diplomas: Laurea, Doctor, in–Economics and Commerce; Philosophy; History; Letters; Oriental Languages and Literature; Foreign Languages and Literature; Industrial Chemistry, 4 yrs.

Libraries: Central Library, *c.* 300,000 vols; specialized libraries, *c.* 25,000.

Publications: Ricerche economiche (quarterly); Annali di Ca' Foscari (weekly).

Academic Staff, 1986-87:

Rank	Full-time	Part-time
Professori di ruolo 1 fascia	18	19
Professori di ruolo 2 fascia	180	20
Professori incaricati	9	–
Assistenti	23	–
Ricercatori	107	–
Total	399	39

Student Enrolment: 1986: 13,135.

3799 **UNIVERSITÀ DEGLI STUDI DI VERONA**

University of Verona

Via S. dell'Artigliere 8, 37129 Verona

Telephone: (39) 45-591100

Rettore: Hrayr Terzian

F. of Medicine and Surgery

F. of Economics and Commerce

F. of Magistero (Teacher Training)

3800 ***POLITECNICO DI MILANO**

Polytechnic Institute of Milan

Piazza Leonardo da Vinci 32, 20133 Milano

Telex: POLIMI 1333467

Telephone: (39) 2-2399-1

Rettore: Arrigo Vallatta (1984-87) Direttore

Direttore Amministrativo: Gesualda Assante

F. of Engineering (including Nuclear Engineering)

Dean: Emilio Massa; *staff* 66 (108)

F. of Architecture (including Town Planning)

Dean: Cesare Stevan; *staff* 80 (64)

Also 34 institutes of the Faculty of Engineering.

Founded 1863, the Polytechnic is a State institution of university rank, enjoying administrative autonomy. Financially supported by the State as well as by the municipal and provincial authorities and other bodies. Governing bodies: the Consiglio di Amministrazione, comprising the Rector, government and municipal representatives, representatives of the academic staff and 5 students; the Senato Accademico, comprising the Rector and the deans of the faculties. Residential facilities for 482 students.

Academic Year: November to October (November-February; March-June; July-October).

Admission Requirements: Secondary school certificate (maturità) or foreign equivalent.

Fees (Lire): 120,000-240,000 per annum.

Language of Instruction: Italian.

Degrees and Diplomas: Laurea, Doctor, in–Aeronautical Engineering; Chemical Engineering; Civil Engineering (constructional, hydraulic, transport); Mechanical Engineering; Electro-technical Engineering; Electrical Engineering; Electronic Engineering; Nuclear Engineering; Architecture, 5 yrs. Dottorato di ricerca, Doctorate of Science, 3-4 yrs. Also postgraduate diploma of specialization, 2 yrs.

Libraries: Engineering, 151,482 vols; Architecture, 24,333; libraries of the insitutes, 340,897.

Academic Staff, 1986-87:

Rank	Full-time	Part-time
Professori di ruolo 1 fascia	143	82
Professori 2 fascia	203	90
Professori incaricati	4	–
Assistenti di ruolo	21	–
Ricercatori	188	–
Contrattisti	1	–
Total	560	172

Student Enrolment, 1986-87:

Men	Women	Total
22,580	6590	29,966*

*Including 796 foreign students.

3801 ***POLITECNICO I TORINO**

Polytechnic Institute of Turin

Corso Duca degli Abruzzi 24, 10129 Torino

Telex: 220646 POLITO I

Telephone: (39-11) 5566315

Fax: (39-11) 5566329

Rettore: Rodolfo Zich

Direttore Amministrativo: A.H. Zecchini

F. of Architecture

Dean: G.B. Vigliano

F. of Engineering

Dean: E. Antonelli

Founded 1859 as School of Engineering, became Politecnico 1906. A State institution of university rank enjoying administrative autonomy. Financially supported by the State and other regional bodies. Governing bodies: the Consiglio di Amministrazione; the Senato Accademico. Some residential facilities for students.

Academic Year: November to October (November-February; March-June).

Admission Requirements: Secondary school certificate (maturità) or recognized foreign equivalent.

Language of Instruction: Italian.

Degrees and Diplomas: Laurea, Doctor, in–Engineering (various fields); Architecture, 5 yrs; Aeronautical Engineering, 2 yrs after Laurea in Engineering. Also Diploma in Graphic Arts, 2 yrs.

Libraries: Central Library, *c.* 21,000 vols; other libraries, *c.* 28,000.

Special Facilities (Museums, etc.): Museo di Mineralogia.

Academic Staff, 1989-90:

Rank	Full-time	Part-time
Professori ordinari	134	44
Professori straordinari	171	70
Professori ricercatori	71	68
Assistenti	16	8
Total	392	190

Student Enrolment, 1989-90:

Of the country	15,208
Of the countries	270
Total	15,478

Other Institutions

Technical Education

3802 **ISTITUTO UNIVERSITARIO DI ARCHITETTURA DI VENEZIA**

Campazzo dei Tolentini 191, 30100 Venezia

Cables: Architettura

Telephone: (39) 41-703377

Rettore: Paolo Ceccarelli (1982-88)

Direttore Amministrativo: S. Lion

Architecture (including Town Planning)

Founded 1926, a State institution. Governing bodies: the Consiglio di Amministrazione; the Consiglio di Facoltà. Some residential facilities for students.

Academic Year: November to October.

Admission Requirements: Secondary school certificate (maturità) or recognized foreign equivalent.
Language of Instruction: Italian.
Degrees and Diplomas: Laurea, Doctor, in Architecture; Town Planning, 5 yrs.
Library: Central Library, 80,000 vols.
Academic Staff: c. 400.
Student Enrolment: c. 7000.

Professional Education

3803 **ISTITUTO UNIVERSITARIO NAVALE**
Via Acton 38, 80133 Napoli
Telephone: (39) 81-312249
Rettore: Arturo De Malo

F. of Maritime Economics
F. of Nautical Sciences

Founded 1920 as Istituto Superiore Navale; adopted present name 1931. The institution is under the jurisdiction of the Ministry of Education. Financially supported by the State, the municipal and provincial authorities and the Chamber of Commerce, Industry, and Agriculture. Governing bodies: the Senato Accademico; the Consiglio di Amministrazione.
Academic Year: November to October.
Admission Requirements: Secondary school certificate (maturità).
Language of Instruction: Italian.
Degrees and Diplomas: Laurea, Doctor, in–Maritime Economics; Nautical Sciences, 4 yrs.
Library: c. 30,000 vols.
Special Facilities (Museums, etc.): Museum of model ships.
Publications: Annali; Annuario (both annually); Collana della Facoltà di Economia Marittima.
Academic Staff: c. 100 (30).
Student Enrolment: c. 1690.

3804 **ISTITUTO UNIVERSITARIO ORIENTALE**
Piazza S. Giovanni Maggiore 30, 80134 Napoli
Telephone: (39) 81-206122
Rettore: Roberto Rubinacci

Oriental Languages and Literature

Founded as Collegio dei Cinesi by Matteo Ripa; recognized by Clement XII 1732, reorganized 1888.
Academic Year: November to October.
Admission Requirements: Secondary school certificate (maturità) or technical or teaching diploma.
Language of Instruction: Italian.
Degrees and Diplomas: Laurea, Doctor, in–Oriental Political Science; Oriental Languages and Civilizations; Eastern European Languages and Institutions; Western European Languages and Institutions, 4 yrs.
Publication: Annali.
Academic Staff: c. 190.
Student Enrolment: c. 2750.

3805 **ISTITUTO UNIVERSITARIO DI LINGUE MODERNE DI MILANO**
Piazza dei Volontari 3, 20145 Milano
Telephone: (39) 2-313922

F. of Foreign Languages and Literature

Teacher Training

3806 **SCUOLA NORMALE SUPERIORE DI PISA**
Piazza dei Cavalieri 7, 56100 Pisa
Telephone: (39) 50-59711
Direttore: Edoardo Vesentini
Direttore Amministrativo: Giovanna Giovannini

Teacher Training (Letters and Philosophy, Mathematics, Physics and Natural Sciences)

Founded 1814 by Napoleon as a 'branch' of the Ecole normale in Paris. Now a State institution under the jurisdiction of the Ministry of Education. Governing body: the Consiglio Direttivo. Residential facilities for some academic staff and for all students.
Academic Year: November to October.
Admission Requirements: Secondary school certificate (maturità) and entrance examination.
Fees: None.
Language of Instruction: Italian.
Degrees and Diplomas: Diploma di licenza, 4 yrs. Diploma di perfezionamento, 2 yrs after graduation.
Library: c. 360,000 vols.
Publications: Annali della Classe di Lettere e Filosofia; Annali della Classe di Scienze.
Academic Staff: c. 120.
Student Enrolment: c. 130.

3807 **SCUOLA SUPERIORE DI STUDI UNIVERSITARI E DI PERFEZIONAMENTO**
Via Carducci 40, 56100 Pisa
Telephone: (39) 50-45377; 46355
Direttore: Bruno Guerrini (1986-89)
Direttore Amministrativo: Mario Nencetti

Sec. of Law and Political Science
Director: Francesco Donato Busnelli; *staff* 4
Sec. of Medicine and Surgery
Director: Arnaldo Arduini; *staff* 5
Sec. of Agriculture
Director: Filiberto Loreti; *staff* 7
Sec. of Engineering
Director: Marino Marini; *staff* 5
Sec. of Economics and Commerce
Director: Roberto Caparvi; *staff* 4

Founded 1967. A State institution under the jurisdiction of the Ministry of Education. Residential facilities for all students.
Academic Year: November to October.
Admission Requirements: Secondary school certificate (maturità) and entrance examination.
Fees: None.
Language of Instruction: Italian.
Degrees and Diplomas: Diploma di Licenza, 4-6 yrs. Diploma di perfezionamento, 2 yrs after graduation.
Library: 16,500 vols.
Publication: Cahiers.
Academic Staff, 1986-87:

Rank	Full-time
Professori 1 fascia	8
Professori 2 fascia	11
Assistenti	1
Ricercatori	6
Total	26

Student Enrolment, 1986-87:

	Men	Women	Total
Of the country	55	26	81

3808 **ISTITUTO UNIVERSITARIO DI MAGISTERO**
Via Ofelia, Angolo Via Fabio Fil 21, 95124 Catania
Telephone: (39) 95-328920
Direttore: Bruno Panvin

Teacher Training (Literature, Education, Modern Languages and Literature)

Founded 1947.
Academic Year: November to October (November-May).
Admission Requirements: Teaching certificate, elementary level, and entrance examination.
Language of Instruction: Italian.
Degrees and Diplomas: Teaching diploma, elementary level, 3 yrs. Laurea, Doctor, in–Literature; Education; Foreign Languages, 4 yrs.
Library: Institute Library.
Publication: Collana dell'Istituto universitario di Magistero di Catania.
Academic Staff: c. 40.
Student Enrolment: c. 3000.

3809 **ISTITUTO UNIVERSITARIO PAREGGIATO DI MAGISTERO FEMMINILE 'SUOR ORSOLA BENINCASA'**
Via Suor Orsola 10, 80135 Napoli
Telephone: (39) 81-418518

Teacher Training (for Women)
Founded 1901.

3810 **ISTITUTO UNIVERSITARIO PAREGGIATO DI MAGISTERO 'MARIA SS. ASSUNTA'**
Via della Traspontina 21, 00193 Roma
Telephone: (39) 6-68277
Direttore: Geogrio Petrocchi

Teacher Training (Letters, Education, Foreign Languages and Literature) (for Women)
Founded 1939. Governing bodies: the Consiglio di Amministrazione; the Consiglio Direttivo; the Consiglio dei Professori.
Academic Year: November to October (November-May).
Admission Requirements: Secondary school certificate (maturità) and entrance examination.
Fees (Lira): *c.* 750,000 per annum.
Language of Instruction: Italian.
Degrees and Diplomas: Teaching diploma, elementary level, 3 yrs. Laurea, Doctor, in–Letters; Education; Foreign Languages and Literature, 4 yrs.
Library: Central Library, 48,700 vols.
Academic Staff, 1986-87: 19 (29).
Student Enrolment, 1986-87:

	Women
Of the country	489
Of other countries	23
Total	512

3811 **ISTITUTO SUPERIORE PAREGGIATO DI EDUCAZIONE FISICA L'AQUILA**
Via F. Crispi, 67100 L'Aquila
Telephone: (39) 862-22104

Physical Education
Founded 1968.

3812 **ISTITUTO SUPERIORE PAREGGIATO DI EDUCAZIONE FISICA**
Via S. Vitale 15, 40125 Bologna
Telephone: (39) 51-239493

Physical Education
Founded 1960.

3813 **ISTITUTO SUPERIORE PAREGGIATO DI EDUCAZIONE FISICA**
Via Nicolidi 2, 50137 Firenze
Telephone: (39) 55-571997
Direttore: Salvatore Carbonaro

Physical Education
Founded 1966. Governing body: the Consiglio di Amministrazione.
Academic Year: November to October.
Admission Requirements: Secondary school certificate (maturità) and entrance examination.
Fees (Lira): 385,000 per annum.
Language of Instruction: Italian.
Degrees and Diplomas: Teaching diploma, 3 yrs.
Library: Central Library.
Academic Staff: c. 40.
Student Enrolment: c. 860.

3814 **ISTITUTO SUPERIORE PAREGGIATO DI EDUCAZIONE FISICA DELLA LOMBARDIA**
Piazza S. Alessandro 1, 20123 Milano
Telephone: (39) 2-803431
Direttore: Angelo Bairati

Physical Education
Founded 1968.

3815 **ISTITUTO SUPERIORE PAREGGIATO DI EDUCAZIONE FISICA**
Via S. Agnes 2, Largo A. Gemelli, 1 Milano 20123
Telex: 321033 UCATMI I
Telephone: (39-2) 8856-311
Fax: (39-2) 8856210
Direttore: Giovanni Peri
Segretario Amministrativo: Emilio Cuzziol

Physical Education
Dean: Giovanni Peri; *staff* 65
Ce. of Psycology
Head: Emilio Bombardieri
Branch in Brescia.
Founded 1964. Governing body: the Board of Directors.
Participates in the ERASMUS programme.
Academic Year: October to June.
Admission Requirements: Secondary school certificate (maturità).
Language of Instruction: Italian.
Degrees and Diplomas: Teaching diploma, 3 yrs.
Library: 1000 vols.
Academic Staff, 1989-90: 65.
Student Enrolment, 1989-90:

	Men	Women	Total
Of the country	421	426	847

3816 **ISTITUTO SUPERIORE PAREGGIATO DI EDUCAZIONE FISICA**
Presso la Mostra d'Oltremare, 80125 Napoli
Telephone: (39) 81-615241
Direttore: Carmine Mensorio

Physical Education
Founded 1960.

3817 **ISTITUTO SUPERIORE PAREGGIATO DI EDUCAZIONE FISICA**
Via Imperatore Federico 61, 90143 Palermo
Telephone: (39) 91-546106
Direttore: Pietro Benigno

Physical Education
Founded 1962 and formally recognized by the State 1965. Governing body: the Consiglio di Amministrazione.
Academic Year: November to October.
Admission Requirements: Secondary school certificate (maturità) and entrance examination.
Language of Instruction: Italian.
Degrees and Diplomas: Teaching Diploma, 3 yrs.
Library: c. 540 vols.
Academic Staff: c. – (50).
Student Enrolment: c. 300.

3818 **ISTITUTO SUPERIORE PAREGGIATO DI EDUCAZIONE FISICA DI PERUGIA**
Via Canali 12, 06100 Perugia
Telephone: (39) 75-754206
Direttore: Mario Pitzurra

Physical Education
Founded 1967.

3819 **ISTITUTO SUPERIORE STATALE PAREGGIATO DI EDUCAZIONE FISICA**
Foro Italico, Piazza Lauro de Bosis 15, 00194 Roma
Telephone: (39) 6-390616
Direttore: Giulio Marinozzi

Physical Education

3820 **ISTITUTO SUPERIORE PAREGGIATO DI EDUCAZIONE FISICA**
Piazza Bernini 12, 10128 Torino
Telephone: (39) 745774
Direttore: Eugenio Meda

Physical Education

3821 **ISTITUTO SUPERIORE PAREGGIATO DI EDUCAZIONE FISICA**

Via SS. Annunziata, 4 61029 Urbino
Telephone: (39-722) 329152
Fax: (39-722) 329198
Direttore: Marina Dacha' (1988-90)
Direttore Amministrativo: Rodolfo Bernini

Physical Education

Founded 1963. Affiliated to the University of Urbino and recognized by the State 1967. Governing bodies: the Consiglio di Amministrazione; the Consiglio Direttivo; the Consiglio di Professori. Residential facilities for academic staff and students.

Academic Year: November to October.

Admission Requirements: Secondary school certificate (maturità) and entrance examination.

Fees (Lira): 900,000-950,000 per annum.

Language of Instruction: Italian.

Degrees and Diplomas: Teaching Diploma, 3 yrs.

Library: c. 20,000 vols.

Publication: Cinesiologia (quarterly).

Press or Publishing House: Centro Stampa.

Academic Staff, 1990: 172.

Student Enrolment, 1989:

	Men	Women	Total
Of the country	792	873	1665
Of other countries	20	2	22
Total	812	875	1687

General Education

3822 **UNIVERSITÀ ITALIANA PER STRANIERI**

Italian University for Foreigners
Palazzo Gallenga, Piazza Fortebraccio 4, 06100 Perugia
Cables: Unitastri-Perugia
Telephone: (39) 75-64344
Rettore: Giorgio Spitella

Italian Language, Literature, and Culture

Founded 1921 as Corsi di Cultura Superiore, became Regia Università Italiana per Stranieri 1925, adopted present title after the Second World War. Under the jurisdiction of the Ministry of Education and responsible also to the provincial and municipal authorities of Perugia. Governing bodies: the Consiglio di Amministrazione; Consiglio Accademico.

Academic Year: January to December (January-March; April-June; July-September; October-December).

Language of Instruction: Italian.

Degrees and Diplomas: Attestato di conoscenza elementare di lingua italiana, 3 months; Attestato di conoscenza della lingua italiana, a further 3 months; Diploma di abilitazione all'insegnamento della lingua italiana all'estero (Diploma qualifying holder to teach Italian abroad), 9 months; Diploma–di Etruscologia e Antichità Italiche; Lingua italiana contemporanea.

Library: c. 60,000 vols.

Academic Staff: c. 50 (80).

Student Enrolment: c. 10,000.

JAPAN

Universities and University Institutions with Graduate Schools[1]

National Institutions

3823 ***AICHI KYOIKU DAIGAKU**

Aichi University of Education

1Hirosawa, Igaya-cho, Kariya-shi, Aichi-ken 448

Telephone: 566-36-3111

F. of Education

Founded as school 1873, reorganized 1949 and acquired present title 1966. Residential facilities for *c.* 150 academic staff and *c.* 300 students.

Academic Year: April to March (April-September; October-March).

Admission Requirements: Graduation from high school or foreign equivalent, and entrance examination.

Language of Instruction: Japanese.

Degrees and Diplomas: Kyoikugakushi, Bachelor of Education, 4 yrs; Kyoikugakushushi, Master of Education, a further 2 yrs. Doctor.

Library: c. 210,000 vols.

Publication: Bulletin.

Academic Staff: c. 230 (110).

Student Enrolment: c. 3450.

3824 **AKITA DAIGAKU**

Akita University

1-1 Tegata Gakuen-machi, Akita-shi, Akita 010

Telephone: (188) 33-5261

Gakucho (President): Yoshitane Watabe (1986-91)

Jimukyokucho (Secretary-General): Kenji Mizuochi

Ce. of Education

Dean: Naoyoshi Niino; *staff* 137 (109)

S. of Medicine

Dean: Tsutomu Watanukiama; *staff* 131 (128)

Mining Ce.

Dean: Sakuro Honda; *staff* 118 (45)

Graduate S. of Medicine

Dean: Tsutomu Watanuki; *staff* – (130)

D. for Advanced Studies in Special Education for the Mentally Handicapped

Dean: Naoyoshi Niino; *staff* – (5)

Graduate S. of Education

Dean: Naoyoshi Niino; *staff* – (55)

C. of Allied Medical Science and Technology (Nursing, Physiotherapy, Occupational Therapy)

Director: Mineko Haryu *staff* 14 (23)

Ce. for Education Technology.

Central Medical Research L.

Natural Resources Research I.

Founded 1949, incorporating Akita Shihan Gakko (Normal School), founded 1875, Akita Kozan Senmon Gakko (Mining College) 1910, Akita Seinen Shihan Gakko (Normal School for Adult Education) 1944, and Igakubu (School of Medicine) 1970. Responsible to the Ministry of Education, Science and Culture. Governing body: the Hyogikai (University Council). Residential facilities for academic staff and students.

Arrangements for co-operation with: St. Cloud State University; Montana College of Mineral Sciences and Technology; South-Central China Institute of Metallurgy, Hunan; Fuxin Mining Institute, Liaoning; Heilongjiang University; Norman Bethune University of Medical Sciences; China Medical University.

Academic Year: April to March (April-September; October-March).

Admission Requirements: Graduation from high school or foreign equivalent, and entrance examination.

Fees (Yen): 169,800 per semester.

Language of Instruction: Japanese.

Degrees and Diplomas: Gakushi, Bachelor–Kyoikugakushi, education; Kogakushi, engineering, 4 yrs; Igakushi, medicine, 6 yrs. Shushi, Master–Kyoikushushi, education; Kogakushushi, engineering, a further 2 yrs. Igakuhakushi, Doctor of Medical Sciences, a further 3-4 yrs.

Libraries: University Library, 333,393 vols; Medical School Library, 78,832.

Special Facilities (Museums, etc.): Mineral Industry Museum; Animal Facilities for Experimental Medicine.

Publications: Memoirs of the Faculty of Education; Akita University (annually); Akita Igaku (quarterly); Scientific and Technical Reports of the Mining College; Reports of Research Institute of Natural Resources (annually).

Academic Staff, 1990:

Rank	Full-time	Part-time
Gakucho (President)	1	–
Kyoju (Professors)	136	–
Jokyoju (Assistant Professors)	139	–
Koshi (Lecturers)	72	310
Joshu (Assistants)	154	–
Kocho (Head Teachers)	–	–
Kyoyu (Teachers)	79	8
Total	581	318

Student Enrolment, 1990:

	Men	Women	Total
Of the country	3381	1104	4485
Of other countries	36	6	42
Total	3417	1110	4527*

*Also 1364 external students.

3825 **ASAHIKAWA IKA DAIGAKU**

Asahikawa Medical College

Nishikagura 4-5, Asahikawa, Hokkaido 078

Telex: 922492

Telephone: (166) 65-2111

Gakucho (President): Akihasa Shimoda (1987-)

Jimukyokucho (Secretary-General): Hajime Kayanuma

S. of Medicine

President: Akihisa Shimoda; *staff* 861 (146)

Animal L. for Medical Research

Director: Tokuji Unno; *staff* 12 (1)

Central L. for Research and Education

Director: Yoshiharu Takemitsu; *staff* 7 (1)

Founded 1973. Graduate course established 1979. Residential facilities for academic staff.

Academic Year: April to March (April-September; October-March).

Admission Requirements: Graduation from senior high school or equivalent, and entrance examination.

Fees (Yen): 339,600 per annum.

Language of Instruction: Japanese.

Degrees and Diplomas: Igakushi, Bachelor of Medicine, 6 yrs. Doctor of Medical Sciences, a further 4 yrs.

Library: 101,105 vols.

Publication: Asahikawa Medical College (annually).

(1) It will be noted that all institutions and higher education included in this chapter bear the title 'Daigaku'. Their classification in various groups is based on a proposal made by the Ministry of Education of Japan.

Academic Staff, 1990-91:

Rank	Full-time	Part-time
Gakucho (President)	1	–
Fukugakucho (Vice-Presidents)	2	–
Kyoju (Professors)	37	–
Jokyoju (Associate Professors)	26	–
Koshi (Assistant Professors)	38	58
Joshu (Research Associates)	136	–
Total	240	58

Student Enrolment, 1990-91:

	Men	Women	Total
Of the country	835	187	1022
Of other countries	5	–	5
Total	840	187	1027

3826 ***CHIBA DAIGAKU**

Chiba University

1-33 Yayoi-cho, Chiba-shi, Chiba 260
Telephone: (472) 51-1111
Fax: (472) 54-1596
Gakucho (President): Ryo Yoshida (1988-92)
Himu-Kyokucho (Secretary-General) Katsuhiko Kurioka

F. of Letters (including Psychology)
Dean: Yuichi Shimomura *staff* 52 (39)
F. of Law and Economics
Dean: Yasuhiko Yuize; *staff* 60 (22)
F. of Education
Dean: Masao Uchida; *staff* 119 (139)
F. of Pharmaceutical Sciences
Dean: Seiyu Hirose; *staff* 53 (16)
F. of Engineering (including Architecture)
Dean: Tsutomu Suzuki; *staff* 185 (177)
F. of Horticulture
Dean: Noritsugu Shimada; *staff* 79 (97)
F. of Science
Dean: Sumio Sakagami; *staff* 67 (69)
S. of Medicine
Dean: Satoshi Murayama; *staff* 167 (520)
S. of Nursing
Dean: Kayoko Yoshitake; *staff* 56 (49)
C. of Arts and Sciences
Dean: Masatoshi Iwashige; *staff* 122 (325)
Research Ce. for Pathogenic Fungi and Microbial Toxicoses
Director: Makoto Miyaji; *staff* 16 (7)
Remote Sensing and Image Research Ce.
Director: Kiyoshi Tsuchiya; *staff* 8
Information Procesing Ce.
Director: Tsutomu Suzuki; *staff* 1
Chemical Analysis C.
Director: Toru Hino; *staff* 3
Health Sciences Ce.
Director: Yasuhiro Kinoshita; *staff* 5 (5)

Also kindergarten, primary, and junior high schools, as well as school for handicapped children.

Founded 1949 as a State university incorporating Chiba Medical College, Chiba Normal School, Chiba Youth Normal School, Tokyo Industrial Senmon Gakko, and Chiba Agricultural College. Graduate School established 1955. Governing body: the Hyogikai (University Council). Residential facilities for students.

Arrangements for co-operation with: Georg-August Universität Göttingen; University of Alabama; Hunan University; University of Alberta; Chulalongkorn University.

Academic Year: April to March (April-September; October-March).

Admission Requirements: Graduation from high school or equivalent or foreign equivalent, and entrance examination.

Fees (Yen): Registration, 206,000; tuition, 339,600 per annum.

Language of Instruction: Japanese.

Degrees and Diplomas: Gakushi, Bachelor–Bungakushi, letters; Hogakushi, law; Keizaigakushi, economics; Rigakushi, science; Kyoikugakushi, education; Yakugakushi, pharmacy; Kangogakushi, nursing; Kogakushi, engineering; Nogakushi, agriculture, 4 yrs. Igakushi, doctor of medicine, 6 yrs. Shushi, Master–Rigakushushi, science; Nogakushushi, agriculture; Kyoikugakushushi, education; Yakugakushushi, pharmacy; Kangogakushushi, nursing; Kogakushushi, engineering, a further 2 yrs. Igakuhakushi, Doctor of Medical Sciences, a further 4 yrs. Yakugakuhakushi, Doctor of Pharmaceutical Sciences, a further 5 yrs.

Library: University Library, 1,087,108 vols.

Special Facilities (Museums, etc.): University Farms.

Publications: Journal of Humanities; Journal of Faculty of General Education; Bulletin of Faculty of Education; Chiba Medical Journal (bimonthly); Journal of Faculty of Engineering; Technical Bulletin of Faculty of Horticulture; Annual Report of Research Centre for Pathogenic Fungi and Microbial Toxicoses; Journal of Law and Economics; Journal of the Arts and Sciences; Journal of the Faculty of Nursing (all annually or biannually).

Academic Staff, 1988-89:

Rank	Full-time	Part-time
Kyoju (Professors)	359	–
Jokyoju (Associate Professors)	309	–
Koshi (Assistant Professors)	124	1453
Joshu (Research Associates)	343	–
Total	1135	1453

Student Enrolment, 1988-89:

	Men	Women	Total
Of the country	8997	3721	12,718
Of other countries	252	111	363
Total	9249	3832	13,081

3827 **DENKI-TSUSHIN DAIGAKU**

University of Electro-Communications

1-5-1 Chofugaoka, Chofu-shi, Tokyo 182
Telex: 2822446 UEC J
Telephone: (424) 83-2161

D. of Communication Systems
D. of Communications Engineering
D. of Applied Electronics Engineering
D. of Electronics Engineering
D. of Industrial Management Engineering
D. of Mechanical Engineering I
D. of Mechanical Engineering II
D. of Materials Research
D. of Engineering Physics
D. of Computer Sciences
D. of Information Mathematics
Junior Technical C.
I. for Communication Sciences
Space Radio Wave Observatory
I. for Laser Science

Founded 1918 by Wireless Association, transferred to Ministry of Communications 1942 and to Ministry of Education 1948. Re-established as university 1949. Junior Technical College established 1953 and Graduate School 1965. Residential facilities for academic staff and students.

Academic Year: April to March (April-October; October-March).

Admission Requirements: Graduation from high school and entrance examination.

Language of Instruction: Japanese.

Degrees and Diplomas: Gakushi, Bachelor, of Engineering, 4 yrs. Shushi, Master, of Engineering, a further 2 yrs.

Library: University Library, *c.* 253,000 vols.

Publications: Reports (biannually); Annual Report of Research.

Academic Staff: c. 220 (130).

Student Enrolment: c. 3040.

3828 **EHIME DAIGAKU**

Ehime University

10-13 Dogo-Himata, Matsuyama-shi, Ehime 790
Telephone: (899) 24-7111
Fax: (899) 24-7149
Gakucho (President): Yasuji Asada
Jimukyokucho (Administrator): Hiroshi Kusaka

F. of Law and Literature (including Economics)
Dean: Senya Misishima; *staff* 90

F. of Education
Dean: Kazuaki Kawabuchi; *staff* 100
F. of Science (Mathematics, Physics, Chemistry, Biology, and Earth Sciences)
Dean: Kei Semba; *staff* 60
S. of Medicine
Dean: Ryo Fukunishi; *staff* 228
F. of Engineering (Mechanical, Electrical, Civil, Industrial, and Ocean Engineering, Metallurgy, Industrial Chemistry, Electronics, Resources Chemistry, and Computer Science)
Dean: Kozo Futagami; *staff* 120
C. of Agriculture
Dean: Koichi Sato; *staff* 96
Graduate S. of Agricultural Sciences
Dean: Ryo Tatsukawa; *staff* 1
F. of General Education
Dean: Katsumi Morita; *staff* 86
Advanced Instrumentation Ce. for Chemical Analysis
Director: Yoshira Sakai; *staff* 3
Data Processing Ce.
Director: Yuzo Takamatsu; *staff* 2
Health Administration Ce.
Director: Akira Tanaka
Also kindergarten, primary, lower secondary, junior and senior high schools, and school for the handicapped.

Founded 1949, incorporating Ehime Normal School, founded 1943, Matsuyama Higher School, 1919, Ehime Youth Normal School, 1944, Niihama Technical College, 1939, and Matsuyama Agricultural College, 1949. Governing body: the Hyogikai (University Council), composed of the dean and 2 professors of each faculty. Some residential facilities for academic staff and for *c.* 430 students.

Arrangements for co-operation with: University of California, Riverside; Southwest Agricultural University, China; Liaoning Normal University; Maejo Institute of Agricultural Technology.

Academic Year: April to March (April-September; October-March).

Admission Requirements: Graduation from high school or equivalent and entrance examination.

Fees (Yen): Registration, 206,000; tuition, 339,600.

Language of Instruction: Japanese.

Degrees and Diplomas: Gakushi, Bachelor–Bungakushi, arts; Rigakushi, science; Shakaigakushi, social science; Hogakushi, law; Kyoikugakushi, education; Kogakushi, engineering; Nogakushi, agriculture, 4 yrs; Shushi, Master–Kogakushushi, engineering; Hogakushushi, law; Rigakushushi, science; Nogakushushi, agriculture, a further 2 yrs. Hakushi, Doctor,of–Medical Sciences; Agriculture, a further 4 yrs.

Libraries: Central and branch libraries, total, 850,659 vols. (Japanese, 603,459; foreign, 247,200).

Academic Staff, 1990:

	Full-time
Kyoju (Professors)	239
Jokyoju (Assistant Professors)	247
Koshi (Lecturers)	85
Joshu (Assistants)	217
Total	789

Student Enrolment, 1990:

	Men	Women	Total
Of the country	6290	2517	8807
Of other countries	76	22	98
Total	6366	2539	8905

3829 **FUKUI DAIGAKU**

Fukui University

9-1 Bunkyo, 3-chome, Fukui-shi, Fukui 910
Telephone: (776) 23-0500
Gakucho (President): Hisao Yagi (1983-87)
Jimukyokucho: Shigetomi Kawadai

F. of Education
Dean: Hiroshi Segawa; *staff* 227 (136)
F. of Engineering (including Architecture)
Dean: Isao Toriumi; *staff* 205 (85)
Textile Engineering Research I.
Director: Togoro Matsuo; *staff* 9 (18)
Experimental I. for Low Temperature Physics
Director: Hiroaki Matsumoto; *staff* 2 (21)
Also primary and junior high schools.

Founded 1949 incorporating Fukui Normal School, Fukui Youth Normal School, and Fukui Technical Senmon Gakko. Financed by the State through the Ministry of Education, Science and Culture. Some residential facilities for academic staff and students.

Arrangements for co-operation with: Rutgers University; Xi'an Institute of Foreign Languages, Shaanxi province; Shaanxi Institute of Mechanical Engineering.

Academic Year: April to March (April-September; October-March).

Admission Requirements: Graduation from high school or equivalent and entrance examination.

Fees (Yen): 300,000 per annum.

Language of Instruction: Japanese.

Degrees and Diplomas: Gakushi, Bachelor–Kyoikugakushi, education; Kogakushi, engineering, 4 yrs; Shushi, Master–Kogakushushi, engineering, a further 2 yrs; Shogakko Kyoyu Menkyosho, Teaching Certificate, elementary level; Chugakko Kyoyu Menkyosho, Teaching Certificate, lower secondary level; Kotogakko Kyoyu Menkyosho, Teaching Certificate, secondary level; Yogo Kyoyu Menkyosho, Teaching Certificate, handicapped children; Yochien Kyoyu Menkyosho, Teaching Certificate, kindergarten, 4 yrs.

Library: University Library, 326,942 vols.

Publications: Report; General Information; Handbook for Students; Memoirs of Faculty of Education; Research Reports of Faculty of Engineering.

Academic Staff, 1986-87:

Rank	Full-time	Part-time
Gakucho (President)	1	–
Kyoju (Professors)	95	–
Jokyoju (Assistant Professors)	121	–
Koshi (Lecturers)	10	183
Joshu (Assistants)	28	–
Kyoyu (Teachers)	65	13
Total	320	196

Student Enrolment, 1986-87:

	Men	Women	Total
Of the country	2407	616	3023
Of other countries	12	10	22
Total	2419	626	3045

3830 **FUKUI IKA DAIGAKU**

Fukui Medical School

23 Shimoaizuki, Matsuoka-cho, Fukui 910-11
Telephone: (776) 61-3111
Fax: (776) 61-3535
Gakucho (President): Kanji Torizuka (1989-92)
Jimukyokucho (Secretary-General): Susumu Saito

F. of Medicine
I. of Laboratory Animals
Director: Yoshinobu Kimura; *staff* 5
Medical Research Ce.
Director: Hideo Negoro; *staff* 7
Medical Information Science Ce.
Director: Masakatsu Sudo; *staff* 7
Radioisotope Research Ce.
Director: Eiichi Kano; *staff* 3

Founded 1978. Graduate School established 1986 and post-graduate school established 1990.

Academic Year: April to March (April-September; October-March).

Admission Requirements: Graduation from high school or equivalent or foreign equivalent, and entrance examination.

Fees (Yen): Registration, 206,000; tuition, 339,600 per annum.

Language of Instruction: Japanese.

Degrees and Diplomas: Igakushi, Bachelor of Medicine, 6 yrs. Igakuhakushi, Doctor of Medical Sciences.

Library: *c.* 78,448 vols.

Academic Staff, 1990:

Rank	Full-time	Part-time
Gakucho (President):	1	–
Fuku Gakucho (Vice-Presidents)	2	–
Kyoju (Professors)	36	–
Jokyoju (Associate Professors)	34	–
Koshi (Assistant Professors)	28	60
Joshu (Research Associates)	130	–
Total	231	60

Student Enrolment, 1990:

	Men	Women	Total
Of the country	539	153	692
Of other countries	3	1	4
Total	542	154	696

3831 **FUKUOKA KYOIKA DAIGAKU**
Fukuoka University of Education
729 Akama, Munakata-shi, Fukuoka 811-41
Telephone: (940) 32-2381

F. of Education

Founded 1943, reorganized 1949.

Academic Year: April to March (April-October; October-February).

Admission Requirements: Graduation from high school and entrance examination.

Degrees and Diplomas: Kyoikugakushi, Bachelor of Education, 4 yrs. Graduate Course, 1 yr.

Academic Staff: c. 320.

Student Enrolment: c. 2900.

3832 **FUKUSHIMA DAIGAKU**
Fukushima University
2 Sugumichi, Asakawa, Fukushima-shi, Fukushima 960-12
Telephone: (245) 48-5151

F. of Economics
F. of Education

Founded 1949.

Academic Year: April to March (April-September; October-March).

Admission Requirements: Graduation from high school or equivalent or foreign equivalent, and entrance examination.

Language of Instruction: Japanese.

Degrees and Diplomas: Gakushi, Bachelor. Shushi, Master.

Library: c. 418,210 vols.

Academic Staff: c. 220.

Student Enrolment: c. 3700.

3833 **GIFU DAIGAKU**
Gifu University
1-1 Yanagido, Gifu-shi, Gifu-ken 501-11
Telephone: (582) 30-1111
Fax: (582) 30-1410
Gakucho (President): Akira Katoh (1949-)
Jimukyokucho (Secretary-General): Sumio Hashimoto

F. of Education
Dean: Saburo Matsuoka; *staff* 154 (42)
S. of Medicine
Dean: Hideo Isono; *staff* 223 (497)
F. of Engineering
Dean: Takeshi Kawamura; *staff* 121 (58)
F. of Agriculture (including Veterinary Science and Forestry)
Dean: Toshio Kinjo; *staff* 64 (15)
F. of General Education (including Physical Education)
Dean: Tomo Horikoshi; *staff* 64 (15)
I. of Equilibrium Research
Director: Ken'ichi Matsunami; *staff* 9 (3)
I. of Anaerobic Bacteriology
Director: Kazue Ueno; *staff* 6 (3)
I. of Mountain Region Development
Director: Masayuki Matsumura; *staff* 8 (3)
S. of Nursing
Principal: Hiromu Yamada; *staff* 4 (21)

Founded 1949, incorporating Gifu Normal College founded 1875, and Gifu College of Agriculture and Forestry founded 1924. Faculty of Engineering of Gifu Prefectural University attached 1952. Gifu Prefectural College of Medicine attached 1964 as Faculty of Medicine. Governing body: the Hyogikai (University Council). Some residential facilities for academic staff and *c.* 340 students.

Arrangements for co-operation with the Universities of: Campinas; Alaska Fairbanks; San Diego State; Zhejiang; Lund. Koshi Institute of Agriculture; University of Electronic Science and Technology of China; Wuxi Institute of Light Industry; Zhejiang Medical University; China Medical University.

Academic Year: April to March (April-September; October-March).

Admission Requirements: Graduation from high school or equivalent or foreign equivalent, and entrance examination.

Fees (Yen): Registration, 206,000 ; tuition, 339,600 per annum.

Language of Instruction: Japanese.

Degrees and Diplomas: Gakushi, Bachelor–Kyoikugakushi, education; Kogakushi, engineering; Nogakushi, agriculture; Juigakushi, veterinary science, 4 yrs. Shushi, Master–Kogakushushi, engineering; Nogakushushi, agriculture; Juigakushushi, veterinary science, a further 2 yrs. Igakushi, doctor of medicine and veterinary science, 6 yrs; Igakuhakushi, doctor of medical and veterinary sciences, a further 4 yrs.

Library: University Library, 558,000 vols.

Special Facilities (Museums, etc.): Gifu Local Museum.

Publications: Faculty Research Reports (annually); Education; Medicine; Engineering; Agriculture; General Education.

Academic Staff, 1989:

Rank	Full-time
Gakucho (President)	1
Kyoju (Professors)	206
Jokyoju (Associate Professors)	174
Koshi (Assistant Professors)	73
Joshu (Research Associates)	191
Teachers of University	54
Other Staff	801
Total	1500

Student Enrolment, 1989:

Of the country	4842
Of other countries	23
Total	4865

3834 **GUNMA DAIGAKU**
Gunma University
4-2 Aramaki-Machi, Maebasi-shi, Gunma 371
Telephone: (272)-32-1611
Gakucho (President): Tadashi Maekawa (1985-89)
Jimukyokucho: Yukio Ando

F. of Education
Dean: Fusao Arai; *staff* 92 (120)
S. of Medicine
Dean: Teruo Nagai; *staff* 150 (193)
F. of Engineering
Dean: Hiroshi Yukawa; *staff* 139 (66)
F. of General Studies (Liberal Arts and Sciences)
Dean: Motohiko Uchida; *staff* 43 (75)
C. of Technology
Director: Shungo Oshiashi; *staff* 26 (24)
I of Endocrinology
Director: Hirao Takigawa; *staff* 24
C. of Medical Care and Technology
Director: Jun Tsuchiya; *staff* 51 (58)

Founded 1949 and incorporating Gunma Normal School, founded 1876, Kiryu Engineering College, 1915, and Maebashi Medical College, 1943. Responsible to the Ministry of Education, Science and Culture. Some residential facilities for academic staff and students.

Academic Year: April to March (April-September; October-March).

Admission Requirements: Graduation from high school or equivalent, and entrance examination.

Fees (Yen): Registration, 300,000 per annum.

Language of Instruction: Japanese.

Degrees and Diplomas: Gakushi, Bachelor–Kyoikugakushi, education; Kogakushi, engineering; 4 yrs. Kogakushushi, Master of Engineering, a further 2 yrs. Igakushi, doctor of medicine, 6 yrs; Igakuhakushi, Doctor of Medical Sciences, a further 4yrs.

Libraries: Central Library, 240,080 vols; Medical library, 99,681; Technological library, 109,197; Others, 38,341.

Publications: Annual Reports; Science Reports; Gunma Journal of Liberal Arts and Science; Gunma Journal of Medical Science; Gunma Symposia on Endocrinology; Annual Reports of Institute of Endocrinology.

Academic Staff, 1986-87:

Rank	Full-time	Part-time
Kyoju (Professors)	180	–
Jokyoyu (Associate Professors)	148	–
Koshi (Lecturers)	86	536
Joshu (Assistants)	226	–
Total	640	536

Student Enrolment, 1986-87:

	Men	Women	Total
Of the country	3210	904	4114
Of other countries	16	5	21
Total	3226	909	4135

3835 **HAMAMATSU IKA DAIGAKU**

Hamamatsu University School of Medicine

3600 Handa-cho, Hamamatsu-shi, Shizuoka 431-31

Telephone: (534) 35-2111

F. of Medicine

Founded 1974. Governing body: the Kyojukai (Council). Residential facilities for *c.* 410 academic staff.

Academic Year: April to March (April-September; October-March).

Admission Requirements: Graduation from high school or equivalent or foreign equivalent, and entrance examination.

Language of Instruction: Japanese.

Degrees and Diplomas: Igakushi, Bachelor of Medicine, 6 yrs. Doctor.

Library: c. 41,410 vols.

Academic Staff: c. 190 (150).

Student Enrolment: c. 600.

3836 **HIROSAKI DAIGAKU**

Hirosaki University

1 Bunkyo-cho, Hirosaki-shi, Aomori-ken 036

Telephone: (172) 36-2111

Gakucho (President): Shuji Tohno (1986-90)

Jimukyokucho: Gihei Henmi

F. of Humanities (including Economics, Business Administration, and Law)
Dean: Kan-eu Akizuki, *staff* 60 (46)
F. of Education (including Fine Arts and Sociology)
Dean: Terumune Takeuchi; *staff* 187 (75)
F. of Science
Dean: Wataru Teshirogi; *staff* 57 (28)
S. of Medicine (including Pharmacy)
Dean: Tomio Yamaguchi; *staff* 147 (141)
F. of Agriculture
Dean: Kaizo Tsubomatsu; *staff* 49 (22)
C. of Liberal Arts (including Physical Education)
Dean: Makoto Akashi; *staff* 50 (96)
S. of Allied Medical Sciences (including Nursing and Midwifery)
Dean: Shuji Tohno; *staff* 62 (125)
Also kindergarten, primary, and junior high schools.

Founded 1949 as a new system national university incorporating Hirosaki High School, founded 1920, Aomori Normal School 1943, Young Men's Normal School 1944, Hirosaki College of Medicine 1948, and Aomori College of Medicine. Governing body: the Board of Directors. The trustees are the President, the deans, and three professors from each of the faculties. Residential facilities for 179 academic staff and 664 students.

Arrangements for co-operation with the University of Tennessee at Martin and at Memphis.

Academic Year: April-March (April-September; October-March).

Admission Requirements: Graduation from high school or equivalent or foreign equivalent, and entrance examination.

Fees (Yen): 300,000 per annum.

Language of Instruction: Japanese.

Degrees and Diplomas: Gakushi, Bachelor–Bungakushi, arts; Keizaigakushi, economics; Kyoikugakushi, education; Rigakushi, science; Nogakushi, agriculture; 4 yrs. Shushi, Master–Nogakushushi, agriculture; Rigakushushi, science, a further 2 yrs. Igakushi, doctor of medicine, 6 yrs; Igakuhakushi, Doctor of Medical Sciences, a further 4 yrs.

Library: University Library, 610,058 vols.

Publication: Faculty Bulletins (annually).

Academic Staff, 1986-87:

Rank	Full-time	Part-time
Kyoju (Professors)	156	–
Jokyoju (Associate Professors)	204	–
Koshi (Assistant Professors)	84	533
Joshu (Research Associates)	174	
Kyoyu (Teachers)	93	–
Total	711	533

Student Enrolment, 1986-87:

	Men	Women	Total
Of the country	3552	1493	5045
Of other countries	12	4	16
Total	3564	1497	5061

3837 ***HIROSHIMA DAIGAKU**

Hiroshima University

1-1-89, Higashisenda-machi, Naka-ku, Hiroshima-shi, Hiroshima 730

Cables: Hiruniv Hiroshima

Telephone: (82) 241-1221

Fax: (02)242-1561

Gakucho (President): Ryuso Tanaka (1989-93)

Jimukyokucho (Secretary-General): Yoshihiro Noguchi

F. of Integrated Arts and Sciences
Dean: Minoru Amano; *staff* 23 (117)
F. of Letters
Dean: Hiroshi Shiomi; *staff* 67 (31)
F. of Education
Dean: Tokuo Kataoka; *staff* 134 (55)
F. of Economics
Dean: Yoshikazu Sunagawa; *staff* 37 (5)
F. of Law (including Political Science and International Relations)
Dean: Hiroyuki Hata; *staff* 35 (4)
F. of Science
Dean: Masahiro Sugagawa; *staff* 161 (19)
F. of Engineering (including Architecture)
Dean: Noriyoshi Yoshida; *staff* 243 (88)
F. of Applied Biological Science
Dean: Shunpei Kakuda; *staff* 64 (10)
F. of School Education (Teacher Training)
Dean: Shigeto Mizuoka; *staff* 93 (60)
S. of Medicine (including Pharmacy)
Dean: Yasuo Harada; *staff* 160 (117)
S. of Dentistry
Dean: Hiroshi Okamoto; *staff* 99 (82)
Higher Education Research Ce.
Director: Masao Seki; *staff* 8
Nuclear Medicine and Biology Research I.
Director: Atsushi Kuramato; *staff* 40 (14)
Information Processing Ce.
Director: Kyoji Nishikawa; *staff* 6
Research Ce. for Integrated Systems
Director: Masataka Hirose; *staff* 4 (1)
Cryogenic Ce.
Director: Takao Kino; *staff* 1
Ce. for Gene Science
Director Osamu Nimi; *staff* 2
Health Service Ce.
Director: Goro Kajiyama; *staff* 7

Founded 1949, incorporating an existing university and seven colleges. Hiroshima Higher Normal School was founded in 1902 and the former Hiroshima University in 1929. Postgraduate courses and faculty of medicine established in 1953. The President is elected by the academic staff and appointed by the Ministry of Education, Science and Culture. Governing body: the Hyogikai (University Council). Residential facilities for foreign students.

Arrangements for co-operation with: University of Michigan; University of Auckland; Eberhard Karl University of Tübingen; University of Oxford, Wadham College; University of North Sumatra; Fudan University; Academy of Medicine, Bulgaria; Thammasat University; University of Hawaii; Graz University; University of Minnesota; Huazhong University of Science and Technology; Dalian University of Science and Technology; Chungnam National University; Medizinische Hochschule, Hannover.

Academic Year: April to March (April-September; October-March).

Admission Requirements: Graduation from high school or recognized equivalent, and entrance examination.

Fees (Yen): Registration, 206,000; tuition, 339,600 per annum.

Language of Instruction: Japanese.

Degrees and Diplomas: Gakushi, Bachelor–Kyoyogakushi, liberal arts; Hogakushi, law; Bungakushi, letters; Kyoikugakushi, education; Keizaigakushi, economics; Rigakushi, science; Yakugakushi, pharmacy; Kogakushi, engineering; Nogakushi, agriculture, 4 yrs; Igakushi, medicine; Shigakushi, dentistry, 6 yrs. Shushi, Master–Bungakushushi, letters; Kyoikugakushushi, education; Hogakushushi, law; Kokusaigakushushi, international relations; Keizaigakushushi, economics; Rigakushushi, science; Yakugakushushi, pharmacy; Kogakushushi, engineering; Nogakushushi, agriculture; Gakujutsushushi, biosphere sciences, social sciences, a further 2 yrs. Hakushi, Doctor–Bungakuhakushi, letters; Kyoikugakuhakushi, education; Rigakuhakushi, science; Gakujutsuhakushi, biosphere sciences, social sciences; Hogakuhakushi, law; Keizaigakuhakushi, economics; Nogakuhakushi, agriculture; Kogakuhakushi, engineering; Yakugakuhakushi, Doctor of Pharmaceutical Sciences, 3 yrs after Shushi. Igakuhakushi, Doctor of Medical Sciences; Shigakuhakushi, Doctor of Dental Sciences, a further 4 yrs.

Library: Central Library and faculty libraries, *c.* 2,390,000 vols.

Publications: Hiroshima University Studies (annually); Bulletin of the Faculty of Education (annually); Journal of Science (three times a year); Memoirs of the Faculty of Engineering (annually); Medical Journal (bimonthly); Research in Higher Education (annually); Research in Higher Education-Daigaku Ronshu (annually).

Academic Staff, 1990-91:

Rank	Full-time	Part-time
Gakucho (President)	1	–
Kyoju (Professors)	484	–
Jokyoju (Associate Professors)	443	–
Koshi (Lecturers)	143	699
Joshu (Assistants)	541	–
Kyoyu (Instructors)	217	
Total	1828	699

Student Enrolment, 1990-91:

	Men	Women	Total
Of the country	11,156	4195	15,351
Of other countries	290	146	436
Total	11,446	4341	15,787

3838 ***HITOTSUBASHI DAIGAKU**

Hitotsubashi University

2-1, Naka, Kunitachi-shi, Tokyo 186

Telex: 2842107 HITOTS J

Telephone: (425) 72-1101

Fax: (425) 75-4055

Gakucho (President): Yuichi Shionoya (1989-92)

Jimukyokucho (Secretary-General): Wataru Konishi

F. of Commerce

Dean: Toshiya Hanawa; *staff* 58 (19)

F. of Economics

Dean: Akira Ono; *staff* 74 (10)

F. of Law

Dean: Morio Takeshita; *staff* 63 (18)

F. of Social Studies

Dean: Sadahiko Fujioka; *staff* 64 (23)

I. of Economic Research

Dean: Ryoshin Minami; *staff* 28 (8)

Founded 1875 as institute of business training; became Tokyo University of Commerce 1920. Reorganized and present title adopted 1949. Governing body: the Board of Councillors. Residential facilities for 544 students.

Arrangements for co-operation with the Universities of: Sheffield; Oxford; Nankai; Stanford; Cologne; Bocconi; Trier; Thammasat; Antwerp; Louvain; California (Berkeley); Shanghai (Finance and Economics). Ecole des hautes Etudes commerciales, Jouy-en-Josas; London School of Economics and Political Science; Massachusetts Instituteof Technology; Harvard Business School.

Academic Year: April to March (April-September; October-March).

Admission Requirements: Graduation from high school or equivalent, and entrance examination.

Fees (Yen): Registration, 206,000; tuition, 339,600 per annum.

Language of Instruction: Japanese.

Degrees and Diplomas: Gakushi, Bachelor–Shogakushi, commerce; Keizaigakushi, economics; Hogakushi, law; Shakaigakushi, social science, 4 yrs. Shushi, Master–Keiegakushushi, business administration; Keizaigakushushi, economics; Hogakushushi, law; Shakaigakushushi, social studies, a further 2 yrs. Hakushi, Doctor–Keiegakuhakushi, business administration; Keizaigakuhakushi, economics; Hogakuhakushi, law; Shakaigakuhakushi, social science, 3 yrs after Shushi.

Libraries: Kunitachi Main Library, *c.* 1,058,100 vols.; Kodaira Branch Library, *c.* 207,300; Ce. for Historical Social Science Literature, *c.* 65,400.

Publications: Journal of Commerce and Management (annually); Journal of Economics (biannually); Journal of Law and Politics; Journal of Arts and Sciences (annually); Journal of Social Studies (annually); Hitotsubashi Ronso (Review) (monthly); Business Review (4 times a year); The Economic Review (4 times a year).

Academic Staff, 1990-91:

Rank	Full-time	Part-time
Gakucho (President)	1	–
Kyoju (Professors)	148	–
Jokyoju (Associate Professors)	45	–
Koshi (Lecturers)	21	161
Gaikokugin kyoshi (Foreign Instructors)	4	–
Gaikokugin koshi (Foreign Lecturers)	–	4
Joshu (Assistants)	81	–
Total	300	166

Student Enrolment, 1990-91:

	Men	Women	Total
Of the country	4498	674	5172
Of other countries	247	90	337
Total	4745	764	5509

3839 ***HOKKAIDO DAIGAKU**

Hokkaido University

Nishi 5, Kita 8, Kita-ku, Sapporo-shi, Hokkaido 060

Telephone: (11) 716-2111

Gakucho (President): Yoshio Ban (1987-)

Jimukyokucho (Secretary-General): Iwao Otani

F. of Letters

Dean: Shoji Oshima; *staff* 111

F. of Education

Dean: Yasuo Takamura; *staff* 37

F. of Law

Dean: Mutsuo Nakamura; *staff* 61

F. of Economics (including Business Administration)

Dean: Shigeo Aramata; *staff* 45

F. of Science

Dean: Yu Hariya; *staff* 252

S. of Medicine

Dean: Tsutomu Hiroshige; *staff* 150

S. of Dentistry

Dean: Masaaki Kawamura; *staff* 94

F. of Pharmaceutical Sciences

Dean: Osamu Yonemitsu; *staff* 48

F. of Engineering (including Architecture)

Dean: Takuji Shibata; *staff* 408

F. of Agriculture (including Forestry and Animal Husbandry)

Dean: Chosei Shichinohe; *staff* 148

F. of Veterinary Medicine

Dean: Tomio Kanno; *staff* 45

F. of Fisheries

Dean: Takahisa Kimura; *staff* 112

D. of General Education

Dean: Hitoshi Yoshida

I. of Language and Culture Studies

Director: Satoshi Okano; *staff* 65

Graduate S. of Environmental Science

Dean: Toshio Kuroyanagi; *staff* 15

I. of Low Temperature Science

Director: Gorow Wakahama; *staff* 47

Research I. of Applied Electricity

Director: Tsuyoshi Ando; *staff* 51

I. of Immunological Science

Director: Ichiro Azuma; *staff* 20

Catalysis Research Ce.

Director: Yuichi Kanaoka; *staff* 23

Slavic Research Ce.
Director: Teruyuki Hara; *staff* 9
Ce. for Information Processing Education
Director: Haruhisa Shirahama; *staff* 3
Ce. for Instrumental Analysis
Director: Tohru Ueda; *staff* 1
Ce. for Experimental Plants and Animals
Director: Mituhiko Hisada
Central I. of Radioisotope Science
Director: Shinzo Nishi; staff 2
Research Ce. for Molecular Genetics
Director: Kazunori Sugimoto; *staff* 2
Computing Ce.
Director: Jin Yoshimura; *staff* 2
C. of Medical Technology
President: Shigeo Suzuki; *staff* 62
I. for the Study of North Eurasian Cultures (Archaeology)
Director: Haruo Ohyi
I. for the Planning of Industrial Education
Director: Kenjiro Michimata
Research and Clinical Ce. for Child Development
Director: Kunio Wakai
Akkeshi Marine Biological Station
Director: Kenji Aketo
I. of Algological Research
Director: Masakazu Tatewaki
Urakawa Seismological Observatory
Director: Hiroshi Okada
Erimo Geophysical Observatory
Director: Hiroshi Okada
Sapporo Seismological Observatory
Director: Hiroshi Okada
L. for Ocean Bottom Seismology
Director: Hideki Shimamura
Usu Volcano Observatory
Director: Hiromu Okada
Research Ce. for Earthquake Prediction
Director: Hiroshi Okada
Balneotherapeutic Research I.
Director: Yuko
Cancer I.
Director: Tokoro Osato
I. for Animal Experiments
Director: Masimichi Kato
Metals Research I.
Director: Yuzo Sanada
Advanced Magnetohydrodynamics
Director: Naoyuki Kayukawa
I. of Dairy Science
Director: Eiich Ueyama
Research I. of North Pacific Fisheries
Director: Kenji Shimazaki
Toya Limnological Station
Director: Takashi Kurohagi
Nanae Fish Culture Experimental Station
Director: Akihiko Hara
Usujiri Fisheries L.
Director: Hirotoshi Yamamoto
Sea-Ice Research L.
Director: Masaaki Aota
Chromosome Research Unit
Director: Michihiro Yoshida
L. for Developing Advanced Electronic Instruments
Director: Masahiro Kawasaki
L. of Animal Experiments
Director: Harue Okuyama

Founded 1872 as school, became Sapporo Agricultural College 1876. Later incorporated as College of Tohuku University, Sendai, became Hokkaido Imperial University 1918 and renamed Hokkaido University 1947. Graduate Schoolestablished 1953. Governing bodies: the University Senate; the Hyogikai (University Council). Residential facilities for academic staff and students.

Arrangements for co-operation with the Universities of: Massachusetts; Portland State; Cornell; Alaska; Wisconsin, Madison; Munich; Beijing; British Columbia; Harbin; Alberta; São Paulo; Pusan; Washington; Maryland; Fudan; Paris III; Oregon Health Sciences. Shenyang College of Agriculture; Northeast College of Agriculture and Forestry.

Academic Year: April to March (April-September; October-March).

Admission Requirements: Graduation from high school or recognized equivalent, and entrance examination.

Fees (Yen): Tuition, 339,600 per annum.

Language of Instruction: Japanese.

Degrees and Diplomas: Gakushi, Bachelor–Bungakushi, letters; Kyoikugakushi, education; Hogakushi, law; Keizaigakushi, economics; Rigakushi, science; Yakugakushi, pharmacy; Kogakushi, engineering; Nogakushi, agriculture; Suisangakushi, fishery, 4 yrs; Igakushi, medicine; Shigakushi, dentistry; Juigakushi, veterinary science, 6 yrs. Shushi, Master–Bungakushushi, letters; Kyoikugakushushi, education; Hogakushushi, law; Keizaigakushushi, economics; Rigakushushi, science; Yakugakushushi, pharmacy; Kogakushushi, engineering; Nogakushushi, agriculture; Suisangakushushi, fishery; Gakujutsushushi, environmental science, a further 2 yrs. Hakushi, Doctor–Bungakuhakushi, letters; Kyoikugakuhakushi, education; Hogakuhakushi, law; Keizaigakuhakushi, economics; Rigakuhakushi, science; Yakugakuhakushi, pharmacy; Kogakuhakushi, engineering; Nogakuhakushi, agriculture; Igakuhakushi, Doctor of Medical Sciences; Shigakuhakushi, Doctor of Dental Sciences; Juigakuhakushi, veterinary science, a further 4 yrs.

Libraries: General Library, 811,476 vols; branch libraries, 1,883,633.

Special Facilities (Museums, etc.): Hokkaido University Museum; Akkeshi Museum; Botanic Garden.

Publications: University Catalogue (English) (biannually); Hokkaido Daigaku Ichiran (annually); Hokudai Jiho (monthly).

Academic Staff, 1989:

Rank	Full-time
Kyoju (Professors)	561
Jokyoju (Assistant Professors)	518
Koshi (Lecturers)	156
Joshu (Assistants)	779
Total	2014

Student Enrolment, 1989:

	Men	Women	Total
Of the country	11,952	2385	14,337
Of other countries	214	77	291
Total	12,166	2462	14,628*

*Also 87 external students.

3840 **HOKKAIDO KYOIKU DAIGAKU**

Hokkaido University of Education

1-1 Minami 24, Nishi 13, Chuo-ku, Sapporo-shi, Hokkaido 064

Telephone: (11) 561-4281

Gakucho (President): Hisashi Ishii (1983-87)

Education

Branches in: Asahikawa; Hakodate; Iwamizawa; Kushiro.

Founded 1943, reorganized 1949. Residential facilities for 57 academic staff and 238 students.

Academic Year: April to March (April-September; October-March).

Admission Requirements: Graduation from high school and entrance examination.

Fees (Yen): Registration, 150,000; tuition, 300,000 per annum.

Language of Instruction: Japanese.

Degrees and Diplomas: Kyoikugakushi, Bachelor of Education, 4 yrs.

Libraries: Total, 729,795 vols; 628,428 (Japanese books); 101,367 (foreign books).

Publications: Journal; Research Bulletin; Science Reports.

Academic Staff, 1986-87:

Rank	Full-time	Part-time
Kyoju (Professors)	176	–
Jokyoju (Assistant Professors)	168	–
Koshi (Lecturers)	46	401
Joshu (Assistants)	24	–
Total	414	401

Student Enrolment, 1986-87:

	Men	Women	Total
Of the country	3126	2235	5361
Of other countries	2	2	4
Total	3128	2237	5365*

*Also 50 external students and students by correspondence.

3841 **HYOGO KYOIKU DAIGAKU**
Hyogo University of Education
942-1 Shimokume, Yashiro-cho, Kato-gun, Hyogo-ken

F. of Education

3842 **IBARAKI DAIGAKU**
Ibaraki University
2-1-1Bunkyo, Mito-shi, Ibaraki 310
Telephone: (292) 26-1621
Fax: (292) 25-0792
Gakucho (President): Tetsuo Hamada
Jimukyokucho (Secretary-General): Shigeru Watanabe

F. of Humanities (including Economics and Social Sciences)
Dean: Shinichi Arai; *staff* 79 (61)
F. of Education
Dean: Tadashi Hiraoka; *staff* 108 (115)
F. of Science
Dean: Mitsuo Hashimoto; *staff* 63 (45)
F. of Engineering
Dean: Mamoru Imabayashi; *staff* 111 (78)
F. of Agriculture
Dean: Tadami Akatsuka; *staff* 61 (47)
C. of General Education
Dean: Shinya Furui; *staff* 65 (77)
Ce. for Co-operative Research and Development
Dean: Susumu Okazaki

Founded 1949, comprising Faculties of Literature and Science, Education and Engineering. Faculty of Literature and Science reorganized as Faculties of Humanities and Science 1967. Governing body: the Hyogikai (University Council). Residential facilities for academic staff and *c.* 450 men and *c.* 70 women students.

Arrangements for academic staff exchanges with the Universities of: Alabama, Birmingham; Fudan.

Academic Year: April to March (April-September; October-March).

Admission Requirements: Graduation from high school or recognized equivalent, and entrance examination.

Fees (Yen): Registration, 206,000; tuition, 169,800 per semester.

Language of Instruction: Japanese.

Degrees and Diplomas: Gakushi, Bachelor–Bungakushi, letters; Shakaikagakushi, social sciences; Rigakushi, science; Kyoikugakushi, education; Kogakushi, engineering; Nogakushi, agriculture, 4 yrs. Shushi, Master–Kogakushushi, engineering; Nogakushushi, agriculture; Rigakushushi, science; Kyoikugakushushi, education, a further 2 years.

Library: University Library, *c.* 642,469 vols.

Special Facilities (Museums, etc.): IZURA (Institute of Arts and Culture); DAIGO (Facilities for Study Camps).

Academic Staff, 1990:

Rank	Full-time	Part-time
Kyoju (Professors)	212	–
Jokyoju (Associate Professors)	181	–
Koshi (Lecturers)	28	423
Joshu (Assistants)	62	–
Total	483	423

Student Enrolment, 1990:

	Men	Women	Total
Of the country	4582	2085	6667*

*Also 139 external students

3843 **IWATE DAIGAKU**
Iwate University
3-18-8 Ueda, Morioka-shi, Iwate 020
Telephone: (196) 23-5171

F. of Humanities and Social Science
F. of Agriculture (including Veterinary Medicine)
F. of Engineering
F. of Education

Founded 1949.

Academic Year: April to March.

Admission Requirements: Graduation from high school and entrance examination.

Language of Instruction: Japanese.

Degrees and Diplomas: Gakushi, Bachelor, 4 yrs. Shushi, Master, afurther 2 yrs.

Academic Staff: *c.* 190.

Student Enrolment: *c.* 2600.

3844 **JOETSU KYOIKU DAIGAKU**
Joetsu University of Education
1 Yamayashiki-machi, Joetsu-shi, Niigata 943
Telephone: (255) 22-2411
Fax: (255) 22-3403
Gakucho (President): Junkoh Matsuno
Jimukyokucho (Secretary-General): Seimu Takeuchi

D. of School Education
Dean: Ikuo Arai; *staff* 24
D. of Early Childhood and Special Education
Dean: Fusaaki Hosei; *staff* 18
D. of Languages
Dean: MichiAnzai; *staff* 20
D. of Social Studies
Dean: Akira Katoh; *staff* 18
D. of Science
Dean: Takeo Osawa; *staff* 28
D. of Fine Arts and Music
Dean: Toyokichi Uruma; *staff* 30
D. of Physical Education, Home Economics, and Industrial Arts
Dean: Isao Shiroda; *staff* 31
Ce. for Educational Research and Development
Director: Akira Morishima; *staff* 5
Ce. for Skills Training (Music, Foreign Languages, Fine Arts)
Director: Goso Kakinoki; *staff* 4
Research Ce. for the Handicapped
Director: Yutaka Wakui; *staff* 2

Founded 1978.

Academic Year: April to March.

Admission Requirements: Graduation from high school and entrance examination.

Fees (Yen): 339,600 per annum.

Language of Instruction: Japanese.

Degrees and Diplomas: Gakushi, Bachelor, 4 yrs. Shushi, Master, a further 2yrs.

Library: Central Library, 153,800 vols.

Publication: Bulletin (biannually).

Academic Staff, 1990:

	Full-time
Kyoju (Professors)	59
Jokyoju (Associate Professors)	71
Koshi (Lecturers)	22
Joshu (Research Assistants)	22
Total	174

Student Enrolment, 1990:

	Men	Women	Total
Of the country	653	617	1270
Of other countries	7	3	10
Total	660	620	1280

3845 **KAGAWA DAIGAKU**
Kagawa University
121, Saiwai-cho, Takamatsu-shi, Kagawa 760
Telephone: (876) 61-4141

F. of Education
F. of Economics (including Business Administration)
F. of Agriculture
F. of Humanities and Social Science

Also kindergarten, elementary, lower secondary schools, and junior college.

Founded 1923 as college, acquired university status 1949. Governing bodies: the Hyogikai (University Council); the Advisory Board, composed of the dean and four professors of each faculty.

Academic Year: April to March (April-October; October-March).

Admission Requirements: Graduation from high school or equivalent, and entrance examination.

Language of Instruction: Japanese.

Degrees and Diplomas: Gakushi, Bachelor, of–Education; Economics; Agriculture, 4 yrs.Shushi, Master, a further 2 yrs.

Libraries: University Library, *c.* 161,000 vols; Agricultural library.

Publications: Memoirs of Faculty of Education; Memoirs of Faculty of Agriculture; Technical Bulletin of Faculty of Agriculture.
Academic Staff: c. 600.
Student Enrolment: c. 2400.

3846 **KAGAWA IKA DAIGAKU**
Kagawa Medical School
1750-1 Ikenobe, Miki-cho, Kita-gun, Kagawa 761-07
Telephone: (878) 98-5111
Fax: (878) 98-7109
Gakucho (President): Isamu Nisida (1990-91)
Jimukyokucho (Secretary-General): Yoshiharu Ogawa

F. of Medicine
Founded 1948. Governing body: the Kyojyukai (Council). Residential facilities for 388 students.
Arrangements for co-operation with the University of Calgary.
Academic Year: April to March (April-July, August-November, December-March).
Admission Requirements: Graduation from high school or equivalent, and entrance examination.
Fees (Yen): 339,000 per annum.
Language of Instruction: Japanese
Degrees and Diplomas: Igakushi, Bachelor of Medicine, 6 years.
Library: 83,177 vols.
Academic Staff, 1990:

Rank	Full-time	Part-time
Kyoju (Professors)	38	–
Jyokyojyu (Associate Professors)	37	–
Koshi (Assistant Professors)	35	186
Joshu (Research Associates)	124	–
Total	234	186

Student Enrolment, 1990:

	Men	Women	Total
Of the country	689	207	896
Of other countries	14	7	21
Total	703	214	917

3847 ***KAGOSHIMA DAIGAKU**
Kagoshima University
1-21-24 Kourimoto, Kagoshima-shi, Kagoshima 890
Telephone: (992) 54-7141
Fax: (992) 59-4986
Gakucho (President): Akihiro Igata (1987-)
Jimukyokucho (Secretary-General): Saiichiro Itou

F. of Law and Letters (including Economics)
Dean: Tunemaro Nakamura; *staff* 75 (24)
F. of Education
Dean: Akira Asaji; *staff* 95 (55)
F. of Science
Dean: Syouzo Hayasaka; *staff* 63 (15)
S. of Medicine
Dean: Kei Matsumoto; *staff* 137 (159)
S. of Dentistry
Dean: Teruhiko Senba; *staff* 102 (52)
F. of Engineering (including Architecture)
Dean: Atsusi Ikari; *staff* 101 (44)
F. of Agriculture (including Forestry, Veterinary Medicine, and Animal Husbandry)
Dean: Hiroshi Ogura, *staff* 117 (51)
F. of Fisheries
Dean: Hachiro Hirata; *staff* 52 (14)
Ce. of Liberal Arts
Dean: Yuzuru Arakawa; *staff* 93 (177)
S. of Allied Medical Sciences
President: Akihiro Igata; *staff* 46 (88)
Research Ce. for the South Pacific
Director: Shinichi Terasi; *staff* 4
Information Processing Ce.
Director: Youji Nagasawa; *staff* 1
Ce. for Educational Research and Training
Director: Toshihide Shimada; *staff* 1
I. for Cancer Research
Director: Shinichi Akiyama; *staff* 4
I. for Laboratory Animal Sciences
Director: Akira Taira; *staff* 2
Fishery Research L.
Director: Akihiko Sinomiya; *staff* 1
Also kindergarten, primary, and junior high schools, and school for retarded children.

Founded 1949, incorporating Seventh High School, Kagoshima Normal School, Kagoshima Youth Normal School, Kagoshima College of Agriculture and Forestry, and Kagoshima College of Fishery. Governing body: the Hyogikai (University Council), comprising the deans and two professors elected from each faculty, and the directors of the University Hospital and Library. Residential facilities for 344 students.

Arrangements for co-operation with: University of Rhode Island; University of Georgia; University of South Carolina; University of Arizona; University College of North Wales; University of Washington; University of the South Pacific; Bogor University of Agricultural Sciences; University of Victoria; University of Papua New Guinea; Papua New Guinea University of Technology; Universiti Pertanian Malaysia; Xiangtan University; Yunnan University of Agriculture; Hunan College of Agriculture.

Academic Year: April to March (April-October; November-March).
Admission Requirements: Graduation from high school or equivalent or foreign equivalent, and entrance examination.
Fees (Yen): Registration, 206,000; tuition, 339,600 per annum.
Language of Instruction: Japanese.
Degrees and Diplomas: Gakushi, Bachelor–Hogakushi, law; Keizaigakushi, economics; Bungakushi, letters; Kyoikugakushi, education; Rigakushi, science; Kogakushi, engineering; Nogakushi, agriculture; Suisangakushi; fishery, 4 yrs; Igakushi, medicine; Shigakushi, dentistry, 6 yrs; Shushi, Master–Bungakushushi, letters; Hogakushushi, law; Rigakushushi, science; Kogakushushi, engineering; Nogakushushi, agriculture; Suisangashushi, fishery, a further 2 yrs. Hakushi, Doctor–Nogakuhakushi, agriculture; Suisangakuhakushi, fishery, a further 3 yrs. Igakuhakushi, Doctor of Medical Sciences; Shigakuhakushi, Doctor of Dental sciences, a further 4 yrs.
Libraries: Central Library, 834,912 vols; Faculty of Medicine, 145,541; Faculty of Fisheries, 68,231.
Special Facilities (Museums, etc.): Experimental Farm; Veterinary Hospital; 2 training Ships.
Publication: Publications of the faculties.
Academic Staff, 1990-91:

Rank	Full-time	Part-time
Gakucho (President)	1	–
Kyoju (Professors)	368	–
Jokyoju (Associate Professors)	322	–
Kennin-Koshi (Lecturers)	82	651
Joshu (Assistants)	311	–
Total	1084	651

Student Enrolment, 1990-91:

	Men	Women	Total
Of the country	7227	2311	9538
Of other countries	72	29	101
Total	7299	2340	9639

3848 ***KANAZAWA DAIGAKU**
Kanazawa University
1-1 Marunouchi, Kanazawa-shi, Ishikawa 920
Telephone: (762) 62-4281
Gakucho (President): Ryohei Honjin (1985-89)
Jimukyokucho: Fusao Goto

F. of Letters
Dean: Yuichi Takazawa; *staff* 53
F. of Education
Dean: Tetsuo Searashi; *staff* 102
F. of Law
Dean: Toshihiko Nonaka; *staff* 36
F. of Economics
Dean: Akio Fujita; *staff* 33
F. of Science
Dean: Kikuo Terada; *staff* 79
S. of Medicine
Dean: Shinjiro Yamamoto; *staff* 141
F. of Pharmacy
Dean: Yasuo Gomi; *staff* 44

F. of Engineering
Dean: Masao Shibahara; *staff* 151
C. of Liberal Arts
Dean: Motomi Seki; *staff* 75
Cancer Research I.
Director: Hotoichi Hatano; *staff* 40
I. for Gene Research
Director: Tadanori Kameyama; *staff* 2
Radioisotope Ce.
Director: Kin-ichi Hisada; *staff* 2
S. of Allied Medical Professions
President: Tatsunosuke Hirake; *staff* 63
Extension I.
Director: Yoshiomi Furuta; *staff* 2

Founded 1949, incorporating Fourth High School, Ishikawa Normal School, Ishikawa Youth Normal School, KanazawaMedical College and Kanazawa Technological College. Governing body: the Hyogikai (University Council). Residential facilities for academic staff and students.

Arrangements for co-operation with: University of Pennsylvania; State University of New York at Buffalo; Universities of Nancy I and II; Technical University of Lublin.

Academic Year: April to March (April-October; October-March).

Admission Requirements: Graduation from high school or recognized equivalent, and entrance examination.

Fees (Yen): 252,000 per annum.

Language of Instruction: Japanese.

Degrees and Diplomas: Gakushi, Bachelor–Bungakushi, arts; Kyoikugakushi, education; Hogakushi, law; Keizaigakushi, economics; Rigakushi, science; Yakugakushi, pharmacy; Kogakushi, engineering, 4 yrs; Igakushi, medicine, 6 yrs. Shushi, Master–Bungakushushi, arts; Kyoikugakushushi, edcuation; Keizaigakushushi, economics; Hogaku-shushi, law; Rigakushushi, science; Yakugakushushi, pharmacy; Kogakushushi, engineering; a further 2 yrs. Hakushi, Doctor–Rigakuhakushi, science; Yakugahakushi, pharmacy, 3 yrs after Shushi. Igakuhakushi, Doctor of Medical Sciences, a further 4 yrs.

Library: Central Library and 7 branch libraries, 1,094,651 vols.

Publications: Studies and Essays of the Faculties of Law, Letters and Economics (annually); Bulletin of the Faculty of Education (annually); Science Reports (biannually); Marine Laboratory Report (annually); Medical Society Journal (monthly); Memoirs of the Faculty of Engineering (biannually); Cancer Research Institute Report (annually); Research Reports and Essays of the College of Liberal Arts (annually); Memoirs of School of Allied Medical Professions (annually); Bulletin of Japan Sea Research Institute; Studies in Curriculum and Teaching Practice; Studies of Educational Technology (annually); Kanazawa Law Review (biannually); Studies and Essays by the Faculty of Economics; Annual Report of the Low Level Radioactivity Laboratory (both annually); Report of Laboratory for Development of Engineering Materials (annually).

Academic Staff, 1986-87:

Rank	Full-time
Kyoju (Professors)	298
Jokyoju (Associate Professors)	257
Koshi (Assistant Professors)	94
Joshu (Research Associates)	276
Total	925

Student Enrolment, 1986-87:

	Men	Women	Total
Of the country	5385	1643	7028
Of other countries	14	6	20
Total	5399	1649	7048

3849 **KANOYA TAIIKU DAIGAKU**

National Institute of Fitness and Sports
1 Shiromizu-cho, Kanoya-shi, Kagoshima 891-23
Telephone: (994) 46-4111
Fax: (994) 46-2516
Gakucho (President): Yoshitaro Hayakawa (1990-)
Jimukyokucho (Secretary-General): Ryouji Kubo

C. of Fitness and Sports Sciences
Marine Sports Ce.
Director: Tetsuo Sakai;
Foreign Language Ce.
Director: Sachiho Taneka; *staff* 3

Founded 1981. Residential facilities for academic staff and 350 students.

Academic Year: April to March (April-November; December-March).

Admission Requirements: Graduation from high school or recognized equivalent, and entrance examination.

Fees (Yen): Registration, 206,000; tuition, 339,600 per annum.

Language of Instruction: Japanese

Degrees and Diplomas: Gakushi, Bachelor, 4 years. Shushi, Master, a further 2 years.

Library: 40,366 vols.

Academic Staff, 1990:

Rank	Full-time	Part-time
Kyoju (Professors)	26	–
Jokyoju (Associate Professors)	15	–
Koshi (Assistant Profesors)	2	24
Joshu (Research Associates)	14	–
Gaikokugin kyoshi (Foreign Instructors)	2	–
Total	59	24

Student Enrolment, 1990:

	Men	Women	Total
Of the country	538	166	704
Of other countries	4	–	4
Total	542	166	708

3850 **KITAMI KOGYO DAIGAKU**

Kitami Institute of Technology
165 Koen-cho, Kitami, Hokkaido 090
Telephone: (157) 24-1010
Fax: (157) 61-9530
Gakucho (President): Makoto Hirabayashi (1990-94)
Jimukyokucho (Secretary-General): Y. Asano

D. of Applied Mechanical Engineering
Head: M. Futamata; *staff* 11
D. of Mechanical Engineering
Head: T. Kitagawa; *staff* 11
D. of Electrical Engineering
Head: T. Takeda; *staff* 12
D. of Electronic Engineering
Head: Yuji Shinada; *staff* 11
D. of Industrial Chemistry
Head: Akira Arase; *staff* 11
D. of Environmental Engineering
Head: M. Matsubara; *staff* 13
D. of Civil Engineering
Head: I. Okumura; *staff* 11
D. of Developmental Engineering
Head: K. Sado; *staff* 11
D. of General Education
; *staff* 26
Graduate S.
President: Makoto Hirabayashi; *staff* 59
Information Processing Ce.
Head: S. Yamashiro; *staff* 3 (6)
L. for Natural Energy Conversion and Solar Cell Engineering
Head: K. Kanayama; *staff* 2 (8)

Founded 1960 as Kitami Junior College of Technology, reorganized 1966 as Kitami Institute of Technology. Graduate School established 1984. Residential facilities for academic staff and students.

Academic Year: April to March (April-September; October-March).

Admission Requirements: Graduation from high school and entrance examination.

Fees (Yen): 340,000 per annum.

Language of Instruction: Japanese.

Degrees and Diplomas: Kogakushi, Bachelor of Engineering, 4 yrs. Kogakushushi, Master of Engineering, a further 2 yrs.

Libraries: Central Library, *c.* 103,740 vols in Japanese and Chinese; *c.* 25,760 in other languages; total, 129,500.

Publication: Research Bulletin (biannually).

Academic Staff, 1986-87:

Rank	Full-time	Part-time
Professors	59	–
Associate Professors	34	–
Assistant Professors	12	94
Research Associate	1	–
Total	106	94

Student Enrolment, 1986-87:

	Men	Women	Total
Of the country	3422	1512	4934*

*Also 11 external students.

4029 ***MEIJI DAIGAKU**

Meiji University

1-1 Kanda Surugadai, Chiyoda-ku, Tokyo 101

Telephone: (3) 296-4545

Gakucho (President): Shinichi Yamamoto

Jimukyokucho: Shigeo Nakamura

S. of Law
Dean: Shoichi Hozumi; *staff* 74 (132)
S. of Commerce
Dean: Mizuho Nakamura; *staff* 84 (108)
S. of Political Science and Economics
Dean: Shiro Shiraishi; *staff* 88 (143)
S. of Letters
Dean: Takashi Matsuda; *staff* 93 (181)
S. of Engineering (including Architecture)
Dean: Takio Oya; *staff* 146 (140)
S. of Agriculture
Dean: Hiroaki Iwamoto; *staff* 45 (72)
S. of Business Administration
Dean: Sekiya Sonoide; *staff* 50 (71)
Women's Junior C.
President: Seiichi Nakahara; *staff* 25 (12)
I. of Social Sciences
Director: Akihiko Hasegawa
I. of Cultural Sciences
Director: Hatsushige Ohtsuka
I. of Science and Technology
Director: Shigeo Shimane
Computer Ce.
Also high schools.

Founded 1881 as Meiji Law School, became university 1903. Reorganized 1925 and 1949. Governing body: the Board of Trustees, comprising 12 members.

Arrangements for co-operation with the University of California, Los Angeles; The University of Alberta; York University.

Academic Year: April to March (April-September; October-March).

Admission Requirements: Graduation from high school or equivalent, and entrance examination.

Fees (Yen): Registration, 220,000; tuition, 503,200 per annum; Agriculture, 783,300-883,300; Engineering, 883,300.

Language of Instruction: Japanese.

Degrees and Diplomas: Gakushi, Bachelor, of–Law; Commerce; Business Administration, 4 yrs. Bungakushi, Bachelor of Arts, in–Political Science, Economics; Letters, 4 yrs. Rigakushi, Bachelor of Science, in–Engineering; Agriculture, 4 yrs. Shushi, Master, a further 2 yrs, Hakushi, Doctor of Law; Commerce; Political Science; Economics; Literature; Business Administration; Science; Agriculture, 3 yrs after Shushi.

Library: Total, 1,099,167 vols.

Special Facilities (Museums, etc.): Archaeological Museum; Commercial Museum; Criminal Museum.

Publications: Law Review (quarterly); Bulletin of the Faculty of Commerce (bimonthly); Review of Economics and Political Science (three times a year); Studies in Literature (biannually); Journal of the Historical Association of Meiji University (biannually); Research Reports of the Faculty of Engineering (annually); Bulletin of the Faculty ofAgriculture (annually); Meiji Business Review (three times a year); Meiji University Bulletin.

Academic Staff, 1986-87:

Rank	Full-time	Part-time
Kyoju (Professors)	406	–
Jokyoju (Associate Professors)	110	–
Koshi (Lecturers)	63	832
Joshu (Assistants)	53	–
Total	632	832

Student Enrolment, 1986-87:

	Men	Women	Total
Of the country	27,597	4899	32,496
Of other countries	120	16	166
Total	27,717	4945	32,662

4030 ***MEIJI GAKUIN DAIGAKU**

Meiji Gakuin University

1-2-37 Shirokane-dai, Minato-ku, Tokyo 108

Cables: Meiji Gakuin 0115269

Telex: J44762PRIME

Telephone: (3) 448-5111

Fax: (3) 447-2684

Electronic mail: CompuServe

Gakucho (President): Kan'ichii Fukuda (1990-)

Jimukyokucho (Secretary-General): Shozo Oi

F. of Literature (including English and French Literature, Arts and Psychology)
Dean: Kenji Oba; *staff* 75
F. of Economics (including Commerce and Business Administration)
Dean: Satoru Kuza; *staff* 38
F. of Sociology and Social Work (including Sociology and Social Welfare Practice)
Dean: Ichiro Yamanaka; *staff* 39
F. of Law (including Law and Politics)
Dean: Mazatoshi Sakeda; *staff* 32
F. of International Studies (including International Politics, Peace Studies and Cross-culture)
Dean: Kentaro Shiozuki; *staff* 37
F. of General Education
Dean: Tomoyoshi Koizumi; *staff* 50
I. of Linguistics and Cultural Studies
Director: Ryuzo Akiba; *staff* 15
Foreign Language Education I.
Director: Hiroki Udono; *staff* 13
Christian Research I.
Director: Hiroshi Shibuya; *staff* 23
Research I. of Industry and Economy
Director: Hiroshi Tuda; *staff* 39
Law Research I.
Director: Masatoshi Sakeda; *staff* 32
I. of the Departement of General Education
Director: Hisao Kayama; *staff* 37
I. of Sociology and Social Welfare
Director: Sadao Ooshima; *staff* 9
International Peace Research I. Heigaku
Director: Toshiyuki Toyada; *staff* 18
Also junior and senior high schools.

Founded 1877 as private Protestant college. Reorganized as university 1949. Governing body: the Board of Trustees. Residential facilities for academic staff from abroad.

Arrangements for co-operation with: Hope College, Michigan; Soong Sil University, Seoul; University of California; Long Island University; Université de Limoges.

Academic Year: April to March (April-September; October-March).

Admission Requirements: Graduation from high school and entrance examination.

Fees (Yen): Registration, 260,000; tuition, 510,000 per annum.

Language of Instruction: Japanese.

Degrees and Diplomas: Gakushi, Bachelor, of–Arts; Economics; Commerce; Sociology and Social Work; Law, 4 yrs. Shushi, Master, of–Arts; Economics; Commerce; Sociology; Social Work; Law, 2 yrs. Hakushi, Doctor, of–Arts; Economics; Commerce; Sociology; Social Work; Law, 3 yrs after Shushi.

Library: c. 550,000 vols.

Publications: University Review (Ronso); Bulletin of Faculties.

Academic Staff, 1990-91:

Rank	Full-time	Part-time
Kyoju (Professors)	158	–
Jokyoju (Assistant Professors)	75	–
Koushi (Lectures)	26	545
Joshu (Research Assistants)	12	–
Total	271	545

Student Enrolment, 1989-90:

	Men	Women	Total
Of the country	7933	3345	11378

4031 **MEIJI YAKKA DAIGAKU**

Meiji College of Pharmacy

1-35-23 Nozawa, Setagaya-ku, Tokyo 154

Telephone: (3) 424-1001

F. of Pharmacy

Founded 1902, reorganized 1949.

Academic Staff: c. 90.

Student Enrolment: c. 1100.

4032 **MEIJO DAIGAKU**

Meijo University

1-501 Shiogamaguchi, Tenpaku-ku, Nagoya-shi, Aichi 468

Telephone: (52) 832-1151

F. of Law
F. of Commerce
F. of Science and Technology
F. of Agriculture
F. of Pharmacy

Founded 1924 as Nagoya School of Science and Engineering. Acquired present name and status 1949.

Academic Year: April to March.

Language of Instruction: Japanese.

Degrees and Diplomas: Gakushi, Bachelor, of–Law; Commerce; Technology; Science; Pharmacy; Agriculture, 4 yrs. Shushi, Master, of Commerce, a further 2 yrs.

4033 **MEISEI DAIGAKU**

Meisei University

2-1-1 Hodokubo, Hino-shi, Tokyo 191

Telephone: (425) 91-5111

C. of Science and Technology
C. of Humanities (including Sociology and Economics)

Founded 1964.

4034 **MUKOGAWA JOSHI DAIGAKU**

Mukogawa Women's University

6-46 Ikebiraki-cho, Nishinomiya-shi, Hyogo 663

Telephone: (798) 47-1212

Fax: 11-81-798-47-1800

Gakucho (President): Akira Kusaka

Fuku-Rijicho (Vice-Chairman): Hashiro Ogino

C. of Letters (including Education and Physical Education)
Dean: Toshiharu Yamamoto; *staff* 74 (133)
C. of Home Economics (including Food Sciences, Textile and Clothing Sciences)
Dean: Masao Kanamori; *staff* 62 (43)
C. of Music
Dean: Teeichi Nakayama; *staff* 21 (35)
S. of Pharmaceutical Sciences (including Pharmaceutical and Biopharmaceutical Sciences)
Dean: Shuzo Takagi; *staff* 64 (34)
I. of Linguistic Cultures (including Communication Process, Comparative Literature, Uses of Computers in Language and Other Fields)
Director: Akira Kusaka; *staff* 7 (1)
Infant Education Research I.
Director: Akira Kusaka; *staff* 4
I. for Education
Director: Michiya Shinbori; *staff* 5 (1)

Also junior college.

Founded as high school 1939, acquired present status 1949. Governing body: the Board of Trustees. Residential facilities for students.

Academic Year: April to March (April-September; October-March).

Admission Requirements: Koko Sotugyo-shosho (certificate of high school graduation).

Fees (Yen): 743,500-176,500.

Language of Instruction: Japanese.

Degrees and Diplomas: Gakushi, Bachelor, of–Letters; Home Economics; Pharmacy; Music, 4 yrs. Master, Shushi, a further 2 yrs. Hakushi, Doctor, of–Home Economics; Pharmacy, a further 3 yrs.

Libraries: Central Library, *c.* 400,000 vols; college libraries.

Publication: Mukogawa Proceedings.

Academic Staff, 1990-91:

Rank	Full-time	Part-time
Kyoju (Professors)	146	–
Jokyoju (Assistant Professors)	80	–
Koshi (Instructors)	48	361
Joshu (Assistants)	111	28
Total	385	389

Student Enrolment, 1990-91:

	Women
Of the country	4511
Of other countries	6
Total	4517

4035 **MUSASHI DAIGAKU**

Musashi University

1-26 Toyotama-kami, Nerima-ku, Tokyo 176

Telephone: (3) 991-1191

D. of Economics
D. of Humanities

Also senior and junior high schools.

Founded 1922 as Musashi High School, became college 1949, acquired present status 1969. Governing body: the Board of Trustees. Some residential facilities for students.

Academic Year: April to March (April-September; October-March).

Admission Requirements: Graduation from high school or equivalent, and entrance examination.

Language of Instruction: Japanese.

Degrees and Diplomas: Gakushi, Bachelor–Keizaigakushi, economics; Bungakushi, arts, 4 yrs. Shushi, Master–Keizaigakushushi, economics, a further 2 yrs. Hakushi, Doctor–Keizaigakuhakushi, economics, 3 yrs after Shushi.

Library: c. 230,000 vols.

Publications: Journal (Economics); Journal (Human and Cultural Sciences).

Academic Staff: c. 90 (220).

Student Enrolment: c. 3810.

4036 **MUSASHI KOGYO DAIGAKU**

Musashi Institute of Technology

1-28-1 Tamazutsumi, Setagaya-ku, Tokyo 158

Telephone: (3) 703-3111

President: Kaoru Ishikawa (1978-87)

F. of Mechanical Engineering
Chairman: Shoichi Furuhama; *staff* 31 (7)
F. of Electrical and Electronic Engineering
Chairman: Hideo Mitsui; *staff* 18 (12)
F. of Electronics and Communication Engineering
Chairman: Mutsuo Konishi; *staff* 12 (6)
F. of Architecture
Chairman: Tadashi Eguchi; *staff* 14 (13)
F. of Civil Engineering
Chairman: Masaru Hoshiya; *staff* 13 (8)
F. of Industrial Engineering
Chairman: Masumasa Imaizumi; *staff* 22 (4)
Atomic Energy Research I.
Director: Tadashi Sato; *staff* 20 (4)
Information Processing Ce.
Director: Shin'ichi Yamada; *staff* 10 (3)

Founded 1929 as technical school, became institute 1949.

Academic Year: April to March (April-October; October-March).

Admission Requirements: Graduation from high school or recognized equivalent or foreign equivalent, and entrance examination.

Fees (Yen): Registration, 200,000; tuition, 900,000.

Language of Instruction: Japanese.

Degrees and Diplomas: Kogakushi, Bachelor of Engineering, 4 yrs. Kogakushushi, Master of Engineering, a further 2 yrs. Kogakuhakushi, Doctor of Engineering, 3 yrs after Shushi.

Library: c. 170,000 vols.

Publications: Guide Book (annually); Musashi Kodai Dayori (quarterly).

Academic Staff, 1986-87:

Rank	Full-time	Part-time
Gakucho (President)	1	–
Kyoju (Professors)	61	–
Jokyoju (Assistant Professors)	51	–
Koshi (Lecturers)	48	162
Joshu (Research Associates)	19	3
Gijutsuin (Teaching Associates)	58	–
Total	238	165

Student Enrolment, 1986-87:

	Men	Women	Total
Of the country	4485	106	4591
Of other countries	5	–	5
Total	4490	106	4596

4037 **MUSASHINO BIJUTSU DAIGAKU**

Musashino Art University

1-736 Ogawa-cho, Kodaira-shi, Tokyo 187

Telephone: (423) 41-5011

Gakucho (President): Hiroshi Mizuo

Rijicho: Munemitsu Tashiro

D. of Japanese Painting
Head: Takashi Asada; *staff* 5 (5)

D. of Painting
Head: Jun Nakano; *staff* 12 (10)

D. of Sculpture
Head: Misaki Kinouchi; *staff* 5 (6)

D. of Visual Communication Design
Head: Mutsuaki Okai; *staff* 9 (23)

D. of Industrial, Interior and Craft Design
Head: Masahiro Miwa; *staff* 16 (22)

D. of Scenography
Head: Ryokichi Mukai; *staff* 8 (21)

D. of Architecture
Head: Hideo Terada; *staff* 8 (27)

D. of Design Theory
Head: Shutaro Mukai; *staff* 5 (21)

Also junior college, including correspondence course.

Founded 1929 as art school, acquired university status 1962. Governing bodies: the Board of Directors; the Board of Trustees. Some residential facilities for women students.

Arrangements for co-operation with: Pratt Institute, Brooklyn; Ecole nationale supérieure des Beaux-Arts, Paris; Hochschule für bildende Künste, Dresden.

Academic Year: April to March (April-July; September-March).

Admission Requirements: Graduation from high school or equivalent, and entrance examination. Provision is made for the recognition of foreign qualifications.

Fees (Yen): Registration, 250,000; tuition, 605,000 per annum.

Language of Instruction: Japanese.

Degrees and Diplomas: Geijutsugakushi, Bachelor of Fine Arts, 4 yrs. Geijutsugakushushi, Master of Fine Arts, a further 2 yrs.

Library: University Library, c. 120,000 vols.

Special Facilities (Museums, etc.): Museum Library.

Publication: Bulletin (annually).

Academic Staff, 1986-87:

Rank	Full-time	Part-time
Kyoju (Professors)	93	–
Jokyoju (Assistant Professors)	3	–
Koshi (Instructors)	2	212
Joshu (Assistants)	–	93
Total	98	305

Student Enrolment, 1986-87:

	Men	Women	Total
Of the country	1412	2313	3725
Of other countries	19	28	47
Total	1431	2341	3772

4038 **MUSASHINO ONGAKU DAIGAKU**

Musashino Academy of Music

1-13-1 Hazawa, Nerima-ku, Tokyo 176

Cables: Musamusik

Telephone: (3) 992-1121

Fax: (3) 991-7599

Gakucho (President): Naotaka Fukui (1981-)

F. of Music

Education and Culture Research Ce.

Also high school and affilated music schools.

Founded 1929 as Musashino School of Music. Officially recognized by the government 1932. Acquired present status 1949. Financially self-supporting. Governing body: the Board of Trustees. Residential facilities for 1112 students.

Academic Year: April to March (April-September; October-March).

Admission Requirements: Graduation from high school and entrance examination.

Fees (Yen): 2,050,000 per annum; graduate school 1,190,000.

Language of Instruction: Japanese.

Degrees and Diplomas: Geijutsugakushi, Bachelor of Fine Arts, 4 yrs. Geijutsushushi, Master of Arts, a further 2 yrs. Also teaching qualifications.

Library: Central Library 177,000 vols.

Special Facilities (Museums, etc.): Musashino Ongaku Daigaku Gakki-Hakubutsukan (Instrument Museum).

Publications: Kenkyu Kiyo (Research Bulletin); Gakusei no rombun (collection of theses, annually).

Academic Staff, 1989-90:

Rank	Full-time	Part-time
Kyoju (Professors)	80	–
Jokyoju (Assistant Professors)	79	–
Koshi (Lecturers)	89	209
Others	193	–
Total	441	209

Student Enrolment, 1989-90:

	Men	Women	Total
Of the country	406	3666	4072
Of other countries	7	49	56
Total	413	3715	4128

4039 **NAGASAKI SOGO KAGAKU DAIGAKU**

Nagasaki Institute of Applied Science

536 Aba-machi, Nagasaki-shin, Nagasaki 851-01

Telephone: (958) 39-3111

F. of Engineering (including Shipbuilding and Architecture)

Founded 1942, became College of Shipbuilding 1965 and recently acquired new title. Governing bodies: the Board of Trustees; the Council. Special arrangements for co-operation with the Harbin Institute of Shipbuilding Engineering.

Academic Year: April to March (April-October; October-March).

Admission Requirements: Graduation from high school and entrance examination.

Language of Instruction: Japanese.

Degrees and Diplomas: Gakushi, Bachelor, of Engineering, 4 yrs. Shushi, Master, a further 2 yrs.

Library: c. 60,000 vols.

Publications: Bulletin (biannually); Studies of Peace Culture (annually).

Academic Staff: c. 90 (80).

Student Enrolment: c. 1920 (Also c. 15 external students).

4040 **NAGOYA SHOKA DAIGAKU**

Nagoya University of Commerce and Business Administration
Sagamine, Nisshin-cho, Aichi-gun, Aichi 470-1
Telex: 4496002 NUCBA
Telephone: (5617) 3-2111
Gakucho (President): Hiroshi Kurimoto (1981-)
Jimukyokucho: Pr. Itaya

D. of Commerce and Business Administration
Management Systems Research Ce.
Ce. for International Economics
Language Ce.
Also high school.

Founded 1950, acquired present status 1953. Governing body: the Board of Trustees of 5 members. Residential facilities for foreign academic staff.

Arrangements for co-operation with the University of Hawaii.

Academic Year: April to March (April-September; October-March).

Admission Requirements: Graduation from high school and entrance examination.

Fees (Yen): 790,000-962,000 per annum.

Languages of Instruction: Japanese and English.

Degrees and Diplomas: Gakushi, Bachelor, of Commerce and Business Administration, 4 yrs. Shushi, Master. Also teaching qualifications.

Library: 273,700 vols.

Special Facilities (Museums, etc.): Centre for Tomorrow.

Publication: Nagoya Shoka Daigaku Ronshu (biannually).

Press or Publishing House: The Society of Commerce, Nagoya University of Commerce and Business Administration.

Academic Staff, 1986-87:

Rank	Full-time	Part-time
Kyoju (Professors)	33	–
Jokyoju (Assistant Professors)	7	–
Koshi (Lecturers)	22	74
Total	62	74

Student Enrolment, 1986-87:

	Men	Women	Total
Of the country	2570	89	2659
Of other countries	13	–	13
Total	2583	89	2672

4041 ***NANZAN DAIGAKU**

Nanzan University
18 Yamazato-cho, Sowa-ku, Nagoya-shi, Aichi 466
Cables: Nanzandaigaku Nagoya
Telephone: (52) 832-3111
Fax: (52) 833-6985
Gakucho (President): Robert J. Riemer (1983-93)

F. of Economics (including Economics, Law and Sociology)
Dean: Shoji Matsuyama; *staff* 22 (20)
F. of Arts and Letters
Dean Katsuhiko Naito; *staff* 91 (130)
F. of Foreign Studies
Dean Roichi Okabe; *staff* 46 (55)
F. of Law
Dean Yutaka Kamiguchi *staff* 20 (14)
F. of Business Administration (including Accountancy)
Dean Reijun Odaka; *staff* 25 (22)
Ce. for Japanese Studies
Director: Shunichi Kato; *staff* 1 (15)
I. of Anthropology
Director: Isamu Kurata; *staff* 6
I. of Religions and Cultures
Director: Jan Van Bragt; *staff* 7 (3)
I. of Japanese Social Ethics
Director: Seiichi Anan; *staff* 6 (1)
Ce. for American Studies
Director: Ichiro Iwano; *staff* 11
Ce. for Latin-American Studies
Director: Hiroshi Matsushita; *staff* 4
Ce. for Australian Studies
Director: Ryozo Kato; *staff* 14

Founded 1932 as Nanzan Middle School for Boys by the Society of the Divine Word, acquired present status and status 1949. Governing body: the Board of Directors. Residential facilities for academic staff and students.

Arrangements for co-operation with: Illinois State University; University of Nebraska; Elmira College, New York; De Pauw University; Oakland University; University of Iowa; St. Lawrence University; St. Louis University; Bowling Green State University; Griffith University; Eckerd College, Florida; Hendrix College, Arkansas; University of North Carolina at Chapel Hill; Dickinson College; University of Wisconsin-Madison, University of Notre Dame.

Academic Year: April to March (April-July; September-February).

Admission Requirements: Graduation from high school or foreign equivalent, and entrance examination.

Fees (Yen): 986,950, first year; 698,500, subsequent years.

Language of Instruction: Japanese.

Degrees and Diplomas: Gakushi, Bachelor, of–Technology; Law; Arts; Economics; Business Administration, 4 yrs. Shushi, Master of Arts in–Anthropoly; Theology; English Literature; French Literature; German Literature; Economics; Business Administration; Law, a further 2 yrs; Hakushi, Doctor, 3 yrs after Shushi.

Libraries: Central Library, *c.* 499,639 vols; Institute libraries, 56,653 vols.

Special Facilities (Museums, etc.): Museum of Anthropology.

Publications: Academia (quarterly); Law Review (quarterly); Theological Review (annually); Nanzan Review of American Studies; Japanese Journal of Religious Studies (quarterly); Asian Folklore Studies (yearly).

Academic Staff, 1989-90:

Rank	Full-time	Part-time
Kyoju (Professors)	97	–
Jokyoju (Assistant Professors)	75	–
Koshi (Lecturers)	30	241
Joshu (Assistants)	1	–
Total	204	241

Student Enrolment, 1986-87:

	Men	Women	Total
Of the country	2711	1769	5480
Of other countries	57	61	118
Total	2768	2830	5598*

*Also 38 external students.

4042 ***NIHON DAIGAKU**

Nihon University
8-24 Kudan-Minami 4-chome, Chiyoda-ku, Tokyo 102
Cables: Nihondaigaku
Telex: 29496 NICHIDAI J
Telephone: (3) 262-2271
Gakucho (President): Shigenori Kinoshita (1990-93)

C. of Law (including Journalism, Political Science, and Public Administration)
Dean: Toshinobu Inada; *staff* 133 (232)
C. of Humanities and Science
Dean: Yoshio Sezai; *staff* 226 (355)
C. of Economics
Dean: Susumu Ide; *staff* 106 (132)
C. of Commerce
Dean: Heizaburo Sonoda; *staff* 106 (132)
C. of Arts (including Photography and Cinema)
Dean: Toru Otake; *staff* 108 (304)
C. of International Relations
Dean: Masayuki Akiyama; *staff* 44 (88)
C. of Science and Technology
Dean: Shigenori Kinoshita; *staff* 397 (370)
C. of Industrial Technology
Dean: Tadatoshi So; *staff* 235 (157)
C. of Medicine
Dean: Yukiyasu Sezai; *staff* 488 (76)
S. of Dentistry
Dean: Eiko Sairenji; *staff* 198 (164)
S. of Dentistry (Matsudo)
Dean: Hisashi Takiguchi; *staff* 193 (78)
C. of Agriculture and Veterinary Medicine
Dean: Sadami Kadota; *staff* 255 (128)
C. of Pharmacy
Dean: Makoto Kirisawa; *staff* 35 (4)
D. for Correspondance Courses
Dean: Yoshio Sezai; *staff* 14 (64)

Also 31 research institutes.

Founded 1889 as Nihon Horitsu Gakki (Japan Law School). Title changed to Nihon Daigaku 1903, acquired present status 1949. Governing body: the Board of Trustees, comprising 27 members. Some residential facilities for students.

Arrangements for co-operation with the Universities of: Washington State; Chung-Ang, Republic of Korea; Berlin (Free); Hawaii; Mainz; São Paulo; Alabama in Birmingham; Kuwait; Toronto; Cambridge; Kyung Hee; Beijing. Massachusetts Institute of Technology.

Academic Year: April to March (April-September; October-March).

Admission Requirements: Graduation from high school or equivalent or foreign equivalent, and entrance examination.

Language of Instruction: Japanese.

Degrees and Diplomas: Gakushi, Bachelor, of–Law; Liberal Arts; Economics; Commerce; Arts; Physical Education; Pharmacy; Science; Engineering; Agriculture; Veterinary Medicine; Fisheries, 4 yrs. Shushi, Master, of–Law; Political Science, Economics; Commerce; Arts; Engineering; Agriculture; Veterinary Medicine; Science, a further 2 yrs. Hakushi, Doctor, of–Law; Literature; Political Science; Economics; Commerce; Science; Engineering; Agriculture; VeterinaryMedicine, 3 yrs after Shushi. Igakuhakushi, Doctor, of–Medical Sciences; Dental Surgery; Dental Science.

Libraries: Central Library, *c.* 204,244 vols; College libraries, total, *c.* 3,947,179.

Publications: Nihon Hogaku (Japanese Law); Kenkyu Kiyo (Studies in Humanities and Sciences); Keizai Shushi (Journal of Economics); Shogaku Shushi (Journal of Commerce); Sangyo Keiei Kenkyu (Journal of Business Research); Nichidai Kogaku Kenkyu Sho (Bulletin of Research Institute of Technology); Journal of the Research Institute of Industrial Technology; Nichidai Igaku Zasshi (Journal of Medicine); Journal of School of Dentistry; Nihon Daigaku Nojuigakubu Gakujutsu Kenkyu Hokoku (Bulletin of Agriculture and Veterinary Medicine Society); Nihon Daigaku Shinbun (Newspaper); Nihon Daigaku Geijutsugakubu Kiyo (College of Art); Kokusai Kankei Gakubu Kenkyu Nenpo (Journal of the College of International Relations); Report of the Mishima Research Institute of Sciences for Living.

Academic Staff, 1990:

Rank	Full-time	Part-time
Kyoju(Professors)	976	–
Jokyoju (Associate Professors)	483	–
Koshi (Lecturers)	612	–
Joshu (Assistant Lecturers)	635	–
Hijokin-koshi (Part-time Lecturers)	–	2390
Kyoyu (Teachers)	807	413
Total	3513	2803

Student Enrolment, 1990:

	Men	Women	Total
Of the country	67,839	17,469	85,308
Of other countries	522	273	795
Total	68,361	17,742	86,103

4043 **NIHON FUKUSHI DAIGAKU**

Nihon Fukushi University

Okuda, Mihama-cho, Chita-gun, Aichi 466

Telephone: (569) 87-2211

F. of Social Welfare

F. of Economics

Founded 1953, acquired present status 1957.

Academic Year: April to March (April-September; October-February).

Admission Requirements: Graduation from high school and entrance examination.

Language of Instruction: Japanese.

Degrees and Diplomas: Shakaigakukushi, Bachelor of Social Science, 8 sem. Shushi, Master.

Library: *c.* 40,000 vols.

Publications: Fukushi Kenkyu (Studies on Social Welfare); Bulletin.

Academic Staff: *c.* 90.

Student Enrolment: *c.* 2300.

4044 ***NIHON JOSHI DAIGAKU**

Japan Women's University

2-8-1 Merjirodai, Bunkyo-ku, Tokyo 112

Telephone: (3) 943-3131

Fax: (3) 942-6518

Gakucho (President): Takako Aoki (1981-92)

F. of Home Economics

Dean: Ihei Iwata; *staff* 116 (181)

F. of Letters and Humanities

Dean: Yoshinobu Aoyama; *staff* 62 (219)

D. of Integrated Arts and Social Sciences

Dean: Yasuko Ichibangase; *staff* 51 (18)

Child Study I.

Head: Shiro Moriue; *staff* – (5)

Rural Life Research I.

Head: Shizue Ono; *staff* 1 (4)

I. of Education for Women

Head: Yasuko Ichibangase; *staff* 2 (2)

Computer Research I.

Head: Tetsu Kaizuka; *staff* 4 (8)

D. for Correspondence Courses

Head: Mitsushige Miyamura; *staff* 140 (173)

Also kindergarten, primary, and high schools.

Founded 1901 as liberal arts college, became university 1948. Faculty of Integrated Arts and Social Sciences established 1990. A private institution for women only. Mainly financed by tuition fees. Governing body: the Board of Trustees, comprising 19 members. Residential facilities for 514 students.

Arrangements for exchanges with: Wellesley College; Marymount College.

Academic Year: April to March (April-September; October-March).

Admission Requirements: Graduation from senior high school or foreign equivalent, and entrance examination.

Fees (Yen): 460,000 per annum.

Language of Instruction: Japanese.

Degrees and Diplomas: Gakushi, Bachelor–Kaseigakushi, home economics; Shakaigakushi, sociology; Bungakushi, letters, 4 yrs. Shushi, Master–Kaseigakushushi, home economics; Bungakushushi, arts; Shakaigakushushi, sociology, a further 2 yrs. Hakushi, Doctor of–Bungakuhakushi, letters; Shakaigakuhakushi, sociology, 3 yrs after Shushi.

Library: University Library, 397,000 vols.

Publication: Journals of the faculties (annually).

Academic Staff, 1990-91:

Rank	Full-time	Part-time
Kyoju (Professors)	106	–
Jokyoju (Associate Professors)	46	–
Kennin-Koshi (Lecturers)	18	418
Joshu (Assistants)	59	73
Total	229	491

Student Enrolment, 1990-91:

	Women
Of the country	5,543
Of other countries	39
Total	5,582*

*Also 4846 external students.

4045 **NIHON RUTERU SHINGAKU**

Japan Lutheran Theological College

3-10-20 Osawa, Mitaka-shi, Tokyo 181

Telephone: (422) 31-4611

F. of Literature

Founded 1928, reorganized 1949 and 1987.

Academic Staff: *c.* 20.

Student Enrolment: *c.* 150.

4046 **NIPPON TAIIKU DAIGAKU**

Nippon College of Physical Education
7-1-1 Fukazawa, Setagaya-ku, Tokyo 158
Telephone: (03) 706-0995
Fax: (3) 5706-0912
Gakucho (President): Yasuji Inagaki (1989-)
Jimukyokucho (Secretary-General): Shoichi Takenaka

S. of Physical Education
Head Masachi Uehira
S. of Health Education
Head Toshihiko Aoyama
S. of Martial Arts
Head Mitsuya Ogawa
S. of Social Recreation
Head Akira Horii
Also junior college.

Founded 1891 as school, became college 1949. Residential facilities for students.

Arrangements for co-operation with: Beijing School of Physical Education; Deutsche Sporthochschule Köln.

Academic Year: April to March (April-September; October-March).

Admission Requirements: Graduation from high school or equivalent, and entrance examination.

Fees (Yen): Tuition, 530,000 per annum.

Language of Instruction: Japanese.

Degrees and Diplomas: Gakushi, Bachelor, of Physical Education. Shushi, Master, a 2 further yrs. Diplomas and Certificates.

Library: College Library, *c.* 166,000 vols.

Publication: Bulletin (biannually).

Academic Staff, 1990-91:

Rank	Full-time	Part-time
Kyoju (Professors)	66	–
Jokyoju (Assistant Professors)	33	–
Koshi (Lecturers)	22	107
Joshu (Assistants)	56	14
Total	177	121

Student Enrolment, 1990-91:

	Men	Women	Total
Of the country	5938	1745	7683
Of other countries	43	7	50
Total	5981	1752	7733

4047 ***NIPPON IKA DAIGAKU**

Nippon Medical School
1-1-5 Sendagi, Bunkyo-ku, Tokyo 113
Telephone: (3) 822-2131
Gakucho (President): Goro Kikuchi (1986-88)
Jimusocho: Yoshitami Kimura

S. of Medicine
Gerontology I.
Head: Masashi Kaneko; *staff* 7 (5)
Tumour and Infectious Diseases I.
Head: Chisato Maruyama; *staff* 3 (1)

Founded 1904 as school, became college 1912, acquired present status 1925. Governing body: the Board of Trustees. Residential facilities for students.

Arrangements for co-operation with: Chiang Mai University; Xi'an University of Medicine.

Academic Year: April to March (April-July; September-December; January-March).

Admission Requirements: Graduation from high school and entrance examination.

Fees (Yen): 2,350,000 per annum.

Language of Instruction: Japanese.

Degrees and Diplomas: Igakushi, doctor of medicine, 6 yrs; Igakuhakushi, Doctor of Medical Sciences, a further 4-6 yrs.

Library: *c.* 165,000 vols.

Publication: Journal (bimonthly).

Academic Staff, 1986-87:

Rank	Full-time	Part-time
Kyoju (Professors)	55	–
Jokyoju (Associate Professors)	89	–
Koshi (Instructors/Lecturers)	105	83
Joshu (Assistants)	476	–
Total	725	83

Student Enrolment, 1986-87:

	Men	Women	Total
Of the country	647	111	758
Of other countries	23	1	24
Total	670	112	782

4048 **NIPPON JUICHIKUSAN DAIGAKU**

Nippon Veterinary and Zootechnical College
1-7-1 Kyonan-cho, Musashino-shi, Tokyo 180
Telephone: (422) 31-4151
Fax: (422) 33-2094

F. of Veterinary Medicine and Animal Husbandry

Founded 1871 as school, acquired present title 1949.

Academic Year: April to March.

Admission Requirements: Graduation from high school.

Fees (Yen): 836,000-1,284,000 per annum.

Language of Instruction: Japanese.

Degrees and Diplomas: Juigakushi, Bachelor of Veterinary Medicine, 6 yrs. Juigakuhakushi, Doctor of Veterinary Medicine, 4 yrs.

Library: *c.* 74,000 vols.

Academic Staff, 1989-90:

Rank	Full-time	Part-time
Kyoju (Professors)	31	–
Jyokyoju (Associate Professors)	22	–
Koshi (Lecturers)	27	65
Joshu (Assistants)	15	–
Fukushu (Junior Assistants)	2	–
Total	97	65

Student Enrolment, 1989-90:

	Men	Women	Total
Of the country	800	389	1189*

*Also 48 external students.

4049 **NIPPON KOGYO DAIGAKU**

Nippon Institute of Technology
4-1 Miyashiro-machi, Minamisaitama-gun, Saitama 345
Telephone: (480) 34-4111
Fax: (480) 34-2941
Gakucho (President): Kiyoyasu Ohkawa (1987-91)
Jimukyobucho (Secretary-General): Haruo Hirose

D. of Mechanical Engineering
Chairman: Tamotsu Tamaki; *staff* 34 (12)
D. of Electrical Engineering
Chairman: Toru Hatta; *staff* 26 (17)
D. of Architectural Engineering
Chairman: Hisashi Hokugo; *staff* 29 (12)
D. of Systems Engineering
Chairman: Hikaru Hasegawa; *staff* 15 (10)
D. of Liberal Arts
Chairman: Yukio Yajima; *staff* 33 (55)
Machining and Processing Ce.
Superintendent: Shigeyoshi Nagata; *staff* 7
Materials Testing Ce.
Superintendent: Masaru Iwase; *staff* 4
Information Technology Ce.
Superintendent: Akiira Watanabe; *staff* 5
Electrical Laboratory Ce.
Superintendent: Katsuhiro Ohkubo; *staff* 5
Ultra High Voltage L.
Superintendent: Tatsuya Harada; *staff* 3
Building Engineering Ce.
Superintendent: Hisashi Hokugo; *staff* 5
Also junior high school, and senior technical high school.

Founded 1967. Graduate School established 1982.

Arrangements for co-operation with the University of Science and Technology of Central China.

Academic Year: April to March (April-September; October-March).
Admission Requirements: Graduation from high school or technical high school, and entrance examination.
Fees (Yen): 1,078,500-1,305,500 per annum.
Language of Instruction: Japanese.
Degrees and Diplomas: Kogakushi, Bachelor of Engineering, 4 yrs. Kogakushushi, Master of Engineering, a 2 further yrs. Kogakuhakushi, Doctor of Engineering, a further 3 yrs.
Library: 143,165 vols.
Special Facilities (Museums, etc.): Museum of Industrial Technology.
Publication: Research Reports (quarterly).
Academic Staff, 1989-90:

Rank	Full-time	Part-time
Kyoju (Professors)	46	–
Jyokyoju (Associate Professors)	29	–
Koshi (Assistant Professors)	39	104
Joshu (Research Associates)	1	–
Technical Assistants	26	–
Total	141	104

Student Enrolment, 1989-90:

	Men	Women	Total
Of the country	3485	47	3532
Of other countries	12	–	12
Total	3497	47	3544

4050 **NIPPON SHIKA DAIGAKU**
Nippon Dental University
1-9-20 Fujimi, Chiyoda-ku, Tokyo 102
Telephone: (3) 261-8311-5

S. of Dentistry
S. of Dentistry (Niigata)

Founded 1907 as Private Kyoritsu Dental School. Reorganized and acquired present name 1949. Graduate School added 1960. Governing body: the Board of Regents. Residential facilities for women students.
Arrangements for co-operation with: University of Michigan; Louisiana University; London University; Gothenburg University.
Academic Year: April to March (April-September; October-March).
Admission Requirements: Graduation from high school or equivalent, and entrance examination.
Language of Instruction: Japanese.
Degrees and Diplomas: Shigakushi, doctor of dentistry, 6 yrs; Shigakuhakushi, Doctor of Dental Sciences, a further 4 yrs.
Library: College Library, *c.* 74,820 vols.
Special Facilities (Museums, etc.): Institution of Dental History.
Publications: Odontology (bimonthly); Bulletin (annually).
Academic Staff: c. 520 (260).
Student Enrolment: c. 310.

4051 **NISHI TOKYO DAIGAKU**
Nishi Tokyo University
2525 Aza Otsukoshi, Yatsusawa, Uenohara-cho, Yamanashi 409-01
Telephone: (554) 63-4411

S. of Science and Engineering
Special S. of Health and Welfare

Founded 1990. Forms part of Teikyo University Group.
Academic Year: April to January (April-July; September-January).
Admission Requirements: Graduation from high school and entrance examination.
Languages of Instruction: Japanese and English.
Academic Staff, 1990: c. 6000 (Teikyo University Group).
Student Enrolment, 1990: c. 30,000 (Teikyo University Group).

4052 **NISHO-GAKUSHA DAIGAKU**
Nisho-Gakusha University
6 Sanban-cho, Chiyoda-ku, Tokyo 102
Telephone: (3) 261-7406

F. of Literature

Founded 1928, reorganized 1949.
Academic Staff: c. 60.
Student Enrolment: c. 2000.

4053 **OKAYAMA RIKA DAIGAKU**
Okayama University of Science
1-1 Ridai-cho, Okayama-shi, Okayama 700
Telephone: (862) 52-3161
Gakucho (President): Tsutoma Kake
Kyokucho (Head, Administration): Shigemitsu Saito

C. of Sciences
Dean: Shoji Wazkabayashi; *staff* 143 (23)
Information Processing Ce.
Head: Hiroyuki Narihisa; *staff* 14
Research I. for Earth Science
Head: Michio Zenki *staff* 5
Ce. for Micro-Analysis
Head: Hatsujiro Hashimote *staff* 3
Ultra Low Temperature Ce.
Head: Kenzo Ohmori; *staff* 4
C. of Engineering

Also nursery, kindergarten, and junior and senior high schools.
Founded 1964. Governing body: the Board of Directors, comprising 8 members. Residential facilities for academic staff and students.
Arrangements for co-operation with: Wright State University of Dayton; Universidade Católica de Paraná; Universidade Federal de Paraná; Hankai University; University of Science and Technology, Beijing; Yunnan University; Sunderland Polytechnic.
Academic Year: April to March (April to October; October-March).
Admission Requirements: Graduation from high school or equivalent, and entrance examination.
Fees (Yen): Registration, 206,000; tuition, 994,400-1070,000 per annum.
Language of Instruction: Japanese.
Degrees and Diplomas: Gakushi, Bachelor–Rigakushi, science; Kogakushi, engineering, 4 yrs. Gakushi, Master–Rigakushushi, science; Kogakushushi, engineering, a further 2 yrs. Hakushi, Doctor, 3 yrs after Shushi.
Library: c. 216,900 vols.
Publications: Ridai-tsushin (bimonthly); Gakuen-tsuchin (bimonthly).
Academic Staff, 1990:

Rank	Full-time	Part-time
Kyoju (Professors)	125	–
Jokyoju (Assistant Professors)	60	–
Koshi (Lecturers)	31	50
Joshu (Assistants)	11	–
Total	227	50

Student Enrolment, 1990:

	Men	Women	Total
Of the country	4573	424	5177
Of other countries	6	–	6
Total	4759	424	5183

4054 **OSAKA GAKUIN DAIGAKU**
Osaka Gakuin University
2-36-1 Kishibe-Minami, Suita-shi, Osaka 564
Telephone: (6) 381-8434

F. of Commerce
F. of Economics
F. of Law
F. of Foreign Languages
D. of Correspondence Courses

Also junior college.
Founded 1962 as Junior College, acquired present status 1963. Postgraduate studies introduced 1967. Governing bodies: the Council; the Senate.
Academic Year: April to March (April-September: October-March).
Admission Requirements: Graduation from high school and entrance examination.
Language of Instruction: Japanese.
Degrees and Diplomas: Gakushi, Bachelor, in all fields, 4 yrs. Shushi, Master, in–Commerce; Economics, a further 2 yrs. Hakushi, Doctor, 3 yrs after Shushi.
Library: c. 1,000,000 vols.
Academic Staff: c. 150 (120).
Student Enrolment: c. 7800 (Also *c.* 870 external students).

4055 **OSAKA GEIJUTSU DAIGAKU**

Osaka University of Arts

469 Higashiyama Kanan-cho, Minami, Kawachi-gun, Osaka 585

Telephone: (721) 93-3781

F. of Arts

Founded 1964.

Arrangements for co-operation with Hong Ig University.

Academic Year: April to March (April-September; October-March).

Admission Requirements: Graduation from high school and entrance examination.

Language of Instruction: Japanese.

Degrees and Diplomas: Bungakushi, Bachelor of Arts, 4 yrs. Diplomas.

Library: 60,000 vols.

Academic Staff: c. 220 (325).

Student Enrolment: c. 7600 (Also *c.* 1100 external students).

4056 **OSAKA IKA DAIGAKU**

Osaka Medical College

2-7 Daigaku-machi, Takatsuki-shi Osaka 569

Telephone: (726) 83-1221

Fax: (726) 81-3723

Gakucho (President): Hideo Matsumoto

Jimukyokucho (Secretary-General): Minoru Matsumara

F. of Medicine

Founded 1927 as Osaka Professional High School of Medicine. Acquired present status and title 1952. Governing body: the Board of Directors.

Arrangements for co-operation with Wilhelms-Universität Münster.

Academic Year: April to March (April-August; September-December; January-March).

Admission Requirements: Graduation from high school or equivalent, and entrance examination.

Language of Instruction: Japanese.

Degrees and Diplomas: Igakushi, doctor of medicine, 6 yrs; Igakuhakushi, Doctor of Medical Sciences, a further 4 yrs.

Library: c. 87,770 vols.

Publications: Journal; Bulletin.

Academic Staff, 1989:

Rank	Full-time
Kyoju (Professors)	37
Jokyoju (Assistant Professors)	91
Joshu (Assistants)	181
Other Staff	1239
Total	1548

Student Enrolment, 1989:

	Men	Women	Total
Of the country	458	151	609
Of other countries	29	6	35
Total	487	157	644

4057 **OSAKA KEIZAI DAIGAKU**

Osaka University of Economics

2-2-8 Osumi, Higashi-yodogawa-ku, Osaka-shi, Osaka 533

Telephone: (6) 328-2431

F. of Economics (day and evening divisions)

F. of Business Administration (day and evening divisions)

Graduate S. of Economics

Japanese Economic History Research I.

Small Business Undertaking Research I.

Industrial and Economics Research I.

I. of Business Administration

Founded as Naniwa College of Commerce 1932, became Showa College of Commerce 1936. Acquired present status 1949. Graduate school added 1966.

Academic Year: April to March (April-September; October-March).

Admission Requirements: Graduation from high school or foreign equivalent, and entrance examination.

Language of Instruction: Japanese.

Degrees and Diplomas: Gakushi, Bachelor–Keizaigakushi, economics; Keieigakushi, business administration, 4 yrs. Shushi, Master–Keizaigakushushi, a further 2 yrs. Hakushi, Doctor–Keizaigakuhakushi, 3 yrs after Shushi.

Library: c. 247,960 vols.

Publications: Osaka Keidai Ronshu (bimonthly); Keiei-Keizai (Business Economy, annually); Chushokigyo kiho (quarterly).

Academic Staff: c. 90 (150).

Student Enrolment: c. 9200.

4058 **OSAKA KOGYO DAIGAKU**

Osaka Institute of Technology

5-16-1 Omiya, Asahi-ku, Osaka-shi, Osaka 535

Telephone: (6) 952-3131

Gakucho (President): Tsugihiko Satoh (1985-87)

Rijicho: Susumu Fujita

F. of Engineering

Graduate S.

Founded 1922 as Kansai College of Engineering, acquired present status 1949. Governing body: the Board of Directors. Residential facilities for 160 men.

Academic Year: April to March (April-September; October-March).

Admission Requirements: Graduation from high school or equivalent, and entrance examination.

Fees (Yen): Registration, 200,000; tuition 865,000-870,000 per annum.

Language of Instruction: Japanese.

Degrees and Diplomas: Kogakushi, Bachelor of Engineering, 4 yrs. Kogakushushi, Master of Engineering, a further 2 yrs. Doctor–Kogakuhakushi, 3 yrs after Master.

Libraries: 188,382 vols in Japanese; 80,191 in other languages.

Publications: Memoirs: Series for Liberal Arts; Series for Science and Technology (biannually); Bulletin of Central ResearchInstitute (quarterly).

Academic Staff, 1986-87:

Rank	Full-time	Part-time
Kyoju (Professors)	78	–
Jokyoju (Assistant Professors)	57	–
Koshi (Lecturers)	76	201
Joshu (Assistants)	2	–
Total	213	201

Student Enrolment, 1986-87:

	Men	Women	Total
Of the country	9601	122	9723
Of other countries	6	–	6
Total	9607	122	9729

4059 **OSAKA ONGAKU DAIGAKU**

Osaka College of Music

1-1-8 Shonai-Saiwa-machi, Toyonaka-shi, Osaka 561

Telephone: (06) 334-2131

Gakucho (President): Yuzuru Nagai (1988-)

Jimukyokucho (Secretary-General): Toyosuke Kurita

C. of Music

Founded 1915 as Osaka School of Music, became high school 1948, junior college 1951. Acquired present status 1958. Governing bodies: the Board of Directors, comprising 17 members; the University Council, comprising 31 members. Residential facilities for women students.

Academic Year: April to March (April-September; October-March).

Admission Requirements: Graduation from high school or foreign equivalent, and entrance examination.

Language of Instruction: Japanese.

Degrees and Diplomas: Geijutsugakushi, Bachelor of Fine Arts, 4 yrs. Shushi, Master, a further 2 yrs.

Library: Central Library, *c.* 85,459 vols.

Special Facilities (Museums, etc.): the Museum of Musical Instruments

Publications: Bulletin (annually); Music Research (annually).

Academic Staff, 1989-90: 75 (282).

Student Enrolment, 1989-90:

	Men	Women	Total
Of the country	123	1305	1428
Of other countries	–	6	6
Total	123	1311	1434

4060 **OSAKA SHIKA DAIGAKU**
Osaka Dental University
5-31, 1-Chome Otemae Chuo-Ku Osaka-shi, Osaka 540
Telephone: (6) 943-6521
Fax: (6) 943-8051
Gakucho (President): Toyoji Hieda

F. of Dentistry
Training S. for Dental Technicians
Dental Technicians S.
Principal: Toshio Tamaki; *staff* 18 (63)
Dental Hygienists S.
Principal: Michiko Miya; *staff* 4 (43)

Founded 1911, acquired present status 1952.

Arrangements for co-operation with Shanghai Second Medical University, Dental School.

Academic Year: April to March (April-June; September-December; January-March).

Admission Requirements: Graduation from high school and entrance examination.

Fees (Yen): 3,500,000 per annum

Language of Instruction: Japanese.

Degrees and Diplomas: Shigakushi, doctor of Dental Surgery, 6 yrs. Shigakuhakushi, Doctor of Dental Sciences, a further 4 yrs.

Libraries: Central Library, *c.* 80,000 vols; branch library, *c.* 40,000.

Publication: Bulletin.

Academic Staff, 1990:

Rank	Full-time	Part-time
Kyoju (Professors)	29	–
Jokyoju (Assistants Professors)	28	–
Koshi (Instructors)	51	254
Joshu (Teaching Assistants)	143	–
Total	251	254

Student Enrolment, 1990:

	Men	Women	Total
Of the country	1204	391	1595

4061 ***OSAKA SHOGYO DAIGAKU**
Osaka University of Commerce
4-1-10 Mikuriya Sakae-machi, Higashiosaka-shi, Osaka 577
Telephone: (6) 781-0383
Fax: (6) 781-8438
Electronic mail: BITNET: nodeno.jpnoucoi
Gakucho (President): Taro Tanioka
Soumu-Bucho (General Manager): Ichiro Tanioka

F. of Commerce and Economics
Dean: Giichi Tomioka; *staff* 9
I. of Industry and Management
Head: Shiro Aimi; *staff* 9
I. of Commercial History
Head: Shigeki Uno; *staff* 11
Information Processing Ce.
Head: Goro Fujioka; *staff* 6

Founded 1928 as commercial school, acquired present status 1949. Present title adopted 1952. Residential facilities for students

Academic Year: April-March (April-September; September-March).

Admission Requirements: Graduation from high school or equivalent, and entrance examination.

Fees (Yen): Registration, 185,400; tuition, 600,000 per annum.

Library: *c.* 200,000 vols.

Academic Staff, 1990:

Rank	Full-time	Part-time
Kyoju (Professors)	50	–
Jokyoju (Associate Professors)	26	–
Koshi (Assistant Professors)	16	73
Joshu (Research Assistants)	–	3
Total	92	76

Student Enrolment, 1990:

	Men	Women	Total
Of the country	3970	61	4031
Of other countries	2	–	2
Total	3972	61	4033

4062 **OSAKA TAIIKU DAIGAKU**
Osaka College of Physical Education
1-1 Gakuen-cho, Ibaraki-shi, Osaka 567
Telephone: (726) 324-3141

F. of Physical Education

Founded 1965.

Academic Year: April to March (April-September; September-March).

Admission Requirements: Graduation from high school and entrance examination.

Language of Instruction: Japanese.

Degrees and Diplomas: Taiikugakushi, Bachelor of Physical Education, 4 yrs.(One year Graduate course).

Academic Staff: *c.* 50 (30).

Student Enrolment: *c.* 1560.

4063 **OSAKA YAKKA DAIGAKU**
Osaka University of Pharmaceutical Sciences
2-10-65 Kawai, Matsubara-shi, Osaka 580
Telephone: (423) 32-1015

F. of Pharmaceutical Sciences

Founded 1925 as school, acquired present status 1950.

Academic Staff: *c.* 25.

Student Enrolment: *c.* 700.

4064 **OTANI DAIGAKU**
Otani University
Kamifusa-cho, Kita-ku, Kyoto-shi, Kyoto 603
Telephone: (75) 432-3131

F. of Letters

Founded as college 1882, became university 1922. Reorganized and present title adopted 1949.

Academic Year: April to March (April-September; October-March).

Admission Requirements: Graduation from high school or equivalent or foreign equivalent, and entrance examination.

Language of Instruction: Japanese.

Degrees and Diplomas: Gakushi, Bachelor–Bungakushi, letters, 4 yrs. Shushi, Master–Bungakushushi, letters, a further 2 yrs.

Library: University Library, *c.* 400,000 vols.

Publications: The Otani Gakuho (quarterly); the Otani Daigaku Kenkyu Nempo (annually); the Mujinto Alumni's Organ (quarterly).

Academic Staff: *c.* 120.

Student Enrolment: *c.* 800.

4065 **OTEMAI JOSHI DAIGAKU**
Otemae College
6-42 Ochayasho-cho, Nishinomiya-shi, Hyogo 662
Telephone: (798) 34-6331

F. of Letters

Founded 1966.

4066 **OTEMON GAKUIN DAIGAKU**
Otemon Gakuin University
2-1-15 Nishiai, Ibaraki-shi, Osaka 567
Telephone: (726) 43-5421
Fax: (726) 43-5427
Gakucho (President): Juichi Oyabu
Jimukyokucho (Secretary-General): Kihei Tsuji

F. of Economics (including Business Administration)
Dean: Akira Katamaki; *staff* 36 (39)
F. of Letters
Dean: Osamu Kondo; *staff* 68 (167)
Ce. for Australian Studies
Head: Yoshihiro Toyama; *staff* 12
Ce. for Education Research
Head: Shosuke Obanawa; *staff* 19

Also kindergarten, primary, junior and senior high schools.

Founded 1888 as elementary school, became university 1966. A private institution receiving some financial support from the government. Residential facilities for *c.* 80 men students.

Arrangements for student exchanges with; Gujarat University; Griffith University, Australia; Normandale Community College, USA.

Academic Year: April to March (April-September; October-March).

Admission Requirements: Graduation from high school or equivalent, or foreign equivalent, and entrance examination.

Fees (Yen): 635,000 per annum.

Languages of Instruction: Japanese and English.

Degrees and Diplomas: Gakushi, Bachelor–Keizaigakushi, economics; Bungakushi, letters, 4 yrs. Shushi, Master–Keizaigakushushi, economics; Bungakushushi, letters, a further 2 yrs.

Library: Central Library, 251,471 vols.

Publications: Otemon Economic Studies (annually); Faculty of Letters Review (annually); Otemon Economic Review (quarterly); Bulletin of Centre for Australian Studies.

Academic Staff, 1989-90:

Rank	Full-time	Part-time
Kyoju (Professors)	60	–
Jokyoju (Associate Professors)	31	–
Koshi (Lecturers)	12	206
Joshu (Assistants)	1	–
Total	104	206

Student Enrolment, 1989-90:

	Men	Women	Total
Of the country	5335	1222	6557
Of other countries	4	5	9
Total	5339	1227	6566

4067 **OTSUMA JOSHI DAIGAKU**

Otsuma Women's University

12 Sanban-cho, Chiyoda-ku, Tokyo 102

Telephone: (3) 261-9841

Gakucho (President): Hideyasu Nakagawa

F. of Domestic Science

F. of Literature

Also junior college.

Founded 1908 as school for Handicrafts and Japanese Traditional Dress, became junior college 1942, acquired present status 1949. Governing bodies: the Board of Trustees; the Board of Councillors. Residential facilities for students.

Academic Year: April to March (April-October; October-March).

Admission Requirements: Graduation from high school and entrance examination.

Language of Instruction: Japanese.

Degrees and Diplomas: Gakushi, Bachelor–Bungakushi, arts; Kaseigakushi, home economics, 4 yrs. Master, a further 2 yrs. Doctor, 2 yrs after Master.

Library: Central Library, *c.* 235,000 vols.

Publications: Otsuma Joshi Daigaku Kaseigakubu Kiyo (Bulletin); Otsuma Joshi Daigaku Bungakubu Kiyo (Bulletin of the Facultyof Language and Literature); Seien.

Academic Staff: c. 180.

Student Enrolment: c. 1750.

4068 **RAKUNO GAKUEN DAIGAKU**

College of Dairy Farming

582-1 Bunkyyolai-Midorimachi, Ebetsu-shi, Hokkaido 069

Telephone: (11) 386-1111/386-1214

Gakucho (President): Jun'ich Ushijima (1985-89)

Jimucho: Kaoru Noguchi

Dairy Farming (including Agricultural Economics and Veterinary Medicine)

Founded 1933 as Hokkai Dairy Farming School, acquired present status 1959. Residential facilities for some academic staff and students.

Arrangements for co-operation with The University of Alberta.

Academic Year: April to March (April-September; October-March).

Admission Requirements: Graduation from high school or equivalent, or foreign equivalent and entrance examination.

Fees (Yen): 115,000-905,000 per annum.

Language of Instruction: Japanese.

Degrees and Diplomas: Bachelor of–Agriculture; Veterinary Medicine, 4 yrs. Master of–Agriculture; Veterinary Medicine, a further 2yrs. Doctor of Veterinary Medicine, 3 yrs after Master.

Library: c. 150,000 vols.

Publication: Journal (annually).

Academic Staff, 1986-87:

Rank	Full-time	Part-time
Kyoju (Professors)	49	14
Jokyoju (Associate Professors)	33	7
Koshi (Lecturers)	30	11
Joshu (Assistants)	9	–
Total	121	32

Student Enrolment, 1986-87:

	Men	Women	Total
Of the country	2288	594	2882
Of other countries	11	1	12
Total	2299	595	2894

4069 ***RIKKYO DAIGAKU**

St. Paul's University

3-chome Nishi-Ikebukuro, Toshima-ku, Tokyo 171

Cables: Rikkyodaigaku

Telephone: (3) 985-2204

President: Yotaro Hamada (1985-90)

C. of Arts (including Theology, Psychology and Education)

Dean: Osamu Tsukada; *staff* 68 (135)

C. of Economics (including Business Administration)

Dean: Yoshinari Maruyama; *staff* 41 (36)

C. of Social Relations (including Tourism)

Dean: Yasuhei Honma; *staff* 32 (64)

C. of Science

Dean: Kumihiko Mizumachi; *staff* 70 (14)

C. of Law and Politics

Dean: Takehisa Awaji; *staff* 27 (37)

F. of General Education (including Cultural and Social Sciences, Natural Sciences, Modern Languages and Physical Education)

Dean: Kichiro Hiida; *staff* 84 (189)

I. of American Studies

Director: Torao Tomita; *staff* 1 (7)

I. of Christian Education

Director: Osamu Tsukada; *staff* 1 (2)

Atomic Energy I.

Director: Manabu Hattori; *staff* 20 (1)

I. of Latin American Studies

Director: Takao Sawaki; *staff* 1 (6)

I. of Industrial Relations

Director: Kakuzou Nonoguchi; *staff* - (26)

I. of Social Welfare

Director: Etsuko Satoh; *staff* - (19)

Psychological and Educational Clinical Ce.

Director: Iwao Ishii; *staff* – (6)

I. of Tourism

Director: Tatsuo Kotani; *staff* 1 (16)

D. of Asian Studies

; *staff* – (4)

Computer Ce.

Director: Kensai Ito; *staff* 5 (1)

Founded 1874 by Bishop Channing Moor Williams of the Episcopal Church of the USA. Acquired university status 1883. Administration taken over by the Japanese 1920. Reorganized and became co-educational 1949. Graduate school established 1951. Governing bodies: the Board of Trustees; the Council of Deans. Residential facilities for women students.

Arrangements for co-operation with: University of Baghdad; University of Chicago; University of The South; Washington and Lee University; Kenyon College; Cuttington University College, Monrovia; Catholic University, Nijmegen; Eberhard Karl University of Tübingen; Humboldt University of Berlin; Monash University; Catholic University, Tilburg; Yonsei University; Western Michigan University; Ateneo de Manila University; University of Warsaw.

Academic Year: April to March (April-September; October-January).

Admission Requirements: Graduation from high school or equivalent, and entrance examination.

Fees (Yen): Registration, 280,000; tuition, 459,000 per annum; Science, 655,000.

Language of Instruction: Japanese.

Degrees and Diplomas: Gakushi, Bachelor–Bungakushi, letters; Rigakushi, science; Hogakushi, law and political science, 4 yrs. Shushi, Master–Shingakushushi, systematic theology; Bungakushushi, letters; Rigakushushi, science; Keizaigakushushi, economics; Shakaigakushushi, sociology; Hogakushushi, law and political science, a further 2-4 yrs. Hakushi, Doctor–Bungakuhakushi, letters; Shingakuhakushi, systematic theology; Keizaigakuhakushi, economics; Rigakuhakushi, science; Shakaigakuhakushi, sociology; Hogakuhakushi, law and political science, 3-6 yrs after Shushi.

Library: University and branch libraries, *c.* 700,000 vols.

Publications: Arts and Letters (Eibei-Bungaku) (annually); Journal of Applied Sociology (biannually); Rikkyo Hogaku (St. Paul's Review of Law and Politics) (annually); Journal of Historical Studies (biannually); Review of Japanese Literature (biannually); St. Paul's Economic Review (quarterly); Rikkyo Quarterly; Christian Studies (KirisutokyoGaku).

Academic Staff, 1989-90:

Rank	Full-time	Part-time
Kyoju (Professors)	232	–
Jokyoju (Assistant and Associate Professors)	68	–
Koshi (Lecturers)	23	–
Joshu (Instructors)	17	–
Hijokin Koshi (Part-time Lecturers)	-	552
Total	340	552

Student Enrolment, 1989-90:

	Men	Women	Total
Of the country	8484	3802	12,286
Of other countries	40	21	61
Total	8524	3823	12,347

4070 **RISSHO DAIGAKU**

Rissho University

4-2-16 Osaki, Shinagawa-ku, Tokyo 141

Telephone: (3) 492-6616

Gakucho (President): Masao Osawa

Kyokucho (Director, Administration): Yoshihiko Hironaka

F. of Buddhism

Dean: Kenyo Mitomo; *staff* 18 (22)

F. of Literature (including General Education)

Dean: Hiroki Takumura; *staff* 59 (124)

F. of Economics

Dean: Katuya Fukuoka; *staff* 21 (26)

F. of Business Administration

Deab: Masaalo Takamatu; *staff* 17 (17)

F. of Law (including Political Science)

Dean: Shoji Iwai; *staff* 13 (23)

Research I. of Nichiren Faith and Teachings

Director: Endo Asai; *staff* – (18)

I. for the Comprehensive Study of the Lotus Sutra

Director: Shinjo Sugoro; *staff* – (18)

Research I. of Industrial Management

Director: Shigeru Suzuki; *staff* – (17)

Legal Research I.

Director: Yukio Nabesawa; *staff* – (13)

Research Ce. for North Sumatra Area Studies

Director: Shozaburo Yamaguchi *staff* – (51)

Research I. of Human Sciences

Director: Hiroshi Iwata; *staff* – (63)

Also junior and senior high schools, and junior college.

Founded 1904 as Buddhist College, became university 1924, incorporating the College. Acquired present status 1949. Financed by the Nichiren Sect. Residential facilities for students.

Special arrangements for co-operation with the University of Southern Maine.

Academic Year: April to March (April-September; October-March).

Admission Requirements: Graduation from high school or equivalent or foreign equivalent, and entrance examination.

Fees (Yen): Registration, 117,000-186,000; tuition, 270,000-541,000 annum.

Language of Instruction: Japanese.

Degrees and Diplomas: Gakushi, Bachelor–Bungakushi, letters; Keizaigakushi, economics, 4 yrs. Bungakushushi, Master of Letters, a further 2 yrs. Bungakuhakushi, Doctor of Letters, 3 yrs after Shushi.

Library: University Library and faculty libraries, total, *c.* 560,216 vols.

Publications: Osakigakuho (Journal of Nichiren and Buddhist Studies); Bungakuburonso (Journal of Faculty of Letters); Keizaigakukiho (Quarterly Report of Economics); Risshochiri (Geographical Review); Risshoshigaku (Report in Historical Researches); Eibungakuronko (Critical Studies in English Literature); Tetsugakuronso (Critical Studies in Philosophy); Kokugokokubungaku (Review of Japanese Philology and Literature); Shakaigakuronso (Critical Studiesin Sociology).

Academic Staff, 1989-90: c. 190 (330).

Student Enrolment, 1990-91:

	Men	Women	Total
Of the country	8034	1511	9545
Of other countries	29	16	45
Total	8063	1527	9590

4071 **RITSUMEIKAN DAIGAKU**

Ritsumeikan University

561-1 Kitamachi, Toji-in, Kita-ku, Kyoto-shi, Kyoto 603

Telephone: (75) 463-1131

F. of Humanities

F. of Law

F. of Economics

F. of Business Administration

F. of Industrial Sociology

F. of Letters

F. of Science and Engineering

Cultural Sciences Research I.

Science and Engineering Research I.

Founded 1900 as a college of law and politics, renamed Ritsumeikan College 1913. Reorganized 1948 as a privateuniversity. Governing bodies: the Board of Trustees; the University Council. Residential facilities for 435 students.

Special arrangements for co-operation with: Institute of Oriental Studies, Academy of Sciences, Moscow; Humboldt University, Berlin; Academy of Sciences, Warsaw.

Academic Year: April to March (April-September; October-March).

Admission Requirements: Graduation from high school and entrance examination.

Language of Instruction: Japanese.

Degrees and Diplomas: Gakushi, Bachelor, of–Law; Economics; Arts; Engineering; Science, 4 yrs. Shushi, Master, of–Law; Economics; Arts; Engineering; Science, a further 2 yrs. Hakushi, Doctor, of–Law; Economics; Arts; Engineering; Science, 3 yrs after Shushi.

Library: University Library, *c.* 889,000 vols.

Publication: Reviews of the Faculties and Research Institutes.

Academic Staff: c. 360 (550).

Student Enrolment: c. 20,540.

4072 ***RYUKOKU DAIGAKU**

Ryukoku University

67 Tsukamoto-cho, Fukakusa, Fushimi-ku, Kyoto-shi, Kyoto 612

Telephone: (75) 642-1111

Gakucho (President): Tyoryu Chiba

F. of Literature (including Philosophy)

F. of Economics

F. of Business Administration

F. of Law

I. of Buddhist Cultural Studies

Social Science Research I.

Also junior college (Buddhist Studies and Social Welfare).

Founded 1679 as Buddhist Seminary, became college 1900 and university 1949. The university is supported by theHonpa Hongawanji denomination. Governing body: the Board of Trustees, of 17 members. Some residential facilities for students.

Academic Year: April to March (April-September; October-March).

Admission Requirements: Graduation from high school or recognized foreign equivalent, and entrance examination.

Language of Instruction: Japanese.

Degrees and Diplomas: Gakushi, Bachelor, of–Letters; Economics; Business Administration; Law, 4 yrs. Shushi, Master, of–Letters; Law, a further 2 yrs and thesis. Hakushi, Doctor, of–Letters; Law, a further 3 yrs and thesis.

Library: University Library, *c.* 628,650 vols.

Publications: Journals of: Law; Economics and Business Administration; Humanities and Science; Social Science Research; Buddhist Culture, Religious Law.

Academic Staff: c. 330 (320).

Student Enrolment: c. 8300.

4073 **RYUTSU-KEIZAI DAIGAKU**

Ryutsu Keizai University
120 Hirahata, Ryguasaki-shi, Ibaraki 301
Telephone: (297) 64-0001
Fax: (297) 64-0011
Gakucho (President): Koji Saeki
Registrar: Shunji Ogawa

F. of Economics (including Business Administration, Accountancy, Law and Foreign Languages)
Dean: Reiko Hayashi; *staff* 56 (50)
F. of Sociology (including Education and Psychology)
Dean: Kazuo Aoi; *staff* 29 (33)

Founded 1965 under the auspices of Nippon Express, an international transportation and distribution company. Governing body: the Council of Trustees. Residential facilities for academic staff and for foreign students.

Arrangements for student exchanges with the Beijing College of Economics.

Academic Year: April to March (April-July; September-March).

Admission Requirements: Graduation from high school and entrance examination.

Fees (Yen): Registration, 203,940; tuition, 695,550 per annum .

Language of Instruction: Japanese.

Degrees and Diplomas: Gakushi, Bachelor, of–Economics; Sociology; Management, 4 yrs. Graduate course in Economics, 1 yr.

Library: c. 78,000 vols.

Publication: Journal of RKU Distribution Studies (biannually). Tsukuba Journal (biannually).

Academic Staff, 1989-90:

Rank	Full-time	Part-time
Kyoju (Professors)	50	–
Jokyoju (Assistant Professors)	21	–
Koshi (Lecturers)	14	83
Total	85	83

Student Enrolment, 1989-90:

	Men	Women	Total
Of the country	3373	279	3652
Of other countries	63	17	80
Total	3436	296	3732

4074 **SAITAMA IKA DAIGAKU**

Saitama Medical School
38 Marohongo, Morayama-machi, Iruma-gun, Saitama 350-04
Telephone: (492) 95-1111

F. of Medicine

Founded 1972. Governing body: the Board of Trustees.

Academic Year: April to March (April-July; September-December; January-March).

Admission Requirements: Graduation from high school and entrance examination.

Language of Instruction: Japanese.

Degrees and Diplomas: Igakushi, Bachelor of Medicine, 6 yrs. Igakuhakushi, Doctor of Medical Sciences, a further 4 yrs.

Library: c. 10,000 vols.

Publication: Saitama Igakukuzasshi (Journal) (quarterly).

Academic Staff: c. 300 (130).

Student Enrolment: c. 720.

4075 **SANGYO IKA DAIGAKU**

University of Occupational and Environmental Health
1-1 Iseigaoka, Yahata-nishi-ku, Kitakyushu-shi, Fukuoka 807
Cables: uoeh kitakyushu
Telephone: (93) 603-1611
Fax: (93) 602-5482
Gakucho (President): Kenzaburo Tsuchiya (1978-90)
Rijicho: Hideo Mori

S. of Medicine
Dean: Osamu Koide; *staff* 176 (122)
S. of Nursing and Medical Technology
Dean: Masayuki Takasugi; *staff* 45 (7)
S. of Occupational and Community Health Nursing
Dean: Masayuki Takasugi; *staff* 4 (14)
I. of Industrial Ecological Sciences
Dean: Kenzaburo Tsuchiya; *staff* 22 (7)

Founded 1978. Graduate School established 1984. Governing body: the Board of Directors. Residential facilities for academic staff and students.

Academic Year: April to March (April-September; October-March).

Admission Requirements: Graduation from high school and entrance examination.

Fees (Yen): 510,700-3,000,000 per annum.

Language of Instruction: Japanese.

Degrees and Diplomas: Igakushi, Doctor of Medicine, 6 yrs. Igakuhakushi, Doctor of Medical Sciences, a further 4 yrs. Diplomas and Certificates.

Library: 90,933 vols.

Publication: Journal (quarterly).

Academic Staff, 1990-91:

Rank	Full-time	Part-time
Kyoju (Professors)	67	–
Jokyoju (Associate Professors)	64	–
Koshi (Assistant Professors)	47	–
Joshu (Instructors)	153	–
Kennin Koshi (Clinical or visiting Professors)	–	176
Total	331	176

Student Enrolment, 1990-91:

	Men	Women	Total
Of the country	593	430	1023
Of other countries	8	3	11
Total	601	433	1034

4076 ***SEIJO DAIGAKU**

Seijo University
6-1-20 Seijo, Setagaya-ku, Tokyo 157
Telephone: (3) 482-1181
Fax: (3) 484-2698
Gakucho (President): Koichi Miyasaki
Jimukyokucho (Secretary-General): Reiko Shimano

F. of Economics (including Administration)
Dean: Itaru Ueno; *staff* 41 (56)
D. of Liberal Arts and Letters (including Japanese, Art Studies, Cultural History, Mass Communication Studies and European Culture)
Dean: Keiji Asanuma; *staff* 68 (114)
F. of Law
Dean: Mitsukuni Yasaki; *staff* 35 (36)
I. of Economic Studies
Director: Hideo Nakamura; *staff* 23
I. of Folklore Studies
Director: Toshio Yamada; *staff* 19

Founded 1917 as elementary school, became high school 1926, acquired university status 1950. Governing body: Seijo Grakun (Board of Directors), comprising 11 members. Residential facilities for foreign students.

Arrangements for co-operation with the University of Wisconsin-Milwaukee

Academic Year: April to March (April-July; September-January).

Admission Requirements: Graduation from high school or foreign equivalent, and entrance examination.

Fees (Yen): Registration, 300,000; tuition 612,000.

Language of Instruction: Japanese.

Degrees and Diplomas: Gakushi, Bachelor–Keizaigakushi, economics; Bungakushi, arts; Hogakushi, law, 4 yrs. Shushi, Master–Keizaigakushushi, economics; Bungakushushi, arts; Hogakushushi, law, a further 2 yrs. Hakushi, Doctor, 3 yrs after Shushi.

Library: University Library, *c.* 500,000 vols.

Publications: Seijo Daigaku Keizai Kenkyu (Economic Studies) (biannually); Seijo Bungei (Arts and Literature) (quarterly); Seijo Law Review; Kokubungaku Ronshu (Monographs on Japanese Literature and Language) (annually); English Monographs (annually); Densho Bunka (Japanese Folklore Studies) (annually).

Academic Staff, 1988:

Rank	Full-time	Part-time
Kyoju (Professors)	104	–
Jokyoju (Associate Professors)	33	–
Koshi (Lecturers)	7	206
Total	144	206

Student Enrolment, 1988:

	Men	Women	Total
Of the country	2486	1880	4366

4077 **SEIKEI DAIGAKU**
Seikei University
3-3-1 Kichijoji, Kita-machi, Musashino-shi, Tokyo 180
Telephone: (422) 51-5181
Fax: (422) 56-0116
Gakucho (President): Hiroya Ueno (1989-91)
Gakuchoshitsucho; Masakazu Ogiso

F. of Economics
Dean: Kazuki Tanaka; *staff* 45 (81)
F. of Engineering (Mechanical, Electrical, Industrial, Chemical and Applied Physics)
Dean: Toshio Nakanishi *staff* 86 (86)
F. of Humanities
Dean: Shigeshi Yana; *staff* 36 (76)
F. of Law
Dean: Shigeru Tasuhara *staff* 36 (76)
Ce. for Asian and Pacific Studies
Director: Takashi Kato; *staff* 5
Information Processing Ce.
Director: Yoshihisa Iida *staff* 4
Also elementary, junior and senior high schools.

Founded 1912 as business school, became university 1949. Reorganized 1969. Governing bodies: the Board of Trustees; the Faculty Meetings. Residential facilities for academic staff.

Arrangements for co-operation with: Griffith University; Chiang Mai University.

Academic Year: April to March (April-September; October-March).

Admission Requirements: Graduation from high school and entrance examination.

Fees (Yen): 560,000-790,000 per annum.

Language of Instruction: Japanese.

Degrees and Diplomas: Gakushi, Bachelor–Bungakushi, arts; Keizaigakushi, economics; Kogakushi, engineering; Hogakushi, law, 4 yrs. Shushi, Master, a further 2 yrs. Hakushi, Doctor, 3 yrs after Shushi.

Library: Central Library, *c.* 481,000 vols.

Publications: Journal of the Faculty of Economics; Proceedings of the Faculty of Engineering; Proceedings of the Faculty of Letters; The Seikei Japanese Literature; The Seikei Legal Sciences.

Academic Staff, 1990-91:

Rank	Full-time	Part-time
Kyoju (Professors)	121	–
Jokyoju (Assistant Professors)	37	–
Koshi (Lecturers)	10	346
Joshu (Assistants)	45	–
Total	213	346

Student Enrolment, 1990-91:

	Men	Women	Total
Of the country	4502	2519	7021
Of other countries	9	5	14
Total	4511	2524	7035

4078 **SEI MARIANNA IKA DAIGAKU**
St. Marianna University School of Medicine
2095 Sogao, Takatsu-ku, Kawasaki-shi, Kanagawa 213
Telephone: (44) 977-8111

F. of Medicine

4079 **SEINAN GAKUIN DAIGAKUKU**
Seinan Gakuin University
6-2-92, Nishijin, Sawara-ku, Fukuoka-shi, Fukuoka 814
Telephone: (92) 841-1311
Fax: (92) 823-3227
Gakucho (President): Teruo Tanaka (1984-90)
Jimukyokucho (Secretary-General): Tsuneemon Watanabe

D. of Theology
Dean: Tashio Aono; *staff* 7 (9)
D. of Literature
Dean: Tsuyoshi Yagi; *staff* 93 (211)
D. of Commerce (including Business Administration)
Dean: Yoshinori Tashiro; *staff* 23 (19)
D. of Economics
Dean: Kaoru Toyama *staff* 24 (16)
D. of Law (including Political Science and International Law)
Dean: Hiroshi Nakamori; *staff* 24 (15)
Also day nursery, kindergarten, middle, and high schools. Also a Study Abroad Programme.

Founded 1916 by the Southern Baptist Missionaries as school, acquired present status 1949. Governing body: the Board of Trustees. Residential facilities for academic staff and students.

Arrangements for co-operation with: Baylor University, Texas; William Jewell College, Missouri; Ouachita Baptist University, Arkansas; Oklahoma Baptist University; State University College at Oneonta, New York; San Diego State University, California; University of Rhode Island; Université de Aix-Marseille III; Université de Grenoble.

Academic Year: April to March (April-September; October-March).

Admission Requirements: Graduation from high school or equivalent, and entrance examination.

Fees (Yen): 490,000 per annum.

Language of Instruction: Japanese, English, French, German, Chinese.

Degrees and Diplomas: Bungakushi, Bachelor of Arts, 4 yrs. Shushi, Master, of–Letters; Business Administration; Law; Economics, a further 2 yrs. Hakushi, Doctor, 3 yrs after Shushi.

Library: *c.* 530,000 vols.

Publications: Studies in: Theology; English Language and Literature; French Language and Literature; Childhood Education; International Cultures; Economic Review; Commercial Review; Law Review.

Academic Staff, 1990-91:

Rank	Full-time	Part-time
Kyoju (Professors)	115	–
Jokyoju (Associate Professors)	44	–
Koshi (Lecturers)	12	270
Total	171	270

Student Enrolment, 1990-91:

	Men	Women	Total
Of the country	4541	2989	7530
Of other countries	5	16	21
Total	4546	3005	7551

4080 **SEIROKA KANGO DAIGAKU**
St. Luke's College of Nursing
10-1 Akashi-cho, Chuo-ku, Tokyo 104
Telephone: (3) 543-639$^{1}/_{3}$

F. of Nursing

Founded 1920 as school, became college 1964. Financially supported by tuition fees and government subsidies. Governing body: the Board of Directors.

Academic Year: April to March (April-September; October-February).

Admission Requirements: Graduation from high school or equivalent, and entrance examination.

Language of Instruction: Japanese.

Degrees and Diplomas: Bachelor of Science in Nursing. Master.

Library: *c.* 24,000 vols.

Publication: Kiyo (Treatise).

Academic Staff: *c.* 40 (50).

Student Enrolment: *c.* 220.

4081 ***SEISHIN JOSHI DAIGAKU**
University of the Sacred Heart
4-3-1 Hiroo, Shibuya-ku, Tokyo 150
Cables: Seishingakuin, Tokyo
Telephone: (3) 407-5811
Fax: (3) 5485-3884
Gakucho (President): Takako Uchiyama (1983-)
Jimukyokucho: Shyugo Kitazawa

D. of Foreign Languages and Literature
; *staff* 14 (43)
D. of Japanese Language and Literature
; *staff* 8 (19)
D. of History and Social Sciences
; *staff* 13 (37)
D. of Philosophy
; *staff* 6 (19)
General Cultural Subjects P.
; *staff* 18 (76)

D. of Education

; *staff* 11 (51)

Founded 1907 as primary and high school. Teachers' training school added 1915. Raised to college status 1948 and university status 1950. Given the right to grant Sho-gakko (State primary school Teachers' Certificate) 1954. Governing body: the Board of Trustees. Residential facilities for *c.* 400 students

Arrangements for co-operation with: Manhattanville College; University of San Diego; Chuen Chen College for Women; Seattle University; Santa Clara University; University of San Francisco; Catholic Faculties of Lyons.

Academic Year: April to March (April-July; October-March).

Admission Requirements: Graduation from high school or recognized foreign equivalent, and entrance examination.

Fees (Yen): 740,000 per annum.

Languages of Instruction: Japanese and English in some courses.

Degrees and Diplomas: Bachelor of Arts, 4 yrs. Master of Arts, at least 2 yrs after Bachelor.

Library: Seishin Joshi Daigaku Library, 270,138 vols.

Publications: Seishin Studies; Christian Cultural Institute Publications.

Academic Staff, 1989-90:

Rank	Full-time	Part-time
Kyoju (Professors)	44	–
Jokyoju (Assistant Professors)	17	–
Koshi (Lecturers)	9	245
Total	70	245

Student Enrolment, 1989-90:

	Women
Of the country	2075
Of other countries	2
Total	2077

4082

*SENSHU DAIGAKU

Senshu University

3-8 Kandakjimbo-cho, Chiyoda-ku, Tokyo 101

Telephone: (3) 265-6211

Gakucho (President): Yoshibumi Odagiri (1986-88)

S. of Economics

Dean: Satoshi Nihei; *staff* 60 (53)

S. of Law

Dean: Hisao Izumi; *staff* 60 (60)

S. of Business Administration

Dean: Masaoshi Deushi; *staff* 58 (56)

S. of Commerce

Dean: Akitaka Sasai; *staff* 65 (54)

S. of Letters

Dean: Yoshiyuki Oshima; *staff* 67 (91)

I. of Social Sciences

Director: Yoshiro Miwa; *staff* – (115)

I. of Law and Political Science

Director: Hiroshi Kamata; *staff* – (60)

I. of Business Administration

Director: Soichi Asajima; *staff* – (61)

I. of Commerce

Director: Kenichi Touji; *staff* – (57)

I. of Accountancy

Director: Yasushito Ozawa; *staff* – (31)

I. of Humanities

Director: Tadao Hisashiga; *staff* – (101)

I. of Physical Education

Director: Hisanoba Yamamoto; *staff* – (18)

I. of Legal Studies

Director: Toshiyuki Nishikawa; *staff* – (44)

I. of Information Sciences

Director: Isao Hayashi; *staff* – (68)

Also junior college.

Founded 1880 as school, became Senshu Daigaku 1913, recognized as private university 1922. Reorganized 1949. Governing bodies: the Board of Trustees; the Board of Councillors. Residential facilities for *c.* 80 men students.

Arrangements for co-operation with: Dankook University; University of Nebraska-Lincoln; Susquehanna University.

Academic Year: April to March (April-July; September-March).

Admission Requirements: Graduation from high school or foreign equivalent, and entrance examination.

Fees (Yen): 380,000 per annum.

Language of Instruction: Japanese.

Degrees and Diplomas: Gakushi, Bachelor–Keizaigakushi, economics; Hogakushi, law; Keieigakushi, business administration; Shogakushi, commerce; Bungakushi, letters, 4 yrs. Shushi, Master–Keizaigakushushi, economics; Hogakushushi, law; Bungakushushi, letters; Keieigakushushi, business administration, a further 2 yrs. Hakushi, Doctor–Keizaigakuhakushi economics; Hogakuhakushi, law; Bungakuhakushi, letters; Shogakuhakushi, commerce; Keieigakuhakushi, business administration, 3 yrs after Shushi.

Library: c. 690,351 vols.

Publications: Journal of Law and Political Science; Economic Bulletin; Studies in the Humanities; Annual Bulletin of Social Science; Business Review; Bulletin of the Institute of Sports, Physical Education and Recreation; Bulletin of the Association of Natural Science; Annual Bulletin of the Humanities.

Academic Staff, 1986-87:

Rank	Full-time	Part-time
Kyoju (Professors)	224	–
Jokyoju (Associate Professors)	69	–
Koshi (Lecturers)	17	314
Total	310	314

Student Enrolment, 1986-87:

	Men	Women	Total
Of the country	16,924	2220	19,144
Of other countries	117	48	165
Total	17,041	2268	19,309

4083

SENZOKU GAKUEN DAIGAKU

Senzoku College of Music

290 Hisamoto, Takatsu-ku, Kawasaki-shi, Kanagawa-ken 213

Telephone: (44) 877-3211

Gakucho (President): Toshikazu Maeda (1986-)

Jimcho: Toru Miyamori

F. of Music

Director: Kunio Toda

Opera I.

Head: Tsunesuke Shimada; *staff* 6 (6)

Also junior college.

Founded 1967. Governing body: 2he Board of Directors. Residential facilities for foreign academic staff and for 70 students.

Arrangements for co-operation with: Hochschule der Künste Berlin; Hochschule für Musik in München.

Academic Year: April to March (April-September; October-March).

Admission Requirements: Graduation from high school or foreign equivalent and entrance examination.

Fees (Yen): Registration, 320,000; tuition, 1,235,000.

Language of Instruction: Japanese.

Degrees and Diplomas: Bungakushi, Bachelor of Arts, 4 yrs. Graduate Course, 1 yr.

Library: Central Library, 52,962 vols.

Publication: Memoirs (annually).

Academic Staff, 1986-87:

Rank	Full-time	Part-time
Kyoju (Professors)	25	11
Jokyoju (Associate Professors)	8	–
Koshi (Assistant Professors)	4	298
Total	37	310

Student Enrolment, 1986-87:

	Men	Women	Total
Of the country	112	1184	1296
Of other countries	1	9	10
Total	113	1193	1306

4084

SHIBAURA KOGYO DAIGAKU

Shibaura College of Technology

3-9-14 Shibaura, Minato-ku, Tokyo 108

Telephone: (3) 452-3201

Fax: (3) 5476-2949

Gakucho (President): Hisayoshi Yanai

Ce. of Education and Research
Head: Hisayoshi Yanai; *staff* 11 (15)
Engineering and Research L.
Chairman: Kunihiro Iida; *staff* 12 (7)
Also Campus at Ohmiya City.
Founded 1927 as Tokyo Higher Technical School, acquired present title and status 1949.
Academic Year: April to January (April-July; September-January).
Admission Requirements: Graduation from high school and entrance examination.
Fees (Yen): Registration, 650,000; tuition, 1,000,000.
Degrees and Diplomas: Gakushi, Bachelor, 4 yrs.
Library: Central Library, 106,089 vols.
Publications: College Identity (monthly); School Catalogue (annualy); Newsletter (monthly); Bulletin (biweekly).
Academic Staff, 1990:

Rank	Full-time	Part-time
Kyoju (Professors)	83	–
Jokyoju (Associate Professors)	62	–
Koshi (Lecturers)	55	217
Joshu (Research Associates)	5	–
Total	205	217

Student Enrolment, 1990:

	Men	Women	Total
Of the country	4341	211	4552
Of other countries	30	3	33
Total	4371	214	4585

4085 **SHIKOKU GAKUIN DAIGAKU**
Shikoku Christian College
3-2-1 Bunkyo-cho, Zentsuji-shi, Kagawa 765
Telephone: (877) 62-2111

F. of Literature
Also junior college.
Founded 1950 on the initiative of American Presbyterian missionaries as school, became junior college 1959, acquired present status 1962. Governing bodies: the Board of Trustees; the College Council. Residential facilities for academic staff and students.
Academic Year: April to March (April-September; October-February).
Admission Requirements: Graduation from high school and entrance examination.
Language of Instruction: Japanese.
Degrees and Diplomas: Bungakushi, Bachelor of Arts, 4 yrs. Bungakushushi, Master of Arts, in Social Welfare, a further 2 yrs. Also Teaching Certificates.
Library: c. 40,000 vols.
Publications: Ronshu (Studies, annually); Karashidane (annually).
Academic Staff: c. 50 (40).
Student Enrolment: c. 1000.

4086 **SHOWA DAIGAKU**
Showa University
1-5-8 Hatanodai, Shinagawa-ku, Tokyo 142
Telephone: (3) 784-1151

S. of Medicine
S. of Pharmaceutical Sciences
S. of Dentistry
Founded 1928 as medical college, became full medical school 1952 and acquired present status 1964.
Academic Year: April to March (April-October; October-March).
Admission Requirements: Graduation from high school and entrance examination.
Language of Instruction: Japanese.
Degrees and Diplomas: Igakushi, doctor of medicine, 6 yrs. Igakuhakushi, Doctor of Medical Sciences, a further 4 yrs. Yakugakushi, Bachelor of Pharmaceutical Sciences, 4 yrs.
Library: University Library, c. 55,000 vols.
Publication: Journal of the Showa Medical Association.
Academic Staff: c. 390.
Student Enrolment: c. 1200.

4087 **SHOWA JOSHI DAIGAKU**
Showa Women's University
1-7 Taishido, Setagaya-ku, Tokyo 154
Telephone: (3) 411-5111
Fax: (3) 487-6850
Electronic mail: jpnswu 10
Gakucho (President): Kusuo Hitomi (1982-)
Jimukyokucho (Secretary-General): Kazunobu Shibuta

F. of Literature
Dean: Chikasada Harada; *staff* 47 (33)
F. of Domestic Science (including Living Arts and Living Science)
Dean: Yasumasa Hayakawa; *staff* 51 (35)
D. of English and American Literature
Professor: Yoshio Tamasaki; *staff* 22 (8)
D. of Living Arts
Professor: Takemitsu Sasho; *staff* 28 (29)
D. of Modern Culture
President: Yukio Miyoshi; *staff* 21
I. of Women's Culture
President: Hiroyasu Fukuba; *staff* 32
Child Education Research I.
President: Hiroyasu Fukuba; *staff* 2
Ship Open C. (including Adult and Lifelong Education)
President: Kinji Yamane; *staff* 19 (163)
Also junior college, and senior and junior high schools.
Founded 1920 as college, acquired present status 1949. Residential facilities for some academic staff and students.
Arrangements for co-operation with: St. Michael's College, Winooski, Vermont.
Academic Year: April to March (April-September; October-March).
Admission Requirements: Graduation from high school and entrance examination.
Fees (Yen): 168,000 per Semester; per faculty.
Language of Instruction: Japanese.
Degrees and Diplomas: Gakushi, Bachelor, of–Letters; Home Economics, 4 yrs.Shushi, Master, a further 2 yrs. Hakushi, Doctor, 2 yrs after Shushi.
Libraries: University Library, c. 290,000 vols; Kindaibunko Library c. 60,000.
Special Facilities (Museums, etc.): Hitomi Memorial Hall; Concert Hall with 2000 seats.
Publications: Gakuen (monthly); Kindai-bungaku-kenkyusosho (Modern Literature Research Series).
Academic Staff, 1990:

Rank	Full-time	Part-time
Kyoju (Professors)	64	–
Jokyoju (Associate Professors)	26	–
Koshi (Assistant Professors)	18	88
Total	108	88

Student Enrolment, 1990:

	Women
Of the country	2122
Of other countries	43
Total	2165

4088 **SHOWA YAKKA DAIGAKU**
Showa College of Pharmaceutical Sciences
5-1-8 Tsurumaki, Setagaya-ku, Tokyo 154

F. of Pharmaceutical Sciences
Founded 1930 as Showa Women's Senmon Gakko of Pharmacy, acquired present status 1949.
Academic Staff: c. 70.
Student Enrolment: c. 800.

4089 ***SOKA DAIGAKU**
Soka University
1-236 Tangi-cho, Hachioji-shi, Tokyo 192
Telephone: (426) 91-2206
Fax: (426) 91-2039
Gakucho (President): Kazuo Takamatsu
Jimukyokucho (Secretary-General): Eiichi Fukada

F. of Economics
Dean: Masasuke Nihei; *staff* 30 (3)

F. of Law (including Political Science)
Dean: Kinnosuke Komuro; *staff* 34 (7)
F. of Letters (including Sociology)
Dean: Toichi Watanabe; *staff* 44 (13)
F. of Business Administration
Dean: Shigeo Mitsumori; *staff* 25 (13)
F. of Education
Dean: Kenkichi Takano; *staff* 40 (20)
I. of Peace Studies
Director: Noboru Yamamoto; *staff* 12 (6)
I. of Applied Economics
Director: Akira Onishi; *staff* 6 (4)
I. of Asian Studies
Director: Chingho A. Chen; *staff* 13 (5)
I. of Japanese Studies
Dean: Kenji Doi
D. for Correspondence Courses
Director: Minoru Sugasawa; *staff* 7 (150)
I. of Life Science
Director: Yuzo Tsukada; *staff* 11 (1)
I for Systems Science
Director: Akira Onishi; *staff* 8 (6)
Also branches in Los Angeles; Paris.

Founded 1971. Graduate schools established 1975. Governing body: the Faculty Conference, comprising 50 members. Residential facilities for academic staff and students.

Arrangements for co-operation with the Universities of: Glasgow; Paris; Texas; Malaya; Nairobi; Philippines; Indonesia; Bologna; London; Manchester; Barcelona; East Asia, Macau; Otago; Parana; Guanjuato; Singapore; Klagenfurt.

Academic Year: April to March (April-July; August-November; December-March).

Admission Requirements: Graduation from high school or equivalent or foreign equivalent, and entrance examination.

Fees (Yen): 514,000-881,000; 53,000-75,000 (Correspondance Courses); Institute (Japanese), 532,000

Language of Instruction: Japanese.

Degrees and Diplomas: Gakushi, Bachelor, of–Economics; Law; Letters; Business Administration; Education, 4 yrs. Shushi, Master, of–Economics; Law; Letters, a further 2 yrs. Hakushi, Doctor, 3 yrs after Shushi. Also Teacher's Certificate.

Library: Total, *c.* 580,000 vols.

Publications: Soka Economic Studies (quarterly); Soka Law Review (quarterly); Studies in English Language and Literature (quarterly); Soka University News (monthly); Catalogue (annually); Sociologica (quarterly); Bulletin of the Educational Society (quarterly); Review of Business Administration (quarterly); Journal of Asian Studies.

Academic Staff, 1990-91:

Rank	Full-time
Kyoju (Professors)	151
Jokyoju (Associate Professors)	52
Koshi (Lecturers)	28
Joshu (Assistants)	17
Total	248

Student Enrolment, 1990-91:

	Men	Women	Total
Of the country	4156	1673	5929
Of other countries	42	58	100
Total	4198	1731	6029*

*Also 10,000 external students.

4090 **SUGIYAMA JOGAKUEN DAIGAKU**
Sugiyama Jogakuen University
17-3 Hoshigaoka-motomachi, Chikusa-ku, Nagoya-shi, Aichi 464
Telephone: (52) 781-1186

F. of Home Economics
Also junior college.

Founded 1949 as college, acquired present status 1972. Governing body: the Board of Trustees. Residential facilities for *c.* 40 students.

Academic Year: April to March (April-October; October-March).

Admission Requirements: Graduation from high school and entrance examination.

Language of Instruction: Japanese.

Degrees and Diplomas: Bungakushi, Bachelor of Arts; Rigakushi, Bachelor of Science, 4 yrs. Shushi, Master.

Library: *c.* 52,330 vols.

Publication: Journal (annually).

Academic Staff: *c.* 100 (90).

Student Enrolment: *c.* 1810.

4091 **TAISHO DAIGAKU**
Taisho University
3-20-1 Nishisugamo, Toshima-ku, Tokyo 170
Telephone: (3) 918)-7311

F. of Buddhism
F. of Letters (including Sociology)

Founded 1926, reorganized 1949.

Academic Year: April to March (April-September; October-March).

Admission Requirements: Graduation from high school or equivalent, and entrance examination.

Languages of Instruction: Japanese and English.

Degrees and Diplomas: Gakushi, Bachelor. Shushi, Master. Hakushi, Doctor.

Library: *c.* 200,000 vols.

Academic Staff: *c.* 100 (60).

Student Enrolment: *c.* 2270.

4092 **TAKUSHOKU DAIGAKU**
Takushoku University
3-4-14 Kobinata, Bunkyo-ku, Tokyo 112
Telephone: (3) 947-2261

F. of Commerce
F. of Political Science and Economics
F. of Foreign Languages
F. of Technology

Founded 1900.

Language of Instruction: Japanese.

Library: *c.* 130,000 vols.

Academic Staff: *c.* 200.

Student Enrolment: *c.* 2800.

4093 **TAMA BIJUTSU DAIGAKU**
Tama Art University
3-15-34 Kaminoge, Setagaya-ku, Tokyo 158
Telephone: (3) 702-1141

F. of Arts and Design

Founded as a private school 1935, became college 1947 and achieved university level 1953. An independent private institution. Governing bodies: the Board of Directors, of 8 members; the Council, of 10 members; the Faculty Meeting, of 74 members. Residential facilities for men students.

Academic Year: April to February (April-September; October-February).

Admission Requirements: Graduation from high school and entrance examination.

Language of Instruction: Japanese.

Degrees and Diplomas: Gakushi, Bachelor, of–Arts, 4 yrs. Shushi, Master, of–Arts, a further 2 yrs.

Library: University Library, *c.* 30,000 vols.

Special Facilities (Museums, etc.): Art Museum; Museum of Ethnology and Folklore.

Academic Staff: *c.* 140.

Student Enrolment: *c.* 1300.

4094 ***TAMAGAWA DAIGAKU**
Tamagawa University
6-1-1 Tamagawa Gakuen, Machida-shi, Tokyo 194
Telephone: (427) 28-3111
Gakucho (President): Tetsuro Obara (1973-)
Dean (Academic Affairs): Hiroya Akabane

F. of Agriculture
Dean: Yoichiro Okimoto; *staff* 66 (26)
F. of Engineering
Dean: Makoto Kanno; *staff* 87 (15)
F. of Arts and Education
Deans: Yoshiaki Obara, Takeya Shibuya; *staff* 75 (243)
D. for Correspondence Courses
Dean: Yoshiaki Obara

Graduate S.
Head: Tetsuo Obara
Educational Research I.
Head: Tetsuo Obara; *staff* 6
Also kindergarten, elementary, junior, and senior high schools, and women's junior college.

Founded 1929 as Tamagawa Academy, became university 1947. Governing body: the Board of Directors. Residential facilities for 284 students.

Academic Year: April to March (April-July; September-March).

Admission Requirements: Graduation from senior high school or equivalent or foreign equivalent, and entrance examination.

Fees (Yen): 940,000-1,320,000 per annum, according to faculty.

Language of Instruction: Japanese.

Degrees and Diplomas: Gakushi, Bachelor–Bungakushi, arts; Nogakushi, agriculture; Kogakushi, technology, 4 yrs. Shushi, Master–Bungakushushi, arts; Nogakushushi, agriculture; Kogakushushi, technology, a further 2 yrs. Hakushi, Doctor–Bungakuhakushi, arts or philosophy; Nogakuhakushi, agriculture; Kogakuhakushi, technology, 3 yrs after Shushi.

Library: 670,427 vols.

Special Facilities (Museums, etc.): Kyoiku Hakubutsu Shiryokan.

Publications: Zenjin (monthly); Shohou (annually); Mitsubachi Kagaku (Honeybee Science Report) (quarterly).

Academic Staff, 1990-91:

Rank	Full-time	Part-time
Kyoju (Professors)	134	–
Jokyoju (Assistant Professors)	107	–
Koshi (Lecturers)	48	–
Joshu (Assistants)	17	–
Junior Assistants	10	–
Total	316	284

Student Enrolment, 1986-87:

	Men	Women	Total
Of the country	3227	3268	6495
Of other countries	7	10	17
Total	3234	3276	6512*

*Also 10,966 external students.

4095 **TEIKYO DAIGAKU**
Teikyo University
2-11-1 Kaga, Itabashi-ku, Tokyo 173
Telex: (3) 962-5067
Telephone: (3) 964-1211
Gakucho (President): Shoichi Okinaga

S. of Liberal Arts (Hachioji Campus)
S. of Economics (Hachioji Campus)
S. of Law (including Foreign Languages, Social, Human and Natural Sciences, and Tourism) (Hachioji Campus)
S. of Medicine
S. of Pharmacy and Biological Pharmacy (Sagamiko Campus)
S. of Science and Engineering (Utsunomiya Campus)
Also kindergarten, junior and senior high schools, special schools, and junior colleges.

Founded 1966. The central institution forming the Teikyo University Group, comprising three universities (Teiky University, Teikyo University of Technology, and Nishi Tokyo University), and four junior colleges.

Arrangements for co-operation with Humboldt University, Berlin.

Academic Year: April to January (April-July; September-January).

Admission Requirements: Graduation from high school and entrance examination.

Languages of Instruction: Japanese and English.

Degrees and Diplomas: Gakushi, Bachelor. Shushi, Master. Hakushi, Doctor.

Libraries: 340,000 vols; Medicine, 180,000; Pharmacy, 76,000.

Publication: Teikyo Journal (bimonthly).

Academic Staff, 1990: c. 6000 (Teikyo University Group).

Student Enrolment, 1990: c. 30,000 (Teikyo University Group).

4096 **TEIKYO KOGYO DAIGAKU**
Teikyo Universityof Technology
2289-23 Uruido Aza Otani, Ichihara, Chiba 290-01
Telephone: (436) 74-5511

F. of Informatics
Special S. of Health and Welfare

Founded 1987. Forms part of Teikyo University Group.

Academic Year: April to January (April-July; September-January).

Admission Requirements: Graduation from high school and entrance examination.

Languages of Instruction: Japanese and English.

Academic Staff, 1990: c. 6000 (Teikyo University Group).

Student Enrolment, 1990: c. 30,000 (Teikyo University Group).

4097 **TOHO DAIGAKU**
Toho University
5-21-16 Omori Nishi, Ota-ku, Tokyo 143
Telephone: (3) 762-4151
Gakucho (President): Toshio Asada (1973-)

S. of Pharmaceutical Sciences
Dean: Mitsuya Tanaka; *staff* 71 (23)
S. of Physical Science (including Biology, Biomolecular Science, Chemistry, Information and Physics)
Dean: Toru Nakazawa; *staff* 91 (46)
S. of Medicine
Dean: Tatsuo Shirai; *staff* 605 (11)
Also middle and high schools.

Founded 1925 as Teikoku Women's Medical College, became private university 1947. Some residential facilities for academic staff and students.

Academic Year: April to March (April-July: September-December; January-March).

Fees (Yen): 1,653,900-10,719,050 per annum.

Language of Instruction: Japanese.

Degrees and Diplomas: Gakushi, Bachelor–Rigakushi, science; Yakugakushi, pharmacy, 4 yrs. Igakushi, doctor of medicine, 6 yrs; Igakuhakushi, Doctor of Medical Sciences, a further 4 yrs.

Library: c. 217,240 vols.

Publication: Toho Medical Journal (Toho Igakukai Zasshi) (monthly).

Academic Staff, 1989-90:

Rank	Full-time	Part-time
Kyoju (Professors)	119	–
Jokyoju (Associate Professors)	92	–
Koshi (Assistant Professors)	118	154
Joshu (Instructors)	429	–
Total	758	154

Student Enrolment, 1990-91:

	Men	Women	Total
Of the country	1790	1371	3161
Of other countries	13	5	18
Total	1803	1376	3179

4098 **TOHO ONGAKU DAIGAKU**
Toho College of Music
84 Imaizumi, Kawagoe-shi, Saitama 356
Telephone: (492) 35-2157
Gakucho (President): Yoshio Nomura (1984-)
Jimukyokucho: Harumitsu Mimurodo

F. of Music

Founded 1965.

Academic Year: April to March (April-September; October-March).

Admission Requirements: Graduation from high school or equivalent or foreign equivalent.

Fees (Yen): Registration, 380,000; tuition, 620,000 per annum.

Language of Instruction: Japanese.

Degrees and Diplomas: Bungakushi, Bachelor or Arts, 4 yrs. Graduate Course, 1 yr.

Library: 22,166 vols.

Academic Staff, 1986-87:

Rank	Full-time	Part-time
Kyoju (Professors)	17	–
Jokyoju (Associate Professors)	13	–
Koshi (Assistant Professors)	4	15
Total	34	15

Student Enrolment, 1986-87:

	Men	Women	Total
Of the country	23	515	538

4099 **TOHOKU FUKUSHI DAIGAKU**
Tohoku Fukushi (Welfare) University
1-8-1 Kunimi, Sendai-shi, Miyagi 980
Telephone: (22) 233-3111
Gakucho (President): Dohki Itoh (1982-90)

F. of Social Welfare
Dean: Yoshito Tsuji; *staff* 81 (62)
Research I. for Buddhist Social Welfare
Director: Dohki Itoh; *staff* – (14)
Research I. for Buddhist Social Education
Director: Dohki Itoh; *staff* – (8)
Research I. for Public Administration
Director: Nobuhide Watanabe; *staff* – (20)

Founded 1958. Acquired present status 1962. Governing bodies: the Board of Directors; the Board of Trustees.

Academic Year: April to March (April-September; October-March).

Admission Requirements: Graduation from high school or equivalent or foreign equivalent, and entrance examination.

Fees (Yen): Registration, 170,000; tuition, 350,000 per annum.

Language of Instruction: Japanese.

Degrees and Diplomas: Gakushi, Bachelor–Shakaigakushi, sociology, 4 yrs. Shushi, Master–Shakaigakushushi, sociology, a further 2 yrs. Professional qualifications.

Library: 114,984 vols.

Special Facilities (Museums, etc.): Keisuke Serizawa's Collection of African Folk Materials.

Publication: Bulletins (annually).

Academic Staff, 1986-87:

Rank	Full-time	Part-time
Kyoju (Professors)	39	–
Jokyoju (Associate Professors and Assistant Professors)	36	–
Koshi (Research Associates)	6	–
Joshu (Lecturers)	–	62
Total	81	62

Student Enrolment, 1986-87:

	Men	Women	Total
Of the country	2401	1599	4000
Of other countries	2	–	2
Total	2403	1599	4002

4100 ***TOHOKU GAKUIN DAIGAKU**
Tohoku Gakuin University
1-3-1 Tsuchitoi, Sendai-shi, Miyagi 980
Telephone: (222) 64-6411
Gakucho (President): Tetsuo Seino (1982-)

F. of Letters
Dean: Matsuji Hasegawa; *staff* 53 (42)
F. of Economics
Dean: Kenzo Sato; *staff* 76 (48)
F. of Law
Dean: Hideo Saito; *staff* 34 (35)
F. of Engineering
Dean: Risaburo Sato; *staff* 34 (35)
Evening S.
Dean: Kenichi Mori; *staff* 20 (27)

Founded 1886 as Sendai Theological Seminary, adopted present title (North Japan College) 1891. Receives support from the Board of International Missions of the Evangelical and Reformed Church.

Arrangements for co-operation with: Ursinus College, Collegeville, Pennsylvania; Franklin and Marshall College, Lancaster, Pennsylvania.

Academic Year: April to March (April-September; October-March).

Admission Requirements: Graduation from high school and entrance examination.

Fees (Yen): Registration, 180,000; tuition, 414,000; Engineering, 620,000 per annum.

Language of Instruction: Japanese.

Degrees and Diplomas: Gakushi, Bachelor–Bungakushi, letters; Keizaigakushi, economics; Kogakushi, engineering; Hogakushi, law, 4 yrs. Shushi, Master–Bungakushushi, letters; Keizaigakushushi, economics; Kogakushushi, engineering; Hogakushushi, law, a further 2 yrs. Hakushi, Doctor, 3 yrs after Master.

Library: University Library, *c.* 359,187 vols.

Publications: Reviews (annually); Science and Engineering Reports (annually).

Academic Staff, 1986-87:

Rank	Full-time	Part-time
Kyoju (Professors)	130	92
Jokyoju (Associate Professors)	88	58
Koshi (Lecturers)	39	21
Joshu (Research Associates)	13	4
Total	270	175

Student Enrolment, 1986-87:

	Men	Women	Total
Of the country	10,577	2348	12,925

4101 **TOHOKU SHIKA DAIGAKU**
Tohoku Dental University
31-1 Mosumi-do, Tomita-machi, Koriyama-shi, Fukushima 963

F. of Dentistry

4102 **TOHOKU YAKKA DAIGAKU**
Tohoku College of Pharmacy
4-4-1 Komatsushima, Sendai-shi, Miyagi 983
Telephone: (22) 234-4181

F. of Pharmaceutical Sciences
Cancer Research I.

Founded 1939 as school, became college 1949. Residential facilities for academic staff.

Academic Year: April to March (April-September; October-March).

Admission Requirements: Graduation from high school or equivalent or foreign equivalent, and entrance examination.

Language of Instruction: Japanese.

Degrees and Diplomas: Yakugakushi, Bachelor of Pharmacy, 4 yrs. Yakugakushushi, Master of Pharmacy, a further 2 yrs. Yakugakuhakushi, Doctor of Pharmacy, 3 yrs after Shushi.

Library: College Library, *c.* 30,000 vols.

Academic Staff: c. 80.

Student Enrolment: c. 800.

4103 ***TOKAI DAIGAKU**
Tokai University
2-28 Tomigaya, Shibuya-ku, Tokyo 151
Cables: Tokai Daigaku
Telex: 2423402 UNITOK J
Telephone: (3) 467-2211
Fax: (3) 467-0197
Socho (President): Tatsuro Matsumae

S. of Letters
Dean: Hachishi Suzuki; *staff* 85 (89)
S. of Political Science and Economics
Dean: Rei Shiratori; *staff* 36 (30)
S. of Law
Dean: Isao Sato; *staff* 26 (5)
S. of Humanities and Culture
Dean: Masamichi Tezeni; *staff* 61 (76)
S. of Physical Education
Dean: Tokimaro Omura *staff* 40 (10)
S. of Science
Dean: Hiroshi Watanabe; *staff* 44 (71)

S. of Engineering (including, Control Engineering, Communication Engineering, Electronics Applied to Physics, Nuclear Engineering, Electro-Photo Optics, Industrial Chemistry, Metallurgy, Architecture and Building Engineering, Civil Engineering, Prime Mover Engineering, Production Engineering, Precision Mechanics, Aeronautics and Astronautics, and Management Engineering)
Dean: Sanni Hagi; *staff* 255 (116)
S. of Marine Science and Technology
Dean: Akira Nagaii; *staff* 93 (53)
S. of Medicine
Dean: Shogo Sasaki; *staff* 439 (2)
Foreign Language Education Ce.
Director: Hajime Yano; *staff* 89 (165)
Ce. for Japanese (for foreign students)
Director: Muneo Hori; *staff* 14 (17)
Librarian and Teacher Training P.
; *staff* 13 (14)
I. of Industrial Science Research
Director: Toru Hirayama; *staff* 1
I. of Civilization Research
Director: Keitaro Syoju; *staff* 4
I. of Social Sciences Research
Director: Rei Shiratori;
I. of Oceanic Research and Development
Director: Aogu Matsumae; *staff* 8
I. of Arts Research
Director: Tatsuo Fukuda; *staff* 4
I. of Research and Development
Director: Tatsuro Matsumae; *staff* 29
Medical Research I.
Director: Kimiyoshi Tuji
I. of Education Research
Director: Sonosuke Katori; *staff* 5
Research and Information Ce.
Director: Koichi Matsuyama; *staff* 1
I. of Sports Medical Science Research
Director: Shoichi Nakano
Asia Minor and Balkan Research Ce.
Director: Keitaru Syoju
Research and Information Ce.
Director: ToshibumiSakata
Space Information Ce.
Director: Tatsuro Matsumae
Strategic Peace and International Affairs Research I.
Director: Shigeyoshi Matsumae
Also Tokai University European Centre (Denmark); Tokai University Boarding School (Denmark); Tokai University Matsumae Budo Centre (Vienna); Tokai University Pacific Centre (Hawaii). Also 2 Universities, 5 junior colleges, 15 senior high schools, 4 junior high schools, 1 elementary school, 4 kindergarten and 3 University Hospitals.

Founded 1946 as a university officially authorized by the Ministry of Education. Governing body: the Board of Trustees. Residential facilities for academic staff and foreignstudents.

Arrangements for co-operation with: University of Sofia; Moscow State University; Far Eastern University, USSR; King Mongkut's Institute of Technology Ladkrabang, Thailand; Technical University of Budapest; Humboldt University of Berlin; University of Kassel; Université d'Aix Marseille III; Université de Montpellier III; University of Essex; Universidad de Salamanca; University of Miami; New York Medical College; Syracuse University; University of Hawaii; Tufts University; University of Alaska Statewide System-Fairbanks; Wake Forest University; San Francisco State University; University of California, Los Angeles; People's University of China; Fudan University; Zhongshan University.

Academic Year: April to March (April-September; September-March).

Admission Requirements: Graduation from high school and entrance examination.

Fees (Yen): Registration and tuition per semester, 802,240-985,240; Medecine, 6,536,860.

Language of Instruction: Japanese.

Degrees and Diplomas: Gakushi, Bachelor–Kogakushi, engineering; Bungakushi, letters; Suisangakushi, fishery; Seijigakushi, political science; Keizaigakushi, economics; Hogakushi, law; Kyoyogakushi, liberal arts; Keieigakushi, business and management; Kyoyogakushi, humanities and culture; Rigakushi, science; Taiikugakushi, physical education, 4 yrs; Igakushi, medicine, 6 yrs. Shushi, Master, a further 2 yrs. Hakushi, Doctor, 3 yrs after Shushi.

Library: University Library, 1,187,530 vols.

Special Facilities (Museums, etc.): Marine Science Museum; Physical Science Museum; Natural History Museum; Human Science Museum; 2 Research and training vessels.

Publication: Faculty publications.

Press or Publishing House: Tokai University Press.

Academic Staff, 1990-91:

Rank	Full-time	Part-time
Kyoju (Professors)	644	–
Jokyoju (Associate Professors)	359	–
Koshi (Lecturers)	242	–
Joshu (Assistants)	250	–
Total	1495	661

Student Enrolment, 1990-91:

	Men	Women	Total
Of the country	27,013	4397	31,410
Of other countries	322	140	462
Total	27,335	4537	31,872

4104 **TOKUSHIMA BUNRI DAIGAKU**

Tokushima Bunri University

1-8 Terashiimaho-cho, Tokushima-shi, Tokushima 770

Telephone: (886) 22-0097

Fax: (886) 26-2998

Gakucho (President): Takashi Soeda

F. of Domestic Science
Dean: Masa Yamamoto
F. of Music
Dean: Shigeru Toyama
F. of Pharmaceutical Sciences
Dean: Sho Ito
F. of Literature
Dean: Motomi Kishida
F. of Engineering (including Mechanical-Electronic and Information Science and Systems)
Dean: Koichi Akizono

Founded 1895, acquired present status 1966.

Academic Year: April to March.

Admission Requirements: Graduation from high school and entrance examination.

Language of Instruction: Japanese.

Degrees and Diplomas: Gakushi, Bachelor, 4 yrs. Shushi, Master, a further 2 yrs.

Academic Staff, 1990: 278.

Student Enrolment, 1990: 3001.

4105 **TOKYO DENKI DAIGAKU**

Tokyo Denki University

2-2 Kanda-Nishikicho, Chiyoda-ku, Tokyo 101

Telephone: (3) 294-1551

F. of Engineering (day and evening courses)
F. of Science and Engineering
Also high school, junior college, and technical institute.

Founded 1907 as evening Institute of Electrical and Mechanical Technology. Became Higher Technical School 1939and college 1949. Some residential facilities for students.

Academic Year: April to March (April-September; October-March).

Admission Requirements: Graduation from high school or equivalent, and entrance examination.

Language of Instruction: Japanese.

Degrees and Diplomas: Kogakushi, Bachelor of Engineering, 4 yrs. Kogakushushi, Master of Engineering, a further 3 yrs. Kogakuhakushi, Doctor of Engineering, 3 yrs after Shushi.

Library: College Library, *c.* 110,000 vols.

Publications: Research Reports (annually); Library Reports (annually).

Academic Staff: c. 180 (190).

Student Enrolment: c. 8300 (Also *c.* 70 external students).

4106 **TOKYO IKA DAIGAKU**
Tokyo Medical College
6-1-1 Shinjuku, Shinjuku-ku, Tokyo 1600
Telephone: (3) 351-6141

F. of Medicine

Founded 1916 as private school, became Tokyo Medical College 1946. Graduate courses started 1957.

Academic Year: April to March (April-August; September-December; January-March).

Admission Requirements: Graduation from high school and entrance examination.

Language of Instruction: Japanese.

Degrees and Diplomas: Igakushi, doctor of medicine, 6 yrs; Igakuhakushi, Doctor of Medical Sciences, a further 4 yrs.

Library: College Library, *c.* 75,420 vols.

Publication: Journal.

Academic Staff: c. 320.

Student Enrolment: c. 950.

4107 ***TOKYO JIKEI-KAI IKA DAIGAKU**
Jikei University School of Medicine
3-25-8 Nishi-shinbashi, Minato-ku, Tokyo 105
Telephone: (3) 433-1111
Gakucho (President): Masakazu Abe (1988-90)
Jimukyokucho: Yoshiki Tanaka

F. of Medicine
Continuing Medical Education Ce.
Head: Kenichi Kobayashi; *staff* 3
I. of Medical Science
Director: Takehiko Fukuhara; *staff* 13
Animal Ce. L.
Director: Shinichi Hayashi; *staff* 2
Radioisotope Research Ce.
Director: Sachio Mochizuki; *staff* 3
Also Colleges of Nursing.

Founded 1881 as school, became college 1921. Acquired university status 1952. Governing body: the Board of Directors, comprising 11 members.

Arrangements for co-operation with: University of London.

Academic Year: April to March (April-July; September-December; January-March).

Admission Requirements: Graduation from high school or equivalent, and entrance examination.

Fees (Yen): 1,800,000 per annum.

Language of Instruction: Japanese.

Degrees and Diplomas: Igakushi, Bachelor of Medicine, 6 yrs; Igakuhakushi, Doctor of Medical Sciences, a further 4-8 yrs.

Library: c. 199,000 vols.

Special Facilities (Museums, etc.): Hyohon-kan (Medical Museum).

Publications: Tokyo Jikeikai Ika Daigaku Zasshi (in Japanese) (bimonthly); Jikeikai Medical Journal (in English) (quarterly).

Academic Staff, 1989-90:

Rank	Full-time	Part-time
Kyoju (Professors)	64	45
Jokyoju (Assistant Professors)	63	34
Koshi (Instructors)	181	285
Joshu (Assistants)	606	443
Total	914	807

Student Enrolment, 1989-90:

	Men	Women	Total
Of the country	599	109	708

4108 ***TOKYO JOSHI DAIGAKU**
Tokyo Women's Christian University
2-6-1 Zempukuji, Suginami-ku, Tokyo 167
Cables: twcutjd tokyo
Telephone: (3) 395-1211
Fax: (3) 399-3123
Gakucho (President): Jun-ichi Kyogoku (1988-92)
Jimukyokucho (Secretary-General): Takeo Terada

C. of Arts and Sciences (Philosophy, Japanese Literature, English, History, Sociology and Economics, Psychology, and Mathematics)
Dean: Kazuo Ohsumi; *staff* 100 (215)
C. of Culture and Communication (including Communication, Cross-Cultural Studies, and Language)
Dean: Aiko Kozaki; *staff* 3 (33)
I. for Comparative Studies of Culture
Director: Zen-ichi Ito; *staff* 1
C. for Women's Studies
Director: Aiko Negishi; *staff* 1

Founded 1918 as college, became university 1948. Graduate school established 1971. College of Culture and Communication established 1988. Governing bodies: the Board of Trustees; the University Council. Residential facilities for foreign academic staff and *c.* 350 students.

Arrangements for co-operation with: Beirut Arab University; Ewha Woman's University; Seoul Woman's University; Silliman University; Harris Memorial College, Manila; Northern Christian College, Laoag City; Scripps College, Claremont, California; Mount Holyoke College, South Hadley, Massachusetts; William Smith College, New York; Yunnan Institute of Nationalities, Kunming.

Academic Year: April to March (April-September; October-March).

Admission Requirements: Graduation from high school or equivalent, and entrance examination.

Fees (Yen): Tuition, 494,000 per annum.

Language of Instruction: Japanese.

Degrees and Diplomas: Gakushi, Bachelor–Bungakushi, arts; Rigakushi, science, 4 yrs. Shushi, Master–Bungakushushi, arts; Rigakushushi, science, a further 2 yrs.

Library: University Library, *c.* 438,000 vols.

Publications: Japanese Literature (biannually); Essays and Studies in British and American Literature (biannually); Historica (annually); Sociology and Economics (annually); Annals of Institute for Comparative Studies of Culture (annually); Science Reports (annually); Essays and Studies (biannually); University Bulletin (monthly).

Academic Staff, 1990-91:

Rank	Full-time	Part-time
Kyoju (Professors)	88	–
Jokyoju (Associate Professors)	22	–
Koshi (Lecturers)	9	277
Joshu (Assistants)	29	–
Total	148	277

Student Enrolment, 1990-91:

	Women
Of the country	3637
Of other countries	5
Total	3642

4109 **TOKYO JOSHI IKA DAIGAKU**
Tokyo Women's Medical College
8-1 Kawada-cho, Shinjuku-ku, Tokyo 162
Telex: TWMLIB J 232-2317
Telephone: (3) 353-8111

F. of Medicine

Founded 1900 by Dr. Yayoi Yoshioka as Medical School, became college, 1951. Governing body: the Board of Trustees.

Academic Year: April to March (April-July; September-December; January-March).

Admission Requirements: Graduation from high school or foreign equivalent, and entrance examination.

Language of Instruction: Japanese.

Degrees and Diplomas: Igakushi, doctor of medicine, 6 yrs; Igakuhakushi, Doctor of Medical Sciences, a further 4 yrs.

Library: c. 64,000 vols.

Publications: Bulletin (annually); College News (quarterly).

Academic Staff: c. 720 (310).

Student Enrolment: c. 1160.

4110 **TOKYO KEIZAI DAIGAKU**
Tokyo Keizai University
1-7 Minamicho, Kokubunji-shi, Tokyo 185
Telephone: (423) 21-1941

F. of Economics (day and evening courses)
F. of Business Administration (day and evening courses)
Also junior college.

Founded 1900 as Okura School of Commerce, became university 1949. Graduate School established 1970. Financially supported by tuition fees and government subsidy. Governing bodies: the Board of Trustees, comprising 15 members; the Board of Councillors, comprising 37 members. Residential facilities for *c.* 116 men students.

Academic Year: April to March (April-September; October-March).

Admission Requirements: Graduation from high school or equivalent, and entrance examination.

Language of Instruction: Japanese.

Degrees and Diplomas: Gakushi, Bachelor–Keizaigakushi, economics; Keieigakushi, business administration, 4 yrs. Shushi, Master–Keizaigakushushi, economics, a further 2 yrs. Hakushi, Doctor–Keizaigakuhakushi, 3 yrs after Shushi.

Library: *c.* 260,000 vols.

Publications: Bulletin; Journal of Humanities and Natural Sciences (3 times a year).

Academic Staff: *c.* 105 (180).

Student Enrolment: *c.* 7600.

4111 **TOKYO KOGEI DAIGAKU**

Tokyo Institute of Polytechnics

1583 Iiyama, Atsugi-shi, Kanagawa 243-02

Telephone: (462) 41-0454

Fax: (462) 42-3000

Gakucho (President): Shinichi Kihuchi

F. of Engineering (Photographic Engineering, Image Technology, Industrial Chemistry, Architecture, and Electronics)

Dean: Hisakazu Kuwosahi; *staff* 90 (74)

Also 2 junior colleges.

Founded 1923.

Academic Year: April to March (April-September; September-March).

Admission Requirements: Graduation from high school and entrance examination.

Language of Instruction: Japanese.

Degrees and Diplomas: Kogakushi, Bachelor of Engineering, 4 yrs. Kogakushushi, Master of Engineering, a further 2 yrs.

Library: *c.* 66,023 vols.

Publication: Bulletin (annually).

Academic Staff, 1990: 90 (74).

Student Enrolment, 1990:

	Men	Women	Total
Of the country	2313	143	2456
Of other countries	3	–	3
Total	2316	143	2459

4112 **TOKYO KOKUSAI DAIGAKU**

Tokyo International University

4-23-20 Takadanobaba, Shinjuku-ku, Tokyo 160

Telephone: (3) 362-9641

F. of Business and Commerce

F. of International Studies and Human Relations

Founded 1965.

Academic Year: April to March (April-September; September-March).

Admission Requirements: Graduation from high school and entrance examination.

Language of Instruction: Japanese.

Degrees and Diplomas: Gakushi, Bachelor. Shushi, Master.

Library: *c.* 160,000 vols.

Academic Staff: *c.* 130 (80

Student Enrolment: *c.* 4620.

4113 **TOKYO NOGYO DAIGAKU**

Tokyo University of Agriculture

1-1-1 Sakuragaoka, Setagaya-ku, Tokyo 156

Telephone: (3) 420-2131

F. of Agriculture (including Forestry, Animal Husbandry, Landscape Architecture, and Nutrition)

Also junior college, senior high schools, and correspondence courses.

Founded 1891 as college, became university 1925.

Academic Year: April to March (April-September; October-March).

Admission Requirements: Competitive entrance examination following graduation from high school.

Language of Instruction: Japanese.

Degrees and Diplomas: Gakushi, Bachelor, of Agriculture, 4 yrs. Shushi, Master, a further 2 yrs. Hakushi, Doctor, a further 2 yrs.

Library: University Library, *c.* 87,850 vols.

Publications: Nogaku Shuho (Agricultural Journal, annually); General Education Journal (quarterly); Memoirs (annually).

Academic Staff: *c.* 260.

Student Enrolment: *c.* 7900.

4114 ***TOKYO RIKA DAIGAKU**

Science University of Tokyo

1-3 Kagurazaka, Shinjuku-ku, Tokyo 162

Telex: SCIENCUNIV

Telephone: (3) 260-4271

Gakucho (President): Masao Yoshiki (1982-89)

Jimukyokuchgo (Secretary-General): Toshikata Sugiyama

F. of Science

Dean: Kenjiro Meguro

F. of Pharmacy

Dean: Kazuhiko Kubata

F. of Engineering

Dean: Ichiro Kijima

F. of Science and Technology

Dean: Keizo Ogino

F of Industrial Science and Technology

Dean: Masaharu Aoki

Research I. of Science Technology

Head: Teruaki Mukaiyama

Founded 1881 as college, reorganized and became university 1949. Governing body: the Board of Trustees.

Academic Year: April to March (April-October; October-March).

Admission Requirements: Graduation from high school or recognized equivalent, and entrance examination.

Fees (Yen): Tuition, 230,000-580,000 per annum, according to faculty.

Language of Instruction: Japanese.

Degrees and Diplomas: Gakushi, Bachelor, of–Science; Pharmacy; Engineering, 4 yrs. Shushi, Master, a further 2 yrs. Hakushi, Doctor, 3 yrs after Shushi.

Library: University Library, 540,924 vols.

Publications: SUT Journal of Mathematics (biannually); Fire Science and Technology (biannually); Collected Papers (annually)

Press or Publishing House: Science University of Tokyo Press

Academic Staff, 1989-90:

Rank	Full-time	Part-time
Kyoju (Professors)	260	–
Jokyoju (Associate Professors)	100	–
Koshi (Lecturers)	116	456
Joshu (Assistants)	179	–
Total	655	456

Student Enrolment, 1989-90:

	Men	Women	Total
Of the country	15,867	2225	18,092
Of other countries	28	4	32
Total	15,895	2229	18,124

4115 **TOKYO SHIKA DAIGAKU**

Tokyo Dental College

1-2-2, Masago, Chiba-shi, Chiba 260

Telephone: (472) 79-2222

Fax: (472) 79-2052

Dean: Tetsuya Kanatake

Vice-Dean: Takashi Nakakuku

S. of Dentistry

Also 25 departments of the school.

Founded 1890 as Takayama Dental School; acquired present title and status 1907. Reorganized 1950. Governing bodies: the Board of Trustees; the Faculty Assembly; the Faculty Council.

Arrangements for academic staff exchange with the Universities of: Yonsei; Florida; Texas.

Academic Year: April to March (April-September; October-March).

Admission Requirements: Graduation from high school and entrance examination.

Language of Instruction: Japanese.

Degrees and Diplomas: Shigakushi, Doctor of Dentistry, 6 yrs; Shigakuhakushi, Doctor of Dental Sciences, 4 yrs.
Libraries: College Library, *c.* 134,380 vols; branch libraries, *c.* 20,600.
Publications: Bulletin; Journal.
Academic Staff, 1990:

Rank	Full-time	Part-time
Kyoju (Professors)	44	2
Jyokyoju (Associate Professors)	37	7
Koshi (Assistant Professors)	78	316
Joshu (Assistants)	129	61
Total	288	386

Student Enrolment, 1990:

	Men	Women	Total
Of the country	825	234	1059
Of other countries	6	–	6
Total	831	234	1065

4116 **TOKYO YAKKA DAIGAKU**
Tokyo College of Pharmacy
1432-1 Horinouchi, Hachioji-shi, Tokyo 192-03
Telephone: (426) 76-5111

F. of Pharmacy

Founded 1880 as school, acquired present name and status 1949. Some residential facilities for academic staff and students.
Academic Year: April to March (April-September; October-March).
Admission Requirements: Graduation from high school and entrance examination. Special provisions for foreign students with similar qualifications.
Language of Instruction: Japanese.
Degrees and Diplomas: Yakugakushi, Bachelor of Pharmacy, 4 yrs. Yakugakushushi, Master of Pharmacy, a further 2 yrs. Yakugakuhakushi, Doctor of Pharmacy, 3 yrs after Master.
Library: College Library, *c.* 50,000 vols.
Publication: Tokyo Yakka Daigaku Nempo (Annual Report).
Academic Staff: c. 140 (40).
Student Enrolment: c. 2120.

4117 **TOYO DAIGAKU**
Toyo University
5-28-20 Hakusan, Bunkyo-ku, Tokyo 112
Telex: 272-3678
Telephone: (3) 945-7557
Fax: (3) 945-7221
Gakucho (President): Koichi Kansaku

F. of Literature (including Buddhist Studies)
Director: Koji Nitta; *staff* 147 (289)
F. of Economics
Director: Teruo Abe; *staff* 30 (23)
F. of Business Administration
Director: Hiroaki Wakuta; *staff* 30 (24)
F. of Law
Director: Kazuo Morioka; *staff* 33 (21)
F. of Sociology
Director: Michito Fujiki; *staff* 34 (63)
F. of Engineering (including Architecture)
Director: Tadataka Yamashita; *staff* 151 (98)
Asia-Africa Cultural Research I.
Director: Kiyohito Haryu; *staff* – (40)
I. of Economics
Director: Iwao Okamoto; *staff* – (29)
I. of Business Administration
Director: Junichi Nomura; *staff* – (29)
I. of Social Relations
Director: Hidehiko Hirose; *staff* – (33)

Founded 1887, became university 1906. Residential facilities in 4 seminar houses.
Academic Year: April to March (April-September; October-March).
Admission Requirements: Graduation from high school and entrance examination.
Fees (Yen): Registration, 123,600-247,200; tuition, 190,000-680,000
Language of Instruction: Japanese.

Degrees and Diplomas: Gakushi, Bachelor, of–Arts; Science, 4 yrs. Shushi, Master, of–Arts; Science, a further 1-2 yrs. Hakushi, Doctor, of–Arts; Science, 2-3 yrs after Shushi.
Library: University Library and branch libraries, total, 774,895 vols.
Publication: Publications of the faculties.
Academic Staff, 1990:

Rank	Full-time	Part-time
Kyoju (Professors)	253	–
Jyokyoju (Associate Professors)	92	–
Koshi (Lecturers)	67	518
Joshu (Assistants)	13	–
Total	425	518

Student Enrolment, 1990:

	Men	Women	Total
Of the country	17,121	3736	20,857
Of other countries	139	98	237
Total	17,260	3834	21,94*

*Also 1605 external students and 36 students by correspondence.

4118 **TOYOTA KOGYO DAIGAKU**
Toyota Technological Institute
2-12 Hisakata, Tempaku-ku, Nagoya-shi, Aichi 468
Telephone: (52) 802-1111

F. of Engineering

Founded 1981.
Academic Year: April to March (April-September; October-March).
Admission Requirements: Graduation from high school or equivalent, and entrance examination.
Language of Instruction: Japanese.
Degrees and Diplomas: Gakushi, Bachelor. Shushi, Master.
Library: c. 28,670 vols.
Academic Staff: c. 20.
Student Enrolment: c. 225.

4119 ***TSUDAJUKU DAIGAKU**
Tsuda College
2-1-1 Tsuda-machi, Kodaira-shi, Tokyo 187
Telephone: (423) 42-5111
Fax: (423) 41-2444
Gakucho (President): Michiko Temma (1988-)
Jimushunin: Jun Adachi

D. of English Language and Literature
Chairman: Toshio Nakao; *staff* 17 (47)
D. of Mathematics
Chairman: Toshio Niwa; *staff* 17 (15)
D. of International and Cultural Studies
Chairman: Hiroshi Momose; *staff* 16 (37)
Graduate S. of Literature
Chairman: Shizuko Kawamoto; *staff* 13 (1)
Graduate S. of Mathematics
Chairman: Shinji Fukuhara; *staff* 12 (3)
Graduate S. of International Studies
Chairman: Charles D. Lummis; *staff* 12
I. for Research in Language and Culture
Head: Minoru Kobayashi; *staff* 18
I. of International Studies
Head: Koh Se-Kai; *staff* 29 (5)
I. of Mathematics and Computer Science
Head: Mitsuo Sugiura; *staff* 19
Computer Ce.
Head: Koji Katayama; *staff* 12
Health Service Ce.
Head: Mihoko Ejiri; *staff* 4
Audio-visual Ce.
Head: Akiko Ueda; *staff* 4

Founded 1900 as school, acquired present status 1948. Governing bodies: the Board of Trustees, comprising 9 members; the Council, comprising 19 members. Residential facilities for *c.* 4,000 students.
Arrangements for co-operation with: Australian National University; Western Washington University; Bryn Mawr College; University of Massachusetts; Ewha Women's University.
Academic Year: April to March (April-July; October-February).

Admission Requirements: Graduation from high school or equivalent, and entrance examination.

Fees (Yen): Registration 267,800; tuition, 520,000 per annum; Mathematics, 570,000.

Languages of Instruction: Japanese and English.

Degrees and Diplomas: Gakushi, Bachelor–Bungakushi, arts; Rigakushi, science, 4 yrs. Shushi, Master–Bungakushushi, arts; Kokusaishushi, international studies; Rigakushushi, science, a further 2 yrs. Hakushi, Doctor–Bungakuhakushi, letters;Geikujutsuhakushi, international studies; Rigakuhakushi, science, 3 yrs after Shushi.

Library: College Library, *c.* 194,000 vols.

Publications: Tsuda Review; Study of International Relations; Journal.

Academic Staff, 1990-91:

Rank	Full-time	Part-time
Kyoju (Professors)	48	–
Jokyoju (Assistant Professors)	29	–
Koshi (Lecturers)	4	–
Hijokin Koshi (Part-time Lecturers)	–	195
Joshu (Assistants)	3	–
otal	84	195

Student Enrolment, 1990-91:

	Women
Of the country	2614
Of other countries	20
Total	2634

4120 **TSURUMI DAIGAKU**

Tsurumi College

2-1-3 Tsurumi, Tsurumi-ku, Yokohama-shi, Kanagawa 230

F. of Literature

F. of Dentistry

Founded 1924 as school, became junior college 1953, acquired present title 1963.

Academic Staff: c. 70.

Student Enrolment: c. 2390.

4121 **WAKO DAIGAKU**

Wako University

2160 Kanai-cho, Machida-shi, Tokyo 194-01

Telephone: (44) 988-1431

F. of Humanities

F. of Economics

Founded 1966. Some residential facilities for academic staff and students.

Academic Year: April to March (April-September; October-March).

Admission Requirements: Graduation from high school and entrance examination.

Language of Instruction: Japanese.

Degrees and Diplomas: Bungakushi, Bachelor of Arts; Keizaigakushi, Bachelor of Economics, 4 yrs.

Library: c. 100,000 vols.

Publication: University News (quarterly).

Academic Staff: c. 90 (130).

Student Enrolment: c. 3660.

4122 ***WASEDA DAIGAKU**

Waseda University

1-6-1 Nishi-Waseda, Shinjuku-ku, Tokyo 169

Cables: Wasedauniv

Telex: 2323280 WASEDA J

Telephone: (3) 203-4141

Fax: (3)208-1032

Socho (President): Haruo Nishihara (1982-90)

S. of Political Science and Economics

Dean: Mitsuro Uchida; *staff* 74 (111)

S. of Law

Dean: Koichi Sakurai; *staff* 94 (207)

S. of Literature I (including Philosophy, and Fine and Dramatic Arts)

Dean: Tetsuo Iwanami; *staff* 185 (202)

S. of Literature II (evening division)

Dean: Eiichi Takahashi; *staff* 185 (101)

S. of Education

Dean: Sadao Tsutsumi; *staff* 114 (269)

S. of Commerce

Dean: Osamu Nishizawa; *staff* 92 (87)

S. of Science and Engineering (including Architecture)

Dean: Hiroshi Hirayama; *staff* 226 (351)

S. of Social Sciences (evening division)

Dean: Hiromitsu Sato; *staff* 49 (98)

S. of Human Sciences

Dean: Kuniji Asai; *staff* 68 (33)

Graduate S. (Political Science, Economics, Law, Literature, Commerce, Science and Engineering)

I. of Social Sciences

Director: Hideo Mineshima; *staff* 6

Science and Engineering Research L.

Director: Takashi Onuki; *staff* 13

Kagami Memorial L. for Materials Science and Technology

Director: Eiichi Kato; *staff* 2

Systems Science I.

Director: Kyoichi Futagami; *staff* 15

I. of Comparative Law

Director: Yoichi Nagahama; *staff* 2

I. of Language Teaching

Director: Mitsuru Mizuno; *staff* 17 (29)

I. for Research in Business Administration

Director: Hiroshi Ishizuka

I. for Research in Contemporary Political and Economic Affairs

Director: Shozo Kobayashi

Advanced Research Ce. for Human Sciences

Director: Tsumoru Ushiyama

Ce. for Japanese Language

Director: Yoshiyuki Morita; *staff* 11 (27)

Ce. for Informatics

Director: Ken Hirose; *staff* 1 (8)

International D.

Director: Nobuo Hozumi; *staff* 2 (22)

Also senior high schools and college of technology.

Founded 1882 as Tokyo Senmon Gakko (College). Renamed Waseda University 1902. Reorganized 1949. Graduate schools established 1951. Governing bodies: the Board of Trustees; the Congregation; and the Executive Board of Directors with the President of the University as ex officio chairman.

Arrangements for co-operation with: University of Paris; University of Bonn; Moscow State University; University of Southern California; University of Augsburg; University of Sydney; Shanghai Jiaotong University; Fudan University; University of Stirling; McGill University; University of Rome; University College, Dublin; Hankuk University of Foreign Studies; University of Toronto; Korea University; De La Salle University; University of Chicago; Washington University; Beijing University; Nankai University; Thammasat University; Ecole supérieure de Commerce, Lyon; Georgetown University; Great Lakes Colleges; California State University; Oregon State System of Higher Education; California Private Universities and Colleges.

Academic Year: April to March (April-July; September-February).

Admission Requirements: Graduation from high school or equivalent or foreign equivalent, and entrance examination.

Fees (Yen): Tuition, 470,000-790,000 per annum, according to field of study.

Language of Instruction: Japanese.

Degrees and Diplomas: Gakushi, Bachelor–Seijigakushi, political science; Keizaigakushi, economics; Hogakushi, law; Bungakushi, literature; Kyoikugakushi, education; Shogakushi, commerce; Rigakushi, science; Kogakushi, engineering; Shakaikagakushi, social sciences; Shakaigakushi, human sciences, 4 yrs. Shushi, Master–Seijigakushushi, political science; Keizaigakushushi, economics; Hogakushushi, law; Bungakushushi, literature; Shogakushushi, commerce; Rigakushushi, science; Kogakushushi, engineering; Kyoikugakushushi, education, a further 2 yrs. Hakushi, Doctor–Seijigakuhakushi, political science; Keizaigakuhakushi, economics; Hogakuhakushi, law; Bungakuhakushi, literature; Shogakuhakushi, commerce; Kogakuhakushi, engineering; Rigakuhakushi, science, 3 yrs after Shushi.

Libraries: University Library, 1,400,000 vols.; Department and Institute Libraries, 1,678,000 vols.

Special Facilities (Museums, etc.): Tsubouchi Memorial Theatre Museum.

Publications: Waseda Political Studies; Waseda Economic Papers; Waseda Business and Economic Studies; Waseda Bulletin of Comparative Law; Journal of Human Development; Waseda Journal of Asia Studies; Reports of Materials Science and Technology; Report of the Science and Engineering Research Laboratory; Studies in Egyptian culture; schools andsociety reviews.

Press or Publishing House: Waseda University Press.

Academic Staff, 1990-91:

Rank	Full-time	Part-time
Kyoju (Professors)	777	–
Kyakuin-Kyoju (Professors)	19	15
Jokyoju (Associate Professors)	138	–
Koshi (Assistant Professors)	55	1970
Kyoyu (Teachers)	109	–
Total	1098	1985

Student Enrolment, 1990-91:

	Men	Women	Total
Of the country	37,607	8749	46,356
Of other countries	739	280	1019
Total	38,346	9029	47,375

Other Universities and University Institutions

National Institutions

4123 **KYOTO KYOIKU DAIGAKU**

Kyoto University of Education

1 Fujinomori-cho, Fushimi-ku, Kyoto-shi, Kyoto 612

Telephone: (75) 641-9281/8

Teacher Training (including Physical and other Specialized Education)

Also elementary, junior high, senior high, and kindergarten schools.

Founded 1876 as school, became university 1947. Formerly known as Kyoto Gakguei Daigaku. Residential facilities for academic staff and students.

Academic Year: April to March (April-September; October-March).

Admission Requirements: Graduation from senior high school or equivalent, and entrance examination.

Language of Instruction: Japanese.

Degrees and Diplomas: Gakushi, Bachelor–Kyoikugakushi, education; Gakgueigakushi, liberal arts, 4 yrs. Also Teaching Certificate.

Library: University Library, *c.* 163,000 vols.

Publication: Bulletin Series A (Literature) and B (Natural Science) (biannually).

Academic Staff: c. 130 (100).

Student Enrolment: c. 1720.

Public Institutions

4124 **AICHI KENRITSU DAIGAKU**

Aichi Prefectural University

3-28 Takada-cho, Mizuho-ku, Nagoya-shi, Aichi 467

Telephone: (52) 851-2191

F. of Letters

F. of Foreign Studies (British, American, French, and Spanish) (day and evening courses)

Also junior women's college.

Founded 1947, became university 1966. Governing body: the Board of Trustees. Residential facilities for academic staff.

Academic Year: April to March (April-September; October-March).

Admission Requirements: Graduation from high school or equivalent, and entrance examination.

Language of Instruction: Japanese.

Degrees and Diplomas: Gakushi, Bachelor, of Arts, 4 yrs.

Libraries: Central Library; specialized libraries.

Publication: Faculty Journals.

Academic Staff: c. 110 (120).

Student Enrolment: c. 1490.

4125 **FUKUOKA JOSHI DAIGAKU**

Fukuoka Women's University

1-1-1 Kasumigaoka, Higashi-ku, Fukuoka-shi, Fukuoka 813

Telephone: (92) 661-2411

Gakucho (President): Ryohei Matsuura (1985-90)

Kyokucho: Hiroshi Notohara

F. of Letters (Japanese and English)

Dean: Yoshimi Uryu; *staff* 19 (35)

F. of Domestic Science

Dean: Shuji Cho; *staff* 20 (63)

I. for Lifelong Education

Head: Makoto Aihara; *staff* 1 (1)

Founded 1923 as college, became university 1950. Residential facilities for some academic staff and *c.* 150 students.

Academic Year: April to February (April-July; September-October; October-February).

Admission Requirements: Graduation from high school and entrance examination.

Fees (Yen): Tuition, 339,600 per annum.

Language of Instruction: Japanese.

Degrees and Diplomas: Bungakushi, Bachelor of Letters; Kaseigakushi, Bachelor of Domestic Science, 4 yrs. Also Diploma in Dietetics and Teaching.

Library: University Library, 103,400 vols.

Publications: Bungei to Shiso (Literature and Thought); Bulletin of the Faculty of Home Life Science.

Academic Staff, 1988-89:

Rank	Full-time	Part-time
Kyoju (Professors)	20	57
Jokyoju (Associate Professors)	14	37
Koshi (Lecturers)	5	3
Joshu (Assistants)	11	5
Total	50	102

Student Enrolment, 1988-89:

	Women
Of the country	720
Of other countries	2
Total	722

4126 **GUNMA KENRITSU JOSHI DAIGAKU**

Gunma Prefectural Women's University

1395-1 Kaminote, Tamamura-machi, Sawa-gun, Gunma 370-11

Telephone: (270) 65-8511

F. of Letters

4127 **HIROSHIMA JOSHI DAIGAKU**

Hiroshima Women's University

1-1-71 Higashi-ujina, Minami-ku, Hiroshima-shi, Hiroshima 734

Telephone: (82) 251-5178

Gakucho (President): Imahori Seiji

F. of Letters

F. of Home Economics

Founded 1920 as Women's College, became Women's Junior College 1950 and university 1965. Residential facilities for academic staff who are officials of the prefectural government and for *c.* 100 students.

Academic Year: April to March (April-October; October-March).

Admission Requirements: Graduation from high school and entrance examination.

Language of Instruction: Japanese.

Degrees and Diplomas: Gakushi, Bachelor, 4 yrs. Also Teaching Certificate and Diploma in Dietetics, 4 yrs.

Library: c. 125,800 vols.

Publication: Bulletins (annually).

Academic Staff: c. 65.

Student Enrolment: c. 920.

4128 **HOSO DAIGAKU**

University of the Air

2-11 Wakaba, Chiba City 260

Telephone: (472) 76-5111

Fax: (472) 76-6130

Gakucho (President): Kazue Koda

Jimukyokucho (Secretary-General): Naomi Onodera

F. of Liberal Arts

Also 6 study centres in the Kanto area and japanese language courses for foreign students.

Founded 1983. Admitted first students 1985. Instruction is given by radio and television and students may attend formal lectures in 6 study centres in the Kanto area. Administered by the University of the Air Foundation and National Centre for the Development of Educational Broadcasting. Governing body: the Board of Trustees

Academic Year: April to March (April-September; October-March).

Admission Requirements: Graduation from high school or equivalent or foreign equivalent, and entrance examination.

Fees (Yen): 94,500 per annum, per 31 credits; non-degree students, 48,800 per annum, per 16 credits.

Degrees and Diplomas: Gakushi, Bachelor, of Liberal Arts, 4 yrs.

Library: 89,270 vols.

Publications: On Air (annually); Journal (quarterly).

Academic Staff, 1990:

Rank	Full-time	Part-time
Kyoju (Professors)	30	243
Jokyoju (Associate Professors)	22	26
Koshi (Assistant Professors)	2	509
Total	54	778

Student Enrolment, 1990:

	Men	Women	Total
Of the country	15,162	14,300	29,462
Of other countries	126	113	239
Total	15,288	14,413	29,701

4129 **KOCHI JOSHI DAIGAKU**

Kochi Women's University

5-10 Eikokuji-cho, Kochi-shi, Kochi 780

Telephone: (888) 73-2156

Fax: (888) 73-2156

Gakucho (President): Junko Ikegawa

F. of Literature

Dean: Shinyu Uku; *staff* 22 (38)

F. of Home Economics

Dean: Yoshihiko Hirami; *staff* 22 (38)

Founded 1947 as Kochi Prefectural Women's College, acquired present status 1949. Residential facilities for some academic staff and for 76 students.

Academic Year: April to March (April-October; October-March).

Admission Requirements: Graduation from high school and entrance examination.

Fees (Yen): Tuition, 151,200 per semester.

Language of Instruction: Japanese.

Degrees and Diplomas: Gakushi, Bachelor, of–Home Economics; Hygiene and Nursing; Letters, 4 yrs.

Library: University Library, *c.* 128,000 vols.

Publication: Bulletin (annually).

Academic Staff, 1990:

Rand	Full-time	Part-time
Kyoju (Professors)	28	–
Jokyoju (Associate Professors)	19	–
Koshi (Assistant Professors)	1	148
Joshu (Research Associates)	11	–
Total	59	148

Student Enrolment, 1990: c. 729 (Women).

4130 **KUMAMOTO JOSHI DAIGAKU**

Kumamoto Women's University

2432-1 Mizuarai, Kengunmachi, Kumamoto-shi, Kumamoto 862

Telephone: (96) 383-2929

Fax: (96) 384-6765

Gakucho (President): Yutaka Mutsugaki

Jimukyokucho (Secretary-General): Akitoshi Ito

F. of Letters (Japanese and English)

Dean: Yoshifumi Hirado; *staff* 22

F. of Living Science (Food and Nutrition, and Environment)

Dean: Naokazu Ota; *staff* 33

Founded 1947 as Kumamoto Prefectural Women's College, acquired present status 1949.

Arrangements for co-operation with San Myung Women's University

Academic Year: April to March (April-September; October-March).

Admission Requirements: Graduation from high school or equivalent or foreign equivalent and entrance examination.

Fees (Yen): Tuition, 339,600 per annum.

Language of Instruction: Japanese.

Degrees and Diplomas: Gakushi, Bachelor–Bungakushi, arts; Kaseigakushi, home economics, 4 yrs.

Library: University library, 124,677 vols.

Publications: Journal; Studies in Domestic Culture (both annually).

Academic Staff, 1990:

Rank	Full-time	Part-time
Kyoju (Professors)	24	21
Jokyoju (Associate Professors)	16	19
Koshi (Assistant Professors)	5	4
Joshu (Research Associates)	10	18
Total	55	63

Student Enrolment, 1990: 863 (Women).

4131 **NAGASAKI-KENRITSU KOKUSAI-KEIZAI DAIGAKU**

Nagasaki Prefectural College of International Economics

123 Kawashimo-cho, Sasebo, Nagasaki 858

Telephone: (956) 47-2191

Gakucho (President): Yakaichi Sakai

Jimukyokucho (Secretary-General): Ryohei Matsuda

F. of Economics

Founded 1951 as junior college of English and commerce. Acquired present status and title 1967. Governing body: the Kyojukai (Faculty Council). Residential facilities for academic staff.

Academic Year: April to March (April-September; October-March).

Admission Requirements: Graduation from senior high school or equivalent or foreign equivalent, and entrance examination.

Fees (Yen): Tuition, 339,000 per annum.

Language of Instruction: Japanese.

Degrees and Diplomas: Gakushi, Bachelor–Keizaigakushi, economics, 4 yrs.

Library: c. 76,500 vols.

Publications: Journal of Liberal Arts and Economics (quarterly); The Research and the Study (biannually).

Academic Staff, 1990: c. 34 (39).

Student Enrolment, 1990:

Men	Women	Total
731	171	902

4132 **OKINAWA KENRITSU GEIJUTSU DAIGAKU**

Okinawa Prefectural College of Fine Arts

1-4 Tonokura-cho, Shuri, Naha-shi, Okinawa 903

Telephone: (988) 31-5000

F. of Fine Arts

Founded 1928.

Academic Year: April to March (April-October; October-March).

Admission Requirements: Graduation from high school or equivalent, and entrance examination.

Language of Instruction: Japanese.

Degrees and Diplomas: Geijutsugakushi, Bachelor of Fine Arts, 4 yrs.

4133 **SHIMONOSEKI SHIRITSU DAIGAKU**

Shimonoseki City College

2-1-1 Daigaku-cho, Shimonoseki-shi, Yamuguchi 751

Telephone: (832) 52-0288

Fax: (832) 52-8099

Gakucho (President): Etsuji Kinoshita (1986-92)

Jimukyokucho (Secretary-General): Haruo Inoue

F. of Economics (including International Commerce)

Founded 1956 as junior college, reorganized by government with present status 1962. Residential facilities for 7 academic staff.

Academic Year: April to March (April-October; November-March).

Admission Requirements: Graduation from high school or equivalent, and entrance examination.

Fees (Yen): 339,600 per annum.

Language of Instruction: Japanese.

Degrees and Diplomas: Gakushi, Bachelor–Keizaigakushi, economics; Shogakushi, commerce, 4 yrs.

Library: Central Library, 100,000 vols.

Publication: Shoukei Ronshu (Review) (three times a year).

Academic Staff, 1989-90:

Rank	Full-time	Part-time
Kyoju (Professors)	24	–
Jokyoju (Associate Professors)	15	–
Koshi (Assistant Professors)	7	51
Total	46	51

Student Enrolment, 1989-90:

	Men	Women	Total
Of the country	1539	356	1895
Of other countries	13	3	16
Total	1552	359	1911

4134 **SHIZUOKA JOSHI DAIGAKU**

Shizuoka Women's University

409 Yata, Shizuoka-shi, Shizuoka 422

Telephone: (542) 62-0336

Gakucho (President): Koji Uchizono (1985-89)

Jimukyokucho: Kanji Yamaguchi

F. of Letters

Dean: Yutaka Haraguchi; *staff* 26 (25)

F. of Food and Clothing Sciences

Dean: Ryonosuke Shinba; *staff* 34 (24)

Founded 1951 as junior women's college, became university 1967. Governing body: the University Council. Residential facilities for academic staff.

Academic Year: April to March (April-September; October-March).

Admission Requirements: Graduation from high school or equivalent or foreign equivalent and entrance examination.

Fees (Yen): Tuition, 300,000-450,000 per annum.

Language of Instruction: Japanese.

Degrees and Diplomas: Bungakushi, Bachelor of Arts; Kaseigakushi, Bachelor of Home Economics, 4 yrs.

Library: 78,371 vols.

Publication: Report (annually).

Academic Staff, 1986-87:

Rank	Full-time	Part-time
Kyoju (Professors)	17	–
Jokyoju (Associate Professors)	20	–
Koshi (Assistant Professors)	4	49
Joshu (Research Associates)	16	–
Total	57	49

Student Enrolment, 1986-87: 617 (Women).

4135 **TAKASAKI KEIZAI DAIGAKU**

Takasaki City University of Economics

1300 Kaminamie-machi, Takasaki-shi, Gunma 370

Telephone: (273) 43-5417

Fax: (273) 43-4830

Gakucho (President): Manabu Ishi

Jimukyokucho: Masao Honda

F. of Economics

; *staff* 51 (77)

I. for Research of Regional Economy

Head: Hideo Hasegawa; *staff* 2 (30)

Founded 1952 as junior college, acquired present status 1957. Residential facilities for academic staff and for *c.* 100 students.

Arrangements for co-operation with the State University of West Texas.

Academic Year: April to March (April-July; September-February).

Admission Requirements: Graduation from high school or equivalent, and entrance examination.

Fees (Yen): 339,600.

Language of Instruction: Japanese.

Degrees and Diplomas: Keizaigakushi, Bachelor of Economics; Keieigakushi, Bachelor of Business Administration, 4 yrs.

Library: c. 120,113 vols.

Publications: Journal; Bulletin of Research Institute of Regional Economics.

Academic Staff: c. 50 (65).

Student Enrolment, 1989-90:

	Men	Women	Total
Of the country	1740	270	2010
Of other countries	11	7	18
Total	1751	277	2028

4136 **TOKYO TORITSU KAGAKU GIJUTSU DAIGAKU**

Tokyo Metropolitan Institute of Technology

6-6 Asahigaoka, Hino-shi, Tokyo 191

F. of Engineering

4137 **TSURU BUNKA DAIGAKU**

Tsuru University

3-8-1 Tahara, Tsuru-shi, Yamanashi 402

Telephone: (554) 43-4341

Gakucho (President): Kaoru Ueda (1984-88)

Jimukyokucho: Toyomaru Sonoda

D. of Education

Head: Yusuke Arimura; *staff* 40 (71)

D. of Japanese Literature

Head: Takeshi Nakano; *staff* 13 (17)

D. of English Literature

Head: Yasuhisa Mikami; *staff* 17 (33)

Also elementary school.

Founded 1955 as Tsuru Junior College, acquired present status and title 1960. Financially supported by tuitionfees, government and municipal subsidies. Residential facilities for academic staff.

Academic Year: April to March (April-September; October-March).

Admission Requirements: Graduation from high school and entrance examination.

Fees (Yen): 300,000 per annum.

Language of Instruction: Japanese.

Degrees and Diplomas: Gakushi, Bachelor–Bungakushi, arts, 4 yrs.

Library: 100,804 vols.

Publications: Bulletins of English Literature; Japanese Literature; Primary Education; Tsuru University Review (all annually).

Academic Staff, 1986-87:

Rank	Full-time	Part-time
Kyoju (Professors)	37	–
Jokyoju (Assistant Professors)	29	–
Koshi (Lecturers)	4	121
Total	70	121

Student Enrolment, 1986-87:

	Men	Women	Total
Of the country	1001	1356	2357

4138 **YAMAGUCHI JOSHI DAIGAKU**

Yamaguchi Women's University

3-2-1 Sakurabatake, Yamaguchi-shi, Yamaguchi 753

Telephone: (839) 28-0211

Gakucho (President): Seiji Nakayama (1984-88)

Jimukyokucho: Kazuo Sumikawa

F. of Letters

Dean: Sachiko Ueno: *staff* 35 (20)

F. of Life Science and Home Economics

Dean Hideo Nakayama; *staff* 35 (20)

Also kindergarten school.

Founded 1941, acquired present status and title 1975. Financed by the Yamaguchi prefectural authorities. Residential facilities for academic staff and 160 students.

Academic Year: April to March (April-October; October-March).

Admission Requirements: Graduation from high school or equivalent or foreign equivalent, and entrance examination.

Fees (Yen): 252,000 per annum.

Language of Instruction: Japanese.

Degrees and Diplomas: Gakushi, Bachelor, of–Arts; Home Economics, 4 yrs. Diplomas in–Nutrition; Clothing; Library Science, 3-4 yrs. Teaching Certificates, 4 yrs.

Library: c. 80,000 vols.

Publications: Bulletin: Section I, Humanities and Social Science; Section II, Natural Sciences (annually).

Academic Staff, 1986-87:

Rank	Full-time
Kyoju (Professors)	28
Jokyoju (Assistant Professors)	13
Koshi (Instructors)	8
Joshu (Assistants)	13
Total	62

Student Enrolment, 1986-87:

	Women
Of the country	680

Private Institutions

4139 **AICHI SHUKUTOKU DAIGAKU**
Aichi Shukutoku College
9 Katahira, Nagakute-cho, Aichi-gun, Aichi 480-11

F. of Literature

4140 **AKITA KEIZAI DAIGAKU**
Akita University of Economics and Law
46-1 Morisiwa, Tezakura, Akita-shi, Akita 010

F. of Economics
F. of Law
Founded 1964.

4141 **AOMORI DAIGAKU**
Aomori University
248 Abeno, Kohata, Aomori-shi, Aomori 030
Telephone: (177) 38-2114

F. of Business Administration
Founded 1962, reorganized 1968.

4142 **ASAHIKAWA DAIGAKU**
Asahikawa College
113-3-23 Nagayama, Asahikawa-shi, Hokkaido 079
Telephone: (166) 48-3121

F. of Economics
Founded 1968.

4143 **ASHIKAGA KOGYO DAIGAKU**
Ashikaga Institute of Technology
268-1 Omae-cho, Ashikaga-shi, Tochigi 326
Telephone: (284) 62-0605

F. of Engineering
Founded 1967.

4144 **ATOMI GAKUEN JOSHI DAIGAKU**
Atomi Gakuen Women's College
1-9-6 Nakano, Niiza-shi, Saitama 352
Telephone: (484) 78-3333

F. of Literature
Founded 1969.

4145 **BAIKO JOGAKUIN DAIGAKU**
365 Myoji-cho, Yoshimi, Shimonoseki-shi, Yamaguchi 759-65
Telephone: (832) 56-1111

F. of Letters
Founded 1964, reorganized 1967.

4146 **BEPPU DAIGAKU**
Beppu University
82 Kita-shigaki, Beppu-shi, Oita 874
Telephone: (977) 67-0101

F. of Literature
Also kindergarten, high schools, and junior college.

Founded 1946 as Beppu Women's Professional School, acquired present status 1954. Residential facilities for academic staff and *c.* 200 students.

Academic Year: April to March (April-September; September-March).

Admission Requirements: Graduation from high school or equivalent, and entrance examination.

Language of Instruction: Japanese.

Degrees and Diplomas: Bungakushi, Bachelor of Arts, 4 yrs. Also teaching qualifications.

Library: University Library, *c.* 50,000 vols.

Special Facilities (Museums, etc.): Jodai Museum.

Publications: Memoirs; Bulletin of Japanese Literature.

Academic Staff: *c.* 40.

Student Enrolment: *c.* 1000.

4147 **BUNKYO DAIGAKU**
Bunkyo University
3337 Minami-Ogishima, Koshigaya-shi, Saitama 343

F. of Education
F. of Human Science
F. of Information and Communication
F. of Language and Literature

4148 **CHIBA KEIAI KEIZAI DAIGAKU**
Chiba Keiai College of Economics
1-5-21 Anagawa, Chiba-shi, Chiba 260
Telephone: (472) 65-7333

F. of Economics
Founded 1951, reorganized 1966.

4149 **CHUKYO JOSHI DAIGAKU**
Chukyo Women's University
55 Nadakayama Yokone-cho, Obu-shi, Aichi 474
Telephone: (562) 46-1291
Fax: (562) 48-4621
Gakucho (President): Kuniko Tanioka
Jimukyokucho (Secretary-General): Kunio Ishihara

F. of Physical Education
Dean: Tetsuo Meshizuka; *staff* 14 (4)
F. of Home Economics
Dean: Akira Ikeda; *staff* 22 (2)

Founded 1950 as junior college, acquired present status 1963. Residential facilities for students.

Arrangements for co-operation with Ewha Women's University.

Academic Year: April to March (April-September; October-March).

Admission Requirements: Graduation from high school or equivalent, and entrance examination.

Language of Instruction: Japanese.

Degrees and Diplomas: Gakushi, Bachelor, of Physical Education, 4 yrs.

Library: College Library, *c.* 14,000 vols.

Academic Staff, 1990: 42.

Student Enrolment, 1990: 1345 (Women).

4150 **CHUO GAKUIN DAIGAKU**
451 Kujike, Abiko-shi, Chiba 270-11
Telephone: (471) 82-1311

F. of Commerce
F. of Law
Founded 1966.

4151 **DAIDO KOGYO DAOGALI**
Daido Institute of Technology
2-21 Daido-cho, Minami-ku, Nagoya-shi, Aichi 457
Telephone: (52) 612-3833/6111
Gakucho (President): Shoshiro Kanaya (1985-87)

D. of Mechanical Engineering
Head: Zenji Andoh; *staff* 24 (6)
D. of Construction Engineering
Head: Hideo Sato; *staff* 20 (7)
D. of Applied Electronics
Head: Ruyuzou Yamada; *staff* 10
Information Processing Ce.
Head: Hanji Satone; *staff* 1 (3)
Materials Engineering L.
Head: Taro Ishikawa; *staff* 21

Founded 1964. Governing body: Board of Directors comprizing 9 members.

Arrangements for co-operation with: University of Oregon; Oregon State University.

Academic Year: April to March (April-October; October-March).

Admission Requirements: Graduation from high school or equivalent or foreign equivalent and entrance examination.

Fees (Yen): Tuition, 1,097,000 per annum.

Language of Instruction: Japanese.

Degrees and Diplomas: Gakushi, Bachelor–Kogakushi, engineering, 4 yrs.

Library: 80,000 vols.

Publication: Bulletin (annually).

Academic Staff, 1986-87:

Rank	Full-time	Part-time
Kyoju (Professors)	34	–
Jokyoju (Associate Professors)	23	–
Koshi (Assistant Professors)	29	73
Joshu (Research Associates)	6	–
Total	92	73

Student Enrolment, 1986-87:

	Men	Women	Total
Of the country	2221	21	2242
Of other countries	1	–	1
Total	2222	21	2243*

*Also 2253 external students.

4152 **DAIICHI KEIZAI DAIGAKU**

Daiichi College of Commerce and Industry

3-11-25 Gojo, Dazaifu-shi, Fukuoka 818-01

Telephone: (92) 922-5131

F. of Economics

Founded 1968.

4153 **DAIICHI KOGYO DAIGAKU**

Dai Ichi University, College of Technology

1-10-2 Chuo, Kokubu-shi, Kagoshima 899-43

Telephone: (995) 45-0640

F. of Technology

4154 **DAIICHI YAKKA DAIGAKU**

Daiichi College of Pharmaceutical Sciences

93 Tamagawa-cho, Minami-ku, Fukuoka-shi, Fukuoka 815

Telephone: (92) 54-0161

F. of Pharmaceutical Sciences

Founded 1960. Some residential facilities.

Academic Year: April to March (April-October; October-February).

Admission Requirements: Graduation from high school or foreign equivalent, and entrance examination.

Language of Instruction: Japanese.

Degrees and Diplomas: Yakugakushi, Bachelor of Pharmacy, 4 yrs. Yakugakushushi, Master of Pharmacy, a further 2 yrs.

Academic Staff: c. 70 (30).

Student Enrolment: c. 1000.

4155 **DOHO DAIGAKU**

Doho University

7-1 Inabaji-cho, Nakamura-ku, Nagoya-shi, Aichi 453

Telephone: (52) 411-1111

F. of Literature

F. of Social Welfare

Founded 1921, reorganized 1950.

Academic Year: April to March (April-July; September-December; January-March).

Admission Requirements: Graduation from high school and entrance examination.

Language of Instruction: Japanese.

Degrees and Diplomas: Gakushi, Bachelor, of–Sociology; Letters, 4 yrs.

Library: University Library, c. 40,000 vols.

Publication: Doho Gakuho.

Academic Staff: c. 60.

Student Enrolment: c. 950.

4156 **DOHTO DAIGAKU**

Dohto University

7 Ochiishi-cho, Mombetsu-shi, Hokkaido

Telephone: 1582-4-8101

Fax: 1582-4-8101

Gakucho (President): Jun Sakurai (1978-)

F. of Social Welfare

Dean: Masaharu Higashino; *staff* 14 (6)

F. of Fine Arts (including Design, Architecture)

Dean: Osamu Satoh; *staff* 17 (2)

D. for General Education

Dean: Kiyoshi Saitoh; *staff* 19

Welfare Research I.

Assistant Director: Nobuyuki Takahashi; *staff* 9 (2)

Design Research I.

Director: Miyoki Hatakeyama; *staff* 12

Marine Biology Research I.

Director: Masashi Mitani; *staff* 5

Founded 1978.

Arrangements for co-operation with: Kyong Hee University; Dong-Eui University; University of Manila; Tennessee Technological University; University of Alaska, Anchorage; Oregon State University; Hawaii Pacific College; University of La Verne; Baker University; Franklin University; Gardner-Webb College; University of Calgary; Ecole nationale supérieure des Arts decoratifs, Paris; University of Stockholm; University of Iceland.

Admission Requirements: Graduation from high school and entrance examination.

Fees (Yen): 685,400-786,600 per annum.

Degrees and Diplomas: Gakushi, Bachelor, 4 yrs.

Library: c. 40,000 vols.

Publications: Bulletins, Faculty of Social Welfare; Faculty of Fine Arts; General Education; Design in Northern Japan; Northern Social Welfare (all annually).

Academic Staff, 1990:

Rank	Full-time	Part-time
Kyoju (Professors)	17	–
Jokyoju (Associate Professors)	19	–
Koshi (Lecturers)	13	8
Joshu (Assistant Lecturer)	1	–
Total	50	8

Student Enrolment, 1990:

	Men	Women	Total
Of the country	1113	145	1258
Of other countries	2	3	5
Total	1115	148	1263

4157 **EICHI DAIGAKU**

Eichi University

2-18-2 Nakoji, Amagasaki-shi, Hyogo 661

Telephone: (6) 491-5083

F. of Liberal Arts

Founded 1963 as a Catholic university under the authority of the Archbishop of Osaka. Recognized by the Ministry of Education, Science and Culture. Financially supported by tuition fees, government subsidy, and donations.

Academic Year: April to March (April-September; October-February).

Admission Requirements: Graduation from high school or equivalent or foreign equivalent, and entrance examination.

Language of Instruction: Japanese.

Degrees and Diplomas: Gakushi, Bachelor, of–Arts; Theology, 4 yrs. Also teaching qualifications.

Library: University Library, c. 54,500 vols.

Publication: Sapientia (annually).

Academic Staff: c. 50 (25).

Student Enrolment: c. 1040.

4158 **FERISU JOGAKUIN DAIGAKU**

Ferris Women's College

37 Yamate-cho, Naka-ku, Yokohama-shi, Kanagawa 231

Telephone: (45) 662-4521

Gakucho (President): Satoshi Oguro (1985-89)

Jimbucho: Ichirou Kikuchi

D. of English Language and Literature
Head: Masaru Makiuchi; *staff* 10 (31)
D. of Japanese Language and Literature
Head: Junnosuke Fukuda; *staff* 7 (19)
Also junior college, and junior and senior high schools.

Founded 1870 as school by the Dutch Reformed Mission Board, became Junior college 1950 and acquired present title 1965. Governing body: the Board of Trustees, comprising 18 members.

Academic Year: April to March (April-September; October-March).

Admission Requirements: Graduation from high school and entrance examination.

Fees (Yen): Registration, 300,000; tuition, 450,000.

Languages of Instruction: Japanese, English, French and German.

Degrees and Diplomas: Bungakushi, Bachelor of Arts, 4 yrs.

Library: College Library, 91,000 vols.

Publication: Kiyoh (Ferris Studies, annually).

Academic Staff, 1986-87:

Rank	Full-time	Part-time
Kyoju (Professors)	15	–
Jokyoju (Assistant Professors)	11	–
Koshi (Instructors)	3	79
Total	29	79

Student Enrolment, 1986-87:

	Women
Of the country	914
Of other countries	7
Total	921

4159 **FUJI DAIGAKU**
Fuji University
450-3 Shimoneko, Hanemaki-shi, Iwate 025
Telephone: (198) 23-6221

F. of Economics

4160 **FUJI JOSHI DAIGAKU**
Fuji Women's College
Nishi 2, Kita16, Kita-ku, Sapporo-shi, Hokkaido 001
Telephone: (11) 736-0311
Gakucho (President): Yoshiko Nagata (1985-)
Jimukyokucho: Hideharu Kondo

English Literature and Japanese Literature
Also kindergarten, junior, and senior high schools.

Founded 1925 as Fuji High School for Girls by German Franciscan Sisters. Acquired present status and title 1961. A private institution financially supported by tuition fees. Governing body: the Board of Trustees, comprising 11 sisters of the Franciscan Order, 1 priest, and 1 layman. Residential facilities for academic staff and for 100 students.

Academic Year: April to March (April-September; October-March).

Admission Requirements: Graduation from high school or recognized equivalent, and entrance examination.

Fees (Yen): 350,000 per annum.

Language of Instruction: Japanese.

Degrees and Diplomas: Bungakushi, Bachelor of Letters, 4 yrs. Teaching diplomas for high and middle schools.

Library: College Library, 165,000 vols.

Publication: Bulletin (collection of research papers, annually).

Academic Staff, 1986-87:

Rank	Full-time	Part-time
Kyoju (Professors)	24	17
Jokyoju (Assistant Professors)	1	9
Koshi (Instructors)	–	3
Total	25	29

Student Enrolment, 1986-87: 542 (Women).

4161 **FUKUOKA KOGYO DAIGAKU**
Fukuoka Institute of Technology
3-30-1 Wajirohigashi, Higashi-ku, Fukuoka-shi, Fukuoka 811-02
Telephone: (92) 606-3131
Fax: (92) 606-8923
Gakucho (President): Shigeo Takata
Jimukyokucho (Secretary-General): Hideo Honda

F. of Engineering
Dean: Shigeo Takata; *staff* 100 (80)
Electronics Research L.
Head: Tomihoko Katoo; *staff* 2 (1530)
Computer and Information Research L.
Head: Tuneo Tamachi; *staff* 10 (3)

Founded 1963.

Academic Year: April to March (April-September; October-Mrach).

Admission Requirements: Graduation from high school or equivalent, and entrance examination.

Fees (Yen): 1,000,000.

Language of Instruction: Japanese

Publications: Reports of the Electronics Research Laboratory (annually); Research Bulletin (biannually)

Student Enrolment, 1990: 740.

4162 **GIFU JOSHI DAIGAKU**
Gifu Women's University
80 Taromaru, Gifu-shi, Gifu 501-25
Telephone: (582) 29-2211

F. of Home Economics
F. of Literature
Founded 1967.

4163 **GIFU KEIZAI DAIGAKU**
Gifu College of Economics
5-5 Kitakata-cho, Ogaki-shi, Gifu 503
Telephone: (584) 74-5151

F. of Economics

Founded 1967. Governing body: the Board of Directors. Financed mainly from tuition fees. Some residential facilities for students. Some residential facilities for students.

Academic Year: April to March (April-September; October-March).

Admission Requirements: Graduation from high school or equivalent, and entrance examination.

Language of Instruction: Japanese.

Degrees and Diplomas: Keisaigakushi, Bachelor of Economics, 4 yrs.

Libraries: c. 26,000 vols (in Japanese); c. 10,600 (in other languages).

Publication: Journal (quarterly).

Academic Staff: c. 40 (60).

Student Enrolment: c. 2200.

4164 **HACHINOHE DAIGAKU**
Hachinohe University
13-98 Mihono, Hachinohe-shi, Aomori 031
Telephone: (178) 25-2711

F. of Commerce
Founded 1981.

4165 **HACHINOHE KOGYO DAIGAKU**
Hachinohe Institute of Technology
88-1 Aza-Obiraki, Oaza-Myo, Hachinohe-shi, Aomori 031
Telephone: (178) 25-3111

F. of Engineering (Mechanical, Industrial Equipment, Electrical, Civil, and Architectural)
D. of General Education

Founded 1972. Governing body: the Board of Regents.

Academic Year: April to March (April-September; September-March).

Admission Requirements: Graduation from high school and entrance examination.

Language of Instruction: Japanese.

Degrees and Diplomas: Kogakushi, Bachelor of Engineering, 4 yrs.

Library: c. 35,000 vols.

Academic Staff: c. 90 (25).

Student Enrolment: c. 1720.

4166 **HAKODATE DAIGAKU**
Hakodate University
51-1 Takaoka-cho, Hakodate-shi, Hokkaido 042
Telephone: (138) 57-1181

F. of Commerce
Founded 1953, reorganized 1968.

4167 **HAKUOH DAIGAKU**
Hakuoh University
1177 Daigyoji, Oyoma-shi, Tochigi 323
Telephone: (285) 222-1111

F. of Management

4168 **HANNAN DAIGAKU**
University of Hannan
5-4-33 Amamihigashi, Matsubara-shi, Osaka 580
Telephone: (0723) 32-1224

F. of Commerce
F. of Economics

Founded 1965. Some residential facilities for students.

Academic Year: April to February (April-July; September-February).

Admission Requirements: Graduation from high school or equivalent, and entrance examination.

Language of Instruction: Japanese.

Degrees and Diplomas: Bachelor of Commercial Science.

Academic Staff: c. 50.

Student Enrolment: c. 650.

4169 **HIROSAKI GAKUIN DAIGAKU**
Hirosaki Gakuin University
13-1 Minori-cho, Hirosaki-shi, Aomori 036

F. of Literature (for women)

Academic Year: April to March (April-September; October-March).

Admission Requirements: Graduation from high school and entrance examination.

Language of Instruction: Japanese.

Degrees and Diplomas: Bachelor of Arts, 4 yrs.

4170 **HIROSHIMA-DENKI DAIGAKU**
Hiroshima Denki Institute of Technology
6-20-1 Nakano, Aki-ku, Hiroshima-shi, Hiroshima 739-03
Telephone: (82) 893-0381

F. of Engineering

Also junior college and high school.

Founded 1964 as junior college, acquired present status and title 1966. Governing body: the Board of Directors.

Academic Year: April to March (April-September; October-March).

Admission Requirements: Graduation from high school and entrance examination. Provisions for recognition of foreign qualifications.

Language of Instruction: Japanese.

Degrees and Diplomas: Gakushi, Bachelor, of Engineering, 4 yrs.

Library: Central Library, *c.* 38,070 vols.

Publication: Research Report (annually).

Academic Staff: c. 60 (30).

Student Enrolment: c. 1290.

4171 **HIROSHIMA JOGAKUIN DAIGAKU**
Hiroshima Jogakuin Women's College
4-13-1 Ushita-Higashi, Higashi-ku, Hiroshima-shi, Hiroshima 730
Telephone: (82) 228-0386

F. of Literature

Also junior college (home economics) and kindergarten and high schools.

Founded 1886 as school by American Methodist Episcopal Church. Became college 1932, and acquired present status 1949. Governing bodies: the Board of Trustees, comprising 15 members; the Council, of 31 members. Residential facilities for *c.* 60 students.

Academic Year: April to March (April-September; October-March).

Admission Requirements: Graduation from high school or equivalent or foreign equivalent, and entrance examination.

Language of Instruction: Japanese.

Degrees and Diplomas: Bungakushi, Bachelor of Arts, 4 yrs.

Library: College Library, *c.* 75,000 vols.

Publication: Research Bulletin (annually).

Academic Staff: c. 55 (45).

Student Enrolment: c. 1270.

4172 **HIROSHIMA KOGYO DAIGAKU**
Hiroshima Institute of Technology
2-1-1 Miyake, Saiki-ku, Hiroshima-shi, Hiroshima 731-51
Telephone: (829) 21-3121
Fax: (829)22-1480
Gakucho (President): Nboru Tsuru (1987-)
Jimukyokucho (Secretary-General): Hitoshi Itoh

F. of Engineering
Engineering Research Ce.
Director: Y. Komura

Also high schools.

Founded 1961, reorganized 1963. Governing body: the Board of Directors, comprising 10 members. Residential facilities for academic staff.

Academic Year: April to March (April-September; October-March).

Admission Requirements: Graduation from high school and entrance examination.

Fees (Yen): Tuition, 770,000 per annum.

Language of Instruction: Japanese.

Degrees and Diplomas: Gakushi, Bachelor–Kogakushi, 4 years. Shushi, Master, a further 2 years.

Library: 155,807 vols.

Publication: Research Bulletin (annually).

Academic Staff, 1990-91:

Rank	Full-time
Gakucho (President)	1
Kyoju (Professors)	100
Jokyoju (Assistant Professors)	50
Koshi (Instructors)	18
Joshu (Assistants)	2
Total	171

Student Enrolment, 1990-91:

Men	Women	Total
3710	101	3811

4173 **HOKKAIGAKUEN KITAMI DAIGAKU**
235 Hokk, Kitami-shi, Hokkaido 090
Telephone: (157) 22-2721

F. of Commerce

Academic Year: April to March (April-September; October-March).

Admission Requirements: Graduation from high school and entrance examination.

Language of Instruction: Japanese.

Degrees and Diplomas: Shogakushi, Bachelor of Commerce, 4 yrs.

4174 **HOKKAIDO KOGYO DAIGAKU**
Hokkaido Institute of Technology
419-2 Maeda, Teine, Nishi-ku, Sapporo-shi, Hokkaido 061-24
Telephone: (11) 681-2161

F. of Engineering

Founded 1967. A private institution under the authority of the Shoshi-Gakuen (Educational Foundation). Financially supported by tuition fees and State subsidies. Residential facilities for *c.* 80 students.

Academic Year: April to March (April-July; September-March).

Admission Requirements: Graduation from senior high school and entrance examination.

Language of Instruction: Japanese.

Degrees and Diplomas: Gakushi, Bachelor, of Engineering, 4 yrs.

Library: c. 58,000 vols.

Publication: Memoirs of the Institute (annually).

Academic Staff: c. 120 (60).

Student Enrolment: c. 2070.

4175 **HOKKAIDO TOKAI DAIGAKU**
Hokkaido Tokai University
224 Chuwa, Kamui-cho, Asahikawa-shi, Hokkaido 070
Telephone: (166) 61-5111

F. of Engineering

Founded 1972 as junior college of design, acquired present status and title 1977. Governing body: the Board of Trustees. Some residential facilities for academic staff.

Academic Year: April to March (April-September; October-March).

Admission Requirements: Graduation from high school and entrance examination.

Language of Instruction: Japanese.

Degrees and Diplomas: Degree and Diploma: Geijutsukogakushi, Bachelor of Art Technology, 4 yrs.
Library: Matsumae Memorial Library, *c.* 35,000 vols.
Publications: Journal of Hokkaido Tokai University; Journal of Research Institute.
Press or Publishing House: University Press.
Academic Staff: c. 35 (25).
Student Enrolment: c. 680.

4176 **IBARAKI KIRISUTOKYO DAIGAKU**
Ibaraki Christian College
6-11-1 Omika-cho, Hitachi-shi, Ibaraki 319-12
Telephone: (294) 52-3215

F. of Literature
Also junior college and senior and junior high schools.
Founded 1967. Governing body: the Board of Trustees. Residential facilities for students.
Arrangements for co-operation with Oklahoma Christian College.
Academic Year: April to March (April-September; October-March).
Admission Requirements: Graduation from high school and entrance examination.
Languages of Instruction: Japanese and English.
Degrees and Diplomas: Gakushi, Bachelor, of Arts, 4 yrs.
Library: c. 40,000 vols
Special Facilities (Museums, etc.): College Museum.
Publication: Journal (annually).
Academic Staff: c. 70.
Student Enrolment: c. 2820.

4177 **IKUTOKU KOGYO DAIGAKU**
Ikutoku Technical University
1030 Shimo-ogino, Atsugi-shi, Kanagawa 243-02
Telephone: (462) 41-1211
Gakucho (President): Kikuo Oki
Jimukyokucho: Yukiniko Baba

F. of Engineering
Founded 1968.
Academic Year: April to March (April-September; October-March).
Admission Requirements: Graduation from high school and entrance examination.
Fees (Yen): Registration, 200,000; tuition, 680,000 per annum.
Language of Instruction: Japanese.
Degrees and Diplomas: Gakushi, Bachelor, of Engineering, 4 yrs.
Library: 100,000 vols.
Publication: Research Reports (annually).
Academic Staff, 1986-87:

Rank	Full-time	Part-time
Kyoju (Professors)	60	–
Jokyoju (Assistant Professors)	30	–
Koshi (Lecturers)	11	–
Joshu (Assistants)	22	–
Others	30	78
Total	153	78

Student Enrolment, 1986-87:

	Men	Women	Total
Of the country	2962	40	3002

4178 **JOBU DAIGAKU**
634 Toyazuka-machi, Isezaki-shi, Gumma 372
Telephone: (270) 32-1011

F. of Commercial Science
F. of Management and Information Science
Founded 1968.

4179 **JOSHI BIJUTSU DAIGAKU**
Women's College of Fine Arts
1-49-8 Wada, Suguinami-ku, Tokyo 166
Cables: Tokyo 7-8381
Telephone: (3) 382-2271

F. of Arts (Painting, Design, and Plastic Arts)
Also junior college.
founded 1900 as school, became college 1929. Reorganized 1949. Residential facilities for *c.* 440 students.
Academic Year: April to March (April-September; October-March).
Admission Requirements: Graduation from high school or equivalent, and entrance examination.
Language of Instruction: Japanese.
Degrees and Diplomas: Bachelor of Fine Arts, 4 yrs.
Library: c. 83,800 vols.
Publication: Bulletin (biannually).
Academic Staff: c. 70 (100).
Student Enrolment: c. 1210.

4180 **KAGOSHIMA JOSHI DAIGAKU**
1904 Uchi, Hayato-cho, Aira-gun, Kagoshima 899-51
Telephone: (995) 43-1111

F. of Literature
Founded 1978.

4181 **KAGOSHIMA KEIZAI DAIGAKU**
Kagoshima Keizai University
8850 Shimofukomoto-cho, Kagoshima-shi, Kagoshima 891-01
Telephone: (992) 61-3211
Gakucho (President): Noriyoshi Nokuo
Jimukyokucho (Secretary-General): Kiyonori Yamaguchi

F. of Economics
Dean: Toorju Tajiri; *staff* 57 (32)
F. of Sociology
Dean: Kinichi Yamashita; *staff* 37 (32)
I. for Regional Studies (Sociology)
Head: Takahiko Manabe; *staff* 2
Founded 1932 as college of commerce, acquired present status 1950.
Academic Year: April to March (April-October; October-March).
Admission Requirements: Graduation from high school or equivalent, and entrance examination.
Fees (Yen): 452,000-697,100 per annum
Language of Instruction: Japanese.
Degrees and Diplomas: Gakushi, Bachelor–Keizaigakushi, economics; Keieigakushi, management; Shakaigakush, sociology, 4 yrs.
Library: College Library, *c.* 207,000 vols.
Publications: Kagoshima Keidai Ronshu (Studies of Cultural and Social Sciences) (quarterly). Kagoshima Keizai Daigaku Shakaigakubu Ronshu (quarterly); Regional Studies (three times a year).
Academic Staff: c. 50.
Student Enrolment, 1990:

	Men	Women	Total
Of the country	3260	206	3466

4182 **KANAZAWA KEIZAI DAIGAKU**
Kanazawa College of Economics
10-1 Ushi, Gosho-machi, Kanazawa-shi, Ishikawa 920
Telephone: (762) 52-2236

F. of Economics
Founded 1967.

4183 **KEIHIN JOSHI DAIGAKU**
Keihin Women's University
1420 Iwase, Kamakura-shi, Kanagawa 247
Telephone: (467) 44-2111

F. of Home Economics
Founded 1943 as Keihin Women's Professional School of Domestic Science, acquired present status 1959.

4184 **KINJO GAKUIN DAIGAKU**
Kinjo Gakuin University
2-1723 Omori, Moriyama-ku, Nagoya-shi, Aichi 463
Telephone: (52) 798-0180
Fax: (52) 799-2087
Gakucho (President): Kaoru Shimamura (1988-92)

F. of Literature (including Sociology)
F. of Home Economics
Also junior college.
Founded 1889 as women's school, became college 1949 and university 1966. Residential facilities for academic staff and students.
Academic Year: April to March (April-September; October-March).

Admission Requirements: Graduation from high school or equivalent, and entrance examination.

Fees (Yen): Registration, 350,000; tuition, 450,000 per annum.

Language of Instruction: Japanese.

Degrees and Diplomas: Gakushi, Bachelor–Bungakushi, arts; Rigakushi, science, 4 yrs.

Libraries: University Library, *c.* 127,000 vols in Japanese; *c.* 26,000 in other languages.

Publications: Kinjo Gakuin Daigaku Ronshu (Bulletin of Faculty of Letters); Kinjo Dai.

Academic Staff, 1990:

Rank	Full-time	Part-time
Kyoju (Professors)	60	–
Jokyoju (Associate Professors)	32	221
Koshi (Assistant Professors)	7	–
Total	99	221

Student Enrolment, 1990:

	Women
Of the country	3616
Of other countries	9
Total	3625

4185 **KOBE KAISEI JOSHI GAKUEN DAIGAKU**

Kobe Kaisei (Stella Maris) College

2-7-1 Aotani cho, Nada-ku, Kobe-shi, Hyogo 657

Telephone: (78) 801-2277

F. of Literature

Founded 1956 as junior college, became college 1965.

Academic Year: April to March (April-October; October-March).

Admission Requirements: Graduation from high school and entrance examination.

Languages of Instruction: English, French and Japanese.

Degrees and Diplomas: Bungakushi, Bachelor of Arts, 4 yrs.

Library: c. 30,115 vols.

Publications: Kiyo; Kaisei Echoes.

Academic Staff: c. 40.

Student Enrolment: c. 330 (Women).

4186 **KOKA JOSHI DAIGAKU**

Koka Women's College

38 Kadono-cho, Nishikyogoku, Ukyo-ku, Kyoto-shi, Kyoto 615

Telephone: (75) 312-1783

Gakucho (President): Kei Hachiya (1983-87)

Jimukyokucho: Nobuyuki Akita

F. of Literature

Also kindergarten, elementary, junior and senior high schools, and junior college.

Founded 1944, reorganized 1964. Governing body: the Board of Trustees. Residential facilities for *c.* 230 students.

Arrangements for co-operation with Buena Vista College, Utah.

Academic Year: April to March.

Admission Requirements: Graduation from high school or foreign equivalent and entrance examination.

Language of Instruction: Japanese.

Degrees and Diplomas: Bungakushi, Bachelor of Arts, 4 yrs.

Library: Central Library, *c.* 60,000 vols.

Publication: Research Bulletin (annually).

Academic Staff: c. 30 (75).

Student Enrolment: c. 990 (Women).

4187 **KOKUSAI BUDO DAIGAKU**

International Budo University

841 Aza Monomizuka, Shinga, Katsuura-shi, Chiba, 299-52

Telephone: (4707) 3-4111

F. of Physical Education

Founded 1984.

Academic Year: April to March (April-September; September-March).

Admission Requirements: Graduation from high school and entrance examination.

Language of Instruction: Japanese.

Degrees and Diplomas: Gakushi, Bachelor.

Library: c. 22,900 vols.

Academic Staff: c. 50.

Student Enrolment: c. 1490.

4188 **KORIYAMA JOSHI DAIGAKU**

Koriyama Women's College

3-25-2 Kaisei, Koriyama-shi, Fukushima 963

Telephone: (249) 32-4848

Fax: (249) 33-6748

Gakucho (President): Fusa Sekiguchi

Jimukyokucho: Osamu Sekiguchi

S. of Home Economics

Also kindergarten and senior high schools and junior college.

Founded 1950 as junior college, acquired present status and title 1966. Governing body: the Board of Trustees, comprising 8 members. Residential facilities for *c.* 250 academic staff and *c.* 360 students.

Arrangements for co-operation with Virginia Polytechnic Institute and State University.

Academic Year: April to March (April-September; September-March).

Admission Requirements: Graduation from high school and entrance examination.

Fees (Yen): 440,000 per annum

Language of Instruction: Japanese.

Degrees and Diplomas: Gakushi, Bachelor, of Home Economics, 4 yrs. Professional and teaching qualifications, 2 yrs.

Library: c. 60,000 vols.

Special Facilities (Museums, etc.): National Costume Museum.

Publication: Bulletin.

Academic Staff, 1990: 28.

Student Enrolment, 1990:

	Women
Of the country	451
Of other countries	3
Total	454*

*Also 35 auditors.

4189 **KOSHIEN DAIGAKU**

Koshien University

10-1 Momijigaoka, Takarazuka-shi, Hyogo 665

Telephone: 797-87-5666

Gakucho (President): Yojiro Kawamura (1983-)

Jimukyokucho (Secretary-General): Yoshio Nakamura

C. of Nutrition

Dean: Hachiro Akehashi; *staff* 33 (11)

C. of Business Administration and Information Science

Dean: Kotaro Watanabe; *staff* 28 (21)

Ce. for Education in Information Processing

Director: Hideyo Ichihashi; *staff* – (7)

Founded 1967 as private University with College of Nutrition, incorporated College of Business Administration and Information Science 1986.

Arrangements for co-operation with Chu Shan Medical and Dental College, China.

Academic Year: April to March (April-September; October-March).

Admission Requirements: Graduation from high school or foreign equivalent and entrance examination.

Fees (Yen): Tuition, 780,000-1,080,000 per annum.

Language of Instruction: Japanese.

Degrees and Diplomas: Gakushi, Bachelor of–Nutrition; Business Administration, 4 yrs.

Library: Library, 50,000 vols.

Publication: Bulletins (annually).

Academic Staff, 1990-91:

Rank	Full-time	Part-time
Kyoju (Professors)	26	–
Jokyoju (Assistant Professors)	12	–
Koshi (Lecturers)	14	31
Total	52	31

Student Enrolment, 1990-91:

	Men	Women	Total
Of the country	1224	276	1500

4190 **KUMAMOTO SHOKA DAIGAKU**

Kumamoto University of Commerce
2-5-1 Oe, Kumamoto-shi, Kumamoto 862
Telephone: (96) 364-5161
Gakucho (President): Katsuyuki Kitakoga (1980-88)
Jimukyokucho: Shoichi Kaihara

F. of Commerce
Dean: Akira Shima; *staff* 30 (19)
F. of Economics
Dean: Hiroshi Nagai; *staff* 18 (6)
Research I. of Economics and Business
Director: Ko Nakatate; *staff* 1 (51)
Research I. of Foreign Affairs
Director: Shiro Tajima; *staff* – (51)
Also kindergarten and high school and junior college.

Founded 1942 as Oriental Language College, became Junior College 1950 and acquired present title and status 1954. Governing body: the Board of Directors. Some residential facilities for academic staff and for 76 students.

Arrangements for co-operation with: University of Montana; Montana State University; Eastern Montana College, Billings; Northern Montana College, Havre; Western Montana College, Dillon; Rocky Mountain College, Billings; College of Great Falls; Carroll College, Helena; Montana College of Mineral Science and Technology, Butte.

Academic Year: April to March (April-September; October-March).

Admission Requirements: Graduation from high school or equivalent, and entrance examination.

Fees (Yen): Registration, 120,000; tuition, 391,000.

Language of Instruction: Japanese.

Degrees and Diplomas: Shogakushi, Bachelor of Commerce; Keizaigakushi, Bachelor of Economics.

Library: c. 300,000 vols.

Publications: Kumamoto Shodai Ronshu (Treatises) (three times a year); Foreign Affairs Studies (biannually); Sangiyou Keiei Kenkyu (annually).

Academic Staff, 1986-87:

Rank	Full-time	Part-time
Kyoju (Professors)	47	–
Jokyoju (Assistant Professors)	21	–
Koshi (Lecturers)	13	84
Joshu (Assistants)	1	–
Total	82	84

Student Enrolment, 1986-87:

	Men	Women	Total
Of the country	4193	258	4451
Of other countries	7	–	7
Total	4200	258	4458

4191 **KURUME KOGYO DAIGAKU**

Kurume Institute of Technology
Kamitsu-machi, Kurume-shi, Fukuoka 830
Telephone: (942) 22-2345

F. of Engineering
Founded 1966.

4192 **KWASSUI JOSHI DAIGAKU**

Kwassui Women's College
1-50 Higashi-Yamate-machi, Nagasaki-shi, Nagasaki 850

F. of Literature

Founded 1952 as junior college, acquired present status 1981.

Academic Year: April to March (April-September; October-March).

Admission Requirements: Graduation from high school and entrance examination.

Language of Instruction: Japanese.

Degrees and Diplomas: Gakushi, Bachelor.

Library: c. 105,780 vols.

Academic Staff: c. 30.

Student Enrolment: c. 510.

4193 **KYOTO GAKUEN DAIGAKU**

Kyoto Gakuen University
Nanjo Otani, Sokabe-cho, Kameoka-shi, Kyoto 621

F. of Economics

Founded 1969. Governing body: the Board of Trustees, comprising 38 members. Residential facilities for *c.* 80 men students.

Academic Year: April to March (April-September; October-March).

Admission Requirements: Graduation from high school and entrance examination.

Language of Instruction: Japanese.

Degrees and Diplomas: Keizaigakushi, Bachelor of Economics; Keiaigakushi, Bachelor of Business Administration, 4 yrs.

Library: c. 580,000 vols.

Publication: Review (biannually).

Academic Staff: c. 50 (40).

Student Enrolment: c. 2380.

4194 **KYOTO SEIKA DAIGAKU**

Kyoto Seika College
37 Kino, Iwakura, Sakyo-ku, Kyoto-shi, Kyoto 606
Telephone: (75) 702-5199
Fax: (75) 722-0838
Gakucho (President): Yoshimitsu Kasahara (1983-)
Jimukyokucho (Secretary-General): Yoshimi Nageyama

F. of Arts
Dean: Jiro Hashida; *staff* 52 (81)
F. of Humanities (including Traditional Japanese Culture and Comparative Cultures)
Dean: Shoji Yagasaki; *staff* 35 (37)

Founded 1979. Some residential facilities for academic staff an students.

Arrangements for co-operation with: Antioch University; Chiang Mai University; University of Adelaide; Wolverhampton Polytechnic; University of Michigan.

Academic Year: April to March (April-September; October-March).

Admission Requirements: Graduation from high school and entrance examination.

Fees (Yen): 1,540,500-1,501,000 per annum; foreign students, 804,000-1,005,000.

Language of Instruction: Japanese.

Degrees and Diplomas: Gakushi, Bachelor, 4 yrs. Shushi, Master, a further 2 yrs.

Library: c. 78,630 vols.

Special Facilities (Museums, etc.): Audio-visual Centre; Papermaking Workshop.

Publications: Kion Hyoron (Japanese language publication, annually); Kyoto Review (English language publication, annually).

Academic Staff, 1990:

Rank	Full-time	Part-time
Kyoju (professors)	47	–
Jokyoju (Associate Professors)	19	–
Koshi (Lecturers)	21	118
Total	87	118

Student Enrolment, 1990:

	Men	Women	Total
Of the country	759	957	1716
Of other countries	14	11	25
Total	773	968	1741

4195 **KYUSHU JOSHI DAIGAKU**

Kyushu Women's University
1 Jiyugaoka, Yahatanishi-ku, Kitakyushu-shi, Fukuoka 802
Telephone: (93) 691-0251

F. of Home Economics
F. of Literature

Founded as college 1962, became university 1965.

Academic Year: April to March (April-September; October-March).

Admission Requirements: Graduation from high school and entrance examination.

Language of Instruction: Japanese.

Degrees and Diplomas: Gakushi, Bachelor, of–Home Economics; Letters, 4 yrs.

Library: c. 32,600 vols.

Publications: Bulletin of Kyushu Women's University (annually); Bulletin of Letters and Linguistics (annually).

Academic Staff: c. 50 (90).

Student Enrolment: c. 750.

4196 **KYUSHU KYORITSU DAIGAKU**

Kyushu Kyoritsu University

1-1 Jiyugaoka, Yahatanishi-ku, Kitakyushu-shi, Fukuoka 807

Telephone: (93) 691-6277

F. of Economics

F. of Engineering

4197 **MATSUMOTO SHIKA DAIGAKU**

Matsumoto Dental College

1780 Hirooka, Gobara, Shiojiri-shi, Nagano 399-07

Telephone: (263) 52-3100

F. of Dentistry

4198 **MATSUSAKA DAIGAKU**

Matsusaka University

1846 Kubo-cho, Matsusaka-shi, Mie 515

Telephone: (598) 29-1122

F. of Political Science and Economics

4199 **MEIJI SHINKYU DAIGAKU**

Meiji College of Oriental Medicine

Hiyoshi-cho, Funai-gun, Kyoto 629-03

Telephone: (7717) 2-1181

Fax: (7717) 2-0326

Gakucho (President): Osamu Mizukoshi

General Director: Kazuhisa Taniguchi

F. of Acupuncture and Moxibustion

; *staff* 67 (28)

Research Ce. for Oriental Medicine

Head: Koji Fukada; *staff* 4

Founded 1978 as junior college, acquired present status and title 1983.

Academic Year: April to March.

Admission Requirements: Graduation from high school and entrance examination.

Fees (Yen): 2,020-2,920 per annum.

Language of Instruction: Japanese.

Degrees and Diplomas: Gakushi, Bachelor–of Acupuncture and Moxibustion, B.A.M., 4 yrs.

Publication: Meiji Shinkyu Igaku (biannually).

Academic Staff, 1990:

Rank	Full-time	Part-time
Kyoju (Professors)	20	
Jokyoju (Assistant Professors)	8	
Koshi (Lecturers)	22	
Joshu (Assistants)	17	
Total	67	28

Student Enrolment, 1990:

	Men	Women	Total
Of the country	398	104	502

4200 **MIMASAKA JOSHI DAIGAKU**

Mimasaka Women's College

32 Kamigawara, Tsuyama-shi, Okayama 708

Telephone: (8682) 2-7718

F. of Home Economics

Also junior college.

Founded 1967. Governing body: the Board of Trustees, comprising 11 members. Some residential facilities for students.

Academic Year: April to March (April-July; September-December; January-March).

Admission Requirements: Graduation from senior high school and entrance examination.

Language of Instruction: Japanese.

Degrees and Diplomas: Gakushi, Bachelor, of–Home Economics, 4 yrs. Also teaching qualifications.

Library: c. 55,000 vols.

Publication: Bulletin (annually).

Academic Staff: c. 90 (60).

Student Enrolment: c. 700.

4201 **MINAMI KYUSHU DAIGAKU**

Minami Kyushu College

6307 Tayoshi, Miyazaki-shi, Miyazaki 884

Telephone: (985) 51-6307

F. of Horticulture

Also junior college.

Founded 1965, acquired present status 1967. Residential facilities for academic staff and students.

Admission Requirements: Graduation from high school and entrance examination.

Language of Instruction: Japanese.

Degrees and Diplomas: Gakushi, Bachelor, 4 yrs.

Publication: Bulletin.

Academic Staff: c. 70 (40).

Student Enrolment: c. 1030 (Also *c.* 15 external students).

4202 **MIYAGI GAKUIN JOSHI DAIGAKU**

Miyagi Gakuin Women's College

9-1-1 Sakuragaoka, Sendai-shi, Miyagi 980

Telephone: (222) 79-1311

F. of Liberal Arts

4203 **MOMOYAMA GAKUIN DAIGAKU**

St. Andrew's University

237-1 Nishino, Sakai-shi, Osaka 588

Telephone: (722) 36-1181

Gakucho (President): Masaharu Inabetsu

Jimubucho: Akio Anada

F. of Economics

Dean: Kenji Fukii; *staff* 36 (43)

F. of Sociology

Dean: Norio Kitagawa; *staff* 34 (36)

F. of Business Administration

Dean: Nobumasa Nakata; *staff* 32 (36)

Research I.

Director: Mitsuhiko Iyoda; *staff* 105

D. of Library Science

Director: Kazutoshi Nishikawa; *staff* 4 (29)

Ce. for Adult Education

Director: Kazutoshi Nishikawa; *staff* 8

Founded 1959 in commemoration of centennial anniversary of the establishment of the Anglican Mission in Japan and tracing origins to high school founded 1884. Governing body: the Rijikai, comprising 13-17 members. Residential facilities for students.

Special arrangements for co-operation with: California State University; Keimyung University.

Academic Year: April to March (April-September; October-March).

Admission Requirements: Graduation from high school or equivalent and entrance examination.

Fees (Yen): Registration, 200,000; tuition, 502,000 per annum.

Language of Instruction: Japanese.

Degrees and Diplomas: Gakushi, Bachelor–Keizaigakushi, economics; Shakaigakushi, sociology; Keieigakushi, business administration, 4 yrs.

Library: Central Library, *c.* 260,000 vols.

Publications: Economic Review (quarterly); Sociological Review (quarterly); Journal of Christian Studies; Bulletin of Research Institute; Journal of Human Sciences.

Academic Staff, 1986-87:

Rank	Full-time	Part-time
Kyoju (Professors)	56	
Jokyoju (Assistant Professors)	46	
Total	102	115

Student Enrolment, 1986-87:

	Men	Women	Total
Of the country	5283	308	5591
Of other countries	71	10	81
Total	5354	318	5672*

*Also 44 external students.

4204 **MORIOKA DAIGAKU**
Morioka University
5-4-1 Kuriyagawa Morioka-shi, Iwate 020-01
Telephone: (196) 41-2193

F. of Literature

4205 **MUSASHINO JOSHI DAIGAKU**
Musashino Women's College
1-1-20 Shin-machi, Hoya-shi, Tokyo 202
Telephone: (424) 62-3111

F. of Literature
Also kindergarten, high schools, and junior college.

Founded 1950, acquired present status 1965. Governing body: the Board of Directors headed by the chief priest of Tokyo Hongan-Ji Temple. Residential facilities for *c.* 260 students.

Academic Year: April to March (April-September; October-March).

Admission Requirements: Graduation from high school and entrance examination.

Language of Instruction: Japanese.

Degrees and Diplomas: Gakushi, Bachelor, of–Arts, 4 yrs. Also teaching qualifications. Diploma in Library Science.

Library: *c.* 81,930 vols.

Publications: Bulletin (annually); English-American Literature (annually).

Academic Staff: *c.* 90 (140).

Student Enrolment: *c.* 2530.

4206 **NAGANO DAIGAKU**
Nagano University
Shimonogo, Ueda-shi, Nagano 386-12
Telephone: (268) 38-2350
Fax: (268) 38-5887
Gakucho (President): Hunio Marui (1987-)
Jimukyokucho (Secretary-General): Fujie Hori

F. of Industrial Science
Dean: Michioki Taniguchi; *staff* 51 (46)

Founded 1966 as Honshu University, acquired present title 1974.

Academic Year: April to March.

Admission Requirements: Graduation from high school or foreign equivalent, and entrance examination.

Fees (Yen): 888,000 per annum

Degrees and Diplomas: Gakushi, Bachelor, of Sociology, 4 yrs.

Academic Staff, 1990:

Rank	Full-time	Part-time
Kyoju (Professors)	26	–
Jokyoju (Associate Professors)	15	–
Koshi (Lecturers)	10	46
Total	51	46

Student Enrolment, 1990:

	Men	Women	Total
Of the country	1003	336	1339

4207 **NAGOYA GAKUIN DAIGAKU**
Nagoya Gakuin University
1350 Kamishinano-cho, Seto-shi, Aichi 480-12
Telephone: (561) 42-0350
Fax: (561) 41-1953
Gakucho (President): Akio Nishimura (1988-)
Jimukyokucho (Secretary-General): Hideki Kasahara

F. of Economics (including Business Administration)
Dean: Yoshio Yamazaki; *staff* 61

F. for Foreign Students (including English and Chinese)
Dean: Ryuji Yamashita; *staff* 30

Institute for Japanese Language and Culture
Director: Shizumu Hirose; *staff* 8 (9)

Founded 1887 as Nagoya Anglo-Japanese Institute, reorganized 1906. Acquired present status and title 1964. Governing body: the Board of Trustees.

Arrangements for co-operation with: University of Alaska; University of Montana; Coe College; Ball State University; Randolph Macon College; University of Iowa; Austin College; University of North Carolina; St. Martin's College; Transylvanian University.

Academic Year: April to December (April-July; September-December) (January-March: Winter Interim).

Admission Requirements: Graduation from high school or foreign equivalent and entrance examination.

Fees (Yen): 525,000-1,000,000 per annum.

Language of Instruction: Japanese.

Degrees and Diplomas: Keizaigakushi, Bachelor of Economics.

Library: *c.* 210,500 vols.

Publications: Review (quarterly); Round Table on Languages, Linguistics and Literature (biannually).

Academic Staff, 1990:

Rank	Full-time
Kyoju (Professors)	46
Jokyoju (Associate University)	31
Koshi (Lecturers)	15
Total	92

Student Enrolment, 1990:

	Men	Women	Total
Of the country	3627	179	3806
Of other countries	10	6	16
Total	3637	185	3822

4208 **NAGOYA GEIJUTSU DAIGAKU**
Nagoya University of Arts
280 Koi Kumanosho, Shikatsu-cho, Nishikasguai-gun, Aichi 481
Telephone: (568) 24-0315
Fax: (568) 24-0317
Gakucho (Rector): Shunzo Oshima (1990-94)
Jimukyokucho (Secretary-General): Shigeru Kato

F. of Music
Dean: Jiro Nagaosa; *staff* 41 (75)

F. of Fine Arts
Dean: Isao Takagi; *staff* 41 (45)

Founded 1970.

Academic Year: April to March (April-September; October-March).

Admission Requirements: Graduation from high school or equivalent or foreign equivalent.

Fees (Yen): Registration, 300,000; tuition, 494,000-780,000 per annum.

Language of Instruction: Japanese.

Degrees and Diplomas: Gakushi, Bachelor of Arts, 4 yrs.

Library: *c.* 52,659 vols.

Publication: Kyo (Faculty Research and Thesis Periodical) (annually).

Academic Staff, 1989-90:

Rank	Full-time	Part-time
Kyoju (Professors)	41	–
Jokyoju (Assistant Professors)	24	–
Koshi (Instructors)	18	121
Joshu (Assistant)	–	–
Total	83	121

Student Enrolment, 1989-90:

	Men	Women	Total
Of the country	658	1076	1734
Of other countries	2	–	2
Total	660	1076	1736

4209 **NAGOYA KEIZAI DAIGAKU**
Nagoya Economics University
61-1 Uchikubo, Inuyama-shi, Aichi 484
Telephone: (568) 67-0511

F. of Economics

4210 **NAGOYA JOSHI DAIGAKU**
Nagoya Women's University
4-30 Shioji-cho, Mizuho-ku, Nagoya-shi, Aichi 467
Telephone: (52) 852-1111

F. of Home Economics

Founded 1950 as junior college, acquired present status 1964. Some residential facilities for students.

Academic Year: April to March (April-October; October-March).

Admission Requirements: Graduation from high school or equivalent, and entrance examination.

Language of Instruction: Japanese.

Degrees and Diplomas: Gakushi, Bachelor, of–Home Economics, 4 yrs. Also teaching qualifications.
Library: College Library.
Publication: Kiyo (annually).
Academic Staff: c. 30.
Student Enrolment: c. 400.

4211 **NAGOYA ONGAKU DAIGAKU**
Nagoya College of Music
7-1 Inabaji, Nagoya-shi, Nakamura 453
Telephone: (52) 411-1111
Gakucho (President): Kyuichiro Miguno (1985-88)
Jimucho: Toshiaki Asano

Music

Founded as college 1965, became university 1976. Governing body: Shinshu Ohtani (Buddhist organization). Residential facilities for students.
Academic Year: April to March (April-September; October-March).
Admission Requirements: Graduation from high school or foreign equivalent.
Fees (Yen): 401,600 per annum.
Language of Instruction: Japanese.
Degrees and Diplomas: Bachelor of Arts in Music, 4 yrs.
Library: 110,000 vols.
Publication: Bulletin (annually).
Academic Staff, 1986-87:

Rank	Full-time	Part-time
Kyoju (Professors)	27	
Jokyoju (Associate Professors)	15	
Koshi (Instructors)	7	
Total	49	72

Student Enrolment, 1986-87:

	Men	Women	Total
Of the country	30	782	812
Of other countries	–	6	6
Total	30	788	818

4212 **NAKAMURA GAKUEN DAIGAKU**
Nakamura Gakuen College
5-7-1 Befu, Jonan-ku, Fukuoka-shi, Fukuoka 814
Telephone: (92) 851-2531

F. of Home Economics

Also junior college.

Founded as high school in 1953, became junior college 1957 and acquired present status 1965. Governing body: the Board of Trustees. Residential facilities for c. 500 students.
Academic Year: April to March (April-September; October-March).
Admission Requirements: Graduation from high school and entrance examination.
Language of Instruction: Japanese.
Degrees and Diplomas: Gakushi, Bachelor, of Home Economics, 4 yrs.
Library: c. 50,000 vols.
Publication: Research Bulletin (annually).
Academic Staff: c. 50 (20).
Student Enrolment: c. 770.

4213 **NARA DAIGAKU**
Nara University
500 Misagi-cho, Nara-shi, Nara 631
Telephone: (742) 44-1251
Fax: (742) 41-0650
Gakucho (President): Ichiro Suizu
Jimukyokucho (Secretary-General): Mitsuyoshi Imanishi

C. of Liberal Arts (including Humanities, Social Science, and Natural Sciences)
Dean: Yoshiya Ichikawa; *staff* 28 (30)
F. of Literature
Dean: Hiroshi Matsuyama; *staff* 31 (45)
F. of Social Research
Dean: Jyuji Misumi; *staff* 20 (13)

Founded 1969. Faculty of Social Research established 1988.
Academic Year: April to March.
Fees (Yen): c. 1,050,000-1,070,000
Language of Instruction: Japanese.
Degrees and Diplomas: Gakushi, Bachelor, 4 yrs.
Library: 138,000 vols.
Academic Staff, 1990:

Rank	Full-time	Part-time
Kyoju (Professors)	46	–
Jokyoju (Associate Professors)	21	–
Koshi (Lecturers)	13	–
Joshu (Assistants)	5	–
Total	85	88

Student Enrolment, 1990:

	Men	Women	Total
Of the country	2022	816	2838

4214 **NARA SANGYO DAIGAKU**
Nara Sangyo University
3-12-1 Tatsunokita, Sangyo-ch, Ikoma-gun, Nara 636

F. of Economics

Founded 1984.

4215 **NIHON RUTERU SHINGAKU DAIGAKU**
Japan Lutheran Theological College
3-10-20 Osawa, Mitaka-shi, Tokyo 181

F. of Theology
F. of Literature

Founded 1909.

4216 **NIHON SEKIJUJI KANGO DAIGAKU**
Japanese Red Cross College of Nursing
4-1-3 Hiroo, Shibuya-ku, Tokyo 150

F. of Nursing

Founded 1890.

4217 **NIHON SHAKAI JIGYO DAIGAKU**
Japan College of Social Work
1-4-19 Jingumae, Shibuya-ku, Tokyo 150

D. of Social Welfare

Founded 1947 as Japan Social Welfare Senmon Gakko, became junior college 1950, acquired present status 1958.
Academic Year: April to March.
Admission Requirements: Graduation from high school and entrance examination.
Degrees and Diplomas: Shakaigakushi, Bachelor of Sociology, 4 yrs.
Library: c. 38,000 vols.
Academic Staff: c. 55.
Student Enrolment: c. 100.

4218 **NIHON TAIIKU DAIGAKU**
Japan Women's College of Physical Education
8-19-1 Kitakarasuyama, Setagaya-ku, Tokyo 157

F. of Physical Education

Founded 1965.

4219 **NIIGATA YAKKA DAIGAKU**
Niigata College of Pharmacy
5-13-2 Kamishin'ei-cho, Niigata-shi, Niigata 950-21
Telephone: (25) 269-3171
Fax: (25) 260-1415
Gakucho (President): Haruaki Yajima

F. of Pharmaceutical Sciences

Founded in 1977 as a private college of pharmacy. Some residential facilities for academic staff.
Academic Year: April to March (April-September; October-March).
Admission Requirements: Graduation from high school and entrance examination.
Fees (yen): 1,827,000 per annum.
Language of Instruction: Japanese.
Degrees and Diplomas: Yakugakushi, Bachelor of Pharmacy, 4 yrs.
Library: Central Library, 27,644 vols.
Special Facilities (Museums, etc.): 2 Medicinal Botanical Gardens.
Publication: Bulletin of the Niigata College of Pharmacy (annually).

Academic Staff, 1990:

Rank	Full-time	Part-time
Kyoju (Professors)	17	–
Jokyoju (Associate Professors)	20	18
Sennin-Koshi (Assistant Professors)	21	–
Total	58	18

Student Enrolment, 1990:

	Men	Women	Total
Of the country	218	269	514

4220 **NIPPON BUNKA DAIGAKU**
977 Katakura-cho, Hachioji-shi, Tokyo 192

F. of Law

4221 **NIPPON BUNRI DAIGAKU**
Nippon Bunri University
Ichigi, Oita-shi, Oita 870-03
Telephone: (975) 92-1600

S. of Engineering
S. of Business and Economics

Founded 1967 as Oita Institute of Technology. Acquired present title 1982.

4222 **NISHIKYUSHU DAIGAKU**
Nishikyushu University
4490-9 Hirayama, Osaki, Kanzaki-gun, Saga 842

F. of Home Economics

4223 **NISHINIPPON KOGYO DAIGAKU**
Nishinippon Institute of Technology
1633 Aratsu, Kanda-machi, Miyako-gun, Fukuoka 800-03
Telephone: (9302) 3-1491
Gakucho (President): M. Konomi
Jimukyokucho: M. Imamiya

Engineering (including Architecture)
Geotechnical Research I.
Information Processing Ce.

Founded 1967. Residential facilities for 160 students.

Academic Year: April to March (April-October; October-March).

Admission Requirements: Graduation from high school or equivalent or foreign equivalent.

Fees (Yen): 990,000 per annum.

Language of Instruction: Japanese.

Degrees and Diplomas: Kogakushi, Bachelor of Engineering, 4 yrs.

Library: Library of Institute, 81,079 vols.

Publication: Memoirs (annually). Technical Report.

Academic Staff, 1986-87:

Rank	Full-time	Part-time
Kyoju (Professors)	15	
Jokyoju (Assistant Professors)	31	
Koshi (Lecturers)	9	
Joshu (Assistants)	9	
Total	64	36

Student Enrolment, 1986-87:

	Men	Women	Total
Of the country	1402	13	1415

4224 ***NOTORUDAMU JOSHI DAIGAKU**
Notre Dame Women's College
1 Minami Nonogami-cho, Shimogamo, Sakyo-ku, Kyoto-shi, Kyoto 606
Telephone: (75) 781-1173
Fax: (75) 702-4060
Gakucho (President): Ume Tashiro
Jimukyokucho (Secretary-General): Hidero Iguchi

F. of Literature
Dean: Ume Tashiro; *staff* 37 (51)
F. of English Language and Literature
Head: Sister Celin Matsumoto

Also elementary and junior and senior high schools.

Founded 1961 by the Congregation of School Sisters of Notre-Dame. Recognized by the Ministry of Education. Financially supported by tuition fees. Governing body: the Board of Directors. Residential facilities for students.

Academic Year: April to March (April-September; October-March).

Admission Requirements: Graduation from high school or equivalent, and entrance examination.

Fees (Yen): 1,148,000 per annum.

Language of Instruction: Japanese.

Degrees and Diplomas: Gakushi, Bachelor, of Arts, 4 yrs.

Library: University Library, 95,000 vols.

Academic Staff, 1990:

Rank	Full-time	Part-time
Kyoju (Professors)	17	–
Jokyoju (Associate Professors)	17	–
Kennin-Koshi (Lecturers)	6	51
Total	40	51

Student Enrolment, 1990: 1164 (Women).

4225 **NOTORUDAMU SEISHIN JOSHI DAIGAKU**
Notre-Dame Immaculate Heart Women's College
2-16-9 Ifukucho, Okayama-shi, Okayama 700
Cables: notredame seishin
Telephone: (862) 52-1155
Fax: (865) 55-7665
Gakucho (President): Mie Saiga (1990-)
Gakucho-Hosa (Vice-President): Kokichi Nishibori

F. of Japanese and English Literature
Head: Hideo Isogai; *staff* 25 (24)
F. of Home Economics (including Child Welfare and Food and Nutrition)
Head: Susumu Miyake; *staff* 54 (63)
I. of Christian Culture Research
Head: Aoi Tsuda; *staff* 2 (1)
I. of Life Style Cultura
Head: Manabu Yokoyama; *staff* 4
I. of Human Studies
Head: Koichi Kasuya; *staff* 2
Culture Research Ce.
Head: Hideo Isogai; *staff* 2
Research I. for Informatics and Science
Head: Kunio Yasue; *staff* 3
Child Clinic I.
Head: Susumu Miyake; *staff* 2

Also kindergarten and elementary schools.

Founded 1949, under the auspices of the Sisters of Notre-Dame de Namur. Recognized by the Ministry of Education, Science and Culture. Financially supported by the government and by tuition fees. Governing body: the Board of Trustees. Some residential facilities for academic staff and students.

Arrangements for co-operation with: Trinity College, Washington D.C.; College of Notre-Dame, Belmont, California; Emmanuel College, Boston; Christ College, Irvine, California; Salve Regina, Newport College, Rhode Island;Notre Dame College Manchester, New Hampshire.

Academic Year: April to March (April-July; October-March).

Admission Requirements: Graduation from high school or recognized equivalent, and entrance examination.

Fees (Yen): Registration, 257,000; tuition, 400,000 per annum.

Language of Instruction: Japanese.

Degrees and Diplomas: Gakushi, Bachelor–Bungakushi, arts; Kaseigakushi, home economics, 4 yrs. Teaching Certificates.

Libraries: Central library, 185,600 vols; Masamune Atsuo Bunko; Kurokawa: 2500.

Special Facilities (Museums, etc.): Seikatsu Bunka Museum (Women's Life Culture).

Publications: Kiyo (Bulletin); Nempo (published by Christian Culture Research Centre and Institute of Life Style Culture); Journal of the Research Institute for Informatics and Science.

Academic Staff, 1990-91:

Rank	Full-time	Part-time
Gakucho (President)	1	–
Kyoju (Professors)	38	56
Jokyoju (Associate Professors)	18	20
Koshi (Instructors)	21	8
Joshu (Assistants)	8	3
Total	85	87

Student Enrolment, 1990-91:

	Women
Of the country	1989
Of other countries	2
Total	1991

4226 **OBIRIN DAIGAKU**
Obirin College
3758 Tokiwa-machi, Machida-shi, Tokyo 194-02
Telephone: (427) 97-2661

F. of Literature
F. of Economics
Founded 1950, acquired present status 1966.

4227 **OKAYAMA SHOKA DAIGAKU**
Okayama College of Commerce
2-10-1 Tsushima, Kyo-machi, Okayama-shi, Okayama 700
Telephone: (862) 52-0642
Fax: (862) 55-6947
Gakucho (President): Yutaka Ijiri
Jimukyokucho (Secretary-General): Jiro Fujiwara

D. of Commerce
; *staff* 19 (10)
D. of Industrial Management
; *staff* 15 (9)

Founded 1955, acquired present status 1965. Financially supported by tuition fees and government subsidies.

Academic Year: April to March (April-October; October-March).

Admission Requirements: Graduation from senior high school and entrance examination.

Fees (Yen): tuition, 360,000 per annum.

Languages of Instruction: Japanese, English, German and Spanish.

Degrees and Diplomas: Gakushi, Bachelor, of Commerce, 4 yrs. Also teaching qualification.

Library: Central Library, *c.* 158,000 vols.

Publication: Okayama Shodai Ronso (3 times a year).

Academic Staff, 1990:

Rank	Full-time	Part-time
Kyoju (Professors)	25	–
Jokyoju (Associate Professors)	23	–
Sennin-Koshi (Assistant Professors)	8	42
Joshu (Research Associate)	1	–
Total	57	42

Student Enrolment, 1990:

	Men	Women	Total
Of the country	2,360	138	2,498

4228 **OKINAWA DAIGAKU**
University of Okinawa
747 Kokuba, Naha-shi, Okinawa 902
Telephone: (988) 32-3216

D. of Law and Economics
Also junior college.

Founded 1961.

Academic Year: April to March (April-September; October-March).

Admission Requirements: Graduation from high school and entrance examination.

Language of Instruction: Japanese.

Degrees and Diplomas: Gakushi, Bachelor, of–Law; Economics.

Library: *c.* 39,990 vols.

Academic Staff: *c.* 50 (70).

Student Enrolment: *c.* 2220.

4229 **OKINAWA KOKUSAI DAIGAKU**
Okinawa Kokusai University
276-2 Ginowan, Ginowan-shi, Okinawa 901-22
Telephone: (9889) 2-1111

C. of Law
C. of Letters
F. of Commerce and Economics
Founded 1972.

4230 **OSAKA DENKITSUSHIN DAIGAKU**
Osaka Electro-Communication University
18-8 Hatsumachi, Neyagawa-shi, Osaka 572
Telephone: (720) 24-1131

F. of Engineering
Also junior college.

Founded 1941, acquired present status 1961. Governing body: the Board of Trustees of 10 members. Some residential facilities for students.

Academic Year: April to March (April-September; October-March).

Admission Requirements: Graduation from high school and entrance examination.

Language of Instruction: Japanese.

Degrees and Diplomas: Gakushi, Bachelor–Rigakushi, science, 4 yrs.

Library: *c.* 40,000 vols.

Publication: Collection of theses (annually).

Academic Staff: *c.* 120.

Student Enrolment: *c.* 4000.

4231 **OSAKA KEIZAI HOKA DAIGAKU**
Osaka University of Economics and Law
6-10 Gakuonji, Yao-shi, Osaka 581

Economics
Law

4232 **OSAKA SANGYO DAIGAKU**
Osaka Sangyo University
3-1-1 Nakagaito, Daito-shi, Osaka 574
Telex: 5349101 SJPOSU J
Telephone: (720) 75-3001
Fax: (720) 71-1253
Gakucho (President): Michiyoshi Kuwahara (1987-91)
Riji, Jimubucho: Shigetake Sugioka

F. of Economics
Dean: Seiichi Ando; *staff* 17 (16)
F. of Business Management
Dean: Yasuo Kawaguchi; *staff* 20 (30)
F. of Engineering (including Transportation, Environmental Design and Electronics)
Dean: Isamu Sakamoto; *staff* 57 (31)
C. of General Education
Dean: Hiroichi Hasegawa; *staff* 52 (132)
I. for Industrial Research
Head: Sadao Komatsu; *staff* 4 (38)
Academic Information Processing Ce.
Head: Ippei Sugiura; *staff* 5 (7)
Also junior college.

Founded 1928 as Railway School, became junior college 1950 and university 1965. Graduate School established 1988. Governing body: the Board of Trustees, comprising 12 members. Residential facilities for some academic staff and 80 students.

Academic Year: April to March (April-September; October-March).

Admission Requirements: Graduation from high school or equivalent or foreign equivalent, and entrance examination.

Fees (Yen): Registration, 340,000; tuition, 670,000-980,000 per annum, according to faculty.

Language of Instruction: Japanese.

Degrees and Diplomas: Gakushi, Bachelor–Keieigakushi, business management; Keizaigakushi, economics; Kogakushi, engineering, 4 yrs.Shushi, Master–Kogakushushi, engineering, a further 2 yrs.

Library: University Library, 211,000 vols.

Publications: Journal (quarterly); Bulletin of the Society of Osaka Sangyo University (annually); Bulletin of the Institute for Industrial Research(annually); Report on education and Research (annually).

Press or Publishing House: Institute for Industrial Research of Osaka Sangyo University; Society of Osaka Sangyo University; Planning andDeveloping Office of School Juridical Person Osaka Sangyo University.

Academic Staff, 1990-91:

Rank	Full-time	Part-time
Kyoju (Professors)	84	–
Jokyoju (Associate Professors)	60	–
Sennin-Koshi (Assistant Professors)	19	266
Joshu (Research Associates)	8	3
Total	171	269

Student Enrolment, 1990-91:

	Men	Women	Total
Of the country	7,350	349	7,699
Of other countries	68	18	86
Total	7,418	367	7,785*

*Also 33 external students.

4233 **OSAKA SHOIN JOSHI DAIGAKU**
Osaka Shoin Women's College
4-2-26 Hishiyanishi, Higashi-Osaka-shi, Osaka 577
Telephone: (6) 723-8181

F. of Liberal Arts

Founded 1926 as Women's Professional High School, acquired present title and status 1949.

Academic Staff: c. 40.

Student Enrolment: c. 140.

4234 **OTANI JOSHI DAIGAKU**
Otani Women's College
Shigakudai, Nishikiori, Tondabayashi-shi, Osaka 584

F. of Letters

Founded 1930, acquired present status 1966.

4235 **REITAKU DAIGAKU**
Reitaku University
2-1-1 Hikarigaoka, Kashiwa-shi, Chiba 277
Telephone: (471) 73-3901
Fax: (471) 73-1100
Gakucho (President): Mototaka Hiroike
Dean of Academic Affairs: Tetsuo Obukata

F. of Foreign Languages
Dean: Shimpei Tanaka; *staff* 73 (55)

Research Ce. for International Cultural Affairs
Director: Jitaro Mizuno; *staff* – (17)

Founded 1950 as junior college, acquired present status and title 1959.

Arrangements for co-operation with: University of Redlands, Virginia; California Lutheran University; University of Stirling; Prince of Songkhla University, Thailand; Tan Kang University, Taipei.

Academic Year: April to March (April-July; September-March).

Admission Requirements: Graduation from high school or equivalent, and entrance examination.

Fees (Yen): 480,000 per annum.

Language of Instruction: Japanese.

Degrees and Diplomas: Bungakushi, Bachelor of Arts, 4 yrs.

Library: Central Library, *c.* 250,000 vols.

Publications: Reitaku Daigaku Kiyo (Bulletin, biannually); Ronso (Journal, annually);

Press or Publishing House: Hiroikegakuen Press.

Academic Staff, 1990:

Rank	Full-time	Part-time
Kyoju (Professors)	34	–
Sennin-Koshi (Assistant Professors)	21	–
Kennin-Koshi (Lecturers)	15	59
Joshu (Assistants)	3	–
Total	72	59

Student Enrolment, 1990:

	Men	Women	Total
Of the country	258	446	704
Of other countries	75	70	145
Total	303	516	849

4236 **SAGAMI JOSHI DAIGAKU**
Sagami Women's University
2-1-1 Bunkyo, Sagamihara-shi, Kanagawa 228
Telephone: (427) 42-1411

F. of Liberal Arts

Also kindergarten and high schools.

Founded 1900 as Nihon Women's School, acquired present status and title 1949. Some residential facilities for students.

Academic Year: April to March (April-July; October-February).

Admission Requirements: Graduation from high school and entrance examination. Fees (Yen): *c.* 35,000.

Language of Instruction: Japanese.

Library: c. 130,000 vols.

Publications: Journal; Sagami English and American Literature.

Academic Staff: c. 115.

Student Enrolment: c. 3300 (Women).

4237 **SAGAMI KOGYO DAIGAKU**
Sagami Institute of Technology
1-1-25 Tsujido Nishikaigan, Fujusawa-shi, Kanagawa 251
Telephone: (466) 34-4111

F. of Engineering

Founded 1963.

Academic Staff: c. 45.

Student Enrolment: c. 350.

4238 **SAITAMA KOGYO DAIGAKU**
Saitama Institute of Technology
1690 Fusaiji, Okabe-machi, Osato-gun, Saitama 369-02
Telephone: (485) 85-2521
Fax: (485) 85-2523
Gakucho (President): Giichi Muto
Jimukyokucho (Secretary-General): Tenaki Marumo

F. of Engineering

Founded 1962 as College of Engineering, acquired present status and title 1976. Financially supported by tuition fees and government subsidies. Governing body: the Board of Directors, comprising 31 members.

Academic Year: April to March (April-September; October-March).

Admission Requirements: Graduation from high school or equivalent or foreign equivalent, and entrance examination.

Language of Instruction: Japanese.

Degrees and Diplomas: Kogakushi, Bachelor of Engineering, 4 yrs.

Library: 25,554 vols.

Academic Staff, 1990:

Rank	Full-time	Part-time
Kyoju (Professors)	26	–
Jojkyoju (Associate Professors)	15	–
Koshi(Lecturers)	15	28
Total	56	28

Student Enrolment, 1990:

	Men	Women	Total
Of the country	1300	50	1350
Of other countries	10	3	13
Total	1310	53	1363

4239 **SAKUYO ONGAKU DAIGAKU**
Sakuyo College of Music
1334-1 Yaide, Tsuyama-shi, Okayama 708
Telephone: (868) 24-1811

F. of Music

Also junior college.

Founded 1951, acquired present status 1966. Financially supported by tuition fees. Governing body: Sakuyo Board of Directors.

Arrangements for co-operation with: University of California, Los Angeles; Music Conservatory, Shenyang; and College of Music, Detmold.

Academic Year: April to March (April-September; October-February).

Admission Requirements: Graduation from high school and entrance examination.

Fees (Yen): Tuition, 810,000 per annum.

Language of Instruction: Japanese.

Degrees and Diplomas: Gakushi, Bachelor, of Arts, 4 yrs. Also teaching qualifications.

Libraries: c. 80,181 vols; also 4906 recordings, including LP, CD and video tapes.

Special Facilities (Museums, etc.): Buddhist cathedral auditorium with pipe organ.

Publication: (Bulletins).

Academic Staff, 1990: 57 (73).

Student Enrolment, 1990:

Men	Women	Total
59	606	665

4240 **SANGYO NORITSU DAIGAKU**

SANNO College

1573 Kami-kasuya, Isehara-shi, Kanagawa 259-11

Telephone: (463) 92-2211

D. of Management and Informatics

Founded 1979.

4241 **SAPPORO DAIGAKU**

Sapporo University

3-1; 3-7 Nishioka, Toyohira-ku, Sapporo-shi, Hokkaido 062

Telephone: (11) 852-1811

F. of Economics

F. of Business Administration

F. of Foreign Languages

Also women's junior college.

Founded 1967. Residential facilities for c. 40 academic staff.

Academic Year: April to March (April-September; October-March).

Admission Requirements: Graduation from high school or equivalent, and entrance examination.

Language of Instruction: Japanese.

Degrees and Diplomas: Gakushi, Bachelor, of–Economics; Economic Administration; Arts, 4 yrs.

Library: c. 650,000 vols.

Academic Staff: c. 110 (220).

Student Enrolment: c. 4750.

4242 **SAPPORO GAKUIN DAIGAKU**

Sapporo Gakuin University

11 Bunkyodai, Ebetsu-shi, Hokkaido 069-01

Telephone: (11) 386-8111

Gakucho (President): Shinzaburo Asuwa (1982-85)

Jimcho: Yoshiaki Taniguchi

F. of Commerce (day and evening studies)

Dean: Sadao Watanabe; *staff* 38 (19)

F. of Letters

Dean: Masao Katabami; *staff* 19 (37)

F. of Law

Dean: Kunio Shoji; *staff* 6 (1)

Founded 1946 as Sapporo College of Liberal Arts, acquired present title 1984.

Academic Year: April to March (April-September; October-March).

Admission Requirements: Graduation from high school or foreign equivalent, and entrance examination.

Language of Instruction: Japanese.

Degrees and Diplomas: Gakushi, Bachelor–Syogakushi, commerce; Bungakushi, letters; Hogakushi, law, 4 yrs.

Library: Central Library, 180,000 vols.

Publications: Review of Economics and Business; Bulletin of the Faculty of Letters; Law Review.

Academic Staff, 1984-85:

Rank	Full-time	Part-time
Kyoju (Professors)	65	–
Jokyoju (Assistant Professors)	32	–
Koshi (Lecturers)	3	99
Total	100	99

Student Enrolment, 1984-85:

	Men	Women	Total
Of the country	3793	272	4065
Of other countries	9	2	11
Total	3802	274	4076

4243 **SEISEN JOSHI DAIGAKU**

Seisen Women's College

3-16-21 Higashi Gotanda, Shinagawa-ku, Tokyo 141

Telephone: (3) 447-5551

Gakucho (President): Yuriko Kuriyama (1984-88)

F. of Literature

Also kindergarten, elementary, junior and senior high schools.

Founded 1950 by the Congregation of the Handmaids of the Sacred Heart. Governing body: the Board of Governors.

Academic Year: April to March (April-September; September-March).

Admission Requirements: Graduation from high school or equivalent, and entrance examination.

Language of Instruction: Japanese.

Degrees and Diplomas: Bungakushi, Bachelor of Arts, 4 yrs.

Library: College Library, c. 12,000 vols.

Publication: Bulletin (annually).

Academic Staff: c. 50 (90).

Student Enrolment: c. 1430.

4244 **SENDAI DAIGAKU**

Sendai College

Minami 2, Shibata-gun, Miyagi 989-16

F. of Physical Education

Founded 1967.

4245 **SETSUNAN DAIGAKU**

Setsunan University

17-8 Ikedanaka-machi, Neyagawa-shi, Osaka 572

Telephone: (720) 26-5101

F. of Engineering (including Architecture)

Founded 1975. Financially supported by tuition fees and grants.

Academic Year: April to March (April-September; October-March).

Admission Requirements: Graduation from high school or equivalent, and entrance examination.

Language of Instruction: Japanese.

Degrees and Diplomas: Gakushi, Bachelor, of Engineering, 4 yrs.

Library: Central Library, c. 400,000 vols.

Publication: Scientific Review (quarterly).

Academic Staff: c. 85 (80).

Student Enrolment: c. 2500.

4246 **SHIKOKU JOSHI DAIGAKU**

Shikoku Women's University

123-1 Ebisuno, Ojin-cho, Tokushima-shi, Tokushima 771-11

Telephone: (886) 65-1300

Fax: (886) 65–1300

Gakucho (President): Shin-ichi Endoh (1980-92)

Jimubucho: Mitsuo Yamamoto

F. of Literature

Dean: Tsuneo Miyaoka; *staff* 22 (35)

F. of Home Economics

Dean: Teruo Abe; *staff* 38 (35)

Ce. for Experimental Instruments

Information Processing Education Ce.

Calligraph's Research Ce.

Also junior college.

Founded 1961, acquired present status 1966. Governing body: the Board of Trustees, comprising 7 members. Residential facilities for 455 students.

Arrangements for co-operation with Saginaw Valley State University.

Academic Year: April to March (April-October; October-March).

Admission Requirements: Graduation from high school or equivalent or foreign equivalent.
Fees (Yen): 338,100-398,700 per annum.
Language of Instruction: Japanese.
Degrees and Diplomas: Gakushi, Bachelor–Bungakushi, literature; Kaseigakushi, home economics, 4 yrs.
Library: 184,064 vols.
Publication: Bulletin (biannually).
Academic Staff, 1989-90:

Rank	Full-time	Part-time
Kyoju (Professors)	55	–
Jokyoju (Assistant Professors)	35	–
Koshi (Lecturers)	21	136
Joshu (Assistants)	15	–
Total	126	136

Student Enrolment, 1989-90:

	Women
Of the country	2157
Of other countries	5
Total	2162

4247 **SHINWA JOSHI DAIGAKU**
Shinwa Women's College
7-13-1 Suzurandai-kitamachi, Kita-ku, Kobe-shi, Hyogo 65-1
Telephone: (78) 591-1651
Fax: (78) 591-3113
Gakucho (President): Tetsuo Santo (1988-)
Jimukyokucho (Secretary-General): Takanori Nanba.

D. of Japanese Literature
Chairman: Kaoru Yamasaki; *staff* 9 (17)
D. of English Literature
Chairman: Seishi Yamagushi; *staff* 10 (20)
D. of Childhood Education
Chairman: Osamu Yamagushi; *staff* 10 (32)

Founded 1966 as an extension of the Shinwa Educational Institution, which has a 100-year history. Residential facilities for students.
Academic Year: April to March
Admission Requirements: Graduation from high school and entrance examination.
Fees (Yen): 500,000 per annum.
Language of Instruction: Japanese.
Degrees and Diplomas: Gakushi, Bachelor, 4 yrs.
Library: 120,000 vols.
Publications: Review of Shinwa Women's College; Studies in Childhood; Studies in english Linguistics and Literature (all annually).
Academic Staff, 1990:

Rank	Full-time	Part-time
Kyoju (Professors)	22	–
Jokyoju (Associate Professors)	14	–
Koshi (Lecturers)	9	–
Total	45	95

Student Enrolment, 1990:

	Women
Of the country	1709
Of other countries	14
Total	1723

4248 **SHIRAYURI JOSHI DAIGAKU**
Shirayuri Women's College
1-25 Midorigaoka, Chofu-shi, Tokyo 182
Telephone: (3) 326-5050
Fax: (3) 328-4550
Gakucho (President): Teruko Kataoka

F. of Liberal Arts

Founded 1965.
Academic Year: April to March
Admission Requirements: Graduation from high school or recognized equivalent, and entrance examination.
Language of Instruction: Japanese

Student Enrolment, 1990:

	Women
Of the country	7347
Of other countries	16
Total	7363

4249 **SHITENNOJI KOKUSAI BUKKYO DAIGAKU**
Shitennoji International Buddhist University (IBU)
3-2-1 Gakuenmae Habikino-shi, Osaka 583
Telephone: (729) 56-3181
Fax: (729) 56-6011
Gakucho (President): Sonkyo Takito (1990-)

F. of Literature

Also junior college.
Founded 1957, acquired present status 1967 and present name 1981.
Academic Year: April to March (April-September; October-March).
Admission Requirements: Entrance examination for foreign students.
Fees (Yen): Tuition, 286,000 per semester.
Language of Instruction: Japanese.
Libraries: Central Library, 123,155 vols; Kangakuin library, 7,846.
Special Facilities (Museums, etc.): Shitennoji Museum.
Publications: Shitennoji (monthly); Bulletin; Research Reports; Studies (all annually).
Academic Staff, 1990:

Rank	Full-time	Part-time
Kyoju (Professors)	58	–
Jokyoju (Assistant Professors)	12	–
Koshi (Lecturers)	20	106
Total	90	106

Student Enrolment, 1990:

	Men	Women	Total
Of the country	1312	2257	3569

4250 **SHOIN JOSHIGAKUIN DAIGAKU**
Shoin Women's University and College
1-2-1 Shinohara-Obanoyama-cho, Nada-ku, Kobe-shi, Hyogo 657
Telephone: (78) 882-6122
Fax: (78) 801-1185
Gakucho (President): Kazuaki Kurozawa (1988-92)
Jimubucho (Registrar): Hiroshi Hirakawa

D. of English and English/American Literature
Chairman: Yoshikazu Katsuyama; *staff* 26 (54)
D. of Japanese Literature
Chairman: Toru Asami; *staff* 20 (38)
D. of Fashion and Interior Design
Chairman: Kazuko Suita; *staff* 8 (22)
D. of Domestic Science
Chairman: Yoshié Ichikawa; *staff* 14 (28)
D. of English
Chairman: Yoshikazu Katsuyama; *staff* 21 (40)
Christian Culture Research I.
Head: Shozo Arai; *staff* 5

Also junior and senior high schools, and junior college.
Founded 1892, acquired present status and title 1966. Financially supported by tuition fees and government grant. Governing body: the Board of Trustees, comprising 17 members. Residential facilities for *c.* 200 students.
Arrangements for co-operation with: New Hampshire State University; Hobart and William Smith Colleges.
Academic Year: April to March (April-July; October-March).
Admission Requirements: Graduation from senior high school or equivalent or foreign equivalent, and entrance examination.
Fees (Yen): Registration, 300,000; tuition, 870,000 per annum.
Language of Instruction: Japanese.
Degrees and Diplomas: Gakushi, Bachelor, of Arts, 4 yrs.
Library: *c.* 180,000 vols.
Publications: Bunrin (Review of Japanese Literature); Shoin Review; Shoin Literary Review; Shoin Theological Review and Review of Living Science (all annually).

Academic Staff, 1990-91:

Rank	Full-time	Part-time
Kyoju (Professors)	47	
Jokyoju (Associate Professors)	26	
Koshi (Lecturers)	16	
Total	89	182

Student Enrolment, 1990-91:

	Women
Of the country	2649
Of other countries	27
Total	2676

4251 **SHOKEI DAIGAKU**

Shokei College

2155-7 Nirenoki, Shimizu-machi, Kumamoto-shi, Kumamoto 860
Telephone: (96) 338-8840
Fax: (96) 338-9301
Gakucho (President): Seiichi Uno
Jimukyokucho (Secretary-General): Hatsugi Motomura

F. of Literature
Dean: Michio Furusawa; *staff* 30 (20)

Founded 1888, acquired present status 1975. Residential facilities for academic staff and students.

Arrangements for co-operation with St. Mary College, Omaha.

Academic Year: April to March.

Admission Requirements: Graduation from high school or recognized equivalent, and entrance examination.

Fees (Yen): Registration, 160,000; tuition 400,000 per annum.

Language of Instruction: Japanese.

Degrees and Diplomas: Bachelor of Arts, 4 yrs.

Publication: Bulletin (annually).

Academic Staff, 1990-91:

Rank	Full-time	Part-time
Kyoju (Professors)	19	11
Jyokyoju (Associate Professors)	3	7
Koshi (Lecturers)	8	2
Total	30	20

Student Enrolment, 1990-91:

	Women
Of the country	522
Of other countries	1
Total	523

4252 **SHUCHIIN DAIGAKU**

Shuchiin College

545 Toji-cho, Hachijo-sagaru, Minami-ku, Kyoto-shi, Kyoto 601
Telephone: (75) 681-6513

F. of Buddhism

Founded 1905, acquired present status 1949. Financed mainly by the Shingon Sect.

Academic Year: April to March (April-September; October-March).

Admission Requirements: Graduation from high school or equivalent, and entrance examination.

Language of Instruction: Japanese.

Degrees and Diplomas: Bungakushi, Bachelor of Letters, 4 yrs.

Library: College Library, *c.* 51,000 vols.

Academic Staff: c. 30.

Student Enrolment: c. 40.

4253 **SHUJITSU JOSHI DAIGAKU**

Shujitsu Joshi University

1-6-1 Nishigawara, Okayama-shi, Okayama 703

F. of Literature

4254 **SHUKUTOKU DAIGAKU**

Shukutoku College

200 Daiganji-cho, Chiba-shi, Chiba 280

F. of Social Welfare

Founded 1965.

4255 **SOAI DAIGAKU**

Soai University

4-4-1 Nanko-Naka, Suminoe-ku, Osaka-shi, Osaka 559
Telephone: (6) 612-5900

F. of Music
F. of Humanities

Founded 1906 as conservatory, acquired present status 1958.

Academic Year: March to February (March-September; October-February).

Admission Requirements: Graduation from high school or recognized equivalent, and entrance examination.

Language of Instruction: Japanese.

Degrees and Diplomas: Gakushi, Bachelor.

4256 **SONODA GAKUEN JOSHI DAIGAKU**

Sonoda Gakuen Women's College

7-29-1 Minami-Tsukaguchi-cho, Amagasaki-shi, Hyogo 661
Telephone: (6) 429-1201
Fax: (6) 422-8523
Gakucho (President): Sodonojo Ichitani

F. of Language and Literature

Also junior college.

Founded 1963, acquired present status 1966. Residential facilities for students.

Arrangements for co-operation with: Griffith University; Brisbane College of Advanced Education; Christchurch Teachers' College, New Zealand; The University of the South Pacific.

Academic Year: April to March.

Admission Requirements: Graduation from high school and entrance examination.

Degrees and Diplomas: Gakushi, Bachelor, 4 yrs. Also Certificates, 2 yrs.

4257 **SUGINO JOSHI DAIGAKU**

Sugino Women's College

4-6-19 Kamiasaki, Shinagawa-ku, Tokyo 141

F. of Home Economics

Founded 1950, acquired present status 1964.

4258 **TACHIBANA JOSHI DAIGAKU**

Tachibana Women's University

34 Oyake Yamada-cho, Yamashina-ku, Kyoto-shi, Kyoto 607
Telephone: (75) 571-1111

F. of Letters

Founded 1967.

4259 **TAKACHIHO SHOKA DAIGAKU**

Takachiho University of Commerce

2-19-1 Omita, Sguinami, Tokyo 168

F. of Commerce

Founded 1912, reorganized 1950.

4260 **TEIKOKU JOSHI DAIGAKU**

Teikoku Women's College

6-173 Toda, Moriguchi-shi, Osaka 570
Telephone: (6) 902-0791
Fax: (6) 901-3716
Gakucho (President): Shogo Okuda (1983-)
Rijicho: Shogo Okuda

D. of Food Sciences
Chairman: Machiko Asano; *staff* 7 (13)
D. of Clothing and Fashion
Chairman: Shuzo Azuma; *staff* 6 (10)
D. of Juvenile Studies
Chairman: Masahiro Tatebe; *staff* 14 (11)

Also kindergarten, junior and senior high schools, and junior college.

Founded 1962 as junior college, acquired present status and title 1965 Governing body: the Board of Trustees. Residential facilities for students.

Academic Year: April to March (April-July; September-March).

Admission Requirements: Graduation from high school and entrance examination.

Fees (Yen): 754,800-930,000.

Language of Instruction: Japanese.

Degrees and Diplomas: Kaseigakushi, Bachelor of Home Economics, 4 yrs. Teaching Certificates.

Library: Central Library, 62,671 vols.

Publication: Bulletin (annually).

Academic Staff, 1990:

Rank	Full-time	Part-time
Kyoju (Professors)	39	–
Jokyoju (Assistant Professors)	28	–
Koshi (Lecturers)	23	154
Joshu (Assistants)	11	3
Total	101	157

Student Enrolment, 1990:

	Women
Of the country	2534
Of other countries	6
Total	2540

4261 **TENRI DAIGAKU**

Tenri University

1050 Somanouchi-cho, Tenri-shi, Nara 632

Telephone: (7436) 3-1511

Gakucho (President): Tadakazu Yamada (1985-)

Jimukyokucho: Koichi Nishizono

F. of Letters

Head: Minoru Jinanishi; *staff* 31 (19)

F. of Foreign Languages

Head: Hisashi Maeda; *staff* 70 (39)

F. of Physical Education

Head: Narao Kishi; *staff* 21 (5)

F. of Liberal Arts

Head: Shinji Nishitani; *staff* 28 (37)

F. of Arts and Sciences (including Library Science and Museology)

Osyasato Research I.

Head: Tadakazu Yamada; *staff* 8 (3)

Founded 1925 as foreign language school, acquired present status and title 1949. Studies based on Tenrikyo doctrine. Financially supported by tuition fees, government subsidies, and Tenrikyo grants. Residential facilities for academic staff and students.

Arrangements for co-operation with Indiana University.

Academic Year: April to March (April-September; October-March).

Admission Requirements: Graduation from high school and entrance examination.

Language of Instruction: Japanese.

Degrees and Diplomas: Gakushi, Bachelor, of–Arts; Physical Education, 4 yrs.

Libraries: 1,456,962 vols; specialized libraries.

Special Facilities (Museums, etc.): Tenri Sankokan Museum.

Publications: Bulletin; Journal of Religion; Biblia; Yamanobenomichi Untei; Yamatobunka; Chosen Gakuho (Journal of the Academic Association of Koreanology in Japan).

Academic Staff, 1986-87:

Rank	Full-time	Part-time
Kyoju (Professors)	64	44
Jokyoju (Assistant Professors)	48	16
Koshi (Lecturers)	30	30
Joshu (Assistants)	9	–
Foreign Teachers	16	13
Total	167	103

Student Enrolment, 1986-87:

	Men	Women	Total
Of the country	1719	919	2638
Of other countries	18	13	31
Total	1737	932	2669

4262 **TEZUKAYAMA DAIGAKU**

Tezukayama University

7-1-1 Tezukayama, Nara-shi, Nara 631

Telephone: (742) 45-4701

F. of Liberal Arts

Also kindergarten and grade schools and junior college.

Founded 1964. Governing body: the Board of Trustees, comprising 67 members. Residential facilities for students.

Academic Year: April to March (April-September; October-February).

Admission Requirements: Graduation from high school or equivalent, and entrance examination.

Language of Instruction: Japanese.

Degrees and Diplomas: Gakushi, Bachelor–Kyoyogakushi, arts, 4 yrs. Diplomas in–Library Science; Museum Work, 2 yrs. Also teaching qualifications, 2 yrs.

Library: c. 110,000 vols.

Publications: Bulletin (annually); Review (4 times a year).

Academic Staff: c. 50 (70).

Student Enrolment: c. 1330.

4263 **TEZUKAYAMA GAKUIN DAIGAKU**

Tezukayama Gakuin University

1823 Imakuma, Sayama-cho, Minamikawachi-gun, Osaka 589

Telephone: (723) 65-0865

F. of Literature

Also kindergarten, elementary, junior and senior high schools, and junior college.

Founded 1916, became university 1966. Residential facilities for students.

Academic Year: April to March (April-October; October-February).

Admission Requirements: Graduation from high school and entrance examination.

Languages of Instruction: Japanese and English.

Degrees and Diplomas: Gakushi, Bachelor–Bungakushi, letters, 4 yrs. Also Teaching, Librarian, and Museum Staff Certificates.

Libraries: Central Library, *c.* 35,000 vols; departmental libraries.

Publications: Bulletin; Studies and Essays of Tezukayama Gakuin University Faculty.

Academic Staff: *c.* 90.

Student Enrolment: 860 (Women).

4264 **TOA DAIGAKU**

University of East Asia

2-1 Tchinomiya Gakuen-cho Shimonoseki-shi, Yamaguchi 751

Telephone: (832) 56-1111

Fax: (832) 56-9577

Gakucho (President): Takefumi Ikui

Jimukyokuchi (Secretary-General): Tetsuzo Tokushige

F. of Business Administration (including Humanities)

Dean: Tetsuhiko Sugihara; *staff* 33 (7)

F. of Engineering (including Mechanical Engineering, Food Sciences and Technology, and System Engineering)

Dean: Toshiro Ohwadano; *staff* 40 (6)

Science Research I.

Director: Hiroshi Sumida; *staff* 9 (3)

Founded 1966. Residential facilities for academic staff and 200 students.

Academic Year: April to March (April-September; October-March).

Admission Requirements: Graduation from high school or recognized equivalent, and entrance examination.

Fees (Yen): Registration, 247,200; tuition, 520,000-620,000.

Language of Instruction: Japanese.

Degrees and Diplomas: Gakushi, Bachelor, of–Business Administration; Engineering, 4 yrs.

Library: Central Library, 50,000 vols.

Special Facilities (Museums, etc.): Tea Ceremony Room.

Publication: Toa Daigaku Gakujutsu Kenkyusho.

Academic Staff, 1990:

Rank	Full-time	Part-time
Kyoju (Professors)	42	–
Jyokyoju (Associate Professors)	19	–
Koshi (Lecturers)	16	13
Total	77	13

Student Enrolment, 1990:

	Men	Women	Total
Of the country	2065	37	2102

4265 **TOHO GAKUEN DAIGAKU**

Toho Gakuen School of Music

41-1-1 Wakaba-cho, Chofu-shi, Tokyo 182

Telephone: (3) 307-4101

S. of Music

Also junior college.

Founded 1952 as junior college, acquired present status 1961. Governing body: the Board of Trustees. Residential facilities for junior college academic staff and for students.

Academic Year: April to March (April-July; September-March).

Admission Requirements: Graduation from high school and entrance examination.

Language of Instruction: Japanese.

Degrees and Diplomas: Geijutsguakushi, Bachelor of Fine Arts, 4 yrs. Also Diploma, 3-7 yrs.

Libraries: University Library, *c.* 45,820 vols; junior college, *c.* 5000.

Publications: Bulletin (quarterly); Toho Education (biannually).

Academic Staff: c. 70 (200).

Student Enrolment: c. 790.

4266 **TOHOKU JOSHI DAIGAKU**

Tohoku Women's College

1-2-1 Toyohara, Hirosaki-shi, Aomori 036

Telephone: (172) 33-2289

F. of Home Economics

Founded 1946, reorganized 1968.

4267 **TOHOKU KOGYO DAIGAKU**

Tohoku Institute of Technology

35-1 Yagiyama-kasumicho Taihakuku, Sendai-shi, Miyagi 982

Telephone: (22) 229-1151

Fax: (22) 228-2781

Gakucho (President): Shun-ichi Iwasaki (1989-91)

Jimubucho (Director of Administrative Affairs): Shohei Segawa

D. of Electronics

Chairman: Yukio Hiratate; *staff* 27 (10)

D. of Communication Engineering

Chairman: Hiroshi Ujiie; *staff* 26 (9)

D. of Architecture

Chairman: Hideo Shinohe; *staff* 31 (6)

D. of Civil Engineering

Chairman: Hikoto Takahashi; *staff* 31 (7)

D. of Industrial Design

Chairman: Jihei Suzuki; *staff* 19 (16)

Informatics L.

Director: Torao Sekio; *staff* 3

Founded 1964. Governing body: the Board of Trustees, comprising 10 members. Residential facilities for 260 students.

Academic Year: April to March (April-September; October-March).

Admission Requirements: Graduation from high school and entrance examination.

Fees (Yen): 857,000-1,125,000 per annum.

Language of Instruction: Japanese.

Degrees and Diplomas: Gakushi, Bachelor–Kogakushi, engineering, 4 yrs.

Library: Central Library, 123,000 vols.

Publication: Memoirs (annually).

Academic Staff, 1990:

Rank	Full-time	Part-time
Kyoju (Professors)	53	56
Jokyoju (Assistant Professors)	47	27
Koshi (Lecturers)	15	12
Joshu (Assistants)	65	–
Total	180	95

Student Enrolment, 1990:

	Men	Women	Total
Of the country	3308	180	3488
Of other countries	1	–	1
Total	3309	180	3489

4268 **TOHOKU SEIKATSU BUNKA DAIGAKU**

Tohoku Living Culture College

1-18 Nijinooka, Izumi-shi, Miyagi 980

Telephone: (22) 272-7511

F. of Domestic Science

Founded 1958.

4269 **TOKAI JOSHI DAIGAKU**

Tokai Women's College

Kirino-cho, Kakamigahara-shi, Gifu 504

Telephone: (583) 89-2200

F. of Liberal Arts

4270 **TOKOHA GAKUEN DAIGAKU**

Tokoha Gakuen University

100 Sena, Shizuoka-shi, Shizuoka 420

Telephone: (542) 63-1125

F. of Education

F. of Foreign Languages

4271 **TOKUYAMA DAIGAKU**

Tokuyama University

843-4-2 Kume-Kurigasako, Tokuyama-shi, Yamaguchi 745

Telephone: (834) 28-0411

Fax: (834) 28-8790

Gakucho (President): Kentaro Murata

F. of Economics

Dean: Ryoko Kaneda; *staff* 19 (1)

F. of Management

Dean: Akira Marukawa; *staff* 15 (6)

Economic Research I.

Director: Kanejiro Tsumori; *staff* 5

Computer Ce.

Head: Kimio Fujimura; *staff* 3

Founded 1971. Residential facilities for students.

Academic Year: April to March.

Admission Requirements: Graduation from high school or recognized equivalent, and entrance examination.

Fees (Yen): Tuition, 436,000 per annum.

Language of Instruction: Japanese.

Degrees and Diplomas: Gakushi, Bachelor, 4 yrs.

Library: Library, 98,000 vols.

Publications: Tokuyama Daigaku Ronso (biannually); Riyo (annually).

Academic Staff, 1990:

Rank	Full-time	Part-time
Kyoju (Professors)	29	–
Jyokyoju (Assistant Professors)	21	–
Koshi (Instructors)	9	21
Joshu (Assistants)	2	–
Total	61	21

Student Enrolment, 1990:

	Men	Women	Total
Of the country	2353	44	2397

4272 **TOKYO JOSHI TAIIKU DAIGAKU**

Tokyo Women's College of Physical Education

620 Tanigawakami, Aoyagi, Kunitachi-shi, Tokyo 186

Telephone: (425) 72-4131

Physical Education

Founded 1962.

Academic Year: April to March (April-September; October-March).

Admission Requirements: Graduation from high school and entrance examination.

Language of Instruction: Japanese.

Degrees and Diplomas: Taiikugakushi, Bachelor of Physical Education, 4 yrs.

Library: College Library, *c.* 50,000 vols.

Academic Staff: c. 80.

Student Enrolment: c. 600.

4273 **TOKYO KASEI DAIGAKU**

Tokyo Kasei University

1-18-1 Kaga, Itabashi-ku, Tokyo 173

Telephone: (3) 961-5226

Fax: (3) 962-7135

Gakucho (President): Yoichi Ikemoto

Jimukyokucho (Secretary-General): Tetsuzo Takahashi

F. of Home Economics

Dean: Ichitaro Uematsu; *staff* 46 (27)

F. of Humanities (including Psychology and Education)
Dean: Toshikazu Horiguchi; *staff* 14 (24)
Domestic Science Research I.
Also kindergarten, high school, junior high school, and junior college.
Founded 1922 as school, became college 1949. Residential facilities for 400 students.
Academic Year: April to March (April-September; October-March).
Admission Requirements: Graduation from high school and entrance examination.
Fees (Yen): Registration, 267,800; tuition, 530,000 per annum.
Language of Instruction: Japanese.
Degrees and Diplomas: Gakushi, Bachelor–Kaseigakushi, domestic science; Bungakushi, humanities, 4 yrs.
Library: University Library, total, 195,580 vols.
Publication: Reports of the Studies of Tokyo Kasei Daigaku (annually).
Press or Publishing House: Tokyo Kasei University Press.
Academic Staff, 1990:

Rank	Full-time	Part-time
Kyoju (Professors)	59	–
Jokyoju (Associate Professors)	40	–
Koshi (Instructors)	30	121
Joshu (Research Assistants)	48	21
Total	177	142

Student Enrolment, 1990:

	Women
Of the country	5713
Of other countries	27
Total	5740

4274 **TOKYO KASEI GAKUIN DAIGAKU**
Tokyo Kasei Gakuin College
2600 Aihara-machi, Machida-shi, Tokyo 194-02
Telephone: (427) 82-9811
Fax: (427) 82-9880
Gakucho (President): Masakazu Uzawa
Jimukyokucho (Secretary-General): Kazuji Morishima

F. of Home Economics
Dean: Nobuo Tamiya; *staff* 62 (55)
F. of Humanities
Dean: Noboru Haga; *staff* 33 (26)
Also junior and senior high schools.
Founded 1927 as Tokyo Vocational School of Home Economics, became junior college 1950, acquired present statusand title 1988. Governing body: the Board of Trustees. Some residential facilities for students.
Academic Year: April to March (April-September; October-March).
Admission Requirements: Graduation from high school or equivalent or foreign equivalent, and entrance examination.
Fees (Yen): Registration, 300,000; tuition, 660,000-700,000 per annum.
Language of Instruction: Japanese.
Degrees and Diplomas: Gakushi, Bachelor–Kaseigakushi, home economics; Bungakushi, arts, 4 yrs.
Library: Central Library, *c.* 156,352 vols.
Special Facilities (Museums, etc.): Museum of Living Culture.
Publication: Journal (annually).
Academic Staff, 1990:

Rank	Full-time	Part-time
Kyoju (Professors):	40	–
Jyokyoju (Associate Professors)	25	–
Koshi (Assistant Professors)	13	81
Joshu (Research Assistants)	17	–
Total	95	81

Student Enrolment, 1990:

	Women
Of the country	1731
Of other countries	3
Total	1734

4275 **TOKYO KOKA DAIGAKU**
Tokyo Engineering University
1404-1 Katakura-cho, Hachioji-shi, Tokyo 192
Telex: 2862-558 TEUN J
Telephone: (426) 37-2111
Fax: (426) 37-2118
Gakucho (President): Noboru Takagi
Jimukyokucho (Secretary-General): Tatsumi Negishi

F. of Engineering
F. of Electronics
Dean: Shoichiro Yamaguchi; *staff* 11 (4)
F. of Information Technology
Dean: Hiroji Nishino; *staff* 11 (2)
F. of Mechatronics (Robotics, Control Engineering, Mechanical System Engineering, and Sensor Engineering)
Dean: Katsuhiko Noda; *staff* 12 (1)
Founded 1986 by the Nippon Denshi Kogakuin Educational Foundation.
Academic Year: April to March.
Admission Requirements: Graduation from high school or recognized equivalent, and entrance examination.
Language of Instruction: Japanese.
Degrees and Diplomas: Gakushi, Bachelor–Kogakushi, science engineering, 4 yrs.
Library: 23,998 vols.
Academic Staff, 1990:

Rank	Full-time	Part-time
Kyoju (Professors)	39	–
Jokyoju (Associate Professors)	9	–
Koshi (Assistant Professors)	10	–
Joshu (Assistants)	–	15
Total	58	15

Student Enrolment, 1990:

	Men	Women	Total
Of the country	1549	63	1612

4276 **TOKYO ONGAKU DAIGAKU**
Tokyo Music College
3-4-5 Minami-Ikebukuro, Toshima-ku, Tokyo 186
Telephone: (3) 982-3186

F. of Music
Founded 1907 as school, acquired present status 1963.
Academic Year: April to March (April-July; September-March).
Admission Requirements: Graduation from high school or equivalent, and entrance examination.
Language of Instruction: Japanese.
Degrees and Diplomas: Bungakushi, Bachelor of Letters, 4 yrs.
Library: College Library, *c.* 11,900 vols.
Academic Staff: c. 100.
Student Enrolment: c. 260.

4277 **TOKYO ZOKEI DAIGAKU**
Tokyo University of Art and Design
3-2707 Motohachioji, Hachioji-shi, Tokyo 193
Telephone: (426) 61-4401
Fax: (426) 61-4401
Gakucho (President): Kyo Toyoguchi (1984-)
Jimukyokucho (Secretary-General): Iwao Ishikura

F. of Art and Design
Founded 1966.
Arrangements for co-operation with Wuxi Institute of Light Industry, China.
Academic Year: April to March.
Admission Requirements: Graduation from high school or equivalent or foreign equivalent, and entrance examination.
Fees (Yen): 1,379,000-1,391,000 per annum.
Language of Instruction: Japanese.
Degrees and Diplomas: Bungakushi, Bachelor of Arts, 4 yrs.

Academic Staff, 1990:

Rank	Full-time	Part-time
Kyoju (Professors)	32	–
Jokyoju (Associate Professors)	24	–
Koshi (Lecturers)	5	80
Total	61	80

Student Enrolment, 1990:

	Men	Women	Total
Of the country	735	605	1340

4278 **TOWA DAIGAKU**
Towa University
1-1-1 Chikushigaoka, Minami-ku, Fukuoka-shi, Fukuoka 815
Telephone: (92) 541-1511

F. of Engineering

Also women's junior college.

Founded 1967. Governing body: the Board of Directors.

Academic Year: April to March (April-September; October-March).

Admission Requirements: Graduation from high school and entrance examination.

Language of Instruction: Japanese.

Degrees and Diplomas: Kogakushi, Bachelor of Engineering, 4 yrs.

Library: 40,000 vols.

Publications: Towa Daigaku Kiyo; Junshin Kiyo (both annually).

Academic Staff: c. 45 (40).

Student Enrolment: c. 410.

4279 **UENO GAKUEN DAIGAKU**
Ueno Gakuen College
4-24-12 Higashiueno, Taito-ku, Tokyo 110
Telephone: (3) 842-1021
Fax: (3) 843-7548
Gakucho (President): Hiro Ishibashi
Somubucho: Seizaburo Yasuno

F. of Music

Head: Hiroshi Hoshino; *staff* 33 (76)

Also junior and senior high schools and junior college.

Founded 1904 as school, became junior college 1952, acquired present status 1958. Governing body: the Board of Trustees, comprising 5 members. Residential facilities for academic staff and students.

Arrangements for co-operation with St. Hilda's College, University of Oxford.

Academic Year: April to March (April-September; October-March).

Admission Requirements: Graduation from high school or recognized equivalent or foreign equivalent, and entrance examination.

Fees (Yen): Registration, 1,270,800; tuition, 767,000.

Languages of Instruction: Japanese and English.

Degrees and Diplomas: Geijutsugakushi, Bachelor of Arts, 4 yrs. Also diplomas for teachers (senior and junior school levels), 2-4 yrs. Diplomas in Music, 2 yrs.

Library: College Library, *c.* 80,000 vols.

Special Facilities (Museums, etc.): The Institute for the Study of Musical Instruments; The Research Archives for Japanese Music.

Publications: Ueno Gakuen Gakuho (bulletin) (annually); Kiyo (every 5 yrs).

Academic Staff, 1990:

Rank	Full-time	Part-time
Kyoju (Professors)	32	–
Jokyoju (Assistant Professors)	14	–
Koshi (Lecturers)	16	106
Total	62	106

Student Enrolment, 1990:

	Women
Of the country	1120

4280 **WAYO JOSHI DAIGAKU**
Wayo Women's University
2-3-1 Kohnodai, Ichikawa-shi, Chiba 272
Telephone: (473) 71-1111

F. of Literature and Home Economics

Founded 1897 as school, renamed Wayo Women's Senmon Gakko 1928, acquired present status 1949.

Academic Staff: c. 100.

Student Enrolment: c. 1500.

4281 **YAHATA DAIGAKU**
Yahata University
5-9-1 Edamitsu,Yahatahigashi-ku, Kitakyushu-shi, Fukuoka 805

F. of Law and Economics

Founded 1947, reorganized 1950.

4282 **YAMANASHI GAKUIN DAIGAKU**
Yamanashi Gakuin University
2-4-5 Sakaori, Kofu-shi, Yamanashi 400
Telephone: (552) 33-1111

F. of Law (including Business Administration)

Founded 1946 as Yamanashi Jissen Women's Koto Gakuin, became junior college 1950, acquired present status 1962.

Academic Staff: c. 40.

Student Enrolment: c. 650.

4283 **YASHIRO GAKUIN DAIGAKU**
St. Michael's University
5-1-1 Manabigaoka, Tarumi-ku, Kobe-shi, Hyogo 655
Telephone: (78) 709-3851

F. of Economics

Founded 1968.

4284 **YASUDA JOSHI DAIGAKU**
Yasuda Women's University
6-13-1 Yasuhigashi, Asaminami-ku, Hiroshima-shi, Hiroshima 731-01
Telephone: (82) 878-8111

F. of Letters

Also kindergarten, junior and senior high schools.

Founded 1915 as school, became junior college 1955, acquired present status 1966. Governing body: the Board of Trustees. Residential facilities for students.

Academic Year: April to March (April-October; October-March).

Admission Requirements: Graduation from high school and entrance examination.

Languages of Instruction: Japanese and English.

Degrees and Diplomas: Bungakushi, Bachelor of Letters, 4 yrs. Also teaching certificates and professional qualifications.

Library: Central Library, *c.* 110,000 vols.

Publication: Journal (annually).

Academic Staff: c. 75 (75).

Student Enrolment: c. 2050.

4285 **YOKOHAMA SHOKA DAIGAKU**
Yokohama College of Commerce
4-11-1 Higashi Terao, Tsurumi-ku, Yokohama-shi, Kanagawa 230
Telephone: (45) 571-3901
Fax: (45) 571-4125
Gakucho (President): Kazuo Ohsawa
Jimukyokucho Dairi (Acting Secretary-General): Katsutoshi Sugimitsu

F. of Commerce

Dean: Yoshitomo Miyahara; *staff* 54 (78)

D. of Commerce

Director: Mitsuo Mochizuki; *staff* 14 (21)

D. of Foreign Trade and Tourism

Director: Tsutomu Hara; *staff* 10 (8)

D. of Management Information (including Tourism)

Director: Masao Ohyama; *staff* 10 (9)

Founded 1967, reorganized 1969. Financially supported by tuition fees and government subsidies. Governing body: the Hyogiinkai (Board of Trustees), comprising 15 members.

Academic Year: April to March (April-July; September-February).

Admission Requirements: Graduation from high school and entrance examination.

Fees (Yen): Registration, 250,000; tuition, 500,000 per annum.

Language of Instruction: Japanese.

Degrees and Diplomas: Bachelor of Commerce, 4 yrs.

Library: College Library, *c.* 86,063 vols.

Publications: Ronshu (biannually); Kiyo (irregular); Yokohama Shokadaigaku Kokaikoza (Summary of Extension Programmes, annually).

Academic Staff, 1990:

Rank	Full-time	Part-time
Kyoju (Professors)	29	–
Jokyoju (Associate Professors)	23	–
Joshu (Assistant Professors)	3	–
Koshi (Lecturers)	–	78
(Visiting Professors)	5	–
Total	60	78

Student Enrolment, 1990:

	Men	Women	Total
Of the country	1770	150	1920
Of other countries	21	21	42
Total	1791	171	1962

JORDAN

Universities

4286 ***BETHLEHEM UNIVERSITY**

Rue des Frères, B.P. 9, Bethlehem (West Bank)
Telex: 26526 NDC IL
Telephone: 74-1241
President: Msgr. Raouf Najjar (1989-)
Vice-Chancellor: Anton de Roeper, FSC

F. of Arts
Dean: Mahmoud Abu Kitteh; *staff* 44 (3)
F. of Science
Dean: Adnan Shqair; *staff* 22
F. of Business Administration
Dean: Sami El-Yousef; *staff* 11
F. of Nursing
Dean: Maria Homberg; *staff* 6 (1)
F. of Education
Dean: Joseph Loewenstein
I. of Hotel Management
Director: Abu El-Walid Dajani; *staff* 4 (12)

Founded 1973 by the American De La Salle Brothers and tracing its origins to a college they opened in 1893. A private institution recognized by the Ministry of Education and sponsored by the Holy See. Governing body: the Board of Trustees. Residential facilities for 36 women students.

Arrangements for co-operation with University College, Dublin.

Academic Year: September to June (September-January; February-June).

Admission Requirements: Secondary school certificate or recognized equivalent, and entrance examination.

Fees (Dinars): 160 per annum.

Languages of Instruction: Arabic and English.

Degrees and Diplomas: Associate Degree in Business Administration, 2 yrs. Bachelor of–Arts; Science; Business Administration; Arts in Elementary Education; Science in Nursing, 4 yrs. Diploma in Tourism, 2 yrs; Hotel Management, 4 yrs.

Library: Central Library, 35,000 vols.

Publication: Journal (annually).

Academic Staff, 1986-87:

Rank	Full-time
Professors	5
Associate Professors	5
Assistant Professors	20
Instructors	64
Lecturers	14
Total	108

Student Enrolment, 1986-87:

	Men	Women	Total
Of the country	832	689	1521

4287 ***BIRZEIT UNIVERSITY**

P.O. Box 14, Birzeit (West Bank)
Telex: 23076 BIRZEIT JO
Telephone: 95-4381
Fax: 956229
President: Hanna Nasir (1972-)
Vice-President: Gabi Baramki

F. of Arts (including Archaeology, Education, and Middle East Studies)
Dean: Naji Abdul Jabbar; *staff* 86 (8)
F. of Science
Dean: Simon Kuttab; *staff* 53 (2)
F. of Commerce and Economics
Dean (Acting): Sameer Hazbon; *staff* 18 (3)
F. of Engineering
Dean: Bishara Abu Ghannam; *staff* 35 (2)
Adult Literacy P.
Director: Hiam Abu Ghazaleh; *staff* 6
Community Health Ce.
Director: Rita Giacaman; *staff* 10 (2)
Ce. for Environmental and Occupational Health Sciences
Director: Ramzi Sansur; *staff* 7
Ce. for Palestinian Research and Documentation
Director: Ali Jarbawi; *staff* 9
I. of Archaeology
Director: Alber Clock; *staff* 8

Founded 1924 as school, acquired present status and title 1972. A private institution financed by student feesand contributions. Governing bodies: the Board of Trustees; the University Council.

Arrangements for co-operation with the Universities of: Bremen; Paris VII; Amsterdam; Indiana; Durham; Carleton; Delft University of Technology; University of Copenhagen; Brussels (Free); Louvain; Umeå; Montpellier III.

Academic Year: October to July (October-February; March-July).

Admission Requirements: Secondary school certificate or foreign equivalent.

Fees (Dinars): 110-150 per semester, according to Faculty.

Languages of Instruction: Arabic and English.

Degrees and Diplomas: Bachelor of–Arts; Science; Commerce, 4 yrs; Engineering, 5 yrs. Teaching qualification (secondary level).

Libraries: 94,000 vols (64,000 in English; 30,000 in Arabic).

Publications: Bulletins and Newsletters; Ataq Filistiniyya (Birzeit Research Review).

Academic Staff, 1986-87:

Rank	Full-time	Part-time
Professors	6	–
Associate Professors	16	–
Assistant Professors	89	5
Lecturers	7	–
Instructors	80	9
Assistant Instructors	14	–
Total	212	14

Student Enrolment, 1986-87:

	Men	Women	Total
Of the country	1689	707	2396

4288 ***UNIVERSITY OF JORDAN**

Amman (East Bank)
Telex: 21629 UNIVJ JO
Telephone: 843555
Fax: (962-6) 832318
President: Mahmud Samra (1989-)
Secretary-General: Mohammad Saleh Abdul-Ati

F. of Arts (including Archaeology, Education, Population Studies, Modern Languages, and Sociology)
Dean: Hussein Atwan; *staff* 117 (6)
F. of Economics and Administration (including Business Administration and Political Science)
Dean: Isma'il Abdul Rahman; *staff* 66 (15)
F. of Science
Dean: Salim Sabri; *staff* 111 (2)
F. of Shari'a (Islamic Studies)
Dean (Acting): Ibrahim Zeid El-Keilani; *staff* 33 (2)
F. of Medicine
Dean: Musleh Tarawneh; *staff* 128 (6)
F. of Agriculture
Dean: Sudki Khader; *staff* 68 (4)
F. of Education
Dean: Omar Sheikh; *staff* 49
F. of Engineering and Technology (including Architecture)
Dean: Isam Za'balawi; *staff* 94 (13)
F. of Law
Dean: Mohammed Hammoury; *staff* 18

F. of Physical Education
Dean: Mohammad Hammouri; *staff* 18
F. of Nursing
Dean: Majida Zaki Eddin; *staff* 36
F. of Pharmacy
Dean (Acting): Omar Shaheen; *staff* 12 (1)
F. of Dentistry
Dean (Acting): Ghazi Bakka'in; *staff* 15 (1)
Deanship of Scientific Research
Dean: Hammam Ghasib; *staff* 19
Language Ce.
Director: Mohammad al-Anani; *staff* 10
Computer Ce.
Director; Taleb Sari'; *staff* 28
Ce. of Islamic Culture
Director: Amin al-Qdah *staff* 8
Water Research and Studies Ce.
Director: Elias Salameh; *staff* 6
Ce. for Strategic Studies
Director: Hussein Touka; *staff* 6
Ce. for Education Development for Health Personnel
Director: Kandil Shaker; *staff* 12
Educational Technology Ce.
Director: Narjis Hamdi; *staff* 15
Ce. of Phonetics Research and Studies
Director: Yousef al-Halees; *staff* 6

Founded 1962 as an independent national institution of higher education. Governing bodies: the Council of Higher Education; the University Council. Residential facilities for academic staff and women students.

Arrangements for co-operation with the Universities of: Baghdad; Mosul; Al-Mustansiriyah; California, Long Beach; Michigan State; Ohio State; Wyoming; New York State; Glasgow; Reading; London; Oxford; Winnipeg; British Colombia; San'a; Tashkent; Algiers; Qatar; Sheffield, Durham, Birmingham; Edinburgh; Dundee; Strathclyde; Wisconsin-Milwaukee; Mercer; Pittsburgh; Lyon II; Washington State; Arizona; Kiel; Frankfurt am Main; Essen; Nice; Ulm; Beijing; Poznań; Trieste; Prague; Brno; Prague Technical. Hatfield Polytechnic.

Academic Year: September to August (September-January; January-May; June-August).

Admission Requirements: Secondary school certificate or recognized equivalent.

Fees (Dinars): 6-20 per credit hour; postgraduate, 15-30. (US$): 60-112.50; postgraduate, 112-225.

Languages of Instruction: Arabic and English.

Degrees and Diplomas: Bachelor of–Arts, B.A.; Science, B.S., 3-6 yrs; Science in Medicine, 6 yrs. Master of–Arts, M.A.; Science, M.S., a further 2-3 yrs. Doctorate, Ph.D. Also Diploma, 2 yrs.

Library: c. 516,680 vols. Centre for Archives and Manuscripts,16,800 manuscripts, 2120 microfiche, 2623 microfilms, 293photostatic files, 537 slides, 15 video films, and 4 cassettes.

Special Facilities (Museums, etc.): Museums of Archaeology; Zoology; National Heritage; Medicine; Insects.

Publications: Dirasat (Research Journal) (biannually); Cultural Journal 'Al-Majallah al-Thaqafiyyahq' (quarterly).

Press or Publishing House: University Publishing House.

Academic Staff, 1988-89:

Rank	Full-time	Part-time
Professors	162	–
Associate Professors	180	–
Assistant Professors	279	–
Assistant Instructors	28	53
Lecturers	46	–
Research Assistants	74	–
Total	769	53

Student Enrolment, 1988-89:

	Men	Women	Total
Of the country	2325	2317	4642
Of other countries	547	305	852
Total	2872	2622	5494

4289 ***AL-QUDS UNIVERSITY/JERUSALEM UNIVERSITY**
P.O. Box 20002, Jerusalem
Vice-Chancellor: Z.M. Al Karmi
C. of Science and Technology
C. of Paramedical Professions
C. of Art (for Women)
C. of Islamic Theology

Founded 1982.

Degrees and Diplomas: Bachelor of–Arts; Science, 4-5 yrs. Master, 6-7 yrs. Higher Studies' Diploma, 5-6 yrs.

Library: c. 85,000 vols.

Academic Staff, 1986-87: 157 (32).

Student Enrolment, 1986-87: 1558.

4290 **JAMI'AT AL KHALIL**
Hebron University
P.O. Box 40, Hebron (West Bank)
Telephone: (2) 963293
President: Khulqi Khanfar (1988-)
Vice-President for Administrative Affairs: Ratib Al-Badawl
C. of Islamic Law (Shari'a)
Dean: H. Al-Sharbati; *staff* 15 (1)
C. of Arts (Arabic and English Languages, History, and Education)
Dean: A. Rajabi; *staff* 35 (12)
C. of Science
Dean: Awni Khatib; *staff* 12
C. of Agriculture (including Animal Husbandry, Plant Production, Ecnomics, Food Processing)
Dean: Sufian Sultan; *staff* 7

Founded 1971 as theological college, acquired present status and title 1980. A private institution. Governing bodies: the Board of Trustees; the University Council.

Academic Year: October to June (October-February; March-June).

Admission Requirements: Secondary school certificate.

Fees (Dinars): 5 per credit hour, per semester.

Languages of Instruction: Arabic and English.

Degrees and Diplomas: Bachelor of–Arts; Science in Agricuture, 4 yrs. Diplomas in Education.

Library: Central Library, 35,000 vols.

Publication: The University Mission.

Press or Publishing House: Hebron University Publishing Office.

Academic Staff, 1989-90: 69.

Student Enrolment, 1989-90:

	Men	Women	Total
Of the country	900	950	1850

4291 ***MU'TAH UNIVERSITY**
P.O. Box 7, Mu'tah (East Bank)
Telex: 63003 MU'TAH JO
Telephone: 629545
President: Awad Khleifat (1990-)
Assistant President: Majed Qteishat
F. of Sciences (including Computer Sciences)
Dean: Sayed El-Ghabaty; *staff* 33 (2)
F. of Engineering
Dean: Inayatallah Glapsa; *staff* 24 (2)
F. of Arts (Arabic Language and Literature, English Language and Literature, Education, History and Archaeology, Social Sciences, Shari'a and Islamic Studies)
Dean: Anwar Abu Sweilem; *staff* 62 (2)
F. of Administration and Law Sciences (including Economics and Political Science)
Dean: Sami Abdella; *staff* 33 (1)
F. of Police Sciences
F. of Military Sciences

Founded 1981. A State institution enjoying academic and administrative autonomy. Governing body: the University Council. Some residential facilities for academic staff and students.

Arrangements for research work and faculty exchange with: Glasgow University; Texas Consortium, and Universities in: Saudi Arabia, Oman, United Arab Emirates.

Academic Year: October to June (October-January; February-June).

Admission Requirements: Secondary school certificate. Admission is highly competitive.

Fees (Dinars): 8-15 per credit hour.

Languages of Instruction: Arabic and English.

Degrees and Diplomas: Bachelor of–Law; Business Administration; Accountancy; Public Administration; Economy; Political Science; Arts in–English; Arabic; History and Archaeology; Social Sciences; Islamic Studies; Science in Engineering, 4-5 yrs. Also Diploma in Education.

Library: Mu'tah University Library, 120,000 vols.

Publications: Mu'tah L.L-Buhooty Wa A-Dirassat (Humanities and Social Sciences; Natural and Applied Sciences).

Academic Staff, 1989-90:

Rank	Full-time	Part-time
Professors	10	–
Associate Professors	11	–
Assistant Professors	121	7
Lecturers	10	–
Total	152	7

Student Enrolment, 1989-90:

	Men	Women	Total
Of the country	2400	588	2988

4292 ***AN-NAJAH UNIVERSITY**

An-Najah National University

P.O. Box 7, Omar Ibn Khattab Street, Nablus (West Bank)
Telephone: (972-53) 70042
Fax: (972-53) 71122
President: Shawkat Z. Kilani
Vice-President: Bahjat Sabri

F. of Arts (Arabic, English, Geography, History and Archaeology, Sociology, Islamic Studies and Fine Arts)
Dean: Ahmad Hamid; *staff* 51
F. of Education
Dean: Husni Masri; *staff* 40
F. of Engineering
Dean: Mazen Rasikh Husni *staff* 22
F. of Economics and Administrative Sciences
Dean: Abdul Fattah Abu Shokor; *staff* 32
F. of Science
Dean: Mohammad Hannoun; *staff* 46
Rural Research Ce.
Director: Jamal Abu Omar; *staff* 6

Founded 1977. A private institution. Governing body: the Board of Trustees.

Arrangements for co-operation with: Milwaukee University; Universidad Autónoma de Madrid; Durham University.

Academic Year: October to June (October-January; March-June).

Admission Requirements: Secondary school Certificate.

Fees (Dinars): 130-160 per annum.

Languages of Instruction: Arabic, and English for Faculty of Science and Engineering.

Library: 126,000 vols.

Publication: Journal of Research (Humanities) (Pure and Applied Sciences) (biannually).

Press or Publishing House: Research and Documentation Centre.

Academic Staff, 1990:

Rank	Full-time
Professors	2
Associate Professors	16
Assistant Professors	82
Lecturers	1
Instructors	64
Assistant Instructors	26
Total	191

Student Enrolment, 1990:

	Men	Women	Total
Of the country	1909	1559	3468

4293 ***JAMI'AT EL-YARMOUK**

Yarmouk University

Irbid (East Bank)
Cables: yarmouk irbid
Telex: 51533 YARMOUK JO
Telephone: 271100
Fax: 2274725
President: Ali Mahafzah (1989-)
Vice-President (Academic Affairs): Fuad Sheikh Salem

F. of Science
Dean: Muhammad Shboul; *staff* 141 (10)
F. of Arts, Humanities, and Social Sciences (including Modern Languages and Journalism)
Dean: Shahir Rashdan; *staff* 152 (1)
F. of Education and Fine Arts (including Physical Education)
Dean: Youssuf Ghawanmeh; *staff* 85 (22)
F. of Economics and Administration
Dean: Abdul-Bari Durrah; *staff* 55 (3)
C. of Applied Engineering
Dean: Ibrahim Dokani; *staff* 17 (1)
I. of Archaeology and Anthropology
Director: Moawiyah; *staff* 14 (1)
F. of Education
Dean: Abdullah Zeid El-Keilani; *staff* 44 (18)
Ce. for Islamic Studies
Director: Abdel-Rahman Saleh; *staff* 9 (5)
Ce. for Jordanian Studies
Director: Talal Akasheh; *staff* 7
Language Ce.
Director: Khalaf El-Makhzoumi; *staff* 21 (2)
Research and Educational Development Ce.
Director: Yacoub Abu Hilo
D. for Lifelong Education and Community Services
Director: Ahmed El-Khatib; *staff* 13
Marine Science Station (Aqabah)

Founded 1975 by Royal Decree with Faculty of Arts and Science. A State institution enjoying academic and adminisrative autonomy. Largely financed by the State. Governing bodies: the Higher Education Council; the University Council. Some residential facilities for academic staff and for women students from remote areas.

Arrangements for co-operation with many Arab, American, European, Asian, and African Universities, together with scientific organizations, institutions, and centres.

Academic Year: September to August (September-January; February-June; June-August).

Admission Requirements: Secondary school certificate or recognized equivalent.

Fees (Dinars): 8-20 per credit hour; 60-113 for foreign students.

Languages of Instruction: Arabic and English.

Degrees and Diplomas: Bachelor of–Arts, B.A.; Science, B.S., 4-5 yrs. Master of–Arts in Education; Science, a further 2-3 yrs. Higher Diploma in Islamic Studies, 2 yrs. Also Teaching Diploma, 1 yr.

Library: c. 250,000 vols.

Special Facilities (Museums, etc.): Museum of Archaeology; Natural Sciences Museum.

Publication: Research Journals for Literature and Language and Humanities and Social Sciences (biannually).

Press or Publishing House: Yarmouk University Press.

Academic Staff, 1990:

Rank	Full-time	Part-time
Professors	29	–
Associate Professors	113	–
Assistant Professors	202	–
Instructors	32	–
Lecturers	57	45
Research Assistants	52	–
Total	505	45

Student Enrolment, 1990:

	Men	Women	Total
Of the country	6114	4123	10,327
Of other countries	102	195	297
Total	6216	4318	10,624

4294 ***JORDAN UNIVERSITY OF SCIENCE AND TECHNOLOGY**

Irbid (East Bank)
Telex: 55545 JUST JO
Telephone: (962-2) 295111
Fax: (962-2) 295123
President: Kamel Ajlouni (1986-)
Vice-President for Administration: F.E. Khasawneh

F. of Engineering
Dean: A. Abu El-Haija; *staff* 83 (3)
F. of Medicine
Dean: S. Hijazi: *staff* 57 (1)

F. of Dentistry
Dean: G. Howe; *staff* 14 (4)
F. of Pharmacy
Dean: El-S. Ebrahim; *staff* 13 (2)
F. of Nursing
Dean (Acting): N. Najib; *staff* 9
F. of Science
Dean: S. Mikbil; *staff* 35 (19)
F. of Agriculture and Veterinary Medicine
Dean: Fayez Khasawneh; *staff* 13

Founded 1986. Governing body: the University Council, comprising 24 members. Residential facilities for expatriate staff and women students.

Academic Year: September to May (September-January; January-May).

Admission Requirements: Secondary school certificate.

Fees (Dinars): 25 per semester.

Language of Instruction: English.

Degrees and Diplomas: Bachelor, 4-5 yrs. Master of Science, a further 2-3 yrs.

Library: J.U.S.T. Library, 40,000 vols.

Special Facilities (Museums, etc.): Agricultural Experiment Station.

Academic Staff, 1989-90:

Rank	Full-times
Professors	27
Associate Professors	34
Assistant Professors	115
Lecturers	34
Instructors	14
Total	253

Student Enrolment, 1989-90:

	Men	Women	Total
Of the country	1775	797	2572
Of other countries	119	57	176
Total	1894	854	2748

Other Institutions

4295 **INTERMEDIATE UNIVERSITY COLLEGE**
P.O. Box 922380, Ein Ghazel Road, Amman (East Bank)
Telephone: 664530
President: Yasin I. Sartawi
Dean: Ahmed Jaser

D. of Engineering and Applied Arts
Head: Samih Ibrahim; *staff* 9 (6)
D. of Paramedical Studies (including Pharmacy)
Head: Rasmeya Shakoor; *staff* 11 (6)
D. of Computer and Business Studies
Head: A'lyan Sharif; *staff* 18 (8)
D. of Academic and Teacher's Training
Head: Omiya Badran; *staff* 16 (6)

Founded 1978. Governing bodies: the Board of Directors; the Board of Trustees. Residential facilities for women students.

Academic Year: September to June (September-January; February-June).

Admission Requirements: Secondary school certificate or equivalent.

Fees (Dinars): 160,000-230,000 per semester.

Language of Instruction: Arabic.

Degrees and Diplomas: Diplomas, 2 yrs.

Academic Staff, 1989-90: 66 (26).

Student Enrolment, 1989-90:

	Men	Women	Total
Of the country	1400	1000	2400

4296 **UNRWA/UNESCO TRAINING CENTRE**
Amman (East Bank)

Founded 1967.

4297 **HUSSEIN INSTITUTE OF AGRICULTURE**
P.O. Box 7, Tulkarm (West Bank)
Telephone: 26

Founded 1931.

4298 **PRINCESS SUMAYA COLLEGE FOR INFORMATICS**
P.O. Box 6945, Amman (East Bank)
Telex: 21276 RAMAH JO
Telephone: 844700

Founded 1977.

4299 **PARAMEDICAL INSTITUTE**
P.O. Box 1097, Amman (East Bank)
Telephone: 775809

Founded 1973.

4300 **AMMAN POLYTECHNIC**
P.O. Box 15008, Marka, Amman (East Bank)
Telephone: 962550

Founded 1975.

4301 **HEBRON POLYTECHNIC**
P.O. Box 198, Hebron (West Bank)
Telephone: 962550

Founded 1978.

4302 **AL-HUSON POLYTECHNIC**
P.O. Box 50, Irbid-al-Husn (East Bank)
Telephone: 210400

Founded 1981.

4303 **INSTITUTE OF PUBLIC ADMINISTRATION**
Jubaiha, Amman (East Bank)

Founded 1968.

4304 **JORDAN COOPERATIVE INSTITUTE**
P.O. Box 1343, Amman (East Bank)
Telex: 21835
Telephone: 661513

Founded 1963.

4305 **INSTITUTE OF FINE ARTS**
Amman (East Bank)

Founded 1967.

4306 **JORDAN COLLEGE OF NURSING**
P.O. Box 491, Amman (East Bank)
Telephone: 773123

Founded 1966.

4307 **ROYAL POLICE COLLEGE**
P.O. Box 925425, Amman (East Bank)
Telephone: 621681

4308 **JORDAN JUNIOR COLLEGE OF SOCIAL WORK**
P.O. Box 8088, Amman (East Bank)
Telephone: 62936

Social Work

Founded 1966 as institute. Acquired present title 1981. A State institution under the jurisdiction of the Ministry of Social Development.

Academic Year: October to June (October-February; February-June).

Admission Requirements: Secondary school certificate.

Language of Instruction: Arabic.

Library: c. 3000 vols.

Academic Staff: c. 20 (20).

4309 **STATISTICAL TRAINING CENTRE**
P.O. Box 2015, Amman (East Bank)
Telephone: 24313
Director: Abdulhadi Alawin
Assistant Director: Fahad Hiyari

Statistics

Founded 1964. A State institution responsible to the Department of Statistics.

Academic Year: October to June (October-January; February-June).
Admission Requirements: Secondary school certificate.
Fees (Dinars): 143 per annum.
Language of Instruction: Arabic.
Degrees and Diplomas: Certificate of Assistant Statistician, 2 yrs.
Academic Staff: c. 15.
Student Enrolment: c. 50.

4310 **AJLOUN COMMUNITY COLLEGE**
Ajloun (East Bank)
Telephone: 26

D. of Education
D. of Commerce
Founded 1964, acquired present status and title 1980. Responsible to the Ministry of Education.
Academic Year: September to June (September-January; February-June).
Admission Requirements: Secondary school certificate.
Language of Instruction: Arabic.
Degrees and Diplomas: Diploma, 2 yrs.
Library: c. 22,000 vols.
Academic Staff: c. 30.
Student Enrolment: c. 950 (Women).

4311 **AMMAN COMMUNITY COLLEGE**
P.O. Box 1705, Amman (East Bank)
Telephone: 639124
Dean: Saleh D. Hindi
Administrative Assistant: Yousuf A. Abu Kaff

D. of Education
Head: Hisham A. Ulayan; *staff* 30
D. of Commerce
Director: Nader F. Ziod; *staff* 3
D. of Library Science and Journalism
Assistant Director: Nader F. Ziod; *staff* 4
Ce. of Educational Audio-Visual Aids
Supervisor: Ahmad H. Aidi; *staff* 2
Founded 1952 as Teacher Training Institute, acquired present status and title 1980. Responsible to the Ministry of Education. Residential facilities for academic staff and students.
Academic Year: September to June (September-January; February-June).
Admission Requirements: Secondary school certificate.
Fees (Dinars): 3 per credit hour.
Language of Instruction: Arabic.
Degrees and Diplomas: Diplomas, 2 yrs.
Library: c. 45,000 vols.
Academic Staff, 1989-90: 30.
Student Enrolment, 1989-90:

	Men	Women	Total
Of the country	150	150	300

4312 **AL-ANDULUS COMMUNITY COLLEGE**
P.O. Box 17215, Amman (East Bank)
Telephone: 816125
President: Al-Jaber H. Tayyem (1985-)

D. of Commerce
; *staff* 1 (8)
D. of Paramedical Studies
Head: Mashhour Al-Rasheid; *staff* 1 (3)
D. of Engineering
Head: Zeid Al-Halabi; *staff* 1
D. of Education
Head: Mohammad Faras; *staff* 3 (8)
Founded 1979 as Institute of Banking, acquired present status 1981. Responsible to the Ministry of Education.
Academic Year: September to June (September-January; February-June).
Admission Requirements: Secondary school certificate.
Fees (Dinars): 250-320 per annum.
Languages of Instruction: Arabic and English.
Degrees and Diplomas: Diplomas, 2 yrs.
Library: 3000 vols.
Academic Staff, 1986-87: 7 (21).
Student Enrolment, 1986-87:

	Men	Women	Total
Of the country	213	220	433
Of other countries	36	9	45
Total	249	229	478

4313 **ARAB COMMUNITY COLLEGE**
P.O. Box 926845, Amman (East Bank)
Telephone: 842181-2
Dean: Ali Abdul-Latif

D. of Engineering
Chairman: Sameeh Ahmad; *staff* 13 (2)
D. of Computer Sciences
Chairman: Mohannad Basbous; *staff* 11
D. of Commerce
Chairman: Salim Rustum; *staff* 20 (1)
D. of Education
Chairman: Ghaleb Ismail; *staff* 27 (3)
D. of Paramedical Studies (including Pharmacy)
Chairman: Jamal Othman; *staff* 9
Founded 1980. A private institution. Residential facilities for women students.
Arrangements for co-operation with the Universities of: Wentworth, Boston; North Carolina; Savannah State; Old Dominion, Virginia; Northern Arizona; Houston; Southern Colorado; Temple, Philadelphia; Memphis State. Rochester Institute of Technology, New York; Milwaukee School of Engineering.
Academic Year: September to June (September-January; February-June).
Admission Requirements: Secondary school certificate.
Fees: 150-180 per semester.
Language of Instruction: Arabic.
Degrees and Diplomas: Diplomas, 2 yrs.
Library: c. 18,000 vols.
Academic Staff, 1989-90: . 80.
Student Enrolment, 1989-90:

	Men	Women	Total
Of the country	1614	1199	2812
Of the countries	242	124	366
Total	1856	1323	3178

4314 **HITTEIN COMMUNITY COLLEGE**
P.O. Box 620914, Amman (East Bank)
Telephone: 780801
Dean: Abdul-Raheem Aref (1986-87)

D. of Engineering
Head: Issa Ali; *staff* 4 (3)
D. of Education
Head: Mohammed Abediseid; *staff* 10 (3)
D. of Economics
Head: Mohammad Shaleek; *staff* 6 (3)
D. of Paramedical Studies
Head: Salim Musleh; *staff* 5 (2)
Computer D.
Head: M. Adel; *staff* 3 (1)
Founded 1984. Responsible to the Ministry of Education.
Academic Year: September to June (September-January; February-June).
Admission Requirements: Secondary school certificate.
Fees (Dinars): 250 per annum.
Languages of Instruction: Arabic and English.
Degrees and Diplomas: Diplomas, 2 yrs.
Library: c. 1000 vols.
Academic Staff, 1986-87: 28 (13).
Student Enrolment, 1986-87:

	Men	Women	Total
Of the country	1450	1632	3082
Of other countries	35	16	51
Total	1485	1648	3133

4315 **HUWWARA COMMUNITY COLLEGE**
P.O. Box 1, Huwwara, Irbid (East Bank)
Telephone: 274967
Principal: Radi A. Wagfi (1952-)

D. of Education
Head: Mohammad Ghazal; *staff* 42 (5)
D. of Commerce
Head: Saleh Radaideh; *staff* 5 (1)
D. of Engineering (including Architecture)
Head: Emad Kofahi; *staff* 5 (1)
D. of Educational Technology
Head: Mahmoud Sharar; *staff* 1 (1)
D. of Nutrition and Home Management
Head: Amjad Sweidan; *staff* 2
D. of Vocational Studies (Agriculture)
Head: Amjad Sweidan; *staff* 1

Founded 1956 as teacher training college, acquired present status 1980. Responsible to the Ministry of Education. Residential facilities for academic staff and students.

Academic Year: September to June (September-January; February-June).
Admission Requirements: Secondary school certificate.
Fees (Dinars): 3-5 per credit hour.
Language of Instruction: Arabic.
Degrees and Diplomas: Diplomas, 2 yrs.
Library: 30,000 vols.
Academic Staff, 1986-87: 50 (9).
Student Enrolment, 1986-87:

	Men	Women	Total
Of the country	1092	1000	2092

4316 **IRBID COMMUNITY COLLEGE**
P.O. Box 1283 Irbid (East Bank)

Founded 1978.

4317 **JERASH COMMUNITY COLLEGE**
Jerash (East Bank)
Telephone: 51113
Dean: Mohammad Ahmed Rabia

D. of Engineering
D. of Education
D. of Commerce

Founded 1980. Responsible to the Ministry of Education. Residential facilities for academic staff.

Academic Year: September to June (September-January; February-June).
Admission Requirements: Secondary school certificate.
Languages of Instruction: Arabic and English.
Degrees and Diplomas: Diplomas, 2 yrs.
Library: c. 4000 vols.
Academic Staff: c. 20.
Student Enrolment: c. 300.

4318 **JORDAN COMMUNITY COLLEGE**
P.O. Box 19029, Amman (East Bank)
Telephone: 669141

Education
Paramedical Studies (Pharmacy)
Engineering
Commerce
Computer Sciences

Founded 1981. A private institution responsible to the Ministry of Education.

Academic Year: September to June (September-January; February-June).
Admission Requirements: Secondary school certificate.
Languages of Instruction: Arabic and English.
Degrees and Diplomas: Diplomas, 2 yrs.
Academic Staff: c. 20 (20).
Student Enrolment: c. 440.

4319 **AL-KARAK COMMUNITY COLLEGE**
AP.O. Box 52, Karak (East Bank)
Telephone: 51083

Founded 1979.

4320 **IBN KHALDOUN COMMUNITY COLLEGE**
P.O. Box 1202, Irbid (East Bank)
Telephone: 74731

Founded 1979.

4321 **KHALEEL COMMUNITY COLLEGE**
Khaleel (West Bank)

4322 **AL-KHAWARIZMI COMMUNITY COLLEGE**
P.O. Box 476, Amman (East Bank)
Telex: 22372 JO
Telephone: 669377

Founded 1974.

4323 **AL QUDS COMMUNITY COLLEGE**
P.O. Box 18334, Amman (East Bank)
Telephone: 22631

Founded 1980.

4324 **PRINCESS THARWAT COMMUNITY COLLEGE**
Queen Misbah Street, P.O. Box 3179, Amman (East Bank)
Telephone: 44249

Founded 1980.

4325 **AL-RAZI COMMUNITY COLLEGE**
P.O. Box 794, Irbid (East Bank)
Telephone: 71185

Founded 1979.

4326 **SALT COMMUNITY COLLEGE**
Salt (East Bank)
Telephone: 55573

Founded 1975.

4327 **SHOBAK COMMUNITY COLLEGE**
P.O. Box 5, Shobak (East Bank)
Telephone: 18

Founded 1975.

4328 **AL-ZARQA COMMUNITY COLLEGE**
P.O. Box 6390, Zarqa (East Bank)
Telephone: 986531

Founded 1978.

4329 **AL-ZARQA NATIONAL COMMUNITY COLLEGE**
P.O. Box 1027, Zarqa (East Bank)
Telephone: 985558

Founded 1979.

4330 **COMMUNITY TEACHER TRAINING COLLEGE OF ARTS OF SCIENCE**
Amman (East Bank)

Founded 1967.

4331 **WOMEN'S TEACHER TRAINING INSTITUTE**
P.O. Box 122, Almahed Street, Rammallah (West Bank)
Telephone: (295) 6526
Principal-General: Bayan Nashashibi (1971-)

Founded 1952. Residential facilities for academic staff and students.

Academic Year: September to June (September-January; January-June).
Admission Requirements: Secondary school certificate.
Fees (Dinars): 55-200.
Languages of Instruction: Arabic and English.
Degrees and Diplomas: Diplomas, 2 yrs. Bachelor of Arts in Arabic Language, 4 yrs.
Library: 17,000 vols.
Academic Staff, 1990: 17.
Student Enrolment, 1990: 220.

4332 **UNRWA/UNESCO MEN'S TEACHER TRAINING CENTRE**
Ramallah (West Bank)

Founded 1960.

4333 **UNRWA WOMEN'S TRAINING CENTRE**
P.O. Box 214, Ramallah (West Bank)
Telephone: 952533

Founded 1962.

4334 **AN-NAJAH NATIONAL COMMUNITY COLLEGE**
Omar Ibn Al-Khattab Street, Nablus (West Bank)
Telephone: 70042
Fax: 71122
Dean: Husni Masri

Sec. of Education
Chairman: Nitham Nabulsi; *staff* 16
Sec. of Commerce
Chairman: Osama Shahwan; *staff* 10
Sec. of Computer Studies
Chairman: Mu'tasim Bia'ba'a; *staff* 4
Sec. of Library and Documentation Sciences
Head: Nimer Sabbobah; *staff* 3

Founded 1965. Attached to An-Najah National University.
Academic Year: October to June (October-January; March-June).
Admission Requirements: Secondary school certificate.
Fees (Dinars): 65 per semester.
Language of Instruction: Arabic.
Degrees and Diplomas: Diplomas, 2 yrs.
Library: An-Najah National University Library, 126,000 vols.
Academic Staff, 1989-90: 41.
Student Enrolment, 1989-90:

	Men	Women	Total
Of the country	172	383	555

4335 **TEACHER INSERVICE CENTRE**
Amman (East Bank)

Founded 1971.

4336 **ISLAMIC EDUCATION INSTITUTE**
P.O. Box 685, Amman (East Bank)

Founded 1972.

KOREA
(Democratic People's Republic)

Universities

4337 ***KIM IL SUNG UNIVERSITY**
Taesong District, Pyongyang
President: Pak Gwan O

F. of Economics
F. of History
F. of Philosophy
F. of Law
F. of Korean Language and Literature
F. of Foreign Languages and Literature
F. of Mathematics and Mechanics
F. of Physics
F. of Chemistry
F. of Biology
F. of Geography
F. of Geology
F. of Automation
I. of Juche Ideas
I. of Social Sciences
Also 3 Research Institutes.

Founded 1946, reorganized 1953. A State institution responsible to the National Education Commission. Governing bodies: Instruction; Scientific Research; Social Science; Natural Science; General Affairs.

Academic Year: September to August (September-February; February-August).

Admission Requirements: Graduation from Senior Middle School.

Fees: None.

Language of Instruction: Korean.

Degrees and Diplomas: Bachelor, 4 ½-5 ½ yrs. Associate Doctorate. Doctorate.

Library: Science Library, 2,247,097 vols.

Publications: Newspaper; Gazette.

Press or Publishing House: University Publishing House.

Academic Staff, 1986-87: 3200.

Student Enrolment, 1986-87: 16,000.

4338 **KIM CHAEK UNIVERSITY OF TECHNOLOGY**
Central District, Pyongyang
President: Kim Gyong Wan

F. of Geological Prospecting
F. of Mining Engineering
I. of Metallurgy
F. of Material Engineering
F. of Machine Building
F. of Mechanical Engineering
F. of Shipbuilding
F. of Electrical Engineering
F. of Electronic Engineering
F. of Communication
F. of Automatic Engineering
F. of Physical Engineering
F. of Industrial Management
Also 6 Research Institutes.

Founded 1948. A State institution responsible to the National Education Commission. Governing bodies: Instruction; Scientific Research; General Affairs.

Academic Year: September to August (September-February; February-August).

Admission Requirements: Graduation from Senior Middle School.

Fees: None.

Language of Instruction: Korean.

Degrees and Diplomas: Bachelor of Engineering, 5 ½ yrs. Associate Doctorate. Doctorate.

Library: Main Library.

Publications: Newspaper; Gazette.

Press or Publishing House: University Publishing House.

Academic Staff, 1986-87: 2400.

Student Enrolment, 1986-87: 12,000.

4339 **PYONGYANG UNIVERSITY OF AGRICULTURE**
Ryongsong District, Pyongyang
President: Chon Si Gon

F. of Agriculture
F. of Veterinary and Animal Husbandry

Founded 1981. A State institution responsible to the National Education Commission. Governing bodies: Instruction; Scientific Research; General Affairs.

Academic Year: September to August (September-February; February-August).

Admission Requirements: Graduation from Senior Middle School.

Fees: None.

Language of Instruction: Korean.

Degrees and Diplomas: Bachelor of Engineering, 4 ½-5 yrs.

Library: 55,102 vols.

Publications: Newspaper; Gazette.

Press or Publishing House: University Publishing House.

Academic Staff, 1986-87: 317.

Student Enrolment, 1986-87: 2533.

4340 **PYONGYANG UNIVERSITY OF CINEMATICS**
Tongdaewon District, Pyongyang
President: To Chan Gu

F. of Social Sciences
F. of Creation
F. of Direction
F. of Cinematography
F. of Actors
F. of Technology
I. of Cinematic Art

Founded 1953. A State institution responsible to the National Education Commission. Governing bodies: Instruction; Scientific Research; General Affairs.

Academic Year: September to August (September-February; February-August).

Admission Requirements: Graduation from Senior Middle School.

Fees: None.

Language of Instruction: Korean.

Degrees and Diplomas: Bachelor, 4 yrs. Doctorate.

Library: 95,784 vols.

Publications: Newspaper; Gazette.

Press or Publishing House: University Publishing House.

Academic Staff, 1986-87: 310.

Student Enrolment, 1986-87: 2482.

4341 **UNIVERSITY OF COMMERCE**
Pyongchon District, Pyongyang
President: Kim Dong Sop

F. of Cookery
F. of Services
F. of Tailoring
F. of Management
Commerce I.

Founded 1970. A State institution responsible to the National Education Commission. Governing bodies: Instruction; Scientific Research; General Affairs.

Academic Year: September to August (September-February; February-August).
Admission Requirements: Graduation from Senior Middle School.
Fees: None.
Language of Instruction: Korean.
Degrees and Diplomas: Bachelor, 4 yrs. Associate Doctorate.
Library: 85,614 vols.
Publications: Newspaper; Gazette.
Press or Publishing House: University Publishing House.
Academic Staff, 1986-87: 458.
Student Enrolment, 1986-87: 3663.

4342 **UNIVERSITY OF CONSTRUCTION AND BUILDING MATERIALS**
Taedonggang District, Pyongyang
President: Rim Gun Bok

F. of Architecture
F. of Architectural Engineering
F. of Construction Engineering
F. of Building Materials
F. of City Management
I. of Construction and Building Materials

Founded 1953. A State institution responsible to the National Education Commission. Governing bodies: Instruction; Scientific Research; General Affairs.
Academic Year: September to August (September-February; February-August).
Admission Requirements: Graduation from Senior Middle School.
Fees: None.
Language of Instruction: Korean.
Degrees and Diplomas: Bachelor, 5 yrs.
Library: 149,796 vols.
Publications: Newspaper; Gazette.
Press or Publishing House: University Publishing House.
Academic Staff, 1986-87: 1166.
Student Enrolment, 1986-87: 9326.

4343 **THE UNIVERSITY OF NATIONAL ECONOMY**
Pyongyang

F. of Industrial Management
F. of Agricultural Management
F. of Finance and Banking
F. of Planning
F. of Trade
F. of Statistics

Founded 1946. A State institution responsible to the National Education Commission. Governing bodies: Instruction; Scientific Research; General Affairs.
Academic Year: September to August (September-February; February-August).
Admission Requirements: Graduation from Senior Middle School.

4344 **PYONGYANG UNIVERSITY OF FINE ARTS**
Tongdaewon District, Pyongyang
President: Choe Won Su

F. of Korean Painting
F. of Paintings
F. of Graphic Art
F. of Sculpture
F. of Industrial Art
F. of Crafts
Fine Arts Research I.

Founded 1947. A State institution responsible to the National Education Commission. Governing bodies: Instruction; Scientific Research; General Affairs.
Academic Year: September to August (September-February; February-August).
Admission Requirements: Graduation from Senior Middle School.
Fees: None.
Language of Instruction: Korean.
Degrees and Diplomas: Bachelor, 4 yrs. Associate Doctorate. Doctorate.
Library: 81,617 vols.
Publications: Newspaper; Gazette.
Press or Publishing House: University Publishing House.
Academic Staff, 1986-87: 330.
Student Enrolment, 1986-87: 2641.

4345 **PYONGYANG UNIVERSITY OF FOREIGN STUDIES**
Taesong District, Pyongyang
President: Ro Yong Uk

F. of Russian, Chinese, Arabic, Japanese
F. of English
F. of French and Spanish
F. of Education
Training I.
I. of Education Theory
I. of Simultaneous Interpretation

Founded 1949. A State institution responsible to the National Education Commission. Governing bodies: Instruction; Scientific Research, General Affairs.
Academic Year: September to August (September-February; February-August).
Admission Requirements: Graduation from Senior Middle School.
Fees: None.
Language of Instruction: Korean.
Degrees and Diplomas: Bachelor, 5 yrs. Associate Doctorate. Doctorate.
Library: 222,648 vols.
Publications: Newspaper; Gazette.
Press or Publishing House: University Publishing House.
Academic Staff, 1986-87: 218.
Student Enrolment, 1986-87: 1739.

4346 **THE UNIVERSITY OF LIGHT INDUSTRY**
Songyo District, Pyongyang
President: Kim Suk Jong

F. of Textile Engineering
F. of Machine Engineering
F. of Chemical Engineering of Daily Necessities
F. of Food Engineering
F. of Management
Light Industry I.
Food Research I.

Founded 1959. A State institution responsible to the National Education Commission. Governing bodies: Instruction; Scientific Research; General Affairs.
Academic Year: September to August (September-February; February-August).
Admission Requirements: Graduation from Senior Middle School.
Fees: None.
Language of Instruction: Korean.
Degrees and Diplomas: Bachelor, 5 yrs. Associate Doctorate. Doctorate.
Library: 255,931 vols.
Publications: Newspaper; Gazette.
Press or Publishing House: University Publishing House.
Academic Staff, 1986-87: 978.
Student Enrolment, 1986-87: 7827.

4347 **PYONGYANG UNIVERSITY OF MECHANICAL ENGINEERING**
Taedonggang District, Pyongyang
President: Pak Bong Chun

F. of Machinery
F. of Mechanical Engineering
F. of Construction Machinery
F. of Automation
F. of Design
I. of Mechanical Engineering

A State institution responsible to the National Education Comission. Governing bodies: Instruction; Scientific Research; General Affairs.
Academic Year: September to August (September-February; February-August).
Admission Requirements: Graduation from Senior Middle School.
Fees: None.
Language of Instruction: Korean.
Degrees and Diplomas: Bachelor of Engineering, 5 yrs. Associate Doctorate. Doctorate.
Library: 308,787 vols.
Publications: Newspaper; Gazette.
Press or Publishing House: University Publishing House.

Academic Staff, 1986-87: 1395.
Student Enrolment, 1986-87: 6975.

4348 **PYONGYANG UNIVERSITY OF MEDICINE**
Central District, Pyongyang
President: Paek Sok Kyu

F. of Clinical Medicine
F. of Korean Traditional Medicine
F. of Basic Medicine
F. of Hygiene
F. of Pharmacy
F. of Stomatology
Also 3 Research Institutes.

Founded 1948. A State institution responsible to the National Education Commission. Governing bodies: Instruction; Scientific Research; General Affairs.

Academic Year: September to August (September-February; February-August).
Admission Requirements: Graduation from Senior Middle School.
Fees: None.
Language of Instruction: Korean.
Degrees and Diplomas: Bachelor, 5-6 yrs. Associate Doctorate. Doctorate.
Library: 260,455 vols.
Publications: Newspaper; Gazette.
Press or Publishing House: University Publishing House.
Academic Staff, 1986-87: 1463.
Student Enrolment, 1986-87: 7315.

4349 **PYONGYANG MUSIC AND DANCE UNIVERSITY**
Taedonggang District, Pyongyang
President: Pang Son Yong

F. of National Instruments
F. of Western Instruments
F. of Vocal Technique
F. of Dance
F. of Composition
Preparatory F.
I. of Music and Dance

Founded 1948. A State institution responsible to the National Education Commission. Governing bodies: Instruction; Scientific Research; General Affairs.

Academic Year: September to August (September-February; February-August).
Admission Requirements: Graduation from Senior Middle School.
Fees: None.
Language of Instruction: Korean.
Degrees and Diplomas: Bachelor, 4 yrs. Associate Doctorate.
Library: 136,370 vols.
Publications: Newspaper; Gazette.
Press or Publishing House: University Publishing House.
Academic Staff, 1986-87: 540.
Student Enrolment, 1986-87: 2934.

4350 **PYONGYANG UNIVERSITY OF PHYSICAL EDUCATION**
Tongdaewon District, Pyongyang
President: Yun Tae Yun

Physical Education

Founded 1958. A State institution responsible to the National Education Commission. Governing bodies: Instruction; Scientific Research; General Affairs.

Academic Year: September to August (September-February; February-August).
Admission Requirements: Graduation from Senior Middle School.
Fees: None.
Language of Instruction: Korean.
Degrees and Diplomas: Bachelor, 4 yrs. Associate Doctorate; Doctorate.
Library: 94,357 vols.
Publications: Newspaper; Gazette.
Press or Publishing House: University Publishing House.
Academic Staff, 1986-87: 206.
Student Enrolment, 1986-87: 1360.

4351 **PYONGYANG UNIVERSITY OF RAILWAYS**
Hyongjesan District, Pyongyang
President: Kim Yong Ryol

Railway Engineering

Founded 1959. A State institution responsible to the National Education Commission. Governing bodies: Instruction; Scientific Research; General Affairs.

Academic Year: September to August (September-February; February-August).
Admission Requirements: Graduation from Senior Middle School.
Fees: None.
Language of Instruction: Korean.
Degrees and Diplomas: Bachelor of Engineering, 5 yrs. Associate Doctorate; Doctorate.
Library: 208,715 vols.
Publications: Newspaper; Gazette.
Press or Publishing House: University Publishing House.
Academic Staff, 1986-87: 1246.
Student Enrolment, 1986-87: 9971.

4352 **HAEJU UNIVERSITY OF AGRICULTURE**
Haeju City, South Hwanghae Province
President: Kim Hong Sik

F. of Agriculture (including Veterinary Medicine, Stockraising, and Forestry)
F. of Pomiculture
F. of Farm Machinery
F. of Agronomics
Agricultural Science Research I.

Founded 1960. A State institution responsible to the National Education Commission. Governing bodies: Instruction; Scientific Research; General Affairs.

Academic Year: September to August (September-February; February-August).
Admission Requirements: Graduation from Senior Middle School.
Fees: None.
Language of Instruction: Korean.
Degrees and Diplomas: Bachelor of Engineering, 4 ½-5 yrs. Associate Doctorate. Doctorate.
Library: 283,349 vols.
Publications: Newspaper; Gazette.
Press or Publishing House: University Publishing House.
Academic Staff, 1986-87: 762.
Student Enrolment, 1986-87: 6106.

4353 **HAMBUK UNIVERSITY OF AGRICULTURE**
Ranam District, Chongjin City, North Hamgyong Province
President: Pak Mu Hon

F. of Agriculture (including Veterinary Medicine, and Animal Husbandry)
F. of Farm Machinery
F. of Pomiculture

Founded 1970. A State institution responsible to the National Education Commission. Governing bodies: Instruction; Scientific Research; General Affairs.

Academic Year: September to August (September-February; February-August).
Admission Requirements: Graduation from Senior Middle School.
Fees: None.
Language of Instruction: Korean.
Degrees and Diplomas: Bachelor of Engineering, 4 1/2-5 yrs. Associate Doctorate.
Library: 105,375 vols.
Publications: Newspaper; Gazette.
Press or Publishing House: University Publishing House.
Academic Staff, 1986-87: 385.
Student Enrolment, 1986-87: 3079.

4354 **HAMHUNG UNIVERSITY OF AGRICULTURE**
Sapo District, Hamhung City, South Hamgyong Province
President: Kim Sang Jong

F. of Agriculture (including Veterinary Medicine and Animal Husbandry)
F. of Pomiculture
F. of Farm Machinery

Agricultural Scientific Research I.

Founded 1958. A State institution responsible to the National Education Commission. Governing bodies: Instruction; Scientific Research; General Affairs.

Academic Year: September to August (September-February; February-August).

Admission Requirements: Graduation from Senior Middle School.

Fees: None.

Language of Instruction: Korean.

Degrees and Diplomas: Bachelor of Engineering, 4 ½-5 yrs. Associate Doctorate. Doctorate.

Library: 182,531 vols.

Publications: Newspaper; Gazette.

Press or Publishing House: University Publishing House.

Academic Staff, 1986-87: 544.

Student Enrolment, 1986-87: 4398.

4355 **HYESAN UNIVERSITY OF AGRICULTURE AND FORESTRY**

Hyesan City, Ryangang Province

President: Kim Ha Zin

F. of Agriculture (including Veterinary Medicine, Animal Husbandry and Forestry)

F. of Management

F. of Forestry Engineering

F. of Wood Processing

Agricultural and Forestry Scientific Research I.

Founded 1955. A State institution responsible to the National Education Commission. Governing body: Instruction, Scientific Research and General Affairs.

Academic Year: September to August (September-February; February-August).

Admission Requirements: Graduation from Senior Middle School.

Fees: None.

Language of Instruction: Korean.

Degrees and Diplomas: Bachelor of Engineering, 4 ½-5 yrs. Associate Doctorate. Doctorate.

Library: 133,762 vols.

Publications: Newspaper; Gazette.

Press or Publishing House: University Publishing House.

Academic Staff, 1986-87: 710.

Student Enrolment, 1986-87: 5681.

4356 **KANGGYE UNIVERSITY OF AGRICULTURE AND FORESTRY**

Kanggye City, Chagang Province

President: Cho Zae Hyong

F. of Agriculture (including Veterinary Medicine, Stockraising, and Forestry)

F. of Sericulture

F. of Farm Machinery

Founded 1970. A State institution responsible to the National Education Commission. Governing bodies: Instruction; Scientific Research; General Affairs.

Academic Year: September to August (September-February; February-August).

Admission Requirements: Graduation from Senior Middle School.

Fees: None.

Language of Instruction: Korean.

Degrees and Diplomas: Bachelor of Engineering, 4 ½-5 yrs. Associate Doctorate.

Library: 127,530 vols.

Publications: Newspaper; Gazette.

Press or Publishing House: University Publishing House.

Academic Staff, 1986-87: 313.

Student Enrolment, 1986-87: 2508.

4357 **NAMPO UNIVERSITY OF AGRICULTURE**

Waudo District, Nampo City

President: Kim Sok Chol

F. of Agriculture

F. of Horticulture

F. of Farm Machinery

Founded 1967. A State institution responsible to the National Education Commission. Governing bodies: Instruction; Scientific Research; General Affairs.

Academic Year: September to August (September-February; February-August).

Admission Requirements: Graduation from Senior Middle School.

Fees: None.

Language of Instruction: Korean.

Degrees and Diplomas: Bachelor of Engineering, 4 ½-5 yrs. Associate Doctorate.

Library: 102,310 vols.

Publications: Newspaper; Gazette.

Press or Publishing House: University Publishing House.

Academic Staff, 1986-87: 620.

Student Enrolment, 1986-87: 4961.

4358 **SARIWON UNIVERSITY OF AGRICULTURE**

Sariwon City, North Hwanghae Province

President: Kang Ung Ryol

F. of Agriculture (including Veterinary Medicine and Animal Husbandry)

F. of Biology

F. of Agrochemistry

F. of Pomiculture

F. of Forest and River Protection

F. of Farm Machinery

F. of Agronomics

Academic Year: September to August (September-February; February-August).

Admission Requirements: Graduation from Senior Middle School.

Fees: None.

Language of Instruction: Korean.

Degrees and Diplomas: Bachelor of Engineering, 4 ½-5 yrs. Associate Doctorate. Doctorate.

Library: 362,941 vols.

Publications: Newspaper; Gazette.

Press or Publishing House: University Publishing House.

Academic Staff, 1986-87: 1833.

Student Enrolment, 1986-87: 9165.

4359 **SINUIJU UNIVERSITY OF AGRICULTURE**

Sinuiju City, North Pyongyang Province

President: Kim Jong Gi

F. of Agriculture (including Veterinary Medicine, and Stockraising)

F. of Pomiculture

F. of Farm Machinery

Founded 1969. A State institution responsible to the National Education Commission. Governing bodies: Instruction; Scientific Research; General Affairs.

Academic Year: September to August (September-February; February-August).

Admission Requirements: Graduation from Senior Middle School.

Fees: None.

Language of Instruction: Korean.

Degrees and Diplomas: Bachelor of Engineering, 4-5 yrs. Associate Doctorate.

Library: 81,007 vols.

Publications: Newspaper; Gazette.

Press or Publishing House: University Publishing House.

Academic Staff, 1986-87: 610.

Student Enrolment, 1986-87: 4884.

4360 **WONSAN UNIVERSITY OF AGRICULTURE**

Wonsan City, Kwangwon Province

President: Kim Jong Hun

F. of Agriculture (including Veterinary Medicine, Animal Husbandry, and Forestry)

F. of Agricultural Machines

F. of Agronomics

F. of Pomiculture

F. of Sericulture

F. of Agro-Chemistry

F. of Agro-Biology

F. of Irrigation Engineering

Also 3 Research Institutes.

Founded 1948. A State institution responsible to the National Education Commission. Governing bodies: Instruction; Scientific Research; General Affairs.

Academic Year: September to August (September-February; February-August).
Admission Requirements: Graduation from Senior Middle School.
Fees: None.
Language of Instruction: Korean.
Degrees and Diplomas: Bachelor of Engineering, 4 ½-5 yrs. Associate Doctorate. Doctorate.
Library: 321,732 vols.
Publications: Newspaper; Gazette.
Press or Publishing House: University Publishing House.
Academic Staff, 1986-87: 1004.
Student Enrolment, 1986-87: 8029.

4361 **HAMHUNG UNIVERSITY OF CHEMICAL INDUSTRY**
Hoesang District, Hamhung City, South Hamgyong Province
President: Kang Won Sik

F. of Inorganic Chemical Engineering
F. of Organic Chemical Engineering
F. of High Polymers Chemical Engineering
F. of Silicate Engineering
F. of Machine Engineering

Founded 1947. A State institution responsible to the National Education Commission. Governing bodies: Instruction; Scientific Research; General Affairs.
Academic Year: September to August (September-February; February-August).
Admission Requirements: Graduation from Senior Middle School.
Fees: None.
Language of Instruction: Korean.
Degrees and Diplomas: Bachelor of Engineering, 5 yrs. Associate Doctorate. Doctorate.
Library: 336,871 vols.
Publications: Newspaper; Gazette.
Press or Publishing House: University Publishing House.
Academic Staff, 1986-87: 2228.
Student Enrolment, 1986-87: 11,140.

4362 **WONSAN UNIVERSITY OF ECONOMICS**
Wonsan City, Kangwon Province
President: Kim Gwan Muk

F. of Planning
F. of Supply and Administration
F. of Finance
F. of Commercial Management

Also Economic Management Research Institute.
Founded 1960. A State institution responsible to the National Education Commission. Governing bodies: Instruction; Scientific Research; General Affairs.
Academic Year: September to August (September-February; February-August).
Admission Requirements: Graduation from Senior Middle School.
Fees: None.
Language of Instruction: Korean.
Degrees and Diplomas: Bachelor, 4 yrs. Associate Doctorate. Doctorate.
Library: 111,718 vols.
Publications: Newspaper; Gazette.
Press or Publishing House: University Publishing House.
Academic Staff, 1986-87: 1006.
Student Enrolment, 1986-87: 8046.

4363 **NAMPO UNIVERSITY OF FISHERIES**
Waudo District, Nampo City
President: Chang Myong Dok

Fisheries

Founded 1977. A State institution responsible to the National Education Commission. Governing bodies: Instruction; Scientific Research; General Affairs.
Academic Year: September to August (September-February; February-August).
Admission Requirements: Graduation from Senior Middle School.
Fees: None.
Language of Instruction: Korean.
Degrees and Diplomas: Bachelor of Engineering, 4 yrs.
Library: 67,198 vols.
Publications: Newspaper; Gazette.
Press or Publishing House: University Publishing House.
Academic Staff, 1986-87: 432.
Student Enrolment, 1986-87: 3459.

4364 **WONSAN UNIVERSITY OF FISHERIES**
Wonsan City, Kangwon Province
President: Kim Su Hong

Fisheries

Founded 1959. A State institution responsible to the National Education Commission. Governing bodies: Instruction; Scientific Research; General Affairs.
Academic Year: September to August (September-February; February-August).
Admission Requirements: Graduation from Senior Middle School.
Fees: None.
Language of Instruction: Korean.
Degrees and Diplomas: Bachelor of Engineering, 5 yrs. Associate Doctorate. Doctorate.
Library: 187,691 vols.
Publications: Newspaper; Gazette.
Press or Publishing House: University Publishing House.
Academic Staff, 1986-87: 748.
Student Enrolment, 1986-87: 5986.

4365 **UNIVERSITY OF GEOLOGY**
Sariwon City, North Hwanghae Province
President: Choe Chong Ryong

Geology

Founded 1970. A State institution responsible to the National Education Commission. Governing bodies: Instruction; Scientific Research; General Affairs.
Academic Year: September to August (September-February; February-August).
Admission Requirements: Graduation from Senior Middle School.
Fees: None.
Language of Instruction: Korean.
Degrees and Diplomas: Bachelor of Engineering, 5 yrs. Associate Doctorate. Doctorate.
Library: 178,385 vols.
Publications: Newspaper; Gazette.
Press or Publishing House: University Publishing House.
Academic Staff, 1986-87: 841.
Student Enrolment, 1986-87: 6766.

4366 **HAMHUNG UNIVERSITY OF HYDRAULICS**
Tonghungsan District, Hamhung City, South Hamgyong Province
President: Kim Sang Chol

F. of Hydraulic Engineering
F. of Electrical Engineering
F. of Irrigation
F. of Mechanical Engineering

Also 4 Research Institutes.
Founded 1959. A State institution responsible to the National Education Commission. Governing bodies: Instruction; Scientific Research; General Affairs.
Academic Year: September to August (September-February; February-August).
Admission Requirements: Graduation from Senior Middle School.
Fees: None.
Language of Instruction: Korean.
Degrees and Diplomas: Bachelor of Engineering, 5 yrs. Associate Doctorate. Doctorate.
Library: 23,927 vols.
Publications: Newspaper; Gazette.
Press or Publishing House: University Publishing House.
Academic Staff, 1986-87: 912.
Student Enrolment, 1986-87: 7295.

4367 **SINUIJU UNIVERSITY OF LIGHT INDUSTRY**
Sinuiju City, North Pyongyang Province
President: Choe Hae Sin

F. of Machine Engineering
F. of Chemical Engineering
F. of Textile Engineering

F. of Food Technology
Also 2 Research Institutes.
Founded 1982. A State institution responsible to the National Education Commission. Governing bodies: Instruction; Scientific Research; General Affairs.
Academic Year: September to August (September-February; February-August).
Admission Requirements: Graduation from Senior Middle School.
Fees: None.
Language of Instruction: Korean.
Degrees and Diplomas: Bachelor of Engineering, 5 yrs.
Library: 71,676 vols.
Publications: Newspaper; Gazette.
Press or Publishing House: University Publishing House.
Academic Staff, 1986-87: 362.
Student Enrolment, 1986-87: 2897.

4368 **CHONGJIN UNIVERSITY OF MEDICINE**
Pohang District, Chongjin City, North Hamgyong Province
President: Kim Gi Ho
Medicine (including Pharmacy and Traditional Medicine)
Also Research Institute.
Founded 1948. A State institution responsible to the National Education Commission. Governing bodies: Instruction; Scientific Research; General Affairs.
Academic Year: September to August (September-February; February-August).
Admission Requirements: Graduation from Senior Middle School.
Fees: None.
Language of Instruction: Korean.
Degrees and Diplomas: Bachelor, 5-6 yrs. Associate Doctorate. Doctorate.
Library: Main Library.
Publications: Newspaper; Gazette.
Press or Publishing House: University Publishing House.
Academic Staff, 1986-87: 669.
Student Enrolment, 1986-87: 5355.

4369 **HAMHUNG UNIVERSITY OF MEDICINE**
Hamhung City, South Hamgyong Province
President: Ri Duk Song
Medicine (including Stomatology and Traditional Medicine)
Also Research Institute.
Founded 1946. A State institution responsible to the National Education Commission. Governing bodies: Instruction; Scientific Research; General Affairs.
Academic Year: September to August (September-February; February-August).
Admission Requirements: Graduation from Senior Middle School.
Fees: None.
Language of Instruction: Korean.
Degrees and Diplomas: Bachelor, 5-6 yrs. Associate Doctorate. Doctorate.
Library: 361,067 vols.
Publications: Newspaper; Gazette.
Press or Publishing House: University Publishing House.
Academic Staff, 1986-87: 619.
Student Enrolment, 1986-87: 4952.

4370 **HAEJU UNIVERSITY OF MEDICINE**
Haeju City, South Hwanghae Province
President: Han Song Uk
Medicine (including Pharmacy and Traditional Medicine)
Also Research Institute.
Founded 1959. A State institution responsible to the National Education Commission. Governing bodies: Instruction; Scientific Research; General Affairs.
Academic Year: September to August (September-February; February-August).
Admission Requirements: Graduation from Senior Middle School.
Fees: None.
Language of Instruction: Korean.
Degrees and Diplomas: Bachelor, 5-6 yrs. Associate Doctorate. Doctorate.
Library: 195,000 vols.
Publications: Newspaper; Gazette.
Press or Publishing House: University Publishing House.
Academic Staff, 1986-87: 710.
Student Enrolment, 1986-87: 5675.

4371 **HYESAN UNIVERSITY OF MEDICINE**
Hyesan City, Ryangang Province
President: Chon Tong Chol
Medicine (including Traditional Medicine and Pharmacy)
Founded 1971. A State institution responsible to the National Education Commission. Governing body: Instruction, Scientific Research and General Affairs.
Academic Year: September to August (September-February; February-August).
Admission Requirements: Graduation from Senior Middle School.
Fees: None.
Language of Instruction: Korean.
Degrees and Diplomas: Bachelor, 5-6 yrs. Associate Doctorate.
Library: 87,958 vols.
Publications: Newspaper; Gazette.
Press or Publishing House: University Publishing House.
Academic Staff, 1986-87: 372.
Student Enrolment, 1986-87: 2980.

4372 **KANGGYE UNIVERSITY OF MEDICINE**
Kanggye City, Chagang Province
President: Chon Rin Sung
Medicine (including Traditional Medicine and Pharmacy)
Founded 1969. A State institution responsible to the National Education Commission. Governing bodies: Instruction; Scientific Research; General Affairs.
Academic Year: September to August (September-February; February-August).
Admission Requirements: Graduation from Senior Middle School.
Fees: None.
Language of Instruction: Korean.
Degrees and Diplomas: Bachelor, 5-6 yrs. Associate Doctorate.
Library: 104,000 vols.
Publications: Newspaper; Gazette.
Press or Publishing House: University Publishing House.
Academic Staff, 1986-87: 356.
Student Enrolment, 1986-87: 2846.

4373 **PYONGSONG UNIVERSITY OF MEDICINE**
Pyongsong City, South Pyongan Province
President: Pak Yong Sam
Medicine (including Traditional Medicine)
Founded 1972. A State institution responsible to the National Education Commission. Governing bodies: Instruction; Scientific Research; General Affairs.
Academic Year: September to August (September-February; February-August).
Admission Requirements: Graduation from Senior Middle School.
Fees: None.
Language of Instruction: Korean.
Degrees and Diplomas: Bachelor, 5-6 yrs. Associate Doctorate.
Library: 105,175 vols.
Publications: Newspaper; Gazette.
Press or Publishing House: University Publishing House.
Academic Staff, 1986-87: 803.
Student Enrolment, 1986-87: 6426.

4374 **SARIWON UNIVERSITY OF MEDICINE**
Sariwon City, North Hwanghae Province
President: Paek Chan Hwa
Medicine (including Traditional Medicine)
Founded 1971. A State institution responsible to the National Education Commission. Governing bodies: Instruction; Scientific Research; General Affairs.
Academic Year: September to August (September-February; February-August).
Admission Requirements: Graduation from Senior Middle School.
Fees: None.
Language of Instruction: Korean.
Degrees and Diplomas: Bachelor, 5-6 yrs. Associate Doctorate.
Library: 198,461 vols.

Publications: Newspaper; Gazette.
Press or Publishing House: University Publishing House.
Academic Staff, 1986-87: 403.
Student Enrolment, 1986-87: 3225.

4375 **SINUIJU UNIVERSITY OF MEDICINE**
Pyonghawa-Dong, Sinuiju City, Pyongan Province
President: Vho Hyong Han

Medicine (including Stomatology and Traditional Medicine)
Also Research Institute.

Founded 1969. A State institution responsible to the National Education Commission. Governing bodies: Instruction; Scientific Research; General Affairs.

Academic Year: September to August (September-February; February-August).
Admission Requirements: Graduation from Senior Middle School.
Fees: None.
Language of Instruction: Korean.
Degrees and Diplomas: Bachelor, 5-6 yrs. Associate Doctorate.
Library: 113,039 vols.
Publications: Newspaper; Gazette.
Press or Publishing House: University Publishing House.
Academic Staff, 1986-87: 678.
Student Enrolment, 1986-87: 5428.

4376 **WONSAN UNIVERSITY OF MEDICINE**
Wonsan City, Kangwon Province
President: Om Gap Bong

Medicine (including Traditional Medicine and Pharmacy)

Founded 1971. A State institution responsible to the National Education Commission. Governing bodies: Instruction; Scientific Research; General Affairs.

Academic Year: September to August (September-February; February-August).
Admission Requirements: Graduation from Senior Middle School.
Fees: None.
Language of Instruction: Korean.
Degrees and Diplomas: Degrees and Diplomas: Doctor, 5 yrs. Associate Doctorate.
Library: 127,425 vols.
Publications: Newspaper; Gazette.
Press or Publishing House: University Publishing House.
Academic Staff, 1986-87: 324.
Student Enrolment, 1986-87: 2916.

4377 **CHONGJIN UNIVERSITY OF MINING AND METALLURGICAL ENGINEERING**
Pohang District, Chongjin City, North Hamgyong Province
President: Hwang Yong Hwan

F. of Geotechnology
F. of Mining
F. of Coal Engineering
F. of Automation
F. of Metallurgy
F. of Mineral Analysis

Founded 1959. A State institution responsible to the National Education Commission. Governing bodies: Instruction; Scientific Research; General Affairs.

Academic Year: September to August (September-February; February-August).
Admission Requirements: Graduation from Senior Middle School.
Fees: None.
Language of Instruction: Korean.
Degrees and Diplomas: Bachelor of Engineering, 4 yrs. Associate Doctorate. Doctorate.
Library: 316,593 vols.
Publications: Newspaper; Gazette.
Press or Publishing House: University Publishing House.
Academic Staff, 1986-87: 1027.
Student Enrolment, 1986-87: 8214.

4378 **PYONGNAM UNIVERSITY OF COAL MINING**
Pyongsong City, South Pyongan Province
President: Hong Du Yong

F. of Coal Mining
F. of Geological Engineering
F. of Mechanical Engineering
F. of Automation
Also Research Institute.

Founded 1968. A State institution responsible to the National Education Commission. Governing bodies: Instruction; Scientific Research; General Affairs.

Academic Year: September to August (September-February; February-August).
Admission Requirements: Graduation from Senior Middle School.
Fees: None.
Language of Instruction: Korean.
Degrees and Diplomas: Bachelor of Engineering, 5 yrs. Associate Doctorate.
Library: 155,811 vols.
Publications: Newspaper; Gazette.
Press or Publishing House: University Publishing House.
Academic Staff, 1986-87: 824.
Student Enrolment, 1986-87: 6593.

4379 **HAMHUNG UNIVERSITY OF PHARMACY**
Hamhung City, South Hamgyong Province
President: An Jong Chol

Pharmacy

Founded 1968. A State institution responsible to the National Education Commission. Governing body: Instruction, Scientific Research, General Affairs.

Academic Year: September to August (September-February; February-August).
Admission Requirements: Graduation from Senior Middle School.
Fees: None.
Language of Instruction: Korean.
Degrees and Diplomas: Bachelor of Engineering, 5 yrs.
Library: 126,667 vols.
Publications: Newspaper; Gazette.
Press or Publishing House: University Publishing House.
Academic Staff, 1986-87: 638.
Student Enrolment, 1986-87: 5107.

4380 **UNIVERSITY OF SEA TRANSPORT**
Rajin City, North Hamgyong Province
President: Kim Sung Hak

Navigation
Marine Engineering
Also Research Institute.

Founded 1968. A State institution responsible to the National Education commission. Governing bodies: Instruction; Scientific Research; General Affairs.

Academic Year: September to August (September-February; February-August).
Admission Requirements: Graduation from Senior Middle School.
Fees: None.
Language of Instruction: Korean.
Degrees and Diplomas: Bachelor of Engineering, 5 yrs. Associate Doctorate. Doctorate.
Library: 157,832 vols.
Publications: Newspaper; Gazette.
Press or Publishing House: University Publishing House.
Academic Staff, 1986-87: 489.
Student Enrolment, 1986-87: 3992.

4381 **THE UNIVERSITY OF SCIENCE**
Pyongsong City, South Pyongan Province
President: Ro Sang Gyun

F. of Mathematics
F. of Physics
F. of Automation
F. of Chemistry
F. of Biology
Also Research Institute.

Founded 1967. A State institution responsible to the National Education Commission. Governing bodies: Instruction; Scientific Research; General Affairs.

Academic Year: September to August (September-February; February-August).
Admission Requirements: Graduation from Senior Middle School.
Fees: None.
Language of Instruction: Korean.
Degrees and Diplomas: Bachelor, 5 yrs. Associate Doctorate. Doctorate.
Library: 250,023 vols.
Publications: Newspaper; Gazette.
Press or Publishing House: University Publishing House.
Academic Staff, 1986-87: 833.
Student Enrolment, 1986-87: 4163.

4382 **HUICHON UNIVERSITY OF TECHNOLOGY**
Huichon City, Chagang Province
President: Kim Jin Pyong

F. of Radio Engineering
F. of Wire Communication Engineering
F. of Electro-Apparatus Engineering
F. of Mechanical Engineering
Also Research Institutes.

Founded 1959. A State institution responsible to the National Education Commission. Governing bodies: Instruction; Scientific Research; General Affairs.
Academic Year: September to August (September-February; February-August).
Admission Requirements: Graduation from Senior Middle School.
Fees: None.
Language of Instruction: Korean.
Degrees and Diplomas: Bachelor of Engineering, 5 yrs. Associate Doctorate. Doctorate.
Library: 17,874 vols.
Publications: Newspaper; Gazette.
Press or Publishing House: University Publishing House.
Academic Staff, 1986-87: 1299.
Student Enrolment, 1986-87: 6496.

4383 **THE UNIVERSITY OF VETERINARY AND ANIMAL HUSBANDRY**
Pyongsong City, South Pyongan Province
President: Pak Yong Hup

Veterinary Medicine
Animal Husbandry

Founded 1955. A State institution responsible to the National Education Commission. Governing bodies: Instruction; Scientific Research; General Affairs.
Academic Year: September to August (September-February; February-August).
Admission Requirements: Graduation from Senior Middle School.
Fees: None.
Language of Instruction: Korean.
Degrees and Diplomas: Bachelor of Engineering, 5 yrs. Associate Doctorate. Doctorate.
Library: 174,088 vols.
Publications: Newspaper; Gazette.
Press or Publishing House: University Publishing House.
Academic Staff, 1986-87: 622.
Student Enrolment, 1986-87: 5294.

Other Institutions

Technical Education

4384 **SARIWON COLLEGE OF AGRICULTURAL CHEMICALS**
North Hwanghae Province

Agricultural Chemistry

Founded 1984. A State institution responsible to the Provincial Committee for Administration and Economic Guidance. Governing bodies: Instruction; Scientific Research; General Affairs.
Academic Year: September to August (September-February; February-August).
Admission Requirements: Graduation from Senior Middle School.
Fees: None.
Language of Instruction: Korean.

4385 **SINCHON COLLEGE OF AGRICULTURE**
South Hwanghae Province
Rector: Choi Chun Hwan

Agriculture (including Veterinary Medicine, Farm Machinery)

Founded 1984. A State institution responsible to the Provincial Committee for Administration and Economic Guidance. Governing bodies: Instruction; Scientific Research; General Affairs.
Academic Year: September to August (September-February; February-August).
Admission Requirements: Graduation from Senior Middle School.
Fees: None.
Language of Instruction: Korean.
Degrees and Diplomas: Bachelor, 4 yrs.

4386 **SUKCHON COLLEGE OF AGRICULTURE**
South Pyongan Province
Rector: Chang Myong Ryul

Agriculture (including Stockraising and Farm Machinery)

Founded 1984. A State institution responsible to the Provincial Committee for Administration and Economic Guidance. Governing bodies: Instruction; Scientific Research; General Affairs.
Academic Year: September to August (September-February; February-August).
Admission Requirements: Graduation from Senior Middle School.
Fees: None.
Language of Instruction: Korean.
Degrees and Diplomas: Bachelor, 4 yrs.

4387 **TOKCHON AUTOMOBILE COLLEGE**
South Pyongan Province
Rector: Ryo Song Hak

Automobile Engineering
Metal Engineering
Machine Building
Welding Engineering

Founded 1984. A State institution responsible to the Provincial Committee for Administration and Economic Guidance. Governing bodies: Instruction; Scientific Research; General Affairs.
Academic Year: September to August (September-February; February-August).
Admission Requirements: Graduation from Senior Middle School.
Fees: None.
Language of Instruction: Korean.
Degrees and Diplomas: Bachelor, 4 yrs.
Academic Staff, 1986-87: 97.
Student Enrolment, 1986-87: 775.

4388 **CHONGSU COLLEGE OF CHEMICAL INDUSTRY**
North Pyongan Province
Rector: Pak Gwang Mun

Industrial Chemistry

Founded 1985. A State institution responsible to the Provincial Committee for Administration and Economic Guidance. Governing bodies: Instruction; Scientific Research; General Affairs.
Academic Year: September to August.
Admission Requirements: Graduation from Senior Middle School.
Fees: None.
Language of Instruction: Korean.
Degrees and Diplomas: Bachelor, 4 yrs.

4389 **HAMHUNG COLLEGE OF CHEMISTRY**
South Hamgyong Province
Rector: Hong Gyong Bo

Inorganic Chemistry Engineering
Analytical Chemistry
Chemical Machinery
Automation of Chemical Process
Organic Synthetic Engineering
Pharmaceutical Chemical Engineering

High Polymer Chemical Engineering

Founded 1984. A State institution responsible to the Provincial Committee for Administration and Economic Guidance. Governing bodies: Instruction; Scientific Research; General Affairs.

Academic Year: September to August (September-February; February-August).

Admission Requirements: Graduation from Senior Middle School.

Fees: None.

Language of Instruction: Korean.

Degrees and Diplomas: Bachelor, 4 yrs.

4390 **LI SU BOK COLLEGE OF CHEMICAL INDUSTRY**

South Pyongan Province

Founded 1984.

4391 **PYONGYANG COLLEGE OF CITY PLANNING**

Pyongyang

Rector: Cho Song Bo

Construction Engineering

Founded 1985. A State institution responsible to the Provincial Committee for Administration and Economic Guidance. Governing bodies: Instruction; Scientific Research; General Affairs.

Academic Year: September to August (September-February; February-August).

Admission Requirements: Graduation from Senior Middle School.

Fees: None.

Language of Instruction: Korean.

Degrees and Diplomas: Bachelor, 4 yrs.

4392 **HAMHUNG COLLEGE OF COMPUTING MACHINES**

South Hamgyong Province

Rector: Li Hak Sun

Computer Sciences

Founded 1985. A State institution responsible to the Provincial Committee for Administration and Economic Guidance. Governing bodies: Instruction; Scientific Research; General Affairs.

Academic Year: September to August.

Admission Requirements: Graduation from Senior Middle School.

Fees: None.

Language of Instruction: Korean.

Degrees and Diplomas: Bachelor, 4 yrs.

4393 **PYONGYANG COLLEGE OF COMPUTING MACHINES**

Pyongyang

Rector: Choi Byong June

Computer Sciences

Founded 1985. A State institution responsible to the Provincial Committee for Administration and Economic Guidance. Governing bodies: Instruction; Scientific Research; General Affairs.

Academic Year: September to August (September-February; February-August).

Admission Requirements: Graduation from Senior Middle School.

Fees: None.

Language of Instruction: Korean.

Degrees and Diplomas: Bachelor, 4 yrs.

Academic Staff, 1986-87: 89.

Student Enrolment, 1986-87: 711.

4394 **PYONGYANG COLLEGE OF CONSTRUCTION**

Pyongyang

Construction Engineering (including Architecture)

Founded 1984. A State institution responsible to the Provincial Committee for Administration and Economic Guidance. Governing bodies: Instruction; Scientific Research; General Affairs.

Academic Year: September to August (September-February; February-August).

Admission Requirements: Graduation from Senior Middle School.

Fees: None.

Language of Instruction: Korean.

Degrees and Diplomas: Bachelor, 4 yrs.

Academic Staff, 1986-87: 87.

Student Enrolment, 1986-87: 699.

4395 **SINUIJU COLLEGE OF FINANCE**

North Pyongan Province

Rector: Ryu Jong Gyu

Finance

Founded 1985. A State institution responsible to the Provincial Committee for Administration and Economic Guidance. Governing bodies: Instruction; Scientific Research; General Affairs.

Academic Year: September to August.

Admission Requirements: Graduation from Senior Middle School.

Fees: None.

Language of Instruction: Korean.

Degrees and Diplomas: Bachelor, 4 yrs.

Academic Staff, 1986-87: 91.

Student Enrolment, 1986-87: 731.

4396 **PYONGYANG ELECTRICAL COLLEGE**

Pyongyang

Rector: So Jae Bom

Electrical Engineering (including Radio Communication)

Founded 1984. A State institution responsible to the Provincial Committee for Administration and Economic Guidance. Governing bodies: Instruction; Scientific Research; General Affairs.

Academic Year: September to August (September-February; February-August).

Admission Requirements: Graduation from Senior Middle School.

Fees: None.

Language of Instruction: Korean.

Degrees and Diplomas: Bachelor, 4 yrs.

Academic Staff, 1986-87: 100.

Student Enrolment, 1986-87: 796.

4397 **SUPUNG ELECTRICAL COLLEGE**

North Pyongan Province

Rector: Kim Sok Jun

Electrical Engineering

Founded 1984. A State institution responsible to the Provincial Committee for Administration and Economic Guidance. Governing bodies: Instruction; Scientific Research; General Affairs.

Academic Year: September to August (September-February; February-August).

Admission Requirements: Graduation from Senior Middle School.

Fees: None.

Language of Instruction: Korean.

Degrees and Diplomas: Bachelor, 4 yrs.

4398 **CHONGJIN COLLEGE OF ELECTRONICS AND AUTOMATION**

North Hamgyong Province

Rector: Pak Gyu Han

Electronics

Automation

Founded 1984. A State institution responsible to the Provincial Committee for Administration and Economic Guidance. Governing bodies: Instruction; Scientific Research; General Affairs.

Academic Year: September to August.

Admission Requirements: Graduation from Senior Middle School.

Fees: None.

Language of Instruction: Korean.

Degrees and Diplomas: Bachelor, 4 yrs.

4399 **HAEJU COLLEGE OF ELECTRONICS AND AUTOMATION**

South Hwanghae Province

Rector: Song Rak Un

Electronics

Automation

Founded 1984. A State institution responsible to the Provincial Committee for Administration and Economic Guidance. Governing bodies: Instruction; Scientific Research; General Affairs.

Academic Year: September to August (September-February; February-August).

Admission Requirements: Graduation from Senior Middle School.

Fees: None.

Language of Instruction: Korean.

Degrees and Diplomas: Bachelor.

4400 **HAMHUNG COLLEGE OF ELECTRONICS AND AUTOMATION**
South Hamgyong Province
Rector: Li Gun Tae

Electronics
Automation

Founded 1984. A State institution responsible to the Provincial Committee for Administration and Economic Guidance. Governing bodies: Instruction; Scientific Research; General Affairs.

Academic Year: September to August (September-February; February-August).

Admission Requirements: Graduation from Senior Middle School.

Fees: None.

Language of Instruction: Korean.

Degrees and Diplomas: Bachelor.

4401 **SONGJIN COLLEGE OF FIREPROOF MATERIAL TECHNOLOGY**
North Hamgyong Province
Rector: Cho Jung Won

Silicate Engineering
Mechanical Engineering
Electrical Engineering

Founded 1978. A State institution responsible to the Provincial Committee for Administration and Economic Guidance. Governing bodies: Instruction; Scientific Research; General Affairs.

Academic Year: September to August.

Admission Requirements: Graduation from Senior Middle School.

Fees: None.

Language of Instruction: Korean.

Degrees and Diplomas: Bachelor, 5-6 yrs.

4402 **SINPO COLLEGE OF FISHERIES**
South Hamgyong Province
Rector: Li Chung Nam

Fisheries

Founded 1984. A State institution responsible to the Provincial Committee for Administration and Economic Guidance. Governing bodies: Instruction; Scientific Research; General Affairs.

Academic Year: September to August (September-February; February-August).

Admission Requirements: Graduation from Senior Middle School.

Fees: None.

Language of Instruction: Korean.

Degrees and Diplomas: Bachelor, 4 yrs.

4403 **RYONGSONG COLLEGE**
Pyongyang
Rector: Mun Kok Hwan

Food Technology

Founded 1960. A State institution responsible to the Provincial Committee for Administration and Economic Guidance. Governing bodies: Instruction; Scientific Research; General Affairs.

Academic Year: September to August.

Admission Requirements: Graduation from Senior Middle School.

Fees: None.

Language of Instruction: Korean.

Degrees and Diplomas: Bachelor, 5-6 yrs.

4404 **KILJU COLLEGE OF FORESTRY**
North Hamgyong Province
Rector: Chang Chong Gil

Forestry

Founded 1984. A State institution responsible to the Provincial Committee for Administration and Economic Guidance. Governing bodies: Instruction; Scientific Research; General Affairs.

Academic Year: September to August (September-February; February-August).

Admission Requirements: Graduation from Senior Middle School.

Fees: None.

Language of Instruction: Korean.

Degrees and Diplomas: Bachelor, 4 yrs.

4405 **TANCHON COLLEGE OF GEOLOGICAL PROSPECTING**
South Hamgyong Province
Rector: Chon Hui Jun

Geological Engineering

Founded 1984. A State institution responsible to the Provincial Committee for Administration and Economic Guidance. Governing bodies: Instruction; Scientific Research; General Affairs.

Academic Year: September to August (September-February; February-August).

Admission Requirements: Graduation from Senior Middle School.

Fees: None.

Language of Instruction: Korean.

Degrees and Diplomas: Bachelor, 4 yrs.

4406 **PUKCHONG COLLEGE OF HORTICULTURE**
South Hamgyong Province
Rector: Kim Hui Sop

Horticulture
Forestry

Founded 1984. A State institution responsible to the Provincial Committee for Administration and Economic Guidance. Governing bodies: Instruction; Scientific Research; General Affairs.

Academic Year: September to August.

Admission Requirements: Graduation from Senior Middle School.

Fees: None.

Language of Instruction: Korean.

Degrees and Diplomas: Bachelor, 4 yrs.

4407 **TOKCHON COLLEGE OF HYDRAULIC POWER CONSTRUCTION**
South Pyongan Province
Rector: Chong Gyu Son

Construction Engineering

Founded 1985. A State institution responsible to the Provincial Committee for Administration and Economic Guidance. Governing bodies: Instruction; Scientific Research; General Affairs.

Academic Year: September to August (September-February; February-August).

Admission Requirements: Graduation from Senior Middle School.

Fees: None.

Language of Instruction: Korean.

Degrees and Diplomas: Bachelor, 4 yrs.

Academic Staff, 1986-87: 127.

Student Enrolment, 1986-87: 1025.

4408 **CHONGJIN COLLEGE OF LIGHT INDUSTRY**
North Hamgyong Province
Rector: Han Myong Se

Light Industrial Engineering

Founded 1984. A State institution responsible to the Provincial Committee for Administration and Economic Guidance. Governing bodies: Instruction; Scientific Research; General Affairs.

Academic Year: September to August (September-February; February-August).

Admission Requirements: Graduation from Senior Middle School.

Fees: None.

Language of Instruction: Korean.

Degrees and Diplomas: Bachelor, 4 yrs.

4409 **HAEJU COLLEGE OF LIGHT INDUSTRY**
South Hwanghae Province
Rector: Paek Chang Hak

Light Industrial Engineering

Founded 1985. A State institution responsible to the Provincial Committee for Administration and Economic Guidance. Governing bodies: Instruction; Scientific Research; General Affairs.

Academic Year: September to August.

Admission Requirements: Graduation from Senior Middle School.

Fees: None.

Language of Instruction: Korean.

Degrees and Diplomas: Bachelor, 4 yrs.

4410 **KAESONG COLLEGE OF LIGHT INDUSTRY**
Kaesong City
Rector: Kim Byong Ryon

Light Industrial Engineering

Founded 1984. A State institution responsible to the Provincial Committee for Administration and Economic Guidance. Governing bodies: Instruction; Scientific Research; General Affairs.

Academic Year: September to August (September-February; February-August).

Admission Requirements: Graduation from Senior Middle School.

Fees: None.

Language of Instruction: Korean.

Degrees and Diplomas: Bachelor, 4 yrs.

4411 **HUICHON COLLEGE OF MECHANICAL ENGINEERING**
Chagang Province
Rector: Chong Sok Jong

Mechanical Engineering

Founded 1984. A State institution responsible to the Provincial Committee for Administration and Economic Guidance. Governing bodies: Instruction; Scientific Research; General Affairs.

Academic Year: September to August (September-February; February-August).

Admission Requirements: Graduation from Senior Middle School.

Fees: None.

Language of Instruction: Korean.

Degrees and Diplomas: Bachelor, 4 yrs.

Academic Staff, 1986-87: 121.

Student Enrolment, 1986-87: 969.

4412 **KUSONG COLLEGE OF MECHANICAL ENGINEERING**
North Pyongan Province
Rector: O Hyen Gap

Mechanical Engineering

Founded 1984. A State institution responsible to the Provincial Committee for Administration and Economic Guidance. Governing bodies: Instruction; Scientific Research; General Affairs.

Academic Year: September to August.

Admission Requirements: Graduation from Senior Middle School.

Fees: None.

Language of Instruction: Korean.

Degrees and Diplomas: Bachelor, 4 yrs.

Academic Staff, 1986-87: 89.

Student Enrolment, 1986-87: 714.

4413 **RYONGSONG COLLEGE OF MECHANICAL ENGINEERING**
South Hamgyong Province
Rector: Chi Chang Se

Mechanical Engineering

Chemical Engineering

Founded 1961. A State institution responsible to the Provincial Committee for Administration and Economic Guidance. Governing bodies: Instruction; Scientific Research; General Affairs.

Academic Year: September to August (September-February; February-August).

Admission Requirements: Graduation from Senior Middle School.

Fees: None.

Language of Instruction: Korean.

Degrees and Diplomas: Bachelor, 5-6 yrs.

4414 **NAMPO COLLEGE OF MEDICINE**
Nampo
Rector: Ryon Hyong Gwan

Medicine

Dentistry

Founded 1985. A State institution responsible to the Provincial Committee for Administration and Economic Guidance. Governing bodies: Instruction; Scientific Research; General Affairs.

Academic Year: September to August.

Admission Requirements: Graduation from Senior Middle School.

Fees: None.

Language of Instruction: Korean.

Degrees and Diplomas: Doctor, 4 yrs.

4415 **CHONGJIN MERCANTILE MARINE COLLEGE**
Chongjin
Rector: Han So Hong

Marine Engineering (including Navigation and Port Management)

Founded 1985. A State institution responsible to the Provincial Committee for Administration and Economic Guidance. Governing bodies: Instruction; Scientific Research; General Affairs.

Academic Year: September to August (September-February; February-August).

Admission Requirements: Graduation from Senior Middle School.

Fees: None.

Language of Instruction: Korean.

Degrees and Diplomas: Bachelor, 4 yrs.

4416 **CHONGJIN COLLEGE OF METALLURGICAL ENGINEERING**
North Hamgyong Province
Rector: Paek Chol Ok

Metallurgy

Founded 1984. A State institution responsible to the Provincial Committee for Administration and Economic Guidance. Governing bodies: Instruction; Scientific Research; General Affairs.

Academic Year: September to August.

Admission Requirements: Graduation from Senior Middle School

Fees: None.

Language of Instruction: Korean.

Degrees and Diplomas: Bachelor, 4 yrs.

4417 **KANGSON COLLEGE OF METALLURGICAL ENGINEERING**
Nampo
Rector: Cho Yong Gil

Metallurgy

Founded 1984. A State institution responsible to the Provincial Committee for Administration and Economic Guidance. Governing bodies: Instruction; Scientific Research; General Affairs.

Academic Year: September to August (September-February; February-August).

Admission Requirements: Graduation from Senior Middle School.

Fees: None.

Language of Instruction: Korean.

Degrees and Diplomas: Bachelor, 4 yrs.

4418 **KIM CHAEK COLLEGE OF METALLURGICAL ENGINEERING**
North Hamgyong Province
Rector: Kim Chi Jong

Metallurgy

Founded 1984. A State institution responsible to the Provincial Committee for Administration and Economic Guidance. Governing bodies: Instruction; Scientific Research; General Affairs.

Academic Year: September to August (September-February; February-August).

Admission Requirements: Graduation from Senior Middle School.

Fees: None.

Language of Instruction: Korean.

Degrees and Diplomas: Bachelor, 4 yrs.

4419 **ANJU COLLEGE OF COAL MINING**
South Pyongan Province
Rector: Kim Ung Chol

Mining

Founded 1985. A State institution responsible to the Provincial Committee for Administration and Economic Guidance. Governing bodies: Instruction; Scientific Research; General Affairs.

Academic Year: September to August.

Admission Requirements: Graduation from Senior Middle School.

Fees: None.

Language of Instruction: Korean.

Degrees and Diplomas: Bachelor, 4 yrs.

Academic Staff, 1986-87: 178.

Student Enrolment, 1986-87: 1426.

4420 **UNDOK COLLEGE OF COAL MINING**
North Hamgyong Province
Rector: Chon Jong Sik

Mining

Founded 1985. A State institution responsible to the Provincial Committee for Administration and Economic Guidance. Governing bodies: Instruction; Scientific Research; General Affairs.

Academic Year: September to August (September-February; February-August).

Admission Requirements: Graduation from Senior Middle School.

Fees: None.

Language of Instruction: Korean.

Degrees and Diplomas: Bachelor, 4 yrs.

4421 **PYONGYANG COLLEGE OF PRINTING**
Pyongyang
Rector: Li Yong Hun

Printing Engineering (including Metal Processing)

Founded 1984. A State institution responsible to the Provincial Committee for Administration and Economic Guidance. Governing bodies: Instruction; Scientific Research; General Affairs.

Academic Year: September to August (September-February; February-August).

Admission Requirements: Graduation from Senior Middle School.

Fees: None.

Language of Instruction: Korean.

Degrees and Diplomas: Bachelor, 4 yrs.

Academic Staff, 1986-87: 168.

Student Enrolment, 1986-87: 1347.

4422 **CHONGJU COLLEGE OF RAILWAY CONSTRUCTION**
North Pyongan Province
Rector: Kim Hui Jong

Railway Engineering

Founded 1985. A State institution responsible to the Provincial Committee for Administration and Economic Guidance. Governing bodies: Instruction; Scientific Research; General Affairs.

Academic Year: September to August.

Admission Requirements: Graduation from Senior Middle School.

Fees: None.

Language of Instruction: Korean.

Degrees and Diplomas: Bachelor, 4 yrs.

4423 **CHONGJIN COLLEGE OF RAILWAY MANAGEMENT**
North Hamgyong Province
Rector: Kim Chang Su

Railway Management

Founded 1985. A State institution responsible to the Provincial Committee for Administration and Economic Guidance. Governing bodies: Instruction; Scientific Research; General Affairs.

Academic Year: September to August (September-February; February-August).

Admission Requirements: Graduation from Senior Middle School.

Fees: None.

Language of Instruction: Korean.

Degrees and Diplomas: Bachelor, 4 yrs.

4424 **NAMPO COLLEGE OF SHIPBUILDING**
Nampo
Rector: Li Gun Ju

Shipbuilding (including Metal Engineering)

Founded 1985. A State institution responsible to the Provincial Committee for Administration and Economic Guidance. Governing bodies: Instruction; Scientific Research; General Affairs.

Academic Year: September to August (September-February; February-August).

Admission Requirements: Graduation from Senior Middle School

Fees: None.

Language of Instruction: Korean.

Degrees and Diplomas: Bachelor, 4 yrs.

Academic Staff, 1986-87: 130.

Student Enrolment, 1986-87: 1040.

4425 **SUNCHON COLLEGE OF SILICATE TECHNOLOGY**
South Pyongan Province
Rector: Kim Nam Yun

Silicate Technology (including Mechanical Engineering)

Founded 1976. A State institution responsible to the Provincial Committee for Administration and Economic Guidance. Governing bodies: Instruction; Scientific Research; General Affairs.

Academic Year: September to August.

Admission Requirements: Graduation from Senior Middle School.

Fees: None.

Language of Instruction: Korean.

Degrees and Diplomas: Bachelor, 5-6 yrs.

4426 **PYONGYANG COLLEGE OF SURGERY**
Pyongyang
Rector: Kim Tae Sil

Medicine (including Korean Traditional Medicine)
Pharmacy (including Korean Traditional Pharmacy)
Nursing

Founded 1985. A State institution responsible to the Provincial Committee for Administration and Economic Guidance. Governing bodies: Instruction; Scientific Research; General Affairs.

Academic Year: September to August (September-February; February-August).

Admission Requirements: Graduation from Senior Middle School.

Fees: None.

Language of Instruction: Korean.

Degrees and Diplomas: Doctor, 4 yrs.

4427 **ANJU COLLEGE OF TECHNOLOGY**
South Pyongan Province
Rector: Choe Han Chun

Chemical Engineering
Mechanical Engineering
Electrical Engineering

Founded 1976. A State institution responsible to the Provincial Committee for Administration and Economic Guidance. Governing bodies: Instruction; Scientific Research; General Affairs.

Academic Year: September to August (September-February; February-August).

Admission Requirements: Graduation from Senior Middle School.

Fees: None.

Language of Instruction: Korean.

Degrees and Diplomas: Bachelor, 5-6 yrs.

4428 **BUKJUNG COLLEGE OF TECHNOLOGY**
North Pyongan Province
Rector: Chang Bong Chol

Mechanical Engineering (including Metal Processing)

Founded 1960. A State institution responsible to the Provincial Committee for Administration and Economic Guidance. Governing bodies: Instruction; Scientific Research; General Affairs.

Academic Year: September to August.

Admission Requirements: Graduation from Senior Middle School.

Fees: None.

Language of Instruction: Korean.

Degrees and Diplomas: Bachelor, 5-6 yrs.

4429 **CHONGJIN COLLEGE OF TECHNOLOGY**
North Hamgyong Province
Rector: Son Gyong Jun

Electrical Engineering
Metallurgical Engineering
Chemical Engineering
Mechanical Engineering

Founded 1960. A State institution responsible to the Provincial Committee for Administration and Economic Guidance. Governing bodies: Instruction; Scientific Research; General Affairs.

Academic Year: September to August (September-February; February-August).

Admission Requirements: Graduation from Senior Middle School.

Fees: None.

Language of Instruction: Korean.

Degrees and Diplomas: Bachelor, 5-6 yrs.

4430 **HONNAE COLLEGE OF TECHNOLOGY**
Kangwon Province
Rector: U Chae Ha

Mechanical Engineering
Silicate Engineering

Founded 1982. A State institution responsible to the Provincial Committee for Administration and Economic Guidance. Governing bodies: Instruction; Scientific Research; General Affairs.

Academic Year: September to August (September-February; February-August).

Admission Requirements: Graduation from Senior Middle School.

Fees: None.

Language of Instruction: Korean.

Degrees and Diplomas: Bachelor, 5-6 yrs.

4431 **DONGRIM COLLEGE OF TECHNOLOGY**
North Pyongyan Province
Rector: Ho Jong Un

Mechanical Engineering (including Metal Processing)

Founded 1976. A State institution responsible to the Provincial Committee for Administration and Economic Guidance. Governing bodies: Instruction; Scientific Research; General Affairs.

Academic Year: September to August.

Admission Requirements: Graduation from Senior Middle School.

Fees: None.

Language of Instruction: Korean.

Degrees and Diplomas: Bachelor, 5-6 yrs.

4432 **FEBRUARY 26 TH COLLEGE OF TECHNOLOGY**
Chagang Province
Rector: Li Byong Gi

Technology (including Machine Building and Metal Processing)

Founded 1985. A State institution responsible to the Provincial Committee for Administration and Economic Guidance. Governing bodies: Instruction; Scientific Research; General Affairs.

Academic Year: September to August (September-February; February-August).

Admission Requirements: Graduation from Senior Middle School.

Fees: None.

Language of Instruction: Korean.

Degrees and Diplomas: Bachelor, 5-6 yrs.

4433 **HAEJU COLLEGE OF TECHNOLOGY**
South Hwanghae Province
Rector: Kim Jong Ho

Electrical Engineering
Mechanical Engineering
Chemical Engineering

Founded 1961. A State institution responsible to the Provincial Committee for Administration and Economic Guidance. Governing bodies: Instruction; Scientific Research; General Affairs.

Academic Year: September to August (September-February; February-August).

Admission Requirements: Graduation from Senior Middle School.

Fees: None.

Language of Instruction: Korean.

Degrees and Diplomas: Bachelor, 5-6 yrs.

4434 **HUNGNAM COLLEGE OF TECHNOLOGY**
South Hamgyong Province
Rector: Maeng Tae Ho

Chemical Engineering
Mechanical Engineering
Automation
Electrical Engineering

Founded 1960. A State institution responsible to the Provincial Committee for Administration and Economic Guidance. Governing bodies: Instruction; Scientific Research; General Affairs.

Academic Year: September to August.

Admission Requirements: Graduation from Senior Middle School.

Fees: None.

Language of Instruction: Korean.

Degrees and Diplomas: Bachelor, 5-6 yrs.

4435 **HWASONG COLLEGE OF TECHNOLOGY**
Pyongyang

Founded 1983. A State institution responsible to the Provincial Committee for Administration and Economic Guidance. Governing bodies: Instruction; Scientific Research; General Affairs.

Academic Year: September to August (September-February; February-August).

Admission Requirements: Graduation from Senior Middle School.

Fees: None.

Language of Instruction: Korean.

4436 **HYESAN COLLEGE OF TECHNOLOGY**
Ryanggang Province
Rector: Choe Bong Taek

Mechanical Engineering
Textile Engineering

Founded 1971. A State institution responsible to the Provincial Committee for Administration and Economic Guidance. Governing bodies: Instruction; Scientific Research; General Affairs.

Academic Year: September to August (September-February; February-August).

Admission Requirements: Graduation from Senior Middle School.

Fees: None.

Language of Instruction: Korean.

Degrees and Diplomas: Bachelor, 5-6 yrs.

4437 **HYONGBONG COLLEGE OF TECHNOLOGY**
South Pyongan Province
Rector: Kim In Sok

Mining Engineering
Mechanical Engineering

Founded 1979. A State institution responsible to the Provincial Committee for Administration and Economic Guidance. Governing bodies: Instruction; Scientific Research; General Affairs.

Academic Year: September to August.

Admission Requirements: Graduation from Senior Middle School.

Fees: None.

Language of Instruction: Korean.

Degrees and Diplomas: Bachelor, 5-6 yrs.

4438 **KANGSON COLLEGE OF TECHNOLOGY**
Nampo
Rector: Pak Yong Chan

Metallurgy
Mechanical Engineering
Automation
Electrical Engineering

Founded 1960. A State Institution responsible to the Provincial Committee for Administration and Economic Guidance. Governing bodies: Instruction; Scientific Research; General Affairs.

Academic Year: September to August (September-February; February-August).

Admission Requirements: Graduation from Senior Middle School.

Fees: None.

Language of Instruction: Korean.

Degrees and Diplomas: Bachelor, 5-6 yrs.

4439 **KAPSAN COLLEGE OF TECHNOLOGY**
Ryanggang Province
Rector: Mun Chang Gwon

Mining Engineering
Mechanical Engineering

Founded 1984. A State institution responsible to the Provincial Committee for Administration and Economic Guidance. Governing bodies: Instruction; Scientific Research; General Affairs.

Academic Year: September to August (September-February; February-August).

Admission Requirements: Graduation from Senior Middle School.

Fees: None.

Language of Instruction: Korean.

Degrees and Diplomas: Bachelor, 5-6 yrs.

4440 **KIYANG COLLEGE OF TECHNOLOGY**
Nampo
Rector: Kim Ju Ho

Mechanical Engineering
Metallurgy
Automation
Electrical Engineering

Founded 1960. A State institution responsible to the Provincial Committee for Administration and Economic Guidance. Governing bodies: Instruction; Scientific Research; General Affairs.

Academic Year: September to August.

Admission Requirements: Graduation from Senior Middle School.

Fees: None.

Language of Instruction: Korean.

Degrees and Diplomas: Bachelor, 5-6 yrs.

4441 **KOGONWON COLLEGE OF TECHNOLOGY**
North Hamgyong Province
Rector: Han Tae Dong

Mining Engineering
Mechanical Engineering

Founded 1981. A State institution responsible to the Provincial Committee for Administration and Economic Guidance. Governing bodies: Instruction; Scientific Research; General Affairs.

Academic Year: September to August (September-February; February-August).

Admission Requirements: Graduation from Senior Middle School.

Fees: None.

Language of Instruction: Korean.

Degrees and Diplomas: Bachelor, 5-6 yrs.

4442 **KOMDOK COLLEGE OF TECHNOLOGY**
South Hamgyong Province
Rector: Yun In Sop

Mining Engineering
Mechanical Engineering

Founded 1961. A State institution responsible to the Provincial Committee for Administration and Economic Guidance. Governing bodies: Instruction; Scientific Research; General Affairs.

Academic Year: September to August (September-February; February-August).

Admission Requirements: Graduation from Senior Middle School.

Fees: None.

Language of Instruction: Korean.

Degrees and Diplomas: Bachelor, 5-6 yrs.

4443 **KUSONG COLLEGE OF TECHNOLOGY**
North Pyongan Province
Rector: Im Bong Ryong

Machine Building Engineering
Machine Tool Engineering
Automation

Founded 1960. A State institution responsible to the Provincial Committee for Administration and Economic Guidance. Governing bodies: Instruction; Scientific Research; General Affairs.

Academic Year: September to August.

Admission Requirements: Graduation from Senior Middle School.

Fees: None.

Language of Instruction: Korean.

Degrees and Diplomas: Bachelor, 5-6 yrs.

4444 **KYONGSONG COLLEGE OF TECHNOLOGY**
North Hamgyong Province
Rector: Cho Byong Ho

Silicate Engineering
Mechanical Engineering
Electrical Engineering

Founded 1960. A State institution responsible to the Provincial Committee for Administration and Economic Guidance. Governing bodies: Instruction; Scientific Research; General Affairs.

Academic Year: September to August (September-February; February-August).

Admission Requirements: Graduation from Senior Middle School.

Fees: None.

Language of Instruction: Korean.

Degrees and Diplomas: Bachelor, 5-6 yrs.

4445 **MAY FOURTH COLLEGE OF TECHNOLOGY**
South Pyongan Province
Rector: Kim Dal Sik

Mining Engineering
Mechanical Engineering

Founded 1984. A State institution responsible to the Provincial Committee for Administration and Economic Guidance. Governing bodies: Instruction; Scientific Research; General Affairs.

Academic Year: September to August.

Admission Requirements: Graduation from Senior Middle School.

Fees: None.

Language of Instruction: Korean.

Degrees and Diplomas: Bachelor, 5-6 yrs.

4446 **MUNPYONG COLLEGE OF TECHNOLOGY**
Kangwon Province
Rector: U Du Dae

Mechanical Engineering
Electrical Engineering
Chemical Engineering
Metallurgy

Founded 1960. A State institution responsible to the Provincial Committee for Administration and Economic Guidance. Governing bodies: Instruction; Scientific Research; General Affairs.

Academic Year: September to August (September-February; February-August).

Admission Requirements: Graduation from Senior Middle School.

Fees: None.

Language of Instruction: Korean.

Degrees and Diplomas: Bachelor, 5-6 yrs.

4447 **MUSAN COLLEGE OF TECHNOLOGY**
North Hamgyong Province
Rector: Kim Jong Song

Mechanical Engineering
Dressing Engineering
Mining
Electrical Engineering
Architectural Engineering

Founded 1960. A State institution responsible to the Provincial Committee for Administration and Economic Guidance. Governing bodies: Instruction; Scientific Research; General Affairs.

Academic Year: September to August (September-February; February-August).

Admission Requirements: Graduation from Senior Middle School.

Fees: None.

Language of Instruction: Korean.

Degrees and Diplomas: Bachelor, 5-6 yrs.

4448 **NAMHUNG COLLEGE OF TECHNOLOGY**
South Pyongan Province
Rector: Li Sung Jin

Automation
Chemical Engineering

Founded 1983. A State institution responsible to the Provincial Committee for Administration and Economic Guidance. Governing bodies: Instruction; Scientific Research; General Affairs.

Academic Year: September to August.

Admission Requirements: Graduation from Senior Middle School.

Fees: None.

Language of Instruction: Korean.

Degrees and Diplomas: Bachelor, 5-6 yrs.

4449 **NAMPO COLLEGE OF TECHNOLOGY**
Nampo
Rector: Han Won Chang

Mechanical Engineering
Chemical Engineering
Electrical Engineering

Metallurgy

Founded 1960. A State institution responsible to the Provincial Committee for Administration and Economic Guidance. Governing bodies: Instruction; Scientific Research; General Affairs.

Academic Year: September to August (September-February; February-August).

Admission Requirements: Graduation from Senior Middle School.

Fees: None.

Language of Instruction: Korean.

Degrees and Diplomas: Bachelor, 5-6 yrs.

4450 **POHANG COLLEGE OF TECHNOLOGY**

North Hamgyong Province

Rector: Ho Song Ryol

Mechanical Engineering

Electrical Engineering

Chemical Engineering

Metallurgy

Founded 1964. A State institution responsible to the Provincial Committee for Administration and Economic Guidance. Governing bodies: Instruction; Scientific Research; General Affairs.

Academic Year: September to August (September-February; February-August).

Admission Requirements: Graduation from Senior Middle School.

Fees: None.

Language of Instruction: Korean.

Degrees and Diplomas: Bachelor, 5-6 yrs.

4451 **PUKCHANG COLLEGE OF TECHNOLOGY**

South Pyongan Province

Rector: Yang Yong Gwon

Mechanical Engineering

Electrical Engineering

Founded 1976. A State institution responsible to the Provincial Committee for Administration and Economic Guidance. Governing bodies: Instruction; Scientific Research; General Affairs.

Academic Year: September to August.

Admission Requirements: Graduation from Senior Middle School.

Fees: None.

Language of Instruction: Korean.

Degrees and Diplomas: Bachelor, 5-6 yrs.

4452 **PYONGCHON COLLEGE OF TECHNOLOGY**

Pyongyang

Rector: Kim Chang Ok

Mechanical Engineering

Electrical Engineering

Automation

Founded 1970. A State institution responsible to the Provincial Committee for Administration and Economic Guidance. Governing bodies: Instruction; Scientific Research; General Affairs.

Academic Year: September to August (September-February; February-August).

Admission Requirements: Graduation from Senior Middle School.

Fees: None.

Language of Instruction: Korean.

Degrees and Diplomas: Bachelor, 5-6 yrs.

4453 **PYONGYANG COLLEGE OF TECHNOLOGY**

Pyongyang

Rector: Li Sang Hyon

Textile Engineering

Chemical Engineering

Electrical Engineering

Mechanical Engineering

Founded 1960. A State institution responsible to the Provincial Committee for Administration and Economic Guidance. Governing bodies: Instruction; Scientific Research; General Affairs.

Academic Year: September to August.

Admission Requirements: Graduation from Senior Middle School.

Fees: None.

Language of Instruction: Korean.

Degrees and Diplomas: Bachelor, 5-6 yrs.

4454 **RAHUNG COLLEGE OF TECHNOLOGY**

South Hamgyong Province

Rector: Kwak Li Gun

Mechanical Engineering

Metallurgy

Founded 1976. A State institution responsible to the Provincial Committee for Administration and Economic Guidance. Governing bodies: Instruction; Scientific Research; General Affairs.

Academic Year: September to August (September-February; February-August).

Admission Requirements: Graduation from Senior Middle School.

Fees: None.

Language of Instruction: Korean.

Degrees and Diplomas: Bachelor, 5-6 yrs.

4455 **RAKWON COLLEGE OF TECHNOLOGY**

North Pyongan Province

Rector: Chae Myong Chol

Mechanical Engineering

Metallurgy

Founded 1960. A State institution responsible to the Provincial Committee for Adminstration and Economic Guidance. Governing bodies: Instruction; Scientific Research; General Affairs.

Academic Year: September to August (September-February; February-August).

Admission Requirements: Graduation from Senior Middle School.

Fees: None.

Language of Instruction: Korean.

Degrees and Diplomas: Bachelor, 5-6 yrs.

4456 **RAKYON COLLEGE OF TECHNOLOGY**

North Hwanghae Province

Rector: Kim Mong Ro

Mechanical Engineering

Mining Engineering

Founded 1984. A State institution responsible to the Provincial Committee for Administration and Economic Guidance. Governing bodies: Instruction; Scientific Research; General Affairs.

Academic Year: September to August.

Admission Requirements: Graduation from Senior Middle School.

Fees: None.

Language of Instruction: Korean.

Degrees and Diplomas: Bachelor, 5-6 yrs.

4457 **RANAM COLLEGE OF TECHNOLOGY**

North Hamgyong Province

Rector: Kim Dong Chol

Mechanical Engineering

Metallurgy

Elementary Technology

Founded 1983. A State institution responsible to the Provincial Committee for Administration and Economic Guidance. Governing bodies: Instruction; Scientific Research; General Affairs.

Academic Year: September to August (September-February; February-August).

Admission Requirements: Graduation from Senior Middle School.

Fees: None.

Language of Instruction: Korean.

Degrees and Diplomas: Bachelor, 5-6 yrs.

4458 **RYONGDUNG COLLEGE OF TECHNOLOGY**

North Pyongan Province

Rector: Han Gyu Jong

Mining

Mechanical Engineering

Founded 1979. A State institution responsible to the Provincial Committee for Administration and Economic Guidance. Governing bodies: Instruction; Scientific Research; General Affairs.

Academic Year: September to August (September-February; February-August).

Admission Requirements: Graduation from Senior Middle School.

Fees: None.

Language of Instruction: Korean.

Degrees and Diplomas: Bachelor, 5-6 yrs.

4459 **RYONGYANG COLLEGE OF TECHNOLOGY**
South Hamgyong Province
Rector: Kim Pil Hwan

Mining
Mechanical Engineering

Founded 1961. A State institution responsible to the Provincial Committee for Administration and Economic Guidance. Governing bodies: Instruction; Scientific Research; General Affairs.

Academic Year: September to August.

Admission Requirements: Graduation from Senior Middle School.

Fees: None.

Language of Instruction: Korean.

Degrees and Diplomas: Bachelor, 5-6 yrs.

4460 **SAPO COLLEGE OF TECHNOLOGY**
South Hamgyong Province
Rector: Sin Dae Hyon

Chemical Engineering
Mechanical Engineering
Electrical Engineering
Automation

Founded 1960. A State institution responsible to the Provincial Committee for Administration and Economic Guidance. Governing bodies: Instruction; Scientific Research; General Affairs.

Academic Year: September to August (September-February; February-August).

Admission Requirements: Graduation from Senior Middle School.

Fees: None.

Language of Instruction: Korean.

Degrees and Diplomas: Bachelor, 5-6 yrs.

4461 **SINCHANG COLLEGE OF TECHNOLOGY**
South Pyongan Province
Rector: Pak Jae Dok

Mining
Mechanical Engineering

Founded 1961. A State institution responsible to the Provincial Committee for Administration and Economic Guidance. Governing bodies: Instruction; Scientific Research; General Affairs.

Academic Year: September to August (September-February; February-August).

Admission Requirements: Graduation from Senior Middle School.

Fees: None.

Language of Instruction: Korean.

Degrees and Diplomas: Bachelor, 5-6 yrs.

4462 **SINUIJU COLLEGE OF TECHNOLOGY**
North Pyongan Province
Rector: Choi Je Hak

Electrical Engineering
Food Engineering
Textile Technology

Founded 1960. A State institution responsible to the Provincial Committee for Administration and Economic Guidance. Governing bodies: Instruction; Scientific Research; General Affairs.

Academic Year: September to August.

Admission Requirements: Graduation from Senior Middle School.

Fees: None.

Language of Instruction: Korean.

Degrees and Diplomas: Bachelor, 5-6 yrs.

4463 **SONGJIN COLLEGE OF TECHNOLOGY**
North Hamgyong Province
Rector: Chon Yong Hun

Metallurgy
Mechanical Engineering
Electrical Engineering

Founded 1960. A State institution responsible to the Provincial Committee for Administration and Economic Guidance. Governing bodies: Instruction; Scientific Research; General Affairs.

Academic Year: September to August (September-February; February-August).

Admission Requirements: Graduation from Senior Middle School.

Fees: None.

Language of Instruction: Korean.

Degrees and Diplomas: Bachelor, 5-6 yrs.

4464 **SONGLIM COLLEGE OF TECHNOLOGY**
North Hwanghae Province
Rector: Choi Hyon Gi

Metallurgy
Chemical Engineering
Automation
Transport Machinery

Founded 1960. A State institution responsible to the Provincial Committee for Administration and Economic Guidance. Governing bodies: Instruction; Scientific Research; General Affairs.

Academic Year: September to August (September-February; February-August).

Admission Requirements: Graduation from Senior Middle School.

Fees: None.

Language of Instruction: Korean.

Degrees and Diplomas: Bachelor, 5-6 yrs.

4465 **SONGPYONG COLLEGE OF TECHNOLOGY**
North Hamgyong Province
Rector: Choi Gi Jong

Architectural Engineering
Mechanical Engineering

Founded 1979. A State institution responsible to the Provincial Committee for Administration and Economic Guidance. Governing bodies: Instruction; Scientific Research; General Affairs.

Academic Year: September to August.

Admission Requirements: Graduation from Senior Middle School.

Fees: None.

Language of Instruction: Korean.

Degrees and Diplomas: Bachelor, 5-6 yrs.

4466 **SOSONG COLLEGE OF TECHNOLOGY**
Pyongyang
Rector: Cho Dal Song

Mechanical Engineering
Electrical Engineering
Electronic Engineering
Wood Processing

Founded 1976. A State institution responsible to the Provincial Committee for Administration and Economic Guidance. Governing bodies: Instruction; Scientific Research; General Affairs.

Academic Year: September to August (September-February; February-August).

Admission Requirements: Graduation from Senior Middle School.

Fees: None.

Language of Instruction: Korean.

Degrees and Diplomas: Bachelor, 5-6 yrs.

4467 **SUNCHON COLLEGE OF TECHNOLOGY**
South Pyongan Province
Rector: Kim Won Ho

Mechanical Engineering
Chemical Engineering

Founded 1961. A State institution responsible to the Provincial Committee for Administration and Economic Guidance. Governing bodies: Instruction; Scientific Research; General Affairs.

Academic Year: September to August (September-February; February-August).

Admission Requirements: Graduation from Senior Middle School

Fees: None.

Language of Instruction: Korean.

Degrees and Diplomas: Bachelor, 5-6 yrs.

4468 **SUNGHO COLLEGE OF TECHNOLOGY**
Pyongyang
Rector: Song Do Hyon

Mechanical Engineering
Silicate Engineering

Chemical and Electrical Technology

Founded 1961. A State institution responsible to the Provincial Committee for Administration and Economic Guidance. Governing bodies: Instruction; Scientific Research; General Affairs.

Academic Year: September to August (September-February; February-August).

Admission Requirements: Graduation from Senior Middle School.

Fees: None.

Language of Instruction: Korean.

Degrees and Diplomas: Bachelor, 5-6 yrs.

4469 **TAEAN COLLEGE OF TECHNOLOGY**

Nampo

Rector: Yun Ho Sok

Electrical Engineering

Metallurgy

Mechanical Engineering

Founded 1960. A State institution responsible to the Provincial Committee for Administration and Economic Guidance. Governing bodies: Instruction; Scientific Research; General Affairs.

Academic Year: September to August (September-February; February-August).

Admission Requirements: Graduation from Senior Middle School.

Fees: None.

Language of Instruction: Korean.

Degrees and Diplomas: Bachelor, 5-6 yrs.

4470 **TANCHON COLLEGE OF TECHNOLOGY**

South Hamgyong Province

Rector: Hwang Ha Jong

Mechanical Engineering

Silicate Engineering

Founded 1971. A State institution responsible to the Provincial Committee for Administration and Economic Guidance. Governing bodies: Instruction; Scientific Research; General Affairs.

Academic Year: September to August.

Admission Requirements: Graduation from Senior Middle School.

Fees: None.

Language of Instruction: Korean.

Degrees and Diplomas: Bachelor, 5-6 yrs.

4471 **TOKCHON COLLEGE OF TECHNOLOGY**

South Pyongan Province

Rector: Li Won Gwan

Mechanical Engineering

Metal Processing

Founded 1960. A State institution responsible to the Provincial Committee for Administration and Economic Guidance. Governing bodies: Instruction; Scientific Research; General Affairs.

Academic Year: September to August (September-February; February-August).

Admission Requirements: Graduation from Senior Middle School.

Fees: None.

Language of Instruction: Korean.

Degrees and Diplomas: Bachelor, 5-6 yrs.

4472 **TOKHYON COLLEGE OF TECHNOLOGY**

North Pyongan Province

Rector: Choe Hae Nam

Mining Engineering

Mechanical Engineering

Elementary Technology

Founded 1978. A State institution responsible to the Provincial Committee for Administration and Economic Guidance. Governing bodies: Instruction; Scientific Research; General Affairs.

Academic Year: September to August (September-February; February-August).

Admission Requirements: Graduation from Senior Middle School.

Fees: None.

Language of Instruction: Korean.

Degrees and Diplomas: Bachelor, 5-6 yrs.

4473 **UIJU COLLEGE OF TECHNOLOGY**

North Pyongan Province

Rector: Cho Bong Sam

Metallurgy

Mechanical Engineering

Electrical Engineering

Founded 1978. A State institution responsible to the Provincial Committee for Administration and Economic Guidance. Governing bodies: Instruction; Scientific Research; General Affairs.

Academic Year: September to August.

Admission Requirements: Graduation from Senior Middle School.

Fees: None.

Language of Instruction: Korean.

Degrees and Diplomas: Bachelor, 5-6 yrs.

4474 **UNDOK COLLEGE OF TECHNOLOGY**

North Hamgyong Province

Founded 1960. A State institution responsible to the Provincial Committee for Administration and Economic Guidance. Governing bodies: Instruction; Scientific Research; General Affairs.

Academic Year: September to August (September-February; February-August).

Admission Requirements: Graduation from Senior Middle School.

Fees: None.

Language of Instruction: Korean.

4475 **UNHUNG COLLEGE OF TECHNOLOGY**

Ryanggang Province

Rector: Park Sam

Mining Engineering

Mechanical Engineering

Founded 1985. A State institution responsible to the Provincial Committee for Adminstration and Economic Guidance. Governing bodies: Instruction; Scientific Research; General Affairs.

Academic Year: September to August (September-February; February-August).

Admission Requirements: Graduation from Senior Middle School.

Fees: None.

Language of Instruction: Korean.

Degrees and Diplomas: Bachelor, 5-6 yrs.

4476 **UNSAN COLLEGE OF TECHNOLOGY**

North Pyongan Province

Rector: Park Kyong Ho

Mechanical Engineering

Founded 1961. A State institution responsible to the Provincial Committee for Administration and Economic Guidance. Governing bodies: Instruction; Scientific Research; General Affairs.

Academic Year: September to August.

Admission Requirements: Graduation from Senior Middle School.

Fees: None.

Language of Instruction: Korean.

Degrees and Diplomas: Bachelor, 5-6 yrs.

4477 **CHAERYONG COLLEGE OF TIDELAND RECLAMATION**

South Hwanghae Province

Rector: Kim Sun Il

Tideland Reclamation (including Irrigation and Land Construction)

Founded 1985. A State institution responsible to the Provincial Committee for Administration and Economic Guidance. Governing bodies: Instruction; Scientific Research; General Affairs.

Academic Year: September to August (September-February; February-August).

Admission Requirements: Graduation from Senior Middle School.

Fees: None.

Language of Instruction: Korean.

Degrees and Diplomas: Bachelor, 4 yrs.

Teacher Training

4478 **KIM HYONG JIK UNIVERSITY OF EDUCATION**
Pyongyang
President: Choe Gum Sun

F. of Revolutionary History
F. of Education
F. of History
F. of Geography
F. of Korean Language and Literature
F. of Foreign Languages
F. of Mathematics
F. of Physics
F. of Chemistry
F. of Biology
F. of Music
F. of Physical Culture
F. of Fine Arts
Also 3 Research Institutes.

Founded 1946. A State institution responsible to the National Education Commission.

Academic Year: September to August (September-February; February-August).
Admission Requirements: Graduation from Senior Middle School.
Fees: None.
Language of Instruction: Korean.
Degrees and Diplomas: Bachelor, 5 yrs.
Library: 389,414 vols.
Publications: Newspaper; Gazette.
Press or Publishing House: University Publishing House.
Academic Staff, 1986-87: 763.
Student Enrolment, 1986-87: 3811.

4479 **KIM JONG SUK UNIVERSITY OF EDUCATION**
Ryanggang Province
President: Rim Juk Son

F. of Revolutionary History
F. of Youth League
F. of Korean Language and Literature
F. of Mathematics and Physics
F. of Biology and Chemistry
F. of Physical Culture
F. of Music and Fine Arts

Founded 1961. A State institution responsible to the National Education Commission. Governing body: Instruction, Scientific Research, General Affairs.

Academic Year: September to August (September-February; February-August).
Admission Requirements: Graduation from Senior Middle School.
Fees: None.
Language of Instruction: Korean.
Degrees and Diplomas: Bachelor, 4 yrs.
Library: 103,372 vols.
Publications: Newspaper; Gazette.
Press or Publishing House: University Publishing House.
Academic Staff, 1986-87: 137.
Student Enrolment, 1986-87: 1094.

4480 **CHONGJIN UNIVERSITY OF EDUCATION NO. 1**
North Hamgyong Province
President: Li Gun Suk

F. of Revolutionary History
F. of History and Geography
F. of Mathematics and Physics
F. of Foreign Languages
F. of Biology and Chemistry
F. of Music and Fine Arts

Founded 1961. A State institution responsible to the National Education Commission. Governing body: Instruction, Scientific Research, General Affairs.

Academic Year: September to August (September-February; February-August).
Admission Requirements: Graduation from Senior Middle School.
Fees: None.
Language of Instruction: Korean.
Degrees and Diplomas: Bachelor, 4 yrs.
Library: 316,255 vols.
Publications: Newspaper; Gazette.
Press or Publishing House: University Publishing House.
Academic Staff, 1986-87: 590.
Student Enrolment, 1986-87: 4724.

4481 **CHONGJIN UNIVERSITY OF EDUCATION NO. 2**
North Hamgyong Province
President: Li Jong Yun

F. of Revolutionary History
F. of History and Geography
F. of Korean Language and Literature
F. of Foreign Languages
F. of Music and Fine Arts
F. of Mathematics and Physics
F. of Biology and Chemistry
F. of Physical Culture

Founded 1961. A State institution responsible to the National Education Commission. Governing body: Instruction, Scientific Research, General Affairs.

Academic Year: September to August (September-February; February-August).
Admission Requirements: Graduation from Senior Middle School.
Fees: None.
Language of Instruction: Korean.
Degrees and Diplomas: Bachelor, 4 yrs.
Library: 231,794 vols.
Publications: Newspaper; Gazette.
Press or Publishing House: University Publishing House.
Academic Staff, 1986-87: 462.
Student Enrolment, 1986-87: 3894.

4482 **HAEJU UNIVERSITY OF EDUCATION**
North Hamgyong Province
President: Kim Do Gyun

F. of Revolutionary History
F. of Youth League
F. of History and Geography
F. of Korean Language and Literature
F. of Mathematics and Physics
F. of Biology and Chemistry
F. of Arts
F. of Physical Culture
F. for Correspondence Courses

Founded 1948. A State institution responsible to the National Education Commission. Governing body: Instruction, Scientific Research, General Affairs.

Academic Year: September to August (September-February; February-August).
Admission Requirements: Graduation from Senior Middle School.
Fees: None.
Language of Instruction: Korean.
Degrees and Diplomas: Bachelor, 4 yrs.
Library: 177,944 vols.
Publications: Newspaper; Gazette.
Press or Publishing House: University Publishing House.
Academic Staff, 1986-87: 482.
Student Enrolment, 1986-87: 3855.

4483 **HAMNAM UNIVERSITY OF EDUCATION NO. 1**
South Hamgyong Province
President: Li Jong Mun

F. of Revolutionary History
F. of History and Geography
F. of Korean Language and Literature
F. of Foreign Languages
F. of Physics
F. of Mathematics
F. of Biology and Chemistry
F. of Physical Culture
F. for Correspondence Courses

Founded 1961. A State institution responsible to the National Education Commission. Governing body: Instruction, Scientific Research, General Affairs.

Academic Year: September to August (September-February; February-August).

Admission Requirements: Graduation from Senior Middle School.
Fees: None.
Language of Instruction: Korean.
Degrees and Diplomas: Bachelor, 4 yrs.
Library: 238,636 vols.
Publications: Newspaper; Gazette.
Press or Publishing House: University Publishing House.
Academic Staff, 1986-87: 536.
Student Enrolment, 1986-87: 4289.

4484 **HAMNAN UNIVERSITY OF EDUCATION NO. 2**
South Hamgyong Province
President: Kim Jin Wang

F. of Revolutionary History
F. of History and Geography
F. of Korean Language and Literature
F. of Physical Culture
F. of Mathematics and Physics
F. of Biology and Chemistry
F. of Music and Fine Arts
F. of Youth League
F. for Correspondence Courses

Founded 1961. A State institution responsible to the National Education Commission. Governing body: Instruction, Scientific Research, General Affairs.

Academic Year: September to August (September-February; February-August).
Admission Requirements: Graduation from Senior Middle School.
Fees: None.
Language of Instruction: Korean.
Degrees and Diplomas: Bachelor, 4 yrs.
Library: 251,996 vols.
Publications: Newspaper; Gazette.
Press or Publishing House: University Publishing House.
Academic Staff, 1986-87: 552.
Student Enrolment, 1986-87: 4418.

4485 **HYESAN UNIVERSITY OF EDUCATION NO. 1**
Ryanggang Province
President: Kim Dong Sam

F. of History and Geography
F. of Korean Language and Literature
F. of Mathematics and Physics
F. for Correspondence Courses

Founded 1967. A State institution responsible to the National Education Commission. Governing body: Instruction, Scientific Research, General Affairs.

Academic Year: September to August (September-February; February-August).
Admission Requirements: Graduation from Senior Middle School.
Fees: None.
Language of Instruction: Korean.
Degrees and Diplomas: Bachelor, 4 yrs.
Library: 189,422 vols.
Publications: Newspaper; Gazette.
Press or Publishing House: University Publishing House.
Academic Staff, 1986-87: 371.
Student Enrolment, 1986-87: 2969.

4486 **KANGGYE UNIVERSITY OF EDUCATION NO. 1**
Chagang Province
President: Choe Won Ha

F. of Revolutionary History
F. of Foreign Languages
F. of Korean Language and Literature
F. of Mathematics and Physics
F. of Biology and Chemistry
F. of Physical Culture
F. for Correspondence Courses

Founded 1967. A State institution responsible to the National Education Commission. Governing body: Instruction, Scientific Research, General Affairs.

Academic Year: September to August (September-February; February-August).
Admission Requirements: Graduation from Senior Middle School.
Fees: None.
Language of Instruction: Korean.
Degrees and Diplomas: Bachelor, 4 yrs.
Library: 196,719 vols.
Publications: Newspaper; Gazette.
Press or Publishing House: University Publishing House.
Academic Staff, 1986-87: 383.
Student Enrolment, 1986-87: 3066.

4487 **KANGGYE UNIVERSITY OF EDUCATION NO. 2**
Chagang Province
President: Rim Ho Chan

F. of Revolutionary History
F. of Youth League
F. of History and Geography
F. of Korean Language and Literature
F. of Mathematics and Physics
F. of Biology and Chemistry
F. of Physical Culture
F. for Correspondence Courses

Founded 1952. A State institution responsible to the National Education Commission. Governing body: Instruction, Scientific Research, General Affairs.

Academic Year: September to August (September-February; February-August).
Admission Requirements: Graduation from Senior Middle School.
Fees: None.
Language of Instruction: Korean.
Degrees and Diplomas: Bachelor, 4 yrs.
Library: 196,571 vols.
Publications: Newspaper; Gazette.
Press or Publishing House: University Publishing House.
Academic Staff, 1986-87: 371.
Student Enrolment, 1986-87: 2968.

4488 **KIM JONG TAE UNIVERSITY OF EDUCATION**
South Hwanghae Province
President: Li Song Man

F. of Revolutionary History
F. of History and Geography
F. of Korean Language and Literature
F. of Foreign Languages
F. of Mathematics and Physics
F. of Biology and Chemistry
F. of Physical Culture
F. for Correspondence Courses

Founded 1961. A State institution responsible to the National Education Commission. Governing body: Instruction, Scientific Research, General Affairs.

Academic Year: September to August (September-February; February-August).
Admission Requirements: Graduation from Senior Middle School.
Fees: None.
Language of Instruction: Korean.
Degrees and Diplomas: Bachelor, 4 yrs.
Library: 292,691 vols.
Publications: Newspaper; Gazette.
Press or Publishing House: University Publishing House.
Academic Staff, 1986-87: 525.
Student Enrolment, 1986-87: 4202.

4489 **NAMPO UNIVERSITY OF EDUCATION**
Nampo
President: Kim Bong Gal

F. of Revolutionary History
F. of History and Geography
F. of Korean Language and Literature
F. of Foreign Languages
F. of Mathematics and Physics
F. of Biology and Chemistry
F. of Music and Fine Arts
F. of Technical Education

F. for Correspondence Courses

Founded 1963. A State institution responsible to the National Education Commission. Governing body: Instruction, Scientific Research, General Affairs.

Academic Year: September to August (September-February; February-August).

Admission Requirements: Graduation from Senior Middle School.

Fees: None.

Language of Instruction: Korean.

Degrees and Diplomas: Bachelor, 4 yrs.

Library: 239,975 vols.

Publications: Newspaper; Gazette.

Press or Publishing House: University Publishing House.

Academic Staff, 1986-87: 391.

Student Enrolment, 1986-87: 3126.

4490 **PYONGSONG UNIVERSITY OF EDUCATION**

South Pyongan Province

President: Sin Dok Il

F. of Revolutionary History
F. of History and Geography
F. of Youth League
F. of Korean Language and Literature
F. of Foreign Languages
F. of Mathematics
F. of Physics
F. of Biology and Chemistry
F. of Music and Fine Arts
F. of Physical Culture
F. for Correspondence Courses

Founded 1961. A State institution responsible to the National Education Commission. Governing body: Instruction, Scientific Research, General Affairs.

Academic Year: September to August (September-February; February-August).

Admission Requirements: Graduation from Senior Middle School.

Fees: None.

Language of Instruction: Korean.

Degrees and Diplomas: Bachelor, 4 yrs.

Library: 231,696 vols.

Publications: Newspaper; Gazette.

Press or Publishing House: University Publishing House.

Academic Staff, 1986-87: 1124.

Student Enrolment, 1986-87: 8991.

4491 **PYONGYANG UNIVERSITY OF EDUCATION NO. 2**

Pyongyang

President: Sim Sang Guk

F. of Revolutionary History
F. of Youth League
F. of History and Geography
F. of Korean Language and Literature
F. of Foreign Languages
F. of Mathematics
F. of Physics
F. of Biology and Chemistry
F. of Music and Fine Arts
F. of Physical Culture

Founded 1946. A State institution responsible to the National Education Commission. Governing body: Instruction, Scientific Research, General Affairs.

Academic Year: September to August (September-February; February-August).

Admission Requirements: Graduation from Senior Middle School.

Fees: None.

Language of Instruction: Korean.

Degrees and Diplomas: Bachelor, 4 yrs.

Library: 246,648 vols.

Publications: Newspaper; Gazette.

Press or Publishing House: University Publishing House.

Academic Staff, 1986-87: 718.

Student Enrolment, 1986-87: 5747.

4492 **SARIWON UNIVERSITY OF EDUCATION NO. 1**

North Hwanghae Province

President: Kim Ung Gol

F. of Revolutionary History
F. of Foreign Languages
F. of Mathematics and Physics
F. of Biology and Chemistry
F. of Physical Culture
F. for Correspondence Courses

Founded 1953. A State institution responsible to the National Education Commission. Governing body: Instruction, Scientific Research, General Affairs.

Academic Year: September to August (September-February; February-August).

Admission Requirements: Graduation from Senior Middle School.

Fees: None.

Language of Instruction: Korean.

Degrees and Diplomas: Bachelor, 4 yrs.

Library: 331,192 vols.

Publications: Newspaper; Gazette.

Press or Publishing House: University Publishing House.

Academic Staff, 1986-87: 409.

Student Enrolment, 1986-87: 3275.

4493 **SARIWON UNIVERSITY OF EDUCATION NO. 2**

North Hwanghae Province

President: Han Dae Bong

F. of Youth League
F. of History and Geography
F. of Korean Language and Literature
F. of Mathematics and Physics
F. of Music and Fine Arts
F. for Correspondence Courses

Founded 1963. A State institution responsible to the National Education Commission. Governing body: Instruction, Scientific Research, General Affairs.

Academic Year: September to August (September-February; February-August).

Admission Requirements: Graduation from Senior Middle School.

Fees: None.

Language of Instruction: Korean.

Degrees and Diplomas: Bachelor, 4 yrs.

Library: 227,890 vols.

Publications: Newspaper; Gazette.

Press or Publishing House: University Publishing House.

Academic Staff, 1986-87: 338.

Student Enrolment, 1986-87: 2709.

4494 **SINUIJU UNIVERSITY OF EDUCATION NO. 1**

North Pyongan Province

President: Choe Ik Chan

F. of Revolutionary History
F. of History and Geography
F. of Korean Language and Literature
F. of Mathematics
F. of Foreign Languages
F. of Physics
F. of Biology and Chemistry
F. for Correspondence Courses

Founded 1961. A State institution responsible to the National Education Commission. Governing body: Instruction, Scientific Research, General Affairs.

Academic Year: September to August (September-February; February-August).

Admission Requirements: Graduation from Senior Middle School.

Fees: None.

Language of Instruction: Korean.

Degrees and Diplomas: Bachelor, 4 yrs.

Library: Main Library.

Publications: Newspaper; Gazette.

Press or Publishing House: University Publishing House.

Academic Staff, 1986-87: 575.

Student Enrolment, 1986-87: 4603.

4495 **SINUIJU UNIVERSITY OF EDUCATION NO. 2**
North Pyongan Province
President: Paek Gyong Sun

F. of Revolutionary History
F. of Youth League
F. of History and Geography
F. of Mathematics and Physics
F. of Biology and Chemistry
F. of Music and Fine Arts
F. of Physical Culture
F. of Korean Language and Literature
F. for Correspondence Courses

Founded 1947. A State institution responsible to the National Education Commission. Governing body: Instruction, Scientific Research, General Affairs.

Academic Year: September to August (September-February; February-August).

Admission Requirements: Graduation from Senior Middle School.

Fees: None.

Language of Instruction: Korean.

Degrees and Diplomas: Bachelor, 4 yrs.

Library: 113,750 vols.

Publications: Newspaper; Gazette.

Press or Publishing House: University Publishing House.

Academic Staff, 1986-87: 575.

Student Enrolment, 1986-87: 4603.

4496 **SONGDO UNIVERSITY**
Kaesong City
President: Ryu Son Taek

F. of Revolutionary History
F. of Foreign Languages
F. of Mathematics and Physics
F. of Korean Language and Literature
F. of Biology and Chemistry
F. of Physical Culture
F. for Correspondence

Founded 1961. A State institution responsible to the National Education Commission. Governing body: Instruction, Scientific Research, General Affairs.

Academic Year: September to August (September-February; February-August).

Admission Requirements: Graduation from Senior Middle School.

Fees: None.

Language of Instruction: Korean.

Degrees and Diplomas: Bachelor, 4 yrs.

Library: 131,997 vols.

Publications: Newspaper; Gazette.

Press or Publishing House: University Publishing House.

Academic Staff, 1986-87: 261.

Student Enrolment, 1986-87: 2087.

4497 **WONSAN UNIVERSITY OF EDUCATION NO. 1**
Kangwan Province
President: Kim Su Duk

F. of Revolutionary History
F. of Korean Language and Literature
F. of Foreign Languages
F. of Mathematics and Physics
F. of Biology and Chemistry
F. of Physical Culture
F. for Correspondence Courses

Founded 1961. A State institution responsible to the National Education Commission. Governing body: Instruction, Scientific Research, General Affairs.

Academic Year: September to August (September-February; February-August).

Admission Requirements: Graduation from Senior Middle School.

Fees: None.

Language of Instruction: Korean.

Degrees and Diplomas: Bachelor, 4 yrs.

Library: 210,694 vols.

Publications: Newspaper; Gazette.

Press or Publishing House: University Publishing House.

Academic Staff, 1986-87: 427.

Student Enrolment, 1986-87: 3417.

4498 **WONSAN UNIVERSITY OF EDUCATION NO. 2**
Kangwon Province
President: Pak Yang Sun

F. of History and Geography
F. of Korean Language and Literature
F. of Physics and Mathematics
F. of Youth League
F. of Arts
F. for Correspondence Courses

Founded 1949. A State institution responsible to the National Education Commission. Governing body: Instruction, Scientific Research, General Affairs.

Academic Year: September to August (September-February; February-August).

Admission Requirements: Graduation from Senior Middle School.

Fees: None.

Language of Instruction: Korean.

Degrees and Diplomas: Bachelor, 4 yrs.

Library: 161,703 vols.

Publications: Newspaper; Gazette.

Press or Publishing House: University Publishing House.

Academic Staff, 1986-87: 221.

Student Enrolment, 1986-87: 1771.

4499 **CHONGJIN TEACHERS' TRAINING COLLEGE**
Chongjin
Rector: Yu Chong Sim

F. of Primary Education
F. of Kindergarten Education
F. of Correspondence Courses

Founded 1968. A State institution responsible to the Provincial Committee for Administration and Economic Guidance. Governing body: Instruction, Scientific Research, General Affairs.

Academic Year: September to August (September-February; February-August).

Admission Requirements: Graduation from Senior Middle School.

Fees: None.

Language of Instruction: Korean.

Degrees and Diplomas: Diploma, 3 yrs.

Library: 146,266 vols.

Press or Publishing House: University Publishing House.

Academic Staff, 1986-87: 187.

Student Enrolment, 1986-87: 1497.

4500 **HAEJU TEACHERS' TRAINING COLLEGE**
South Hwanghae Province
Rector: O Ok Ryon

Teacher Training (Primary and Kindergarten levels)

Founded 1967. A State institution responsible to the Provincial Committee for Administration and Economic Guidance. Governing body: Instruction, Scientific Research, General Affairs.

Academic Year: September to August (September-February; February-August).

Admission Requirements: Graduation from Senior Middle School.

Fees: None.

Language of Instruction: Korean.

Degrees and Diplomas: Diploma, 3 yrs.

Library: 229,450 vols.

Press or Publishing House: Teacher Training College Publishing House.

Academic Staff, 1986-87: 601.

Student Enrolment, 1986-87: 4805.

4501 **HAMHUNG TEACHERS' TRAINING COLLEGE NO. 1**
South Hamgyong Province
Rector: Cho Byong Hui

Teacher Training (Primary and Kindergarten levels)

Founded 1968. A State institution responsible to the Provincial Committee for Administration and Economic Guidance. Governing body: Instruction, Scientific Research, General Affairs.

Academic Year: September to August (September-February; February-August).

Admission Requirements: Graduation from Senior Middle School.
Fees: None.
Language of Instruction: Korean.
Degrees and Diplomas: Diploma, 3 yrs.
Library: 110,910 vols.
Press or Publishing House: Teacher Training College Publishing House.
Academic Staff, 1986-87: 391.
Student Enrolment, 1986-87: 3128.

4502 **HAMHUNG TEACHERS' TRAINING COLLEGE NO. 2**
South Hamgyong Province
Rector: Chon Ul Ryong

Teacher Training (Primary level)
F. for Correspondence Courses

Founded 1972. A State institution responsible to the Provincial Committee for Administration and Economic Guidance. Governing body: Instruction, Scientific Research, General Affairs.

Academic Year: September to August (September-February; February-August).

Admission Requirements: Graduation from Senior Middle School.
Fees: None.
Language of Instruction: Korean.
Degrees and Diplomas: Diploma, 3 yrs.
Library: 93,570 vols.
Press or Publishing House: Teacher Training College Publishing House.
Academic Staff, 1986-87: 193.
Student Enrolment, 1986-87: 1545.

4503 **HOIRYONG TEACHERS' TRAINING COLLEGE**
North Hamgyong Province
Rector: Hyon Gwang Won

Teacher Training (Primary and Kindergarten levels)

Founded 1972. A State institution responsible to the Provincial Committee for Administration and Economic Guidance. Governing body: Instruction, Scientific Research, General Affairs.

Academic Year: September to August (September-February; February-August).

Admission Requirements: Graduation from Senior Middle School.
Fees: None.
Language of Instruction: Korean.
Degrees and Diplomas: Diploma, 3 yrs.
Library: 99,554 vols.
Press or Publishing House: Teacher Training College Publishing House.
Academic Staff, 1986-87: 260.
Student Enrolment, 1986-87: 2080.

4504 **HYESAN TEACHERS' TRAINING COLLEGE**
Ryanggang Province
Rector: Pak Gum Ok

Teachers Training (Primary and Kindergarten levels)

Founded 1968. A State institution responsible to the Provincial Committee for Administration and Economic Guidance. Governing body: Instruction, Scientific Research, General Affairs.

Academic Year: September to August (September-February; February-August).

Admission Requirements: Graduation from Senior Middle School.
Fees: None.
Language of Instruction: Korean.
Degrees and Diplomas: Diploma, 3 yrs.
Library: 103,740 vols.
Press or Publishing House: Teacher Training College Publishing House.
Academic Staff, 1986-87: 273.
Student Enrolment, 1986-87: 2186.

4505 **KANGGYE TEACHERS' TRAINING COLLEGE**
Chagang Province
Rector: Li Won Ok

Teacher Training (Primary and Kindergarten levels)

Founded 1968. A State institution responsible to the Provincial Committee for Administration and Economic Guidance. Governing body: Instruction, Scientific Research, General Affairs.

Academic Year: September to August (September-February; February-August).

Admission Requirements: Graduation from Senior Middle School.

Fees: None.
Language of Instruction: Korean.
Degrees and Diplomas: Diploma, 3 yrs.
Library: 90,870 vols.
Press or Publishing House: Teacher Training College Publishing House.
Academic Staff, 1986-87: 342.
Student Enrolment, 1986-87: 2735.

4506 **NAMPO TEACHERS' TRAINING COLLEGE**
Nampo
Rector: Tong Il

Teacher Training (Primary and Kindergarten levels)

Founded 1967. A State institution responsible to the Provincial Committee for Administration and Economic Guidance. Governing body: Instruction, Scientific Research, General Affairs.

Academic Year: September to August (September-February; February-August).

Admission Requirements: Graduation from Senior Middle School.
Fees: None.
Language of Instruction: Korean.
Degrees and Diplomas: Diploma, 3 yrs.
Library: 69,529 vols.
Press or Publishing House: Teacher Training College Publishing House.
Academic Staff, 1986-87: 143.
Student Enrolment, 1986-87: 147.

4507 **PYONGSON TEACHERS' TRAINING COLLEGE**
South Pyongan Province
Rector: Kim Gyong Jun

Teacher Training (Primary and Kindergarten levels)

Founded 1972. A State institution responsible to the Provincial Committee for Administration and Economic Guidance. Governing body: Instruction, Scientific Research, General Affairs.

Academic Year: September to August (September-February; February-August).

Admission Requirements: Graduation from Senior Middle School.
Fees: None.
Language of Instruction: Korean.
Degrees and Diplomas: Diploma, 3 yrs.
Library: 111,213 vols.
Press or Publishing House: Teacher Training College Publishing House.
Academic Staff, 1986-87: 624.
Student Enrolment, 1986-87: 4992.

4508 **PYONGYANG TEACHERS' TRAINING COLLEGE**
Pyongyang
Rector: Nam Sun Hui

Teacher Training (Primary and Kindergarten levels)

Founded 1968. A State institution responsible to the Provincial Committee for Administration and Economic Guidance. Governing body: Instruction, Scientific Research, General Affairs.

Academic Year: September to August (September-February; February-August).

Admission Requirements: Graduation from Senior Middle School.
Fees: None.
Language of Instruction: Korean.
Degrees and Diplomas: Diploma, 3 yrs.
Library: 133,346 vols.
Press or Publishing House: Teacher Training College Publishing House.
Academic Staff, 1986-87: 389.
Student Enrolment, 1986-87: 3109.

4509 **SARIWON TEACHERS' TRAINING COLLEGE**
North Hwanghae Province
Rector: Kim Sun Ok

Teacher Training (Primary and Kindergarten levels)

Founded 1968. A State institution responsible to the Provincial Committee for Administration and Economic Guidance. Governing body: Instruction, Scientific Research, General Affairs.

Academic Year: September to August (September-February; February-August).

Admission Requirements: Graduation from Senior Middle School.
Fees: None.
Language of Instruction: Korean.

Degrees and Diplomas: Diploma, 3 yrs.
Library: 108,576 vols.
Publication: Gazette.
Press or Publishing House: Teacher Training College Publishing House.
Academic Staff, 1986-87p: 319.
Student Enrolment, 1986-87: 2556.

4510 **SINUIJU TEACHERS' TRAINING COLLEGE**
North Pyongan Province
Rector: Li Sil Ok

Teacher Training (Primary and Kindergarten levels)

Founded 1972. A State institution responsible to the Provincial Committee for Administration and Economic Guidance. Governing body: Instruction, Scientific Research, General Affairs.

Academic Year: September to August (September-February; February-August).

Admission Requirements: Graduation from Senior Middle School.
Fees: None.
Language of Instruction: Korean.
Degrees and Diplomas: Diploma, 3 yrs.
Library: 84,500 vols.
Publication: Gazette.
Press or Publishing House: Teacher Training College Publishing House.
Academic Staff, 1986-87: 241.
Student Enrolment, 1986-87: 1929.

4511 **SONCHON TEACHERS' TRAINING COLLEGE**
South Pyongan Province
Rector: Kim Gwang Yon

Teacher Training (Primary and Kindergarten levels)

Founded 1968. A State institution responsible to the Provincial Committee for Administration and Economic Guidance. Governing body: Instruction, Scientific Research, General Affairs.

Academic Year: September to August (September-February; February-August).

Admission Requirements: Graduation from Senior Middle School.
Fees: None.
Language of Instruction: Korean.
Degrees and Diplomas: Diploma, 3 yrs.
Library: 83,651 vols.
Press or Publishing House: Teacher Training College Publishing House.
Academic Staff, 1986-87: 401.
Student Enrolment, 1986-87: 3212.

4512 **WONSAN TEACHERS' TRAINING COLLEGE**
Kangwon Province
Rector: Pae Gye Suk

Teacher Training (Primary and Kindergarten levels)

Founded 1968. A State institution responsible to the Provincial Committee for Administration and Economic Guidance. Governing body: Instruction, Scientific Research, General Affairs.

Academic Year: September to August (September-February; February-August).

Admission Requirements: Graduation from Senior Middle School.
Fees: None.
Language of Instruction: Korean.
Degrees and Diplomas: Diploma, 3 yrs.
Library: 116,432 vols.
Press or Publishing House: Teacher Training College Publishing House.
Academic Staff, 1986-87: 257.
Student Enrolment, 1986-87: 2055.

KOREA
(Republic of)

Universities and Colleges

National Institutions

4514 **ANDONG NATIONAL UNIVERSITY**
388 Songchon-dong, Andong City, Kyongbuk 660
Telephone: (571) 55-1661/71
President: Yub Kim (1984-88)
Head of Academic Affairs: Yeon-Kyu Sohn

Sec. of Humanities
; *staff* 24 (8)
Sec. of Education
; *staff* 17 (7)
Sec. of Social Sciences (including Law)
; *staff* 23 (14)
Sec. of Natural Sciences
; *staff* 13 (4)
Sec. of Arts and Physical Education
; *staff* 21 (40)
I. of Andong Culture
Director: Se-gwon Im; *staff* 2
I. of Language Research
Director: Sang-Kie Kim; *staff* 3
Saemaul Research I.
Director: Won-dal Bae; *staff* 2

Founded 1948 as Andong Normal School. Closed 1962 and opened as Junior Teachers' College 1965. Acquired present status and title 1979. A State institution financed by the central government. Residential facilities for 108 students.

Academic Year: March to December (March-June; September-December).

Admission Requirements: Graduation from high school or equivalent, and entrance examination.

Fees (Won): 389,500-4433,500 per semester.

Language of Instruction: Korean.

Degrees and Diplomas: Bachelor of–Arts; Business Administration; Economics; Law; Public Administration; Science; Home Economics; Music; Fine Arts; Physical Education, 4 yrs.

Library: University Library, 50,000 vols.

Special Facilities (Museums, etc.): University Museum.

Publications: Research Review (annually); Andong Culture (annually); Saemaul Review (annually).

Press or Publishing House: Andong National University Press.

Academic Staff, 1986-87:

Rank	Full-time	Part-time
Gyosu (Professors)	16	–
Bu-gyosu (Associate Professors)	24	–
Jo-gyosu (Assistant Professors)	55	–
Jeon-nim-gangsa (Lecturers)	11	71
Jogyo (Assistants)	25	–
Total	131	71

Student Enrolment, 1986-87:

	Men	Women	Total
Of the country	1467	1261	2728

4515 **BUSAN NATIONAL UNIVERSITY**
30 Changion-dong, Kumjong-gu, Busan 609-735
Telephone: (2) 56-0171
Chongang (President): Jae-Hoon Choi (1983-87)
Samu-gukjang (Director of Business Affairs): Soon-Tae Jung

C. of Engineering
C. of Humanities
C. of Social Sciences
C. of Natural Sciences
C. of Law and Political Science
C. of Education
C. of Business Administration
C. of Pharmacy
C. of Medicine
C. of Dentistry
C. of Home Economics
C. of Arts
Graduate S.
Graduate S. of Business Administration
Graduate S. of Public Administration
Graduate S. of Industrial Management
Graduate S. of Education
Coastal Region Development Research I.
I. of Solid State Physics
Language Research I.
Unification Research I.
Research I. of New Community Movement
I. of Science Education
I. of Mechanical Technology
Computer Ce.

Also 14 departments of the Coastal Region Research Institute and high school.

Founded 1946 as college, became a national university 1953. Controlled by the National Government and receivesfinancial support from the National Treasury. Governing body: the University Council. Residential facilities for academic staff and men students.

Arrangements for co-operation with: National Taiwan University; National Chengchi University; University of Alabama; Northeast Missouri State University; University of California, Los Angeles; Osaka University.

Academic Year: March to December (March-June; September-December).

Admission Requirements: Graduation from high school or equivalent qualification recognized by the Ministry of Education, and entrance examination.

Language of Instruction: Korean.

Degrees and Diplomas: Bachelor of–Arts; Physical Education; Fine Arts; Home Economics; Public Administration; Business Administration; Nursing; Political Science; Economics; Science; Commerce; Laws; Engineering; Pharmacy; Medicine; Dentistry, 4 yrs. Master in any of the above fields, a further 2 yrs. Doctorate, a further 3 yrs.

Library: Central Library, 330,000 vols.

Special Facilities (Museums, etc.): Archaeological Museum.

Publications: Research Reports of Engineering; Humanities Review; Medical Journal; Study in Law; Research publications; Japanese Study; Chinese Study; New Community Review; Language Study.

Press or Publishing House: University Press.

Academic Staff: c. 750.

Student Enrolment: c. 19,000.

4516 **CHANGWON NATIONAL UNIVERSITY**
Toechon-dong, Changwon CT, Kyung-nam 641-773
Telephone: (551) 83-2151
Fax: (551) 83-2970
President: Dong-Wa Park

F. of Liberal Arts
F. of Economics and Management
F. of Law and Administration
F. of Natural Science
F. of Arts and Music

'. of Engineering and Technology
). of Graduate Studies
Jnification Research I.
.abour Problems Research I.
Computer Ce.
. of Industrial Management
'. of Industrial Technology

Founded 1971 as a National Teachers College, acquired present title 1982. Residential facilities for foreign academic staff and 350 students.

Academic Year: March to December (March-June; August-December).

Admission Requirements: Graduation from high school and entrance examination.

Fees (Won): 548,000-68,000 per semester; Graduate Division, 500,000.

Language of Instruction: Korean.

Degrees and Diplomas: Bachelor, 4 yrs. Master, a further 2 yrs.

Library: Central Library, 100,000 vols.

Special Facilities (Museums, etc.): Archaeological Museum; Broadcasting Station.

Publications: Bulletins (in Korean and English); Publications of the Institutes.

Academic Staff, 1990:

Rank	Full-time
Professors	15
Associate Professors	68
Assistant Professors	58
Instructors	29
Assistants	49
Visiting Instructors	120
Total	339

Student Enrolment, 1990: 5825.

4517 **CHONBUK NATIONAL UNIVERSITY**

Dukjin-dong, Chongju City, Chonbuk 560-756
Telex: 760429
Telephone: 70-2023
Fax: 760429
President: Won Sub Kim
Dean of Academic Affairs: Seung Beom Choi

C. of Humanities (Korean, Library Science, German, French, History, English, Japanese, Chinese, Philosophy, Archaeology and Anthropology, Spanish)
Dean: Chung Taik Suh; *staff* 78 (89)
C. of Natural Sciences
Dean: Young Jin Sin; *staff* 67 (32)
C. of Commerce
Dean: Won Ho Yunn; *staff* 34 (14)
C. of Engineering (including Architectural, Metallurgical, Mechanical, Mechanical Design, Industrial Design, Textile, Mining and Mineral Resources, Materials, Electrical, Electronic, Computer, Precision Mechanical, Information and Telecommunications, Civil, Chemical, and Environmental Engineering)
Dean: Jae Ha Lee; *staff* 104 (33)
C. of Law
Dean: Kyu Lin Cho; *staff* 11 (8)
S. of Medicine
Dean: Ho Yeol Choi; *staff* 106
C. of Education
Dean: Hee Jin Lee; *staff* 106 (44)
C. of Social Sciences (including Political Science and Diplomacy, Public Administration, Social Welfare, Journalism and Communication, and Psychology)
Dean: Keun Sup Yoon; *staff* 27 (25)
C. of Arts
Dean: Hye Hee Lee; *staff* 13 (57)
C. of Agriculture (including Food Science and Technology, Horticulture, Forestry, Landscape Architecture, and Animal Husbandry)
Dean: Dae Shik Koh; *staff* 66 (25)
C. of Veterinary Medicine
Dean: Byeong Kirl Back; *staff* 13 (3)
Graduate S.
Dean: Sang Ho Kim
Graduate S. of Education
Dean: Beom Suk Han
Graduate S. of Public Administration
Dean: Key Yung Park
Graduate S. of Business Administration
Dean: Jae Duck Cha
Graduate S. of Industrial Technology
Dean: Ki Joo Kim
Computer Ce.
Semiconductor Research I..
Director: Choon Ho Lee
Language Research I.
Director: Gwong Hyeon Choi
I. of Science Education
Director: Seung Tai Park
L. of Electronics Industry and Development
Director: Hak Shin Kim
Also University Hospital.

Founded 1951 by Ministry of Education under programme for the decentralization of higher education. Governing body: the University Council. Financially supported by the government. Some residential facilities for academic staff and students.

Academic Year: April to February (April-July; September-February).

Admission Requirements: Graduation from high school or foreign equivalent, and entrance examination.

Language of Instruction: Korean.

Degrees and Diplomas: Bachelor of–Agriculture; Arts; Business Administration; Commerce; Dentistry; Economics; Education; Engineering; Home Economics; Library Science, Law, Medicine, Music; Nursing; Physical Education; Politics; Public Administration; Science, Veterinary Medicine; Visual Arts, 4 yrs. Master of–Agriculture; Economics; Veterinary Medicine; Engineering; Arts; Law; Political Science; Public Administration; Business Administration; Commerce; Education; Science; Home Economics; Medical Science, a further 2 yrs. Doctor of–Agriculture; Economics; Veterinary Medicine, Engineering; Literature; Philosophy; Law; Political Science; Business Administration; Science; Medical Science; Education, 3 yrs after Master.

Libraries: Central Library, 354,000 vols; libraries of each department.

Special Facilities (Museums, etc.): University Museum; University Broadcasting; Health Centre.

Press or Publishing House: Science Education Newsletter and the Journal of Science Education (biannually); The Law Research Journal (annually); the Chonbuk National University Medical Journal (quarterly); Social Sciences Studies (annually).

Academic Staff, 1990:

Rank	Full-time	Part-time
Professors	221	–
Associate Professors	200	–
Assistant Professors	141	–
Lecturers	83	333
Total	645	333

Student Enrolment, 1990:

	Men	Women	Total
Of the country	15,024	6247	21,271
Of other countries	13	3	16
Total	15,037	6250	21,287

4518 **CHONNAM NATIONAL UNIVERSITY**

Yongbong-dong, Puk-gu, Kwangiu 500-757

C. of Humanities
C. of Natural Sciences
C. of Business Administration
C. of Law
C. of Medicine
C. of Dentistry
C. of Agriculture
C. of Engineering
C. of Education
Graduate S.

Founded 1952.

4519 **CHUNGBUK NATIONAL UNIVERSITY**
48 Kaeshin-dong, Chongju, Chungbuk 360-763
Telephone: (431) 4-2131/9
President: Seong-Jin Cho (1986-90)
Dean of Academic Affairs: Nang-Ho Lee

C. of Humanities
Dean: Suk-Lin Seon; *staff* 46
C. of Social Sciences (including Political Science, Law, Psychology, Economics, and Administration)
Dean: Dji-Hoon Lee; *staff* 577
C. of Natural Sciences
Dean: Chi-Kyong Kim; *staff* 47
C. of Engineering (including Architecture)
Dean: Jung-Kyun Lee; *staff* 65
C. of Agriculture (including Animal Husbandry, Forestry, and Tobacco Science)
Dean: Song-Il Park; *staff* 66
C. of Education (including Physical Education and Home Economics)
Dean: Yong-Dae Kim; *staff* 100
C. of Pharmacy
Dean: Kyong-Soon Lee; *staff* 12
C. of Medicine
Dean: Kee-Bok Lee
Graduate S.
Also 8 research institutes and Middle School.

Founded 1951 as junior agricultural college, acquired present status and title 1978. Residential facilities for academic staff and women students.

Arrangements for co-operation with the Universities of: Illinois; California State at Fresno.

Academic Year: March to December (March-June; September-December).

Admission Requirements: Graduation from high school and entrance examination.

Fees (Won): 650,000-1,400,000 per annum

Language of Instruction: Korean.

Degrees and Diplomas: Bachelor of–Engineering; Agriculture; Arts; Science; Physical Education; Home Economics; Fine Arts; Pharmacy; Management; Administration; Economics; Law; Political Science, 4 yrs. Master, a further 2-3 yrs. Doctor of–Agriculture; Engineering; Pharmacy, 3 yrs after Master.

Library: Central Library, 200,000 vols.

Special Facilities (Museums, etc.): University Museum.

Publications: Annual Reports; Reports of Tobacco Research Institute (annually).

Press or Publishing House: University Press.

Academic Staff, 1986-87:

Rank	Full-time
Gyosu (Professors)	86
Bu-gyosu (Associate Professors)	96
Jo-gyosu (Assistant Professors)	178
Jeon-nim-gangsa (Instructors)	20
Jo-gyo (Teaching Assistants)	94
Total	474

Student Enrolment, 1986-87:

	Men	Women	Total
Of the country	12,625	3360	15,985
Of other countries	2	1	3
Total	12,627	3361	15,988

4520 **CHUNGNAM NATIONAL UNIVERSITY**
Kung-dong, Yusong-ku, Taejon 305-764
Telex: CNUCIE K 45571
Telephone: (42) 821-5114
Fax: (42) 823-1469
President: Duck-Kyun Oh

C. of Humanities (including Korean, English, German, French, Chinese, Japanese Language and Literature, Sino-Korean Literature, History, Korean History, Philosophy, and Education)
Dean: Duck-Kee Jung; *staff* 91 (92)
C. of Social science (including Library and Information Science, Psychology, Local Government, Political Science and Diplomacy)
Dean: Jae-Chang Ka; *staff* 31 (18)
C. of Natural Sciences
Dean: Chin-Ku Chu; *staff* 96 (48)
C. of Economics and Management
Dean: Keun-Sik Lee; *staff* 38 (20)
C. of Engineering (including Industrial Engineering Education, Naval Architecture, Architectural Engineering, and Environmental Engineering)
Dean: Bo-Sung Rhee; *staff* 100 (64)
C. of Agriculture (including Horticulture, Forestry, Animal Husbandry, and Veterinary Medicine)
Dean: Chab-Jo Kim; *staff* 79 (29)
C. of Law
Dean: Min Suh; *staff* 9 (7)
C. of Pharmacy
Dean: Ung-Kil Jee; *staff* 12 (9)
C. of Medicine
Dean: Se-Jin Choi; *staff* 93 (20)
C. of Home Economics
Dean: Jae-sook Kim; *staff* 16 (20)
C. of Fine Arts and Music
Dean: Pan-Kil Part; *staff* 21 (15)
Graduate S.
Dean: Ki-Suck Maeng; *staff* 2
Graduate S. of Business Administration
Dean: Yun-Jae Rhie; *staff* 2
Graduate S. of Education
Dean: Boog-Joo Kim; *staff* 2
Graduate S. of Public Administration
Dean: Tong-Hoon Kim; *staff* 2
Graduate S. of Public Health
Dean: Un-Taek Shim; *staff* 2
Graduate S. of Industry
Dean: Boog-Sik Hong; *staff* 2
Language Research I.
Basic Science Research I.
Community Development Research I.
Unification Research I.
American Studies I.
Educational Research and Development I.
I. of Environment Science and Technology
Research I. of Physical Education and Sports Science
Research I. of Biological Engineering
Paekje Research I.
Humanities Research I.
Research I. of Natural Sciences
I. of Management and Economics
Industrial Education Research Ce.
Industrial Technology Research I.
I. of Agricultural Science and Technology
I. of Law and Public Administration
I. of Medicine Development
I. of Community Medicine
I. of Home Economics
I. of Arts
Also University Hospital.

Founded 1952, a State institution financed by the government. Residential facilities at College of Agriculture and School of Nursing.

Arrangements for co-operation with: Stenhen F. Austin State University; National Taiwan Normal University; Srinakharinwirot University, Thailand; Tottori University; Kyushu University; Hiroshima University.

Academic Year: March to December (March-June; August-December).

Admission Requirements: Graduation from high school and entrance examination.

Fees (Won): 450,000-600,000 semester.

Language of Instruction: Korean.

Degrees and Diplomas: Bachelor, 4 yrs. Master, a further 2 yrs. Doctor, 3 yrs after Master.

Libraries: Central Library, *c.* 300,000 vols; Medical College Library, *c.* 15,000.

Special Facilities (Museums, etc.): University Museum; Experimental Station; Arboretum.

Publications: Campus Newspaper (in Korean and English); Papers of the Faculties.

Press or Publishing House: The University Press.

Academic Staff, 1990:

Rank	Full-time	Part-time
Professors	180	–
Associate Professors	198	–
Assistant Professors	180	–
Instructors	23	–
Teaching Assistants	150	–
Total	731	336

Student Enrolment, 1990:

	Men	Women	Total
Of the country	15,620	5731	21,351

4521 **GUNSAN NATIONAL UNIVERSITY**
Maryong-dong, Gunsan CT, Chonbuk 573-360
Telephone: 62-4171

Founded 1965.

4522 **GYEONGSANG NATIONAL UNIVERSITY**
92 Kajoa-dong, Chinju CT, Kyongnam 600-300
Telephone: 54-8331

C. of Agriculture (including Forestry, Veterinary Medicine, and Food Technology)
C. of Education
C. of Law and Business Management (including Economics)
Graduate S.
Graduate S. of Education
Agricultural Resources Research I.
I. of Applied Science
I. of Science
I. of Computer Sciences
I. of Education Research and Development
I. of Provincial Culture
Humanities Research I.
Livestock Research I.
Research I. of New Community Movement
Science Research I.
Social Science Research I.
Computer Ce.

Founded 1948 as junior agricultural college. Became 4 year provincial college 1953 and national institution 1968. Graduate courses introduced 1975. Acquired present status and title 1980. Financially supported by the government.

Academic Year: March to February (March-August; September-February).

Admission Requirements: Graduation from high school or equivalent and entrance examination.

Language of Instruction: Korean.

Degrees and Diplomas: Bachelor of–Agriculture; Arts; Fine Arts; Economics; Engineering; Home Economics; Law; Business Management; Physical Education; Public Administration; Science; Veterinary Medicine. Master of–Arts; Science, a further 2 yrs. Doctor of Philosophy. Also Teaching Certificate.

Libraries: Central Library, *c.* 50,000 vols; branch library, *c.* 6500.

Publication: Journal (annually).

Press or Publishing House: University Press.

Academic Staff: c. 300 (20).

Student Enrolment: c. 6000.

4523 **JEJU NATIONAL UNIVERSITY**
Ara-Dong, Cheju CT, Cheju-do 690-121
Telephone: 23-6141

D. of Korean Language and Literature
D. of English Language and Literature
D. of Law
D. of Agriculture
D. of Veterinary Science
D. of Fishery
D. of Animal Husbandry
D. of Home Economics
D. of Horticulture
D. of Food Production
D. of Business Administration
D. of Mathematics
D. of Marine Biology

Founded 1952.

Academic Year: April to March (April-September; October-March).

Admission Requirements: Graduation from high school and entrance examination.

Degrees and Diplomas: Bachelor of–Arts; Law; Commerce; Agricultural Science; Veterinary Science, 4 yrs.

Academic Staff: c. 60.

Student Enrolment: c. 600.

4524 **KANGREUNG NATIONAL UNIVERSITY**
1 Chipyen-dong, Kangreung CT, Kangwon-do 210-320
Telephone: 42-7001

D. of Business Administration
D. of Accountancy
D. of English Language and Literature
D. of Korean Language and Literature
D. of Physics, Chemistry, and Biology
D. of Regional Development
D. of Music and Fine Arts
Saemul Research I.
Unification Research I.

Founded 1969 as teacher training college, acquired present status 1979. A State institution financed by the central government. Residential facilities for 140 women students.

Arrangements for co-operation with New York State University at Old Westbury.

Academic Year: March to February (March-August; September-February).

Admission Requirements: Graduation from high school or equivalent, and entrance examination.

Language of Instruction: Korean.

Degrees and Diplomas: Bachelor, 4 yrs.

Library: Central Library, 26,000 vols.

Special Facilities (Museums, etc.): University Museum.

Publication: Kangreung Herald.

Press or Publishing House: Kangreung University Press.

Academic Staff: c. 90 (30).

Student Enrolment: 1850.

4525 **KANGWEON NATIONAL UNIVERSITY**
Hyoja-dong, Chunchon, Kangwondo 200-701
Telephone: 53-9000
President: Sang-joo Lee (1981-89)
Dean of Academic Affairs: Hyung-sik Lim

C. of Agriculture (including Food Technology)
Dean: Sang-young Lee; *staff* 42 (11)
C. of Humanities and Social Sciences
Dean: Han-seol Park; *staff* 67 (72)
C. of Education
Dean: Keun-seong Choi; *staff* 89 (51)
C. of Law
Dean: Jeung-hu Kim; *staff* 19 (7)
C. of Business Administration
Dean: Jong-seop Shim; *staff* 35 (15)
C. of Natural Sciences (including Pharmacy)
Dean: Chong-hyeok Lee; *staff* 63 (52)
C. of Engineering
Dean: Je-seon Park; *staff* 48 (12)
C. of Forestry
Dean: Jae-man Shin; *staff* 17 (14)
Graduate S.
Graduate S. of Education
Graduate S. of Business and Public Administration
Computer Ce.
Head: Bok-you Choi

Also 16 research institutes.

Founded 1947 as Agricultural College, became university 1978. A State institution under the jurisdiction of the Ministry of Education. Residential facilities for students.

Arrangements for co-operation with the Universities of: Pittsburgh; Alberta.

Academic Year: March to December (March-June; September-December).

Admission Requirements: Graduation from high school or foreign equivalent, and entrance examination.

Fees (Won): 256,000-567,000

Language of Instruction: Korean.

Degrees and Diplomas: Bachelor in all fields, 4 yrs. Master in–Business Administration; Engineering; Agriculture; Literature; Law; Natural Sciences; Public Administration; Education, a further 2 yrs. Doctor or Ph.D. in–Agriculture; Law; Natural Sciences; Public Administration; Engineering, a further 3 yrs.

Library: c. 100,000 vols.

Special Facilities (Museums, etc.): University Museum.

Publications: Journal of Social Sciences; Journal of the Humanities; Research Bulletin (Science and Technology).

Press or Publishing House: University Press.

Academic Staff, 1986-87:

Rank	Full-time	Part-time
Gyosu (Professors)	75	–
Bu-gyosu (Associate Professors)	109	–
Jo-gyosu (Assistant Professors)	173	–
Gangsa (Lecturers)	19	235
Total	376	235

Student Enrolment, 1986-87:

	Men	Women	Total
Of the country	13,562	3481	17,043

4526 **KONG JU NATIONAL TEACHERS' COLLEGE**

9-6 Shinkwan-dong, Konju CT, Chungnam 314-110
Telephone: 53-2151
President: Jae-Kyu Park (1980-88)
Secretary-General: Byung-gap Cho

Teacher Training (secondary level)

Founded 1948 as Provincial Junior Teachers' College, acquired present status 1954. Under the jurisdiction of the Ministry of Education. Residential facilities for foreign academic staff and students.

Academic Year: March to February (March-August; September-February).

Admission Requirements: Graduation from high school or foreign equivalent, and entrance examination.

Language of Instruction: Korean.

Degrees and Diplomas: Bachelor of–Arts; Science; Physical Education; Home Economics; Music; Education; Library Science; Business Administration, 4 yrs. Master of Education, 9 yrs.

Library: c. 65,000 vols.

Special Facilities (Museums, etc.): College Museum

Publications: Thesis Collection (annually); Backje Culture (annually); Science Education (annually).

Press or Publishing House: College Press.

Academic Staff: c. 170 (20).

Student Enrolment: c. 4500.

4527 **KOREA AIR AND CORRESPONDENCE UNIVERSITY**

169 Dongsung-dong, Chongro-ku, Seoul 110-791
Telephone: 740-4114
Fax: (02) 744-5882
President: Byung Ho Le (1989-)
Dean of Academic Affairs: Ki-Baik Lee

D. of General Education
Head: Jae-Jeong Chung; *staff* 7 (8)
D. of Korean Language and Literature
Head: Nam-Chul Cho; *staff* 3
D. of English Language and Literature
Head: Moon-Soo Kim; *staff* 7
D. of Chinese Language and Literature
Head: Sung-Ju Park; *staff* 7
D. of French Language and Literature
Head: Young-Ran Chung; *staff* 7
D. of Law
Head: Syng-Woo Lee; *staff* 7
D. of Public Administration
Head: Myung-Ki Kim; *staff* 7
D. of Economics
Head: Chi-Won Chang; *staff* 8
D. of Business Administration
Head: Jae-Young Shim; *staff* 8
D. of Agriculture
Head: Won Moon; *staff* 9
D. of Home Economics
Head: Young CHo; *staff* 9
D. of Computer Sciences and Statistics
Head: Chi-Soo Lee; *staff* 6
D. of Education
Head: Jong Moon Lee; *staff* 6
D. of Education (Early Childhood Education)
Head: Young-Rye Kwon; *staff* 6
I. of Distance Learning
Director: Symhan H. Kim; *staff* 10
I. for Educational Media Development
Director: Jong Gon An; *staff* 38
Computer Ce;
Director: Duck-Hoon Kwak; *staff* 34
Student Guidance Ce.
Director: Iong-Sung Kim; *staff* 6

Founded 1972 as junior college of Seoul National University. Reorganized as an independent university 1981. Instruction is given by radio and correspondence and students may attend lectures at 50 co-operating universities and colleges throughout the country. A State institution under the jurisdiction of the Ministry of Education.

Arrangements for co-operation with: Mississippi State University; University of the Air, Tokyo; Ramkhamhaeng University, Thailand; Mississippi State University; Allama Iqbal Open University, Pakistan; Open University, Heerlan; National Open University, Taepei.

Academic Year: March to February (March-August; September-February).

Admission Requirements: Graduation from high school or equivalent.

Fees (Won): c. 75,000 per annum.

Language of Instruction: Korean.

Degrees and Diplomas: Bachelor, 5 yrs.

Library: University Library, c. 160,000 vols.

Publications: Journal (biannually); Distance Education Forum (quarterly)

Press or Publishing House: KACU Press.

Academic Staff, 1989-90:

Rank	Full-time	Part-time
Gyosu (Professors)	12	–
Bu-gyosu (Associate Professors)	41	–
Jo-gyosu (Assistant Professors)	29	–
Jogyo (Assistants)	50	–
Gangsa (Lecturers)	19	3154
Total	155	3154

Student Enrolment, 1989-90:

	Men	Women	Total
Of the country	84,715	64,112	148,827*

*All external.

4528 **KOREA MARITIME UNIVERSITY**

1 Dongsam-dong, Yeongdo-ku, Busan 606-791
Telex: KOMAUNI K53665
Telephone: (49) 0031-34

Navigation
Marine Engineering
Mechanical Engineering
Maritime Law
Shipping Management
Naval Architecture
Electronics and Communication
Foreign Trade
Oceanography
Graduate S.
Also junior college.

Founded 1945 at Chinhae, moved to Busan 1953. A national university financed by the central government. Residential facilities for c. 60 academic staff and c. 1400 students.

Arrangements for co-operation with: Taiwan National Institute of Marine Technology; U.S. Merchant Marine Academy.

Academic Year: March to December (March-June; August-December).

Admission Requirements: Graduation from high school.

Language of Instruction: Korean.

Degrees and Diplomas: Bachelor of–Engineering; Laws; Management; Trade, 4 yrs. Master, a further 2 yrs. Doctor of Engineering, 3 yrs.

Library: c. 42,500 vols.
Publication: Journals (annually).
Academic Staff: c. 100 (40).
Student Enrolment: c. 2350.

4529 **KOREA NATIONAL COLLEGE OF PHYSICAL EDUCATION**
88-15 Oryoon-dong, Songpa-gu, Seoul 138-763
Telephone: (8) 418-1001
Fax: (8) 418-1877
President: Chung Tong Gu
Chairman of Academic Affairs: Woo Yung Lee

D. of Physical Education
Head: Jong Hun Nam; *staff* 42 (20)
Research I. of Physical Education and Sports Science
Head: Choi Yong Ei; *staff* 5 (10)
Research I. of Physical Education
Head: Sang Chul Lee; *staff* 3 (10)
Computer Ce.
Head: Hee Joong Yun; *staff* 4
Saemul Undong Research Ce.
Head: Choong Tae Kim; *staff* 2
Graduate S.
Head: Kwang Sub Lee; *staff* 6 (3)

Founded 1977. A State institution under the jurisdiction of the Ministry of Education.

Arrangements for co-operation with: Cleveland State University; Taiwan National College of Physical Education and Sports; Australian College of Physical Education.

Academic Year: March to December (March-June; August-December)
Admission Requirements: Graduation from high school.
Language of Instruction: Korean.
Degrees and Diplomas: Bachelor, 4 yrs. Master, a further 2 yrs. Doctor, Ph.D., 3 yrs after Master.
Libraries: College Library, 100,000 vols; Science and Liberal Arts.
Special Facilities (Museums, etc.): The Central Sports Museum.
Academic Staff, 1990:

Rank	Full-time	Part-time
Professors	7	–
Associate Professors	33	–
Assistant Professors	21	–
Instructors	3	25
Total	64	25

Student Enrolment, 1990:

	Men	Women	Total
Of the country	644	178	822

4530 **KOREA NATIONAL UNIVERSITY OF EDUCATION**
Darak-ri, Kangnae-myeon, Cheongwon-gun, Chungbuk 363-890
Founded 1984.

4531 ***KYUNGPOOK TAEHAK-GYO**
Kyungpook National University
1370 Sankyok-dong, Puk-gu, Taegu 702-701
Telex: PUBLICD K 54400 (12)
Telephone: (53) 955-5001-35
Fax: (53) 954-6806
President: Shi-Kwon Cheon (1987-90)
Dean of Academic Affairs: Tong-Soo Park

C. of Humanities
Dean: Moon-ho Lee; *staff* 62 (44)
C. of Social Sciences (including Political Science, Library Science, and Psychology)
Dean: Byung-gon Lee; *staff* 35 (30)
C. of Economics and Commerce
Dean: Sang-han Kim; *staff* 32 (25)
C. of Engineering
Dean: Hyun-kee Cho; *staff* 118 (45)
C. of Agriculture (including Horticulture and Veterinary Medicine)
Dean: Woo-sung Lee; *staff* 72 (40)
C. of Natural Sciences
Dean: Jun Chung; *staff* 70 (60)
C. of Law
Dean: Won-joo Kim; *staff* 23 (15)
C. of Education
Dean: Joon-kee Chae; *staff* 115 (55)
C. of Music and Visual Arts
Dean: Jong-wook Oh; *staff* 27 (64)
S. of Medicine (including Nursing and Pharmacy)
Dean: Tae-ho Chung; *staff* 113 (19)
S. of Dentistry
Dean: Jae-hyun Seong; *staff* 23 (25)
Graduate S.
Dean: Tae-hwa Shon
Graduate S. of Education
Dean: Sang-loh Lee
Graduate S. of Public Administration
Dean: Jong-yul Han; *staff* 11 (10)
Graduate S. of Health
Dean: Doo-hei Kim; *staff* 11 (15)
Graduate S. of Business Administration
Dean: Woon-sung Park; *staff* 10 (15)
Graduate S. of Industrial Engineering
Dean: Wu-Il Lee; *staff* 10 (10)
Audio-Visual Education Ce. (Music)
; *staff* – (10)
Language I.
Director: Munho Cho; *staff* 5 (5)
Toegye I. of Philosophy and Korean Studies
Director: Kwang-soon Kim; *staff* 3 (25)
I. of Electronic Technology
; *staff* 3 (10)
Computer Ce.
Director: Soon-jung Kim; *staff* 18 (5)
I. of Basic Science
Director: Chang-Un Lee
Saemaul Research I.
Director: Sam-Tak Chung
I. of Genetic Engineering
Director: U-Ik Sohn
Peace Research I.
Director: In-Hee Park
Research I. of Industrial Technology
Director: Byong-Ha Yoon
Humanities I.
Director: Young-Soo Pak
I. of Agricultural Science and Technology
Director: Hyung-Sik Yoon
Law Research I.
Director: Joon-Gu Lee
Social Science Research I.
Director: Shi-Chung Ryu
I. of Economic and Managerial Research
Director: Young-Ho Kim
Research I. of Physical Education and Sports Science
Director: Chong-Won Chae
Environmental Science I.
Director: Sang-oh Oh
I. for Pacific Rim Studies
Director: Woo-Young Ri
I. of Electronic Technology
Director: Byung-Ki Sohn
Science Education Research I.
Director: Soo-Dong Yio
Language I.
Director: Moon-Ho Cho

Also 10 research institutes and elementary and high schools.

Founded as university 1952 incorporating 3 existing (Teachers, 1923; Medicine, 1933; Agriculture, 1944) and 2 newly established colleges (Liberal Arts and Sciences). The main Campus at Sankyuk-dong and the Medical Campusat Tongin-dong. Under the jurisdiction of the Ministry of Education. Governing bodies: the Office of Academic Affairs; the Office of Student Affairs; the Office of General Affairs. Residential facilities for academic staff and 2000 students.

Arrangements for co-operation with: State University of New York at Buffalo; University of South Florida; National Tsing Hua University (Taipei); Kyoto University; University of California, Los Angeles; George Mason University; Queen's University, Canada. Participation in programme for developing Agricultural Technology in underdeveloped countries under an agreement with FAO.

Academic Year: March to February (March-June; September-December).

Admission Requirements: Graduation from high school or foreign equivalent, and competitive entrance examination.

Fees (Won): Tuition, 600,000-800,000 per semester.

Language of Instruction: Korean.

Degrees and Diplomas: Bachelor, 4 yrs. Master, a further 1-2 yrs. Doctor, Ph.D., 2-3 yrs after Master.

Library: Central Library, 450,000 vols.

Special Facilities (Museums, etc.): University Museum (antiques of Sill, Koryo, and Yi Dynasty); Auditorium, capacity of 3000 (Movie Studio, Orchestra Performance Stage); Green House; Animal Feeding House and Veterinary clinic.

Publications: Research Review of Kyungpook University (biannually); Abstracts of thesis Graduate School (annually); Journal of Graduate School of Education (annually); Journal of Humanities (annually); Journal of Social Sciences (annually); Journal of Natural Sciences (annually); Review of Economics and Business (annually); Journal of Law and Political Science (annually); Journal of Kyungpook Engineering (annually); Agricultural Research Bulletin of Kyungpook National University (annually); Kyungpook Education Forum (annually); Kyungpook University Medical Journal (biannually); Philosophy of Korea (annually); Journal of Science Education (annually); Oriental Culture Research (annually); Bulletin of the Institute for Industrial and Social Development (annually); Saemaul Research Review (annually); Journal of Language and Literature (annually); Electronic Technology Reports (annually); Peace Research (annually); Journal of Student Guidance (biannually); Kyungpook Historical Review (annually); Journal of Korean Language and Literature (annually); Nak-Dong Geography (annually); Zeitschrift für Germanistik (annually); Magazine of Geology (annually); Thesis Collection of Korean Language and Literature (annually); History Education Review (annually); Journal of English Language and Literature (annually); Journal of Physical Education (biannually); Kyungpook Mathematical Journal (biannually). Publishing House: Kyung Dae Shin Moon (University Press).

Press or Publishing House: The University Press.

Academic Staff, 1990-91:

Rank	Full-time	Part-time
Gyosu (Professors)	208	78
Bu-gyosu (Associate Professors)	171	52
Jo-gyosu (Assistant Professors)	182	65
Jeon-nim-gangsa (Instructors)	85	—
Jogyo (Assistants)	128	50
Total	774	245

Student Enrolment, 1990-91:

	Men	Women	Total
Of the country	12,710	6957	19,638
Of other countries	58	29	87
Total	12,768	6986	19,725

4532 **MOKPO NATIONAL UNIVERSITY**

Torim-ri, Chonggye-myon, Muan-gun, Chonnam 534-729
Telephone: (631) 72-8153
Fax: (636) 52-4793
President: Chong-Moo Bae
Administrative Officer: Man-Kyu Choe

C. of Humanities (Korean Language and Literature, English Language and Literature, History, Chinese Language and Literature, Archaeology and Anthropology, Japanese Language and Literature, Education, National Ethics Education, Commercial Education, Music, Fine Art)
Dean: Kyung-Hoe Heo; *staff* 76
C. of Social Science (Business Administration, International Trade, Economics, Regional Development, Law, Public Administration, Land Administration, Finance and Insurance)
Dean: Chun-Sik Kim; *staff* 47
C. of Natural Science
Dean: Kong-Rae Park; *staff* 59
C. of Engineering (Electronic, Food, Mechanical, Computer, Electrical, and Architecture Engineering)
Dean: Hae-Deok Jeong; *staff* 15
Graduate S.
Dean: Kyung-Jung Kim; *staff* 57
Welfare Improvement I.
Director: Oang-Yeul Lyu; *staff* 8
Unification Research I.
Director: Se-Weon Mo; *staff* 10
I. of Littoral Biota (including Environmental Pollution, and Preservation of the Coastal Ecosystms)
Director: Sook Shin; *staff* 12
I. of Basic Sciences
Director: Heong-Kuk Kim; *staff* 5

Founded 1946 as normal school. Acquired present statue and title 1990. Residential facilities for students.

Arrangements for joint research with 3 universities in: USA; People's Republic of China; Taiwan.

Academic Year: March to February.

Admission Requirements: Graduation from high school and entrance examination.

Fees (Won): 900,000-1,100,000 per annum.

Language of Instruction: Korean.

Degrees and Diplomas: Bachelor, 4 yrs. Master, a further 2 yrs.

Library: Central Library, 80,000 vols.

Special Facilities (Museums, etc.): Museum. Broadcasting System.

Publication: Journals of Research Institutes (annually).

Press or Publishing House: University Press.

Academic Staff, 1990: 238.

Student Enrolment, 1990:

	Men	Women	Total
Of the country	2971	2272	5243

4533 **NATIONAL FISHERIES UNIVERSITY OF BUSAN**

599-1 Taeyon-dong, Nam-gu, Busan 608
Telephone: (51) 622-3951

F. of Fishing Technology
F. of Food Science and Technology
F. of Fisheries Biology
F. of Oceanography
F. of Social Sciences
I. of Marine Sciences
I. of Fisheries Management
I. of Aquatic Organisms Pathology

Founded 1946 as State institution, incorporated in Busan National University, detached as independent institution 1964. Responsible to Ministry of Education.

Arrangements for co-operation with Tokyo Daigaku.

Academic Year: March to February (March-August; September-February).

Admission Requirements: Graduation from high school and entrance examination.

Language of Instruction: Korean.

Degrees and Diplomas: Bachelor of–Science; Engineering; Fisheries Commerce; Management, 4 yrs. Master, a further 2 yrs. Doctorate,3 yrs, postgraduate.

Library: 50,000 vols.

Publications: Theses Collection; Bulletin.

Academic Staff: c. 150 (40).

Student Enrolment: c. 5700.

4534 ***SEOUL NATIONAL UNIVERSITY**

Shinnim-dong, Kwanak-gu, Seoul 151
Telex: SAUROK K29664
Telephone: 886-0101/9
President: Hyun-Jae Lee (1983-87)
Dean of Academic Affairs: Sin-Taek Kang

C. of Humanities (including Archaeology)
C. of Social Sciences (including Political Science and Psychology)
C. of Natural Sciences (including Computer Sciences, Astronomy,and Oceanography)
C. of Home Economics
C. of Business Administration
C. of Engineering (Architectural, Mining, Metallurgical, Mechanical, Textile, Nuclear, Electrical, Electronic, Marine, and Aeronautical)
C. of Agriculture (including Forestry and Animal Husbandry)
C. of Fine Arts
C. of Law
C. of Education
C. of Veterinary Medicine
C. of Pharmacy
C. of Music
C. of Medicine
C. of Dentistry

Graduate S. of Public Administration
Graduate S. of Environmental Studies
Graduate S. of Public Health
Natural Products Research I.
Language Research I.
I. of Communication Research
I. of Environmental Science
Research I. for Molecular Biology and Genetics
I. of Social Sciences
I. of Economic Research Law Research I.
I. of Korean Culture
I. of American Studies
I. of Saemaul Udong Studies
Research I. of Basic Sciences
Also 22 Research Institutes of the Colleges.

Founded 1946 in succession to former Keijo Imperial University. Reorganized in 1975. A State institution underthe jurisdiction of the Ministry of Education. Governing body: the University Council. Residential facilities for academic staff and students.

Academic Year: March to February (March-June; September-December).

Admission Requirements: Graduation from high school or teachers' college, or equivalent qualification recognized by the Ministry of Education in Korea, and entrance examination.

Language of Instruction: Korean.

Degrees and Diplomas: Bachelor of–Natural Sciences; Engineering; Agriculture; Political Science; Economics; Literature; Business Administration; Physical Education; Veterinary Medicine; Pharmacy; Music; Nursing; Home Economics; Fine Arts; Law, 4 yrs; Medicine and Dentistry, 6 yrs. Master in the above fields and Education; Public Health; Public Administration; Urban Planning; Landscape Architecture, a further 2 yrs. Doctor of–Engineering; Agriculture; Literature; Philosophy; Political Science; Business Administration; Education; Public Health; Public Administration; Natural Sciences; Law; Economics; Medicine; Pharmacy; Veterinary Medicine, 3 yrs after Master.

Library: Central Library and specialized libraries, *c.* 1,200,000 vols.

Special Facilities (Museums, etc.): University Museum.

Publications: Social Science Review (quarterly); Proceedings of the College of Natural Sciences (biannually); Home Economics Journal (annually); Engineering Report (annually); Economic Review (annually); Korean Development Policy Studies (annually); Journal of the College of Education (biannually); Journal of Pharmaceutical Sciences (annually); Seoul Journal of Medicine (quarterly); Korean Journal of Public Health (biannually); Korean Journal of Public Administration (biannually); Journal of Environmental Studies (biannually); Social Sciences and Policy Studies (quarterly); Korean Economic Journal (quarterly); Law Journal (quarterly); Journal of Humanities (biannually); Korean Business Journal (quarterly). Publications of the Research Institutes.

Press or Publishing House: Seoul University Press.

Academic Staff: *c.* 1600 (750).

Student Enrolment: *c.* 31,000.

4535 **SUNCHON NATIONAL UNIVERSITY**
Maegok-dong, Cunch'on, Chonnam 540-742
Telex: 29664 SNUROK K
Telephone: 52-8131
Fax: 53-5606
President: Jin-Ho Kim
Secretary-General: Bum-Suk Suh

Agricultural S.
Dean: Heang-Jin Lim; *staff* 64 (7)
Educational S.
Dean: Chung-Koo Cho; *staff* 37 (8)
Humanities and Social Science S.
Dean: Jong-Young
Engineering S.
Dean: Jee-Ju Kwak; *staff* 27 (10)
Natural Science S.
Dean: Young-Ki Kim; *staff* 23 (13)
Computer Ce.
Regional Development Research I.
Head: Lan- Sik Shin; *staff* 1
Industrial Technology Research I.
Head: Hyeng-Joo Jeon; *staff* 1
Natural Science Research I.
Head: Jong-Hong Kim; *staff* 1

Founded 1935 as Agricultural School. Acquired present status and title 1982. Reseidential facilities for 304 students.

Arrangements for co-operation with: the National Taiwan University.

Academic Year: March to February (March-August; September-February).

Admission Requirements: Graduation from high school and entrance examination.

Fees (Won): 529,500-638,500 per semester.

Language of Instruction: Korean.

Degrees and Diplomas: Bachelor, 4 yrs. Master, a further 2 yrs.

Libraries: Central Library, 39,835 vols (Oriental, 28,898; Western, 10,937).

Special Facilities (Museums, etc.): University Museum; University Broadcasting Station; University Farm; University Forests; University Breeding Farm; University Farming Promotion Centre.

Press or Publishing House: Sunchon National University Bulletin.

Academic Staff, 1989-90:

Rank	Full-time	Part-time
Professors	35	–
Associate Professors	42	–
Assistant Professors	79	–
Lecturers	24	–
Total	180	52

Student Enrolment, 1989-90:

	Men	Women	Total
Of the country	4198	1569	5767
Of other countries	3	1	4
Total	4201	1570	5771

4536 **YOSU NATIONAL FISHERIES COLLEGE**
Kuk-dong, Yosu CT Chonnam 550-180
Telephone: 42-7141
Fax: 41-5520
President: Seong-Koo Kang
Director of Academic Afffairs: Tai-Jung Kang

Fisheries

Founded 1917 as school. Acquired present status and title 1987. Residential facilities for students.

Academic Year: March to February.

Admission Requirements: Graduation from high school.

Fees (Won): 553,000 per semester.

Language of Instruction: Korean.

Degrees and Diplomas: Bachelor, 4 yrs.

Library: Yosu National Fisheries College Library, 25,853 vols.

Academic Staff, 1989-90:

Rank	Full-time	Part-time
Professors	30	–
Assistant Professors	10	–
Associate Professors	20	–
Instructors	15	16
Total	75	16

Student Enrolment, 1989-90: 1720.

Public Institutions

4537 **SEOUL CITY UNIVERSITY**
Chonnong-dong, Tongdaemun-gu, Seoul 130-743
Telephone: 245-5303

Founded 1918

Private Institutions

4538 **AJOU UNIVERSITY**
Wonchon-dong, Suwon CT, Kyongji 440-749
Telephone: 33-5141

C. of Engineering
C. of Business Administration

C. of Liberal Arts and Science
Graduate S.
Founded 1972.

4539 **BUSAN WOMEN'S UNIVERSITY**
Dongrae-gu, Busan

D. of Home Economics
D. of Nutrition
D. of Fine Arts
D. of Physics
D. of Music
Founded 1969.

4540 **CATHOLIC UNIVERSITY**
Haewha-dong, Chongno-gu, Seoul 110-530
Telephone: 762-2501
Fax: 741-2801
President: Eui-Chai Tjeng

F. of Theology
Dean: Joo-Byong Youn; *staff* 33 (9)
F. of Medicine (including Nursing)
Dean: Kyu-Chul Cho; *staff* 530 (18)
Also 12 Research Institutes and Centres of the Faculties.

Founded 1885 as St. Joseph's Seminary. Acquired present statue and title 1959. Residential facilities for academic staff and students.

Arrangements for academic exchange programmes with other Catholic Universities, etc., in Europe, America and Asia.

Academic Year: March to December (March-June; September-December).

Admission Requirements: Graduation from high school and entrance examination.

Fees (Won): 655,000-1,000,000 per semester.

Language of Instruction: Korean.

Degrees and Diplomas: Bachelor of–Theology, Nursing, 4 yrs, Medicine, 6 yrs. Master, a further 2 yrs. Doctor of Medical Science, 3 yrs after Master.

Libraries: Theology, 62,000 vols; Medicine, 31,000.

Special Facilities (Museums, etc.): University Museum.

Publications: Catholic Theology and Thought (biannually); Journal; Journal of Catholic Research Institute; Bulletin of Clinical Research Institute; Bulletin of the Catholic Medical; Korean Journal of Occupational Health.

Press or Publishing House: Catholic University Press.

Academic Staff, 1990:

Rank	Full-time	Part-time
Professors	107	–
Associate Professors	86	–
Assistant Professors	160	–
Instructors	180	–
Teaching Assistants	31	9
Visiting Professors	–	18
Total	564	27

Student Enrolment, 1990:

	Men	Women	Total
Of the country	1093	425	1518*

*Also 35 external students.

4541 **CHEONGJU UNIVERSITY**
Naedok-dong, Chongju CT, Chungbuk 360-764
Telephone: 54-2111

C. of Economics and Business Administration
C. of Law and Political Science
C. of Liberal Arts and Science
C. of Natural Sciences and Engineering
C. of Education
C. of Arts
Graduate S.

Founded 1946 as college of commerce.

Academic Year: March to February (March-August; September-February).

Admission Requirements: Graduation from high school and entrance examination. Provision is made for the recognition of foreign qualifications.

Degrees and Diplomas: Bachelor of–Arts; Science; Engineering; Commerce; Economics; Law; Political Science. Master of–Commerce; Economics; Political Science; Law.

Academic Staff: c. 50.

Student Enrolment: c. 1000.

4542 **CHOSUN UNIVERSITY**
Sosok-dong, Dong-gu, Kwangiu 501-759
Telephone: 232-8151

C. of Law and Political Science
C. of Liberal Arts and Science
C. of Education
C. of Commerce and Economics
C. of Foreign Languages
C. of Engineering (including Architecture)
Medical C. (including Nursing)
C. of Pharmacy
C. of Dentistry
C. of Physical Education
Evening C.
Women's Junior C.
Graduate S.
Also 16 research institutes.

Founded 1946 as private institution. Some residential facilities for academic staff and students.

Academic Year: March to February (March to August; September February).

Admission Requirements: Graduation from high school and entrance examination.

Language of Instruction: Korean.

Degrees and Diplomas: Bachelor of–Law, LL.B.; Political Science B.Pol.Sc.; Economics, B.Econ.; Commerce, B.Com.; Arts, B.Art; Music B.Music; Science, B.Sc.; Home Economics, B.Home Econ.; Physical Education, B.Phys.Educ.; Engineering, B.Engin.; Pharmacy, B.Phar., 4 yrs. Medicine, B.M., 6 yrs. Master of–Law, LL.M.; Political Science, M.Pol.Sc. Economics, M.Econ.; Commerce, M.Com.; Arts, M.Art; Sciences, M.Sc. Management, M.Manage.; Physical Education, M.Phys.Educ.; Music M.Music; Medicine, M.Med.; Nursing, M.Nur.; Engineering, M.Engin. Pharmacy, M.Phar., a further 2 yrs. Doctor of–Law, LL.D.; Economics D.Econ.; Commerce, D.Com.; Science, D.Sc.; Engineering, D.Engin. Pharmacy, D.Phar., 3-4 yrs after Master.

Library: c. 380,000 vols.

Publications: Chosun World (English); Cho Dae Shin Moon; Ye-dae Shin Moon; Cho Dae Hag Bo; Chong-Hap Theses Collection; Maek.

Academic Staff: c. 500.

Student Enrolment: c. 13,000.

4543 **CHUNG ANG UNIVERSITY**
221 Huksok-dong, Dongssak-ku, Seoul 151
Cables: Chunganguniv Seoul
Telex: CAUNIV K 24763
Telephone: 813-3811
President: Jae Chul Ri (1987-)
Dean of Academic Administration: Dong Kyo Chun

C. of Liberal Arts and Science (including Library Science)
Dean: Hee Young Hwang; *staff* 75 (112)
C. of Engineering (including Architecture and Computer Science)
Dean: Woo Hyun Lee; *staff* 39 (24)
C. of Education (including Home Economics)
Dean: Sung Yoon Hong; *staff* 33 (37)
C. of Law
Dean: Jung Kun Park; *staff* 11 (5)
C. of Political Science and Economics (including Journalism)
Dean: Seung Park; *staff* 30 (15)
C. of Business Administration (including Accountancy)
Dean: Meen Ju Kahng; *staff* 20 (16)
C. of Industrial Studies (including Animal Husbandry, Food Technology, Regional Development, and Horticulture)
Dean: Chong Hoon Lee; *staff* 19 (5)
C. of Pharmacy
Dean: Johng Kap Kim; *staff* 13 (1)
C. of Medicine (including Nursing)
Dean: Bong Hin Rah; *staff* 82 (13)
C. of Arts
Dean: Jeong Ok Kim; *staff* 33 (73)
C. of Foreign Languages
Dean: Ok Ro Lee; *staff* 25 (14)

C. of Social Sciences
Dean: Cheol Ho Cha; *staff* 20 (34)
C. of Home Economics
Dean: Seo Seok Yoon; *staff* 12 (9)
C. of Music
Dean: Jae Dong Chung; *staff* 22 (72)
C. of Architecture and Construction Engineering
Dean: Hyun Shik Shin; *staff* 1
Graduate S.
Dean: Byung Chul Kim; *staff* 366
Graduate S. of Social Development
Dean: Chang Joo Kim; *staff* 52
Graduate S. of International Management
Dean: Meen Ju Kahng; *staff* 50
Graduate S. of Education
Dean: Mok Sang Yuh; *staff* 50
Graduate S. of Mass Communication
Dean: Min Ha Kim; *staff* 34
Graduate S. of Construction Engineering
Dean: Myung Ho Lee; *staff* 34
I. of Law
Director: Yeol Kim
I. of Humanities
Director: Jun Taik Park
I. of Community Development
Director: Chung Joo Kim
I. of Oriental Medicine
Director: Dug Ryong Hahn
I. of Korean Studies
Director: Kun Soo Kim
Japanese Studies Ce.
Director: Sung Kyu Whang
Research I. of New Community Movement
Director: Chang Joo Kim
Evening C.
Also 10 research institutes, and kindergarten, primary, middle and girls' and boys' high schools, and junior college of art.

Founded 1918 as normal college for women, became Chungoang (Central) Women's College 1945, co-educational 1948. Accredited with university status by Ministry of Education 1953 as private, non-denominational institution. Financed by tuition fees and donations. Governing bodies: the Board of Trustees, composed of 16 members; the Executive Council, composed of the deans of the faculties and directors of the institutes. Some residential facilities for academic staff and for 1500 students.

Special arrangements for co-operation with: Nihon University; University of Alberta; University of Pennsylvania; University of Minnesota; University of Pittsburgh; University of Wisconsin; University of Sheffield; Southwest State University; George Washington University; University of Southern California, Los Angeles; Alaska Pacific University; Colombia College, Hollywood; Universitas Sjiah Kuala; Florida International University; King Abdul-Aziz University; Long Island University; Findlay College, Ohio; National Taiwan University; National Taiwan Normal University; Tatung Institute of Technology; De La Salle University.

Academic Year: March to February (March-June; September-December).

Admission Requirements: Graduation from high school or foreign equivalent, and entrance examination.

Fees (Won): Tuition, 1,176,000-1,400,000 per annum; Graduate School, 1,340,000-1,424,000.

Language of Instruction: Korean.

Degrees and Diplomas: Bachelor of–Arts, B.A.; Science, B.S.; Pharmacy, B.P.; Laws, B.L., 4 yrs; Medicine, M.D., 6 yrs. Master, a further 2-3 yrs. Doctorate, Ph.D., a further 3-4 yrs and thesis.

Libraries: Central Library *c.* 300,000 vols; Ansung Campus, 30,000.

Special Facilities (Museums, etc.): University Museum; Folk Art Museum.

Publications: Theses Collection; Mun Gyong (Liberal Arts); Engineering Review; Education Review; Law Review; Review of Political Science and Economics; Agriculture Review; Pharmacy Journal; Business Administration Review; Journal of College of Arts; Journal of Medicine (all biannually); Korean Journal of Comparative Law (annually); Korean Studies Journal (monthly); Journal of Economic Development (annually).

Press or Publishing House: Chung-Ang University Press; Chung-Ang Publishing Company.

Academic Staff, 1986-87:

Rank	Full-time	Part-time
Professors	195	–
Associate Professors	132	–
Assistant Professors	117	–
Instructors	79	429
Clinical Instructors	36	–
Professor Emeritus	4	–
Assistants	168	–
Total	713	429

Student Enrolment, 1986-87:

	Men	Women	Total
Of the country	20,491	6049	26,540
Of other countries	45	12	57
Total	20,536	6061	26,597

4544 **DANKOOK UNIVERSITY**
San 8-2 Hannam-dong, Yongsan-gu, Seoul 140-714
Telephone: 797-0581
President: Choong Sik Chang

C. of Liberal Arts and Science
C. of Commerce and Economics
C. of Law and Political Science
C. of Engineering (including Architecture)
C. of Education (including Physical Education)
C. of Evening Studies
Graduate S.
Graduate S. of Business Administration
Graduate S. of Education
Graduate S. of Public Administration
I. of Oriental Studies
I. of Anglo-American Studies
Research I. of New Community Movement
Industrial Research I.
Chinese Studies I.
I. of Folk Arts
Technology Research I.
I. of Statistics
Evening S.
Also campus at Cheonan.

Founded 1947. A private institution. Governing body: the Board of Trustees.

Academic Year: March to February (March-August; September-February).

Admission Requirements: Graduation from high school and entrance examination.

Language of Instruction: Korean.

Degrees and Diplomas: Bachelor in all fields, 4 yrs. Master, a further 2 ½ yrs. Doctor in–Humanities; Social Sciences; Science; Engineering, a further 3 yrs.

Libraries: Central Library, *c.* 200,000 vols; Cheonan Campus library, *c.* 5000; Oriental Studies library, *c.* 100.

Special Facilities (Museums, etc.): Central Museum; Suk Ju-son Folk Arts Museum.

Publications: Bulletin; Essays on Korean Language and Literature; Home Economic Studies; Business Studies; Dongyang Hak; Law Review; Historical Journal; Journal of Industrial Studies; The China Quarterly; Commerce and Economics Review.

Press or Publishing House: University Press.

Academic Staff: c. 250 (350).

Student Enrolment: c. 13,650.

4545 **DONG-A UNIVERSITY**
Hadan-dong, Saha-gu, Pusan 604-714
Telephone: 204-0171
Fax: 201-5430
President: Soon-Gi Shin
Dean of Academic Affairs Office: Ta-Il Lee

C. of Humanities
Dean: Chong-Tak Kim; *staff* 91 (86)
C. of Natural Sciences
Dean: Jong-Won Yu; *staff* 49 (27)

C. of Law
Dean: Won-Yeong Park; *staff* 13 (4)
C. of Social Sciences
Dean: Sung-Gyun Park; *staff* 39 (10)
C. of Business Administration
Dean: Hai-Sil Sohn; *staff* 43 (10)
C. of Agriculture
Dean: Jung-Ki Park; *staff* 38 (6)
C. of Engineering
Dean: Yong Kil Hwang; *staff* 112 (36)
C. of Physical Education
Dean: Young-Pil An; *staff* 19 (15)
C. of Arts
Dean: Il-Sang Cho; *staff* 38 (69)
C. of Medicine
Dean: Joon-Youn Kim; *staff* 56
Graduate S.
Dean: Byung-Tae Cho
Graduate S. of Business Administration
Dean: Yong-Dal See
Graduate S. of Education
Dean: Hae-Woo Shin
Graduate S. of Industry
Dean: Sun-Sok Kwon
Sokdang Academic Research I. of Korean Culture
Head: Myung-Jong Yu
Language Research I.
Dean: Woong-Dal Ryoo
Enviromental Problems Research I.
Dean: Soo-Saeng Kim
Population Research Ce.
Dean: Nam-Il Kim
Business Management Research I.
Dean: Yong-Dae Kim
Social Science Research I.
Dean: Mo-Shong Choi
Research I. of Sports Science
Dean: Chel-Ho Part
I. of German Studies
Dean: Young-Su Lee
I. of Law Studies
Dean: Jo-Kun Chung
Basic Science Research I.
Dean: Dae-Dong Sung
Korea Agricultural Technology Research I.
Dean: Young-Kil Kim
I. of Korean Resources Development
Dean: Myung-Ki Kim
Ocean Resources Research I.
Dean: Sae-Wook Oh
Tourism and Leisure Research I.
Dean: Hai-Sik Sohn
Life Science Research I.
Research I. for Industrial Medicine
Dean: Joon-Youn Kim
Also University Hospital (opened 1990).

Founded as college 1947, became university 1959. A private institution. Governing body: the Board of Directors. Some residential facilities for academic staff and 150 students.

Arrangements for co-operation with the Universities of: Aachen; Munich; Chinese Culture, Taiwan; Chukyo; Liverpool; Oriente, Venezuela; California State, Fresno.

Academic Year: March to February (March-August; September-December).

Admission Requirements: Graduation from high school or equivalent, and entrance examination.

Language of Instruction: Korean.

Degrees and Diplomas: Bachelor of–Arts; Science; Home Economics; Fine Arts; Music; Physical Education; Political Science; Law; Economics; Business Administration; Administration; Medicine; Agriculture; Engineering, 4 yrs. Master of–Arts; Science; Home Economics; Physical Education; Political Science; Law; Commerce; Education; Fine Arts; Music; Public Administration; Economics; Business Administration; Agriculture; Engineering, a further 2 yrs. Doctor of–Law; Science Economics; Education; Political Science; Administration; Philosophy; Agriculture; Engineering; Literature, 2 yrs after Master.

Library: Central Library, *c.* 522,300 vols.

Special Facilities (Museums, etc.): University Museum (Collections from Chosan Dynasty); Broadcasting System.

Publications: University Newspaper (weekly); Journal; Journals of: Law and Economics; Agriculture; Engineering; Student Guidance.

Press or Publishing House: Publishing House.

Academic Staff, 1989-90:

Rank	Full-time	Part-time
Professors	114	–
Associate Professors	169	–
Assistant Professors	169	–
Instructors	48	281
Total	500	281

Student Enrolment, 1989-90:

	Men	Women	Total
Of the country	20,338	6293	26,631
Of other countries	1	1	2
Total	20,339	6294	26,633

4546 **DONG EUI UNIVERSITY**
24 Kaya-dong, Busanjin-gu, Busan 614-010
Telephone: 804-1500

F. of Liberal Arts
F. of Law and Political Science
F. of Business Administration and Economics
F. of Science
F. of Engineering
F. of Fine Arts and Music
I. of Political Science
I. of Industrial Management
I. of Marine Biology

Founded 1979 by the Dong Eui Foundation. A private institution financed by tuition fees (80%) and the Foundation. Governing body: the Board of Trustees.

Academic Year: March to February (March-July; September-December).

Admission Requirements: Graduation from high school or foreign equivalent, and entrance examination.

Language of Instruction: Korean.

Degrees and Diplomas: Bachelor, 4 yrs.

Library: Central Library, *c.* 27,300 vols.

Publications: Bulletin (monthly); Hyomin Journal (annually); Theses collection (annually).

Academic Staff: c. 80 (60).

Student Enrolment: c. 2250.

4547 **DONG-SHIN ENGINEERING COLLEGE**
Taeho-dong, Naju CT, Chonnam 520-180
Telephone: 33-2901

Founded 1985.

4548 **DONGDUCK WOMEN'S UNIVERSITY**
23-1 Hawolgok-dong, Sungbug-ku, Seoul 136-714
Telephone: 913- 2001/10
Fax: 913-0731
President: Jong-Hyup Kim (1983-90)
Dean of General Affairs: Sang-Soon Lee

C. of the Humanities (including Korean, English, Japanese, French, German Language and Literature, and Korean History)
Dean: Eui Gyu Kim; *staff* 26 (55)
C. of Social Sciences (including Business Administration, Economics, International Trade, and Library Science)
Dean: Do Kyung Kim; *staff* 12 (28)
C. of Natural Science (including Home Economics, Pharmacy, Food and Nutrition, Health Science, Computer Science, Child Education, andPhysical Education)
Dean: Yoon Sook Lee; *staff* 23 (31)
C. of Pharmacy
Dean: Sang Hak Do; *staff* 7 (6)
C. of Arts (including Fine Arts, Applied Arts,Visual and Industrial Design, and Music)
Dean: Suck Whan Park; *staff* 19 (49)
D. of General Studies and Teaching
Dean: Hong Tae Yoon; *staff* 25 (23)

Graduate S.
Dean: Young Yeon Yoon; *staff* 25 (23)
Computer Ce.
Korean Studies I.
Director: Young Oh Moon; *staff* 4
Business Administration I.
Director: Se Young Oh
Environmental Health Research Ce.
Director: Byeung Gi Chol; *staff* 7
Industrial Design Research Ce
Director: Hyun Kim;E4
Natural Drugs Research I.
Director: Sang Hak Do; *staff* 7

Founded 1950. A private institution. Governing body: the Board of Trustees.

Academic Year: March to February (March-August; September-February).

Admission Requirements: Graduation from high school and entrance examination.

Fees (Won): *c.* 900,000 per semester.

Language of Instruction: Korean.

Degrees and Diplomas: Bachelor of–Arts; Science; Home Economics; Business Administration; Economics, International Trade; Pharmacy; Library Science; Fine Art; Music; Physical Education, 4 yrs. Master of–Arts; Science; Home Economics; Business Administration; Pharmacy; Fine Art; Music; Physical Education, a further 2 yrs. Doctor of Pharmacy, a further 3yrs.

Library: Choonkang Memorial Library, 107,323 vols.

Special Facilities (Museums, etc.): Dongduck Women's Museum.

Publications: Journal of Korean Studies; Treaties (annually).

Press or Publishing House: Dongduck Women's University Press.

Academic Staff, 1990:

Rank	Full-time	Part-time
Gyosu (Professors)	17	29
Bu-gyosu (Associate Professors)	28	28
Jo-gyosu (Assistant Professors)	39	30
Jeon-nim-gangsa (Lecturers-Instructors)	8	90
Total	92	177

Student Enrolment, 1990: 3882 (Women).

4549 **DONGGUK UNIVERSITY**
26, 3-ga Pil-dong,Chung-gu, Seoul 100-715
Telephone: 267-8131

C. of Buddhism
C. of Liberal Arts and Sciences
C. of Law and Political Science
C. of Economics and Commerce
C. of Agriculture and Forestry
C. of Engineering
C. of Education
Graduate S.
Graduate S. of Public Administration
Graduate S. of Business Administration
Graduate S. of Education
Buddhist Research I.
National Security Research I.
Ce. for Dhyana (Zen Studies)
Buddhist Scriptures Translation
Computer Ce.
Extension D.
Branch at Kyongju

Founded 1906 as Myong Zin School, became Choong Ang Buddhist College 1930, Hye Wha College 1940, Dongguk College 1946, acquired present name and status 1953. Governing body: the Board of Trustees of 9 members. Residential facilities for students.

Academic Year: March to February (March-July; September-December).

Admission Requirements: Graduation from high school or recognized foreign equivalent, and entrance examination.

Language of Instruction: Korean.

Degrees and Diplomas: Bachelor of–Arts; Fine Arts; Science; Law; Political Science; Public Administration; Economics; Commerce; Business Administration; Agriculture; Engineering; Physical Education; Home Economics, 4 yrs; Oriental Medicine, 6 yrs. Master of–Arts; Science; Law; Political Science; Public Administration; Economics; Commerce; Business Administration; Agriculture; Engineering; Education, a further 2 yrs. Doctor of–Literature; Philosophy; Law; Science; Political Science; Economics; Agriculture; Engineering, 3 yrs after Master.

Library: Central Library, *c.* 350,000 vols.

Special Facilities (Museums, etc.): University Museum.

Publications: Dongguk Sasang (Buddhist philosophy); Dongguk Munhak (Korean literature); Bulgyo Hakpo (Buddhist Studies); Tripitaka Korean.

Academic Staff: c. 500.

Student Enrolment: c. 16,000.

4550 **DUKSUNG WOMEN'S UNIVERSITY**
Sangmun-dong, Dobong-gu, Seoul 132-030
Telephone: 902-8121

D. of General Education
D. of Liberal Arts
D. of Social Science (including Library Science and Business Administration)
D. of Natural Sciences (including Home Economics and Food Technology)
D. of Arts

Founded 1950. A private institution.

Academic Year: March to February (March-August; September-February).

Admission Requirements: Graduation from high school or foreign equivalent, and entrance examination.

Language of Instruction: Korean.

Degrees and Diplomas: Bachelor of–Arts; Science; Home Economics; Fine Arts; Business Administration; Pharmacy, 4 yrs. Master of–Arts; Home Economics; Pharmacy, a further 2 yrs. Also Teaching Certificate.

Library: c. 110,000 vols.

Publications: Woon Hyun (student Magazine); Duksung Women's College Press (bimonthly); Journal of Professors' Research (annually).

Academic Staff: c. 70 (140).

Student Enrolment: 3210 (Women).

4551 ***EWHA WOMEN'S UNIVERSITY**
11-1, Tahyon-dong, Sudaemun-gu, Seoul 120-750
Telephone: 362-6151
President: Li Sook Chung (1979-)
Dean of Faculty: Bong Ho Ryu

C. of Liberal Arts
Dean: Hong-Keun Hahm; *staff* 84 (136)
C. of Natural Sciences
Dean: Heh-Jeong Moh; *staff* 23 (33)
C. of Music
Dean: Yun-Kyung Yoon; *staff* 36 (104)
C. of Fine Arts
Dean: Dong-Sook Ahn; *staff* 36 (65)
C. of Physical Education
Dean: Chong Sun Kim; *staff* 15 (40)
C. of Education
Dean: Young-jai Chung; *staff* 63 (85)
C. of Law and Political Science
Dean: Duk-Kyu Jhin; *staff* 33 (34)
C. of Medicine
Dean: Nak-Eung Sung; *staff* 66 (13)
C. of Nursing
Dean: Young Hee Choi; *staff* 10 (3)
C. of Pharmacy
Dean: Hea Chung Yun; *staff* 15 (3)
C. of Home Economics
Dean: Sook He Kim; *staff* 14 (9)
Graduate S.
Dean: Woo Chul Kang; *staff* 1 (104)
Graduate S. of Education
Dean: Chung Han Kim; *staff* – (28)
Graduate S. of Industrial Design
Dean: Dong-Sook Ahn; *staff* – (5)
S. for Lifelong Education
Dean: Dong-Chol Kim; *staff* 2 (21)
Also 14 research institutes.

Founded 1886 as school by Mary Scranton (Methodist Missionary), became college 1910 and university 1945. A private institution financed by tuition fees, a government grant, and donations. Governing body: the University Council. Residential facilities for students.

Academic Year: March to February (March-August; September-February).

Admission Requirements: Graduation from high school or equivalent, and entrance examination.

Fees (Won): Registration, 681,600; tuition, 600,400 per semester; Graduate School, 784,000; 714,000

Language of Instruction: Korean.

Degrees and Diplomas: Bachelor of–Arts; Science; Music; Fine Arts; Public Administration; Law; Political Science; Business Administration; Home Economics; Pharmacy, 4 yrs; Medicine, 6 yrs. Master of–Arts, Science, Medicine; Fine Arts; Law; Political Science; Business Administration; Home Economics; Nursing; Pharmacy; Education; Music; Physical Education, a further 2 yrs. Doctor of–Philosophy; Law; Political Science; Science; Medicine; Pharmacy; Business Administration.

Library: 485,987 vols.

Special Facilities (Museums, etc.): University Museum; Natural History Museum.

Press or Publishing House: University Press.

Academic Staff, 1986-87:

Rank	Full-time	Part-time
Gyosu (Professors)	197	–
Bu-gyosu (Associate Professors)	88	–
Jo-gyosu (Assistant Professors)	95	–
Jeon-nim-gangsa (Instructors)	18	683
Jogyo (Assistants)	23	–
Total	421	683

Student Enrolment, 1986-87:

	Women
Of the country	16,440
Of other countries	1
Total	16,441

4552 **HALLYM COLLEGE**

Okchon-dong, Chunchon CT, Kangwon 200-010

Telephone: 53-5411

Founded 1982.

4553 **HAN NAM UNIVERSITY**

Ojung-dong, Taeduk-Gu, Taejon CT, Chungnam 300-791

Telephone: 623-7111

Fax: (42) 625-5874

President: Won Sul Lee

C. of Liberal Arts
; *staff* 61 (109)

C. of Education
; *staff* 27 (55)

C. of Natural Science
; *staff* 32 (39)

C. of Engineering
; *staff* 20 (19)

C. of Economics and Administration
; *staff* 40 (29)

Natural Science I.
Head: Won hoi Ku; *staff* – (10)

East-West Cultural Science I.
Head: Deuk ryoong Kim; *staff* – (6)

Regional Development I.
Dean: Sun Mo Jung; *staff* – (4)

Language I.
Dean: Kyun Tae Kim; *staff* – (5)

I. of Industrial Management
Dean: Hyeon Lib Jeong

Chung-Cheon Cultural I.
Dean: Yo Sun Park

Information Science I.
Dean: Su Man Lee; *staff* – (5)

New Community Research Ce.
Dean: Yun Pyo Shin

Ce. for Study of Christianity and Culture
Dean: Eun Yong Kim

I. for Japanese Studies
Dean: Eun Tong-Key

I. of Social Science Research

I. of Economics

Founded in 1956 by a Presbyterian Missionary Foundation. Residential facilities for 92 men and 39 women students.

Arrangements for co-operation with: Shikoku Christian College, Japan; St. Andrews College, USA; Lynchburg College, USA; Seattle Pacific University; Queens College; King College, USA; Bangkok University; De La Salle University, Philippines; Tunghai University

Academic Year: March to December (March-June; August-December).

Admission Requirements: Graduation from high school and entrance examination.

Fees (Won): Tuition, 714,500-912,000 per semester.

Language of Instruction: Korean.

Degrees and Diplomas: Bachelor, 4 yrs; Master, a further 1-2 yrs (M.A./M.S./MBA); Doctor, Ph.D., 3-5 yrs (Ph.D./Ed.D).

Library: Central Library, 210,000 vols.

Special Facilities (Museums, etc.): University Museum; Natural History Museum; Broadcasting Station.

Publications: Han Nam Press (weekly); Han Nam Times (in English, monthly); Vision in Action (in English, quarterly).

Press or Publishing House: Han Nam University Press.

Academic Staff, 1989-90:

Rank	Full-time	Part-time
Professors	34	–
Associate Professors	89	–
Asistant Professor	58	–
Instructor	16	281
Total	191	281

Student Enrolment, 1989-90:

	Men	Women	Total
Of the country	5619	3370	8989
Of other countries	6	3	9
Total	5625	3323	8998

4554 **HAN SHIN UNIVERSITY**

Yangsan-ri, Osan-eup, Hwasong-gun, Kyonggi 445-8OO

Telephone: 45-8480

Founded 1940.

4555 **HANKOOK AVIATION UNIVERSITY**

200-1, Hwajon-ri, Hwajon-up, Koyang-gun, Kyonggi 411-910

Telephone: 372-5771

Fax: 307-5769

President: Hang-Wook Kim

Dean of Academic Affairs: Sang-Sin Yoo

D. of General Studies
Head: Chul-Se Shin; *staff* 8 (16)

D. of Flight Operation
Head: Yil-Kyoo Choi; *staff* 6 (2)

D. of Business Administration
Head: Gun-Ho Cha; *staff* 6 (8)

D. of Aeronautical Engineering
Head: Keun-Myung Lee; *staff* 7 (4)

D. of Telecommunication and Information Engineering
Head: Yun-Hyun Lee; *staff* 4 (7)

D. of Avionics Engineering
Head: Won-Hoo Kim; *staff* 4 (6)

D. of Aviation Administration
Head: Wan-Sik Choi; *staff* 3

D. of Materials Engineering
Head: Myong-Gwa Park; *staff* 3

D. of Mechanical Engineering and Design
Head: Sang-Sin Yoo; *staff* 3 (1)

D. of Computer Science
Head: Dong-Sohn Yoo; *staff* 3 (2)

Graduate S.
Head: Keun-Myung Lee; *staff* 13 (1)

D. of Telecommunication and Information Engineering
Head: Yun-Hyun Lee; *staff* 6

D. of Flight Operation and Administration
Head: Yil-Kyoo Choi; *staff* 15

Aviation Research Ce.
Head: Bong-Joon Lee; *staff* 19 (1)

I. for Electronic, Information and Telecommunication Development Research
Head: Byong Won Hwang; *staff* 11 (13)
I. for Aviation Industry and Policy Studies
Head: Soon-Kil Hong; *staff* 15 (1)
Computer Ce.
Also Aviation School and Aviation Personnel Training Centre.

Founded 1952 by Ministry of Transport. Administrative control transferred to Ministry of Education 1968. Transferred to Hanjin Group under government plan for systematizing the aviation-related circles 1978. Governing body: the Jung-Suck Foundation. Residential facilities for academic staff and students.

Arrangements for the exchanges for joint research with: Northrop University; Leningrad Academy of Civil Aviation; Institute of Air and Space Law; McGill University.

Academic Year: March to February (March-August; September-February).

Admission Requirements: Graduation from high school and entrance examination.

Fees (Won): 700,000 per semester.

Language of Instruction: Korean.

Degrees and Diplomas: Bachelor, 4 yrs. Master, a further 2 yrs. Doctor, Ph.D., 3 yrs after Master.

Library: Central Library, 60,000 vols.

Special Facilities (Museums, etc.): Aircraft Maintenance Workshop; Wireless Experiment Room; Air Traffic Control Station.

Publication: Collected Theses (biannually).

Press or Publishing House: Hankuk Aviation University Press.

Academic Staff, 1990:

Rank	Full-time	Part-time
Professors	24	8
Associate Professors	6	5
Assistant Professors	15	6
Instructors	8	22
Total	53	41

Student Enrolment, 1990:

Men	Women	Total
2198	202	2400

4556 **HANKOOK UNIVERSITY OF FOREIGN STUDIES**
270 Imun-dong, Tongdaemun-gu, Seoul 131-791
Telephone: 965-7001

C. of Occidental Studies
C. of Oriental Studies
C. of Law and Political Science
C. of Trade and Economics
C. of Education
C. of Liberal Arts and Natural Sciences
Graduate S.
Graduate S. of Interpretation and Translation
Graduate S. of International Trade
Graduate S. of Education
Language Research Ce.
Evening D.

Founded 1954 with the approval of the Ministry of Education. Receives some financial support from the government. Governing body: the Board of Trustees. Residential facilities for foreign academic staff.

Academic Year: March to December (March-July; September-December).

Admission Requirements: Graduation from high school or equivalent, and entrance examination.

Language of Instruction: Korean.

Degrees and Diplomas: Bachelor of Arts, B.A., 4 yrs; Master of Arts, M.A.; Master of Political Science, a further 2 yrs. Doctorate, Ph.D., in–Arts; Economics; Politics.

Library: Central Library, *c.* 180,600 vols.

Publication: Collections of articles (annually).

Press or Publishing House: University Press.

Academic Staff: c. 200 (180).

Student Enrolment: c. 11,600.

4557 **HANSUNG UNIVERSITY**
Samson-dong, Songbuk-gu, Seoul 136–042
Telephone: 742-2201

Founded 1972.

4558 ***HANYANG UNIVERSITY**
17 Haengdang-dong, Songdong-gu, Seoul 133-791
Telephone: 292-3111
President: Pyung Hee Lee

C. of Engineering
C. of Humanities
C. of Social Sciences
C. of Natural Sciences
C. of Home Economics
C. of Law
C. of Commerce and Economics
C. of Education
C. of Music
C. of Physical Education
C. of Medicine
C. of General Studies
Graduate S.
Graduate S. of Industrial Management
Graduate S. of Education
Graduate S. of Public Administration
Graduate S. of Business Administration
I. of Research of New Community Movement
Also 4 colleges at Panwol Campus, 13 research institutes, women's junior college and evening college of engineering, and elementary and high schools.

Founded 1939 as Dong-Ah Polytechnic Academy, reorganized as Kunkuk College 1945 and Hanyang College of Engineering 1948. Acquired present title and status 1956. A private institution financed by the Hanyang Educational Foundation. Governing body: the Board of Trustees. Residential facilities for academic staff and students.

Arrangements for co-operation with the Universities of: Texas (Tech); Georgetown; Southern Illinois; Toledo; Eastern Illinois; Windsor; Chengchi.

Academic Year: March to February (March-June; September-December).

Admission Requirements: Graduation from high school and entrance examination.

Language of Instruction: Korean.

Degrees and Diplomas: Bachelor in all fields, 4 yrs. Master, a further 2 yrs. Doctorate, 3 yrs after Master. Doctor of Medicine, 6 yrs.

Libraries: Central Library, *c.* 250,000 vols; College of Medicine library, *c.* 20,000; College of Engineering library, *c.* 30,000.

Publications: Institute Research Publication (biannually); Students' Papers (weekly, in Korean; monthly, in English).

Press or Publishing House: Hanyang Printing Press.

Academic Staff: c. 600.

Student Enrolment: c. 24,000.

4559 **HONAM UNIVERSITY**
Sangchon-dong 148, Seo-gu, Kwangiu 502-260
Telephone: (62) 34-8211
Fax: (62) 363-7500
President: In-Ok Yang

I. of East European Studies
Director: Yong Hwa Kim; *staff* 1 (5)
I. of Social Studies
Director: Yeo Song Yun; *staff* 1 (2)
I. of Industrial Administration
Director: Yun Hong Choi; *staff* 1 (16)

Founded 1981.

Academic Year: March to December (March-June; August December).

Admission Requirements: Graduation from high school and entrance examination.

Fees (Won): 917,000 per semester.

Language of Instruction: Korean.

Degrees and Diplomas: Bachelor, 4 yrs. Master, a further 2 yrs.

Libraries: Central Library, 81,640 vols; 2nd Campus Library, 18,126.

Academic Staff, 1989-90:

Rank	Full-time	Part-time
Professors	1	–
Associate Professors	33	–
Assistant Professors	47	–
Full-time Lecturers	20	–
Visiting Professors	–	3
Total	101	3

Student Enrolment, 1989-90:

	Men	Women	Total
Of the country	2385	1843	4228

4560 **HONG IK UNIVERSITY**

72-1 Sangsu-dong, Mapo-gu, Seoul 121-791
Telephone: 322-0151
President: Myeon Young Lee (1985-88)

C. of Engineering
Dean: Suk Yoon Kim; *staff* 53 (56)
C. of Business Administration and Economics
Dean: Sang-Pil Shim; *staff* 24 (20)
C. of Fine Arts
Dean: Seo Bo Park; *staff* 31 (95)
C. of Liberal Arts
Dean: Chong-Hiok Yoon; *staff* 21 (7)
C. of Education
Dean: Kyung Hwa Hong; *staff* 28 (71)
Graduate S.
Graduate S. of Industrial Arts
Graduate S. of Environmental Studies
Graduate S. of Education
I. of Environmental Studies
Director: Myung Hyan Chun; *staff* 10 (2)
Computer Ce.
Also 8 research institutes, and junior college and primary and high schools.

Founded 1946 as college, incorporated Soo-Do Engineering College and acquired university status 1971. A private institution. Governing body: the Board of Trustees.

Arrangements for co-operation with: Osaka University of Arts; Connecticut State Central College; College of Chinese Culture, Taipei.

Academic Year: March to February (March-July; September-December).

Admission Requirements: Graduation from high school and entrance examination.

Language of Instruction: Korean.

Degrees and Diplomas: Bachelor of–Arts, B.A.; Fine Arts, B.F.A.; Economics, B.E.; Science, B.S.; Engineering, B.E.; Business Administration, B.B.A., 4 yrs. Master, a further 2 yrs. Doctorate, PhD., 3 yrs after Master.

Library: Central Library, *c.* 250,000 vols.

Special Facilities (Museums, etc.): University Museum.

Publications: Management Review (annually); Journal of Educational Development (annually).

Press or Publishing House: University Press.

Academic Staff, 1986-87:

Rank	Full-time	Part-time
Gyosu (Professors)	74	
Bu-gyosu (Associate Professors)	36	
Jo-gyosu (Assistant Professors)	24	
Jeon-nim-gangsa (Lecturers)	23	
Total	157	249

Student Enrolment, 1986-87:

	Men	Women	Total
Of the country	9300	2910	12,210

4561 **HYOSUNG WOMEN'S UNIVERSITY**

Kumrak-dong, Hayang-eup, Kyungsan-gun, Kyungbuk 713-900

C. of Liberal Arts and Sciences
C. of Law and Political Science
C. of Education
C. of Pharmacy
C. of Art
C. of Home Economics
Graduate S.

Founded 1952.

4562 ***IN HA UNIVERSITY**

253 Yonghyon-dong, Nam-gu, Inchon 402-751
Telex: 32771 INHAUNI K
Telephone: 862-0077
President: Tai Won Park

C. of Engineering
C. of Natural Sciences
C. of Business Administration and Economics
C. of Law and Public Administration
C. of Liberal Arts and Sciences
C. of Education
Graduate S. of Education
Graduate S. of Business Administration
Also 5 Research Institutes.

Founded 1954 as Institute of Technology, became university 1971. A private institution. Governing bodies: the Board of Trustees; the University Council.

Academic Year: March to December (March-July; August-December).

Admission Requirements: Graduation from high school and entrance examination.

Language of Instruction: Korean.

Degrees and Diplomas: Bachelor of–Arts; Science, 4 yrs. Master of–Arts; Science; Education; Business Administration, a further 2-3yrs. Doctor of–Literature; Engineering; Science.

Library: c. 200,000 vols.

Academic Staff: c. 200 (100).

Student Enrolment: c. 13,200.

4563 **INCHEON UNIVERSITY**

177 Towha-dong, Nam-gu, Incheon 402-749
Telephone: 74-5301

F. of Humanities
F. of Natural Sciences (including Home Economics and Physical Education)
F. of Social Sciences (including Law and Political Science)
F. of Engineering (including Architecture)
F. of Business Administration
National Unification Research Ce.
Research Ce. of New Community Movement
Industrial Development Research Ce.
Foreign Language I.
Also technical college, and kindergarten, primary, middle and high schools.

Founded 1979. A private institution supervised by the Sunin Academic Foundation.

Academic Year: March to February (March-August; September-February).

Admission Requirements: Graduation from high school and entrance examination.

Language of Instruction: Korean.

Degrees and Diplomas: Bachelor, 4 yrs.

Library: c. 8500 vols.

Publications: Collections of Papers (annually); University Press (monthly).

Press or Publishing House: University Press.

Academic Staff: c. 70 (20).

Student Enrolment: c. 1960.

4564 **INJE UNIVERSITY**

18-3, Obang-dong, Kimhae, Kyongsangnam-do 621-749
Telephone: (51) 463-1341
Fax: (525) 34-0712
President: Nak Hwan Paik
Director of General Affairs: Young Euy Choi

C. of Medicine
Dean: Duck Whan Chung: *staff* 191 (104)
C. of Natural Sciences
Dean: Jung Tai Shin; *staff* 52 (32)
C. of Humanities and Social Sciences (Korean, English and Chinese Language and Literature, Business Administration, International Trade, Economics, Law, Health Management)
Dean: Kook Hyon Um; *staff* 27 (43)
C. of Public Health
Medical I.
Director: Soon Yong Lee; *staff* 8
I. of Medical Sciences
Director: Yong Je Choo; *staff* 2

I. of Industrial Medicine
Director: Duck Hwan Moon; *staff* 2 (10)
I. of Basic Sciences
Director: Sang Joon Choi; *staff* 1 (33)
Also 3 attached Hospitals.

Founded as College 1979. Acquired present status and title 1989. A private institution. Governing body: the Inje Educational Foundation. Residential facilities for students.

Arrangements for co-operation with the University of Hawaii.

Academic Year: March to February (March-August; September-February).

Admission Requirements: Graduation from high school and entrance examination.

Fees (Won): 960,000-744,000 per semester.

Language of Instruction: Korean.

Degrees and Diplomas: Bachelor, 4 yrs. Master, a further 2 yrs. Doctor, Ph.D., 3-4 yrs after Master. Doctor of Medicine, M.D., 6 yrs.

Library: 125,000 vols.

Publications: In Je Medical Journal (quarterly); In Je Newspaper (quarterly); Bulletin (monthly); In Je Journal (biannually).

Press or Publishing House: University Press.

Academic Staff, 1990:

Rank	Full-time	Part-time
Professors	53	–
Associate Professors	40	–
Assistant Professors	101	–
Instructors	83	184
Total	277	184

Student Enrolment, 1990:

	Men	Women	Total
Of the country	2339	1700	4039

4565 **INTERNATIONAL UNIVERSITY**
Chongneung-dong, Songbuk-gu, Seoul 136-104
Telephone: 919-0411

Founded 1955.

4566 **JEON JU UNIVERSITY**
Hyoja-dong, Chonju CT, Chonbuk 560-759
Telephone: 6-5011

D. of Korean Language and Literature
D. of English Language and Literature
D. of Law
D. of Home Economics
D. of Commerce
Founded 1964.

4567 **JEONJU WOOSUK UNIVERSITY**
Hujong-ri, Samrae-eup, Wanju-gun, Chonbuk 565-800
Telephone: 73-8001

S. of Humanities
S. of Social Sciences
S. of Education
S. of Science
S. of Pharmacy
S. of Home Economics
S. of Physical Education and Art
Graduate S.
Evening S.

Founded 1979. Residential facilities for students.

Academic Year: March to February (March-August; September-February).

Admission Requirements: Graduation from high school and entrance examination.

Language of Instruction: Korean.

Degrees and Diplomas: Bachelor of Arts, 4 yrs. Master of Arts. Master of Science in Pharmacy.

Library: c. 60,000 vols.

Special Facilities (Museums, etc.): College Museum.

Academic Staff: c. 90 (50).

Student Enrolment: c. 4000.

4568 **KEIMYUNG UNIVERSITY**
2139 Taemyung-dong, Taegu 705-701
Telephone: (53) 626-1321
Fax: (53) 623-9935
President: Ilhi Synn (1988-)
Senior Administrative Officer for Academic Affairs: Yung Tae Kim

C. of Humanities (including Korean, Chinese, Japanese, English, German, French, Language and Literature, Philosophy, National Ethics, and Theology)
Dean: Hi Sup Kim
C. of Teacher Training
Dean: Moon Yong Lee
C. of Foreign Studies
Dean: Kil Sung Choi
C. of Business Administration (including Accountancy)
Dean: Bong Jin Cho
C. of Social Sciences (including Economics, International Trade, Public Administration, Mass Communication, Psychology, and Library Science)
Dean: Gu Ho Yun
C. of Law
Dean: Jin Yuhn Jung
C. of Natural Sciences (including Statistics, Microbiology, Public Health, Food Science and Technology, and Pre-Medicine)
Dean: Eui Rak Kim
C. of Engineering (including Architectural, Urban, Industrial, Chemical, Material, and Transport Engineering)
Dean: Jong Woo Lee
S. of Medicine (including Pharmacy and Nursing)
Dean: Jin Sung Kang
C. of Home Economics (including Food Science)
Dean: Pil Sook Huh
C. of Music
Dean: Sang Dae Kim
C. of Fine Arts
Dean: Yung Ryung Lee
C. of Physical Education
Dean: Yung Sang Pae
I. for International Education
Director: Yong Sang Cho
I. for Industrial Management
Director: Byung Ha Kim
I. for Domestic Science
Director: Duk Hwan Ryu
I. for German Studies
Director: Ki Do Kim
I. for Japanese Studies
Director: Kil Sung Choi
I. for Chinese Studies
Director: Jong Dong Hwang
I. for Educational Studies
Director: Deuk Ryul Synn
I. for Industrial Technology
Director: Jong Sik Kim
I. for Mathematical Science
Director: Nam Sik Lee
I. for Natural Sciences
Director: Dae Sik Yu
Research I. for Social Sciences
Director: Dae In Kang
I. for Medical Science
Director: Young Uk Suh
I. for Arts and Culture
Director: Won Kyung Kim
I. for Theological Studies
Director: Sung Chan Choi
I. for Local Communication
Director: Sey Chul Kim
East-West Ce.
Director: Chang Suk Pak
Ce. for Behavioural Sciences
Director: Yung Chae Kim
Evening C.
Dean: Yung Tae Kim
I. for Lifelong Education
Director: Jung Bin Lee
Also 16 research institutes.

Founded 1954 by the Presbyterian Church in Korea as a small Christian liberal arts college. Received charter from the government 1956 and became University 1978. Residential facilities for academic staff.

Arrangements for co-operation with the Universities of: Missouri; Rhode Island; Long Island; St. Andrew's, Japan; National Taiwan Normal. Whitworth College, Spokane.

Academic Year: March to December (March-June; August-December).

Admission Requirements: Graduation from high school or recognized equivalent, and entrance examination.

Fees (Won): Tuition, 1,500,000 per annum.

Language of Instruction: Korean.

Degrees and Diplomas: Bachelor of Arts and Science in–Literature; Divinity; Business Administration; Economics; Laws; Public Administration; Science; Engineering; Home Economics; Music; Fine Arts, 4 yrs; Medicine, 6 yrs. Master, a further 2 yrs. Doctor of–Literature; Philosophy; Education; Business Administration; History; Economics; Accountancy; Engineering, 3 yrs after Master.

Library: Dong San Memorial Library, 300,000 vols.

Special Facilities (Museums, etc.): University Museum (including Kaya Kingdom relics).

Publications: Journal of Cross-Cultural Studies; Business Management Review; Journal of Japanese Studies; Journal of Community and Adult Education; Zeitschrift für Deutsche Studien; Research Review; Industrial Technology Bulletin (all annually).

Press or Publishing House: The Keimyung University Press.

Academic Staff, 1990:

Rank	Full-time
Gyosu (Professors)	111
Bu-gyosu (Associate Professors)	167
Jo-gyosu (Assistant Professors)	132
Jeon-nim-gangsa (Instructors)	25
Total	435

Student Enrolment, 1990:

	Men	Women	Total
Of the country	9454	6219	15,673

4569 **KING SEJONG UNIVERSITY**

Kunja-dong, Songdong-gu, Seoul 133-150

Telephone: 467-5121

Founded 1954.

4570 ***KONKUK UNIVERSITY**

93-1, Mojin-dong, Seongdong-gu, Seoul 133-701

Telephone: 457-0061

Fax: (2) 452-3094

President: Yong-han Kim (1988-)

Director of Academic Affairs: Chang-han Kim

C. of Liberal Arts (including Korean, English, German, French, and Chinese Languages and Literature)

Dean: Do-hee Choi; *staff* 46 (77)

C. of Sciences

Dean: Myon-yong Park; *staff* 22 (22)

C. of Engineering (including Architectural, Civil, Mechanical, Electrical, Electronic, Industrial, Chemical, Textile, Microbiological, Environment, and Space Engineering, and Industrial Chemistry)

Dean: Tae-woong Ko; *staff* 56 (31)

C. of Law and Political Science

Dean: Dong-hee Park; *staff* 8 (33)

C. of Commerce and Economics

Dean: Yong-kuk Kim; *staff* 28 (17)

C. of Animal Husbandry

Dean: Won-jae Maeng; *staff* 32 (9)

C. of Agriculture (including Forestry and Horticulture)

Dean: Ki-joon Kim; *staff* 21 (10)

C. of Arts and Home Economics

Dean: In-ja Lee; *staff* 15 (10)

C. of Education (including Foreign Language Education, Mathematics, Physical Education, and Music)

Dean: Choong-ki Kim; *staff* 28 (55)

C. of Humanities (including Korean, English, German, and French Languages and Literature; and Library Science)

Dean: Yong-sik Park; *staff* 21 (17)

C. of Social Sciences (including Law, Public Administration, Mass Communication, Economics, Business Administration, and International Trade)

Dean: Seong-chan Hong; *staff* 22 (11)

C. of Natural Sciences

Dean: Hyung-ha Kim; *staff* 29 (16)

C. of Medicine

Dean: In-seong Lee; *staff* 57 (33)

C. of Political Science

Dean: Chang-ho Choi; *staff* 22

C. of Art and Design

Dean: Ha-sin Chung; *staff* 12 (20)

I. of Humanities

I. of Industrial Science and Technology

Agriculture Development I.

I. of Economics and Management

I. for Genetic Engineering

I. of Environmental Studies

I. of Basic Sciences

I. of Social Sciences

I. of Public Administration Affairs

I. of Animal Husbandry

I. of Arts and Home Economics

I. of Education

I. of Cheongwon Humanities

I. of Social Policy

I. of Natural Sciences

I. of Formative Arts

I. of Medical Sciences

I. of Chinese Affairs

I. of Real Estate Policy

Founded 1946 as Cho-Sun Political Science School, acquired present status and title 1959. A private institution financed by the Kon-Kuk University Foundation, but supervised by the Ministry of Education. Residential facilities for foreign academic staff and students.

Arrangements for co-operation with: Free University of Berlin; University of Hohenheim; Ben Gurion University of the Negev; Tung Hai University; Chinese Culture University; National Chung Hsing University, Taichung; Catholic University of America; California State University, Fresno; University of Akron; Obihiro University; University of British Columbia; University of Quebec; Hebrew University of Jerusalem; Israel Institute of Technology, Technion.

Academic Year: March to December (March-June; September-December).

Admission Requirements: Graduation from high school and entrance examination.

Fees (Won): Tuition, 1,600,000 per annum

Language of Instruction: Korean.

Degrees and Diplomas: Bachelor of–Literature; Science; Engineering; Political Sciences; Law; Public Administration; Economics; Management; Commerce; Agriculture; Veterinary Medicine; Home Economics; Physics; Fine Art, 4 yrs; Medicine, 6 yrs. Master of–Political Science; Economics; Law; Public Administration; Management; Literature; Science; Agriculture; Engineering, a further 2 yrs. Doctor of–Literature; Philosophy; Economics; Law; Science; Agriculture; Political Science, a further 3 yrs.

Library: Central Library, *c.* 400,000 vols.

Special Facilities (Museums, etc.): Kon-Kuk Museum.

Publication: Journals of the Research Institutes.

Press or Publishing House: University Press.

Academic Staff, 1990-91:

Rank	Full-time	Part-time
Gyosu (Professors)	188	–
Bu-gyosu (Associate Professors)	115	–
Jo-gyosu (Assistant Professors)	92	–
Gangsa (Lecturers)	30	463
Total	425	463

Student Enrolment, 1990-91:

	Men	Women	Total
Of the country	14,772	4508	19,280
Of other countries	6	6	12
Total	14,778	4514	19,292

4571 **KOOKMIN UNIVERSITY**
861-1 Chongnung-dong, Songbuk-gu, Seoul 136-702
Telephone: 914-3141
President: Bom-suk Chung (1979-85)

C. of Liberal Arts
Dean: Du-ha Jeon; *staff* 33 (63)
C. of Law and Political Science
Dean: Jae-yoon Park; *staff* 25 (21)
C. of Economics and Business Administration
Dean: Oh-youn Oh; *staff* 22 (25)
C. of Engineering
Dean: Tai-yoon Yoon; *staff* 27 (12)
C. of Architecture and Design
Dean: Chul-soo Kim; *staff* 22 (36)
C. of Education
Dean: Joong-shik Shin; *staff* 28 (49)
C. of Forestry
Also 12 research institutes.

Founded 1946 as night college, acquired present status and title 1981. A private institution financed by the Kookmin Foundation, but supervised by the Ministry of Education.

Arrangements for co-operation with: University of Chinese Culture, Taipei; National Chung Hsing University, Taichung; Tunghai University; Taichung; National Kaohsiun Normal College; University of Iowa; Texas Southern University; Appalachian State University; University of Alabama; Winthrop College, South Carolina; Santa Clara University; Willamette University.

Academic Year: March to February (March-August; September-February).

Admission Requirements: Graduation from high school, or recognized equivalent, and entrance examination.

Fees (Won): 1.3m per annum.

Language of Instruction: Korean.

Degrees and Diplomas: Bachelor in all fields, 4 yrs. Master, a further 2 yrs. Doctor, Ph.D., a further 6 yrs.

Library: Central Library, 200,000 vols.

Publications: Law and Political Review; Economics and Business Review; Thesis of Engineering; Thesis of Korean Studies; Papers in Chinese Studies; Journal of Language and Literature; Design Review; Journal of Scientific Institute.

Press or Publishing House: University Press.

Academic Staff, 1986-87:

Rank	Full-time	Part-time
Gyosu (Professors)	55	
Bu-gyosu (Associate Professors)	52	
Jo-gyosu (Assistant Professors)	41	
Gangsa (Lecturers)	9	
Total	157	206

Student Enrolment, 1986-87:

	Men	Women	Total
Of the country	5793	1827	7620
Of other countries	6	–	6
Total	5799	1827	7626

4572 **KOREA UNIVERSITY**
1,5-ka, Anam-dong, Sungbuk-gu, Seoul 136-701
Telex: KOREA KU 34138
Telephone: (2) 920-1114
Fax: (2) 922-5820
President (Acting): Chin-Woong Kim (1989-)

C. of Law
Dean: Tal-Kon Choi; *staff* 18
C. of Business Administration (including Accountancy)
Dean: Dong-Ki Kim; *staff* 23
C. of Liberal Arts
Dean: Il-Chul Shinn; *staff* 90
C. of Agriculture (including Forestry, Horticulture, Animal Husbandry, and Food Technology)
Dean: Sung-Bok Kim; *staff* 35
C. of Political Sciences and Economics
Dean: Ki-Shik Han; *staff* 40
C. of Science (including Computer Science)
Dean: Woo-Kap Kim; *staff* 39
C. of Engineering (including Architecture)
Dean: Dong-Sup Doh; *staff* 45
C. of Medicine (including Nursing and Midwifery)
Dean: Sae-Min Kim; *staff* 184
C. of Education
Dean: Sang-Kyem Kim; *staff* 38
Graduate S.
Dean: Bae-Ho Hahn
Graduate S. of Business Administration
Dean: Hae-Chun Kim
Graduate S. of Education
Dean: In-Jong You
Graduate S. of Food and Agriculture
Dean: Beyoung-Hwa Kwack
Also 26 research institutes and junior college.

Founded 1905 as Posung College, acquired present status and title 1946. A private institution operated by the Korea-Choongang Educational Foundation but supervised by the Ministry of Education. Governing body: the University Council. Residential facilities for students.

Arrangements for co-operation with the Universities of: Waseda; Washington, Seattle.

Academic Year: March to December (March-July; August-December).

Admission Requirements: Graduation from high school or equivalent, and entrance examination.

Fees (Won): Registration, 800,000; tuition, 700,000 per semester.

Language of Instruction: Korean.

Degrees and Diplomas: Bachelor of Arts in–Law; Public Administration; Liberal Arts; Education; Business Administration; Arts; Agriculture; Political Sciences; Economics; Science; Engineering; Medicine, 4 yrs. Master, a further 2 yrs. Doctorate, Ph.D. in–Law; Political Sciences, Business Administration; Liberal Arts; History; Psychology; Sociology; Philosophy; Economics; Education; Science; Engineering; Medicine; Agriculture, 3 yrs after Master. Also teaching qualification, and Certificates in–Business Administration; Education; Food Technology and Agriculture.

Libraries: Central Library, *c.* 500,000 vols; Medicine, *c.* 30,000; Science, *c.* 120,000; Graduate School, 80,000.

Special Facilities (Museums, etc.): Museum of Korean Antiquities.

Publications: The Kodai Shinmoon (University Newspaper); The Granite Tower (English Newspaper); Kodai Munwha (Culture); the Phoenix (English Department); Sa Chong (Historical Review); Journal of Asiatic Studies.

Press or Publishing House: University Press.

Academic Staff: c. 530 (680).

Student Enrolment: c. 23,400.

4573 **KOREAN CHRISTIAN COLLEGE**
Deungchon-dong, Kangso-gu, Seoul 157-010
Telephone: 605-2989

Founded 1958.

4574 **KOREAN SAHMYOOK UNIVERSITY**
223Kongneung 2-dong, Nohwon-gu, Seoul 139-742
Cables: adventist, aeoul, korea
Telex: KUM SDA K 25329
Telephone: (2) 972-3606 12
Fax: (2) 979-5318
President: Chong Wha Kim
Academic Dean: Hong Ryang Kim

D. of Theology
Director: Hai Chong Pak; *staff* 15
D. of English Language and Literature
Director: Deuk Ki Ahn; *staff* 8 (4)
D. of Business Administration
Director: Joon Hwan Choi; *staff* 4 (2)
D. of Nursing
Director: Bok Ja Oh; *staff* 4 (5)
D. of Pharmacy
Director: Chong Hwa Lee; *staff* 5 (8)
D. of Nutrition
Director: Sang Up Lee; *staff* 3 (3)
D. of Chemistry
Director: Chong Byok Choi; *staff* 4 (5)
D. of Music
Director: Moon Yang Cho; *staff* 3 (29)

D. of Biology
Director: Kang Oh Lee; *staff* 3 (3)
D. of Horticulture
Director: Sank Kyung Han; *staff* 2 (2)
D. of Industrial Education
S. of Graduate Studies
Dean: Hai Chong Pak
Theological Research I.
Director: Dae Keuk Nam; *staff* 13 (2)
Evangelistic Research I.
Director: Hyun Chui Shin; *staff* 9
Christian Education Research I.
Director: Young Il Cho; *staff* 2
Behavioural Science Research I.
Director: Hong Ryang Kim; *staff* 5 (2)
Life Science Research I.
Director: Kang Oh Lee; *staff* 8 (1)
Language Research I.
Director: Deuk Ki Ahn; *staff* 7 (1)
Basic Science Research I.
Director: Chong Byok Choi; *staff* 4 (2)
Also agricultural and nursing junior colleges, and seminary.

Founded as Seventh-day Adventist Denominational Training School 1906, became college 1961 and university 1985.Graduate School established 1981. Governing bodies: the Board of Management; the Executive Board. Residential facilities for academic staff and 189 men and 162 women students.

Arrangements for co-operation with: Pacific Union Colege, California; Philippines Union College.

Academic Year: March to February (March-July; August-December).

Admission Requirements: Graduation from high school and entrance examination.

Language of Instruction: Korean.

Degrees and Diplomas: Bachelor of–Arts; Science; Business Administration; Music; Theology, 4 yrs. Master, a further 2 yrs. Also junior college diplomas, 2-3 yrs.

Library: Central Library, 80,000 vols.

Publications: Korean Sahmyook University Journal; Sahmyook Hag Bo (monthly); Sahmyook Herald (bimonthly).

Academic Staff, 1990:

Rank	Full-time
Professors	23
Associate Professors	25
Assistant Professors	14
Instructors	8
Total	70

Student Enrolment, 1990:

	Men	Women	TotaL
Of the country	830	1387	2217
Of other countries	3	1	4
Total	833	1388	2221

4575 **KOREAN TOURISM UNIVERSITY**
Hyohyen-dong, Kyongju CT, Kyungbuk 780-210
Telephone: 3-5558

Founded 1988.

4576 **KOSIN COLLEGE**
Dongsam-dong, Youngdo-gu, Busan 606-080
Telephone: (11-82-51) 257-5133
President: Ho Jim Jun

D. of Natural Sciences (including Health Science, Biology, Nutrition, Mathematics, Chemistry, Home Management, and Nursing)
Dean: Yong Dae Hong; *staff* 36
D. of Medicine
Dean: Jong Dak Lee; *staff* 98
D. of Theology
Dean: Sung Lin Kim; *staff* 23
Graduate S.
Director: Ga Tae Han
Graduate S. of Theology
Director: Sun Gin Ho
Also College Hospital.

Founded 1970. A private institution operated by the Presbyterian Church of Korea.

Academic Year: March to December (March-July; September-Dcember).

Admission Requirements: Graduation from high school and entrance examination.

Fees (Won): 1,200,000 per annum.

Language of Instruction: Korean.

Degrees and Diplomas: Bachelor of–Arts; Science, 4 yrs; Medicine, 6 yrs. Master, a further 2 yrs. Doctor, Ph.D. in Medicine, 3 yrs after Master.

Library: Total, 80,350 vols.

Special Facilities (Museums, etc.): Educational Broadcasting Station.

Academic Staff, 1989-90: 161 (156).

Student Enrolment, 1989-90:

	Men	Women	Total
Of the country	1164	1251	3915

4577 **KUM-OH INSTITUTE OF TECHNOLOGY**
188 Shinpyung-dong, Kumi CT, Kyung Buk 730-701
Telephone: (546) 461-0131-9
Fax: (546) 461-0136
President: Hyun Ki Paik (1989-)

D. of Mechanical Engineering
Head: Joong-cheol Bang; *staff* 5 (4)
F. of Mechanical and Production Engineering
Head: Sung-dong Kim; *staff* 5 (1)
D. of Mechanical and Precision Engineering
Head: Joong-Youn Park; *staff* 4 (2)
D. of Engineering Science and Mechanics
Head: Eun-Ha Hwang; *staff* 5 (3)
D. of Electronic Engineering
Head: Jeon Heung Woo; *staff* 6 (3)
D. of Electronics Communication
Head: Saw Dong Shin; *staff* 4 (1)
D. of Electronic and Control Engineering
Head: Chang Hyun Chae; *staff* 4 (2)
D. of Architectural Engineering
Head: Yoon Keun Kwak; *staff* 5 (3)
Civil Engineering D.
Head: Han Sang Mook; *staff* 5 (4)
D. of Industrial Engineering
Head: Hoekyun Shin; *staff* 6 (6)
D. of Polymer Science and Engineering
Head: Hyun Park; *staff* 5 (4)
D. of Materials Science and Engineering
Head: Sung-Jin Kim; *staff* 2 (4)
D. of Applied Mathematics
Head: Hong Taek Hwang; *staff* 5 (6)
Research I. of Manufacturing Productivity
Head: Young Tae Kim; *staff* 5 (20)
Community Research I.
Head: Yong Hyun Choi; *staff* 1 (1)
Ce. for Continuing Education
Head: Yong Hyun Choi; *staff* 1 (50)
Graduate S.
Head: Sim Woo Jin; *staff* 45 (1)
Graduate S. of Industry
Head: Yoon Dong Han; *staff* 50
Computer Engineering Ce.
Head: Yoons Ik Shin; *staff* 7 (1)

Founded 1979. A State institution under the jurisdiction of the Ministry of Education. Financially supported by the government and tuition fees. Residential facilities for academic staff and for students.

Academic Year: March to February (March-August; September-February).

Admission Requirements: Graduation from high school and entrance examination.

Language of Instruction: Korean.

Degrees and Diplomas: Bachelor, 4 yrs. Master, a further 2 yrs.

Library: c. 15,000 vols.

Publications: Newspaper; Academic Journal (annually).

Academic Staff, 1989-90: c. 60.

Student Enrolment, 1989-90: c. 4000.

4578 **KWAN DONG UNIVERSITY**
72-1 Naegok-dong, Kangreung CT, Kangwon 210-160
Telephone: 3-7721

C. of Education
C. of Humanities
C. of Social Sciences (including Law, Administration, and Economics)
C. of Engineering (including Architecture)
Evening C.

Founded 1955 as junior college, acquired present status and title 1959.

Academic Year: March to February (March-September; September-February).

Admission Requirements: Graduation from high school and entrance examination.

Language of Instruction: Korean.

Degrees and Diplomas: Bachelor of–Humanities; Natural Science; Engineering; Physical Education; Fine Arts; Music; Business Administration; Economics, 4 yrs.

Library: Central Library, 100,000 vols.

Academic Staff: c. 110 (50).

Student Enrolment: c. 6200.

4579 **KWANGJU CATHOLIC COLLEGE**
Sangchon-dong, So-gu, Kwangju 502-260
Telephone: (62) 365-5111
Fax: (62) 365-6444
President: Sylvester Pang, J.C.L. (1985-)
Registrar: Francis Ahn, S.T.L.

C. of Theology and Philosophy
Head: Francis Ahn, S.T.L.; *staff* 19 (4)
Graduate S.

Founded 1962. Residential facilities for 18 priests and 250 students.

Academic Year: March to February (March-August; September-February).

Admission Requirements: Graduation from high school and entrance examination.

Fees (US$): 3400 per annum.

Language of Instruction: Korean.

Degrees and Diplomas: Bachelor of Theology, 4 yrs; Master, a further 2 yrs.

Library: 56,000 vols.

Academic Staff, 1990: 19 (4).

4580 **KWANGWOON UNIVERSITY**
447-1 Wolkye-dong, Nowon-gu, Seoul 139-050
Telephone: 918-1021
President: Kook Chull Seo (1985-88)
Director of the Office of Planning and Management: Soo Il Jeon

D. of Engineering
Head: Dong Chan Moon; *staff* 35 (12)
D. of Natural Sciences (including Computer Science)
Head: Jae Hong Shim; *staff* 12 (15)
D. of Business Administration and Economics
Head: Chun Sik Kim; *staff* 15 (7)
D. of Law and Political Science
Head: Gye Hwan Kim; *staff* 14 (8)
D. of Social Sciences
Graduate S.
Dean: Sang Man Kim; *staff* 20 (12)
Graduate S. of Engineering and Management Information
Dean: Chang Ook Kim; *staff* 18 (7)
Also kindergarten, middle and high schools.

Founded 1962 as Institute of Technology, acquired present status and title 1983. A private institution operated by the Kwangwoon Foundation but supervised by the Ministry of Education.

Academic Year: March to February (March-August; September-February).

Admission Requirements: Graduation from high school and entrance examination.

Fees (Won): 578,500-585-500 per semester.

Language of Instruction: Korean.

Degrees and Diplomas: Bachelor of–Engineering; Science; Business and Economics; Law and Political Science, 4 yrs. Master, a further2 yrs. Doctorate, Ph.D..

Library: Central Library, 110,000 vols.

Academic Staff, 1986-87:

Rank	Full-time	Part-time
Gyosu (Professors)	28	–
Bu-gyosu (Associate Professors)	21	47
Jo-gyosu (Assistant Professors)	32	60
Gangsa (Lecturers)	15	–
Total	96	107

Student Enrolment, 1986-87:

	Men	Women	Total
Of the country	4315	172	4487

4581 **KYONGGI UNIVERSITY**
Iui-ri, Suji-myon, Yongin-gun, Kyonggi 449-840
Telephone: 6-2175

D. of Physical Education
D. of Korean Language and Literature
D. of English Language and Literature
D. of Tourism
D. of Business Administration
D. of Public Administration
D. of International Trade
D. of Tourism Development
D. of Accountancy
D. of Civil Engineering
D. of Architecture
D. of Industrial Management
I. of Production Management
I. of Tourism Development (Hotel Administration)
I. of Social Studies
I. of American Culture and Language
I. of Chinese Studies

Founded 1956 as Teacher Training College, acquired present status and title 1976. A private institution financed by tuition fees and Foundation support. Residential facilities for *c.* 150 students.

Academic Year: March to February (March-August; September-February).

Admission Requirements: Graduation from high school and entrance examination.

Language of Instruction: Korean.

Degrees and Diplomas: Bachelor of Arts in–Korean Language and Literature; English Language and Literature; Physical Education; Tourism; Business Administration; International Trade; Tourism Development; Accountancy; Public Administration, 4 yrs. Bachelor of Science in–Architecture; Civil Engineering; Industrial Management, 4 yrs.

Library: c. 60,000 vols.

Publications: Research Journals (annually); Study on Tourism; Journal of Industrial Business Problems; Kyonggi Magazine.

Academic Staff: c. 60 (90).

Student Enrolment: c. 2020.

4582 **KYUNG HEE UNIVERSITY**
Hoegi-dong, Dongdaemun-ku, Seoul 130-701
Telephone: (2) 961-0114
Fax: (2) 962-4343
Chancellor: Young Seek Choue

C. of Liberal Arts and Science (including Korean and English Languages and Literature, History, Philosophy, Physics, Chemistry, Biology, Geography, and Mathematics)
Dean: Tae Young Kim
C. of Law
Dean: Byung Mook Kim
C. of Political Sciences and Economics (including Business Administration, Mass Communication, Trade and Accountancy)
Dean: Kee Ho Chun
C. of Education
Dean: Jae Bong Yoo
C. of Medicine
Dean: Young Han Baek
C. of Oriental Medicine
Dean: Wan Hee Kim
C. of Dentistry
Dean: Han Kook Cho
C. of Pharmacy
Dean: Shin Kyu Kim

C. of Foreign Languages and Literature (including English, French, Chinese, Japanese, and Spanish Languages and Literature)
Dean: Tae Young Bae
C. of Social Sciences (including Public Administration, Business Administration, and International Trade)
Dean: Kea Tak Lee
C. of Music
Dean: Bong Lim Kim
C. of Natural Sciences
Dean: Hee Chan Choi
Graduate S.
Dean: Jong Il Ra
C. of Engineering (Mechanical, Textile, Electronic, Chemical, Architectural, Civil, Industrial, Nuclear, and Computer Engineering)
Dean: Jong Nam Kim
C. of Industry (Agriculture, Forestry, Horticulture, Food Processing, Landscape Architecture, Ceramic Arts, and Industrial Arts)
Dean: Shin Han Kwon
C. of Physical Education and Sports
Dean: Sang Kook Kim
S. of Nursing
International C. of Hotel Administration
Graduate S. of Education
Dean: Byung Oh Won
Graduate S. of Public Administration
Dean: Sae Duk Oh
Graduate S. of Business Administration
Dean: Jung Kyu Lee
Graduate I. of Peace Studies
Graduate S. of Technology and International Sciences
Dean: Dae Young Lee
Graduate S. of Journalism and Mass Communication
Dean: Byung Ku Hahn
Also 26 affiliated Research Centres, University and Dental Hospitals, Oriental Hospital, and kindergarten, elementary, and high schools.

Founded 1949 as Shin Hung College, acquired present status and title 1951. A private institution. Financially supported by private business interests. Governing body: the Board of Trustees. Residential facilities for some academic staff.

Academic Year: March to December (March-July; September-December).

Admission Requirements: Graduation from high school and entrance examination.

Languages of Instruction: Korean and some English.

Degrees and Diplomas: Bachelor in all fields of study, 4 yrs. Master, a further 2 ½ yrs. Degree of Doctor, 3 yrs after Master.

Library: Central Library and branch libraries, *c.* 130,000 vols.

Special Facilities (Museums, etc.): University Museum; Natural History Museum; Computer Centre; Audio-visual Education Centre; Bureau of Mass Communication; Central Laboratory for Instrumental Analysis; Crown Concert Hall.

Publications: College publications; Research Institutes' magazines.

Press or Publishing House: Kyung Hee University Press.

Academic Staff, 1989: c. 1070.

Student Enrolment, 1989: c. 25,000.

4583 **KYUNGNAM UNIVERSITY**
449 Wolyong-dong, Masan CT 630-260
Telephone: 2-8112

C. of Liberal Arts and Science
C. of Education
C. of Commerce and Economics
C. of Law and Political Science
C. of Engineering (including Architecture)
Graduate S.
Graduate S. of Education
Graduate S. of Business Administration
I. for Far Eastern Studies
I. of Industrial Management
I. of Environmental Research

Founded 1946 as school in Seoul. Moved to Masan 1954 and acquired present status and title 1982. A private institution. Governing body: the Board of Trustees. Residential facilities for students.

Arrangements for co-operation with the University of Iowa.

Academic Year: March to February (March-August; September-February).

Admission Requirements: Graduation from high school and entrance examination.

Language of Instruction: Korean.

Degrees and Diplomas: Bachelor, 4 yrs. Master in–Business Administration; Economics; Korean Language and Literature; English Language and Literature; Law; Political Administration; Diplomatic Science; Physical Education, a further 2 yrs. Doctor of–Economics; Law; Political Administration; Diplomatic Science, at least a further 3 yrs.

Library: c. 160,000 vols.

Special Facilities (Museums, etc.): Collection from local excavations.

Publications: Kyungnam Times; Korean University Newspaper.

Press or Publishing House: University Printing Department.

Academic Staff: c. 230 (190).

Student Enrolment: c. 15,500.

4584 **KYUNGSUNG UNIVERSITY**
Taeyon-dong, Nam-gu, Busan 608-020
Telephone: 622-5331

Founded 1955.

4585 **KYUNGWON UNIVERSITY**
Pokjon-dong, Songnam CT, Kyonggi 461-200
Telephone: 752-3220

Founded 1981.

4586 **MOKWON METHODIST COLLEGE**
24 Mok-dong, Chung-gku, Taejon CT, Chungnam 301-070
Telephone: 252-9941
President: Kun Ho Lee (1988-89)

C. of Humanities
Head: Soon Kil Hong; *staff* 26 (38)
C. of Social Sciences (including Business Administration, Economics, Law, and Applied Statistics)
Head: Young Dal Kim; *staff* 25 (31)
C. of Science and Engineering (including Computer Sciences)
Head: Sung Do Back; *staff* 14 (21)
C. of Music
; *staff* 12 (50)
C. of Fine Arts
Head: Young Ja Yoon; *staff* 11 (54)
C. of Liberal Arts and Science
Head: Yong Nyun Kim
Graduate S.
Graduate S. of Theology
Head: Ik Won Kim; *staff* 14 (5)
Industrial Management I.
Director: Kyu Sang Lee
Computer Ce.
Director: Ho Kun Yoon

Founded 1954 as Seminary, acquired present status and title 1980. A private institution. Residential facilities for students.

Academic Year: March to February (March-August; September-February).

Admission Requirements: Graduation from high school or foreign equivalent, and entrance examination.

Fees (Won): 410,000-560,000 per semester.

Language of Instruction: Korean.

Degrees and Diplomas: Bachelor, 4 yrs. Master in–Theology; Music; Fine Arts, a further 2 yrs.

Library: 124,000 vols.

Academic Staff, 1986-87:

Rank	Full-time	Part-time
Gyosu (Professors)	4	–
Bu-gyosu (Associate Professors)	18	–
Jo-gyosu (Assistant Professors)	45	–
Gangsa (Lecturers)	41	220
Total	118	220

Student Enrolment, 1986-87:

	Men	Women	Total
Of the country	2800	1485	4285

4587 **MYONG JI UNIVERSITY**
Nam-ri, Yongin-gun, Kiyonggi 120-728
President: Il-Kyong Park

C. of Humanities
C. of Law and Political Science
C. of Business Administration and Economics
C. of Science
C. of Engineering
C. of Humanities and Social Science
Graduate S.
Public Administration Research I.
Industrial Research I.
I. of Humanities
I. for Saemul

Founded 1948 as a private institution of higher education for women, reorganized 1962 as Seoul Moon-Lee College of Business and Technology, and achieved present status 1983.

Admission Requirements: Graduation from high school or equivalent and entrance examination.

Language of Instruction: Korean.

Degrees and Diplomas: Bachelor, 4 yrs. Master, a further 2 yrs. Doctorate, Ph.D., 4 yrs.

Library: Total, c. 200,000 vols.

Academic Staff: 260 (80).

Student Enrolment: 10,000.

4588 ***PAI CHAI UNIVERSITY**
439-6 Toma-dong, So-gu, Taejon CT, Chungnam 302-162
Telephone: 522-0335

D. of Korean Language and Literature
D. of English Language and Literature
D. of German Language and Literature
D. of French Language and Literature
D. of Early Childhood Studies
D. of Home Economics
D. of Music
D. of Horticulture
D. of Art
D. of Business Management

Founded 1885 as school, became junior college 1978 and acquired present status and title 1981. A private institution supervised by the Ministry of Education.

Academic Year: March to February (March-August; September-February).

Admission Requirements: Graduation from high school and entrance examination.

Language of Instruction: Korean.

Degrees and Diplomas: Bachelor of–Arts; Science, 4 yrs.

Library: Central Library, c. 15,000 vols.

Publications: Pai Chai Hag Bo (monthly); Theses Collection (annually).

Academic Staff: c. 50.

Student Enrolment: c. 930.

4589 **POHANG INSTITUTE OF SCIENCE AND TECHNOLOGY**
P.O. Box 125, Pohang CT, Kyungbuk 790-330
Telephone: 75-0900

Founded 1986.

4590 **PUSAN UNIVERSITY OF FOREIGN STUDIES**
Uam-dong, Nam-gu, Pusan 608-060
Telephone: (51) 643-5111-7
Fax: (51) 645-4525
President: Dong-Son Kim
Dean of Academic Affairs: Chang-Hee Lee

F. of Foreign Studies (English, French, German, Spanish, Portuguese, Russian, Japanese, Chinese, Thai, Malay-Indonesian, Arabic, Hindi) ; *staff* 63 (41)
F. of Humanities and Social Science ; *staff* 19 (18)
F. of Economics and Trade ; *staff* 14 (8)
F. of Natural Sciences and Engineering ; *staff* 11 (5)
Evening S. ; *staff* 40 (15)
Graduate S.
Dean: Dong-Son Kim; *staff* 23
Audio-visual Education I.
Director: Jung-Soo Kim; *staff* 5
Linguistic Research Ce.
Director: Young-Kil Kim; *staff* 5
Cultural Studies Ce.
Director: Sang-Jin Chung; *staff* 5
Social Science Research Ce.
Director: Hae-Min Yoo; *staff* 9
Computer Ce.
Director: Mok-Dong Chung; *staff* 6
Trade and Management Research Ce.
Director: Dong-Ryul Kim; *staff* 12
I. of Law
Director: Shi-Jo Yoo; *staff* 5
I. of International Studies
Director: Son-Hong Kwon; *staff* 14
Foreign Language Training I.
Director: Jung-Soo Kim; *staff* 5

Founded 1981. Governing body: the Board of Trustees. Residential facilities for 12 athlete students.

Arrangements for co-operation with Chian-Mai University, Thailand.

Academic Year: March to December (March-June; September-December).

Admission Requirements: Graduation from school and entrance examination.

Fees (Won): 666,000-699,000; Graduate Studies, 847,000.

Language of Instruction: Korean.

Degrees and Diplomas: Bachelor, 4 yrs. Master, a further 2 yrs.

Library: Central Library, 81,000 vols.

Special Facilities (Museums, etc.): Museum; Broadcasting Station.

Publications: Journal of Social Science; Culture Research; Journal of International Affairs; P.U.F.S. Journal of Phonology; Journal of Business and Trade.

Press or Publishing House: The Pusan University of Foreign Studies Press.

Academic Staff, 1989-90:

Rank	Full-time	Part-time
Professors	1	–
Associate Professors	22	–
Assistant Professors	67	–
Instructors	9	72
Total	99	72

Student Enrolment, 1989-90: 6653.

4591 **SONGSIM YOJA DAEHAK**
Sacred Heart College for Women
San 43-1, Yokkgok 2-Dong, Puchon CT, Kyonggi 422-743
Telephone: (32) 62-8251
Fax: (32) 665-9798
President: Jeong-mi Park (1989-93)
Dean of Studies: Yoong-il Kim

D. of Korean Language and Literature
Chairperson: Bong-gun Kim; *staff* 7 (6)
D. of English Language and Literature
Chairperson: Myung-ja Kim; *staff* 9 (9)
D. of French Language and Literature
Chairperson: Gwan-sik Kim; *staff* 6 (7)
D. of Chinese Language and Literature
Chairperson: Jong-rye Won; *staff* 3 (8)
D. of Korean History
Chairperson: Byung-wook Ahn; *staff* 5 (10)
D. of Social Service
Chairperson: Jong-hae Kim; *staff* 5 (6)
D. of Sociology
Chairperson: Dong-ok Park; *staff* 4 (9)
D. of Business Administration
Chairperson: Gi-chan Kim; *staff* 4 (9)
D. of Accountancy
Chairperson: Sung-gyu Park; *staff* 3 (5)
D. of Psychology
Chairperson: Ho-gyun Yun; *staff* 3 (5)
D. of Home Economics
Chairperson: Mi-sook Lee; *staff* 6 (9)

D. of Nutrition
Chairperson: Joong-hee Lee; *staff* 6 (3)
D. of Textile Engineering and Clothing
Chairperson: Gyung-jo Ahn; *staff* 3 (9)
D. of Chemistry
Chairperson: Gang-ryul Lee; *staff* 6 (4)
D. of Mathematics
Chairperson: Geum-hee Han; *staff* 4 (7)
D. of Biology
Chairperson: Ha-gyu Lee; *staff* 4 (6)
D. of Music
Chairperson: Hye-son Lee; *staff* 7 (30)
Graduate S.
Dean: Tae-sung Huh; *staff* 21 (3)
Graduate S. of Korean Language and Literature
Graduate S. of English Language and Literature
Graduate S. of French Language and Literature
Graduate S. of Social Service
Graduate S. of Chemistry
I. of Natural Sciences
Director: Min-chol Park; *staff* 15
I. of Life Science
Director: I-sik Kim; *staff* 12
I. for Religious Educaton
Director: Hye-jeong Roh; *staff* 2 (6)
I. of Sacred Music
Director: Byung-chol Choi; *staff* 4
Research I. of Social Sciences
Director: Si-jae Lee; *staff* 19
Also 5 research institutes.

Founded 1964 by the Society of the Sacred Heart. Governing body: the Songsim School Corporation, comprising 9 trustee members.

Arrangements for co-operation with University of the Sacred Heart, Tokyo.

Academic Year: March to December (March-July; September-December).

Admission Requirements: Graduation from high school and entrance examination.

Fees (Won): 778,000-972,500 per semester.

Language of Instruction: Korean.

Degrees and Diplomas: Bachelor of–Arts, B.A.; Science, B.S.; Business Administration, B.B.A.; Music, B.M.; Home Economics, B.H.E., 4 yrs. Master, a further 2 yrs.

Library: Songsim Central Library, *c.* 132,710 vols.

Publications: Sacred Heart College Press (weekly); Songsim Scene (English newspaper, bimonthly).

Academic Staff, 1990:

Rank	Full-time	Part-time
Professors	34	–
Associate Professors	30	–
Assistant Professors	24	–
Instructors	8	159
Total	96	159

Student Enrolment, 1990: *c.* 3505 (Women).

4592 **SANG MYUNG WOMEN'S UNIVERSITY**
Hongji-dong,, Chongno-gu, Seoul 110-743
Telephone: 737-0291

D. of Home Economics
D. of Fine Arts
D. of Physical Education
D. of Korean Literature
D. of English Philology
D. of Music
D. of Sociology

Founded 1965.

Academic Year: March to December (March-August; September-December).

Admission Requirements: Graduation from high school or recognized equivalent, and entrance examination.

Language of Instruction: Korean.

Library: Central Library, *c.* 560,000 vols.

Special Facilities (Museums, etc.): Folklore Museum.

Academic Staff: *c.* 30 (60).

Student Enrolment: 700.

4593 **SANG JI COLLEGE**
1082 Woosan-dong, Wonju CT, Kangwon 220-130
Telephone: 42-1121

D. of Law
D. of Public Administration
D. of Economics
D. of Business Administration
D. of Social Welfare

Founded 1974.

4594 **SEOUL WOMEN'S UNIVERSITY**
Kongreung-dong, Nowon-gu, Seoul 139-240
Telephone: 972-2031
President: Koo-Young Chung (1984-87)

D. of Humanities
; *staff* 24 (39)
D. of Social Sciences (including Business Administration, Economics, Library Science, and Physical Education)
; *staff* 15 (46)
D. of Natural Sciences (including Food Technology)
; *staff* 11 (25)
D. of Fine Arts and Physical Education
; *staff* 11 (34)
I. of Saemaul Studies
Director: In-Don Lee; *staff* 1 (5)
Rural Development I.
Director: Byeong-Gi Im; *staff* 5 (10)
I. for Women's Studies
Director: Moon-Hee Kang; *staff* 2 (9)
Also primary and middle schools.

Founded 1960, by Korean Presbyterian Church. A private institution. Residential facilities for academic staff and 553 students.

Academic Year: March to February (March-August; September-February).

Admission Requirements: Graduation from high school and entrance examination.

Fees (Won): Tuition, 379,000-399,500.

Language of Instruction: Korean.

Degrees and Diplomas: Bachelor of–Science, B.Sc.; Arts, B.A.; Agriculture, B.Ag.; Fine Arts, B.F.A.; Business Administration, B.B.Ad.; Home Economics, B. Home Econ.; Physical Education, 4 yrs. Master, a further 2 yrs. Doctorate in–Food Technology and Nutrition; Korean Language and Literature; Education; Home Economics; Rural Science.

Library: 94,095 vols.

Publications: Seoul Women's University News (monthly); Seoul Women's University Journal (annually); Seoul Women's UniversityBulletin (annually); Rural Development Research Series (annually).

Press or Publishing House: Seoul Women's University Press.

Academic Staff, 1986-87:

Rank	Full-time	Part-time
Gyosu (Professors)	19	–
Bu-gyosu (Associate Professors)	16	8
Jo-gyosu (Assistant Professors)	18	10
Jeon-nim-gangsa (Lecturers)/(Instructors)	8	126
Total	61	144

Student Enrolment, 1986-87: 3059 (Women).

4595 **SEPWON UNIVERSITY**
Mochung-dong, Chungju CT, Chungbuk 360-140
Telephone: 62-8813

Founded 1972.

4596 ***SOGANG UNIVERSITY**
Shinsu-dong, Mapo-gu, Seoul 121-742
Cables: jesuitmis
Telephone: 715-0141
Fax: 701-8962
President: Hong Park, S.J. (1989-93)
Vice-President: Ha-Soon Cha

C. of Liberal Arts (Korean, English, German, French Language and Literature, History, Philosophy, Religious Studies)
Dean: Yun-Chan Chung; *staff* 58 (81)

C. of Science and Engineering (Mathematics, Physics, Chemistry, Biology, Electronic Engineering, Chemical Engineering, and Computer Science)
Dean: Yong-Duk Kim; *staff* 51 (34)
C. of Commerce
Dean: Sung-Huan Jo; *staff* 15 (2)
Graduate S.
Dean: Sang-Jun Kim
Graduate S. of Business Administration
Dean: Sang-Ryong Sye
Humanities Research I.
Director: Seung-Ki Hong
I. of Basic Science Research
Director: Kye-Chil Oh
I. of Religious Studies
Director: Yang-Mo Chung
Communications and Culture I.
Director: Yong-Ho Chang
I. of Economic and Business Research
Director: Hyo-Koo Lee
I. of East-Asian Studies
Director: Tai-Wook Rhee
I. of Labour and Management Studies
Director: Young-Ki Park
I. of Technology Management
Dean: Kwang-Du Kim
I. of Accountancy
Director: Jong-Hyun Baek
I. of English
Director: Norbert J. Tracy
C. of Social Science (including Mass Communication, Political Science, and Law)
Dean: Jung-Ho Sye; *staff* 25
C. of Business Administration
Dean: Nei-Nei Park; *staff* 22 (18)
General Education D.
Director: Jung-Taek Kim; *staff* 14 (63)
I. of Industrial Technology Research
Director: Chul Ahn
I. of Philosophy
Director: Jong-Dae Park

Founded 1960 as college by the Society of Jesus, acquired university status 1970. A private institution financed by tuition fees (82%) and grants. Governing body: the Board of Trustees. Residential facilities for academic staff.

Arrangements for co-operation with: Sophia University, Tokyo; Creighton University, Omaha; University of Munich; Pennsylvania State University; Geogetown University, Washington; Heilongjang University, Harbin; Universityof Athens; Gregorian University, Rome.

Academic Year: March to December (March-July); August-December).

Admission Requirements: Graduation from high school or equivalent, and entrance examination.

Fees (Won): 700,000-1,000,000 per semester.

Language of Instruction: Korean.

Degrees and Diplomas: Bachelor of–Arts; Science, 4 yrs. Master of–Arts; Science, a further 2-3 yrs. Doctorate, 3-4 yrs after Master.

Library: Loyola Library, 400,000 vols.

Special Facilities (Museums, etc.): University Museum.

Publications: Sogang Harvard Business (quarterly); Journal of East Asian Studies (biannually); Theological Series; ReligiousSeries.

Press or Publishing House: Sogang Herald (English newspaper); Sogang Harkbo (weekly).

Academic Staff, 1989-90:

Rank	Full-time	Part-time
Gyosu (Professors)	95	–
Bu-gyosu (Associate Professors)	54	–
Jo-gyosu (Assistant Professors)	28	–
Jeon-nim-gangsa (Instructors)	8	226
Total	185	226

Student Enrolment, 1989-90:

	Men	Women	Total
Of the country	7544	1126	8670*

*Also 954 postgraduate students.

4597 **SOOKMYUNG WOMEN'S UNIVERSITY**
San 2-1, Chungpa-dong, Yongsan-gu, Seoul 140-132
Telephone: 713-9391
Fax: 718-2337
President: Kyu-Sun Chung
Dean of Office of Academic Affairs: Jong-Kyu Ham

C. of Liberal Arts (including Library Science)
Dean: Kwi-Kyung Lee; *staff* 45 (138)
C. of Natural Sciences
Dean: Myung-Ja Kim; *staff* 27 (26)
C. of Home Economics
Dean: Jung-Woo Lee; *staff* 17 (32)
C. of Political Science and Economics
Dean: Yo-Sup Chung; *staff* 11 (27)
C. of Music
Dean: Man-Bok Kim; *staff* 17 (113)
C. of Pharmacy
Dean: Sook-Yeon Lee; *staff* 10 (8)
C. of Fine Arts
Dean: Chung-un Ahn; *staff* 12 (35)
Graduate S.
Dean: Chan-Woo Shin
Research C. for Asian Women
Director: In-Bok Lee; *staff* 6
Research I. of Political Affairs and Economics
Director: Kyung-Ui Rhee; *staff* 2
Research I. of Languages and Literature
Director: Jin-Song Cha; *staff* 3
Research I. of Pharmaceutical Science
Director: Sook-Yeon Lee; *staff* 2
Reunification Research I.
Director: Ok-Yul Kim; *staff* 2

Founded 1938 as college, acquired university status 1955. A private institution governed by a Board of Trustees of 9 members. Some residential facilities for students.

Arrangements for co-operation with: Western Michigan University; Seton Hall University; University of Chinese Culture, Taipei.

Academic Year: March to December (March-July; September-December).

Admission Requirements: Graduation from high school and entrance examination.

Fees (Won): 92,800,000-835,240,000.

Language of Instruction: Korean.

Degrees and Diplomas: Bachelor of–Arts; Science, 4 yrs. Master of Arts, a further 2 yrs. Doctor of Philosophy, Ph.D.

Library: c. 500,000 vols.

Special Facilities (Museums, etc.): Museum: Collections of Ornaments; Folk Arts; Calligraphy and Porcelain.

Publications: Weekly Newspaper; Faculty members' Papers; Papers of the Research Centre for Asian Women.

Press or Publishing House: Sookmyung Women's University Press.

Academic Staff, 1989-90:

Rank	Full-time	Part-time
Professors	80	–
Associate Professors	51	–
Assistant Professors	18	–
Instructors	3	447
Total	152	447

Student Enrolment, 1989-90: c. 7030.

4598 **SOONCHUNGYANG UNIVERSITY**
Asan-gun, Chungnam 337-880
Telephone: 42-4601
President: Kum Haw (1983-86)
Dean of General Affairs: Jeong Ung Rhim

C. of Humanities
Dean: Duck Ok Kim; *staff* 15 (11)
C. of Economics and Commerce
Dean: Chung Hyo Lee; *staff* 10 (5)
C. of Sciences
Dean: Kee Soo Kim; *staff* 24 (2)
C. of Industrial Sciences
Dean: Suck Kyoon Suh; *staff* 5 (1)
C. of Medicine
Dean: Sang Kyoon Kang; *staff* 170

I. of Cancer Research
Director: Kyung Bal Hur; *staff* 12
I. of Obstetrics and Gynaecology
Director: Hun Yoo; *staff* 14
I. of Industrial Medicine
Director: Taeg Seung Nam; *staff* 15
I. of Population and Community Health Studies
Director: Sook Bang; *staff* 9

Founded 1978 as Medical College, acquired present status and title 1979. Residential facilities for 40 academic staff and 300 students.

Academic Year: March to February (March-August; September-February).

Admission Requirements: Graduation from high school and entrance examination.

Fees (Won): *c.* 800,000 per semester.

Language of Instruction: Korean.

Degrees and Diplomas: Bachelor of–Arts; Science; Business Administration; Economics; Physical Education, 4 yrs; Medicine, 6 yrs. Master of–Science; Medicine, a further 2 yrs.

Library: Central Library, 70,000 vols.

Publications: University Quarterly; Hyangrock Hagbo (monthly newspaper).

Academic Staff, 1986-87:

Rank	Full-time
Gyosu (Professors)	44
Bu-gyosu (Associate Professors)	26
Jo-gyosu (Assistant Professors)	58
Jeon-nim-gangsa (Instructors)	96
Total	224

Student Enrolment, 1986-87:

	Men	Women	Total
Of the country	3110	618	3728
Of other countries	1	1	2
Total	3111	619	3730

4599 ***SOONG SIL UNIVERSITY**
1-1 Sangdo 1 dong, Dongjak-ku, Seoul 156-743
Telephone: (2) 814-9611
Fax: (2) 816-1513
President: Johann Zoh (1989-93)
Dean of Academic Affairs: Sang Suk Lee

C. of Liberal Arts (including Korean, English, German, and French Language and Literature, Philosophy, and History)
Dean: Moon Gyong Kim; *staff* 40 (84)
C. of Natural Sciences
Dean: Myung Soo Kim; *staff* 19 (21)
C. of Law
Dean: Kyung Keun Kang; *staff* 6 (10)
C. of Social Sciences (including Public Administration, Political Science and Diplomacy)
Dean: Tuk Chu Chun; *staff* 13 (16)
C. of Economics and Commerce
Dean: Dong Kil Yoo; *staff* 22 (35)
C. of Engineering (including Chemical, Textile, Electrical, Electronic, Mechanical, Industrial, and Architectural Engineering; Computer Sciences, and Industrial Education)
Dean: Choong Kyu Park; *staff* 48 (54)
D. for Evening Studies
Dean: Il Woong Lim; *staff* 80 (108)
Graduate S.
Dean: Myung Kwan Choi; *staff* 125 (25)
Graduate S. of Industry
Dean: Hong Sik Yoon; *staff* 23 (5)
Graduate S. of Small Business Studies
Dean: Kwang Bae Lee; *staff* 26 (6)
Graduate S. of Information Science
Dean: Chul Hee Lee; *staff* 7 (4)
Graduate S. of Labour and Industrial Relations
Dean: Song Chin Kim; *staff* 6 (3)
I. of Humanities
Head: Jae Young So; *staff* 38 (2)
I. of Basic Sciences
Head: Chong In Yu; *staff* 20
I. of Law
Head: Doo Hwan Kim; *staff* 6 (3)
I. of Social Sciences
Head: Kyu Il Kim; *staff* 12 (3)
Christian I. of Social Sciences
Head: Sam Yeul Lee; *staff* 3 (6)
I. of Industrial and Economics Research
Head: Tae Ha Park
I. of Christian Culture
Head: Young Han Kim; *staff* 2 (2)
I. of Small Business Development
Head: Yoon Bae Ouh
Korean I. of Labour and Industrial Relations
Head: Song Chin Kim; *staff* 2
Computer Ce.

Founded 1897 by the Northern Presbyterian Church of the United States and became 4-year college 1905. Merged with Tae Jon College and became Soong Jun University 1971. Tae Jon College separated from the main campus 1983,and the school restored to its original name of Soong Sil 1987. A private institution. Governing body: the University Council. Residential facilities for academic staff and students.

Arrangements for co-operation with: University of Alaska-Fairbanks; Whitworth College, Spokane; Pratt Institute, New York; Meiji Gakuin University, Tokyo.

Academic Year: March to February (March-June; August-December).

Admission Requirements: Graduation from high school or equivalent, and entrance examination.

Fees (Won): 600,000-700,000 per semester.

Language of Instruction: Korean.

Degrees and Diplomas: Bachelor of–Literature; Natural Sciences; Engineering; Business Administration; Economics; Law; Public Administration, Political Science, 4 yrs. Master, a further 2-3 yrs. Doctor of–Literature; Natural Sciences; Law; Social Work; Economics; Business Administration; Engineering, 3 years after Master.

Library: Central Library, 200,000 vols.

Special Facilities (Museums, etc.): Korean Christian Museum; The Central Library; Central Computer Centre; Audio-visual Education Institute; University Theatre.

Publications: Soong Sil University Essays and Papers (Natural Science, Humanities, Social Sciences); Journal of Social Sciences; Soong Sil Law Review; Journal of Graduate School of Regional Development; Essays and Papers of the Graduate School; Joong Sil Sahak.

Press or Publishing House: Soong Sil University Press.

Academic Staff, 1990:

Rank	Full-time	Part-time
Gyosu (Professors)	69	2
Byu-gyosu (Associate Professors)	55	–
Jo-gyosu (Assistant Professors)	24	–
Jeon-nim-gangsa (Instructors)	2	–
Lecturers	–	220
Total	150	222

Student Enrolment, 1990:

	Men	Women	Total
Of the country	6030	1501	7531
Of other countries	1	–	1
Total	6031	1501	7532

4600 **SUNG KYUN KWAN UNIVERSITY**
53, 3-ka Myungryun-dong, Chongro-gu, Seoul 110-745
Telephone: 762-5021
President: Cho Chwa-ho

C. of Liberal Arts (including Education and Psychology)
C. of Science
C. of Engineering
C. of Law and Political Science
C. of Economics and Commerce (including Business Administration)
C. of Pharmacy
C. of Confucian Studies
C. of Agriculture (including Animal Husbandry)
C. of Home Economics
C. of Education
S. of Economics
Graduate S.
Research I. of Oriental Culture

Science Research I.
I. of Humanities
S. of Library Science
I. of Social Sciences
I. of Korean Industrial Studies
Graduate S. of Foreign Trade
Graduate S. of Industrial Development

Founded 992 as sole national institute of higher learning in Koryo Dynasty based on Confucian doctrine and principles. Re-established 1398 on present site under Yi Dynasty. Recognized by the government as a college 1937 and private university 1953. Governing body: the Board of Trustees.

Academic Year: March to February (March-July; September-February).

Admission Requirements: Graduation from high school or equivalent qualification recognized by the Ministry of Education, and entrance examination.

Language of Instruction: Korean.

Degrees and Diplomas: Bachelor of–Arts; Science; Library Science; Laws; Political Science; Economics; Education; Pharmacy; Engineering; Agriculture; Business Administration; Public Administration; Physical Education; Home Economics, 4 yrs. Master, a further 2 yrs. Doctor, 3-5 yrs after Master.

Library: Total, *c.* 297,000 vols.

Special Facilities (Museums, etc.): Sung Kyun Kwan Museum.

Publications: University Journal; Social Science Review; Journal of Far Eastern Studies; Journal of International Studies.

Academic Staff: c. 240.

Student Enrolment: c. 15,000.

4601 **SUNGSHIN WOMEN'S UNIVERSITY**
3ga Tongson-dong, Songbug-gu, Seoul 136-742
Telephone: 94-0124

D. of Home Economics
D. of Economics
D. of Foreign Languages
D. of Fine Arts
D. of Korean Language and Literature
D. of Music
D. of Social Sciences

Founded 1963.

4602 **SUWEON UNIVERSITY**
Wawoo-ri,Pongdam-myon, Hwasong-gun, Kyonggi 445-890
Telephone: 33-1402

Founded 1981.

4603 **SUWON CATHOLIC COLLEGE**
Wongrim-ri, Pongdam-myon, Hwasong-gun, Kyonggi 445-890
Telephone: 33-1081

Founded 1983.

4604 **TAEGU CATHOLIC COLLEGE**
Pongduk-dong, Nam-gu, Taegu 705-020
Telephone: 626-9581

Founded 1981.

4605 **TAEGU ORIENTAL MEDICAL COLLEGE**
Chumchon-dong, Kyongsan-gun, Kyongbuk 713-800
Telephone: 83-0551

Medicine

Founded 1980.

4606 **TAEGU UNIVERSITY**
Taemyong-dong, Nam-gu, Taegu 705-030
Telephone: 67-2081

Founded 1956.

4607 **TAEJEON COLLEGE**
96-3 Yongun-dong, Tong-gu, Taejon CT, Chungnam 300-120
Telephone: 252-0213

D. of Korean Language and Literature
D. of English
D. of National Ethics
D. of Law
D. of Public Administration
D. of Management Economics
D. of International Trade
D. of Mathematics
D. of Economics
D. of Oriental Medicine
D. of Biology
D. of Electronics
D. of Architecture
Evening D.

Also 6 Research Institutes.

Founded 1981. A private institution.

Arrangements for co-operation with China Medical College, Taichung.

Academic Year: March to December (March-August; September-February).

Admission Requirements: Graduation from high school or foreign equivalent, and entrance examination.

Language of Instruction: Korean.

Degrees and Diplomas: Bachelor of Arts, 4 yrs, except Oriental Medicine, 6 yrs.

Library: c. 30,800 vols.

Publication: Research Papers (annually).

Press or Publishing House: College Press.

Academic Staff: c. 40 (50).

Student Enrolment: c. 50.

4608 **UNIVERSITY OF ULSAN**
Mugo-dong, Ulsan CT Kyongnam 680-749
Telephone: 77-3101

D. of Mechanical Engineering
D. of Electrical Engineering
D. of Material Sciences
D. of Civil Engineering
D. of Chemistry and Industrial Chemistry
D. of Architecture
D. of General Studies
Junior Technical C.
Computer Ce.

Founded 1969 with the aid of the Colombo Plan and Ulsan Foundation. Residential facilities for some academic staff and for *c.* 100 students.

Academic Year: March to February (March-July; September-February).

Admission Requirements: Graduation from high school and entrance examination.

Language of Instruction: Korean.

Degrees and Diplomas: Bachelor of Engineering, 4 yrs.

Library: c. 20,000 vols.

Publication: Technical Research Reports.

Academic Staff: c. 40 (50).

Student Enrolment: c. 1560.

4609 **WON KWANG UNIVERSITY**
Shinyong-dong, Iri CT, Chonbuk 570-749
Telephone: 52-2111

C. of Liberal Arts and Science
C. of Education
C. of Law and Political Science
C. of Pharmacy
C. of Commerce and Economics
C. of Education
C. of Agriculture
C. of Oriental Medicine
C. of Dentistry
C. of Engineering
C. of Home Economics
Graduate S.
Graduate S. of Education

Founded 1953 as college.

4610 **YEUNGNAM UNIVERSITY**
Taedong-dong, Kyungsan-eup, Kyungsan-gun, Kyungbuk 713-800
Telephone: 82-5111

C. of Liberal Arts

C. of Science
C. of Engineering (including Architecture)
C. of Law and Political Science
C. of Commerce and Economics
C. of Medicine
C. of Pharmacy
C. of Home Economics
C. of Education (including Physical Education)
C. of Agriculture and Animal Husbandry
C. of Music
C. of Fine Arts
Evening C.
Graduate S.
Graduate S. of Business Administration
Graduate S. of Environmental Studies
Graudate S. of Education
Also technical junior college.

Founded 1967, incorporating Taegu College and Chonggu College founded 1947 and 1950 respectively. A private institution. Governing body: the Board of Trustees. Residential facilities for academic staff and students.

Special arrangements for co-operation with the Universities of: Ball State; Maryland; St. John's, New York; Chinese Culture, Taipei.

Academic Year: March to February (March-August; September-February).

Admission Requirements: Graduation from high school or equivalent, and entrance examination.

Language of Instruction: Korean.

Degrees and Diplomas: Bachelor of–Literature; Science; Engineering; Agriculture; Home Economics; Physical Education; Fine Arts; Music; Economics; Law; Public Administration; Political Science; Business Administration; Commerce; Pharmacy, 4 yrs; Medicine, 6 yrs. Master of–Literature; Law; Public Administration; Political Science; Economics; Business Administration; Engineering; Pharmacy; Science; Home Economics; Fine Arts; Medicine; Music, a further 2 yrs. Doctor of–Literature; Engineering; Philosophy; Science; Law; Pharmacy; Economics; Political Science; Public Administration; Medicine.

Library: Central Library, *c.* 230,000 vols.

Special Facilities (Museums, etc.): University Museum.

Publications: These Collections (Humanities, Social and Natural Sciences); Yeungdae Shinmum; Yeungnam Chronical; Business Administration Memoirs (annually); Journal of Oriental Culture (annually); Industrial Economy (annually); Journal of Silla-Kaya Culture (annually); Public Administration Review (annually).

Press or Publishing House: University Press.

Academic Staff: *c.* 480 (240).

Student Enrolment: *c.* 20,000.

4611 ***YONSEI UNIVERSITY**

134 Shinchon-dong, Sodaemun-gu, Seoul 120-749
Telex: K29127
Telephone: 392-0131
President: Se Hee Ahn (1980-88)
Dean: Kyoung Bae Min

C. of Liberal Arts
Dean: Chong Young Lee; *staff* 79 (111)
C. of Business Administration and Economics (including Statistics)
Dean: Suk Bum Yoon; *staff* 48 (35)
C. of Science
Dean: Choong Hyun Chung; *staff* 66 (75)
C. of Engineering (including Architecture)
Dean: Hanju Lee; *staff* 65 (46)
C. of Theology
Dean: Sang Hee Moon; *staff* 20 (8)
C. of Social Sciences
Dean: Jung Karp Surh; *staff* 26 (15)
C. of Law
Dean: Ju Chan Sonn; *staff* 11 (5)
C. of Music
Dean: Jai Youl Park; *staff* 25 (104)
C. of Home Economics
Dean: Soo Jae Moon; *staff* 22 (24)
C. of Education and Physical Education
Dean: In Whoe Kim; *staff* 15 (44)
C. of Medicine
Dean: Yoo Bock Lee; *staff* 287 (2)
C. of Dentistry
Dean: Chung Suck Lee; *staff* 31
C. of Nursing
Dean: Yun Soon Choi; *staff* 24 (8)
Graduate S.
Dean: Jae Shi Choi
Graduate S. of Business Administration
Dean: Ik Soon Im
Graduate S. of Theology
Dean: Sang Hee Moon
Graduate S. of Education
Dean: Chung Hoon Choy
Graduate S. of Public Administration
Dean: Hyoung Sup Yoon
Graduate S. of Engineering
Dean: Kun Duk Kim
Graduate S. of Health Sciences and Management
Dean: Il Soon Kim
Graduate S. of International Studies
Dean: Heung Soo Park
I. of Agricultural Development
Director: Young Hee Kang
I. of Medical Technology
Director: Jae Duk Lew
I. of Korean Studies
Director: Sok Duk Kim
I. of East and West Studies
Director: Dal Choong Kim
I. of Urban Studies and Development
Director: Chung Hyon Ro
Korean-French Ce.
Director: Myun Sung
I. of Christianity and Korean Culture
Director: Jung Ki Kim
I. of Tropical Medicine
Director: Keun Tae Lee
I. for Occupational Health Studies
Director: Young Han Moon
Also 12 research institutes.

Founded 1885 as Severance Union Medical Clinic. Merged with Chosun Christian College, established 1915, to form present university 1957. The university is related to the United Board for Christian Higher Education in Asia and has a local Board of Directors. Recognized by the government as a university entitled to award degrees. Subject to the educational law and ordinances of the government. Governing body: Board of Directors comprising representatives of Protestant churches in Korea and North America. Some residential facilities for academic staff and *c.* 500 students.

Academic Year: March to February (March-August; August-December).

Admission Requirements: Graduation from high school, government qualifying examination and university entrance examination.

Language of Instruction: Korean.

Degrees and Diplomas: Bachelor of–Arts (Literature), B.A.; Science, B.S.; Engineering, B.E.; Theology, Th.B.; Law, LL.B.; Political Science, B.Pol.Sci.; Mass Communication; Economics, B.Econ.; Business Administration, B.B.Ad.; Public Administration, B.Pub.Admin.; Music, B.Mus., 4 yrs; Medicine, B.M.; Dentistry, B.D., 6 yrs. Master of–Arts (Literature), M.A.; Business Administration, M.B.Ad.; Science, M.S.; Engineering, M.Eng.; Political Science, M.Pol.Sc.; Medicine, M.Med.; Public Health, M.Pub.H.; Economics, M.Econ.; Theology, M.Th.; Law, M.L.; Public Administration, M.Pub.Admin.; Music, M.Mus.; Physical Education, M.Phy.Ed., a further 2 yrs. Doctor of–Arts; Business Administration; Public Administration; Law; Science; Engineering; Theology; Medicine; Philosophy; Education; Economics; Political Science; Dentistry.

Library: Central Library, *c.* 451,600 vols.

Special Facilities (Museums, etc.): University Museum.

Publications: Journal of Humanities; Yonsei Social Science Review; Yonsei Nonchong; The Dong Bang Hak Chi (Journal of Far Eastern Studies); Yonsei Business Review; Yonsei Engineering Review; Etudes Franco-Coréennes; Journal of East and West Studies; Journal of Educational Science.

Press or Publishing House: University Press.

Academic Staff, 1986-87:

Rank	Full-time	Part-time
Gyosu (Professors)	363	
Bu-gyosu (Associate Professors)	134	
Jo-gyosu (Assistant Professors)	189	
Jeon-nim-gangsa (Instructors)	96	
Total	782	583

Student Enrolment, 1986-87: 26,356.

Other Institutions

Teacher Training

4612 **BUSAN NATIONAL TEACHERS COLLEGE**
Koje-dong, Tongnae-gu, Busan 607-070
Telephone: 84-5055

Founded 1946.

4613 **CHE JU NATIONAL TEACHERS COLLEGE**
Hwabuk-dong, Cheju CT 690, Cheju 690-060
Telephone: 53-5691

Founded 1953.

4614 **CHEONG JU NATIONAL TEACHERS COLLEGE**
Sugok-dong, Chongju CT, Chungbuk 360-150
Telephone: 4-8151

Founded 1941.

4615 **CHINJU NATIONAL TEACHERS COLLEGE**
Shinan-dong, 380, Chinju CT, Kyungnam 660-756
Telephone: 43-6001
Fax: 745-8941
President: Yoon Hwan Rho
Secretary-General: Se Han Kim

Teacher Training (elementary level)

Founded 1940. Acquired present status 1983. Residential facilities for 80 women students.

Academic Year: March to December (March-July; September-December).

Admission Requirements: Graduation from high school.

Fees (Won): 500,000 per semester.

Language of Instruction: Korean.

Degrees and Diplomas: Bachelor of Education, 4 yrs.

Library: Central Library, 50,000 vols.

Publication: Thesis Collection (annually).

Press or Publishing House: Chinju Teachers College Press.

Academic Staff, 1989-90: 61 (10).

Student Enrolment, 1989-90:

	Men	Women	Total
Of the country	381	936	1317

4616 **CHONJU KYOYUK DACHAK**
Chonju National Teachers College
Dongseohak-dong, Chonju CT, Chonbuk 560-759
Telephone: (652) 85-7101
Fax: (657) 81-0102
President: Hyung-ho Song
Head of Administration: Soo-don Kim

D. of Ethics Education
; *staff* 3
D. of Korean Language
; *staff* 4 (1)
D. of Social Studies
; *staff* 4 (2)
D. of Mathematics
; *staff* 3 (1)
D. of Sciences
; *staff* 3 (1)
I. of Science Education
Research I. of Education
Retraining I. for Primary School Teachers

Also primary and secondary schools.

Founded 1936, as Chonju Normal School. Acquired present status and title 1983.

Arrangements for co-operation with Hiroshima Bunkyo Women's College.

Academic Year: March to February (March-August; September-February).

Admission Requirements: Graduation from high school.

Fees (Won): 548,000 per semester.

Language of Instruction: Korean.

Degrees and Diplomas: Bachelor of Education, 4 yrs.

Library: College Library, 39,820 vols.

Special Facilities (Museums, etc.): Chonju National Teachers College Museum.

Publications: College Newspaper (in Korean, monthly); Hwanghak Herald (in English, quarterly); The Hwanghak (annually).

Academic Staff, 1990:

Rank	Full-time	Part-time
Professors	30	–
Associate Professors	7	–
Assistant Professors	3	–
Lecturers	3	15
Assistants	12	
Total	55	15

Student Enrolment, 1990:

	Men	Women	Total
Of the country	246	476	722

4617 **CHUNCHEON NATIONAL TEACHERS COLLEGE**
Soksa-dong, Chunchon CT, Kangwon 200-180
Telephone: 2-5691
President: Seong-Tag Jeon
General Affairs Section Chief: Joon-Kyu Choi

D. of Ethics
Chairman: Hyuk-Nai Kwon; *staff* 3
D. of Korean Language and Literature
Chairman: Byeong-Ha Seo; *staff* 4 (2)
D. of Social Studies
Chairman: Jong-Yeul Park; *staff* 4 (1)
D. of Elementary
Chairman: Yang-Seop Song; *staff* 7 (1)
D. of Mathematics
Chairman: Whan-Yong Song; *staff* 3
D. of Science
Chairman: Kwang-Myoung Kim; *staff* 4
D. of Vocational Education
Chairman: Jong-Un Hong; *staff* 4
D. of Music
Chairman: In-Won Cho; *staff* 3 (1)
D. of Fine Arts
Chairman: Jin-Ku Han; *staff* 3 (1)
D. of Physical Education
Chairman: Eui-Yong Sung; *staff* 5
D. of Pre-school Education
Chairman: Un-Choo Kim; *staff* 1 (1)
D. of Foreign Languages
Chairman: Kwang-Su Kim; *staff* 2 (2)
Elementary Education Research Ce.
Director: Wan-Sup Lee
Science Education Research Ce.
Director: Whan-Yong Son
Moral Education Research Ce.
Director: Sang-Soon Lee
National Education Research Ce.
Director: Jong-Yeul Park
East Province Culture Research Ce.
Director: Byeong-Ha Seo
Community Development Research Ce.
Director: Jong-Un Hong

Founded 1939 as normal school. Acquired present statue and title 1983. Residential facilities for 240 women students.

Academic Year: March to February (March-August; September-February).

Admission Requirements: Graduation from high school and entrance examination.
Fees (Won): 548,500 per semester.
Language of Instruction: Korean.
Degrees and Diplomas: Bachelor, 4 yrs.
Library: College Library, 45,919 vols.
Publications: Journal; Research publications.
Press or Publishing House: Chunchon Teachers College Press.
Academic Staff, 1990: 43 (9).
Student Enrolment, 1990:

	Men	Women	Total
Of the country	365	618	983

4618 **INCHON NATIONAL TEACHERS COLLEGE**
Sungeui-dong, Nam-gu, Inchon 402-010
Telephone: 883-5151
Fax: 882-5024
President: Il-choul Lee

D. of Ethics
Chairman: Chol-ja Kim; *staff* 5 (1)
D. of Korean Language
Chairman: Young-ki Lim; *staff* 7 (3)
D. of Social Sciences
Chairman: Young-tae Oh; *staff* 8 (3)
D. of Mathematics
Chairman: Dong-gweon Jeong; *staff* 4 (2)
D. of Science
Chairman: An-chim Han; *staff* 7 (1)
D. of Physical Education
Chairman: Gee-ho Park; *staff* 8 (1)
D. of Music
Chairman: Chin-no Yang; *staff* 7 (1)
D. of Art
Chairman: Jong-hak Park; *staff* 6 (3)
D. of Practical Arts
Chairman: Chung-soon Park; *staff* 5 (2)
D. of General Education
Chairman: Hee-seun Chio
D. of Early Childhood Studies
Chairman: Og-soon Shin
Science Education Research I.
Director: Hyun-iae Kim; *staff* 1 (10)
Elementary Education Research I.
Director: Choong-haeng Kim; *staff* 1 (7)
Computer and Publishing Ce.
Director: Hyun-kyung Seong; *staff* 3 (6)
Kijeon Culture Research I.
Director: Jin-sik Kim; *staff* 1 (10)
Also elementary school and In-service Training Institute.
Founded 1962. Acquired present status 1982.
Academic Year: March to February (March-August; September-February).
Admission Requirements: Graduation from high school or equivalent.
Fees (Won): 545,000 per semester.
Language of Instruction: Korean.
Degrees and Diplomas: Bachelor, 4 yrs.
Library: College Library, 62,690 vols.
Special Facilities (Museums, etc.): Broadcasting Centre.
Publications: Research Journal; Research of Mathematics and Science Education; Journal of Kyeongki Cultural Studies (all annually).
Academic Staff, 1989-90:

Rank	Full-time	Part-time
Professors	41	–
Associate Professors	18	–
Assistant Professors	12	–
Lecturers	2	24
Assistants	14	–
Total	87	24

Student Enrolment, 1989-90:

	Men	Women	Total
Of the country	647	1320	1967

4619 **KONGJU NATIONAL TEACHERS COLLEGE**
Ponghwang-dong, Kongju CT, Chungnam 314-060
Telephone: 2-2661
Founded 1938.

4620 **KWANGJU NATIONAL TEACHERS COLLEGE**
Punghyang-dong, Puk-gu, Kwangju 500-090
Telephone: (62) 524-6001
Fax: (62) 528-2622
Dean: Moon-Ju Kang

Teacher Training (elementary level)
Also elementary school.
Founded 1938.
Academic Year: March to December (March-July; September-December).
Admission Requirements: Graduation from high school and entrance examination.
Fees (Won): 463,500 per semester.
Language of Instruction: Kerean.
Degrees and Diplomas: Bachelor of Arts, 4 yrs.
Library: 50,000 vols.
Publications: Kwanqju Teachers College Review; Journal of Elementary Education Research; Science Education Review (all annually).
Academic Staff, 1990: 55 (17).
Student Enrolment, 1990:

	Men	Women	Total
Of the country	366	773	1139

4621 **SEOUL NATIONAL TEACHERS COLLEGE**
Socho-dong, Kangnam-gu, Seoul 137-070
Telephone: 583-4091
Founded 1946.

4622 **TAE GU NATIONAL TEACHERS COLLEGE**
Taemyong-dong, Nam-gu, Taegu 705-030
Telephone: 66-4971
Founded 1949.

Also 119 junior colleges.

KUWAIT

4624 ***JAMI'AT AL-KUWAIT**
Kuwait University
Khaldia, P.O. Box 5969, Kuwait Safat 13060
Telex: KT 22616
Telephone: 4811188
Rector: Shueb Abdulla (1985-)
Secretary-General: Hussain Al-Mahmoud

C. of Commerce, Economics and Political Science
Dean: Moudy Al-Holoud; *staff* 102
C. of Law
Dean: Adel Al-Tebtabaie; *staff* 33
C. of Arts
Dean: Khaldoun Al-Naquib; *staff* 190
C. of Science
Dean: Fayza Al-Khorafy; *staff* 184
F. of Medicine
Dean: A.A. Al-Abdul Razzaq; *staff* 180
C. of Engineering and Petroleum Technology
Dean: Hassan Al-Alawi; *staff* 88
F. of Allied Health Sciences and Nursing
Dean: Farida Al-Awadi
C. of Education
Dean: Saad Al-Hashel; *staff* 58
C. of Shari'a (Islamic Law) and Islamic Studies
Dean: Ahmed Al-Ghandour; *staff* 52
Ce. for Community Service and Continuing Education
Director: Rasha Al-Sabah

Founded 1966. A State institution under the jurisdiction of the Ministry of Education. Governing body: the University Council of which the Minister of Education is chairman. Some residential facilities for academic staff and students.

Arrangements for co-operation with: George Washington University; Howard University; University of Texas.

Academic Year: September to June (September-January; February-June).

Admission Requirements: Secondary school certificate or equivalent.

Fees (Kuwait Dinar): Registration, 5 per semester; tuition, 5 per course.

Languages of Instruction: Arabic and English.

Degrees and Diplomas: Bachelor of–Arts, B.A.; Arts and Education, B.A.Ed.; Science, B.Sc.; Science and Education, B.Sc.Ed.; Commerce, B.Com.; Economics, B.Econ.; Political Science, B.P.Sc.; Law and Shari'a (Islamic Law), B.L.S., 4 yrs; Engineering, B.Sc.Eng., 4 ½ yrs; Medical Science, 7 yrs. Master of–Arts, M.A.; Science, M.Sc.

Library: Total, *c.* 433,520 vols.

Publications: Gulf and Arabian Peninsular Studies (in Arabic, quarterly); Arab Journal for the Humanities (English and Arabic); Journal of the University of Kuwait (Science) (annually); Social Sciences Journal (Arabic and English–quarterly); Journal of Palestine Studies.

Academic Staff, 1986-87: 887.

Student Enrolment, 1986-87:

	Men	Women	Total
Of the country	5178	7238	12,416
Of other countries	2438	2560	4998
Total	7616	9798	17,414

4625 **COLLEGE OF BASIC EDUCATION**
P.O. Box 34053, Adiyilia 73251
Telephone: 2514200/2514323
Dean: Marzoug Al Gounaim (1986-)

D. of Arabic
Head: Hassan A. Mohsen; *staff* 21
D. of Islamic Education
Head: Yusuf A. Al Firt; *staff* 17
D. of Social Studies
Head: Zuhdi Sammour; *staff* 12
D. of Science
Head: Saeed A. Mahfouz; *staff* 39
D. of Mathematics
Head: Mohamed S. Abd Al Ellah; *staff* 23
D. of Fine Arts
Head: Jassem A.J. Jumma; *staff* 36
D. of Physical Education
Head: Jawad K.S. Hashim; *staff* 43
D. of Library Science
Head: Abdel Wahab Abou Al Nour; *staff* 16
D. of Education and Psychology
Head: Sabria Al Wakeel; *staff* 49
D. of Interior Design
Head: Taher Abdulla Al Zaher; *staff* 8
D. of Home Economics
Head: Samia Abdel Majeed; *staff* 7

Founded 1962 as Teachers' Institute, acquired present status and title 1986. Under the supervision of the Public Authority for Applied Education and Training.

Academic Year: September to June (September-January; February-June).

Admission Requirements: Secondary school certificate.

Fees: None.

Language of Instruction: Arabic.

Degrees and Diplomas: Bachelor of Arts, 4 yrs.

Library: College Library.

Publications: Cultural Season; Cultural Horizon; Journal.

Academic Staff, 1986-87: 290.

Student Enrolment, 1986-87:

	Men	Women	Total
Of the country	395	768	1163
Of other countries	20	13	33
Total	415	781	1196

4626 **COLLEGE OF BUSINESS STUDIES**
P.O. Box 43197, Hawalli 32046
Telex: KT 22615A
Telephone: 2614962
Dean: Hassan Al-Tayeb (1986-)
Administrative Deputy: Sami Al-Ali

Business Administration (including Computer Sciences, Accountancy, Banking and Statistics)

Founded 1975 as institute, acquired present status and title 1986. Under the supervision of the Public Authority for Applied Education and Training.

Arrangements for co-operation with: Georgetown University; Florida International University.

Academic Year: September to June (September-January; February-June).

Admission Requirements: Secondary school certificate.

Fees: None.

Language of Instruction: Arabic.

Degrees and Diplomas: Diploma, 2 yrs. Bachelor, 4 yrs (planned).

Library: College Library.

Academic Staff, 1986-87: 177.

Student Enrolment, 1986-87:

	Men	Women	Total
Of the country	711	1386	2097
Of other countries	152	189	341
Total	863	1575	2438

4627 **COLLEGE OF HEALTH SCIENCES**

P.O. Box 14281, Fayha 72853
Telephone: 2541044
Dean: Abdul Rahman Al-Muhailan (1986-)

Health Sciences (including Nursing, Pharmacy, Food Technology, and Environmental Health)

Founded 1974 as institute. Acquired present status and title 1986. Under the supervision of the Public Authority for Applied Education and Training.

Academic Year: September to June (September-January; February-June).

Admission Requirements: Secondary school certificate.

Fees: None.

Languages of Instruction: Arabic and English.

Degrees and Diplomas: Diploma, 2 yrs. Bachelor of Science, 4 yrs (planned).

Academic Staff, 1986-87: 42 (32).

Student Enrolment, 1986-87:

	Men	Women	Total
Of the country	85	156	241
Of other countries	–	283	283
Total	85	439	524

4628 **COLLEGE OF TECHNOLOGICAL STUDIES**

P.O. Box 42325, Shuwaikh 70654
Telex: 22269 PTT TRG
Telephone: 846471; 847100
Dean: Yaqoob Fahed Al-Obaid (1986-)

D. of Applied Sciences
Head: Abdulmohsen Alkhorqfi; *staff* 40

D. of Mechanical Engineering
Head: Ismail Nasif; *staff* 53

D. of Electrical Engineering
Head: Yousof Abed; *staff* 16

D. of Chemical Engineering
Head: Abdul Majeed Alobaid; *staff* 21

D. of Electronics
Head: Abdulaziz Alsaqr; *staff* 30

D. of Civil Engineering
Head: Forat Tawfik Elrobee; *staff* 15

Founded 1976 as institute. Acquired present status and title 1986. Under the supervision of the Public Authority for Applied Education and Training. Residential facilities for expatriate academic staff and scholarship students.

Academic Year: September to June (September-January; February-June).

Admission Requirements: Secondary school certificate.

Fees: None.

Languages of Instruction: Arabic and English.

Degrees and Diplomas: Diploma, 2 ½-3 yrs.

Library: College Library.

Academic Staff, 1986-87: 179.

Student Enrolment, 1986-87:

	Men	Women	Total
Of the country	1075	110	1185
Of other countries	327	5	332
Total	1402	115	1517

LAO PEOPLE'S DEMOCRATIC REPUBLIC

4629 **UNIVERSITÉ DES SCIENCES MÉDICALES**
Ministère de la Santé publique, Vientiane
Recteur: Nhénara Chounlamany

F. of Medicine
Dean: M. Phokham
F. of Pharmacy
Dean: Phiĕnephén
S. of Public Health
Director: M. Khampiene
S. of Dentistry
Director: M. Phokham

Founded 1958. Under the supervision of the Ministry of Health. Arrangements for co-operation with the University of Strasbourg.

Academic Year: October to August.

Admission Requirements: Secondary school certificate (baccalauréat).

Fees: None.

Language of Instruction: Lao.

Degrees and Diplomas: Diplôme in–Pharmacy; Dentist Assistantship, 4-5 yrs. Doctorat in Medicine, 6 yrs.

Library: Central Library, 28,000 vols.

Academic Staff, 1990: 70 (100).

Student Enrolment, 1990:

	Men	Women	Total
Of the country	517	597	1114

4630 **ÉCOLE SUPÉRIEURE DE PÉDAGOGIE DONGDOK**
Ministère de l'Education, Vientiane

Education
Founded 1958.

4631 **INSTITUT NATIONAL POLYTECHNIQUE**
Ministère de l'Education, Vientiane

Founded 1984.

4632 **ÉCOLE SUPÉRIEURE DES PONTS ET CHAUSSÉES**
Ministère de la Communication et des Transports, Vientiane

Civil Engineering
Founded 1983.

4633 **ÉCOLE SUPÉRIEURE DU BÂTIMENT**
Ministère de la Construction, Vientiane

Construction Engineering
Founded 1979.

4634 **NATIONAL POLYTECHNIC INSTITUTE**
Ministry of Education, Vientiane
Telephone: 5934
Director: Boun Thone Seng Khammy

D. of Electrical and Electronic Engineering
Head: Seng Prasong; *staff* 10
D. of Electronics
D. of Civil Enginnering
Head: Sai Khong; *staff* 12
D. of Mechanical Engineering
Head: Boun Hom; *staff* 11 (7)
D. of Basic Sciences
Head: M. Seuak; *staff* 25

Founded 1984.

Arrangements for co-operation with: Kalinin Polytechnic Institute; Moscow Construction Institute; Hanoi University of Technology; Federal Institute of Technology.

Academic Year: January to September (September-January; February-May).

Admission Requirements: Secondary school certificate (baccalauréat).

Language of Instruction: Lao.

Degrees and Diplomas: Diplomas.

Academic Staff, 1989-90: 108.

Student Enrolment, 1990:

	Men	Women	Total
Of the country	436	84	520

4635 **INSTITUT NATIONAL DES SCIENCES DE L'ÉDUCATION**
Ministère de l'Education, Vientiane

Educational Sciences
Founded 1982.

4636 **INSTITUT NATIONAL DES SCIENCES SOCIALES**
Ministère de l'Education, Vientiane

Social Sciences
Founded 1986.

LEBANON

Universities

4637 ***AL-JÂMI'AH AL-LUBNANIYAH**
Lebanese University
Museum Square, Beirut
Telex: 42151 LE FANSUL
Telephone: 386817/18
President: George Tohmé (1980-90)

F. of Fine Arts
Dean: San'a Abd-El-Samad; *staff* 34 (120)
F. of Science
Dean: Raji Abou-Chacra; *staff* 241 (20)
F. of Law, Political Science and Administration
Dean: Mouhammad Majzoub; *staff* 83 (115)
F. of Letters and Human Sciences
Dean: Sassine Assaf; *staff* 341 (172)
F. of Education
Dean: Sami Abi Tayeh; *staff* 72
F. of Journalism and Communication
Dean: Michel Assi; *staff* 24 (25)
F. of Economics and Business Administration
Dean: Zouhair Shokor; *staff* 36 (85)
F. of Engineering
Dean: Robert Hanna; *staff* 68 (123)
F. of Social Sciences
Dean: Hachem Haydar; *staff* 48 (34)
F. of Agriculture (including Veterinary Science)
Dean: Moin Hamzeh; *staff* 11
F. of Public Health (including Nursing)
Dean: Mahmoud Nasr-Eddine; *staff* 20 (17)
F. of Medicine (including Dentistry and Pharmacy)
Dean: Mounir Abou Assaly; *staff* – (111)

Founded 1951 as teacher training college, reorganized by decree as university 1953. An autonomous State institution under the patronage of the Minister of Education. Financially supported by the State. Governing body: the University Council which, together with the Councils of the faculties and institutes, deals with administrative matters.

Academic Year: October to July.

Admission Requirements: Secondary school certificate (baccalauréat) or recognized equivalent.

Fees: None.

Languages of Instruction: Arabic, French and English.

Degrees and Diplomas: Licence in–Science; Literature and Human Sciences; Communication; Economics and Business Administration; Law, Political Science and Administration, 4 yrs. Diplôme in–Dramatic Art; Fine Arts, 4 yrs; Engineering; Agriculture; Veterinary Medicine; Dentistry; Pharmacy, 5 yrs; Architecture, 6 yrs; Medicine, 8 yrs. Diplôme d'études supérieures (D.E.S.), a further 2 yrs. Doctorate, 3-5 yrs.

Libraries: Central Library; libraries of the Faculties of Science, and Law, 20,000-30,000 vols each.

Publications: Beryte, Juridic Magazine; Hannan (Geography); Dirassat (Science, Literature, and Philosophy) (all biannually).

Student Enrolment, 1986-87:

	Men	Women	Total
Of the country	11,591	11,777	23,368
Of other countries	574	618	1132
Total	12,165	12,395	24,560

4638 ***AMERICAN UNIVERSITY OF BEIRUT**
Beirut U.S. Office: 850 Third Avenue, New York N.Y. 10022
Cables: amunob le
Telex: 20801 LE
Telephone: 340740
President: Frederick P. Herter (1987-)
Registrar: Fuad Haddad

F. of Arts and Sciences
Dean: Lutfy Diab
F. of Medicine (including Nursing)
Dean: Raja N. Khuri
F. of Health Sciences (including Public Health)
Dean: Haroutune Armenian
F. of Engineering and Architecture
Dean: Nassir Sabah
F. of Agriculture and Food Sciences
Dean: Thomas M. Sutherland
D. of Education
Director: George Za'rour
S. of Nursing
Director: Wadad Khalaf
Computer Ce.
Director: Muhammad Manasfi
I. of Money and Banking
Director: Samir Makdisi

Founded 1866 as Syrian Protestant College with school of medicine added 1867 and pharmacy 1871. Re-chartered as American University of Beirut 1920. The university is a private non-denominational institution under a charter from the educational authorities of the State of New York, USA with a self-perpetuating Board of Trustees. Supported by fees, income from an endowment, and private gifts and donations. No organic relationship with anygovernment, religious body, etc. Governing body: the Senate, composed of elected representatives of the faculties. Residential facilities for academic staff and 1000 students.

Arrangements for co-operation with the Universities of: Bari; Perugia; Naples; Johns Hopkins; Michigan.

Academic Year: October to June (October-February; February-June).

Admission Requirements: Graduation from a high school recognized by the university or a secondary school certificate recognized by theuniversity, and entrance examination.

Language of Instruction: English.

Degrees and Diplomas: Bachelor of–Arts, B.A.; Science, B.S.; Science in Public Health; Business Administration, B.B.A.; Science in Dietetics and Nutrition; Science in Nursing, 4 yrs; Engineering, B.E.; Science in Agriculture, 5 yrs; Architecture, B.Arch., 6 yrs. Master of–Arts, M.A.; Science, M.S.; Science in Health Sciences; Business Administration, M.B.A.; Engineering, M.E.; Science in Agriculture; Arts in Education; Public Health, M.S.P.H., 1-3 yrs after Bachelor. Doctor of–Philosophy, 3-4 yrs; postgraduate Medicine, 8 yrs. Nursing Diploma, 3 yrs. Also diplomain Public Health, and Teaching Diploma.

Library: Jafet Memorial Library and branch libraries, *c.* 435,000 vols.

Special Facilities (Museums, etc.): Archaeology Museum; Geology Museum. Herbarium.

Publications: Al-Abhath (annually); Berytus (Archaeological Studies) (annually); Arab Political Documents (annually).

Press or Publishing House: Office of University Publications.

Academic Staff: *c.* 370 (180).

Student Enrolment: *c.* 4460 (Including *c.* 740 foreign students. Also *c.* 800 part-time students in Extension Programme).

4639 ***JAMI'AT AL-QIDDIS YUSSUF**
UNIVERSITÉ SAINT JOSEPH
St. Joseph University
Rue Huvelin, B.P. 293, Beirut
Cables: Medifac
Telephone: 326-636
Recteur: Jean Ducruet, S.J. (1975-90)
Secretaire général: Henri Awit

I. of Religious Sciences
Director: Thom Sicking, S.J.; *staff* 4 (27)
I. of Islamic-Christian Studies
Director: Augustin Dupré La Tour,S.J.; *staff* – (13)
F. of Medicine
Dean: Antoine Ghossain; *staff* 77 (80)

F. of Pharmacy
Dean: Edouard Masri; *staff* 10 (29)
F. of Dentistry
Dean: Elie Aramouni; *staff* 69 (72)
F. of Engineering
Dean: Sélim Catafago; *staff* 39 (134)
F. of Law and Political Science
Dean: Richard Chemaly; *staff* 16 (38)
F. of Economics
Dean: Louis Hobeika; *staff* 8 (15)
F. of Business Administration and Management
Dean: Claude Boustany; *staff* 7 (28)
F. of Letters and Human Sciences
Dean: Sélim Abou, S.J.; *staff* 15 (50)
F. of Nursing and Midwifery
Dean: Isabelle Guernigou; *staff* 10 (80)
I. of Modern Languages and Translation
Director: Jarjoura Hardane; *staff* 12 (35)
S. of Social Welfare
Director: Hyam Kahi; *staff* 6 (8)
I. of Teacher Training (kindergarten and primary levels, and handicapped children)
Director: Aïda Roukos; *staff* 7 (22)
Ce. of Modern Arabic Studies
Director: John Donohue, S.J.
Ce. of Banking
Director: Pierre Nasrallah; *staff* – (15)
Ce. of Insurance Studies
Director: Charles Dahdah; *staff* – (19)
I. of Telecommunications
University Centres at: Tripoli, Saïda, Zahlé.

Founded 1881 by Society of Jesus. Title of University confirmed by Pope Leo XIII 1881. Faculty of medicine established 1883 by agreement with French Government. A private institution. Received some financial assistance from the French State until 1975 when the university became an autonomous institution financed by tuition fees and government subsidies. Governing body: the Conseil de l'Université.

Academic Year: October to July (October-February; February-July).

Admission Requirements: Secondary school certificate (baccalauréat) or foreign equivalent, and entrance examination.

Fees (Pounds): 16,000-24,000, according to field of study.

Languages of Instruction: French and English.

Degrees and Diplomas: Diplôme–d'études universitaires générales (D.E.U.G.); d'études scientifiques préparatoires, 2 yrs. Licence–en Sciences religieuses; en Sciences biologiques et techniques agro-alimentaires; en Gestion des Entreprises; en Sciences commerciales; ès Lettres et des Sciences humaines, 3 yrs; en Droit; en Sciences économiques; d'enseignement en langue et littérature arabes, 4 yrs. Maîtrise, 1 yr after Licence. Diplôme d'études approfondies (D.E.A.); Diplôme d'études superieures spécialisées (D.E.S.S.), 1 yr after Maîtrise. Doctorat by thesis. Doctorat en Médecine, 7 yrs. Also Diplômes de specialité in various fields of medicine. Diplôme de Sage-Femme, midwifery, 3 yrs. Chirurgien dentiste, 5 yrs.

Library: Libraries of the faculties.

Special Facilities (Museums, etc.): Musée de préhistoire.

Publications: Proche-Orient, Etudes Juridiques (biannually); Proche Orient, Etudes Economiques (every 2 months); Mélanges de l'Université Saint-Joseph (annually); Centre d'Etude pour le Monde Arabe Moderne Reports (annually); Annales de la Faculté des Lettres et des Sciences humaines; Collections: 'Documents Huvelin'; 'Publications Techniques et Scientifiques'; 'Annales de la Faculté de Droit'.

Academic Staff, 1986-87:

Rank	Full-time	Part-time
Professeurs titulaires	323	–
Chargés de cours et Assistants	–	660
Total	323	660

Student Enrolment, 1986-87:

Of the country	5479
Of other countries	530
Total	6009*

*Including 3207 women.

4640 ***JÂMI'AT BÂYRUT AL-'ARABIYA**
Beirut Arab University
Tarik El-Jadidé, P.O. Box 11-5020, Beirut
Telex: 22844 ABU
Telephone: 300-110; 301-820
President: Mohamed Ali Abdelrahran (1986-89)
Secretary-General: Issam Houry

F. of Arts (including Sociology)
Dean: Omar Abd-El-Aziz; *staff* 11 (24)
F. of Law (including Islamic Law)
Dean: Mustafa Shiha; *staff* 8 (10)
F. of Commerce (including Business Administration and Economics)
Dean: Ahmed Nour; *staff* 9 (23)
F. of Engineering
Dean: Mohamed Abdel Salam Fathi Ali; *staff* 26 (123)
F. of Architecture
Dean: Mohamed Abd El-Al; *staff* 6 (34)
F. of Science
Dean: Ibrahim Elkholy; *staff* 11 (16)
F. of Pharmacy
Dean: Ibrahim Elkholy; *staff* 2 (13)

Founded 1960 by the Muslim Welfare Society in Beirut. Financed by the Society and by tuition fees. Governing body: the University Council, composed of the Rector, the deans of the faculties, a representative of University Board of Alexandria, and 2 representatives of the Muslim Welfare Society. Affiliated with University of Alexandria.

Academic Year: November to June.

Admission Requirements: Secondary school certificate (baccalauréat) or equivalent.

Fees (Pounds): 1000-3000 per annum.

Languages of Instruction: Arabic and English.

Degrees and Diplomas: Licence in Law, 4 yrs. Bachelor of–Commerce; Arts, 4 yrs; Engineering; Pharmacy; Architecture, 5 yrs. Master of Science, a further 2 yrs. Diploma in Engineering.

Library: Central Library, department libraries, total, *c.* 265,000 vols.

Publication: Research Publications.

Academic Staff, 1986-87: 74 (243).

Student Enrolment, 1986-87:

	Men	Women	Total
Of the country	2141	691	2832
Of other countries	752	212	964
Total	2893	903	3796*

*Also 33,931 external students.

4641 ***UNIVERSITÉ SAINT-ESPRIT**
University of the Holy Ghost
Kaslik, Jounieh
Telex: 45777LE USEK
Telephone: 930124; 932124
Recteur: Louis Hage (1986-92)
Secrétaire général: Ayoub Chahwan

F. of Theology
Dean: Pierre Azzi; *staff* 15 (30)
F. of Philosophy and Human Sciences
Dean: Choukrallah Choufani; *staff* 12 (55)
F. of Letters
Dean: Joseph Mouanes
F. of Commerce
Dean: Antoine Karam; *staff* 10 (38)
F. of Law
Dean: Antoine Khalife; *staff* – (3)
F. of Fine and Applied Arts (including Cinema and Television)
Dean: Abda Badwi; *staff* 3 (89)
I. of History
Director: Augustin Mouhanna; *staff* 4 (9)
I. of Liturgy
Director: Emmanuel Khoury; *staff* 4 (8)
I. of Musicology
Director: Youssef Tannous; *staff* 2 (6)
I. of Pedagogy
Director: Charbel Akiki; *staff* 3 (8)
I. of Liturgy
Director: Jean Tabet; *staff* 10 (6)
Sec. of Languages
Director: Choukrallah Choufani; *staff* 3 (6)

S. of Music
Director: Jacques Badwi; *staff* – (34)
Peace and Development Research Ce.
Director: Joseph Azizi

Founded 1949 by the Lebanese Maronite Order, recognized by the government 1962. A private institution. Financed by the Maronite Order. Some residentialfacilities for students.

Academic Year: October to July (October-January; February-July).

Admission Requirements: Secondary school certificate (baccalauréat) or foreign equivalent.

Languages of Instruction: Arabic and French.

Degrees and Diplomas: Diplôme d'études universitaires générales (D.E.U.G.), 2 yrs. Licence d'Enseignement, 2 yrs. Diplôme d'études approfondies (D.E.A.), 1 further yr. Doctorat (3ème cycle), 2-4 yrs after D.E.A. Also Diplôme-de Langues vivantes, 3 months-3 yrs.

Library: Central Library, 73,000 vols.

Publications: Parole de l'Orient (quarterly); Bulletin; Cahiers de Philosophie et de Théologie (annually).

Academic Staff, 1986-87: 59 (301).

Student Enrolment, 1986-87:

Men	Women	Total
1213	1652	2865*

*Including 82 foreign students.

Other Institutions

4642 **AL-AKADIMIYAH AL-LUBNANIYAH LIL-FÛNÛN AL-JAMILAH**
Lebanese Academy of Fine Arts
Beirut

S. of Decorative Arts
S. of Architecture
S. of Music
S. of Painting

Founded 1937.

4643 **MA'HAD HAÏGAZIAN**
Haigazian College
Rue du Mexique, Kantari, P.O. Box 17480, Beirut
Cables: Haigazcol
Telephone: 349230; 353011

Ce. for Armenian Studies
D. of Business Administration and Economics
D. of Humanities, Language, and Literature
D. of Science
D. of Social and Behavioural Sciences (including Education, Political Science, and Psychology)

Founded 1955 by the Union of Armenian Evangelical Churches of the Near East, Armenian Missionary Association of America and a private grant. Recognized by the Ministry of Education and degrees equated with Licence conferred by the Lebanese University. Governing bodies: the Board of Trustees in the U.S.A.; Board of Managers in Lebanon.

Academic Year: October to June (October-February; February-June).

Admission Requirements: Secondary school certificate (baccalauréat) or equivalent, and entrance examination.

Language of Instruction: English.

Degrees and Diplomas: Bachelor of–Arts, B.A.; Science, B.S.; Business Administration, B.B.A., 4 yrs. Also Diplomas in Teaching.

Libraries: Barsumian (English) Library, *c.* 20,000 vols; Armenian Library, *c.* 18,000.

Publication: The Haigazian Armenological Review (in Armenian) (annually).

Academic Staff: c. 20 (30).

Student Enrolment: c. 360.

4644 **KULLIYAT BEIRUT AL-JAMEIYA**
Beirut University College
P.O. Box 13-5053, Lebanon
Cables: becoge
Telex: 23389 LE
Telephone: (New York) (202) 870-2562
President: Riyad F. Nassar (1982-90)
Vice-President for Administration and Finance: Fawzi Hajjar

D. of Education
Head: Hadia Harb; *staff* 3 (17)
D. of Business Studies
Head: Nihad Pasha *staff* 6 (36)
D. of Business Studies (including Journalism) (Byblos)
Head: Fuad Awad; *staff* 3 (5)
D. of Humanities (including Journalism)
Head: Jean Makdissi; *staff* 15 (37)
D. of Humanities (Byblos)
Head: Ruth Maalouf; *staff* 7 (11)
D. of Natural Sciences
Head: Leila Khoury; *staff* 7 (31)
D. of Social Sciences
Chairman: Mounir Khoury; *staff* 6 (6)
D. of Social Sciences (Byblos)
Head: George Nasr; *staff* 4 (4)
I. for Women's Studies in the Arab World
Head: Julinda Abu Nasr; *staff* 3 (5)
Also Branches in Byblos and Sidon.

Founded 1835 as school for women by the Board of Foreign Missions of the Presbyterian Church, U.S.A., became two-year junior college 1924 and liberal arts college 1950. Acquired present title 1973 and admitted men students 1975. Governing body: the Board of Trustees, comprising as 21 members. Residential facilities for academic staff and woman students.

Arrangements for co-operation with the Board of Regents of the University of the State of New York awarding BA/BS diplomas for students who enrol as Freshman. Dual degrees for engineering students with a number of universities in the USA. Pre-pharmacy programmes with 4 Colleges of Pharmacy in the USA.

Academic Year: October to June (October-February; February-June).

Admission Requirements: Secondary school certificate (baccalauréat) for Lebanese students, or graduation from higher school and entrance examination.

Fees (Pounds): 900,000 per annum.

Language of Instruction: English.

Degrees and Diplomas: Associate in–Arts, A.A.; Applied Science, A.A.S., 2 yrs. Bachelor of–Arts, B.A.; Science, B.Sc., a further 2yrs. Master in Business Studies, M.B.S., a further 1 ½ yrs.

Library: 110,000 vols.

Special Facilities (Museums, etc.): Fine Arts Building for Art Exhibits; Theatre; Radio-TV film studio.

Publications: Alumni Bulletin (quarterly); BUC Newsletter (biannually); BUC Shares - New York Office (biannually); Al-Raida Newsletter (quarterly).

Academic Staff, 1989-90:

Rank	Full-time	Part-time
Professors	8	2
Associate Professors	10	11
Assistant Professors	8	31
Lecturers	3	–
Instructors	26	93
Assistant Instructors	–	36
Total	60	173

Student Enrolment, 1989-90:

	Men	Women	Total
Of the country	1661	1335	2996
Of other countries	130	120	250
Total	1791	1455	3246

4645 **MA'HAD AL-HIKMAT AL-ALI LIL-HÛQÛQ**
College of Law
1961, rue de Hikmat, Beirut

Founded 1961.

4646 **MA'HAD AL-SHARQ AL-AWSUT**
Middle East College
B.P. 1170, Beirut

D. of Religious Studies
D. of History
D. of Business Administration
D. of Engineering
D. of Natural Sciences

Founded 1949.

4647 **KULLIYAT AL-IMAM AL-OUZAI LI-DIRASAT AL-ISLAMIYA**
Imam Ouzai College of Islamic Studies
P.O. Box 14-5355, Beirut
Telephone: 317708
Director: Abdullah Khalidy (1979-)
Registrar: Badr Eddine Nawar

Islamic Studies

Founded 1979 by the Islamic Centre for Education. Nucleus of new university to be called Iram Ouzai University.

Academic Year: October to June.

Admission Requirements: Secondary school certificate (baccalauréat) or equivalent.

Fees (Pounds): 2000 per annum.

Language of Instruction: Arabic.

Degrees and Diplomas: Bachelor of Arts in Islamic Studies, 4 yrs. Master, a further 2 yrs. Doctor, Ph.D.

Library: 25,000 vols.

Academic Staff, 1986-87: 45.

Student Enrolment, 1986-87: 200.

4648 **ISLAMIC COLLEGE OF BUSINESS ADMINISTRATION**
P.O. Box 14-5355, Beirut

Business Administration

Founded 1987 by the Islamic Centre for Education.

LIBERIA

Universities

4649 ***UNIVERSITY OF LIBERIA**

P.O. Box 9020, Capital Hill, Monrovia
Telephone: 22448
President: Joseph Morris

Ce. of Social Sciences and Humanities (including Political Science)
Teachers' Training Ce.
Ce. of Agriculture and Forestry
Ce. of Business and Public Administration
Ce. of Science and Technology
S. of Law
Ce. of Medicine (including Pharmacy and Public Health)
I. of African Studies and Research
D. of Lifelong Education

Founded 1851 as Liberia College, opened 1862. Became university 1951. The institution is responsible to the Ministry of Education and is financed by the State. Governing bodies: the Faculty Senate; the University Council. Residential facilities for *c.* 420 students.

Academic Year: March to December (March-July; August-December).

Admission Requirements: Secondary school certificate and entrance examination.

Language of Instruction: English.

Degrees and Diplomas: Bachelor of–Laws, LL.B., 3 yrs (4 yrs evening); Arts, B.A.; Science, B.Sc., 4 yrs. Doctor of Medicine, 7 yrs.

Library: Total, *c.* 107,400 vols.

Publications: Journal; The Liberian Economic and Management Review; Science Magazine; Research Institute Newsletter (quarterly); Law Journal (biannually); University Spokesman (bimonthly).

Academic Staff: c. 250.

Student Enrolment: c. 3320.

Other Institutions

4650 **CUTTINGTON UNIVERSITY COLLEGE**

P.O. Box 277, Monrovia
Cables: Pecusam
Telephone: 224243
President: Melvin J. Mason
Dean of Academic Affairs: William Saa Salifu

D. of Education
Head: Josephine Nimley; *staff* 7 (4)
D. of Humanities
Head: Saaim Naame; *staff* 5 (2)
D. of Nursing
Head: Cecelia Morris; *staff* 7 (1)
D. of Sciences
Head: A. Korli Korheina; *staff* 10 (1)
D. of Social Science
Head: Joseph S. Guannu; *staff* 10 (3)
D. of Theology
Head: A. Bani Collins; *staff* 2 (1)
I. of Rural Development
Director: Patrick B. Kiadii; *staff* 6 (7)

Founded 1889 as Hoffman Institute. Renamed Cuttington College and Divinity School 1897. Closed 1929 to 1949. Acquired present title 1976. Administered by the Protestant Episcopal Church. Governing body: the Board of Trustees, of which the Episcopal Bishop is President, and including the Minister of Education. Residential facilities for academic staff and students.

Arrangements for co-operation with: Kingston Polytechnic, London; Susquehanna University; Kalamazoo College; Rekiyyo University.

Academic Year: March to December (March-June; August-December).

Admission Requirements: Secondary school certificate or recognized equivalent, and entrance examination.

Language of Instruction: English.

Degrees and Diplomas: Bachelor of–Arts, B.A.; Science, B.Sc., 4 yrs. Doctorate (Honoris Causa).

Library: William V.S. Tubman Library, 100,000 vols.

Special Facilities (Museums, etc.): Africana Collection.

Publication: Cuttington Research Journal (biannually).

Academic Staff, 1986-87:

Rank	Full-time	Part-time
Professors	4	–
Associate Professors	7	2
Assistant Professors	8	1
Lecturers	32	12
Assistant Lecturers	20	–
Total	71	15

Student Enrolment, 1986-87:

	Men	Women	Total
Of the country	478	296	774
Of other countries	37	11	48
Total	515	307	822

LIBYA
(Socialist People's Libyan Arab Jamahirya)

4651 ***UNIVERSITY OF GARYOUNIS**

P.O. Box 1308, Benghazi
Telephone: 87462
Vice-Chancellor: Salem Shebani

F. of Letters and Education
F. of Economics and Commerce
F. of Law
F. of Science
F. of Engineering
F. of Agriculture
F. of Dentistry
Research Ce. for Social Sciences and Economics

Founded 1955 as University of Libya, reorganized as two separate Universities in Benghazi and Tripoli, 1974. Under the jurisdiction of the Ministry of Education and financed by the government. Governing body: the University Council. Residential facilities for students living outside Benghazi.

Academic Year: October to June (October-January; February-June).
Admission Requirements: Secondary school certificate or equivalent.
Fees: None.
Languages of Instruction: Arabic and English.
Degrees and Diplomas: Degree of Bachelor, 4 yrs.
Library: c. 250,000 vols.
Publications: Faculty Journals; Arts; Law; Economics (all annually).
Academic Staff: c. 510.
Student Enrolment: c. 4720 (Also *c.* 4040 external students).

4652 ***UNIVERSITY OF AL-FATEH**

P.O. Box 13482, Tripoli
Telephone: 36010/8
President: Ibraheim El-Muntases

F. of Science (including Zoology)
F. of Agriculture
F. of Engineering
F. of Letters
F. of Petroleum Technology
F. of Nuclear Engineering and Electronics
F. of Medicine
F. of Pharmacy
F. of Veterinary Medicine
F. of Education (Zawia)

Founded 1957 as University of Libya, reorganized as two separate universities in Tripoli and Benghazi, 1974. Under the jurisdiction of the Ministry of Education and financed by the government.

Academic Year: September to June (September-January; February-June).
Admission Requirements: Secondary school certificate or equivalent.
Fees: None.
Languages of Instruction: Arabic and English.
Degrees and Diplomas: Degree of Bachelor, 4-5 yrs. Master of Science, M.Sc., a further 2 yrs.
Library: c. 10,000 vols.
Academic Staff: c. 1000.
Student Enrolment: c. 24,000.

4653 **SEBHA UNIVERSITY**

P.O. Box 18758, Sebha
Telex: 30622
Telephone: (071) 21575/76
Secretary, People's Committee: Mansoor Rahdi Saleh (1985-)

F. of Education
Head: Sanusi Amer Sanusi; *staff* 85 (3)
F. of Science
Head: Idris Al-Hadi; *staff* 111 (6)
Research Ce. for African Studies

Founded 1983, incorporating the Faculty of Education of the University of Al-Fateh. Residential facilities for academic staff and students.

Academic Year: September to June (September-November; December-February; March-June).
Admission Requirements: Secondary school certificate.
Language of Instruction: Arabic.
Degrees and Diplomas: Bachelor, 3-4 yrs.
Library: Central Library, 78,000 vols.
Academic Staff, 1986-87: 178 (9).
Student Enrolment, 1986-87: c. 2000.

4654 **AL-ARAB MEDICAL UNIVERSITY**

Benghazi

F. of Medicine
F. of Dentistry

Founded 1984.

4655 **HIGHER INSTITUTE OF ELECTRONICS**

P.O. Box 8645, Beni Walid/Souk Jin

Founded 1976.

4656 **HIGHER INSTITUTE OF MECHANICS AND ELECTRICAL ENGINEERING**

P.O.Box 61160, Hon
Telex: 30254 EM HON LY
Telephone: (57) 2841
Fax: (57) 2842
Dean: Abulghassem M. Mohamed
Registrar: Ahmed A. Ehmeda

D. of Mechanical Engineering
Head: Mohd. Ahmed Al-Rifi
D. of Electrical Engineering
Head: Al-Amin A. Ehmeda
Sec. of English
Head: Ahmed Younus
Sec. of Mathematics
Head: Basim Al-Khafaji

Founded 1976. Residential facilities for academic staff and atudents.

Academic Year: October to July.
Admission Requirements: Secondary school certificate.
Fees: None.
Language of Instruction: Arabic.
Degrees and Diplomas: Bachelor of Engineering Technology, 4 yrs.
Publication: Technical Journal of HIMEE.
Academic Staff, 1990: 20.
Student Enrolment, 1990: 350.

4657 **HIGHER INSTITUTE OF TECHNOLOGY**

P.O. Box 68, Brack
Telex: 30621 BK HIT LY
Telephone: 45300
Dean: Abdussalam Mohamed Almethnani (1988-)
Registrar: Abdulgader Mohamed Almethnani

D. of Medical Laboratory Technology
Head: Omar Mohamed Abukhres; *staff* 8 (2)
D. of Food Technology
Head: Salem Sassi Shamekh; *staff* 9 (2)
D. of Environmental Technology
Head: Mohamed Ibrahim Chirgawi; *staff* 12 (2)
D. of General Sciences
Head: Abdulgader Ali Ajaili; *staff* 5 (2)

Founded 1976. Residential facilities for academic staff.

Academic Year: October to June.
Admission Requirements: Secondary school certificate.
Fees: None.
Degrees and Diplomas: Degree of Bachelor, 4 yrs.
Library: 10,000 vols.
Academic Staff, 1989-1990:

Rank	Full-time	Part-time
Associate Professors	2	–
Assistant Professors	7	–
Lecturers	19	2
Assistant Lecturers	8	–
Total	36	2

Student Enrolment, 1989-1990:

	Men
Of the country	245
Of other countries	15
Total	260

LUXEMBOURG

4658 **CENTRE UNIVERSITAIRE DE LUXEMBOURG**
162A, avenue de la Faïencerie, Luxembourg 1511
Telephone: 216-21
Président: Pierre Seck (1987-91)
Directeur administratif: Gilbert Trausch

D. of Law and Economics
Head: Paul Margue; *staff* 1 (69)
D. of Letters and Human Sciences
Head: M.-Thérèse Schroeder-Hartmann; *staff* – (54)
D. of Science
Head: Pierre Seck; *staff* 4 (39)
D. of Education
Head: J.P.R. Strainchamps; *staff* – (21)
D. of Law
Head: Robert Biever; *staff* – (10)
Sem. of Mathematics
Head: Jean-Paul Pier

Founded 1848 as Cours supérieur. Centre Universitaire established 1968 and achieved present status 1974. Financed by the State. Governing body: the Conseil d'administration. Limited residential facilities for students.

Arrangements for co-operation with Universities in: France, Belgium, Austria, Federal Republic of Germany, United Kingdom, and Canada.

Academic Year: October to May (October-January; February-May).

Admission Requirements: Secondary school certificate or foreign equivalent.

Fees: None.

Language of Instruction: French.

Degrees and Diplomas: Certificats, 2 sem. Diplôme d'études universitaires pratiques en économie et en droit (D.E.U.P.E.D.). Diplôme de Gradué en gestion, 4 sem.

Library: 160,000 vols.

Academic Staff, 1986-87:

Rank	Full-time	Part-time
Professeurs	5	65
Chargés de cours	–	47
Chargés d'enseignement	–	72
Assistants	–	9
Total	5	193

Student Enrolment, 1986-87:

	Men	Women	Total
Of the country	305	278	583
Of other countries	51	47	93
Total	356	320	676

4659 **INSTITUT UNIVERSITAIRE INTERNATIONAL DE LUXEMBOURG**
162A, avenue de la Faïencerie, Luxembourg

Ce. for Juridical Studies and Comparative Law
Ce. for Political Economics
Ce. for European Studies and Research

Founded 1958, reorganized 1974. Financed by the State. Governing body: the Conseil universitaire.

Academic Year: October to June (October-February; February-June).

Admission Requirements: Licence.

Language of Instruction: French.

Degrees and Diplomas: Certificats.

4660 **INSTITUT SUPÉRIEUR D'ÉTUDES ET DE RECHERCHES PÉDAGOGIQUES**
B.P. 2, 7201 Wolferdange
Telephone: 33-14-14
Fax: 33-32-56
Directeur: Georges Wirtgen (1985-)

Education

Founded 1960. Reorganized 1983.

Academic Year: October to July (October-January; February-July).

Admission Requirements: Secondary school certificate.

Fees: None.

Languages of Instruction: French and German.

Degrees and Diplomas: Certificat d'Etudes pédagogiques, 3 yrs.

Publication: Cahiers.

Academic Staff, 1989-90: 10 (50).

Student Enrolment, 1989-90:

	Men	Women	Total
Of the country	74	132	206

4661 **INSTITUT SUPÉRIEUR DE TECHNOLOGIE**
Rue R. Coudenhove-Kalergie, Luxembourg-Kirchberg
Telex: 3586 LST DR
Telephone: 43-66-61
Fax: 43-21-24
Directeur: Paul Feidert
Sécretaire général André Bouteiller

Civil Engineering
Industrial Computer Sciences
Ce. for Applied Microelectronics Research

Founded 1976.

Participates in the ECTS programme.

Academic Year: October to July.

Admission Requirements: Secondary school certificate.

Fees: None.

Languages of Instruction: French and German.

Degrees and Diplomas: Ingénieur technicien, 3 yrs.

Library: Centre de Documentation scientifique et technique.

Academic Staff, 1989: 41 (11).

Student Enrolment, 1989:

Of the country	215	9	224
Of other countries	41	1	42
Total	256	10	266

4662 **INSTITUT EUROPÉEN POUR LA GESTION DE L'INFORMATION**
13, rue de Bragance, Luxembourg

Information Management

Founded 1982.

MACAU

4663 ***UNIVERSIDADE DA ÁSIA ORIENTAL**

University of East Asia
P.O. Box 3001, Macau
Cables: Ueastasia
Telex: 88397 UEA OM
Telephone: 27322
Rector: Shou Sheng Hsueh
Secretary: K.W.J. Topley

S. of Arts
Dean: M. Macmillan; *staff* 8 (2)
S. of Business Administration
Dean: G.H. Hines; *staff* 12 (3)
S. of Social Sciences ; *staff* 6 (3)
Ce. of Education (planned)
Graduate Ce.
Principal: G.H. Hines; *staff* 1 (20)
Ce. Polytechnic
Principal: T.L. Tomáz; *staff* – (13)
Also junior and open colleges.

Founded 1981. A private institution. Financially supported by tuition fees and donations. Governing bodies: the Board of Trustees, comprising 9 members; the Council, comprising 53 members. Residential facilities for students.

Arrangements for co-operation with: South China Normal University; Shenzhen University.

Academic Year: September to June (September-January; February-June).

Admission Requirements: A recognized General Certificate of Education with minimum 2-3 passes at Advanced Level.

Fees (Pataca): 30,000 per annum.

Languages of Instruction: English and Chinese.

Degrees and Diplomas: Associate, 2 yrs. Bachelor of–Arts; Science; Business Administration; Social Sciences, 3 yrs. Master, a further 2 yrs. Also postgraduate diplomas, 1-2 yrs.

Library: 52,899 vols.

Press or Publishing House: University of East Asia Press.

Academic Staff, 1986-87:

Rank	Full-time	Part-time
Professors	7	5
Associate Professors	14	13
Assistant Professors	7	8
Lecturers	40	82
Assistant Lecturers	9	–
Tutors	–	166
Total	77	274

Student Enrolment, 1986-87:

	Men	Women	Total
Of the country	1791	637	2428
Of other countries	220	45	265
Total	2011	682	2693*

*Also 3746 external students.

MADAGASCAR

4664 ***UNIVERSITÉ D'ANTANANARIVO**

University of Antananarivo
B.P. 566, Ambohitsaina, Antananarivo
Telex: 22304 RECUMT MG
Telephone: 241-14
Recteur: Raymond Ranjeva
Secrétaire général: Guy Anselme Rakotovao

S. of Law, Economics, Administration, and Sociology
President: Willy Leonard
S. of Sciences
President: Emile Ralaisoa Rakotomahanina
S. of Health Sciences (Medicine)
President: Joseph Andrianjatovo
Polytechnic S.
President: Solonjatovo Rakotonirina
S. of Letters
President: Jeannine Rambeloson
S. of Agriculture (including Forestry, Stockbreeding, and Food Industries)
S. of Teacher Training (including Physical Education)
Director: Josiane Ranaivo Rabgetokotany

Founded 1955 as Institut des hautes Etudes tracing origins to school of medicine (1896) and school of law (1941). Became Université de Madagascar 1960. Reorganized 1973 with six main divisions, and in 1976 as a decentralized institution with six Regional Centres. Acquired present status as independent university 1988.

Arrangements for co-operation with university institutions in: France; La Réunion; Germany; Algeria; Switzerland; U.S.A.; USSR.

Academic Year: November to July.

Admission Requirements: Secondary school certificate (baccalauréat) or equivalent, and entrance examination.

Languages of Instruction: French and Malgache.

Degrees and Diplomas: Diplôme universitaire d'études scientifiques (D.U.E.S.); Diplôme universitaire d'études littéraires (D.U.E.L.); Diplôme universitaire d'études technologiques (D.U.E.T.), 2 yrs; Licence, 1 further yr; Maîtrise, 1 yr after Licence. Diplôme d'études approfondies (D.E.A.), 1 yr after Maîtrise; Diplôme d'études supérieures (D.E.S.), 2 yrs after Maîtrise. Diplôme d'Ingénieur, 4 yrs. Doctorat (3ème cycle). Doctorat en Médecine, 7 yrs. Also teaching qualifications.

Library: c. 120,000 vols.

Special Facilities (Museums, etc.): Museum of Art and Archaeology.

4665 **UNIVERSITÉ D'ANTSIRANANA**

University of Antsiranana
B.P. 0, Antsiranana
Recteur: M. Befeno

Polytechnic S.
S. of Letters

Founded 1975 as Regional Centre of Université de Madagascar. Acquired present status as independent university 1988.

Academic Year: November to July.

Admission Requirements: Secondary school certificate (baccalauréat) or equivalent, and entrance examination.

Languages of Instruction: French and Malgache.

Degrees and Diplomas: Diplôme universitaire d'études scientifiques (D.U.E.S.); Diplôme universitaire d'études littéraires (D.U.E.L.); Diplôme universitaire d'études technologiques (D.U.E.T.), 2 yrs; Licence, 1 further yr; Maîtrise, 1 yr after Licence. Diplôme d'études approfondies (D.E.A.), 1 yr after Maîtrise; Diplôme d'études supérieures (D.E.S.), 2 yrs after Maîtrise. Diplôme d'Ingénieur, 4 yrs. Doctorat (3é cycle). Doctorat en Médecine, 7 yrs. Also teaching qualifications.

4666 **UNIVERSITÉ DE FIANARANTSOA**

University of Fianarantsoa
B.P. 1264, Fianarantsoa
Recteur: Michel Dieudonné Razafindrantsimaniry

S. of Law
S. of Sciences

Founded 1977 as Regional Centre of the Université de Madagascar. Acquired present status as independent university 1988.

Academic Year: November to July.

Admission Requirements: Secondary school certificate (baccalauréat) or equivalent, and entrance examination.

Languages of Instruction: French and Malgache.

Degrees and Diplomas: Diplôme universitaire d'études scientifiques (D.U.E.S.); Diplôme universitaire d'études littéraires (D.U.E.L.); Diplôme universitaire d'études technologiques (D.U.E.T.), 2 yrs; Licence, 1 further yr; Maîtrise, 1 yr after Licence. Diplôme d'études approfondies (D.E.A.), 1 yr after Maîtrise; Diplôme d'études supérieures (D.E.S.), 2 yrs after Maîtrise. Diplôme d'Ingénieur, 4 yrs. Doctorat (3é cycle). Doctorat en Médecine, 7 yrs. Also teaching qualifications.

4667 **UNIVERSITÉ DE MAHAJANGA**

University of Mahajanga
B.P. 652, Mahajanga
Recteur: M. Rajabo

S. of Dentistry
S. of Sciences
S. of Medicine

Founded 1977 as Regional Centre of Université de Madagascar. Acquired present status as independent university 1988.

Academic Year: November to July.

Admission Requirements: Secondary school certificate (baccalauréat) or equivalent, and entrance examination.

Languages of Instruction: French and Malgache.

Degrees and Diplomas: Diplôme universitaire d'études scientifiques (D.U.E.S.); Diplôme universitaire d'études littéraires (D.U.E.L.); Diplôme universitaire d'études technologiques (D.U.E.T.), 2 yrs; Licence, 1 further yr; Maîtrise, 1 yr after Licence. Diplôme d'études approfondies (D.E.A.), 1 yr after Maîtrise; Diplôme d'études supérieures (D.E.S.), 2 yrs after Maîtrise. Diplôme d'Ingénieur, 4 yrs. Doctorat (3é cycle). Doctorat en Médecine, 7 yrs. Also teaching qualifications.

4668 **UNIVERSITÉ DE TOAMASINA**

University of Toamasina
B.P. 591, Toamasina
Recteur: Emile Tsizaraina

S. of Law, Economics, Business Administration, and Sociology
S. of Letters

Founded 1977 as Regional Centre of Université de Madagascar. Acquired present status as independent university 1988.

Academic Year: November to July.

Admission Requirements: Secondary school certificate (baccalauréat) or equivalent, and entrance examination.

Languages of Instruction: French and Malgache.

Degrees and Diplomas: Diplôme universitaire d'études scientifiques (D.U.E.S.); Diplôme universitaire d'études littéraires (D.U.E.L.); Diplôme universitaire d'études technologiques (D.U.E.T.), 2 yrs; Licence, 1 further yr; Maîtrise, 1 yr after Licence. Diplôme d'études approfondies (D.E.A.), 1 yr after Maîtrise; Diplôme d'études supérieures (D.E.S.), 2 yrs after Maîtrise. Diplôme d'Ingénieur, 4 yrs. Doctorat (3é cycle). Doctorat en Médecine, 7 yrs. Also teaching qualifications.

4669 **UNIVERSITÉ DE TOLIARA**

University of Toliara
B.P. 185, Toliara
Recteur: Philibert Ndata

S. of Law
S. of Sciences

Founded 1977 as Regional Centre of the Université de Madagascar. Acquired present status as independent university 1988.

Academic Year: November to July.

Admission Requirements: Secondary school certificate (baccalauréat) or equivalent, and entrance examination.

Languages of Instruction: French and Malgache.

Degrees and Diplomas: Diplôme universitaire d'études scientifiques (D.U.E.S.); Diplôme universitaire d'études littéraires (D.U.E.L.); Diplôme universitaire d'études technologiques (D.U.E.T.), 2 yrs; Licence, 1 further yr; Maîtrise, 1 yr after Licence. Diplôme d'études approfondies (D.E.A.), 1 yr after Maîtrise; Diplôme d'études supérieures (D.E.S.), 2 yrs after Maîtrise. Diplôme d'Ingénieur, 4 yrs. Doctorat (3é cycle). Doctorat en Médecine, 7 yrs. Also teaching qualifications.

MALI

4670 **ÉCOLE DES HAUTES ÉTUDES PRATIQUES**

B.P. 242, Bamako

Directeur: Adoulaye Haidara

Business Administration (including Accountancy)

Secretarial Studies

Founded 1974.

4671 **ÉCOLE NATIONALE D' ADMINISTRATION**

B.P. 276, Bamako

Telephone: 22-17-19

Directeur: Yaya Doumbia

Sec. of Public Administration

Sec. of Law

Sec. of Economics

Founded 1963. A State institution responsible to the Ministry of Education.

Arrangements for co-operation with: Institut international d'Administration publique, Paris; University of Pittsburgh.

Academic Year: October to June (October-February; February-June).

Admission Requirements: Secondary school certificate (baccalauréat) or equivalent, and entrance examination.

Language of Instruction: French.

Degrees and Diplomas: Diplôme, 4 yrs.

Academic Staff: c. 30 (60).

Student Enrolment: c. 1750.

4672 **ÉCOLE NATIONALE D'INGÉNIEURS**

B.P. 242, Bamako

Telephone: 22-27-36

Directeur: Siné Camara Mamadou

Sec. of Civil Engineering

Sec. of Electro-Mechanical Engineering

Sec. of Geology

Sec. of Topography

Sec. of Science

Founded 1950 as School of Public Works, acquired present status and title 1963. A State institution. Financed by the State with assistance from Unesco.

Academic Year: October to June (October-February; February-June).

Admission Requirements: Secondary school certificate (baccalauréat) and entrance examination.

Language of Instruction: French.

Degrees and Diplomas: Diplôme d'Ingénieur des Sciences appliquées.

Library: Total, c. 2300 vols.

Academic Staff: c. 80 (20).

Student Enrolment: c. 470.

4673 **ÉCOLE NATIONALE DE MÉDECINE ET DE PHARMACIE DU POINT G**

B.P. 1805, Bamako

Telephone: 22-52-77; 22-59-23

Directeur: Aliou Ba

Medicine

Pharmacy

Founded 1968. Financed by the State. Governing bodies: the Conseil pédagogique et scientifique; the Conseil de perfectionnement. Residential facilities for *c.* 60 students.

Academic Year: October to June (October-December; January-March; April-June).

Admission Requirements: Secondary school certificate (baccalauréat) and entrance examination.

Fees: None.

Language of Instruction: French.

Degrees and Diplomas: Diplôme de–Docteur en Médecine; Pharmacien, 5 ½ yrs.

Library: Central Library.

Academic Staff: c. 10 (60).

Student Enrolment: c. 300.

4674 **ÉCOLE NATIONALE DES POSTES ET TÉLÉCOMMUNICATIONS**

Bamako

Directeur: Alfarooye Sanfo

Telecommunication Engineering

Founded 1969.

4675 **ÉCOLE NORMALE SUPÉRIEURE**

B.P. 241, Bamako

Telephone: 22189

Teacher Training (secondary level)

Founded 1962. Financed by the State. Residential facilities for *c.* 200 students.

Academic Year: October to June (October-December; January-March; April-June).

Admission Requirements: Secondary school certificate (baccalauréat) and entrance examination.

Fees: None.

Language of Instruction: French.

Degrees and Diplomas: Diplôme, 4 yrs.

Library: c. 2150 vols.

Academic Staff: c. 120.

Student Enrolment: c. 1760.

4676 **INSTITUT POLYTECHNIQUE RURAL DE KATIBOUGOU**

B.P. 6, Koulikoro

Telephone: 26-20-12

Directeur: Kalifa Sanogo

Agriculture

Stockraising

Forestry

Veterinary Medicine and Animal Husbandry (Bamako)

Founded 1966. A State institution responsible to the Ministry of Education. Some residential facilities for academic staff and students.

Academic Year: October to September (October-February; June-September).

Admission Requirements: Secondary school certificate (baccalauréat) and entrance examination. Technicien supérieur, Diplôme (D.E.F.) and entrance examination.

Language of Instruction: French.

Degrees and Diplomas: Diplôme de–Technicien supérieur; d'Ingénieur des Sciences appliquées, 4 yrs. Diplôme de Docteur-Ingénieur ès Sciences, a further 3 yrs.

Library: c. 3200 vols.

Special Facilities (Museums, etc.): Forestry Museum.

Academic Staff: c. 300.

Student Enrolment: c. 12,000.

4677 **INSTITUT SUPÉRIEUR DE FORMATION ET RECHERCHE APPLIQUÉE**

B.P. 241, Bamako

Directeur: Moustapha Soumaré

Teacher Training (postgraduate studies)

Founded 1970 as Centre Pédagogique Supérieur. Acquired present status and title 1982.

MARTINIQUE

4678 **UNIVERSITÉ DES ANTILLES ET DE LA GUYANE**
Route de Bellevue, 97260 Fort-de-France
Telephone: 72-60-24
President: Philippe Saint-Cyr (1982-87)

F. of Law and Economics (Schoelcher)
Ut. of Letters and Human Sciences
Also courses at Pointe-à-Pitre (Guadeloupe), and at Cayenne (French Guiana).

Founded 1850 as School of Law, became Centre Universitaire des Antilles-Guyane 1949 and Université 1982. Attached to the Académie de Bordeaux. Financially supported by the Ministry of Education. Residential facilities for students.

Academic Year: October to June (October-December; January-March; April-June).

Admission Requirements: Secondary school certificate (baccalauréat) or foreign equivalent, or special entrance examination.

Language of Instruction: French.

Degrees and Diplomas: Capacité en Droit, 2 yrs. Diplôme d'études universitaires générales (D.E.U.G.), 2 yrs. Licence, 4 yrs. Diplôme d'études supérieures spécialisées (D.E.S.S.) in Foreign Trade, 1 further yr.

Library: 15,000 vols.

Academic Staff: c. 40.

Student Enrolment: c. 1220.

MAURITANIA

4679 **UNIVERSITÉ DE NOUAKCHOTT**
B.P. 227, Nouakchott
Recteur: M. Haibetna O. Sidi Haiba

F. of Letters and Humanities
F. of Law and Economics
Founded 1986.

4680 **CENTRE SUPÉRIEUR D'ENSEIGNEMENT TECHNIQUE**
B.P. 227, Nouakchott

D. of Mechanical Engineering
D. of Electrical Engineering
Founded 1981.

4681 **INSTITUT SUPÉRIEUR DES SCIENCES**
B.P. 5026, Nouakchott
Directeur: Simone Ba

Applied Sciences
Founded 1970 as Ecole normale supérieure, acquired present status and title 1986.

4682 **INSTITUT SUPÉRIEUR SCIENTIFIQUE**
B.P. 227, Nouakchott

D. of Mathematics
D. of Physics
D. of Chemistry
D. of Biology
D. of Geology
Founded 1986.

MEXICO

Universities

Public Institutions

4683 **UNIVERSIDAD AUTÓNOMA AGRARIA 'ANTONIO NARRO'**
Domicilio Conocido, Buena Vista, 25315 Saltillo, (Coahuila)
Telex: 038128
Telephone: 4-31-00
Fax: 21481
Rector: Oswaldo Garcia Martńez
Secretario General: Luis Alberto Aguirre Uribe

F. of Agronomy (including Parasitology, Forestry, and Horticulture)
Co-ordinator: César Estrada Torres; *staff* 138 (8)
F. of Engineering
Co-ordinator: Salvador Muñoz Castro; *staff* 110 (4)
F. of Socioeconomic Science
Co-ordinator: José Gpe. Narro Reyes; *staff* 27 (25)
F. of Animal Science
Co-ordinator: Humberto González Morales; *staff* 34 (12)
F. of Agronomy (Torreón)
Co-ordinator: Armando Moreno Rubio; *staff* 37 (64)
F. of Animal Science (Torreón)
Co-ordinator: Manuel Hernández Valenzuela; *staff* 30 (8)
Branches in Laguna, Torreón, and Coahuila.

Founded 1923. An autonomous institution financially supported by the State and federal governments. Residential facilities for students.

Academic Year: August to May (August-December; January-May).

Admission Requirements: Secondary school certificate (bachillerato).

Fees (Pesos): 36,000 per semester; Graduate, 59,000.

Language of Instruction: Spanish.

Degrees and Diplomas: Licenciado and Professional titles, 4 yrs. Degree of Maestría, a further 2 yrs. Doctorado, after 3 yrs.

Library: Biblioteca Egidio Rebonato, 17,000 vols.

Special Facilities (Museums, etc.): Biological Garden; Observatory; Meterological Station.

Publications: Comuna (monthly); Revista Agraria (every 2 months); Avances de Investigación (6 cassettes).

Academic Staff, 1989: 246 (135).

Student Enrolment, 1989:

	Men	Women	Total
Of the country	3034	318	3352

4684 ***UNIVERSIDAD AUTÓNOMA DE AGUASCALIENTES**
Autonomous University of Aguascalientes
Jardín del Estudiante 1, 20000 Aguascalientes (Aguascalientes)
Telephone: 4-32-07
Fax: (491) 4-55-91
Presidente: Gonzalo González Hernández (1990-92)
Secretario General: Santiago Cortés Chvez

Ce. of Basic Studies
Dean: Juan José Martínez Guerra; *staff* 75 (56)
Ce. of Biomedical Sciences
Dean: Antonio Ávila Storer; *staff* 19 (122)
Ce. for Agriculture and Veterinary Medicine
Dean: Javier Hernández Dueñas; *staff* 32 (15)
Ce. for Technology
Dean: Héctor Elizalde González; *staff* 43 (79)
Ce. of Economics and Administration
Dean: Jaime Medina Rodríguez; *staff* 27 (99)
Ce. of Arts and Humanities
Dean: Genaro Zalpa Ramírez; *staff* 87 (108)
Also 3 Medical Clinics and secondary and high schools.

Founded 1867 as Instituto Autónomo de Ciencias y Tecnología, acquired present title and status 1973. An autonomous institution financially supported by the State and federal governments. Governing bodies: the Consejo Universitario (University Council), comprising 14 members of the academic staff, 14 students, and 7 others; the Consejo de Representantes, including equal academic staff and student representation.

Academic Year: August to June (August-December; January-June).

Admission Requirements: Secondary school certificate (bachillerato).

Fees (Pesos): 312,000 per semester.

Language of Instruction: Spanish.

Degrees and Diplomas: Licenciado in–Law, Communication; Letters; Social work; History; Applied Mathematics; Informatics; Chemico-Biology Analysis; Optometry; Education; Public Health; Busines Administration; Industrial Relations; Economics; Tourism; Town Planning, 8-10 sem. Professional titles in–Veterinary Medicine; Sociology; Biology; Engineering; Nursing; Medicine; Accountancy; Architecture; Graphic Design, 6-10 sem. Maestría, Master, a further 2 yrs.Also postgraduate diplomas of specialization.

Library: Total, 78,844 vols.

Special Facilities (Museums, etc.): Biological Garden. Varvente Radio Station.

Publication: Voz Universitaria (quarterly).

Academic Staff, 1989-90: 303 (619).

Student Enrolment, 1986-87:

	Men	Women	Total
Of the country	3364	3555	6919
Of other countries	384	327	711
Total	3748	3882	7630

4685 ***UNIVERSIDAD AUTÓNOMA DE BAJA CALIFORNIA**
Autonomous University of Baja California
Avenida Alvaro Obregón y Julián Carrillo s/n, 21100 Mexicali (Baja California)
Cables: igual
Telex: 569888
Telephone: 54-22-00
Rector: Héctor Manuel Gallego García (1983-87)
Secretario General: Luis Javier Garavito Elias

S. of Accountancy
Director: Magdaleno Chávez Lara; *staff* 10 (65)
S. of Architecture
Director: Jorge Nuñez Verdugo; *staff* 17 (65)
S. of Agriculture (including Animal Husbandry)
Director: Alfredo Ruiz Mendez; *staff* 31 (24)
S. of Education
Director: Clara Elena Gallego Salas; *staff* 14 (28)
S. of Social and Political Sciences
Director: Mauricio Esparza Enriquez; *staff* 13 (37)
S. of Law
Director: Miguel Figueroa Zavala; *staff* 10 (36)
S. of Pedagogy
Director: Bardomiano González Pérez; *staff* 10 (43)
S. of Veterinary Medicine and Animal Husbandry
Director: Héctor Torres Fdz. Cuerra; *staff* 25 (15)
S. of Medicine
Director: Humberto Torres Sangines; *staff* 13 (113)
S. of Dentistry
Director: Xavier Aguilera; *staff* 13 (32)
S. of Accountancy and Business Administration (Tijuana)
Director: Sergio Octavio Vázquez; *staff* 18 (98)
S. of Chemistry
Director: Héctor Felipe Salgado; *staff* 26 (18)
S. of Law (Tijuana)
Director: Jesús Alfredo Osuna Lafarga; *staff* 12 (49)
S. of Economics
Director: Alejandro Mungaray; *staff* 8 (12)

S. of Medicine (Tijuana)
Director: Héctor Rivera Valenzuela; *staff* 10 (98)
S. of Tourism
Director: Raquel Stabinsky Velasco; *staff* 9 (28)
S. of Marine Science
Director: María Guadalupe García; *staff* 41 (52)
S. of Biology
Director: Alejandro Martínez Ruiz; *staff* 20 (47)
S. of Engineering
Director: Pablo Fok Pun; *staff* 21 (120)
S. of Dentistry (Tijuana)
Director: Alberto Contreras Sánchez; *staff* 10 (41)
S. of Engineering (Ensenada)
Director: Miguel Mario Juarez Villarreal; *staff* 3 (13)
S. of Accountancy (Ensenada)
Director: Héctor Manuel Miramontes; *staff* 3 (29)
S. of Nursing
Director: José Mayagoitia Gómez; *staff* 7 (45)
S. of Agricultural Technology
Director: Luis Febronio Diaz Nuñez; *staff* 2 (11)
S. of Humanities
Director: Gustavo Almaraz Montaño; *staff* 2 (10)
I. of Geography and History Research
Director: Adalberto Walther Meade; *staff* 1 (1)
I. of Marine Research
Director: Román Lizarraga Arciniega; *staff* 33 (4)
I. of Engineering Research
Director: Ruben Roa Quiñonez; *staff* 12 (2)
I. of Social Research
Director: Gabriel Estrella Valenzuela; *staff* 5 (2)
Ce. for Historical Research
Director: David Piñera Ramírez; *staff* 4 (1)
I. of Economic and Social Research
Director: Alejandro Mungaray; *staff* 6 (1)
S. of Social Work
Director: Alejandro Iñigo Soto; *staff* – (15)

Founded 1957. An autonomous institution financially supported by the State and federal governments. Governing bodies: the Junta de Gobierno consisting of 11 honorary members; the Consejo Universitario, including representatives of the academic and administrative staffs and of the students.

Arrangements for co-operation with: Fullerton College; University of California Davis and Los Angeles; University of San Diego; State University of New York.

Academic Year: August to June (August-December; January-June).

Admission Requirements: Secondary school certificate (bachillerato).

Fees (Pesos): 8800-19,000.

Language of Instruction: Spanish.

Degrees and Diplomas: Licenciado in–Public Administration and Political Science; Education; Sociology; Business Administration; Computer Sciences, 4 yrs; Communication; Psychology; Law, 4 ½ yrs; Economics; Tourism, 5 yrs. Professional titles of–Técnico agropecuario, 2 yrs; Enfermera(o), 3 yrs; Partero, midwife; Cirujano dentista; Contador público, accountancy, 4 yrs; Arquitecto; Químico; Ingeniero (various fields); Oceanólogo; Médico veterinario y Zootecnista, 4-5 yrs; Biólogo; Físico, 5 yrs; Médico general, 6 yrs. Degree of Maestría in–Biopharmacy; Solar Architecture. Also postgraduate diplomas of specialization.

Libraries: Central Library, 37,162 vols; Tijuana, 12,938; Ensenada, 9496.

Special Facilities (Museums, etc.): University Museum.

Publication: Revistas.

Academic Staff, 1986-87: 763 (17,192).

Student Enrolment, 1986-87: 22,000.

4686 UNIVERSIDAD AUTÓNOMA DE BAJA CALIFORNIA SUR

Autonomous University of Baja California South
Ciudad Universitaria, Km. 5 Carretera Al Sur, 23000 La Paz (Baja California Sur)
Telephone: 4-22-00

Ce. of Social Sciences (including Political Science and Economics)
Ce. of Marine Sciences
Ce. of Agricultural Sciences (including Animal Husbandry)
Extension D.

Founded 1975. An autonomous State university financially supported by the State and federal government. Governing body: the Consejo Universitario.

Academic Year: January to December (January-June; August-December).

Admission Requirements: Secondary school certificate (bachillerato) and entrance examination.

Language of Instruction: Spanish.

Degrees and Diplomas: Licenciado in–Political Science and Public Administration; Economics, 9 sem. Professional titles of–Biólogo marino; Geólogo marino; Ingeniero agrónomo; Médico zootecnista, 9 sem; Ingeniero en Pesquerías, fishery, 10 sem.

Libraries: Social Sciences, *c.* 1000 vols; Biology, *c.* 1000.

Publications: Revista Panorama (bimonthly); Gaceta Universitaria (monthly).

Academic Staff: c. 30 (40).

Student Enrolment: c. 540.

4687 UNIVERSIDAD AUTÓNOMA DEL CARMEN

Autonomous University of Carmen
Calle 31 x 56, 24176 Ciudad del Carmen (Campeche)
Telephone: 2-11-33
Rector: Luis Alberto Fuentes Mena
Secretary-General: Melchor Ahumada Jiménez

F. of Law
Director: Efren Requena Espinosa
F. of Education
Director: Andrés E. Salazar Dzib.
F. of Commerce and Administration
Director: Ma. Manuela Inurreta N.; *staff* 4
F. of Fishery
Director: Maria C. Rosano Hdez. *staff* 3
F. of Chemistry
Director: José del C. Zavala Loría; *staff* 4
F. of Engineering
Director: Ernesto Mellado Gutiérrez; *staff* – (6)
S. of Nursing
Director: Javier Reyes Naal
S. of Languages
Director: Martha Orterga Roldan.; *staff* – (3)
S. of Commerce
Director: Trinidad A. Trujillo C.; *staff* 2

Founded 1967.

Academic Year: September to June (September-February; March-June).

Admission Requirements: Secondary school certificate (bachillerato) and entrance examination.

Degrees and Diplomas: Licenciado. Professional titles.

Library: Total, 5709.

Academic Staff: c. 340.

Student Enrolment: c. 4480.

4688 UNIVERSIDAD AUTÓNOMA DE CHAPINGO

Autonomous University of Chapingo
Km. 38.5 Carretera México-Texcoco, 56230 Chapingo (Estado de México)
Telephone: (5) 5-10-88-80
Fax: (595) 4-61-40
Rector: Hugo Ramirez Maldonado
Academic Director: Agustin López Herrera

Agriculture

Also 8 Regional Centres, and a Unit for Arid Zones.

Founded 1854 as school of agriculture, became university 1974. An autonomous institution under the jurisdiction of the Ministry of Agriculture, and financially supported by the State and federal governments. Governing body: the Consejo Universitario. Residential facilities for academic staff and students.

Arrangements for co-operation with: Instituto Superior de Ciencias Agropecuarias de La Habana; Universität Humboldt, Berlin; Universidad del Salvador.

Academic Year: August to June (August-December; February-June).

Admission Requirements: Secondary school certificate (bachillerato) and entrance examination.

Language of Instruction: Spanish.

Degrees and Diplomas: Title of Ingeniero agrónomo, in various fields, 4 yrs. Degree of Maestría, 2 yrs.

Library: Central Library, *c.* 55,040 vols.

Special Facilities (Museums, etc.): Museo Nacional de Agricultura.

Academic Staff, 1989: 1157.
Student Enrolment, 1989:

	Men	Women	Total
Of the country	4814	641	5455

4689 ***UNIVERSIDAD AUTÓNOMA DE CHIAPAS**
Autonomous University of Chiapas
Avenida Norte-Poniente 151, 29050 Tuxtla Gutiérrez (Chiapas)
Telephone: 2-53-55
Rector: Jorge Cruz Toledo T.

Administration
Physics and Mathematics
Biomedicine
Humanities
Law (San Cristóbal Las Casas)
Sociology (San Cristóbal Las Casas)
Business Administration (Tapachula)
Agriculture (Tapachula)
Acccountancy
Chemistry (Tapachula)
Agriculture (Villa Flores)
Agriculture (Huehuetan)

Founded 1975 incorporating previously existing schools. An autonomous institution supported by the State and federal governments. Governing bodies: the Junta de Gobierno; the Consejo Universitario.

Academic Year: September to June (September-January; February-June).

Admission Requirements: Secondary school certificate (bachillerato).

Degrees and Diplomas: Licenciado in–Business Administration; Accountancy; Tourism; Industrial Relations; Agricultural Development; Law; Economics; Sociology; Anthropology; Public Administration, 9 sem. Professional titles of–Ingeniero, in various fields; Químico en alimentos; Químico agrícola; Químico farmacobiólogo, 9 sem; Médico cirujano odontólogo, dentistry, 10 sem; Médico cirujano, medicine, 11 sem.

Library: Specialized libraries of the Departments.

Publications: Vida Universitaria; Criterio Universitario.

Academic Staff: c. 470.

Student Enrolment: c. 6820.

4690 **UNIVERSIDAD AUTÓNOMA DE CHIHUAHUA**
Autonomous University of Chihuahua
Escorza y B. Carranza s/n, 31000 Chihuahua (Chihuahua)
Telephone: 5-24-27
Rector: Rudolfo Torres M. (1985-89)

F. of Agriculture
Director: Raúl Castillo L.
F. of Accountancy and Administration
Director: Mario Salcido O.
F. of Law
Director: Rodolfo Acosta M.
F. of Physical Education
Director: José Agripino Medina Z.
F. of Nursing and Midwifery
Director: Leticia Moriel Corral
F. of Philosophy and Letters
Director: Enrique Macín Rascón
S. of Public Administration and Political Science
Director: Jesús Jasso Reyes

Founded 1954. An autonomous institution, financially supported by the State and federal governments. Governing body: the Consejo Universitario.

Academic Year: September to June (September-January; February-May).

Admission Requirements: Secondary school certificate (bachillerato).

Language of Instruction: Spanish.

Degrees and Diplomas: Licenciado and Professional titles, 4-5 yrs. Degree of Maestría, a further 2 yrs.

Academic Staff, 1986-87: 288 (1061).
Student Enrolment, 1986-87:

	Men	Women	Total
Of the country	7800	3450	11,250
Of other countries	9	–	9
Total	7809	3450	11,259

4691 **UNIVERSIDAD AUTÓNOMA DE CIUDAD JUÁREZ**
Autonomous University of Ciudad Juárez
Avenida López Mateos 20, Apartado postal 1594D, 32310 Ciudad Juárez (Chihuahua)
Telephone: 3-12-22
Rector: Enrique Villareal Macias

I. of Biomedicine
I. of Social Sciences and Administration
I. of Engineering (including Architecture)

Founded 1973. An autonomous institution financially supported by the State and federal governments.

Academic Year: September to June (September-January; February-June).

Admission Requirements: Secondary school certificate (bachillerato) and entrance examination.

4692 ***UNIVERSIDAD AUTÓNOMA DE COAHUILA**
Autonomous University of Coahuila
Bulevar Venustiano Caranza y Licenciado Salvador González Lobo, 25280 Saltillo (Coahuila)
Telephone: 2-01-55
Rector: Jaime Isaías Ortiz Cárdenas (1985-88)
Secretario General: Germán de J. Froto Madariaga

F. of Education
F. of Law
S. of Chemistry
S. of Economics
S. of Civil Engineering
S. of Architecture
S. of Psychology
S. of Nursing and Midwifery
S. of Social Work
S. of Plastic Arts
S. of Medicine
S. of Medicine (Torreón)
S. of Dentistry (Torreón)
S. of Commerce and Administration (Torreón)
S. of Political Science (Torreón)
S. of Law and Social Sciences (Torreón)
S. of Economics (Torreón)
S. of Nursing (Torreón)
Open U.I. (Torreón)
S. of Mechanical and Electrical Engineering (Norte)
S. of Mining and Metallurgy (Norte)
Also preparatory schools.

Founded 1867 as 'Ateneo Fuente', became university by decree 1957. An autonomous institution receiving financial support from the State and federal governments. Governing body: the Consejo Universitario.

Academic Year: August to June (August-December; January-June).

Admission Requirements: Secondary school certificate (bachillerato) and entrance examination.

Language of Instruction: Spanish.

Degrees and Diplomas: Licenciado or Professional titles in all fields. Degree of Maestría. Postgraduate degrees of specialization in Medicine.

Library: Total, *c.* 81,500.

Special Facilities (Museums, etc.): Museo 'Ateneo Fuente'; Museo Preparatorio 'Venustiano Carranza'.

Publication: Gazeta de la Universidad de Coahuila.

Academic Staff, 1986-87: c. 900.
Student Enrolment, 1986-87:

Of the country	24,000
Of other countries	500
Total	24,500

4693 ***UNIVERSIDAD DE COLIMA**
University of Colima
Avenida Universidad 333, 28000 Colima (Colima)
Telex: 62248 UCOLME
Telephone: 2-54-36
Rector: Jorge Humberto Silva Ochoa (1984-88)

F. of Education
Director: Juan Eliezer de Los S.; *staff* – (3)
F. of Accountancy and Administration
Director: Heriberto Ibañez Jimenez; *staff* 5 (36)

F. of Medicine
Director: Francisco Lepe Auguayo; *staff* 6 (48)
F. of Mechanical and Electrical Engineering
Director: Abraham Castillo V.; *staff* 29 (5)
F. of Biological Sciences
Director: José Ma. Salas González; *staff* – (5)
F. of Architecture
Director: Gonzalo Villa Chavez; *staff* – (4)
F. of Law
Director: Héctor G. Anguiano S.; *staff* 1 (21)
S. of Political and Social Sciences
Director: Josué Noé de la Vega; *staff* 2 (34)
S. of Social Work
Director: Ana Cecilia García; *staff* 4 (29)
S. of Economics
Director: Roberto Langarica A.; *staff* – (17)
S. of Civil Engineering
Director: José Luis García P.; *staff* 6 (21)
S. of Chemistry
Director: Salvador Rodríguez Huerta; *staff* 17 (8)
S. of Nursing
Director: Sonia I. Serrano Barreda; *staff* 2 (31)
S. of Veterinary Medicine and Animal Husbandry
Director: Gustavo Cerna Elizondo; *staff* 11 (10)
S. of Marine Sciences
Director: José Ramón Luna Hernández; *staff* 25 (20)
S. of Letters and Communication
Director: Salvador G. Silva Padilla; *staff* 4 (24)
S. of Foreign Languages
Director: Carlos A. Sánchez Mancilla; *staff* 3 (3)
Also 8 research centres.

Founded 1940 as Universidad Popular. Acquired present status and title 1960. An autonomous State institution.

Arrangements for co-operation with the Universities of: Oregon State; Iowa; Córdoba, Spain; Nicaragua.

Academic Year: August to July (August-January; February-July).

Admission Requirements: Secondary school certificate (bachillerato) and entrance examination.

Language of Instruction: Spanish.

Degrees and Diplomas: Licenciado in–Nursing; Letters and Journalism; Rural Communication, 4 yrs; Sociology; Political Science; Public Administration; Economics; Education, 4 ½ yrs; Social Work; Business Administration; Oceanology, 5 yrs. Professional titles of–Ingeniero (various fields), 3-5 yrs; Químico farmacéutico biólogo, 4 yrs; Contador público, accountancy; Arquitecto; Médico veterinario y zootecnista, 5 yrs; Médico cirujano, 6 yrs. Degree of Maestría.

Libraries: Central Library; specialized libraries, total, 42,000 vols.

Publication: Revistas.

Academic Staff, 1986-87: 161 (476).

Student Enrolment, 1986-87:

	Men	Women	Total
Of the country	3064	2068	5132
Of other countries	1	–	1
Total	3065	2068	5133

4694 **UNIVERSIDAD JUÁREZ DEL ESTADO DE DURANGO**
Juárez University of Durango
Constitución 404 Sur, 34000 Durango (Durango)
Telephone: 2-00-44
Rector: José Hugo Martínez Ortiz
Secretario General: Alejandro Gaitán Manuel

S. of Law
S. of Medicine
S. of Accountancy and Administration
S. of Mathematics
S. of Forestry
S. of Social Work
S. of Sociology
S. of Music
S. of Dentistry
S. of Nursing and Midwifery
S. of Commerce
S. of Veterinary Medicine and Animal Husbandry
S. of Zoology (Gomez Palacio)
S. of Food Technology (Gomez Palacio)
S. of Agricultural Engineering (Gomez Palacio)
S. of Civil Engineering (Gomez Palacio)
S. of Medicine (Gomez Palacio)

Founded 1856 as Colegio Civil, became Instituto Juárez 1872. Acquired present rank and title 1957. An autonomous institution financially supported by the State and federal governments. Governing bodies: the Consejo Universitario; the Junta Directiva.

Academic Year: February to November.

Admission Requirements: Secondary school certificate (bachillerato).

Language of Instruction: Spanish.

Degrees and Diplomas: Licenciado in–Law; Biology; Food Technology; Administration, 9-10 sem. Professional titles of–Enfermera, nursing; Contador público, accountancy; Médico veterinario; Ingeniero agrónomo; Ingeniero civil, 9-10 sem. Médico cirujano; Médico cirujano dentista.

Library: Total, *c.* 65,200 vols.

Academic Staff: *c.* 1190.

Student Enrolment: *c.* 21,790.

4695 **UNIVERSIDAD AUTÓNOMA DEL ESTADO DE HIDALGO**
Autonomous University of Hidalgo
Abasolo 600, 42000 Pachuca (Hidalgo)
Telephone: 2 65 34
Rector: Juan Alberto Flores Álvarez

I. of Law and Social Sciences
I. of Accountancy and Administration
I. of Industrial Engineering
I. of Exact Sciences
S. of Medicine
S. of Dentistry
S. of Social Work
S. of Nursing
Also high school.

Founded 1869 as school, acquired present status and title 1961. An autonomous institution financially supported by the State and federal governments. Governing body: the Consejo Universitario.

Academic Year: September to June (September-January; February-June).

Admission Requirements: Secondary school certificate (bachillerato) and entrance examination.

Language of Instruction: Spanish.

Degrees and Diplomas: Licenciado in–Law; Public Administration; Business Administration, 4 ½ yrs. Professional titles in–Nursing, 3 yrs; Social Work, 4 yrs; Dentistry; Industrial Engineering; Accountancy, 4 ½ yrs; Medicine, 5 yrs.

Libraries: Central Library, *c.* 32,100 vols; Social Sciences, *c.* 5110; Accountancy and Administration, *c.* 2490; IndustrialEngineering, *c.* 2460; Medicine, *c.* 1820; Dentistry, *c.* 120; Social Work, *c.* 830; Nursing, *c.* 610.

Academic Staff: *c.* 110 (340).

Student Enrolment: *c.* 9530.

4696 **UNIVERSIDAD AUTÓNOMA DEL ESTADO DE MÉXICO**
Autonomous University of the State of Mexico
Instituto Literario 100 Oriente, 50000 Toluca (Estado de México)
Telex: 174426 UAMME
Telephone: 5-45-04
Rector: Jorge Guadarrama López (1984-85)
Secretario Administrativo: Victor Ortega García

F. of Architecture and Fine Arts
Director: Héctor Serrano Barquín
F. of Behavioural Sciences
Director: Pilar Gallegos Vargas
F. of Political Science and Public Administration
Director: Juan Miguel Morales
F. of Accountancy and Administration
Director: Felipe Nemer Naime
F. of Humanities
Director: Eugenio Nuñez Ang
F. of Engineering
Director: José Luis Cortés Martínez
F. of Law
Director: Reynaldo Robles Martínez
F. of Medicine
Director: Javier Sánchez Guerro
C. of Dentistry
Director: Joel Nava Romero

C. of Agriculture
Director: Aristeo Alvarez Arratia
C. of Chemistry
Director: Roberto Laureles Solano
C. of Economics
Director: Román López Flores
C. of Geography
Director: Carlos Reyes Torres
C. of Veterinary Medicine
Director: Joel Nava Romero
Also 8 high schools.

Founded 1828 as Institute of Science and Letters, acquired autonomous status 1943, became university 1956. An autonomous institution. Financially assisted from State and federal funds. Governing body: the Consejo Universitario.

Arrangements for co-operation with the Universities of: Santiago de Compostela; Laval; Warsaw; Oviedo.

Academic Year: September to August (September-February; March-August).

Admission Requirements: Secondary school certificate (bachillerato) or foreign equivalent, and entrance examination.

Fees (Pesos): Foreign students, 65,000 per annum.

Language of Instruction: Spanish.

Degrees and Diplomas: Licenciado and Professional titles in–Agriculture; Anthropology; Business Administration; Philosophy; History; Tourism; Geography, 4 yrs; Civil Engineering; Mechanical Engineering; Veterinary Medicine; Political Science; Economics; Nursing; Psychology; Medicine; Dentistry; Chemistry, 4-5 yrs; Law; Architecture, 5 yrs. Degree of Maestría in–Public Administration; Construction Engineering; Computer Sciences; Urban and Regional Planning; Sociology; Law; Philosophy.

Library: c. 125,000 vols.

Special Facilities (Museums, etc.): Museum of Natural History; Museum of History; Pinacoteca; University Museum.

Publications: Revista (quarterly); Universidad (monthly); Collections: Sciences and Technics; Semillas; Nuestro Mexico; Research; Faculty Magazines.

Press or Publishing House: Departamento Editorial de la U.A.E.M.

Academic Staff: c. 230 (40).

Student Enrolment: c. 27,030.

4697 **UNIVERSIDAD AUTÓNOMA DEL ESTADO DE MORELOS**

Autonomous University of the State of Morelos
Avenida Universidad 1001, 62210 Cuernavaca (Morelos)
Telex: 173392 UAMME
Telephone: 13-10-90; 13-88-09
Rector: Fausto Gutiérrez Aragón (1982-88)
Secretario General: Federico García Rodríguez

F. of Accountancy and Business Administration
F. of Chemistry and Industrial Engineering
S. of Agriculture
S. of Law and Social Sciences
S. of Biology
S. of Psychology
S. of Medicine
S. of Education and Human Communication
S. of Architecture

Founded 1939 as a State institution of higher education and tracing history to a literary college founded 1872. Became university 1953. By decree of 1967 granted independence from federal and State governments as autonomous university. An autonomous institution financially supported by the State and federal governments. Governing body: the Consejo Universitario.

Academic Year: September to June.

Admission Requirements: Secondary school certificate (bachillerato) and entrance examination.

Language of Instruction: Spanish.

Degrees and Diplomas: Bachiller in various fields. Licenciado in–Business Administration; Law; Psychology. Professional titles in–Biochemical Technology; Nursing, 3 yrs; Biology; Industrial Chemistry, 4 yrs; Architecture; Accountancy; Business Administration; Industrial Engineering, 5 yrs. Teaching qualifications.

Libraries: Central Library, c. 20,000 vols; Science library, c. 5000; specialized libraries, c. 16,000.

Special Facilities (Museums, etc.): Geology and Mineralogy Museum.

Publication: Extensión Universitaria.

Press or Publishing House: University Press.

Student Enrolment: c. 16,540.

4698 ***UNIVERSIDAD DE GUADALAJARA**

University of Guadalajara
Avenida Juárez 975, 44100 Guadalajara (Jalisco)
Telex: 0681744 XHUG MEX
Telephone: 26-72-86
Fax: 26-40-48
Rector: Raul Padilla López (1989-95)
Secretario General: Guillermo Arturo Gómez Reyes

F. of Administration
Director: Agustín Alva Castillo; *staff* 34
F. of Agronomy
Director: J. Antonio Sandoval Madrigal; *staff* 32
F. of Agriculture (Autlán)
Director: José Flores Sandoval
F. of Accountancy
Director: Jorge Rodríguez Santana; *staff* 48
F. of Architecture
Director: Carlos Correa Ceseña; *staff* 34
F. of Chemistry
Director: Antonio Oropeza Chávez; *staff* 27
F. of Dentistry
Director: José Humberto Muñoz López; *staff* 34
F. of Economics
Director: J. Abelino Torres Montes de Oca; *staff* 16
F. of Engineering
Director: Luis Castillo Jiminez; *staff* 36
F. of Geography
Director: Manuel Morales García; *staff* 11
F. of Law
Director: Jesús Villalobos; *staff* 9
F. of Medicine
Director: Raúl Vargas López
S. of Nursing
Director: Laura M. Padilla Gutierrez; *staff* 12
S. of Nursing (Ciudad Guzman)
Director: José Francisco Espinoza Cardenas; *staff* 15
S. of Nursing (Ocotlán)
Director: Abigail Medina Velarde
F. of Philosophy and Letters
Director: Carlos Fregoso Gennis; *staff* 18
S. of Plastic Arts
Director: Sergio Zepeda Castañeda; *staff* 13
F. of Psychology
Director: Jorge Arauz Contreras; *staff* 9
F. of Science
Director: Adolfo Espinoza de los Monteros; *staff* 15
F. of Social Work
Director: Margarita Garza de Villareal; *staff* 12
F. of Tourism
Director: Virginia Marcela Gómez Reyes; *staff* 13
F. of Veterinary Medicine and Animal Husbandry
Director: José Rizo Ayala; *staff* 24
F. of Veterinary Medicine and Animal Husbandry (Ciudad Guzmán)
Director: Juan Mercado Agredano
Polytechnic S.
Director: Ignacio Mora Luna; *staff* 28
Polytechnic S. (Ocotlán)
Director: José Luis Zamora Vargas; *staff* 7
I. of Human Settlement
Director: Jorge Camberos Garibi
I. of Astronomy and Meteorology
Director: Enrique Flores Tritschler
I. of Botany
Director: Luz Ma. Villareal de Puga
I. for the Development of Capital Goods
Director: Juan Villalvazo Naranjo
I. of Economic and Regional Studies
Director: Jesús Arroyo Alejandre
I. of Social Studies
Director: Mario Rodríguez Lapuente
I. of Geography and Statistics
Director: Rosier Omar Barrera Rodríguez

I. of Limnology
Director: Manuel Guzmán Arroyo
I. for Wood, Cellulose and Paper Studies
Director: José Turrado Saucedo
I. of Infectious and Experimental Pathology
Director: Eduardo Rodríguez Noriega
I. for Psychiatry and Psychosomatic Disorders
Director: Carlos Corona Ibarra
Regional I. for Public Health Research
Director: Osmar Juan Matsui Santana
Also 24 preparatory schools and vocational centres, and 13 research laboratories and centres.

Founded 1791 by Royal Decree of Charles IV of Spain. An autonomous State institution. Governing bodies: the Dirección General Académia; the Dirección General de Extensión Universitaria.

Arrangements for co-operation with the Universities of: Quebec; California, Los Angeles, Berkeley; North Carolina; New Mexico; Oregon State; Moorhead State; Pittsburgh; Washington; Washington State; Wisconsin, Madison; El Salvador; Centraoamerican Managua, Nicaragua; Nicaragua; Los Andes, Bogota; INCCA de Colombia; Colombia (National); Zulia, Venezuela; Dresden (Technical); Leipzig; Hamburg; Tübingen; Oviedo; Valladolid; Compultense de Madrid; Autónoma de Madrid; Pais Vasco; Montpellier III; Rennes II; Reading; Lublin; Warsaw; Kyoto; Oran. Polytechnic of North London; University College of London; Fachhochschule Münster; National University of the South, Bahia Blanca.

Academic Year: September to August (September-February; March-August).

Admission Requirements: Secondary school certificate (bachillerato) and entrance examination.

Language of Instruction: Spanish.

Degrees and Diplomas: Licenciado in–Economics; Business Administration; Philosophy; Letters; Sociology; Psychology; History; Accountancy; Physical Education; Social Work; Tourism; Public Administration; Biology; Physics; Mathematics; Industrial Design; Interior Design; Geography; Teaching English. Professional titles of–Médico cirujano y Partero; Abogado, law; Ingeniero (various fields); Cirujano dentista; Químico, chemistry; Químico farmacobiólogo; Arquitecto; Enfermera, nursing; Médico veterinario y zootecnista. Degree and Maestría. Doctorado. Postgraduate titles and specialization.

Library: Total, 379,000 vols.

Publications: Amatl; Argumentos; Carta Economica Regional; Ciencia Animal; Comunicación y Sociedad; Cuadernos; Dimensiones; Estudios Sociales; Función; Palabra; Prometeo; Reforma y Utopia; Sociedad y Estado; Tiempos de Arte; Tiempos de Ciencia.

Press or Publishing House: Depártamento Editorial.

Academic Staff, 1989-90: c. 900 (6000).

Student Enrolment, 1989-90: c. 209,700.

4699 **UNIVERSIDAD DE GUANAJUATO**

University of Guanajuato
Lascuraín de Retana 5, 36000 Guanajuato (Guanajuato)
Telephone: 2-03-04
Rector: Santiago Hernández Ornelas (1983-)
Secretario General: Juan Carlos Romero Hicks

S. of Accountancy and Administration
Director: Cecilia H. Barrios Cebassos; *staff* 10 (60)
S. of Law
Director: Pedro Vázquez Nieto; *staff* 13 (24)
S. of Mining, Geology, and Metallurgy
Director: Antonio Nieto Antunez; *staff* 17 (18)
S. of Medicine
Director: Ricardo Santoyo Valenzuela; *staff* 24 (113)
S. of Chemistry
Director: Francisco Barajas Arredondo; *staff* 36 (34)
S. of Electronics, and Mechanical and Electrical Engineering
Director: Arturo Lara López; *staff* 30 (33)
S. of Architecture
Director: Salvador Covarrubias Alcocer; *staff* 19 (34)
S. of Plastic Arts
Director: José Escalera Chagoyán; *staff* 5 (7)
S. of Business Administration
Director: Germán Rodríguez Frias; *staff* 13 (61)
S. of Interior Design
Director: Gloria del Rosario Toranzo; *staff* 3 (13)
S. of Nursing and Midwifery (4)
Director: Irene Mora Martínez; *staff* 14 (19)
S. of Philosophy and Letters
Director: Luis Palacios Hernández; *staff* 11 (23)
S. of Civil Engineering
Director: Luis Mario Zamarripa; *staff* 12 (19)
S. of Topography
Director: Rodrigo Ogaz Muñoz; *staff* 7 (17)
S. of Music
Director: Mario Ruiz Santillán; *staff* 4 (20)
S. of Industrial Relations
Director: Francisco Montiel Domínguez; *staff* 7 (25)
S. of Agriculture and Animal Husbandry
Director: Rafael Ramírez Malagón; *staff* 22 (7)
S. of Psychology
Director: Augusto Vázquez Aguilar; *staff* 13 (37)
S. of Mathematics
Director: Arturo Ramírez Flores; *staff* 2 (11)
S. of Auxiliary Accountancy
Director: Guadalupe Ochoa Duarte; *staff* 5 (16)
I. of Physics
Director: Clicerio Avilez Valdez; *staff* 9
I. of Education Research
Director: María del Carmen Carrasco Hernández; *staff* 9
Agriculture and Food Technology Research Ce.
Director: Victor Rios Mercadillo; *staff* 15 (7)
Language Ce.
Director: Virgilio Fernández Wrenches; *staff* 3 (4)
Also 58 affiliated high (preparatory) schools.

Founded 1732 as Colegio de la Purísima, became a State institution 1870, raised to university rank 1945. Financially supported by the State and federal governments. Governing body: the Consejo Universitario. Residential facilities for visiting academic staff.

Arrangements for co-operation with the Universities of: California, Fresno, Davis; San Diego State; Southern Oregon State; Chicago State; Campiñas State; California, Riverside; Warsaw (Technical); Texas Tech.; Valencia; Seville; Laval; São Paulo.

Academic Year: August to June (August-December; January-June).

Admission Requirements: Secondary school certificate (bachillerato) and entrance examination.

Language of Instruction: Spanish.

Degrees and Diplomas: Licenciado in–Interior Design, 3 ½ yrs; Nursing; Philosophy; History; Letters, 4 yrs; International Commerce; Psychology, 4 ½ yrs; Law; Industrial Relations; Mathematics; Business Administration; Industrial Relations, 5 yrs. Professional titles of–Ingeniero, various fields, 3-5 yrs; Químico, 4 yrs; Contador público, accountancy; Arquitecto; Químico farmacobiólogo, 5 yrs; Médico cirujano, 6 ½ yrs. Degree of Maestría. Doctorado in–Physics; Biology. Postgraduate titles of specialization. Teaching qualifications in Music.

Libraries: Central Library, 33,116 vols; Architecture, 4064; Chemistry, 5137; Accountancy and Administration, 4097; Medicine, 7697; Engineering, 3503; Mining and Metallurgy, 2777; Agriculture and Animal Husbandry, 3024; Business Administration, 6741; Nursing, 11,066; Civil Engineering, 3649; Psychology, 927.

Special Facilities (Museums, etc.): Museums: Natural History; Mineralogy; Anatomy.

Publication: Colmena Universitaria (every 3 months).

Academic Staff, 1986-87: 366 (699).

Student Enrolment, 1986-87:

	Men	Women	Total
Of the country	9470	7475	16,945
Of other countries	30	4	34
Total	9500	7479	16,979

4700 **UNIVERSIDAD AUTÓNOMA DE GUERRERO**

Autonomous University of Guerrero
Avenida Abasolo 33, 39020 Chilpancingo (Guerrero)
Telephone: 2-25-36
Rector: José Enrique González Ruiz

S. of Social Sciences (Acapulco)
S. of Philosophy and Letters
S. of Engineering
S. of Education
C. of Law
C. of Architecture and Town Planning
C. of Economics
C. of Biological and Chemical Sciences

C. of Commerce and Administration (Acapulco)
C. of Tourism (Acapulco)
C. of Agriculture (Iguala)
C. of Medicine (Acapulco)
C. of Marine Ecology (Acapulco)
C. of Veterinary Medicine and Animal Husbandry (Ciudad Altamirana)
C. of Earth Sciences (Taxco el Viejo)
Also preparatory schools.

Founded 1869, reorganized 1960. An autonomous institution financially supported by the State and federal governments.

Degrees and Diplomas: Licenciado in–Law; Economics; Tourism; Philosophy; Ibero-American Literature; Sociology; History; Professional titles of–Ingeniero Topógrafo y Geodesta; Químico biólogo; Ingeniero agrónomo; Contador público; accountancy; Médico cirujano; Ecólogo marino.

4701 ***UNIVERSIDAD AUTÓNOMA METROPOLITANA**
Metropolitan Autonomous University
Boulevard Manuel Avila Camacho 90, Col. El Parque, 53390 Naucalpan de Juárez (Estado de México)
Telex: 1772152 AUMRME
Telephone: 576-79-00
Fax: 5766529
Rector: Gustavo A. Chapela Castañares (1989-93)
Secretario General: Enrique Fernández Fasaracht

D. of Social Sciences and Humanities (including Law and Economics) (Azcapotzalco)
Director: Jorge Fernández Souza; *staff* 358 (28)
D. of Basic Sciences and Engineering (Azcapotzalco)
Director: Eduardo de la Garza Vizcaya; *staff* 3528 (229)
D. of Arts and Design (Azcapotzalco)
Director: Emilio Martínez de Velasco; *staff* 267 (30)
D. of Social Sciences and Humanities (including Political Science and Psychology) (Iztapalapa)
Director: Ignacio Llamas Buitrón; *staff* 276 (64)
D. of Basic Sciences and Engineering (Iztapalapa)
Director: José Luis Gázquer Mateos; *staff* 276 (64)
D. of Biological and Health Sciences (including Food Technology) (Iztapalapa)
Director: José Ramírez Pulido; *staff* 193 (95)
D. of Social Sciences and Humanities (Xochimilco)
Director: Sonia Comboni Salinas; *staff* 368 (11)
D. of Biological and Health Sciences (including Dentistry, Veterinary Medicine and Animal Husbandry) (Xochimilco)
Director: Fernando de la Mora Carrasco; *staff* 365 (8)
D. of Arts and Design (including Town Planning and Architecture) (Xochimilco)
Director: Concepción Vargas Sánchez; *staff* 166 (20)

Founded 1973. An autonomous State institution financed by the federal government. Governing body: the Academic Councils.

Academic Year: September to July (September-December; January-April; May-July).

Admission Requirements: Secondary school certificate (bachillerato) and entrance examination.

Fees (Pesos): Foreign students, 500,000 per annum.

Language of Instruction: Spanish.

Degrees and Diplomas: Licenciado in–Administration; Nursing; Law; Economics; Sociology; Communication; Psychology; Social Anthropology; Political Science; Humanities, 4 yrs. Professional titles of–Ingeniero, in various fields; Matemático; Químico; Cirujano dentista; Biólogo, biology; Químicobiólogo; Farmacobiólogo; Estomatólogo; Médico veterinario y zootecnista, veterinary medicine and animal husbandry; Arquitecto, architecture; Diseñador, in various fields, 4 yrs. Médico, medicine, 5 yrs. Degree of Maestría. Doctorado in Science.

Library: Campus libraries, total 320,144 vols.

Publications: Campus Bulletins; Organo Informativo (weekly); Pauta; Contactos; Argumentos; Gutemberg Dos; Sociológica Azc (quarterly); Cuadernos; Casa del Tiempo (monthly); Revista A; Revista Aleqatos; Universidad Futura (seasonal).

Press or Publishing House: University Press.

Academic Staff, 1989-90:

Rank	Full-time	Part-time
Profesores Titulares	676	95
Profesores Asociados	1491	318
Profesores Asistentes	462	102
Total	2629	515

Student Enrolment, 1989-90:

	Men	Women	Total
Of the country	25,722	14,974	40,696
Of other countries	586	246	822
Total	26,298	15,220	41,518

4702 ***UNIVERSIDAD NACIONAL AUTÓNOMA DE MÉXICO**
National Autonomous University of Mexico
Ciudad Universitaria, 4510 México (D.F.)
Telex: 1777429 UNAMME
Telephone: 548-40-40; 548-89-31
Fax: 550-87-72
Rector: José Sarukhán Kermez (1989-93)
Secretario General: José Narro Robles

F. of Architecture
Director: Ernesto José Velasco León; *staff* 35 (456)
S. of Plastic Arts
Director: Juan A. Madrid Vargas; *staff* 53 (150)
F. of Science
Director: Francisco Ramos Gómez; *staff* 175 (995)
F. of Political and Social Sciences (including Journalism, Communication Studies and International Relations)
Director: Ricardo Méndez Silva; *staff* 252 (597)
F. of Chemistry
Director: Francisco J. Barnés de Castro; *staff* 144 (436)
F. of Business Administration and Accountancy
Director: Salvador Ruiz de Chávez Ochoa; *staff* 127 (638)
F. of Law
Director: José Dálvalos Morales; *staff* 50 (506)
F. of Economics
Director: Juan Pablo Arroyo; *staff* 83 (359)
F. of Nursing and Midwifery
Director: Graciela Arroyo de Cordero; *staff* 28 (59)
F. of Philosophy and Letters
Director: Juliana González Valenzuela; *staff* 159 (580)
F. of Engineering
Director: Daniel Reséndiz Núñez; *staff* 197 (949)
F. of Medicine
Director: Fernando Cano Valle; *staff* 261 (2810)
S. of Music
Director: Jorge Eduardo Suárez Angeles; *staff* 39 (109)
S. of Social Work
Director: Ma. de Lourdes Apodaca Rangel; *staff* 10 (112)
F. of Dentistry
Director: Javier Portilla Robertson; *staff* 83 (432)
F. of Veterinary Medicine and Animal Husbandry
Director: Leopoldo Henri Pasch Martínez; *staff* 140 (209)
F. of Psychology
Director: Javier Urbina Soria; *staff* 149 (129)
Ce. for Atmospheric Sciences
Director: Julián Adem Chahin; *staff* 66 (1)
Ce. of Ecology
Director: Daniel Piñero Dalmau; *staff* 34
Ce. of Instruments
Director: Claudio Firmani Clementi; *staff* 59
Ce. for Research on Nitrogen Fixing
Director: Rafael Palacios de la Lama; *staff* 46
Ce. for Genetic Engineering and Biotechnology
Director: Francisco Bolívar Zapata; *staff* 64
I. of Astronomy
Director: Alfonso Serrano Pérez Grovas; *staff* 94
I. of Biology
Director: Antonio Lot Helgueras; *staff* 140 (2)
I. of Marine Sciences and Limnology
Director: Jorge Carranza Fraser; *staff* 103
I. of Nuclear Sciences
Director: Marcos Rosenbaum Pitluck; *staff* 34

I. of Physics
Director: Miguel José Yacamán; *staff* 161
I. of Cellular Physiology
Director: Antonio Peña Díaz; *staff* 71
I. of Geophysics
Director: Gerardo Suárez Reynoso; *staff* 107
I. of Geography
Director: Román Alvarez Bejar; *staff* 72 (1)
I. of Geology
Director: Fernando Ortega Gutiérez; *staff* 93 (4)
I. of Engineering
Director: Luis Esteva Maraboto; *staff* 151 (8)
I. of Biomedical Research
Director: Librado Ortíz Ortíz; *staff* 133 (1)
I. of Applied Mathematics and Systems
Director: Ignacio Méndez Ramirez; *staff* 95
I. of Research in Materials
Director: Ariel A. Valladares Clemente; *staff* 88 (1)
I. of Mathematics
Director: Raymundo Bautista Ramos; *staff* 45
I. of Chemistry
Director: Fernando Walls Armijo; *staff* 53
National Astronomical Observatories (San Pedro Mártir; Tonantzintla, and Zacatecas)
F. of Higher Studies (Cuautitlán)
Director: Jaime Keller Torres; *staff* 353 (461)
National S. of Professional Studies (Acatlán)
Director: Victor José Palencia Gómez; *staff* 249 (948)
National S. of Professional Studies (Iztacala)
Director: Arlette López Trujillo; *staff* 541 (775)
National S. of Professional Studies (Aragón)
Director: Claudio Carl Merifiel Castro; *staff* 54 (779)
National S. of Professional Studies (Zaragoza)
Director: Benny Weiss Steider; *staff* 268 (804)
Also 27 research institutes, stations, and centres, and 10 preparatory schools.

Founded 1551 under Felipe II of Spain as Royal and Pontifical University recognized by Papal Bull 1555. Closed following the independence of Mexico, re-established by law in 1910 as the National University of Mexico incorporating a number of existing institutions. Granted full autonomy 1929, reorganized 1944. Moved to new site 1954. Financed by the federal government. Governing body: the Junta de Gobierno (Board of Governors), the Consejo Universitario (University Council), including the Rector, the Secretary-General and the directors of all faculties, schools and institutes, as well as members of the academic staff and student body.

Arrangements for exchanges of researchers, academic staff, and students with institutions worldwide.

Academic Year: November to September (November-April; May-September).

Admission Requirements: Secondary school certificate (bachillerato) or recognized foreign equivalent, and entrance examination.

Language of Instruction: Spanish.

Degrees and Diplomas: Bachiller, 3 yrs. Licenciado in–Accountancy; Applied Art and Publicity; Archives; Biomedical Research; Business Administration; Classical Literature; Dramatic Art; Economics; Education; Geography; Graphic Art; Hispanic Language and Literature; History; Information Sciences; Instrumental Music; International Relations; Latin American Studies; Law; Library Science; Modern Languages and Literature; Musical Composition; Nursing and Midwifery; Painting; Philosophy; Political Science and Public Administration; Psychology; Sculpture; Singing; Social Work; Sociology; Industrial Design, 4-5 yrs. Professional titles in–Actuarial Studies, 3 ½ yrs; Veterinary Medicine; Biology, 4 yrs; Mathematics; Physics, 4 ½ yrs; Architecture; Dentistry; Public Accountancy, 5 yrs; Engineering, in various fields: Electrical; Topography and Surveying, 3 yrs; Civil; Geophysical; Geological; Mining and Metallurgical, 5 yrs; Chemistry; Pharmacology and Biology, 4 ½ yrs; Medicine, 7 yrs. Degree of Maestría, 1-2 yrs after degree of Licenciado or corresponding professional qualifications and thesis. Doctorado by thesis. Postgraduate titles of specialist in various fields. Also lower level technical qualifications.

Libraries: Central Library, *c.* 3,000,000 vols; 167 specialized libraries of the faculties, schools, and institutes, 2,500,000.

Special Facilities (Museums, etc.): National Astronomic Observatory (San Pedro Mártir, B.C. and Tonantzintla, Puebla); Arts and Sciences Museum;Geology Museum; Elk Chopo Museum; History and Philosophy of Medicine Museum; Palacio de Minería Museum.

Publications: Revista de Intercambio Académico; Biblioteca Universitaria; Perfiles Educativos; Voices of Mexico (quarterly); Agenda Estadística; Informe Universidad Nacional Autónoma de México (annually); Cuadernos de Legislación Universitaria (every 4 months); Los Universitarios; Punto de Partida (monthly). Also publications of thefaculties, schools and research centres.

Press or Publishing House: Dirección General de Publicaciones y Distribuidora de Libros UNAM.

Academic Staff, 1990:

Rank	Full-time	Part-time
Ayudantes de Profesor de Asignatura	–	5611
Ayudantes de Carrera	–	37
Técnicos Académicos	1949	187
Profesores de Asignatura	–	23,158
Profesores de Carrera	3184	–
Investigadores	1484	–
Personal Académico por honorarios y Profesores Eméritos	–	397
Total	6617	29,390

Student Enrolment, 1990:

	Men	Women	Total
Of the country	79,098	61,775	140,873*

*Also 5299 external students (Open University System).

4703 ***UNIVERSIDAD MICHOACANA DE SAN NICOLÁS DE HIDALGO**

Michoacan University of Saint Nicholas of Hidalgo
Edificio 'A' Cd. Universitaria, Morelia (Mich.)
Telephone: 2-05-69
Rector: Cuauhtémoc Olmedo Ortiz (1983-87)
Secretario General: Salvador Tomayo Sánchez

F. of Medicine
F. of Dentistry
F. of Law and Sociology
F. of Agrobiology (Uruapan)
S. of Civil Engineering
S. of Mechanical Engineering
S. of Chemistry
S. of Wood Technology
S. of Architecture
S. of Chemistry
S. of Pharmacy and Biological Sciences
S. of Nursing
S. of Accountancy and Administration
S. of Physics and Mathematics
S. of Biological Sciences
S. of Philosophy
S. of History
S. of Veterinary Medicine and Zoology
C. of Agriculture (Apatzingan)

Founded 1843 as Colegio de San Nicolás and traces its history back to the college originally established in 1542. Became university 1917. Reorganized 1939. An autonomous institution financially supported by State and federal governments.

Arrangements for co-operation with the University of Helsinki.

Academic Year: September to July (September-February; March-July).

Admission Requirements: Secondary school certificate (bachillerato) or equivalent, and entrance examination.

Fees (Pesos): Registration, 32; foreign students, 385.22. Tuition, 6500 per annum; foreign students, 78,200.

Language of Instruction: Spanish.

Degrees and Diplomas: Licenciado, 5 yrs. Degree of Maestría and Doctorado in Metallurgy.

Library: c. 50,000 vols.

Special Facilities (Museums, etc.): Museo Michoacano.

Publication: Research Collections.

Press or Publishing House: Editorial Universitaria.

Academic Staff: c. 270 (1810).

Student Enrolment: c. 45,000.

4704 ***UNIVERSIDAD AUTÓNOMA DE NAYARIT**

Autonomous University of Nayarit
Ciudad de la Cultur 'Amado Nervo', 63190 Tepic (Nayarit)
Telephone: 3-38-39
Rector: Salvador Villaseñor Anguiano (1986-90)
Secretario General: Carlos González Morteo

S. of Agriculture (Xalisco)
Director: Ildefonso López Castillo
S. of Industrial Chemical Engineering
Director: Martha Meza Ortega
S. of Economics
Director: Raúl Pérez González
S. of Tourism
Director: Miguel Angel de la Rosa Pacheco
S. of Commerce and Administration (including Accountancy)
Director: Ricardo Gómez Jiménez
S. of Law
Director: María Lourdes Yerena Galeana
S. of Medicine
Director: José Rodríguez Naya
S. of Dentistry
Director: Eusebio Martínez Sánchez
S. of Veterinary Medicine and Animal Husbandry
Director: Mario Jáuregui Medina
S. of Fishery
Director: José María Robles Naya
S. of Nursing
Director: Arcelia María Santos Padilla
Also 14 preparatory schools.

Founded 1962 as institute, became university 1969 and acquired present status and title 1975. An autonomous institution financially supported by the State and federal governments.

Academic Year: September to July (September-January; March-July).

Admission Requirements: Secondary school certificate (bachillerato) and entrance examination.

Degrees and Diplomas: Licenciado in–Economics; Tourism, 5 yrs. Professional titles of–Enfermera general, nursing, 3 yrs; Ingeniero, 4-5 yrs; Contador público, accountancy, Abogado, law; Cirujano dentista; Médico veterinario zootecnista,5 yrs; Médico cirujano, 6 yrs.

Libraries: Central Library; libraries of the schools.

Publication: Revista Convergencia (biannually).

Academic Staff, 1986-87: 356 (705).

Student Enrolment, 1984-85:

	Men	Women	Total
Of the country	8500	9064	17,564*

*Also 4 foreign students.

4705 ***UNIVERSIDAD AUTÓNOMA DE NUEVO LEÓN**

Autonomous University of Nuevo León
Ciudad Universitaria, 64000 Monterrey (Nuevo León)
Telex: 382989 UNALNME
Telephone: 76-41-40
Rector: Gregorio Farias Longaria (1985-88)
Secretario General: Lorenzo Vela Peña

F. of Agriculture (including Animal Husbandry)
Director: Fermín Montes; *staff* 284 (12)
F. of Architecture
Director: Humberto A. Montemayor; *staff* 32 (144)
F. of Biology
Director: Luis J. Galan Wong; *staff* 78 (57)
F. of Mathematics and Physics
Director: Luis V. García González; *staff* 43 (32)
F. of Chemistry
Director: Ezequiel Castillo Prieto; *staff* 10 (63)
F. of Accountancy and Administration
Director: Gumersindo Hinojoso Cantu; *staff* 79 (277)
F. of Law and Social Sciences (including Criminology)
Director: Francisco Rivera Bedoya; *staff* 39 (167)
F. of Economics
Director: Manuel Silos Martínez; *staff* 9 (10)
F. of Nursing
Director: Magdalena Alonso Castillo; *staff* 35 (72)
F. of Philosophy and Letters
Director: Bernardo Flores Flores; *staff* 38 (102)
F. of Political Science
Director: Rogelio García Paéz; *staff* 1 (38)
F. of Communication Sciences
Director: Ernesto Rocha Ruiz; *staff* 24 (70)
F. of Civil Engineering
Director: David Fernández Camargo; *staff* 30 (70)
F. of Mechanical and Electrical Engineering
Director: Guadalupe Cedilla Garza; *staff* 305 (422)
F. of Medicine
Director: Alfredo Piñeyro López; *staff* 144 (138)
F. of Dentistry
Director: José L. Valdez Iruegas; *staff* 13 (131)
F. of Sport
Director: Jorge G. Solís Alanís; *staff* 12 (41)
F. of Psychology
Director: Humberto Leal Benavides; *staff* 17 (94)
F. of Public Health Administration
Director: Horacio González Santos; *staff* 8 (22)
F. of Social Work
Director: Josefina García G.; *staff* 32 (33)
F. of Veterinary Medicine and Animal Husbandry
Director: Telesforo Vera Garza; *staff* 17 (7)
F. of Political Science
Director: Eliseo Castillo Tejeda; *staff* 3 (27)
F. of Communication Sciences
Director: Fernando Esquivel Lozano; *staff* 30 (67)
F. of Earth Sciences
Director: Juan Manuel Barbarin Castillo; *staff* 16 (1)
F. of Forestry
Director: Ernesto I. Salinas Ahumada
F. of Visual Arts
Director: Salvador Aburto Morales; *staff* 2 (19)
F. of Music
Director: Ricardo Gómez Chavarria; *staff* 2 (19)
S. of Scenic Arts
Director: Luis G. Lozano Lozano; *staff* 6 (21)
Also 8 research centres, 24 preparatory schools, 6 technical schools, and junior college.

Founded 1826 as Colegio civil del Estado de Nuevo León, became university 1933 and acquired present status and title 1971. An autonomous institution financially supported by the State and federal governments. Governing body: the Consejo Universitario.

Arrangements for co-operation with the Universities of: Arizona; California, Santa Barbara; Texas; Cincinnati;Missouri; Paris I; de las Villas, Cuba; Heidelberg. Technical College, Darmstadt.

Academic Year: August to July (August-January; February-July).

Admission Requirements: Secondary school certificate (bachillerato).

Fees (Pesos): 12,000 per semester.

Language of Instruction: Spanish.

Degrees and Diplomas: Licenciado in–Nursing; Psychology; Mathematics; Physics; Computer Sciences; Business Administration; Law; Political Science; Criminology; Journalism; Economics; Philosophy; Letters; Social Work; Interior Design, 5 yrs. Professional titles of–Biólogo; Químico; Enfermera, nursing; Médico cirujano; Cirujano dentista; Médico veterinario zootecnista; Ingeniero agrónomo; Arquitecto; Ingeniero, in various fields; Contador público, accountancy. Degree of Maestría. Doctorado.

Library: Central Library, 200,000 vols.

Publications: Universidad en Cifras (annually); Humanitas (annually); Armas y Letras (quarterly); Revista 'Ensayos' (quarterly).

Press or Publishing House: Imprenta Universitaria.

Academic Staff, 1986-87: 2060 (3878).

Student Enrolment, 1986-87:

	Men	Women	Total
Of the country	62,833	39,488	102,321
Of other countries	194	129	323
Total	63,027	39,617	102,644

4706 **UNIVERSIDAD AUTÓNOMA 'BENITO JUÁREZ' DE OAXACA**

'Benito Juárez' Autonomous University of Oaxaca
Ciudad Universitaria, Ex-Hacienda 'Cinco Señores', 68120 Oaxaca (Oaxaca)
Telex: 18601 UBJOME
Telephone: 6-46-86
Rector: César Mayoral Figueroa

F. of Accountancy and Public Administration
F. of Medicine and Surgery
S. of Law and Social Sciences
S. of Medicine
S. of Chemistry
S. of Architecture
S. of Veterinary Medicine and Zoology
S. of Nursing

S. of Dentistry
Also preparatory schools at Oaxaca, León, and Tehuantepec.

Founded 1827 as an institute, became university 1955. An autonomous institution financially supported by the State and federal governments. Governing bodies: the Consejo Universitario; the Asamblea Universitaria (University Board); the Consejo Técnico (Board of Schools).

Academic Year: February to November (February-June; July-November).

Admission Requirements: Secondary school certificate (bachillerato).

Language of Instruction: Spanish.

Degrees and Diplomas: Bachiller in–Science; Humanities, 3 yrs. Licenciado in–Sociology, 4 yrs; Law; Business Administration, 5 yrs. Professional titles of–Contador privado, private accountancy, 2 yrs; Técnico en Laboratorio clínico; Artes plásticas, 4 yrs; Médico veterinario; Médico; Odontología; Contador público, accountancy; Arquitecto, 5 yrs.

4707 **UNIVERSIDAD DE OCCIDENTE**

Avenida Benito Juárez 435, Poniente, Apartado postal 936, 81200 Los Mochis (Sinaloa)
Telephone: 2-66-17
Fax: 5-39-00
Rector: Ruben Elias Gil Leyva
Secretario General: José Guillermo Alvarez Guerrero

D. of Administration
D. of Engineering (Civil and Agricultural Industrial Engineers)
D. of Psychology
D. of Communication
D. of Law
D. of Biology
D. of Accountancy and Economics
D. of Mathematics
Anthropological and Social Research I.
Aquacultural and Fishing Development Technology Research I.
Also Units in: Guasave, Guamuchil, Culiacan (Capital), Mazatlán (Tourist Port).

Founded 1980. An autonomous institution under the jurisdiction of the State of Sinaloa and financially supported by the Centro de Estudios Superiores de Occidente. Governing body: the Consejo Académico.

Academic Year: August to July (August-November; January-April; May-July).

Admission Requirements: Secondary school certificate (bachillerato) and entrance examination.

Fees (Pesos): 137,680 per semester.

Language of Instruction: Spanish.

Degrees and Diplomas: Licenciado in–Administration (Agricultural, Public, Financial, Tourism, Computer Systems, Marketing and Educational); Psychology; Communication; Law; Rural Sociology; Biology, 4 yrs. Professional title of Ingeniero. Degree of Maestría in Agro-Industrial Administration.

Library: Central Library, 8000 vols.

Special Facilities (Museums, etc.): Valley of Fuerte Regional Museum.

Academic Staff, 1990: 74 (330).

Student Enrolment, 1990:

	Men	Women	Total
Of the country	1484	2151	3635

4708 ***UNIVERSIDAD AUTÓNOMA DE PUEBLA**

Autonomous University of Puebla
4 Sur No. 104, 72000 Puebla (Puebla)
Telex: 178350 IUAPME
Telephone: 42-88-02
Rector: M. C. Samuel Malpica Uriba
Secretario General: Daniel Cazés Menache

S. of Public Administration
S. of Architecture
S. of Accountancy
S. of Physics and Mathematics
S. of Chemistry
S. of Law and Social Sciences
S. of Economics
S. of Nursing and Midwifery
S. of Philosophy and Letters
S. of Civil Engineering
S. of Chemical Engineering
S. of Medicine
S. of Veterinary Medicine and Zoology (Tecamachalco)
S. of Dentistry
S. of Languages
S. of Music
I. of Scientific Research
D. of Physical Education
Extension D.
Also 9 preparatory schools.

Founded 1937 as Universidad de Puebla but tracing its origins to College of Holy Spirit 1578, subsequently State College 1825. Reorganized and granted present status 1956. An autonomous institution financed by State and federal governments. Governing body: the Consejo Universitario, comprising 125 members. Residential facilities for 500 students.

Arrangements for co-operation with the Universities of: Camagüey; Nicaragua; El Salvador; Łódź; Dresden (Technical); Paris VIII; Prague; Florence; Campinas; McMaster, Canada; Ohio; Altiplano.

Academic Year: February to November (February-June; July-November).

Admission Requirements: Secondary school certificate (bachillerato) and entrance examination.

Language of Instruction: Spanish.

Degrees and Diplomas: Licenciado or Professional titles in all fields, 3-6 yrs. Maestría in–Physics; Mathematics; Languages; Social Sciences; Physiology; Chemistry, a further 3 yrs. Doctor in Physics.

Libraries: Central Library, *c.* 80,000 vols; libraries of the schools, *c.* 120,000.

Special Facilities (Museums, etc.): Museo Universitario de Ciencia y Arte.

Publication: Revistas.

Press or Publishing House: Editorial Universidad.

Academic Staff: c. 920 (2300).

Student Enrolment: c. 77,490.

4709 ***UNIVERSIDAD AUTÓNOMA DE QUERÉTARO**

Autonomous University of Querétaro
Centro Universitario, Cerro de las Campanas, 76010 Querétaro (Querétaro)
Telephone: 6-32-42
Rector: Braulio Guerra Malo (1982-88)
Secretario Administrativo: Armando Pérez Nuñez

F. of Chemistry
Director: Alfonso Pérez Buenrostro; *staff* 18 (72)
F. of Engineering
Director: Agustin Pacheco Cardenas; *staff* 20 (65)
F. of Accountancy and Business Administration
Director: José Sosa Padilla; *staff* 17 (26)
F. of Law
Director: Arturo García Peña; *staff* 11 (44)
F. of Psychology
Director: Adolfo Chacón Gallardo; *staff* 16 (57)
S. of Medicine
Director: Carlos Alcocar Cuarón; *staff* 9 (80)
F. of Veterinary Medicine and Animal Husbandry
Director: Eduardo Cabello Frias; *staff* 3 (20)
S. of Sociology
Director: Carlos Dorantes Gutiérrez
S. of Nursing
Director: Juana Sánchez Cabrera; *staff* 12 (28)
I. of Fine Arts
Director: Adalberto Martínez; *staff* 2 (45)
S. of Languages
Director: Aurora Y. Silva Rodríguez; *staff* 8 (21)
S. of Journalism
Director: Raúl Martínez Merling; *staff* – (9)
Also 5 Research Centres and preparatory school.

Founded 1625 as college, became university 1951. An autonomous institution financially supported by the State and federal governments. Governing body: the Consejo Universitario.

Arrangements for co-operation with the Universities of: Valladolid; Salamanca; McGill; Laval; Humboldt, Berlin; Leiden; Western Illinois; York, Ontario.

Academic Year: September to July (September-February; March-July).

Admission Requirements: Secondary school certificate (bachillerato) or equivalent, and entrance examination.

Fees (Pesos): 40,000 per semester.

Language of Instruction: Spanish.

Degrees and Diplomas: Licenciado in–Psychology; Business Administration; Law; Sociology, 4-10 sem. Professional titles of–Químico (various fields); Ingeniero civil; Ingeniero en Instrumentación y Control de Procesos; Biólogo; Contador público; Médico; Médico veterinario zootecnista; Enfermera general, 6-12 sem. Degree of Maestría in–Food Technology; Hydrology; Law; Clinical Psychology; Education; Construction; Administration; Mathematics; Philosophy.

Library: Central Library, *c.* 60,000 vols.

Publications: Investigación; Bulletin; Universidad.

Press or Publishing House: Imprenta Universitaria.

Academic Staff, 1986-87: 226 (834).

Student Enrolment, 1986-87:

	Men	Women	Total
Of the country	7598	5502	13,100
Of other countries	15	7	22
Total	7613	5509	13,122

4710 **UNIVERSIDAD AUTÓNOMA DE SAN LUIS POTOSÍ**

Autonomous University of San Luis Potosí

Alvaro Obregón 64, 78000 San Luis Potosí (San Luis Potosí)

Telephone: (91-48) 12-34-61

Fax: (91-48) 12-89-28

Electronic mail: Lastras A. SEP Rodr@7iguez Al. Medell@7in P

Rector: Alfonso Lastras Ramírez (1988-92)

Secretario General: Jaime Valle Méndez

S. of Agriculture (including Animal Husbandry)
Director: Rodolfo Loza Márquez Labastida; *staff* 41 (1)
S. of Chemistry
Director: Roberto Leyva Ramos; *staff* 26 (9)
F. of Commerce and Administration (including Accountancy)
Director: Héctor A. Díaz Pedroza; *staff* 34 (6)
F. of Law
Director: Héctor Aldasoro Velasco; *staff* 22 (10)
F. of Economics
Director: Héctor Montoya Espinoza; *staff* 23 (2)
S. of Stomatology
Director: Sergio López Moctezuma; *staff* 28 (3)
S. of Nursing
Director: Isabel Villarreal Guzmán; *staff* 19 (22)
F. of Science
Director: Guillermo Marx Reyes; *staff* 14 (2)
F. of Engineering
Director: David Atísha Castillo; *staff* 55 (16)
S. of Medicine
Director: José Luis Leiva Garza; *staff* 61 (50)
S. of Psychology
Director: Juan Manuel Tejeda Tayabas; *staff* 21
S. of Habitat (including Architecture, Construction, Industrial Design and Graphic Design)
Director: Alfredo Tellez Arellano; *staff* 22
D. of Communication Sciences
Director: Raúl Camacho; *staff* 2 (2)
I. of Geology
Director: Guillermo Labarthe Hernández; *staff* 4 (2)
Arid Zones Research I.
Director: Nicolas Vazquez Rosillo; *staff* 15 (4)
I. of Educational Sciences
Director: Adrián Pesina Zamarripa; *staff* 8 (9)
Language Ce.
Director: Arsenio Lobo Ramírez; *staff* 3
I. of Physics
Director: Juan Fernando Cárdenas Rivero; *staff* 20 (9)
I. of Metallurgy
Director: José de Jesús Negrete S.; *staff* 14 (3)
Humanistic Research I.
Director: Eudoro Fonsea Yerena; *staff* 5
Chemistry Research Ce.
Co-ordinator: Jesús Navarro Contreras
I. of Agriculture and Stockraising
Co-ordinator: Humberto Cuellar Torres
Economic Research I.
Co-ordinator: Martha Miranda de Torres
Law Research I.
Co-ordinator: Adriana López Ledezma

Founded 1859, became an autonomous institution with full university status 1923. Governing body: the Junta de Gobierno.

Arrangements for co-operation with the Universities of: Cantabria; Valladolid; Seville; California, Los Angeles; Ohio State; Brown, New York; Laval, Canada; Québec; Altiplano, Puno; Maranhão; California, Berkeley; Louisiana (Technical); Arizona State; Cornell.

Academic Year: August to May (August-December; February-May).

Admission Requirements: Secondary school certificate (bachillerato) and entrance examination.

Fees (Pesos): *c.* 30,000.

Language of Instruction: Spanish.

Degrees and Diplomas: Licenciado in–Mathematics, 7 sem; Library Science; Nursing; Electronics; Physics; Communication Sciences; Psychology, 8-9 sem; Agricultural Administration; Public Administration; Administration; Industrial Design; Architecture; Economics, 10 sem. Professional titles of–Técnico, 4-5 sem; Químico Farmacobiólogo; Químico, 8 sem; Ingeniero, various fields, 9-10 sem; Edificador y Administrador de Obras; Contador público; Abogado, law; Cirujano dentista, 10 sem; Médico cirujano, 6 yrs. Degree of Maestría. Doctorado. Postgraduate titles of specialist in various fields. Teaching qualfications.

Libraries: Central Library, 2,318,600 vols; libraries of the faculties and schools, total, 40,756.

Special Facilities (Museums, etc.): Botanic Garden (Arid Zones Research I.).

Publications: Revistas; Periódicos; Folletos; Cuadrante (Ciencias Sociales y Literatura); Acta Científica (Investigación en General); Conciencia Universitaria (Suplemento Periodístico) (monthly).

Academic Staff, 1989-90:

Rank	Full-time	Part-time
Profesores Titulares	99	9
Profesores Asociados	125	61
Profesores Asistentes	139	73
Total	363	143

Student Enrolment, 1989-90:

Men	Women	Total
12,085	10,593	22,678

4711 **UNIVERSIDAD AUTÓNOMA DE SINALOA**

Autonomous University of Sinaloa

Angel Flores y Riva Palacio, s/n. 80000 Culiacán (Sinaloa)

Telephone: 2-35-50

Rector: Jorge Medina Viedas (1981-85)

F. of Law and Social Sciences
C. of Agriculture (including Animal Husbandry)
C. of Agriculture (Juan José Rios)
S. of Biology
S. of Accountancy and Administration
S. of Engineering (Los Mochis)
S. of Engineering (Mazatlán)
S. of Economics
S. of Marine Sciences
S. of Fishery
S. of Social Sciences
S. of Medicine and Surgery
S. of Social Work
S. of Nursing
S. of Meteorology
S. of Plastic Arts
S. of Physics and Mathematics
S. of Philosophy
S. of Agricultural Administration
I. of Languages
Musical Ce.
S. of Dentistry
S. of Psychology
S. of Veterinary Medicine and Zoology
Also 26 preparatory schools.

Founded 1873 as Liceo Rosales, became Universidad de Occidente 1922 and Universidad Socialista del Noroeste 1937, Universidad de Sinaloa 1941 and Universidad Autónoma 1965. An autonomous institution financially supported by the State and federal governments. Governing body: the Consejo Universitario.

Academic Year: September to June (September-January; February-June).

Admission Requirements: Secondary school certificate (bachillerato).

Language of Instruction: Spanish.

Degrees and Diplomas: Licenciado and Professional titles, 5 yrs. Degree of Maestría, a further 2 yrs. Diploma, 3 yrs.

Library: Central Library, libraries of the schools.

Publications: La Verdad; Gaceta; Centenario.

Press or Publishing House: University Press.
Academic Staff: c. 1270 (2030).
Student Enrolment: c. 67,830.

4712 **UNIVERSIDAD DE SONORA**
University of Sonora
Campos de la Universidad, 83000 Hermosillo (Sonora)
Telephone: 2-10-46
Rector: Manuel Rivera Zamudio

S. of Law and Social Sciences
S. of Psychology and Communications Studies
S. of Engineering
S. of Chemistry
S. of Agronomy and Stock-Raising
S. of Engineering (Caboria)
S. of Chemistry (Caboria)
S. of Law and Sciences (Caboria)
S. of Engineering (Navojoa)
S. of Chemistry (Navojoa)
S. of Law and Social Sciences (Navojoa)
S. of Agronomy and Stockraising (Navojoa)
D. of Social Sciences
D. of Accountancy and Administration
D. of Economics
D. of Humanities
D. of Physics
D. of Mathematics
D. of Geology
D. of Chemistry and Biology
D. of Geology (Caboria)
D. of Social Sciences (Caboria)
D. of Accountancy and Administration (Caboria)
D. of Economics (Caboria)
D. of Chemistry and Biology (Caboria)
D. of Physics (Caboria)
D. of Mathematics (Caboria)
D. of Physics (Navojoa)
D. of Mathematics (Navojoa)
D. of Geology (Navojoa)
D. of Social Sciences (Navojoa)
D. of Accountancy and Administration (Navojoa)
D. of Economics (Navojoa)
D. of Chemistry and Biology (Navojoa)
Also preparatory schools and high school.

Founded 1938, first students admitted 1942. An autonomous institution financially supported by the State and federal governments. Governing body: the University Council, the Rector, Directors of Schools and Institutes, and a Board of Trustees.

Academic Year: August to June (August-December; February-June).

Admission Requirements: Secondary school certificate (bachillerato) and entrance examination.

Language of Instruction: Spanish.

Degrees and Diplomas: Bachiller, 3 yrs. Licenciado in–Economics; Business Administration; Law, 5 yrs; Mathematics; Physics; Letters, 4 yrs. Professional titles in–Social Work; Accountancy and Business Administration; Ranch Administration, 3yrs; Engineering, in various fields; Biology; Chemistry; Agriculture; Animal Husbandry, 5 yrs.

Library: Central Library and specialized school libraries, total, c. 100,560 vols.

Special Facilities (Museums, etc.): Anthropology and History Museum..

Publications: Anuario General; Revista Universidad de Sonora; Boletín Informativo; Gaceta Universitaria.

Academic Staff: c. 140 (280).
Student Enrolment: c. 18,000.

4713 **UNIVERSIDAD DEL SUDESTE**
University of the South East
Ciudad Universitaria, 24030 Campeche (Campeche)
Telephone: 6-55-03

F. of Law
F. of Engineering
C. of Chemistry and Biology
C. of Commerce
C. of Medicine
C. of Political Science and Public Administration
C. of Medicine
C. of Accountancy
C. of Technology
C. of Dentistry

Founded 1756, reorganized 1957. An autonomous institution financially supported by the State and federal governments.

Degrees and Diplomas: Licenciado in Law. Professional titles of–Contador público, accountancy; Médico cirujano; Ingeniero civil; Ingeniero topógrafo geodesta; Técnico agropecuario; Cirujano dentista.

Academic Staff: c. 180.
Student Enrolment: c. 1960.

4714 **UNIVERSIDAD 'JUÁREZ' AUTÓNOMA DE TABASCO**
'Juárez' Autonomous University of Tabasco
Zona de la Cultura, Carretera Frontera s/n, 86020 Villahermosa (Tabasco)
Telephone: (91-931) 2-29-93
Fax: (91-931) 2-16-37
Rector: Fernando Rabelo Ruiz de la Peña. (1988-92)
Academic Services Secretary: Walter Ramírez Izquierdo

D. of Economics and Administration
Director: Jorge A. Rosas Castero; *staff* 55 (33)
D. of Social Sciences and Humanities
Director: José Luis Ocaña A.; *staff* 55 (29)
D. of Health Sciences (Medicine, Dentistry, and Nursing)
Director: Edmundo Batres Ledón; *staff* 79 (68)
D. of Engineering and Technology
Director: Rodolfo Mayo Oropeza; *staff* 70 (16)
D. of Basic Studies
Director: Tito Ocaña Zurita; *staff* 35 (3)
D. of Agriculture and Stockraising
Director: Victorio P. Alriero G.; *staff* 45 (5)
D. of Basic Sciences (Biology)
Director: Raúl Fco. Pineda L.; *staff* 32 (13)
D. of Informatics
Director: Hugo Milla Martínez; *staff* 12 (4)
Social Sciences and Humanities Research Ce.
Co-ordinator: Miguel A. Díaz C.
Health Research Ce.
Co-ordinator: Esmelin Trinidad V.
Biology and Biotechnology Research Ce.
Co-ordinator: Jorge A. Goño Arevalo
Agriculture Research Ce.
Co-ordinator: José del C. Hernández
Economics-Administration Research Ce.
Co-ordinator: López Naranjo
Engineering and Technology Research Ce.
Co-ordinator: Rito Javier Rodriguez Lozoya
Basic Sciences Research Ce.
Co-ordinator: Rodolfo Conde del Agiula.

Founded 1879 as Instituto Juárez. Acquired university status 1958. An autonomous institution financially supported by the State and federal governments. Governing body: the Consejo Universitario.

Arrangements for co-operation with: University of New Mexico; University of Missouri.

Academic Year: September to July (September-January; March-July).

Admission Requirements: Secondary school certificate (bachillerato) and entrance examination.

Fees (Pesos): Registration, 7000 per annum; tuition, 35,000 per annum.

Language of Instruction: Spanish.

Degrees and Diplomas: Licenciado in–Law; Economics; Education; Accountancy; Commercial Relations; Sociology; History; Mathematics; Physics; Chemistry; Biology; Informatics; Nursing; 4-5 yrs. Professional titles of–Médico veterinario zootécnico, veterinary medicine and animal husbandry; Médico cirujano; Cirujana Dentista; Ingeniero (various fields), 4-7 yrs. Also Degree of Maestría in–Hydraulics; Education; Administration. Also postgraduate titles of specialist in various fields.

Library: Central Library and six specialized libraries, total, 80,331 vols.

Special Facilities (Museums, etc.): Herbarium; Art Gallery; Theater; Zoology Museum.

Publication: Revistas.

Academic Staff, 1989-90: 383 (392).
Student Enrolment, 1989-90:

	Men	Women	Total
Of the country	8413	6774	15,187

4715 **UNIVERSIDAD AUTÓNOMA DE TAMAULIPAS**

Autonomous University of Tamaulipas
Calle Matamoros 8-altos, 87000 Ciudad Victoria (Tamaulipas)
Telex: 31260UATYME
Telephone: 2-70-00

F. of Law
F. of Agriculture
F. of Commerce and Administration (including Accountancy)
F. of Social Work
F. of Veterinary Medicine and Zoology
F. of Education
F. of Agriculture (Ciudad Mante)
F. of Commerce and Administration (including Accountancy) (Nuevo Laredo)
F. of Law and Social Sciences (Tampico)
F. of Engineering (Tampico)
F. of Architecture (Tampico)
F. of Nursing and Midwifery (Tampico)
F. of Medicine (Tampico)
C. of Music (Tampico)
F. of Commerce and Administration (including Accountancy) (Tampico)
F. of Dentistry (Tampico)
F. of Medicine (H. Matamoros)
F. of Nursing (Matamoros)
F. of Chemistry (Reynosa)
F. of Agro-Industrial Sciences (Reynosa)
Also preparatory schools at Ciudad Mante and Valle Hermoso.

Founded 1956 incorporating existing schools. An autonomous institution financially supported by the State and federal governments.

Academic Year: September to June (September-January; February-June).

Admission Requirements: Secondary school certificate (bachillerato).

Language of Instruction: Spanish.

Degrees and Diplomas: Licenciado in–Law; Business Administration; Education. Professional titles of–Ingeniero agrónomo; Contador público, accountancy; Médico veterinario zootecnista; Enfermera, nursing; Partera, midwifery; Trabajador social, social work; Ingeniero civil; Arquitecto; Médico cirujano; Cirujano dentista; Quimico farmacobiólogo; Quimico industrial.

Library: Central Library.

Special Facilities (Museums, etc.): History Museum.

Academic Staff: c. 1040.

Student Enrolment: c. 14,240.

4716 **UNIVERSIDAD AUTÓNOMA DE TLAXCALA**

Avenida Universidad 1, 90000 Tlaxcala (Tlaxcala)
Telephone: 2-11-67
Rector: Héctor I. Ortiz Ortiz (1983-87)
Secretario: Héctor Vazquez Galicia

D. of Social Sciences and Administration (including Economics, Law and Political Sciences)
Director: Rafael Estrada Aguilar; *staff* 5 (17)
D. of Education (including Education for the Disabled)
Director: Josefina Espinoza Cuellar; *staff* 2 (6)
D. of Human Sciences (including Languages)
Director: Eugenio Romero Melgarejo; *staff* 4 (5)
D. of Industrial Engineering and Chemistry
Director: Magdiel Xicotencatl Preza; *staff* 3 (4)
D. of Agriculture (including Veterinary Medicine and Animal Husbandry)
Director: Rolando M. Romero López; *staff* 6 (3)
D. of Health Sciences (Dentistry, Nursing and Midwifery)
Director: Jesús George Cruz; *staff* 9 (4)

Founded 1976. An autonomous State institution financially supported by the State and federal governments. Governing body: the Consejo Universitario.

Academic Year: September to June (September-January; February-June).

Admission Requirements: Secondary school certificate (bachillerato) and entrance examination.

Fees (Pesos): 2900.

Language of Instruction: Spanish.

Degrees and Diplomas: Licenciado in–Social Work; Law; Accountancy; Administration, 4 ½ yrs; Biology; Political Science and Public Administration; Languages; Education; Economics, 5 yrs; Special Education, 5-6 yrs. Professional titles in–Nursing; Languages, 3 yrs; Dentistry; Accountancy, 4-4 ½ yrs; Engineering and Chemistry; Veterinary Medicine and Animal Husbandry, 5 yrs. Degree of Maestría in–Law; Biology; Education, a further 2 yrs. Doctorado in Biology.

Library: Central Library.

Special Facilities (Museums, etc.): Botanical Garden and Herbarium.

Publications: Comunidad (monthly); Vox Populi (monthly); Summa (quarterly); Enfoque (quarterly).

Academic Staff, 1986-87: 29 (55).

Student Enrolment, 1986-87:

	Men	Women	Total
Of the country	2505	3208	5713
Of other countries	–	1	1
Total	2505	3209	5714

4717 **UNIVERSIDAD VERACRUZANA**

University of Veracruz
Zona Universitaria, Lomas del Estadio, 91090 Xalapa (Veracruz)
Telex: 015516 DIUVME
Telephone: 7-34-27
Rector: Carlos Manuel Aguirre Gutiérrez (1983-87)

F. of Business Administration
F. of Agriculture
F. of Anthropology
F. of Architecture
F. of Bioanalysis
F. of Biology
F. of Dentistry
F. of Music
F. of Theatre
F. of Commerce
F. of Engineering
F. of Physics
F. of Dance
F. of Law
F. of Economics
F. of Statistics
F. of Philosophy
F. of History
F. of Languages
F. of Chemistry
F. of Spanish Literature
F. of Mathematics
F. of Medicine
F. of Nutrition
F. of Pedagogics
F. of Psychology
F. of Sociology
F. of Dentistry (Ciudad Mendoza)
F. of Medicine (Ciudad Mendoza)
F. of Mechanical and Electrical Engineering (Ciudad Mendoza)
F. of Administration (Coatzacoalcos)
F. of Engineering (Coatzacoalcos)
F. of Chemistry (Coatzacoalcos)
F. of Agriculture (Córdoba)
F. of Biology (Córdoba)
F. of Architecture (Córdoba)
F. of Medicine (Minatitlán)
F. of Dentistry (Minatitlán)
F. of Social Work (Minatitlán)
F. of Commerce (Nogales)
F. of Architecture (Poza Rica)
F. of Engineering (Poza Rica)
F. of Chemistry (Poza Rica)
F. of Medicine (Poza Rica)
F. of Dentistry (Poza Rica)
F. of Psychology (Poza Rica)
F. of Pedagogics (Poza Rica)
F. of Social Work (Poza Rica)
F. of Commerce (Veracruz)
F. of Administration (Veracruz)
F. of Pedagogics (Veracruz)
F. of Tourism (Veracruz)
F. of Engineering (Veracruz)
F. of Physics (Veracruz)
F. of Psychology (Veracruz)
F. of Dentistry (Veracruz)
F. of Naval Engineering (Veracruz)
F. of Chemistry (Veracruz)

F. of Veterinary Medicine and Zoology (Veracruz)
F. of Bioanalysis (Veracruz)
F. of Medicine (Veracruz)
F. of Nutrition (Veracruz)
F. of Journalism (Veracruz)
F. of Agriculture (Tuxpán)
F. of Biology (Tuxpán)
F. of Veterinary Medicine and Zoology (Tuxpán)
F. of Commerce (Tuxpán)
Branches in: Xalapa, Veracruz, Córdoba-Orizaba, Coatzacoalcos-Minatlán, Poza Rica, Tuxpán.

Founded 1944 incorporating existing faculties and schools. The university has its seat at Xalapa. An autonomous institution financially supported by the State and federal governments. Governing body: the Consejo Universitario. Some residential facilities for students.

Arrangements for co-operation with the Universities of: Murcia; Extremadura; Barcelona; Zaragoza; Granada; León; Córdoba, Spain.

Academic Year: September to August (September-February; March-August).

Admission Requirements: Secondary school certificate (bachillerato) and entrance examination.

Language of Instruction: Spanish.

Degrees and Diplomas: Licenciado in–Law; Business Administration; Economics; Statistics; Biology; Physics; Mathematics; Sociology; Anthropology; Archaeology; Psychology; Nutrition; Languages; Spanish Literature; Philosophy; History; Journalism; Agriculture; Atmospherics; Tourism; Computer Sciences; Clinical Chemistry; Physical Education; Social Work; Education, 4 yrs; Arts; Actuarial Sciences, 5 yrs. Professional titles of–Médico cirujano; Contador público, accountancy; Cirujano dentista; Arquitecto; Químico, chemistry; Químico farmacéutico; Ingeniero (various fields); Enfermera, nursing; Médico veterinario zootecnista, 4 yrs. Degree of Maestría in–Administration; Spanish Literature; Penal Science; Forensic Medicine; Engineering.

Special Facilities (Museums, etc.): Anthropology Museum.

Publications: Cuadernos Antropológicos; La Palabra y El Hombre; Texto Crítico; Semiosis (biannually).

Academic Staff: c. 2520.

Student Enrolment: c. 49,850.

4718 **UNIVERSIDAD AUTÓNOMA DE YUCATÁN**

Autonomous University of Yucatán
Calle 60 y 57, 97000 Mérida (Yucatán)
Telephone: 24-80-00
Rector: Alvaro J. Mimenza Cuevas (1987-90)
Secretario General: Felipe Escalante Ruz

F. of Anthropology
Director: Carlos Bojorquez U.; *staff* 15 (19)
F. of Architecture
Director: Fernando Medina Casares; *staff* 8 (59)
F. of Business Administration and Accountancy
Director: Miguel Vidal Vazquez; *staff* 11 (132)
F. of Law
Director: Carlos Herrera Heredia; *staff* 11 (57)
F. of Economics
Director: Raúl Vela Sosa; *staff* 6 (14)
F. of Engineering
Director: Eduardo Escalante; *staff* 39 (50)
F. of Chemical and Industrial Engineering
Director: Juan Soto Cruz; *staff* 8 (22)
F. of Mathematics
Director: René Torres León; *staff* 7 (7)
F. of Medicine
Director: Carlos Urzáiz J.; *staff* 15 (116)
F. of Veterinary Medicine
Director: Ignacio Vado Sólis; *staff* 55
F. of Dentistry
Director: Carlos Núñez Erosa; *staff* 22 (18)
F. of Psychology
Director: Elias Góngora C.; *staff* 10 (3)
F. of Education
Director: Julia González Cervera; *staff* 12 (7)
S. of Chemistry
Director: Wilberth Villegas; *staff* 11 (25)
S. of Nursing
Director: Amada Rendón Sarlat; *staff* 8 (113)
Also 2 preparatory schools.

Founded 1624, reorganized 1922. An autonomous institution financially supported by the State and federal governments. Governing body: the Consejo Universitario.

Arrangements for co-operation with the Universities of: Wisconsin; Gainesville, Florida; Brno; Laval; Essex. Loughborough University of Technology.

Academic Year: September to July (September-February; February-July).

Admission Requirements: Secondary school certificate (bachillerato).

Language of Instruction: Spanish.

Degrees and Diplomas: Bachiller, 3 yrs. Licenciado, 4-5 yrs. Degree of Maestria, a further 2-3 yrs.

Libraries: Central Library, 57,608 vols; libraries of the faculties and schools.

Publication: Revista de la Universidad de Yucatán.

Academic Staff, 1986-87: 310 (880).

Student Enrolment, 1986-87:

	Men	Women	Total
Of the country	8041	5303	13,344

4719 **UNIVERSIDAD AUTÓNOMA DE ZACATECAS**

Autonomous University of Zacatecas
Galeana No. 1, 98000 Zacatecas (Zacatecas)
Telephone: 2-01-60
Rector: Francisco García Hernández (1984-88)
Secretario General: Delfino Garcia Hernández

S. of Agriculture
Director: José Luis Espana Téllez
S. of Chemistry
Director: Javier Aguayo Pérez
S. of Accountancy and Administration
Director: Jesús Limones Hernández
S. of Law
Director: Aquiles González Navarro
S. of Economics
Director: Juan Alcalá Frias
S. of Nursing
Director: Maria Isabel Medina Hernández
S. of Engineering
Director: Raúl Fernández Avalos
S. of Mining
Director: Rubén de J. del Pozo Mendoza
S. of Medicine
Director: Octavio Angel Flores Medina
S. of Dentistry
Director: Juan Manuel Garcia González
S. of Veterinary Medicine and Animal Husbandry
Director: Jesús Dávila Escobedo
S. of Social Sciences
Director: Ramón Vera Salvo
Ce. for Mathematics
Director: David Mayer Foulkes
Ce. for Languages
Director: Laura García Medina
Also preparatory schools and secondary schools.

Founded 1832 as State college, became Institute of Sciences 1920 and granted autonomy 1959. Acquired present title 1968. An institution financially supported by the State and federal governments. Governing body: the Consejo Universitario.

Academic Year: August to June (August-December; February-June).

Admission Requirements: Secondary school certificate (bachillerato).

Fees (Pesos): Registration, 600-8000; foreign students, 22,500-45,000.

Language of Instruction: Spanish.

Degrees and Diplomas: Licenciado in–Law; Accountancy; Mathematics; Nursing, 4 yrs; Economics, 5 yrs. Professional titles of–Ingeniero químico; Químico farmacobiólogo; Contador público, accountancy; Ingeniero, in various fields; Médico veterinario y zootecnista, veterinary medicine and animal husbandry; Enfermera Partera y Obstetra, nursing and midwifery; Médico cirujano dentista; Médico cirujano, 6-10 sem. Degree of Maestría, a further 2 yrs.

Library: c. 35,260.

Special Facilities (Museums, etc.): Museo de Mineralogía. Academic Staff 1986-87: 396 (1062).

Student Enrolment, 1984-85:

Of the country	16,818
Of other countries	50
Total	16,868

4720 **UNIVERSIDAD PEDAGÓGICA NACIONAL**

Km. ½ Carretera al Ajusco, Héroes de Padierna, 14201 México (D.F)
Telephone: 571-85-66

Education

Founded 1979. The University has its seat in México, with 75 units throughout the country. An autonomous institution financially supported by the State and federal governments.

Private Institutions

4721 **UNIVERSIDAD DE LAS AMÉRICAS, A.C.**

University of the Americas
Puebla 223, Col. Roma, 067000 Mexico (D.F.)
Telephone: 525-14-05
Fax: 511-6040
Rector: Margarita Gómez-Palacio (1988-)

D. of Business Administration
D. of Psychology
Director: Ismael Garcia; *staff* 11 (24)
D. of International Studies
Director: Victor M. Godinez; *staff* 9 (20)
D. of Education
Directors: Georgina N. Eardman; Janet Saenz; *staff* 7 (8)
Language Ce.
I. of Oaxacan Studies
Director: David Peterson
Also Clinic for Human Communication Disorders.

Founded 1940 as junior college, acquired present title 1963. Moved to Cholula, Puebla, 1970, returned to present site 1985. A private bilingual institution accredited by the U.S. Southern Association of Colleges and Schools, and recognized by the State. Governing body: the Board of Trustees.

Arrangements for co-operation with the Universities of: Arizona; Alabama.

Academic Year: September to May (September-December; January-April; May-August).

Admission Requirements: Secondary school certificate (bachillerato) or equivalent.

Fees (Pesos): 82,800 per annum; graduate, 114,000.

Languages of Instruction: Spanish and English.

Degrees and Diplomas: Licenciado and Bachelor of Arts, 4-4 ½ yrs. Degree of Maestría and Master of Arts. Honorary Doctorates.

Library: 13,028 vols.

Special Facilities (Museums, etc.): Frissell Museum of Zapotec Art.

Academic Staff, 1989-90: 110 (20).

Student Enrolment, 1988-89: 1248.

4722 **UNIVERSIDAD ANAHUAC**

Lomas de Anahuac, Apartado Postal 10-844, 1000 Mexico (D.F.)
Telephone: (525) 589-22-00
Fax: (525) 589-97-96
Rector: Raymund Cosgrave (1990-93)
Secretario General: Gregorio Lopez Zarraga

S. of Medicine
Director: José Kuthy Porter; *staff* 5 (134)
S. of Communications
Director: Fernando Santibañez y Flores; *staff* 13 (42)
S. of Social Sciences
S. of Actuarial Sciences
Director: Oliva Sánchez García; *staff* 4 (14)
S. of Psychology
Director: Rosamaria Vallf. Gómez Tagle; *staff* 11 (28)
S. of Architecture
Director: Fernando Paz y Puente; *staff* 9 (32)
S. of Computer Sciences
Director: Nicolas Haidar Salazar; *staff* 7 (19)
S. of Law
Director: Ignacio Melo Ruiz; *staff* 4 (39)
S. of Economics
Director: Gerardo Jacob Rocha; *staff* 5 (18)
S. of Education
Director: Isabel Ogalde Careaga; *staff* 7 (8)
S. of Business Administration
Director: Javier Larraza Hernández; *staff* 13 (61)
S. of Tourism
Director: Lorenzo Salsamendi Rius; *staff* 10 (22)
S. of Industrial Design
Director: Tullia Bassani Antivare; *staff* 17 (52)
S. of Engineering
Director: Rafael López Meneses; *staff* 19 (63)

Founded 1965. A private institution.

Academic Year: January to December (January-June; August-December).

Admission Requirements: Secondary school certificate (bachillerato) and entrance examination.

Fees (Pesos): 3,604,000 per annum.

Degrees and Diplomas: Licenciado, 8-10 sem; Medicine, 12 sem.

Publication: Generación Anáhuac (every 2 months).

Academic Staff, 1989-90: 124 (532).

Student Enrolment, 1989-90:

	Men	Women	Total
Of the country	1918	2004	3922
Of other countries	45	44	89
Total	1963	2048	4011

4723 **UNIVERSIDAD ANÁHUAC DEL SUR**

Anáhuac University
Avenida de las Torres 131, Col. Oliver de los Padres, 01780 México (D.F.)
Telephone: 589-22-00
Rector: Faustino Pardo Villa

S. of Graphic Design
Director: Rafael Medina Dela Cerda; *staff* 8 (15)
S. of Actuarial Sciences
Director: Camilo Reynaud Guerrero del Villar; *staff* 4 (12)
S. of Business Administration and Accountancy
Director: Manuel Rañal Luaña; *staff* 7 (20)
S. of Engineering
Director: Fernando Ocampo Canabal; *staff* 6 (17)
S. of Tourism
Director: Manuel Rodriguez Woog; *staff* 5 (10)
S. of Computer Science
Director: Camilo Reynaud Guellero del Villar; *staff* 4 (10)
S. of Industrial Relations
Director: Manuel Rañal Luaña; *staff* 4 (14)

Founded 1964. A private institution. Degrees recognized by the National Autonomous University.

Academic Year: August to June (August-December; January-May).

Admission Requirements: Secondary school certificate (bachillerato) and entrance examination.

Fees (Pesos): Registration, 110,000; tuition, 40,500 per month.

Language of Instruction: Spanish.

Degrees and Diplomas: Licenciado.

Library: Central Library, 11,000 vols.

Academic Staff, 1986-87: 58 (98).

Student Enrolment, 1986-87:

	Men	Women	Total
Of the country	425	460	885
Of other countries	13	8	21
Total	438	468	906

4724 **UNIVERSIDAD DEL BAJÍO A.C.**

Falda del Cerro Gordo s/n, Fraccionamiento Lomas del Campestre, 37150 León (Guanajuato)
Telex: 1772861 ULSAME
Telephone: 7-17-40
Rector: Ronaldo Henderson Calderón
Administrador: Jorge Zuñiga Ramos

S. of Administration
S. of Communication Studies
S. of Dentistry

S. of Accountancy
S. of Veterinary Medicine and Zoology
S. of Tourism and Hotel Management
S. of Engineering (Industrial, Civil, Mechanical and Electrical)
S. of Architecture
S. of Law
S. of Computer Engineering
S. of Agriculture
Art and Design Ce.
Extension Ce. (Computer Systems, Design, Dentistry)

Also campuses in Salamanca; San Francisco del Rincón.

Founded 1968 as institute, acquired present status and title 1973. Recognized by the State 1985. A private institution attached to the University of Guanajuato. Governing body: the Consejo Universitario. Residential facilities for 116 students.

Academic Year: August to June (August-December; February-June).

Admission Requirements: Secondary school certificate (bachillerato) and entrance examination.

Language of Instruction: Spanish.

Degrees and Diplomas: Licenciado in–Tourism; Communication, 4 yrs; Accountancy; Law; Business Administration; Engineering; Agriculture; Architecture; Computer Engineering; Journalism, 4 ½ yrs; Industrial Design, 5 yrs. Professional titles of–Odontologia, dentistry; Médico veterinario, 5 yrs.

Library: Central Library, 50,000 vols.

Publication: Research Publications.

Academic Staff: c. 50 (120).

Student Enrolment: c. 1970.

4725 **UNIVERSIDAD CHAPULTEPÉC**

Chihuahua 156, Col. Roma, 06700 México (D.F.)
Telephone: 584-57-74

S. of Commerce and Administration
S. of Medicine
S. of Architecture
S. of Law
S. of Systems Engineering

Academic Year: August to September (August-February; April-September).

Admission Requirements: Secondary school certificate (bachillerato).

Language of Instruction: Spanish.

Degrees and Diplomas: Licenciado, 4 ½ yrs.

4726 **UNIVERSIDAD DE LA COMMUNICACIÓN**

José Vasconcelos 70, Col. Condesa, 06140 México (D.F.)
Telephone: 286-08-49
Rector: Salvador Corrales Ayala (1980-87)
Vice-Rector Administrativo: Alfonso Méndez

D. of Advertising
Director: Hilario Arreola; *staff* 3
D. of Administration
Director: Elisa Silva de Castillo; *staff* 1
D. of Accountancy
Director: Elisa Silva de Castillo; *staff* 1

Founded 1977. A private institution recognized by the State. Governing body: the Consejo de Gobierno.

Academic Year: August to July (August-January; February-July).

Admission Requirements: Secondary school certificate (bachillerato) and entrance examination.

Fees (Pesos): 2,290,000 per semester.

Language of Instruction: Spanish.

Degrees and Diplomas: Licenciado, 4-4 ½ yrs.

Library: 5000 vols.

Publication: Revista Tinta Joven (annually).

Academic Staff, 1990: – (74).

Student Enrolment, 1990:

	Men	Women	Total
Of the country	270	265	535
Of other countries	2	2	4
Total	272	267	539

4727 **UNIVERSIDAD 'CRISTÓBAL COLÓN'**

Carretera Boticaria Km. 1(½), 91930 Veracruz (Veracruz)
Telephone: 7-21-89

S. of Architecture
S. of Computer Sciences and Administration
S. of Law
S. of Pedagogics
S. of History of Art
S. of Agricultural Development
S. of Psychology

A private institution. Degrees recognized by the Universidad Veracruzana.

Academic Year: March to February (March-August; September-February).

Admission Requirements: Secondary school certificate (bachillerato) and entrance examination.

Degrees and Diplomas: Licenciado in–Business Administration; Law, 5 yrs. Professional titles of–Arquitecto; Contador público, accountancy, 5 yrs.

4728 **UNIVERSIDAD CUAUHTÉMOC**

Jalpan y Tlacomulco. Colonia La Paz, 72160 Puebla (Puebla)
Telephone: 48-20-44

S. of Commerce and Administration
S. of Law
S. of Engineering
S. of Dentistry
S. of Psychology

Also preparatory school.

Founded 1977. A private institution recognized by the State.

Academic Year: August to July (August-January; February-July).

Admission Requirements: Secondary school certificate (bachillerato) or recognized foreign equivalent.

Language of Instruction: Spanish.

Degrees and Diplomas: Licenciado. Professional titles. Degree of Maestria.

Student Enrolment: c. 1000.

4729 **UNIVERSIDAD CUETLAXCOAPAN, S.C.**

Boulevard Valsequillo y 3B Sur. Residencial Boulevares, 72000 Puebla (Puebla)

Veterinary Medicine
Animal Science

4730 **UNIVERSIDAD FEMENINA DE MÉXICO**

Women's University of Mexico
Avenida Constituyentes 151, Col. San Miguel Chapultepec, 11850 México (D.F.)
Telephone: 515-13-11
Rector: Luz Antonieta Polanco de Garzón (1989-)
Secretaria General: Guillermina Mayorga Olague

S. of Psychology
Director: Norma Malpica Flores
S. of Law
Director: Javier Mejia Estañol
S. of Education
Director: Isabel Muñoz Urias
S. of International Relations
Director: José Antonio Gómez Cangas
S. of Pharmacobiological Chemistry
Director: Enrique Calderón García
S. of Bilingual Executive Secretarial Studies
Director: Silvia García Montes de Oca
S. of Clinical Laboratory Technology
Director: José Aguilar Castillo
S. of Tourism
Director: Luis Sergio González Puebla
S. of Social Work
Director: Margarita Ruiz Valdepeña
S. of Graphic and Decorative Design
Director: Luz Alba Tlapalcoyoa

Also preparatory school.

Founded 1943 as a centre of higher education for women. A private institution. Degrees recognized by the National University of Mexico. Governing bodies: the Administrative Council; the Board of Directors.

Academic Year: September to July (September-January; February-July).

Admission Requirements: Secondary school certificate (bachillerato) and entrance examination.
Languages of Instruction: Spanish and English.
Degrees and Diplomas: Bachiller, 3 yrs; Licenciado in–Psychology; Law; Pharmacobiological Chemistry; Education; International Relations, 4 ½-5 yrs. Professional titles of–Trabajadora social, social work; Técnica, various fields, 3-4 yrs.
Library: c. 12,000 vols.
Academic Staff, 1989: c. 240.
Student Enrolment, 1989: c. 1300.

4731 **UNIVERSIDAD FEMENINA DE VERACRUZ-LLAVE**
Balboa 524, 91910 Veracruz (Veracruz)
Telephone: 7-14-60

Social Work

A private institution attached to the Universidad de Vera Cruz.
Academic Year: March to February (March-August; September-February).
Admission Requirements: Secondary school certificate (bachillerato).
Language of Instruction: Spanish.
Degrees and Diplomas: Licenciado, 4 yrs.

4732 **UNIVERSIDAD FRANCO-MEXICANA**
Colina del Kan 1, Fracc. Boulevares, 53140 Naucalpan (Estado de México)

Business Administration and Tourism
Communication Studies
Accountancy
Law
Education
Psychology
Industrial Relations

4733 **UNIVERSIDAD GALILEA, A.C.**
5 de Mayo 535, Zona Centro, 78000 San Luis Potosí (S.L.P.)

S. of Psychology
S. of Nursing

4734 **UNIVERSIDAD DEL GOLFO**
Obregon 203 Pte., 89000 Tampico (Tamaulipas)
Telephone: 12-92-22
Rector: Heriberto Florencia Menéndez

E. of Economics
Director: Alberto A. Rivera
E. of Law
Director: Pascual Mora Morales
E. of Accountancy and Business Administration
Director: Alberto A. Rivera
Also preparatory schools.

Founded 1972, attached to the National Autonomous University of Mexico. A private institution recognized by the State government.
Academic Year: September to June (September-January; February-June).
Admission Requirements: Secondary school certificate (bachillerato).
Language of Instruction: Spanish.
Degrees and Diplomas: Licenciado in–Economics; Accountancy; Business Administration, 4 yrs; Law, 5 yrs.
Library: c. 8000 vols.
Publication: Boletín de Administración (monthly).
Academic Staff, 1989-90: c. – (36).
Student Enrolment, 1989-90:

	Men	Women	Total
Of the country	76	18	94

4735 **UNIVERSIDAD AUTÓNOMA DE GUADALAJARA**
Autonomous University of Guadalajara
Avenida la Patria 1201, 3a, Sección Lomas del Valle, 44100 Guadalajara (Jalisco)
Telex: 682785 UAG PME
Telephone: 41-50-51
Rector: Luis Garibay Gutiérrez (1957-)
Secretario General: Carlos Pérez Vizcaíno

D. of Medicine (including Dentistry, Pharmacy, Biology, and Nursing)
Director: Néstor Velásco Pérez; *staff* 248 (65)
D. of Science and Technology
Director: David Soto Ramírez; *staff* 111 (88)
D. of Humanities and Social Sciences (including Law, Economy, Business Administration, Education, Philosophy and Architecture)
Director: Humberto López Delgadillo; *staff* 237 (122)
S. of Dentistry
S. of Nursing
S. of Civil Engineering
S. of Mechanical and Electrical Engineering
S. of Computer Sciences
S. of Agricultural Engineering
S. of Biology
S. of Mathematics
S. of Accountancy
S. of Tourism
S. of Economics
S. of Industrial Design
S. of Plastic Arts
S. of Anthropology
S. of Philosophy and Letters
S. of Languages
S. of Psychology
S. of Communication Studies
I. of Humanities and Social Sciences
Director: Héctor López Rodríguez; *staff* 87 (51)
I. of Biology
Director: Jesús Flores Sánchez; *staff* 12 (4)
I. of Exact and Earth Sciences
Director: José Manuel Muro Martínez; *staff* 73 (36)
Ce. for Lifelong Education
Director: José Morales González; *staff* 26
Also 3 preparatory and 2 secondary schools.

Founded 1935 as a private autonomous institution. Degrees recognized by the National University of Mexico. Independent of State and federal governments. Governing body: the Consejo Universitario, composed of equal numbers of administrators, teaching staff and students.
Arrangements for co-operation with the Universities of: Arizona State; California, Los Angeles; Colorado State; Florida International; New York at Potsdam; Texas A & M; Arizona; Nebraska; New Mexico; Wisconsin; Houston; Southwestern Louisiana; Eastern New Mexico; Miami; Hankuk (Foreign Studies); Kyoto; Kyushu; Petrópolis (Catholic); Campinas; Santa Catarina; Lima; Morón.
Academic Year: January to December (January-June; August-December).
Admission Requirements: Secondary school certificate (bachillerato) or foreign equivalent, and entrance examination.
Fees (Pesos): Registration, 75,000-90,000; tuition, 150,000-412,000 per semester.
Language of Instruction: Spanish.
Degrees and Diplomas: Licenciado or Professional title in–Business Administration; Tourism; Architecture; Accountancy; Economics; Anthropology; Archaeology; Chemistry; Chemical Engineering; Pharmacy; Biology; Law; Social Work; Nursing and Midwifery; Mathematics; Library Science; Hispanic Languages and Literature; History; Civil Engineering; Electrical Engineering; Industrial Design; Visual Arts; Dentistry; Computer Sciences; Computer Engineering; Education; Agricultural Engineering; Journalism; Psychology, 3-5 yrs; Medicine, 6 yrs. Diplomado in–Tourism; Graphic Design; Languages, 2 ½-3 yrs. Degree of Maestría in–Languages; Education; Architecture; Law; Chemistry; Administration and Economics; Public Health. Doctorado in–Chemistry; Education. Postgraduate titles of specialist in Medicine. Also lower level technical qualifications, 3 yrs.
Libraries: Central Library, 90,000 vols; Health Sciences, 29,358.
Publications: Ocho Columnas; Docencia; Actas de la Facultad de Medicina.
Press or Publishing House: University Press.
Academic Staff, 1986-87: 1285 (498).
Student Enrolment, 1986-87:

	Men	Women	Total
Of the country	10,134	8174	18,308
Of other countries	788	339	1127
Total	10,922	8513	19,435

4736 **UNIVERSIDAD HISPANO MEXICANA**
Emilio Castelar 63 Esq. con Eugenio Sué 44, Col. Polanco, 11590 México (D.F.)
Telephone: 545-17-82

Tourism
Administration
International Relations

A private institution. Degrees recognized by the National University of Mexico.

4737 ***UNIVERSIDAD IBEROAMERICANA**
The Ibero-American University
Prolongcación Paseo de la Reforma 880, Col. Lomas de Santa Fé, 01210 México, D.F.
Telephone: 570-70-70
Rector: Carlos Escandón Domínguez (1988-92)
Director General Académico: Armando Rugarcia Torres

D. of Business Administration
Director: Florentino Velásquez Garaña; *staff* 6 (6)
D. of Economics
Director: Julian Barquin Liaño; *staff* 3 (3)
D. of Accountancy
Director: Virgilio Saldívar Casteñeda; *staff* 5
D. of Architecture and Town Planning
Director: Jorge Ballina Garza-Galindo; *staff* 6 (4)
D. of Art (including Art History)
Director: Estela Eguiarte Sakar; *staff* 4 (3)
D. of Industrial and Graphic Design
Director: Raúl Torres Maya ; *staff* 7 (5)
D. of Nutrition and Food Technology
Director: Angel Torreblanca Roldán; *staff* 9 (1)
D. of Civil Engineering
Director: Santiago Martínez Hernández; *staff* 4 (3)
D. of Mechanical and Electrical Engineering
Director: Francisco Martin del Campo; *staff* 12 (6)
D. of Engineering and Chemical Engineering
Director: Gilberto Fabila Carrera; *staff* 8
D. of Physics
Director: Gustavo Soto de la Vega; *staff* 8
D. of Mathematics
Director: Juan Cristóbal Cárdenas Oviedo; *staff* 6 (4)
D. of Systems Technology
Director: Raymundo Cantú Latapí; *staff* 8 (5)
D. of Political and Social Sciences
Director: Ricardo Macouzet Noriega; *staff* 16 (3)
D. of Communication
Director: Pablo Casares Arrangoiz; *staff* 13 (1)
D. of Law
Director: Raúl González Schmal; *staff* 6 (4)
D. of Psychology
Director: José Antonio Virseda Heras; *staff* 8 (6)
D. of Human Development
Director: Francisco Favier Palencia; *staff* 8 (3)
D. of Religious Sciences
Director: Rubén Murillo Díaz; *staff* 3 (3)
D. of Philosophy
Director: Antonio Ibargüengoitia Chico; *staff* 7 (5)
D. of History
Director: Cristina Torales Pacheco; *staff* 8 (6)
D. of Letters
Director: Gerald Nyenhuis Hendrickse; *staff* 6
Ce. for Didactics
Director: José Ramón Ulloa Herrero; *staff* 6 (2)
Social Service Ce.
Director: Alberto Fierro Garza; *staff* 10 (4)
Extension Ce.
Director: Milena Gout Ortiz; *staff* 3

Branches at: León; Tijuana; Laguna; Golfo Centro.

Founded 1943 as university cultural centre with faculty of philosophy, became university 1952. Departments fall under Divisions of: Economics and Administration, Art, Science and Engineering, Human Sciences. Degrees recognized by the National University of Mexico or by the Ministry of Education 1974. Financially supported by tuition fees. Governing bodies: the Senado Universitario; the Consejo Universitario; the Comités Académicos.

Arrangements for co-operation with the Universities of: Jerusalem (Hebrew); Tel-Aviv; Eichstätt (Catholic); Comillas; Havana; Gonzaga; Loyola, Chicago. Ecole nationale supérieure d'Arts et Métiers, France.

Academic Year: January to December (January-May; August-December).

Admission Requirements: Secondary school certificate (bachillerato) or recognized foreign equivalent, and entrance examination.

Fees (Pesos): Registration, 965,200; tuition, 84,600-184,800.

Language of Instruction: Spanish.

Degrees and Diplomas: Licenciado in–Political Science and Public Administration; Architecture; International Relations; Hotel Administration; Sociology; Philosophy; History; History of Art; Latin American Literature; Industrial Relations; Economics; Theology; Chemical Engineering; Nutrition and Food Technology; Business Administration; Architecture; Mass Communication and Technology; Accountancy; Law; Graphic Design; Biomedical Engineering; Electronic and Communication Engineering Industrial Engineering; Chemical Engineering; Physics Computer systems; Civil Engineering; Mechanical and Electrical Engineering; Psychology; 4 yrs. Degree of Maestría in–Philosophy; Law; Systems Analysis; Food Technology; Psychology; Human Development; Social Anthropology; History; Business Administration; Construction; Sociology; Communication; Social Anthropology; Modern Literature, 2 yrs. Doctorado in–Philosophy; Education Research; History; Social Sciences; Psychology; Modern Literature, 2 yrs.

Library: 252,000 vols.

Publications: Revista Jurídica; Revista DIDAC; Anuario de Humanidades; Revista de Filosofía; Revista CALDERO; Revista UMBRAL XXI.

Academic Staff, 1986-87: 1013.

Student Enrolment, 1990:

	Men	Women	Total
Of the country	4581	5127	9708

4738 **UNIVERSIDAD INTERCONTINENTAL**
Avenida Insurgentes Sur 4135, 14420 México (D.F.)
Telephone: 573-85-44

S. of Architecture
S. of Communication Sciences
S. of Accountancy and Administration
S. of Law
S. of Philosophy
S. of Design
S. of Dentistry
S. of Education
S. of Psychology
S. of Theology
S. of Tourism

Founded 1976. A private institution. Degrees recognized by the National University of Mexico. Governing bodies: the Consejo de Gobierno; the Claustro Universitario.

Academic Year: September to June (September-January; February-June).

Admission Requirements: Secondary school certificate (bachillerato).

Language of Instruction: Spanish.

Degrees and Diplomas: Licenciado in–Hotel Administration; Communication Sciences; Philosophy; Dentistry; Education; Tourism; Theology, 8 sem; Accountancy; Psychology, 9 sem; Architecture, 10 sem. Also diploma in Languages, 5 sem.

Library: c. 30,430 vols.

Publication: Ediciones de la Rectoria (biannually).

Academic Staff: c. 380.

Student Enrolment: c. 1820.

4739 **UNIVERSIDAD JOSÉ VASCONCELOS**
Guadalupe 312 norte, 34000 Victoria de Durango (Durango)
Telephone: (181) 3-37-51
Rector: Miguel C. Jarquín Marín

D. of Psychology
Director: Catalina Salazar; *staff* – (17)
D. of Communications
Director: Elvira Flores de Rodríguez; *staff* 4 (19)
D. of Design
Director: Roberto Delahanty Matuk; *staff* – (7)
D. of Pedagogy
Director: Enrique Medina Vidaña; *staff* – (7)
D. of Lifelong Education
Director: Catalina Salazar Hernández; *staff* – (12)

Academic Year: January to December (January-June; August-December).

Admission Requirements: Secondary school certificate (bachillerato) and entrance examination.
Degrees and Diplomas: Licenciado; Diplomas.
Library: 1000 vols.
Academic Staff, 1989-90: 5 (54).
Student Enrolment, 1989-90:

	Men	Women	Total
Of the country	46	106	152

4740 **UNIVERSIDAD KINO, A.C.**
Kino University
Marruecos Final Oriente, Col. Casa Blanca, 83070 Hermosillo (Sonora)
Rector: José Luis Bojórquez Siordia
Secretario General: Roberto Arizmendi Rodríguez

D. of Social Sciences
Director: Enrique Gómez Can; *staff* 1 (17)
D. of Management Sciences
Director: Héctor Pérez Gastelum; *staff* 1 (11)
Research D. (Economics, Education, Communication, Sociology)
Director: Ricardo Arechavala Vargas; *staff* 2 (9)

Founded 1985. A private institution.
Arrangements for co-operation with Stanford University.
Academic Year: September to June (September-January; February-June).
Admission Requirements: Secondary school certificate (bachillerato).
Fees (Pesos): 300,000 per semester.
Language of Instruction: Spanish.
Degrees and Diplomas: Licenciado in–Journalism; Accountancy; Administration, 4 yrs; Education, 5 yrs.
Library: 10,000 vols.
Academic Staff, 1986-87: 4 (37).
Student Enrolment, 1986-87:

	Men	Women	Total
Of the country	29	83	112

4741 ***UNIVERSIDAD LA SALLE**
La Salle University
Avenida Benjamin Franklin 47, 06140 México (D.F.)
Cables: ulsalle mexico
Telephone: 516-99-60
Fax: 271-85-85
Rector: José Cervantes Hernández
Vice-Rector: Ambrosio Luna Sallas

S. of Accountancy and Administration
Director: María Teresa Ayala Uribe; *staff* – (170)
S. of Law
Director: Luis Rodríguez Manzanera; *staff* – (46)
S. of Engineering
Director: Arturo Rojas de Bengardi; *staff* 7 (113)
S. of Architecture
Director: Oscar Castro Almeida; *staff* – (85)
S. of Medicine
Director: Abdo Bisteni Adem; *staff* 1 (216)
S. of Chemistry
Director: Araceli Sánchez de Corral; *staff* 2 (68)
S. of Philosophy
Director: Jorge Muñoz Batista; *staff* – (21)
S. of Religious Sciences
Director: Manuel Alarcón Vázquez; *staff* 5 (25)
D. of Education
Director: Rita Ferrini Ríos; *staff* 13 (10)
D. for Lifelong Education
Director: Norma Angélica Mora; *staff* 7 (25)
Also preparatory school and 2 Data Processing Centres.

Founded 1962, a private institution attached to National University of Mexico. Governing bodies: the Junta de Gobierno; the Consejo Universitario.
Arrangements for co-operation with Arizona State University.
Academic Year: August to June (August-January; February-June).
Admission Requirements: Secondary school certificate (bachillerato), or recognized foreign equivalent, and entrance examination.
Fees (Pesos): 270,000-637,000 per semester.
Language of Instruction: Spanish.
Degrees and Diplomas: Bachiller, 3 yrs. Licenciado in–Law; Philosophy; Administration, 5 yrs. Professional titles of–Contador público, accountancy; Arquitecto; Ingeniero, 5 yrs; Médico cirujano; Químico. Degree of Maestría, a further 2-3 yrs.
Libraries: Central Library, 85,000 vols; Medicine, 2890.
Publications: La Gaceta (monthly); Logos (quarterly); Revista de la Escuela de Ingeniería (biannually); Revista Médica.
Academic Staff, 1986-87: 39 (968).
Student Enrolment, 1986-87:

	Men	Women	Total
Of the country	5424	2136	7560
Of other countries	88	32	120
Total	5512	2168	7680

4742 **UNIVERSIDAD LASALLISTA BENAVENTE**
Avenida Universidad s/n, 38040 Celaya (Guanajuato)
Telephone: 2-45-08

Law
Academic Year: September to June (September-January; February-June).
Admission Requirements: Secondary school certificate (bachillerato).
Language of Instruction: Spanish.
Degrees and Diplomas: Licenciado in Law, 5 yrs.

4743 **UNIVERSIDAD LATINA, A.C.**
Chihuahua 202, 006700 México (D.F.)
Telephone: 574-18-09

Administration
Accountancy
Degrees recognized by the National University of Mexico.
Academic Year: August to July (August-December; January-July).
Admission Requirements: Secondary school certificate (bachillerato).
Language of Instruction: Spanish.
Degrees and Diplomas: Licenciado, 4 yrs.

4744 **UNIVERSIDAD LATINOAMERICANA**
S.C., Gabriel Mancera 1402, Col. del Valle, 03100 México (D.F.)
Telephone: 604-53-52
Rector: Benito Guillén-Nieyemer
Secretario General: Sergio González Villar

S. of Dentistry
Director: Manuel Saavedra García; *staff* 3 (63)
S. of Communications and Public Relations
Director: Sergio Montero Olivares; *staff* 3 (27)
S. of Administration and Accountancy
Director: Enrique Paz Zavala; *staff* 3 (46)
S. of Informatics
Director: José Argueta Ramírez; *staff* – (11)
S. of Law
Director: Alfredo Reyes Krafft; *staff* 2 (9)
Also preparatory school.

Founded 1976. Attached to the National Autonomous University of Mexico and the Ministry of Education. Governing body: the Consejo de Administración.
Academic Year: September to June (September-January; February-June).
Admission Requirements: Secondary school certificate (bachillerato) and entrance examination.
Fees (Pesos): 1,500,000 per semester; foreign students, 2,000,000.
Language of Instruction: Spanish.
Degrees and Diplomas: Licenciado in–Public Relations; Accountancy, Law; Informatics, 4 yrs; Business Administration, 4 ½ yrs. Professional title of Cirujano dentista, 4 ½ yrs. Degree of Maestría in Dentistry, a further 2 yrs.
Library: 8645 vols.
Academic Staff, 1989-90: c. 10 (190).
Student Enrolment, 1989-90:

	Men	Women	Total
Of the country	672	1045	1717*

*Also 42 foreign students.

4745 **UNIVERSIDAD DE MATAMOROS**
Diagonal Cuauhtémoc y 7a, Zona Centro, 87300 Matamoros (Tamaulipas)

S. of Communications
S. of Law and Social Sciences
S. of Accountancy and Administration
S. of Economics

S. of Dentistry
S. of Architecture
S. of Agriculture

4746 **UNIVERSIDAD MAYAB**
Km. 15.5 Carretera Mérida-Progresso, 97000 Mérida (Yucatan)
S. of Accountancy and Administration
S. of Law
S. of Computer Sciences
S. of Communications and Social Sciences
S. of Psychology

4747 **UNIVERSIDAD DE MAZATLAN, A.C.**
Guillermo Nelson 100 Desp. 104, 82000 Mazatlán (Sinaloa)
Mechanical Engineering Administration
Business Administration
Law
Public Accountancy
Computer Systems Administration

4748 **UNIVERSIDAD MEXICANA DEL NORESTE**
Quinta Zona 409, Col. Caracol, 64810 Monterrey (Nuevo León)
Telephone: 40-12-05
Rector: Juan Antonio González Arechiga y de la Cueva
Directora de Servicios Escolares: Josefina Espinoza Jara
D. of Administration and Social Sciences
Co-ordinator: Ernesto Cortazar Martínez; *staff* 8 (35)
D. of Engineering and Science
Co-ordinator: Guadalupe Moreno Soto; *staff* 9 (45)
D. of Systems Engineering
D. of Library Science
Director: Alfonso Gómez S.
D. of Cultural Diffusion
Director: Rogelio Ojeda Ch.
D. of Education Systems
Director: Jesús Castilleja

Founded 1976. A private institution recognized by the State government. Governing body: the Board of Directors, comprising 13 members.

Academic Year: January to December (January-June; August-December).

Admission Requirements: Secondary school certificate (bachillerato).

Language of Instruction: Spanish.

Degrees and Diplomas: Licenciado or Professional titles, 4-4 ½ yrs.

Library: Department libraries.

Publications: Aprender a Ser (quarterly); Imagen (monthly).

Academic Staff: *c.* 80.

Student Enrolment: *c.* 420 (Also *c.* 60 external students).

4749 **UNIVERSIDAD MEXICANA DE TECNOLOGÍA**
Czda. de Tlalpan 450, Col. Viaducto, 08200 México (D.F.)
Telex: 1771-300 ACHAME
Telephone: 530-98-04
Rectora: María del Carmen Pérez Herrera (1982-87)
D. of Law
D. of Accountancy
D. of Business Administration
D. of Computer Sciences

Founded 1959 as college, acquired present status and title 1982. A private institution. Governing body: the Consejo.

Academic Year: September to June (September-January; February-June).

Admission Requirements: Secondary school certificate (bachillerato) and entrance examination.

Language of Instruction: Spanish.

Degrees and Diplomas: Licenciado and Professional titles in all fields. Degree of Maestría. Doctorado.

Library: *c.* 12,000 vols.

Publication: Boletines (monthly).

Academic Staff: *c.* 40 (50).

Student Enrolment: *c.* 3020.

4750 **UNIVERSIDAD MÉXICO AMERICANA DEL NORTE**
Guerrero y Plutarco Elías Calles 1317, Col. de Prado, 88560 Ciudad Reynosa (Tamaulipas)
Telephone: 2-20-86
Rectora: Edith Cantu de Luna
S. of Commerce and Administration
S. of Communication Sciences
S. of Engineering
S. of Medicine (including Nursing)
S. of Architecture and Computer Sciences
S. of Law
S. of Veterinary Medicine

Founded 1982. A private institution.

Academic Year: September to August (September-December; January-April; May-August).

Admission Requirements: Secondary school certificate (bachillerato).

Language of Instruction: Spanish.

Degrees and Diplomas: Professional titles.

4751 **UNIVERSIDAD MIGUEL ALEMÁN**
Antonio Alzate y Press Palmito, Col. Hercilia, 88300 Ciudad Miguel Alemán (Tamaulipas)
F. of Architecture
F. of Accountancy and Administration
F. of Law and Social Sciences

4752 **UNIVERSIDAD DE MONTEMORELOS**
University of Montemorelos
Apartado postal 16, Montemorelos (Nuevo León)
Telex: 30104
Telephone: 3-30-80
S. of Education
S. of Accountancy and Administration
S. of Nursing
S. of Medicine
S. of Fine Arts
S. of Chemistry and Biology
S. of Theology

Founded 1942 as college. Later attached to the Autonomous University of Nuevo León. Acquired present status and title 1973. A private institution recognized by the State government. Residential facilities for academic staff and students.

Academic Year: September to June (September-November; December-March; March-June).

Admission Requirements: Secondary school certificate (bachillerato).

Language of Instruction: Spanish.

Degrees and Diplomas: Licenciado in–Education; Music; Nursing, 4 yrs. Professional titles of–Contador público, accountancy, 5 yrs; Médico cirujano.

Library: *c.* 32,980 vols.

Academic Staff: *c.* 100.

Student Enrolment: *c.* 1690.

4753 ***UNIVERSIDAD DE MONTERREY**
University of Monterrey
Ave. Morones Prieto 4500 Pte., San Pedro, 66238 Garza García (Nuevo León)
Telephone: (83) 38-50-38
Fax: (83) 38-56-19
Rector: Jorge Santisteban Pria (1983-)
Registrar: Francisco Ramirez Armenta
D. of Art, Design, and Environmental Sciences (including Architecture)
Director: José Francisco Narro López; *staff* 12 (65)
D. of Economic and Administrative Sciences
Director: José Manuel Aguiar López; *staff* 13 (70)
D. of Educational Sciences and Humanities
Director: Maria de los Angeles Cavazos; *staff* 25 (63)
D. of Engineering, Exact and Natural Sciences
Director: Jesús Antonio Garza Gutiérrez; *staff* 21 (63)
D. of Health Sciences (including Medicine)
Director: Zeta Melva Triana de Arreola; *staff* 4 (106)
D. of Law and Social Sciences
Director: Heriberto Anselmo Amaya; *staff* 28 (36)
S. of Nursing and Midwifery
S. of Nursing

Research and Development P.
Head: Manuel Sepúlveda; *staff* 1 (3)
P. for the Development of Academic Personnel
Head: Oswaldo Reyes; *staff* 1
Ce. for Health and Development
Director: Alfredo Zapata; *staff* 10 (3)
Also preparatory school (two local units).

Founded 1969. A private autonomous institution accredited by the State of Nuevo León and consequently recognized nationally. Governing body: the Board of Trustees.

Arrangements for co-operation with the Universities of: Pennsylvania State; Heidelberg. Universidad Peruana Cayetano Heredia, Peru; Katholieke Universiteit Leuven.

Academic Year: August to June (August-December; January-June).

Admission Requirements: Secondary school certificate (bachillerato) or foreign equivalent.

Fees (Pesos): 2,930,000 per semester; students from Latin America, 3,340,000-4,277,000; students from the USA, 9,97

Fees: 7,000.

Language of Instruction: Spanish.

Degrees and Diplomas: Licenciado in–Graphic Design; Industrial Design; Industrial Interior Design; Art; Business Administration; Economics; Education; Letters; Psychology; Human Relations; International Studies; Communication Sciences; Sociology; Chemistry, 8 sem; Law, 9 sem. Professional titles of–Arquitecto; Contador público, accountancy; Ingeniero, various fields, 7-9 sem; Médico, 6 ½ yrs. Diplomado in–Education; International Commerce. Degree of Maestria in–Education; Organizational Development; Law; International Trade; Quality Administration; Administration. Also lower level technical qualifications, 5 sem.

Library: Central Library, 58,000 vols.

Special Facilities (Museums, etc.): Art Gallery.

Publications: Diálogo (biannually); Boletín (annually); Enlace; Desarrollo; Nuevo Foro (monthly); Boletin de Investigación Educativa (biannually).

Press or Publishing House: Imprenta UDEM.

Academic Staff, 1989-90:

Rank	Full-time	Part-time
Profesores Titulares	1	1
Profesores Asociados	12	2
Profesores Adjuntos	74	27
Instructor	1	–
Profesores Auxiliares	–	430
Total	88	457

Student Enrolment, 1989-90:

	Men	Women	Total
Of the country	1266	1749	3015
Of other countries	146	85	231
Total	1412	1834	3246

4754 **UNIVERSIDAD MOTOLINÍA, A.C.**

Motolinia University

Cerrado de Ameyalco 227, Col. del Valle, 03100 México (D.F.)
Telephone: 523-48-13

Law
Chemistry
Also preparatory school.

Founded 1918, acquired university status 1944 in relationship with the National University of Mexico. For women only.

Academic Year: September to July (September-January; February-July).

Admission Requirements: Secondary school certificate (bachillerato).

Language of Instruction: Spanish.

Degrees and Diplomas: Licenciado in Law, 5 yrs. Professional title of Químico farmacéutico biólogo, 5 yrs.

4755 **UNIVERSIDAD MOTOLINÍA DEL PEDREGAL**

Avenida de las Fuentes 525, Pedregal de San Angel, 01900 México (D.F.)

S. of Design

4756 **UNIVERSIDAD DEL NORESTE**

Prol. Av. Hidalgo s/n Km. 137, Apartado postal 469, Tampico (Tamaulipas)
Telephone: 3-58-31
Rector: Héctor García Herrera (1983-87)
Secretario General: Octaviano Guzmán Medina

E. of Medicine
E. of Psychology
S. of Chemistry
E. of Public Relations and Communications
E. of Chemistry
E. of Dentistry

Founded as Institute of Biology 1970. Acquired present status and title 1977. A private institution. Governing body: the Consejo Universitario.

Academic Year: January to December (January-June; August-December).

Admission Requirements: Secondary school certificate (bachillerato).

Language of Instruction: Spanish.

Degrees and Diplomas: Licenciado or Professional titles, 3-6 yrs.

Library: c. 8390 vols.

Publication: Revista.

Academic Staff: c. 60 (140).

Student Enrolment: c. 1650.

4757 **UNIVERSIDAD AUTÓNOMA DEL NORESTE**

Monclova 1561, Col. República, 25280 Saltillo (Coahuila)
Telephone: (91-841) 4-82-58
Fax: (91-841) 6-31-53
Rector: Pablo Adolfo Longoria Treviño (1989-)
Secretario General: Gabriel Duran Maltos

Architecture
Accountancy
Industrial Engineering Administration
Industrial and Systems Engineering
Mechanical Engineering Administration
Business Administration
Educative Administration
Tourism
Human Resources Administration
Political Science and Public Administration
Law
Graphic Design
Human Development
Psychology
Computer Sciences

Founded 1974. A private institution recognized by the State government.

Academic Year: August to June (August-December; January-June).

Admission Requirements: Secondary school certificate (bachillerato) and entrance examination.

Fees (Pesos): 1,539,000 per semster.

Language of Instruction: Spanish.

Degrees and Diplomas: Licenciado or Professional titles, 4-4 ½ yrs. Degree of Maestria. Postgraduate title a specialist, 1 yr.

Library: Central Library, 18,649 vols.

Academic Staff, 1990: 8 (700).

Student Enrolment, 1990:

	Men	Women	Total
Of the country	2240	1985	4225

4758 **UNIVERSIDAD DEL NORTE**

Venustiano Carranza 1350 Nte., 64000 Monterrey (Nuevo León)
Telephone: 48-97-30
Rector: Luis Castillo González
Director General: Antonio J. González Villarreal

D. of Engineering (including Mechanical, Computer Information Systems, Industrial and Electrical)
Director: Conrado Davila Garcia; *staff* 3
D. of Administration
Director: Jesús Castro Pérez; *staff* 5 (1)

A private institution recognized by the State government.

Academic Year: January to December (January-April; May-August; September-December).

Admission Requirements: Secondary school certificate (bachillerato).

Fees (Pesos): 650,000-1,100,000.

Language of Instruction: Spanish.

Degrees and Diplomas: Licenciado, 4 yrs. Professional titles of Ingeniero, 4 yrs.
Library: 5,000 vols.
Academic Staff, 1990: 30 (90).
Student Enrolment, 1990:

	Men	Women	Total
Of the country	1839	615	2454
Of other countries	15	5	20
Total	1854	620	2474

4759 **UNIVERSIDAD NUEVO MUNDO**
Bosque Moctezuma 124, 53920 Fracc. La Herradura (Estado de México)
Telephone: 89-17-00

Mass Communication
Business Administration
Accountancy
Law
Graphic Design
Industrial Design
Philosophy
Mechanical Engineering
Psychology

A private institution attached to the National Autonomous University of Mexico.
Academic Year: September to June (September-January; February-June).
Admission Requirements: Secondary school certificate (bachillerato).
Language of Instruction: Spanish.
Degrees and Diplomas: Licenciado or Professional titles, 4-5 yrs.

4760 **UNIVERSIDAD PANAMERICANA**
Augusto Rodin 498, Col. Mixcoac, 03910 México (D.F.)
Telephone: 563-00-22
Fax: 611-22-65
Rector: Carlos Llano Cifuentes (1990-93)
Vice-Rector: Jesús Magaña Bravo

S. of Administration (including Accountancy)
Director: Fernando Cabrera; *staff* 19 (11)
S. of Law
Director: Miguel Angel Ochoa; *staff* 8 (6)
S. of Economics
Director: Salvador Cerón; *staff* 5 (6)
S. of Philosophy
Director: Luis Guerrero Martínez; *staff* 5 (9)
S. of Industrial and Electromechanical Engineering
Director: Pedro Creuheras Vallcorba; *staff* 17 (9)
S. of Education
Director: Alfredo López Juárez; *staff* 13 (11)
I. of Higher Business Studies
Dean: Sergio Raimond-Kedilhac
S. of Institution Administration
Director: Carmen Ramos
I. of Business Administration
Director: Sergio Raimond-Kedilhac
I. of Education
Co-ordinator: Marcela Chavarría Olarte; *staff* 2 (8)
Branches in Guadalajara City and Monterrey City.

Founded 1966 as institute, became university 1978. A private institution attached to the National Autonomous University of Mexico. Governing body: the Junta de Gobierno.

Arrangements for co-operation with the University of Navarra; Harvard University; Instituto de Estudios Superiores de la Empresa, Barcelona.
Academic Year: August to June (August-December; February-June).
Admission Requirements: Secondary school certificate (bachillerato).
Language of Instruction: Spanish.
Degrees and Diplomas: Licenciado, 4-5 yrs. Degree of Maestria in Law, a further 2 yrs.
Library: 30,000 vols.
Publications: Boletín (monthly); Revista Istmo (every 2 months).
Academic Staff, 1988-89: 311 (40).
Student Enrolment, 1988-89: 3720.

4761 **UNIVERSIDAD POPULAR AUTÓNOMA DEL ESTADO DE PUEBLA**
Edificio Central, 21 Sur 1103, 72160 Puebla (Puebla)
Telex: 178432
Telephone: 49-08-80

D. of Humanities
D. of Technology
D. of Health Sciences (includinng Medicine and Dentistry)
D. of Economics and Administration (including Accountancy)
D. of Agriculture (including Forestry and Animal Husbandry)

A private institution recognized by the State government.
Academic Year: January to December (January-July; August-December).
Admission Requirements: Secondary school certificate (bachillerato).
Language of Instruction: Spanish.
Degrees and Diplomas: Licenciado. Professional titles.

4762 ***UNIVERSIDAD REGIOMONTANA A.C.**
Villagrán Sur 328, 64000 Monterrey (Nuevo León)
Telex: 382316 URACME
Telephone: 42-52-94
Fax: 44-34-70
Rector: Francisco Abel Treviño Cisneros
Secretario General: Hector Valdes Treviño

D. of Humanities and Social Sciences (including Law, Psychology, Education, Music, Philosophy and Literature)
Director: Baudelio Castillo Flores; *staff* 5 (134)
D. of Engineering and Exact Sciences
Director: Elsa Contreras Meza; *staff* 16 (61)
D. of Architecture and Design
Director: José Sanchez Villarreal; *staff* 3 (20)
D. of Communication and Cultural Studies
Director: José M. Vega Prado; *staff* 8 (55)
D. of Business Administration
Director: Carlos Olivares Leal; *staff* 11 (113)
D. of Graduate (Master) Studies (Business Administration, Communication, Architecture, Education, and Law)
Director: Gilberto Montemayor Cantu; *staff* – (50)
D. of Training and Development
Director: José Rangel; *staff* – (15)
Also high school and research centres of the divisions.

Founded 1951 as Instituto Modelo de Enseñanza, became university 1969. A private institution recognized by the State government.

Arrangements for co-operation with Texas A & I University; University of North Texas; Southwest Texas State University; Texas Technical University.
Academic Year: September to August (September-December; January-April; May-August).
Admission Requirements: Secondary school certificate (bachillerato).
Fees (Pesos): 616,000-2,400,000.
Language of Instruction: Spanish.
Degrees and Diplomas: Bachelor, 3-4 yrs. Master, a further 2-3 yrs.
Library: Total, 24,408 vols.
Publication: Veritas (annually).
Academic Staff, 1989-90: 159 (511).
Student Enrolment, 1989-90:

	Men	Women	Total
Of the country	4194	2638	6832
Of other countries	101	57	158
Total	4295	2695	6990

4763 **UNIVERSIDAD REGIONAL 'MIGUEL HIDALGO'**
16 de Septiembre 102 Ote, Col. Arbol Grande, 89490 Ciudad Madero (Tamaulipas)

4764 **UNIVERSIDAD DE SALTILLO**
Calle Juarez Ote 595, 25000 Saltillo (Coahuila)

Public Accountancy
Business Administration
Political Science and Public Administration
Law
English Literature
Psychology

Communications

4765 **UNIVERSIDAD DE LA SIERRA, A.C.**
Avenida de los Técnicos s/n, Fracc. El Paraíso, 73160 Huauchinango (Puebla)

Business Administration
Public Accountancy
Law

4766 **UNIVERSIDAD REGIONAL DEL SURESTE**
Prolongación 20 de Noviembre s/n, Col. Alemán, 62120 Oaxaca (Oaxaca)
Telephone: 6-86-22
Rector: Gerardo J. Corres González

S. of Administration and Accountancy
S. of Architecture
S. of Dentistry
S. of Law and Social Sciences
S. of Medicine
S. of Psychology
S. of Chemistry
S. of Nursing
S. of Technology
S. of Computer Science
Also preparatory schools.

Founded 1977.
Academic Year: August to June (August-December; January-June).
Admission Requirements: Secondary school certificate (bachillerato).
Language of Instruction: Spanish.
Degrees and Diplomas: Professional titles, 4-5 yrs.
Publication: The New Review.
Academic Staff, 1989-90: 400.
Student Enrolment, 1989-90:

	Men	Women	Total
Of the country	1000	519	1519

4767 **UNIVERSIDAD TECNOLÓGICA DE MÉXICO**
Technical University of Mexico
Avenida Marina Nacional 162, Col. Anáhuac, 11320 México (D.F.)
Telephone: 399-20-00
Rector: Ignacio Guerra Pellegaud

F. of Dentistry
Director: Elias Grego; *staff* 80
F. of Administrative and Social Sciences (including Economics, Business Administration and Tourism)
Also high school.

Founded 1966. A private institution. Degrees recognized by the National Autonomous University of Mexico and the Ministry of Education.
Academic Year: September to August (September-December; January-April; May-August).
Admission Requirements: Secondary school certificate (bachillerato) and entrance examination.
Language of Instruction: Spanish.
Degrees and Diplomas: Licenciado, 3 yrs. Professional titles, 3-4 yrs.
Library: c. 10,000 vols.
Academic Staff: c. 40 (380).
Student Enrolment: c. 4830.

4768 **UNIVERSIDAD DEL TEPEYAC**
Callao 842, Col. Lindavista, 07300 México (D.F.)
Telephone: 781-40-33
Rector: Rodrigo Valle-Orozco (1975-)

S. of Architecture
Director: Concepción Allende R.; *staff* – (26)
S. of Business Administration
Director: José Guillermo del Rio Zuñiga; *staff* 8 (51)
S. of Communication Sciences
Director: Víctor Mendoza Martínez; *staff* 7 (42)
S. of Accountancy
Director: José Guillermo del Rio Zuñiga; *staff* 8 (51)
S. of Law
Director: Carlos Pelaez Casabianca; *staff* 2 (33)
S. of Tourism
Director: Juan Carlos González López; *staff* – (44)
S. of Engineering
Director: Francisco Antelmo Diaz Guerra; *staff* – (11)
Language Ce.
Co-ordinator: Rosa María Robles; *staff* – (35)
Computer Ce.
Co-ordinator: Juan Andres Preza y Mansilla; *staff* – (9)
Research Ce.
Director: Pablo Romero Vazquez; *staff* – (18)
D. of Psychology
Head: Clauria Albor Juarez; *staff* – (2)
D. of Public Relations
Head: Juan Manuel Rodríguez González Meza; *staff* – (2)
Also elementary and preparatory schools.

Founded 1941 as college, became university 1975. A private institution recognized by the State.
Academic Year: September to June (September-January; February-June).
Admission Requirements: Secondary school certificate (bachillerato) or equivalent, and entrance examination.
Fees (Pesos): 2,580,000 per semester.
Language of Instruction: Spanish.
Degrees and Diplomas: Licenciado or Professional titles, 4-5 yrs. Diplomas in Languages, 2 ½ yrs.
Library: c. 25,000 vols.
Special Facilities (Museums, etc.): Movie and T.V. Studios; Radio Station.
Academic Staff, 1989-90: 61 (180).
Student Enrolment, 1989-90:

	Men	Women	Total
Of the country	3915	1690	5605

4769 **UNIVERSIDAD DEL VALLE DE ATEMAJAC**
Avenida Tepeyac 4800, Fracc. Prados Tepeyac, 45050 Guadalajara (Jalisco)
Telephone: 21-95-06
Rector: Santiago Méndez Bravo

D. of Humanities and Social Sciences (including Communication, Psychology, Education, and Nutrition)
Director: Jesús Suárez González; *staff* 10 (60)
D. of Engineering (including Computer Systems and Architecture)
Director: Víctor Barba Arellano; *staff* 3 (92)
D. of Economics and Administration
Director: Francisco Austreberto Guitérrez Fonseca; *staff* 10 (137)
Ce. for Lifelong Education
Director: Occtavio Salazar Arellano; *staff* – (57)
D. of Research
Head: Gabriel Sánchez; *staff* 4 (7)
Also Branches in La Piedad and Zamora.

Founded 1960 as institute, became university 1979. A private institution recognized by the State.
Academic Year: January to December (January-April; May-August; September-December).
Admission Requirements: Secondary school certificate (bachillerato) and entrance examination.
Fees (Pesos): 1,350,000-1,800,000.
Language of Instruction: Spanish.
Degrees and Diplomas: Licenciado or Professional titles, 4-5 yrs. Diplomado in–Anthropology; Theology; Public Relations. Degree of Maestria.
Library: 15,000 vols.
Academic Staff, 1990: 32 (495).
Student Enrolment, 1990:

	Men	Women	Total
Of the country	2131	1420	3551
Of other countries	9	9	14
Total	2140	1425	3565*

*Also 4303 students in the two branches.

4770 **UNIVERSIDAD VALLE DEL BRAVO**
Herón Ramírez 155 Nte, Col. Rodriguez, 88630 Ciudad Reynosa (Tamaulipas)
Telephone: 2-42-49

Business Administration
Public Accountancy
Law
Communications
Tourism
Spanish Literature

Psychology
Biology
Medicine, Surgery and Obstetrics
Dentistry
Agricultural Engineering Administration
Civil Engineering
Mechanical Engineering
Electrical Engineering Administration
Petroleum Engineering
Industrial Administration Engineering
Industrial Relations
Agricultural and Zoological Engineering
Architecture
Computer Science Systems
Branches in Monte, Nuevo Laredo, Orizatlán, Reynosa, Tampico, Ciudad Victoria.

A private institution recognized by the State government.

Academic Year: September to March (September-January; February-March).

Admission Requirements: Secondary school certificate (bachillerato).

Language of Instruction: Spanish.

Degrees and Diplomas: Licenciado or Professional titles, 4-5 yrs.

4771 **UNIVERSIDAD DEL VALLE DE MÉXICO**
Tehuantepec 250, Colonia Roma Sur, 06760 México (D.F.)
Telephone: 584-77-55
Fax: 574-04-22
Rector: Aurelio Romero Fernández (1990-)
Vice-Rector Administrativo: Martha Elena Sierra Gómez

Architecture (Tlalpan, San Rafael)
Economics and Administration (including Business Administration, Accountancy, Public and Industrial Relations, Tourism, Finance, Marketing)
Social Sciences (including Communication, Law, Education, Psychology)
Exact Sciences (including Architec0ure, Industrial Engineering, Computer Systems, Graphic Design, Ecology)
Computer Ce.
Campuses in: Guadalupe, San Angel, Lomas Verdes, San Rafael, Tlalpan

Founded 1960 as Institución Harvard, became university 1968. A private institution recognized by the State. Governing body: the Junta de Gobierno.

Academic Year: August to June (September-January; February-June).

Admission Requirements: Secondary school certificate (bachillerato) and entrance examination.

Fees (Pesos): 230,000-240,000 per month.

Language of Instruction: Spanish.

Degrees and Diplomas: Bachiller, 3 yrs. Licenciado or Professional title, 8-10 sem. Degree of Maestría.

Library: Total, 36,240 vols.

Special Facilities (Museums, etc.): Centro de Educación Especial y Desarrollo Humano.

Publications: Fusión (bimonthly); Nuestro Valle (monthly).

Press or Publishing House: Editorial Universidad del Valle de México.

Academic Staff, 1989-90: 1587.

Student Enrolment, 1989-90: 23,200.

4772 **UNIVERSIDAD DEL VALLE DE PUEBLA, A.C.**
Avenida 12 Oriente 204, 72000 Puebla (Puebla)
Telephone: 40-61-35

Administration
Public Accountancy
Industrial Relations
Tourism
Computer Science Administration

A private institution recognized by the State government.

4773 **UNIVERSIDAD DEL VALLE DE TOLUCA**
Calle 21 de Marzo 101, Toluca (Estado de México)
Telephone: 8-00-56

Economics and Administration
Architecture and Town Planning
Accountancy
Social Sciences

A private institution recognized by the State government.

Academic Year: August to July (August-January; February-July).

Admission Requirements: Secondary school certificate (bachillerato).

Language of Instruction: Spanish.

Degrees and Diplomas: Licenciado or Professional titles, 4-5 yrs.

4774 **UNIVERSIDAD EJECUTIVOS DE VENTAS Y MERCADOTECNIA DE MÉXICO, A.C.**
Rio Niágara 26, Col. Cuauhtémoc, 06500 México (D.F.)

Merchandise

4775 **UNIVERSIDAD VILLA RICA**
Avenida Díaz Mirón 2242, 91700 Veracruz (Veracruz)
Telephone: 7-53-64

Accountancy and Administration
Law
Economics
Psychology

A private institution attached to the National Autonomous University of Mexico.

Academic Year: September to July (September-January; February-July).

Admission Requirements: Secondary school certificate (bachillerato).

Language of Instruction: Spanish.

Degrees and Diplomas: Licenciado, 4-5 yrs.

4776 **UNIVERSIDAD XICOTEPETL, A.C.**
Aldama 122, B73080 Col. Xicotepec de Juarez (Puebla)
Telephone: 91-776-413-10
Rector: José Luis Aldana López

D. of Veterinary Medicine and Zoology
Director: Luis Vargas Galindo; *staff* 4 (14)
D. of Agricultural and Plant Engineering
Director: Severo Piedra Rodriguez; *staff* 5 (17)
D. of Agricultural Business Administration
Director: Antonio Maldonado Garnica; *staff* 5 (12)
D. of Business Administration
Director: Meliton Amador Quiroz; *staff* 6 (15)
D. of Public Accountancy
Director: Ruben Becerra Lecona; *staff* 5 (15)

Founded 1983. A private institution.

Academic Year: September to June (September-January; February-June).

Admission Requirements: Secondary school certificate (bachillerato) or equivalent.

Fees (Pesos): 600,000 per semester.

Language of Instruction: Spanish.

Degrees and Diplomas: Bachelor, 5 yrs.

Library: Juventino Fosado Paredes Library, 1,200 vols.

Publication: El Xicote Universitario (monthly).

Academic Staff, 1990: 25 (73).

Student Enrolment, 1990:

	Men	Women	Total
Of the country	191	46	237

Other Institutions

Technical Education

4777 **CENTRO DE ENSEÑANZA TÉCNICA Y SUPERIOR**
Calz, Cetys s/n, Apartado postal 3-797, Mexicali (Baja California)
Telephone: 65-01-11
Fax: 65-02-41
Rector: J. Alfonso Marin Jimenez
Director Educativo: Enrique C. Blancas de la Cruz

S. of Engineering
Director: Ezequiel Rodríguez; *staff* 15 (23)
S. of Business Administration and Accountancy
Director: Francisco Villarba R. *staff* 10 (35)
S. of Psychology (Tijuana) *staff* 9 (15)
S. of Accountancy and Engineering Administration (Tijuana)
S. of Accountancy and Administration (Ensenada)
S. of Engineering (Tijuana)
Director: Rodrigo Gutiérrez; *staff* 5 (22)

S. of Business Administration and Accountancy (Tijuana)
Director: Pedro A. Adame S. *staff* 15 (17)
S. of Engineering (Ensenada)
Director: Socorro Lomeli; *staff* 3 (30)
S. of Business Administration and Accountancy
Director: Tomas Soto; *staff* 2 (26)
S. of Vocational and Technical Studies
Director: Omar Garcia G. *staff* 3 (23)
Also preparatory schools at Mexicali, Ensenada, and Tijuana.

Founded 1961, a private institution and authorized by the Secretary for Education to award degrees including doctorates. Governing body: the Board of Trustees.

Academic Year: August to June (August-December; January-June).

Admission Requirements: Secondary school certificate (bachillerato).

Language of Instruction: Spanish.

Degrees and Diplomas: Licenciado in–Business Administration; Human Resources Administration; Marketing Administration; Computer Systems; Psychology, 8 sem. Professional titles of–Ingeniero, various fields; Contador público, accountancy, 8sem.

Library: c. 30,000 vols.

Libraries: Mexicali, 38,000 vols; Tijuana, 20,000 vols; Ensenada, 8,000 vols.

Academic Staff: c. 60 (190).

Student Enrolment, 1990:

	Men	Women	Total
Of the country	1305	1216	2521

4778 **CENTRO DE ENSEÑANZA TÉCNICA INDUSTRIAL**
Avenida del Chaco 3223, Fraccionamiento Providencia, 44620
Guadalajara (Jalisco)
Telephone: 47-64-29

Mechanical Engineering
Industrial Engineering
Processing

A State institution responsible to the federal authorities.

Academic Year: August to June (August-January; February-June).

Admission Requirements: Secondary school certificate (bachillerato).

Language of Instruction: Spanish.

Degrees and Diplomas: Professional title of Ingeniero industrial, 4 yrs.

4779 **ESCUELA DE INGENIERÍA MUNICIPAL**
Dr. Lucio 191A, México (D.F.)
Telephone: 588-17-91

Engineering

A private institution.

Academic Year: September to June (September-January; February-June).

Admission Requirements: Secondary school certificate (bachillerato).

Language of Instruction: Spanish.

Degrees and Diplomas: Professional title of Ingeniero municipal, 4 yrs.

4780 **INSTITUTO POLITÉCNICO NACIONAL**
National Polytechnic Institute
Unidad Profesional Zacateco, 07738 México (D.F.)
Telephone: 754-41-02
Director General: Raúl Talán Ramírez (1985-88)
Secretario Académico: José Luis Rodríguez Garcia

S. of Mechanical and Electrical Engineering
Director: René Torres Bejarano
S. of Civil Engineering and Architecture (including Geology)
Director: Jaime Rueda Gaxiola
S. of Chemical and Industrial Engineering (including Metallurgy)
Director: Guillermo Marroquin Juárez
S. of Textile Engineering
Director: Alfredo García González
S. of Physics and Mathematics
Director: José Antonio Irán Díaz Góngora
S. of Medicine (including Optometry)
Director: Teodoro Bazán Sosa
S. of Homeopathic Medicine
Director: Armando Barocio Lozano
S. of Biological Sciences
Director: Roberto Ibarra Rivas
S. of Commerce and Administration
Director: José Angel Escobar Arvizú
S. of Tourism
Director: Lino Ceja Fernández
S. of Economics
Director: Benito Reyes Gutiérrez
Interdisciplinary Ce. of Engineering, Social Sciences, and Administration
Director: Ernesto Angeles Mejía
Interdisciplinary Ce. of Health Sciences
Director: José Luis Rivas Hernández
Biotic Products Research Ce.
Director: Luz María del Castillo
Computer Ce.
Director: Cuauhtémoc Rodríguez Díaz Fernández
Digital Research Ce.
Director: Héctor Ruiz Veraza
D. for Lifelong Education
Also 16 scientific and technological studies centres.

Founded 1937 when several technical schools in the City of Mexico were grouped and others created. A State institution under the jurisdiction of the Ministry of Education. Governing bodies: the Dirección General; the Secretaría General; the Dirección Administrativa.

The institute co-operates with many other countries under the terms of various cultural conventions and agreements.

Academic Year: September to July (September-February; February-July).

Admission Requirements: Secondary school certificate (bachillerato) or foreign equivalent, and entrance examination.

Language of Instruction: Spanish.

Degrees and Diplomas: Licenciado in–Physics and Mathematics; Commercial Relations; Tourism; Industrial Administration; Computer Sciences; Nursing; Nutrition; Optometry; Social Work, 4 yrs; Economics, 5 yrs. Professional titles of–Ingeniero, in various fields, 4-5 yrs; Enfermera partera, midwifery, 2 yrs; Enfermera, nursing; Optometrista, optometry, 3 yrs; Contador público, accountancy, 4 yrs; Biólogo, biology; Químico, chemistry; Químico farmacéutico, 5 yrs; Médico cirujano, 6 yrs. Degree of Maestría. Doctorado in Science. Also lower level technical qualifications, 3 yrs.

Library: Total, 500,000 vols.

Special Facilities (Museums, etc.): Geology Museum.

Publications: Acta Mexicana de Ciencia y Tecnología; Anales de la Escuela Nacional de Ciencias Biológicas; Acta Médica.

Academic Staff, 1986-87: 7200 (4800).

Student Enrolment, 1986-87:

	Men	Women	Total
Of the country	77,400	51,600	129,000
Of other countries	1040	260	1300
Total	78,440	51,860	130,300

4781 ***INSTITUTO TECNOLÓGICO AUTÓNOMO DE MÉXICO**
Rio Hondo 1, Tizapán, San Angel, 10200 México (D.F.)
Telephone: 550-93-00
Rector: Javier Beristáin Iturbide (1972-)
Registrar: Carlos López Santibañez

D. of Accountancy and Administration
Director: Octavio Colmenares; *staff* 32 (65)
D. of Social Sciences
Director: Federico Estevez; *staff* 5 (12)
D. of Computer Sciences
Director: Victoria Bajar Simsolo; *staff* 34 (28)
D. of Economics
; *staff* 26 (39)
D. of General Studies
Director: Rodolfo Vázquez; *staff* 27 (43)
D. of Applied Mathematics and Actuarial Sciences
Director: Enrique de Alba; *staff* 28 (51)
D. of Law
Director: Víctor Blanco; *staff* 8 (18)
Ce. for Economic Research and Analysis
Director: Manuel Sánchez; *staff* 10 (30)
Ce. for Public Policy
Ce. for International Business
Extension Ce.
Director: Matthias Sachse Steinbrecher; *staff* 12 (52)

Founded 1946. A private autonomous institution recognized by the State 1963. Governing body: the Junta de Gobierno.

Arrangments for co-operation with: Trent University; Thames Polytechnic; ESADE, Barcelona; University of California, Los Angeles; University of Texas. Also participates in the International Students Exchange Program, USA.

Academic Year: August to June (August-December; January-June; June-July).

Admission Requirements: Secondary school certificate and entrance examination.

Fees (Pesos): 1,584,000-2,800,000.

Language of Instruction: Spanish.

Degrees and Diplomas: Licenciado, 4 yrs. Degree of Maestria in–Economics; Public Policy, Administration and International Business, 2 yrs. Also Diplomado in Graduate Programmes.

Library: c. 95,000 vols.

Publication: Estudios (biannually).

Academic Staff, 1990: c. 121 (300).

Student Enrolment, 1990:

	Men	Women	Total
Of the country	2219	1508	3727
Of other countries	7	3	10
Total	2226	1511	3737

4782 **INSTITUTO TECNOLÓGICO MEXICANO**

5 de Febrero 91, México 1 (D.F.)

Telephone: 512-16-23

Business Administration

Accountancy

A private institution.

Academic Year: September to August (September-March; April-August).

Admission Requirements: Secondary school certificate (bachillerato).

Language of Instruction: Spanish.

Degrees and Diplomas: Professional title of Contador público, accountancy, 4 yrs.

4783 **INSTITUTO TECNOLÓGICO Y DE ESTUDIOS SUPERIORES DE MONTERREY**

Monterrey Institute of Technology

Avenida Eugenio Garza Sada 2501, Sucursal de Correos 'J', 64849 Monterrey (Nuevo León)

Telex: 382975

Telephone: 58-20-00

Rector: Rafael Rangel Sostmann (1986-)

D. of Administration and Social Sciences (including Economics)

D. of Agriculture and Marine Sciences (including Animal Husbandry)

D. of Science and Humanities

D. of Engineering and Architecture

D. of Health Sciences

Extension D.

Campuses at: Guaymas; Ciudad Obregón; Chihuahua; Saltillo; San Luis Potosi; Querétaro; Irapuato; León; Ciudad de México; Toluca; Guadalajara; Cuernavaca; Morelos; Colima; Tuxtla Gutiérrez; Cordóba, Estado de Veracruz; Ciudad Juárez; Atizpán de Zaragoza; Pachuca, Hidalgo; Mazatlán; Monterrey; Torreón, Coahuila; Hermosillo; Culiacán; Altamira; Zacatecas.

Founded 1943, a private institution approved of by the Board of Education of the federal government. Governing body: the Board of Trustees. Residential facilities for students.

Arrangements for co-operation with: University of Wisconsin; University of Colorado; Colorado State University; Cornell University; Texas A & M University; Southern Illinois University; University of Missouri; Iowa State University; University of Nebraska; University of New Mexico; University of Utah; University of Texas; State University of New York.

Academic Year: August to May (August-December; January-May).

Admission Requirements: Secondary school certificate (bachillerato) or equivalent, and entrance examination.

Language of Instruction: Spanish.

Degrees and Diplomas: Licenciado in–English; Spanish; Physics; Chemistry; Business Administration; Communication; Marketing; Administration; Journalism; Human Resources Management; Law; Organizational Psychology; Economics, 9 sem. Professional titles of–Ingeniero, in various fields, including Agriculture and Animal Husbandry, 8-10 sem; Contador público, accountancy; Arquitecto, 9 sem; Médico cirujano y Partero, 6 yrs. Degree of Maestria in most fields, a further 2 yrs. Doctorado in–Chemistry; Agriculture.

Libraries: Total, 221,516 vols; History of Mexico, 36,848.

Publications: Tetlani; publications of the campuses.

Academic Staff, 1987: 1190.

Student Enrolment, 1986-87:

	Men	Women	Total
Of the country	15,270	6544	21,814
Of other countries	636	272	908
Total	15,906	6816	22,722

4784 ***INSTITUTO TECNOLÓGICO Y DE ESTUDIOS SUPERIORES DE OCCIDENTE**

Fuego 1031 Jardines Del Bosque, 31175 Guadalajara (Jalisco)

Telephone: 84-25-43

Fax: 84-29-27

Rector: Luis González-Cosío Elcoro (1989-94)

Secretario Académico: Miguel Bazdresch Parada

D. of Engineering

Director: Javier Glez. Orozco; *staff* 38 (109)

D. of Economics and Administration

Director: Pedro Núñez Hermosillo; *staff* 43 (125)

S. of Architecture

Director: Carlos Petersen Farah; *staff* 7 (57)

S. of Human Social Sciences

Director: Carlos Luna Cortés; *staff* 13 (22)

D. of Physics and Mathematics

Co-ordinator: Gerardo Aguilera Pérez

D. of Social Sciences

Director: Pablo Lasso Gómez

Computer Ce.

Co-ordinator: Fernando Escobar Zúñiga

Ce. for Agriculture and Stockraising

Co-ordinator: Oscar Hernández Valdés; *staff* 12 (5)

Extension D.

D. of Postgraduate Studies

Director: Miguel Bazdresch Parada

Founded 1957 as a private institution, became incorporated with the Universidad Nacional Autónoma de México 1968. Recognized by the State 1975. Governing bodies: the Junta de Gobierno; the Consejo Académico.

Academic Year: August to May (August-November; January-May).

Admission Requirements: Secondary school certificate (bachillerato) and entrance examination.

Fees (Pesos): 2,145,000 per semester.

Language of Instruction: Spanish.

Degrees and Diplomas: Licenciado in–Industrial Relations; Business Administration; Accountancy; Civil Engineering; Industrial Engineering; Electrical Engineering and Electronics; Computer Sciences; Marketing; Agricultural and Stockraising Administration; Systems Analysis; Psychology; Communication; Chemical Engineering, 8-9 sem; Architecture, 10 sem. Degree of Maestria, a further 3 sem.

Libraries: Central Library, 58,000 vols; libraries of the divisions and schools.

Publications: Revista Renglones; Revista Huella (quarterly); Boletín Informativo (monthly).

Academic Staff, 1989-90:

Rank	Full-time	Part-time
Numerarios	2	1
Titulares	37	80
Asociados	50	459
Adjuntos Especiales	–	116
Adjuntos	–	119
Ayudantes	–	41
Total	89	816

Student Enrolment, 1989-90:

	Men	Women	Total
Of the country	2570	1767	4337
Of other countries	30	29	59
Total	2600	1796	4396

4785 **INSTITUTO TECNOLÓGICO Y DE ESTUDIOS SUPERIORES POTOSINO**

Avenida Madero 335, Apartado postal 743, 78220 San Luis Potosí (San Luis Potosí)
Telephone: 3-37-39

Accountancy

Founded 1967. Attached to the Universidad Nacional Autónoma de México.

Academic Year: September to July (September-January; March-July).

Admission Requirements: Secondary school certificate (bachillerato).

Language of Instruction: Spanish.

Degrees and Diplomas: Licenciado in Business Administration, 4 yrs. Professional title of Contador público, accountancy, 4 yrs.

Academic Staff: c. 5 (80).

Student Enrolment: c. 400.

4786 **INSTITUTO TECNOLÓGICO DE SONORA**

5 de Febrero 818 Sur, 85000 Ciudad Obregón (Sonora)
Telephone: 4-14-29
Rector: Oscar Amézaga (1979-87)
Vice-Rector Administrativo: Jorge Orozco P.

D. of Agriculture (including Animal Husbandry)
Head: Ramón Zavala F.; *staff* 9 (12)
D. of Administration and Accountancy
Head: José J. Franco J.; *staff* 17 (61)
D. of Psychology
Head: Alejandro Jacobo C.; *staff* 7 (13)
D. of Industrial Engineering
Head: Ignacio Palomares U.; *staff* 10 (17)
D. of Civil Engineering and Hydrology
Head: Héctor A. López; *staff* 14 (22)
D. of Chemistry and Chemical Engineering
Head: Gerardo Vega P.; *staff* 13 (23)
D. of Humanities
Head: Dora E. Garcia; *staff* 11 (20)
D. of Veterinary Medicine and Animal Husbandry
Head: José M. Aceves; *staff* 10 (26)
D. of Mathematics and Physics
Head: Jaime R. Pablos; *staff* 15 (68)
D. of Nursing (2)
Head: Rose E. Vizcarra; *staff* 12 (13)
Extension D.

Branches in: Navojoa; Guaymas.

Founded 1955 as preparatory school, acquired present status and title 1973. A State institution financed by the federal government. Governing body: the Consejo Directivo.

Academic Year: August to July (August-December; January-May).

Admission Requirements: Secondary school certificate (bachillerato) and entrance examination.

Fees (Pesos): 7500-27,500 per semester.

Language of Instruction: Spanish.

Degrees and Diplomas: Licenciado in–Administration; Psychology; Education, 8 sem. Professional titles of–Ingeniero, various fields, 8-9 sem; Contador público, accountancy; Químico, 8 sem; Médico veterinario zootecnista, 10 sem. Degreeof Maestría in Administration, a further 2 yrs.

Library: 26,784 vols.

Academic Staff, 1986-87: 147 (356).

Student Enrolment, 1986-87:

	Men	Women	Total
Of the country	3738	2873	6611
Of other countries	4	1	5
Total	3742	2874	6616*

*Also 980 external students.

4787 **INSTITUTO TECNOLÓGICO AGROPECUARIO NO. 20**

Km. 18 Carretera Ags. S.L.P., 20270 Aguascalientes (Aguascalientes)
Telephone: 5-56-60

Plant Technology
Agricultural Engineering
Zoology

A State institution.

4788 **INSTITUTO TECNOLÓGICO AGROPECUARIO NO. 4**

Km. 24.5 Carretera Tampico-Mante, Altimara (Tamaulipas)
Telephone: 3-36-04

Plant Technology

A State institution

Academic Year: September to June (September-January; February-June)

Admission Requirements: Secondary school certificate (bachillerato).

Language of Instruction: Spanish.

Degrees and Diplomas: Professional titles, 2-4 yrs.

4789 **INSTITUTO TECNOLÓGICO AGROPECUARIO NO. 5**

Ejido China, 24000 Campeche (Campeche)

Plant Technology
Zoology

A State institution.

Academic Year: September to June (September-January; February-June)

Admission Requirements: Secondary school certificate (bachillerato).

Language of Instruction: Spanish.

Degrees and Diplomas: Professional titles, 2-4 yrs.

4790 **INSTITUTO TECNOLÓGICO AGROPECUARIO NO. 16**

Avenida Insurgentes s/n, Apartado postal 207, 77000 Chetumal (Quintana Roo)
Telephone: 2-15-02

Rural Development
Agriculture

Academic Year: September to June (September-January; February-June)

Admission Requirements: Secondary school certificate (bachillerato).

Language of Instruction: Spanish.

Degrees and Diplomas: Professional titles, 2-4 yrs.

4791 **INSTITUTO TECNOLÓGICO AGROPECUARIO NO. 25**

Domicilio Conocido, Municipio Pangarabato, 0660 Ciudad Altamirano (Guerrero)

Plant Technology
Rural Development

A State institution.

4792 **INSTITUTO TECNOLÓGICO AGROPECUARIO NO. 18**

Prol. de Pipila s/n, Mpio. Ursulo Galván, 91680 Cd. Curdel (Veracruz)
Telephone: 2-91-13

Plant Technology
Zoology

A State institution.

4793 **INSTITUTO TECNOLÓGICO AGROPECUARIO NO. 24**

Km. 14.5 Carretera Cuauhtémoc, Col. Alvaro Obregón, 31500 Ciudad Cuauhtémoc (Chihuahua)

Plant Technology
Administration

A State institution.

4794 **INSTITUTO TECNOLÓGICO AGROPECUARIO NO. 31**

Dom. Conocido, Rancho J.B., Comitán (Chiapas)

Zoology
Rural Development

4795 **INSTITUTO TECNOLÓGICO AGROPECUARIO NO. 22**

Km. 4 de la Carretera Valles-Ingenio Plan de Ayala, 79000 Ciudad Valles (San Luis Potosí)
Telephone: 2-32-75

Plant Technology
Zoology

A State institution.

4796 **INSTITUTO TECNOLÓGICO AGROPECUARIO NO. 1**

Carretera Durango-México, Km. 22, Apartado postal 393, Durango (Durango)
Telephone: 2-95-56

Plant Technology
Zoology

Administration

Founded 1973. A State institution.

Academic Year: September to June (September-January; February-June).

Admission Requirements: Secondary school certificate (bachillerato).

Language of Instruction: Spanish.

Degrees and Diplomas: Professional titles, 4 yrs.

Academic Staff: c. 40 (10).

Student Enrolment: c. 860.

4797 **INSTITUTO TECNOLÓGICO AGROPECUARIO NO. 6**

Apartado postal 94, 43000 Huejutla de Reyes (Hidalgo)

Plant Technology

Zoology

A State institution

Academic Year: September to June (September-January; February-June).

Admission Requirements: Secondary school certificate (bachillerato).

Language of Instruction: Spanish.

Degrees and Diplomas: Licenciado, 4 yrs.

4798 **INSTITUTO TECNOLÓGICO AGROPECUARIO NO. 8**

Centenaro 61, San Pedro Comitancillo (Oaxaca)

Rural Development

A State institution.

Academic Year: September to June (September-January; February-June).

Admission Requirements: Secondary school certificate (bachillerato).

Language of Instruction: Spanish.

Degrees and Diplomas: Professional title, 4 yrs.

4799 **INSTITUTO TECNOLÓGICO AGROPECUARIO NO. 13**

Apartado postal No. 26, 71600 Santiago Pinotepa Nacional (Oaxaca)

Plant Technology

Zoology

A State institution.

Academic Year: September to June (September-January; February-June).

Admission Requirements: Secondary school certificate (bachillerato).

Language of Instruction: Spanish.

Degrees and Diplomas: Professional titles, 2 yrs.

4800 **INSTITUTO TECNOLÓGICO AGROPECUARIO NO. 12**

Apartado postal 5, Ejido Emiliare Zapata, 67700 Linares (Nuevo León)

Plant Technology

Zoology

A State institution.

Academic Year: September-June (September-January; February-June).

Admission Requirements: Secondary school certificate (bachillerato).

Language of Instruction: Spanish.

Degrees and Diplomas: Professional titles, 2 yrs.

4801 **INSTITUTO TECNOLÓGICO AGROPECUARIO NO. 2**

Carretera Mérida-Motul Km. 16.3, Apartado postal 53-D, 97110 Mérida (Yucatán)

Telephone: 3-10-40

Plant Technology

Rural Development

A State institution.

Academic Year: September to June (September-January; February-June).

Admission Requirements: Secondary school certificate (bachillerato).

Language of Instruction: Spanish.

Degrees and Diplomas: Professional titles, 2-4 yrs.

4802 **INSTITUTO TECNOLÓGICO AGROPECUARIO NO. 9**

Cerro de la Trilla, Apartado postal 18, 62600 Micatlán (Morelos)

Telephone: 4-34-00

Plant Technology

Zoology

A State institution.

Academic Year: September to June (September-January; February-June).

Admission Requirements: Secondary school certificate (bachillerato).

Language of Instruction: Spanish.

Degrees and Diplomas: Professional titles, 2-4 yrs.

4803 **INSTITUTO TECNOLÓGICO AGROPECUARIO NO. 7**

Km. 7 Carretera Morelia-Guanajuato, Apartado postal 39 'B', 58000 Morelia (Michoacán)

Zoology

Forestry

Plant Technology

Rural Development

A State institution.

Academic Year: September to June (September-January; February-June).

Admission Requirements: Secondary school certificate (bachillerato).

Language of Instruction: Spanish.

Degrees and Diplomas: Professional titles, 2-4 yrs.

4804 **INSTITUTO TECNOLÓGICO AGROPECUARIO NO. 28**

Km. 15 Carretera Villa Kermosa-Frontera, Villahermosa (Tabasco)

Plant Technology

Zoology

A State institution.

4805 **INSTITUTO TECNOLÓGICO AGROPECUARIO NO. 29**

Km. 7.5 Carretera San Diego, 90122 San Diego Xocoyucán (Tlaxcala)

Industrial Engineering

Zoology

A State institution.

4806 **INSTITUTO TECNOLÓGICO AGROPECUARIO NO. 23**

23, Ex-Hacienda de Nazerono, Sta. Cruz Xoxocotlan (Oaxaca)

Telephone: 6-18-94

Director: Federico Sada Solana (1984-88)

Plant Technology

Zoology

Founded 1981. A State institution.

Academic Year: September to June (September-January; February-June).

Admission Requirements: Secondary school certificate (bachillerato).

Language of Instruction: Spanish.

Degrees and Diplomas: Professional titles of Ingeniero agrónomo, 4 yrs. Degree of Maestría, a further 2 yrs.

Library: c. 2000 vols.

Academic Staff: c. 30 (10).

Student Enrolment: c. 290.

4807 **INSTITUTO TECNOLÓGICO AGROPECUARIO NO. 27**

Pozo de Ibarra, 63300 Santiago Ixcuintla (Nayarit)

Plant Technology

Rural Development

A State institution.

4808 **INSTITUTO TECNOLÓGICO AGROPECUARIO NO. 19**

Apartado postal 79, 97700 Tizimín (Yucatán)

Telephone: 3-21-88

Zoology

Rural Development

A State institution.

Academic Year: September to June (September-January; February-June).

Admission Requirements: Secondary school certificate (bachillerato).

Language of Instruction: Spanish.

Degrees and Diplomas: Professional titles, 2-4 yrs.

4809 **INSTITUTO TECNOLÓGICO AGROPECUARIO NO. 26**

Domicilio Conocido, Km. 4 Carretera Tlacomulco-San Miguel Coyutlan, Municipio Tlacomulco de Zúñiga, 45640 Tlacomulco (Jalisco)

Zoology

Plant Technology

Administration

A State institution.

4810 **INSTITUTO TECNOLÓGICO AGROPECUARIO NO. 10**

Carretera Torreón, Km. 14.5, La Partida, 27000 Torreón (Coahuila)

Plant Technology

Zoology

Rural Development

A State institution.

Academic Year: September to June (September -January; February-June).
Admission Requirements: Secondary school certificate (bachillerato).
Language of Instruction: Spanish.
Degrees and Diplomas: Professional titles, 4 yrs.

4811 **INSITUTO TECNOLÓGICO AGROPECUARIO NO. 3**
Daniel Soto No. 370, Esq. Sebastián Ortíz, Apartado Postal 38, 68300 Tuxtepec (Oaxaca)
Telephone: 5-16-97

Plant Technology
Zoology

A State institution.
Academic Year: September to June (September-January; February-June).
Admission Requirements: Secondary school certificate (bachillerato).
Language of Instruction: Spanish.
Degrees and Diplomas: Professional titles, 2 yrs.

4812 **INSTITUTO TECNOLÓGICO AGROPECUARIO NO. 21**
Block No. 611, Municipio de Bacum, 85000 Valle del Yaqui (Sonora)

Plant Technology
Administration
Industrial Engineering

A State institution.
Academic Year: September to June (September-January; February-June).
Admission Requirements: Secondary school certificate (bachillerato).
Language of Instruction: Spanish.
Degrees and Diplomas: Professional titles, 4 yrs.

4813 **INSTITUTO TECNOLÓGICO AGROPECUARIO NO. 30**
Ejido el Mezguite, Vila de Arista (S.L.P.)

Plant Technology
Zoology

4814 **INSTITUTO TECNOLÓGICO FORESTAL DE EL SALTO NO. 1**
Mesa del Tecnológico s/n, Apartado postal 59, El Salto, 34950 P. Nuevo (Durango)

Forestry

A State institution.
Academic Year: September to June (September-January; February-June).
Admission Requirements: Secondary school certificate (bachillerato).
Language of Instruction: Spanish.
Degrees and Diplomas: Professional titles, 2-4 yrs.

4815 **INSTITUTO TECNOLÓGICO DEL MAR**
Km. 12 Carretera Internacional, Veracruz-México Via Córdoba, 94290 Boca del Rio (Veracruz)
Telephone: 6-01-39

Fishery Industry
Marine Technology

A State institution.
Academic Year: August to June (August-January; February-June).
Admission Requirements: Secondary school certificate (bachillerato).
Language of Instruction: Spanish.
Degrees and Diplomas: Licenciado or Professional titles.

4816 **INSTITUTO TECNOLÓGICO DEL MAR**
Apartado postal 742, 85480 Quaymas (Sonora)

4817 **INSTITUTO TECNOLÓGICO DEL MAR**
Apartado postal 557, 82000 Mizatlán (Sinaloa)

4818 **INSTITUTO TECNOLÓGICO DE ACAPULCO**
Apartado postal 600, 39300 Acapulco (Guerrero)
Telephone: 4-6-19

Commercial Relations
Electrical Engineering
Biochemical Engineering
Tourism Administration
Food Technology
Architecture

Founded 1975. A State institution financed by the federal government.
Academic Year: January to December (January-June; August-December).
Admission Requirements: Secondary school certificate (bachillerato) and entrance examination.
Language of Instruction: Spanish.
Degrees and Diplomas: Licenciado. Professional titles, 4-6 yrs.
Library: c. 3500 vols.
Academic Staff: c. 80 (170).
Student Enrolment: c. 900.

4819 **INSTITUTO TECNOLÓGICO DE AGUASCALIENTES**
Blvd. Adolfo López Mateos, Apartado postal 263, 20000 Aguascalientes (Aguascalientes)
Telephone: 5-01-51
Director: Carlos Jesús Aguilera Batista

Industrial Engineering
Computer Sciences
Electrical Engineering
Thermal Mechanics
Business Administration
Chemical Products

Founded 1967. A State institution financed by the federal government.
Academic Year: August to December (August-December; February-July).
Admission Requirements: Secondary school certificate (bachillerato) and entrance examination.
Language of Instruction: Spanish.
Degrees and Diplomas: Licenciado in–Business Administration; Administrative Sciences. Professional titles of–Ingeniero industrial; Contador público, accountancy; Técnico, in various fields, 3 yrs. Degree of Maestría in Industrial Engineering.
Library: c. 12,760 vols.
Academic Staff: c. 110 (90).
Student Enrolment: c. 2020.

4820 **INSTITUTO TECNOLÓGICO DE APIZACO**
Calz. Instituto Tecnológico s/n, Apartado postal 19, 90300 Apizaco (Tlaxcala)
Telex: 128857 ITRCME

Industrial Engineering
Civil Engineering
Business Administration
Community Development
Production Engineering

Founded 1975. A State institution financed by the federal government.
Academic Year: February to December (February-June; August-December).
Admission Requirements: Secondary school certificate (bachillerato) and entrance examination.
Language of Instruction: Spanish.
Degrees and Diplomas: Licenciado. Professional titles.
Library: c. 5000 vols.
Publications: Tiza (monthly); Itoloca (weekly).
Student Enrolment: c. 1040.

4821 **INSTITUTO TECNOLÓGICO DE CAMPECHE**
Apartado postal 347, 24500 Campeche (Campeche)

Industrial Engineering
Business Administration
Architecture
Production Engineering

A State institution financed by the federal government.
Academic Year: September to June.
Admission Requirements: Secondary school certificate (bachillerato) and entrance examination.
Language of Instruction: Spanish.
Degrees and Diplomas: Licenciado in Business Administration. Professional title of Ingeniero industrial en producción.

4822 **INSTITUTO TECNÓLOGICO REGIONAL DE CELAYA**
Avenida Tecnológico Irrigación, Apartado postal 57, 38010 Celaya (Guanajuato)
Telex: 12857 ITRCME
Telephone: 2-10-23

Industrial Engineering
Business Administration
Biochemical Engineering
Food Technology
Computer Science Systems
Production Engineering
Chemical Engineering

Founded 1958, a State institution financed by the federal government.

Arrangements for cooperation with: University of Wisconsin, Madison; University of Texas A & M; University of California-Davis.

Academic Year: September to May (September-December; February-May).

Admission Requirements: Secondary school certificate (bachillerato) and entrance examination.

Language of Instruction: Spanish.

Degrees and Diplomas: Licenciado in Business Administration. Professional titles of Ingeniero industrial; Ingeniero bioquímico, 4 yrs. Degree of Maestría in Chemical Engineering, a further 2 yrs.

Library: c. 1200 vols.

Academic Staff: c. 250 (20).

Student Enrolment: c. 3020.

4823 **INSTITUTO TECNOLÓGICO DE CERRO AZUL**
Avenida Hidalgo s/n. Col. Campo Comercial, 92510 Cero Azul (Veracruz)
Telephone: 2-07-41
Director: Enrique Vargas Rivas (1984-)

D. of Civil Engineering
Head: Sergio Arrieta Vera
D. of Electro-mechanical Engineering
Head: Iraiz Lara Zumaya
D. of Business Administration
Head: Esperanza Rodriguez Mar

Founded 1982. A State institution financed by the federal government.

Academic Year: August to June (August-December; February-June).

Admission Requirements: Secondary school certificate (bachillerato).

Language of Instruction: Spanish.

Degrees and Diplomas: Licenciado in–Business Administration; Computer Sciences. Professional title of Ingeniero, 4 ½-6 yrs.

Library: 3000 vols.

Academic Staff, 1986-87:

Rank	Full-time	Part-time
Profesores Titulares	6	–
Profesores Asociados	16	–
Profesores Asistentes	12	–
Profesores de Asignatura	–	9
Total	34	9

Student Enrolment, 1986-87:

	Men	Women	Total
Of the country	392	216	608

4824 **INSTITUTO TECNOLÓGICO DE CHETUMAL**
Avenida Andrés Q. Roo Esq. Insurgentes, 5 Col. Centro, Ciudad Chetumal, Apartado postal 267, 77000 Othón Blanco (Quintana Roo)
Telephone: 2-10-19

Industrial Engineering
Business Administration
Civil Engineering
Biology
Tourism Administration
Accountancy
Electrical Engineering

A State institution financed by the federal government.

Academic Year: August to June.

Admission Requirements: Secondary school certificate (bachillerato) and entrance examination.

Language of Instruction: Spanish.

Degrees and Diplomas: Licenciado in Business Administration, 4 yrs. Professional title of Ingeniero industrial, 4 yrs.

4825 **INSTITUTO TECNOLÓGICO DE CHIHUAHUA**
Avenida Tecnológico 2909, Apartado postal 119, 31310 Chihuahua (Chihuahua)
Telex: 349682 ITCHME
Telephone: 3-74-74
Director: Sergio Villezcas Armendariz (1984-90)
Subdirector: Guillermo Medina Vega

Industrial Engineering
Mechanical Engineering
Electrical Engineering
Chemical Engineering
Production Engineering
Electronics
Metallurgy
Commercial Relations
Industrial Relations

Founded 1948, a State institution financed by the federal government.

Arrangements for co-operation with the University of New Mexico.

Academic Year: September to July (September-January; February-July).

Admission Requirements: Secondary school certificate (bachillerato) or equivalent, and entrance examination.

Language of Instruction: Spanish.

Degrees and Diplomas: Professional titles in–Industrial Engineering; Metallurgy; Commercial Relations; Industrial Relations, 4-5 yrs. Degree of Maestría in Electronics, a further 1 ½-2 yrs.

Library: c. 20,000 vols.

Academic Staff: c. 80 (100).

Student Enrolment: c. 2970.

4826 **INSTITUTO TECNOLÓGICO DE CHIPANCINGO**
Avenida de la Juventud s/n, Col. Burócrata, Chipancingo, (Gro.)

Accountancy
Computer Sciences
Civil Engineering
Geology

4827 **INSTITUTO TECNOLÓGICO DE CIUDAD GUZMÁN**
Carretera al Fresnita s/n, Apartado postal 150, 49100 Ciudad Guzmán (Jalisco)
Telephone: 2-17-18

Electrical and Mechanical Engineering
Industrial Relations
Industrial Engineering
Electronics
Accountancy
Business Administration
Computer Sciences

A State institution financed by the federal government.

Academic Year: September to June.

Admission Requirements: Secondary school certificate (bachillerato) and entrance examination.

Language of Instruction: Spanish.

Degrees and Diplomas: Licenciado in Business Administration, 4 yrs. Professional title of Ingeniero, 4 yrs.

4828 **INSTITUTO TECNOLÓGICO DE CIUDAD JUÁREZ**
Km. 6 Carretera Panamericana, 32000 Ciudad Juárez (Chihuahua)
Telex: 333888ITRJME
Telephone: 7-36-46

Industrial Engineering and Technology
Business Administration (including Accountancy)
Tourism Administration
Electronics Engineering
Mechanical Engineering
Production Engineering

Founded 1964. A State institution financed by the federal government.

Arrangements for co-operation with Texas Tech University.

Academic Year: August to June (August-December; January-June).

Admission Requirements: Secondary school certificate (bachillerato) and entrance examination.

Language of Instruction: Spanish.

Degrees and Diplomas: Licenciado in Business Administration; Accountancy, 4 ½ yrs. Professional titles of–Ingeniero industrial, in various fields, 4 ½ yrs. Degree of Maestría in–Engineering; Education, a further 2 yrs.

Library: c. 17,400 vols.

Publications: Boletín; Revista.
Academic Staff: c. 90 (150).
Student Enrolment: c. 3390.

4829 **INSTITUTO TECNOLÓGICO DE CIUDAD MADERO**
Calle 1 de Mayo y Sor Juana Inés de la Cruz, 89440 Ciudad Madero (Tamaulipas)
Telephone: 5-21-53

Electrical Engineering
Mechanical Engineering
Industrial Engineering
Chemical Industrial Engineering

Founded 1954. A State institution financed by the federal government.
Academic Year: September to June (September-January; February-June).
Admission Requirements: Secondary school certificate (bachillerato) and entrance examination.
Language of Instruction: Spanish.
Degrees and Diplomas: Professional titles of–Ingeniero, 4 yrs; Técnico, 3 yrs. Degree of Maestro in–Petrochemistry; Petroleum Technology; Business Administration, 2 ½ yrs.
Library: c. 14,000 vols.
Special Facilities (Museums, etc.): Huasteca Regional Museum.
Publications: Difutec (monthly); Ecos Periodísticos (monthly); Gaceta Académica.
Academic Staff: c. 170 (180).
Student Enrolment: c. 3800.

4830 **INSTITUTO TECNOLÓGICO DE CIUDAD VICTORIA**
Boulevard Lic. Emilio Portes Gil y Camino a la Libertad, 87080 Ciudad Victoria (Tamaulipas)
Telephone: 2-43-58

Civil Engineering
Industrial Engineering
Biology
Computer Science
Production Engineering

Founded 1975. A State institution financed by the federal government.
Academic Year: August to June (August-December; February-June).
Admission Requirements: Secondary school certificate (bachillerato) and entrance examination.
Language of Instruction: Spanish.
Degrees and Diplomas: Professional titles.
Publication: Senda (monthly).
Academic Staff: c. 20 (50).
Student Enrolment: c. 630.

4831 **INSTITUTO TECNOLÓGICO DE COLIMA**
Avenida Tecnológico 1, 28000 Colima (Colima)
Telex: 62234 INTRME
Telephone: 2-63-93

Industrial Engineering
Biochemical Engineering
Architecture
Tourism
Business Administration
Computer Sciences

Founded 1976. A State institution financed by the federal government.
Academic Year: September to June.
Admission Requirements: Secondary school certificate (bachillerato) and entrance examination.
Language of Instruction: Spanish.
Degrees and Diplomas: Licenciado. Professional titles.
Library: c. 1340 vols.
Academic Staff: c. 30.
Student Enrolment: c. 330.

4832 **INSTITUTO TECNOLÓGICO DE CULIACÁN**
Avenida Ing. Juan de Dios Bátiz s/n, y R. Corral, Apartado postal 1273, Culiacán (Sinaloa)
Telex: 665436 ITRCME
Telephone: 3-38-04

Computer Sciences
Food Technology
Electrical Engineering
Industrial Engineering

Founded 1968. A State institution financed by the federal government.
Academic Year: September to June (September-January; February-June).
Admission Requirements: Secondary school certificate (bachillerato) and entrance examination.
Language of Instruction: Spanish.
Degrees and Diplomas: Licenciado in Computer Sciences. Professional qualifications in various fields, 6 sem. Professional title of Ingeniero industrial, 9 sem.
Library: c. 3800 vols.
Academic Staff: c. 10 (80).
Student Enrolment: c. 900.

4833 **INSTITUTO TECNOLÓGICO DE DURANGO**
Boulevard Felipe Pescador 1830, Apartado postal 465, 34080 Durango (Durango)
Telex: 066311 ITRD ME
Telephone: 8-55-86
Fax: 8-57-06
Director: Héctor Arreola Soria
Subdirector Administrativo: Rubén Rosales Diaz

Industrial Engineering
Civil Engineering
Computer Sciences Engineering
Food Technology
Mechanical Engineering
Electrical Engineering
Electronics
Production Engineering
Chemical Engineering
Graduate and Research Ce.
Head: Jesús Rodríguez Alonso

Founded 1948. A State institution financed by the federal government.
Academic Year: January to December (January-June; August-December).
Admission Requirements: Secondary school certificate (bachillerato) and entrance examination.
Language of Instruction: Spanish.
Degrees and Diplomas: Professional titles of Técnico and Ingeniero (Industrial and Civil), in various fields, 5-12 sem. Degree of Maestría in–Industrial Planning; Food Technology; Construction.
Library: c. 13,000 vols.
Special Facilities (Museums, etc.): Science and Technology Museum..
Academic Staff, 1990: 226 (85).
Student Enrolment, 1990:

	Men	Women	Total
Of the country	1785	990	2775

4834 **INSTITUTO TECNOLÓGICO DE HERMOSILLO**
Apartado postal 518, 83170 Hermosillo (Sonora)
Telephone: 4-58-75

Industrial Engineering
Commercial Relations
Computer Sciences
Mechanical Engineering
Electronics

A State institution financed by the federal government.
Academic Year: August to June.
Admission Requirements: Secondary school certificate (bachillerato) and entrance examination.
Language of Instruction: Spanish.
Degrees and Diplomas: Licenciado. Professional title of Ingeniero industrial, 4 yrs.

4835 **INSTITUTO TECNOLÓGICO DEL JUCHITÁN**
Km. 821, Carretera Panamericana, Apartado postal 63, 70000 Juchitán de Zaragoza (Oaxaca)
Telephone: 2-00-42

Industrial Engineering
Civil Engineering
Electro-mechanical Engineering
Electrical Engineering
Electronics
Accountancy
Community Development

Production Engineering
A State institution financed by the federal government.
Academic Year: August to June.
Admission Requirements: Secondary school certificate (bachillerato) and entrance examination.
Language of Instruction: Spanish.
Degrees and Diplomas: Professional title of Ingeniero, 4 yrs.

4836 **INSTITUTO TECNOLÓGICO DE JIQUILPAN**
Avenida Presidente Lázaro Cárdenas 366, Jiquilpan (Michoacán)
Telephone: 3-02-37

Accountancy
Biological Engineering
Commercial Relations
Food Technology
Production Engineering
Chemical Engineering
Industrial Engineering
Administration
Founded 1976. A State institution financed by the federal government.
Academic Year: February to December (February-June; August-December).
Admission Requirements: Secondary school certificate (bachillerato) and entrance examination.
Language of Instruction: Spanish.
Degrees and Diplomas: Professional titles.
Academic Staff: c. 20.
Student Enrolment: c. 290.

4837 **INSTITUTO TECNOLÓGICO DE LA LAGUNA**
Bulevar Revolución y Calzada Cuauhtémoc, Apartado postal 681, 27000 Torreón (Coahuila)
Telephone: 3-18-23

Mechanical and Electrical Engineering
Industrial Engineering
Electronics
Production Engineering
Chemical Engineering
Founded 1965. A State institution financed by the federal government.
Academic Year: September to June (September-January; February-June).
Admission Requirements: Secondary school certificate (bachillerato) and entrance examination.
Language of Instruction: Spanish.
Degrees and Diplomas: Professional qualifications in various fields, 6 sem. Title of Ingeniero industrial, 9 sem.
Library: c. 6000 vols.
Academic Staff: c. 110 (5).
Student Enrolment: c. 1410.

4838 **INSTITUTO TECNOLÓGICO DE LA PAZ**
Apartado postal 243, 23050 La Paz (Baja California Sur)
Telephone: 2-24-24

Civil Engineering
Industrial Biochemical Engineering
Business Administration
Food Engineering
Accountancy
Computer Science
Planning
A State institution financed by the federal government.
Academic Year: August to June.
Admission Requirements: Secondary school certificate (bachillerato) and entrance examination.
Language of Instruction: Spanish.
Degrees and Diplomas: Licenciado in Business Administration, 4 yrs. Professional title of Ingeniero, 4 yrs.

4839 **INSTITUTO TECNOLÓGICO DE LEÓN**
Carretera a León-Silao, Avenida Tecnológico s/n, Fracc. Julián de Obregón, 37000 León (Guanajuato)
Telephone: 4-08-19
Director: Bulmaro Fuentes Lemus (1983-)

Industrial Engineering
Founded 1972. A State institution financed by the federal government.
Academic Year: August to June (August-December; February-June).
Admission Requirements: Secondary school certificate (bachillerato) and entrance examination.
Fees (Pesos): 12,000 per semester.
Language of Instruction: Spanish.
Degrees and Diplomas: Licenciado, 4 yrs.
Academic Staff, 1986-87: 71 (73).
Student Enrolment, 1986-87:

	Men	Women	Total
Of the country	1005	333	1338
Of other countries	–	1	1
Total	1005	334	1339

4840 **INSTITUTO TECNOLÓGICO DE LOS MOCHIS**
Boulevard Juan de Dias Bátiz y Prolongación 20 de Noviembre, Apartado postal 766, 81200 Los Mochis (Sinaloa)
Telephone: 2-58-58

Industrial Engineering
Business Administration
Accountancy
Biochemical Engineering
Food Technology
Chemical Engineering
Architecture
A State institution financed by the federal government.
Academic Year: August to June.
Admission Requirements: Secondary school certificate (bachillerato) and entrance examination.
Language of Instruction: Spanish.
Degrees and Diplomas: Licenciado in–Business Administration; Accountancy, 4 yrs. Professional title of Ingeniero, 4 yrs.

4841 **INSTITUTO TECNOLÓGICO DEMATAMOROS**
Km. 6 Carretera Lauro Villar, 87490 Matamoros (Tamaulipas)
Telephone: 2-41-62

Industrial Engineering
Electrical Engineering
Civil Engineering
Industrial Relations
Electromechanical Engineering
Urban Planning
Chemical Engineering
Production Engineering
A State institution financed by the federal government.
Academic Year: August to June.
Admission Requirements: Secondary school certificate (bachillerato) and entrance examination.
Language of Instruction: Spanish.
Degrees and Diplomas: Licenciado in Industrial Relations, 4 yrs. Professional title of Ingeniero, 4 yrs.

4842 **INSTITUTO TECNOLÓGICO DE MÉRIDA**
Carretera Mérida-Progreso Km. 5,Apartado postal 561, 97118 Mérida (Yucatán)
Telex: 753760 ITRMMO
Telephone: 27-23-00

Industrial and Mechanical Engineering
Chemical and Production Engineering
Biochemical Engineering
Civil Engineering
Tourist Administration
Air conditioning
Business Administration
Industrial Planning
Lifelong Education
Founded 1961. A State institution financed by the federal government.
Academic Year: September to June (September-January; February-June).
Admission Requirements: Secondary school certificate (bachillerato) and entrance examination.
Language of Instruction: Spanish.
Degrees and Diplomas: Licenciado in–Business Administration; Tourism, 4 yrs. Professional titles of Ingeniero, various fields, 4 ½ yrs. Degree of Maestría.
Library: c. 13,000 vols.

Publications: Imágenes; Una Mirada al Futuro.
Academic Staff: c. 180 (170).
Student Enrolment: c. 3110.

4843 **INSTITUTO TECNOLÓGICO DE MEXICALI**
Blvd. Lázaro Cárdenas, Col. P. Elías Calles, Mexicali (Baja California)
Telephone: 8-19-81

Industrial Engineering
Electrical Engineering
Electronics
Control Engineering
Chemical Engineering

A State institution financed by the federal government.

4844 **INSTITUTO TECNOLÓGICO DE MINATITLÁN**
Km. 27 Carretera Transistmica, Apartada postal 777, 96700 Minatitlán (Veracruz)
Telephone: 4-1685; 4-1983

Business Administration
Electronic Engineering
Industrial Chemical Engineering
Electro-mechanical Engineering
Production Engineering
Instruments

Founded 1972. A State institution financed by the federal government.
Academic Year: September to July (September-January; February-July).
Admission Requirements: Secondary school certificate (bachillerato) and entrance examination.
Language of Instruction: Spanish.
Degrees and Diplomas: Licenciado in Business Administration. Professional title of Ingeniero, in various fields. Also lower level technical qualifications.
Library: c. 8000 vols.
Academic Staff: c. 180.
Student Enrolment: c. 2250.

4845 **INSTITUTO TECNOLÓGICO DE MORELIA**
Avenida Tecnológico 1500, 58120 Morelia (Michoacán)
Telex: 69654 ITMLME
Telephone: 2-10-88

Mechanical Engineering
Electrical Engineering
Industrial Engineering
Production Engineering
Tourism Administration

Founded 1965. A State institution financed by the federal government.
Academic Year: August to June (August-January; February-June).
Admission Requirements: Secondary school certificate (bachillerato) and entrance examination.
Language of Instruction: Spanish.
Degrees and Diplomas: Title of Ingeniero, 4 yrs.
Library: c. 8200 vols.
Academic Staff: c. 100 (60).
Student Enrolment: c. 3000.

4846 **INSTITUTO TECNOLÓGICO DE NOGALES**
Calz. de los Nogales s/n, Apartado postal 796, 84000 Nogales (Sonora)
Telex: 54125 ITXNME
Telephone: 2-10-88

Industrial Engineering
Ironworks
Production Engineering
Tourism Administration
Community Development
Electronics
Business Administration
Civil Engineering
Industrial Relations

A State institution financed by the federal government.
Academic Year: August to June.
Admission Requirements: Secondary school certificate (bachillerato) and entrance examination.
Language of Instruction: Spanish.
Degrees and Diplomas: Licenciado. Professional titles.

4847 **INSTITUTO TECNOLÓGICO DE NUEVO LAREDO**
Avenida Reforma Sur 2007, 88000 Nuevo Laredo (Tamaulipas)
Telephone: 2-34-44

Industrial and Electronic Engineering
Business Administration
Civil Engineering
Tourism Administration
Electronics
Mechanical Engineering
Thermal Engineering
Production Engineering

Founded 1964. A State institution financed by the federal government.
Academic Year: September to June (September-January; February-June).
Admission Requirements: Secondary school certificate (bachillerato) and entrance examination.
Language of Instruction: Spanish.
Degrees and Diplomas: Title of Ingeniero, 4 yrs.
Library: c. 6000 vols.
Academic Staff: c. 30 (20).
Student Enrolment: c. 1020.

4848 **INSTITUTO TECNOLÓGICO DE NUEVO LEÓN**
Avenida Eloy Cavazos s/n, Ciudad Guadalupe Nuevo León, 67170 Guadalupe (Nuevo León)
Telex: 36658 ITNLME
Telephone: 79-10-49

Industrial Engineering
Business Administration
Electronics
Computer Systems
Production Engineering

A State institution financed by the federal government.
Academic Year: August to June.
Admission Requirements: Secondary school certificate (bachillerato) and entrance examination.
Language of Instruction: Spanish.
Degrees and Diplomas: Licenciado, 4-4 ½ yrs. Professional title of Ingeniero industrial, 4 yrs.

4849 **INSTITUTO TECNOLÓGICO DE OAXACA**
Calz. Tecnológico s/n, 68030 Oaxaca (Oaxaca)
Telephone: 6-17-22

Industrial Engineering
Civil Engineering
Business Administration
Electrical Engineering
Mechanical Thermal Engineering
Chemical Engineering
Engineering Structures
Tourism Administration

A State institution financed by the federal government.
Academic Year: August to June.
Admission Requirements: Secondary school certificate (bachillerato) and entrance examination.
Language of Instruction: Spanish.
Degrees and Diplomas: Licenciado, 4 yrs. Professional title of Ingeniero, 4 yrs.

4850 **INSTITUTO TECNOLÓGICO DE ORIZABA**
Prolongación de Oriente 9 s/n, Apartado postal 324, 94320 Orizaba (Veracruz)
Telex: 15439 ITOME
Telephone: 4-40-96

Industrial Engineering
Computer Science
Mechanical Thermal Engineering
Chemical Engineering
Production Engineering

Founded 1957. A State institution financed by the federal government.
Academic Year: August to June.
Admission Requirements: Secondary school certificate (bachillerato) and entrance examination.
Language of Instruction: Spanish.
Degrees and Diplomas: Licenciado in Computer Sciences. Professional title of Ingeniero industrial, 4 yrs. Degree of Maestría, a further 2 yrs.

Library: c. 15,000 vols.
Academic Staff: c. 150 (160).
Student Enrolment: c. 2380.

4851 **INSTITUTO TECNOLÓGICO DE PACHUCA**
Apartado postal 276, 42080 Venta Prieta (Hidalgo)
Telephone: 2-50-20

Industrial Engineering
Civil Engineering
Chemical Engineering

A State institution financed by the federal governmmet;
Academic Year: August to June.
Admission Requirements: Secondary school certificate (bachillerato) and entrance examination.
Language of Instruction: Spanish.
Degrees and Diplomas: Professional titles of Ingeniero, 4 yrs.

4852 **INSTITUTO TECNOLÓGICO DE PARRAL**
Avenida Tecnólogico s/n, Apartado postal 216, 33850 Parral (Chihuahua)
Telephone: 2-24-52

Industrial Engineering
Electromechanics
Mining
Production Engineering
Accountancy
Business Administration
Chemical Engineering
Electro-mechanical Engineering

Founded 1975. A State institution financed by the federal government.
Academic Year: February to December (February-June; August-December).
Admission Requirements: Secondary school certificate (bachillerato) and entrance examination.
Degrees and Diplomas: Licenciado in Business Administration, 4 yrs. Professional titles of Técnico and Ingeniero (industrial and civil), 3-4 yrs.
Academic Staff: c. 30 (50).
Student Enrolment: c. 900.

4853 **INSTITUTO TECNOLÓGICO DE PIEDRAS NEGRAS**
Avenida Tecnológico Prolongación Poniente., 26080 Piedras Negras (Coahuila)
Telex: 37258 ITPNME
Telephone: 2-10-41

Electronics
Business Administration
Commercial Relations
Planning
Industrial Engineering
Accountancy

Founded 1976. A State institution financed by the federal government.
Academic Year: August to June (August-December; February-June).
Admission Requirements: Secondary school certificate (bachillerato) and entrance examination.
Language of Instruction: Spanish.
Degrees and Diplomas: Licenciado in–Business Administration; Commercial Relations, 4-6 yrs. Professional title of Ingeniero, 4-6 yrs.
Library: c. 820 vols.
Academic Staff: c. – (20).
Student Enrolment: c. 220.

4854 **INSTITUTO TECNOLÓGICO DE PUEBLA**
Avenida Tecnológico 420, Apartado postal 1145, 72000 Puebla (Puebla)
Telephone: 42-96-19

Industrial Engineering
Electrical Engineering
Electronics
Mechanical Engineering
Design

A State institution financed by the federal government.
Academic Year: August to June.
Admission Requirements: Secondary school certificate (bachillerato) and entrance examination.
Language of Instruction: Spanish.
Degrees and Diplomas: Professional title of Ingeniero industrial, 4 yrs.

4855 **INSTITUTO TECNOLÓGICO DE QUERÉTARO**
Avenida Tecnológico y Calle Mariano Escobedo, 76000 Querétaro (Querétaro)
Telex: 121625 ITQME
Telephone: 2-22-81

Industrial Engineering
Architecture
Administration
Computer Systems
Mechanical Engineering
Electrical Engineering
Production Engineering

Founded 1967. A State institution financed by the federal government.
Academic Year: September to June (September-January; February-June).
Admission Requirements: Secondary school certificate (bachillerato) and entrance examination.
Language of Instruction: Spanish.
Degrees and Diplomas: Professional title of Ingeniero industrial, 4 yrs.
Library: c. 10,000 vols.
Academic Staff: c. 15 (50).
Student Enrolment: c. 1530.

4856 **INSTITUTO TECNOLÓGICO DE SALTILLO**
Avenida Universidad y Boulevard V. Carranza 2400, 25280 Saltillo (Coahuila)
Telex: 38165 ITRSME
Telephone: 2-31-01
Director: Jesús Horacio Cano Rios

Industrial Engineering
Mechanical Engineering
Metallurgy
Electrical Engineering
Computer Sciences

Founded 1951. A State institution financed by the federal government.
Arrangements for cooperation with: Ecole nationale supérieure de la Métallurgie et de l'Industrie des Mines, Nancy; University of Leeds.
Academic Year: August to June (August-December; January-June).
Admission Requirements: Secondary school certificate (bachillerato) and entrance examination.
Fees (Pesos): 10,000 per semester.
Language of Instruction: Spanish.
Degrees and Diplomas: Professional titles of Ingeniero industrial and Ingeniero metalúrgico, 4-6 yrs. Also professional titles of Técnico in various fields, 2 ½-4 yrs.
Library: c. 8000 vols.
Academic Staff, 1986-87: 352.
Student Enrolment, 1986-87:

	Men	Women	Total
Of the country	2085	484	2569
Of other countries	14	–	14
Total	2099	484	2583

4857 **INSTITUTO TECNOLÓGICO DE SAN LUIS POTOSÍ**
Km. 1, Carretera San Luis Potosí Rio Verde, 78070 San Luis Potosí (San Luis Potosí)
Telex: 13669
Telephone: 2-32-75

Industrial Engineering
Computer Systems
Industrial Relations
Civil Engineering
Electrical Engineering
Electronics
Production Engineering
Tourism Administration

Founded 1970. A State institution financed by the federal government.
Academic Year: August to June (August-December; February-June).
Admission Requirements: Secondary school certificate (bachillerato).
Fees (Pesos): Registration, 800 per semester.
Language of Instruction: Spanish.
Degrees and Diplomas: Licenciado in–Industrial Relations, Tourism Administration, 4-6 yrs. Professional titles of–Ingeniero industrial; Ingeniero en Sistemas computacionales; Ingeniero civil, 4-6 yrs.
Library: c. 10,000 vols.

Academic Staff: c. 70 (20).
Student Enrolment: c. 1700.

4858 **INSTITUTO TECNOLÓGICO DE TAPACHULA**
Km. 2 Carretera Tapachula-Puerto Madero, Tapachula (Chiapas)

Civil Engineering
Industrial Engineering

4859 **INSTITUTO TECNOLÓGICO DE TEPIC**
Carretera Tepic-Guadalajara, Apartado postal 343, 63000 Tepic (Nayarit)
Telex: 61144 INTEME
Telephone: 2-60-83

Civil Engineering
Food Technology
Biochemical Engineering
Development
Commercial Relations
Architecture
Industrial Relations

Founded 1975. A State institution financed by the federal government.
Academic Year: August to June (August-December; February-June).
Admission Requirements: Secondary school certificate (bachillerato) and entrance examination.
Language of Instruction: Spanish.
Degrees and Diplomas: Licenciado. Professional title of Ingeniero.
Student Enrolment: c. 380.

4860 **INSTITUTO TECNOLÓGICO DE TEHUACÁN**
Apartado postal 247, 75700 Tehuacán (Puebla)
Telephone: 2-24-48

Civil Engineering
Business Administration
Industrial Engineering
Biochemical Engineering
Accountancy
Food Technology

Founded 1975. A State institution financed by the federal government.
Academic Year: September to June (September-January; February-June).
Admission Requirements: Secondary school certificate (bachillerato) and entrance examination.
Language of Instruction: Spanish.
Degrees and Diplomas: Licenciado in Business Administration, 4 ½ yrs. Professional title of Ingeniero, 4 ½ yrs. Also lower levelqualification, 3 yrs.
Library: c. 4990 vols.
Student Enrolment: c. 1100.

4861 **INSTITUTO TECNOLÓGICO DE TIJUANA**
Col. Fraccionamiento Tomás de Aquino, 22000 Tijuana (Baja California Norte)
Telex: 566796 ITRTME
Telephone: 82-10-55

Civil Engineering
Commercial Relations
Biochemistry
Industrial Engineering
Electro-mechanical Engineering
Architecture
Production Engineering
Accountancy
Computer Sciences
Industrial Relations
Food Technology
Engineering Structures
Town Planning
Electronics

Founded 1971. A State institution financed by the federal government.
Academic Year: August to June (August-December; January-June).
Admission Requirements: Secondary school certificate (bachillerato) and entrance examination.
Language of Instruction: Spanish.
Degrees and Diplomas: Licenciado in–Industrial Relations; Commercial Relations; Computer Sciences; Accountancy, 9-12 sem. Professional titles of–Ingeniero; Arquitecto, 9-12 sem. Degree of Maestría in Chemistry.
Library: c. 20,550 vols.
Publication: Tecamatl (quarterly).
Academic Staff: c. 90 (180).
Student Enrolment: c. 2850.

4862 **INSTITUTO TECNOLÓGICO DE TLALNEPANTLA**
Avenida Tecnológico s/n, Apartado postal 750, 54070 Tlalnepantla (Estado de México)
Telephone: 5-65-67-77

Industrial Engineering
Electrical Engineering
Mechanical Engineering
Electronics
Administration
Production Engineering

A State institution financed by the federal government.
Academic Year: August to June.
Admission Requirements: Secondary school certificate (bachillerato) and entrance examination.
Language of Instruction: Spanish.
Degrees and Diplomas: Professional title of Ingeniero, 4 yrs.

4863 **INSTITUTO TECNOLÓGICO DE TOLUCA**
Rancho de La Virgen Metepec, Apartado postal 890, 50000 Toluca (Estado de México)
Telex: 174403 ITRTME
Telephone: 6-03-24

Electronic Engineering
Industrial Engineering
Chemical Engineering
Electro-mechanical Engineering
Production Engineering
Administration

Founded 1972 as college, acquired present status and title 1974. A State institution financed by the federal government.
Academic Year: August to June (August-January; January-June).
Admission Requirements: Secondary school certificate (bachillerato) and entrance examination.
Language of Instruction: Spanish.
Degrees and Diplomas: Professional title of Ingeniero, 7-12 sem. Degree of Maestría in Computer Sciences.
Library: c. 13,500 vols.
Academic Staff: c. 40 (20).
Student Enrolment: c. 600.

4864 **INSTITUTO TECNOLÓGICO DE TUXTEPEC**
Calzada Tecnológico s/n, Col. Centro, 68300 San Juan B. Tuxtepec (Oaxaca)

Civil Engineering
Electro-Mechanical Engineering
Accountancy
Business Administration
Biochemical Engineering
Food Technology
Community Development

Founded 1975. A State institution financed by the federal government.
Academic Year: August to June (August-December; February-June).
Admission Requirements: Secondary school certificate (bachillerato).
Language of Instruction: Spanish.
Degrees and Diplomas: Licenciado, 4 yrs. Professional title of Ingeniero, 4 yrs.
Library: Information Centre, *c.* 3400 vols.
Publication: Bulletin (monthly).
Academic Staff: c. 40.
Student Enrolment: c. 380.

4865 **INSTITUTO TECNOLÓGICO DE TUXTLA GUTIÉRREZ**
Carretera Panamericana Km. 1080, 29020 Tuxtla Gutiérrez (Chiapas)
Telephone: 2-18-99

Industrial Engineering
Biochemical Engineering
Natural Products
Electrical Engineering
Production Engineering

Chemical Engineering
A State institution financed by the federal government.
Academic Year: August to June.
Admission Requirements: Secondary school certificate (bachillerato) and entrance examination.
Language of Instruction: Spanish.
Degrees and Diplomas: Professional title of Ingeniero, 4 yrs.

4866 **INSTITUTO TECNOLÓGICO DE VERACRUZ**
Circunvalación Norte e Icazo, 96700 Veracruz (Veracruz)
Telex: 151626 DIRVME
Telephone: 2-41-77

Industrial Engineering
Biochemical Engineering
Systems Engineering
Computer Sciences
Food Technology
Electrical Engineering
Electronics
Production Engineering
Chemical Engineering
Founded 1944, acquired present status 1957. A State institution financed by the federal government.
Academic Year: September to June (September-January; February-June).
Admission Requirements: Secondary school certificate (bachillerato) and entrance examination.
Language of Instruction: Spanish.
Degrees and Diplomas: Professional titles of Ingeniero, 4 yrs.
Publication: Diálogo (monthly).
Academic Staff: c. 30 (40).
Student Enrolment: c. 1670.

4867 **INSTITUTO TECNOLÓGICO DE VILLAHERMOSA**
Carretera a Frontera Km. 3, Apartado postal 424, 86000 Villahermosa (Tabasco)
Telephone: 2-48-65

Biochemical Engineering
Industrial Chemistry
Business Administration
Civil Engineering Food Technology
Community Development
A State institution financed by the federal government.
Academic Year: August to June.
Admission Requirements: Secondary school certificate (bachillerato) and entrance examination.
Language of Instruction: Spanish.
Degrees and Diplomas: Licenciado in Business Administration, 4 yrs. Professional title of Ingeniero, 4 yrs.

4868 **INSTITUTO TECNOLÓGICO DE ZACATECAS**
Domicilio Conocido 'La Escondida', 99559 Zacatecas (Zacatecas)
Telephone: 2-41-08

Industrial Engineering
Metallurgy
Architecture
Business Administration
Production Engineering
Electronics
Founded 1976. A State institution financed by the federal government.
Academic Year: August to June (August-December; January-June).
Admission Requirements: Secondary school certificate (bachillerato) and entrance examination.
Language of Instruction: Spanish.
Degrees and Diplomas: Licenciado in Business Administration, 4-6 yrs. Professional titles of–Ingeniero industrial; Ingeniero metalúrgico; Arquitecto, 6-8 yrs.
Academic Staff: c. 40 (30).
Student Enrolment: c. 760.

4869 **INSTITUTO TECNOLÓGICO DE ZACATEPEC**
Calz. Tecnológico 27, Apartado postal 45, 63780 Zacatepec (Morelos)
Telephone: 2-13-94

Industrial Chemistry
Industrial Engineering
Tourist Administration
Civil Engineering
Production Engineering
Town Planning
A State institution financed by the federal government.
Academic Year: August to June.
Admission Requirements: Secondary school certificate (bachillerato) and entrance examination.
Language of Instruction: Spanish.
Degrees and Diplomas: Licenciado in Tourist Administration, 4 yrs. Professional title of Ingeniero, 4 yrs.

Professional Education

4870 **ASOCIACIÓN SATÉLITE DE ESTUDIOS CULTURALES 'SOR SUANA' A.C.**
Colibri 6 Primera Sección de Lomas Verdes, 53120 Naucalpan de Juárez (Estado de México)

Humanities

4871 **CENTRO DE ARTE MEXICANO, A.C.**
Cascada 180, Pedregal San Angel, 01900 México (D.F.)
Telephone: 568-32-44

History of Art

4872 **CENTRO DE BACHILLERES Y ESTUDIOS PROFESIONALES DE SALAMANCA**
Camino la Ordeña Km. 1, Fracc. el Monte Apartado postal 462, Salamanca (Guanajuato)

Industrial Engineering
Architecture
Industrial Relations
Work Psychology

4873 **CENTRO DE EDUCACIÓN PROFESIONAL, S.C.,**
Puebla 162, Col. Roma, 06700 México (D.F.)
Telephone: 514-26-54

Business Administration
A private institution.

4874 **CENTRO ESCOLAR 'BENITO JUÁREZ'**
5 de Febrero No. 443 Sur, Ciudad Obregón (Sonora)
Telephone: 3-32-82

Social Work
A private institution.
Academic Year: September to July (September-January; February-July).
Admission Requirements: Secondary school certificate (bachillerato).
Language of Instruction: Spanish.
Degrees and Diplomas: Licenciado, 4 yrs.

4875 **CENTRO ESCOLAR 'MIGUEL ALEMÁN V'**
Calle 27 No. 150, Fracc. San Miguel, 7140 Mérida (Yucatan)

Public Accountancy
Physics

4876 **CENTRO DE ESTUDIOS EN CIENCIAS DE LA COMUNICACIÓN**
Valle 23, Pedregal de San Angel, 01900 México (D.F.)
Telephone: 559-36-04

Publicity
Public Relations
A private institution.
Academic Year: September to June (September-January; February-June).
Admission Requirements: Secondary school certificate (bachillerato) and entrance examination.
Language of Instruction: Spanish.
Degrees and Diplomas: Licenciado, 4 yrs.

4877 **CENTRO DE ESTUDIOS SUPERIORES DE DISEÑO DE MONTERREY**

Padre Mier 1545 Poniente, Col. Obispado, 64000 Monterrey (Nuevo León)
Telephone: (83) 43-35-63
Rector: Alejandro García Villareal (1985-90)
Administrador: Gustavo M. de Luna

Graphic and Interior Design
Fashion Design

Founded 1978, acquired present status and title 1985. A State institution.

Arrangements for co-operation with similar institutions in: U.S.A.; Canada; Netherlands.

Academic Year: September to June (September-December; January-June).

Admission Requirements: Secondary school certificate (bachillerato).

Fees (Pesos): Registration, 35,000-40,000; tuition, 300,000-420,000 per annum.

Language of Instruction: Spanish.

Degrees and Diplomas: Professional titles, 4 yrs. Diplomas, 3 yrs.

Library: 4270 vols.

Academic Staff, 1986-87: 22 (24).

Student Enrolment, 1986-87:

	Men	Women	Total
Of the country	70	756	826
Of other countries	1	3	4
Total	71	759	830

4878 **CENTRO DE ESTUDIOS SUPERIORES DEL ESTADO DE SONORA**

Americas y Tetabiate 2, Col. Valle Verde, 83200 Hermosillo (Sonora)

D. of Economics
D. of Science and Engineering
D. of Chemistry and Biology

4879 **CENTRO DE ESTUDIOS SUPERIORES DE GUAMUCHIL, S.C.**

Silverio Trueba y Fernando Amilpa, Guamuchil (Sinaloa)

Administration and Accountancy
Law

A private institution recognized by the State government.

4880 **CENTRO DE ESTUDIOS SUPERIORES DE OAXACA**

M. Alcalá 801-A, 68000 Oaxaca (Oaxaca)

Communications

A private institution attached to the National Autonomous University of Mexico.

4881 **CENTRO DE ESTUDIOS SUPERIORES**

Andador 16 de Setiembre 74, 76000 Querétaro (Querétaro)
Telephone: 4-17-79
Director General: Martha E. Ortiz de Romero
Secretaria Oficina: Gloria Sánchez H.

Social Work
Economics

Attached to the National Autonomous University of Mexico.

Academic Year: September to June.

Admission Requirements: Secondary school certificate (bachillerato).

Language of Instruction: Spanish.

Degrees and Diplomas: Licenciado.

4882 **CENTRO DE ESTUDIOS SUPERIORES TURÍSTICOS, A.C. (COAHUILA)**

Presidente Cárdenas 651, 25000 Saltillo (Coah.)

Tourism

4883 **CENTRO DE ESTUDIOS TECNOLÓGICOS Y UNIVERSITARIOS, S.D.**

Guillermo Prieto No. 2, Col. San Rafael, 06470 México (D.F.)

4884 **CENTRO DE ESTUDIOS UNIVERSITARIOS DE MONTERREY**

Avenida Hidalgo Pte. 546, 64000 Monterrey (N.L.)

4885 **CENTRO DE ESTUDIOS UNIVERSITARIOS DE XOCHICALCO**

Avenida A. López Mateos 1277, Apartado postal 1377, Ensenada (B.C. Norte)

4886 **CENTRO DE INVESTIGACIONES Y ESTUDIOS SUPERIORES EN ANTROPOLOGÍA SOCIAL**

General Victoria 75, Apartado postal 22048, Tlalpan, 14000 México (D.F.)

4887 **CENTRO SINDICAL DE ESTUDIOS SUPERIORES DE LA CTM, A.C.**

Camelia 108, Fracc. Rancho Cortez, Apartado postal 134-C, Sucursal C., 62050 Cuernavaca (Mor.)

4888 **CENTRO UNIVERSITARIO HISPANOAMERICANO**

Avenida Cruz del Sol 3, Esq. Avenida Cerro de las Torres, 3103 Col. Satélite (Estado de México)
Telephone: 393-15-33
Rector: Eduardo A. Ituarte Verduzco

Business Administration (including Accountancy)
Law
Education
Tourism

Branch in Coacalco.

Founded 1976. A private institution recognized by the State.

Academic Year: September to June.

Admission Requirements: Secondary school certificate (bachillerato) and entrance examination.

Language of Instruction: Spanish.

Degrees and Diplomas: Licenciado in–Acccountancy; Business Administration; Education; Tourism, 4-4 ½ yrs; Law, 5 yrs.

Library: Total, 5500 vols.

Student Enrolment, 1986-87:

	Men	Women	Total
Of the country	1400	1600	3000

4889 **CENTRO UNIVERSITARIO KENNEDY**

Insurgentes 1616, San Jerónimo, Apartado postal 1803, Monterrey (N.L.)

4890 **CENTRO UNIVERSITARIO DE MAZATLÁN**

Calle Cruz No. 2, Apartado postal 275, Mazatlán

4891 **CENTRO UNIVERSITARIO DEL NORESTE, A.C.**

Lic. Guillermo Martínez Domínguez 116, 87360 H. Matamoros (Tamps.)
Telephone: 3-88-35
Director: Ricardo Díaz

S. of Law
Head: Mario Garza; *staff* 22
S. of Accountancy and Administration
Head: Protasio Guerra; *staff* 14
S. of Business Administration
Head: Roberto Sosa; *staff* 16
S. of Agriculture
S. of Psychology
Head: Cristina Fernández

Founded 1976 as preparatory school, acquired present status and title 1982. A private institution recognized by the State.

Academic Year: August to June (August-December; January-June).

Admission Requirements: Secondary school certificate (bachillerato) or equivalent.

Fees (Pesos): 150,000.

Language of Instruction: Spanish.

Degrees and Diplomas: Licenciado.

Student Enrolment, 1986-87:

	Men	Women	Total
Of the country	275	250	525

4892 **CENTRO UNIVERSITARIO DE CIENCIAS HUMANAS**
Ex-Convento de San Jerónimo, Plaza de San Jerónimo 47, 06080 México (D.F.)
Telephone: 5-108999

Human Sciences

Founded 1980. A private autonomous institution recognized by the federal government. Under the supervision of the Claustro de Sor Juana, A.C.

Academic Year: August to June (August-December; January-June).

Admission Requirements: Secondary school certificate (bachillerato) and entrance examination.

Language of Instruction: Spanish.

Degrees and Diplomas: Licenciado, 4 ½ yrs.

Library: Biblioteca Claustro de Sor Juana, 10,641 vols.

Academic Staff: c. 70.

Student Enrolment: c. 230.

4893 **EL COLEGIO DE MÉXICO**
The College of Mexico
Camino al Ajusco 20, 10740 México (D.F.)
Telex: 1777585 COLME
Telephone: 568-60-33
Fax: 652-6233
Presidente: Mario Ojeda Gómez
Secretario General: José Luis Reyna

Linguistic and Literary Studies Ce.
Director: Beatriz Garza Cuarón *staff* 23 (5)
Historical Studies Ce.
Director: Alicia Hernández Chavez *staff* 19
International Studies Ce.
Director: Soledad Loaeza
Economic Studies Ce.
Director: Adalberto Garcia *staff* 24
Demographic and Urban Development Studies Ce.
Director: José B. Morelos; *staff* 33
Ce. of Asian and North African Studies
Director: Jorge Silva; *staff* 9
Ce. of Social Studies
Director: Orlandina de Oliveira; *staff* 19

Founded 1940, acquired present status 1962. An autonomous institution financed by the federal government, national decentralized and private institutions, international bodies, and foreign private foundations. Degrees are recognized by Ministry of Education. Governing body: the Junta de Gobierno (Administrative Committee).

Arrangements for co-operation with the Universities of: Sofia; Brown, USA; Indiana; Harvard; Louvain; Osaka; Puerto Rico; Tsukuba; Toulouse Le Mirail; Warsaw.

Academic Year: September to July (September-February; March-July).

Admission Requirements: Licenciado and entrance examination.

Fees (US$): 2000 per semester.

Language of Instruction: Spanish.

Degrees and Diplomas: Licenciado in International Relations; Public Administration, 4 yrs. Degree of Maestria in–Asian and African Studies, 3 yrs; Economics; Demography and Urban Development, 2 yrs. Doctorado in–History; Spanish Language and Literature; Social Studies; Demographic Studies, 3 yrs.

Library: c. 500,000 vols.

Publications: Historia Mexicana; Foro Internacional; Estudios de Asia y África; Nueva Revista de Filología Hispánica; Estudios Sociológicos; Estudios Económicos; Estudios Demográficos y Urbanos.

Academic Staff, 1989-90: 197 (25).

Student Enrolment, 1989-90:

	Men	Women	Total
Of the country	131	85	210
Of other countries	27	14	41
Total	158	99	257

4894 **COLEGIO SAN AGUSTÍN, A.C.**
Calle 58 No. 484, 97000 Mérida (Yucatan)

Tourism

4895 **COLEGIO SUPERIOR AGROPECUARIO DEL ESTADO DE GUERRERO**
Carretera Iguala Tuxpan Km. 2, 40000 Iguala (Guerrero)
Telephone: 2-43-28

Agriculture (including Animal Husbandry)

Founded 1975 as institute, acquired present status and title 1982. An autonomous State institution.

Academic Year: August to June (August-December; January-June).

Fees: None.

Language of Instruction: Spanish.

Degrees and Diplomas: Professional titles, 3-4 ½ yrs.

Library: Total, 12,000 vols.

Publication: Revista (every 4 months).

Academic Staff: c. 50 (25).

Student Enrolment: c. 850.

4896 **COMPLEJO EDUCATIVO HISPANO-AMERICANO A.C.**
Avenida Morelos 220 Col. Penitas, 37180 León (Guanajuato)
Telephone: 7-56-12
Directora: Patricia Aranda Orozco (1983-)

Education
Psychology

Founded 1978. A private institution recognized by the State. Attached to the Universidad de Guanajuato.

Academic Year: August to June (August-December; January-June).

Admission Requirements: Secondary school certificate (bachillerato) and examination.

Language of Instruction: Spanish.

Degrees and Diplomas: Licenciado, 5 yrs.

Library: 2000 vols.

Academic Staff, 1986-87: – (19).

Student Enrolment, 1986-87:

	Men	Women	Total
Of the country	26	69	95

4897 **COLEGIO ESPAÑOL DE MÉXICO**
Artículo 123 No. 44, México (D.F.)
Telephone: 5212-98-34

Accountancy

A private institution.

Academic Year: September to June (September-January; February-June).

Admission Requirements: Secondary school certificate (bachillerato).

Degrees and Diplomas: Professional title of Contador público, accountancy, 3 yrs.

4898 **ESCUELA SUPERIOR DE ADMINISTRACIÓN DE INSTITUCIONES**
Canteras de Oxtopulco 16, 04310 México (D.F.)
Telephone: 5-48-41-79

Institution Administration

Founded 1969. A private institution.

Academic Year: January to December (January-August; August-December).

Admission Requirements: Secondary school certificate (bachillerato) and entrance examination.

Language of Instruction: Spanish.

Degrees and Diplomas: Licenciado, 4 yrs.

Academic Staff: c. 40.

Student Enrolment: c. 210 (Women).

4899 **ESCUELA SUPERIOR DE ADMINISTRACIÓN DE RECURSOS NATURALES**
Blvd. Ortíz Mena s/n, Col. Centro, 33800 Hidalgo del Parral (Chihuahua)
Telephone: 2-12-09

Natural Resources Administration

A private institution attached to the Autonomus University of Chihuahua.

4900 **ESCUELA SUPERIOR DE AGRICULTURA 'HERMANOS ESCOBAR'**
Apartado postal 29, Ciudad Juárez (Chihuahua)
Telephone: 6-25-11

Agriculture

Founded 1906 as private school, became institution of further education 1962, acquired present title and status 1973. Attached to the University of Chihuahua. Receives some financial support from the federal government.

Academic Year: August to June (August-December; January-June).

Admission Requirements: Secondary school certificate (bachillerato) and entrance examination.

Language of Instruction: Spanish.

Degrees and Diplomas: Bachiller in Biology, 3 yrs. Professional title of Ingeniero agrónomo, 4 ½ yrs. Degree of Maestría, a further 2 yrs.

Library: c. 8000 vols.

Special Facilities (Museums, etc.): Desert Plants Collection; Botanical Garden.

Publications: Renovación; Nueva Era; Zootecnia.

Academic Staff: c. 60 (40).

Student Enrolment: c. 1870.

4901 **ESCUELA SUPERIOR DE AGRICULTURA Y VETERINARIA**
de la Puente 216 Poniente, San Buenaventura (Coahuila)

Agricultural Engineering
Veterinary Medicine and Animal Husbandry

A private institution recognized by the State government.

Academic Year: September to June (September-January; February-June).

Admission Requirements: Secondary school certificate (bachillerato).

Language of Instruction: Spanish.

Degrees and Diplomas: Professional titles, 4 ½-5 yrs.

4902 **ESCUELA SUPERIOR EN ORGANIZACIÓN Y ADMINISTRACIÓN AGROPECUARIA DE LA LAGUNA, A.C. (COAHUILA)**
Bravo y Degollado, 27000 Torreón (Coahuila)

Agricultural Organization and Administration

4903 **ESCUELA NACIONAL DE ANTROPOLOGÍA E HISTORIA**
Periférico Sur y Calle Zapote, Col. Isidro Fabela, 14030 México (D.F.)
Telephone: 655-7018

Anthropology
Archaeology
Ethnology
History
Linguistics

Founded 1938 as department of anthropology of the National School of Biological Sciences at the Instituto Politécnico Nacional, acquired present status and title 1942. A State institution under the jurisdiction of the Board of Public Education of the federal government.

Academic Year: September to August (September-March; May-August).

Admission Requirements: Secondary school certificate (bachillerato) or equivalent.

Fees: None.

Language of Instruction: Spanish.

Degrees and Diplomas: Licenciado in–Anthropology; Archaeology; Ethnology; Linguistics; Physical Anthropology; History; Ethnohistory; Social Anthropology, 5 yrs with 3 months of field work, and a thesis. Degree of Maestría in–Social Anthropology; Linguistics; History.

Library: c. 300,000 vols.

Publication: Revista.

Academic Staff: c. 50.

Student Enrolment: c. 1050.

4904 **ESCUELA DE ARQUITECTURA DE CHIHUAHUA,A.C.**
Calzada H. Colegio Militar Antiguo Colegio La Salle s/n, Chihuahua (Chihuahua)
Telephone: 4-18-42

Architecture

Founded 1970. A private institution attached to the Autonomous University of Chihuahua.

Academic Year: August to May.

Admission Requirements: Secondary school certificate and entrance examination.

Language of Instruction: Spanish.

Degrees and Diplomas: Professional title, 5 yrs.

Academic Staff: c. 25.

Student Enrolment: c. 180.

4905 **ESCUELA DE ARTE TEATRAL**
Auditorio nacional, México 18 (D.F.)
Telephone: 520-71-66

Dramatic Art

A State institution attached to the Instituto Nacional de Bellas Artes.

Academic Year: September to June (September-December; January-June).

Admission Requirements: Secondary school certificate (bachillerato).

Language of Instruction: Spanish.

Degrees and Diplomas: Professional titles, 4 yrs.

4906 **ESCUELA BANCARIA Y COMERCIAL**
Paseo de la Reforma 202, 06600 México (D.F.)
Telephone: 5-66-01-77
Director: Alejandro Prieto
Secretario General: Enrique Cepeda Accountancy and Administration
Banking and Finance

D. for Correspondence Courses

Founded 1929 by the Banco de México. Became independent 1932, diplomas recognized by the Mexican Government Educational authorities 1939. Governing bodies: the Consejo Académico; the Consejo Ejecutivo.

Academic Year: August to June (August-December; February-June).

Admission Requirements: Secondary school certificate (bachillerato) or recognized foreign equivalent and entrance examination.

Language of Instruction: Spanish.

Degrees and Diplomas: Licenciado in–Ciencias administrativas; Contaduría pública, accountancy; Banca y Finanzas, 4 yrs.

Library: c. 3000 vols.

Publication: Banca y Comercio (quarterly).

Academic Staff, 1986-87: – (250).

Student Enrolment, 1986-87:

	Men	Women	Total
Of the country	2950	2550	4500*

*Also 4000 external students.

4907 **ESCUELA NACIONAL DE BIBLIOTECONOMÍA Y ARCHIVONOMÍA**
Viaducto Miguel Alemán 155, México 13 (D.F.)
Telephone: 530-13-52

Library Science
Archives

A State institution.

Academic Year: January to December.

Admission Requirements: Secondary school certificate (bachillerato) and entrance examination.

Language of Instruction: Spanish.

Degrees and Diplomas: Licenciado, 2-4 yrs.

4908 **ESCUELA NACIONAL DE CAPACITACIÓN ADUANERA**
Calz. Tlalpan 2775, Col. El Reloj, Tlalpán (D.F)
Telephone: 522-30-02

Customs and Revenue

Founded 1972. A State institution.

Academic Year: September to July (September-January; February-July).

Admission Requirements: Secondary school certificate (bachillerato).

Language of Instruction: Spanish.

Degrees and Diplomas: Licenciado, 4 yrs. Diploma.

Library: Central Library, c. 3500 vols.

Publication: Revista Aduanera.

Academic Staff: c. 20.

Student Enrolment: c. 4050.

4909 **ESCUELA PROFESIONAL DE COMERCIO Y ADMINISTRACIÓN DE LEÓN**
Independencia 1706, 37380 León (Guanajuato)
Telephone: 2-09-38

Accountancy and Administration

Founded 1960. A private institution attached to the Universidad de Guanajuato.

Academic Year: September to July.

Admission Requirements: Secondary school certificate (bachillerato).

Language of Instruction: Spanish.

Degrees and Diplomas: Licenciado in Business Administration. Professional title of Contador público, 5 yrs.

Library: c. 3000 vols.

Academic Staff: c. – (40).

Student Enrolment: c. 350.

4910 **ESCUELA SUPERIOR DE COMERCIO Y ADMINISTRACIÓN 'COLEGIO GUASAVE'**
Domicilio Conocido, Colonia Ejidal, 81020 Guasave (Sinaloa)
Telephone: 2-00-06

Accountancy

A private institution recognized by the State government.

Academic Year: September to June.

Admission Requirements: Secondary school certificate (bachillerato).

Language of Instruction: Spanish.

Degrees and Diplomas: Professional title of Contador público, 4 ½ yrs.

4911 **ESCUELA SUPERIOR DE COMUNICACIÓN GRÁFICA**
Avenida División del Norte 3102, Col. Bellavista 31320 Altavista (Chihuahua)
Telephone: 7-03-05

Graphics
Communication

A private institution attached to the Autonomous University of Chihuahua.

4912 **ESCUELA DE COMUNICACIÓN SOCIAL**
Riva Palacio No. 684 Note., 80000 Culiacán (Sinaloa jour, rel publ.)
Telephone: 3-58-29

Journalism
Public Relations

A private institution.

4913 **ESCUELA NACIONAL DE CONSERVACIÓN, RESTAURACIÓN Y MUSEOGRAFÍA 'MANUEL DEL CASTILLO NEGRETE'**
Ex-Convento de Churubusco, Xicoténcatl y Grl. Anava, 04120 Coyoacán (D.F.)
Cables: Celarmex, México
Telephone: 688-25-40
Director: Jaime Cama Villafranca (1983-88)

Architectural Restoration
Museology

Founded 1964. A State institution under the supervision of the National Institute of Anthropology and History and financially supported by the Ministry of Public Education.

Academic Year: September to June (September-January; February-June).

Admission Requirements: Secondary school certificate (bachillerato) or recognized foreign equivalent.

Language of Instruction: Spanish.

Degrees and Diplomas: Licenciado in Architectural Restoration, 5 yrs. Professional titles of–Maestro en Arquitectura; Maestro en Museología, 2 yrs. Técnico en Restauración de Bienes Culturales, 2 ½ yrs.

Library: c. 6000 vols.

Special Facilities (Museums, etc.): Museo de Historia Natural.

4914 **ESCUELA PROFESIONAL DE CONTABILIDAD Y ADMINISTRACIÓN 'MITRO. JOSÉ CALVO' A.C.**
Avenida Cuauhtémoc 60, México 7 (D.F.)
Telephone: 578-78-27

Business Administration
Accountancy

A private institution.

Academic Year: September to June (September-January; February-June).

Admission Requirements: Secondary school certificate (bachillerato).

Language of Instruction: Spanish.

Degrees and Diplomas: Licenciado in Business Administration, 4 yrs. Professional title of Contador público, accountancy, 4 yrs.

4915 **ESCUELA SUPERIOR DE CONTADURÍA Y ADMINISTRACIÓN**
Avenida Monterrey s/n, Col. Chapultepec, 26860 Nueva Rosita (Coahuila)
Telephone: 4-37-45

Administration
Accountancy

A private institution attached to the Autonomous University of Coahuila.

4916 **ESCUELA LIBRE DE DERECHO**
Arcos de Belén, México 7 (D.F.)
Telephone: 588-02-11

Law

A private institution.

Academic Year: September to June (September-January; February-June).

Admission Requirements: Secondary school certificate (bachillerato) or recognized foreign equivalent.

Language of Instruction: Spanish.

Degrees and Diplomas: Licenciado, 5 yrs.

4917 **ESCUELA LIBRE DE DERECHO DE SINALOA**
Rosales 266 Pte, Culiacán (Sinaloa)
Telephone: 2-71-68

Law

A private institution.

Academic Year: September to June (September-January; February-June).

Admission Requirements: Secondary school certificate (bachillerato).

Language of Instruction: Spanish.

Degrees and Diplomas: Licenciado, 5 yrs.

4918 **ESCUELA DE DIETÉTICA Y NUTRICIÓN DEL ISSTE**
Avenida San Fernando 15, Col. Toriello Guerra, 14050 Tlalpan (D.F.)
Telephone: 559-55-54

Dietetics and Nutrition

A State institution.

4919 **ESCUELA DE DISEÑO DEL INBA**
Balderas 125, México 1 (D.F.)
Telephone: 521-71-94

Design

A State institution.

Academic Year: September to June (September-January; February-June).

Admission Requirements: Secondary school certificate (bachillerato).

Language of Instruction: Spanish.

Degrees and Diplomas: Professional titles, 4 yrs.

4920 **ESCUELA DE DISEÑO**
Belisario Domínguez 2202, Col. Obispado, 64010 Monterrey (Nuevo León)
Telephone: 46-20-42

Design

4921 **ESCUELA DE CIENCIAS DE LA EDUCACIÓN**
Juan Escutia y M. del Llano, Col. Obrero, 64010 Monterrey (Nuevo León)
Telephone: 44-67-03

Education

A State institution.

4922 **ESCUELA DE MEDICINA FÍSICA Y REHABILITACIÓN**
Avenida Observatorio y Esq. Sur 136, Col. Tacubaya, México 18 (D.F.)
Telephone: 271-50-00

Physical Therapy

A private institution.

4923 **ESCUELA DE FISICOTERAPÍA DEL HOSPITAL ABC**
Avenida Observatorio y Esq. Sur 136, Col. Tacubaya, México 18 (D.F.)

Physiotherapy
A private institution.

4924 **ESCUELA LIBRE DE HOMEOPATÍA**
Primera de Santa Lucia 6, 06200 México 2 (D.F.)
Telephone: 526-09-49

Homeopathy
Founded 1912. A private institution.
Academic Year: October to June.
Admission Requirements: Secondary school certificate (bachillerato).
Language of Instruction: Spanish.
Degrees and Diplomas: Professional titles of–Médico Homeópatía; Cirujano Partero, 6 yrs; Enfermera y Partera, nursing and midwifery, 4 yrs.
Publication: Homeopatía de México (monthly).
Academic Staff: c. 60.
Student Enrolment: c. 590.

4925 **ESCUELA PANAMERICANA DE HOTELERÍA**
Prolong. Martin Mendalde 1795, Col. Valle, 03100 México (D.F.)
Hotel Administration

4926 **ESCUELA DE INGENERÍA MUNICIPAL**
Doctor Lucio 191A. Col. Doctores, 06720 México (D.F.)
Engineering
A private institution.
Academic Year: September to June (September-January; February-June).
Admission Requirements: Secondary school certificate (bachillerato).
Language of Instruction: Spanish.
Degrees and Diplomas: Professional title of Ingeniero municipal, 4 yrs.

4927 **ESCUELA NÁUTICA MERCANTE 'CAP. DE ALT. ANTONIO GÓMEZ MAQUEO'**
Calz. Gabriel Leyva s/n, 82040 Mazatlán (Sinaloa)
Telephone: 1-24-86
Marine Engineering
A State institution.
Academic Year: September to July (September-January; February-July).
Admission Requirements: Secondary school certificate (bachillerato) and entrance examination.
Language of Instruction: Spanish.
Degrees and Diplomas: Professional titles, 3-4 yrs.

4928 **ESCUELA NÁUTICA MERCANTE DE TAMPICO**
Boulevard López Mateos y Constitución, 89070 Tampico (Tamaulipas)
Telex: 14763 ENMTMO
Telephone: 12-55-21
Director: Pedro Vélazquez San Miguel
Marine Engineering
Founded 1945. A State institution. Residential facilities for academic staff and 156 students.
Academic Year: September to June (September-January; February-June).
Admission Requirements: Secondary school certificate (bachillerato) and entrance examination.
Language of Instruction: Spanish.
Degrees and Diplomas: Professional titles, 3-4 yrs.
Academic Staff, 1986-87: 24 (10).
Student Enrolment, 1986-87:

	Men	Women	Total
Of the country	77	6	83
Of other countries	3	–	3
Total	80	6	86

4929 **ESCUELA NÁUTICA MERCANTE 'FERNANDO SILICEO'**
Boulevard Avila Camacho s/n, 91700 Veracruz (Ver.)
Telephone: 31-08-73
Director: Humberto Roffiel Gutiérrez
Marine Engineering
Founded 1919 as institute, acquired present status and title 1926. A State institution. Residential facilities for *c.* 200 students.
Academic Year: September to June (September-February; March-June).
Admission Requirements: Secondary school certificate (bachillerato) and entrance examination.
Languages of Instruction: Spanish and English.
Degrees and Diplomas: Professional titles, 3-4 yrs.
Library: c. 4000 vols.
Academic Staff, 1986-87: 7 (31).
Student Enrolment, 1986-87:

	Men	Women	Total
Of the country	450	16	466
Of other countries	24	–	24
Total	474	16	490

4930 **ESCUELA SUPERIOR DE PEDAGOGÍA, A.C.**
División del Norte 3102, Col. Bellavista, 31320 Altavista (Chihuahua)
Telephone: 4-07-77
Pedagogy
A private institution attached to the Autonomous University of Chihuahua.

4931 **ESCUELA DE PERIODISMO 'CARLOS SEPTIEN GARCÍA'**
Basilio Badillo 43, 1er Piso, 06030 México (D.F.)
Telephone: 510-49-01
Journalism
A private institution.
Academic Year: September to June (September-January; February-June).
Admission Requirements: Secondary school certificate (bachillerato) and entrance examination.
Language of Instruction: Spanish.
Degrees and Diplomas: Licenciado, 4 yrs.

4932 **ESCUELA NACIONAL DE PINTURA, ESCULTURA Y GRABADO 'LA ESMERALDA' DEL INBA**
San Fernando No. 14, Col. Guerrero, 06300 México (D.F.)
Painting
Sculpture
Engraving

4933 **ESCUELA DE PSICOLOGÍA Y PEDAGOGÍA 'SIGMUND FREUD'**
Morelos 417-419, 31000 Chihuahua (Chihuahua)
Telephone: 3-19-23
Psychology
Pedagogy
A private institution attached to the Autonomous University of Chihuahua.
Academic Year: August to July.
Admission Requirements: Secondary school certificate (bachillerato) and entrance examination.
Language of Instruction: Spanish.
Degrees and Diplomas: Licenciado, 4 ½ yrs.

4934 **ESCUELA INDEPENDIENTE DE PSICOLOGÍA**
Calle 3a y Méndez, Col. Santa Rosa, Chihuahua (Chihuahua)
Telephone: 5-71-86
Psychology
A private institution.

4935 **ESCUELA LIBRE DE PSICOLOGÍA**
Paseo Bolívar 419, Chihuahua (Chihuahua)
Telephone: 6-39-79
Psychology
A private institution attached to the Autonomous University of Chihuahua.

4936 **ESCUELA DE PSICOLOGÍA DEL VALLE DE TANGAMANGA**
5 de Mayo 535, 78000 San Luis Potosí (San Luis Potosí)
Telephone: 4-17-47
Psychology
Nursing
A private institutions.

4937 **ESCUELA SUPERIOR DE RELACIONES INDUSTRIALES**
Calz. Valle de Juárez 6922, Col. San Lorenzo, 32320 Ciudad Juárez (Chihuahua)
Telephone: 7-26-00

Industrial Relations

A private institution attached to the Autonomous University of Chihuahua.

4938 **ESCUELA DE TRABAJO SOCIAL DE TAMPICO**
Boulevard López Mateos No. 3401, Col. Santo Niño, Tampico (Tamaulipas)

Social Work

4939 **ESCUELA DE TRABAJO SOCIAL DE TIJUANA**
Calz. de Guadalupe 6, Fraccionamiento La Villa, La Mesa, Apartado postal 885, Tijuana (Baja California Norte)
Telephone: 86-8911
Secretaria Administrativa: María de la Luz Porras Arvizu

Social Work

Founded 1970. A private institution attached to the National Autonomous University of Mexico.

Arrangements for co-operation with San Diego State University.

Academic Year: August to June (August-December; January-June).

Admission Requirements: Secondary school certificate (bachillerato) and entrance examination.

Language of Instruction: Spanish.

Degrees and Diplomas: Licenciado, 4 yrs.

Academic Staff: c. – (15).

Student Enrolment: c. 150.

4940 **ESCUELA SUPERIOR DE MEDICINA VETERINARIA Y ZOOTECNIA, A.C.**
Km. 125.5 Carretera Federal México Puebla, Momoxpán, 72760 San Pedro Cholula (Puebla)

Veterinary Medicine
Animal Husbandry

4941 **FACULTADES UNIVERSITARIAS DE SALTILLO, A.C.**
Hidalgo Norte 160, Saltillo (Coahuila)
Telephone: 3-91-50

Business Administration
Accountancy

A private institution attached to the Autonomous University of Coahuila.

Academic Year: August to June.

Admission Requirements: Secondary school certificate (bachillerato) and entrance examination.

Language of Instruction: Spanish.

Degrees and Diplomas: Licenciado in Business Administration. Professional title of Contador público, accountancy, 5 yrs.

4942 **INSTITUTO SUPERIOR DE ARQUITECTURA**
Insurgentes Sur, 1027-402, Co. Nápoles, México 18 (D.F.)
Telephone: 598-47-00

Architecture

A private institution.

Academic Year: September to June (September-January; February-June).

Admission Requirements: Secondary school certificate (bachillerato) and entrance examination.

Language of Instruction: Spanish.

Degrees and Diplomas: Professional titles, 6 yrs.

4943 **INSTITUTO MEXICANO DE LA AUDICIÓN Y EL LENGUAJE**
Progreso 141A, Col. Escandón, 11800 México 18 (D.F.)

Hearing and Speech Therapy

Founded 1951. A private institution recognized by the Ministries of Health and Education.

Academic Year: September to July (September-February; February-July).

Admission Requirements: Secondary school certificate (bachillerato).

Language of Instruction: Spanish.

Degrees and Diplomas: Bachelor of Arts.

Library: 3000 vols.

Academic Staff: c. – (19).

Student Enrolment: c. 40.

4944 **INSTITUTO CELAYENSE**
Paseo del Bajío y Magnolia, Celaya (Guanajuato)
Telephone: 2-48-37

Psychology

A private institution attached to the University of Guanajuato.

4945 **INSTITUTO DE CIENCIA Y CULTURA, A.C.**
Victoria Pte. 525, Saltillo (Coahuila)
Telephone: 3-00-53

Administration
Biology

A private institution attached to the Autonomus University of Coahuila.

Academic Year: August to July.

Admission Requirements: Secondary school certificate (bachillerato) and entrance examination.

Language of Instruction: Spanish.

Degrees and Diplomas: Licenciado, 4-4 ½ yrs.

4946 **INSTITUTO DE CIENCIAS Y ARTES**
2a Avenida Norte y 3a Calle Ote., 29000 Tuxtla Gutiérrez (Chiapas)
Telephone: 2-37-82

C. of Topography
C. of Biology
C. of Dentistry
C. of Psychology

An autonomous State institution.

4947 **INSTITUTO DE CIENCIAS Y ESTUDIOS SUPERIORES DE TAMAULIPAS, A.C.**
Calle 7 Rayón y Victoria 706, 87300 H. Matamoros (Tamaulipas)
Telephone: 3-34-49

Medicine
Psychology
Social Work
Education
Accountancy
Business Administration

Founded 1979. A private institution recognized by the State government. Governing body: the Consejo.

Academic Year: September to August (September-February; March-August).

Admission Requirements: Secondary school certificate (bachillerato).

Language of Instruction: Spanish.

Degrees and Diplomas: Licenciado, 5 yrs.

Academic Staff: c. 40 (15).

Student Enrolment: c. 1000.

4948 **INSTITUTO SUPERIOR DE CIENCIAS Y TECNOLOGÍA DE LA LAGUNA, A.C.**
Héroes de Nacozari s/n, Col. Bellavista, 35050 Gómez Palacio (Durango)
Telephone: 4-26-33

S. of Civil Engineering
S. of Architecture
S. of Psychology
S. of Social Communication
S. of Graphic Design

Founded 1974 and attached to the Autonomous University of Coahuila. Transferred to Gómez Palacio 1977 and officially recognized as a fully autonomous institution by the State. Financially supported by tuition fees. Governing body: the Consejo Directivo de la Asociación Civil.

Academic Year: August to June (August-December; January-June).

Admission Requirements: Secondary school certificate (bachillerato).

Language of Instruction: Spanish.

Degrees and Diplomas: Licenciado in–Psychology; Social Communication; Graphic Design, 4 yrs. Professional titles of–Ingeniero civil, 4 yrs; Arquitecto, 5 yrs.

Library: c. 5500 vols.

Academic Staff: c. 5 (100).

Student Enrolment: c. 430.

4949 **INSTITUTO DE ENSEÑANZA E INVESTIGACION SUPERIOR EN COMERCIO INTERNACIONAL**

Monterrey 242, 06760 México 7 (D.F.)
Telephone: (5) 564-16-28
Fax: (5) 264-15-63
General Director: Becerra Gailo Belisario

External Commerce
International Trade
Customs and Excise
International Administration

Founded 1979.

Academic Year: February-February (February-July; September-February).

Admission Requirements: Secondary school certificate (bachillerato) and entrance examination.

Fees (Pesos): Registration, 400,000; tuition, 350,000 per month.

Language of Instruction: Spanish.

Degrees and Diplomas: Professional title of Técnico, 1 ½-2 ½ yrs; Licenciado, 4 yrs.

Academic Staff, 1989-90: – (48).

Student Enrolment, 1989-90:

	Men	Women	Total
Of the country	400	250	650
Of other countries	20	10	30
Total	420	260	680

4950 **INSTITUTO NACIONAL DE LA COMUNICACIÓN HUMANA, 'DR. ANDRÉS BUSTAMANTE GURRIA'**

Dr. Francisco P. Miranda 167, Col. Merced Gómez (Plateros), México (D.F.)
Telephone: 593-37-42
Director: Francisco Hernández Orozco (1973-)

Human Communication Studies

Founded 1952 as National Institute of Audiology, acquired present status and title 1969. Under the supervisionof the Health Department.

Academic Year: March to February.

Admission Requirements: Secondary school certificate (bachillerato) and entrance examination.

Language of Instruction: Spanish.

Degrees and Diplomas: Diploma, 4 yrs. Postgraduate qualifications as Specialist in Human Communication Medicine, 3 yrs.

Academic Staff, 1986-87: 43 (17).

Student Enrolment, 1986-87:

	Men	Women	Total
Of the country	28	204	232

4951 **INSTITUTO TECNOLÓGICO DE LA CONSTRUCCIÓN, A.C.**

Colima 254, Col. Roma, 06793 México (D.F.)

Construction Engineering

4952 **INSTITUTO DE CULTURA SUPERIOR**

Prado Norte 664, Lomas de Chapultepec, 11000$ México (D.F.)
Telephone: 540-2792

History of Art

A private institution.

Academic Year: September to June.

Admission Requirements: Secondary school certificate (bachillerato).

Language of Instruction: Spanish.

Degrees and Diplomas: Licenciado, 4 yrs.

4953 **INSTITUTO SUPERIOR DE CULTURA Y ARTE DE MONTERREY**

Avenida San Jerónimo 201 Pte, 64460 Monterrey (Nuevo León)
Telephone: 47-19-17

Design
Interior Decoration

A private institution attached to the University of Monterrey

Academic Year: August to June.

Admission Requirements: Secondary school certificate (bachillerato) and entrance examination.

Language of Instruction: Spanish.

Degrees and Diplomas: Licenciado, 4 yrs.

4954 **INSTITUTO CULTURAL DON VASCO, A.C.**

Entronque Nueva Carretera a Pátzcuaro s/n, Apartado postal 66, Uruapán (Michoacán)

Business Administration
Accountancy

A private institution attached to the National Autonomous University of Mexico.

Academic Year: September to June (September-January; February-June).

Admission Requirements: Secondary school certificate (bachillerato).

Language of Instruction: Spanish.

Degrees and Diplomas: Licenciado in Business Administration, 4 ½ yrs. Professional title of Contador público, 4 ½ yrs.

4955 **INSTITUTO CULTURAL ISIDRO FABELA, S.C.**

Quintano Roo, Sur 836, Toluca (Estado de México)
Telephone: 5-37-91

Business Administration
Accountancy
Anthropology
Law
History
Geography

A private institution attached to the Autonomous University of the State of Mexico.

Academic Year: October to September.

Admission Requirements: Secondary school certificate (bachillerato) and entrance examination.

Language of Instruction: Spanish.

Degrees and Diplomas: Licenciado, 5 yrs.

4956 **INSTITUTO MICHOACANO DE CIENCIAS DE LA EDUCACIÓN 'JOSÉ MARÍA MORELOS'**

Calzada Juárez 1600, 580060 Morelia (Michoacán)
Telephone: 3-50-75
Director: Gerardo Díaz Valdés

Teacher Training

Founded 1972 as Escuela Normal Superior, acquired present status and title 1986. A State institution.

Academic Year: September to June (September-January; February-June).

Admission Requirements: Secondary school certificate (bachillerato) and Titulo de Maestro en Educación primaria.

Language of Instruction: Spanish.

Degrees and Diplomas: Licenciado, 4 yrs. Degree of Maestria, a further 5 sem.

Library: 7232 vols.

Academic Staff, 1986-87: 1 (65).

Student Enrolment, 1986-87: 1045.

4957 **INSTITUTO UNIVERSITARIO DE CIENCIAS DE LA EDUCACIÓN, A.C.**

Calle Colegio Salesiano 35, Col. Anáhuac, México 3 (D.F.)
Telephone: 531-40-42

Communication
Pedagogy
Psychology
Sociology

A private institution attached to the National Autonomous University of Mexico.

Academic Year: August to June (August-January; February-June).

Admission Requirements: Secondary school certificate (bachillerato).

Language of Instruction: Spanish.

Degrees and Diplomas: Licenciado, 3-4 yrs.

4958 **INSTITUTO DE ESTUDIOS PROFESIONALES, A.C.**

Hidalgo Sur 468, 25000 Saltillo (Coahuila)
Telephone: 3-34-38

Civil Engineering
Architecture
Business Administration

A private institution attached to the Autonomous University of Coahuila.

Academic Year: August to June.

Admission Requirements: Secondary school certificate (bachillerato).

Language of Instruction: Spanish.

Degrees and Diplomas: Licenciado in–Business Administration, 4 yrs. Professional titles of Contador público; Ingeniero civil; Arquitecto, 5 yrs.

4959 **INSTITUTO DE ESTUDIOS PROFESIONALES PARA LA ADMINISTRACIÓN DEL TIEMPO LIBRE**
Avenida Ejército Nacional 253, Col. Anzures, 11300 México (D.F.)
Telephone: 531-05-74
Recreation Administration

4960 **INSTITUTO MANTENSE DE ESTUDIOS PROFESIONALES**
Calle Ocampo 212 Sur, 89800 Ciudad Mante (Tamaulipas)
Telephone: 2-17-78
Rectora: María Olga Trevino Arizmendi
Secretario General: José Luis Arzola Dominguez
F. of Law
Director: Juan Ploneda Hernández; *staff* – (15)
F. of Commerce
Director: José Luis Arzola Domínguez
F. of Administration
Director: José Luis Arzola Domínguez; *staff* – (14)
F. of Agricultural Administration
Director: Soe Gómez Enriquez
Also preparatory school.

Founded 1980 and attached to the Universidad Valle del Bravo. Became an independent autonomous institution recognized by the State 1983.

Academic Year: January to December (January-April; May-August; September-December).

Admission Requirements: Secondary school certificate (bachillerato).

Fees (Pesos): 62,000 per annum.

Language of Instruction: Spanish.

Degrees and Diplomas: Professional titles.

Library: 10,000 vols.

Academic Staff, 1986-87: c. 50.

Student Enrolment, 1986-87:

	Men	Women	Total
Of the country	337	298	635

4961 **INSTITUTO MEXICANO DE ESTUDIOS SUPERIORES**
Avenida Ocampo con Privada Rayón 245, 27000 Torreón (Coahuila)
Telephone: 2-32-54
Rector: José Bernal Gómez
Director Administrativo: Juan Bernal Imperial
D. of Social Work
Co-ordinator: Gabriela Macotela; *staff* 5 (10)
D. of Nutrition
Co-ordinator: Rosario Moncayo; *staff* 4 (10)
Also junior college and high school.

Founded 1959. A private institution.

Academic Year: September to June (September-January; January-June).

Admission Requirements: Secondary school certificate (bachillerato) and entrance examination.

Fees (Pesos): 900,000 per semester.

Language of Instruction: Spanish.

Degrees and Diplomas: Professional titles, 6-9 sem.

Library: 5000 vols.

Academic Staff: c. 15 (30).

Student Enrolment: c. 1250.

4962 **INSTITUTO DE ESTUDIOS SUPERIORES DE TAMAULIPAS**
Calle Divisonia Tampico, Altimara Ponientes s/n, Tampico (Tamaulipas)
Telephone: 2-11-02
Philosophy
Psychology
Computer Sciences
Civil Engineering
Administration
Accountancy

A private institution recogized by the State government.

Academic Year: January to December (January-June; August-December).

Admission Requirements: Secondary school certificate (bachillerato).

Language of Instruction: Spanish.

Degrees and Diplomas: Licenciado, 4-4 ½ yrs.

4963 **INSTITUTO DE ESTUDIOS SUPERIORES VASCO DE QUIROGA, A.C.**
Prol. V. do Mendoza 1678, Col. Félix Ireta, 58070 Morelia (Michoacán)
Telephone: 2-17-46
Business Administration
Architecture
Accountancy

A private institution recognized by the State government.

4964 **INSTITUTO DE ESTUDIOS SUPERIORES DE TURISMO, S.C.**
Privada del Lago 40, Col. Américas Unidas, 03610 México (D.F.)
Telephone: 539-03-08
Tourism

A private institution.

Academic Year: September to July (September-January; February-July).

Admission Requirements: Secondary school certificate (bachillerato).

Language of Instruction: Spanish.

Degrees and Diplomas: Licenciado, 4 ½ yrs.

4965 **INSTITUTO SUPERIOR DE INTÉRPRETES Y TRADUCTORES**
Río Rhin 40, 06500 México (D.F.)
Telephone: 566-77-22
Director: Jacobo Chencinsky (1963-87)
Translation
Interpretation

Founded 1963. A private institution recognized by the State.

Academic Year: September to June (September-January; February-June).

Admission Requirements: Secondary school certificate (bachillerato) and entrance examination.

Fees (Pesos): 115,000-125,000.

Languages of Instruction: Spanish and English.

Degrees and Diplomas: Licenciado, 4 yrs. Professional title of Técnico, 3 yrs. Degree of Maestría in English, 3 yrs.

Library: c. 2000 vols.

Academic Staff, 1986-87: 6 (26).

Student Enrolment, 1986-87:

	Men	Women	Total
Of the country	8	150	158
Of other countries	1	3	4
Total	9	153	162

4966 **INSTITUTO LEONARDO BRAVO**
Ezequiel Montes 115, México 4 (D.F.)
Telephone: 535-29-40
Accountancy

A private institution.

Academic Year: September to July (September-January; February-July).

Admission Requirements: Secondary school certificate (bachillerato).

Language of Instruction: Spanish.

Degrees and Diplomas: Professional title of Contador público, accountancy, 3 yrs.

4967 **INSTITUTO LITERARIO Y DE ESTUDIOS SUPERIORES DE CAMPECHE**
Avenida Malecón, Miguel Alemán s/n, 24000 Campeche (Campeche)
Telephone: 6-13-32
Social Work
Tourism
Journalism

A State institution.

4968 **INSTITUTO MEXICANO MADERO**
17 Poniente 503, 72000 Puebla (Puebla)
Telephone: 43-82-80
Administration
Accountancy
Journalism
Communication Planning
Economics
Agriculture Engineering

Animal Husbandry Administration
A private institution attached to the National Autonomous University of Mexico.

4969 **INSTITUTO DEL NORESTE**
Angel Flores 247 Ote, Culiacán (Sinaloa)
Telephone: 2-72-63

Psychology
A private institution recognized by the State government.
Academic Year: September to June (September-January; February-June).
Admission Requirements: Secondary school certificate (bachillerato).
Language of Instruction: Spanish.
Degrees and Diplomas: Licenciado, 4 ½ yrs.

4970 **INSTITUTO UNIVERSITARIO DEL NORTE**
Calle Bolivar 112, 31000 Chihuahua (Chihuahua)
Telephone: 5-81-15

Dentistry

4971 **INSTITUTO REGIOMONTANO**
Virgilio Garza y José Benitez, Col. Chepe Vera. Apdo. Postal 492, 64030 Monterrey (N.L.)
Telephone: 46-58-59
Director General: Miguel A. Alba Carpio (1983-)

Education
Founded 1983. Attached to the Universidad Autónoma de Nuevo León.
Academic Year: June to June (June-December; January-June).
Admission Requirements: Secondary school certificate (bachillerato).
Fees (Pesos): 145,000 per semester.
Language of Instruction: Spanish.
Degrees and Diplomas: Licenciado.
Academic Staff, 1986-87: 1 (16).

4972 **INSTITUTO SUPERIOR DE TURISMO**
Calle 9A No. 2211, 31000 Chihuahua (Chihuahua)
Telephone: 6-40-14

Tourism
A private institution attached to the Autonomous Univiversity of Chihuahua.
Academic Year: September to June (September-January; February-June).
Admission Requirements: Secondary school certificate (bachillerato) and entrance examination.
Language of Instruction: Spanish.
Degrees and Diplomas: Licenciado, 4 yrs.

4973 **LICEO PROFESIONAL DE COMERCIO Y ADMINISTRACIÓN, A.C.**
Bravo y 7a, H. Matamoros (Tamaulipas)
Telephone: 3-08-15

Business Administration
Accountancy
A private institution recognized by the State government.

4974 **TECNOLÓGICO DE ESTUDIOS CONTABLES Y ADMINISTRACIÓN**
Viaducto Pte. Miguel Alemán 255, Col. Roma Sur, México 7 (D.F.)
Telephone: 564-25-54

Business Administration
Accountancy
Tourist Administration
A private institutions.
Academic Year: March to January.
Admission Requirements: Secondary school certificate (bachillerato).
Language of Instruction: Spanish.
Degrees and Diplomas: Licenciado, 4 yrs. Professional title of Contador público, 5 yrs.

4975 **TECNOLÓGICO UNIVERSITARIO DE MÉXICO**
Avenida Azcapotzalco 308, Col. Clavería, 02080 México (D.F.)
Telephone: 561-86-46

Administration

Accountancy

Teacher Training

4976 **ESCUELA NORMAL SUPERIOR FEDERAL DE AGUASCALIENTES**
Boulevard Nazario Ortiz Garza s/n, 20000 Aguascalientes (Aguascalientes)
Telephone: 6-26-76

Teacher Training (secondary level)
Founded 1977. A State institution.
Academic Year: September to June.
Admission Requirements: Secondary school certificate (bachillerato) and teaching qualification (primary level) or degree of Licenciado.
Language of Instruction: Spanish.
Degrees and Diplomas: Licenciado, 4 yrs.
Library: c. 3500 vols.
Academic Staff: c. 20 (50).
Student Enrolment: c. 510.

4977 **ESCUELA NORMAL SUPERIOR DE CELAYA**
Luis de Velasco 225, Celaya (Guanajuato)
Telephone: 2-07-06

Teacher Training
A private institution recognized by the State.
Academic Year: September to June (September-January; February-June).
Admission Requirements: Secondary school certificate (bachillerato) and Título de Maestro en Educación primaria.
Language of Instruction: Spanish.
Degrees and Diplomas: Teaching qualification (secondary level), 4 yrs.

4978 **ESCUELA NORMAL SUPERIOR DEL ESTADO 'JOSÉ E. MADRANE'**
Calle Ramírez y 6a, Chihuahua (Chihuahua)
Telephone: 2-12-32

Teacher Training
A private institution recognized by the State.
Academic Year: September to June (September-January; February-June).
Admission Requirements: Secondary school certificate (bachillerato) and Título de Maestro en Educación primaria.
Language of Instruction: Spanish.
Degrees and Diplomas: Teaching qualification (secondary level), 4 yrs.

4979 **ESCUELA NORMAL SUPERIOR DE CIUDAD MADERO, TAMAULIPAS, A.C.**
Brasil y 5 de Mayo No. 406 Pte., 89400 Ciudad Madero (Tamaulipas)

Teacher Training
A private institution recognized by the State.

4980 **ESCUELA DE EDUCACIÓN FÍSICA 'PROF. ANTONIO ESTOPIER E.'**
Zaragoza 443 Norte, 35150 Col. Lerdo (Durango)

Physical Education
A State institution.

4981 **ESCUELA NORMAL SUPERIOR DE TAMAULIPAS, A.C.**
Carretera Soto la Marina Km. 2, Apartado postal 338, Ciudad Victoria (Tamaulipas)
Telephone: 2-43-05

Teacher Training
A private institution recognized by the State.
Academic Year: September to June (September-January; February-June).
Admission Requirements: Secondary school certificate (bachillerato) and Título de Maestro en Educación primaria.
Languages of Instruction: Spanish. Dissertations and theses may also be presented in English and French.
Degrees and Diplomas: Teaching qualification (secondary level), 4 yrs.

4982 **ESCUELA NORMAL SUPERIOR DEL ESTADO DE MORELOS**
Avenida Palmas No. 13, Col. Bellavista, Cuernavaca (Morelos)
Telephone: 3-25-28

Teacher Training (secondary level)
A State institution.
Academic Year: September to June (September-January; February-June).
Admission Requirements: Secondary school certificate (bachillerato) and Título de Maestro en Educación primaria.
Language of Instruction: Spanish.
Degrees and Diplomas: Licenciado, 4 yrs.

4983 **ESCUELA NORMAL SUPERIOR DE DURANGO**
Calle Pino Suárez 3000 Ote., Durango (Durango)
Telephone: 6-45-64

Teacher Training (secondary level)
A State institution.
Academic Year: September to June (September-January; February-June).
Admission Requirements: Secondary school certificate (bachillerato) and Título de Maestro en Educación primaria.
Language of Instruction: Spanish.
Degrees and Diplomas: Licenciado, 4 yrs.

4984 **ESCUELA NORMAL SUPERIOR DEL ESTADO DE MÉXICO NO. 2**
Avenida Revolución y Avenida de Los Maestros, Ecatepec (Estado de México)
Director: Roberto Ruiz Llano

Teacher Training (secondary level)
Founded 1977. A State institution.
Academic Year: September to June (September-January; February-June).
Admission Requirements: Secondary school certificate (bachillerato) and Título de Maestro en Educación primaria.
Language of Instruction: Spanish.
Degrees and Diplomas: Licenciado in Pedagogy, 4 yrs.
Library: c. 9000 vols.
Academic Staff: c. 10.
Student Enrolment: c. 1650.

4985 **ESCUELA NORMAL SUPERIOR LABASTIDA**
José Vasconcelos Ote. 110, Col. de Valle, 66220 Garza García (Nuevo León)
Telephone: 56-90-30

Teacher Training (secondary level)
A private institution recognized by the State.
Academic Year: September to June (September-January; February-June).
Admission Requirements: Secondary school certificate (bachillerato) and Título de Maestro en Educación primaria.
Language of Instruction: Spanish.
Degrees and Diplomas: Licenciado, 4 yrs.

4986 **ESCUELA NORMAL SUPERIOR DE JALISCO**
Lisboa 488, Col. Sta. Elena Estadio, 44230 Guadalajara (Jalisco)
Telephone: 24-54-01
Directora: Alicia Velasco Aldana (1986-)
Subdirector Secretario: J. Manuel Luna Figueroa

Teacher Training (secondary level)
Founded 1973. A State institution.
Academic Year: September to June (September-January; February-June).
Admission Requirements: Secondary school certificate (bachillerato) and Título de Maestro en Educación primaria.
Fees (Pesos): 5000 per annum.
Language of Instruction: Spanish.
Degrees and Diplomas: Licenciado, 4 yrs.
Library: 6997 vols.
Special Facilities (Museums, etc.): Museum of Biology and Geology.
Academic Staff, 1986-87: 19 (50).
Student Enrolment, 1986-87:

	Men	Women	Total
Of the country	337	479	816

4987 **ESCUELA NORMAL SUPERIOR 'NUEVA GALICIA'**
Luis Pérez Verdía 361, 44680 Guadalajara (Jalisco)
Telephone: 15-60-17
Director: Nabor González Gómez (1976-)

Teacher Training (secondary level)
Founded 1947. A private institution recognized by the State.
Academic Year: August to June (August-January; February-June).
Admission Requirements: Secondary school certificate (bachillerato) and Título de Maestro de Educación primaria.
Fees (Pesos): 230,000 per annum.
Language of Instruction: Spanish.
Degrees and Diplomas: Licenciado, 4 yrs.
Library: c. 45,000 vols.
Academic Staff, 1986-87: 8 (56).
Student Enrolment, 1986-87:

	Men	Women	Total
Of the country	549	1106	1655

4988 **ESCUELA NORMAL DE ESPECIALIZACIÓN**
Francisco Siles No. 1279, Fracc. Jardines Plaza del Sol, 04500 Guadalajara (Jalisco)
Telephone: 22-52-71

Teacher Training (for the handicapped)
A State institution.

4989 **ESCUELA NORMAL SUPERIOR DE GUANAJUATO**
Paseo de la Presa 76, Guanajuato (Guanajuato)
Telephone: 2-19-76

Teacher Training (secondary level)
A State institution.
Academic Year: September to June (September-January; February-June).
Admission Requirements: Secondary school certificate (bachillerato) and Título de Maestro en Educación primaria.
Language of Instruction: Spanish.
Degrees and Diplomas: Licenciado, 4 yrs.

4990 **ESCUELA NORMAL SUPERIOR DE LA LAGUNA**
Blvd. Miguel Alemán, Frente a la Termoeléctrica, Gómez Palacio (Durango)
Telephone: 3-16-43

Teacher Training (secondary level)
A State institutions.
Academic Year: September to June (September-January; February-June).
Admission Requirements: Secondary school certificate (bachillerato) and Título de Maestro en Educación primaria.
Language of Instruction: Spanish.
Degrees and Diplomas: Licenciado, 4 yrs.

4991 **ESCUELA NORMAL SUPERIOR DEL ESTADO DE BAJA CALIFORNIA SUR**
República y Altamirano, La Paz (Baja California Sur)
Telephone: 2-10-69

Teacher Training (secondary level)
A State institution.
Academic Year: September to June (September-January; February-June).
Admission Requirements: Secondary school certificate (bachillerato) and Título de Maestro en Educación primaria.
Language of Instruction: Spanish.
Degrees and Diplomas: Licenciado, 4 yrs.

4992 **ESCUELA 'JUSTO SIERRA'**
Juárez 523, León (Guanajuato)

4993 **INSTITUTO AMÉRICA**
Calz. del Tepeyac s/n, León (Guanajuato)
Telephone: 3-14-72

Teacher Training (secondary level)
A private institution recognized by the State.
Academic Year: September to June (September-January; February-June).
Admission Requirements: Secondary school certificate (bachillerato) and Título de Maestro en Educación primaria.
Language of Instruction: Spanish.
Degrees and Diplomas: Licenciado, 4 yrs.

4994 **ESCUELA NORMAL SUPERIOR DE SINALOA, A.C.**
Tejeira No. 10C, Col. Juan Cerrasco, Mazatlán (Sinaloa)
Telephone: 1-54-91

Teacher Training (secondary level)
A State institution.
Academic Year: July to August.
Admission Requirements: Secondary school certificate (bachillerato) and Título de Maestro en Educación primaria.
Language of Instruction: Spanish.
Degrees and Diplomas: Licenciado, 4 yrs.

4995 **ESCUELA NORMAL SUPERIOR DE YUCATÁN**
Calle 56 No. 426, Mérida (Yucatán)
Telephone: 1-23-14

Teacher Training (secondary level)
A State institution.
Academic Year: September to June (September-January; February-June).
Admission Requirements: Secondary school certificate (bachillerato) and Título de Maestro en Educación primaria.
Language of Instruction: Spanish.
Degrees and Diplomas: Licenciado, 4 yrs.

4996 **ESCUELA NORMAL SUPERIOR DE MÉXICO**
Fresno 15, 06400 México 4 (D.F.)
Telephone: 592-33-27

Teacher Training (secondary level)
Founded 1936. A State institution.
Academic Year: September to July (September-January; February-July).
Admission Requirements: Secondary school certificate (bachillerato) and Título de Maestro en Educación primaria.
Language of Instruction: Spanish.
Degrees and Diplomas: Licenciado, 4 yrs.

4997 **ESCUELA NORMAL DE ESPECIALIZACIÓN**
Campos Elíseos y Bernard Shaw, México 25 (D.F.)
Telephone: 540-29-61
Director: Humberto Galeana Romano (1981-)

Teacher Training (for the handicapped)
Founded 1943. A State institution.
Academic Year: September to June (September-January; February-June).
Admission Requirements: Secondary school certificate (bachillerato) and Título de Maestro en Educación primaria.
Language of Instruction: Spanish.
Degrees and Diplomas: Licenciado, 4 yrs.
Library: c. 10,000 vols.
Academic Staff, 1986-87: 34 (182).
Student Enrolment, 1986-87:

	Men	Women	Total
Of the country	67	1042	1109
Of other countries	3	4	7
Total	70	1046	1116

4998 **ESCUELA NORMAL SUPERIOR 'F.E.P.'**
Sadi Carnot 44, 06470 México 25 (D.F.)
Telephone: 535-86-83

Teacher Training (secondary level)
A private institution recognized by the State.
Academic Year: September to June (September-January; February-June).
Admission Requirements: Secondary school certificate (bachillerato) and Título de Maestro en Educación primaria.
Language of Instruction: Spanish.
Degrees and Diplomas: Licenciado, 4 yrs.

4999 **ESCUELA SUPERIO DE EDUCACIÓN FÍSICA**
Puerta 4 Ciudad Deportiva, Magdalena Mixcuca, 08010 México (D.F.)
Telephone: 519-50-60

Physical Education
Founded 1936. A State institution.
Academic Year: September to June (September-February; February-June).
Admission Requirements: Secondary school certificate (bachillerato).
Language of Instruction: Spanish.
Degrees and Diplomas: Licenciado, 4 yrs.
Academic Staff: c. 40 (80).
Student Enrolment: c. 1170.

5000 **ESCUELA NORMAL SUPERIOR DEL ESTADO DE NUEVO LEÓN**
Centro Escolar Venustiano Carranza, Venustiano Carranza y Ruperto Martinez, 64000 Monterrey (Nuevo León)
Telephone: 43-83-66

Teacher Training (secondary level)
Founded 1961. A State institution.
Academic Year: September to June (September-January; February-June).
Admission Requirements: Secondary school certificate (bachillerato) and Título de Maestro en Educación primaria.
Language of Instruction: Spanish.
Degrees and Diplomas: Teaching qualification (secondary level), 4 yrs.
Library: c. 5200 vols.
Special Facilities (Museums, etc.): Museo de Ciencias Biológicas.
Publication: Comunicación.
Academic Staff: c. 210.
Student Enrolment: c. 2680.

5001 **ESCUELA NORMAL DE ESPECIALIZACIÓN**
Avenida Tepeyac 1666 Pte. y Priv. Castelar 'D', Colonia Pío X, 64710 Monterrey (Nuevo León)

Teacher Training (for the handicapped)
A State institution.
Academic Year: September to June (September-January; February-June).
Admission Requirements: Secondary school certificate (bachillerato) and Título de Maestro en Educación primaria.
Language of Instruction: Spanish.
Degrees and Diplomas: Licenciado, 4 yrs.

5002 **ESCUELA NORMAL SUPERIOR DE OAXACA**
Arteaga No. 44, 68000 Oaxaca (Oaxaca)
Telephone: 6-98-68

Teacher Training (secondary level)
A private institution recognized by the State.
Academic Year: September to June (September-January; February-June).
Admission Requirements: Secondary school certificate (bachillerato) and Título de Maestro en Educación primaria.
Language of Instruction: Spanish.
Degrees and Diplomas: Licenciado, 4 yrs.

5003 **ESCUELA NORMAL SUPERIOR DE HIDALGO**
Mina No. 110, 42000 Pachuca (Hidalgo)
Telephone: 2-47-77

Teacher Training
A State institution.

5004 **ESCUELA NORMAL SUPERIOR DEL ESTADO**
11 Sur No. 1102, 7200 Puebla (Puebla)
Telephone: 38-84-73

Teacher Training (secondary level)
A State institution.
Academic Year: September to June (September-January; February-June).
Admission Requirements: Secondary school certificate (bachillerato) and Título de Maestro en Educación primaria.
Language of Instruction: Spanish.
Degrees and Diplomas: Licenciado, 6 yrs.

5005 **ESCUELA NORMAL SUPERIOR BENAVENTE**
Calle 25 Oriente 9, 72000 Puebla (Puebla)
Telephone: 43-63-00

Teacher Training (secondary level)
Founded 1956. A private institution recognized by the State. Financially supported by the Colegio Benavente.
Academic Year: September to June (September-January; February-June).
Admission Requirements: Secondary school certificate (bachillerato) and Título de Maestro en Educación primaria.
Language of Instruction: Spanish.
Degrees and Diplomas: Licenciado, 4 yrs.
Library: c. 6300 vols.

Academic Staff: c. 170.
Student Enrolment: c. 700.

5006 **ESCUELA NORMAL SUPERIOR 'JUSTO SIERRA MENDEZ'**
Avenida Kermanas Serdán s/n, 72000 Puebla (Puebla)
Telephone: 45-37-78

Teacher Training (secondary level)
A private institution recognized by the State.
Academic Year: July to August.
Admission Requirements: Secondary school certificate (bachillerato) and Título de Maestro en Educación primaria.
Language of Instruction: Spanish.
Degrees and Diplomas: Licenciado, 6 yrs.

5007 **ESCUELA NORMAL SUPERIOR DE QUERÉTARO, A.C.**
Domicilio Conocido, Colonia Vista Alegre, 76090 Querétaro (Querétaro)

Teacher Training (secondary level)
A private institution recognized by the State.
Academic Year: September to June (September-January; February-June).
Admission Requirements: Secondary school certificate (bachillerato) and Título de Maestro en Educación primaria.
Language of Instruction: Spanish.
Degrees and Diplomas: Licenciado, 4 yrs.

5008 **ESCUELA NORMAL SUPERIOR**
Calle Aldama Pte. 858, Saltillo (Coahuila)
Telephone: 3-65-39

Teacher Training
A State institution.
Academic Year: September to June (September-January; February-June).
Admission Requirements: Secondary school certificate (bachillerato) and Título de Maestro en Educación primaria.
Language of Instruction: Spanish.
Degrees and Diplomas: Teaching qualification (secondary level), 4 yrs.

5009 **ESCUELA NORMAL REGIONAL DE ESPECIALIZACIÓN**
Hidalgo y Aldama, Saltillo (Coahuila)
Telephone: 3-61-59

Teacher Training (for the handicapped)
A State institution.
Academic Year: July to August.
Admission Requirements: Secondary school certificate (bachillerato) and Título de Maestro en Educación primaria.
Language of Instruction: Spanish.
Degrees and Diplomas: Teaching qualification, 4 yrs.

5010 **ESCUELA NORMAL SUPERIOR DEL SUR DE TAMAULIPAS**
Ayuntamiento y Nicolás Bravo, Col. Martock, Tampico (Tamaulipas)
Telephone: 2-43-05

Teacher Training (secondary level)
A private institution recognized by the State.
Academic Year: September to June (September-January; February-June).
Admission Requirements: Secondary school certificate (bachillerato) and Título de Maestro en Educación primaria.
Language of Instruction: Spanish.
Degrees and Diplomas: Teaching qualification, 4 yrs.

5011 **ESCUELA NORMAL SUPERIOR DE NAYARIT**
Ciudad de la Cultura 'Amado Nervo', Tepic (Nayarit)
Telephone: 2-01-06

Teacher Training (secondary level)
Academic Year: September to June (September-January; February-June).
Admission Requirements: Secondary school certificate (bachillerato) and Título de Maestro en Educación primaria.
Language of Instruction: Spanish.
Degrees and Diplomas: Teaching qualification, 4 yrs.

5012 **ESCUELA NORMAL SUPERIOR DEL ESTADO DE MÉXICO**
Natalia Carasco 400, Col. Federal, 50070 Toluca (Estado de México)
Telephone: 4-00-63

Teacher Training
Founded 1968. A State institution.
Academic Year: September to June (September-January; February-June).
Admission Requirements: Secondary school certificate (bachillerato) and Título de Maestro en Educación primaria.
Language of Instruction: Spanish.
Degrees and Diplomas: Licenciado in Pedagogy, 4 yrs.
Library: 15,000 vols.
Academic Staff: c. 35 (5).
Student Enrolment: c. 3600.

5013 **ESCUELA NORMAL SUPERIOR DE CHIAPAS**
Avenida 20 de Noviembre s/n, Col. Albania, Tuxtla Gutierrez (Chiapas)
Telephone: 2-68-76

Teacher Training (secondary level)
A State institution.
Academic Year: September to June (September-January; February-June).
Admission Requirements: Secondary school certificate (bachillerato) and Título de Maestro en Educación primaria.
Language of Instruction: Spanish.
Degrees and Diplomas: Teaching qualification, 4 yrs.

5014 **ESCUELA NORMAL SUPERIOR 'JUAN DE ASBAJE'**
Dr. Verduzco 380 Sur, Zamora (Michoacán)
Telephone: 2-07-14

Teacher Training (secondary level)
A private institution recognized by the State.
Academic Year: September to June (September-January; February-June).
Admission Requirements: Secondary school certificate (bachillerato) and Título de Maestro en Educación primaria.
Language of Instruction: Spanish.
Degrees and Diplomas: Licenciado, 4 yrs. Also 130 other institutions of teacher training.

Also 130 other institutions of Teacher Training

MONGOLIA
(People's Republic)

5016 ***MONGOL ULSYN IKH SURGUULI**
Mongolian State University
p.b. 377, Ulan Bator 11
Telephone: 20668
Rector: Osoryn Shagdarsüren (1982-)
Director of Studies: S. Turmur-Ochir

F. of Physics and Mathematics
Dean: A. Mekei; *staff* 61 (26)
F. of Natural Sciences
Dean: G. Samden; *staff* 59 (17)
F. of Social Sciences
Dean: Ya. Dolgorjab; *staff* 42 (29)
F. of Philology
Dean: Sukh Bator; *staff* 74 (21)
F. of Economics
Dean: T. Namjaa; *staff* 42 (11)
F. of Trade Economics
Dean: A. Damdin; *staff* 20 (17)
Preparatory F.
Dean: Z. Munkhee; *staff* 19
D. for Evening and Correspondence Studies
Dean: Sh. Davaasambuu

Founded 1942 as a State institution. Governing bodies: the Rectorial Council; the Academic Council. Residential facilities for academic staff and *c.* 1000 students.

Arrangements for co-operation with the Universities of: Moscow; Irkutsk; Halle; Berlin (Humboldt); Prague; Habana; Beijing; New Delhi; Leeds; Osaka; Tokyo; Paris-Sorbonne.

Academic Year: September to July (September-January; February-July).

Admission Requirements: Secondary school certificate (gerchilgee).

Fees: None.

Language of Instruction: Mongolian.

Degrees and Diplomas: Diploma of Specialist in relevant fields, 5 yrs. Postgraduate qualifications, 3 further years and thesis.

Library: Educational and Scientific Library, 375,000 vols.

Special Facilities (Museums, etc.): Zoology Museum; Botany Museum.

Publication: Research Bulletin.

Academic Staff, 1986-87: 317 (121).

Student Enrolment: *c.* 4000 (Also *c.* 350 external students).

5017 **POLITECHNIKYN DEED SURGUULI**
Mongolian Polytechnical Institute
P.O. 46, Box 520, Ulan Bator
Telephone: 25109
Rector: Ch. Avdai (1976-)

F. of Geology and Mining
Dean: A. Samdan; *staff* 44
F. of Mechanical Engineering
Dean: Kh. Chimeddash; *staff* 50
F. of Energetics
Dean: Kh. Tsagaan; *staff* 37
F. of Construction Engineering and Architecture
Dean: D. Sambu; *staff* 47
F. of Automated Control Systems
Dean: G. Tsogbadrakh; *staff* 42
F. of Civil Engineering
Dean: Ts. Jadambaa; *staff* 40
Preparatory F.
Dean: Kh. Purevdagva; *staff* 80
F. for Evening and Extramural Studies
Dean: Ya. Bavuudorji; *staff* 30

Founded 1969 as part of the Mongolian State University. Became an independent institution 1983. Residential facilities for academic staff and 800 students.

Arrangements for co-operation with: Irkutsk Polytechincal Institute; Ural Polytechnical Institute; Institute of Civil Engineering, Moscow; Institute of Architecture, Moscow; Freiberg Mining Academy; Institute of Electrical and Mechanical Engineering, Sofia; Technical University, Budapest.

Academic Year: September to July (September-January; February-July).

Admission Requirements: Secondary school certificate (gerchilgee).

Fees: None.

Language of Instruction: Mongolian.

Degrees and Diplomas: Diploma of Specialist in relevant fields of Engineering.

Library: 200,000 vols.

Publication: Mineralogy.

Academic Staff, 1986-87:

Rank	Full-time
Professors	3
Associate Professors	70
Senior Lecturers	60
Lecturers	261
Assistant Lecturers	6
Total	400

Student Enrolment, 1986-87:

	Men	Women	Total
Of the country	430	400	830
Of other countries	11	6	17
Total	441	406	847*

*Also 630 external students.

5018 **FOREIGN LANGUAGE INSTITUTE**
p.b. 46/53, Ulan Bator
Telephone: 22702

Russian Language
Romanic and Germanic (including English, German, French, and Spanish)
Mongolian and Eastern languages
Mongolian and Foreign Literature
Social Science (including Economics and Political Sciences)
Pedagogics
Translation

Founded 1979 as Russian Language Institute. Acquired present title 1990. Governing body: Vice-Minister of People's Education. Residential facilities for students.

Arrangements for co-operation with similar institutions in USSR and People's Republic of China.

Academic Year: September to June.

Languages of Instruction: Mongolian, Russian, English, German, French, Spanish, Chinese, and Japanese.

Degrees and Diplomas: Bachelor, 5 yrs.

Library: Central Library, 85,000 vols.

Publication: Scientific Notebook (annually).

Press or Publishing House: Copy-writing Bureau

Academic Staff, 1989-90: 110.

Student Enrolment, 1989-90:

	Men	Women	Total
Of the country	85	715	800

5019 **INSTITUTE FOR MANAGEMENT PERSONNEL**
University Street 3, Ulan Bator 46

Management Studies

Founded 1979.

5020 **KHOBDIN ULSIN BAGSHIIN DEED SURGUUL**
Khobdo State Pedagogical Institute
Khobdo City, Khobdo Province
Telephone: 2500
Rector: Jadamba Nimyin (1979-)

F. of Natural Sciences
Dean: L. Demberel; *staff* 39
F. of Social Sciences
Dean: D. Batchubuun; *staff* 39

Founded 1979. Residential facilities for academis staff and 500 students. Arrangements for co-operation with Pedagogical Institutions in USSR.
Academic Year: September to June (September-January; February-June).
Admission Requirements: Secondary school certificate (gerchilgee).
Fees: None.
Language of Instruction: Mongolian.
Degrees and Diplomas: Teaching qualifications (secondary level), 4-5 yrs.
Library: Central Library, 100,000 vols.
Special Facilities (Museums, etc.): Biological and Geographical Museum.
Publication: Scientific Publications (annually).
Academic Staff, 1989-90: 78.
Student Enrolment, 1989-90:

	Men	Women	Total
Of the country	210	230	440

5021 **STATE PEDAGOGICAL INSTITUTE**
p.b. 48/103, Peace Street 2, Ulan Bator

F. of Mongolian Language and Literature
F. of Russian Language
F. of Mathematics and Physics
F. of Natural and Social Sciences
F. of Art and Labour Studies
F. of Physical Education
F. of Teachers Retraining
External F.

Founded 1951 as part of Mongolian State University.

5022 **STATE AGRICULTURAL INSTITUTE**
Post Office 53, Ulan Bator

F. of Agricultural Engineering
F. of Veterinary Medicine
F. of Animal Husbandry
F. of Agricultural Economics

Founded 1942 as part of Mongolian State University.

5023 **STATE MEDICAL INSTITUTE**
Post Office 48, Ulan Bator

F. of Medicine
F. of Pediatrics
F. of Dentistry
F. of Pharmacy
F. of Hygiene
F. of Therapy

Founded 1942 as part of Mongolian State University.

MOROCCO

Universities

5024 **UNIVERSITÉ HASSAN II**

Hassan II University
B.P. 9167, Mers-Sultan, Casablanca
Telephone: 26-26-72
Recteur: Abdelouahed Belkziz (1985-)

F. of Law, Economics and Social Sciences
Dean: Mohamed Bennani; *staff* 200 (26)
F. of Pharmacy
Dean: Abderrahim Harouchi; *staff* 261
F. of Dentistry
Dean: Mohamed Himmiche; *staff* 28 (24)
F. of Letters and Human Sciences I (History, Geography, French, English, Spanish, and German Literature and Language)
Dean: Abdelfattah Benkaddour; *staff* 167 (7)
F. of Letters and Human Sciences II (Arabic, French and English Language and Literature, History, Geography, Islamic Studies)
Dean: Hassan Esmili; *staff* 121
F. of Letters and Human Sciences III (French and Arabic Language and Literature, Geography, History, English, Islamic Studies)
Dean: Aziza Bennani; *staff* 75 (3)
F. of Science I (Mathematics, Chemistry, Biology, Physics, Geology)
Dean: Driss Khiari; *staff* 176
F. of Science II (Mathematics, Chemistry, Biology, Physics, Geology)
Dean: Mohamed Berada *staff* 170
S. of Engineering (E.N.S.E.M.)
Director: Zouheir Guessouss; *staff* 36
C. of Technology
Director: Ahmed Berkaoui; *staff* 35 (3)

Founded 1975. Residential facilities for students in Cités universitaires.

Arrangements for co-operation with: Université des Sciences et Techniques de Lille; Université d'Aix-Marseille III; Université de Montpellier I; Université de Nancy; Université Provence-Aix-Marseille; Université de Lyon; Université de Droit et de Santé de Lille; Université de Laval, Canada; Université François Rabelais-Tours; Université de Nantes; Université de Bordeaux III; Faculté de Lettres La Manoubia; Ecole supérieure des Enseignants, Tunisia.

Academic Year: September to July (September-December; January-March; April-July).

Admission Requirements: Secondary school certificate (baccalauréat).

Fees: None.

Languages of Instruction: Arabic and French.

Degrees and Diplomas: Licence, 4 yrs. Diplôme d'études supérieures (D.E.S.), 1-2 yrs after Licence. Professional title of Ingénieur, 5 yrs. Doctorat.

Library: Faculty libraries, 136,415 vols.

Publications: Annales; Publications de thèses, colloques.

Academic Staff, 1988-89:

Rank	Full-time
Professeurs	85
Maîtres de conférences	149
Maîtres-Assistants	728
Assistants	136
Professeurs 2e cycle	–
Autres	171
Total	1269

Student Enrolment, 1988-89: 35,773.

5025 ***JAMI'AT MUHAMMAD AL-AWWAL**

Mohammed I University
Complexe Universitaire, B.P. 524, Oujda
Telephone: (212-68) 0521-22
Fax: (212-68) 6171
Recteur: Hassan Mekouare (1989-)
Secrétaire général: Abderrahman Houtch

F. of Letters and Human Sciences (Islamic Studies, French and English Language and Literature, History, Geography)
Dean: Mohammed Taifi; *staff* 121 (13)
F. of Juridical, Economic and Social Sciences (including Political Science)
Dean: M'hammed Jalal; *staff* 73 (3)
F. of Science
Dean: Abdelkrim Ramdani; *staff* 176 (17)
C. of Technology
Director: Mohammed Barrocha

Founded 1978. Governing body: the Conseil. Residential facilities for students in Cité universitaire.

Academic Year: October to June.

Admission Requirements: Secondary school certificate (baccalauréat) or equivalent.

Fees: None.

Languages of Instruction: Arabic and French.

Degrees and Diplomas: Licence, 4 yrs. Diplôme d'études supérieures (D.E.S.), 1-2 yrs after Licence. Doctorat d'Etat.

Library: Faculty libraries, total, 61,180 vols.

Publications: Al Maiadin (annually); Majallat Kulliat al-Adab (annually).

Academic Staff, 1989-90:

Rank	Full-time	Part-time
Professeurs	13	–
Maîtres de Conférences	44	2
Maîtres-Assistants	266	5
Assistants	13	–
Autres	34	26
Total	370	33

Student Enrolment, 1989-90:

	Mrn	Women	Total
Of the country	10,188	6415	16,603
Of other countries	273	13	286
Total	10,461	6428	16,889

5026 ***UNIVERSITÉ MOHAMMED V/JÂMIÂT MOHAMMED EL KHÂMISS**

Mohammed V University
B.P. 554, rue Michlifen Agdal, Rabat-Chellah
Telex: RECUNIV 32603
Telephone: 713-18; 713-33
Recteur: Abdellatif Benabdeljalil

F. of Law, Economics and Social Sciences
Dean: Abdelaziz Benjelloun
F. of Science
Dean: Ahmed Kerkour
F. of Letters and Human Sciences
Dean: Hassan Mekouar
F. of Medicine and Pharmacy
Dean: Taïb Chkili
F. of Dentistry
Dean: Bouchaïb Jidal
S. of Engineering
Director: Ahmed Jebli
F. of Education
Dean: M'hamed Zaimi
F. of Letters and Human Sciences (Kénitra)
Dean: Larbi Mezzine

F. of Science (Kénitra)
Dean: Mohamed Zinoun
C. of Translation (Tanger)
Director: Bouchaïb Idrissi Bouyahyaoui
Research I. for African and Moroccan Studies
Director: Abdelhadi Tazi
Scientific Research I.
Director: Hajjoub Lamsougar

Founded 1957 incorporating former institutes of letters (1912), law (1920), and science (1940). Reorganized 1975. A State institution. Governing body: the Conseil, including members of the academic staff, 2 representatives of the student body and 8 members appointed by the Ministry of Education. Some residential facilities for students in Cités universitaires.

Arrangements for exchange of academic staff and students, and research projects with institutions in: Belgium;Canada; France; Federal Republic of Germany; Iraq; Tunisia; Mauritania; USA; USSR.

Academic Year: September to July (September-December; January-March; April-July).

Admission Requirements: Secondary school certificate (baccalauréat) or equivalent. Entrance examination for Medicine. Diploma of Licence for Education.

Fees: None.

Languages of Instruction: Arabic and French.

Degrees and Diplomas: Capacité en Droit, Law, 2 yrs. Licence–en Droit; en Sciences économiques; ès Lettres; ès Sciences, 4 yrs. Diplôme d'études supérieures (D.E.S.) in various fields–1-2 yrs after Licence. Doctor of–Dentistry, 5 yrs; Pharmacy; Medicine, 7 yrs. Professional title of Ingénieur, 5 yrs and practical work. Doctorates by theses. Also Diplôme universitaires de technologie (D.U.T.), 2 yrs.

Library: 17,409 vols.

Publications: Revues (Droit, Lettres, Education) (biannually); La Recherche scientifique.

Academic Staff, 1985-86:

Rank	Full-time	Part-time
Professeurs	262	41
Maîtres de conférences	218	13
Maîtres-Assistants	819	25
Assistants	163	15
Professeurs du second degré	121	20
Autres	132	136
Total	1715	250

Student Enrolment, 1985-86:

	Men	Women	Total
Of the country	20,456	11,722	32,178
Of other countries	654	144	798
Total	21,110	11,866	32,976

5027 **UNIVERSITÉ SIDI MOHAMMED BEN ABDALLAH**
Boulevard des Almohades, B.P. 2626, Fès
Telephone: 224-01
Recteur: Mohamed Hilali
Secrétaire général: Mohamed Ferhane

F. of Law, Economics and Social Sciences
Dean: Amal Jelal; *staff* 123 (13)
F. of Letters and Human Sciences (Literature, Languages, Social Sciences, Philosophy, History, Geography, Islamic Studies)
Dean: Tazi Saoud Abkelouahab; *staff* 244 (20)
F. of Science (Mathematics, Informatics, Physics, Chemistry, Geology, Biological Sciences)
Dean: Daoudi Saad; *staff* 232 (10)
F. of Letters
S. of Technology
Director: Makrini Mohamed; *staff* 38 (5)

Founded 1975. Governing body: the Council. Residential facilities for 5000 students.

Academic Year: September to June (September-February; February-June).

Admission Requirements: Secondary school certificate (baccalauréat) or equivalent.

Fees: None.

Languages of Instruction: Arabic and French.

Degrees and Diplomas: Diplôme d'études universitaires générales (D.E.U.G.), 2 yrs. Licence, 4 yrs. Diplôme des études supérieures (D.E.S.), a further 2 yrs. Doctorat d'Etat. Also Diplôme universitaire de technologie (D.U.T.), 2 yrs.

Academic Staff, 1989-90:

Rank	Full-time	Part-time
Professeurs	47	–
Maîtres de conférances	70	5
Maîtres-Assistants	422	4
Assistants	28	39
Autres	70	–
Total	637	48

Student Enrolment, 1989-90:

	Men	Women	Total
Of the country	16,091	8763	24,854
Of other counties	541	40	581
Total	16,632	8803	25,435

5028 **UNIVERSITÉ CADI AYYAD**
Boulevard de Safi, Marrakech
Telex: 74013
Telephone: 346-49

F. of Science
F. of Law, Economics, and Social Sciences
F. of Letters and Human Sciences

Founded 1975.

Academic Year: September to June (September-December; January-April).

Admission Requirements: Secondary school certificate (baccalauréat) or equivalent.

Fees: None.

Language of Instruction: French.

Degrees and Diplomas: Certificat universitaire, 2 yrs. Licence, 4 yrs. Certificat d'études approfondies, 1 further year. Certificat des études universitaires supérieures, 2 yrs after Licence. Doctorat de 3ème cycle. Doctorat d'Etat.

5029 **UNIVERSITÉ QUARAOUIYINE**
Dhar El Mahraz, B.P. 60, Fès
Telex: 31016
Telephone: (06) 411-99; 421-23

F. of Islamic Law (Sha'ria)
F. of Arabic Language and Literature (Marrakech)
F. of Theology and Philosophy (Tétouan)
F. of Islamic Law (Sha'ria) (Agadir)

Also 8 further institutes of Islamic Studies in: Marrakech; Taroudant; Larache; Meknès; Al Hoceima; El Ksar;El Kebir; Oujda.

Founded 859, reorganized 1788-89 by Mohammed III. Became Moroccan State institution 1947. The head of the university is the Minister of State for Cultural and Traditional Education. Some residential facilities for students.

Academic Year: November to June (November-December; January-March; April-June).

Admission Requirements: Secondary school certificate (baccalauréat) or equivalent.

Fees: None.

Language of Instruction: Arabic.

Degrees and Diplomas: Licence, 4 yrs. Diplôme d'études supérieures, a further 2 yrs; Doctorat.

Libraries: Central Library; faculty libraries.

Publication: Revues (quarterly).

Academic Staff: c. 90.

Student Enrolment: c. 5000.

Other Institutions

5030 **ÉCOLE NATIONALE D'ADMINISTRATION PUBLIQUE**
1, avenue de la Victoire, Rabat
Telephone: 250-61

Public Administration

Founded 1948.

5031 **ÉCOLE NATIONALE D'AGRICULTURE DE MEKNÈS**

B.P. S/40, Haj Kaddour, Route d'Ifrane, Meknès
Telex: 41969
Telephone: 223-89
Directeur: Mohamed Rochdi (1986-)
Directeur des Etudes: Zoubida Bensouda

D. of Agronomy
Head: Abderrazak Bentassil; *staff* 8
D. of Animal Husbandry
Head: Ahmed Kabbali; *staff* 7
D. of Food Technology
Head: Mohamed Akasbi; *staff* 3
D. of Ecology
Head: My Mustapha El Youssoufi; *staff* 2
D. of Tree Culture and Viticulture
Head: Saïd Hjaouj; *staff* 3
D. of Agricultural Mechanization
Head: Chekli Hassan; *staff* 2
D. of Rural Equipment
Head: B. Abdelouaheb Filali; *staff* 1
D. of Basic Sciences
Head: Zoubida Bensouda; *staff* 6
D. of Earth Sciences
Head: Bousselham Loudyi; *staff* 3
D. of Agricultural Zoology
Head: Ahmed Sekkat; *staff* 4
D. of Rural Economy
Head: Agled Driouchi; *staff* 4
D. of Agricultural Diffusion
Head: Abderrazak Lakjaa; *staff* 3
D. of Plant Pathology
Head: Mohammed Boulif; *staff* 3
Also Continuing Agricultural Education and Advanced Programmes.

Founded 1945. A State institution under the jurisdiction of the Ministry of Agriculture and Agrarian Reform. Governing body: le Conseil d'administration.

Arrangements for co-operation with similar institutions in: France; Canada; U.S.A.

Academic Year: September to July (September-December; January-March; April-July).

Admission Requirements: Secondary school certificate (baccalauréat).

Fees: None.

Language of Instruction: French.

Degrees and Diplomas: Diplôme d'Ingénieur agronomo spécialisé, 6 yrs.

Library: Cental Library and departmental libraries.

Special Facilities (Museums, etc.): Two Farms.

Publication: Bulletin.

Academic Staff, 1989-90:

Rank	Full-time	Part-time
Professeurs	3	–
Maîtres de conférences	12	–
Maîtres-Assistants	32	–
Assistants	3	26
Total	50	26

Student Enrolment, 1989-90:

	Men	Women	Total
Of the country	202	40	242
Of other countries	30	–	30
Total	232	40	272

5032 **INSTITUT AGRONOMIQUE ET VÉTÉRINAIRE HASSAN II**

Avenue Maa El Aïnïne, Haut Agdal, Rabat
Telex: 31873
Telephone: 717-58
Directeur: M'hammed Sedrati
Secrétaire général: M. Larbi Firdawcy

Agriculture
Veterinary Sciences
Topography
Food Technology
Horticulture
S. of Agriculture
S. of Forestry
Agricultural Engineering
Agricultural Machinery
Sea Food Science
Landscape Architecture
Ce. for Lifelong Education
Also 35 departments for teaching and research.

Founded 1966 by Royal Decree as Institut d'Agronomie, reorganized 1968 and acquired present title 1972. A State institution. Financed by the State. Governing bodies: the Conseil d'administration, with the Minister of Agriculture as chairman; the Conseil de perfectionnement. Residential facilities for 2400 students.

Arrangements for co-operation with similar institutions in other countries, including: Belgium, Canada, Denmark, France, Tunisia, United Kingdom, U.S.A.

Academic Year: September to July (September-December; January-March; April-July).

Admission Requirements: Secondary school certificate (baccalauréat) and entrance examination. Age limit, 23 years.

Fees (Dirhan): 5000-6000 per annum, for students not supported by the government.

Language of Instruction: French.

Degrees and Diplomas: Professional titles of–Ingénieur, 4 yrs. Ingénieur d'Etat en Agronomie, 6 yrs. Docteur vétérinaire, 6yrs and thesis. Doctorat ès Sciences agronomiques.

Library: Central Library, and specialized libraries, *c.* 15,000 vols.

Publications: Hommes, Terre et Eaux (quarterly); Actes of IAV (quarterly).

Academic Staff, 1989-90: 350 (140).

Student Enrolment, 1989-90:

	Men	Women	Total
Of the country	1800	300	2100
Of other countries	200	15	215
Total	2000	315	2315

5033 **INSTITUT NATIONAL D'AMÉNAGEMENT ET D'URBANISME**

Avenue Maa El Aïnïne, Haut Agdal, Rabat
Telephone: 735-10

Town Planning and Development

Founded 1981. A State institution under the jurisdiction of the Ministry of Housing and Development.

Arrangements for co-operation with: University of Aix-Marseilles; University of Tours; University of Paris XII.

Academic Year: October to July (October-February; March-July).

Admission Requirements: University qualification and 4 yrs professional experience, and entrance examination.

Language of Instruction: French.

Degrees and Diplomas: Diplôme d'études supérieures en Aménagement et Urbanisme (D.E.S.A.U.) (3e cycle).

Academic Staff: c. 25.

Student Enrolment: c. 50.

5034 **ÉCOLE NATIONALE D'ARCHITECTURE**

Charia Errahba, Terre Plein, Hassan, Rabat
Telephone: (7) 224-27
Directeur: Saïd Tazi (1983-)

Architecture

Founded 1980.

Arrangements for co-operation with the Ecoles d'Architecture, Paris.

Academic Year: October to June (October-December; January-March; April-June).

Admission Requirements: Secondary school certificate (baccalauréat) and entrance examination.

Fees: None.

Language of Instruction: French.

Degrees and Diplomas: Diplôme, 6 yrs.

Library: 4000 vols.

Academic Staff, 1986-87: 18 (47).
Student Enrolment, 1986-87:

	Men	Women	Total
Of the country	255	57	312
Of other countries	31	9	40
Total	286	66	352

5035 **INSTITUT SUPÉRIEUR DE COMMERCE ET D'ADMINISTRATION DES ENTREPRISES**
Km. 9-5, Route de Nouasseur, Casablanca
Cables: Iscae Casablanca
Telephone: 34-55-01

Commerce
Business Administration
Lifelong Administration

Founded 1971. A State institution under the jurisdiction of the Ministry of Commerce and Industry. Financed bythe State. Residential facilities for students.

Academic Year: October to June (October-February; February-June).
Admission Requirements: Secondary school certificate (baccalauréat) and competitive entrance examination.
Fees: None.
Language of Instruction: French.
Degrees and Diplomas: Diplôme, 4 yrs. Diplôme (cycle supérieur de Gestion, business administration), a further 2 yrs and thesis.

5036 **INSTITUT DAR EL HADITH EL HASSANIA**
Institute of Islamic Studies
Rue de la Côte d'Ivoire, Rabat
Telephone: 225-87

Islamic Studies

Founded 1964. A State institution.

Academic Year: October to June (October-December; January-March; April-June).
Admission Requirements: Diploma of Licence from the Université Quaraouyine or equivalent, and entrance examination.
Language of Instruction: Arabic.
Degrees and Diplomas: Diplôme d'études supérieures en Sciences Islamiques (D.E.S.), 2 yrs. Doctorat d'Etat, by theses.
Library: c. 13,000 vols.
Publication: Revue (annually).
Academic Staff: c. 10 (10).
Student Enrolment: c. 60.

5037 **ÉCOLE NATIONALE FORESTIÈRE D'INGÉNIEURS TABRIQUET**
Tabriquet, B.P. 511, Salé
Telephone: 871-49
Directeur: M. Tijani

Forestry

Founded 1968. Under the jurisdiction of the Ministry of Agriculture and Agrarian Reform. Residential facilities for academic staff and students.

Academic Year: October to July.
Admission Requirements: Secondary school certificate (baccalauréat).
Fees: None.
Language of Instruction: French.
Degrees and Diplomas: Professional title of Ingénieur d'Application des Eaux et Forêts, 4 yrs.

5038 **INSTITUT ROYAL DE FORMATION DES CADRES DE LA JEUNESSE ET DES SPORTS**
Belle-Vue, Avenue Ibn Sina, Agdal, Rabat
Telephone: 726-73

Founded 1980.

5039 **CENTRE DE FORMATION DES CONSEILLERS EN PLANIFICATION DE L'ÉDUCATION**
Avenue Maa Al Aïnaïne, Haut Agdal, Rabat
Telephone: 30007
Directeur: Khallati Abdelati (1985-)

Educational Planning

Founded 1961, reorganized 1976, 1982 and 1985. A State institution responsible to the Direction centrale de laPlanification. Residential facilities for 200 students.

Academic Year: September to June (September-December; January-March; April-June).
Admission Requirements: University degree (D.E.U.G.).
Fees: None.
Languages of Instruction: Arabic and French.
Degrees and Diplomas: Diplôme de Conseiller, 2 yrs.
Library: 2400 vols.
Academic Staff, 1986-87: 17 (16).
Student Enrolment, 1986-87:

	Men	Women	Total
Of the country	190	10	200

5040 **CENTRE DE FORMATION DES CONTRÔLEURS DE LA PROPRIÉTÉ FONCIÈRE**
c/o I.A.V. Hassan II, B.P. 704, Rabat

Land Ownership

5041 **CENTRE NATIONAL DE FORMATION DES INSPECTEURS DE L'ENSEIGNEMENT**
Bab Tamesna, Rabat
Telephone: 301-96
Directeur: Mohammed Yousfi Malki (1980-)

School Inspection

Founded 1969.

Academic Year: September to June (September-December; January-March; April-June).
Admission Requirements: 4-7 yrs teaching experience and entrance examination.
Fees: None.
Language of Instruction: Arabic.
Degrees and Diplomas: Diplôme.
Library: 3450 vols.
Academic Staff, 1986-87: 37 (16).
Student Enrolment, 1986-87:

	Men	Women	Total
Of the country	354	37	391

5042 **ÉCOLE DES SCIENCES DE L'INFORMATION**
Avenue Maa Al Aïnïne, B.P. 6204, Haut Agdal, Rabat
Telephone: 77-49-49-04
Fax: 77-02-32
Directeur: Mohamed Benjelloun (1978-)
Secrétaire général Mohamed Iaazane

Library Science
Documentation
Archives

Founded 1974, under the authority of the Ministry of Planning.

Arrangements for co-operation with the Universities of: Sheffield; Wisconsin; Montreal; Pittsburgh; Boras, Sweden; King Abdulaziz; Algiers. Pratt Institute, USA. Also similar institutions in France.

Academic Year: October to June (October-December; January-March; April-June).
Admission Requirements: Secondary school certificate (baccalauréat) or equivalent, or 5 yrs professional experience, and entrance examination.
Fees: None.
Languages of Instruction: French and Arabic.
Degrees and Diplomas: Diplôme of–Informaticien, 4 yrs; Informaticien spécialisé, a further 2 yrs.
Library: 10,000 vols.
Publication: La Revue de l'E.S.I.

Academic Staff, 1989-90:

Rank	Full-time	Part-time
Maîtres de conférences	4	–
Maîtres-Assistants	11	–
Assistants	3	–
Enseignants vacataires	–	35
Total	18	35

Student Enrolment, 1989-90:

	Men	Women	Total
Of the country	155	180	335

5043 **INSTITUT SUPÉRIEUR DE JOURNALISME**
Avenue Maa Al Aïnïne, B.P.6205, Haut Agdal, Rabat
Telex: ISJ 32786 M
Telephone: 733-40
Fax: 727-89 isj
Directeur: Mohamed Lamouri
Sécretaire général: Mounir Jellal

Journalism
Audio-visual Studies
General Education

Founded 1970. A State institution under the jurisdiction of the Ministry of Information.

Arrangements for co-operation with: Institut français de Presse et des Sciences de l'Information; Institut de Presse et des Sciences de l'Infor-mation, Tunis.

Academic Year: September to July (September-December; January-March; May-December; April-July).

Admission Requirements: University degree (Licence or equivalent).

Fees: None.

Languages of Instruction: Arabic and French.

Degrees and Diplomas: Diplôme des Etudes supérieures de Journalisme, 2 yrs.

Library: Bibliothèque de l'Institut.

Special Facilities (Museums, etc.): Movie-room; Television Studio; Radio Studio.

Publication: IS. Journal (School newspaper in Arabic and French).

Academic Staff, 1990: 23 (22).

Student Enrolment, 1990:

	Men	Women	Total
Of the country	77	45	122
Of other countries	30	3	33
Total	107	48	155

5044 **INSTITUT NATIONAL D'ÉTUDES JUDICIAIRES**
Avenue Beni Snassen, Haut Souissi, Rabat
Telephone: 502-53

Law

Founded 1970.

5045 **INSTITUT SUPÉRIEUR D'ÉTUDES MARITIMES**
Km. 7, Route d'El Jadida, Casablanca
Telephone: 34-44-45

Marine Engineering

Founded 1957.

5046 **ÉCOLE NATIONALE DE L'INDUSTRIE MINÉRALE**
Rue Abderrahman El Ghafiqui, Rabat-Agdal
Telephone: 713-60; 716-67

Mineral Technology

Founded 1972. A State institution responsible to the Ministry of Energy and Mines. Residential facilities for 614 students.

Arrangements for co-operation with similar institutions in: Paris; Besançon; Nancy; Compiègne; Lyon; Toulouse; Louvain; Montréal.

Academic Year: October to June.

Admission Requirements: Secondary school certificate (baccalauréat) and entrance examination.

Fees (Dirhams): Registration, 150 per annum.

Language of Instruction: French.

Degrees and Diplomas: Diplôme–d'Ingénieur d'application, 4 yrs; d'Ingénieur d'Etat, 6 yrs.

Library: c. 7000 vols.

Publication: Publications sur les colloques, séminaires et conférences.

Press or Publishing House: Imprimerie.

Academic Staff: c. 80 (15).

Student Enrolment: c. 480.

5047 **ÉCOLE NORMALE SUPÉRIEURE**
Route d'El Jadida, Casablanca
Telephone: 23-22-77
Directeur: Rachid Cherkaoui
Secrétaire général: Abdelaziz Benaicha

D. of Education Sciences (secondary level)
Head: Ahmed Al Motamassik; *staff* 14
D. of Mathematics and Computer Sciences
Head: Azhari Abdelhak; *staff* 12
D. of Physical Education and Sport
Head: Michel Marcos; *staff* 30
D. of Biology and Geology
Head: Abdelatif Belkouri; *staff* 10
D. of Physics and Chemistry
Head: Bourak Benachou; *staff* 17
D. of Languages (Arabic, French, English)
Head: Mohamed El Askary; *staff* 7

Founded 1978, under the supervision of the Ministry of Education.

Arrangements for co-operation with the Institut national de Sport et de l'Education physique.

Academic Year: September to June (September-December; January-March; April-June).

Admission Requirements: Secondary school certificate (baccalauréat).

Languages of Instruction: French and Arabic.

Degrees and Diplomas: Diplôme, 4 yrs. Diplôme (1st and 2nd cycle).

Library: Central library, 6181 vols.

Academic Staff, 1989-90: 93.

Student Enrolment, 1989-90:

	Men	Women	Total
Of the country	402	34	436

5048 **ÉCOLE NORMALE SUPÉRIEURE**
Route Bensouda, Fès
Telephone: 20
Directeur: Saidi El Kebir (1981-)

Teacher Training

Founded 1978. A State institution responsible to the Ministry of Education.

Arrangements for co-operation with: Université libre de Bruxelles; Université de Bordeaux I; Université de Nice; Université de Paris VI; Université de Toulouse.

Academic Year: September to May.

Admission Requirements: Secondary school certificate (baccalauréat) and entrance examination.

Fees: None.

Languages of Instruction: French and Arabic.

Degrees and Diplomas: Diplôme, 4 yrs. Doctorat de 3e cycle, 3 yrs.

Library: Central Library, 11,300 vols.

Academic Staff, 1986-87: 104.

Student Enrolment, 1986-87:

	Men	Women	Total
Of the country	320	260	580

5049 **ÉCOLE NORMALE SUPÉRIEURE**
Cité Mohammedia, Daoudiate, Marrakech

Teacher Training

5050 **ÉCOLE NORMALE SUPÉRIEURE**
Boîte postale S/60, Meknès
Telephone: (05) 229-50

Teacher Training

Founded 1983. A State institution responsible to the Ministry of Education.

Arrangements for co-operation with: Ecole normale supérieure de Fontenay-aux-Roses; Ecole normale supérieure de Saint-Cloud; Université de Grenoble.

Academic Year: September to June (September-December; January-March; April-June).

Admission Requirements: Secondary school certificate (baccalauréat).

Fees: None.
Languages of Instruction: French and Arabic.
Degrees and Diplomas: Diplôme (1er et 2ème cycles).
Library: c. 2500 vols.
Publication: Cahiers.
Academic Staff: c. 40.
Student Enrolment: c. 410.

5051 **ÉCOLE NORMALE SUPÉRIEURE (ENSEIGNEMENT TECHNIQUE)**
Avenue Maa El Aïnïne, Haut Agdal, Rabat

Teacher Training (Technical)

5052 **ÉCOLE NORMALE SUPÉRIEURE DE TAKADDOUM-RABAT**
Avenue Oued Akrach, Takaddoum-Rabat
Telephone: 500-25

Teacher Training

Founded 1978. A State institution responsible to the Ministry of Education.

Arrangements for co-operation with several French universities.

Academic Year: September to June (September-December; January-March; April-June).

Admission Requirements: Secondary school certificate (baccalauréat) and entrance examination.

Fees: None.
Languages of Instruction: French, Arabic and English.
Degrees and Diplomas: Diplôme (1er-3ème cycles), 4 yrs.
Academic Staff: c. 160.
Student Enrolment: c. 1180.

5053 **ÉCOLE NORMALE SUPÉRIEURE SOUISSI**
Zankat Cadi Ahmed Bennani, Rabat

Teacher Training

5054 **ÉCOLE DE PERFECTIONNEMENT DE CADRES DU MINISTÈRE DE L'INTÉRIEUR**
Base Aérienne, Kénitra
Telephone: 32-18

Diplomatic Studies

Founded 1964.

5055 **INSTITUT NATIONAL DES POSTES ET TÉLÉCOMMUNICATIONS**
Maa Al Aïnïne, Haut Agdal, Rabat
Telephone: 730-77

Telecommunication Engineering

Founded 1971.

5056 **INSTITUT NATIONAL DE STATISTIQUE ET D'ÉCONOMIE APPLIQUÉE**
B.P. 6217, Rabat-Instituts, Rabat
Telex: 32719 M
Telephone: 709-15/23/26
Directeur: Mustapha Benykhlef (1977-)

Statistics
Economics
Computer Sciences
Demography and Human Sciences
Mathematics

Founded 1961 as Centre de Formation des Ingénieurs des Travaux Statistiques, acquired present status and title 1965. A State institution responsible to the Ministry of Planning. Residential facilities for 567 students.

Academic Year: September to July (September-December; January-March; April-July).

Admission Requirements: Secondary school certificate (baccalauréat) and entrance examination.

Languages of Instruction: French and Arabic.

Degrees and Diplomas: Professional titles of–Ingénieur d'Application de la Statistique; Analyste, 4 yrs. Ingénieur Statisticien-Economiste, 2 yrs after Licence or title of Ingénieur and 3 yrs professional experience in certain cases. Also lower level qualifications.

Library: 15,000 vols.
Publication: Revue.
Academic Staff, 1989-90:

Rank	Full-time	Part-time
Professeurs	13	3
Maîtres de conférences	5	1
Maîtres-Assistants	27	38
Assistants	6	11
Total	51	53

Student Enrolment, 1989-90:

	Men	Women	Total
Of the country	366	143	509
Of other countries	52	6	58
Total	418	149	567

5057 **HIGH TECH**
Angle rue Fès-Meknès-Quartier de la Résidence, Rabat
Telephone: 333-31
Directeur: Anis Balafrej (1985-)

Computer Sciences

Founded 1985 by the Société Maroc Technologie. A private institution.

Academic Year: October to June.
Admission Requirements: Secondary school certificate (baccalauréat).
Fees (Dirham): 16,200 per annum.
Languages of Instruction: French and English.
Degrees and Diplomas: Associate, 2 yrs. Licence, 4 yrs.
Academic Staff, 1986-87: – (9).
Student Enrolment, 1986-87:

	Men	Women	Total
Of the country	16	4	20

5058 **INSTITUT SUPÉRIEUR DE TOURISME**
13, avenue Allal Ben Abdallah, Tanger
Telephone: 394-29

Tourism

Founded 1972.

5059 **INSTITUT NATIONAL DES TRAVAILLEURS SOCIAUX**
Tanger Correspondence: Ministère des Affaires sociales, 15 rue Marrakech, Rabat

Social Work

Founded 1983.

5060 **ÉCOLE HASSANIA DES TRAVAUX PUBLICS**
Km. 6, Route d'El Jadida, B.P. 8108, Casablanca
Telephone: 36-47-27

Civil Engineering

Founded 1971.

MOZAMBIQUE

5061 ***UNIVERSIDADE EDUARDO MONDLANE**
Praça 25 de Junho, P.O. Box 257, Maputo
Telephone: 27851
Reitor: Fernando dos Reis Ganhão (1975-)

F. of Law
F. of Economics
F. of Agricultural Sciences
F. of Biology
F. of Geology
F. of Medicine
F. of Veterinary Medicine
F. of Mathematics
F. of Arts
F. of Physics
F. of Electrical Engineering
F. of Civil Engineering
F. of Chemistry
F. of Mechanical Engineering
I. of Scientific Research
Ce. of African Studies
Ce. of Ecology
Ce. of Communication Studies
Ce. of Psychopedagogics

Founded 1962 as Estudios Gerais Universitários, became Universidade de Lourenço Marques 1968, acquired present title 1976. A State institution responsible to the Ministry of Education and Culture. Governing body: the Conselho Universitario. Residential facilities for *c.* 45 academic staff and *c.* 210 students.

Academic Year: February to December (February-August; August-December).

Admission Requirements: Secondary school certificate or equivalent, and entrance examination.

Language of Instruction: Portuguese.

Degrees and Diplomas: Bacharelato in–Law, 2 yrs; Economics; Letters; History; Geography; Physics; Mathematics; Chemistry; Geology; Agriculture; Engineering; Biology, 3 yrs. Licenciatura in above fields, 2 yrs after Bacharelato; Veterinary Medicine, 5 yrs.

Libraries: c. 68,000 vols; faculty libraries.

Special Facilities (Museums, etc.): Natural History Museum.

Academic Staff: c. 260.

Student Enrolment: c. 840.

MYANMAR

Universities and University Institutions

5062 **ARTS AND SCIENCE UNIVERSITY OF MANDALAY**
University P.O., Mandalay
Telephone: 659

F. of Arts
F. of Science

Founded 1958 as separate university. Formerly a college of the University of Rangoon, originated as an intermediate college 1923, and an agricultural college 1938. Recognized 1964 and faculties of Medicine and Agriculture detached as separate institutions. Financed by the Central Government and responsible to the Ministry of Education.

Academic Year: July to March (July-December; January-March).

Admission Requirements: Secondary school certificate.

Language of Instruction: Myanmar.

Degrees and Diplomas: Bachelor of–Arts; Science, 4 yrs; Arts (Honours); Science (Honours), 5 yrs. Master of Arts or Science, at least 1 yr after Bachelor (Honours).

Academic Staff: c. 430.

Student Enrolment: c. 7000.

5063 **MOULMEIN UNIVERSITY**
Moulmein
Telephone: (32) 21180

Founded 1953.

5064 **ARTS AND SCIENCE UNIVERSITY OF YANGON**
University P.O., Yangon
Telephone: Auto 31144

F. of Arts
F. of Science

Founded 1920 incorporating Government College, Rangoon, and Judson College, both established in the late 19th century and formerly affiliated to the University of Calcutta. The university was closed during the Japanese occupation of Burma and reopened as University of Rangoon 1946. Reorganized 1964 and faculties of Social Science, Medicine, Forestry, Education, and Engineering, and college of Veterinary Science detached as separate institutions. Financed by the Central Government and responsible to the Ministry of Education. Residential facilities for members of the academic staff and students.

Academic Year: July to March (July-December; January-March).

Admission Requirements: Secondary school certificate.

Language of Instruction: Myanmar.

Degrees and Diplomas: Bachelor of–Arts; Science, 4 yrs; Arts (Honours); Science (Honours), 5 yrs; Law, 2 yrs after Bachelor of Arts. Master of–Arts or Science, at least 1 yr after Bachelor (Honours).

Academic Staff: c. 430.

Student Enrolment: c. 7200.

5065 **INSTITUTE OF AGRICULTURE**
Ye Zin, Pyinmana
Telephone: 98

Agriculture

Founded 1924 as College and Research Institute. Reorganized 1937 as college of former University of Rangoon. Became Faculty of University of Rangoon 1946 and Faculty of University of Mandalay on its establishment in 1958. Detached as independent institute following reorganization of university education 1964. Financed by the Central Government and responsible to the Ministry of Education and the Central Academic and Administrative councils of the Universities. Governing bodies: the Academic Board; the Administrative Board. Some residential facilities for academic staff and students.

Academic Year: November to September (November-March; May-September).

Admission Requirements: Secondary school certificate or equivalent.

Languages of Instruction: Myanmar and English.

Degrees and Diplomas: Bachelor of Agriculture, B.Ag. Master of Agricultural Science, M.Ag.Sc..

Academic Staff: c. 100.

Student Enrolment: c. 1500.

5066 **INSTITUTE OF ANIMAL HUSBANDRY AND VETERINARY SCIENCE**
Yangon

Animal Husbandry and Veterinary Science

Founded 1964. Formerly part of University of Rangoon.

5067 **RANGOON INSTITUTE OF TECHNOLOGY**
Gyogon, Insein
Telephone: 40526

D. of Mechanical Engineering
D. of Civil Engineering
D. of Electrical Engineering
D. of Chemical Engineering
D. of Mining Engineering
D. of Petroleum Engineering
D. of Textile Engineering
D. of Metallurgy
D. of Architecture
D. of Geology

Founded 1924 as department of the former University of Rangoon. Became faculty 1947. Detached as independent institute following reorganization of university education 1964. Financed by the Central Government and responsible to the Ministry of Education. Governing bodies: the Senate; the Administrative Board. Residential facilities for academic staff and students.

Academic Year: October to July (October-March; May-July).

Admission Requirements: Secondary school certificate.

Languages of Instruction: Myanmar and English.

Degrees and Diplomas: Bachelor of–Engineering, B.E.; Architecture, B.Arch., 6 yrs. Master of Engineering, M.E., a further 2 yrs. Also Diplomas in Food Technology.

Library: c. 35,000 vols.

Academic Staff: c. 130.

Student Enrolment: c. 2760.

5068 **WORKERS' COLLEGE**
Botataung Pagoda Road, Yangon

D. of Arts
D. of Science

Founded 1964. Formerly University for Adult Education founded 1947.

Student Enrolment: c. 3000.

5069 **AKYAB COLLEGE**
Akyab

Founded 1973.

5070 **BASSEIN COLLEGE**
Bassein

Founded 1958.

5071 **MAGWE COLLEGE**
Magwe

Founded 1958.

5072 **THWAR BET SAINGYA SEI THEKATHO**
Institute of Dental Medicine
Schwedagon Padoga Road, Yangon
Telephone: 70866

Dentistry

Founded 1964, acquired present status 1974. A State institution responsible to the Ministry of Health. Governing body: the Board.

Academic Year: November to September (November-March; April-September).

Admission Requirements: Secondary school certificate or foreign equivalent.

Language of Instruction: English.

Degrees and Diplomas: Bachelor of Dental Surgery, B.D.S.

Special Facilities (Museums, etc.): Pathology Museum.

Academic Staff: c. 40.

Student Enrolment: c. 200.

5073 **INSTITUTE OF ECONOMICS**
University P.O., Yangon 11041
Rector: Khin Maung Nyunt
Pro-Rector: Than Nyun

D. of Economics
Head: U Myat Thein; *staff* 51 (2)
D. of Applied Economics
Head: Daw Khin Lay; *staff* 23
D. of Commerce
Head: U Tin Htut; *staff* 67 (8)
D. of Management Studies
Head: Daw Khin Than Kywe; *staff* 18
D. of Statistics
Head: U Ko Ko; *staff* 74 (2)

Founded 1964. Formerly part of University of Rangoon. Under the jurisdiction of the Ministry of Higher Education. Governing body: the Board of Management. Residential facilities for academic staff and students.

Academic Year: November to September (November-March; June-September).

Admission Requirements: Secondary school certificate.

Fees (Kyats): 360 per annum.

Languages of Instruction: Myanmar and English.

Degrees and Diplomas: Bachelor of–Economics; Commerce. Honours Degrees. Postgraduate Master. Diplomas in–Management and Administration; Economical Planning; Statistics.

Library: 519,000 vols.

Academic Staff, 1990:

Rank	Full-time	Part-time
Professors	4	–
Associate Professors	1	–
Lecturers	56	12
Assistant Lecturers	60	–
Tutors	112	–
Total	233	12

Student Enrolment, 1990:

	Men	Women	Total
Of the country	1659	3736	5395

5074 **INSTITUTE OF EDUCATION**
University P.O., Yangon
Telephone: 30919

Teacher Training (Education, Liberal Arts, Sciences)

Founded 1930, a Constituent College of former University of Rangoon, became Faculty of Education 1946 and detached as independent institute following reorganization of University 1964. Financed by the Central Government and responsible to the Ministry of Education and the Central Academic Administrative Councils of the Universities. Governing bodies: the Academic Board; the Administrative Board. Residential facilities for academic staff and for students from outside Rangoon.

Academic Year: August to July (September-December; January-April; May-July).

Admission Requirements: Secondary school certificate.

Language of Instruction: Myanmar.

Degrees and Diplomas: Bachelor of Education, B.Ed., 5 yrs. Master of Education, M.Ed., a further 2 yrs. Diploma in Education, Dip.Ed., 1 yr (postgraduate).

Library: Institute Library.

Publication: Magazine (annually).

Academic Staff: c. 120.

Student Enrolment: c. 2100 (Also *c.* 400 external students).

5075 **INSTITUTE OF MEDICINE**
Mandalay
Telephone: 1012

Medicine
D. of Adult Education (including Retraining)

Founded 1954 as branch faculty, became faculty of University of Mandalay 1958 and acquired present title and status 1964. A State institution. Some residential facilities for academic staff and students.

Academic Year: September to August (September-December; January-April; May-August).

Admission Requirements: Secondary school certificate.

Languages of Instruction: Myanmar and English.

Degrees and Diplomas: Bachelor of Medicine and Surgery, M.B.B.S., 6 ½ yrs. Master of Science, M.Sc., 2 yrs, postgraduate.

Library: c. 17,210 vols.

Academic Staff: c. 190.

Student Enrolment: c. 900 (Also *c.* 5 external students).

5076 **INSTITUTE OF MEDICINE I**
Godwin Road, Yangon

Medicine

Founded 1964. Formerly part of University of Rangoon.

5077 **INSTITUTE OF MEDICINE II**
Mingaladon P.O., Rangoon

Medicine

Founded 1964. Formerly part of University of Rangoon.

5078 **MYITKYINA COLLEGE**
Myitkyina

Founded 1963.

5079 **TAUNGGYI COLLEGE**
Taunggyi

Founded 1961.

Other Institutions

Technical Institutions

5080 **GOVERNMENT TECHNICAL INSTITUTE**
Insein

Engineering

Founded 1890.

5081 **GOVERNMENT TECHNICAL INSTITUTE**
Kalaw

Engineering

Founded 1968.

5082 **GOVERNMENT TECHNICAL INSTITUTE**
Mandalay

Engineering

Founded 1955.

Universities and University Institutions

Professional Education

5083 **STATE AGRICULTURAL INSTITUTE**
Pyinmana

Agriculture
Founded 1954.

5084 **STATE AGRICULTURAL INSTITUTE**
Thaton

Agriculture
Founded 1967.

5085 **INSTITUTE FOR FOREIGN LANGUAGES**
University Avenue, Yangon

Foreign Languages
Founded 1963.

5086 **INSTITUTE OF PARAMEDICAL SCIENCES**
General Hospital Compound, Yangon

Paramedical Sciences
Founded 1964.

Other Institutions

Teacher Training

5087 **STATE TEACHERS' TRAINING SCHOOL**
Bogalay

Teacher Training
Founded 1970.

5088 **STATE TEACHERS' TRAINING SCHOOL**
Kyaukpyu

Teacher Training
Founded 1953.

5089 **STATE TEACHERS' TRAINING COLLEGE**
Mandalay

Teacher Training
Founded 1952.

5090 **STATE TEACHERS' TRAINING SCHOOL**
Meiktila

Teacher Training
Founded 1953.

5091 **STATE TEACHERS' TRAINING COLLEGE**
CMoulmein

Teacher Training
Founded 1953.

5092 **STATE TEACHERS' TRAINING SCHOOL**
Myaungmya

Teacher Training
Founded 1953.

5093 **STATE TEACHERS' TRAINING SCHOOL**
Myitkyina

Teacher Training
Founded 1962.

5094 **STATE TEACHERS' TRAINING SCHOOL**
Prome

Teacher Training
Founded 1968.

5095 **STATE TEACHERS' TRAINING COLLEGE**
Kanbe, Yangon

Teacher Training
Founded 1947.

5096 **STATE TEACHERS' TRAINING SCHOOL**
Thinkangyung, Yangon

Teacher Training
Founded 1969.

5097 **STATE TEACHERS' TRAINING SCHOOL**
Sagaing

Teacher Training
Founded 1968.

5098 **STATE TEACHERS' TRAINING SCHOOL**
Taunggyi

Teacher Training
Founded 1964.

5099 **STATE TEACHERS' TRAINING SCHOOL**
Thegon, Prome District

Teacher Training
Founded 1965.

5100 **STATE TEACHERS' TRAINING SCHOOL**
Toungoo

Teacher Training
Founded 1967.

NAMIBIA

5101 ***THE ACADEMY**

13 Storch Street, Windhoek 9000
Telex: (50) 908-7271
Telephone: (61) 307-9111
Rector and Vice-Chancellor: A.J.H. Buitendacht
Registrar: I.F.W. Steyn

University of Namibia
Principal: H. Schlagbauer
F. of Arts (African Languages, Afrikaans, English, Biblical Studies, Geography, German, History, Library and Information Sciences, Psychology, Social Work, Sociology)
Dean: B.A. Harlech-Jones; *staff* 37
F. of Economics and Management
Dean: G.K.H. Tötemeyer; *staff* 14
F. of Science
Dean: A.C. Marsh; *staff* 21
F. of Management Science
F. of Education
Dean: G.H. Lübbert; *staff* 10
F. of Health Sciences (Nursing)
Dean (Acting): A.S.B. van Dyk; *staff* 31
Technikon
Principal: A.V. du Plessis
Curriculum Group of Management and Administration
Director: B.G. Hollick; *staff* 8
Curriculum Group of Agriculture and Nature Conservation
Director: W. Jankowitz; *staff* 7
Curriculum Group of Accountancy and Information Systems
Director: I.R. Thompson; *staff* 5
Curriculum Group of Secretarial Training
Director Mrs F.A. Du Preez; *staff* 4
Curriculum Group of Legal Training
Director (Acting): I.R. Thompson; *staff* 3
Curriculum Group of Communicative Training
Director: Mrs A. Geel; *staff* 4
C. for Out of School Training
Principal: Svan Staden
Technical Sec.
Head (Acting): J.v D. West Huizen; *staff* 13
General and Commercial Sec.
Head (Acting): Mrs M. De Klerk; *staff* 13
Bureau of Research
Director: E. Stals; *staff* 3
I. for Social and Economic Research (NISER)
Director: G.K.H. Tötemeyer; *staff* 2
Also Teaching Hospital.

Founded 1981 under the Academy for Tertiary Education Act. An autonomous institution comprising the University of Namibia, Technikon Namibia, and the College for Out of School Training. Primarily funded by the State withsupplementary funds from student fees and private sector support. Governing bodies: the Council; the Senate; the Board of Studies. Residential facilities for students in 4 hostels.

Academic Year: February to November (February-June; July-November).

Admission Requirements: Matriculation Certificate or equivalent issued by the Joint Matriculation Board. Diploma courses, Senior Certificate.

Fees (Rand): (University) 2500-300 per annum; (Technikon) 1000-1300; (College) 800-1000.

Language of Instruction: English.

Degrees and Diplomas: Certificates (College for Out of School Training), 1-2 yrs. National Diplomas (Technikon), 3-4 yrs. Diplomas (University) 1-4 yrs. Bachelor of–Arts; Science; Commerce; Primary Education; Curationis Progression Praxis, 3-4 yrs.

Library: 33,000 vols.

Academic Staff, 1988-89: 164.

Student Enrolment, 1988-89:

	Men	Women	Total
Of the country	1110	2202	3312
Of other countries	100	136	236
Total	1210	2338	3548*

*Also 1412 distance teaching students.

NEPAL

5102 ***TRIBHUVAN VISHWAVIDYALAYA**

Tribhuvan University
Kirtipur, Kathmandu
Cables: Trivarsity
Telephone: 15313
Rector: Chandra Prasad Gorkhali

F. of Humanities and Social Sciences
F. of Science
F. of Commerce, Business and Public Administration
F. of Law
F. of Education
I. of Forestry
I. of Engineering
I. of Agriculture and Animal Husbandry
I. of Medicine
Economic Development and Administration Research Ce.
Research Ce. for Applied Science and Technology
Research Ce. for Nepal and Asian Studies
Educational Innovation and Development Research Ce.

Founded 1958 as a teaching and affiliating university. Reorganized 1971. An autonomous institution financed bythe State. Governing bodies: the Senate; the Syndicate; the Academic Council. Some residential facilities for students.

Academic Year: July to June.

Admission Requirements: Secondary school certificate and entrance examination.

Languages of Instruction: English and Nepali.

Degrees and Diplomas: Proficiency certificate, 2-3 yrs, Bachelor in–Education; Humanities and Social Sciences; Commerce and Business Administration; Science; Animal Husbandry, 4 yrs; Law; Engineering, 5 yrs; Medicine, 6 ½ yrs. Master in–Commerce and Business Administration; Science; Animal Husbandry; Engineering; Medicine, a further 2 yrs and 1 yr National Development Service. Doctor, Ph.D. Also postgraduate degree in Medicine.

Library: 144,145 vols.

Academic Staff, 1986-87: 4164.

Student Enrolment: c. 50,000.

NETHERLANDS

Universities and University Institutions

5103 ***UNIVERSITEIT VAN AMSTERDAM**

University of Amsterdam
Maagdenhuis, Spui 21, 1012 WX Amsterdam
Telex: 16526 UNASD
Telephone: (31-20) 5259111
Fax: (31-20) 5252136
President: J.K.M. Gevers (1988-)
Secretary-General: R.H.T. Bleijerveld

F. of Theology
Dean: K.A. Deurloo; *staff* 28
F. of Law
Dean: J.A. Ankum; *staff* 244
F. of Medicine
Dean: A.E. Becker; *staff* 602
F. of Mathematics and Information Sciences
Dean: J.F.K. van Benthem; *staff* 114
F. of Letters (Arts)
Dean: J.C.H. Blom; *staff* 604
F. of Economics and Econometrics
Dean: H. Nevolecker; *staff* 107
F. of Physics and Astronomy
Dean: E.P.J. van den Heuvel; *staff* 192
F. of Chemistry
Dean: A.J.M. van Renswoude; *staff* 340
F. of Biology
Dean: L.A. Grivell; *staff* 240
F. of Psychology
Dean: G.J. Mellenbergh; *staff* 165
F. of Education
Dean: G. Snel; *staff* 131
F. of Environmental Studies
Dean: G.J. Borger; *staff* 193

Also more than 150 clinics, laboratories, institutes, and seminars of the different faculties.

Founded 1632 as 'Athenaeum Illustre', became university 1876. Responsible to municipal authorities until 1961,now independent. Financially supported by the State. Governing bodies: the Universitiesraad (University Council), comprising 35 members; the College van Bestuur (Executive Board). Residential facilities for students.

Arrangement for co-operation with the Universities of: Cairo; Cusco and Puno, Peru; Nicaragua; Benin; Hanoi; Bir Zeit; Philippines; Suriname; Antilles, Curaçao. National University, Costa Rica; University of the Andes, Colombia; Autonomous University of Mexico; Moi University, Kenya; Gadia Mata University, Indonesia; University Mohammed V, Morocco; University of Warsaw; University Eövös Loránd, Budapest; University of Economics, Budapest; University of Bucharest; Inter-University Centre of Post-Graduate Studies, Dubrovnik; University of Leningrad; Moscow University; Herzen Institute, Leningrad; Tartu University; European Network of Capital Cities Universities; University of Hull; Autonomous University of Madrid; University of Salamanca; Université Louis Pasteur, Strasbourg; The City of London University; University College, London; University of Oslo; Tufts University, Boston; University of Minnesota, Minneapolis; New School of Social Research, New York; San Francisco State University; Columbia University, New York; Montana State University; University of West Florida; University of Nebraska;International Student Exchange Program (ISEP); Hebrew University, Jerusalem; University of Tel Aviv; Xiamen University; Nanjing University; University of Technology, Shanghai; Shenyang Institute of Metal Research; Beijing University. Participates in the ERASMUS programme.

Academic Year: September to July (September-December; January-April; April-July).

Admission Requirements: Secondary school certificate in subjects appropriate to faculty requirements (diploma eindexamen Gymnasium A or B, or Atheneum A or B) or equivalent.

Fees (Guilders): Registration, 1750, per annum.

Languages of Instruction: Dutch and English.

Degrees and Diplomas: In all faculties Doctoraal examen leading, in Law, to degree of Meester in de Rechten, mr., 4 yrs, and in all other fields to doctorandus, drs., 5 yrs. Professional qualifications–Arts, medicine; Tandarts, dentistry, atleast 2 yrs after relevant doctorandus. Doctorate, by thesis, in all fields.

Libraries: Central Library, *c.* 3,000,000 vols; libraries of faculties and institutes.

Special Facilities (Museums, etc.): Allard Pierson Museum (Archaeology); Zoology Museum; Geology Museum; University Museum (History of the University).

Publications: Studiegids; Folia Civitatis; School en Universiteit.

Academic Staff, 1989-90:

Rank	Full-time
Professoren	360
Others	2400
Total	2760

Student Enrolment, 1989-90:

	Men	Women	Total
Of the country	12,000	13,000	25,000

5104 **VRIJE UNIVERSITEIT, AMSTERDAM**

Free University, Amsterdam
De Boelelaan 1105, 1081 HV Amsterdam
Telex: 11329 DPVVUNL
Telephone: (31-20) 5489222
Rector: Cornelis Datema
Secretaris College van Bestuur: D.M. Schut

F. of Theology
Dean: H. Heene
F. of Law
Dean: J.E. Doek
F. of Medicine
Dean: N.F.Th. Arts
F. of Dentistry
Dean: P.F. vander Stelt
F. of Mathematics and Science
Dean: J. Oosterhoff
F. of Arts (including Archaeology)
Dean: G.E. Booij
F. of Economics and Econometrics
Dean: A.H.Q.M. Merkies
F. of Social Sciences (including Education and Political Science)
Dean: J. Tennekes
F. of Philosophy
Dean: J.A. Aertsen
F. of Earth Sciences
Dean: Th.W.M. Hevelt
F. of Physical Education
Dean: H.C.G. Kemper
F. of Physics and Astronomy
Dean: E. Boeker
F. of Chemistry
Dean: E.J. Baerends
F. of Biology
Dean: R. Kraaijenhof

F. of Psychology and Pedagogics
Dean: J.F. Orfebeke

5105 **TECHNISCHE UNIVERSITEIT DELFT**
Delft University of Technology
Julianalaan 134, 2628 BL, Delft
Telex: 38151 BHTHD NL
Telephone: (015) 789111
Rector: J.M. Dirken (1984-89)
Secretaris: P.A. Vuurens

F. of Mathematics and Computer Sciences
Dean: D.H. Wolbers
F. of Philosophy and Humanities
Dean: R. Roe
F. of Civil Engineering
Dean: H.P.S. van Lohuizen
F. of Geodesy
Dean: J.E. Alberda
F. of Architecture (including Town Planning)
Dean: L.M.K.J. van Wilder
F. of Mechanical Engineering
Dean: G. Prins
F. of Electrical Engineering
Dean: H.R. van Nauta Lemke
F. of Chemical Engineering and Chemistry
Dean: L. de Galan
F. of Mining
Dean: D. Price
F. of Applied Physics
Dean: J.J.J. Kokkedee
F. of Naval Architecture and Marine Engineering
Dean: C. Gallin
F. of Aerospace Engineering
Dean: H. Wittenberg
F. of Metallurgy and Materials Engineering
Dean: G. den Ouden
F. of Industrial Design Engineering
Dean: R. den Buurman
Nuclear Reacter I.
Computer Ce.
Interfaculty for Graduate Studies in Architecture and Town Planning
Interfaculty for Graduate Studies in Civil Engineering

Founded 1905 as Technische Hogeschool in succession to the Royal Academy for civil engineers, founded 1842 and the Polytechnische School, founded 1864. Acquired present title 1986. A State institution financed by the government. Governing bodies: the Universiteitsraad (University Council); the College van Bestuur (Executive Board).

Special arrangements for co-operation with: Technion-Israel Institute of Technology; Tsinghua University, Beijing; Technical University of Berlin; Chulalongkorn University, Bangkok; Universidad Politécnica de Nicaragua; Eduardo Mondlane University, Maputo; Federal University of Technology, Oweri; Technical University of Hanoi;University of Zambia.

Academic Year: September to June (August-October; November-January; January-March; April-June).

Admission Requirements: Secondary school certificate in appropriate subjects (diploma eindexamen Gymnasium B and Atheneum B), or foreign equivalent.

Fees (Guilders): Tuition, 1650 per annum.

Language of Instruction: Dutch.

Degrees and Diplomas: Diploma of–Wiskundig -ingenieur, mathematics; Civiel-, civil engineering; Geodetisch-, surveying; Bouwkundig-, architecture; Werktuigkundig-, mechanical engineering; Elektrotech-nisch-, electrical engineering; Sheikundig-, chemical engineering; Mijn-, mining; Natuurkundig-, physical engineering; Scheepsbouwkundig-, naval architecture; Vliegtuigbouwkundig-, aeronautical engineering; Metaalkundig-, metallurgy; Ingenieur industriële vormgever, industrial design; Materials Science; Computer Sciences, 4-6 yrs. The degree of Doctor is awarded on the basis of a thesis or experimental work following the diploma.

Libraries: Central Library, *c.* 460,000 vols; department libraries.

Special Facilities (Museums, etc.): History of Technology Museum.

Publications: Delft Integraal (quarterly); departmental publications.

Press or Publishing House: University Press.

Academic Staff, 1986-87:

Rank	
Hoogleraren	522
Lektoren	1110
Wetenschappelijke staf	2451
Total	4083

Student Enrolment, 1986-87:

	Men	Women	Total
Of the country	10,855	1219	12,074
Of other countries	673	116	789
Total	11,528	1335	12,863

5106 ***TECHNISCHE UNIVERSITEIT EINDHOVEN**
Eindhoven University of Technology
Postbus 513, 5600 MB Eindhoven
Telex: 51163 TUEHV NL.
Telephone: (040) 479111
Fax: (040) 445187
Rector: M. Tels
Secretaris: H.P.J.M. Roumen

D. of Philosophy and Social Sciences (Technology and Development, Transfer Technological Know-how, Women, Work and Technology, and Environmental Psychology Related to Social and Industrial Aspects)
Dean: N.H. Douben; *staff* 93 (23)
D. of Mathematics and Computer Sciences
Dean: J.H. van Lint; *staff* 164 (16)
D. of Physics
Dean: F.W. Sluyjter; *staff* 201 (13)
D. of Mechanical Engineering
Dean: D.H. van Campen; *staff* 255 (6)
D. of Electrical Engineering (Communication, Microelectronics, Power Engineering, Systems Engineering)
Dean: J. Jess; *staff* 258 (13)
D. of Chemical Engineering
Dean: H.M. Buck; *staff* 248 (9)
D. of Architecture, Building Construction, and Town Planning
Dean: M.F.T. Bax; *staff* 155 (16)
D. of Industrial Engineering
Dean: C.H.V.A. Botter; *staff* 131 (19)
I. of Perception Research (Hearing and Speech, Vision and Reading, Cognition and Communication, Information Ergonomics, Communication Aids)
Director: H. Bouma; *staff* 15
I. for Continuing Education
Director: S.T.M. Ackermans; *staff* 3 (49)
Eindhoven International I. (Telecommunications Engineering, Engineering, Energy and Logistics) (in preparation)
Director: A. Heetman; *staff* 6
Computer Ce.
Director: W.J.M. Senden; *staff* 87 (3)

Founded 1956 as Technische Hogeschool. Acquired present title 1986. A State institution financed by the government. Governing bodies: the Universiteitsraad (University Council), comprising 29 members; the College van Bestuur (Executive Board), comprising 3 members. Some residential facilities for students.

Participates in ERASMUS, SEFI, DELTA, COMETT, BRITE-EURAM, ESPRIT-II programmes. Member of CLUSTER, Santander-group, CESAR-foundation.

Academic Year: September to August (September-December; December-March; March-August).

Admission Requirements: Secondary school certificate in appropriate subjects (diploma eindexamen Gymnasium, Atheneum, or H.B.S., B, HTO), or recognized equivalent.

Fees (Guilders): 1750 per annum.

Language of Instruction: Dutch.

Degrees and Diplomas: In all departments Doctoraal examen leading to degree of Ingenieur, Ir.: Diploma of Wiskundig Ingenieur, mathematics; Natuurkundig-, physics; Bouwkundig-, architecture; Werktuigkundig-, mechanical engineering; Electrotechnisch-, electrical engineering; Scheikundig-, chemical engineering; Bedrijfskundig-, industrial engineering, at least 5 yrs. The title of Doctor is awarded on basis of a thesis or experimental work following the diploma.

Library: Central Library, *c.* 300,000 vols.

Publications: Gids; Wetenschappelijk Verslag (annually).

Academic Staff, 1989-90: c. 1085.

	Men	Women	Total
Of the country	5795	695	6490
Of other countries	113	22	135
Total	5908	717	6625

5107 **UNIVERSITEIT TWENTE**

University of Twente

P.O. Box 217, 7500AE Enschede

Telex: 44200

Telephone: (053) 899111

Fax: 357956

Rector: J.H.A. de Smit (1988-91)

Secretaris: F.C. Verschoor

D. of Philosophy and Social Science
Dean: A. Rip
D. of Applied Mathematics
Dean: R. Martini
D. of Mechanical Engineering
Dean: W. Bakker
D. of Electrical Engineering
Dean: Sh.J.A. Popma
D. of Industrial Management
Dean: P.A.E. van de Bunt
D. of Chemical Engineering
Dean: W.R. van der Linden
D. of Applied Physics
Dean: J. Greve
D. of Technology and Social Science
Dean: A. Rip
D. of Public Administration
Dean: C.L. Menting
D. of Educational Sciences
Dean: W.J. van der Linder
D. of Computer Science
Dean: A. Mÿholt

Founded 1961 as Technische Hogeschool. Acquired present title 1986. A State institution financed by the government. Governing bodies: the Universiteitsraad (University Council), composed of 27 university members and 6 non-university members; the College van Bestuur (Executive Board), of 3 members. Residential facilities for students.

Arrangements for co-operation with: Bandung Institute of Technology; University of Dortmund; University of Münster; University of Zambia; University of Palo Alto.

Academic Year: September to July (August-December; January-April; April-June).

Admission Requirements: Secondary school certificate in appropriate subjects (diploma eindexamen Gymnasium B, or H.B.S. B) or recognized foreign equivalent.

Fees (Guilders): *c.* 1650 per annum.

Language of Instruction: Dutch.

Degrees and Diplomas: The degree of Doctor is awarded on the basis of a thesis or experimental work following the diploma, *c.* 4 yrs. Technical Propaedeuse, 1 yrs; Doctoraal, 3 yrs; Diploma of Ingenieur, Ir, Social Sciences Propaedeuse, 1 yrs;Doctoraal, 3 yrs. Diploma of Doctorandus, Drs.

Library: 100,000 vols.

Publication: Ut-Mediair (8 times a year).

Academic Staff, 1990:

Rank	Full-time
Hoogleraren	109
Buitengewoon of bijzonder hoogleraren	12
Overig wetenschappelijk personeel	700
Total	821

Student Enrolment, 1990:

	Men
Of the country	5302
Of other countries	88
Total	5390*

*Also 1036 Women students.

5108 **RIJKSUNIVERSITEIT GRONINGEN**

University of Groningen

Postbus 72, 9700 AB, Groningen

Telex: 53410

Telephone: (50) 639111

Fax: (50) 635380

President: E. Bleumink

Secretaris (Registrar): H.J.D. Bruins

F. of Theology (including Religious Studies)
Dean: J. Roldanus; *staff* 25
F. of Law
Dean: J. Griffiths *staff* 165
F. of Medicine (including Dentistry)
Dean: H.J. Huisjes; *staff* 440
F. of Mathematics and Science (including Astronomy, Biology, Chemistry, Chemical Engineering, Computer Science, Environmental Science, Mathematics, Pharmacy, Physics, Applied Physics and Technical Pharmacy)
Dean: M.J. Janssen; *staff* 415
F. of Arts (Modern European Languages, Art History, History, Classic, Slavic and Semitic Languages, General Art Studies including Computer Application, American Studies, Communication)
Dean: M. Maaskant; *staff* 260
F. of Economics (including Econometry, Fiscal Economics, Eastern European Studies, Studies of Labour)
Dean: H.J. Wagener; *staff* 170
F. of Psychological, Pedagogical and Sociological Sciences
Dean: G. Lang; *staff* 165
F. of Philosophy
Dean: T.A.F. Kuipers; *staff* 25
F. of Organization and Management
Dean: M. van Gils; *staff* 80
F. of Spatial Sciences (Human Geography, Demography of Non-Western World)
Dean: H. Voogd
Nuclear Physics Acceleration I.
Materials Science Ce.
Traffic Research Ce.
Ce. for Hungarian Studies
Also clinics, laboratories, and institutes of the various faculties.

Founded 1614 as an academy by the Province of Groningen. In 1811, during the Napoleonic invasion, the university was attached to the Université impériale. Became a State university in 1876. Governing bodies: the Universiteitsraad (University Council), comprising 29 members; the College van Bestuur (Executive Board), comprising 3 members.

Participates in the ERASMUS and ISEP (USA) programmes. Member of the Coïmbra-Group.

Academic Year: September to July (September-December; December-March; Maech-July).

Admission Requirements: Secondary school certificate in subjects appropriate to faculty requirements (diploma eindexamen Gymnasium A or B, Atheneum A or B) or foreign equivalent.

Fees (Guilders): Tuition, 1750 per annum.

Languages of Instruction: Dutch, and some English.

Degrees and Diplomas: In all faculties Doctoraal examen leading, in Law, to degree of Meester in de Rechten, mr., and in all other fields to doctorandus, drs., or to degree of Ingenieur, Ir. Professional qualifications–Arts, medicine; Tandarts, dentistry; Apotheker, pharmacy; Psycholoog, psychology; Accountant, at least 2 yrs after relevant doctorandus. Undergraduate studies take 4 yrs. Doctorate, by thesis, in all fields.

Library: University Library, including faculty and institute libraries, more than 2,000,000 vols.

Special Facilities (Museums, etc.): University Museum; Gerardus van der Leeuwmuseum (Ethnographic Museum).

Publications: Groninger Universiteitsgids; Universiteitskrant. Annual reports: General; Education; Scientific; and Financial.

Academic Staff, 1989:

Rank	Full-time
Hoogleraren	290
Wetenschappelijke staf	1600
Total	1890

Student Enrolment, 1989-90:

Men	Women	Total
10,000	7000	17,000

5109 **OPEN UNIVERSITEIT**

Open University

Valkenbrugerweg 167, 6401 DL Heerlen
Telex: 56559
Telephone: 45-762222
Fax: 45-711486

Chairman of the Executive Board: B. de Haan
Secretary-General: G.M. J. Prick

D. of Law
Head: J.M. Reijntjes
D. of Economics
Head: H.W.S.M. Peek
D. of Business and Administration and Politics
Head: J.C. van Dalen
D. of Natural Sciences
Head: W.H. de Jen
D. of Technology
Head: K.L. Boon
D. of Cultural Sciences
Head: R. Rolf
D. of Social Sciences
Head: J.F.M. Claessen

Founded 1982, admitted first student 1984. A State institution for distance education. Governing bodies: the Universiteitsraad; the College van Bestuur (Executive Board).

Admission Requirements: No qualifications required. Minimum age, 18.

Fees (Guilders): 220 per course of 100 hours.

Language of Instruction: Dutch.

Degrees and Diplomas: Course certificate. University diploma or degree of 164 credits, 5400 hours. Doctorate, Ph.D., with dissertation. Also higher vocational education diploma, 108-150 credits.

Publication: Modulair (monthly magazine for students and relations)

Academic Staff, 1990: 477 (344).

Student Enrolment, 1990:

	Men	Women	Total
Of the country	25,393	15,337	40,730
Of other countries	690	232	922
Total	26,083	15,569	41,652*

*All by correspondence

5110 ***RIJKSUNIVERSITEIT TE LEIDEN**

Leiden University

stationsweg 46, POB 9500, 2300 RA Leiden
Telex: 39427 (BURUL NL)
Telephone: (71) 27-2727
Fax: (71) 273118

Rector: J.J.M. Beenakker (1985-91)
Secretaris: D.P. den Os

F. of Theology
Dean: M. de Jonge; *staff* 21
F. of Law
Dean: J.M. Nieuwenhuis; *staff* 240
F. of Medicine
Dean: W.Th. Daems; *staff* 493
F. of Mathematical and Physical Sciences
Dean: G. van Dyk; *staff* 514
F. of Arts
Dean: J.G. Wooij *staff* 361
F. of Social Sciences (including Education)
Dean: H.J.M. Claessen; *staff* 311
F. of Philosophy
Dean: H. Philipse; *staff* 11
F. of Pre-and Protohistory
Dean: L. Louwe Kooijmans; *staff* 12
Computer Ce.
Ce. for Environmental Studies
Director: H.A. Udo de Haes; *staff* 25
Medical-Genetic Ce. of South-West Netherlands
D. of Bio-Pharmaceutical Science
Director: D.D. Breines
Interuniversity Research I. for Radiopathology and Radiation Protection
Director: A.A. van Zeeland; *staff* 34

Also University Hospital and clinics, institutes and laboratories of the various faculties; Research Information Centre; The Academic Business Centre; International Centre and International Exchange Co-ordinator.

Founded 1575 by William the Silent, Prince of Orange, became a State institution in the 19th century. The university is financially supported by the State. Governing bodies: the Universiteitsraad (University Council), composed of 8 members of the non-scientific staff, and 8 representatives of the student body, and 5 non-university members; the College van Bestuur (Executive Board), comprising 3 members. Some residential facilities for foreign academic staff and for students.

Academic Year: September to July (September-December; January-Easter; Easter-July).

Admission Requirements: Secondary school certificate in subjects appropriate to faculty requirements (diploma eind examen, Gymnasium Aor B, Atheneum A or B, or H.B.S. A or B), or foreign equivalent.

Fees (Guilders): 1750 per annum.

Language of Instruction: Dutch.

Degrees and Diplomas: In all faculties Doctoraal examen leading, in Law, to degree of Meester in de Rechten, mr., 4-5 yrs, and in all other fields to doctorandus, drs., 5 yrs. Professional qualifications–Arts, medicine; Apotheker, pharmacy, at least 2 yrs after relevant doctorandus; Wetenschappelijk onderzoeker, 1 yr; Leraar, 6 months. Doctorate, bythesis, in all fields.

Libraries: University Library, *c.* 2,000,000 vols; faculty and institute libraries.

Special Facilities (Museums, etc.): Natural History Museum; Archaeological Museum; Geological and Mineralogical Museum; Ethnological Museum; Museum of Natural Sciences; Historical Museum; Botanical Garden (16th century).

Press or Publishing House: DSWO-press.

Academic Staff, 1989-90: 2086.

Student Enrolment, 1989-90: 17,194.

5111 **RIJKSUNIVERSITEIT LIMBURG**

University of Limburg

P.O. Box 616, 6200 MD Maastricht
Telephone: (43) 88-88-88/88-77-77
Fax: (43) 25-21-95

Rector: F.I.M. Bonke
Secretaris: B.C.M.E. Niessen

F. of Medicine
Dean: F. Sturmans
F. of Health Sciences
Dean: A.J. Boon
F. of Law
Dean: M.J. Cohen
F. of Economics (including Business Administration, Accountancy, and International Management)
Dean: A. Beek
F. of General Studies
Dean: O.J. Vrieze

Founded 1974 as Medische Faculteit te Maastricht. Governing bodies: the Universiteitsraad (University Council), comprising 18 members; the College van Bestuur (Executive Board), comprising 3 members.

Academic Year: September to June (September-December; January-June).

Admission Requirements: Secondary school certificate. If over 21 years of age, diploma eindexamen VWA, Gymnasium, Atheneum, or HBO.

Fees (Guilders): Tuition, 1750 per annum.

Language of Instruction: Dutch.

Degrees and Diplomas: Doctorandus, drs., 4 yrs.

Library: Central Library, *c.* 375,000 vols.

Publications: Bibliotheekbulletin; Bulletin Gezondheidswetenschappen; Carabas (Law); EForum (Economics); Flexibel (Medical Faculty); Huisartsgeneeskundebulletin; Ikonomix; Intercom; Kozijn; Meesterlijk (Law); Nieuwsbrief; Nieuwsbulletin (Economic Faculty); NSEM-Nieuwsbrief; Observant; Onderwijsnieuwsbrief; Perspectief; Reliëf; Theezeef.

Academic Staff, 1990: c. 600.

Student Enrolment, 1990:

	Men	Women	Total
Of the country	2642	2973	5615

5112 ***KATHOLIEKE UNIVERSITEIT NIJMEGEN**

Catholic University, Nijmegen
Comeniuslaan 4, 6500 HC Nijmegen
Telex: 48211 NM NL
Telephone: (080) 519333
Rector: B.M.F. van Iersel
Secretaris: A.F. van der Laan

F. of Theology
Dean: A.H.M. Scheer; *staff* 33 (7)
F. of Literature and Arts
Dean: J.M.G.A. Aarts; *staff* 174 (88)
F. of Law
Dean: J.M.M. Maeijer; *staff* 85 (19)
F. of Medicine (including Dentistry)
Dean: F.J.M. Daemen; *staff* 534 (176)
F. of Mathematics and Natural Sciences
Dean: J.J. Steggerda; *staff* 278 (62)
F. of Social Sciences (including Education)
Dean: O. Schreuder; *staff* 314 (135)
Central Interfaculty (Philosophy)
Dean: H.A.G. Braakhuis; *staff* 34 (10)
Interfaculty of Geography and Prehistory
Dean: P.J.W. Kouwe; *staff* 52 (12)
I. of Psychology
I. of Sociology
I. of Educational Research
I. of Religious Studies
I. of Social Medicine
Catholic Documentation Ce.
Human Scientific Research Ce.
Also 75 institutes, clinics, and laboratories of the various faculties.

Founded 1923 by decree of the Sacred Congregation of Studies and by Royal Decree. The university is based on the principles of the doctrine of the Roman Catholic Church. Although a private institution, the university receives financial support from the State. Its degrees are recognized as equivalent to and as affording the same rights as those of the State universities. Governing bodies: the Universiteitsraad (University Council), comprising a maximum of 39 members; the College van Bestuur (Executive Board). Residential facilities for students.

Arrangements for co-operation with University institutions in: U.S.A.; Federal Republic of Germany; France; Japan; Poland; Indonesia; China; Tanzania; Belgium.

Academic Year: September to July (September-December; January-March; April-July).

Admission Requirements: Secondary school certificate in subjects appropriate to faculty requirements (diploma eindexamen Gymnasium A or B, Atheneum A or B, or H.B.S. A or B), or equivalent.

Fees (Guilders): Registration, 1604.

Language of Instruction: Dutch.

Degrees and Diplomas: In all faculties Doctoraal examen leading, in Law, to degree of Meester in de rechten, mr., 4 yrs, and in all other fields to doctorandus, drs., 5-6 yrs. Professional qualifications–Arts, medicine; Tandarts, dentistry, at least 2 yrs after relevant doctorandus. Doctorate, by thesis, in all fields.

Library: Central Library, *c.* 1,000,000 vols.

Publications: KU-Nieuws (weekly); Gids; Jaarverslag.

Academic Staff, 1984-85:

Rank	Full-time	Part-time
Professoren	289	–
Others	944	573
Total	1233	573

Student Enrolment, 1986: 14,265.

5113 ***ERASMUS UNIVERSITEIT ROTTERDAM**

Erasmus University Rotterdam
Burgemeester Oudlaan 50, Postbus 1738, 3000 DR Rotterdam
Telex: 24421
Telephone: (10) 4081111
Fax: 452 0204
Rector: C.J. Rijnvos (1989-)

F. of Economics
Dean: J. Verhulp; *staff* 385
F. of Law
Dean: R. van Delden; *staff* 143
F. of Medicine
Director: K. Kerrebijn; *staff* 408
F. of Philosophy
Dean: J. Sperna Weiland; *staff* 23
Sub-F. of Social Sciences
Dean: J. Berting; *staff* 122
Sub-F. of Societal History and Study of the Arts
Dean: H.V. Dyk; *staff* 250
F. of Management
Dean: P. van Berkel; *staff* 133
D. of Health Services Administration
Chairman: A.F. Casparie; *staff* 18
Ce. of Business Economics
Director: C.H. Buitenhuis; *staff* 10
I. of Econometrics
Director: T. Kloek; *staff* 35
Economic Research I.
Director: W. Siddke; *staff* 6
Fiscal Economic I.
Director: L.G.M. Stevens; *staff* 15
Ce. for Development Planning
Director: J.J. Terhal; *staff* 16
I. of Economic Geography
Director: G.A. van der Knaap; *staff* 10

Founded 1973, incorporating the former Netherlands School of Economics, founded 1913, and the Medical School, Rotterdam Governing bodies: the Universiteitsraad (University Council), comprising 40 members; the College van Bestuur (Executive Board), comprising 3 members. Residential facilities for *c.* 2100 students.

Arrangements for co-operation with: Bogor Agricultural University; Hasanuddin University; University of Aix-en-Provence; Michigan State University; University of Gdańsk; University of Łódź; Central School of Planning and Statistics, Warsaw; University of Hull; Indiana University; Catholic University of Louvain; University of Pennsylvania; Northwestern University; University of Western Ontario; Centre d'Enseignement supérieur des Affaires, Jouy-en-Josas; Christian University of Indonesia; Syiah Kuala University; University of Paris IX;University of Glasgow; University of Dijon; University of the Andes, Bogota; University of Rochester.

Academic Year: September to June (September-January; January-June).

Admission Requirements: Secondary school certificate (diploma eindexamen Gymnasium A or B, H.B.S. A or B, or Atheneum A or B), or recognized equivalent.

Fees (Guilders): Total, 1250 per annum.

Languages of Instruction: Dutch and English.

Degrees and Diplomas: In all faculties Doctoraal examen leading, in Law, to degree of Meester in de Rechten, mr., 4 yrs, and in all other fields to doctorandus, drs., 4 yrs. Professional qualification–Arts, Medical doctor, at least 2 yrs after doctorandus. MBA, at least 2 yrs after Doctorandus. Doctorate, by thesis, in all fields.

Libraries: Central Library, 498,000 vols; Medical library, 197,500; 'Rotterdamsch Leeskabinet', 184,500.

Special Facilities (Museums, etc.): Economic Archives; Historisch Kabinet.

Publications: Quod Novum (University newspaper, weekly); Scientific Report (annually).

Academic Staff, 1989-90:

Rank	Full-time
Gewone hoogleraren A	88
Gewone hoogleraren B	108
Wetenschappelijk personeel	794
Total	990

Student Enrolment, 1989-90:

	Men	Women	Total
Of the country	9914	3897	13,811*

*Also 808 external students.

5114 ***KATHOLIEKE UNIVERSITEIT BRABANT**

Tilburg University
Hogeschoollaan 225, 5037 GC Tilburg
Telex: 52426
Telephone: (13) 669111
Fax: (13) 663019
Rector: R.A. de Moor (1983-91)
Secretaris: R.H.A.M. Kraakman

D. of Economics
Dean: A. Kapteyn; *staff* 103 (21)
D. of Social Sciences (Psychology, Sociology, Leisure Studies, Social Security, Human Resource Management, Administrative Policy)
Dean: J.A.P. Hagenaars; *staff* 70 (45)
D. of Law
Dean: C.P.A. Geppaart
D. of Philosophy
Dean: E.E. Berns
D. of Letters
Dean: H. Verdaasdont
I. of Fiscal Research
Director: T.A. Stevers
I. of Social Research
Director: J.H.G. Segers
I. of Development Research
Director: B.H. Evers; *staff* 12 (5)
I. of Economic Research
Director: W.G.H. van Hulst; *staff* 13 (5)
I. Tilburg I. of Advanced Studies (TIAS)
Director: H.F.M. Peeters; *staff* 7 (200)
Ce. for Economics Research
Director: E. van Damme

Founded 1927 as R.K. Handelshogeschool, name changed to Katholieke Economische Hogeschool 1938 and to Katholieke Hogeschool 1963. The degrees awarded by the institution are recognized as equivalent to and affording the same rights as those of State universities. A private institution financially supported by the State. Governing bodies: the Universiteitsraad (University Council); the College van Bestuur (Executive Board).

Arrangements for co-operation with the Universities of: Cambridge; Warsaw; Indiana; Connecticut. National University of San Antonio Abad, Cuzco; National University of the Plateau; Academies of Economics, Cracow and Poznań; National University of Costa Rica, Centre Popular de Estudios Superiores, Matagalpa, Nicaragua; Free University of Brussels; Universidad de Deusto, Bilbao; Washington University, St Louis.

Academic Year: September to April (September-December; January-April).

Admission Requirements: Secondary school certificate in subjects appropriate to faculty requirements (diploma eindexamen Gymnasium A or B, H.B.S. A or B, or Atheneum A or B), or equivalent.

Fees (Guilders): Tuition, 1604 per annum.

Language of Instruction: Dutch.

Degrees and Diplomas: Doctoraal examen leading to degree of Meester, mr., in Law and in Faculties of Economics and Social Sciences to doctorandus, drs., 3-4 yrs. Doctorate by thesis. Certificate of Advanced Studies (not leading to a formal degree) for programmes in TIAS.

Library: c. 400,000 vols.

Publications: Economie; Social Wetenschappen; Exerpta Informatica Annual Report; KUBUS.

Press or Publishing House: Tilburg University Press.

Academic Staff, 1988:

Rank	Full-time	Part-time
Hoogleraaren	72	24
Overig Wetenschappelijk	–	–
Personeel	283	161
Assistenten in opleiding	68	14
Student assistenten	–	123
Total	423	322

Student Enrolment, 1989-90:

Men	Women	Total
5233	2826	8059

5115 ***RIJKSUNIVERSITEIT UTRECHT**

Utrecht University
Heidelberglaan 8, P.O.Box 80125, 3584 TC Utrecht
Telex: 40087
Telephone: (30) 53911
Fax: (30) 521818
Rector: J.A. van Ginkel
Secretaris: W.G. van der Purten

F. of Theology
Dean: O.J. de Jong; *staff* 48 (50)
F. of Philosophy
Dean: J. Mansfeld; *staff* 33 (16)
F. of Arts
Dean: C.B. Wels; *staff* 335 (374)
F. of Law
Dean: C.M. Jaspers; *staff* 233 (164)
F. of Social Sciences
Dean: H.P.M. Adriaansen; *staff* 344 (354)
F. of Geography
Dean: J. Hauer; *staff* 169 (94)
F. of Medicine
Dean: M.F. Kramer; *staff* 721 (461)
F. of Veterinary Medicine
Dean: S.G. v.d. Bergh; *staff* 662 (219)
F. of Mathematics and Computer Sciences
Dean: T.A. Springer; *staff* 115 (54)
F. of Physics and Astronomy
Dean: H.P. Hooymayers; *staff* 326 (82)
F. of Chemistry
Dean: J. de Gear; *staff* 323 (69)
F. of Pharmacy
Dean: A. Bult; *staff* 131 (53)
F. of Biology
Dean: M.J.A. Werger; *staff* 326 (86)
F. of Geology and Geophysics
Dean: N.J. Vlaar; *staff* 165 (44)
I. for Molecular Biology and Biotechnology
Dean: M.O. Voorma; *staff* 39 (26)
I. of Education

Founded 1636 and established as a State University. The status of the university is defined in the Higher Education Act of 1961, and it is financially supported by the State. Governing bodies: the Universiteitsraad (University Council); the College van Bestuur (Executive Board). Some residential facilities for Students.

Arrangements for co-operation with the Universities of: Antwerp; Aarhus; Bochum; Bologna; Coimbra; Hull; Madrid; Lille; Lund; Florida; Gainesville; Strasbourg; Wisconsin; Costa Rica; Zimbabwe; Gadjah Mada; Yogyakarta; Bénin; Eduardo Mondlane, Maputo; Ahmadu Bello; Zaria.

Academic Year: September to June.

Admission Requirements: Secondary school certificate in subjects appropriate to faculty requirements (eindexamen Gymnasium A or B, or Atheneum).

Fees (Guilders): 1750 per annum.

Language of Instruction: Dutch.

Degrees and Diplomas: In all faculties Doctoraal examen leading, in Law, to degree of Meester in de rechten, mr., 4 yrs, and in all other fields to doctorandus, drs., 5-6 yrs. Professional qualificiations–Arts, medicine; Tandarts, dentistry;Veterinary Medicine, at least 2 yrs after relevant doctorandus. Doctorate, by thesis, in all fields.

Library: Central Library.

Special Facilities (Museums, etc.): University Museum.

Publications: Gids der Rijksuniversiteit te Utrecht; Jaarboek der Rijksuniversiteit te Utrecht.

Academic Staff, 1986-87: 667.

Student Enrolment, 1989-90:

	Men	Women	Total
Of the country	10,038	11,634	21,672
Of other countries	242	238	480
Total	10,280	11,872	22,152

5116 ***LANDBOUWUNIVERSITEIT WAGENINGEN**

Wageningen Agricultural University
P.O.B. 9101, 6700 HB Wageningen
Telex: 45854
Telephone: (8370) 89111
Fax: (8370) 84449
Electronic mail: bg@rcl.wau.nl
President: W.P.M. Vos
Secretary: H.M. van den Hoofdakker

F. of Agricultural and Environmental Sciences (including Plant and Animal Science, Technology, Land Use, Social Sciences and Economics)
Rector: H.C. Van der Plas

International Courses (including Animal Production and Agriculture, Crop Science, Management of Agricultural Knowledge Systems, Soil and Water Management, Tropical Forestry, Biotechnology. And Ecological Agriculture, Geographic Information Systems) (in preparation)

Founded 1876 as national agricultural college, granted university status 1918. Under the jurisdiction of the Ministry of Agriculture. Nature Conservation, and Fisheries. Governing bodies: the Executive Board; the University Council. Residential facilities for *c.* 4000 students.

The University has three Permanent Centres abroad, Turrialba (Costa Rica), Adiopodoume (Ivory Coast), and Sahel Centre (Burkina Faso). Also currently involved in projects in Africa (Benin, Mozambique, Nigeria, Zambia, Zimbabwe), South America (Costa Rica, Nicaragua), and Asia (Bangladesh, Indonesia, Viet Nam). On the initiative of Wageningen, a network of European agricultural faculties has been set up, known as Natura. Bilateral relations established with Universities of: Guelph; Reading; Córdoba; Spain; Hohenheim; Vila Real, Portugal; Perugia, Italy; Chania, Greece; Leuven; Gent; Gödöllö, Hungary; Nitra; Nanjin.

Academic Year: September to August (September-December; January-May; June-August).

Admission Requirements: Secondary school certificate in appropriate subjects (diploma V.W.O.) or equivalent.

Fees (Guilders): 1750 per annum.

Languages of Instruction: Dutch and English.

Degrees and Diplomas: Landbouwkundig Ingenieur (LR), 4-6 yrs. Doctor in de Landbouwwetenschappen (Dr.), a further 2-4 yrs. Master ofScience (MSc), after 1 ½-2 yrs special (English) programme. Ph.D., a further 3-4 yrs.

Library: Central Library, *c.* 1,000,000 vols.

Special Facilities (Museums, etc.): Biological Garden De Dreijen; Arboretum Belmonte.

Publications: Wageningen University Papers (6-10 per annum); Wageningen Economic Studies (5 per annum); Wageningen Social Studies (5 per annum); Wagenings Universiteitsblad (40 per annum).

Press or Publishing House: PUDOC (Publikaties en Documentatie).

Academic Staff, 1989: c. 600 (160).

Student Enrolment, 1989-90:

	Men	Women	Total
Of the country	*c.* 4000	*c.* 2500	*c.* 6500*

*Also *c.* 350 foreign students.

Institutions Offering International Courses

5117 ***STICHTING INTERNATIONAAL INSTITUUT VOOR SOCIALE STUDIËN**

Institute of Social Studies

Badhuisweg 251, 2509 LS Den Haag

Cables: socinst

Telex: 31 491 NL

Telephone: (70) 3510100

Fax: (70) 3549851

Rector: G. Lycklama A Nyeholt (1990-)

Managing Director: F. Koopman

D. of Social Sciences (including Public Administration, International and National Development, Economic Planning, Industrial Development, Rural and Urban Development, International Relations, Population and Development)

Dean: W. Boelman; *staff* 60

Research D.

Dean: E. Mulder

Founded 1952 by the universities of the Netherlands to promote graduate and advanced international research and training in the social sciences. Granted independent status 1956. Largely financed by the State. Governing body: the Board of Trustees, comprising 10 members.

Academic Year: September to May (September-December; January-February; March-May).

Admission Requirements: University degree in appropriate field and good command of English. Preference is given to candidates with several years' professional experience.

Fees (Guilders): Tuition, 3750-6500.

Language of Instruction: English.

Degrees and Diplomas: Diplomas in–Socio-Economic Planning; Project Analysis; Statistics and National Accounting; Regional Development Planning; International and National Development; Urban Social Development; Rural Development; Industrial Relations; Development Administration, 6 months. Master of Development Studies, 15 months. Doctorate (Ph.D.).

Libraries: Library and Documentation Division, *c.* 33,000 vols; *c.* 30,000 documents.

Publication: Development and Change (three times a year).

Academic Staff, 1989-90:

Rank	Full-time	Part-time
Professors	13	5
Lecturers	52	2
Total	65	7

Student Enrolment, 1989-90:

	Men	Women	Total
Of the country	2	1	3
Of other countries	120	80	200
Total	122	81	203

5118 **STICHTING DER NEDERLANDSE UNIVERSITEITEN EN HOGESCHOLEN VOOR INTERNATIONALE SAMENWERKING**

Netherlands Universities Foundation for International Co-operation (NUFFIC)

'De Wittebrug', Badhuisweg 251, P.O. Box 90734, 2509 LS Den Haag

Telex: 33565 NUFIC NL

Telephone: (070) 502681

Director: T.G. Veenkamp

Secretary: J.A. Willinge

Founded 1952 by the universities of the Netherlands to promote international co-operation in the academic and scientific fields, parti-cularly in relation to developing countries. Largely financed by the State. Governing body: the Board of Governors.

International Courses: Hydraulic and Sanitary Engineering; Environmental Science and Technology (in co-operation with the Technological University of Delft). Health Development (in co-operation with the Institutes for Tropical Medicine, Amsterdam, Leiden, Rotterdam, and Antwerp). European Integration (in co-operation with University of Amsterdam). Food Science and Nutrition (in co-operation with State University, Utrecht; Agricultural University, Wageningen; State University of Ghent; Catholic University of Louvain; General Department of Development Co-operation, Brussels); Management Service Research; Port Management. Also specialized summer courses.

Admission Requirements: University degree in an appropriate field and professional experience.

Languages of Instruction: English and some French.

Degrees and Diplomas: Most courses lead to the award of a Diploma. Also degree of Master of Public Health.

Publications: Higher Education and Research in the Netherlands (quarterly: also in Spanish); Basic Data on International Courses offered in the Netherlands (annually: also in Spanish and French); Overzicht-internationale universitairesamenwerking (monthly, in Dutch).

Academic Staff: c. 1950.

Student Enrolment: c. 280.

5119 **INTERNATIONAL AGRICULTURAL CENTRE**

11 Lawickse Allee, P.O. Box 88, 6700 AB Wageningenen

Cables: Intas

Telex: 45888 INTAS NL

Telephone: 08370-19040

Agriculture and Animal Husbandry

Founded 1951. Operated in co-operation with the Netherlands Universities Foundation for International Co-operation (NUFFIC).

Admission Requirements: University degree and relevant professional experience.

Fees (Guilders): 1000.

Languages of Instruction: English. Also French and German in Rural Extension.

Degrees and Diplomas: Certificate of Attendance, 14 weeks.

5120 **INSTITUTE FOR HOUSING STUDIES**

P.O. Box 20718, 3001 JA Rotterdam

Telex: 24548 IHS NL

Telephone: (010) 4309540

Director: Cor Dijkgraaf

Housing, Planning and Building (including Architecture)

Housing Policy in Developing Countries (Design and Technology, Settlement Planning, Building Process and Resource Management)

Founded 1946. Reorganized 1971. An independent, private foundation. Operated in co-operation with the Netherlands Universities Foundation for International Co-operation (NUFFIC). The course is designed to aid professionals from other countries working in the field of human settlements to reassess policy measures and projects relating to the urban poor. Regional courses are also held in India, Indonesia, Sri Lanka, Tanzania, Thailand. Governing body: the Board.

Academic Year: Courses: January-June; August-January.

Admission Requirements: University degree and relevant professional experience.

Fees (Guilers): *c.* 10,000.

Language of Instruction: English.

Degrees and Diplomas: Diploma, 5 months. Also Certificate of Attendance.

Library: c. 7000 vols.

Special Facilities (Museums, etc.): Exhibition area, 11,000 sq. m.

Publications: Bouw; Documentatie Bouwwezen; Studies.

Academic Staff, 1986-87: 23.

Student Enrolment: c. 200.

5121 **INTERNATIONAL INSTITUTE FOR AEROSPACE SURVEY AND EARTH SCIENCES (ITC)**
INTERNATIONAAL INSTITUUT VOOR LUCHT-EN RUIMTEKAARTERING EN AARDKUNDE (ITC)
350 Boulevard 1945, P.O. Box 6, 7500 AA Enschede
Cables: Aersur
Telex: 44525
Telephone: (053) 320330

D. of Photogrammetry
D. of Aerial Photography and Remote Sensing
D. of Cartography
D. of Land Resource Surveys and Rural Development
D. of Earth Resources Surveys
Chairman: S. Dijkstra; *staff* 28 (14)
D. of Urban Settlement Analysis
Chairman: M. Juppenplatz; *staff* 10 (4)

Founded 1951 as the International Training Centre. Acquired present status and title 1966. Supports regional centres in Columbia, Nigeria, India, and Indonesia. Operated in co-operation with the Netherlands Universities Foundation for International Co-operation (NUFFIC). Governing bodies: the Board of Governors; the Scientific Council. Residential facilities for students.

Admission Requirements: University degree in an appropriate field and professional experience.

Fees (Guilders): Registration, 100; tuition, 500 per month, 1000 per seminar or short course of less than 2 months.

Languages of Instruction: English and French.

Degrees and Diplomas: Diplomas, 8-12 months. Degree of Master of Science, M.Sc., a further 16-22 months and thesis. Research Doctorate, Ph.D.

Library: c. 12,000 vols.

Publication: Journal (quarterly).

Academic Staff: c. 100 (25).

Student Enrolment: c. 400.

5122 **EINDHOVEN INTERNATIONAL INSTITUTE OF TECHNOLOGICAL STUDIES**
TUE-RC, P. O. Box 218, 5600 MB Eindhoven
Telex: 51 136 TUEHV NLT(40) 474600 Fax: (40) 455515
Director of Studies: A.Heetman
Secretary-General: M. Paulussen

Electronics
Telecommunication

Founded 1957 as Philips International Institute. Operated in co-operation with the Netherlands Universities Foundation for International Co-operation (NUFFIC).

Academic Year: January to December (January-May; September-December).

Admission Requirements: University degree in Engineering (B.Sc. Engineering)

Fees (Guilders): 15,000 per annum.

Language of Instruction: English.

Degrees and Diplomas: Diploma, 1 yr. Degree of Master, 17 months.

Academic Staff, 1990: 3 (14).

Student Enrolment, 1990:

	Men	Women	Total
Of other countries	18	1	19

5123 **NETHERLANDS INTERNATIONAL INSTITUTE FOR MANAGEMENT**
Mijnbouwplein 11, 2628 RT Delft
Cables: RVB Delft
Telex: 38323 RVB NL
Telephone: (015) 561100

Industrial Management
Regional Industrial Development

Founded 1952 as an independent institution for research in fields of management, particularly in relation to developing countries. Operated in co-operation with the Netherlands Universities Foundation for International Co-operation (NUFFIC). Largely financed by the State. Governing body: the Board of Trustees, comprising 3 members from the Delft University of Technology, 3 members from the Netherlands Universities Foundation for International Co-operation, and 3 co-opted members.

Academic Year: Courses: January-June; July-December.

Admission Requirements: University degree and relevant professional experience.

Fees (Guilders): 15,500.

Language of Instruction: English.

Degrees and Diplomas: Diplomas, 3 months.

Library: c. 5000 vols.

Publication: Newsletters and Research Papers (biannually).

Academic Staff: c. 20 (100).

5124 **INTERNATIONAL INSTITUTE FOR HYDRAULIC AND ENVIRONMENTAL ENGINEERING**
P. O. Box 3015, 2601 DA Delft
Telex: 38099 IHE NL
Telephone: (015) 78-3402

Hydraulic and Environmental Engineering

Founded 1957. Operated in co-operation with the Netherlands Universities Foundation for International Co-operation (NUFFIC). Financed by the government, fees, and grants from Unesco, World Meteorological Organization (WMO), and World Health Organization (WHO).

Academic Year: October to September (October-February; March-July; July-September).

Admission Requirements: University degree and a minimum of 3 yrs professional experience.

Fees (Guilders): 4000 per annum.

Language of Instruction: English.

Degrees and Diplomas: Diplomas, 11 months.

Library: c. 4500 vols.

Publications: Report Series (five times a year); Newsletter (bi-annually).

Academic Staff: c. 20 (190).

Student Enrolment: c. 260.

5125 **KONINKLIJK INSTITUUT VOOR DE TROPEN**
Royal Tropical Institute Amsterdam
Mauritskade 63, 1092 AD Amsterdam
Cables: Intropen Amsterdam
Telex: 15080 KIT NL
Telephone: (020) 5688477

Tropical Agriculture
Tropical Hygiene
Social Research

Founded 1910. Operated in co-operation with the Netherlands Universities Foundation for International Co-operation (NUFFIC). Governing bodies: the Board of Directors; the Executive Board. Residential facilities for 156 students.

Arrangements for co-operation with: Institut de Médecine tropicale Prince Léopold, Antwerp; University of Nairobi; Airlangga University; Padjajaran University, Bandung; Institut d'Economie rurale, Mali.

Academic Year: September to July.

Admission Requirements: Degree of Medical Doctor and at least 4 yrs experience in developing countries.

Fees (Guilders): 9450.

Languages of Instruction: English and French.

Degrees and Diplomas: Degree of Master, 1 yr.

Library: Central Library.

Special Facilities (Museums, etc.): Tropenmuseum.
Publications: Tropical Geographical Medicine; Communications (Tropical Agriculture); Tropical Man (Anthropology).

5126 **EUROPA INSTITUTE OF THE UNIVERSITY OF AMSTERDAM**
P. O. Box 19123, 1000 GC Amsterdam
Telephone: (020) 5252162
Director: Richard H. Lauwaars
Executive Director: Robert Adolfs

European Integration Studies

Founded 1960 and attached to the University of Amsterdam. Financed by the Netherlands Universities Foundation for International Co-operation (NUFFIC) and the University of Amsterdam. Some residential facilities for foreign students.

Special arrangements for co-operation with the University of Minnesota.
Academic Year: September to May.
Admission Requirements: University degree.
Fees (Guilders): 2100 per annum.
Languages of Instruction: Dutch and English.
Degrees and Diplomas: Diploma, 1 yr.
Library: c. 10,000 vols.
Publications: Europese Mongrafieën (triannually); Legal Issues of European Integration (biannually); Occasional Papers.
Academic Staff, 1986-87: 6 (2).
Student Enrolment, 1986-87:

	Men	Women	Total
Of the country	1	1	2
Of other countries	17	8	25
Total	18	9	27

5127 **INTERNATIONAL INSTITUTE FOR LAND RECLAMATION AND IMPROVEMENT**
P. O. Box 45, 6700 AA Wageningen
Cables: intas, iac.
Telex: 45888 INTAS NL
Telephone: 08370-22938

Rural Development

Founded 1955 with initial financial support from the Kellogg Foundation. Under the jurisdiction of and financially supported by the government. Governing body: the Board of Governors on which the State Agricultural University is represented, together with the Ministriesof Agriculture and Fisheries, Transport and Public Works, and Development Aid.

Admission Requirements: University degree in an appropriate field and professional experience.
Fees (Guilders): 1000.
Language of Instruction: English.
Degrees and Diplomas: Certificate.
Library: Library and Documentation Centre, c. 21,000 vols.
Academic Staff: c. 20.
Student Enrolment: c. 30.

5128 **INTERNATIONAL UNION OF LOCAL AUTHORITIES (TRAINING DEPARTMENT)**
P. O. Box 90646, 2509 LP The Hague
Cables: IULA
Telex: 32504 INTA IULA
Telephone: (070) 24-40-32
President: Lars Eric Ericsson (1985-89)
Secretary-General: J.G. van Putten

Local Government

Founded 1913 in response to a need for international contact among local authorities and national local government associations. Operated in co-operation with the Netherlands Universities Foundation for International Co-operation (NUFFIC). Financed by membership fees, sales of publications, etc. Governing body: the Executive Committee elected by members.

Academic Year: March to December (March-May; October-December).
Admission Requirements: Experienced officials or elected members of local authorities.
Fees (Guilders): 9500.
Languages of Instruction: English, French, and Spanish.
Degrees and Diplomas: Certificate of Attendance, 8 weeks.
Library: c. 20,000 vols.
Publications: Planning and Administration (biannually); Biblio-graphia (every two months); IULA Newsletter (monthly).
Academic Staff, 1986-87: 3 (7).
Student Enrolment, 1986-87:

	Men	Women	Total
Of other countries	40	10	50

5129 **HAAGSE ACADEMIE VOOR INTERNATIONAAL RECHT THE HAGUE ACADEMY OF INTERNATIONAL LAW L'ACADÉMIE DE DROIT INTERNATIONAL DE LA HAYE**
Peace Palace, Carnegieplein 2, 2517 KJ The Hague
Cables: Acintlaw
Telex: 32323 ICJ NL
Telephone: (70) 469680
Secretary-General: Daniel Bardonnet (1985-)
Head of Secretariat: Ms M. Croese

International Law and International Relations

Founded 1923 with the support of the Carnegie Foundation. The Academy established its Centre for Studies and Research in 1957. Governing bodies: the Curatorium; the Administrative Council.

Academic Year: Summer Session only: 2 July to 10 August.
Admission Requirements: Advanced academic degree or 3 yrs practice in international affairs.
Languages of Instruction: English and French.
Degrees and Diplomas: Diploma.
Library: Library of the Peace Palace, 550,000 vols.

5130 **TELECOMMUNICATIONS INSTITUTE PITTC**
Postbox 1168, 1200 BD Hilversum
Cables: Signal-Hilversum
Telex: 43894 PHVS NL
Telephone: 31-35872750
Director: J.A. Samwel (1978-)

Telecommunications

Founded 1962. Operated in co-operation with the Netherlands Universities Foundation for International Co-operation (NUFFIC).

Academic Year: August to May.
Admission Requirements: A university degree in Technology.
Language of Instruction: English.
Degrees and Diplomas: Certificate, 2 weeks to 8 months.
Academic Staff, 1986-87: 25.
Student Enrolment, 1986-87:

	Men	Women	Total
Of the country	403	5	408
Of other countries	499	19	518
Total	902	24	926

5131 **RIJKS HOGERE LANDBOUWSCHOOL**
National Agricultural College Deventer
P.O. Box 7, 7400 AA Deventer
Telephone: 05700-22150
Director: J.W. Kijne (1982-)

Agriculture
Tropical Animal Husbandry

Founded 1912. Operated in co-operation with the Netherlands Universities Foundation for International Co-operation (NUFFIC). Financially supported by the Ministry of Agriculture and Fisheries. Some residential facilities for foreign students.

Arrangements for co-operation with the Universities of: Edinburgh; Reading.

Academic Year: August to July (August-December; January-July).
Admission Requirements: University degree and at least 4 yrs working experience.
Fees (Guilders): 1300 per annum.
Languages of Instruction: Dutch and English.
Degrees and Diplomas: Diploma, 10 months.
Library: c. 12,000 vols.

Academic Staff, 1986-87: 66 (20).
Student Enrolment, 1986-87:

	Men	Women	Total
Of the country	722	204	926
Of other countries	36	5	41
Total	758	209	967

5132 **PRAKTIJKSCHOOL 'BARNEVELD'**

Barneveld College
P.O. Box 64, 3770 AB Barneveld
Cables: 0018 (bacol nl)
Telephone: (31-0) 3420-14881
Managing Director: H. Broekhuizen

D. of International Studies and Projects (Animal Husbandry, Animal Nutrition and Animal Feed Manufacturing Technology)

Director: G.J. Koeslag; *staff* 25 (25)

Founded 1961 by the Netherlands Farmers' and Market Gardeners' Organization as an international Society with branches in Barneveld and abroad. A private institution receiving financial support from the Ministry of Agriculture, Nature Management and Fisheries. International programmes funded by Netherlands government, by international bodies and NGO's. Governing body: the Board.

Arrangements for co-operation for projects with local counterpart organizations in Colombia, Indonesia, Philippines, Yemen Arab Republic and Tunisia.

Academic Year: August to June (August-December; January-March; April-June).

Admission Requirements: Secondary school certificate or equivalent and a minimum 3 yrs professional experience, depending on type of course taken.

Languages of Instruction: Dutch, English, French, and possibly Spanish.

Degrees and Diplomas: Diplomas.

Academic Staff, 1989-90: 60.

Student Enrolment, 1989-90:

	Men	Women	Total
Of other countries	45	25	70

5133 **RADIO NEDERLAND TRAINING CENTRE**

P. O. Box 222, 1200 JG Hilversum
Cables: mundivox
Telex: 43336 WOMR NL
Telephone: (35) 16151
General Manager: Yaap Swart
General-Secretary: Hans Trompetter

Journalism

Radio and Television

Also Radio Netherland Training Centre; Branch in San José, Costa Rica

Founded 1968. Operated in co-operation with the Netherlands Universities Foundation for International Co-operation (NUFFIC). The courses are for experienced radio and television programmers from developing countries. On-the-spot training on request is also offered. Residential faculties (hostels) for trainees.

Academic Year: January-December (January-May; August-December).

Admission Requirements: Secondary school certificate or equivalent, and minimum 2 yrs professional experience.

Fees (Guilders): 22,500.

Language of Instruction: English.

Degrees and Diplomas: Certificate, 4 months.

5134 **NIJENRODE, THE NETHERLANDS SCHOOL OF BUSINESS**

Straatweg 25, 3621 BG Breukelen
Telex: 40553
Telephone: 03462-912111

F. of Business Administration

Founded 1946 as college, acquired present status and title 1982. A private institution supported by the Ministry of Education and Science. Operated in co-operation with the Netherlands Universities Foundation for International Co-operation (NUFFIC). Governing body: the Algemeen Bestuur (Board of Trustees). Residential facilities for *c.* 600 students.

Arrangements for co-operation in exchange programmes with universities in the U.S.A.

Academic Year: September to June (September-November; November-February; March-June).

Admission Requirements: University degree and entrance examination.

Fees (Guilders): 14,750-41,480.

Languages of Instruction: Dutch and English.

Degrees and Diplomas: Bachelor of Business Administration, 3 yrs; Master, 1 further yr. Also Diplomas.

Library: *c.* 20,000 vols.

Academic Staff: *c.* 30 (35).

Student Enrolment: *c.* 610.

NETHERLANDS ANTILLES

5135 **UNIVERSIDAT NASHONAL DI ANTIA UNIVERSITEIT VAN DE NEDERLANDSE ANTILLEN**
University of the Netherlands Antilles
Jan Noorduynweg 111, P.O. Box 3059, Willemstad, Curaçao
Telex: 1411 UNA NA
Telephone: 84422
Rector: Alex J.G. Reinders (1985-87)
Secretaris: Harold F. Hollander

F. of Law
Dean: Brian M. Mezas; *staff* 7 (8)
F. of Social Sciences and Economics
Dean: Roy Evers; *staff* 7 (25)
F. of Engineering (including Architecture)
Dean: H.A. Th. Cruden; *staff* 31 (25)
Computer Ce.

Founded 1970 as Law School, became Institute of Higher Studies 1973 and acquired present status and title 1979, incorporating the School of Engineering, founded 1972. The university is responsible to the Ministry of Education. Governing bodies: the Board of Trustees; the University Council. Some residential facilities for foreign students and students from other islands in the area.

Arrangements for co-operation with: State University of Groningen; University of Leiden; Delft University of Technology; Eindhoven University of Technology; Twente University of Technology; State University of Utrecht; State University of Leiden; Florida International University; University of the West Indies.

Academic Year: September to June (September-December; January-April).

Admission Requirements: Secondary school certificate or equivalent.

Fees (Antillean Guilders): 650.

Language of Instruction: Dutch.

Degrees and Diplomas: Kandidaat in Law, 2 yrs. Doctoraal examen leading to Meester, mr., in Law and in all other fields to doctorandus, drs., 4 ½ yrs. Also Certificate in Public Administration, 2 yrs.

Library: 70,000 vols.

Academic Staff, 1986-87: 39 (58).

Student Enrolment, 1986-87:

	Men	Women	Total
Of the country	245	172	417
Of other countries	80	51	131
Total	325	223	548

NEW CALEDONIA

5136 **UNIVERSITÉ FRANÇAISE DU PACIFIQUE**
B.P. 4477, Nouméa
Telex: 175
Telephone: 687-25-49-55
Directeur: Yves Pimont

D. of Law
Director: M. Orfila; *staff* 6 (11)
D. of Humanities and Literature
Director: P. Riegel; *staff* 4 (7)
D. of Languages
Director: M. Tolron; *staff* 3 (11)
D. of Sciences
Director: M. Garrrigos; *staff* 8 (7)
D. of Biology
Director: M. Valet; *staff* 8 (7)

Founded 1987. The University has Centres universitaires in Nouméa and Tahiti.

Academic Year: March to December.

Admission Requirements: Secondary school certificate (baccalauréat) and entrance examination.

Fees (Francs C.F.P.): 17,000 per annum.

Language of Instruction: French.

Degrees and Diplomas: Diplôme d'études universitaires générales (D.E.U.G), 2 yrs. Licence, a further 1 yr. Maîtrise, 1 yr following Licence. Diplôme détudes approfondies (D.E.A.), 1 further yr.

Academic Staff, 1989-90: 58 (86) (Total).

Student Enrolment, 1989-90: 1125 (Total).

5137 **CENTRE RÉGIONAL ASSOCIÉ DU C.N.A.M. (CENTRE NATIONAL DES ARTS ET MÉTIERS)**
Chambre de Commerce et de l'Industrie de Nouvelle-Calédonie, B.P. 3562, 10, rue Verdun, Nouméa
Telephone: 28-37-07
Directeur: Bernard Schall (1984-)

Founded 1971. Attached to the Conservatoire national des Arts et Métiers, Paris.

Academic Year: February to December (February-May; June-August; September-December).

Admission Requirements: Secondary school certificate (baccalauréat).

Fees (Francs, C.F.P.): 8000.

Language of Instruction: French.

Degrees and Diplomas: Diplôme d'Ingénieur, 9-10 yrs.

Academic Staff, 1986-87: – (14).

Student Enrolment, 1986-87:

	Men	Women	Total
Of the country	304	188	492
Of other countries	5	–	5
Total	309	188	497

5138 **CENTRE DE DROIT**
B.P.G. 4, 98300 Nouméa Cedex
Telephone: 27-59-44
Vice-Recteur: M. Vidal (1984-)

Law and Economics

Founded 1962. Attached to the Université de Bordeaux I.

Academic Year: February to December (February-May; June-August; September-December).

Admission Requirements: Secondary school certificate (baccalauréat).

Fees (Francs, C.F.P): Registration, 2400 per annum.

Language of Instruction: French.

Degrees and Diplomas: Capacité en Droit, 2 yrs. Diplôme d'études universitaires générales (D.E.U.G.), 2 yrs; Licence–en Droit, 3 yrs. Maîtrise, 1 yr after Licence.

Academic Staff: c. – (20).

Student Enrolment: c. 180.

5139 **ÉCOLE NORMALE D'INSTITUTEURS**
B.P. 19, Nouméa
Directeur: J. Tortonese

Teacher Training

Founded 1954.

5140 **CENTRE DE FORMATION ET DE RECHERCHE PÉDAGOGOGIE (ECOLE NNORMALE D'INSTITUTEURS DE L'ENSEIGNEMENT CATHOLIQUE)**
B.P. 3580, Nouméa
Telephone: 27-63-95
Directeur: Frère Huin

Education

Founded 1964. A private institution.

Academic Year: March to December (March-May; June-August; September-December).

Admission Requirements: Secondary school certificate (baccalauréat).

Language of Instruction: French.

Degrees and Diplomas: Diplôme.

Academic Staff, 1986-87: 8 (3).

Student Enrolment, 1986-87:

	Men	Women	Total
Of the country	14	40	54

5141 **ÉCOLE DE FORMATION DES PERSONNELS MÉDICAUX 'V. BUDILLON'**
B.P. 3278, Nouméa

Nursing

5142 **LYCÉE LA PÉRUSE**
B.P. M5, Nouméa Cedex

5143 **LYCÉE JULES GARNIER DE NOUVILLE**
B.P. H3, Nouméa Cedex

5144 **ÉCOLE DE GESTION ET DE COMMERCE DU PACIFIQUE SUD**
Chambre de Commerce et de l'Industrie, 15, rue de Verdun, B.P. M3, Nouméa
Telex: COMIN 3045 NM
Telephone: 27.43.33
Fax: 27.81.14
Président: Jean Lanchon
Directeur: Denis Baranger

D. of Commerce
Head: Sylvie Beaujouan; *staff* – (8)
D. of Gestion
Head: Denis Amice; *staff* – (12)
D. of Management
Head: Denis Mège; *staff* – (15)

Founded 1986. Under the supervision of the Chambre de Commerce et d'Industrie de Nouvelle-Calédonie.

Academic Year: March to December.

Admission Requirements: Secondary school certificate (baccalauréat) and entrance examination.

Fees (Francs C.F.P.): 120,000.

Language of Instruction: French.

Degrees and Diplomas: Diplôme, 3 yrs.

Publication: Initiatives.

Academic Staff, 1989-90: – (26).
Student Enrolment, 1990:

	Men	Women	Total
Of the country	12	17	29
Of other countries	1	1	2
Total	13	18	31

NICARAGUA

Universities

5145 **UNIVERSIDAD CENTROAMERICANA**
Central American University
Apartado postal 69, Managua
Telephone: (505) 70352-3; 70587
Rector: César Jerez, S.J.
Secretario General: Otilio Miranda, S.J.

F. of Business Administration
Dean: William Lau; *staff* 35 (38)
F. of Law
Dean: Rafael Chamorro Mora; *staff* 4 (17)
F. of Engineering
Dean: Irma de la Torre; *staff* 9
F. of Humanities (including Library Science, Sociology, and Journalism)
Dean: Angel López; *staff* 105 (53)
F. of Animal Husbandry and Agriculture
Dean: Carlos Saénz Bellanger; *staff* 61 (70)
Ce. for Languages (English and Russian)
Director: Otilio Miranda S.J.; *staff* 15 (8)
Central American History Research I.

Founded 1960 as a private autonomous university by the Society of Jesus. Mainly financed by student fees and grants, but receives some support from the State. Governing bodies: the Board of Trustees, comprising 9 members; the University Council, comprising 11 members.

Arrangements for co-operation with: University of Washington; Georgetown University; Universidad de Guadalajara; Escuela Superior de Administración y Dirección de Empresas, Barcelona; Catholic University of Louvain.

Academic Year: March to December (March-July; August-December).

Admission Requirements: Secondary school certificate (bachillerato). Entrance examination for the Faculty of Engineering.

Fees (Córdobas): 860 per annum.

Language of Instruction: Spanish.

Degrees and Diplomas: Licenciado in–Humanities; Agricultural Administration, 4 yrs; Business Administration, 4-5 yrs; Psychology; Law; Journalism; Accountancy; Computer Sciences; Animal Husbandry; Farm Management, 5 yrs. Professional title of Ingeniero in various fields, 5 yrs. Master of Science in Civil Engineering, 2-3 yrs. Doctor en Derecho, law,6 yrs. Profesor de Educación media, teaching qualification, 4 yrs.

Libraries: Central Library, 42,000 vols; Institute of Central American History, *c.* 12,000.

Special Facilities (Museums, etc.): Instituto Histórico Centroamericano.

Publications: Revista Encuentro (quarterly); Boletín informativo UCA.

Academic Staff: c. 340.

Student Enrolment, 1986-87: 4109.

5146 **UNIVERSIDAD NACIONAL AUTÓNOMA DE NICARAGUA**
National University of Nicaragua
León
Cables: Unan
Telephone: 26-12
Rector: Octavio Martínez Ordoñez

F. of Law and Social Sciences
F. of Medicine
F. of Chemistry
F. of Dentistry
F. of Physical and Mathematical Sciences (including Architecture and Surveying) (Managua)
F. of Humanities (including Education, Journalism, and Social Services) (Managua)
F. of Economics (including Business Administration) (Managua)
F. of Science and Letters
F. of Education (Managua)
F. of Agriculture (Managua)
F. of Health Sciences (Managua)
S. of Education
Extension D.

Founded 1812 as Universidad de León in succession to a 17th century seminary. Retained characteristics of Spanish colonial university until reorganization at end of 19th century. Accorded autonomous status 1958 and reforms initiated. Financially supported by the State through the Ministry of Education (88%), tuition fees (10%), other sources (2%). Governing body: the Junta Universitaria, composed of the Rector as Chairman, the deans of the faculties, the Secretary-General, the Vice-Rector, a representative of the Ministry of Education, and a representative of the students. Residential facilities in León and Managua for students and for foreign academic staff.

Academic Year: June to May (June-October; November-March; April-May).

Admission Requirements: Secondary school certificate (bachillerato) or foreign equivalent. Entrance examination for Medicine, Psychology, Dentistry, and Architecture.

Language of Instruction: Spanish.

Degrees and Diplomas: Licenciado in–Chemistry; Physics and Mathematics; Biology; Journalism; Social Work; Education; Orientation, 4 yrs; Law; Business Administration; Accountancy; Economics; Marketing; Psychology, 5 yrs. Professional titles of–Topógrafo, 2 yrs; Tecnólogo médico, 4 yrs; Ingeniero civil; Ingeniero agrónomo; Arquitecto; Cirujano Dentista, dentist, 5 yrs. Doctorado en Medicina, 7 yrs. Profesor de Educación media, teaching qualification, 4 yrs. Also Master in Applied Ecology, 2 yrs after Licenciado.

Libraries: Central Library, *c.* 120,000 vols; Managua district library, *c.* 55,000; Carazo regional library, *c.* 8500; Puerto Cabezas, *c.* 3000.

Publications: Cuadernos Universitarios (quarterly); Revista Médica (semestral); Gaceta Universitaria (bimonthly); Taller (student literary review in English).

Academic Staff: c. 800.

Student Enrolment: c. 22,000.

5147 **UNIVERSIDAD NACIONAL DE INGENIERÍA**
Managua
Telephone: 73709
Rector: Juan Sánchez Barquero
Secretario General: Julio Maltez Montiel

F. of Basic Sciences
Dean: Mayra Calero Silva; *staff* 70 (6)
F. of Construction Engineering and Architecture
Dean: Sergio Obregón Aguilar; *staff* 51 (7)
F. of Industrial Engineering
Dean: Pablo Lanzas Ayon; *staff* 49 (18)
F. of Technical Studies
Dean: Mariano González Meléndez; *staff* 36 (51)

Founded 1983. A State institution.

Arrangements for co-operation with: University of Guadalajara; Autonomous University of Mexico; Autonomous University of Yucatan; Royal Institute of Technology, Stockholm; Delft University of Technology.

Academic Year: March to November (March-July; August-November).

Admission Requirements: Secondary school certificate (bachillerato).

Fees (Córdobas): 500 per annum.

Language of Instruction: Spanish.

Degrees and Diplomas: Professional titles of–Ingeniero; Arquitecto, 5-6 yrs.

Academic Staff, 1986-87: 265 (23).

Student Enrolment, 1986-87: 4030.

5148 **UNIVERSIDAD POLITÉCNICA DE NICARAGUA**
Apartado postal 3595, Managua
Telephone: 97740
Rector: Sergio Denis García Velásquez
Registrar: Mayra Rodríguez

S. of Education (Technical)
S. of Administration, Commerce, and Finance
Director: Guillermo Zambrana; *staff* 11
S. of Nursing
Director: Lidya Ruth Zamora; *staff* 14
S. of Design
Director: Maria Vargas; *staff* 8 (24)
S. of Statistics
Director: Melba Castillo; *staff* 4 (14)

Founded 1968 by the Nicaraguan Baptist Convention with the aid of the American Baptist Home Mission Society. Became university 1976. A private university receiving government subsidy for operating expenses. Relies on outside contributions for the other costs. Governing body: the Board of Trustees.

Academic Year: February to November (February-July; August-November).

Admission Requirements: Secondary school certificate (bachillerato).

Fees: None.

Language of Instruction: Spanish.

Degrees and Diplomas: Professional titles and Técnico Superior in–Administration; Commercial Art and Publicity; Electro-Mechanical Engineering; Interior Decoration and Design; Nursing; Physical Education; Industrial Arts; Vocational Industrial Education; Professional Design; Insurance; Marketing; Agricultural Administration; Communication Graphics; Architectural Drawing and Supervision of Construction; Statistics; Banking and Finance; Nursing, 2 ½-3 yrs. Licenciado in Nursing, a further 2 yrs.

Library: c. 1500 vols.

Academic Staff, 1990: 37 (38).

Student Enrolment, 1990:

	Men	Women	Total
Of the country	424	1158	1582

Other Institutions

5149 **CENTRO POPULAR DE ESTUDIOS SUPERIORES**
Frente al Parque Morazan, Matagalpa
Telephone: 2474
Director: Eduardo Jaen Aráuz (1981-)

Accountancy and Finance

Founded 1980. A State institution.

Academic Year: February to November (February-June; July-November).

Admission Requirements: Secondary school certificate (bachillerato).

Fees: None.

Language of Instruction: Spanish.

Degrees and Diplomas: Licenciado. Certificate of Técnico.

Library: c. 1400 vols.

Academic Staff: c. 40.

Student Enrolment: c. 400 (External).

5150 **ESCUELA DE AGRICULTURA Y GANADERÍA**
Apartado postal 81, Esteli
Telephone: 071-2347
Rector: José María Martín Mateo

Animal Husbandry
Agriculture
Veterinary Medicine

Founded 1968. A private Catholic institution. Residential facilities for 80 students.

Academic Year: March to December (March-August; August-December).

Admission Requirements: Secondary school certificate (bachillerato).

Language of Instruction: Spanish.

Degrees and Diplomas: Professional titles of Técnico, 5 sem.

Library: 4491 vols.

Academic Staff, 1986-87: 27.

Student Enrolment, 1986-87:

	Men	Women	Total
Of the country	196	116	312
Of other countries	2	–	2
Total	198	116	314

5151 **ESCUELA INTERNACIONAL DE AGRICULTURA Y GANADERÍA**
Apartado postal 5, Rivas

Animal Husbandry
Agriculture

Founded 1969.

5152 **ESCUELA DE ENFERMERÍA**
Jinotepe-Carazo

Nursing

Founded 1984.

5153 **ESCUELA ENFERMERÍA**
Puerto Cabezas

Nursing

Founded 1982.

5154 **ESCUELA DE ENFERMERÍA DE LA TRINIDAD**
Esteli

Nursing

Founded 1982.

5155 **INSTITUTO POLITÉCNICO DE LA SALUD**
Apartado postal 'Antiguo Colegio Francés', Managua

Industrial Food Technology
Nursing
Medical Statistics
Clinical Laboratory Technology
Physiotherapy

Founded 1980.

5156 **INSTITUTO TÉCNICO AERONÁUTICO**
Managua

Commercial Aviation

Founded 1982.

5157 **INSTITUTO TÉCNICO 'LA SALLE'**
Apartado postal 4, León
Telephone: 0311-2584
Director: Eduardo Muñoz Calzada (1985-)

Industrial Mechanics
Electro-Energetics
Agricultural Mechanization
Electrical Engineering and Refrigeration

Founded 1982. A private institution receiving some financial support from the State.

Academic Year: March to December.

Admission Requirements: Secondary school certificate (bachillerato).

Language of Instruction: Spanish.

Degrees and Diplomas: Professional titles of Ingeniero. Also Diploma of Técnico.

Library: 10,000 vols.

Academic Staff, 1986-87: – (8).

Student Enrolment, 1986-87:

Men	Women	Total
36	8	44

5158 **INSTITUTO TECNOLÓGICO DE ESTUDIOS SUPERIORES 'PEDRO ARAUZ PALACIOS'**
Apartado postal 35, Managua

Civil Engineering
Mechanical Engineering
Telecommunications
Electro-Energetics

Founded 1979.

5159 **INSTITUTO TECNOLÓGICO NACIONAL**
Apartado postal 162, Granada
Rector: Guillermo Martinez

Industrial Mechanics
Electro-Energetics

Industrial Chemistry
Agricultural Mechanization

Founded 1974.

NIGER

5160 **UNIVERSITÉ DE NIAMEY**

University of Niamey
B.P. 237, Niamey
Telex: 5258
Telephone: 73-2713/15
Recteur: Sidikou Arouna Hamidou (1988-)
Secrétaire général: Maman Amatagar

F. of Science
Dean: Issoufou Kouada; *staff* 55 (26)
F. of Letters and Human Sciences
Dean: Aboubakar Adamou; *staff* 45 (30)
F. of Health Sciences
Dean: Hamidou Sékou; *staff* 16 (28)
F. of Agriculture and Animal Husbandry
Dean: Alhassane Yenokoye; *staff* 15 (9)
F. of Economics and Law
Dean: Amadou Tankoano; *staff* 20 (29)
F. of Education
Dean: Karmago Ibrahim Konate; *staff* 27 (10)
Mathematics Research I.
Director: Abou Traoré; *staff* 3 (12)
Human Sciences Research I.
Director: Boubé Gado; *staff* 7
Radioisotope Research I.
Director: M. Marini; *staff* 5 (7)

Founded 1971 as Centre d'Enseignement supérieur. Became university 1973. Under the jurisdiction of the Ministry of Higher Education and Research. Governing body: the Conseil, composed of the Rector, deans and directors of the faculties and institutes, representatives of the academic staff and student body, and representatives of the government. Residential facilities for academic staff and students.

Arrangements for co-operation with the Universities of: Orléans; Toulouse; Montpellier; Paris VI; Clermont-Ferrand; Aix-Marseille; Dijon; Grenoble; Bordeaux; Toulon et du Var; Tours; Tunis; Würzburg.

Academic Year: October to June (October-December; January-March; April-June).

Admission Requirements: Secondary school certificate (baccalauréat) or special entrance examination.

Fees (Francs C.F.A.): 5000 per annum.

Language of Instruction: French.

Degrees and Diplomas: Diplôme d'études universitaires générales (D.E.U.G.) in Law and Economics, 2 yrs; Diplôme universitaire d'études scientifiques (D.U.E.S.) in–Mathematics and Physics; Physics and Chemistry; Chemistry and Biology; Biology and Geology; Diplôme universitaire d'études littéraires (D.U.E.L.), 2 yrs. Licence–ès Sciences physiques; ès Sciences naturelles; ès Lettres, 1 yr after D.E.U.G., D.U.E.S. or D.U.E.L. Maîtrise ès Sciences agronomiques, 1 yr after Licence. Diplôme–d'Agronomie approfondie; d'Ingénieur agronome, 5 yrs. Doctorat en Médecine, Doctorat (3e cycle) in Letters and Science. Doctorat d'Etat. Also diplomas in school counselling and teaching (lower level).

Library: 62,000 vols.

Academic Staff, 1986-87:

Rank	Full-time	Part-time
Professeurs	11	10
Maîtres de conférences	25	10
Maîtres-Assistants	73	29
Assistants	117	76
Total	226	125

Student Enrolment, 1986-87:

	Men	Women	Total
Of the country	2442	473	2915
Of other countries	266	42	308
Total	2708	515	3223

5161 **UNIVERSITÉ ISLAMIQUE DU NIGER**

Niamey
In process of development

5162 **ÉCOLE NATIONALE D'ADMINISTRATION NIVEAU SUPÉRIEUR**

B.P. 542, Niamey
Telephone: 72-2853

Administration

5163 **ÉCOLE AFRICAINE ET MALGACHE DE L'AVIATION CIVILE**

B.P. 746, Niamey
Telephone: 72-3661

Aviation

5164 **ÉCOLE NATIONALE DE LA SANTÉ PUBLIQUE NIVEAU SUPÉRIEUR**

B.P. 290, Niamey
Telephone: 72-3001

Public Health

5165 **CENTRE AGRHYMET**

Niamey

NORWAY

Universities and University Institutions

5166 ***UNIVERSITETET I BERGEN**
University of Bergen
Muséplass 1, 5007 Bergen
Telex: 42690 UBBNTELETEX: 2421-441023 UIBTA
Telephone: 475-21-30-50
Fax: 475-32-85-85
Rektor: Ole Didrik Lærum (1990-92)
Direktør: Kåre Rommetveit

F. of Arts
Dean: Ingvild Sælid Gilhus; *staff* 209 (5)
F. of Mathematics and Natural Sciences (including Computer Sciences)
Dean: Harald Høiland; *staff* 418 (20)
F. of Medicine (including Nursing)
Dean: Dagfinn Aarskog; *staff* 293 (36)
F. of Social Sciences (including Political Science)
Dean: Svein Nordbotten; *staff* 117 (7)
F. of Dentistry
Dean: Nils Skaug; *staff* 169 (1)
F. of Law
Dean: Nils Nygaard; *staff* 44 (3)
F. of Psychology
Dean: Tordis Dalland Evans; *staff* 76 (3)
Ce. for Development Studies
Director: Gunnar Sørbø
Ce. for Environmental and Resource Studies
Director: Ulf Lie
Ce. for International Health
Director: Bjarne Bjorvatn
Ce. for Middle East and Islamic Studies
Ce. for the Study of Science and Humanities

Founded as Bergen Museum 1825, became university 1948. A State institution enjoying considerable autonomy in both academic and financial matters. Financed by a grant voted by parliament. Governing bodies: the Akademiske Kollegium (Senate), consisting of the Rector, Prorector, 6 representatives of the academic staff, 2 representatives of the non-academic staff, and 3 representatives of the student body; the Faculty Councils. Some residential facilities for students.

Arrangements for co-operation with the Universities of: California; Washington, Seattle; Minnesota; Oregon; Newfoundland; York; Khartoum; Kiel; Lübeck; Dar es Salaam; Caen.

Academic Year: August to June (August-December; January-June).

Admission Requirements: Secondary school certificate (examen artium) or recognized equivalent.

Fees: Tuition, none.

Language of Instruction: Norwegian.

Degrees and Diplomas: Candidatus magisterii, cand.mag. in–Natural Sciences; Social Sciences; Arts, 4-4 ½ yrs. Candidatus in–Dentistry, cand.odont., 5 yrs; Law, cand.jur.; Natural Sciences, cand.scient., 5-6 yrs; Arts, cand.philol.; Social Sciences, cand.polit., 5 ½-6 yrs; Medicine, cand.med., 6-6 ½ yrs; Psychology, cand.psychol., 6 ½-7 yrs. Magister artium, 6-7 yrs. Doctorate in–Philosophy; Medicine; Dentistry; Natural Sciences; Law; Social Sciences; Arts; Psychology. Also Licentiatus in Dentistry.

Library: Bergen University Library, 1,100,000 vols.

Special Facilities (Museums, etc.): Historical Museum; Natural History Museum; Bryggen Museum of Medieval Archaeology; Museum of Theatre and Drama; Botanical Garden; the Norwegian Arboretum.

Publication: Bulletin (in English, biannually).

Academic Staff, 1989-90:

Rank	Full-time
Professors	285
Lecturers	427
Research Assistants	131
Others	28
Total	861

Student Enrolment, 1989-90:

	Men	Women	Total
Of the country	4985	6225	11,210
Of other countries	458	328	786
Total	5443	6553	11,966

5167 ***UNIVERSITETET I OSLO**
University of Oslo
Postboks 1072, Blindern, 0316 Oslo 3
Cables: oslo 3
Telex: 72425 UNIOS N
Telephone: (2) 45-50-50
Fax: (2) 45-44-42
Rektor: Inge Lønning (1984-92)
Universitetsdirektør: Kjell Stahl

F. of Theology
Dean: Svein Aage Christoffersen
F. of Law
Dean: Erling Selvig
F. of Medicine
Dean: Erik Thorsby
F. of Liberal Arts
Dean: Sivert Langholm
F. of Mathematics and Natural Sciences
Dean: Tor Amundsen
F. of Dentistry
Dean: Edward B. Messelt
F. of Social Sciences (including Education Economics, and Politics)
Dean: Rolv Mikkel Blakar
D. of Nursing
Head: Margarethe Lorensen
International Summer S.
Head: Andus Lysne
Summer Session for School Teachers
Ce. for Teacher Training and School Service
Director: Sigmund Lieberg
Also Norwegian Institutes in Rome and Athens.

Founded 1811 as Kongelige Frederiks Universitet, named after the King of Denmark. Title changed to Universitetet i Oslo 1939. The university is a State institution and government financed. Professors are now appointed bythe Senate. Governing body: the Akademiske Kollegium (Senate), composed of the Rector, Prorector, 6 representatives of the permanent academic staff, 2 representatives of the non-academic staff, and 2 representatives of the student body. The Rector is elected from among the permanent academic staff and serves for a period of 3 years. Residential facilities for students and some academic staff.

Arrangements for co-operation with Humboldt-Universität zu Berlin; Technische Universität (Otto von Guericke), Magdeburg; Christian-Albrechts Universität zu Kiel; Eberhard-Karls-Universität Tübingen; Wilhelm Pieck Universität Rostock; Università degli Studi di Firenze; Universitatea Bucaresti; Universiteit van Amsterdam; Inter-University Centre of Post-Graduate Studies, Dubrovnik; University of Zimbabwe; University of North Dakota.

Academic Year: August to June (August-December; January-June).

Admission Requirements: Secondary school certificate (examen artium) or recognized equivalent.

Fees (Kroner): 330 per term.

Language of Instruction: Norwegian.

Degrees and Diplomas: Candidatus in–Dentistry, cand. odont.; Pharmacy, cand.pharm.; Law, cand.jur.; Science, cand.scient.; Economics, cand.oecon., 5 yrs; Politics, cand.polit.; Sociology, cand. sociol.; Medicine, cand.med.; Psychology, cand.psychol.; Theology, cand.theol.; Philology, cand.philol.; Education, cand.paed., 6-8 yrs. Cand.mag. in Arts or Science, 3 ½-4 yrs. Licentiatius in–Law, lic. juris.; Dentistry, lic.odont.; Theology, lic.theol., 5-6 yrs; Economics, lic.oecon.; Philosophy, lic.philos., 6-7 yrs. Magister artium in–Liberal Arts; Social Sciences, 6-7 yrs. Doctorates in–Theology; Law; Medicine; Philosophy; Dentistry; Psychology; Science.

Library: Universitetsbiblioteket, total, *c.* 4,000,000 vols.

Special Facilities (Museums, etc.): Museums: Botany; Ethnography; Geology; Palaeontology; Zoology. Botanical Garden; Collection of National Antiquities; Numismatic Cabinet.

Publications: UNIFORUM (c. 25-30 issues per annum); Akademisk Kvartal (quarterly).

Academic Staff, 1989: c. 1700.

Student Enrolment, 1989:

	Men	Women	Total
Of the country	11,280	14,426	25,706
Of other countries	–	–	1852
Total	11,280	14,426	27,558

5168 ***UNIVERSITETET I TROMSØ**

University of Tromsø

Breivika, 9000 Tromsø

Telephone: (4783) 44000

Fax: (4783) 80094

Rektor: Ole D. Mjøs

Direktør: Harald Overvaag

S. of Medicine
Dean: Jarie Aarbakke; *staff* 191

S. of Law
Dean: Jens Edvin Andrasservl; *staff* 14

I. of Social Sciences
Dean: Helge O. Larsen; *staff* 80

S. of Languages and Literature
Dean: Öse Hlorth Lervik; *staff* 40

I. of Biology and Geology
Dean: Børre Robertsen; *staff* 62

I. of Mathematics, Physics, and Chemistry (including Computer Sciences and Statistics)
Dean: Per N. Skancke; *staff* 90

S. of Fisheries
Dean: Kjell Olsen; *staff* 45

I. of Museology
Dean: Roger Jørgensen; *staff* 47

D. of Education
Head: Einar Størkersen; *staff* 8

Founded 1968, officially opened by King Olav V 1972. A State institution enjoying considerable autonomy in both academic and financial matters. Financed by the government. Governing body: the Styret, comprising 9 members.

Participates in the NORDPLUS programme.

Academic Year: August to June (August-December; January-June).

Admission Requirements: Secondary school certificate (examen artium) or recognized equivalent.

Fees: Tuition, none.

Language of Instruction: Norwegian.

Degrees and Diplomas: Candidatus magisterii, cand.mag.; Fiskerikandidat, 4-5 yrs; Candidatus scientiarum, cand.scient., 5-5 ½ yrs; Candidatus philologiae, cand.philol.; Candidatus rerum politicarum, cand.polit.; Candidatus medicinae, cand.med., 6 yrs; Magister artium, mag.art., 5-6 yrs. Doctorate in–Philosophy; Medicine; Science.

Library: c. 400,000 vols.

Special Facilities (Museums, etc.): Museology Museum.

Publications: Uniternt (9 times a year); Ottar.

Academic Staff, 1986-87:

Rank	Full-time	Part-time
Professorer	99	37
Amanuenser	177	8
Stipendiater	34	–
Total	310	45

Student Enrolment, 1990:

	Men	Women	Total
Of the country	1916	1773	3689
Of other countries	125	70	195
Total	2041	1843	3884

5169 ***UNIVERSITETET I TRONDHEIM**

University of Trondheim

Postboks 4392, Sverres gt.15, 7002 Trondheim

Telephone: (7) 59-50-00

Fax: (7) 59-68-93

Rektor: Rolf Lenschow (1987-93)

Administrerende Direktør: Toe H. Johansen

I. of Technology
Rector: Dag Kavlie; *staff* 717 (73)

C. of Arts and Science
Dean: Magne Dybvig; *staff* 236 (7)

I. of Technology
Dean: Karsten Jakobsen; *staff* 730 (86)

Museum of Natural History and Archaeology
Director: Gunnar Sundnes; *staff* 33

D. of Architecture
Chairman: G. Aschehoug

D. of Mining and Metallurgy
Chairman: Jon Kleppe

D. of Civil Engineering
Chairman: Hallvard Ødegaard

D. of Mechanical Engineering
Chairman: Asbjørn Rolstadås

D. of Electrical and Computer Engineering
Chairman: Hans H. Faanes

D. of Chemistry
Chairman: Norvald Nesse

D. of Physics and Mathematics
Chairman: Olav Njåstad

D. of Economics and Administration
Chairman: Steinar Nijgaard

D. of Naval Architecture and Marine Engineering
Chairman: Carl M. Larsen

F. of Arts (including Applied Linguistics, Drama, Film, Theatre, English, French, German, History, Linguistics, Music, Scandinavian Languages and Literature, Philosophy, Phonetics, Religious Studies, and Social Anthropology)
Dean: Per Øverland

F. of Sciences (including Aqua-Culture, Bio-Chemistry, Biology, Bio-Technology, Botany, Chemistry, Environmental Science, Informatics, Marine Biology, Mathematics, Physics, Statistics, and Zoology)
Dean: Eivin Røskaft

F. of Social Sciences (including Advanced Studies for Social Workers, Education, Geography, Psychology, Economics, Social and Political Science, Sociology, Higher Economic and Administrative Studies)
Dean: Per Morten Schiefloe

I. of Teacher Training
Rector: Rolf Grankvist

D. of Medicine
Dean: Kåre Molne; *staff* 47 (36)

D. of Archaeology

D. of Natural History

Founded 1968, integrating the Institute of Technology, founded 1910, the College of Arts and Science, founded 1922, and the Museum of Natural History and Archaeology, founded 1766. Governing body: the Senate, comprising 9 members.

Academic Year: September to June (September-December; January-June).

Admission Requirements: Secondary school certificate (examen artium) or equivalent.

Fees: None.

Language of Instruction: Norwegian.

Degrees and Diplomas: Sivilingeniør, siv.ing., engineering, in all fields, except Architecture, Arkitekt, arch., 4-4 1/2 yrs. Doctor ingeniør, dr.ing., 2 1/2-3 yrs. Doctor scientarum, Dr.scient.; Doctor artium, Dr.art.; Doctor rerum politicarum, Dr.polit., 2 1/2 yrs; Doctor technicae, dr.techn., Doctor philosophiae, Dr.philos.; Doctor medicinae, Dr.med., awarded by thesis showing independent research. Candidatus, in–Science, cand.scient., 5 yrs; Arts, cand.philol.; cand.polit, 6 yrs; Candidatus Magisterii, cand.mag., 4-5 yrs. Also diploma in Teacher Training, 6months.

Libraries: The Technical University Library of Norway; the University Library of Trondheim, total, *c.* 2,000,000 vols.

Special Facilities (Museums, etc.): Trondhjem Biologiske Stasjon (Marine Station); Ringve Botanical Garden.

Publication: UNITNYTT (8-10 times per year).

Academic Staff, 1989-90: 1018 (141).

Student Enrolment, 1989-90: 13,000.

5170 ***NORGES LANDBRUKSHØGSKOLE**

Norwegian College of Agriculture
1432 Ås-NLH
Telephone: (02) 94-00-60

D. of Animal Husbandry
D. of Food Technology
D. of Mathematics and Natural Sciences
D. of Plant Production
D. of Social Sciences (including Forestry and Land Consolidation and) Architecture
D. of Agricultural Technology
Forest Research I.
Plant Protection I.
I. of Agricultural Engineering
D. of Agricultural Vocational Education

Founded 1859, became university institution 1919 and acquired present status and title 1972. The college is under the jurisdiction of the Ministry of Agriculture. Governing bodies: the Collegium (Senate), including all full and associate professors; the Executive Board of 9 members. The students are represented on both bodies. Residential facilities for academic staff and students.

Academic Year: August to August (August-December; January-May; May-August).

Admission Requirements: Secondary school certificate (examen artium) or equivalent, as well as qualification from a vocational agricultural school and 2 or 3 yrs practical work.

Fees: Tuition, none.

Language of Instruction: Norwegian.

Degrees and Diplomas: Professional titles of–Candidat of Agriculture, cand.agric., 5 yrs. Licentiat of Agriculture, lic.agric., a further 3-4 yrs. Doctor of Agriculture, Dr.Agric.

Library: Main Library, *c.* 365,000 vols.

Publication: Meldinger fra Norges Landbrukshøgskole (scientific reports).

Academic Staff: c. 120.

Student Enrolment: c. 970.

5171 **ARKITEKTHØGSKOLEN I OSLO**

Oslo School of Architecture
Postboks 6768, St. Olavsgt. 2-4, 0130 Oslo 1
Telephone: (02) 20-83-16
Rektor: Odd Kjeld Østbye (1990-93)
Direktør: Inger Stray Lien

Architecture

Founded 1945 as Statens Arkitektskole, acquired present title 1969. A State institution governed by a Board appointed by the Ministry of Education and Research.

Participates in: ILAUD, NORDPLUS-programme, EAAE and NOFUA.

Academic Year: September to June (September-December; January-June).

Admission Requirements: Secondary school certificate (examen artium).

Fees: None.

Language of Instruction: Norwegian.

Degrees and Diplomas: Diploma, 5 1/2 yrs.

Library: c. 30,000 vols.

Special Facilities (Museums, etc.): Gallery AHO.

Publication: The Yearbook, 1990

Academic Staff, 1989-90: 32.

Student Enrolment: c. 270.

5172 **NORGES HANDELSHØYSKOLE**

Norwegian College of Economics and Business Administration
Helleveien 30, 5035 Bergen
Telex: 40642
Telephone: (05) 25-65-00

D. of Economics (including Business Administration)
D. of General Studies
Extension D.
Administrative Research Foundation
Applied Research Ce.

Founded 1936 following legislation passed in 1917. A State institution of university rank. Governing bodies: the Kollegium (Board) of 7 members; the Division Boards; the Staff Council. The students have elected representatives in all governing bodies. Some residential facilities for students.

Academic Year: September to June (September-December; January-June).

Admission Requirements: Secondary school certificate (examen artium).

Fees: None.

Language of Instruction: Norwegian.

Degrees and Diplomas: Siviløkonomeksamen, economics and business administration, 4 yrs. Handelslærereksamen, teaching qualification, 2 further yrs. Siviløkonom Hae in–business administration, economics, or behavioural sciences, 2 yrs. Høyere Revisoreksamen, accountancy, 1 further yr. Licentiatus, 3-4 yrs after Siviløkonom, by thesis. Dr.oecon, Doctor of Economics, by thesis showing independent research.

Library: c. 200,000 vols.

Academic Staff: c. 140 (20).

Student Enrolment: c. 1460 (Also *c.* 2600 extension department students).

5173 ***NORGES IDRETTSHØGSKOLE**

Norwegian University of Sport and Physical Education
Sognsveien 220, 0807 Oslo 8
Telephone: (2) 23-46-85
Rector: Kari Fasting

I. of Sport
Director: Kåre Nicolaysen
I. of Biology and Sportmedizin
Director: Sigmund B. Strømme
I. of Social Sciences
Director: Gunnar Breivik

Founded 1968. A State institution financially supported by the Ministry of Education and Research. Governing body: the Styre (Board), comprising 9 members.

Academic Year: August to June (August-December; January-June).

Admission Requirements: Secondary school certificate (examen artium) and physical fitness examination.

Fees: None.

Language of Instruction: Norwegian.

Degrees and Diplomas: Diploma, 6-7 yrs. Also minor subject courses, 1 yr.

Library: c. 25,000 vols.

Publications: LITTomLITT (c. 10 times a year); Informasjon (c. 5 times a year); Notater og rapporter fra NIH; Kopendier; Bibliografier og dokumentasjons studier.

Academic Staff, 1989-90: 50 (6).

Student Enrolment, 1989-90:

	Men	Women	Total
Of the country	170	170	340
Of other countries	5	5	10
Total	175	175	350

5174 **NORGES MUSIKKHØGSKOLE**

Norwegian College of Music
Postboks 5190, Majorstua, 0302 Oslo 3
Telephone: (2) 46-40-55
Fax: (2) 46-70-74
Principal: Benny Dahl-Hansen
Direktør: Sigmund Skrinde

Music

Founded 1973. A State institution governed by an elected Board.

Academic Year: September to June (September-December; January-June).

Admission Requirements: Secondary school certificate (examen artium) and entrance examination.

Fees: None.
Language of Instruction: Norwegian.
Degrees and Diplomas: Degree, 4 yrs except School Music, 3 yrs. Postgraduate specialization, a further 2 yrs.
Academic Staff: c. 50 (50).
Student Enrolment: c. 290.

5175 **NORGES VETERINÆRHØGSKOLE**
Norwegian College of Veterinary Medicine
Postboks 8146, DEP, 0033 Oslo 1
Telephone: (2) 69-36-90
Fax: (2) 56-57-04
Rektor: Kåre Fossum (1989-)
Direktør: Kjell Gjfevenes

Veterinary Medicine (including Animal Husbandry)

Founded 1935, an autonomous State institution responsible to the Ministry of Agriculture. Financed by the State, Agricultural Research Council, other research councils, and industry. Governing body: the Board.
Academic Year: August to June (August-December; January-June).
Admission Requirements: Secondary school certificate (examen artium) and 6 months practical farm work.
Fees: None.
Language of Instruction: Norwegian.
Degrees and Diplomas: Candidatus Medicinae Veterinariae, 5 ½-6 yrs. Doctor scientiarum, Dr.scient., a further 3 yrs. Doctor Medicinae Veterinariae, 4-5 yrs by thesis showing independent research.
Library: College Library, 62,500 vols.
Special Facilities (Museums, etc.): Veterinary Museum.
Publication: Annual Report.
Academic Staff, 1989-90: 87 (10).
Student Enrolment, 1986-87:

Men	Women	Total
115	155	270*

*Including 9 foreign students.

Other Institutions

Regional, Engineering and Other Colleges

5176 **AGDER DISTRIKTSHØGSKOLE**
Agder College
Postboks 407, 4601 Kristiansand
Telephone: (42) 27040
Fax: (42) 27041
President: Sylfest Lomheim
Managing Director: Arne Holme

I. of Economics and Business Administration
Head: Harald Knudsen; *staff* 20 (20)
I. of Public Administration (including Political Science)
Head: Pål Repstad; *staff* 8 (10)
I. of Mathematics
Head: Hanserin Borgersen; *staff* 6 (4)
I. of Computer Sciences
Head: Tore Funker; *staff* 10 (4)
I. of Languages
D. of Chemistry
Head: Texje Ostensen; *staff* 5 (2)
I. of Translation (Norwegian, English, French)
Head: Francine Lomheim; *staff* 5 (5)
I. of Norwegian
Head: Marit Chaistoffersen; *staff* 5 (3)
I. of English
Head: Peter Young; *staff* 5 (2)
Extension D.
Head: Jan Duvalano; *staff* 3 (25)

Founded 1969 by Act of Parliament as one of several new regional colleges designed to offer short professional courses in areas not covered by universities and other institutions. A State institution financially supported by the Ministry of Education and Research. Governing body: the Regional Styre (Board), of 10 members. Residential facilities for c. 100 students.

Arrangements for co-operation with: Pacific Lutheran University, Tacoma; Luther College; St. Olavs College; Monterrey Institute of International Studies; University of California-Santa Barbara; Université de Toulouse III; Université d'Aix-Marseille III; Ecole supérieure d'Interprétes et de Traducteurs, Paris; University of Surrey, Guildford; Darlington College of Technology; University of Cracow; Institute of Development Management, Tanzania.
Academic Year: August to June (August-November; January-June).
Admission Requirements: Secondary school certificate (examen artium).
Fees: None.
Language of Instruction: Norwegian.
Degrees and Diplomas: Degree of Høgskolekandidat, 2-3 yrs. Candidatus magisterii, Cand.mag., 4 yrs. Avd. Kandidat, 4 yrs.
Library: c. 60,000 vols.
Publications: Studiehandbok (annually); Katalog; ADH-nytt; ADH-Skrifter; ADH-årsmelding (annual report); Research at APH (every third year).
Academic Staff, 1989: 55.
Student Enrolment, 1989:

	Men	Women	Total
Of the country	553	842	1395
Of other countries	26	19	45
Total	579	861	1440*

*Also 283 external students.

5177 **HEDMARK DISTRIKTSHØGSKOLE**
Hedmark College
Postboks 104, 2450 Rena
Telephone: (064) 40800
Rektor: Erik Mønness (1986-88)
Kontorschef: Anne Myhre

Sec. of Business Administration
Sec. of Economics
Sec. of Computer Sciences

Founded 1979. A State institution financially supported by the Ministry of Cultural and Scientific Affairs. Residential facilities for students.
Academic Year: August to June (August-December; January-June).
Admission Requirements: Secondary school certificate (examen artium).
Language of Instruction: Norwegian.
Degrees and Diplomas: Degree of Høgskolekandidat, 2 yrs. Candidatus magisterii, cand.mag., 4 yrs.
Library: c. 5000 vols.
Publication: Research Papers.
Academic Staff, 1986-87: 14.
Student Enrolment, 1986-87:

	Men	Women	Total
Of the country	93	165	258
Of other countries	2	–	2
Total	95	165	260

5178 **FINNMARK DISTRIKTSHØGSKOLE**
Finnmark College
Postboks 301, 9501 Alta
Telephone: (084) 34011

Sec. of Economics and Administration
Sec. of Electronics
Sec. of Computer Sciences
Sec. of Christian Studies
Sec. of Finnish

Founded 1973. A State institution financially supported by the Ministry of Cultural and Scientific Affairs. Governing body: the Høgskolestyre (Board). Some residential facilities for academic staff and students.
Academic Year: September to June (September-December; January-June).
Admission Requirements: Secondary school certificate (examen artium).
Fees: None.
Language of Instruction: Norwegian.
Degrees and Diplomas: Certificate, 3 yrs. Also diploma, 1 yr. Candidatus magisterii, cand.mag., 4 yrs.
Library: c. 18,000 vols.
Academic Staff: c. 70.
Student Enrolment: c. 380 (Also c. 400 external students).

5179 **SOGN OG FJORDANE DISTRIKTSHØGSKOLE**

Sogn and Fjordane College
Postboks 39, 5801 Sogndal
Telephone: (56) 76000
Fax: (56) 76100
Rektor: Aage Engesater (1989-91)
Director: Hans Jörgen Binningsbö

Social Sciences
Natural Sciences
Economics and Business Administration

Founded 1970 by Act of Parliament as one of several new regional colleges designed to offer short professional courses in areas not covered by universities and other institutions. A State institution financially supported by the Ministry of Education and Research. Governing body: the Högskulerádit (Board) of 11 members.

Academic Year: August to June (August-December; January-June).

Admission Requirements: Secondary school certificate (examen artium).

Fees: None.

Language of Instruction: Norwegian.

Degrees and Diplomas: Degree of Høgskolekandidat, 3 yrs. Candidatus magisterii, cand.mag., 4 yrs.

Library: c. 18,000 vols.

Academic Staff, 1990: 36 (1).

Student Enrolment, 1990:

	Men	Women	Total
Of the country	221	297	518
Of other countries	3	–	3
Total	224	297	521

5180 **HØGSKOLEN I HARSTAD**

Postboks 2140, 9405 Kanebogen

Economics and Administration
Health Administration

5181 **MØRE OG ROMSDAL DISTRIKTSHØGSKOLE**

Møre and Romsdal College
Postboks 208, 6401 Molde
Telephone: 072-51077

Sec. of Economics and Administration
Sec. of Transport Studies
Sec. of Electronics
Sec. of Computer Sciences
Sec. of Mathematics

Founded 1970 by Act of Parliament as one of several new regional colleges designed to offer short professional courses in areas not covered by universities and other institutions. A State institution, financially supported by the Ministry of Cultural and Scientific Affairs. Governing body: the Høgskoleråd, comprising 22 members.

Academic Year: August to June (August-December; January-June).

Admission Requirements: Secondary school certificate (examen artium).

Fees: None.

Language of Instruction: Norwegian.

Degrees and Diplomas: Degree of Høgskolekandidat, 2-3 yrs. Candidatus magisterii, cand.mag., 4 yrs.

Library: c. 20,000 vols.

Publication: Research Works.

Academic Staff: c. 40 (20).

Student Enrolment: c. 550 (Also c. 100 external students).

5182 **MØRE OG ROMSDAL DISTRIKTSHØGSKOLE**

Møre and Romsdal College
Postboks 188, 6101 Volda
Telephone: (070) 770666

Sec. of Norwegian Language and Literature
Sec. of German
Sec. of Local History
Sec. of Communication Studies (including Journalism)
Sec. of Social Work
Sec. of Regional Planning
Sec. of Theology and Sociology
Sec. of Child Welfare

Founded 1970 by Act of Parliament as one of several new regional colleges designed to offer short professional courses in areas not covered by universities and other institutions. A State institution financially supported by the Ministry of Cultural and Scientific Affairs. Governing body: the Styre (Board).

Academic Year: August to June (August-December; January-June).

Admission Requirements: Secondary school certificate (examen artium).

Fees: None.

Language of Instruction: Norwegian.

Degrees and Diplomas: Degree of Høgskolekandidat, 2 yrs. Candidatus magisterii, cand.mag., 4 yrs.

Library: c. 15,000 vols.

Academic Staff: c. 30.

Student Enrolment: c. 320.

5183 **NORD-TRØNDELAG DISTRIKTSHØGSKOLE**

North Trøndelag College
Postboks 145, 7701 Steinkjer

Sec. of Economics and Administration
Sec. of Agricultural Economics

A State institution financially supported by the Ministry of Church and Education. Governing body: the Styre (Board).

Academic Year: August to June (August-December; January-June).

Admission Requirements: Secondary school certificate (examen artium).

Fees: None.

Language of Instruction: Norwegian.

Degrees and Diplomas: Degree of Høgskolekandidat, 2 yrs.

5184 **HØGSKOLESENTERET I NORDLAND**

Nordland University Centre
Postboks 6003, 8016 Mørkved-Bodø
Telephone: (81) 17200
Fax: (81) 17457
Rektor: Nils M. Nielsen (1990-92)
Directør: Eivind Sommerseth

S. of Economics and Business Administration
Dean: Finn Jørgensen; *staff* 22

S. of Social Sciences
Dean: Aksel Bikset; *staff* 26

S. of Fisheries and Aquaculture
Dean: Magne Haakstad; *staff* 8

Research I.
Director: Hallgeir Aalbu; *staff* 42

Founded 1971 by Act of Parliament as one of several new regional colleges designed to offer short professional courses in areas not covered by universities and other institutions. Acquired present status and title 1985. A State institution financially supported by the Ministry of Education and Research. Governing body: the Rådet (Board). Residential facilities for students.

Arrangements for special inter-Nordic exchanges. Also exchange agreements with institutions in Germany (Ruhr-gas) and France (Troll-gas), and with universities in the USA and Canada.

Academic Year: August to June (August-December; January-June).

Admission Requirements: Secondary school certificate (examen artium).

Fees: None.

Language of Instruction: Norwegian.

Degrees and Diplomas: Siviløkonomeksamen, economics and business administration, 4 yrs. Degree of Høgskolekandidat; Sosionom, 2-3 yrs. Candidatus magisterii, cand.mag., 4 yrs.

Library: Central Library, c. 70,000 vols.

Publication: Scientific Research Reports.

Academic Staff, 1990-91:

Rank	Full-time	Part-time
Professorer	7	6
Høgskoledosentaer	5	–
Undervisningsleder	2	–
Førsteamanuenser	14	–
Amanuenser	38	1
Vitenskapelige assistenter	4	–
Total	70	7

Student Enrolment, 1990-91:

	Men	Women	Total
Of the country	601	532	1133
Of other countries	7	8	15
Total	608	540	1148*

*Also 436 external students.

5185 **OPPLAND DISTRIKTSHØGSKOLE**

Oppland College

Postboks 1004, Skurva, 2601 Lillehammer

Telephone: (062) 55600

Sec. of Economics and Administration
Sec. of Education
Sec. of Education for the Handicapped
Sec. of Tourism
Sec. of Political Science and Public Administration
Sec. of History

Founded 1970 by Act of Parliament as one of several new regional colleges designed to offer short professional courses in areas not covered by universities and other institutions. A State institution financially supported by the Ministry of Cultural and Scientific Affairs. Governing body: the Styre (Board), of 21 members. Residential facilities for *c.* 200 students.

Academic Year: August to June (August-December; January-June).

Admission Requirements: Secondary school certificate (examen artium) or equivalent.

Fees: None.

Language of Instruction: Norwegian.

Degrees and Diplomas: Degree of Høgskolekandidat, 2 yrs. Diplomkandidat, 4-5 yrs. Candidatus magisterii, cand.mag., 4 yrs.

Library: *c.* 26,000 vols.

Academic Staff: *c.* 40.

Student Enrolment: *c.* 420.

5186 **ØSTFOLD DISTRIKTSHØGSKOLE**

Østfold College

Os allé 9, 1750 Halden

Telephone: (479) 18-54-00

Fax: (479) 18-64-75

Principal: Knut Aarvak

Direktør: Bodo J. Schneede

Data Processing
Economics and Business Administration
Foreign Languages and International Economics (including German and French)
Leadership and Organization

Founded 1977. A State institution financially supported by the Ministry of Education and Research. Governing body: the Academic Senate of 12 members.

Arrangements for co-operation with the University of Stirling.

Academic Year: August to June (August-December; January-June).

Admission Requirements: Secondary school certificate (examen artium).

Fees: None.

Language of Instruction: Norwegian.

Degrees and Diplomas: Degree of Høgskolekandidat, 2-3 yrs. Candidatus magisterii, cand. mag., 4 yrs.

Academic Staff, 1989-90: 28.

Student Enrolment, 1989-90: 422 (Also 126 external students).

5187 **HØGSKOLESENTERET I ROGALAND**

Rogaland University Center

Postboks 2557, Ullandhaug, 4004 Stavanger

Telephone: (4) 87-43-00

Fax: (4) 87-43-00

Rektor: Dag Tresselt (1986-91)

Høgskoledirektør: Tore Husebø

D. of Science and Technology
Head: Magnus Dalva; *staff* 90
D. of Culture and Social Sciences (including Journalism)
Head: Lennart Rosenlund; *staff* 15
D. of Economics and Business Administration
Head: Roald M. Martinussen; *staff* 12
D. of Humanities and Art (including Languages and History)
Head: Per Moen; *staff* 10

Founded 1969 by Act of Parliament as one of several new regional colleges designed to offer short professional courses in areas not covered by universities and other institutions. Acquired present status and title 1986. A State institution financially supported by the Ministry of Education and Research. Governing body: the Styre (Executive Board). Some residential facilities for students.

Academic Year: September to June (September-December; January-June).

Admission Requirements: Secondary school certificate (examen artium) or equivalent.

Fees (Kroner): Tuition, 205 per semester.

Language of Instruction: Norwegian.

Degrees and Diplomas: Degree of–Høgskolekandidat, 2 yrs; Høgskoleingeniør, 3 yrs. Candidatus magisterii, cand.mag., 4 yrs. Sivilingeniør, siv.ing., 5 yrs.

Library: Research Library.

Academic Staff, 1989-90:

Rank	Full-time	Part-time
Professorer	8	7
Høgskoledosentar	7	3
Førsteamanuensis/Amanuensis/Høgskolelektor	101	–
Total	116	10

Student Enrolment, 1989-90: 3000.

5188 **TELEMARK DISTRIKTSHØGSKOLE**

Telemark College

3800 Bø i Telemark

Telephone: (036) 60200

Rektor: Nils Røttingen (1985-87)

Direktør: Asmund Brenden

D. of Economics and Administration Studies (including Computer Sciences)
Head: Vidar Ringstad; *staff* 16
D. of Environmental Studies
Head: Olav Hesjedal; *staff* 14
D. of Cultural Development Studies and Sports Administration
Head: Per Mangset; *staff* 9
D. of History
Head: Ellen Schrumpf; *staff* 4
D. of Norwegian Studies
Head: Eivind Landmark; *staff* 4
D. of Mathematics
Head: Knut Dale; *staff* 3
D. of English
Head: Øyvind T. Gulliksen; *staff* 4

Founded 1970 by Act of Parliament as one of several new regional colleges designed to offer professional courses in areas not covered by universities and other institutions. A State institution financially supported by the Ministry of Cultural and Scientific Affairs. Governing body: the Senate (Høgskoleting). Residential facilities for students.

Arrangements for co-operation with Luther College, Decorah, Iowa.

Academic Year: August to June (August-December; January-June).

Admission Requirements: Secondary school certificate (examen artium) or equivalent.

Fees: None.

Language of Instruction: Norwegian.

Degrees and Diplomas: Degree of Høgskolekandidat, 2-3 yrs. Also Diploma, 1 yr. Candidatus magisterii, cand.mag., 4 yrs.

Library: 50,000 vols.

Academic Staff, 1986-87:

Rank	Full-time
Høgskoledosentar	4
Undervisningsleiar	1
Amanuensar	46
Hjelpestillingar	3
Total	54

Student Enrolment, 1986-87:

	Men	Women	Total
Of the country	308	372	680
Of other countries	5	4	9
Total	313	376	689*

*Also 200 external students.

5189 **AGDER INGENIØR- OG DISTRIKTSHØGSKOLE**

Agder Technical College and College of Engineering

Groosveien 36, 4890 Grimstad

Telephone: (041) 41811

Sec. of Civil Engineering
Sec. of Electronics
Sec. of Mechanical Engineering

Sec. of Technology and Economics

Founded 1967 as school, acquired present status and title 1977. A State institution financially supported by the Ministry of Cultural and Scientific Affairs. Governing body: the Styre (Council). Residential facilities for students.

Academic Year: August to June (August-December; January-June).

Admission Requirements: Secondary school certificate (examen artium) or equivalent.

Language of Instruction: Norwegian.

Degrees and Diplomas: Høgskolekandidat; Høgskoleingeniør, 3 yrs. Candidatus magisterii, cand.mag., 4 yrs.

Library: c. 7500 vols.

Academic Staff: c. 40.

Student Enrolment: c. 60.

5190 **BERGEN INGENIØRHØGSKOLE**

Bergen College of Engineering

Lars Hillesgatan 34, 5000 Bergen

Telephone: (05) 333040

Rektor: Harald Dalen (1965-90)

D. of Electrical Engineering
D. of Control Engineering
D. of Civil Engineering
D. of Industrial Engineering
D. of Computer Sciences
D. of Chemistry
D. of Mechanical Engineering (including Marine Architecture)
D. of General Studies

Founded 1875 as technical college, acquired present status and title 1977. A regional State institution financially supported by the Ministry of Cultural and Scientific Affairs.

Arrangements for co-operation with South Dakota School of Mines and Technology.

Academic Year: August to June (August-December; January-June).

Admission Requirements: Secondary school certificate (examen artium) or equivalent.

Language of Instruction: Norwegian.

Degrees and Diplomas: Høgskoleingeniør, 3 yrs.

Library: College Library.

Academic Staff: 55 (10).

Student Enrolment: c. 670.

5191 **GJØVIK INGENIØRHØGSKOLE**

Gjøvik College of Engineering

Postboks 191, 2801 Gjøvik

Telephone: (061) 73548

D. of Civil Engineering
D. of Mechanical Engineering
D. of Electrical Engineering
D. of Computer Sciences
D. of Basic Studies

Founded 1966. A regional State institution. Residential facilities for students.

Academic Year: August to June (August-December; January-June).

Admission Requirements: Secondary school certificate (examen artium).

Language of Instruction: Norwegian.

Degrees and Diplomas: Høgskoleingeniør, 3 yrs.

Academic Staff: c. 40.

Student Enrolment: c. 550.

5192 **HÆRENS INGENIØRSHØGSKOLE**

Army of Engineering

Hvalsmoen, 3500 Hønefoss

Telephone: (67) 23022

Fax: (67) 23022 (line 920)

Head Teacher: Fagernes, Ivar

Administrative Officer: Fenrik Nordang

F. of Military Building Construction

Founded 1955.

Academic Year: January to December (August-December; January-June).

Admission Requirements: Secondary school certificate (examen artium).

Language of Instruction: Norwegian.

Degrees and Diplomas: Diploma of Engineer, 3 yrs.

Academic Staff, 1990: 5 (8).

Student Enrolment, 1990:

	Men	Women	Total
Of the country	60	3	63

5193 **HORTEN INGENIØRHØGSKOLE**

Horten College of Engineering

Skippergt. 6, 3190 Horten

Telephone: 4735-43091

Rektor: Knut Gråthan (1985-87)

Administrativ leder: Bjørn Jakobsen

D. of Electronic Engineering

Head: Per G. Waitz; *staff* 10 (2)

D. of Mechanical Engineering

Head: Svein Wendel; *staff* 10

D. of Industrial Engineering

Head: Rolf Klemmetsen; *staff* 9 (8)

Founded 1855, acquired present status and title 1977. A regional State institution supported by the Ministry of Cultural and Scientific Affairs.

Academic Year: August to June (August-December; January-June).

Admission Requirements: Secondary school certificate (examen artium).

Language of Instruction: Norwegian.

Degrees and Diplomas: Høgskoleingeniør, 3 yrs. Candidatus magisterii, cand.mag., 4 yrs.

Academic Staff, 1986-87: 29 (10).

Student Enrolment, 1986-87: 330.

5194 **KONGSBERG INGENIØRHØGSKOLE**

Kongsberg College of Engineering

Postboks 235, 3601 Kongsberg

Telephone: (03) 73-40-60

D. of Control Engineering
D. of Computer Engineering
D. of Mechanical Engineering
D. of Optometry
D. of Applied Mathematics and Physics

Founded 1977. A regional State institution financially supported by the Ministry of Cultural and Scientific Affairs. Governing body: the Styre (Board), comprising 13 members.

Academic Year: August to June (August-October; October-January; January-March; March-June).

Admission Requirements: Secondary school certificate (examen artium).

Language of Instruction: Norwegian.

Degrees and Diplomas: Høgskoleingeniør, 3 yrs.

Academic Staff: c. 40.

Student Enrolment: c. 360.

5195 **MØRE OG ROMSDAL INGENIØRHØGSKOLE**

Møre and Romsdal College of Engineering

Fogdegården, 6009 Ålesund

Engineering

Academic Year: August to June (August-December; January-June).

Admission Requirements: Secondary school certificate (examen artium).

Language of Instruction: Norwegian.

Degrees and Diplomas: Høgskoleingeniør, 3 yrs.

5196 **NARVIK INGENIØRHØGSKOLE**

Narvik College of Engineering

Lodve Langesgt 2, 8501 Narvik

Telephone: (82) 44130

Fax: (82) 45726

Rektor: Olav Soleng (1989-90)

Direktør: Eva Opshang Teigen

D. of Electrical Engineering

Head: S.A. Munkvold; *staff* 18

D. of Civil Engineering

Head: Eigil Roaldset; *staff* 12 (1)

D. of Mechanical Engineering

Head: Kjell Fostervold; *staff* 8 (1)

D. of General Studies

Head: B. Sivertsen; *staff* 10 (1)

Concrete Test Station

Head: B. Linder; *staff* 2

D. of Extension Course

Founded 1955 as a municipal college, acquired present status 1978. A regional State institution financially supported by the Ministry of Education and Research. Governing body: the Høgskolestyre (Board). Residential facilities for students.

Academic Year: August to June (August-December; January-June).

Admission Requirements: Secondary school certificate (examen artium), with A levels in Mathematics and Physics.

Fees: None.

Language of Instruction: Norwegian.

Degrees and Diplomas: Høgskoleingeniør, 3 yrs. Diplôme in–Management and Economics; Computer Technology; Production Technology, 1 yr. Master, 5 yrs.

Library: Central Library, 4000 vols.

Academic Staff, 1989-90: 50.

Student Enrolment, 1989-90:

	Men	Women	Total
Of the country	500	100	600
Of other countries	5	–	5
Total	505	100	605

5197 **NKI INGENIØRHØGSKOLEN**

The NKI College of Engineering

Postboks 10, 1321 Stabekk

Telephone: (2) 12-29-50

Fax: (2) 53-05-00

Rektor: Stein Tore Jenssen

D. of Mechanical Engineering

Head: Wenehe Haugstuen; *staff* 2 (4)

D. of Construction Engineering

Head: Leiflugar Finborud; *staff* 2 (25)

D. of Electrical Engineering

Head: Ivar Mortensenen; *staff* 9 (40)

D. of Research and Development

Head: Torstein Rekkedal; *staff* 2

Founded 1964. Offers full-time tuition in 18 sites throughout the country. A private enterprise owned by the NKI Foundation.

Arrangements for co-operation with the Open University, United Kingdom.

Academic Year: August to June.

Admission Requirements: Secondary school certificate (advanced level).

Fees (Kroner): 12,400-31,300 per annum.

Language of Instruction: Norwegian.

Degrees and Diplomas: Høgskoleingeniør, 3 yrs.

Press or Publishing House: The NKI Publishing House.

Academic Staff, 1989-90: c. 20 (450).

Student Enrolment, 1989-90:

	Men	Women	Total
Of the country	1125	175	1300
Of other countries	130	20	150
Total	1255	195	1450*

*Also *c.* 17,000 students by correspondence and open classes (Technical and Non-Technical).

5198 **OSLO INGENIØRHØGSKOLE**

Oslo College of Engineering

Cort Adelersgt. 30, 0254 Oslo 2

Telephone: (2) 55-30-00

Fax: (02) 56-11-22

Rektor: Kjell Gustavsen (1986-)

D. of Civil Engineering

Head: Ola Hovind

D. of Electrical Engineering

Head: Gunnar Slungaard

D. of Chemical Engineering

Head: Gunnar Eia

D. of Mechanical Engineering

Head: Olav Skjeggedal

D. of Mathematics, Data Processing, and Physics

Head: Birger Emblem

Founded 1873, acquired present status and title 1977. A regional State institution financially supported by the Ministry of Education and Research.

Academic Year: August to June (August-December; January-June).

Admission Requirements: Secondary school certificate (examen artium).

Language of Instruction: Norwegian.

Degrees and Diplomas: Høgskoleingeniør, 3 yrs.

Academic Staff, 1986-87: 62.

Student Enrolment, 1989-90:

	Men	Women	Total
Of the country	670	200	870

5199 **ØSTFOLD INGENIØRHØGSKOLE**

Østfold College of Engineering

Postboks 1192, Valaskjold, 1701 Sarpsborg

Telephone: (9) 142011

Fax: (9) 142802

Rektor: Kåre Sørby (1985-)

Studies jef: Marit Dahl

Engineering (Building and Construction, Electrical, Mechanical and Chemical Engineering)

Founded 1965, acquired present status and title 1977. A regional State institution financially supported by the Ministry of Education and Research.

Academic Year: August to June (August-December; January-June).

Admission Requirements: Secondary school certificate (examen artium).

Fees: None.

Language of Instruction: Norwegian.

Degrees and Diplomas: Høgskoleingeniør, 3 yrs.

Academic Staff, 1989-90: 40.

Student Enrolment, 1989-90: 687

5200 **TELEMARK INGENIØRHØGSKOLE**

Telemark College of Engineering

Kjølnes, 3900 Porsgrunn

Telephone: (035) 55080

Rektor: Rolf Ergon (1985-87)

Kontorsjef: Torbjørn Lindaas

D. of Civil Engineering

Head: Olav Torsholt; *staff* 9

D. of Electrical Engineering

Head: Torleif Røvter; *staff* 37

D. of Electronics

Head: Rolf Palmgren; *staff* 7

D. of Mechanical Engineering

Head: Hans Robert Kaasa; *staff* 8

D. of Chemical Engineering

Head: Jens Mosbye; *staff* 11

Founded 1971. A regional State institution financially supported by the Ministry of Cultural and Scientific Affairs. Residential facilities for students.

Academic Year: August to June (August-December; January-June).

Admission Requirements: Secondary school certificate (examen artium).

Language of Instruction: Norwegian.

Degrees and Diplomas: Høgskoleingeniør, 3 yrs.

Library: c. 12,700 vols.

Academic Staff, 1986-87: 6 (2).

Student Enrolment, 1986-87:

	Men	Women	Total
Of the country	307	71	378
Of other countries	10	2	12
Total	317	73	390

5201 **TRONDHEIM INGENIØRHØGSKOLE**

Trondheim College of Engineering

Gunnerusgt. 1, 7013 Trondheim

Telephone: (075) 21-670

D. of Civil Engineering

D. of Electrical Engineering

D. of Mechanical Engineering

D. of Science and Liberal Studies

D. of Computer Sciences

D. of Chemistry

Founded 1870. A regional State institution financially supported by the Ministry of Cultural and Scientific Affairs. Governing body: the Høgskoleråd, comprising 9 members. Residential facilities for students.

Academic Year: August to June (August-October; October-December; January-March; March-June).
Admission Requirements: Secondary school certificate (examen artium).
Language of Instruction: Norwegian.
Degrees and Diplomas: Høgskoleingeniør, 3 yrs.
Academic Staff: c. 60 (10).
Student Enrolment: c. 820.

5202 **AGDER MARITIME HØGSKOLE**
Agder College of Maritime Studies
Fløyveien 28, 4800 Arendal

5203 **HAUGESUND MARITIME HØGSKOLE**
Skåregt. 103, 5500 Haugesund

5204 **OSLO TEKNISKE MARITIME SKOLE**
Etterstadsletta 5, Postboks 6009, Etterstad, 0601 Oslo 6
Cables: Maskiniskolen
Telephone: (02) 19-31-31
Rektor: Sigmund Soma
Undervisningsinspektør: Tor Urdal

D. of Marine Technology
Head: Øivind Andreassen; *staff* 2 (6)
D. of Mechanical Engineering
Head: Jan R. Haugen; *staff* 1 (6)
Academic Year: August to June (August-December; January-June).
Admission Requirements: Secondary school certificate (examen artium).
Language of Instruction: Norwegian.
Degrees and Diplomas: Høgskoleingeniør, 2-3 yrs.
Academic Staff, 1986-87: 3 (10).
Student Enrolment, 1986-87:

	Men	Women	Total
Of the country	45	1	46
Of other countries	3	–	3
Total	48	1	49

5205 **TROMSØ MARITIME HØGSKOLE**
Sommerfeldtsgt. 74/76, 9000 Tromsø

5206 **TRONDHEIM MARITIME HØGSKOLE**
Ladehammerveien 6, 7041 Trondheim

5207 **TØNSBERG MARITIME HØGSKOLE**
Postboks 38, 3101 Tønsberg

5208 **STATENS KUNSTAKADEMI**
National Academy of Fine Arts
St. Olavsgate 32, 0166 Oslo 1
Telephone: (02) 20-01-50
Rector: Boge Berg (1984-87)
Registrar: Aina Helgesen

Fine Arts
Founded 1909.
Academic Year: September to May (September-December; January-May). Normal period of study 4-5 yrs.
Languages of Instruction: Norwegian and English.
Library: 7000 vols.
Academic Staff, 1986-87: 9 (10).
Student Enrolment, 1986-87:

	Men	Women	Total
Of the country	35	59	94
Of other countries	11	8	19
Total	46	67	113

5209 **VESTLANDETS KUNSTAKADEMI**
National Academy of Fine Arts
C. Sundtsgaten 53, 5000 Bergen

Fine Arts

5210 **KUNSTAKADEMIET I TRONDHEIM**
Aasta Hensteens vei 22, 7000 Trondheim

Fine Arts

5211 **STATENS HØGSKOLE FOR KUNSTHÅNDVERT OG DESIGN I BERGEN**
Bergen College of Art and Design
Strønsgt. 1, 5000 Bergen
Telephone: (05) 312214
Rektor: Rolf Hermansen (1983-96)

Craft and Design
Founded 1909, acquired present status 1981. A State institution.
Academic Year: September to June (September-December; January-June).
Admission Requirements: Secondary school certificate (examen artium) and entrance examination.
Fees: Tuition, none.
Language of Instruction: Norwegian.
Degrees and Diplomas: Diploma in–Interior Architecture; Textiles and Ceramics; Graphic Design, 4-4 ½ yrs.
Library: c. 2500 vols.
Academic Staff: c. 20 (20).
Student Enrolment: c. 150.

5212 **STATENS HÅNDVERKS- OG KUNSTINDUSTRISKOLE**
The National College of Art and Design
Ullevålsveien 5, N-0165 Oslo 1
Telephone: (2) 20-12-35
Fax: (2) 111496
Rektor: Rovar Høyland (1989-)
Høgskolesekretær: Dag Mathiesen

D. of Fine Art
Head: Hilmar Freedriksen; *staff* 4 (3)
D. of Ceramics
Head: Arne Åse; *staff* – (4)
D. of Metal and Jewellery
Head: Arne Magnus Joansrød; *staff* 3 (2)
D. of Fashion and Costume Design
Head: Mabi Helwes; *staff* 9 (2)
D. of Textile-Printing and Weaving
Head: Brith. Fuglevaas; *staff* 4 (2)
D. of Graphic Design and Ilustration
Head: Peter Haars; *staff* 3 (2)
I. for Interior Arts and Decoration
Head: Geir Stormoen; *staff* – (2)
Also section in Brummundoal and Risør.
Founded 1818. Governing body: the Board.
Participates in the NORDPLUS exchange programmes.
Academic Year: August to May (August-December; January-May).
Admission Requirements: Secondary school certificate (examen artium).
Fees: None.
Language of Instruction: Norwegian.
Degrees and Diplomas: Høgskolekandidat, 3 yrs. Designkandidat/Kunstfagkandidat, a further 1 ½ yrs.
Library: 45,000 vols.
Academic Staff, 1989-90: c.50
Student Enrolment, 1986-87:

	Men	Women	Total
Of the country	110	160	270
Of other countries	9	14	23
Total	119	174	293*

*Also 19 students by correspondence.

5213 **STATENS BALLETTHØGSKOLE**
National College of Ballet
Tjuvholmen, Bygning 13, 0250 Oslo 2

Ballet

5214 **DEN NORSKE BALLETTHØGSKOLE**
Sørbyhangen 33, 0377 Oslo 3

5215 **STATENS TEATERHØGSKOLE**
National College of Dramatic Art
Stranden 3, P.O.Box 1501, Vika, 0117 Oslo 1
Telephone: 830010
Fax: 838358
Rektor: Bente Børsum

Dramatic Art (including Directing)

Founded 1953. A State institution financially supported by the Ministry of Education and Research.

Academic Year: August to May (August-December; January-May).

Admission Requirements: Secondary school certificate (examen artium).

Fees: None.

Language of Instruction: Norwegian.

Degrees and Diplomas: Diplomas, 3 yrs.

Academic Staff, 1990: 8 (5).

Student Enrolment, 1990:

	Men	Women	Total
Of the country	15	14	29

5216 **STATENS OPERAHØGSKOLE**
National College of Operatic Art
Tjuvholmen, bygning B, 0250 Oslo 2
Telephone: (02) 42-52-74

Operatic Art

Founded 1964. Under the direct supervision of the Ministry of Cultural and Scientific Affairs. Governing body: the Board, comprising 5 members.

Academic Year: September to May (September-December; January-May).

Admission Requirements: Secondary school certificate.

Fees: None.

Language of Instruction: Norwegian.

Degrees and Diplomas: Diploma, 3 yrs.

Library: Operatic music and literature.

5217 **ØKONOMISK COLLEGE**
Oslo College of Business and Economics
Parkveien 65, 0245 Oslo 2
Telephone: (47-2) 434621
Fax: (47-2) 562472
Rektor: Johannes Øvereng
Studierektor: Kristian K. Saxegaard

Administration
Economics
Accountancy and Auditing
International Business P.

Founded 1970. Under the supervision of the City of Oslo.

Admission Requirements: Secondary school certificate (examen artium).

Fees: None.

Language of Instruction: Norwegian.

Degrees and Diplomas: Høskolekandidat, 2 yrs. Bachelor in International Business, 3 yrs. Title of Registered Accountant.

Academic Staff, 1990: 15 (17).

Student Enrolment, 1990:

	Men	Women	Total
Of the country	102	203	305
Of other countries	1	2	3
Total	103	205	308*

*Also 50 external students.

5218 **TRONDHEIM ØKONOMISKE HØGSKOLE**
Trondheim College of Economics and Business Administration
Klostergt. 90, 7000 Trondheim

Economics and Business Administration
Auditing

5219 **BEDRIFSØKONOMISK INSTITUTT**
Oslo School of Business and Management
Postboks 69, 1341 Bekkestua
Rektor: Jørgen Randers (1981-89)
Direktør: Bjørn R. Berntsen

Management Studies

Founded 1968 as an autonomous Foundation.

Academic Year: July to June (August-December; January-June).

Admission Requirements: Secondary school certificate (examen artium).

Language of Instruction: Norwegian.

Degrees and Diplomas: Bachelor. Master.

Library: 22,000 vols.

Academic Staff, 1986-87: 61 (372).

Student Enrolment, 1986-87: 10,000.

5220 **STEFELSEN NORGES MARKEDSHØGSKOLE**
Norwegian School of Marketing
Postboks 210 Økern, 0510 Oslo 5

5221 **NORGES FISKERIHØGSKILE**
Norwegian College of Fishery Science

Fishery

Founded 1972. Courses are given by the Universities of Bergen and Tromsø, University of Trondheim, and National College of Economics and Business Administration, Bergen.

5222 **MØRE OG ROMSDAL FISKERITEKNISKE HØGSKOLE**
College of Fishery Technology
Postboks 1555 Nørve, 6021 Ålesund

5223 **STATENS NAERINGSMIDDELTEDNISKE HØGSKOLE**
College of Food Technology
Tungaveien 32, 7004 Trondheim

5224 **NORSK HOTELL HØGSKOLE**
Box 2536, Ullandhaug. 400, Stavanger

Hotel Management

5225 **NORSK JOURNALISTHØGSKOLE**
Norwegian College of Journalism
Frysjaveien 33c, Oslo 1
Telephone: (02) 23-63-85

Journalism

Founded 1965 as school, acquired present status and title 1979. A State institution. Governing body: the Styre (Board), comprising 13 members.

Academic Year: September to May (September-December; March-May).

Admission Requirements: Secondary school certificate (examen artium).

Fees: None.

Language of Instruction: Norwegian.

Degrees and Diplomas: Diploma, 2 yrs.

Library: c. 8910 vols.

Publication: Oppslag (Research Papers, 2-3 times a year).

Academic Staff: c. 10.

Student Enrolment: c. 80.

5226 **STATENS BIBLIOTEK- OG INFORMASJONSHØGSKOLE**
Norwegian School of Library and Information Sciences
Dæleneggaten 26, 0567 Oslo 5
Telephone: (02) 357390
Rektor: Tor Henrinsen

Library and Information Science

Founded 1940. An autonomous State institution. Governing body: the Høgskolerådet (Board), comprising 15 members.

Arrangements for co-operation with similar institutions in many countries, particularly in the north countries.

Academic Year: August/September to June (August/September-December; January-June).

Admission Requirements: Secondary school certificate (examen artium) or equivalent.

Fees: None.

Language of Instruction: Norwegian.

Degrees and Diplomas: Diploma Bibliotekareksamen, 3 yrs. Postgraduate Diploma, a further 2 yrs.

Library: c. 40,000 vols.

Academic Staff: c. 30 (10).

Student Enrolment: c. 800.

5227 **DET NORSKE DIAKONHJEM SOSIALHØGSKOLEN**
Norwegian Lutheran Hospital and College, Department of Social Work
Borgebveien 3c, 0319 Oslo 3
Telephone: (02) 46-59-50

S. of Nursing
S. of Social Studies
S. of Theology and Administration
S. of Auxiliary Nursing (Adult Education)

Founded 1890 as a Lutheran institution. Acquired present status 1981.
Academic Year: August to June (August-December; January-June).
Admission Requirements: Secondary school certificate (examen artium).
Language of Instruction: Norwegian.
Degrees and Diplomas: Diplome, 3 yrs.
Academic Staff: c. 70 (10).

5228 **NORGES KOMMUNAL- OG SOSIALHØGSKOLE**
Norwegian State College of Public Administration and Social Work
Tjernveien 12, 0957 Oslo 9
Telephone: 472-16-43-1
Fax: 472-16-36-16
Dean of Faculties: Steinar Stjernø (1988-92)
Directør: Geir Fr. Finnsen

D. of Public Administration and Social Work (including Economics, and Law)
Head: Gunnar Fahren; *staff* 10
D. for Social Work (including Psychology, Law, Political Science, Sociology, and Social Policy)
Head: Ingeveig Andersen; *staff* 18
D. for Child Care
Head: Per Lilleengen; *staff* 13
D. for Further Education
Head: Ingar Onsúm; *staff* 4
D. Research D. (Social Welfare, Social Security, Social Policy)
Leader: Knut Halvorsen; *staff* 9 (2)

Founded 1949. A State institution financially supported by the Ministry of Education and Research.
Academic Year: September to June (September-December; January-June).
Admission Requirements: Secondary school certificate (examen artium).
Fees: None.
Language of Instruction: Norwegian.
Degrees and Diplomas: Diplomas of–Barnevernspedagogeksamen, child care; Kommunalkandidateksamen; Sosionomeksamen, 3 yrs.
Academic Staff, 1986-87: 45.
Student Enrolment, 1989-90:

	Men	Women	Total
Of the country	117	479	596
Of other countries	9	13	22
Total	126	492	618

5229 **SOSIALHØGSKOLEN, STAVANGER**
Stavanger College of Social Work
Møllegt. 66, 4000 Stavanger
Telephone: (04) 52-10-80
Rektor: Inger Jo Haaland (1975-)

Social Work (including Child Care)

Founded 1966. A State institution financially supported by the Ministry of Cultural and Scientific Affairs.
Academic Year: August to June (August-December; January-June).
Admission Requirements: Secondary school certificate (examen artium) or equivalent.
Language of Instruction: Norwegian.
Degrees and Diplomas: Diplomas of–Barnevernspedagogeksamen, child care; Sosionomeksamen, 3 yrs. Candidatus magisterii, cand.mag., 4yrs.
Library: 11,000 vols.
Academic Staff, 1986-87: 21.
Student Enrolment, 1986-87:

	Men	Women	Total
Of the country	53	219	272

5230 **SOSIALHØGSKOLEN, TRONDHEIM**
Trondheim College of Social Work
Tunnerusgt. 1, 7000 Trondheim

Social Work

5231 **RUDOLF STEINERHØGSKOLEN**
Sporveisgt, 35 Oslo 3
Telephone: (2) 56-69-61
Direktør: D.L. Brierley

Teacher Training (Steiner Education)

Founded 1981 and recognized by the Department of Education.
Academic Year: August to June.
Admission Requirements: Secondary school certificate (examen artium).
Fees (Kronen): 9000-10,000.
Language of Instruction: Norwegian.
Degrees and Diplomas: Diploma, 2 yrs. Teaching certificate in Steiner Kindergarten Education, 3 yrs.
Publication: Steinerskolen (4 times a year).
Academic Staff, 1990: 13 (5).
Student Enrolment, 1990-91:

	Men	Women	Total
Of the country	6	39	45
Of other countries	1	4	5
Total	7	43	50

5232 **NORSK DIAKONIHØGSKOLE**
Louisenberggt. 11, 0456 Oslo 4

5233 **MISJONSHØGSKOLEN**
School of Theology and Missiology
Misjonsveien 34, 4000 Stavanger
Telephone: (04) 521000
Dekanus: Ingemar Øberg
Høgskolesekretær: Erik Larsen

Theology and Missiology

Founded 1843, acquired present status and title 1977. Financially supported (45%) by the government. Governing body: the Styre (Board). Residential facilities for students.
Academic Year: September to June (September-December; January-June).
Admission Requirements: Secondary school certificate (examen artium) or equivalent.
Fees (Kroner): 1200 per annum.
Language of Instruction: Norwegian.
Degrees and Diplomas: Candidatus theologiae, 6 ½ yrs. Also basic course of 1 yr duration.
Library: 40,000 vols.
Publication: Misjonsmarka (four times a year).
Academic Staff, 1986-87:

Rank	Full-time	Part-time
Professorer	5	2
Amanuenser	5	–
Stipendiater	2	–
Lecturers	4	6
Total	16	8

Student Enrolment, 1986-87:

	Men	Women	Total
Of the country	78	38	116
Of other countries	1	–	1
Total	79	38	117

5234 **DET TEOLOGISKE MENIGHETSFAKULTET**
Free Faculty of Theology
Gydas vei 4, 0363 Oslo 3
Telephone: (02) 46-79-00

Theology

Founded 1908. Financially supported by the State (45%) and donations (55%).
Academic Year: September to June (September-December; January-June).
Admission Requirements: Secondary school certificate (examen artium) or equivalent.
Fees: None.
Language of Instruction: Norwegian.

Degrees and Diplomas: Candidatus theologiae, cand.theol. Also Diploma in Parish Education.
Publications: Tidsskrift for Teologi og Kirke (quarterly); Ung Teologi (quarterly); Lys og Liv (eight times a year).
Academic Staff: c. 20.
Student Enrolment: c. 970.

Colleges of Nursing and Health Sciences

5235 **STATENS SYKEPLEIERHØGSKOLE**
National College of Nursing
Bjerregaardsgt. 21, 0172 Oslo 1

Nursing
Academic Year: August to June (August-December; January-June).
Admission Requirements: Secondary school certificate (examen artium).
Fees: None.
Language of Instruction: Norwegian.
Degrees and Diplomas: Diploma, 3 yrs.

5236 **AKER SYKEPLEIERHØGSKOLE**
Aker College of Nursing
Trondheimsveien 235, 0514 Oslo 5
Telephone: 150892

Nursing
Founded 1924. Acquired present status 1981. A State institution.
Academic Year: August to June (August-December; January-June).
Admission Requirements: Secondary school certificate (examen artium).
Fees: None.
Language of Instruction: Norwegian.
Degrees and Diplomas: Diploma, 3 yrs.
Academic Staff: c. 20 (10).
Student Enrolment: c. 320.

5237 **AUST-AGDER SYKEPLEIERHØGSKOLE**
East Agder College of Nursing
14800 Arendal

Nursing
Academic Year: August to June (August-December; January-June).
Admission Requirements: Secondary school certificate (examen artium).
Fees: None.
Language of Instruction: Norwegian.
Degrees and Diplomas: Diploma, 3 yrs.

5238 **BERGEN DIAKONISSEHJEMS SYKEPLEIERHØGSKOLE**
Bergen Nursing Sisters' College of Nursing
Haraldsplass, 5000 Bergen

Nursing
Academic Year: August to June (August-December; January-June).
Admission Requirements: Secondary school certificate (examen artium).
Fees: None.
Language of Instruction: Norwegian.
Degrees and Diplomas: Diploma, 3 yrs.

5239 **BETANIEN SYKEPLEIERHØGSKOLE**
Betanien College of Nursing
Vestlundveien 19, 5033 Fyllingsdalen

Nursing
Academic Year: August to June (August-December; January-June).
Admission Requirements: Secondary school certificate (examen artium).
Fees: None.
Language of Instruction: Norwegian.
Degrees and Diplomas: Diploma, 3 yrs.

5240 **BETANIEN SYKEPLEIERHØGSKOLE**
Betanien College of Nursing
Akersbakken 35, 0172 Oslo 1

Nursing
Academic Year: August to June (August-December; January-June).
Admission Requirements: Secondary school certificate (examen artium).
Fees: None.
Language of Instruction: Norwegian.

Degrees and Diplomas: Diploma, 3 yrs.

5241 **DIAKONHJEMS SYKEPLEIERHØGSKOLE**
Postboks 23, Vindern 0391 Oslo 3

5242 **DIAKONISSEHUSETS SYKEPLEIERSKOLE**
Deaconess College of Nursing
Lovisenbergveien 15, 0456 Oslo 4
Telephone: (02) 357135
Rektor: Berit Hovland

Nursing (including Gerontology)
Lifelong Education
Founded 1868. Acquired present status 1981. A private institution under the supervision of The Deaconess Houseof Oslo. Some residential facilities for students.
Academic Year: August to June (August to December; January-June).
Admission Requirements: Secondary school certificate (examen artium).
Fees: None.
Language of Instruction: Norwegian.
Degrees and Diplomas: Diploma in–Nursing, 3 yrs; Gerontological Nursing, 4 yrs.
Library: 4000 vols.
Student Enrolment, 1986-87: 197.

5243 **FINNMARK SYKEPLEIERHØGSKOLE**
Finnmark College of Nursing
Postboks 1216, 9601 Hammerfest
Telephone: (084) 12022
Rektor: Erik Fjeldstad

Nursing
Founded 1960. Acquired present status and title 1983. A State institution financially supported by the Ministry of Cultural and Scientific Affairs.
Academic Year: August to June (August-December; January-June).
Admission Requirements: Secondary school certificate (examen artium).
Fees: None.
Language of Instruction: Norwegian.
Degrees and Diplomas: Diploma, 3 yrs.
Student Enrolment, 1986-87:

	Men	Women	Total
Of the country	2	109	111
Of other countries	–	5	5
Total	2	114	116

5244 **HAUGESUND SJUKEPLEIERHØGSKOLE**
Haugesund College of Nursing
Skåregate 105, 5500 Haugesund
Telephone: (4) 71-27-77
Fax: (4) 71-57-87
Direktør: Alfhild Allertsen

Nursing
Academic Year: August to June (August-December; January-June).
Admission Requirements: Secondary school certificate (examen artium).
Fees: None.
Language of Instruction: Norwegian.
Degrees and Diplomas: Diploma, 3 yrs.
Library: c. 6000 vols.
Student Enrolment, 1990:

	Men	Women	Total
Of the country	8	176	184

5245 **HAUKELAND SYKEPLEIERHØGSKOLE**
Haukeland College of Nursing
Haukelandsbakken 45, 5000 Bergen
Telephone: (5) 29-80-90
Fax: (5) 29-15-85
Rektor: Guro Barkve (1979-)

Nursing and Health Visiting Education
Founded 1961 as school. Acquired present status and title 1982. A State institution financially supported by the Ministry of Education and Research. Governing body: the Regional College Board.
Academic Year: August to June (August-December; January-June).
Admission Requirements: Secondary school certificate (examen artium).

Fees: None.
Language of Instruction: Norwegian.
Degrees and Diplomas: Diploma in–General Nursing; Health Visiting, 1 yr.
Student Enrolment, 1989: 369.

5246 **HEDEMARK SYKEPLEIERHØGSKOLE**
Hedemark College of Nursing
Kirkevegen, 2400 Elverum
Telephone: (064) 10066
Rektor: Berit Bjerkamp Solvang (1981-)
Undervisningsinspektør: Marianne Vestli Johnsen

Nursing
Founded 1927 by the Red Cross. Taken over by the Hedmark County 1962. Acquired present status 1986. A State institution financially supported by the Ministry of Cultural and Scientific Affairs.
Academic Year: August to June (August-December; January-June).
Admission Requirements: Secondary school certificate (examen artium).
Fees: None.
Language of Instruction: Norwegian.
Degrees and Diplomas: Diploma, 3 yrs. Diploma in Advanced Nursing, a further 1 ½ yrs.
Library: c. 8500 vols.
Academic Staff, 1986-87: 22.
Student Enrolment, 1986-87:

	Men	Women	Total
Of the country	13	229	242

5247 **INNHERRED SYKEPLEIERHØGSKOLE**
Innherd College of Nursing
7600 Levanger
Telephone: (076) 80022
Rektor: Asgjerd Valstad

Nursing
Founded 1928. Acquired present status 1981. A State institution financially supported by the Ministry of Cultural and Scientific Affairs.
Academic Year: August to June (August-December; January-June).
Admission Requirements: Secondary school certificate (examen artium).
Fees: None.
Language of Instruction: Norwegian.
Degrees and Diplomas: Diploma, 3 yrs.
Academic Staff, 1986-87: 14 (9).
Student Enrolment, 1986-87:

	Men	Women	Total
Of the country	18	163	181

5248 **KRISTIANSAND SYKEPLEIERHØGSKOLE**
Kristiansand Nursing College
Solbergvn, 14, 4615 Kristiansand
Telephone: (42) 26990
Fax: (42) 26880
Rektor: Karin Kin Nicolaysen
Inspektør: Astrid Birkeland

Nursing
Founded 1972. Governing body: the Agder Høgskolestyre.
Academic Year: August to June.
Admission Requirements: Secondary school certificate (examen artium).
Fees: None.
Language of Instruction: Norwegian.
Degrees and Diplomas: Diploma, 3 yrs.
Academic Staff, 1989-90: 18.
Student Enrolment, 1989-90:

	Men	Women	Total
Of the country	8	170	178

5249 **MENIGHETSSØSTERHJEMMETS SYKEPLEIERHØGSKOLE**
Parish Sisters' College of Nursing
Rosenborggt. 8, 0356 Oslo 3
Telephone: (02) 693890

Nursing
Founded 1916 as school. Acquired present status and title 1981.
Academic Year: August to June (August-December; January-June).
Admission Requirements: Secondary school certificate (examen artium).
Fees: None.
Language of Instruction: Norwegian.
Degrees and Diplomas: Diploma, 3 yrs.

5250 **NAMDAL SYKEPLEIERHØGSKOLE**
Namdal College of Nursing
7800 Nansos

Nursing
Academic Year: August to June (August-December; January-June).
Admission Requirements: Secondary school certificate (examen artium).
Fees: None.
Language of Instruction: Norwegian.
Degrees and Diplomas: Diploma, 3 yrs.

5251 **SYKEPLEIERHØGSKOLEN I OPPLAND**
Oppland College of Nursing
Ludvig Skattumsgt. 30/32, 2800 Gjøvik
Telephone: (61) 74064
Fax: (61) 72189
Rektor: Bodhild Hoff Sagli

Nursing
Founded 1928. Acquired present status 1981. A State institution financially supported by the Ministry of Education and Research.
Academic Year: August to June (August-December; January-June).
Admission Requirements: Secondary school certificate (examen artium).
Fees: None.
Language of Instruction: Norwegian.
Degrees and Diplomas: Diploma, 3 yrs.
Academic Staff, 1989-90: c. 30.
Student Enrolment, 1989: 245.

5252 **NORDLAND SYKEPLEIERHØGSKOLE**
Nordland College of Nursing
Leiteveien 7, 8000 Bodø

Nursing
Academic Year: August to June (August-December; January-June).
Admission Requirements: Secondary school certificate (examen artium).
Fees: None.
Language of Instruction: Norwegian.
Degrees and Diplomas: Diploma, 3 yrs.

5253 **DRAMMEN SYKEPLEIERHØGSKOLE**
Drammen College of Nursing
Konggt. 51, 3000 Drammen

Nursing
Academic Year: August to June (August-December; January-June).
Admission Requirements: Secondary school certificate (examen artium) or equivalent.
Language of Instruction: Norwegian.
Degrees and Diplomas: Diploma, 3 yrs.

5254 **SYKEPLEIERHØGSKOLEN I LØRENSKOG**
Lørenskog College of Nursing
Postbox 3, 1474 Nordbyhagen
Rektor: Anne Marie Grønningsæter
Avdelingsleder: Sidsen Tveiten

Nursing
Founded 1895. Acquired present status 1986. A State institution.
Academic Year: August to June (August-December; January-June).
Admission Requirements: Secondary school certificate (examen artium).
Language of Instruction: Norwegian.
Degrees and Diplomas: Diploma, 3 yrs.
Library: c. 7000 vols.
Academic Staff, 1990: 13 (10).
Student Enrolment, 1990:

	Men	Women	Total
Of the country	20	196	216
Of other countries	4	3	7
Total	24	199	223

5255 **SYKEPLEIERHØGSKOLE I TRØMSØ**
Åsgårdveien 9A, 9000 Tromsø

Nursing
Public Health
Psychology

Academic Year: August to June (August-December; January-June).
Admission Requirements: Secondary school certificate (examen artium).
Language of Instruction: Norwegian.
Degrees and Diplomas: Diploma, 3 yrs.

5256 **HØGSKOLEN I HARSTAD SYKEPLEIERUTDANNINGEN**
Postboks 2144, 9405 Kanebogen

Nursing

Academic Year: August to June (August-December; January-June).
Admission Requirements: Secondary school certificate (examen artium).
Language of Instruction: Norwegian.
Degrees and Diplomas: Diploma, 3 yrs.

5257 **SJUKEPLEIARHØGSKOLEN I ALESUND**
Alesund College of Nursing
Postboks 40, 6017 Asestrandra
Telephone: (071) 41990
Rektor: Pauline Solberg (1980-87)

Nursing

Founded 1974. Acquired present status 1981. A State institution financially supported by the Ministry of Cultural and Scientific Affairs.
Academic Year: August to June (August-December; January-June).
Admission Requirements: Secondary school certificate (examen artium).
Fees: None.
Language of Instruction: Norwegian.
Degrees and Diplomas: Diploma, 3 yrs. Diploma in Advanced Nursing, a further 1 ½ yrs.
Academic Staff, 1986-87: 12.
Student Enrolment, 1986-87:

	Men	Women	Total
Of the country	16	152	168

5258 **SJUKEPLEIERHØGSKOLE I MOLDE**
Molde College of Nursing
Glomstuveien 33, 6400 Molde
Telephone: (72) 51944
Fax: (72) 15850
Rektor: Annie Bakke (1981-)

D. of Nursing
Head: Edel Marie Kjølstad; *staff* 15 (6)
D. of Psychiatric Nursing
Head: Solfrid Vatne; *staff* 2 (1)

Founded 1958. Acquired present status 1981. A State institution financially supported by the Ministry of Education and Research. Governing body: the Høgskolestyret.
Academic Year: August to June (August-December; January-June).
Admission Requirements: Secondary school certificate (examen artium).
Fees: None.
Language of Instruction: Norwegian.
Degrees and Diplomas: Diploma, 3 yrs. Diploma in Advanced Nursing, 1 further yr.
Library: c. 3000 vols.
Academic Staff, 1988-89: 17 (6).
Student Enrolment, 1988-89:

	Men	Women	Total
Of the country	28	179	207

5259 **SOGN OG FJORDANE SJUKEPLEIARHØGSKOLEN**
Sogn and Fjordane College of Nursing
6800 Førde
Telephone: (057) 22011

Nursing

Founded 1979. Acquired present status 1981. A State institution. Residential facilities for students.
Academic Year: August to June (August-December; January-June).
Admission Requirements: Secondary school certificate (examen artium).
Language of Instruction: Norwegian.
Degrees and Diplomas: Diploma, 3 yrs.
Student Enrolment: c. 130.

5260 **STAVANGER SYKEPLEIERHØGSKOLE**
Stavanger College of Nursing
Madlaveien 13, 4000 Stavanger
Telephone: (04) 53-30-95

Nursing

Founded 1946 as school. Acquired present status and title 1981. A State institution. Governing body: the Styre (Board). Residential facilities for academic staff and for c. 100 students.
Academic Year: August to June (August-December; January-June).
Admission Requirements: Secondary school certificate (examen artium).
Fees: None.
Language of Instruction: Norwegian.
Degrees and Diplomas: Diploma, 3 yrs.
Library: c. 6400 vols.
Academic Staff: c. 20.
Student Enrolment: c. 190.

5261 **STORD SJUKEPLEIERHØGSKOLE**
Stord College of Nursing
5400 Stord

Nursing

Academic Year: August to June (August-December; January-June).
Admission Requirements: Secondary school certificate (examen artium).
Fees: None.
Language of Instruction: Norwegian.
Degrees and Diplomas: Diploma, 3 yrs.

5262 **SYKEPLEIERHØGSKOLEN I SØR-TRØNDELAG**
South Trøndelag College of Nursing
Håkon Jarlsgate 12, 7000 Trondheim
Telephone: (075) 29145

Nursing

Founded 1967. Acquired present status 1981. A State institution financially supported by the government and county of Sør-Trøndelag. Governing body: the Styre (Board), comprising 7 members. Residential facilities for academic staff and students.
Academic Year: August to June (August-December; January-June).
Admission Requirements: Secondary school certificate (examen artium).
Fees: None.
Language of Instruction: Norwegian.
Degrees and Diplomas: Diploma, 3 yrs.
Library: College Library.
Academic Staff: c. 20 (10).
Student Enrolment: c. 360.

5263 **TELEMARK SJUKEPLEIERSKOLE**
Telemark College of Nursing
Postboks 1408, 3701 Skien
Telephone: 035-25583

Nursing

Founded 1908 as school, acquired present status and title 1982. A State institution financially supported by the Ministry of Cultural and Scientific Affairs. Some residential facilities for students.
Academic Year: August to June (August-December; January-June).
Admission Requirements: Secondary school certificate (examen artium).
Fees: None.
Language of Instruction: Norwegian.
Degrees and Diplomas: Diploma, 3 yrs.
Academic Staff: c. 15.
Student Enrolment: c. 180.

5264 **ULLEVÅL SYKEPLEIERHØGSKOLE**
Ullevål College of Nursing
PB 86, Ullevål Sykehus, 0407 Oslo 4
Telephone: (2) 607025
Fax: (2) 466887
Rektor: Ellen Askeland (1979-)
Avdelingsleder: Karin Evje Olsen

Nursing

Founded 1900. Acquired present status 1982. A State institution financially supported by the Ministry of Education and Research.
Arrangements for co-operation with: University of Linkøping.
Academic Year: August to June (August-December; January-June).
Admission Requirements: Secondary school certificate (examen artium).

Fees: None.
Language of Instruction: Norwegian.
Degrees and Diplomas: Diploma, 3 yrs. Diploma in Psychiatric Nursing, a further 1 ½ yrs.
Library: c. 8000 vols.
Academic Staff, 1990: 42.
Student Enrolment, 1989-90:

	Men	Women	Total
Of the country	60	455	515
of other countries	8	16	24
Total	68	471	539

5265 **VESTFOLD SYKEPLEIERHØGSKOLEN**
Vestfold College of Nursing
Skiringsalsgt. 9 A, 3100 Tønsberg
Telephone: (33) 17010
Rektor: Kåre Myhrer (1972-)
Undervisningsinspektør: Torunn Eik

Nursing

Founded 1919 as Red Cross College of Nursing. Acquired present status 1983. A State institution financially supported by the Ministry of Education and Research.

Academic Year: August to June (August-December; January-June).
Admission Requirements: Secondary school certificate (examen artium).
Fees: None.
Language of Instruction: Norwegian.
Degrees and Diplomas: Diploma, 3 yrs.
Academic Staff, 1989-90: 7 (7).
Student Enrolment, 1989-90:

	Men	Women	Total
Of the country	8	160	168
Of other countries	7	1	8
Total	15	161	176

5266 **ØSTFOLD SYKEPLEIERHØGSKOLE**
Østfold College of Nursing
Rektor Østbyegate 2, 1600 Fredrikstad
Telephone: (9) 311245
Rektor: Inger Reitan (1969-)

Nursing
Psychiatric Nursing

Founded 1955. Acquired present status 1982. A State institution financially supported by the Ministry of Education and Research.

Academic Year: August to June (August-December; January-June).
Admission Requirements: Secondary school certificate (examen artium) or equivalent.
Language of Instruction: Norwegian.
Degrees and Diplomas: Diploma, 3 yrs. Diploma in Advanced Nursing, 1 further yr.
Library: c. 9400.
Academic Staff: c. 25.
Student Enrolment, 1990:

	Men	Women	Total
Of the country	21	269	290

5267 **STATENS UTDANNINGSSENTER FOR HELSEPERSONELL**
National Postgraduate Training Centre for Health Personnel
Huk Aveny 56, 0287 Oslo 2
Telephone: (2) 438000
Fax: (2) 562045
Direktør: Ingrid Tveot Evensen

Public Health
Midwifery
Psychiatric Nursing

Founded 1961.

Academic Year: January to December/September to July.
Admission Requirements: 3 yrs of nursing school and minimum 1 yr of practical work.
Language of Instruction: Norwegian.
Student Enrolment, 1990: 135.

5268 **STATENS SPESIALSKOLE I PSYKIATRISK SYKEPLEIE**
National Special College of Psychiatric Nursing
Neståsen, 8000 Bodø
Telephone: 081-22-315

Psychiatric Nursing

Founded 1960 as school under the Department of Social Affairs. Acquired present status and title 1981. A Stateinstitution financially supported by the Ministry of Cultural and Scientific Affairs. Governing body: the Styre (Board). Residential facilities for students.

Academic Year: September to June (September-December; January-June).
Admission Requirements: Nursing diploma and 1 yr practical experience.
Fees: None.
Language of Instruction: Norwegian.
Degrees and Diplomas: Diploma.
Library: c. 4000 vols.
Academic Staff: c. 5 (30).
Student Enrolment: c. 20.

5269 **HØGSKOLEN I PSYKIATRISK SYKEPLEIE**
College of Psychiatric Nursing
Haukelandsbakken 45, 5009 Bergen
Telephone: 29-80-90
Rektor: Ingebørg Voldsæter

Psychiatric Nursing (postgraduate)

Founded 1980. Acquired present status 1981. A State institution financially supported by the Ministry of Education and Research.

Academic Year: August to June (August-December; January-June).
Admission Requirements: Nursing diploma and 1 yr practical experience.
Fees: None.
Language of Instruction: Norwegian.
Degrees and Diplomas: Diploma, 3 yrs.
Academic Staff, 1986-87: 5 (1).
Student Enrolment, 1986-87:

	Men	Women	Total
Of the country	4	24	28

5270 **ULLEVÅM SYKEPLEIERHØGSKOLE SPESIALUTDANNING I PSYKIATRISK SYKEPLEIE**
Special College of Psychiatric Nursing
Dikemark, 1385 Solberg

Psychiatric Nursing

Founded 1954. Became administratively associated with Ullevål College of Nursing, Oslo 1983.

5271 **BERGEN JORDMORHØGSKOLE**
Bergen College of Midwifery
Sundtsevi 57, 5050 Nesttun

Midwifery (postgraduate)

5272 **HELSESØTERSKOLEN I TRONDHEIM**
College of Public Health Nursing
Eirik Jarlsgate 4, 7000 Trondheim

Public Health Nursing (postgraduate)

5273 **HØGSKOLEN I HARSTAD**
College of Mental Nursing
Vernepleierutdanningen, Postboks 2144, 9405 Harstad

Nursing (for the Mentally Handicapped)

Academic Year: August to June (August-December; January-June).
Admission Requirements: Nursing diploma and 1 yr practical experience.
Language of Instruction: Norwegian.
Degrees and Diplomas: Diploma, 3 yrs.

5274 **AKERSHUS VERNEPLEIERHØGSKOLE**
Akershus College for Mental Nursing
Emma Hjorthsvei 1, Postboks 372, 1301 Sandvika

Nursing (for the Mentally Handicapped)

Academic Year: August to June (August-December; January-June).
Admission Requirements: Nursing diploma and 1 yr practical experience.
Language of Instruction: Norwegian.
Degrees and Diplomas: Diploma, 3 yrs.

5275 **BERGEN VERNEPLEIERHØGSKOLE**
Bergen College of Mental Nursing
Willy Valentinskei 34, 5034 Laksevåg
Telephone: (05) 34-22-10

Nursing (for the Mentally Handicapped)

Founded 1979. Acquired present status 1981. A State institution.

Academic Year: September to June (September-December; January-June).

Admission Requirements: Nursing diploma and 1 yr practical experience.

Language of Instruction: Norwegian.

Degrees and Diplomas: Diploma, 3 yrs.

Library: c. 2000 vols.

Academic Staff: c. 10.

Student Enrolment: c. 70.

5276 **OSLO VERNEPLEIERHØGSKOLE**
Oslo College of Mental Nursing
H.N. Haugesgt. 44, 0481 Oslo 4

Nursing (for the Mentally Handicapped)

Academic Year: August to June (August-December; January-June).

Admission Requirements: Nursing diploma and 1 yr practical experience.

Language of Instruction: Norwegian.

Degrees and Diplomas: Diploma, 3 yrs.

5277 **ROGALAND VERNEPLEIERHØGSKOLEN**
College of Mental Nursing
4350 Nærbø

Nursing (for the Mentally Handicapped)

Academic Year: August to June (August-December; January-June).

Admission Requirements: Nursing diploma and 1 yr practical experience.

Language of Instruction: Norwegian.

Degrees and Diplomas: Diploma, 3 yrs.

5278 **VERNEPLEIERHØGSKOLEN I SØR-TRØNDELAG**
South Trøndelag College of Mental Nursing
7060 Klæbu

Nursing (for the Mentally Handicapped)

Academic Year: August to June (August-December; January-June).

Admission Requirements: Nursing diploma and 1 yr practical experience.

Language of Instruction: Norwegian.

Degrees and Diplomas: Diploma, 3 yrs.

5279 **ØSTFOLD VERNEPLEIERHØGSKOLE**
Østfold College of Mental Nursing
Postboks 1189, Gamle Fredrikstad, 1601 Fredrikstad/F13

OMAN

5324 ***SULTAN QABOOS UNIVERSITY**
Al Khoudh, P.O. Box 32500, Muscat
Cables: Jam'iah
Telex: 5602 SQU ON
Telephone: 513333
Fax: 513254
Vice-Chancellor: Yahya M. Al-Manthari
Secretary-General: Hammad H. Al-Ghafri

C. of Education and Islamic Sciences (including Home Economics)
Dean: M. Shibini; *staff* 74
C. of Engineering (Civil, Mechanical, and Electrical)
Dean: J. Hunt; *staff* 52
C. of Science (Biology, Chemistry, Computing, Mathematics, Physics, Earth Sciences)
Dean: G. Gamlen; *staff* 110
C. of Agriculture (including Rural Studies, Animal Sciences, Fisheries, and Plant Sciences)
Dean: L. Hogan; *staff* 98
C. of Medicine (including Pharmacy)
Dean: G. Heseltine; *staff* 103
Computer Ce.
Director: S. Jensen; *staff* 28
Language Ce.
Director: James Melia; *staff* 62
Islamic Research Ce.
Ce. for Education Research
Director: T. Barwani; *staff* 5
Also University Hospital.

Founded 1980 with construction starting 1983. First students admitted 1986. An autonomous institution. Governing bodies: the University Council; the Academic Council. Residential facilities for academic staff and students.

Academic Year: September to June (September-January; February-June).

Admission Requirements: Secondary school certificate or equivalent.

Fees: None.

Degrees and Diplomas: Bachelor of–Arts, B.A.; Education, B.Ed.; Science, B.Sc.; Engineering, B.Eng.; Agriculture, B.Agr.; Science in Health Sciences; Medicine, B.Med.

Press or Publishing House: University Printing Press.

Academic Staff, 1989-90:

Rank	Full-time
Professors	38
Associate Professors	77
Assistant Professors	59
Lecturers	44
Assistant Lecturers	56
Total	274

Student Enrolment, 1989-90: c. 2800.

PANAMA

5325 ***UNIVERSIDAD DE PANAMÁ**

University of Panamá

Ciudad Universitaria, Dr. Octavio Méndez Pereira, El Cangrejo-Estafeta Universitaria, Panamá 3

Telephone: 63-6133

Rector: Abdiel J. Adames (1987-)

F. of Business Administration and Accountancy
F. of Public Administration
F. of Agriculture (including Animal Husbandry)
F. of Architecture
F. of Natural Sciences and Pharmacy (including Nursing)
F. of Social Communication
F. of Economics
F. of Law and Political Science
F. of Philosophy, Letters, and Education
F. of Medicine
F. of Dentistry
Criminology Research I.
I. of Earth Sciences
Education Administration Research I.

Also Vocational Centres (Universidad Popular) at Coclé, Azuero, and Darién. Regional Centres at Azuero, Coclé, Colón, Chiriquí, Veraguas.

Founded 1935. Autonomy granted by decree 1946. The institution falls under the jurisdiction of the Ministry ofEducation. Reorganized 1981. Governing bodies: the Consejo General Universitario; the Consejo Académico; the Consejo Administrativo.

Arrangements for co-operation with the University of Delaware.

Academic Year: April to January (April-September; September-January).

Admission Requirements: Secondary school certificate (bachillerato) or recognized equivalent.

Language of Instruction: Spanish.

Degrees and Diplomas: Licenciado in–Agricultural Engineering, 3 yrs; Public Administration; Commerce; Business Administration; Accountancy; Economics; International Relations; Social Work; Chemistry; Mathematics; Physics; Biology; Pharmacy; Philosophy and Letters; Spanish; French; English; Geography; Geography and History; Library Science; Journalism; Public Relations; Music; Physical Education; Psychology; Education, 4 yrs; Agriculture; Architecture; Plastic Arts; Interior Design; Graphic Design; Law and Political Science; Engineering, various fields, 5 yrs. Professional title of–Técnico, in various fields, 2-3 yrs. Professional titles in–Nursing, 3 yrs; Chemistry; Physics; Philosophy and Letters; Spanish; French; English; Geography and History; Physical Education, 5 yrs. Degree of Maestría in–Mathematics; Entomology; Educational Development, a further 2 yrs. Doctor in–Dentistry,5 yrs; Medicine, 6 yrs. Also teaching qualifications, primary level, 3 yrs. Diplomas and certificates.

Library: Central Library, *c.* 300,000 vols.

Publications: Boletines Estadísticos (biannually); Acción y Reflexión Educativa (quarterly); Revistas.

Press or Publishing House: Imprenta Universitaria.

Academic Staff: c. 1370 (1050).

Student Enrolment: c. 37,000.

5326 **UNIVERSIDAD SANTA MARÍA LA ANTIGUA**

Santa Maria La Antigua University

Apartado 6-1696, Estafeta El Dorado, Panamá 6

Telephone: 36-1868

Rector: Stanley Muschett Ibarra

Registrar: Noemí C. de Miranda

D. of Administration
Dean: Gladys M. de Moreno
D. of Technology and Natural Sciences (including Architecture)
Dean: Isaac Lowinger
D. of Humanities, Religious Studies, and Social Sciences
Dean: Francisco Beens
D. of Law and Political Science
Dean: Bonifacio Diez

Also University Centres at Colón and Chiriquí.

Founded 1965 with the Archbishop of Panamá as Grand Chancellor of the University. Reorganized 1973. Governing bodies: the Junta de Directores, composed of 9 members; the Consejo Académico.

Academic Year: April to December (April-July; August-December).

Admission Requirements: Secondary school certificate and entrance examination.

Fees (Balboa): 5400-6200 per semester.

Language of Instruction: Spanish.

Degrees and Diplomas: Licenciado in all fields, 4-5 yrs. Master, a further 2 yrs. Also professional qualifications.

Library: c. 52,130 vols.

Publications: Revista 'La Antigua'; Boletín Secretaría General.

Press or Publishing House: Editorial Santa María La Antigua.

Academic Staff, 1990: 38 (221).

Student Enrolment, 1990:

Men	Women	Total
2278	2003	4321

5327 **UNIVERSIDAD TECNOLÓGICA**

Panamá

F. of Civil Engineering
F. of Electrical Engineering
F. of Mechanical Engineering
F. of Computer Systems
D. of Natural and Social Sciences

Regional Centres in: Azuero; Bocas del Toro; Coclé; Colón; Chorrea; Chiriquí; Veraguas.

Founded 1984.

5328 **ESCUELA NÁUTICA DE PANAMÁ**

Apartado 5936, Panamá 2

Telephone: (64) 8625

Director: Antonio Motta Donadio

Marine Studies

Founded 1958, acquired present status 1971. A State institution financially supported by the central government. Governing body: the Board of Directors. Residential facilities for students.

Academic Year: April to February (April-August; September-February).

Admission Requirements: Secondary school certificate (bachillerato).

Language of Instruction: Spanish.

Degrees and Diplomas: Licenciado en Ingeniería Náutica, 5 yrs.

Library: 3000 vols.

Academic Staff, 1986-87:

Rank	Full-time	Part-time
Professores Titulares	4	–
Professor Adjunto	1	–
Professores Auxiliares	12	21
Instructores	6	–
Total	23	21

Student Enrolment, 1986-87:

	Men
Of the country	300
Of other countries	10
Total	310

5329 **INSTITUTO SUPERIOR DE TURISMO**
Panamá

Tourism
Founded 1972.

5330 **INSTITUTO SUPERIOR DE ENSEÑANZA**
Panamá

Teacher Training (for the Physically and Mentally Handicapped)
Founded 1969.

PARAGUAY

5331 ***UNIVERSIDAD CATÓLICA 'NUESTRA SEÑORA DE LA ASUNCIÓN'**

Catholic University of 'Our Lady of Asunción'

Independencia Nacional y Comuneros, Casilla 1718, Asunción

Telephone: (595-21) 41044

Fax: (595-21) 445245

Rector: Juan Oscar Usher Tapponier (1985-90)

Secretario General: Sixto Volpe Ríos

F. of Philosophy and Human Sciences (including Political Science and Education)

Dean: Ramiro Domínguez; *staff* 3 (7)

F. of Law and Diplomatic Studies

Dean: Elixeno Ayala; *staff* 3 (7)

F. of Accountancy and Business Administration

Dean: Cesar Guillermo Cruz Roa; *staff* 5 (5)

F. of Science and Technology (including Architecture)

Dean: Enrique Marin Fernández; *staff* 4 (12)

F. of Science and Letters (Villarrica)

Dean: Nidia Arguello de Garcete; *staff* 3 (1)

F. of Science and Letters (Encarnación)

Dean: Manfredo Wilhelm; *staff* 3

F. of Science and Letters (Concepción)

Dean: María Isabel Valdez de Araújo; *staff* 3

F. of Science and Letters (Ciudad del Este)

Dean: Reinaldo Quintana; *staff* 3

I. of Theology

Director: Michel Gibaud; *staff* 2 (2)

S. of Nursing

Director: Magdalena Genest, A.M.J.; *staff* 3

F. of Science and Letters (Pedro Juan Caballero)

Director: Humberto Villalba; *staff* 3

Also 4 Research Centres.

Founded 1960 by the Conferencia Episcopal del Paraguay and reorganized by the Sacred Congregation of Seminaries and University Studies. Recognized by the State on the same basis as the National University. The Archbishopof Asunción is Grand Chancellor of the University. Governing bodies: the Consejo Universitario; the Consejo Administrativo.

Arrangements for co-operation with the Universities of: Milan; Brussels (Free); Kansas; La Plata, Argentina; Frankfurt-am-Main; Université catholique de l'Ouest, Angers.

Academic Year: March to December (March-July; August-December).

Admission Requirements: Secondary school certificate (bachillerato) or equivalent, and entrance examination.

Fees (Guaranís): 431,600-577,400 per annum.

Language of Instruction: Spanish.

Degrees and Diplomas: Licenciado in–Philosophy; History; Psychology; Sociology; Political Science; Diplomatic Studies; Accountancy; Letters; Mathematics; Pastoral Studies; Business Administration; Education; Nursing; Midwifery, 5-6 yrs. Professional titles of–Notario; Enfermería, nursing; Economista, 4 yrs; Abogado,law, 6 yrs; Ingeniero; Arquitecto; Químico farmacéutico; Médico cirujano. Postgraduate degrees of–Materno infantil y Nutrición (Obstetrícia); Máster en Administración de Empresas. Doctorado.

Library: Central Library, 45,000 vols.

Publications: Revista del Centro de Estudios Antropológicos; Estudios Paraguayos (Revista de la Universidad).

Press or Publishing House: Centro de Publicaciones de la Universidad Católica (CEPUC).

Academic Staff, 1989:

Rank	Full-time
Profesores Titulares	12
Profesores Asistentes	229
Profesores Encargados de Cátedra	988
Total	1229

Student Enrolment, 1989:

Of the country	10,059
Of other countries	670
Total	10,729

5332 **UNIVERSIDAD NACIONAL DE ASUNCIÓN**

National University of Asunción

España 1198, Asunción

F. of Law and Social Sciences

F. of Philosophy

F. of Medicine

F. of Physics and Mathematics

F. of Economics

F. of Dentistry

F. of Chemistry and Pharmacy

F. of Agricultural and Veterinary Science

F. of Architecture

S. of Library Science

I. of Social Work

I. of Nursing

I. of Midwifery

Founded 1890. Granted autonomous status 1929. Financed by the State. Governing body: the Consejo Superior Universitario, composed of the Rector, the deans, one professor from each faculty, an alumnus, and one student.

Academic Year: March to November.

Admission Requirements: Secondary school certificate (bachillerato) or equivalent, and entrance examination.

Language of Instruction: Spanish.

Degrees and Diplomas: Licenciado in–Philosophy; Mathematics; Education; Letters, 3 yrs; History; Exact Sciences; Physico-Chemistry; Natural Sciences; Public Administration, 4 yrs; Economics, 6 yrs. Doctor by thesis in–History, 1 yr after Licenciado; Philosophy; Letters; Mathematics; Education, 2 yrs after Licenciado; Dentistry, 5 yrs; Medicine; Biochemistry; Industrial Chemistry, 6 yrs; Economics; Law and Social Sciences. Professional titles of–Topógrafo; Partera, midwifery, 3 yrs; Químico farmacéutico; Notario; Agrónomo, 4 yrs; Ingeniero agrónomo; Médico veterinario, 5 yrs; Arquitecto; Abogado, law, 6 yrs; Ingeniero civil; Ingeniero industrial, 6 yrs and thesis.

Library: University Library, *c.* 120,000 vols.

Academic Staff: c. 500.

Student Enrolment: c. 6000.

5333 **ESCUELA SUPERIOR DE FILOSOFÍA, CIENCIAS Y EDUCACIÓN**

Asunción

D. of Chemistry

D. of Education

D. of Philosophy and Letters

D. of Science

D. of Social Sciences

Founded 1944.

5334 **INSTITUTO SUPERIOR DE EDUCACIÓN**

Avenida Eusebio Ayala Km. 4.5, Asunción

Education

5335 **INSTITUTO NACIONAL DE INVESTIGACIONES CIENTÍFICAS**

P.O. Box 1141, Asunción

D. of Physics

D. of Chemistry

D. of Mathematics

D. of Psychology and Education

Founded 1957, under the auspices of Unesco.

Academic Year: April to December.

Admission Requirements: Secondary school certificate (bachillerato) or equivalent.

PERU

Universities and Technical Universities

National Institutions

5336 **UNIVERSIDAD NACIONAL DE 'SAN AGUSTÍN'**
National University of San Agustín
Santa Catalina 117, Casilla postal 23, Arequipa, Arequipa
Cables: santa catalina
Telephone: 227678
Rector: Manuel Zavallos Avara

P. of Law
P. of Humanities
P. of History and Social Sciences
P. of Biology
P. of Chemistry
P. of Geology
P. of Education
P. of Accountancy and Economics
P. of Medicine (including Nursing and Nutrition)
P. of Architecture and Town Planning
P. of Physics and Mathematics
I. of Geophysics

Founded 1825 as academy, became university 1928. Reorganized 1969 and faculties replaced by academic programmes. Governing bodies: the Asamblea Universitaria; the Consejo Ejecutivo.

Academic Year: September to August (September-January; March-August).

Admission Requirements: Secondary school certificate and entrance examination.

Fees: None.

Language of Instruction: Spanish.

Degrees and Diplomas: Licenciado in–Industrial Relations; History; Sociology; Anthropology; Philosophy; Literature and Languages; Education; Chemistry; Mathematics; Physics; Nutrition, 5 yrs. Professional titles of–Enfermera, nursing; Biólogo; Ingeniero Agropecuario; Asistente Social; Contador Público, accountancy; Arquitecto; Ingeniero Civil; Ingeniero Químico; Ingeniero Metalurgista; Ingeniero Geólogo; Ingeniero Geofisico, 5 yrs; Abogado, law; Psicólogo, 6 yrs; Médico-Cirujano, 7 ½ yrs.

Libraries: Central Library, *c.* 40,700 vols; Medicine, *c.* 14,500; programme libraries.

Special Facilities (Museums, etc.): Archaeology and History Museum.

Publications: Boletín Informativo de la Universidad; Memoria anual; Boletín de la Dirección Universitaria de Planificación; Boletín del Instituto Geofísico.

Academic Staff: c. 410 (360).

Student Enrolment: c. 12,500.

5337 **UNIVERSIDAD NACIONAL DE 'SAN CRISTÓBAL DE HUAMANGA'**
National University of 'San Cristóbal de Huamanga'
Portal Independencia 57, Apartado 120, Ayacucho, Ayacucho
Telephone: 2522

P. of Engineering
P. of Social Sciences
P. of Nursing and Midwifery
P. of Education
P. of Agriculture
P. of Chemical Engineering
P. of Mining Engineering
P. of Law

Founded 1677. Closed in 1886 and reopened 1959. Reorganized 1969 and faculties replaced by academic programmes. Financed by the government and under the jurisdiction of the Ministry of Education. Governing bodies: the Consejo Universitario; the Consejos de Programas; the Consejo de Administración Económica; the Consejode Instituto. Residential facilities for students.

Academic Year: April to December (April-July; August-December).

Admission Requirements: Secondary school certificate and entrance examination.

Language of Instruction: Spanish.

Degrees and Diplomas: Bachiller and professional titles in–Agri-culture; Mining; Chemistry; Midwifery; Biology; Anthropology; Law; Social Service; Education. Doctorates in–Midwifery; Biology; Anthropology; Social Service; Education, after Bachiller. Teaching qualifications, primary and secondary level.

Library: c. 12,000 vols.

Special Facilities (Museums, etc.): Natural History; Archaeology and Petrology.

Publication: Universidad y Wamaní.

Academic Staff: c. 370.

Student Enrolment: c. 6100.

5338 **UNIVERSIDAD NACIONAL DE CAJAMARCA**
National University of Cajamarca
Correos Villa Universitaria, Cajamarca, Cajamarca
Telephone: 922796
Fax: 923356
Rector: César Paredes Canto (1989-94)
Vice-Rector Administrativo: Aurelio Martos Díaz

F. of Agriculture and Forestry
Dean: Alonso Vela Ahumada; *staff* 63
F. of Education
Dean: Josué Tejada Atalaya; *staff* 50
F. of Engineering
Dean: Víctor Collantas Díaz *staff* 75
F. of Health Sciences (Nursing and Midwifery)
Dean: Jorge Céspedes Abanto; *staff* 92
F. of Social Sciences
Dean: Felipe Cogorno Vásquez; *staff* 27
F. of Veterinary Medicine
Dean: Roberto Acosta Gálvez; *staff* 42
F. of Economics, Accountancy, and Administration
Dean: Segundo Cieza Yánez; *staff* 28
F. of Animal Husbandry
Dean: Tulio Mondragón Roncal; *staff* 24
Soil Microbiology L.
Co-ordinator: Judith La Rosa; *staff* 5
Research and Control of Transmissible Diseases Ce.
Co-ordinator: Elio Delgado Azañero; *staff* 7
Fisheries Development and Promotion Ce.
Co-ordinator: Edgar Marino Valle; *staff* 6

Also branches in Jaén and Chota (Nursing).

Founded 1962. A State institution. Governing bodies: the Asamblea Universitaria; the Consejo Universitario.

Academic Year: March to December.

Admission Requirements: Secondary school certificate.

Language of Instruction: Spanish.

Degrees and Diplomas: Bachiller. Professional titles.

Library: Central Library, *c.* 40,000 vols.

Special Facilities (Museums, etc.): Natural History Museum; Archaeological Museum; Herbarium.

Press or Publishing House: Editorial Universitaria de la Universidad Nacional de Cajamarca.

Academic Staff, 1989-90:

Rank	Full-time
Profesores Principales	70
Profesores Asociados	92
Profesores Auxiliares	199
Jefes de Prácticas	40
Total	401

Student Enrolment, 1990: 5700.

5339 **UNIVERSIDAD NACIONAL DEL 'CALLAO'**
National University of Callao
Colina 310, Apartado 138, Callao, Callao
Telephone: 296607
Rector: Nicanor Ninahuaman Mucha

P. of Engineering
P. of Accountancy
P. of Economics
Founded 1966.
Academic Staff: c. 250.
Student Enrolment: c. 6600.

5340 **UNIVERSIDAD NACIONAL 'DANIEL ALCIDES CARRIÓN'**
National University 'Daniel Alcides Carrión'
Edificio Estatal 4, Apartado 77, Cerro de Pasco, Pasco
Telephone: 2197

P. of Education
P. of Economics and Commerce
P. of Engineering
P. of Animal Husbandry
P. of Nursing
P. of Geology
Founded 1965. Reorganized 1969 and faculties replaced by academic programmes.

5341 **UNIVERSIDAD NACIONAL DE SANTA**
Avenida Pacífico 508, Urb. Buenos Aires, Chimbote, Ancash

5342 **UNIVERSIDAD NACIONAL DE SAN ANTONIO ABAD**
National University of San Antonio Abad
Avenida de la Cultura s/n, Casilla 367-167, Cuzco, Cuzco
Telephone: 22271

P. of Economics
P. of Commerce
P. of Education
P. of Technology
P. of Geology
P. of Mining
P. of Animal Husbandry
Founded 1598, reorganized 1692. Reorganized 1969 and faculties replaced by academic programmes.

5343 **UNIVERSIDAD NACIONAL 'JOSÉ FAUSTINO SÁNCHEZ CARRIÓN'**
National University 'José Faustino Sánchez Carrión'
Avenida Grau 592, Calle Colón 461, Huacho, Lima
Telephone: 324741; 322773
Rector: Daniel Valenzuela San Martín

P. of Industrial Engineering
P. of Fisheries
P. of Business Administration
P. of Accountancy
P. of Sociology
P. of Nursing
P. of Nutrition
Founded 1968. A State institution.
Academic Year: January to December.
Admission Requirements: Secondary school certificate and entrance examination.
Language of Instruction: Spanish.
Degrees and Diplomas: Bachiller, 5 yrs. Professional titles in all fields.
Academic Staff: c. 120.
Student Enrolment: c. 3030.

5344 **UNIVERSIDAD NACIONAL DEL CENTRO DEL PERÚ**
National University of Central Peru
Calle Real 160, Apartado 77, Huancayo, Junín
Telex: 6400 PE
Telephone: 233032
Rector: Gustavo Ramírez Piza

P. of Agriculture
Dean: Juan Bullon Ames
P. of Chemical Engineering
Dean: Esau Caro Meza
P. of Forestry
Dean: Hugo Ayala Sinchez
P. of Animal Husbandry
Dean: Armando Borja Cueva
P. of Economics
Dean: Meliton Vilchez Perales
P. of Education and Humanities
Dean: Anibal Cardenas Ayala
P. of Social Services
Dean: Layli Maravi Baldeón
P. of Architecture
Dean: Pedro Carrillo Ruíz
P. of Mechanical and Electrical Engineering
Dean: Francisco Borja Salcedo
P. of Food Technology
Dean: Luz Buendia Sotelo
P. of Nursing
Dean: Sherin Krederdt Araujo
P. of Administration
Dean: Eutimio Jara Rodríguez
P. of Electrical Engineering
Dean: Ovidio Ascencio Castro
P. of Metallurgical Engineering
Dean: Alejandro Barrantes Peralta
P. of Mining Engineering
Dean: Ernesto Rosales Galarza
Research Ce.
Director: Humberto Rodríguez Landeo
P. of Sociology
Dean: Pablo Mosombite Pinedo
P. of Anthropology
Dean: Augusto Cruzatt Añaños
P. of Accountancy
Dean: Maximiliano Vila Poma
Founded 1959, acquired present status 1961. A State institution. Reorganized 1969 and faculties replaced by academic programmes.
Academic Year: April to December (April-July; July-December).
Admission Requirements: Secondary school certificate and entrance examination.
Language of Instruction: Spanish.
Degrees and Diplomas: Bachiller. Licenciado in–Anthropology; Nursing; Sociology; Social Work; Business Administration; Journalism. Professional titles of–Ingeniero (various fields); Contador Público, accountancy; Economista; Arquitecto;, 5 yrs. Teaching qualifications (primary level, 3 yrs; secondary level, 5 yrs). Degrees of specialization.
Library: c. 3600 vols.
Special Facilities (Museums, etc.): Museums: Ethnology, Archaeology and Regional History.
Publications: Anales Cientificos; Revista de Ciencias Agrarias; Proceso (quarterly).
Academic Staff: c. 290 (20).
Student Enrolment: c. 8500.

5345 **UNIVERSIDAD NACIONAL 'HERMILIO VALDIZÁN'**
National University 'Hermilio Valdizán'
Dos de Mayo 680, Apartado 278, Huánuco, Huánuco
Telephone: 2341
Rector: Edgardo Torres Vera

P. of Agriculture
P. of Education
P. of Economics and Commerce
P. of Nursing

P. of Engineering

Founded 1964. Reorganized 1969 and faculties replaced by academic programmes.

Academic Staff: c. 140.

Student Enrolment: c. 5550.

5346 **UNIVERSIDAD NACIONAL 'SANTIAGO ANTÚNEZ DE MAYOLO'**

National University 'Santiago Antúnez de Mayolo'

Avenida Centenario s/n, Apartado 70, Huaraz, Ancash

Telephone: 721393

Rector: Jaime Minaya Castromonte

P. of Mining

P. of Civil Engineering

P. of Agricultural Engineering

P. of Industrial Engineering

Founded 1977.

5347 **UNIVERSIDAD NACIONAL 'SAN LUIS GONZAGA'**

National University of 'San Luis Gonzaga'

Jr. Cajamarca 194, Ica, Ica

Telephone: 2868; 2437

Rector: César Angeles Caballero

P. of Economics and Administration

P. of Law

P. of Engineering

P. of Applied Sciences

P. of Natural Sciences

P. of Medicine

P. of Veterinary Medicine

P. of Dentistry

Founded 1955, became university 1961. Reorganized 1969 and faculties replaced by academic programmes. The university is an autonomous institution.

Academic Year: April to December (April-July; August-December).

Student Enrolment: c. 2000.

5348 **UNIVERSIDAD NACIONAL DE LA 'AMAZONÍA PERUANA'**

National University of the 'Peruvian Amazon'

Apartado 496, Iquitos, Loreto

Telephone: 235351

Rector: Rusbel Arevalo Melendez

P. of Engineering

P. of Biology

P. of Nursing

P. of Education

P. of Administration

General Research I.

S. of General Studies

Teacher Training S.

Founded 1962. Reorganized 1969 and faculties replaced by academic programmes.

Academic Year: April to March (April-July; August-December).

Admission Requirements: Secondary school certificate and entrance examination.

Fees: None.

Language of Instruction: Spanish.

Degrees and Diplomas: Bachiller. Licenciado. Professional titles of–Ingeniero de agronomía y forestal, agriculture and forestry; Ingeniero Químico; Biólogo; Enfermera(o); Contador Público; Normalista Superior, teaching qualification, secondary level.

Academic Staff: c. 200.

Student Enrolment: c. 4500.

5349 **UNIVERSIDAD NACIONAL 'PEDRO RUÍZ GALLO'**

National University of Lambayeque

Jr. 8 de Octubre 637, Casilla 557, Lambayeque, Lambayeque

Telephone: 2080; 2134

Rector: Ángel Dias Celis

P. of Biology

P. of Law

P. of Nursing

P. of Engineering (including Animal Husbandry)

P. of Veterinary Medicine

P. of Economics and Social Sciences (including Accountancy)

Founded 1960 as high school, acquired present name and status 1970, incorporating the former Universidad Nacional Agraria del Norte and the Universidad Nacional de Lambayeque. Reorganized 1972.

Academic Year: July to January (July-November; February-June; September-January).

Admission Requirements: Secondary school certificate and entrance examination.

Fees: None.

Language of Instruction: Spanish.

Degrees and Diplomas: Bachiller. Licenciado in Biology. Professional titles of–Ingeniero Agrónomo; Biólogo; Contador Público; Abogado, law; Enfermera, nursing; Ingeniero Civil; Ingeniero Agrícola; Médico Veterinario; Sociólogo; Ingeniero Zootecnista, animal husbandry, 5 yrs.

Library: c. 15,700 vols.

Academic Staff: c. 240 (60).

Student Enrolment: c. 5500.

5350 **UNIVERSIDAD NACIONAL AGRARIA**

National University of Agriculture

Apartado 456, La Molina, Lima, Lima

Cables: uniagraria

Telephone: 35-2035

Rector: Alfonso Flores Mere

Secretario General: Menandro Ortiz Pretel

F. of Science

Dean: Pedro Cueva M.

F. of Forestry

Dean: Roberto López C.

F. of Economics and Planning

Dean: Walter Fegan E.

F. of Food Technology

Dean: Carlos Lescano Anadón

F. of Agricultural Engineering

Dean: Rodolfo Muànante Sanguinetti

F. of Agriculture

Dean: Carmen Felipe-Morales

F. of Fishery

Dean: Roberto Shirasaka Kanno

F. of Animal Husbandry

Dean: Juan Kalinowski Echegaray

Arid Zones Research Ce.

Director: Carlos López Ocaña

Ce. for Investment and Development Studies

Ce. of Statistics and Data Processing

Head: Gonzalo Fano Miranda

Graduate S.

Director: Luis Maezono Yamashita

Also 18 Research Programmes and 3 Regional institutions.

Founded 1901 at Santa Beatriz as school of agriculture, moved to La Molina 1933. Became university 1960. Reorganized 1969 and faculties replaced by academic programmes. The university is an autonomous institution financed by the State. Governing bodies: the Asamblea Universitaria (University Assembly); the Consejo Universitario. Some residential facilities for students.

Academic Year: April to December (April-July; August-December; January-March).

Admission Requirements: Secondary school certificate, and entrance examination.

Language of Instruction: Spanish.

Degrees and Diplomas: Bachiller. Professional titles of–Ingeniero (various fields); Biólogo; Economista; Alimentarias; Meteorólogo, by thesis after Bachiller. Magister in Scientiae, Mag.Sc., 2 yrs postgraduate study.

Libraries: National Agricultural Library, c. 32,000 vols; faculty libraries.

Special Facilities (Museums, etc.): Museo Antropológico.

Publications: Universitas, Boletín Informativo de la Universidad; Anales Científicos, Organo Científico Oficial de la Universidad.

Academic Staff: c. 400.
Student Enrolment, 1990:

	Men	Women	Total
Of the country	2995	1326	4321
Of other countries	13	5	18
Total	3008	1331	4339

5351 **UNIVERSIDAD NACIONAL DE EDUCACIÓN 'ENRIQUE GUZMÁN Y VALLE'**
National University of Education 'Enrique Guzmán y Valle'
La Cantuta, Chosica, Lima
Telephone: 910052
Rector: Milciades Hidalgo Cabrera

Education

Founded 1905 as Escuela Normal, became college 1960 and then national university. A State institution. Residential facilities for some members of the academic staff and for all students.

Academic Year: April to December (April-July; August-December).

Admission Requirements: Secondary school certificate and entrance examination.

Fees: None.

Language of Instruction: Spanish.

Degrees and Diplomas: Teaching qualification (primary, secondary, and technical levels).

Library: College Library.

Publication: Review.

Academic Staff: c. 190.

Student Enrolment: c. 9700.

5352 **UNIVERSIDAD NACIONAL DE 'INGENIERÍA'**
National University of Engineering
Avenida Túpac Amaru s/n, Apartado 1301, San Martín de Porres Lima, Lima
Cables: Uni
Telephone: 811035
Rector: Javier Sota Nadal
Secretario General: Telmo Goyzueta Meiggs

P. of Architecture and Town Planning (including Fine Arts)
Dean: José García Bryce
P. of Science
Dean: Jaime Avalos Sánchez
P. of Geological, Mining, and Metallurgical Engineering
Dean: Maximo Romero Rojas
P. of Civil Engineering
Dean: Genaro Humala Aybar
P. of Mechanical and Electrical Engineering
Dean: Juan Hori Asano
P. of Industrial Engineering
Dean: Luis Flores Fonseca
P. of Sanitary Engineering
Dean: Sara Pisfil Herrera
P. of Petroleum Engineering
Dean: Wilfredo Salinas Ruiz-Conejo
Graduate S.
Dean: María Jesús Ojeda
S. of Fine Arts
S. of Technology
Regional S. of Mathematics
Planning I.
Director: Víctor Cataño Cauti
Standards I.
Director: German Grajeda Reyes
I. of Industrial Research
I. of Pure and Applied Mathematics
I. of Structural Engineering
Energetics I.
Electrical Testing I.
I. for Hydraulics and Fluid Mechanics
Director: José Nicolas de Pierola
I. of Electrical Engineering
Director: Jubert Chávez Serrano
I. of Economics and Social Sciences
Director: Víctor García Gonzáles
I. of Chemical Engineering
Director: Mario Rojas Delgado
I. of Research
Director: Ernesto López Carranza
I. of Petroleum Research
Director: Edgar Argume Chávez

Founded 1875 as special school of Construction and Mining. Became National Engineering School 1941 and National Engineering University 1954. An autonomous institution financed by the State. Reorganized 1969 and facultiesreplaced by academic programmes. Governing bodies: the General Assembly, consisting of 12 professors and 4 students from each programme, presided over by the Rector; the University Council, consisting of one dean, one professor, and one student from each programme, the Rector, the Vice-Rector, and the President of the Students' Association; the Council of Economic Administration; the Programme Councils. Residential facilities for students.

Academic Year: April to December (April-July; August-December).

Admission Requirements: Secondary school certificate and entrance examination.

Fees: None.

Language of Instruction: Spanish.

Degrees and Diplomas: Bachiller, 4 yrs. Professional title of Ingeniero Fisico-Matemático or Arquitecto, by thesis after Bachiller. Magister, 2 yrs postgraduate study.

Libraries: Central Library, c. 122,000 vols; faculty libraries, c. 37,000.

Special Facilities (Museums, etc.): Museums: Mineralogy; Palaeontology.

Publications: Amaru; Boletín Informativo; Notas de Matemáticas; Rector's Annual Report; Reports of different organisms; Catalogues of Programmes and Schools; Several non-periodical technical publications.

Academic Staff, 1989: c. 990.

Student Enrolment, 1989: c. 12,240.

5353 **UNIVERSIDAD NACIONAL 'MAYOR DE SAN MARCOS'**
National University of San Marcos
Avenida República de Chile 295, Lima, Lima
Telephone: 283727
Rector: Jorge Campos Rey de Castro

P. of Physics and Mathematics (including Statistics)
P. of Chemistry and Chemical Engineering
P. of Engineering
P. of Geology and Geological Engineering
P. of Biological Sciences
P. of Pharmacy and Biochemistry
P. of Veterinary Medicine
P. of Medicine
P. of Dentistry
P. of Social Sciences
P. of Economics
P. of Law and Political Science
P. of Accountancy and Administrative Studies
P. of Philosophy, Psychology, and Art
P. of Linguistics, Philosophy, and Spanish Literature
P. of Education
P. of Metallurgical Engineering
P. of Nutrition

Also 51 academic departments and research centres and institutes.

Founded 1551 by Royal Decree and reorganized by Papal Bull 1571. Closed at the time of the establishment of the Republic, reinaugurated 1861. Became an autonomous institution 1874, reorganized 1946. Reorganized 1969 and faculties replaced by academic programmes. Receives financial assistance from the State. Governing bodies: the University Assembly; the University Council; Programme Councils; the Council of Economic Administration.

Academic Year: April to December (April-July; September-December).

Admission Requirements: Secondary school certificate and entrance examination.

Language of Instruction: Spanish.

Degrees and Diplomas: Bachiller. Licenciado in–Mathematics; Statistics; Research; Physics; Anthropology; Sociology; Social Work; Archaeology; Administration; Philosophy; Art; Languages; Hispanic Literature. Professional titles of–Abogado, law; Médico-Cirujano; Obstétriz, midwifery; Ingeniero Geólogo; Biólogo Matemático; Economista; Contador Público, accountancy; Químico Farmacéutico; Cirujano Dentista; Médico Veterinario; Ingeniero Químico; Ingeniero Industrial; Ingeniero Mecánico de Fluidos; Ingeniero Electrónico; Geógrafo; Psicólogo; Periodista, journalism; Químico. Teaching qualification (secondary level).

Libraries: Central Library; specialized libraries.
Special Facilities (Museums, etc.): Museum: Archaeology and Ethnology; Natural History; Art and History.
Publications: Anales de Medicina; Anales del Programa de Farmacia y Bioquímica; Boletín Bibliográfico de la Biblioteca Central; Boletín del Programa de Medicina; Boletín del Instituto de Investigaciones Económicas; Odontologia; Archivos del Instituto de Biologia Andina; Revistas de: Educación; Letras; Nueva Crónica (History); Derecho y Ciencias Políticas; Ciencias Comerciales; Farmacia; Medicina Veterinaria; Neuro-Psiquiatria-Sphinx; Investigaciones Pecuarias; Peruana de Medicina Tropical; Sanidad Avícola; Derecho de Trabajo.
Academic Staff: c. 3150.
Student Enrolment: c. 35,000.

5354 **UNIVERSIDAD NACIONAL DE PIURA**
National University of Piura
Prolongación Avenida Grau s/n, Piura, Piura
Telephone: 321931
Rector: Arturo Davies Guaylupo (1984-89)
Secretario General: Ferrer Farías Alburqueque

F. of Agriculture
Dean: Martín Augusto Delgado Junchayo; *staff* 40 (1)
F. of Administration
Dean: Gloria Isabel Castillo Rosales; *staff* 14 (1)
F. of Accountancy and Finance
Dean: José Víctor Huiman Silva; *staff* 31 (3)
F. of Physics and Mathematics
Dean: Jorge Huamanchumo Miranda; *staff* 47
F. of Social Sciences and Education
Dean: Rita Janet Lamas Fuentes; *staff* 24 (2)
F. of Economics
Dean: Eddie Hugo Agurto Plata; *staff* 24 (7)
F. of Industrial Engineering
Dean: Andrés Lorenzo Oruna Cisneros; *staff* 20
F. of Mining
Dean: Alberto Winchonlong Coronado; *staff* 22 (3)
F. of Fishery
Dean: Manuel Mogollón López; *staff* 21
F. of Medicine
Dean: Manuel Purizaca Benites; *staff* 19
F. of Animal Husbandry
Dean: Alejandro Alfonso Carrasco Vásquez; *staff* 16 (1)
I. of Art and Culture
Director: Luisa Sánchez de Heredia; *staff* 6
I. of Sport
Director: Marzo Zapata Briceno; *staff* 6
Ce. for Lifelong Education
Head: José Carlos Palacios Altuna

Founded 1961 as technical institution, reorganized 1969 as national university. Governing bodies: the Asamblea Universitaria; the Consejo Universitario.
Academic Year: April to December (April-July; August-December).
Admission Requirements: Secondary school certificate.
Fees: None.
Language of Instruction: Spanish.
Degrees and Diplomas: Bachiller and Professional titles in all fields, 5 yrs.
Library: Central Library, 23,000 vols.
Publication: Revistas.
Academic Staff, 1986-87: c. 300.
Student Enrolment, 1986-87: 5183.

5355 **UNIVERSIDAD NACIONAL DE PUCALLPA**
National University of Pucallpa
Pucallpa, Ucayali
Telephone: 6044
Rector: Víctor Manuel Chávez Vasquez (1986-88)
Secretario General: Alfonso Gonzáles Machedo

F. of Forestry
Dean: César Olivera Orellana
F. of Agriculture
Dean: Víctor Fernández Delgado
F. of Nursing
Dean: Emilio Pascual Valentin

Founded 1979.
Academic Year: April to December.
Admission Requirements: Secondary school certificate.
Fees: None.
Language of Instruction: Spanish.
Degrees and Diplomas: Bachiller and Professional titles.
Library: 7380 vols.
Academic Staff, 1986-87: 52 (4).
Student Enrolment, 1986-87:

	Men	Women	Total
Of the country	262	171	433

5356 **UNIVERSIDAD NACIONAL DEL 'ALTIPLANO'**
National University of 'Altiplano'
Ciudad Universitaria, Apartado 291, Puno, Puno
Telephone: 673
Rector: Luis Salas Arones (1984-89)
Secretario General: Juan Moises Mamani Mamani

F. of Agriculture
F. of Veterinary Medicine and Animal Husbandry
F. of Economics
F. of Accountancy and Administration
F. of Health Sciences
F. of Social Work
F. of Social Sciences
F. of Statistics
F. of Mining Engineering
F. of Law
F. of Chemical Engineering
F. of Education
F. of Nursing
Ce. for Rural Development
Social Development Research I.

Founded 1856. Closed for almost 100 years. Reopened 1961. A national autonomous university financed by the State. Governing bodies: the Asamblea Universitaria with two-thirds academic staff and one-third student membership; the Consejo Universitario. The Rector is elected by secret ballot of the General Assembly.
Academic Year: April to December (April-July; August-December).
Admission Requirements: Secondary school certificate and entrance examination.
Fees: None.
Language of Instruction: Spanish.
Degrees and Diplomas: Bachiller in–Agriculture; Veterinary Medicine and Animal Husbandry; Economics; Accountancy; Statistics; Sociology; Social Work; Mining Engineering; Law; Chemistry; Biology; Health Sciences. Licenciado in–Statistics; Sociology; Mining Engineering; Education. Professional titles of–Ingeniero Agrónomo; Ingeniero Economista; Ingeniero Químico; Médico Veterinario y Zootecnista; Contador Público, accountancy; Trabajador Social, social work; Abogado, law; Biólogo; Médico; Nutricionista; Enfermera(o), nursing.
Libraries: Central Library, 25,000 vols; libraries of the faculties, c. 4200.
Publication: Revista.
Academic Staff: c. 290 (20).
Student Enrolment: c. 7500.

5357 **UNIVERSIDAD NACIONAL 'FEDERICO VILLARREAL'**
National University 'Federico Villarreal'
Calle Carlos González 285, San Miguel, Lima
Telephone: 644370
Rector: Luis Cotillo Zegarra

F. of Architecture and Town Planning
F. of Administration
F. of Economics
F. of Finance and Accountancy
F. of Natural Sciences and Mathematics
F. of Social Sciences
F. of Co-operative Studies
F. of Law and Political Science
F. of Education and Human Sciences
F. of Civil Engineering
F. of Geographic Engineering
F. of Industrial and Systems Engineering
F. of Medicine
F. of Oceanography, Fishery, and Food Technology
F. of Dentistry

F. of Psychology
F. of Medical Technology
I. of Physical Education
I. of Languages
I. of Antarctic Studies
D. for Lifelong Education
Also 10 Research Centres.

Founded 1963. An autonomous institution financed by the State. Governing body: the Asamblea Universitaria, presided over by the Rector.

Academic Year: April to December.

Admission Requirements: Secondary school certificate and entrance examination.

Fees: None.

Language of Instruction: Spanish.

Degrees and Diplomas: Bachiller and professional titles in–Architecture; Law; Fishery; Civil Engineering; Education; Industrial Engineering; Economics; Accountancy; Dentistry; Administration; Psychology; Medicine; Nursing; Co-operative Studies; Sociology; History; Social Service; Geographic Engineering, 10-14 sem.

Library: Total, 54,000 vols.

Special Facilities (Museums, etc.): Art, Painting and Sculpture.

Publications: Boletín Estadístico (annually); Research publications; Revista of the Faculty of Law and Political Science.

Academic Staff: c. 680 (1250).

Student Enrolment: c. 30,000.

5358 **UNIVERSIDAD NACIONAL JORGE BASADRE GROHMANN**

National University Jorge Basadre Grohmann
Avenida Bolognesi con Pinto s/n, Casilla 316, Tacna, Tacna
Telephone: 721385
Rector: Alberto Coayla Vilca
Secretario General: José Avilés Hinojosa

F. of Administration
Dean: Pedro Riveros Valderrama
F. of Accountancy and Finance
Dean: Fernando Tenorio Vicente
F. of Mining
Dean: Zenón Sarmiento Mejia; *staff* 34
F. of Metallurgy
Dean: Humberto Molero Contrera
F. of Fishery
Dean: Luis Muñante Angulo
F. of Midwifery
Dean: Carlos Valente Rossi
F. of Agriculture
Dean: Vicente Castañeda Chávez
F. of Food Technology
Dean: Miguel Larrea Céspedes
F. of Education
Dean: José Acosta Eyzaguirre

Founded 1971. Governing bodies: the Asamblea Universitaria; the Consejo Universitario.

Academic Year: April to December.

Admission Requirements: Secondary school certificate and entrance examination.

Fees: None.

Language of Instruction: Spanish.

Degrees and Diplomas: Bachiller. Licenciado in–Business Administration; Midwifery. Professional titles of–Ingeniero, various fields; Contador público, accountancy.

Libraries: Central Library; Ciudad Universitaria Library.

Academic Staff, 1989: c. 200.

Student Enrolment, 1989: c. 2560.

5359 **UNIVERSIDAD NACIONAL DE SAN MARTÍN**

National University of San Martín
Martínez de Compagñón 527, Tarapoto, San Martín
Rector: Augusto Montes Gutierres

Agriculture and Forestry
Civil Engineering
Agricultural Engineering
Sciences and Humanities
Mother and Child Care

Founded 1979.

5360 **UNIVERSIDAD NACIONAL AGRARIA DE 'LA SELVA'**

National University of Agriculture of 'La Selva'
Apartado 156, Tingo María, Huánuco
Telephone: 2341

Ut. of Tropical Agriculture
P. of Agriculture
P. of Agricultural Engineering
P. of Animal Husbandry

Founded 1964.

5361 **UNIVERSIDAD NACIONAL DE 'LA LIBERTAD'**

National University of Trujillo
Independencia 431, Oficina 216, Casilla 315, Trujillo, La Libertad
Cables: diego de almagro 396
Telephone: 243721
Rector: Carlos Chirinos Villanueva

P. of Economics
P. of Science
P. of Metallurgy
P. of Law and Political Science
P. of Social Sciences
P. of Education
P. of Engineering
P. of Pharmacy and Biochemistry
P. of Biology
P. of Physics and Mathematics
P. of Medicine

Founded 1824, by decree of Simón Bolívar, opened 1831. The university was closed between 1878 and 1894. Reorganized 1969 and faculties replaced by academic programmes. Some residential facilities for students.

Academic Year: June to May (June-September; November-May).

Admission Requirements: Secondary school certificate and entrance examination.

Fees: None.

Language of Instruction: Spanish.

Degrees and Diplomas: Bachiller in–Law; Economics; Social Anthropology; Archaeology, 4 yrs; Education; Chemical Engineering; Pharmacy and Biochemistry; Biology; Physics and Mathematics, 5 yrs; Medicine, 8 yrs. Licenciado in–Business Administration; Social Anthropology; Archaeology; Mathematics; Physics; Statistics, 5 yrs. Professional titles of–Enfermero, 4 yrs; Abogado, law; Economista, economics; Contador Público, accountancy; Ingeniero Químico; Químicofarmacéutico; Biólogo, 5 yrs; Médico-Cirujano, 8 yrs. Doctorado in all fields. Teaching qualification (secondary level).

Libraries: Central Library, c. 15,460 vols; Education and Social Sciences, c. 11,840; Chemical Engineering, c. 2950; Physics and Mathematics, c. 2470; Languages, c. 3600; Biology, c. 2730; Pharmacy, c. 1600; Medicine, c. 4030; Economics, c. 4700; Law and Political Science, c. 5200; Nursing, 1000; Archaeology, c. 2460.

Publications: Memoria Rectoral (annually or biannually); Revista Universitaria (annually); Boletín Informativo (monthly).

Academic Staff: c. 640.

Student Enrolment: c. 11,000.

5362 **UNIVERSIDAD NACIONAL DE TUMBES**

National University of Tumbes
Bolognesi 218, Tumbes, Tumbes
Telephone: 3081

Private Institutions

5363 **UNIVERSIDAD PARTICULAR DE APURIMAC**

Apurimac University
Apartado 140, Abancay, Apurimac
Rector: Jorge Elias Monzón Pesantes
Secretario General: Pedro Pablo Chambi Condori

F. of Agriculture
Dean: Vicente Mamani Pari
F. of Accountancy
Dean: Pedro Julián Santos Carpio
F. of Law
Dean: Jorge Ramirez Aragón

F. of Education
Dean: Julián Casaverde Agrada
F. of Nursing
Dean: María Antonieta Flores
Founded 1984. A private institution.
Academic Year: April to December (April-July; September-December).
Admission Requirements: Secondary school certificate.
Fees (Intis): 400 per semester.
Language of Instruction: Spanish.
Degrees and Diplomas: Bachiller and Professional titles.
Library: Central Library, 60 vols.
Academic Staff, 1986-87: 13 (37).
Student Enrolment, 1986-87: 1575.

5364 **UNIVERSIDAD CATÓLICA DE SANTA MARÍA**
Avenida Santa Catalina 410, Casilla 1350, Arequipa, Arequipa
Telephone: 224401
Rector: Norberto Cevallos Quequezama
P. of Social Communications
P. of Accountancy
P. of Law
P. of Economics and Management
P. of Nursing
P. of Dentistry
P. of Social Service
P. of Education
Teacher Training S.
Founded 1961. Reorganized 1969 and faculties replaced by academic programmes.
Academic Staff: c. 260.
Student Enrolment: c. 5600.

5365 **UNIVERSIDAD PARTICULAR DE CHICLAYO**
Chiclayo University
Avenida Quinones 615, Urb. San Juan, Chiclayo, Lambayeque
Telephone: 22-78-06
F. of Architecture
Co-ordinator: Jorge Cubas Ruiz; *staff* 7 (8)
F. of Midwifery
Co-ordinator: Juan Serrepe Ascencio; *staff* 2 (19)
Founded 1985. A private institution.
Academic Year: April to December (April-July; August-December).
Admission Requirements: Secondary school certificate.
Fees (Intis): 1280-5120 per semester.
Language of Instruction: Spanish.
Degrees and Diplomas: Bachiller and Licenciado, 5 yrs. Magister in Education Administration, 2 yrs postgraduate study.
Library: Central Library.
Publication: Revista.
Academic Staff, 1986-87: 14 (40).
Student Enrolment, 1986-87:

	Men	Women	Total
Of the country	217	369	586

5366 **UNIVERSIDAD PARTICULAR 'LOS ANGELES' DE CHIMBOTE**
University 'Los Angeles' of Chimbote
José Olaya 981, Chimbote, Ancash
Telephone: 321621

5367 **UNIVERSIDAD ANDINA DEL CUSCO**
Parque la Madre 186, Cusco, Cusco
Telephone: 226377

5368 **UNIVERSIDAD PRIVADA 'LOS ANDES'**
Jr. Cusco 259, Huancayo, Junin
Telephone: 234480

5369 **UNIVERSIDAD DE HUÁNUCO**
University of Huánuco
Jirón Constitución 650, Huánuco, Huánuco
Telephone: 3154
Presidenta de la Comisión Organizadora: Rosa Abarca de Ruiz
F. of Law and Political Sciences
Dean: Bernabé Mato Cori; *staff* 9 (11)
F. of Midwifery
Dean: Cróver Chávez Tapia; *staff* 4 (22)
F. of Animal Husbandry
Dean: José Ríos Navarro; *staff* 5 (6)
Founded 1989. Previously Universidad 'Víctor Andrés Belaúnde'.
Academic Year: April to December (April-July; September-December).
Admission Requirements: Secondary school certificate.
Fees (US$): 200 per semester.
Language of Instruction: Spanish.

5370 ***UNIVERSIDAD DEL PACÍFICO**
University of the Pacific
Avenida Salaverry 2020, Apartado 4683, Jesús María, Lima 11, Lima
Cables: udelpa
Telex: 25650 PE CP SHERA
Telephone: 712277
Fax: 706121
Rector: Raimundo Villagrasa Novoa, S.J. (1989-94)
Secretario General: Carlos Gatti Murriel
F. of Economics
Dean: Jorge González Izquierdo
F. of Business Administration (including Accountancy)
Dean: Gregorio Leong Chávez
Graduate S.
Dean; Estuardo Marrou Loayza
D. of General Studies
Vice-Dean: Jorge Wiesse Rebagliati
Management Development Ce.
Director: Alejandro Valdés
Research Ce.
Director: Juan Julio Wicht Rossel, S.J.
Founded 1962. A private institution. Governing body: the Consejo Universitario.
Arrangements for co-operation with: University of Texas at Austin; Pittsburgh University; Georgetown University; Iona Collge; Pontificia Universidade Católica do Rio de Janeiro; Pontificia Universidad Javeriana, Bogotá; Ecole supérieure de Commerce, Paris.
Academic Year: May to April (May-August; September-December; February-April).
Admission Requirements: Secondary school certificate and entrance examination.
Language of Instruction: Spanish.
Degrees and Diplomas: Bachiller and Licenciado, 5 yrs. Magister in–Economics; Administration, 2 yrs postgraduate study.
Libraries: General Library, 35,554 vols; specialized library, 9017.
Publication: Apuntes (biannually).
Academic Staff, 1989:

Rank	Full-time	Part-time
Profesores Principales	12	5
Profesores Asociados	7	14
Profesores Auxiliares	13	8
Total	32	27

Student Enrolment, 1989:

	Men	Women	Total
Of the country	1077	509	1585
Of other countries	12	5	17
Total	1089	514	1603

5371 **UNIVERSIDAD ANDINA 'NÉSTOR CÁCARES VELÁSQUEZ'**
Carretera Km. 19, Apartado 4896, Juliaca, Puno
Telephone: 540

5372 **UNIVERSIDAD UNIÓN INCAÍCA**
Inca Union University
Villa Unión, Casilla 4896, Naña (Lima)
Cables: incaunion, lima
Telephone: 971333
Rector: Maximo Vicuña Arrieta
Secretario General: Carlos Bendezú Luna Victoria

F. of Education and Social Sciences
Dean: Rubén Castillo Anchapuri
F. of Theology
Dean: Merling Alomía Bartra
F. of Natural and Food Sciences
Dean: Judith de Jamison
F. of Accountancy and Administration
Dean: Santo Farfán Peña
F. of Health Sciences (Nursing)
Dean: Víctor Canaval Barroso

Founded 1983. Governing body: the Board of Trustees. Residential facilities for academic staff and students.

Academic Year: March to December (March-July; August-December).

Admission Requirements: Secondary school certificate and entrance examination.

Fees (US$): 700 per semester.

Language of Instruction: Spanish.

Degrees and Diplomas: Bachiller, 5 yrs. Magister, a further 2 yrs. Doctorate, 2 yrs.

Library: c. 30,000 vols.

Publications: El Eco; Theologika; Paideia.

Press or Publishing House: Imprenta Editorial Unión.

Academic Staff, 1990:

Rank	Full-time	Part-time
Profesores Principales	14	–
Profesores Asociados	16	–
Profesores Auxiliares	15	–
Profesores Contratados	–	10
Total	45	10

Student Enrolment, 1990:

	Men	Women	Total
Of the country	608	726	1334
Of other countries	37	19	56
Total	645	745	1390

5373 **UNIVERSIDAD RICARDO PALMA**
Avenida Prolongación Benavides Gda. 54, Las Gardenias, Surco, Lima
Telephone: 459035
Rector: Edmundo Velarde Laos (1984-89)
Secretario General: Edwin Rondón Vásquez

F. of Architecture and Town Planning
F. of Psychology
F. of Biology
F. of Engineering
F. of Economics and Business Administration
F. of Modern Languages

Founded 1969. A private autonomous institution.

Academic Year: April to December (April-July; July-September; October-December).

Admission Requirements: Secondary school certificate.

Fees: According to income of parents.

Language of Instruction: Spanish.

Degrees and Diplomas: Bachiller in–Psychology, 5 yrs; Architecture; Mechanical Engineering; Industrial Engineering; Electrical Engineering; Electronics; Accountancy; Business Administration; Economics; Translation; Biology; Sociology; Education, 6 yrs. Professional titles of– Licenciado en Psicología, 5 yrs; Ingeniero Civil; Ingeniero Electrónico; Ingeniero Industrial; Contador Público, accountancy; Economista; Educación; Asistente Social; Técnico en Laboratorio Químico; Licenciado en Biología; Licenciado en Administración de Empresas, business administration; Licenciado en Traducción, 6 yrs.

Libraries: Central Library, 15,000 vols; Architecture, 1000; Psycho-logy, 1200; Modern Languages, 1800.

Publication: Revista (biannually).

Academic Staff: 200 (40).

Student Enrolment: c. 12,000.

5374 **UNIVERSIDAD MARCELINO CHAMPAGNAT**
Jr. Mártir Olaya 162, Lima, Lima
Telephone: 47-30-64
Rector: Antonio Castagnetti Morini

F. of Education (Religious Sciences and Natural Sciences)

Founded 1948 as school. Became Institute 1983 and is now of University status.

Fees (Intis): 1000 per annum.

Language of Instruction: Spanish.

Degrees and Diplomas: Title of Profesor(a), 5 yrs.

Academic Staff, 1986-87: c. 15.

Student Enrolment, 1990:

	Men	Women	Total
Of the country	150	750	900
Of other countries	2	7	9
Total	152	757	909

5375 **UNIVERSIDAD 'SAN MARTÍN DE PORRES'**
Calle Bolívar 348, Miraflores, Lima, Lima
Telephone: 442905
Rector: Luis Gazzallo Miano

P. of Letters
P. of Education
I. of Philosophy and Social Science
I. of History
I. of Geography

Founded 1962. Reorganized 1969 and faculties replaced by academic programmes.

Academic Staff: c. 260.

Student Enrolment: c. 10,000.

5376 ***PONTIFICIA UNIVERSIDAD CATÓLICA DEL PERÚ**
Pontifical Catholic University of Peru
Avenida Universitaria, s/n, San Miguel, Lima, 32, Lima
Telephone: 622540
Fax: (51-14) 611785
Rector: Hugo Sarabia Swett (1989-94)
Secretario General: Alberto Varillas

F. of Administrative Sciences
Dean: José Cabrera Winkelried; *staff* 9
F. of Social Sciences (including Anthropology, Economics)
Dean: Máximo Vega-Centeno Bocangel; *staff* 46 (7)
F. of Science and Engineering
Dean: Luis Guzmán Barrón Sobrevilla; *staff* 113 (13)
F. of Law
Dean: Jorge Avendaño Valdez; *staff* 6 (7)
F. of Education
Dean: Elsa Tueros Way; *staff* 10 (2)
F. of Letters and Human Sciences (including Archaeology, Library and Information Sciences, Linguistics and Psychology)
Dean: Roberto Criado Alzamora; *staff* 34 (26)
F. of General Studies (Letters)
Dean: Beatriz Mauchi Laynez
F. of General Studies (Science)
Dean: Dionisio Ugaz Mont
F. of Art
Dean: Adolfo Winternitz Wurmser; *staff* 5 (5)
F. of Social Work
Dean: Clemencia Sarmiento Sánchez
Graduate S.
Director: José Tola Pasquel
S. of Social Service (Trujillo)
Director: Segundo Carbajal Honores
Language Ce.
Director: Ana María Delaitre; *staff* 9 (3)
I. of Languages
Director: Aldo Higashi B.; *staff* – (2)
Ce. for Archaeology, Philosophy, History, Linguistics and Literature Research
Director: Armando Nieto Vélez
Ce. for Anthropology, Political Science, Economics, and Sociology Research
Director: Carlos Wandorff Montenegro
I. of Legal Research

Founded 1917 as catholic university. Classified by law in 1949 in the category of national universities and entitled to award degrees and titles under the same conditions. Honorary title of Pontifical University conferred by the Vatican 1942. Reorganized 1969 and faculties replaced by major academic programmes. An Episcopal Council, presided over by the Archbishop of Lima, Grand Chancellor of the university, has since been established by decree of the Sacred Congregation of Seminaries and Universities. Governing bodies: the Asamblea Universitaria; the Consejo Universitario.

Academic Year: March to December (March-July; August-December).

Admission Requirements: Secondary school certificate or foreign equivalent, and entrance examination.

Language of Instruction: Spanish.

Degrees and Diplomas: Bachiller in–Science; Education; Art; Engineering; Administration; Social Science; Law; Humanities; Social Work; Statistics, 4 yrs. Licenciado in–Anthropology; Social Services; Economics; Sociology; Physics; Mathematics; Archaeology; Geography; Library Science; Chemistry; Education; Philosophy; Language and Literature; History; Psychology, 5 yrs. Professional titles of–Ingeniero Agrónomo, agriculture; Ingeniero Civil; Ingeniero Mecánico; Ingeniero Industrial; Ingeniero de Minas; Contador Público, accountancy; Administrador de Empresas, business administration; Abogado, law; Asistente Social. Magister, 1-2 yrs postgraduate study. Doctorates in–Philosophy; History; Literature. Teaching qualifications, primary and secondary level.

Library: Central Library, 300,000 vols.

Special Facilities (Museums, etc.): Archaeology Museum.

Publications: Pro-Mathematica; Química; Anthropológica; Debates en Sociología; Derecho; Economía; Lexis (Revista de Lingüística y Literatura); Histórica; Psicología; Espacio y Desarrollo; Areté; Boletín del Instituto Riva-Agüero; Sinopsis.

Press or Publishing House: Fondo Editorial de la Pontificia Universidad Católica del Perú.

Academic Staff, 1990:

Rank	Full-time	Part-time
Profesores Principales	72	18
Profesores Asociados	52	10
Profesores Auxiliares	69	18
Contratados	51	24
Asistentes de Docencia	30	2
Total	274	72

Student Enrolment, 1990:

Of the country	10,545
Of other countries	50
Total	10,595

5377 **UNIVERSIDAD FEMENINA DEL SAGRADO CORAZÓN**

Women's University of the Sacred Heart

Avenida Los Frutales s/n, Monterrico, Lima, Lima

Telephone: 364641

Rector: Luz María Alvarez Calderón Fernandini

P. of Architecture

P. of Education

P. of Sociology

P. of Psychology

P. of Translation and Interpretation

P. of General Studies

Ce. of Social and Educational Research

Founded 1962, opened 1967 by the Sisters of the Sacred Heart. An autonomous institution.

Academic Year: April to December (April-July; August-December).

Admission Requirements: Secondary school certificate and entrance examination.

Language of Instruction: Spanish.

Degrees and Diplomas: Bachiller and professional titles in–Education; Psychology; Sociology; Translation and Interpretation. Also Magister and Doctorate. Teaching qualification, secondary level.

Library: c. 22,000 vols.

Academic Staff: c. 130.

Student Enrolment: c. 1370 (Women).

5378 **UNIVERSIDAD DE LIMA**

University of Lima

Avenida Javier Prado s/n, Monterrico, Lima 33, Lima

Telephone: 350677

Fax: 356552

Rector: Desiderio Blanco López (1989-94)

Secretario General: Antonino Espinosa Laña

F. of Administration

Dean (Acting): Fernando Rafael Parodi Larco; *staff* 8 (52)

F. of Economics

Dean: Luis Revolledo Soberón; *staff* 13 (27)

F. of Accountancy

Dean: Edilberto Sánchez Rubianes; *staff* 9 (43)

F. of Communication Sciences

Dean: Isaac León Frias; *staff* 46 (72)

F. of Industrial Engineering

Dean: Manuel Rufino Chumbiray Quilichi; *staff* 24 (92)

F. of Metallurgy

Dean: José Francisco Patroni Olcese; *staff* 5 (20)

F. of Systems Engineering

Dean: Alex Mahamud Ubillús; *staff* 4 (13)

F. of Human Sciences

Dean: Fernando Silva Santisteban Bernal; *staff* 2 (2)

F. of Law and Political Sciences

Dean: Carlos Torresy Torres Lara; *staff* 14 (186)

P. of General Studies

Director: Teresa Mouchard de Hidalgo; *staff* 27 (56)

P. of Education Administration

Director: María Gabriela Porto Cárdenas de Power; *staff* – (7)

I. of Co-operative Studies

Director: Lily Chan Sánchez

I. of Philosophy Research

Director: Francisco Miro Quesada Cantuarias

Economics and Social Research I.

Director: Javier Masias Astengo

Ce. for Accountancy Research

Director: Manuel Luna Victoria Sánchez

Ce. for Social Communication Research (CICOSUL)

Director: Oscar Quezada Macchiavello

Ce. for Study and Qualification, Mass Media (CECOM)

Director: Fernando Semillán Cavero

Ce. for Legal Research

Director: Carlos Fernández Sesarego

Ce. for Industrial Production Research (CIPI)

Director: Mioara Dunitrache de Gutiérrez

Computer Ce.

Founded 1962 as a private autonomous institution. Governing bodies: the Asamblea Universitaria; the Consejo Universitario.

Arrangements for co-operation with: State University of New York; College of Saint Thomas, USA; Westfalische Wilhelms Universität, Münster; University of Ottawa; University of Alabama; Universidad de La Habana.

Academic Year: March to December (March-July; August-December).

Admission Requirements: Secondary school certificate and entrance examination.

Language of Instruction: Spanish.

Degrees and Diplomas: Degree of Bachiller and professional titles, 5 yrs; Law, 6 yrs. Magister, a further 2 yrs.

Library: Central Library, c. 60,000 vols.

Publications: Lienzo; Ciencia Económica; IUS ET PRAXIS; Cuadernos de Historia; Cuaderno CICOSUL; Contratexto, Cuadernos deLingüistica y Literatura; Cuaderno de Psicología; Cuadernos de Sociología.

Academic Staff, 1990: c. 670.

Student Enrolment, 1990: c. 9480.

5379 **UNIVERSIDAD DE PIURA**

University of Piura

Ciudad Universitaria San Eduardo, Apartado 3208, Piura, Piura

Telephone: 328171

Rector: José Navarro Pascual

F. of Engineering

F. of Economics and Business Administration

F. of Journalism

F. of Science and Humanities

Extension D. (Education)

Founded 1968. Governing body: the Consejo Superior. Residential facilities for students.

Arrangements for co-operation with the University of British Colombia.

Academic Year: March to December (March-July; August-December).

Admission Requirements: Secondary school certificate and entrance examination.

Language of Instruction: Spanish.

Degrees and Diplomas: Bachiller of Arts (Journalism); Science (Business Administration), 4-5 yrs; Engineering, 5 yrs. Licenciado in–Business Administration; Journalism, 5-6 yrs. Professional titles of–Ingeniero Industrial; Ingeniero Civil, 6 yrs.

Library: Central Library, 56,000 vols.

Publications: Colección Algarrabo; Colección de Ciencias Sociales' Revista Amigos.

Academic Staff: c. 50 (65).

Student Enrolment: c. 1500.

5380 **UNIVERSIDAD PARTICULAR INCA GARCILASO DE LA VEGA**

Avenida Arequipa 1841, Lince, Lima
Telephone: 711421
Rector: Jorge Lazo Arrasco

P. of Administration
P. of Psychology
P. of Sociology and Social Work
P. of Accountancy
P. of Economics
P. of Education
P. of Industrial Engineering
P. of Political Science

Founded 1964. Reorganized 1969 and faculties replaced by academic programmes.

Academic Staff: c. 200.

Student Enrolment: c. 7000.

5381 ***UNIVERSIDAD PERUANA 'CAYETANO HEREDIA'**

Avenida Honorio Delgado 932, Urb. Ingeniería, San Martín de Porres, Lima
Telephone: 815772
Rector: Alberto Cazorla Talleri (1984-89)
Vice-Rector Administrativo: Naldo Balarezo Gerstein

F. of Sciences and Philosophy
Dean: Renán Manrique Mejía; *staff* 66 (58)
F. of Medicine
Dean: César Torres Zamudio; *staff* 171 (230)
F. of Stomatology
Dean: Hernán Villena Martínez; *staff* 18 (32)
Graduate S.
Director: Ernesto Salem A.
I. of Tropical Medicine
Director: Humberto Guerra A.
I. for High Altitude Studies
Director: Francisco Simé Barbadillo
I. for Population Studies
Director: Luis Sobrevilla A.

Founded 1961 by the faculty members of the National University of San Marcos Medical School. An autonomous private institution. Governing bodies: the Asamblea Universitaria; the Consejo Universitario.

Arrangements for co-operation with the Universities of: Johns Hopkins; Alabama at Birmingham; Miami; Baylor; Tulane; Texas Tech, Minnesota.

Academic Year: April to December (April-July; August-December).

Admission Requirements: Secondary school certificate and entrance examination.

Fees (Intis): 332-13,281 per semester, according to income of parents.

Language of Instruction: Spanish.

Degrees and Diplomas: Bachiller in–Dentistry; Sciences, 5 yrs; Medicine, 8 yrs. Licenciado in–Biology; Chemistry; Physics; Mathe-matics; Cirujano dentista, 5 yrs; Statistics; Psychology, 6 yrs; Professional titles of–Médico cirujano, 8 yrs. Magister in–Sciences; Medicine, a further 2 yrs. Doctorate in–Sciences; Medicine, 2 yrs after Magister.

Libraries: Central Library, 15,300 vols; High Altitude Studies, 1720; Tropical Medicine, 1370.

Special Facilities (Museums, etc.): Museo de Pre-historia.

Publications: Acta Herediana (each semester); Bulletin (monthly).

Academic Staff, 1986-87:

Rank	Full-time	Part-time
Profesores Principales	70	35
Profesores Asociados	49	31
Profesores Auxiliares	96	190
Jefes de Prácticas	40	64
Total	255	320

Student Enrolment, 1986-87:

	Men	Women	Total
Of the country	942	1075	2017
Of other countries	1	6	7
Total	943	1081	2024

5382 **UNIVERSIDAD DE TACNA**

Opus Sacerdotale Cooperationis Hispano-Americanae P.J. Vigil, Calle San Camilo 1000, Tacna, Tacna
Telephone: 725343

Other Institutions

Professional Education

Amazonas

5383 **INSTITUTO SUPERIOR TECNOLÓGICO 'GUSTAVO LANANTA LUJÁN'**

Chachapoyas-Leymebariba, Amazonas

Education
Agriculture
Construction Engineering
Mechanical Engineering

Founded 1980 as Escuela Superior de Educación Profesional. Acquired present status and title 1983. A State institution.

5384 **INSTITUTO SUPERIOR TECNOLÓGICO 'PERÚ-JAPAN'**

Jr. Amazonas 120, Chachapoyas
Telephone: 179

Founded 1984.

5385 **INSTITUTO SUPERIOR TECNOLÓGICO 'UTCUBAMBA'**

Bagua Grande, Amazonas

Forestry
Civil Engineering

Founded 1987.

5386 **INSTITUTO SUPERIOR TECNOLÓGICO 'BAGNA'**

Distrito La Peca, Amazonas

Forestry
Civil Engineering

Founded 1987.

5387 **INSTITUTO SUPERIOR TECNOLÓGICO 'AMAZONAS'**

Jr. Comercio 849, Bagna, Amazonas

Accountancy
Nursing

Founded 1984.

Ancash

5388 **INSTITUTO SUPERIOR TECNOLÓGICO 'AIJA'**

Fundo Monserrate, Aija, Ancash

Agriculture

Founded 1985.

5389 **INSTITUTO SUPERIOR TECNOLÓGICO 'DANILE VILAR'**
Caraz, Ancash
Electrical Engineering
Mechanical Engineering
Founded 1984.

5390 **INSTITUTO SUPERIOR TECNOLÓGICO 'CASMA'**
Casma, Ancash
Information Technology
Civil Engineering
Founded 1987.

5391 **INSTITUTO SUPERIOR TECNOLÓGICO 'CARLOS SALAZAR ROMERO'**
Avenida El Pacífico s/n, Urban, Buenos Aires, Chimbote, Ancash
Telephone: 325512
Mechanical Engineering
Metallurgy
Electrical and Electronic Engineering
Administration
Accountancy
Founded 1977 as Escuela Superior de Educación Profesional. Acquired present status and title 1983. A State institution.

5392 **INSTITUTO SUPERIOR TECNOLÓGICO 'CHIQUIÁN'**
Mishay Alto, Chiquián, Ancash
Telephone: 325512
Mechanical Engineering
Electrical Engineering
Founded 1984.

5393 **INSTITUTO SUPERIOR TECNOLÓGICO 'ELEAZAR GUZMÁN BARRÓN'**
Huaraz, Ancash
Mechanical Engineering
Health Sciences
Agriculture
Tourism
Electrical and Electronic Engineering
Metallurgy
Founded 1980 as Escuela Superior de Educación Profesional. Acquired present status and title 1983. A State institution.

5394 **INSTITUTO SUPERIOR TECNOLÓGICO 'HUARAZ'**
Huaraz, Ancash
Accountancy

5395 **INSTITUTO SUPERIOR TECNOLÓGICO 'HUARÍ'**
Barrio Magisterial, Huarí, Ancash
Agriculture

5396 **INSTITUTO SUPERIOR TECNOLÓGICO 'HUARMEY'**
Huarmey, Ancash
Agriculture

5397 **INSTITUTO SUPERIOR TECNOLÓGICO 'PISCOBAMBA'**
Piscobamba, Ancash
Agriculture

Apurimac

5398 **INSTITUTO SUPERIOR TECNOLÓGICO 'ABANCAY'**
Abancay, Apurimac
Agriculture
Civil Engineering

Arequipa

5399 **INSTITUTO SUPERIOR TECNOLÓGICO 'PEDRO P. DÍAZ'**
Francisco Pizarro, 13, Porongoche, Paucarpata, Apartado 1290, Arequipa, Arequipa
Telephone: 225672
Accountancy
Electrical and Electronic Engineering
Agricultural Engineering
Automation
Construction Engineering
Mechanical Engineering
Founded 1976 as Escuela Superior de Educación Profesional. Acquired present status and title 1983. A State institution.
Academic Year: April to December (April-August; September-December).
Admission Requirements: Secondary school certificate.
Fees: None.
Language of Instruction: Spanish.
Degrees and Diplomas: Title of Especialista Profesional.
Academic Staff: c. 40 (20).
Student Enrolment: c. 1700.

5400 **INSTITUTO SUPERIOR TECNOLÓGICO 'MONSEÑOR JÚLIO GONZÁLEZ RUIZ'**
Catahuasi, La Unión, Arequipa
Agriculture
Civil Engineering

5401 **INSTITUTO SUPERIOR TECNOLÓGICO CIENCIAS TECNOLÓGICAS**
Calle Santa Marcha 209, Arequipa
Telephone: 214045

5402 **INSTITUTO TÉCNICO SUPERIOR DE ADMINISTRACIÓN DE EMPRESAS**
Calle Paral, 217, Arequipa

5403 **INSTITUTO SUPERIOR TECNOLÓGICO 'CAYETANA HEREDIA'**
Avenida Independencia 946, Arequipa
Telephone: 225441
Information Technology
Computing

5404 **INSTITUTO SUPERIOR TECNOLÓGICO 'ECAN'**
Avenida Salaverry 302, Vallacito, Arequipa
Telephone: 222705
Administration

5405 **INSTITUTO SUPERIOR TECNOLÓGICO 'AREQUIPA'**
Calle Rivero 311, Arequipa
Telephone: 214704
Electronics
Computer Science

5406 **INSTITUTO SUPERIOR TECNOLÓGICO 'ALBERT EINSTEIN'**
Calle Rivero 306 y la Nerced 425, Arequipa
Telephone: 219125
Computer Science
Electronics

5407 **INSTITUTO SUPERIOR TECNOLÓGICO 'ISIPRODA'**
Calle Rivero 306, Arequipa
Telephone: 219125
Computer Science
Accountancy

5408 **INSTITUTO SUPERIOR TECNOLÓGICO 'DEL SUR'**
Calle Palacio Viojo 114, Arequipa

Administration
Banking
Accountancy

5409 **INSTITUTO SUPERIOR TECNOLÓGICO 'LA RECOLETA'**
Calle Recoleta 117, Yanahuara, Arequipa
Electrical Engineering
Mechanical Engineering

5410 **INSTITUTO SUPERIOR TECNOLÓGICO 'JAVIER PRADO'**
Avenida Prolongación, Mariscal Castilla 72LB, Arequipa
Information Technology

5411 **INSTITUTO SUPERIOR TECNOLÓGICO 'MARIA MONTESSORI'**
La Merced 212, Arequipa
Telephone: 213521
Information Technology

5412 **INSTITUTO SUPERIOR TECNOLÓGICO 'FAUSTINO B. FRANCO'**
Camaná, Arequipa
Agriculture

Ayacucho

5413 **INSTITUTO SUPERIOR TECNOLÓGICO 'VÍCTOR ALVAREZ HUAPAYA'**
Jr. San Martín 367, Ayacucho
Agriculture
Mechanical Engineering
Health Sciences
Education
Administration
Founded 1978 as Escuela Superior de Educación Profesional. Acquired present status and title 1983. A State institution.

5414 **INSTITUTO SUPERIOR TECNOLÓGICO 'CHIPAS'**
Chipas-Lucanas, Ayacucho
Agriculture
Information Technology

5415 **INSTITUTO SUPERIOR TECNOLÓGICO 'AUCUARA'**
Aucara-Lucanas, Ayacucho
Agriculture

5416 **INSTITUTO SUPERIOR TECNOLÓGICO 'CORA CORA'**
Coracora, Ayacucho
Agriculture
Civil Engineering

5417 **INSTITUTO SUPERIOR TECNOLÓGICO 'HUANCAPI'**
Huancapi, Ayacucho
Agriculture
Information Technology

5418 **INSTITUTO SUPERIOR TECNOLÓGICO 'HUANTA'**
Huanta, Ayacucho
Agriculture
Electronics

Cajamarca

5419 **INSTITUTO SUPERIOR TECNOLÓGICO 'BAMBAMARCA'**
Miguel Glau s/n, Bambamarca, Cajamarca
Agriculture
Metallurgy
Electronics

5420 **INSTITUTO SUPERIOR TECNOLÓGICO 'CAJABAMBA'**
Balta 193, Cajabamba (Cajamarca)
Director: Edwin Eslava Contreras
Secretaria: Bernardita Arana Cruchaga
D. of Agriculture
Head: Ignacio Salazar Marquin; *staff* 8
D. of Electrical Engineering
Head: José Chuquez Lezama; *staff* 8
D. of Mechanics
Head: Silva Araujo Evert; *staff* 5
D. of Technical Nursing
Head: Betty Torres Novoa; *staff* 8
Founded 1986.
Academic Year: April to December.
Admission Requirements: Secondary school certificate and entrance examination.
Fees: None.
Language of Instruction: Spanish.
Degrees and Diplomas: Bachelor, 4 yrs.
Academic Staff, 1990: 4.
Student Enrolment, 1990:

	Men	Women	Total
Of the country	200	300	500

5421 **INSTITUTO SUPERIOR TECNOLÓGICO 'CAJAMARCA**
Km 3 ½ Carretera Baños del Inca, Cajamarca
Agriculture
Forestry

5422 **INSTITUTO SUPERIOR TECNOLÓGICO 'CASCAS'**
Cascas-Contumaza, Cajamarca
Agriculture

5423 **INSTITUTO SUPERIOR TECNOLÓGICO 'MARIANO IBERICO RODRÍGUEZ'**
José Gálvez 683, Cajamarca
Accountancy
Administration

5424 **INSTITUTO SUPERIOR TECNOLÓGICO 'PEDRO ORTÍZ MONTOYA'**
Celendín, Cajamarca
Agriculture
Construction Engineering
Mechanical Engineering
Health Sciences
Founded 1980 as Escuela Superior de Educación Profesional. Acquired present status and title 1983. A State institution.

5425 **INSTITUTO SUPERIOR TECNOLÓGICO 'CHOTA'**
Fundo Tuctuhuasi, Chota, Cajamarca
Agriculture
Mechanical Production

5426 **INSTITUTO SUPERIOR TECNOLÓGICO 'FELIPE ALVA Y AVA'**
Contumaza, Cajamarca
Agriculture
Accountancy

5427 **INSTITUTO SUPERIOR TECNOLÓGICO 'CUTERVO'**
Cutervo, Cajamarca
Agriculture
Electricity
Technical nursing

5428 **INSTITUTO SUPERIOR TECNOLÓGICO ' 4 DE JUNIO DE 1821'**

Avenida 4 de Junio de 1821 s/n, Cruce Montegrande, Jaén, Cajamarca

Director: Hermógenes Mejia Solf

Agriculture
Construction Engineering
Mechanical Engineering
Pharmaceutical Techniques
Accountancy

Founded 1980 as Escuela Superior de Educación Profesional. Acquired present status and title 1983. A State institution.

Academic Year: April to December.

Admission Requirements: Secondary school certificate and entrance examination.

Language of Instruction: Spanish.

Degrees and Diplomas: Title of Especialista, 3 yrs.

Library: c. 2000 vols.

Special Facilities (Museums, etc.): Archaeological Museum.

5429 **INSTITUTO SUPERIOR TECNOLÓGICO 'SAN IGNACIO'**

Santa Rosa Cdra 3, San Ignacio, Cajamarca

Agriculture
Forestry
Accountancy
Administration

5430 **INSTITUTO SUPERIOR TECNOLÓGICO 'SAN MARCOAS'**

Huayabamba, San Marcoas, Cajamarca

Agriculture
Accountancy

5431 **INSTITUTO SUPERIOR TECNOLÓGICO 'SAN MIGUEL'**

San Miguel, Cajamarca

Agriculture

5432 **INSTITUTO SUPERIOR TECNOLÓGICO ' 13 DE JULIO'**

San Pablo, Cajamarca s/n

Agriculture
Accountancy

5433 **INSTITUTO SUPERIOR TECNOLÓGICO 'SANTA CRUZ'**

Santa Cruz, Cajamarca

Agriculture
Accountancy
Technical Nursing

Callao

5434 **INSTITUTO SUPERIOR TECNOLÓGICO 'SIMÓN BOLÍVAR'**

Avenida Colonial Cdra, 32, Bellavista, Callao

Health Sciences
Electrical and Electronic Engineering
Laboratory Technology
Chemistry

Founded 1976 as Escuela Superior de Educación Profesional. Acquired present status and title 1983. A State institution.

5435 **INSTITUTO SUPERIOR TECNOLÓGICO 'SAN ANTONIO'**

Avenida Saenz Peña 1330, Bellavista, Callao

Telephone: 292524

Health Sciences

Cuzco

5436 **INSTITUTO SUPERIOR TECNOLÓGICO 'TÚPAC AMARÚ'**

Avenida La Cultura s/n, San Sebastián, Casilla ZE 51, Cuzco

Telephone: 231461

Director: Silvio Chura Quisocala (1979-)

Agriculture
Tourism
Mechanical Engineering
Health Sciences
Accountancy and Economics
Electrical and Electronic Engineering

Founded 1975 as Escuela Superior de Educación Profesional. Acquired present status and title 1983. A State institution.

Academic Year: April to December (April-August; September-December).

Admission Requirements: Secondary school certificate.

Fees (Intis): 10 per semester.

Language of Instruction: Spanish.

Degrees and Diplomas: Title of Técnico Profesional.

Library: 2500 vols.

Academic Staff, 1986-87: 57.

Student Enrolment, 1986-87:

	Men	Women	Total
Of the country	415	296	599
Of other countries	184	56	352
Total	599	352	951

5437 **INSTITUTO SUPERIOR TECNOLÓGICO 'ESPINAS'**

Espinas, Cuzco

Agriculture
Technical Nursing

5438 **INSTITUTO SUPERIOR TECNOLÓGICO 'VILCANOTA'**

Sicuani, Cuzco

Agriculture
Civil Engineering

5439 **INSTITUTO SUPERIOR TECNOLÓGICO 'TAYAPAMPA'**

Tayapampa, Cuzco

Agriculture

5440 **INSTITUTO SUPERIOR TECNOLÓGICO 'URUBAMBA'**

Urubamba, Cuzco

Agriculture
Forestry
Civil Engineering

Founded 1978 as Escuela Superior de Educación Profesional. Acquired present status and title 1983. A State institution.

Huancavelica

5441 **INSTITUTO SUPERIOR TECNOLÓGICO 'HUANCAVELICA'**

Jr. Huayne Cápac 350, San Cristobal, Huancavelica

Agriculture
Technical nursing
Accountancy

5442 **INSTITUTO SUPERIOR TECNOLÓGICO 'PAMPAS'**

Pampas-Tayacaja, Huancavelica

Agriculture
Electricity

5443 **INSTITUTO SUPERIOR TECNOLÓGICO 'AMBO'**

Ambo, Huancavelica

Agriculture

Huánuco

5444 **INSTITUTO SUPERIOR TECNOLÓGICO 'APARICIO POMARES'**

Huánuco

Administration
Construction Engineering
Health Sciences

Founded 1980 as Escuela Superior de Educación Profesional. Acquired present status and title 1983. A State institution.

5445 **INSTITUTO SUPERIOR TECNOLÓGICO 'GLICERIO GOMÉZ I.'**
Huamalies, Llata, Huánuco

Administration
Construction Engineering

5446 **INSTITUTO SUPERIOR TECNOLÓGICO 'NARANJILLO'**
Huánuco

Agriculture
Electricity

5447 **INSTITUTO SUPERIOR TECNOLÓGICO 'RICARDO SALINAS VARA'**
Dos de Mayo, Huánuco

Agriculture
Technical Nursing

Ica

5448 **INSTITUTO SUPERIOR TECNOLÓGICO 'CHINCHA'**
Avenida Unión s/n, Pueblo Nuevo, Chincha Alta, Ica
Director: Héctor Olivares Pachas

Agriculture
Accountancy
Construction Engineering

Founded as Escuela Superior de Educación Profesional. Acquired present status and title 1983. A State institution.

Academic Year: April to December (April-July; August-December).

Admission Requirements: Secondary school certificate.

Fees (Intis): 100.

Language of Instruction: Spanish.

Degrees and Diplomas: Title of Técnico Profesional.

Academic Staff, 1986-87: 23 (10).

Student Enrolment, 1986-87:

	Men	Women	Total
Of the country	321	297	618

5449 **INSTITUTO SUPERIOR TECNOLÓGICO 'CATALINA BUENDIA DE PECHO'**
Ica
Telephone: 232245

Accountancy
Electrical and Electronic Engineering
Mechanical Engineering
Metallurgy

Founded 1980 as Escuela Superior de Educación Profesional. Acquired present status and title 1983. A State institution.

5450 **INSTITUTO SUPERIOR TECNOLÓGICO 'MARCONA'**
Colegio Nacional San Juan, Ica
Telephone: 232245

Electrical and Electronic Engineering

5451 **INSTITUTO SUPERIOR TECNOLÓGICO 'SAN AGUSTIN'**
Municipalidad 234, Ica
Telephone: 234540

Administration
Accountancy

5452 **INSTITUTO SUPERIOR TECNOLÓGICO**
Panamericana Sur s/n, Nasca, Ica

Agriculture
Electronics
Mechanical Engineering
Visual Arts

Founded 1980 as Escuela Superior de Educación Profesional. Acquired present status and title 1983. A privateinstitution under the jurisdiction of the Ministry of Education. Governing body: the Consejo de Gobierno.

Academic Year: April to December (April-August; July-December).

Admission Requirements: Third yr of secondary school.

Language of Instruction: Spanish.

Degrees and Diplomas: Title of Bachiller Profesional, 3 ½ yrs.

Library: c. 500 vols.

Academic Staff: c. 20.

Student Enrolment: c. 150.

5453 **INSTITUTO SUPERIOR TECNOLÓGICO 'PALPA'**
Rio Grande, Palpa, Pisco, Ica

Agriculture

5454 **INSTITUTO SUPERIOR TECNOLÓGICO 'PISCO'**
Pisco, Ica

Agriculture
Accountancy

Junín

5455 **INSTITUTO SUPERIOR TECNOLÓGICO 'ANDRÉS AVELINO CACERES'**
San Agustín de Cajas, Huancayo, Junín
Telephone: 46414

Administration
Executive Secretarial Studies
Marketing
Industrial Relations

Founded 1980 as Escuela Superior de Educación Profesional. Acquired present status and title 1983. A State institution.

Academic Year: October to June (October-January; March-June).

Admission Requirements: Secondary school certificate and entrance examination.

Language of Instruction: Spanish.

Degrees and Diplomas: Titles of Especialista Profesional.

Academic Staff: c. 40.

Student Enrolment: c. 430.

5456 **INSTITUTO SUPERIOR TECNOLÓGICO 'SANTIAGO ANTÚNEZ DE MAYOLO'**
Apartado 287, Palián, Huancayo, Junín
Telephone: 231632

Agriculture
Mechanical Engineering
Health Sciences
Administration
Metallurgy
Construction Engineering

Founded 1976 as Escuela Superior de Educación Profesional. Acquired present status and title 1983. A State institution.

5457 **INSTITUTO SUPERIOR TECNOLÓGICO 'CONTINENTAL'**
Calle Real 125, Huancayo, Junín

Computer Sciences
Electricity
Administration

5458 **INSTITUTO SUPERIOR TECNOLÓGICO 'SAN PEDRO'**
Calle Real 235, Huancayo, Junín

Accountancy
Computer Science

5459 **INSTITUTO SUPERIOR TECNOLÓGICO 'ALEJANDRO O. DEUSTUA'**
Jr. Ancash 441, Huancayo, Junín

Accountancy
Administration

5460 **INSTITUTO SUPERIOR TECNOLÓGICO 'SAN IGNACIO DE LAYOLA'**
Calle Simón Bolivar 250, Junín

Accountancy
Agriculture

5461 **INSTITUTO SUPERIOR TECNOLÓGICO 'SAUSA'**
Augusto Hector Aliaga E., Jauja, Junín

Agriculture

5462 **INSTITUTO SUPERIOR TECNOLÒGICO 'RAMIRO PRIALE PRIALE'**
9 de Julio, Concepción, Junín

Agriculture

5463 **INSTITUTO SUPERIOR TECNOLÓGICO 'HUASICANCHA'**
Victor Raúl Castellar Z., Junín

Agriculture

5464 **INSTITUTO SUPERIOR TECNOLÒGICO 'ADOLFO VIENRICH'**
Malecón Galvez s/n, Casilla 232, Tarma, Junín
Telephone: 2699

D. of General Studies
D. of Production Technology
D. of Automation
D. of Electrical Engineering
D. of Civil Engineering
D. of Accountancy
D. of Electronics
D. for Evening Studies

Founded 1967 as regional college and became Escuela Superior de Educación Profesional 1979. Acquired presentstatus and title 1983. A State institution under the jurisdiction of the Ministry of Education.

Academic Year: April to December (April-August; August-December).
Admission Requirements: Secondary school certificate.
Language of Instruction: Spanish.
Degrees and Diplomas: Professional titles.
Library: Department libraries.
Academic Staff: c. 25 (5).
Student Enrolment: c. 300.

La Libertad

5465 **INSTITUTO SUPERIOR TECNOLÓGICO 'CHOCOPE'**
Chocope, Ascope, La Libertad

Agriculture

5466 **INSTITUTO SUPERIOR TECNOLÓGICO 'PAÍJAN'**
Ascope, La Libertad

Food Industry

5467 **INSTITUTO SUPERIOR TECNOLÓGICO 'BOLÍVAR'**
Bolivar, La Libertad

Agriculture

5468 **INSTITUTO SUPERIOR TECNOLÓGICO 'CIRO ALEGRÍA BAZÁN'**
Avenida Panamericana Norte s/n, Chepén, La Libertad

Accountancy
Administration
Technical Nursing
Mechanics

5469 **INSTITUTO SUPERIOR TECNOLÓGICO 'GUADALUPE'**
Avenida Ayacucho 284, Guadalupe, La Libertad

Agriculture
Accountancy

5470 **INSTITUTO SUPERIOR TECNOLÓGICO 'JORGE DEMAISON S.'**
Jr. Sarmiento 1138, Pacasmayo, La Libertad
Telephone: 2305

Agriculture
Electrical Engineering
Mechanical Engineering

5471 **INSTITUTO SUPERIOR TECNOLÓGICO 'ERASMO ARELLANO G'**
Pataz, La Libertad

Mining

5472 **INSTITUTO SUPERIOR TECNOLÓGICO 'HUAMACHUCO'**
Sanchez Carrión, Santiago de Chuco, La Libertad

Agriculture
Civil Engineering

5473 **INSTITUTO SUPERIOR TECNOLÓGICO 'VICTOR ANDRÉS B.'**
Santiago de Chuco, La Libertad

Agriculture

5474 **INSTITUTO SUPERIOR TECNOLÓGICO 'CHAN CHAN'**
Trujillo, La Libertad

Electrical Engineering
Civil Engineering
Production Engineering
Agricultural Mechanics
Fishery Production

A private institution.

5475 **INSTITUTO SUPERIOR TECNOLÓGICO 'DEL NORTE'**
Trujillo, La Libertad

Accountancy
Executive Secretarial Studies
Computer Sciences
Clinical Laboratory Technology
Pharmacy

A private institution.

5476 **INSTITUTO SUPERIOR TECNOLÓGICO JOHN F. KENNEDY**
Jr. Bolívar, Truijillo, La Libertad

Accountancy
Tourism

Founded 1980 as Escuela Superior de Educación Profesional. Acquired present status and title 1983. A privateinstitution.

5477 **INSTITUTO SUPERIOR TECNOLÓGICO 'NUEVAA ESPERANZA'**
Avenida José Castelli s/n, Trujillo, La Libertad

Founded 1982 as Escuela Superior de Educación Profesional. Acquired present status and title 1983. A State institution.

5478 **INSTITUTO SUPERIOR TECNOLÓGICO 'TRUJILLO'**
Calle Albrecht 319, Urb., Los Quinteros, Trujillo, La Libertad

Accountancy
Executive Secretarial Studies
Tourism

A private institution.

5479 **INSTITUTO SUPERIOR TECNOLÓGICO 'TRUJILLO'**
Jr. Amazonas 204, Trujillo, La Libertad

Administration
Agriculture
Accountancy

Founded 1979 as Escuela Superior de Educación Profesional. Acquired present status and title 1983. A State institution.

Academic Year: April to December (April-July; August-December).
Admission Requirements: Third yr of secondary school.
Language of Instruction: Spanish.
Degrees and Diplomas: Title of Bachiller Profesional, 3-4 yrs.
Academic Staff: c. 44.
Student Enrolment: c. 520.

5480 **INSTITUTO SUPERIOR TECNOLÓGICO 'MANUEL GONZÁLES PRADA'**
El Provenir, Trujillo, La Libertad
Electrical Engineering
Mechanical Engineering

5481 **INSTITUTO SUPERIOR TECNOLÓGICO 'INDOAMERICANO'**
Trujillo, La Libertad
Agriculture
Accountancy
Civil Engineering

5482 **INSTITUTO SUPERIOR TECNOLÓGICO 'CIMA'**
Calle San Martin 540, Trujillo, La Libertad
Computer Science
Electrical Engineering

5483 **INSTITUTO SUPERIOR TECNOLÓGICO 'JORGE BASADRE'**
Ricardo Palma 348-Urb., Palermo, Trujillo, La Libertad
Telephone: 234561
Computer Science
Interior Design
Technical Nursing

5484 **INSTITUTO SUPERIOR TECNOLÓGICO 'LOS LIBERTADORES'**
Avenida 29 de Diciembre 113, Trujillo, La Libertad
Tourism
Laboratory Technology

5485 **INSTITUTO SUPERIOR TECNOLÓGICO 'SAN LUIS'**
Avenida Salvador Lara 30, Urb. Huerta, Trujillo, La Libertad
Computer Science
Technical Nursing

5486 **INSTITUTO SUPERIOR TECNOLÓGICO 'SAN LUIS'**
Avenida Salvador Lara 30 Urb. Huerta Granda Trujillo La Libertad
Computer Science
Technical Nursing

5487 **INSTITUTO SUPERIOR TECNOLÓGICO 'VIRÚ'**
Virú, La Libertad
Agriculture
Accountancy
Laboratory Technology

Lambayeque

5488 **INSTITUTO SUPERIOR TECNOLÓGICO 'CHICLAYO'**
Avenida Batta 658, Chiclayo, Lambayeque
Telephone: 23-2801
Marketing
Accountancy
A private institution.

5489 **INSTITUTO SUPERIOR TECNOLÓGICO 'REPÚBLICA ARGENTINA'**
Calle Arica 845, Chiclayo, Lambayeque
Telephone: 23-3573
Accountancy
Secretarial Studies
Marketing
A private institution.

5490 **INSTITUTO SUPERIOR TECNOLÓGICO 'REPÚBLICA FEDERAL DE ALEMANIA'**
Avenida Elvira García y García 755, Los Parques, Chiclayo, Lambayeque
Telephone: 23-8578
Administration
Accountancy
Electrical and Electronic Engineering
Mechanical Engineering
Industrial Processes
Founded 1980 as Escuela Superior de Educación Profesional. Acquired present status and title 1983. A State institution.

5491 **INSTITUTO SUPERIOR TECNOLÓGICO 'ELIAS AGUIRRE'**
Jr. Torres Paz 199, Chiclayo, Lambayeque
Telephone: 227065
Computer Science

5492 **INSTITUTO SUPERIOR TECNOLÓGICO 'BERTRAND RUSSELL'**
Calle 7 de Enero 632, Chiclayo, Lambayeque
Telephone: 234442
Computer Science
Electricity

5493 **INSTITUTO SUPERIOR TECNOLÓGICO 'CAYETANO HEREDIA'**
Batte 1624, Chiclayo, Lambayeque
Technical Nursing

5494 **INSTITUTO SUPERIOR TECNOLÓGICO 'MANUEL MESONES MURO'**
Alicia 1168, Chiclayo, Lambayeque
Accountancy
Technical Nursing

5495 **INSTITUTO SUPERIOR TECNOLÓGICO 'ENRIQUE LÓPEZ ALBUJAR'**
Libertad 314, Ferreñafe, Chiclayo, Lambayeque
Directora: Carmen Clara Gamallo Palao (1980-)
Agriculture
Construction Engineering
Administration
Accountancy
Founded 1980 as Escuela Superior de Educación Profesional. Acquired present status and title 1983. A State institution.
Academic Year: April to December (April-August; September-December).
Admission Requirements: Secondary school certificate and entrance examination.
Fees (Intis): 35.
Language of Instruction: Spanish.
Degrees and Diplomas: Title of Técnico Profesional.
Student Enrolment, 1986-87:

	Men	Women	Total
Of the country	440	321	761

5496 **INSTITUTO SUPERIOR TECNOLÓGICO 'MOTUPE'**
Motupe, Lambayeque
Agriculture
Administration

5497 **INSTITUTO SUPERIOR TECNOLÓGICO 'OLMOS'**
Calle Sto. Domingo 112, Via Chiclayo, Olmos, Lambayeque
Telephone: 12
Agriculture
Mechanical Engineering

Lima

5498 **INSTITUTO SUPERIOR TECNOLÓGICO 'COSMETOLOGIA'**
Psje. Nacarino 120, Breña, Lima 5
Telephone: 321644

5499 **INSTITUTO SUPERIOR TECNOLÓGICO**
Apartado 11, Quilmaná, Cañete, Lima
Telephone: 007

Agriculture
Administration
Founded 1977.

5500 **INSTITUTO SUPERIOR TECNOLÓGICO AMAUTA**
Avenida Bolivia 288, Cercado, Lima

Administration
Founded 1979 as Escuela Superior de Educación Profesional. Acquired present status and title 1983. A privateinstitution.

5501 **INSTITUTO SUPERIOR TECNOLÓGICO DE LIMA**
Avenida Uruguay 390, Cercado, Lima

Administration
Electrical and Electronic Engineering
Founded 1980 as Escuela Superior de Educación Profesional. Acquired present status and title 1983. A privateinstitution.

5502 **INSTITUTO SUPERIOR TECNOLÓGICL 'PEDRO RUÍZ GALLO'**
Plaza 2 de Mayo 26, Altos 301, Cercado, Lima 1
Telephone: 285941

Founded 1980.

5503 **INSTITUTO SUPERIOR TECNOLÓGICO 'ADEC', ASESORÍA DE EMPRESAS COMERCIALES**
Cercado, Lima 1
Telephone: 230939

Executive Secretarial Studies
Accountancy
A private institution.

5504 **INSTITUTO SUPERIOR TECNOLÓGICO 'SEGUROS'**
Cercado, Lima 1
Telephone: 283986

Administration
A private institution.

5505 **INSTITUTO SUPERIOR TECNOLÓGICO 'PERUANO ALEMÁN'**
Avenida Garcilazo de la Vega 1218, Cercado, Lima 1
Telephone: 236427

Clinical Laboratory Technology
Nursing
Pharmacy
Accountancy
Executive Secretarial Studies
A private institution.

5506 **INSTITUTO SUPERIOR TECNOLÓGICO 'VICTOR ANDRÉS BELAUNDÉ'**
Jr. Antonio Miro Quesada 113, Cercado, Lima 1
Telephone: 286458

Education
Administration
Languages and Literature
Economics
Founded 1980 as Escuela Superior de Educación Profesional. Acquired present status and title 1983. A privateinstitution.
Arrangements for co-operation with Uppsala University.
Academic Year: April to December (April-August; September-December).
Admission Requirements: Secondary school certificate.
Fees (Soles): 80,000.
Language of Instruction: Spanish.
Degrees and Diplomas: Title of Especialista Profesional.
Library: 2000 vols.
Student Enrolment: c. 2500.

5507 **INSTITUTO SUPERIOR TECNOLÓGICO 'COMPUTRONIC TECH'**
Avenida Urguay 135, Cercado, Lima 1

Computer Science

5508 **INSTITUTO SUPERIOR TECNOLÓGICO 'LIMA'**
Carabaua 474, Jr. de la Unión 1143, Lima 1
Telephone: 330510

Electrical and Electronic Engineering
Technical Nursing
Accountancy

5509 **INSTITUTO SUPERIOR TECNOLÓGICO 'IDAT'**
Avenida Arequipa 599, Cercado, Lima 1

Accountancy
Administration
Electrical Engineering

5510 **INSTITUTO SUPERIOR TECNOLÓGICO 'SANTA MARÍA REYNA'**
Avenida Uruguay 316, Cercado, Lima 1
Telephone: 247084

Accountancy
Technical Nursing

5511 **INSTITUTO SUPERIOR TECNOLÓGICO 'SAN MARCOS 2'**
Jr. Rufino Torrico 640, Cercado, Lima 1

Administration
Accountancy

5512 **INSTITUTO SUPERIOR TECNOLÓGICO 'FEDERICO W. TAYLOR'**
Jr. Chancay 515, Cercado, Lima 1
Telephone: 311208
Director: Luis Roger Beltrán Vergara

D. of Accountancy
Head: Carlos Suárez Delencia
D. of Administration
Head: Luis Roger Beltrán Vergara
D. of Nursing
Head: Elizabeth Zegarra Silva
D. of Secretarial Studies
Head: Rosa Jimenez Venturi
D. of Computer Studies
Head: Héctor Temoche Temoche
Founded 1982.
Academic Year: March to August.
Admission Requirements: Secondary school examination.
Fees (Intis): 3m. per semester.
Languages of Instruction: Spanish and English.
Degrees and Diplomas: Title of Técnico Profesional.
Library: Total, 480 vols.
Student Enrolment, 1990:

	Men	Women	Total
Of the country	380	162	542

5513 **INSTITUTO SUPERIOR TECNOLÓGICO 'MAX UHLE'**
Jr. Carabaya 1127, Cercado, Lima 1

Civil Engineering
Accountancy
Computer Sciences
Founded 1980.

5514 **INSTITUTO SUPERIOR TECNOLÓGICO 'SEBASTIÁN SALAZAR'**
Jr. Puno 722, Cercado, Lima

Accountancy

5515 **INSTITUTO SUPERIOR TECNOLÓGICO 'DANIEL ALCIDES CARRIÓN'**
Avenida Arequipa 955, Cercado, Lima 1
Telephone: 237246

Accountancy
Administration
Pharmacy
Technical Nursing

5516 **INSTITUTO SUPERIOR TECNOLÓGICO 'ESAE'**
Jr.Chancay 869, Cercado, Lima 1
Telephone: 277798

Computer Sciences
Tourism

5517 **INSTITUTO SUPERIOR TECNOLÓGICO 'ETA'**
Jr.Carabava 1133, Cercado, Lima 1
Telephone: 2219858

Accountancy
Electronics

5518 **INSTITUTO SUPERIOR TECNOLÓGICO 'GARCILAZO DE LA VEGA'**
Psje. Nueva Rosita 175, Lima
Telephone: 323020

Accountancy
Agriculture
Electronics
Technical Nursing

5519 **INSTITUTO SUPERIOR TECNOLÓGICO 'JULIO C. TELIO'**
Avenida 28 de Julio 787, Cercado, Lima 1
Telephone: 246959

Accountancy
Computer Science
Advertising and Design

5520 **INSTITUTO SUPERIOR TECNOLÓGICO 'CESAEN'**
Jr.Chancay 834, Cercado, Lima 1
Telephone: 239327

Accountancy
Administration

5521 **INSTITUTO SUPERIOR TECNOLÓGICO 'NUESTRA SENORA DEL CARMEN'**
Jr. Washington 1270, Cercado, Lima 1
Telephone: 246959

Accountancy

5522 **INSTITUTO SUPERIOR TECNOLÓGICO 'ALBERTO LEOPOLDO BARTON'**
Paseo de la Republica 786, Cercado, Lima 1
Telephone: 232235

Accountancy
Technical Nursing

5523 **INSTITUTO SUPERIOR TECNOLÓGICO 'FEDERICO VILLAREAL'**
Jr. Callao 229, Cercado, Lima 1
Telephone: 285274

Accountancy
Clinical Laboratory Technician
Industrial Chemistry
Technical Nursing

5524 **INSTITUTO SUPERIOR TECNOLÓGICO 'ESADE'**
Avenida Arequipa 331, Cercado, Lima 1
Telephone: 244563

Accountancy
Administration
Computer Sciences

5525 **INSTITUTO SUPERIOR TECNOLÓGICO 'OSCAR MIRO QUESADA DE LA GUERRA-RACSO'**
Avenida Garcilazo de la Vega 1538, Cercado, Lima 1
Telephone: 236792

Accountancy
Administration
Computer Sciences

5526 **INSTITUTO SUPERIOR TECNOLÓGICO 'COOPIP'**
Avenida Rep. de Portugal 181, Brena, Cercado, Lima 1

Accountancy
Electrical Engineering
Electronics

5527 **INSTITUTO SUPERIOR TECNOLÓGICO 'SEÑOR DE LOS MILAGROS'**
Jr. 338, Cercado, Lima 1
Telephone: 272976

Accountancy
Administration

5528 **INSTITUTO SUPERIOR TECNOLÓGICO 'SANTIAGO DE SUCRO'**
Jr. Chancay Cdra. 7, Cercado, Lima 1

Accountancy
Administration
Secretarial Studies

5529 **INSTITUTO SUPERIOR TECNOLÓGICO 'ÓPTICA Y OPTOMETRÍA'**
Camana 615, Cercado, Lima 1

Optics

5530 **INSTITUTO SUPERIOR TECNOLÓGICO 'CAYETANO HEREDIA DE LIMA'**
Avenida Uruguay 315, Cercado, Lima 1

Technical Nursing

5531 **INSTITUTO SUPERIOR TECNOLÓGICO 'DATAPRO'**
Avenida Los Rosales 373, Lima 7
Telephone: 424914

Accountancy
Electronics

5532 **INSTITUTO SUPERIOR TECNOLÓGICO 'PERÚ'**
Es. Jr. Chota y Pasco Coló, Cercado, Lima 1
Telephone: 240405

Accountancy
Secretarial Studies
Tourism

5533 **INSTITUTO SUPERIOR TECNOLÓGICO 'ALMIRANTE GRAU'**
Calle Acieclo Villaren 330, Cercado, Lima 1
Telephone: 324313

Accountancy
Computer Science
Secretarial Studies

5534 **INSTITUTO SUPERIOR TECNOLÓGICO 'HARVARD'**
Avenida España 267, Cercado, Lima 1
Telephone: 324313

Accountancy
Clinical Laboratory
Secretarial Studies

Technical Nursing

5535 **INSTITUTO SUPERIOR TECNOLÓGICO 'SERGIO BERNALES'**
Avenida Arequipa 991, Cercado, Lima 1
Telephone: 248248

Clinical Laboratory Technician
Pharmacy Technician
Technical Nursing

5536 **INSTITUTO SUPERIOR TECNOLÓGICO 'GEORGE BOOLE'**
Avenida Arequipa 2865, Cercado, Lima 1
Telephone: 240204

Accountancy
Computer Science
Electronics

5537 **INSTITUTO SUPERIOR TECNOLÓGICO 'PERUANO'**
Jr. Washington 1369, Cercado, Lima 1

Civil Engineering
Electrical Engineering
Electronics
Mechanical Engineering

5538 **INSTITUTO SUPERIOR TECNOLÓGICO 'SALESIANO'**
Avenida Brasil 210, Cercado, Lima 1

Electrical Engineering
Electronics
Mechanical Engineering
Philosophy and Religion

5539 **INSTITUTO SUPERIOR TECNOLÓGICO 'GRAN MARISCAL RAMÓN CASTILLA'**
Avenida Arequipa 199 Cercado Lima 1

Computer Science

5540 **INSTITUTO SUPERIOR TECNOLÓGICO 'DISEÑO'**
Jr. Ica 376, Cercado, Lima 1

Design

5541 **INSTITUTO SUPERIOR TECNOLÓGICO 'MANUEL SEOANE G.'**
Avenida Fernando Wiesso y Avenida Bayevar, Canto Grande, Lima 1

Mechanical Engineering
Electrical Engineering
Industrial Chemistry

5542 **INSTITUTO SUPERIOR TECNOLÓGICO 'MANUEL ARÉVALO C.'**
Avenida Alises y Avenida Las Palmeras, Lima 31

Electrical Engineering
Food Industry
Technical Nursing

5543 **INSTITUTO SUPERIOR TECNOLÓGICO 'ANTENOR ORROG ESPINOZA'**
Avenida Ciro Alegrín, Buenos Aires de Villa, Lima 9

Computer Sciences
Electrical Engineering
Food Industry

5544 **INSTITUTO SUPERIOR TECNOLÓGICO 'LUIS NEGREIRES VEGA'**
Avenida JoséGrande, Cendevilla, Lima 31

Civil Engineering
Electrical Engineering

5545 **INSTITUTO SUPERIOR TECNOLÓGICO 'HUAROCHIRÍ'**
Huarochiri, Urb. Chacarilla, Lima

Agriculture

5546 **INSTITUTO SUPERIOR TECNOLÓGICO 'COMERCIO EXTERIOR'**
Avenida Salaveray 1910, Jesús Maria, Lima 11
Telephone: 717007

International Business Administration

5547 **INSTITUTO SUPERIOR TECNOLÓGICO 'PERUANO DE COMPUTACIÓN E INFORMÁTICA'**
Jr. Arnaldo Marquez 1512, Jesús Maria, Lima 11
Telephone: 235726

Computer Science

5548 **INSTITUTO SUPERIOR TECNOLÓGICO 'CEPEA'**
Avenida República de Chile 314, Jesús María, Lima
Telephone: 245441

Business Administration
Tourism
Secretarial Studies
Accountancy

Founded 1979 as Escuela Superior de Educación Profesional. Acquired present status and title 1983. A privateinstitution. Supervised by the Asociación de Expositores de Promoción Empresarial Cultural.

Academic Year: April to December (April-July; August-December).

Admission Requirements: Secondary school certificate and entrance examination.

Languages of Instruction: Spanish. Degrees and diplomas: Titles of Especialista Profesional, 3 yrs.

Student Enrolment: c. 1600.

5549 **INSTITUTO SUPERIOR TECNOLÓGICO 'CESCA'**
Jr. Talara 774, Jesús María, Lima 11
Telephone: 328853

Accountancy
Clincal Laboratory Technician
Computer sciences
Electronics
Technical Nursing
Tourism

5550 **INSTITUTO SUPERIOR TECNOLÓGICO 'JOSÉ PARDO'**
Avenida Grau 620, La Victoria, Lima
Telephone: 315040

Construction Engineering
Mechanical Engineering
Electrical and Electronic Engineering

Founded 1977 as Escuela Superior de Educación Profesional. Acquired present status and title 1983. A State institution.

5551 **INSTITUTO SUPERIOR TECNOLÓGICO 'VICTOR RAÚL HAYA DE LA TORRE'**
E.P.S. '18 de Enero', Jirón Stat., Catalina, Malva Rosa-Barranca, Lima

Agriculture
Accountancy

5552 **INSTITUTO SUPERIOR TECNOLÓGICO 'CÉSAR VALLEJO'**
Avenida Arequipa 2515, Lince, Lima
Telephone: 450895

Tourism
Hotel Administration

5553 **INSTITUTO SUPERIOR TECNOLÓGICO 'ERNEST WILHELM MIDDENDORF'**
San Antonio, Miraflores, Lima 18
Telephone: 450895

Administration
Laboratory Chemistry

Translation

Founded 1976 as Escuela Superior de Educación Profesional. Acquired present status and title 1983. A privateinstitution.

5554 **INSTITUTO SUPERIOR TECNOLÓGICO DE ADMINISTRACIÓN DE EMPRESAS ITAE**

Jr. Bolognesi 364, Miraflores, Lima 18
Telephone: 460628
Director: Francisco Flores Bao
Secretario General: Carlos Egas Talla

D. of Accountancy
Head: Adolfo Saavedra
D. of Business Administration
Head: Marco Espinoza Ordoñez
D. of Executive Secretarial Studies
Head: Olga Buatista Granacos
D. of Tourism
Head: Cesár Moran Tello
D. of Marketing
Head: Luis Valqui López
Branch in Lima City.

Founded 1968. A private institution.
Academic Year: April to December (April-July; August-December).
Admission Requirements: Scondary school certificate.
Fees (Intis): 10,000 per annum.
Language of Instruction: Spanish.
Degrees and Diplomas: Title of Técnico Profesional.
Library: c. 5000 vols.
Academic Staff, 1990:

Rank	Full-time	Part-time
Profesores Principales	25	32
Profesores Asistentes	31	48
Auxiliares	29	38
Total	85	118

Student Enrolment, 1990:

	Men	Women	Total
Of the country	920	418	1338
Of other countries	25	7	32
Total	945	425	1360*

*Also 318 external students.

5555 **INSTITUTO SUPERIOR TECNOLÓGICO-ESCUELA DE DECORACIÓN DE INTERIORES**

Avenida 2 de Mayo 535, Miraflores, Lima 18
Telephone: 461386

Interior Design

A private institution.

5556 **INSTITUTO SUPERIOR TECNOLÓGICO METROPOLITANO**

Avenida Central 126, Cd. 36, Miraflores, Lima 18

Founded 1980 as Escuela Superior de Educación Profesional. Acquired present status and title 1983. A privateinstitution.

5557 **INSTITUTO SUPERIOR TECNOLÓGICO 'SAN IGNACIO DE LOYOLA'**

Avenida Santa Cruz 410, Miraflores, Lima 18
Telephone: 459366

Computer Sciences
Accountancy
Secretarial Studies
Technical Sciences

5558 **INSTITUTO SUPERIOR TECNOLÓGICO 'SISE'**

Avenida 28 de Julio 745, Miraflores, Lima 18
Telephone: 44958

Computer Sciences

5559 **INSTITUTO SUPERIOR TECNOLÓGICO 'SIGLO XXI'**

León García 3ra Cuadra, Miraflores, Lima 18
Telephone: 485781

Computer Sciences
Electrical Engineering
Electronics

5560 **INSTITUTO SUPERIOR DE DISEÑO Y PUBLICIDAD 'TOULOUSE LAUTREC'**

Malecón Balta 1070, Miraflores, Lima 18
Telephone: 472999
Fax: 472998
Director: Luis Guillermo Deza Espinosa

D. of Graphic Design
Head: Ana María Rita Vidal Chavarri
D. of Publicity Design
Head: Ernesto Fuentes Cole
D. of Interior Design
Head: Alfredo Sánchez-Griñan C.
D. of Publicity Science
Head: Ernesto Fuentes Cole

Founded 1984.
Agreement with Universidad Autónoma de Guadalajara, Mexico.
Admission Requirements: Secondary school certificate and entrance examination.
Fees (Intis): c. 11,300,000 per month.
Language of Instruction: Spanish.
Degrees and Diplomas: Title of Técnico Profesional, 3 yrs.
Library: c. 500 vols.
Academic Staff, 1990: 85.
Student Enrolment, 1990: c. 700.

5561 **INSTITUTO SUPERIOR TECNOLÓGICO 'ANTONIO RAIMONDI'**

Antonieta Angelica, Avenida 28 de Julio 487, Miraflores, Lima 18

Computer Sciences
Secretarial Studies

5562 **INSTITUTO SUPERIOR TECNOLÓGICO UNIÓN**

Km. 19, Carretera Central, Ñaña, Lima 8
Telephone: 910842

Administration
Accountancy
Health Sciences
Electrical Engineering
Industrial Food Technology

Founded 1979 as Escuela Superior de Educación Profesional. Acquired present status and title 1983. A privateinstitution.

5563 **INSTITUTO SUPERIOR TECNOLÓGICO 'CIBERTEC'**

Jr. Manuel Bañón 360, San Isidro, Lima 27
Telephone: 224184
Fax: 427666
Presidente: Alfredo Miró-Quesada Howard
Directora Ejecutiva: Mariana Rodríguez Risco

Computer Sciences and Informatics
Computer Science and Informatics
Extension D.
Graduate P. in Informatics.

Founded 1983 by the CIBERTEC Educational Association.
Arrangements for co-operation with Universidad Autónoma de Guadalajara, México.
Academic Year: April to December.
Admission Requirements: Secondary school certificate and entrance examination.
Fees (US$): 400 per semester.
Language of Instruction: Spanish.
Degrees and Diplomas: Title of Técnico Profesional, 3 yrs.
Library: c. 3000 vols.

Academic Staff, 1990: 85
Student Enrolment, 1990:

	Men	Women	Total
Of the country	600	400	1000

5564 **INSTITUTO SUPERIOR TECNOLÓGICO 'MONTEMAR'**
Avenida Arequipa 3420, San Isidro, Lima 27

5565 **INSTITUTO SUPERIOR TECNOLÓGICO 'ISETEC'**
Avenida Coronel Portillo 474, San Isidro, Lima 27
Telephone: 406511

Computer Sciences
Design

5566 **INSTITUTO SUPERIOR TECNOLÓGICO 'INSTITUTO PERUANO DE PUBLICIDAD'**
Avenida El Bosque 350, San Isidro, Lima 27
Telephone: 406238

Advertising

5567 **INSTITUTO SUPERIOR TECNOLÓGICO 'SENTUR'**
Avenida Arequipa 2633, San Isidro, Lima 27
Telephone: 404841

Tourism

5568 **INSTITUTO SUPERIOR TECNOLÓGICO 'SISTEMA PERÚ'**
Juan de Arona 150, San Isidro, Lima 27
Telephone: 428186

Television

5569 **INSTITUTO SUPERIOR TECNOLÓGICO 'MONTESSORI'**
Los Pinos 530, San Isidro, Lima 27
Telephone: 409576

Design

5570 **INSTITUTO SUPERIOR TECNOLÓGICO 'SAN AGUSTÍN'**
Avenida Javier Prado 980, San Isidro, Lima 27

Computer Sciences

5571 **INSTITUTO SUPERIOR TECNOLÓGICO 'GILDA LILIANA BALLIVÍAN ROSADO'**
Lizardo Montero s/n, San Juan de Miraflores, Lima 29

Administration
Accountancy
Construction Engineering
Electrical Engineering
Electronics

Founded 1980 as Escuela Superior de Educación Profesional. Acquired present status and title 1983.

5572 **INSTITUTO SUPERIOR TECNOLÓGICO 'MARÍA ROSARIO ARAOZ PINTO'**
José Marti 150, San Miguel, Lima 32

Administration
Construction Engineering
Visual Arts
Mechanical Engineering

Founded 1976 as Escuela Superior de Educación Profesional. Acquired present status and title 1983. A State institution.

5573 **INSTITUTO SUPERIOR TECNOLÓGICO 'TUSAN'**
Jr. Cantuarias 155, San Miguel, Lima 32

Electronics
Computer Sciences

5574 **INSTITUTO SUPERIOR TECNOLÓGICO 'TECSUP'**
Avenida Industrial s/n, Carretera Central, Km. 5.7, Santa Anita, Lima 18-755
Telex: 20037 PEMHO
Telephone: 371905
Fax: (51-14) 371909
Presidente: Luis Hochschild
Director Ejecutivo: Raúl Fajardo

D. of Industrial Electronics
Head: Daniel Carbonel; *staff* 9 (5)
D. of Industrial Electrotechnics
Head: Alberto Bejarano; *staff* 10 (5)
D. of Chemical and Metallurgical Operations
Head: Luis Espinoza; *staff* 4 (4)
D. of Mechanical Maintenance
Head: Juan Musayón; *staff* 16 (5)
Continuing Capacitation P.
Head: Javier Ugarte; *staff* 2 (18)

Founded 1982.
Arrangements for co-operation with Cambrian College of Canada.
Academic Year: March to December (March-July; August-December).
Admission Requirements: Secondary school certificate.
Language of Instruction: Spanish.
Degrees and Diplomas: Title of Técnico Profesional, 3 yrs.
Library: c. 5000 vols.
Academic Staff, 1990: 44 (19).
Student Enrolment, 1990:

	Men	Women	Total
Of the country	426	21	547

5575 **INSTITUTO SUPERIOR TECNOLÓGICO 'JATUM YAUYOS'**
Yauyos, Lima

Agronomy
Civil Engineering

5576 **INSTITUTO SUPERIOR TECNOLÓGICO 'JULIO CÉSAR TELLO'**
Avenida Mariategui s/n, Villa El Salvador, Lima 42

Administration
Accountancy
Mechanical Engineering
Metallurgy
Industrial Processing

Founded 1980 as Escuela Superior de Educación Profesional. Acquired present status and title 1983. A privateinstitution.

5577 **INSTITUTO SUPERIOR TECNOLÓGICO 'SANTA MARIANA DE JESÚS'**
Sr. Tiachuanaco 679, Zarate, Lima 36
Telephone: 811914

Chemical Industry
Technical Nursing

5578 **INSTITUTO SUPERIOR TECNOLÓGICO 'PEDRO DEL AGUILA HIDALGO'**
Avenida del Ejército s/n, Iquitos, Lima
Telephone: 234451

Health Sciences
Mechanical Engineering
Administration
Construction Engineering
Agronomy
Forestry
Electrical and Electronic Engineering

Founded 1976 as Escuela Superior de Educación Profesional. Acquired present status and title 1983. A State institution.

5579 **INSTITUTO SUPERIOR TECNOLÓGICO 'CORPUS CHRISTI'**
Km. 4 Carretera Abelardo, Quillones, Lima

Technical Nursing
Tourism

Accountancy

Madre de Dios

5580 **INSTITUTO SUEPRIOR TECNOLÓGICO 'JORGE BASADRE G.'**
Avenida Fitzcarrald Cdra. 14, Puerte Maldonado, Madre de Dios

Agriculture
Mechanical Engineering
Health Sciences

Founded 1980 as Escuela Superior de Educación Profesional. Acquired present status and title 1983. A State institution.

Moquegua

5581 **INSTITUTO SUPERIOR TECNOLÓGICO 'JOSÉ CARLOS MARIATEGUI'**
Samegua, Moquegua
Telephone: 374

Health Sciences
Administration
Metallurgy
Mechanical Engineering
Accountancy

Founded 1976 as Escuela Superior de Educación Profesional. Acquired present status and title 1983. A State institution.

5582 **INSTITUTO SUPERIOR TECNOLÓGICO 'MARIANO LINO URQUIETA'**
Avenida Uruguay 173, Urb. Garibaldi I 20, Moquegua

Computer Sciences
Technical Nursing
Accountancy

5583 **INSTITUTO SUPERIOR TECNOLÓGICO 'LUIS E. VALCARCEL' DE ILO**
Urbanización 'Villa del Mar', Ilo, Moquegua
Telephone: 782931
Director: Galino Tomás Revilla Salas

Accountancy
Executive Secretarial Studies
Fishery

Founded 1988.

Academic Year: April to December (April-August; August-December).

Admission Requirements: Secondary school certificate and entrance examination.

Fees (Intis): 8000 per month.

Language of Instruction: Spanish.

Degrees and Diplomas: Title of Técnico Profesional, 3 yrs.

Academic Staff, 1990: 27.

Student Enrolment, 1990: 381.

Pasco

5584 **INSTITUTO SUPERIOR TECNOLÓGICO**
Avenida Los Incas s/n, San Juan Pampa, Pasco
Telephone: 2110

Mechanical Engineering
Civil Engineering
Electrical Engineering
Electronics

Founded 1980 as Escuela Superior de Educación Profesional. Acquired present status and title 1983. A State institution.

5585 **INSTITUTO SUPERIOR TECNOLÓGICO 'HUARIACA'**
Carretera Central de Tunaspampa s/n, Huariaca, Pasco

Agriculture
Accountancy
Technical Nursing

Founded 1982 as Escuela Superior de Educación Profesional. Acquired present status and title 1983. A State institution.

5586 **INSTITUTO SUPERIOR TECNOLÓGICO 'DANIEL A. CARRIÓN G.'**
Avenida 28 de Julio s/n, Yanahuanca, Pasco

Agriculture
Technical Nursing

5587 **INSTITUTO SUPERIOR TECNOLÓGICO 'OXAPAMPA'**
Jr. Enrique Battger s/n, Oxapampa, Pasco

Technical Nursing
Accountancy

5588 **INSTITUTO SUPERIOR TECNOLÓGICO 'PAUCARTAMBA'**
Pasco

Agriculture

Piura

5589 **INSTITUTO SUPERIOR TECNOLÓGICO 'ALMIRANTE MIGUEL GRAU'**
Prolongación Avenida Grau, Apartado 466, Piura
Telephone: 32 3068

Agriculture
Health Sciences
Electrical and Electronic Engineering
Mechanical Engineering
Administration
Metallurgy
Industrial Processing

Founded 1976 as Escuela Superior de Educación Profesional. Acquired present status and title 1983. A State institution.

5590 **INSTITUTO SUPERIOR TECNOLÓGICO COSMOS**
Jr. Libertad 714, Piura, Piura

Advertising
Accountancy
Administration
Secretarial Studies

Founded 1980 as Escuela Superior de Educación Profesional. Acquired present status and title 1983. A privateinstitution.

5591 **INSTITUTO SUPERIOR TECNOLÓGICO 'SULLANA'**
Sullana, Piura

Agriculture
Civil Engineering
Accountancy
Technical Nursing
Mechanical Production
Technical Sciences

Founded 1980 as Escuela Superior de Educación Profesional. Acquired present status and title 1983. A State institution.

5592 **INSTITUTO SUPERIOR TECNOLÓGICO NO ESTATAL 'SAN JUAN'DE SULLANA**
Avenida José de Lama 195, Apartado postal 200, Sullana, Piura
Telephone: 2354
Director: Teodoro Uriol Gálvez (1969-)
Secretario General: Victor Urión Gavidia

D. of Executive Secretarial Studies
Head: Gladys Coronado; *staff* 10
D. of Computer and Informatic Studies
Head: Manuel Icanaquo Yesan; *staff* 5
D. of Accountancy
Head: Blanca Lopez de Rivera; *staff* 6 (9)
D. of Administration
Head: Yolanda Calderón Castillo; *staff* 5 (8)
D. of International Negotiation Studies
Head: Carlos Zapata Z.; *staff* 5 (6)

Founded 1984.

Academic Year: April to December.

Admission Requirements: Secondary school certificate and entrance examination.

Degrees and Diplomas: Title of Técnico Profesional, 3 yrs.

Academic Staff, 1990: 87.
Student Enrolment, 1990:

Men	Women	Total
548	435	983

5593 **INSTITUTO SUPERIOR TECNOLÓGICO 'SAN MIGUEL DE PIURA'**
Avenida Guardia Civil 222, Piura, Piura
Computer Sciences

5594 **INSTITUTO SUPERIOR TECNOLÓGICO 'OTTO TONSMANN'**
Huancavelice G-10, Buenos Aires, Piura
Technical Nursing
Pharmacy

5595 **INSTITUTO SUPERIOR TECNOLÓGICO 'NESTOR MARTES GARRIDO'**
Huancabamba, Piura
Agriculture

5596 **INSTITUTO SUPERIOR TECNOLÓGICO 'VICUS'**
Calle Lima 323, Chulucanas, Piura
Technical Nursing
Agriculture

5597 **INSTITUTO SUPERIOR TECNOLÓGICO 'AYABACA'**
Piura, Piura
Agriculture

5598 **INSTITUTO SUPERIOR TECNOLÓGICO 'HERMANES CARCAMO'**
Paita, Piura
Electrical Engineering
Agriculture

5599 **INSTITUTO SUPERIOR TECNOLÓGICO 'LUCIANO CASTILLO C.'**
Talara, Piura
Chemical Industry
Mechanical Engineering
Accountancy

5600 **INSTITUTO SUPERIOR TECNOLÓGICO 'LA UNIÓN'**
La Unión, Piura
Agriculture
Electrical Engineering

Puno

5601 **INSTITUTO SUPERIOR TECNOLÓGICO 'JULI'**
Ciudad de Juli, Puno
Agriculture

5602 **INSTITUTO SUPERIOR TECNOLÓGICO 'JOSÉ ANTONIO ENCINAS'**
Fundo Salcedo Rinconada, Puno
Telephone: 207
Agriculture
Mechanical Engineering
Administration
Construction Engineering
Electrical and Electronic Engineering

Founded 1976 as Escuela Superior de Educación Profesional. Acquired present status and title 1983. A State institution.

5603 **INSTITUTO SUPERIOR TECNOLÓGICO 'MANUEL NUÑEZ BUTRÓN'**
Morales Huascar 762, Juliaca, Urb. La Capilla, Puno
Mechanical Engineering
Accountancy
Secretarial Studies
Technical Nursing

Founded 1976 as Escuela Superior de Educación Profesional. Acquired present status and title 1983. A State institution.

5604 **INSTITUTO SUPERIOR TECNOLÓGICO 'AYAVIRI'**
Balsaspata, Ayaviri, Puno
Accountancy
Agriculture

5605 **INSTITUTO SUPERIOR TECNOLÓGICO 'HUANCANÉ'**
Huancané, Puno
Agriculture
Technical Nursing

5606 **INSTITUTO SUPERIOR TECNOLÓGICO 'PEDRO VILCAPAZA'**
Azangaro, Puno
Agriculture
Technical Nursing

5607 **INSTITUTO SUPERIOR TECNOLÓGICO 'YUNGUYO'**
Yunguyo, Puno
Agriculture
Technical Nursing

San Martín

5608 **INSTITUTO SUPERIOR TECNOLÓGICO 'NOR ORIENTAL DE LA SELVA'**
Calle Tupac Amarú 398, Banda Silcayo, Tarapoto, San Martin
Mechanical Engineering
Electrical Engineering
Agriculture
Civil Engineering
Forestry

Founded 1978 as Escuela Superior de Educación Profesional. Acquired present status and title 1983. A State institution.

5609 **INSTITUTO SUPERIOR TECNOLÓGICO 'ALTO MAYO'**
Mayamba, San Martín
Agriculture
Accountancy

5610 **INSTITUTO SUPERIOR TECNOLÓGICO 'RIOJA'**
Rioja, San Martín
Agriculture
Mechanical Engineering
Technical Nursing

5611 **INSTITUTO SUPERIOR TECNOLÓGICO 'HUALLAGA'**
Saposa, San Martín
Agriculture
Computer Sciences

5612 **INSTITUTO SUPERIOR TECNOLÓGICO 'TOCACHE'**
Tocache, San Martín
Agriculture

5613 **INSTITUTO SUPERIOR TECNOLÓGICO 'BELLAVISTA'**
Bellavista, San Martín
Agriculture
Civil Engineering

5614 **INSTITUTO SUPERIOR TECNOLÓGICO 'SAN CRISTO DE BOGAZÓN'**
Mance Inca 415, Tarapoto, San Martin
Director: Luis Cusco Cruz
Administration

Accountancy
Technical Nursing
Auxiliary Nursing

Founded 1985.

Academic Year: March to December (March-July; August-December).

Admission Requirements: Secondary school certificate and entrance examination.

Language of Instruction: Spanish.

Degrees and Diplomas: Title of Técnico Profesional, 3 yrs.

Student Enrolment, 1990:

	Men	Women	Total
Of the country	150	50	200
Of other countries	10	8	18
Total	160	58	218

Tacna

5615 **INSTITUTO SUPERIOR TECNOLÓGICO 'FRANCISCO DE PAULA GONZÁLEZ VIGIL'**

Avenida Circunvalación s/n, Tacna (Tacna)
Telephone: 721201
Director: Luis B. Rodríguez Hinojosa (1984-)

Agriculture
Electrical and Electronic Engineering
Construction Engineering
Mechanical Engineering
Accountancy

Founded 1977 as Escuela Superior de Educación Profesional. Acquired present status and title 1983. A State institution.

Academic Year: April to December (April-August; September-December).

Admission Requirements: Secondary school certificate.

Language of Instruction: Spanish.

Degrees and Diplomas: Title of Técnico Profesional.

Library: 3500 vols.

Academic Staff, 1986-87: 62 (11).

Student Enrolment, 1986-87:

	Men	Women	Total
Of the country	673	293	966

5616 **INSTITUTO SUPERIOR TECNOLÓGICO 'RAMÓN COPAJA'**

Tarata, Tacna

Agriculture

Tumbes

5617 **INSTITUTO SUPERIOR TECNOLÓGICO 'JOSÉ ABELARDO QUIÑONES'**

Apartado 73, Tumbes, Tumbes
Telephone: 3833

Mechanical Engineering
Technical Nursing
Electronics
Civil Engineering
Secretarial Studies
Administration

Founded 1977 as Escuela Superior de Educación Profesional. Acquired present status and title 1983. A State institution.

Ucayali

5618 **INSTITUTO SUPERIOR TECNOLÓGICO 'SUIZA'**

Km. 6 de la Carretera 'Federico Basadre', Coronel Portillo, Pucallpa, Ucayali

Agriculture
Forestry
Health Sciences
Mechanical Engineering
Civil Engineering
Electrical Engineering
Accountancy
Secretarial Studies

Founded 1980 as Escuela Superior de Educación Profesional. Acquired present status and title 1983. A State institution.

5619 **INSTITUTO SUPERIOR TECNOLÓGICO 'ATALAYA'**

Raymundy, Ucayali

Agriculture

Teacher Training

5620 **INSTITUTO SUPERIOR PEDAGÓGICO 'SAN JUAN BAUTISTA DE LA SALLE' DE ABANCAY**

Calle Lima 135, Apartado 60, Abancay, Apurímac

Teacher Training

Founded 1981. A State institution.

5621 **INSTITUTO SUPERIOR PEDAGÓGICO 'JOSÉ MARÍA ARQUEDAS' DE ANDAHUAYLAS**

Coyahuacho s/n, San Jerónimo, Andahuaylas, Apurímac

Teacher Training

A State institution.

5622 **INSTITUTO SUPERIOR PEDAGÓGICO DE AREQUIPA**

Jr. La Merced 313, Arequipa, Arequipa

Teacher Training

5623 **INSTITUTO SUPERIOR PEDAGÓGICO 'NUESTRA SRA. DE LOURDES' DE AYACUCHO**

Avenida 28 de Julio 393, Ayacucho, Ayacucho

Teacher Training

A State institution.

5624 **INSTITUTO SUPERIOR PEDAGÓGICO DE AZÁNGARO**

Jr. Villacampa s/n, Azángaro, Puno

Teacher Training

A State institution.

5625 **INSTITUTO SUPERIOR PEDAGÓGICO PARTICULAR 'SALESIANA'**

Avenida Brasil 210, Apartado 999, Lima 6

Teacher Training

A private institution.

5626 **INSTITUTO SUPERIOR PEDAGÓGICO 'CIRO ALEGRÍA BAZÁN'**

Jr. Odonován 740, Cajabamba, Cajamarca

Teacher Training

A State institution.

5627 **INSTITUTO SUPERIOR PEDAGÓGICO DE CAJAMARCA**

Apartado 15, Avenida El Maestro, Cajamarca, Cajamarca

Teacher Training

A State institution.

5628 **INSTITUTO SUPERIOR PEDAGÓGICO PARTICULAR 'SAN JOSÉ'**

Yauyos, Cañete, Lima

Teacher Training

A private institution.

5629 **INSTITUTO SUPERIOR PEDAGÓGICO DE CAÑETE**

Mercado Modelo Norte, Cañete, Lima

Teacher Training

5630 **INSTITUTO SUPERIOR PEDAGÓGICO DE CELENDÍN 'ARISTIDES MERINO NERINO'**

Jr. Pardo 731, Celendín, Cajamarca

Teacher Training
A State institution.

5631 **INSTITUTO SUPERIOR PEDAGÓGICO DE CERRO DE PASCO**
Avenida 6 de Diciembre, San Juan de Yanacancha, Cero de Pasco, Pasco
Teacher Training
A State institution.

5632 **INSTITUTO SUPERIOR PEDAGÓGICO 'TORIBIO RODRÍGUEZ DE MENDOZA' DE CHACHAPOYAS**
Jr. Triunfo s/n 6ta., Chachapoyas, Amazonas
Teacher Training
A State institution.

5633 **INSTITUTO SUPERIOR PEDAGÓGICO 'SAGRADO CORAZÓN DE JESÚS' DE CHICLAYO**
Jr. Leonardo Ortíz Cahuide s/n, Chiclayo, Lambayeque
Teacher Training
A State institution.

5634 **INSTITUTO SUPERIOR PEDAGÓGICO PARTICULAR 'STO. TORIBIO DE MOGROVEJO'**
Jr. Leticia 318, Chiclayo, Lambayeque
Telephone: 238698
Director: Dionisio Quiroz Tequén
Secretario general: Luis Chang Ching
Teacher Training
Sub-Director: Juan Llanos Figueredo; *staff* 5
Ce. of Research and Development Education
Sub-Director: Jorge Pérez Uriarte; *staff* 2
Founded 1981 as a private institution.
Academic Year: April to December (April-July; August-December)
Admission Requirements: Secondary school certificate.
Language of Instruction: Spanish.
Degrees and Diplomas: Title of Profesor(a), 5 yrs.
Academic Staff, 1990: 61 (54).
Student Enrolment, 1990:

	Men	Women	Total
Of the country	277	1169	1446

5635 **PROGRAMA DE FORMACIÓN DE PROF. DE EDUCACIÓN PRIMARIA**
Chimbote, Ancash
Telephone: 324171
Teacher Training
A State institution.

5636 **INSTITUTO SUPERIOR PEDAGÓGICO DE CHINCHA**
Avenida América 201, Chincha, Ica
Teacher Training
A State institution.

5637 **INSTITUTO SUPERIOR PEDAGÓGICO 'NUESTRA SRA. DE CHOTA'**
Jr. Atahualpa 106, Chota, Cajamarca
Teacher Training
A State institution.

5638 **INSTITUTO SUPERIOR PEDAGÓGICO 'TEODORO PEÑALOZA' DE CHUPACA**
Avenida Los Héroes 380, Chupaca-Huancayo, Junín
Teacher Training
A State institution.

5639 **INSTITUTO SUPERIOR PEDAGÓGICO 'GREGORIO MENDEL' DE CHUQUIBAMBILLA**
Prelatura de Chuquibambilla, Graú, Apurímac
Teacher Training
A State institution.

5640 **PROGRAMA DE FORMACIÓN DE PROFESORES DE PRIMARIA**
Jr. Melgar s/n, Contumazá, Cajamarca
Teacher Training
A State institution.

5641 **INSTITUTO SUPERIOR PEDAGÓGICO DE CORACORA**
Plaza Jorge Chávez, Coracora, Ayacucho
Teacher Training
A State institution.

5642 **INSTITUTO SUPERIOR PEDAGÓGICO 'OCTAVIO MATTA CONTRERAS' DE CUTERVO**
Jr. Obrero s/n, Cutervo, Cajamarca
Teacher Training
A State institution.

5643 **INSTITUTO SUPERIOR PEDAGÓGICO 'SANTA ROSA' DE CUZCO**
Calle San Andrés, Apartado 267, Cuzco, Cuzco
Teacher Training
A State institution.

5644 **INSTITUTO SUPERIOR PEDAGÓGICO 'FAUSTINO SÁNCHEZ CARRIÓN' DE HUAMACHUCO**
Prolongación Sánchez Carrión s/n, Huamachuco, La Libertad
Teacher Training
A State institution.

5645 **INSTITUTO SUPERIOR PEDAGÓGICO DE HUANCAVELICA**
Plaza Santa Domingo s/n, Huancavelica, Huancavelica
Teacher Training
A State institution.

5646 **INSTITUTO SUPERIOR PEDAGÓGICO 'JOSÉ SALVADOR CAVERO' DE HUANTA**
Jr. Ayacucho 567, Huanta, Ayacucho
Teacher Training
A State institution.

5647 **INSTITUTO SUPERIOR PEDAGÓGICO 'MARIOS DURÁN MARTEL'**
Carretera Central s/n, Paucarbamba, Huánuco, Huánuco
Teacher Training
A State institution.

5648 **INSTITUTO SUPERIOR PEDAGÓGICO DE HUARÁZ**
Jr. Víctor Vélez s/n, Barrio de Nicrupampa, Apartado 82, Huaráz, Ancash
Teacher Training
A State institution.

5649 **INSTITUTO SUPERIOR PEDAGÓGICO DE ICA 'JUAN XXIII'**
Calle Dos de Mayo 158, Ica, Ica
Teacher Training
A State institution.

5650 **INSTITUTO SUPERIOR PEDAGÓGICO DE IQUÍTOS**
Jirón Putmayo 355, Maynas, Iquítos, Loreto
Teacher Training
A State institution.

5651 **INSTITUTO SUPERIOR PEDAGÓGICO 'VÍCTOR ANDRÉS BELAÚNDE' DE JAÉN**
Jirón Bolívar 1695, Jaén, Cajamarca
Teacher Training
A State institution.

5652 **INSTITUTO SUPERIOR PEDAGÓGICO DE JULIACA**
Carretera Norte, Salida al Cuzco, Juliaca, Puno
Teacher Training
A State institution.

5653 **INSTITUTO SUPERIOR PEDAGÓGICO 'HERMILIO VALDIZÁN' DE LA UNIÓN**
Jr. San Antonio s/n, La Unión, Huánuco
Teacher Training
A State institution.

5654 **INSTITUTO SUPERIOR PEDAGÓGICO DE EDUCACIÓN FÍSICA DE LAMPA**
Prolongación J.M. Ríos s/n, Lampa, Puno
Teacher Training
A State institution.

5655 **INSTITUTO SUPERIOR PEDAGÓGICO PARTICULAR 'STO. DOMINGO DE GUZMÁN'**
Prolongación Arenales 420, Lima, Lima
Teacher Training
A private institution.

5656 **INSTITUTO PEDAGÓGICO NACIONAL DE EDUCACIÓN INICIAL**
Jr. Víctor Criado Tejado 2712, Urb. Elio, Lima, Lima
Teacher Training
A State institution.

5657 **INSTITUTO PEDAGÓGICO NACIONAL DE MONTERRICO**
Apartado 247 Monterrico, Lima
Teacher Training
A State institution.

5658 **INSTITUTO SUPERIOR PEDAGÓGICO 'MERCEDES CABELLO DE CARBONARA'**
Carretera Moquegua, Moquegua, Moquegua
Teacher Training
A State institution.

5659 **INSTITUTO SUPERIOR PEDAGÓGICO 'GENERALÍSIMO JOSÉ DE SAN MARTÍN' DE MOYOBAMBA**
Jr. Pedro Pascasio Noriega s/n, Moyobamba, San Martín
Teacher Training
A State institution.

5660 **INSTITUTO SUPERIOR PEDAGÓGICO 'NTRA. SEÑORA DE LA ASUNCIÓN' DE OTUZCO**
Otuzco, La Libertad
Teacher Training
A State institution.

5661 **INSTITUTO SUPERIOR PEDAGÓGICO 'DAVID SÁNCHEZ INFANTE' SAN PEDRO DE LLOC**
Panamericana Norte Km. 659, San Pedro de Lloc, La Libertad
Teacher Training
A State institution.

5662 **INSTITUTO SUPERIOR PEDAGÓGICO DE PIURA**
Avenida Chulucanas s/n, Santa Rosa, Piura
Teacher Training
A State institution.

5663 **INSTITUTO SUPERIOR PEDAGÓGICO DE POMABAMBA**
Pomabamba, Ancash
Teacher Training
A State institution.

5664 **INSTITUTO SUPERIOR PEDAGÓGICO DE PUCALLPA**
Jirón Sáenz Peña s/n, Pucallpa, Ucayali
Teacher Training
A State institution.

5665 **INSTITUTO SUPERIOR PEDAGÓGICO BILINGUE DE YARINACOCHAS**
Yarinacochas, Pucallpa, Ucayali
Teacher Training
A State institution.

5666 **INSTITUTO SUPERIOR PEDAGÓGICO PARTICULAR CATEQUÉTICA**
Avenida cre 1200, Lima 21, Lima
Teacher Training
A private institution.

5667 **INSTITUTO SUPERIOR PEDAGÓGICO 'NUESTRA SEÑORA DEL ROSARIO' DE PUERTO MALDONADO**
Puerto Maldonado, Madre de Dios
Teacher Training

5668 **INSTITUTO SUPERIOR PEDAGÓGICO DE PUQUIO**
Avenida Mariano Salas s/n, Lucanas, Ayacucho
Teacher Training
A State institution.

5669 **INSTITUTO SUPERIOR PEDAGÓGICO DE PUNO**
Fundo Salsedo s/n, Apartado 81, Puno, Puno
Teacher Training
A State institution.

5670 **INSTITUTO SUPERIOR PEDAGÓGICO 'FRAY FLORENCIO PASCUAL ALEGRE GONZÁLES' DE REQUENA**
Barrio Tarapacá s/n, Requena, Loreto
Teacher Training
A State institution.

5671 **INSTITUTO SUPERIOR PEDAGÓGICO 'VICTORINO ELORZ GOICOECHEA' DE SULLANA**
Avenida Victorino Elorz s/n, Apartado 122, Sullana, Piura
Teacher Training
A State institution.

5672 **INSTITUTO SUPERIOR PEDAGÓGICO 'JOSÉ JIMÉNEZ BORGA'**
Jr. Billingurst 150, Tacna, Tacna
Teacher Training
A State institution.

5673 **INSTITUTO SUPERIOR PEDAGÓGICO DE TARAPOTO**
Jirón Orellana s/n, Tarapoto, San Martín
Teacher Training
A State institution.

5674 **INSTITUTO SUPERIOR PEDAGÓGICO DE TARMA**
Tarma, Junín
Teacher Training
A State institution.

5675 **INSTITUTO SUPERIOR PEDAGÓGICO DE TAYABAMBA**
Jirón Sucre 200, Tayabamba La Libertad
Teacher Training
A State institution.

5676 **INSTITUTO SUPERIOR PEDAGÓGICO 'TÚPAC AMARÚ' DE TINTA**
Tinta, Cuzco

Teacher Training
A State institution.

5677 **INSTITUTO SUPERIOR PEDAGÓGICO DE LA LIBERTAD**
Avenida América Sur, Trujillo, La Libertad

Teacher Training
A State institution.

5678 **INSTITUTO SUPERIOR PEDAGÓGICO PARTICULAR 'SANTO TOMÁS DE AQUINO' DE TRUJILLO**
Jr. Ayacucho 510, Trujillo, La Libertad

Teacher Training
A private institution.

5679 **INSTITUTO SUPERIOR PEDAGÓGICO 'JOSÉ ANTONIO ENCINAS' DE TUMBES**
Panamericana Norte Km. 03, Tumbes, Tumbes

Teacher Training
A State institution.

5680 **INSTITUTO SUPERIOR PEDAGÓGICO DE URUBAMBA**
Apartado 379, Urubamba, Cuzco

Teacher Training
A State institution.

5681 **INSTITUTO SUPERIOR PEDAGÓGICO 'IGNACIO A. RAMOS OLIVERA' DE YUNGAY**
Jr. Yungay s/n, Yungay, Ancash

Teacher Training
A State institution.

5682 **INSTITUTO SUPERIOR PEDAGÓGICO 'ELIAS OLAZAR' DE YURIMAGUAS**
Avenida Mariscal Castilla, Yurimaguas, Loreto

Teacher Training
A State institution.

Professional Education

Ica

5683 **INSTITUTO SUPERIOR TECNOLÓGICO 'PARAKAS'**
Urb. 'La Morales', Ica, Ica

Tourism

PHILIPPINES

Universities

Public Institutions

5684 **BENGUET STATE UNIVERSITY**
La Trinidad, Benguet

Agriculture
Forestry
Agricultural Business Management
Engineering
Veterinary Medicine
Education
Technical Sciences

Founded 1960, reorganized 1965. A State institution.

5685 **BICOL UNIVERSITY**
Legazpi City 4500
Telephone: 4913-4932
President: Patria Gregorio-Lorenzo (1988-)
Administrative Officer: Emiliano A. Aberin

C. of Engineering
Head: Atanacio A. Barajas; *staff* 55 (6)
C. of Education (including Secondary and Elementary Education)
Dean: Violeta M. Diaz; *staff* 53 (1)
C. of Agriculture
Dean: Justino R. Arboleda; *staff* 60 (3)
C. of Fisheries
Director: Nimea Pelea; *staff* 43
C. of Arts and Science (including Sociology, Political Science and Economics)
Dean: Jaime R. Recama
C. of Nursing
Dean: Paz G. Muñoz; *staff* 21 (21)
S. of Arts and Trade
Director: Eulalio Del Ayre; *staff* 50 (1)
Graduate S.
Dean: Lazara V. Julianda; *staff* 14 (23)
Ce. for Research and Statistics
Director: Virginia C. Orense; *staff* 12 (4)
Extension Ce.
Director: Ramon Salire; *staff* 9 (4)
Also elementary school and high school.

Founded 1969 incorporating several existing schools, including Bicol Teachers' College; Roxas Memorial Agricultural School; Bicol Regional School of Arts and Trades; and Bicol School of Fisheries. A State institution. Governing body: the Board of Regents, with the Secretary of Education, Culture and Sports as Chairman. Residential facilities for academic staff and students.

Arrangements for co-operation with the Universities of: Tsukuba; Kochi; New South Wales; Exeter; Melbourne; Queensland; Rhode Island; Strathclyde.

Academic Year: June to March (June-October; November-March).

Admission Requirements: Graduation from high school and entrance examination.

Fees (Pesos): 138-368 per semester.

Languages of Instruction: English and Pilipino

Degrees and Diplomas: Bachelor of–Arts, A.B.; Science, B.S., Bachelor of Science in–Education, B.S.E.; Elementary Education, B.S.E.E.; Agriculture, B.S.A., Agricultural Education, B.S.A.E.; Fisheries, B.S.F.; Industrial Education, B.S.I.E.; Architecture, B.S.Arc.; Nursing, 4 yrs; Agricultural Engineering, B.S.A.Eng.; Civil Engineering; Mechanical Engineering; Electrical Engineering, 5 yrs. Master of Arts–in Education, M.A.Ed.; Teaching, M.A.T.; Public Administration, M.A.P.A; Educational Management, M.A.E.M.; Industrial Education, M.A.I.E.; Management, M.A.M. Master of Science in Agriculture, M.S.A., a further 2 yrs. Doctor of Education, Ed.D., at least 2 yrs after Master.

Library: Central Library 60,000 vols.

Special Facilities (Museums, etc.): Natural History Museum.

Publications: Gearcast (Engineering); Bicol Universitarian; Coverall; publications of the colleges.

Academic Staff, 1989-90:

Rank	Full-time	Part-time
Professors	22	7
Associate Professors	80	18
Assistant Professors	172	6
Instructors	302	10
Lecturers	–	40
Total	576	81

Student Enrolment, 1989-90:

	Men	Women	Total
Total	5947	6735	12,682

5686 **CAGAYAN STATE UNIVERSITY**
Tuguegarao, Cagayan

Engineering
Arts and Science
Agricultural Business
Education
Industrial Technology
Technical Sciences

Founded 1978. A State institution.

5687 **PAMPAMAHALAANG PAMANTASAN NG GITNANG LUZON**
Central Luzon State University
Muñoz, Nueva Ecija 2320
Cables: CLSU, Muñoz, N.E.
Telephone: 107 (PLDT)
President: Eliseo L. Ruiz
Administrative Officer: Ricardo C. Bernardo

C. of Agriculture (including Animal Husbandry and Horticulture)
Dean: Guillermo Rillon; *staff* 60
C. of Arts and Sciences
Dean: Teresita Maquiso; *staff* 83
C. of Engineering (Agricultural, Civil, Electrical, and Mechanical)
Dean: Honorato L. Angeles; *staff* 28
C. of Education
Dean: Vivencio Esteban; *staff* 36
C. of Inland Fisheries
Dean: Rodolfo G. Arce; *staff* 14
C. of Veterinary Medicine
Dean: Oscar D. Quines; *staff* 15
C. of Business Administration
Dean: Oscar O. Gulmatico; *staff* 19
C. of Home Economics (including Food Technology)
Dean: Lourdes F. San Juan; *staff* 12
Also high school.

Founded 1907 as school, became agricultural college 1950, acquired university status 1964. Governing body: the Board of Regents, with the Ministry of Education, Culture and Sports as ex officio Chairman. Residential facilities for academic staff and students.

Academic Year: June to March (June-October; November-March).

Admission Requirements: Graduation from high school and entrance examination.

Fees (Pesos): 25 per unit, per annum.

Language of Instruction: English.

Degrees and Diplomas: Bachelor of Science in–Agriculture; Agriculture Education; Home Economics; Agricultural Extension; Education; Food Technology; Biology; Chemistry; Secondary Education; Elementary Education; Garment Technology; Business Administration; Inland Fisheries, 4 yrs; Agricultural Engineering. Master of Science, 1-2 yrs after Bachelor. Master of Arts in Teaching (Agriculture) (elementary level). Doctor of Veterinary Medicine, 6 yrs.

Library: 43,078 vols.

Special Facilities (Museums, etc.): Ilongot Museum.

Publications: Scientific Journal (biannually); Newsletter (quarterly); Bulletin (bimonthly).

Press or Publishing House: CLSU Publishing House.

Academic Staff, 1986-87:

Rank	Full-time
Professors	12
Associate Professors	24
Assistant Professors	82
Instructors	222
Total	340

Student Enrolment, 1986-87:

	Men	Women	Total
Of the country	1923	2481	4404
Of other countries	94	8	102
Total	2017	2489	4506

5688 **PAMANTASAN NG KALAGITNAANG MINDANAO**

Central Mindanao University
University Town, Musuan, Bukidnon 8710
President: Leonardo A. Chua
Registrar: Leonilo M. Moralde

C. of Agriculture (including Animal Husbandry)
Dean: Angelo R. Josue; *staff* 63
C. of Arts and Sciences
Dean: Marcelino N. Maceda; *staff* 69
C. of Education
Dean: Emmanuel A. Lariosa; *staff* 28
C. of Engineering (Agricultural and Civil)
Dean: Deogracias B. Navaja; *staff* 28
C. of Forestry
Dean: Amado M. Exile; *staff* 16
C. of Home Economics
Dean: Norma R. Montemayor; *staff* 8
C. of Veterinary Medicine
Dean: Medino A. Yebron; *staff* 14
Graduate S.
Dean: Mardonio N. Lao; *staff* 84
Also elementary school and high school.

Founded 1910, became Mindanao Agricultural College 1952 and acquired present status 1965. Governing body: the Board of Regents of which the Minister of Education, Culture and Sports is Chairman. Residential facilities for students.

Academic Year: June to March (June-October; November-March).

Admission Requirements: Graduation from high school and entrance examination.

Fees (Pesos): Tuition, 15 per unit.

Languages of Instruction: English and Pilipino.

Degrees and Diplomas: Bachelor of–Arts, A.B.; Science, B.S.; Science in Agriculture, B.S.A.; Science in Development Communication, B.S.; Science in Agribusiness Management, B.S.A.M.; Science in Biology, B.S.; Science in Mathematics, B.B.; Science in Secretarial Administration, B.S.; Science in Home Economics, B.S.H.E.; Science in Education, B.S.Ed.; Science in Agricultural Education, B.S.A.Ed.; Science in Forestry, B.S.F.; Science in Civil Engineering, B.S.C.Eng.; Science in Agricultural Engineering, B.S.A.Eng.; Science in Electrical Engineering, B.S.E.E.; Science in Mechanical Engineering, B.S.M.E.; Science in Nutrition and Dietetics, B.S.N.D.; Business Education, B.S.B.Ed., 4-5 yrs. Master of Arts, M.A.; Master of Science, M.S., a further 2 yrs. Doctor of Philosophy in Education; Doctor of Education. Doctor of Veterinary Medicine, D.V.M., 6 yrs. Also vocational diplomas.

Library: Central Library, *c.* 17,397 vols.

Special Facilities (Museums, etc.): Anthropological Museum; Herbariums; Fernery; Biological and Medicinal Garden; Arboretum; Radio Station.

Publications: Journal of Science and Agriculture (biannually); CMU This Week (CMU Newsletter).

Press or Publishing House: CMU Printing Press.

Academic Staff, 1989-90:

Rank	Full-time
Professors	34
Associate Professors	46
Assistant Professors	83
Instructors	139
Total	302

Student Enrolment, 1989-90:

	Men	Women	Total
Of the country	2703	3041	5744

5689 **DON MARIANO MARCOS MEMORIAL STATE UNIVERSITY**

Bacnotan, La Union

Agriculture
Agronomy (Forestry)
Sciences
Business Administration
Education
Home Technology
Fishery
Hotel and Restaurant Management
Arts
Law
Industrial Technology
Midwifery
Technical Sciences

Founded 1960, reorganized 1972. A State institution.

5690 **ISABELA STATE UNIVERSITY**

Echague, Isabela

S. of Arts and Sciences
S. of Agricultural Industries
S. of Vocational and Industrial Studies
S. of Forestry
S. of Engineering
S. of Education
S. of Home Technology
S. of Technical Sciences

Founded 1926, reorganized 1963 and 1979. A State institution.

5691 **MARIANO MARCOS STATE UNIVERSITY**

Batac, Ilocos Norte 0305
Cables: MMSU, Batac, Ilocos Norte
President: Felipe B. Cachola
Registrar: Alegria T. Visaya

C. of Arts and Sciences
Dean: Freddie Pagdilao; *staff* 72
C. of Agriculture and Forestry
Dean: Nancy A. Balantac; *staff* 76
C. of Education
Dean: Vicente A. Bonoan; *staff* 104
C. of Nursing
Dean: Violeta Glova; *staff* 16
I. of Technology
Dean: Gregorio Amano; *staff* 42
S. of Fishery
Director: Andres Tungpalan; *staff* 9
C. of Economics and Management
Dean: Marietta Bonoan; *staff* 23
C. of Engineering and Technology
Dean: Carlos Ungson; *staff* 20
Science Research L.
Director: Constancio Ragual; *staff* 60
Ce. for Applied Research and Technology Transfer (Dingras)
Director: Salomon Basilio; *staff* 8
Ce. for Applied Research and Technology Transfer (Paoay)
Director: Isabel Diaz; *staff* 11
Business Resource Development Ce.
Director: Gloria Alano; *staff* 3
Also high school.

Founded 1978, incorporating the Mariano Marcos Memorial College of Science and Technology; Northern Luzon State College, Laoag City; Ilocos

Norte College of Arts and Trades; and Ilocos Norte Agricultural College. A Stateinstitution. Governing bodies: the Board of Regents of which the Secretary of Education, Culture and Sports is ex officio Chairman and comprising 7 members; the University Council. Residential facilities for academic staff and students.

Academic Year: June to March (June-October; November-March).

Admission Requirements: Graduation from high school and entrance examination

Fees (Pesos): 7.50 per unit; Graduate, 17.50-20.

Languages of Instruction: English and Pilipino.

Degrees and Diplomas: Associate in–Industrial Technology; Radio Communications; Fisheries; Arts and Design, 2 yrs. Bachelor of–Science; Science in Agriculture; Agricultural Education; Agricultural Engineering; Forestry; Nursing; Home Technology; Education; Elementary Education; Industrial Technology; Biology; Mathematics; Business Administration; Civil Engineering; Electrical Engineering; Mechanical Engineering; Fishery; Industrial Education; Ceramics Engineering, 4-5 yrs. Master of–Arts; Arts in Teaching; Public Administration; Arts in Public Administration; Agriculture, a further 2 yrs. Doctor of Education, 2-3 yrs.

Library: Central Library, 47,110 vols.

Publications: Ilocos Forum; The Mahogany; Sirmata; ILARCC; Insight; Ilocos Journal of Science and Technology, all quarterly.

Academic Staff, 1989-90:

Rank	Full-time	Part-time
Professor	17	
Associate Professors	25	–
Assistant Professors	113	–
Instructors	318	2
Total	473	2

Student Enrolment, 1989-90: 88 (21).

5692 **PAMANTASANG BAYAN NG MINDANAO**

Mindanao State University

Marawi City

Telex: MSU MANILA INFO OFFICE VASQUEZ STREET MALATE, METRO MANILA

Telephone: 589232

President: Ahmad E. Alonto, Jr.

C. of Agriculture
Dean: Cosain Derico; *staff* 45
C. of Business Administration
Dean: Macacuna Moslem; *staff* 45
C. of Community Development and Public Administration
Dean: Danice Lucman; *staff* 30
C. of Education
Dean: Maimona Sumpingan; *staff* 28
C. of Engineering
Dean: Medior Mamako; *staff* 67
C. of Fisheries
Dean: Pedro Escudero; *staff* 22
C. of Forestry
Dean: Gerardo Gavine; *staff* 20
C. of Health Sciences
Dean: Cynthia Filipinas; *staff* 14
C. for Hotel and Restaurant Management
Head: Gerardo Cortez; *staff* 8
C. of Law
Head: Abdul Aguam; *staff* 6
C. of Medicine
Head: Ombra Tamano; *staff* 3
C. of Physical Education and Sports
Head: Edna de los Santos; *staff* 21
Graduate S.
Dean: Macaurog Derogongan; *staff* 3
I. for Fisheries Research and Development
Head: William Adam
C. of Natural Science and Mathematics
Dean: Gervacio Riconella; *staff* 79
Ce. for Arabic and Islamic Studies
Head: Pama Muti; *staff* 22
C. of Social Sciences and Humanities
Dean: Rolando Gripaldo; *staff* 118
Science Training Ce.
Director: Fortunato Portugaleza; *staff* 16
Also elementary and secondary schools.

Founded 1961, the first students admitted June 1966. A State institution. Governing bodies: the Board of Regents of which the Minister of Education, Culture and Sports is ex officio Chairman and comprising 13 members; the University Council. Some residential facilities for academic staff and students.

Arrangements for co-operation with the Universities of: Hawaii; Malaysia.

Academic Year: June to March (June-October; November-March).

Admission Requirements: Graduation from high school and entrance examination.

Fees (Pesos): 80-100 per semester.

Language of Instruction: English.

Degrees and Diplomas: Bachelor of–Arts, A.B.; Science, B.S.; Science in Agriculture, B.S.A.; Science in Agricultural Education; B.S.A.E.; Science in Public Administration, B.S.P.A.; Science in Business Administration, B.S.B.A.; Science in Community Development, B.S.C.D.; Science in Elementary Education, B.S.E.Ed.; Science in Education, B.S.E.; Science in Fisheries, B.S.Fisheries, 4 yrs; Science in Chemical Engineering, B.S.Ch.E.; Science in Civil Engineering, B.S.C.E.; Science in Electrical Engineering, B.S.E.E.; Science in Mechanical Engineering, B.S.M.E.; Science in Agricultural Engineering, B.S.A.E.; Science in Geophysical Engineering, B.S.G.E.; 5 yrs. Diploma in–Agricultural Technology; Fisheries Technology, 2 yrs; Engineering Technology, 3 yrs. Bachelor of Laws, Ll.B., 4 yrs after first degree. Master of–Arts in Education; Science in Biology; Arts in Philippine Studies; School Administration; Arts in Teaching; Public Administration. Doctor of Philosophy in Philippine Studies. Honorary Degree of Doctor of Laws.

Library: c. 102,800 vols.

Special Facilities (Museums, etc.): Aga Khan Museum; Natural Science Museum.

Publications: Mindanao Journal; Arts and Science Journal; Development Administration Journal; Fisheries and Aquaculture Journal.

Press or Publishing House: University Publishing House.

Academic Staff, 1986-87: 676

Student Enrolment, 1986-87:

	Men	Women	Total
Of the country	2854	3318	6172
Of other countries	7	–	7
Total	2861	3318	6179

5693 **ILIGAN INSTITUTE OF TECHNOLOGY**

Tibanga, Iligan City 8801

Telephone: 2 0800/1; 20484/5

Chancellor: Camar A. Umpa (1988-)

C. of Engineering
Dean: Eliseo Villanueva; *staff* 22 (18)
C. of Engineering Technology
Director: Marcelo Salazar
C. of Arts and Social Sciences
Dean: Rhodora Englis; *staff* 90 (5)
C. of Science and Mathematics
Dean: Harry Carpio; *staff* 71 (5)
S. of Management Technology
S. of Development Management (Business Administration)
C. of Education (including Physical Education)
Head: Eduardo Arugay; *staff* 54
S. of Physical Education
S. of Graduate Studies
Head: Edelyn Martinez: *staff* – (21)
C. for Instructional Staff Development
C. of Business Administration (including Accountancy and Economics)
Dean: Salvacion Capistiano; *staff* 35
Coordination Ce. for Research and Development
Head: Severino Jervacio
D. of Ceramics
Also high school.

Founded 1946 as high school, became technical school 1957 and acquired present title 1968. Attached to Mindanao State University. Financially supported by the government. Governing body: the Board of Regents.

Academic Year: June to March (June-October; November-March).

Admission Requirements: Graduation from high school and entrance examination.

Fees (Pesos): 10-30 per unit

Language of Instruction: English.

Degrees and Diplomas: Bachelor of–Arts; Science in Engineering; Science in Business Administration; Science in Industrial Education; Science in Mathematics, Physics and Biology; Science in Chemistry; Physical Education, 4-5 yrs. Master in–Business Administration; Library Science; Teaching Technology; Arts in Teaching, a further 2 yrs. Diplomas in–Engineering Technology; Secretarial Sciences.

Libraries: Central Library, *c.* 17,000 vols; Engineering, *c.* 4000; Development Management, *c.* 1300.

Academic Staff: c. 530.

Student Enrolment: c. 6700.

5694 ***PAMANTASAN NG LUNGSOD NG MAYNILA**

University of the City of Manila

Intramuros, Manila

Telephone: 40-76-21

President: Jose D. Villanueva (1990-)

Vice-President for Administration: Edelita F. Reyes

C. of Business Administration

Dean: Marcelo V. Fernandez; *staff* 22 (21)

C. of Arts and Sciences

Dean: Rebecca R. Abid; *staff* 58 (41)

C. of Engineering and Technology

Dean: Felix F. Aspiras; *staff* 31 (10)

C. of Nursing

Dean: Mary Vita V. Jackson; *staff* 9 (21)

C. of Education

Dean: Corazon T. Veridiano; *staff* 6 (4)

C. of Law

Dean: Raul I. Goco; *staff* 1 (7)

C. of Medicine

Dean: Eustaquia T. Acevedo; *staff* 39 (29)

Graduate S.

Dean: Virsely M. de la Cruz

Founded 1967, acquired university status 1976. Responsible to the authorities of the City of Manila. Governing body: the Board of Regents.

Arrangements for co-operation with: University of Nebraska; University of Indonesia.

Academic Year: June to March (June-October; November-March).

Admission Requirements: Graduation from high school and entrance examination.

Fees (Pesos): 20-100 per unit.

Languages of Instruction: English and Pilipino.

Degrees and Diplomas: Associate in–Accountancy; Marketing; Banking; Computer Science; Secretarial Studies, 2 yrs. Bachelor of–Arts in Psychology; Mass Communication; Management and Social Work; Science in–Chemistry; Mathematics; Zoology; Business Administration; Education; Computer Science; Nursing, 4 yrs; Engineering (various fields), 5 yrs. Master of-Arts; Science; Engineering; Engineering Management; Business Administration, a further 2 yrs. Doctor of–Education; Business Administration; Medicine, 3-4 yrs after Master.

Library: c. 36,257 vols.

Publications: PLM Review (3 times a year); Ang Pamantasan (bimonthly); Education Newsletter (biannually); Engineering Newsletter (quarterly).

Academic Staff, 1989-90:

Rank	Full-time	Part-time
Professors	6	–
Associate Professors	12	–
Lecturers	–	297
Assistants	21	–
Instructors	133	–
B—		
Total	171	297

Student Enrolment, 1989-90:

	Men	Women	Total
Of the country	2402	4506	6908

5695 **PANGASINAN STATE UNIVERSITY**

Lingayen, Pangasinan 0706

Telephone: 252

President: Rufino O. Eslao

Administrative Officer: Gil A. Madrid

C. of Education

Dean: Apolinario O. Bautista; *staff* 162

C. of Arts, Sciences and Technology

Dean: Victoriano E. Estira; *staff* 123

C. of Agriculture

Dean: Lydio E. Calonge; *staff* 64

C. of Agriculture (San Carlos City)

Dean: Rodolfo Tamondong; *staff* 50

C. of Agriculture (Infanta)

Dean: Antonio Repollo; *staff* 50

C. of Arts and Technology

Dean: Ester C. Lomboy; *staff* 25

C. of Fisheries

Dean: Porferio L. Basilio; *staff* 50

C. of Engineering

Dean: Adelina M. Dingle; *staff* 49

Graduate S.

Dean: Alfredo F. Aquino; *staff* 31

Fisheries Research Station

Dean: Porferio Basilio; *staff* 10

Also elementary and high schools.

Founded 1922 as normal school, became college 1969 and university 1978, incorporating 7 previously existing institutions. A State institution receiving financial support from the government. Governing body: the Board of Regents of which the Secretary of Education, Culture and Sports is Chairman. Some residential facilities for academic staff and students.

Academic Year: June to April (June-October; October-April).

Admission Requirements: Graduation from high school and entrance examination.

Fees (Pesos): 30-60 per unit.

Languages of Instruction: English and Pilipino.

Degrees and Diplomas: Bachelor of Science in–Education, B.S.E.; Elementary Education, B.E.Ed.; Mathematics, B.S.Math.; Food and Nutrition, B.S.F.N.; Agriculture, B.S.A.; Industrial Education, B.S.I.E.; Industrial Technology, B.S.I.T.; Fisheries Education,B.S.F.E.; Fisheries Management, B.S.F; Nutrition and Dietetics; Engineering, various fields. Master of–Education; Development Management; Science, a further 2 yrs.

Library: c. 27,500.

Publications: Academic Review (biannually); Journal of Education Research (biannually).

Academic Staff, 1989-90:

Rank	Full-time
Professors	29
Associate Professors	43
Assistant Professors	102
Instructors	198
Total	372

Student Enrolment, 1989-90:

	Men	Women	Total
Of the country	1759	2962	4541

5696 ***POLITEKNIKONG UNIBERSIDAD NG PILIPINAS**

Polytechnic University of the Philippines

Anonas St., Sta. Mesa, Manila

Cables: Pup Manila

Telephone: 616775-616779

President: Nemesio E. Prudente (1986-)

Vice President for Administration: Flora G. Gonzalez

C. of Accountancy

Dean: Armando Garcia; *staff* 61 (108)

C. of Business

Dean: Julita Gomez; *staff* 6 (48)

C. of Arts and Sciences

Dean: Paz Abad; *staff* 119 (129)

C. of Economics and Politics

Chairman: Teresita Bernardino; *staff* 23 (29)

C. of Computer Management and Information Technology

Dean: Ofelia Caragüe; *staff* 15 (52)

C. of Engineering

Dean: Alberto C. Canete; *staff* 36 (61)

C. of Language and Mass Communication

Dean: Rustica Carpio; *staff* 87 (43)

College of Hotel and Restaurant Management, Food Science and Technology

Dean: Nora Herrera; *staff* 12 (22)

C. of Physical Education and Sports

Chairman: Aida Mangabat; *staff* 43 (31)

C. of Office Administration and Business Teacher Education
Dean: Soledad Villena; *staff* 122 (40)
Branches at Bataan, Lopez, Unisan and Maragondon. Also high school.

The school was founded 1904 as the Manila Business School under the Manila City School system organized by theAmerican Colonial Government in the Philippines. Acquired present title 1977. Governing body: the Board of Regents of which the Minister of Education, Culture and Sports is Chairman.

Academic Year: June to March (June-October; November-March).

Admission Requirements: Graduation from high school and entrance examination.

Fees (Pesos): Tuition, 252-324 (12 per unit).

Language of Instruction: English.

Degrees and Diplomas: Bachelor of Science in Mathematics, B.S.M.; Human Behavior Technology, B.H.B.T.; Industrial Psychology, B.I.P.; Applied Statistics, B.A.S.; Accounting, B.A.; Science in Applied Sociology, B.S.A.S.; Business Management, B.B.M.; Marketing, Management, Advertising, P.R.; Enterpreuneurial Management, B.E.M.; Tourism, B.T.; Information Technology, B.I.T.; Computer Data Processing Management, B.C.D.P.M.; Arts in Political Economy, A.B.P.E.; International Trade Management, B.I.T.M.; Applied Economics, B.A.E.; Banking and Finance, B.B.F.; Arts in Public Administration, A.B.P.A.; Arts in Political Science, A.B.P.S.; Hotel and Restaurant Management, B.H.R.M.; Science in Nutrition and Dietetics, B.S.N.D.; Science in Food Technology, B.S.F.T.; Arts in English, A.B.E.; Business Journalism, B.B.U.J.; Physical Education, 4 yrs;Science in–Enginering, various fields; Architecture, B.S.Arch., 5 yrs. Master. Doctor.

Library: Central Library, 54,447 vols.

Publications: Graduate School Forum; Journal.

Press or Publishing House: University Press.

Academic Staff, 1989-90:

Rank	Full-time	Part-time
Professors	21	22
Associate Professors/Associate Lecturers	77	17
Assistant Professors/Assistant Lecturers	136	34
Instructors	288	430
Special Lecturers	–	12
Total	522	1015

Student Enrolment, 1989-90:

	Men	Women	Total
Of the country	13,732	23,152	36,884

5697 ***PAMANTASANG PANTEKNOLOHIYA NG PILIPINAS**

Technological University of the Philippines

Ayala Boulevard corner San Marcelino Street, Ermita, Manila 2801

Telephone: 58-63-55; 59-30-05; 521-40-63

President: Jose R. Vergara (1978-)

Administrative Officer: Erlinda F. Manalang

C. of Arts and Sciences
Dean: Vilam C. Bati; *staff* 88 (28)
C. of Industrial Education
Dean: Teofilo A. Sison; *staff* 43 (3)
C. of Architecture and Fine Arts
Dean: Diosdado C. Nicdao; *staff* 17 (17)
C. of Industrial Technology
Dean: Rodolfo Y. Baking; *staff* 72 (11)
C. of Engineering
Dean: Perla S. Roxas; *staff* 11 (3)
Graduate S.
Dean: Iluminada Galang Espino; *staff* 8 (20)
Also high school.

Founded 1901 as school, became College of Arts and Trades 1959. Reorganized as a university 1978 to include the Manila Technician Institute, Taguig, Bocolod Technician Institute, Talisay, and Iligan Institute of Technology, and 10 Regional Manpower Training Centres. Financed partly by the State and partly from tuition fees. Governing body: the Board of Regents of which the Minister of Education, Culture and Sports is Chairman. The President is appointed by President of the Philippines upon recommendation of the Board of Regents.

Academic Year: June to March (June-October; November-March).

Admission Requirements: Graduation from high school and entrance examination.

Fees (Pesos): 120; Graduate School, 20 per unit.

Language of Instruction: English.

Degrees and Diplomas: Bachelor of Science in–Fine Arts; Industrial Education, B.S.I.E., 4 yrs; Engineering, various fields; Architecture, 5 yrs. Master of Arts in–Industrial Education, M.A.I.E.; Teaching, M.A.T., a further 2 yrs. Doctor of Education Management. Diploma of Technician, 3 yrs.

Library: Central Library, 31,023 vols.

Publication: Artisan (triannual).

Press or Publishing House: University Press.

Academic Staff, 1986-87:

Rank	Full-time
Professors	13
Associate Professors	30
Assistant Professors	62
Instructors	191
Assistant Instructors	8
Total	304

Student Enrolment, 1986-87: 2065.

5698 **PAMANTASAN NG SILANGANING PILIPINAS**

University of Eastern Philippines

University Town, Catarman, Northern Samar

President: Leonor A. Ong Sotto

Registrar: Rogelio L. Noble

C. of Agriculture (including Forestry and Fisheries)
Dean: Norman T. Diaz; *staff* 26
C. of Arts and Sciences (including Community Development and Zoology)
Dean: Alma C. Manaog; *staff* 34
C. of Business Administration
Dean: Gerardo C. Delorino; *staff* 16 (2)
C. of Engineering
Dean: Rosendo Cinco; *staff* 18
C. of Education
Dean: Nilo E. Colinares; *staff* 33
C. of Veterinary Medicine
Dean: Jaime Jumadiao; *staff* 8
Graduate S.
Dean: Leonor A. Ong Sotto; *staff* 2 (45)
Also elementary and high schools.

Founded 1918 as Catarman Farm School supported by municipal and provincial funds of the Province of Samar. Became Catarman Agricultural School 1951, supported by national and provincial funds and then Catarman National Agricultural High School supported entirely by the national government. Became Samar Institute of Technology 1957 and a university 1964. Governing body: the Board of Regents of which the Secretary of Education, Culture and Sports is Chairman. Some residential facilities for academic staff and students.

Academic Year: July to April (July-November; November-April).

Admission Requirements: Graduation from high school or foreign equivalent, and entrance examination.

Fees (Pesos): 200-400 per semester.

Languages of Instruction: English and Pilipino.

Degrees and Diplomas: Associate in Secretarial Science, 2 yrs. Bachelor of–Arts, A.B.; Science in Agriculture, B.S.A.; Science in Agricultural Education, B.S.A.Ed.; Science in Industrial Arts, B.S.I.A.; Science in Industrial Education, B.S.I.E.; Science in Fisheries, B.S.Fish.; Science in Forestry, B.S.Forest.; Science in Zoology, B.S.Zoo.; Science in Chemistry, B.S.Chem.; Science in Community Development, B.S.C.D.; Science in Education, B.S.E.; Science in Elementary Education, B.S.E.Ed.; Science in Elementary Education and Home Economics, B.S.E.Ed.-H.E.; Science in Home Economics, B.S.H.E..; Science in Business Administration, B.S.B.A., 4 yrs; Science in Agricultural Engineering, B.S.A.E.; Science in Mechanical Engineering, B.S.M.E., 5 yrs. Master of–Arts in Education; Arts in Economics; Arts in Teaching Agriculture; Science in Home Economics Education. Doctor of Veterinary Medicine, 6 yrs.

Library: Central Library, *c.* 14,000.

Academic Staff, 1990: 178.

Student Enrolment, 1990:

	Men	Women	Total
Of the country	1275	1876	3151

5699 **PAMANTASAN NG HILAGANG PILIPINAS**
University of Northern Philippines
Tanay, Ilocos Sur 0401
Telephone: 30-93

C. of Arts and Sciences
C. of Nursing
C. of Engineering
C. of Architecture
I. of Fine Arts
C. of Criminology
C. of Teacher Education
C. of Business Administration
Graduate S.
I. of Social Work
I. of Technical Education and Cottage Industries Development
Also elementary and high schools.

Founded 1910 as trade school, became Northern Luzon School of Arts and Trades 1951, acquired present status and title 1965. Governing body: the Board of Regents, of which the Minister of Education, Culture and Sports is Chairman. Residential facilities for women students.

Academic Year: June to March (June-October; November-March).

Admission Requirements: Graduation from high school or recognized foreign equivalent, and entrance examination.

Languages of Instruction: English, Pilipino, and Ilocano.

Degrees and Diplomas: Associate in–Commercial Arts; Architectural Drafting; Midwifery, 2 yrs; Secretarial Science, A.S.S., 3 yrs. Bachelor of–Arts, B.A.; Fine Arts; Science in Criminology; Science in Industrial Education, B.S.I.E.; Science in Physics, B.S.P.; Science in Chemistry; Science in Biology; Science in Mathematics, B.S.M.; Science in Elementary Education, B.S.E.E.; Science in Business Administration, B.S.B.A.; Science in Nursing, B.S.N.; Science in Social Work, B.S.S.W., 4 yrs; Science in Civil Engineering, B.S.C.E.; Science in Architecture, B.S.Arch.; Sanitary Engineering, B.S.S.E., 5 yrs. Master of–Teaching Elementary Agriculture, M.A.T.E.A; Arts in–Teaching,M.A.T.; Education, M.A.Ed.; Public Administration, M.P.A. Doctor of Education, Ed.D.

Libraries: Central Library, *c.* 9000 vols; Graduate School, *c.* 900.

Special Facilities (Museums, etc.): Ilocano Museum.

Publications: Tandem (quarterly); New Vision (biannually).

Academic Staff: c. 300.

Student Enrolment: c. 6300.

5700 ***UNIBERSIDAD NG PILIPINAS**
University of the Philippines
Diliman, Quezon City 3004
Cables: Univerphil
Telex: 2231 UP DIL PU
Telephone: 96-15-72
President: Jose Abueva
Executive Vice-President: Irene R. Cortés

Main Campus, Diliman
C. of Architecture
Dean: Geronimo V. Manahan
C. of Arts and Sciences
Dean: Pablo K. Botor Sr.
C. of Business Administration
Dean: Magdaleno B. Albarracin, Jr.
C. of Education
Dean: Julieta Savellano
C. of Engineering
Dean: Ruben Garcia
C. of Fine Arts
Dean: Napoleon V. Abueva
C. of Science
Dean: Roger R. Posadas
C. of Social Sciences and Philosophy
Dean: Leslie E. Bauzon
C. of Home Economics
Dean: Estrella F. Alabastro
C. of Law
Dean: Bartolome S. Carale
C. of Music
Dean: Ramon P. Santos
C. of Public Administration
Officer-in-charge: Gabriel U. Iglesias
Asian Ce.
Dean: Ajit Singh Rye
Asian I. of Tourism
Dean: Jose P. Mananzan
Ce. for Statistics
Dean: Walfredo R. Javier
S. of Economics
Dean: José Encarnación, Jr.
I. of Industrial Relations
Dean: Jose C. Gatchalian
I. of Urban and Regional Planning
Dean: Leandro A. Viloria
I. of Islamic Studies
Dean: Wadjc K. Esmula
I. of Library Science
Dean: Rosa M. Vallejo
I. of Mass Communication
Dean: Georgina R. Encanto
I. of Population Studies
Dean: Zelda Z. Zablan
I. of Social Work and Community Development
Dean: Sylvia H. Guerrero
I. of Physical Education and Sports
Dean: Cynthia V. Abad Santos
Graduate S.
Head: Emerenciana Y. Arcellana
Campus at Los Baños
C. of Agriculture
Dean: Ruben Villareal
C. of Arts and Sciences
Dean: Edelwina C. Legaspi
C. of Development Economics and Management
Dean: Tirso B. Paris
C. of Forestry
Dean: Celso B. Lantican
C. of Veterinary Medicine
Dean: Rodolfo S. Pereyra
I. of Plant Breeding
Dean: Eufemio T. Rasco
I. of Agricultural Engineering and Technology
Dean: Ernesto P. Lozada
I. of Human Ecology
Director: Josefa S. Eusebio
Graduate S.
Dean: Dolores A. Ramirez
Health Sciences Ce. (Manila)
Dean: Manuel G. Roxas
Campus at Manila
C. of Dentistry
Dean: Aurelio B. Ramos
C. of Medicine
Dean: Alberto G. Romualdez
C. of Nursing
Dean: Aurora S. Yapchiongco
C. of Pharmacy
Dean: Amorita V. Castillo
C. of Arts and Sciences
Dean: Benjamin V. Lozare
I. of Public Health
Dean: Amanda V. Valenzuela
S. of Allied Medical Professions
Director: Guillermo R. Damian
Campus in the Visayas
C. of Arts and Sciences (Iloilo)
Dean: Lourdes De Castro
C. of Fisheries (Miagao)
Dean: Jose A. Carreon
S. of Development Management
Dean: Tomas A. Sajo
Also Regional Units in: Baguio City, Cebu City, Clark Air Base, and Tacloban City. Also 48 research and extension service centres and programmes.

Founded 1908 by Act of the National Legislature as a State institution incorporating Medical School established 1905. The university has 4 autonomous campuses. Responsible to the Ministry of Education, Culture and Sportsand is a statutory body financed 60% by the government but operating autonomously. Governing bodies: the Board of Regents, of 12 members, with the Minister of Education, Culture and Sports as Chairman, and including the Chairmen of the Committees on Education of the

Senate and the House of Representatives, the President of the University and the Director of Public Schools and 7 nominated members; the University Council, composed of the President of the University and all academic staff holding rank of professor or associate or assistant professor. Some residential facilities for academic staff and students.

Arrangements for co-operation with the Universities of: Aix-Marseilles II and III; Paris III; McGill; Michigan State; Illinois; Queensland; Guam; Kyoto. Obihiro University of Stockraising; Ecole des hautes Etudes en Sciences sociales, Paris; Institut national des Langues et Civilisations orientales, Paris.

Academic Year: June to March (June-October; November-March).

Admission Requirements: Graduation from high school recognized by Department of Education and entrance examination.

Degrees and Diplomas: Bachelor of–Fine Arts, B.F.A.; Science in Fisheries, B.S.Fish.; Science in Occupational Therapy, B.S.O.T.; Science in Physical Therapy, B.S.P.T.; Science in Nursing, B.S.N.; Science in Business Administration, B.S.B.A.; Science in Education, B.S.E.; Science in Elementary Education, B.S.E.Ed.; Science in Home Economics, B.S.H.E.; Science in Forestry, B.S.F.; Science in Community Development; Arts, A.B.; Science, B.S.; Science in Agriculture, B.S.A.; Science in Chemistry, B.S.Chem.; Science in Geology, B.S.Geol.; Science in Social Work, B.S.S.W.; Library Science, B.L.S.; Science in Statistics, B.S.Stat.; Science in Tourism, B.S.T.; Science in Architecture, B.S. Arch.; Science in Food Technology, B.S.F.T.; Science in Pharmacy, B.S.Phar.; Science in Industrial Pharmacy, B.S.Ind.Phar.; Science in Agricultural Engineering, B.S.Ag.E.; Science in Chemical Engineering, B.S.Ch.E.; Science in Civil Engineering, B.S.C.E.; Science in Electrical Engineering, B.S.E.E.; Science in Geodetic Engineering, B.S.G.E.;Science in Industrial Engineering, B.S.I.E.; Science in Mechanical Engineering, B.S.M.E.; Science in Applied Mathematics, B.S.A.M.; Science in Metallurgical Engineering, B.S.Met.E.; Science in Mining Engineering, E.M., 4-5 yrs. Law, a further 4 yrs. Master of–Arts, M.A.; Arts in Teaching, M.A.T.; Education, M.E.; Science, M.S.; Music, M.M.; Business Administration, M.S.B.A.; Engineering, M.E.; Library Science; Public Administration, M.S.P.A.; Fine Arts; Home Economics, M.S.H.E.; Social Work, M.S.S.W.; Hospital Administration M.S.H.A.; Forestry; Science in Forestry; Music; Nursing; Public Administration; Public Health Engineering, M.S.P.H.; Statistics; Laws, LL.M., a further 2 yrs. Doctor of–Veterinary Medicine D.V.M.; Dental Medicine, D.D.M.; Medicine, M.D, 4-6 yrs after first degree; Philosophy, Ph.D. in–Nursing; Economics; Agricultural Economics; Education, Ed.D.; Public Administration; Business Administration; Laws, honoris causa. Teacher's Certificate in Agricultural Education. Certificate in various fields of Administration and Management.

Libraries: Central Library, *c.* 800,000 vols; Los Baños, *c.* 200,000.

Publications: Asian Studies (3 times a year); Philippine Planning Journal (biannually); The Diliman Review (quarterly); Philippine Social Sciences and Humanities Review (quarterly); Natural and Applied Science Bulletin (quarterly); Journal of Philippine Librarianship (biannually); Education Quarterly (quarterly); AIT Tourism Journal (triannually); Home Economics Journal (biannually); Law and Development (annually) Musika Journal (annually); Philippine Engineering Journal (quarterly); Journal of Communication Studies (annually); Journal of Industrial Relations (biannually); Review of Business and Economics (quarterly); The Pterocarpus Journal (biannually); Philippine Journal of Veterinary Medicine (biannually); Philippine Journal of Public Administration (quarterly); Index to Philippine Periodicals (biannually); The Acta Medica Philippina Journal (quarterly); Small Industry Journal (quarterly); Philippine Law Journal (quarterly); Agriculture at Los Baños; UP Gazette (monthly); UP Newsletter (weekly); Carillon (monthly); Philippine Collegian (weekly).

Press or Publishing House: University of the Philippines Press.

Academic Staff: *c.* 2700 (700).

Student Enrolment: *c.* 29,000.

5701 **UNIVERSITY OF SOUTHEASTERN PHILIPPINES**

Barrio Obrero, Davao City
Telephone: 7-86-53
President: Rufino O. Eslao (1982-)
Registrar: Mauro Raras

C. of Engineering
C. of Education
C. of Engineering and Technology
C. of Industrial Technology
C. of Arts and Sciences
C. of Agriculture
C. of Agribusiness
C. of Forestry
Graduate S.
C. of Statistics
Extension D.

Founded 1979. A State institution. Governing body: the Board of Regents, comprising 4 members and of which the Minister of Education, Culture and Sports is Chairman.

Academic Year: June to March (June-October; November-March).

Admission Requirements: Graduation from high school and entrance examination.

Languages of Instruction: English and Pilipino.

Degrees and Diplomas: Bachelor of–Science in–Agricultural Technology; Forestry; Agriculture; Agricultural Education; Agricultural Engineering; Mathematics; Statistics; Biology; Community Development; Public Administration; Agricultural Economics; Agri-business; Education; Elementary Education; Industrial Education; Industrial Technology; Arts, 4 yrs; Civil Engineering; Electrical Engineering; Mechanical Engineering, 5 yrs. Master of–Public Administration; Business Administration; Human Settlement; Agri-business; Social Work; Arts in–Education; Mathematics; Educational Science, Agricultural Economics.

Library: College libraries, *c.* 10,400 vols.

Publications: The Fruitbowl (biannually); the Seedbed (quarterly).

Academic Staff: *c.* 240.

Student Enrolment: *c.* 3400.

5702 **UNIVERSITY OF SOUTHERN MINDANAO**

Kabacan, North Cotabato 9311
Cables: Kabacan, North Cot.
President: Jaman S. Imlan (1984-90)
Administrative Officer: Zacarias S. Dulay

C. of Agriculture (including Horticulture, Veterinary Medicine and Animal Husbandry)
C. of Agribusiness
C. of Arts and Sciences
C. of Education
C. of Engineering
C. of Home Ecological Sciences (including Nutrition)
C. of Industrial Technology
C. of Technical Sciences
Regional Training Ce. for Rural Development

Branches at Arakan and Buluan. Also elementary school.

Founded 1952 as Institute of Technology, became university 1978. A State institution. Governing body: the Board of Regents of 8 members and of which the Minister of Education, Culture and Sports is Chairman. Someresidential facilities for academic staff and students.

Academic Year: June to March (June-October; November-March).

Admission Requirements: Graduation from high school and entrance examination.

Languages of Instruction: English and Pilipino.

Degrees and Diplomas: Bachelor of Science in–Agriculture, B.S.A.; Biology, B.S.Bio.; Chemistry, B.S.Chem.; Agricultural Education, B.S.Ag.Ed.; Agricultural Home Economics, B.S.A.H.E.; Elementary Education, B.S.E.Ed.; Foods and Nutrition, B.S.F.N.; Home Economics, B.S.H.E.; Industrial Education, B.S.I.E.; Industrial Arts, B.S.I.A.; Industrial Technology, B.S.I.T.; Nutrition and Dietetics, B.S.N.D.; Development Communication, B.S.C.D.; Agricultural Business, B.S.A.B.; Agricultural Economics, B.S.Ag.Econ.; Home Extension, B.S.H.E, 4 yrs; Agricultural Engineering, B.S.Ag.Eng.; Civil Engineering, B.S.C.E., 5 yrs. Veterinary Medicine, D.V.M., 6 yrs.

Library: Central Library, *c.* 23,000 vols.

Special Facilities (Museums, etc.): USM Museum.

Publications: USMARC Monitor (Quarterly); College of Education-Future; Teachers Club News Letter; College of Agriculture News Letter.

Academic Staff: *c.* 300.

Student Enrolment: *c.* 3100.

5703 **WEST VISAYAS STATE UNIVERSITY**

Iloilo City

Agriculture
Education
Nursing
Medicine
Forestry
Arts

Founded 1924. A State institution.

5704 **PAMPAMAHALAANG PAMANTASAN NG KANLURANG MINDANAO**
Western Mindanao State University
Baliwasan, Zamboanga City
Telephone: 34-86

C. of Agriculture (including Agri-Business)
Dean: Jawali K. Mandain; *staff* 25 (1)
C. of Arts and Sciences (including Political Science, Home Economics)
Dean: Esmeraluna L. Pide; *staff* 86
C. of Home Economics and Nutrition
Dean: Concepcion L. Tubaran; *staff* 10 (2)
C. of Education
Dean: Julieta Y. Tabacug; *staff* 75
C. of Engineering (including Architecture)
Dean: Godofredo S. Estepha; *staff* 60
C. of Science and Mathematics
Dean: Linda S. Dimaguila; *staff* 70 (2)
C. of Forestry
Dean: Alito R. Baguinat; *staff* 88
C. of Law
Dean: Felisberto C. Gonzales; *staff* 4 (10)
C. of Nursing
Dean: Teodorica T. Calderon; *staff* 18
C. of Social Work
Dean: Cecilia L. Bernal; *staff* 5 (2)
Graduate S.
Dean: Grace J. Rebellos; *staff* 6 (40)
Research Ce.
Dean: Orlando B. Cuartocruz; *staff* 5 (4)

Founded 1918 as secondary school. Became teacher training school 1955 and college 1961. Acquired present status and title 1978. An autonomous State institution financed by the government. Governing body: the Board of Regents of which the Secretary of Education, Culture and Sports is Chairman. Residential facilities for students.

Academic Year: June to March (June-October; November-March; April-May).

Admission Requirements: Graduation from high school and entrance examination.

Degrees and Diplomas: Bachelor of–Arts, A.B.; Science in Social Work, B.S.S.W.; Science in Nursing, B.S.N.; Science in Forestry, B.S.F.; Science in Agriculture, B.S.A.; Science in Home Economics, B.S.H.E.; Science in Education, B.S.E.; Science in Elementary Education, B.S.E.Ed.; Science in Nutrition and Dietetics, B.S.N.D., 4 yrs; Science in Chemistry, B.S. Chem.; Science in Electrical Engineering, B.S.E.E.; Science in Mechanical Engineering, B.S.M.E.; Science in Civil Engineering, B.S.C.E.; Science in Architecture, B.S.Arch., 5 yrs. Bachelor of Laws, Ll.B., 4 yrs after first degree. Master of–Arts in Education; Education; Public Administration, a further 2-5 yrs. Doctor of Education, Ed.D., 3-7 yrs after Master.

Library: Central Library, *c.* 36,372 vols.

Special Facilities (Museums, etc.): Ethnological Museum.

Publications: Research Journal; Curriculum Bulletin (biannually).

Academic Staff, 1988-89:

	Full-time	Part-time
Professors	12	5
Associate Professors	55	36
Assistant Professors	95	35
Instructors	233	16
Total	395	92

Student Enrolment, 1988-89:

	Men	Women	Total
Of the country	9359	13,788	23,147*

*Also 734 external students.

Private Institutions

5705 **ADAMSON UNIVERSITY**
900 San Marcelino Street, Ermita, Manila 1000
Telephone: 502-011
President: Rolando dela Goza, C.M. (1986-89)
Registrar: Benito Resurreccion

C. of Liberal Arts and Science
Dean: Lourdes Peralta; *staff* 43 (44)
C. of Engineering
Dean: Peter Ureta; *staff* 40 (59)
C. of Education
Dean: Domingo Bendero; *staff* – (4)
C. of Commerce and Business Administration
Dean: Jose Ma. Quintos; *staff* 15 (28)
C. of Pharmacy
Dean: Eladio M. Tinio; *staff* 3 (5)
C. of Law
Dean: Ponciano Subido; *staff* – (4)
C. of Sciences
Dean: Adria Jocano; *staff* 62
Graduate S. of Education and Chemistry
Dean: Rosario Alberto; *staff* – (16)
C. of Architecture
Dean: Victoriano Aviguetero; *staff* 8 (4)
I. for Continuing and Professional Development
Director: Rosario Alberto

Also elementary school and high schools.

Founded 1932 as Adamson School of Industrial Chemistry by Dr. George Lucas Adamson, attained university status 1941. A private institution operated under the supervision of the Department of Education, Culture and Sports. Governing bodies: the Board of Trustees, comprising 10 members; the Executive Committee; the Academic Council. Residential facilities for academic staff.

Academic Year: June to March (June-October; November-March).

Admission Requirements: Graduation from high school or foreign qualifications accredited by the Bureau of Private Schools, and entrance examination.

Fees (Pesos): 611.08-747.25 per 10 units; Graduate School, 725.70-1001.30

Language of Instruction: English.

Degrees and Diplomas: Bachelor of–Arts, A.B.; Economics, A.B.Eco.; English, A.B.Eng.; Philosophy, A.B.Philo.; Political Science, A.B.Pol.Sci.; Science, B.S.; Biology, B.S.Biol.; Chemistry, B.S.Ch.; Mathematics, B.S.Math.; Psychology, B.S.Psycho.; Secondary Education, B.S.Ed.; Elementary Education, B.S.E.Ed.; Architecture, B.S.Arch.; Commerce and Business Administration, B.S.C.; Accounting, B.S.C.Acctg.; Banking and Finance, B.S. Bkg.&Fin.; Economics, B.S.C.Eco.; Management, B.S.C.Mgt.; Secretarial Administration, B.S.S.A.; Office Management, B.S.S.A. Off.Mgt.; Computer Secretarial Education, B.S.S.A.C.S.E.; Chemical Engineering, B.S.Ch.E.; Civil Engineering, B.S.C.E.; Ceramics Engineering, B.S.Cer.E.; Computer Engineering, B.S.Cp.E.; Electrical Engineering, B.S.E. Electronics & Communications Engineering, B.S.E.C.E.; Geology, B.S.Geol.; Industrial Engineering, B.S.I.E.; Mechanical Engineering, B.S.M.E.; Mining Engineering, B.S.E.M.; Pharmacy, B.S.Pharm., 4-5 yrs. Bachelor of Laws, Ll.B., 4 yrs after first degree. Master of–Arts in Education; Science in–Chemistry, M.S.Chem.; Pharmacy, M.S.Pharm.; Management Engineering, M.S.Man.E.; Business Administration, M.B.A., 2 further yrs. Doctor of Philosophy in–Education; Management. Also Diplomas in–Pharmacy Aide; Junior Secretarial, Jr.Sec.; Junior Computer Secretarial, Jr.Com.Sec.

Library: 69,628 vols.

Publications: Adamson Chronicle (monthly); Vincere (monthly); Sophia (quarterly report of academic research and opinion).

Academic Staff, 1989-90:

Rank	Full-time	Part-time
Professors	1	11
Associate Professors	6	14
Assistant Professors	67	28
Instructors	93	64
Assistant Instructors	95	80
Total	262	197

Student Enrolment, 1989-90:

	Men	Women	Total
Of the country	10,616	6564	17,180
Of other countries	332	31	363
Total	10,948	6595	17,543

5706 **ANGELES UNIVERSITY FOUNDATION**
MacArthur Highway, Angeles City 2017
Telephone: 2958; 3608
President: Emmanuel Y. Angeles (1975-)

C. of Medicine
Dean: Rodolfo C. Dimayuga; *staff* 40 (87)
C. of Nursing
Dean: Marietta H. Gaddi; *staff* 22 (1)

C. of Civil Engineering
Dean: Rufo M. Guzman; *staff* 5 (16)
C. of Criminology
Dean: Jose B. Manivang; *staff* 4 (14)
C. of Business and Economics
Dean: Romeo C. Mascardo; *staff* 20 (17)
C. of Arts and Sciences
Dean: Corazon D. Sampang; *staff* 35 (22)
C. of Education
Dean: Milagros M. Laxamana; *staff* 6 (8)
Graduate S.
Director: Sancho B. Cuyugan; *staff* 12 (5)
S. for Secretarial Studies
Director (Acting): Angelita M. Canlas; *staff* 5 (4)
Also elementary and high schools.

Founded 1962 as Angeles City Institute of Technology, became university 1971 and University Foundation 1977. Formally inaugurated as Catholic university 1978. A private institution financed by students' fees and donations. Governing bodies: the Board of Trustees; the University Council. Residential facilities for students of College of Nursing.

Academic Year: June to March (June-October; November-March).

Admission Requirements: Graduation from high school and entrance examination.

Fees (Pesos): 200-250.

Languages of Instruction: English and Pilipino.

Degrees and Diplomas: Bachelor of–Arts, A.B.; Science in Civil Engineering, B.S.C.E.; Science in Commerce, B.S.C.; Science in Education, B.S.E.; Science in Elementary Education, B.S.E.Ed.; Science in Nursing, B.S.N.; Science in Secretarial Administration; Science in Psychology; Science in Mathematics; Science in Criminology; Science in Foreign Service, 4-5 yrs. Master of–Arts in Education, M.A.Ed.; Arts in Teaching, M.A.T.; Business Administration, M.B.A.;Science in Mathematics. Doctor of Philosophy, Ph.D., in Educational Administration; Medicine.

Libraries: Central Library, 50,872 vols; Graduate School, 4020.

Publications: Bulletin; Pioneer; Journal.

Academic Staff, 1986-87: 194 (172).

Student Enrolment, 1986-87:

	Men	Women	Total
Of the country	3440	4084	7524
Of other countries	83	58	141
Total	3523	4142	7665

5707 ***AQUINAS UNIVERSITY INC.**
Rawis, Legazpi City 4901
President: Manuel T. Pinon, O.P. (1979-)

C. of Law
C. of Engineering (Civil, Chemical, Industrial, and Architecture)
C. of Education
D. of Business Administration
C. of Arts and Sciences (including Political Science and Social Work)
C. of Commerce
C. of Nursing (including Nutrition)
D. of Religious Studies
D. of Physical Education
C. of Architecture and Fine Arts
Graduate S.
Computer Ce.
Regional Science Teaching Ce.
Socio-Economic Research Ce.
Regional Audio-visual Ce.
Also high school.

Founded 1948 as junior college, administration transferred to the Dominican Fathers 1965, acquired university status 1969. A private institution. Governing body: the Board of Trustees with the Provincial of the Dominican Province of the Philippines as chairman. Residential facilities for women students.

Arrangements for co-operation with Memphis State University.

Academic Year: June to April (June-November; November-April).

Admission Requirements: Graduation from high school or foreign equivalent, and entrance examination.

Languages of Instruction: English and Pilipino.

Degrees and Diplomas: Bachelor of–Arts, A.B.; Arts in Publication Administration, B.A.P.A.; Science in Business Administration, B.S.B.A.; Science in Education, B.S.E.; Science in Elementary Education, B.S.E.Ed.; Science, B.S.; Science in Nutrition and Dietetics; Science in Social Work, B.S.S.W., 4 yrs; Science in Civil Engineering, B.S.C.E.; Science in Chemical Engineering; Science in Industrial Engineering; Science in Architecture, B.S.Arch.;Science in Nursing, B.S.N., 5 yrs. Bachelor of Laws, Ll.B., 4 yrs after first degree. Master of–Arts, M.A.; Business Administration, M.B.A.; Arts in Education, M.A.Ed., 3 yrs after Bachelor. Also diploma in Secretarial Science, D.S.S., 2 yrs, and teaching qualifications.

Library: Central Library, *c.* 50,000 vols.

Publication: Aquinas Research Journal (quarterly).

Academic Staff: c. 90 (60).

Student Enrolment: c. 4300.

5708 **PAMANTASANG ARELLANO**
Arellano University
2600 Legarda, Sampaloc, Manila
Telephone: 60-74-41
President: Jose T. Enriquez

C. of Arts and Sciences
Dean: Jose Enriquez; *staff* 34 (31)
C. of Education
Dean: Amparo S. Lardizabal; *staff* 4 (11)
C. of Commerce
Dean: Francisco Cayco; *staff* 24 (36)
C. of Law
; *staff* 21
C. of Nursing
Dean: Praxedes de la Rosa; *staff* 30 (4)
Graduate S. of Arts
Dean: Amparo S. Lardizabal; *staff* 1 (18)
Also high school and elementary school.

Founded 1938 as law college, university status attained and present title adopted 1947. A private institution. Governing body: the Board of Directors.

Academic Year: June to March (June-October; October-March).

Admission Requirements: Graduation from high school or recognized equivalent, and entrance examination.

Languages of Instruction: English and Pilipino.

Degrees and Diplomas: Bachelor of–Arts, A.B.; Science in Education, B.S.E.; Science in Elementary Education, B.S.E.E.D.; Science in Elementary Education in Home Economics, B.S.E.E.D.H.E.; Science in Commerce, B.S.C.; Science in Commercial Education, B.S.Com.Ed., Science in Nursing, B.S.N. 4 yrs. Bachelor of Laws, Ll.B., 4 yrs after first degree. Master of–Arts, M.A., 2 yrs; Arts in Education, English, Nursing and Political Science. Doctor of Education, Ed.D., 4 yrs. Certificate in Secretarial Science, C.S.S., 1 yr. Diploma in Secretarial Science, D.S.S.A., 4 yrs.

Library: c. 32,672 vols.

Publications: Philippine Education Quarterly; The Arellano Standard (monthly); Alumni Publication (annually).

Academic Staff: c. 215.

Student Enrolment, 1986-87:

	Men	Women	Total
Of the country	882	3951	4833
Of other countries	6	3	9
Total	888	3954	4842

5709 **ATENEO DE DAVAO UNIVERSITY**
P.O. Box 13, Davao City 9501
Telephone: 7-33-49

C. of Arts and Sciences, Commerce, and Mass Communication
Graduate S.
Graduate I. of Education (Mindanao)
S. of Medicine (including Dentistry)
S. of Engineering
C. of Law D. of Agriculture
D. of Accountancy
D. of Business Administration
D. of Humanities
D. of Social Science
D. of Natural Sciences
D. of Religious Studies
I. of Small-scale Industries
Also elementary and high schools.

Founded 1948 as a college, acquired present status and title 1977. A private institution under the supervisionof the Society of Jesus and recognized by the Ministry of Education, Culture and Sports. Governing body:

the Board of Trustees, comprising 8 Jesuit Fathers and 7 lay members. Residential facilities for 150 students.

Academic Year: June to March (June-October; November-March).

Admission Requirements: Graduation from high school and entrance examination.

Languages of Instruction: English and Pilipino.

Degrees and Diplomas: Bachelor of–Arts, A.B.; Science, B.S., 4 yrs. Bachelor of Laws, Ll.B., 4 yrs after first degree. Master of–Arts, M.A.; Science, M.S., a further 1-2 yrs. Doctor of Education, D.Ed., 2-3 yrs. Doctor of–Medicine; Dental Medicine, 4-5 yrs after first degree.

Library: c. 35,000 vols.

Academic Staff: c. 120 (60).

Student Enrolment: c. 3900.

5710 **ATENEO DE MANILA UNIVERSITY**

P.O. Box 154, Manila
Telephone: 99-87-21
Fax: (6-32) 921 61 59
President: Joaquin G. Bernas, S.J. (1984-)
Executive Vice-President: Edmundo M. Martinez, S.J.

S. of Arts and Sciences
Dean: Leovino Ma. Garcia, S.J.; *staff* 143 (151)
Graduate S. of Business Administration
Dean: Edmundo M. Martinez, S.J.; *staff* – (27)
C. of Law
Dean: Cynthia R. del Castillo; *staff* – (41)
Ateneo Computer Technology Ce.
Director Edmundo M. Martinez; *staff* – (9)
I. of Philippine Culture
Director Romana P. de los Reyes; *staff* 7

Also elementary school and high school.

Founded 1859 as public primary school placed under the supervision of the Society of Jesus. Started teacher training 1863 and became college 1865 under Spanish government. Medium of instruction changed from Spanish to English 1898. Became private school 1901. Closed 1941, reopened 1945. Granted university status 1959, now administered by independent Philippine Province of the Society of Jesus. Under the jurisdiction of the Department ofEducation, Culture and Sports. Governing body: the Board of Trustees, comprising 15 members (8 Jesuits and 7 others). Residential facilities for students.

Arrangements for co-operation with: Sophia University, Japan; International Christian University, Japan.

Academic Year: June to March (June-October; November-March).

Admission Requirements: Graduation from high school and entrance examination.

Fees (Pesos): 6065 per semester.

Language of Instruction: English.

Degrees and Diplomas: Bachelor of Arts in–Communication, A.B.Com., 4 years, A.B.Development Studies; Economics, A.B.Eco.; Management Economics, A.B.Mgt.Eco.; Humanities, A.B.Humanities; Interdisciplinary Studies, A.B.I.S.; Philosophy, A.B.Philo.; Political Science, A.B.Pol.Sci.; Pre-Divinity, A.B.Pre-Divinity; Psychology, A.B.Psy.; Social Science, A.B.Social Science; Literature (English), A.B.Lit. (English); Literature (Filipino), A.B.Lit.(Filipino). Bachelor of Science in–Biology, B.S. Bio.; Chemistry, B.S.Ch.; Computer Engineering, B.S.C.S.; Management, B.S.Mgt.; Legal Management, B.S.Legal Mgt.; Managaement Engineering, B.S.Mgt.Eng.,4-5 yrs.; Mathematics, B.S.Math,; Physics, B.s.Physics; Psychology, B.S.Psy. Bachelor of Law, Ll.B., 4 yrs after first degree. Master of Arts in–Communication, M.A.Com.; Economics, M.A.Eco.; Education, M.A.Education; Literature (English), M.A.Lit.(English); Literature (Filipino), M.A.Lit.(Filipino); Language Teaching, M.A.Language Teaching; Linguistics, M.A.Ling.; Philosophy, M.A.Philo.; Psychology, M.A.Psy.; Anthropology, M.A.Anthro.; Sociology, M.A. Socio.; Religious Education, M.A.Religious Education; Theology, M.A.Theology; Theological Studies, M.A.Theological Studies; Pastoral Studies, M.A.Pastoral Studies.Master in–Business Administration, M.B.A.; Business and Government Administration; Hospital Administration.Master of Science in–Computer Science, M.S.C.S.; Information Management, M.S.I.M.; Chemistry, M.S.Ch.; Chemistry Education, M.S.Ch.Education; Mathematics, M.S.Math.; Teaching Mathematics, M.S.Teaching Math.; Physics, M.S.Physics; Teaching Physics, M.S.Teaching Physics; Psychology, M.S.Psy.; Social Development, M.S. Social Development; Applied Sociology and Anthropology, M.S.Applied Socio.& Anthro., a further 2-3 years.Doctor of Philosophy in–Chemistry, Ph.D.Ch.; Literature, Ph.D.Lit.; Mathematics, Ph.D.Math.; Psychology, Ph.D.Psy.; Theology, Ph.D.Theology, a further 3-4 years.

Libraries: Rizal Library, 123,985 vols; Ateneo Professional Schools Library, 50,004.

Special Facilities (Museums, etc.): Ateneo Art Gallery.

Publication: Philippine Studies (quarterly).

Press or Publishing House: University Press.

Academic Staff, 1989-90:

Rank	Full-time	Part-time
Professors	26	1
Associate Professors	18	1
Assistant Professors	36	1
Instructors	32	1
Assistant Instructors	31	1
Lecturers	–	146
Total	143	151

Student Enrolment, 1989-90:

	Men	Women	Total
Of the country	3029	2607	5636
Of other countries	47	20	67
Total	3076	2627	5703

5711 **BAGUIO CENTRAL UNIVERSITY**

18 Bonifacio Street, Baguio City

Founded 1951, acquired present status 1977.

5712 **CENTRAL PHILIPPINE UNIVERSITY**

Iloilo City 5000
Telephone: 7-34-71/9
Fax: (63-33) 7-34-70
President: Augustin A. Pulido (1971-)
Registrar: Esther S. Basiao

C. of Arts and Sciences (including Medical Technology, Nutrition, English, Education and Political Science)
Dean: Leda G. Alba; *staff* 69 (21)
C. of Agriculture
Dean: Enrique S. Altis; *staff* 10 (3)
C. of Commerce (including Economics and Business Administration)
Dean: Milagros V. Dignadice; *staff* 10 (15)
C. of Education (including Home Economics and Physical Education)
Dean: Lorna D. Gellada; *staff* 18 (13)
C. of Engineering
Dean: Walden S. Rio; *staff* 27 (5)
C. of Law
Officer-in-Charge Juanito M. Acanto; (16)
C. of Nursing
Officer-in-Charge Betty S. Polido; *staff* 49 (1)
C. of Theology
Dean: Johnny V. Gumban; *staff* 9 (4)
S. of Graduate Studies
Dean: Elma S. Herradura; *staff* – (10)
Social Research Ce.
Director: Fely P. David; *staff* – (27)

Also kindergarten, elementary, and high schools, and 10 departments attached to the colleges.

Founded 1905 as Jaro Industrial School by American Baptist Foreign Mission Society. Became high school 1915, junior college 1922, senior college 1938. University status attained 1953 and placed under Filipino control 1969. The university is a private institution, financed by tuition fees and grants, and operated under the supervision of the Department of Education, Culture and Sports. Governing body: the Board of Trustees, composed of 15 regular members and 4 ex officio members. Residential facilities for academic staff and students.

Academic Year: June to March (June-October; November-March).

Admission Requirements: Graduation from high school and entrance examination.

Fees (Pesos): 66-108.85 per unit.

Language of Instruction: English.

Degrees and Diplomas: Bachelor of–Arts, A.B.; Science, B.S.; Science in Agriculture, B.S.A.; Science in Commerce, B.S.C.; Science in Medical Technology, B.S.M.T.; Science in Social Work, B.S.S.W.; Science in Education, B.S.E.; Science in Elementary Education, B.S.E.Ed.; Science in Food Technology and Nutrition, B.S.F.N.; Science in Agricultural Education, B.S.Ag.Ed.; Theology, B.Th.; Divinity, B.D., 4 yrs; Science in Chemistry, B.S.Chem.; Science in Civil Engineering, B.S.C.E., Science in Mechanical

Engineering, B.S.M.E.; Science in Chemical Engineering, B.S.Ch.E.; Science in Electrical Engineering, B.S.E.E.; Science in Agricultural Engineering, B.S.Ag.E.; Science in Nursing, B.S.N., 5 yrs. Bachelor of Laws, Ll.B. 4 yrs after first degree. Master of–Arts; Science; Business Administration; Arts in Nursing; Arts in Teaching Physical Education, M.A.T.P.E.; Arts in Teaching Agriculture, M.A.T.A.; Science in Guidance and Counselling, M.S.Guid.; Social Work, 2 yrs after Bachelor. Doctor of Education, Ed.D., at least 2 yrs after Master.

Libraries: University Library, *c.* 58,320 vols; Theology, *c.* 7360.

Publications: The Centralite (annually); The South East Asia Journal; The Link (monthly); Kasanag (weekly); Tuburan (bimonthly); Shalom (biannually); Central Echo.

Academic Staff, 1990: c. 420 (105).

Student Enrolment, 1990: c. 10,715.

5713 ***PAMANTASANG CENTRO ESCOLAR**

Centro Escolar University

9 Mendiola Street, San Miguel, Manila

Cables: ceuniv

Telephone: 741-04-47; 742-20-91-7

President: Dionisio C. Tiongco (1973-)

Registrar: Lucia D. Gonzales

C. of Liberal Arts and Sciences
Dean: Feliciana A. Reyes; *staff* 46 (25)
C. of Science
Dean: Zenaida M. Austria; *staff* 10 (4)
C. of Commerce and Secretarial Administration
Dean: Conrado E. Iñigo; *staff* 22 (14)
C. of Dentistry
Dean: Renato Sison; *staff* 116 (8)
C. of Education and Social Work
Dean: Paz I. Lucido; *staff* 7 (9)
C. of Medical Technology
Dean (Acting): Priscilla A. Panlasigui; *staff* 29 (5)
C. of Music
Dean: Alfredo Buenaventura; *staff* 5 (4)
C. of Nursing
Dean: Ida Kimseng; *staff* 19 (4)
C. of Nutrition and Home Economics
Dean: Julieta Tadle; *staff* 11 (9)
C. of Optometry
Dean: Avelino Reyes; *staff* 15 (2)
C. of Pharmacy
Dean: Epifania Plana; *staff* 20 (2)
C. of Social Work
Dean: Leonora Guzman; *staff* 4 (3)
Graduate S.
Dean: Rosita L. Navarro
Ce. for Data Analysis
Administrator: Rosita G. Santos
D. of Religion
Head: Pelilia V. Hernandez
D. of Basic Languages
Head: Cecilia G. Valmonte
D. of Behavioural Sciences
Head: Aida G. Soliven
D. of Educational Technology
Head: Paz. I. Lucido
Research and Statistics D.
Head: Rosita G. Santos
D. of Religious Studies
Also kindergarten, elementary, and high schools.

Founded 1907 as a private institution, reorganized by the State. Courses leading to the award of the doctorateformally recognized by the State 1952. Financed mainly by tuition fees. Governing bodies: the Board of Directors, comprising 7 members; the Administrative Council.

Academic Year: June to March (June-October; November-March).

Admission Requirements. Graduation from high school or recognized foreign equivalent, and entrance examination.

Languages of Instruction: English and Pilipino.

Degrees and Diplomas: Associate in–Secretarial Administration, A.S.A.; Arts, A.A., 2 yrs; Music, A.M. Bachelor of–Arts, A.B.; Science, B.S.; Science in Education, B.S.E.; Science in Home Economics, B.S.H.E.; Science in Elementary Education, B.S.E.Ed.; Science in Chemistry Education, B.S.Chem.Ed.; Science in Physical Education, B.S.P.E.; Science in Nursing, B.S.N.; Science in Social Work, B.S.S.W.; Science in Chemistry, B.S.Chem.; Science in Foods and Nutrition, B.S.F.N.; Science in Medical Technology, B.S.M.T.; Science in Commerce, B.S.C.; Music, B.M.; Science in Secretarial Administration, B.S.S.A., 4 yrs; Science in Pharmacy, B.S.Phar., 5 yrs. Master of–Arts, M.A.; Science in Social Work, M.S.S.W.; Science in Home Economics, M.S.H.E.; Science in Foods and Nutrition, M.S.F.N.; Music, M.Mus.; Science in Chemistry, M.S.Chem.; Science in Pharmacy, M.S.Phar.; Public Administration, M.P.A., one further yr. Doctorates in–Philosophy, Ph.D.; Education, Ed.D.; Pharmacy, Phar.D.; Dentistry, D.M.D.; Public Admininistration, D.P.A.;Mathematics Education, D.Math.Ed.; Optometry, O.D., 4 yrs. Preparatory courses in–Dentistry, 2 yrs; Law; Medicine, 4 yrs. Teaching certificates, secondary, intermediate and primary levels, 4 yrs. Diploma in–Music Teaching. Secretarial Science; Home Economics, 4 yrs; Dental Technology, 2 yrs. Also professional diploma in Mathematics; Administration; Curricular and Supervision. Doctor, Ph.D., in Southeast Asia Studies.

Library: University Library, 75,300 vols.

Special Facilities (Museums, etc.): Centro Escolar University Archives and Museum.

Publications: The Scholar (monthly); The Clarion (quarterly);

Academic Staff, 1989-90: 260 (40).

Student Enrolment, 1989-90: 20,478.

5714 ***DE LA SALLE UNIVERSITY**

2401 Taft Avenue, P.O Box 3819, Manila 1004

Cables: Delasal

Telephone: 50-46-11

Fax: 5223661

President: Andrew A. Gonzalez, F.S.C. (1979-)

Administrative Officer: Paulino Y. Tan

C. of Business and Economics
Dean: Lydia Echauz; *staff* 43 (74)
C. of Computer Studies
Dean: Emma Teodoro; *staff* 34 (12)
C. of Engineering
Dean: Servillano Olaño *staff* 55 (35)
C. of Liberal Arts
Dean: Maria Lourdes Bautista; *staff* 88 (76)
C. of Science
Dean: Herminia Torres; *staff* 55 (55)
C. of Education
Dean: Estrellita Gruenberg; *staff* 7 (9)
Graduate S. of Business and Economics
Dean: Lydia Echauz; *staff* 6 (46)
Social Science Research Ce.
Director: Robert Salazar
Also 2 colleges in Dasmariñas.

Founded 1911 at elementary and secondary level, first collegiate courses started in 1920s. Formally granted university status 1975. A private institution conducted by the Brothers of the Christian Schools. Degrees recognized by the government. Governing body: the Board of Trustees.

Arrangements for co-operation with the Universities of: Waseda; Ohio; Soochow and Tamkang, Taiwan; Han Nam, Republic of Korea. Loughborough University of Technology; Brighton Polytechnic, United Kingdom.

Academic Year: May to April (May-August; September-December; January-April).

Admission Requirements: Graduation from high school and entrance examination.

Fees (Pesos): 6100-8500 per trimester, according to subject.

Languages of Instruction: English and Pilipino.

Degrees and Diplomas: Bachelor of–Arts, B.A. Bachelor of–Science; Accountancy; Commerce; Applied Economics; Mathematics; Biology; Chemistry; Physics; Chemical Engineering; Mechanical Engineering; Industrial Engineering and Management; Commerce; Electronics and Communications Engineering; Manufacturing Engineering and Management; Civil Engineering; Computer Sciences, 4 yrs. Master in–Business Administration (part-time). Master of Science in–Biology; Chemistry; Mathematics; Physics; Computer Sciences; Educational Management; Educational Measurement and Evaluation; Guidance and Counselling; Psychology; Teaching. Master of Arts in–Educational Management; Engineering Education; Guidance and counseiling; Language and Literature; Philippine Studies; Philosophy; Religious Education. Doctor of Arts in–Education; Management; Philosophy.

Library: Central Library, 137,000 vols.

Special Facilities (Museums, etc.): DLSU Art Gallery.

Publications: Abut-Tanaw (Campus activities monthly); Agham (Science, quarterly); Alumnews (quarterly); Ang Pahayagang Plaridel, The La

Sallian (student papers, monthly); Business and Economics Review (biannually); Computer Issues (quarterly); Dialogue (University journal, biannually); Engineering Journal (biannually); GSBE Bulletin (every trimester); Malate Literary Journal (quarterly); Sophia (Humanities, quarterly).

Press or Publishing House: De La Salle University Press.

Academic Staff, 1989-90:

Rank	Full-time	Part-time
Professors	19	
Associate Professors	53	
Assistant Professors	98	
Instructors	84	
Assistant Instructors	12	
Visiting Professors	11	
Total	277	265

Student Enrolment, 1989-90:

	Men	Women	Total
Of the country	4804	3896	8700
Of other countries	338	188	526
Total	5142	4084	9226

5715 **DIVINE WORD UNIVERSITY OF TACLOBAN**

Tacloban City 6500, Leyte
Cables: Dwut
Telephone: 3212310

President: Florante S. Camacho, S.V.D. (1987-)
Registrar: Anselmo P. Bugal

C. of Law
Dean: Fortunato B. Cuna; *staff* 1 (15)

C. of Arts and Sciences (including Political Science, Sociology, Medical Technology, and Theology)
Dean: Clarita C. Filipinas; *staff* 81 (15)

C. of Commerce
Dean: Conrita T. Tudtud; *staff* 30 (29)

C. of Engineering
Dean: Joveniano C. Nerves; *staff* 12 (11)

C. of Medicine
Dean: Belen C. Diamante; *staff* 35 (17)

C. of Nursing
Dean: Socorro S. Gasco; *staff* 15

C. of Education
Dean: Emilienne M. Acosta; *staff* 7 (2)

Graduate S.
Dean: Efleda K. Bautista; *staff* 1 (7)

Leyte-Samar Research Ce.
; *staff* 1 (6)

Also elementary and high schools and a teaching hospital.

Founded as school 1929, became college 1945, and university 1966. A private institution conducted by the Society of the Divine Word. Governing body: the Board of Trustees, comprising 10 members. Residential facilities for *c.* 60 women students

Academic Year: June to March (June-October; November-March).

Admission Requirements: Graduation from high school and entrance examination.

Fees (Pesos): 1600-2300 per semester; Nursing, 2000-3000; Medicine, 6100-14100.

Languages of Instruction: English and Pilipino.

Degrees and Diplomas: Bachelor of–Arts, A.B.; Science, B.S., 4 yrs. Bachelor of Science in–Elementary Education, B.S.E.Ed.; Secondary Education, B.S.Ed.; Medical Technology, B.S.M.T.; Social Work, B.S.S.W.; Commerce, B.S.C.; Criminology, B.S.Crim.; Secretarial Administration, B.S.S.A.; Nursing, B.S.N.; Civil Engineering, B.S.C.E.; Mechanical Engineering, B.S.M.E.; Chemical Engineering, B.S.Ch.E.; Electrical Engineering, B.S.E.E., 5 yrs. Bachelor of Laws, Ll.B, 4 yrs after first degree. Master of Arts, M.A.,1-2 years after first degree. Doctor of Philosophy, Ph.D. 2-3 years after M.A.; Doctor of Medicine, M.D., 4 years after first degree.

Libraries: Central Library, *c.* 66,000 vols; Law, *c.* 5000.

Special Facilities (Museums, etc.): Leyte-Samar Museum.

Publications: Bulletin (quarterly); Leyte-Samar Studies (biannually); Pulong A Research Forum (monthly); The Power (biannually).

Press or Publishing House: DWU Printing Press.

Academic Staff, 1989-90:

Rank	Full-time	Part-time
Associate Professors	3	2
Assistant Professors	11	2
Senior Instructors	45	18
Junior Instructors	103	20
Assistant Instructors	61	43
Lecturers	–	34
Total	223	119

Student Enrolment, 1989-90:

	Men	Women	Total
Of the country	2938	3879	6817
Of other countries	21	6	27
Total	2959	3885	6844

5716 ***FAR EASTERN UNIVERSITY**

Quezon Boulevard, P.O. Box 609, Manila
Cables: Farsternu
Telephone: 7413421

President: Felixberto C. Sta. Maria (1989-)
Executive Assistant: Leopoldo C. Gonzalez

I. of Accountancy, Finance and Business Administration
Dean: Felino L. Ampil; *staff* 65 (71)

I. of Architecture and Fine Arts
Dean: Marylou Ventura; *staff* 45 (22)

I. of Education
Dean: Rizalina Oteyza; *staff* 29 (15)

I. of Law
Dean: Oscar Victoriano.; *staff* – (32)

I. of Nursing
Dean: Lydia Palaypay; *staff* 20 (44)

I. of Technology
Dean: Jose S. Cuejilo; *staff* 83 (15)

I. of Graduate Studies
Officer-in-Charge: Felicidad C. Robles; *staff* – (8)

I. of Arts and Sciences
Dean: Wilson Faderon

Also high school.

Founded 1928 as Institute of Accountancy and Business Administration, consolidated with Far Eastern College and incorporated under present title 1933. A private institution. Governing body: the Board of Trustees.

Academic Year: June to March (June-October; November-March).

Admission Requirements: Graduation from high school and entrance examination.

Fees (Pesos): 95 per unit per semester; Graduate, 180 per unit per semester.

Language of Instruction: English.

Degrees and Diplomas: Associate in Commercial Science, 2 yrs. Bachelor of–Arts; Science; Science in Commerce; Science in Education; Science in Elementary Education; Fine Arts; Nursing, 4 yrs; Science in Engineering (various fields); Science in Architecture, 5 yrs. Bachelor of Laws, Ll.B., 4 yrs after first degree. Master of–Arts; Arts in Education;Arts in Educational Administration; Business Administration, 2 yrs after Bachelor. Doctor of Education.

Publications: Newsletter (quarterly); Ambon (annually).

Academic Staff, 1989-90:

Rank	Full-time	Part-time
Full Professors	2	6
Associate Professors	26	7
Assistant Professors	60	13
Instructors	113	5
Professional Lecturers	101	172
Total	302	203

Student Enrolment, 1989-90: 58,946.

5717 **FEATI UNIVERSITY**

Helios Street, Santa Cruz, Manila
Telephone: 48-59-51

I. of Engineering and Technology

I. of Liberal Arts and Education

I. of Architecture

I. of Commerce

I. of Science

I. of Vocational and Technical Sciences
I. of Maritime Transport
Graduate S.
Finance
Also secondary school.

Founded 1946 as the Far Eastern School of Aeronautics, became Feati Institute of Technology 1947, attained university status 1959. The university is a private institution dependent on tuition fees. Governing body: the Board of Trustees, composed of 5 members.

Academic Year: June to March (June-October; October-March).

Admission Requirements: Graduation from high school and entrance examination.

Language of Instruction: English.

Degrees and Diplomas: Associate in–Arts, A.A.; Electrical Engineering, A.E.E.; Marine Engineering, A.M.E.; Radio and Electronics Engineering, A.R.E.E.; Surveying, As.Surv.; Textile Engineering, A.T.E.; Business Administration, A.B.A.; Secretarial Science, A.S.S., 2 yrs. Bacherlor of–Arts; Science in–Aeronautical Engineering, B.S.Ae.E.; Chemical Engineering, B.S.Ch.E.; Civil Engineering, B.S.C.E.; Electrical Engineering, B.S.E.E.; Management Engineering, B.S.Man.E.; Mechanical Engineering, B.S.M.E.; Radio and Electronics Engineering, B.S.R.E.E.; Sanitary Engineering, B.S.S.E., 5 yrs; Textile Engineering, B.T.E.; Chemistry, B.S.Chem.; Physics, B.S.Phy.; Mathematics, B.S.Math.; Architecture, B.S.Arch.; Industrial Education, B.S.I.E.; Business Administration, B.S.B.A. Master of–Arts in Education, M.A.Education; Management Engineering, M.Man.E.; Science in–Electrical Engineering, M.S.E.E.; Mathematics, M.S.Math.; Actuarial Mathematics; Pure Mathematics; Mechanical Engineering, M.S.M.E.; Physics, M.S.Physics;Management Engineering, M.S.Man.E., 1 yr after Bachelor. Certificates in–Commercial Art; Education; Secretarial Science; Aircraft Maintenance Engineering; Television Technology; Radio Telegraphy; Radio Technology; Radio Mechanics; Automotive Mechanics; Diesel Engine Mechanics; Internal Combustion Engine Technology; Refrigeration Technology; Machine Shop Technology; Sheet Metal Technology; Bakery, 1-2 yrs.

Library: University Library, *c.* 23,450 vols.

Academic Staff: c. 600.

Student Enrolment: c. 35,300.

5718 **FOUNDATION UNIVERSITY**

Dr.E. Meciano Road, Dumaguete City, Negros Occidental 6501
Telephone: 33-89; 2930
President (Acting): Willie C. Depositario (1986-87)
Executive Vice-President: Luciano C. Maxino

S. of Arts and Sciences
Dean: Ester V. Tan; *staff* 17 (5)
S. of Law
Dean: Luciano C. Maxino; *staff* 4 (3)
S. of Agricultural Technology (including Animal Husbandry)
Dean: Willie C. Depositario; *staff* 15 (4)
S. of Business Administration and Economics
Dean: Whilma S. Yap; *staff* 14 (11)
S. of Education
Dean: Maternidad G. Villarin; *staff* 8 (6)
Graduate S.
Dean: Timoteo Oracion; *staff* 4 (4)
Also elementary and high schools.

Founded 1949 as a College, a private and independent institution. Became university 1969. Governing body: the Board of Trustees, composed of 5 members.

Academic Year: June to March (June-October; November-March).

Admission Requirements: Graduation from high school and entrance examination.

Fees (Pesos): 83-100 per unit, per semester.

Languages of Instruction: Pilipino and English.

Degrees and Diplomas: Bachelor of Science in–Education; Arts; Elementary Education; Industrial Engineering; Physics; Jurisprudence; Commerce; Biology; Agriculture, 4 yrs. Bachelor of Laws, 4 yrs after first degree. Master of–Arts in Education; Science in Agricultural Education; Science in Business Administration, a further 2-3 yrs. Doctor of Education.

Library: Total, 43,853 vols.

Special Facilities (Museums, etc.): Mini Museum.

Publication: Foundation Time (monthly).

Academic Staff, 1986-87:

Rank	Full-time	Part-time
Professors	5	3
Instructors	72	10
Lecturers	2	10
Librarians	3	–
Total	82	23

Student Enrolment, 1986-87:

	Men	Women	Total
Of the country	1602	1977	3579
Of other countries	1	–	1
Total	1603	1977	3580

5719 **GREGORIO ARANETA UNIVERSITY FOUNDATION**

Victoneta Park, Malabon, Metro Manila, Rizal
Telephone: 361-90-53
President: Obed Jose Meneses

I. of Agriculture and Forestry (including Horticulture)
I. of Arts and Sciences
I. of Education and Sports
I. of Business and Agricultural Administration
I. of Engineering
I. of Veterinary Medicine
I. of Graduate Studies and Applied Research
Also kindergarten, elementary and high schools.

Founded 1946 as Araneta Institute of Agriculture, acquired university status 1958. Became a university foundation 1965. A semi-governmental non-profit corporation. Governing body: the Board of Trustees of 7 members, the Secretary of Foreign Affairs, and the Secretary of Finance.

Academic Year: June to March (June-October; October-March).

Admission Requirements: Graduation from high school or recognized foreign equivalent, and entrance examination.

Languages of Instruction: English and Pilipino.

Degrees and Diplomas: Associate in–Agriculture, A.A.; Forestry, A.F. Secretarial Science, A.S.S., 2 yrs. Bachelor of Science, B.S.; Science in–Agriculture, B.S.A.; Forestry, B.S.F.; Animal Husbandry, B.S.A.H.; Education, B.S.E.; Agricultural Extension, B.S.A.Ext.; Elementary Education B.S.E.Ed.; Agricultural Administration, B.S.A.A.; Food Technology, B.S.F.T.; Agricultural Education, B.S.A.Ed.; Commerce, B.S.C.; Agricultural Technology; Business Administration, B.S.B.A.; Secretarial Administration, B.S.S.A., 4 yrs; Bachelor of Arts, 4 yrs; Agricultural Engineering, B.S.A.E.; Mechanical Engineering, B.S.M.E.; Electrical Engineering, B.S.E.E., 5 yrs. Master in Management, M.M.; Master of Arts in Teaching M.A.T.; Master of Science in–Agriculture, M.S.A.; Agricultural Education, M.S.A.Ed.; Forestry, M.S.F.; Agricultural Administration, M.S.A.A.; Biology; Botany; Animal Husbandry, M.S.A.H.; Master of Arts in Education, M.A., 2 yrs after Bachelor. Doctor of Veterinary Medicine, D.V.M., 6 yrs. Doctor of Philosophy in Agricultural Science, Ph.D.; Doctor of Philosophy, 3 yrs after Master.

Library: Central Library, *c.* 33,740 vols.

Publication: Research Journal (quarterly).

Academic Staff: c. 120 (20).

Student Enrolment: c. 6390.

5720 **HOLY ANGEL UNIVERSITY**

Santo Rosario, 2009 Angeles City
Telephone: 241-30
President: Josefina G. Nepomuceno O.S.B. (1985-)
Vice-President for Administration: Teresita N. Wilkerson

C. of Arts and Sciences
Dean: Edna M.C. Santos; *staff* 4 (15)
C. of Business Administration
Dean: Arlyn S. Villanueva; *staff* 22 (61)
C. of Education
Dean (Acting): Edna M.C. Santos; *staff* 11 (24)
C. of Engineering
Dean: Abigail P. Arcilla; *staff* 42 (21)
C. of Secretarial Studies
Dean: Aurora K. Mercado; *staff* 12 (14)
Computer Studies Ce.
Head: Renato M. Santiago; *staff* 1
Vocational/Technical D.
Head: Rudy B. Pamintuan; *staff* 8 (5)

Graduate S.
Dean: Josefina G. Nepomuceno; *staff* – (6)

Founded 1933 as Academy, became college 1962 and acquired university status 1981. A private institution under the supervision of the Department of Education, Culture and Sports. Governing body: the Board of Trustees.

Academic Year: June to April (June-October; November-April).

Admission Requirements: Graduation from high school and entrance examination.

Fees (Pesos): 62 per unit; Graduate school, 150 per unit; Vocational/technical courses: 1000.20 per semester.

Languages of Instruction: English and Pilipino.

Degrees and Diplomas: Bachelor of–Arts, A.B.; Elementary Education, B.E.E.D.; Science in Secretarial Education, B.S.S.A.; Science in Business Administration, B.S.B.A.; Science in Secondary Education, B.S.E.,4 yrs; Science in–Electrical Engineering; Civil Engineering; Industrial Engineering; Mechanical Engineering, 5 yrs. Master of Arts, a further 2yrs. Also vocational/technical courses, 1 yr.

Library: Central Library, 24,790 vols.

Publications: Digest (quarterly); student publications.

Academic Staff, 1989-90: 89 (158).

Student Enrolment, 1989-90:

	Men	Women	Total
Of the country	4589	4576	9165
Of other countries	127	118	245
Total	4716	4694	9410

5721 **INTERNATIONAL HARVARDIAN UNIVERSITY**
123 Malvar Street, Davao City
Telephone: 7-50-14/5

C. of Law
C. of Commerce
C. of Education
C. of Criminology
C. of Engineering
S. of Arts and Sciences (including Political Science)
Graduate S.

Also elementary and high schools.

Founded 1951 as college, acquired university status 1969. Operated under the supervision of the Ministry of Education, Culture and Sports.

Academic Year: June to April (June-October; November-March).

Admission Requirements: Graduation from high school and entrance examination.

Languages of Instruction: English and Pilipino.

Degrees and Diplomas: Bachelor of–Arts, A.B.; Science in Education, B.S.E.; Science in Elementary Education; Science in Civil Engineering, B.S.C.E.; Science in Commerce, 4-5 yrs. Bachelor of Laws, Ll.B, 4 yrs after first degree. Master of Arts in Education, a further 2 yrs. Doctor of Education, ED.D.

Library: c. 20,000 vols.

Publication: Harvardian Star (bimonthly).

Academic Staff: c. 45 (50).

Student Enrolment: c. 4300.

5722 **MANILA CENTRAL UNIVERSITY**
V. Fugoso Street, Santa Cruz, Manila 2805
Cables: Mcu Manila
Telephone: 26-45-86/7; 35-35-61; 34-18-19
President: Purificacion G. Tanchoco (1963-)

C. of Arts and Sciences
C. of Medicine
C. of Dentistry
C. of Optometry
C. of Commerce
C. of Pharmacy and Medical Technology
C. of Nursing
Graduate D. of Education
S. of Midwifery
Extension D.

Also elementary and high schools.

Founded 1904 as School of Pharmacy, became Manila College of Pharmacy and Dentistry 1929. Closed 1941. Became Manila Central Colleges after liberation of the Philippines, with the addition of departments of liberal arts, education, and business administration. Medical and nursing courses added 1948. Recognized as a university by the government and adopted present title 1948. A private non-sectarian institution governed by the Board of Trustees of 5 members. Residential facilities for students of nursing and midwifery.

Academic Year: July to April (July-November; November-April).

Admission Requirements: Graduation from high school and entrance examination.

Language of Instruction: English.

Degrees and Diplomas: Bachelor of–Arts, A.B.; Science, B.S.; Science in Business Administration; Science in Medical Technology, 4 yrs; Science in Nursing; Science in Pharmacy, 5 yrs. Master of Arts in Education, a further 2 yrs. Doctor of–Optometry; Dental Medicine, 4 yrs; Medicine, 5 yrs after 4 yr pre-medical course. Certificate of Midwifery, 3 semesters.

Libraries: Central Library, *c.* 11,500 vols; Medical library, *c.* 5100; Nursing, *c.* 1500; Education and Graduate library, *c.* 2710; Business Administration, *c.* 1200.

Academic Staff: c. 60 (170).

Student Enrolment: c. 5500.

5723 **MANUEL L. QUEZON UNIVERSITY**
916 R. Hidalgo Street, Quiapo, Manila
Cables: Mlqu Manila
Telephone: 47-05-41

F. of Law
F. of Arts and Sciences (including Journalism)
F. of Education
F. of Commerce (including Economics)
F. of Engineering and Architecture
F. of Criminology
F. of Graduate Studies

Also high and elementary schools.

Founded 1947 as School of Law. Faculty of arts and science opened 1948, faculty of education, elementary school, and high school added 1949. Graduate school and faculty of commerce established 1952, faculty of engineering and architecture 1954. Granted university status 1958. Operated under the supervision of the Ministry of Education, Culture and Sports. Financed solely by tuition fees. Governing body: the Board of Regents.

Academic Year: July to April (July-November; November-April; May-June).

Admission Requirements: Graduation from high school or recognized foreign equivalent, and entrance examination.

Language of Instruction: English.

Degrees and Diplomas: Bachelor of–Arts, A.B.; Criminal Science, B.C.S.; Science in Chemistry, B.S.Chem.; Science in Foreign Service, B.S.F.S.; Science in Education, B.S.E.; Science in Elementary Education, B.S.E.Ed.; Science in Education Major in Home Economics, B.S.E.H.E.; Science in Commerce, B.S.C.; Science in Chemical Engineering, B.S.Ch.E.; Science in Civil Engineering, B.S.C.E.; Science in Electrical Engineering, B.S.E.E.; Science in Mechanical Engineering, B.S.M.E.; Science in Architecture, B.S.Arch., 4 yrs. Bachelor of Laws, Ll.B., 4 yrs after first degree. Master of–Laws (General), Ll.M., 1 yr after Bachelor; Arts. M.A. Laws (Taxation), Ll.M.; Science in Commerce; Science in Mathematics, M.S.Math., 2 yrs after Bachelor. Doctor of–Education, Ed.D.; Philosophy in Linguistics, Ph.D. in L., 3 yrs after Bachelor.

Libraries: Main Library, *c.* 11,250 vols; Law, *c.* 5300; Graduate, *c.* 1380 Engineering and Architecture, *c.* Roman L. SunicoMemorial, *c.* 240; Miscellaneous, *c.* 6720.

Publications: Acquitas; Law Quarterly; Quezonian; Graduate School Review.

Academic Staff: c. 650.

Student Enrolment: c. 22,800.

5724 **MANUEL S. ENVERGA UNIVERSITY FOUNDATION**
Lucena City 3901
Telephone: 71-25-41
President: Wilfrido C. Enverga (1984-)

C. of Arts and Sciences
C. of Commerce
C. of Education
C. of Engineering
I. of Applied Business
C. of Agriculture (including Animal Husbandry)
S. of Architecture
Graduate S.
Vocational Studies

Lifelong Education
Also elementary and 3 high schools.

Founded 1947 as college, acquired present status 1968. A private institution. Governing body: the Board of Trustees.

Academic Year: June to March (June-October; October-March).

Admission Requirements: Graduation from high school and entrance examination.

Languages of Instruction: English and Pilipino.

Degrees and Diplomas: Bachelor of–Arts; Science; Science in Business Administration; Science in Education; Science in Elementary Education; Science in Agricultural Technology; Science in Agricultural Education; Science in Secretarial Education, 4 yrs; Science in Civil Engineering; Science in Architecture, 5 yrs. Master of–Science in Business Administration; Arts a further 2-5 yrs. Doctor of Educational Management. Also Diploma in Secretarial Science, 2 yrs.

Library: Total, *c.* 42,930 vols.

Publication: The Luzonian (quarterly).

Academic Staff: c. 100 (70).

Student Enrolment: c. 8100.

5725 **MISAMIS UNIVERSITY**
Mabini and Bonifacio St., Ozamis City
President: Nestor M. Feliciano (1983-)

C. of Agriculture and Forestry
C. of Commerce and Secretarial Studies
C. of Arts and Sciences
C. of Dentistry
C. of Nursing and Midwifery
C. of Engineering
C. of Criminology
C. of Education
C. of Social Work and Community Development
C. of Law
I. of Graduate Studies
Community Extension P.
Also branch in Oroquista City, elementary and high schools.

Founded 1929 as school. Became institute 1931 and college 1955. Acquired present status and title 1977. A private institution. Governing body: the Board of Trustees. Residential facilities for academic staff and students.

Academic Year: June to March (June-October; November-March).

Admission Requirements: Graduation from high school and entrance examination.

Languages of Instruction: English and Pilipino.

Degrees and Diplomas: Bachelor of–Arts; Science in–Nursing; Commerce; Secretarial Studies; Social Work; Community Development; Forestry; Agricultural Technology; Agriculture; Agricultural Education; Elementary Education; Education; Criminology; Home Economics, 4 yrs. Bachelor of Science in–Electrical Engineering; Civil Engineering; Mechanical Engineering; Agricultural Engineering, 5 yrs. Diploma of Dentistry, 6 yrs. Master of Arts in–Education; Teaching; Master in–Business Administration; Public Administration. Doctor of–Philosophy; Education. Also Diplomas in–Junior Secretarial Studies; Midwifery; Engineering; Pre-Dentistry, 2 yrs. Clinical and Health Aide qualifications, 1 yr.

Libraries: Central Library, *c.* 28,000 vols; Oroquieta Unit, *c.* 13,900 vols.

Publication: Misamis Collegian (biannually).

Academic Staff: c. 130 (50).

Student Enrolment: c. 7600.

5726 ***NATIONAL UNIVERSITY**
551 M.F. Jhocson Street, Sampaloc, Manila
Telephone: 60-81-67
President: Domingo L. Jhocson (1945-)

C. of Commerce
C. of Liberal Arts
C. of Dentistry
C. of Pharmacy
C. of Education
C. of Engineering
S. of Arts and Architecture
C. of Law
C. of Technical Sciences
Graduate S.
Also high school.

Founded 1900 as Colegio filipino, became Colegio mercantil 1905. English replaced Spanish as medium of instruction 1913. Became National Academy 1916, present title adopted 1921. A private institution. Governing bodies: the Board of Trustees; the University Council.

Academic Year: June to March (June-October; November-March).

Admission Requirements: Graduation from high school or equivalent and aptitude test, or foreign equivalent recognized by the Government Department of Education.

Language of Instruction: English.

Degrees and Diplomas: Bachelor of–Arts, A.B., 4 yrs; Science in Education, B.S.E.; Science in Elementary Education, B.S.E.Ed.; Science in Commerce, B.S.C., 4 yrs; Science in Architecture, B.S.Arch.; Science in Pharmacy, B.S.Phar.; Bachelor of Science in Chemistry, B.S.Chem.; Science in Industrial Engineering, B.S.I.E.; Science in Chemical Engineering, B.S.Ch.E.; Science in Electrical Engineering, B.S.E.E.; Science in Mechanical Engineering, B.S.M.E.; Science in Civil Engineering, B.S.C.E.; Science in Sanitary Engineering, B.S.E.E., 5 yrs. Master of–Arts, M.A.; Arts in Education; Education major in Elementary Education, 2 yrs after Bachelor; Science in Sanitary Engineering, M.S.S.E., at least 1 yr after Bachelor. Doctor of Dentistry D.D.M., 6 yrs. Diploma: Elementary Teacher's Certificate, 2 yrs. Also Associate in–Pharmacy Aide; Architectural Drafting, 2 yrs.

Library: c. 120,000 vols.

Academic Staff: c. 90 (90).

Student Enrolment: c. 7200.

5727 ***NOTRE DAME UNIVERSITY**
Notre Dame Avenue, Cotabato City 9301
Telephone: 26-98
President: Jose D. Ante (1982-91)
Vice-President: Alfonso E. Cariño

C. of Arts and Sciences
Dean: Ofelia L. Durante; *staff* 80 (15)
C. of Engineering
Dean: Jose M. Rodriguez, Jr.; *staff* 14 (8)
C. of Law
Dean: Ramon T. dela Fuente; *staff* 14
C. of Commerce
Dean: Myrna B. Lim; *staff* 13 (7)
C. of Nursing
Dean: Grace B. Barranco; *staff* 26 (2)
Teachers' C.
Dean: Aurora R. Carag; *staff* 11 (5)
Graduate S.
Director: Ceferino D. Costales; *staff* 16 (6)
Socio-Economic Research Ce.
Director: Eva K. Tan; *staff* 12
Small Busines I.
Director: Myrna B. Lim; *staff* 3 (2)
Community Extension Service
Director: Bata A. Amba; *staff* 3 (4)
Training D. (Elementary Education)
Principal: Erlinda P. Zurita; *staff* 33 (2)

Founded 1948 as Notre Dame Colleges, acquired university status 1969. A private institution under the supervision of the Oblates of Mary Immaculate. Governing body: the Board of Trustees, comprising 10 members. Residential facilities for religious academic staff.

Academic Year: June to March (June-October; November-March).

Admission Requirements: Graduation from high school and entrance examination.

Languages of Instruction: English, Pilipino and Spanish.

Degrees and Diplomas: Bachelor of–Arts, A.B.; Science, B.S.; Science in Commerce, B.S.C.; Elementary Education, B.E.Ed.; Secondary Education, B.S.E.Ed.; 4 yrs; Science in Nursing, B.S.N.; Science in Mechanical Engineering, B.S.M.E.; Science in Electrical Engineering, B.S.E.E.; Science in Civil Engineering, B.S.C.E., 5 yrs. Bachelor of Laws, Ll.B., 4 yrs after first degree. Master of–Arts, M.A.; Business Administration, M.B.A.; Public Administration, M.P.A., 2 yrs after Bachelor. Doctor of–Education, Ed.D., 3 yrs; Philosophy. Also Diploma in Secretarial Science.

Libraries: Main Library, *c.* 62,773 vols; Socio-Economic Research Centre Library, 600.

Publication: Notre Dame Journal (biannually).

Academic Staff, 1989-90:

Rank	Full-time	Part-time
Professors	7	3
Associate Professors	16	1
Instructors	66	31
Lecturers	22	3
Assistants	53	8
Total	170	46

Student Enrolment, 1989-90:

	Men	Women	Total
Of the country	4697	6442	11,139

5728 **ORTAÑEZ UNIVERSITY**
942 Aurora Boulevard, Cubas, Quezon City

Engineering
Arts
Law
Criminology
Nursing
Education
Technical Sciences

Founded 1945, acquired present status and title, 1958, 1973.

5729 **PAMANTASAN NG ARAULLO**
Araullo University
Bitas, Cabanatuan City 3100
Telephone: 963-2215; 963-3369
President: Rolan C. Esteban (1987-)
Registrar: Raoul S. Esteban

C. of Arts and Sciences (including Political Science and Economics)
Dean: Lily G. Buencamino; *staff* 41 (3)
C. of Commerce
Dean: Lourdes B. de Guzman; *staff* 45 (14)
C. of Criminology
Dean: Pedro Villanueva; *staff* 12 (2)
C. of Education
Dean: Edisteo B. Bernardez; *staff* 12 (2)
C. of Engineering (including Architecture)
Dean: Fernando C. Hernandez, Jr.; *staff* 37 (5)
C. of Law
Dean: Juan S. Esteban; *staff* 2 (7)
C. of Nutrition
Head: Maridel V. Khajehi; *staff* 3
D. of Graduate Studies
Dean: Leonila V. Cruz; *staff* 10 (2)
Computer Ce.
Head: Lourdes de Guzman; *staff* 7

Also kindergarten, elementary, and high schools.

Founded 1950 as law school, became college 1953 and acquired university status 1983. A private institution. Governing body: the Board of Trustees.

Academic Year: June to March (June-October; November-March).

Admission Requirements: Graduation from high school and entrance examination.

Fees (Pesos): 1302 per 21 units; Graduate Studies, 1191.70-1470.60 per 12-18 units.

Languages of Instruction: English and Pilipino.

Degrees and Diplomas: Bachelor of–Arts; Science in Commerce; Science in Education; Science in Elementary Education; Science in Criminology, 4 yrs; Science in Geodetic Engineering; Science in Industrial Management Engineering; Science in Civil Engineering; Architecture, 5 yrs. Bachelor of Laws, 4 yrs after first degree. Master of–Arts; Science; Public Management; Management; Business Administration; Teaching Business Education, a further 2-3 yrs. Doctor of Philosophy, 3-4 yrs.

Libraries: Central Library, 38,443 vols; Law, 1293; Graduate School, 2909.

Publications: Sandigan (quarterly); Araullian (quarterly); The Horizon (annually).

Press or Publishing House: Gonzales Printing House

Academic Staff, 1989-90:

Rank	Full-time	Part-time
Professors	2	–
Associate Professors	17	3
Assistant Professors	32	8
Instructors	74	8
Total	125	19

Student Enrolment, 1989-90:

	Men	Women	Total
Of the country	4569	4243	8812

5730 **PHILIPPINE CHRISTIAN UNIVERSITY**
Desmainas, Cavite

Agricultural Technology
Business Administration
Education
Social Work

Founded 1946.

5731 **PHILIPPINE CHRISTIAN UNIVERSITY**
1648 Taft Avenue and Corner Pedro Gil, Manila
Telephone: 57-24-35
President: Carlito S. Puno (1990-95)

C. of Business Administration (including Economics and Accountancy, Marketing, Management, Banking and Finance)
Dean: Isagani Santiago; *staff* 26 (26)
C. of Arts and Sciences (including Political Science and Sociology)
Dean: Corazon C. Obnamia; *staff* 45 (20)
C. of Education (Filipino, English, History, General Science, Mathematics)
Dean: David G. Tovera; *staff* 10 (15)
C. of Nursing
Dean: Remedios Santiago; *staff* 9 (7)
C. of Agricultural Technology
Dean: Oscar J. Tayko
Graduate S. of Education
Dean: David G. Tovera; *staff* 1 (6)
Graduate S. of Commerce
Dean: Isagani Santiago; *staff* – (24)
P. for Rural Development
Head: Oscar J. Tayko
Extension D. (Theology)
S. of Computer and Secretarial Sciences (including Computer Education, Computer Secretarial)
Officer-in-Charge: Richard L. Schwenk; *staff* 14 (11)
C. of Social Work
Dean: Betty I. Molina; *staff* 1 (3)

Also kindergarten and elementary and high schools.

Founded 1947 as college, acquired present status and title 1976. A private institution supported by the UnitedMethodist Church and United Church of Christ in the Philippines. Governing body: the Board of Trustees.

Arrangements for co-operation with the Mokwon Methodist University, Republic of Korea.

Academic Year: June to March (June-October; November-March).

Admission Requirements: Graduation from high school and entrance examination.

Fees (Pesos): 47.65-59.65 per unit.

Languages of Instruction: English, Spanish, and Pilipino.

Degrees and Diplomas: Bachelor of–Arts; Science in–Education; Elementary Education; Pre-school Education; Social Work; Nursing; Business Administration; Secretarial Science, 4 yrs. Master of–Arts in Education; Business Administration, a further 2 yrs. Also Diploma in Secretarial Science; Food Service Management, 2 yrs.

Library: *c.* 33,162 vols.

Publications: Academic Review (biannually); Journal of Education Research (biannually).
Academic Staff, 1989-90: 202 (109).
Student Enrolment, 1989-90:

Men	Women	Total
3026	6842	9868

Student Enrolment, 1986-87:

	Men	Women	Total
Of the country	707	5274	5981
Of other countries	18	66	84
Total	725	5340	6065

5732 ***PHILIPPINE WOMEN'S UNIVERSITY**
1743 Taft Avenue, Manila D-406
Telephone: 59-25-15
President: Rosa Santos Munda (1980-)
Senior Vice-President: Eugenio V. Guillermo

D. of Education (including Library Science, Psychology, Economics, Home Economics, Physical Education, Music, and Fine Arts)
Vice-President: Eva Gonzalez; *staff* 216 (136)
D. of Science and Technology (including Food Technology and Hotel Management)
Vice-President: Ignacio S. Pablo; *staff* 33 (29)
D. of Business Industry
Vice-President: Eugenio B. Guillermo; *staff* 16 (34)
D. of Allied Health Sciences and Social Development (including Pharmacy and Nursing)
Vice-President: Milagros P. Ocampo; *staff* 29 (24)
Computer Ce.
Head: Lilian P. Umipig; *staff* 7 (11)
Ce. for Lifelong Education
Also elementary and high schools.

Founded 1919 as Philippine Women's College. College of Home Economics added 1928, Graduate School established 1932. Granted university status 1932. Community College established 1949. Governing body: the Board of Trustees, composed of 10 members. Residential facilities for academic staff and students.

Arrangements for co-operation with: Mercy College, New York; University of Minnesota; University of Munich.

Academic Year: June to March (June-October; November-March).

Admission Requirements: Graduation from high school and entrance examination.

Fees (Pesos): 76.85 per unit.

Languages of Instruction: English and Pilipino.

Degrees and Diplomas: Bachelor of–Arts, A.B.; Fine Arts, B.F.A.; Music, B.M.; Science in Foods and Nutrition, B.S.F.N.; Science in Food Technology; Science in Administration; Science in Home Economics, B.S.H.E.; Science in Education, B.S.E.; Science in Elementary Education, B.S.E.E.; Science in Business Administration, B.S.B.A.; Science in Hotel and Restaurant Management, B.S.H.R.M.; Science in International Food Administration, B.S.I.F.A.; Science in Social Work, B.S.S.W.; Science in Economics, B.S.Eco., 4 yrs; Science in Pharmacy, B.S.Pharm.; Science in Chemistry, B.S.Chem.; Science in Nursing, B.S.N.; Science in Medical Technology, B.S.Mec.Tech., 5 yrs. Master of–Business Administration; Arts in Education; Arts in Psychology; Arts in Guidance and Counselling; Science in Home Economics; Science in Foods and Nutrition; Science in Pharmacy; Arts in Environmental Management; Science in Chemistry; Science in Pharmaceutical Chemistry; Science in Biology; Science in Social Work, at least 1 yr after Bachelor. Doctor of–Education, Ed.D; Business Management, D.B.M.

Library: Ramona S. Tirona Memorial Library, 74,837 vols.

Special Facilities (Museums, etc.): Bayamiham Folk Arts Center.

Publications: The Philiwomenian (monthly); The Alumna Link (quarterly); Bayanihan Batita (quarterly); PWU Bulletin (bimonthly).

Academic Staff, 1986-87:

Rank	Full-time	Part-time
Professors	6	9
Associate Professors	16	40
Assistant Professors	72	99
Instructors	44	36
Total	138	184

5733 **PAMANTASAN NG SAN LUIS**
Saint Louis University
P.O. Box 71, A. Bonifacio Street, Baguio City 0216
Telephone: 30-43; 27-93
President: Joseph Van den Daelen, CICM (1983-)
Registrar: Violeta C. Garcia

C. of Law
Dean: Galo Reyes; *staff* – (11)
C. of Humanities (including Political Science and Economics)
Dean: Josefina Domingo; *staff* 28 (9)
C. of Commerce and Business Administration
Dean: Gabino Garoy; *staff* 54 (4)
C. of Engineering and Architecture
Dean: Eufracio delos Reyes; *staff* 128 (7)
C. of Education
Dean: Salud S. Idio; *staff* 26 (6)
C. of Natural Sciences (including Pharmacy)
Dean: Gerard Braeckman; *staff* 48 (14)
C. of Medicine
Dean: Honorata Yabut; *staff* 27 (57)
C. of Nursing
Dean: Fatima Fangayen; *staff* 27 (3)
Graduate S. of Arts and Sciences
Dean: Lucita Jacalne; *staff* – (8)
Sociological Research I.
Regional Science Teaching Ce.
Director: Gregorio S. Rimas; *staff* 3
Ce. of Guidance and Counselling
Director: Evarist Verlinden; *staff* 1 (6)
I. for Small-Scale Industries
Director: Erlinda T. Manopol; *staff* 6
Research and Extension Services Ce.
Director: Josefina N. Domingo; *staff* 2 (1)
Information and Computer Science I.
Director: Florian B. Generalao; *staff* 8 (1)

Founded 1911 as primary school. Began offering college courses 1952 and acquired university status 1963. Governing body: the Board of Trustees, comprising 5 members. Residential facilities for students.

Arrangements for co-operation with: Catholic University of Louvain; Universitaire Faculteiten Sint-Aloysuis; Parahuangan Catholic University.

Academic Year: June to March (June-October; November-March).

Admission Requirements: Graduation from high school or recognized foreign equivalent, and entrance examination.

Fees (Pesos): 1500-2000 per semester; Medicine, 8775.50; Nursing, 1800-4500.

Language of Instruction: English.

Degrees and Diplomas: Bachelor of–Arts, B.A.; Literature in English; Philosophy; Arts in Communication; Science in Commerce, B.S.C.; Science in Elementary Education, B.S.E.Ed.; Science in Elementary Education Home Economics, B.S.E.Ed.H.E.; Science in Education, B.S.E.; Science in Chemistry, B.S.(Chem.); Science in Medical Technology, B.S.Med.Tech.; Science in Biology, Science in Social Work, B.S.S.W.; Science in Psychology, B.S.Psycho.; Science in Sociology, B.S.Socio.; Science in Nursing, B.S.N.; Science in Pharmacy, B.S. Pharm., 4 yrs; Science in Chemical Engineering, B.S.Ch.E.; Science in Civil Engineering, B.S.C.E.; Science in Electrical Engineering, B.S.E.E.; Science in Electronic Engineering; Science in Industrial Engineering, B.S.I.E.; Science in Architecture, 5 yrs. Bachelor of Laws, Ll.B., 4 yrs after first degree. Master of–Arts in Economics, M.A.Econ.; Arts in Education, M.A.Educ.; Arts in English,

M.A.Engl.; Arts in Philosophy, M.A.Philos.; Arts in Teaching, M.A.T.; Science in Biology; Science in Chemistry;Science in Business Administration, M.S.B.A.; Science in Management Engineering, M.S.M.E.; Science in Psychology, a further 2 yrs. Doctor of–Education, Ed.D.; Philosophy; Philosophy in Education, at least 2 yrs after Master. Doctor of Medicine, 4 yrs after first degree.

Library: Main Library, 180,475 vols.

Special Facilities (Museums, etc.): Museums: Arts and Culture; Natural Sciences; Archives.

Publications: Saint Louis Chronicle (once every 2 mos.); Research Journal (quarterly); Journal of Medicine (quarterly); SLU-EISSIF Newsletter(quarterly).

Academic Staff, 1989-90:

Rank	Full-time	Part-time
Professors	26	6
Associate Professors	41	10
Assistant Professors	159	49
Instructors	114	33
Assistant Instructors	34	1
Others	2	–
Total	376	100

Student Enrolment, 1989-90:

	Men	Women	Total
Of the country	7371	7514	14,885
Of other countries	137	86	223
Total	7508	7600	15,108

5734 **SAINT PAUL UNIVERSITY**

Mabini Street, Tuguerao, Cagayan
Telephone: 446-1863
President: Mary Angela Barrios, spc
Registrar: Emilia Lagasca,spc

C. of Education
Dean: Miriam Raymond Victoriano, spc; *staff* 8 (3)
C. of Arts and Sciences
Dean: Marie Marcelle Navarro; *staff* 10 (2)
C. of Business and Administration
Dean: Paulina Dy; *staff* 11 (6)
C. of Nursing
Dean: Carolina Agravante, spc; *staff* 11
C. of Engineering
Dean (Acting): Agripina Maribbay; *staff* 11 (6)
C. of Nutrition and Dietetics
Dean: Mary Priscilla Manalang; *staff* 5
Graduate S.
Dean: Levita Manglapus Castro; *staff* 7 (5)
Secretarial D.
Director: Josephine Campanano; *staff* 7 (5)
Also elementary and high schools.

Founded 1907 as college, became university 1982. A private institution. Governing body: the Board of Trustees. Residential facilities for students.

Academic Year: June to March (June-October; November-March).

Admission Requirements: Graduation from high school and entrance examination.

Fees (Pesos): 66.20-74.40 per annum.

Languages of Instruction: English and Pilipino.

Degrees and Diplomas: Associate in Geodetic Engineering, AGE, 3 yrs. Bachelor of Arts, A.B.; Science in–Social Work, B.S.S.W.; Psychology, B.S.P.; Secretarial Administration, B.S.S.A.; Nursing, B.S.N.; Mathematics, B.S.M.; Guidance, B.S.G.; Food and Nutrition, B.S.N.D.; Education, B.S.E.; Elementary Education, B.S.S.E.; Business Administration, B.S.B.A., 4 yrs; Civil Engineering, B.S.C.E., 5 yrs. Information and Computer Science, B.S.I.C.S., 4 yrs.; Geodetic Engineering, B.S.G.E., 3 yrs.; Master of–Education; Arts in Home Economics, M.A.H.E.; Business Administration, M.B.A., a further 2-3 yrs. Doctor of–Philosophy; Elementary and High School Management, 2-3 yrs.

Library: College Library, 23,664 vols.

Publications: The Paulinian (quarterly); Pauleen (biannually); Paulinette (biannually); Search (Faculty Journal) (annually).

Academic Staff, 1989-90:

Rank	Full-time	Part-time
Professors	4	1
Associate Professors	12	1
Assistant Professors	17	1
Instructors	20	5
Assistant Instructors	32	15
Total	85	23

Student Enrolment, 1989-90:

	Men	Women	Total
Of the country	783	2,429	3,212
Of other countries	83	183	266
Total	866	2,612	3,478

5735 **SILLIMAN UNIVERSITY**

Dumaguete City 6501, Negros Oriental
Telephone: 32-00
President: Quintin S. Doromal

C. of Arts and Science
C. of Education
C. of Engineering
C. of Nursing
C. of Medical Technology
C. of Social Work
C. of Law
C. of Business Administration
C. of Agriculture
S. of Divinity
S. of Mass Communications
S. of Music and Fine Arts
Graduate S.
D. of Physical Education and Atheletics
Also elementary and high schools.

Founded 1901 as Silliman Institute, following gift by Dr. Horace B. Silliman to the Presbyterian Board of Foreign Missions (USA). Became university 1938. A private institution supported by fees, gifts, and grants. Since 1957 support from the U.S.A has been channelled through the United Board for Christian Higher Education in Asia, New York. Governing body: the Board of Trustees, composed of 15 members. Some residential facilities for academic staff and for students.

Academic Year: June to March (June-October; November-March).

Admission Requirements: Graduation from high school and entrance examination.

Language of Instruction: English.

Degrees and Diplomas: Bachelor of–Arts, A.B.; Science, B.S.; Science in Agriculture, B.S.A.; Science in Chemistry, B.S.Chem.; Business Administration, B.B.A.; Mass Communications, B.M.C.; Science in Education, B.S.E.; Science in Elementary Education, B.S.E.Ed.; Science in Industrial Education, B.S.I.E.; Science in Nursing, B.S.N.; Theology, B.Th.; Ministry, B.Min.; Divinity, B.D.; Science in Social Work, B.S.S.W.; Science in Home Economics, B.S.H.E.; Science in Mathematics; Science in Medical Technology, B.S.M.T., 4 yrs; Music, B.M.; Science in Civil Engineering, B.S.C.E.; Science in Electrical Engineering, B.S.E.E.; Science in Mechanical Engineering, B.S.M.E., 5 yrs. Bachelor of Laws, Ll.B., 4 yrs after first degree. Master of–Arts, M.A.; Arts in Education; Arts in Teaching, M.A.T.; Fine Arts; Arts in Nursing; Science; Divinity; Ministry, a further 2 yrs. Doctor of–Philosophy in Education, Ph.D.; Education, Ed.D.; Philosophy in English and Literature, Ph.D., 2 yrs after Master.

Library: Total, *c.* 120,000 vols.

Special Facilities (Museums, etc.): Museums: Anthropology; Biology.

Publications: Weekly Calendar; Weekly Sillimanian; Silliman Journal (quarterly); Sands and Coral (annually).

Press or Publishing House: University Press.

Academic Staff: c. 260 (70).
Student Enrolment: c. 6750.

5736 **SOUTHWESTERN UNIVERSITY**
Villa Aznar, Urgello, Private Road, Cebu City
Telephone: 9-66-90; 9-07-21; 9-07-97
President: Manolo S. Fornolles
Registrar: Benjamin Abellana

C. of Medicine
Dean (Acting): Alfredo Paguio; *staff* 24 (62)
C. of Dentistry
Dean: Oscar Villaluz; *staff* 23 (2)
C. of Medical Technology
Assistant Dean: Niñan Oplado; *staff* 15 (22)
C. of Nursing
Dean: Loreto Lucas; *staff* 17
C. of Pharmacy
Dean: Rosario T. Barcenilla; *staff* 7 (8)
C. of Optometry
Dean: Arlene Dorio; *staff* 5 (7)
C. of Law
Dean: Froilan Quijqno; *staff* 2 (9)
C. of Arts and Sciences (including Political Science, Psychology, Economics Biology, and Zoology)
Dean: A.T. Adelaida; *staff* 66 (12)
C. of Commerce
Dean: Eugenio Gabuya; *staff* 13 (20)
C. of Engineering
Dean: Gregorio Segura; *staff* 20 (3)
C. of Education
Dean: Frances Lumain; *staff* 14
C. of Social Work
Chairman: Jimmy Labajo; *staff* 1 (2)
D. of Agricultural Technology
Dean: Ernesto Gemota; *staff* 3 (1)
C. of Veterinary Medicine
Dean: Enrico Flores; *staff* 6 (1)
Graduate S.
Dean: Alicia P. Cabatingan; *staff* 1 (15)
C. of Physical Therapy
Dean: Vicente Villareal; *staff* 10 (1)
I. of Computer Sciences
Dean: Roland Go; *staff* 8 (8)
I. of Physical Education
Director: Melquiades Gonzales; *staff* 6 (2)
Also elementary and high schools.

Founded 1946 as Southwestern Colleges, became university 1959. A private institution financially supported by tuition fees. Governing body: the Board of Directors. Residential facilities for women students.

Academic Year: June to March (June-October; November-March).

Admission Requirements: Graduation from high school and entrance examination.

Languages of Instruction: English, Tagalog, and Cebuano.

Degrees and Diplomas: Bachelor of–Arts, A.B.; Science in Pre-Medicine, B.S.Pre-Med.; Science in Biology, B.S.Biology; Science in Education, B.S.E.; Science in Elementary Education, B.S.E.Ed.; Science in Home Economics, B.S.H.E.; Science in Foods and Nutrition, B.S.F.N.; Science in Commerce, B.S.C.; Science in Medical Technology, B.S.M.T.; Science in computer Sciences, B.S.C.S.; Science in Nursing, B.S.N., 4 yrs; Science in Pharmacy, B.S.Pharm.; Science in Chemical Engineering, B.S.Ch.E.; Science in Mechanical Engineering, B.S.M.E.; Science in Electrical Engineering, B.S.E.E.; Science in Civil Engineering, B.S.C.E.; Science in Physical Therapy, B.S.P.T., 5 yrs. Bachelor of Laws, Ll.B., 4 yrs after first degree. Master of–Arts, M.A.; Business Administration; Nursing, a further yr. Doctor of–Optometry, O.D.; Dental Medicine, D.D.M.; Medicine, M.D.; Veterinary Medicine, D.V.M., 4-6 yrs after first degree. Also Doctorates in–Education; Agricultural Education; Science Education.

Libraries: Central Library, c. 50,000 vols; Medicine, c. 10.175.

Special Facilities (Museums, etc.): Biological Garden; Aznar Coliseum; Amphitheatre; Audio-visual Rooms.

Publications: Southwestern Journal (quarterly); The Quill; The Beacon (annually).

Press or Publishing House: University Press.

Academic Staff, 1989-90:

Rank	Full-time	Part-time
Professors	6	2
Associate Professors	12	7
Assistant Professors	15	7
Instructors	99	51
Assistant Instructors	12	10
Others	98	91
Total	242	168

Student Enrolment, 1989-90:

	Men	Women	Total
Of the country	3700	7368	11,068

5737 **UNIVERSITY OF THE ASSUMPTION**
San Fernando, Pampanga 2001
Cables: San Fernando, pamp. Phil
Telephone: 61-36-17
President: Jesus C. Galang (1985-90)
Registrar: Adelaida M. Lansangan

C. of Education
Dean: Eriberta T. Maglaqui; *staff* 24 (21)
C. of Commerce
Dean: Faustina A. Castro; *staff* 13 (13)
C. of Architecture
Officer-in-Charge: Remedios M. Dizon; *staff* 5 (2)
C. of Engineering
Dean: Helen T. Dagdag; *staff* 22 (15)
C. of Nursing
Dean: Lydia Dizon; *staff* 10 (2)
C. of Nutrition and Dietetics
Officer-in-Charge: Leonida G. David; *staff* 4
C. of Liberal Arts
Dean: Lolita Nicodemus; *staff* 23 (21)
Graduate S.
Dean: Elizabeth Y. Manugue; (12)
Also elementary and high schools.

Founded 1963 as college, became university 1980. A private institution. Governing body: the Board of Trustees.

Academic Year: June to March (June-October; November-March).

Admission Requirements: Graduation from high school and entrance examination.

Fees (Pesos): 373.46 per unit, per year; Graduate studies, 383.45.

Languages of Instruction: English, Pilipino and Spanish.

Degrees and Diplomas: Bachelor of Arts, A.B., 4 yrs; Bachelor of Science in–Architecture, B.S.A.; Commerce, B.S.C.; Education, B.S.E.; Elementary Education, B.S.E.E.D.; Nursing, B.S.N.; Nutrition and Dietetics, B.S.N.D.; Civil Engineering, B.S.C.E; Industrial Engineering, B.S.I.E., 5 yrs. Master of Arts in–Education; Business Administration, M.B.A.Doctor of Education, Ed.D.

Library: Central Library, 26,084 vols.

Publications: Regina (quarterly); Research Journal (biannual); Veritas (quarterly).

Academic Staff: c. 100 (80).
Student Enrolment: c. 5790.

5738 ***UNIVERSITY OF BAGUIO**
17 Gen Luna, Baguio City 2600
Cables: unibaguio
Telephone: (63-74) 442-3071
Fax: (63-74) 442-6501
President: Wilfredo A. Wi (1989-)

C. of Arts and Sciences
Dean: Eduard H. Rillorta; *staff* 30 (5)
C. of Commerce
Dean: Cristeta Leung; *staff* 44 (3)
C. of Criminology
Dean: Rodolfo Sabinian; *staff* 10 (8)
C. of Education
Dean: James Malaya; *staff* 38 (5)
C. of Engineering
Dean: Nancy G. Cruz; *staff* 28 (6)
C. of Dentistry
Dean: Brenda Banda-ay; *staff* 5 (15)

Graduate S.
Dean: Felipe L. de Guzman; *staff* 5
Also elementary and high schools.
Founded 1948 as Technical Institute, acquired university status 1969. A private institution. Governing body: the Board of Trustees, composed of five members. Residential facilities for some academic staff and students.
Arrangements for co-operation with: Nagasaki Wesleyan College; Phon Commercial College; Tamkang University.
Academic Year: June to March (June-October; October-March).
Admission Requirements: Graduation from high school and entrance examination.
Fees (Pesos): 1300 per semester.
Languages of Instruction: English, Pilipino and Spanish.
Degrees and Diplomas: Bachelor of Science in–Elementary Education, B.S.E.Ed.; Commerce, B.S.C.; Commercial Education, B.S. Com. Ed.; Education, B.S.E.; Civil Engineering, B.S.C.E.; Sanitary Engineering, B.S.M.E.; Medical Technology, B.S.M.T.; Criminology, B.S.Crim.; Biology, B.S.Bio.; Bachelor of Arts, A.B., 4-5 yrs. Master of Arts in–Education, M.A.Ed.; English, M.A.English; Business Administration, M.B.A.; College Teaching, M.A.C.T.; Science Education, M.A.S.E., Doctor of Education, Ed.D.; Dental Medicine.
Library: Central Library, *c.* 80,000 vols.
Special Facilities (Museums, etc.): Anthropology Museum.
Publications: Journal (biannually); Bulletin (quarterly).
Press or Publishing House: Black and White Press.
Academic Staff: c. 160 (42).
Student Enrolment: c. 10,000.

5739 ***UNIVERSITY OF BOHOL**
Maria Clara Street, Tagbilaran, Bohol 6301
Telephone: 3101 ITT
President: David B. Tirol (1946-)
Vice-President: Nuevas T. Montes

C. of Law
Dean: Ulysses B. Tirol; *staff* 5 (4)
C. of Technology (including Architecture)
Dean: Jes B. Tirol; *staff* 36 (11)
C. of Pharmacy
Dean: Elvigia Magallano; *staff* 4 (2)
C. of Nursing
Dean: Florencia Estrera; *staff* 47 (1)
C. of Commerce and Business Administration
Dean: Victor B. Tirol; *staff* 22 (8)
Teachers' C.
Dean: Felix A. Lao; *staff* 37 (4)
C. of Arts and Sciences (including Political Science)
Dean: Ines T. Bernaldez; *staff* 14 (6)
C. of Forestry
Head (Acting): Edna Elbambo; *staff* 2 (1)
C. of Architecture
Head: Eufracio Araneta; *staff* 3 (1)
C. of Criminology
Dean: Daniel Lao; *staff* 4 (2)
C. of Home Economics
Dean: Iluminada B. Tirol; *staff* 3 (1)
Graduate S.
Dean: Henya T. Sotela; *staff* 16 (4)
Also elementary and high schools.
Founded 1946 as college, acquired present status and title 1970. A private institution. Governing body: the Board of Trustees.
Academic Year: June to March (June-October; November-March).
Admission Requirements: Graduation from high school and entrance examination.
Languages of Instruction: English, Pilipino, and Spanish.
Degrees and Diplomas: Associate in–Agricultural Technology, A.A.T.; Secretarial Science, A.S.S., 2 yrs; Civil Engineering, A.C.E.; Electrical Engineering, A.E.E.; Geodetic Engineering, A.F.E.; Mechanical Engineering, A.M.E., 3 yrs. Bachelor of–Arts, A.B.; Science in–Pharmacy, B.S.Pharm.; Commerce, B.S.C.; Business Administration, B.S.B.A.; Education, B.S.E.; Elementary Education; Elementary Education in Home Economics; Home Economics, B.S.H.E.; Nursing, B.S.N.; Criminology, B.S.Crim.; Forestry, B.S.F, 4 yrs.; Architecture, B.S. Arch.; Civil Engineering, B.S.C.E.; Chemical Engineering, B.S.Ch.E.; Mechanical Engineering, B.S.M.E.; Electrical Engineering, B.S.E.E., 5 yrs. Bachelor of Laws, Ll.B., 4 yrs after first degree. Master of–Arts, M.A.; Science in Management Engineering, M.S.Man.E.; Science in Business Administration, a further 2-3 yrs. Doctor of Philosophy, Ph.D., at least 3-4 yrsafter Master.
Libraries: Central Library, 19,500 vols; Law, 389; Engineering and High School, 5923.
Special Facilities (Museums, etc.): Research Centre and Museum.
Publications: The Forum; Varsitarian; The Beginner; The Penmasters.
Academic Staff, 1989-90:

Rank	Full-time	Part-time
Professors	15	6
Assistant Professors	109	36
Instructors	71	12
Total	195	54

Student Enrolment, 1989-90:

	Men	Women	Total
Of the country	3307	5333	8,640
Of other countries	–	–	1
Total	3307	5333	8,641

5740 ***UNIVERSITY OF THE EAST**
Claro M. Recto Avenue, Manila
Cables: Philcolcom
Telephone: 741-95-01
President: Oscar C. Limlingan
Vice-President for Academic Affairs: Herminia M. Barcelona

C. of Arts and Sciences (including Political Sciences, Sociology, Physical and Biological Sciences, Mathematics, English and Filipino)
Dean: Rosario V. Lamug; *staff* 238 (15)
C. of Business Administration
Dean: Mercedes J. Manadis; *staff* 121 (53)
C. of Dentistry
Dean: Diampo J. Lim; *staff* 53 (9)
C. of Education
Dean: Amelita A. Cruz; *staff* 49 (8)
C. of Engineering
Dean: Pacifico T. Santos; *staff* 81 (32)
C. of Law
Dean: Dante O. Tinga; *staff* (31)
C. of Medicine
Dean: Joven R. Cuanang; *staff* 41 (145)
C. of Nursing
Dean: Carmelita Divinagracia; *staff* 11 (7)
S. of Fine Arts
Dean: Florencio B. Concepcion; *staff* 3 (9)
Graduate S.
Dean: Pocidio C.M. Quiambao, Jr.; *staff* 8 (15)
I. of Technical Education
Dean: Pacifico T. Santos
Computer I.
Dean: Nati C. San Gabriel; *staff* 15
Founded 1946, became Philippine College of Commerce and Business Administration 1947. Became university 1951. The university is a private institution operated under the supervision of the Department of Education, Cultureand Sports. Financed by student fees and income from investments. Governing body: the Board of Trustees, comprising 11 members.
Academic Year: June to March (June-October; November-March).
Admission Requirements: Graduation from high school or recognized foreign equivalent, and entrance examination.
Fees (Pesos): Tuition, 2,000.
Languages of Instruction: English and Pilipino.
Degrees and Diplomas: Bachelor of–Arts, A.B.; Science, B.S.; Science in Business Administration, B.S.B.A.; Science in Secretarial Education, B.S.S.E.; Science in Education, B.S.E.; Science in Elementary Education, B.S.E.Ed.; Science in Nutrition and Dietetics, B.S.N.D., 4 yrs; Science in Nursing, B.S.N.; Science in Electronics and Communications Engineering; Science in Civil Engineering, B.S.C.E.; Science in Mechanical Engineering, B.S.M.E.; Science in Electrical Engineering, B.S.E.E., 5 yrs. Bachelor of Laws, Ll.B, 4 yrs after first degree. Master of–Arts, M.A.; Business Administration, M.B.A., a further 2 yrs. Doctorates in–Dentistry, D.D.M., 6 yrs; Medicine, M.D., 8 yrs. Doctor of Education, Ed.D.
Library: Total, *c.* 183,230 vols.
Publications: The Dawn (weekly); UE Today (monthly).

Academic Staff: c. 1500.
Student Enrolment, 1990:

	Men	Women	Total
Of the country	16581	16092	32,673
Of Other countries	224	53	277
Total	16805	16145	32,950

5741 **UNIVERSITY OF ILOILO**
Rizal Street, La Paz, Iloilo City

C. of Education
C. of Law
C. of Liberal Arts (including Nutrition)
C. of Science
C. of Commerce
C. of Criminology
C. of Engineering
C. of Agriculture
C. of Nursing
C. of Social Work
S. of Secretarial Studies

Founded 1947, acquired university status 1968.

5742 ***THE UNIVERSITY OF MANILA**
588 Dr. M.V. de Los Santos Street, Manila 2806
Cables: Univman
Telephone: 7413645
President: Virgilio de los Santos

C. of Law
C. of Education
C. of Business Administration
C. of Liberal Arts (including Mathematics and Journalism)
C. of Criminology and Penology
C. of Graduate Studies
C. of Engineering
C. of Sciences

Also high school.

Founded 1913 as Instituto de Manila, a private high school. Became university 1921. Independent private institution operated under the supervision of the Ministry of Education, Culture and Sports. Governing bodies: the Board of Trustees, of 7 members; the Administrative Council. Financed by student fees and income from investments.

Academic Year: June-March (June-October; November-March).

Admission Requirements: Graduation from accredited high school or equivalent, and entrance examination.

Language of Instruction: English.

Degrees and Diplomas: Associate in–Business Administration; Foreign Service; Criminology and Police Administration. Bachelor of–Arts, A.B.; Business Administration, B.B.A.; Science in Foreign Service, B.S.F.S.; Science in Education, B.S.E.; Science in Elementary Education, B.S.E.Ed.; Science in Criminology and Police Administration, B.S.C.P.A., 4 yrs. Bachelor of Laws, Ll.B., 4 yrs after first degree. Master of–Arts in Education, M.A.Educ.; Arts in Political Science, M.A.Pol.Sci.; Arts in History, M.A.Hist.; Public Administration, M.P.A.; Laws, Ll.M., 1 yr after Bachelor. Certificate in Secretarial Science, 1 yr.

Libraries: Central Library, *c.* 19,300 vols; Law and Criminology, *c.* 5700; High School and Elementary Library, *c.* 4990; Tondo Unit Library, *c.* 5680.

Special Facilities (Museums, etc.): Dr. M.V. de los Santos Memorial Museum.

Publications: The Campus Leader; Journal of East Asiatic Studies; The Gold Leaf; Law Gazette; Business Logbook.

Academic Staff: c. 220.
Student Enrolment: c. 12,000.

5743 **UNIVERSITY OF LA SALLE**
La Salle Avenue, Bacolod City, Negros Occidental 6001
Telephone: 2-05-77; 2-65-50
President: Rolando R. Dizon, F.S.C.
Academic Vice-President: Elsa M. Coscollueza

C. of Arts and Science
Associate Dean: Aurora Ang; *staff* 51 (22)
C. of Engineering
Associate Dean: Florita Napauatan; *staff* 7 (2)
C. of Commerce
Associate Dean: Claro Zubia; *staff* 11 (20)
C. of Business Management
C. of Education
Associate Dean: Teretita Atotkbo; *staff* 2 (2)
C. of Nursing
Associate Dean: Zenaida Hilado; *staff* 55
Graduate S.
Dean: Dolores Ramos; *staff* 6 (6)

Also elementary and high schools.

Founded a college 1952 by the La Salle Brothers of the Christian Schools. Became university 1988. A private institution. Governing body: the Board of Trustees, comprising 10 members.

Arrangements for co-operation with La Salle University, Philadelphia.

Academic Year: June to March (June-October; November-March).

Admission Requirements: Graduation from high school and entrance examination.

Fees: 2500-4000 per semester; Graduate, 2000-2500.

Languages of Instruction: English and Pilipino.

Degrees and Diplomas: Bachelor of–Science in Commerce; Science; Arts; Science in Education; Science in Engineering; Science in Nursing, 4 yrs. Master of–Business Administration; Educational Management, a further 3 yrs.

Library: c. 30,000 vols.

Publications: Management Review; Spectrum.

Academic Staff, 1989-90:

	Full-time	Part-time
Professors	12	6
Associate Professors	16	4
Assistant Professors	45	15
Instructors	70	32
Total	143	57

Student Enrolment, 1989-90:

	Men	Women	Total
Of the country	4251	2611	3862

5744 **UNIVERSITY OF MINDANAO**
Bolton Street, Davao City, Mindanao Island
Telephone: 7-54-56
President: Guillermo E. Torres (1945-88)

C. of Commerce
Dean: Thelma S. Ledesma; *staff* 45 (41)
C. of Criminology
Dean: Leo Carillo; *staff* 1 (8)
C. of Education
Dean: Paquita Gavino; *staff* 13 (10)
C. of Engineering and Architecture
Dean: Uldarico D. Dumdum; *staff* 76 (28)
C. of Forestry
Dean: Libertad Duran; *staff* 5 (4)
C. of Law
Dean: Cornelto Maskarino; *staff* 10 (15)
C. of Liberal Arts
Head: Leonides G. Soriano; *staff* 14 (11)
D. of Radio Communication
Dean: Nestor Villagomeza; *staff* 11
Graduate S.
Dean: Julian Rodriguez; *staff* – (24)

Branches at: Panabo, Tagum, Digos, Ilang-Tibungco, Guinga, Peñaplata, Cotabato, Bansalan, Sta. Ana. Also elementary and high schools.

Founded as a private non-sectarian college 1946. Became university 1963. Independent private institution operated under the supervision of the Ministry of Education, Culture and Sports. Governing body: the Board of Trustees.

Academic Year: June to March (June-October; November-March).

Admission Requirements: Graduation from high school or recognized foreign equivalent, and entrance examination.

Languages of Instruction: English and Pilipino.

Degrees and Diplomas: Bachelor of Science in–Agri-Business, B.S.Agri-Bus., 2 yrs. Bachelor of–Arts, A.B.; Science, B.S.; Science in Commerce, B.S.C.; Science in Education, B.S.E.; Science in Elementary Education, B.S.E.Ed.; Science in Social Work, B.S.S.W.; Science in Forestry, B.S.F.; Science in Elementary Education, B.S.E.Ed.; Science in Criminology, B.S.Crim.; Science in Public Administration, B.S.P.A.; Science in Secretarial Administration, B.S.S.A., 4 yrs; Science in Civil Engineering, B.S.C.E.; Science in Chemical Engineering, B.S.Ch.E.; Science in Mechanical Engineering, B.S.M.E.; Science in Architecture, B.S.Arch., 5 yrs. Bachelor of

Laws, Ll.B., 4 yrs after firstdegree. Master of Arts, M.A., 2 yrs after Bachelor. Doctor of Education, Ed.D., 2-3 yrs after Master.
Library: Central Library, 72,474 vols.
Publication: The Mindanao Collegian (monthly).
Academic Staff, 1986-87: 188 (128).
Student Enrolment, 1986-87:

	Men	Women	Total
Of the country	7547	5939	13,486

5745 **UNIVERSITY OF NEGROS OCCIDENTAL-RECOLETOS**
P.O. Box, 214, Lizares Avenue, Bacolod City
Cables: Uno-Recoletos
Telephone: 2-50-36
Fax: 2-50-36
President: Jose Antonio Rodrigalvarez, O.A.R. (1985-)
Registrar: Ismael L. Exito

C. of Law
Dean: Nelson Lo
C. of Arts and Sciences
Dean: Celia Mahinay
C. of Engineering
Dean: Nicanor P. Navarro
C. of Education
Dean: Jose B. Ferraris
C. of Criminology
Dean: Jose Manuel Lopez Vito
S. of Agriculture
Dean: Evangeline D. Orellanes
C. of Commerce
Dean: Edgar L. Grino
C. of Medical Technology
Graduate S.
Dean: Jose B. Ferraris
Also elementary and high schools.

Founded 1941 as institute, became university 1957. Administered since 1962 by the Recollect Fathers of St. Augustine. Under the supervision of the Department of Education, Culture, and Sports. Residential facilities for Recollect Fathers.

Academic Year: June to March (June-October; November-March).
Admission Requirements: Graduation from high school and entrance examination.
Language of Instruction: English.
Degrees and Diplomas: Bachelor of–Arts, A.B.; Elementary Education, B.E.Ed.; Science in–Criminology, B.S. Crim.; Secondary Education, B.S.Ed.; Social Work, B.S.S.W.; Agriculture, B.S.A.; Medical Technology, B.S.M.T.; Psychology, B.S.Psycho.; General Science, B.S.G.S.; Secretarial Administration, B.S.S.A.; Computer Science, B.S.C.S.; Commerce, B.S.C.; Industrial Management, B.S.I.M., 4 yrs.; Civil Engineering, B.S.C.E.; Mechanical Engienering, B.S.M.E.; Electrical Engineering, B.S.E.E.; Chemical Engineering, B.S.Ch.E., 5 yrs. Bachelor of Laws, Ll.B., 4 yrs. after first degree. Master of–Arts in Education, M.A.; Public Administration, M.P.A.; Business Administration, M.B.A., 2 yrs after Bachelor. Doctor of Philosophy, Ph.D., 2 yrs.
Library: Central Library, *c.* 63,889 vols.
Publication: Journal.
Academic Staff: c. 130 (100).
Student Enrolment: c. 10,000.

5746 ***UNIVERSITY OF NORTHEASTERN PHILIPPINES**
Iriga City
President: Ciriaco R. Alfelor

C. of Arts
C. of Architecture
C. of Engineering
C. of Law
C. of Education
C. of Commerce
C. of Nursing (including Midwifery)
C. of Criminology
C. of Social Work
Graduate S.
I. of Technology

Founded 1948. A private institution. Governing body: the Board of Trustees, comprising 6 members.

Degrees and Diplomas: Bachelor, 4 yrs. Bachelor of Laws, 4 yrs after first degree. Master, a further 2 yrs. Doctor in Education.
Library: c. 20,000 vols.
Academic Staff: c. 160 (30).
Student Enrolment: c. 4020.

5747 **UNIVERSITY OF NUEVA CACERES**
Igualdad Street, Naga City 4721
Cables: Unc
Telephone: 9287
President: Jaime Hernandez

C. of Liberal Arts and Sciences
C. of Engineering
C. of Law
C. of Commerce
C. of Education
C. of Nursing
Graduate S. (Educational Management)
Also elementary and high schools.

Founded 1948 as the Nueva Caceres Colleges. Became university 1954. Governing body: the Board of Trustees. The university is a private institution operated under the supervision of the Ministry of Education, Culture and Sports. Some residential facilities for students of nursing and for some academic staff.

Academic Year: June to March (June-October; November-March).
Admission Requirements: Graduation from high school and entrance examination.
Languages of Instruction: English and Pilipino.
Degrees and Diplomas: Graduate in Nursing, G.N., 3 yrs; Bachelor of–Arts, A.B.; Science, B.S.; Science in Commerce, B.S.C.; Science in Business Administration, B.S.B.A.; Science in Public Administration, B.S.P.A., Science in Nursing, B.S.N.; Science in Botany; Science in Zoology; Science in Education, B.S.E.; Science in Elementary Education, B.S.E.Ed., 4 yrs; Science in Civil Engineering, B.S.C.E.; Science in Industrial Engineering, B.S.I.E.; Science in Chemical Engineering, B.S.Ch.E.; Mechanical Engineering, B.S.M.E., 5 yrs. Bachelor of Laws, Ll.B., 4 yrs after first degree. Master of–Arts, M.A.; Science in Business Administration, M.S.B.A., 2 yrs after Bachelor. Doctor of Educational Management, Ed.D., 3 yrs after Master.
Libraries: Central Library, *c.* 14,500 vols; libraries of various schools and departments, *c.* 12,620.
Special Facilities (Museums, etc.): University Museum.
Publications: University of Nueva Caceres Bulletin (monthly); Education Journal; Bikol Culture; Journal of Graduate Studies and Research.
Academic Staff: c. 260.
Student Enrolment: c. 7280.

5748 **UNIVERSITY OF PANGASINAN**
Arellano-Bani Street, Dagupan City
Telephone: 38-50
President: George O. Rayos (1975-)

C. of Architecture
Dean: Bonifacio C. Langit; *staff* 12
C. of Commerce
Dean: Manuel R. Poco; *staff* 42 (15)
C. of Education
Dean: Juliya R. Pamintyan; *staff* 31 (4)
C. of Engineering
Dean: Manuel F. Fernandez; *staff* 31 (2)
C. of Law
Dean: Hermogenes S. Decano; *staff* 2 (12)
C. of Liberal Arts
Dean: Rufino F. Fernandez; *staff* 54 (6)
C. of Medical Technology
Dean: Gustavo U. Reyes; *staff* 4
C. of Nursing
Head: Oliva R. Coquia; *staff* 22
C. of Secretarial Studies
Dean: Manuel R. Poco; *staff* 6
S. of Graduate Studies
Director: Cristeta M. Dumaran; *staff* 6 (4)
Also elementary and high schools and junior division.

Founded 1925, acquired university status 1968. A private institution operated under the supervision of the Ministry of Education, Culture and Sports. Governing body: the Board of Trustees, composed of 5 members. Residential facilities for students of nursing.

Academic Year: June to March (June-October; November-March).

Admission Requirements: Graduation from high school and entrance examination.

Fees (Pesos): 36.20 per unit.

Languages of Instruction: English and Pilipino.

Degrees and Diplomas: Bachelor of–Arts, A.B.; Philosophy, Ph.B.; Science in Architecture, B.S.Arch.; Science in Education, B.S.E.; Science in Elementary Education, B.S.E.Ed.; Science in Industrial Education, B.S.I.E.; Science in Home Economics, B.S.H.E.; Science in Food and Nutrition, B.S.F.N.; Science in Commerce, B.S.C.; Literature in Journalism, Litt.B.Journalism; Science in Medical Technology, B.S. Med.Tech.; Science in Nursing, B.S.N., 4 yrs; Science in Sanitary Engineering, B.S.S.E.; Civil Engineering, B.S.C.E., 5 yrs. Bachelor of Laws, Ll.B., 4 yrs after first degree. Master of Arts in–Business Education, M.A.B.Ed.; Education, M.A.Ed.; Philosophy, M.A.Phil. Master of Science in–Management Engineering, M.S.Man.E.; Business Administration, M.S.B.A., a further 2 yrs. Doctor of Education, Ed.D.

Library: Total, *c.* 45,000 vols.

Special Facilities (Museums, etc.): Lichauco Marine Museum.

Publication: Researcher (annually).

Academic Staff, 1986-87:

Rank	Full-time	Part-time
Professors	3	–
Associate Professors	5	1
Assistant Professors	10	5
Instructors	174	21
Lecturers	18	16
Total	210	43

Student Enrolment, 1986-87:

	Men	Women	Total
Of the country	4317	5775	10,092
Of other countries	10	2	12
Total	4327	5777	10,104

5749 **UNIVERSITY OF SAINT ANTHONY**

San Miguel, Iriga City, Camarines Sur 4431

Telephone: 401

President: Santiago D. Ortega Jr.

Registrar: Teodoro J. Nacario

C. of Engineering (including Architecture)

; *staff* 14 (4)

C. of Commerce

Dean: Millicent C. Obias; *staff* 14 (3)

C. of Education (including Political Science, Mathematics, English, Filipino, Science, Social Studies, Home Economics)

; *staff* 17 (9)

C. of Nursing (including Midwifery)

Dean: Teresita M. Berina; *staff* 17 (5)

C. of Criminology

Dean: Marito T. Bernales; *staff* 4 (5)

C. of Arts and Sciences (including Economics and Political Science, English, Mass Communication, Mathematics and Science)

Dean: Antonio Cortez; *staff* 16 (5)

C. of Technical Vocational Studies, (including Automotive, Radio Communication, Electronics and Electrical Studies)

Dean Luis T. Laniog; *staff* 7 (3)

Graduate S. (including School Administration, Filipino, Home Economics, Science Teaching, Educational Management, Business Management)

Dean: Nenita Ll. Madara; *staff* 11 (8)

Founded 1947 as academy, became college 1963. Acquired present status and title 1973. A private institution under the supervision of the Ministry of Education, Culture and Sports. Governing body: the Board of Trustees.

Academic Year: June to March (June-October; November-March).

Admission Requirements: Graduation from high school and entrance examination.

Language of Instruction: English.

Degrees and Diplomas: Bachelor of–Arts, A.B.; Science, B.S.; Science in Elementary Education, B.S.E.E.; Science in Home Economics, B.S.H.E.; Science in Industrial Education, B.S.I.Ed.; Science in Education, B.S.E.; Science in Criminology, B.S.Crim.; Science in Commerce, B.S.C.; Science in Nursing, B.S.N.; Science in Architecture, B.S.A., 5 yrs; Science in Civil Engineering, 5 yrs. Master of–Arts in Education, M.A.Ed.; Business Administration, M.B.A., a further 2-3 yrs. Doctor of Philosophy in Education, Ph.D.

Library: Central Library, 27,540 vols.

Special Facilities (Museums, etc.): Audio-visual Centre; Coliseum; Radio Room; Guidance and Testing Centre.

Publications: The Anthonian (quarterly); Research Journal (biannually).

Academic Staff, 1990:

Rank	Full-time	Part-time
Full Professors	2	–
ssociate Professors	1	9
Assistant Professors	13	11
Instructors	41	25
Assistant Instructors	15	4
Total	72	49

Student Enrolment, 1990:

	Men	Women	Total
Of the country	937	1987	2924

5750 **UNIVERSITY OF SAN AGUSTÍN**

General Luna Street, Iloilo City 5000

Telephone: 7-484½

President: Mamerto A. Alfeche, O.S.A. (1988-91)

Registrar: Madela O. Duero

S. of Law

Dean: Cesar Tirol; *staff* 1 (19)

Teachers' C.

Dean: Celia A. Cabaluna; *staff* 27 (31)

C. of Commerce

Dean: Felonila Triste; *staff* 60 (10)

C. of Liberal Arts

Dean: Teresita Aportadera; *staff* 15 (30)

C. of Pharmacy and Medical Technology

Dean: Flora S. Salas; *staff* 30 (4)

C. of Technology (including Architecture)

Dean: Conrado Silvederio; *staff* 50 (15)

C. of Nursing

Dean: Mary Concepcion Cajilig; *staff* 20 (14)

Graduate S.

Dean: Remedios S. Somcio; *staff* – (16)

Conservatory of Music

Dean: Salvacion Jardenil; *staff* 3 (5)

Also pre-elementary, elementary and high schools.

Founded 1904 by the Augustinian Fathers, became university 1953. A private institution under the supervision of the Department of Education, Culture and Sports. Governing body: the Board of Trustees.

Academic Year: June to March (June-October; October-March).

Admission Requirements: Graduation from high school or foreign equivalent and entrance examination.

Fees (Pesos): 62.50-85.09 per unit; Graduate School, 81.59-115.18.

Languages of Instruction: English and Filipino.

Degrees and Diplomas: Bachelor of–Arts, A.B.; Science, B.S.; Science in Commerce, B.S.C.; Science in Education, B.S.E.; Music, B.M.; Science in Food and Nutrition, B.S.F.N.; Science in Food Service Administration, B.S.F.S.A.; Science in Chemistry, B.S.Chem.; Science in Home Economics, B.S.H.E.; Science in Nursing, B.S.N.; Science in Elementary Education, B.S.E.Ed., 4 yrs; Science in Medical Technology, B.S.M.T.; Science in Pharmacy, B.S.Phar.; Science in Civil Engineering, B.S.C.E.; Science in Architecture, B.S.Arch.; Science in Mechanical Engineering, B.S.M.E.; Science in Chemical Engineering, B.S.C.E., 4 yrs. Bachelor of Laws, Ll.B., 4 yrs after first degree. Master of–Arts, M.A.; Arts in Teaching, M.A.T.; Business Administration, M.B.A.; Public Administration, M.P.A.; Science in Economics, M.S.E., 2-3 yrs after Bachelor. Doctor of Philosophy, Ph.D. in Education.

Library: Main Library, 103,260 vols.

Special Facilities (Museums, etc.): Radio Station; Audio-visual Room.

Publications: Mirror; departmental publications; Views (annually).

Press or Publishing House: University Press.
Academic Staff: c. 285 (70).
Student Enrolment, 1989-90:

	Men	Women	Total
Of the country	4109	6307	10,416

5751 **PAMANTASAN NG SAN CARLOS**
University of San Carlos
P. del Rosario Street, Cebu City 6401
Cables: steyl, cebu
Telephone: 7-72-02; 7-07-91
Fax: (1) 332-5-43-41
President: Roderickl C. Salazar (1987-92)
Registrar: Roberto Tratagotia

C. of Architecture and Fine Arts (including Interior Design and Advertising Arts)
Dean: Melva Java; *staff* 18 (7)
C. of Commerce (including Business Administration, Accountancy and Secretarial Science)
Dean: Victoria Satorre; *staff* 28 (36)
C. of Engineering
Dean: Elsa Roska; *staff* 49 (14)
C. of Law
Dean: Expedito Bugarin; *staff* 4 (5)
C. of Liberal Arts and Sciences (including Psychology, Political Science, Sociology, Philosophy, Anthropology, Library Science, and Marine Biology)
Dean: Louie Punzalan; *staff* 115 (52)
C. of Nursing
Dean: Rosario Ailes; *staff* 30
C. of Pharmacy
Dean: Leticia Cabrera; *staff* 8 (1)
Teachers' C. (including Elementary Education, Secondary Education, Nutrition and Dietetics, and Home Economics)
Dean: Clara Lucero; *staff* 17 (5)
Ce. for Cebu Studies
Director: Resil Mojares
Graduate S.
Dean: Montana Saniel; *staff* 6 (26)

Founded 1595 as a parish school by Jesuit Fathers. Closed between 1769 and 1783 following the expulsion of the Jesuits from the Philippines. Reopened 1783 and renamed Colegio-Seminario de San Carlos. Administered by Dominican Fathers 1852-1867; by Vincentian Fathers, 1867-1935, and subsequently by the Society of the Divine Word (S.V.D.). In 1924 the institution became an institution of higher learning for the laity. Suspended 1941, reopened 1945. Acquired university status 1948. A private institution operated under the authority of the Society of the Divine Word, recognized by the Ministry of Education, Culture and Sports. Financed by tuition fees and subsidies from the Society of the Divine Word. Governing bodies: the Board of Trustees, composed of 10 members; the President's Cabinet; the Academic Senate, composed of academic deans, heads of departments and senior administrative officers. Some residential facilities for students.

Academic Year: June to March (June-October; November-March).

Admission Requirements: Graduation from high school and entrance examination.

Language of Instruction: English.

Degrees and Diplomas: Bachelor of–Arts, A.B.; Philosophy, Ph.B.; Science, B.S.; Science in Physics, B.S.Phys.; Science in Mathematics, B.S.Math.; Science in Education, B.S.E.; Science in Home Economics, B.S.H.E.; Science in Secretarial Administration, B.S.S.A.; Science in Pharmacy, B.S.Pharm,; Science in Nursing, B.S.N.; Science in Nutrition and Dietetics, B.S.N.D.; Science in Elementary Education, B.S.E.Ed.; Science in Commerce, B.S.C.; Science in Business Administration, B.S.B.A., 4 yrs; Science in Chemistry, B.S.Chem.; Science in Architecture, B.S.Arch.; Science in Chemical Engineering, B.S.Ch.E.; Science in Electrical Engineering, B.S.E.E.; Science in Civil Engineering, B.S.C.E.; Science in Mechanical Engineering, B.S.M.E.; Electronics and Communications Engineering, 5 yrs. Bachelor of Laws, Ll.B., 4 yrs after first degree. Master of–Arts, M.A.; Science, M.S., a further 2 yrs. Doctorof Philosphy, Ph.D. in Education; Anthropology; Philosophy, after Master.

Library: Total, c. 193,387 vols.

Special Facilities (Museums, etc.): Museums: Anthropological and Ethnological; Science (Biology and Geology).

Publications: University Bulletin (bimonthly); Semper Fidelis (annually); San Carlos Publications, monographs: Series A Humanities, B Natural Sciences, C. Religion; the Philippine Scientist; Philippine Quarterly of Culture and Society.

Academic Staff, 1990:

Rank	Full-time	Part-time
Professors	5	5
Associate Professors	6	1
Assistant Professors	48	5
Professorial Candidates	6	2
Senior Instructors	85	4
Junior Instructors	30	26
Assistant Instructors	95	90
Total	275	133

Student Enrolment, 1990:

	Men	Women	Total
Of the country	6533	6881	13,414
Of other countries	36	3	39
Total	6569	6884	13,453

5752 **UNIVERSITY OF SAN JOSE-RECOLETOS**
Corner Magallanes and P. Lopez Streets, Cebu City 6401
Cables: recoletos, cebu
Telephone: 5-38-02; 7-22-71-79
Fax: 5-38-02
President: Emeterio D. Bunao, O.A.R.
Registrar: Felix G. Eturma

C. of Arts and Science (including Political Science and Tourism)
Dean: Milagros C. Espina; *staff* 30-46
C. of Law
Dean: Alicia E. Bathan; *staff* – (14)
C. of Education
Dean: Lucilla Bonilla; *staff* 19 (15)
C. of Engineering
Dean: Benedicto M. Mantos; *staff* 31 (35)
C. of Commerce
Dean: Mariano M. Lerin; *staff* 43 (59)
Graduate S.
Dean: Lourdes H. Torrefranca; *staff* 6 (5)
Research, Planning and Scholarship Ce. (including Primary Health Care, and Social Sciences)
Director: Carmen M. Eturma; *staff* 7 (28)
Instructional Media Ce.
Head: Rosario C. Pasion; *staff* 5
I. of Management
Head: Mariano M. Lerin; *staff* 9
Also elementary and high schools.

Founded 1947 as college by the Recollect Fathers; Graduate School established 1960. Acquired university status 1984. Became a grantee of the International Development Research Centre (Ottawa, Canada) for research on primary health care 1989-1991. Governing bodies: the School Chapter, comprising 15 members; the Academic Council, comprising 21 members.

Academic Year: June to March (June-October; November-March).

Admission Requirements: Graduation from high school and entrance examination.

Fees (Pesos): Tuition, 58,28 per unit; Graduate School, 82,28-174,57.

Languages of Instruction: English and Pilipino.

Degrees and Diplomas: Bachelor of–Arts; Science in Education; Science in Commerce; Science in Elementary Education, 4 yrs; Science in Electrical Engineering; Civil Engineering; Mechanical Engineering; Chemical Engineering; Sanitary Engineering, 5 yrs. Bachelor of Laws, 4 yrs after first degree. Master of–Arts; Science in Business; Management, a further 3 yrs. Doctor of Management.

Library: Central Library, 68,377 vols.

Special Facilities (Museums, etc.): Mass Communication Studio.

Academic Staff, 1989-90:

Rank	Full-time	Part-time
Professors	10	5
Associate Professors	13	–
Assistant Professors	50	–
Instructors	81	141
Total	154	146

Student Enrolment, 1989-90:

	Men	Women	Total
Of the country	5156	7430	12,586
Of other countries	6	–	6
Total	5162	7430	12,592

5753 ***UNIVERSITY OF SANTO TOMAS**

España Street, Sampalac, Manila 2806
Telephone: 731-31-01
Rector: Norberto M. Castillo, O.P. (1982-90)
Secretary-General: Vicente Cajilig, O.P.

Fs. of Philosophy, Theology and Canon Law
Dean: Lamberto Pasion, O.P.
F. of Medicine
Dean: Tito Torralba; *staff* 180 (153)
F. of Civil Law
Dean: Justice Eduardo Caguioa; *staff* 9 (22)
F. of Pharmacy
Dean: Norma V. Lerma; *staff* 71 (6)
F. of Arts and Letters (including Political Science and Journalism)
Dean: Magdalena Villaba; *staff* 53 (25)
F. of Engineering
Dean: Alberto Laurito; *staff* 111 (35)
C. of Education
Dean: Teresita Infante; *staff* 62 (12)
C. of Science
Dean: Carmen G. Kanapi; *staff* 95 (19)
C. of Commerce and Business Administration
Dean: Manuel A. Reyes; *staff* 132 (25)
C. of Architecture and Fine Arts
Dean: Mauro Simpliciano; *staff* 63 (26)
C. of Nursing
Dean: Conchita T. Maceda; *staff* 71 (6)
Graduate S.
Dean: Paul Zwaenepoel; *staff* – (56)
Conservatory of Music
Director: Alejandra Atabug; *staff* 9 (25)
Research Ce.
I. of Religion
Dean: Pompeyo de Mesa, O.P.
I. of Human Reproduction
Director: Vicente J.A. Rosales
I. of Nutrition
Director: Fe M. San
I. of Spanish
Director: Fidel Vallaroel
I. of Oriental Religion and Culture
Director: Fausto Gomez, O.P.
I. of Small-scale Industries
Director: Santiago Solis
I. of Technology
Director: Milagros Quintero
Also elementary and high schools.

Founded 1611 as College of Our Lady of the Rosary by the Most Rev. Fr. Miguel de Benavides, O.P., Archbishop of Manila and the Dominican Fathers. Became College of Santo Tomas 1616. Royal confirmation granted 1785 by the Spanish Government. In 1902 Pope Leo XIII decreed and granted the title of Pontifical University. Pope Pius XII granted the title of Catholic University of the Philippines in 1947. The university is a private institution operated under the supervision of the Ministry of Education, Culture and Sports. Governing bodies: the Board of Trustees; the Council of Regents; the Academic Senate, composed of the Vice-Grand Chancellor as Chairman, and the deans of the faculties, and the Secretary-General; the Economic Council. Residential facilities for nursing students.

Academic Year: June to March (June-October; November-March).

Admission Requirements: Graduation from high school or foreign qualifications approved by the Government Bureau of Private Schools, and entrance examination.

Fees (Pesos): 900-1500 per semester; Medicine, 5000-10,000; Graduate School, 1500.

Languages of Instruction: English, Pilipino, and Spanish.

Degrees and Diplomas: Bachelor of–Fine Arts; Music, 4 yrs. Bachelor of Arts, and Bachelor of Science in various fields, 4-5 yrs. Bachelor of Laws, 4 yrs after first degree. Master of Arts; Master of Science, a further 2 yrs. Doctorate in–Law; Philosophy; Psychology; Political Science; Literature; English; Education; Pharmacy; Chemistry; Biology; Commerce; Guidance and Counselling. Doctor of Medicine, 4 yrs after first degree. Also diplomas of Technician, in various fields, 2 yrs. Associate in Secretarial Science, 2 yrs.

Libraries: Library, 253,100 vols; college and faculty libraries.

Special Facilities (Museums, etc.): Museum of Arts and Sciences; Art Gallery, Bibliographical Section, Philippine Cartography Section, Ethnology and Numismatic Section, Natural History.

Publications: The Varsitarian; Unitas; Thomasian Engineer; The Flame; Pax Roman Bulletin; Journals of Medicine, Nursing, Law, Education, Commerce; Acta Manilana; Boletin Eclesiastico; Philippiniana Sacra; Purple Gazette; Vision; Journal of Graduate Research; The Thomasian Engineer; Veritas; Academia; College of Science Journal; Chemical Bulletin; Medical Forum (quarterly or biannually).

Press or Publishing House: U.S.T. Press.

Academic Staff, 1986-87: c. 1590.

Student Enrolment, 1986-87:

	Men	Women	Total
Of the country	18,351	25,697	44,048
Of other countries	523	584	1,107
Total	18,874	26,281	45,155

5754 **UNIVERSITY OF SOUTHERN PHILIPPINES FOUNDATION**

Mabini Street, Cebu City
Telephone: 7-29-26; 7-23-31

C. of Liberal Arts and Sciences (including Nutrition)
C. of Social Sciences
C. of Engineering (including Architecture)
C. of Commerce
C. of Education
Graduate S. (Law, Social Work, Education)
Southern C.
Don Felix Montinola Memorial C. (Victorias)
Also elementary and secondary schools.

Founded 1927 as Southern Institute, became Southern College 1933, granted university status 1949. A private institution operated by a Foundation. Governing body: the Board of Trustees, comprising 10 members. Residential facilities for academic staff.

Academic Year: June to March (June-October; October-March).

Admission Requirements: Secondary school certificate or recognized equivalent, and entrance examination.

Languages of Instruction: English and Pilipino.

Degrees and Diplomas: Bachelor of–Arts, A.B., 4 yrs; Science in–Education, B.S.E.; Elementary Education, B.S.E.Ed.; Elementary Education, Home Economics, B.S.C.Ed.H.E.; Home Economics, B.S.H.E.; Foods and Nutrition, B.S.F.N.; Social Work, B.S.S.W.; Commerce, B.S.C., 4 yrs; Geodetic Engineering, B.S.G.E.; Civil Engineering, B.S.C.E.; Mechanical Engineering, B.S.M.E.; Electrical Engineering, B.S.E.E.; Electronics and Commercial Engineering, 5 yrs. Master of–Arts in Education; Science in Social Work; Laws, a further 2 yrs. Diploma in Secretarial Science, D.S.S., 2 yrs.

Libraries: Central Library, *c.* 25,700 vols; Graduate School, *c.* 1040; Engineering, *c.* 2880; Commerce, *c.* 2500.

Special Facilities (Museums, etc.): Filipiniana Museum.

Publications: The Southern Scholar; The Junior Scholar.

Academic Staff: c. 170.

Student Enrolment: c. 4060.

5755 **UNIVERSITY OF THE VISAYAS**
Colon Street, Cebu City 6401
Telephone: 9-38-12
President: Eduardo R. Gullas (1983-)

C. of Medicine
Dean: Renato Espinosa; *staff* 64 (20)
C. of Law
Dean: Amadeo D. Seno; *staff* 10 (4)
C. of Engineering and Architecture
Dean: Alberto Olan; *staff* 39 (12)
C. of Arts and Sciences
Dean: Celestina Alino; *staff* 36 (10)
C. of Nursing
Dean: Lourdes Fernan; *staff* 10 (16)
C. of Pharmacy
Dean: Carmen Yap; *staff* 7 (2)
Teachers' C.
Dean: Aurora Econg; *staff* 15 (5)
C. of Commerce and Business Administration
Dean: Ursula Cumba; *staff* 32 (11)
C. of Criminology
Dean: Emmanuel Y. Pepito; *staff* 9 (3)
Graduate S.
Dean: Fe S. Necesrio; *staff* 12 (5)
S. of Marine Engineering
Head: Carmelo T. Simolde; *staff* 9 (3)
Also kindergarten, elementary and secondary schools.

Founded 1919 as institute, became university 1948. A private institution. Financed by tuition fees. Governing body: the Board of Trustees. Some residential facilities for students.

Academic Year: July to April (July-November; November-April).

Admission Requirements: Graduation from high school or recognized foreign equivalent.

Fees (Pesos): 34.15 per unit, per semester; Medicine, 69.83; Graduate School, 80.41; Technology, 921.09 per semeste

Fees: r.

Language of Instruction: English.

Degrees and Diplomas: Bachelor of–Arts, A.B.; Science in Education, B.S.E.; Science in Elementary Education, B.S.E.Ed.; Science in Business Administration, B.S.B.A.; Science in Commerce, B.S.C.; Science in Criminology, B.S.Criminology; Science in Pharmacy, B.S. Pharm.; Science in Civil Engineering, B.S.C.E., 4 yrs. Bachelor of Laws, Ll.B., 4 yrs after first degree. Master of Arts, M.A., 2 yrs after Bachelor on completion of a thesis. Doctor in Education. Associate in Secretarial Science A.C.S., 2 yrs.

Libraries: Main College Library, *c.* 60,000 vols; Graduate School, *c.* 18,000; Medicine, 12,000; Law, 6000.

Publications: UV Journal; Visayanian; The UV Spirit; Alumni Review; UV Bulletin; Research Journal (biannually).

Academic Staff: c. 328.

Student Enrolment: c. 14,604.

5756 **WESLEYAN UNIVERSITY**
Mabini Street, Cabantuan City

Agriculture
Commerce
Engineering
Arts and Sciences
Nutrition
Nursing
Social Work
Education
Technical and Vocational Studies

Founded 1946.

5757 **PAMANTASAN NG XAVIER**
Xavier University
Corrales Avenue, Cagayan de Oro City 9000
Telephone: 37-42; 32-52; 28-60; 62-17
Fax: 6069
President: Benvenido F. Nebres, S.J. (1990-)
Registrar: Aurora M. Gapuz

C. of Law
Dean: Florentino G. Dumlao; *staff* 1 (17)
C. of Medicine
Dean: Francisco L. Oh; *staff* 16 (33)
C. of Arts and Sciences
Dean: Cipriano E. Unson; *staff* 96 (43)
C. of Commerce
Dean: Carolina S. Tandog; *staff* 9 (11)
C. of Education
Dean: Rustica T. Racines; *staff* 11 (2)
C. of Engineering
Dean: Ernesto San Juan; *staff* 15 (6)
C. of Agriculture
Dean: Antonio Ledesma; *staff* 19 (3)
Computer Ce.
Director: Joanne M. Ferraris; *staff* 2
Industrial Technology Ce.
Director: Nenita E. Esmejarda; *staff* 22 (1)
Graduate S.
Dean: Augustin A. Cabrera; *staff* 4 (8)
C. of Nursing
Head: Norma Mangano, S.P.C.
Also high school.

Founded 1933 as elementary school, became college 1940, and university 1958. The university is a private institution recognized by the Ministry of Education, Culture and Sports, and is directed by the Society of Jesus. Financially supported by tuition fees and donations. Governing body: the Board of Trustees, comprising 15 members. Residential facilities for the Jesuit faculty (Loyola House) and students.

Arrangements for co-operation with the Virginia Polytechnic Institute and State University.

Academic Year: June to March (June-October; November-March).

Admission Requirements: Graduation from high school or equivalent, and entrance examination.

Fees (Pesos): 79-108 per unit, per semester; Medicine, 9,500 per semester.

Language of Instruction: English.

Degrees and Diplomas: Bachelor of–Arts, A.B.; Science, B.S.; Science in–Agriculture, B.S.A.; Nursing, B.S.N.; Food Technology, B.S.F.T.; Development Communication, B.S.D.C.; Commerce, B.S.C.; Business Administration, B.S.B.A.; Education, B.S.Ed.; Elementary Education, B.S.E.Ed., 4 yrs; Agricultural Engineering, B.S.A.E.; Chemical Engineering, B.S.Ch.E.; Civil Engineering, B.S.C.E.; Electrical Engineering, B.S.E.E.; Mechanical Engineering, B.S.M.E., 5 yrs. Bachelor of Laws, Ll.B., 4 yrs after first degree. Master of–Arts, M.A.; Arts in Teaching Elementary Agriculture, M.A.T.E.A.; Business Administration, M.B.A.; Public Administration, M.P.A., a further 2 yrs. Doctor of Philosophy, Ph.D. in–Education; Sociology, 3-5 yrs after Master.

Libraries: Central Library, *c.* 58,333 vols; Graduate School, 4104; Law, 1159; Medical, 3519; Engineering Technology, 4350.

Special Facilities (Museums, etc.): Folk-life Museum.

Publication: Kinaadman Journal (annually).

Academic Staff, 1989-90:

Rank	Full-time	Part-time
Professors	11	–
Associate Professors	25	8
Assistant Professors	24	20
Instructors	59	24
Assistant Instructors	44	26
Others	40	103
Total	203	181

Student Enrolment, 1989-90:

	Men	Women	Total
Of the country	2301	2995	5296
Of other countries	31	13	44
Total	2332	3005	5340

Other Institutions

Public Institutions – Chartered

5758 **ABRA STATE INSTITUTE OF SCIENCE AND TECHNOLOGY**
Langangiland, Abra
Agriculture
Forestry
Education
Technical Sciences
Founded 1908, acquired present status and title 1983.

5759 **BASILIAN STATE COLLEGE**
Santa Clara, Lamitan, Basilan
Technical Sciences
Founded 1966, acquired present status and title 1984.

5760 **BUKIDNON STATE COLLEGE**
Fortich Street, Malaybalay, Bukidnon 8201
C. of Liberal Arts (including Education, Social Work, Commerce)
C. of Commerce
Graduate S.
Also elementary and high schools.

Founded 1924 as teacher training school, and acquired present status and title 1976. Graduate courses introduced 1969. A State institution financed mainly by the government. Governing body: the Board of Trustees, of which the Minister of Education, Culture and Sports is Chairman. Residential facilities for academic staff and students.

Academic Year: June to March (June-October; November-March).

Admission Requirements: Graduation from high school and entrance examination.

Languages of Instruction: English and Pilipino.

Degrees and Diplomas: Bachelor of–Arts, B.A.; Science in Education, B.S.E.; Science in Social Work, B.S.S.W.; Science in Commerce, 4 yrs. Master of–Arts in Education, M.A.E.; Arts in Teaching, M.A.T.; Arts in Public Administration, M.A.P.A., a further 2 yrs.

Library: c. 43,000 vols.

Academic Staff: c. 110.

Student Enrolment: c. 4800.

5761 **KOLEHIYO NG BULAKAN SA SINING AT HANAP-BUHAY**
Bulacan College of Arts and Trades
Malolos, Bulacan
Telephone: 797-4114
President: Rosoria Pimentel (1983-89)
S. of Arts and Sciences
Dean: Francisco L. Cruz; *staff* 38 (16)
S. of Engineering
Dean: Divinia Abracosa; *staff* 17 (13)
S. of Education
Dean: Marino C. de Jesus; *staff* 18
S. of Technology
Dean: Salvador P. Peredo; *staff* 36
Also high school.

Founded 1904 as intermediate school, reorganized 1920, acquired present status and title 1965. Mainly financedby the government. Governing body: the Board of Trustees of which the Minister of Education, Culture and Sports is Chairman.

Academic Year: June to March (June-October; November-March).

Admission Requirements: Graduation from high school and entrance examination.

Fees (Pesos): 10 per unit, per semester; Graduate, 12.

Language of Instruction: English.

Degrees and Diplomas: Bachelor of Science in–Industrial Technology; Industrial Education, B.S.I.E., in various fields, 4 yrs; Architecture; Civil Engineering, B.S.C.E.; Mechanical Engineering, B.S.M.E.; Electrical Engineering, B.S.E.E., 5 yrs. Master of Arts in–Teaching, M.A.T.; Industrial Education, a further 2 yrs. Also Certificates.

Library: c. 12,250 vols.

Publications: Pace Setter; The Busy Bee.

Academic Staff, 1986-87:

Rank	Full-time	Part-time
Professors	1	4
Associate Professors	9	–
Assistant Professors	40	–
Instructors	124	15
Total	174	19

Student Enrolment, 1986-87:

	Men	Women	Total
Of the country	3577	1903	5480

5762 **CAMARINES SUR STATE AGRICULTURAL COLLEGE**
San Jose Pili, Camarines Sur 4418
Telephone: 7206
President: Ciriaco N. Divinagracia (1985-91)
Administrative Officer: Job B. Sanchez
D. of Animal Science
Chairman: Luz P. Napoles; *staff* 15
D. of Crop Science (including Agronomy, Horticulture)
In-Charge: Santos R. Balderas; *staff* 25
D. of Agricultural Education and Extension
Chairman: Emily I. Curtina; *staff* 6
D. of Agricultural Economics and Agricultural Business
Chairman: Georgina J. Bordado; *staff* 5
D. of Agricultural Engineering (including Crop Processing, and Environmental Sanitation)
Chairman: Henry A. Mabesa; *staff* 10
D. of Biological Sciences (including Crop Protection, Plant Pathology, and Entomology)
Chairman: Luduvina C. Savilla; *staff* 13
D. of Home and Food Technology
Chairman: Magdalena F. Villareal; *staff* 10
D. of Soil Science
Chairman: Fe B. Perlas; *staff* 5
D. of Agricultural Technology
Chairman: Paz P. Balders; *staff* 6
D. of Humanities (including Agricultural Technology)
Chairman: Belen A. Relleno; *staff* 6
D. of Physical Sciences
Chairman: Asuncion A. Orbeso; *staff* 8
D. of Physical Education and Sports
Chairman: Mariano C. Galvan; *staff* 9
Research D. (including Agriculture, Forestry, and Natural Resources)
Director: Roman N. Bucad; *staff* 9
Extension D.
Director: Aniceto A. Binova; *staff* 6 (15)
Also high school.

Founded 1918 as school, became college 1973. Acquired present status and title 1982. Under the supervision of the Department of Education, Culture and Sports, with specific Chapter for its governance and operation. Governing body: the Board of Trustees. Residential facilities for 403 academic staff and 60% of the students.

Academic Year: June to March (June-October; November-March).

Admission Requirements: Graduation from high school and entrance examination.

Fees (Pesos): 326 per 24 units, per semester; Graduate School, 232.

Languages of Instruction: English and Pilipino.

Degrees and Diplomas: Bachelor of Science in–Agriculture; Agricultural Engineering; Food Technology; Agricultural Business, 4 yrs. Master of Science in–Animal Science; Crop Science, Crop Protection; Agricultural Education, a further 2 yrs.

Library: Central Library, 10,000 vols.

Publications: Newsletter (monthly); Research Journal (biannually); Countryside Journal (biannually).

Academic Staff, 1989-90:

Rank	Full-time	Part-time
Professors	17	2
Associate Professors	9	4
Assistant Professors	43	–
Instructors	69	–
Teachers	33	–
Total	171	6

Student Enrolment, 1989-90:

	Men	Women	Total
Of the country	1050	1082	2132

5763 **CAMARINES SUR POLYTECHNIC COLLEGES**

Nabua, Camarines Sur 4434

President: Lylia Corporal-Sena

Administrative Officer: Ferdinand B. Valencia

D. of Office Administration

Head: Romeo V. Mirando; *staff* 5 (3)

D. of Entrepreneurship (including Civil Engineering, Electrical Engineering, and Mechanical Engineering)

Head: Asuncion P. Orciga; *staff* 13 (4)

D. of Rural Health Care Technology (including Obstetrics, Pediatrics, and Public Health)

; *staff* 1 (4)

Electronics and Communication Service Technology

Head: Huberto I. Ursua; *staff* 1 (5)

Founded 1983. Governing body: the Board of Trustees.

Academic Year: June to March.

Admission Requirements: Graduation from high school or equivalent, and entrance examination.

Fees (Pesos) Tuition, 100,00 per semester.

Language of Instruction: English.

Degrees and Diplomas: Bachelor, 4-5 yrs. Also certificates, 2 yrs.

Library: CSPC-Library, 3,273 vols.

Academic Staff, 1989-90: 21

Student Enrolment, 1989-90:

	Men	Women	Total
Of the country	505	575	1080

5764 **CATANDUANES STATE COLLEGES**

Virac, Catanduanes

President: Rodolfo V. Azanza (1986-)

Secretary-General: Hector B. Abada

C. of Agriculture

Dean: Rufino T. Stalome; *staff* 12 (1)

C. of Fishery

Dean: Rufino T. Salome; *staff* 5

C. of Business Administration (Commerce)

Dean: Gabriel T. Rodulfo; *staff* 19 (12)

C. of Engineering

Dean: Solon T. Arcilla; *staff* 10

C. of Arts and Sciences

Officer-in-Charge: Reynaldo L. Dolores; *staff* 42 (27)

C. of Nutrition

Officer-in-Charge: Reynaldo Dolores; *staff* 21

C. of Nursing

Dean: Aida S.Bonafe; *staff* 13 (5)

C. of Education

Dean: Corazon S. Abad; *staff* 33 (12)

C. of Arts and Trades

Dean: Adolfo S. Bagadiong; *staff* 21 (7)

C. of Public Administration and Community Development

Dean: Reynaldo L. Dolores; *staff* 3 (5)

Graduate S.

Dean: Rosario T. Azanza; *staff* 9 (1)

Research Ce.

Dean: Jose Fernandez; *staff* 2 (1)

Founded 1971. Governing body: the Board of Trustees. Residential facilities for women.

Academic Year: June to March (June-October; November-March

Admission Requirements: Graduation from high school and entrance examination.

Fees (Pesos): 5-15 per unit; Graduate School, 20.

Languages of Instruction: English and Pilipino.

Degrees and Diplomas: Bachelor of-Science in Agri-Fisheries; Arts, A.B.; Science in Business Administration, B.S.B.A.; Elementary Education, B.E.Ed.; Secondary Education, B.S.E.; Science in Community Development, B.S.C.D.; Science in Public Administration, B.S.P.A.; Science in Industrial Education, B.S.I.E.; Science in Nursing, B.S.N.; Science in Nutrition and Dietetics, B.S.N.D., 4 yrs; Science in Engineering, B.S.C.E., 5 yrs.

Libraries: Central Library, 7442 vols; Graduate School, 3821.

Academic Staff, 1990:

Rank	Full-time	Part-time
Professors	3	–
Associate Professors	28	8
Assistant Profssors	46	24
Instructors	95	39
Total	172	71

Student Enrolment, 1989-90:

	Men	Women	Total
Of the country	1260	1662	2922

5765 **CEBU STATE COLLEGE**

Osmeña Boulevard, Cebu City, Cebu

Telephone: 61537

President: Jaime M. Gellor

Administrative Officer: Cleofas C. Dahon

Engineering

Arts

Nursing

Tourism

Education

Industrial Technology

Agriculture

Fishery

Secretarial Studies

Graduate S.

Technical Sciences

Founded 1954, acquired present status and title 1976. Governing body: the Board of Trustees

Academic Year: June to March (June-October; November-March).

Admission Requirements: Graduation from high school and entrance examination.

Languages of Instruction: English and Pilipino.

Degrees and Diplomas: Bachelor of Science in–Education; Nursing, B.S.N., 3-4 yrs. Master, 3-4 yrs. Doctor of Education, Ed.D., 3-4 yrs.

Library: Central Library, 13,801 vols.

Academic Staff, 1990:

Rank	Full-time	Part-time
Professors	19	–
Associate Professors	22	–
Assistant Professors	26	–
Instructors	26	6
Total	93	6

Student Enrolment, 1990:

	Men	Women	Total
Of the country	364	2202	2566

5766 **DALUBHASAANG POLITEKNIKO SA GITNANG LUSON**

Central Luzon Polytechnic College

General Tinio Street, Cabanatuan City 2301

Telephone: 963-2621; 963-2495

President: Eduardo E. Agno (1987-93)

Administrative Officer: Ruben S. Yambot

C. of Engineering

Dean: Alejandro P. Donato; *staff* 63 (4)

C. of Education

Dean: Zearge V. Ducay; *staff* 37 (2)

D. of Graduate S.

Dean: Gonzalo P. Serezo; *staff* 3 (19)

C. of Industrial Technology

Dean: Federico A. Tadeaman; *staff* 28 (2)

Research and Development Ce.

Director: Manuel O.Criez; *staff* 3 (2)

Extension and Community Services

Director: Bueuaventura; *staff* 2 (12)

Founded 1929 as Trade School, acquired present status and title 1964. A State institution mainly financed by the government. Governing body: the Board of Trustees of which the Secretary of Education, Culture and Sports is Chairman. Residential facilities for students.

Academic Year: June to March (June-October; November-March).

Admission Requirements: Graduation from high school and entrance examination.

Fees (Pesos): 8 per unit, per semester; Graduate Studies, 15.

Languages of Instruction: English and Pilipino.

Degrees and Diplomas: Bachelor of–Secondary Education, B.S.E.; Science in–Industrial Education, B.S.I.E., 4 yrs; Civil Engineering, B.S.C.E.; Electrical Engineering, B.S.E.E.; Mechanical Engineering, B.S.M.E., 5 yrs. Master of–Management, M.M.; Art in Industrial Education, M.A.I.E.; Arts in Education, M.A.Ed.; Arts in Building Technology, M.A.Bldg.Tech.; Arts in Drafting Technology, M.A.Draft.Tech.; Arts in Girl's Trades Technology; Arts in Teaching Vocational-Technical Education; Arts in Teaching, M.A.T., a further 2 yrs. Doctor in Education, 4 yrs.

Library: Central Library, 20,984 vols.

Publications: Research Journal; Trade Journal.

Academic Staff, 1989-90: c. 240 (20).

Student Enrolment, 1989-90: c. 10,900.

5767 **CENTRAL VISAYAS POLYTECHNIC COLLEGE**

Dumaguete City 6501
Telephone: 3072
President: Marcelo C. Jalandoon (1985-)
Administrative-Officer: Socrates T. Diputado

C. of Industrial Technology
Vice-President: Santiago D. Quiso; *staff* 32 (16)
Office of Industrial Education
C. of Planning and Research
Head: Marcelo C. Jalandoon; *staff* 3 (1)
C. of Agriculture
Dean: Juan D. Evangelista; *staff* 68
C. of Fishery
Dean: Marciano G. Vergara; *staff* 34
Graduate S.
Dean: Ruth L. Velasco; *staff* 1 (12)
Also elementary and secondary schools.

Founded 1956 as school of arts and trades, acquired present status and title 1983. A State institution. Governing body: the Board of Trustees of which the Secretary of Education, Culture and Sports is Chairman.

Academic Year: June to March (June-October; November-March).

Admission Requirements: Graduation from high school and entrance examination.

Fees (Pesos): 271-403.50 per annum; Graduate School, 242-292 per annum.

Languages of Instruction: English and Pilipino.

Degrees and Diplomas: Bachelor of Science in–Industrial Education; Industrial Technology, 4 yrs. Master of Arts in–Teaching; Educational Management, a further 2 yrs. Also Certificate of Proficiency in Technical Education, 2 yrs.

Library: 14,501 vols.

Special Facilities (Museums, etc.): Observatory, Biological Garden, Art Gallery, Movie Studio.

Press or Publishing House: Asian Printer, Dumaguete City

Academic Staff, 1990:

Rank	Full-time
Professors	5
Associate Professors	7
Assistant Professors	50
Instructors	83
Total	145

Student Enrolment, 1990:

	Men	Women	Total
Of the country	1032	263	1295

5768 **COTABATO CITY STATE POLYTECHNIC COLLEGE**

Sinsuat Avenue, Rosary Heights, Cotabato City
Telephone: 29-82
President: Bologiong P. Pendaliday
Vice-President: Kuisan K. Go

C. of Agriculture, Forestry and Fisheries
Dean: Dammang S. Bantala; *staff* 21 (2)
C. of Industrial Technology
Dean: Hasanaddin Mama
C. of Education
Dean: Zenaida S. Solaiman; *staff* 12

Founded 1983. A State institution. Governing body: the Board of Trustees of which the Secretary of Education, Culture and Sports is Chairman.

Admission Requirements: Graduation from school or equivalent or foreign equivalent, and entrance examination.

Languages of Instruction: English and Filipino.

Degrees and Diplomas: Bachelor, 4 yrs. Also Diplomas, 2-3 yrs.

Library: College Library, 277 vols.

Academic Staff, 1990:

Rank	Full-time	Part-time
Instructors	92	5
Assistant Professors	10	–
Assistant Professors	4	–
Total	106	5

Student Enrolment, 1989-90: 1,914

5769 **COTABATO FOUNDATION COLLEGE OF SCIENCE AND TECHNOLOGY**

Dorolumna, Magpet, North Cotabato

Agriculture
Home Economics
Forestry
Agricultural Business
Technical Sciences

Founded 1973, acquired present status 1983.

5770 **DON HONORIO VENTURY COLLEGE OF ARTS AND TRADES**

Bacolor, Pampanga
Telephone: 910-691
President: Ernesto T. Nicdao (1985-)
Administrative Officer: Andrea N. Ferrer

D. of Architecture
Dean: Benjamin C. Guevarra; *staff* 7 (2)
D. of Engineering
Dean: Benjamin C. Guevarra; *staff* 15 (5)
D. of Education
Officer-in-Charge: Laurencita N. Villanueva; *staff* 25
D. of Technical/Technician Education
Dean: Mariano P. Cadiang; *staff* 66

Founded as Escuela 1861, became Trade School 1905. Acquired present title 1964 and present status as state college 1978. Governing body: Board of Trustees of which the Secretary of Education, Culture and Sports is the Chairman.

Academic Year: June to March (June-October; November-March).

Admission Requirements: Graduation from high school and entrance examination.

Fees (Pesos): 420 per semester.

Language of Instruction: English.

Degrees and Diplomas: Certificate of Proficiency, 2 yrs. Bachelor of Science in–Industrial Education, B.S.I.E., 4 yrs.; Architecture; Civil Engineering, B.S.C.E.; Mechanical Engineering, B.S.M.E., 5 yrs. Master of–Arts in Industrial Education, M.A.I.E., a further 2 yrs.

Publication: The Industrialist (quarterly).

Academic Staff, 1989-90:

Rank	Full-time
Professors	3
Associate Professors	20
Assistant Professors	25
Instructors	110
Total	158

Student Enrolment, 1989-90:

	Men	Women

50d /Total/F350d /COOf the country

5771 **DON MARIANO MARCOS MEMORIAL POLYTECHNIC STATE COLLEGE**

Lapasan, Cagayan de Oro City 9000
Cables: Dmmmpsc, Cagayan de Oro
Telephone: 38-40; 60-65;30-19
President: Eduardo S. Canlas

C. of Engineering and Industrial Technology
Dean: Briccio A. Bullecer; *staff* 74 (8)
C. of Fisheries and Agriculture
Dean: Francisco Aclan; *staff* 44 (1)
C. of Education
Dean: Fe B. Caperida; *staff* 26 (1)
Graduate S.
Dean: Roberto N. Padua; *staff* 2 (5)
Research and Extension Services Ce.
Director: Alfredo Cahansa; *staff* 2
Also branches in: Camiguin, Medina, Alubijid, Panaon, and Jasaan. Also laboratory secondary schools.

Founded 1927 as school. Acquired present status and title 1978. A State institution. Governing body: the Board of Trustees, of which the Secretary of Education and Culture is Chairman.

Academic Year: June to March (June-October; November-March).

Admission Requirements: Graduation from high school and entrance examination.

Fees (Pesos): 184, per annum; education, 304.

Languages of Instruction: English and Pilipino.

Degrees and Diplomas: Associate in Trade Technical Education, 2 yrs. Bachelor of Science in–Industrial Education; Industrial Technology; Agricultural Education; Fisheries; Forestry, 4 yrs; Electrical Engineering; Electronics and Communication Engineering, 5 yrs. Master of Arts in–Educational Management; Teaching, a further 1 ½-2 yrs. Doctor of Philosophy in–Educational Planning and Management. Doctor of Education, 3-5 yrs after Master. Also Certificatesin–Technology, 2 yrs; Technician Education, 9 trimesters.

Library: Central Library, 15,559 vols.

Publication: State College Bulletin (quarterly), Graduate Journal, Trailblazer, Campus Beat.

Academic Staff, 1989-90:

Rank	Full-time	Part-time
Professors	8	5
Associate Professors	24	–
Assistant Professors	30	–
Instructors	119	10
Total	181	15

Student Enrolment, 1989-90:

	Men	Women	Total
Of the country	1754	1026	2780

5772 **DON SEVERINO AGRICULTURAL COLLEGE**

Indang, Cavite 4122
President: Ruperto S. Sangalang (1986-92)
Registrar: Irene F. Baes

D. of Agricultural Economics and Agribusiness
Chairman: Maria A. Ersando; *staff* 10
D. of Agricultural Engineering and Agro-Industrial Technology
Chairman: Jaime Q. Dilidili; *staff* 12
D. of Animal Husbandry
Chairman: Reynaldo E. Samonte; *staff* 12
D. of Biological Sciences
Chairman: Josefina R. Rint; *staff* 13
D. of Languages and Humanities
Chairman: Priscilla M. Dones; *staff* 13
D. of Physical Education
Chairman: Maximo V. Nova; *staff* 4
D. of Physical Sciences
Chairman: Trinidad M. Ocampo; *staff* 12
D. of Plant Science
Chairman: Amornita C. Sanchez; *staff* 19
D. of Rural Development Studies
Chairman: Constancia G. Cueno; *staff* 17
D. of Advanced Education
Head: Constancia G. Cueno; *staff* – (20)
Also elementary and secondary schools.

Founded 1906 as school, acquired present status and title 1964. A State institution mainly financed by the government. Governing body: the Board of Trustees of which the Secretary of Education, Culture and Sports is Chairman. Residential facilities for academic staff and students.

Arrangements for co-operation with the University of Tsukuba.

Academic Year: June to April (June-November; November-April).

Admission Requirements: Graduation from high school and entrance examination.

Fees (Pesos): 370 per semester; Graduate, 760 per semester.

Languages of Instruction: English and Pilipino.

Degrees and Diplomas: Bachelor of Science in–Agriculture; Education; Elementary Education; Agribusiness, 4 yrs; Agricultural Engineering, 5 yrs. Master, a further 3-4 yrs. Also Certificates, 1-2 yrs.

Library: Central Library, *c.* 13,000 vols.

Publications: DSAC Newsletter (monthly); Ugnayan Newsletter (quarterly); Midland Forum (annually); DSAC Research Journal (biannually); PROD (monthly).

Academic Staff, 1989-90:

Rank	Full-time
Professors	8
Associate Professors	17
Assistant Professors	41
Instructors	88
Total	154

Student Enrolment, 1989-90:

	Men	Women	Total
Of the country	810	892	1702
Of other countries	2	–	2
Total	812	892	1704

5773 **EASTERN SAMAR STATE COLLEGE**

Borongan, Eastern Samar
President: Antonio B. Mendoza (1984-90)

Agriculture
Technical Sciences
Also secondary school.

Founded 1960 as school, acquired present status and title 1983. A State institution mainly financed by the government. Governing body: the Board of Trustees of which the Minister of Education, Culture and Sports is Chairman. Residential facilities for academic staff and students.

Academic Year: June to March (June-October; November-March).

Admission Requirements: Graduation from high school and entrance examination.

Language of Instruction: English.

Degrees and Diplomas: Bachelor of Science in–Agriculture, 4 yrs; Agricultural Engineering, 5 yrs. Master of Science, a further 2 yrs.

Library: College Library.

Publication: The Farmhand (biannually).

Academic Staff: c. 50.

Student Enrolment: c. 1700.

5774 **EULOGIO 'AMANG' RODRIGUEZ INSTITUTE OF SCIENCE AND TECHNOLOGY**

Nagtahan, Sampaloc, Manila 2802
Telephone: 601366
President: Frederick So. Pada (1982-)

S. of Engineering, Architecture and Fine Arts
Dean: Alfonso P. Licud; *staff* 56 (49)
S. of Arts and Science
Dean: Rosalina C. Vinluan; *staff* 26 (9)
S. of Business Education
Dean: Maura V. Bautista; *staff* 43 (14)
S. of Teacher Education
Dean: Elvira P. Robles; *staff* 35 (6)
S. of Industrial Technology
Dean: Alberto A. Celestial; *staff* 48 (21)
Graduate S.
Dean: Emillie D. Guevarra; *staff* 4 (37)
Also high school.

Founded 1940 as school, acquired present status and title 1978. A State institution. Governing body: the Board of Trustees, comprising 16 members, of which the Minister of Education, Culture and Sports is Chairman.

Academic Year: June to March (June-October; November-March).

Admission Requirements: Graduation from high school and entrance examination.

Fees (Pesos): 7.50 per unit; Graduate School, 15-20.

Languages of Instruction: English and Pilipino.

Degrees and Diplomas: Bachelor of–Fine Arts; Science in Chemistry; Mathematics; Music Education; Physics; Statistics; Hotel and Restaurant Management; Industrial Education; Secretarial Administration; Business Administration; Industrial Technology, 4 yrs; Architecture; Civil Engineering; Chemical Engineering; Electrical Engineering; Mechanical Engineering; Industrial Management Engineering; Electronics and Communication Engineering; Sanitary and Environmental Engineering; Geodetic Engineering, 5 yrs. Master of Arts in–Education; Industrial Education; Teaching; Business Education, a further 2-3 yrs. Doctor of Education, 3-4 yrs.

Library: 10,552 vols.

Special Facilities (Museums, etc.): Museum, Art Gallery and Post Exchange Service.

Publications: EARIST Journal; EARIST Voice; The Technozettes; The Power; The Evening Post.

Academic Staff, 1986-87:

Rank	Full-time
Professors	18
Associate Professors	42
Assistant Professors	90
Instructors	284
Total	434

Student Enrolment, 1986-87:

Of the country	8427
Of other countries	3
Total	8430

5775 **IFUGAO STATE COLLEGE OF AGRICULTURE AND FORESTRY**

Mayon, Lamut, Ifugao

Agriculture

Forestry

Education

Home Technology

Technical Sciences

Founded 1973, acquired present status and title 1983.

5776 **ILOILO STATE COLLEGE OF FISHERIES**

Tiwi, Barotac Nuevo, Iloilo

Cables: Iscof Btac. Nvo. Phil.

President: Benigno P. (1986-)

Fisheries Technology

Also elementary and high schools.

Founded 1954 as secondary school, became vocational college 1968 and acquired present status and title 1978. Governing body: the Board of Trustees, of which the Minister of Education, Culture and Sports is Chairman. Residential facilities for academic staff and students.

Academic Year: June to April (June-October; November-April).

Admission Requirements: Graduation from high school and entrance examination.

Fees (Pesos): 90 per semester.

Languages of Instruction: English and Pilipino.

Degrees and Diplomas: Bachelor of Science in–Fisheries; Fisheries Education; Marine Transportation; Practical Arts, 4 yrs. Also Diploma in Fishery Technology, 3 yrs.

Library: c. 12,940 vols.

Publications: Ang Perlas (biannually); H.S. Scroll (biannually); Sea Treasure (quarterly).

Academic Staff, 1986-87:

Rank	Full-time
Professors	2
Associate Professors	6
Assistant Professors	18
Instructors	25
Total	51

Student Enrolment, 1986-87:

	Men	Women	Total
Of the country	242	293	535

5777 **JASAAN COLLEGE OF SCIENCE AND TECHNOLOGY**

Jasaan, Misamis Oriental

Engineering

Education

Midwifery

Technical and Vocational Studies

5778 **KALINGA-AAPAYAO STATE COLLEGE**

Kalinga-Apayao

5779 **LAGUNA STATE POLYTECHNIC COLLEGE**

Wawa East, L. de Leon Street Siniloan, Laguna

President: Ricardo A. Wagan (1985-91)

Administrative Officer: Eugenio E. Agellon

C. of Agriculture (Animal Science, Crop Science)

Director: Conrado S. Padilla;

Founded 1952 as high school, became college 1971. Acquired present status and title 1983. Governing body: the Board of Trustees of which the Secretary for Education, Culture and Sports is Chairman. Residential facilities for academic staff and students.

Academic Year: June to March (June to October; November to March).

Admission Requirements: Graduation from high school and entrance examination.

Fees (Pesos): 10 per unit.

Language of Instruction: English.

Degrees and Diplomas: Associate in Agriculture, 2 yrs. Bachelor of Science in–Agriculture; Agricultural Education; Agricultural Technology; Agricultural Business Administration, 4 yrs; Agricultural Engineering, 5 yrs.

Library: Central Library, c. 7286 vols.

Publications: Baybay Echo (quarterly); Binhi (annually); Gintong Ani (annually); Research Journal (annually).

Academic Staff, 1989-90: 74.

Student Enrolment, 1989-90: c. 640.

5780 **LEYTE STATE COLLEGE**

Paterno Street, Tacloban City, Leyte

Telephone: 321-2177

President: Purificacion Flores (1986-92)

Vice-President: Cres V. Chan-Gonzaga

C. of Education

Dean: Norma Fe C. Ricafort; *staff* 65 (10)

C. of Arts and Sciences

Dean: Nenita Sy; *staff* 39

D. of Tourism

Head: Gemma Leonor; *staff* 5

D. of Hotel and Restaurant Management

Head: Arsenia Maye; *staff* 5

Graduate S.

Dean: Felipa Aboy; *staff* 1 (25)

Research D.

Director: Ofelia Triste; *staff* 1 (1)

D. of Community and Extension Services

Director: Dolores Umacob; *staff* 1 (5)

Also elementary school and high school.

Founded 1921 as a provincial normal school, became a college 1952 and acquired present status and title 1976. A State institution. Governing body: the Board of Trustees of which the Secretary of Education, Culture and Sports is Chairman.

Academic Year: June to April (June-October; November-April).

Admission Requirements: Graduation from high school and entrance examination.

Fees (Pesos): 438-538 per semester, per 18-24 units; graduate 525-730, per semester.

Languages of Instruction: English and Pilipino.

Degrees and Diplomas: Diplomas. Bachelor, 4 yrs. Master, a further 2-3 yrs. Doctor, 3-5 yrs following Master.

Library: College Library, 20,025 vols.

Publications: L.S.C. Chronicle; Graduate Studies Newsletter; Graduate Studies Education Review.

Academic Staff, 1989-90:

Rank	Full-time	Part-time
Professors	15	–
Associate Professors	18	–
Assistant Professors	17	–
Instructors	41	15
Total	91	15

Student Enrolment, 1989-90:

	Men	Women	Total
Of the country	392	2249	2641*

*Also 95 external students.

5781 **SURIANE TEKNOLOHIYA NG LEYTE**

Leyte Institute of Technology
Salazar Street, Tacloban City 7101
Telephone: 3212185; 3212186; 3212187
President: Santiago C. Simpas (1984-90)
Administrative Officer: Wilfredo V. Tan

C. of Engineering
Dean: Clodualdo S. Patano; *staff* 54 (61)
C. of Vocational Education
Dean: Eleno C. de la Cruz; *staff* 77 (16)
C. of Arts and Sciences
Dean: Gaudencia A. Genotiva; *staff* 57 (48)
Graduate S.
Dean: Balbino G. Loro; *staff* 5 (19)
Extension D.
Also elementary, secondary, and high schools.

Founded 1907 as part of Leyte Provincial High School, became Provincial Trade School 1915, and Regional School of Arts and Trades 1957. Acquired present status and title 1965. A State institution. Governing body: the Board of Trustees of which the Minister of Education, Culture and Sports is Chairman.

Academic Year: June to April (June-October; November-April).

Admission Requirements: Graduation from high school and entrance examination.

Fees (Pesos): 14 per unit, per semester; Graduate, 23-30.

Languages of Instruction: English and Pilipino.

Degrees and Diplomas: Associate in Marine Engineering, 2 yrs. Bachelor of–Arts, A.B.; Science in Industrial Education, B.S.I.E.; Hotel and Restaurant Administration; Home Economics; Business Education; Science in Education, B.SE.; Science in Civil Engineering, B.S.C.E.; Science in Chemical Engineering, B.S.Chem.E.; Science in Electrical Engineering, B.S.E.E.; Science in Industrial Engineering, B.S.I.E.; Science in Architecture, B.S.Arch.; Science in Home Technology, B.S.H.T.; Science in Mechanical Engineering, B.S.M.E., 4-5 yrs. Master of Arts in–Education, M.A.; Industrial Education, M.A.I.E.; Teaching Vocational Education; Industrial Education, a further 2 yrs. Doctor of Philosophy, Ph.D. 4 yrs.

Library: Central Library, 17,650 vols.

Publications: LIT Graduate Journal (annually); College Journal (annually); Industrial wiel (quarterly).

Academic Staff, 1986-87:

Rank	Full-time	Part-time
Professors	14	–
Associate Professors	36	–
Assistant Professors	97	–
Instructors	39	–
Lecturers	–	158
Total	186	158

Student Enrolment, 1986-87:

	Men	Women	Total
Of the country	2510	1616	4126*

*Also 24 external students.

5782 **MAMBUSAO AGRICULTURAL AND TECHNICAL COLLEGE**

Mambusao, Capiz

Agriculture
Education
Technical Services

5783 **MARINDUQUE INSTITUTE OF SCIENCE AND TECHNOLOGY**

Boac, Marinduque

Industrial Technology
Education
Agriculture
Fisheries
Engineering

Founded 1954.

5784 **MISAMIS ORIENTAL STATE COLLEGE OF AGRICULTURE AND TECHNOLOGY**

Claveria, Misamis Oriental
President: Arsenio B. Gonzales
Registrar: Monico E. Sabejon

D. of Agricultural Technology
Chairman: Romeo Dongallo; *staff* 6
D. of Agricultural Education
Chairman: Pablo R. Tomines; *staff* 12
D. of Engineering
Also academic and vocational high schools.

Founded 1963, acquired present status and title 1983. Governing body: the Board of Trustees, of which the Secretary of Education, Culture and Sports is Chairman. Residential facilities for academic staff and students.

Academic Year: June to March (June-October; November-March).

Admission Requirements: Graduation from high school or recognized equivalent, and entrance examination.

Fees (Pesos): 300 per semester.

Language of Instruction: English

Degrees and Diplomas: Bachelor of–Science in Agricultural Education, BSAEd; Agricultural Technology, BAT, 4 yrs. Diploma in Agricultural Technology, DAT, 2 yrs.

Academic Staff, 1990:

Rank	Full-time	Part-time
Assistant Professors	4	–
Instructors	12	1
Secondary School Teachers	18	1
Total	34	2

Student Enrolment, 1990:

	Men	Women	Total
Of the country	400	417	834

5785 **NATIONAL MARITIME POLYTECHNIC**

Barangay Cabalawan, Tacloban City 6500
Executive Director: George M. Pimentel
Administrative Officer: Benjamin A. Umipig

D. of Maritime Training
Head: Exequiel S. Campo; *staff* 50

Founded 1978, acquired present status and title 1980. A national government agency and training institution. Governing body: the Board of Trustees. Residential facilities for academic staff and students.

Academic Year: May to November.

Fees (Pesos): 513-1888

Languages of Instruction: English and Pilipino.

Degrees and Diplomas: Certificates.

Academic Staff, 1990: c. 50

Student Enrolment, 1990: 203 (Men).

5786 **NAVAL INSTITUTE OF TECHNOLOGY**

Biliran Sub-Province

Education
Technical Sciences

Founded 1965, acquired present status and title 1972.

5787 **NORTHERN ILOILO POLYTECHNIC STATE COLLEGE**
Estancia, Iloilo
President: Nacianeno S. Albaran (1984-)
Administrative Officer: Hilda A. Magtiza

Midwifery
Fisheries
Marine Engineering
Secretarial and Business Management

Founded 1952 as institute, acquired present status and title 1983. A State institution. Governing body: the Board of Trustees of which the Minister of Education, Culture and Sports is Chairman.

Academic Year: June to April (June-October; November-April).

Admission Requirements: Graduation from high school and entrance examination.

Fees (Pesos): 74-89 per semester.

Language of Instruction: English.

Degrees and Diplomas: Associate in–Business Management; Marine Engineering, 2 yrs. Bachelor of Science in–Fisheries; Fisheries Education, 4 yrs. Graduate in Midwifery, 2 yrs.

Library: Central Library, 10,399 vols.

Academic Staff, 1986-87:

Rank	Full-time
Associate Professors	3
Assistant Professors	15
Instructors	35
Teachers	34
Total	86

Student Enrolment, 1986-87:

	Men	Women	Total
Of the country	276	301	577

5788 **NORTHERN MINDANAO STATE INSTITUTE OF SCIENCE AND TECHNOLOGY**
Estancia, Iloilo

Fishery
Education
Engineering
Business Management
Technical Services

Founded 1965, acquired present status and title 1983.

5789 **NUEVA VIZCAYA STATE INSTITUTE OF TECHNOLOGY**
Bayombong, Nueva Vizcaya 3700
Telephone: 321-2280
President: Fortunato A. Battad (1987-)
Administrative Officer: Jose B. Tamani

C. of Education (including Ceramics, Furniture and Cabinet-Making)
Dean: Maria G. Cacacho; *staff* 27
C. of Agriculture (including Animal Science)
Dean: Felicisimo B. Gale; *staff* 41
C. of Engineering (Soil and Water Conservation, Farm Mechanization, and Crop Processing)
Dean: Sulpicio C. Sermonia; *staff* 15
C. of Fisheries
Dean: Victorio D. Gilo; *staff* 7
C. of Home Technology
Dean: Juanita P. Reyes; *staff* 16
C. of Forestry
Dean: Cesar E. Cansanay; *staff* 13
C. of Arts and Sciences
Dean: Emilia I. Bareng; *staff* 28 (4)
Graduate S.
Dean: Dionisio G. Ducusin; *staff* – (10-15)
Research P.
Director: Gideon A. Andres; *staff* 5 (10)
Extension Services P.
Director: Roberto J. Braña; *staff* 5 (6)
Also secondary schools.

Founded 1916 as school, became college of agriculture 1964 and acquired present status and title 1973. A Stateinstitution mainly financed by the government. Governing body: the Board of Trustees of which the Secretary of the Department of Education, Culture and Sports is Chairman. Residential facilities for academic staff.

Academic Year: June to May (June-October; November-March; April-May).

Admission Requirements: Graduation from high school and entrance examination.

Fees (Pesos): 7 per unit.

Languages of Instruction: English, Pilipino, and Spanish.

Degrees and Diplomas: Bachelor of Science in–Agriculture; Agricultural Education; Animal Science; Home Technology; Agricultural Engineering; Forestry; Industrial Education; Extension Education; Fishery; Agribusiness; Elementary Education; Mathematics, 4 yrs. Master of Science in–Agricultural Education; Agriculture, a further 1-2 yrs.

Library: Central Library, 16,000 vols.

Special Facilities (Museums, etc.): Collection of 1300 artefacts.

Publications: Vizcaya Tech Courier (semestral); Rang-Ay (irregular); Info Bits (irregular); Information Bulletin (irregular); NVSIT Bulletin (irregular); READ (irregular); NVSIT Scientific Journal (irregular).

Academic Staff, 1990:

Rank	Full-time
Professors	5
Associate Professors	22
Assistant Professors	58
Instructors	154
Total	239

Student Enrolment, 1990:

	Men	Women	Total
Of the country	745	743	1488

5790 **NUEVA VIZCAYA STATE POLYTECHNIC COLLEGE**
Bambang, Nueva Vizcaya

Education
Arts
Technical Sciences

Founded 1947, reorganized 1957 and 1983.

5791 **OCCIDENTAL MINDORO NATIONAL COLLEGE**
San José, Occidental Mindoro

Agriculture
Commerce
Education
Midwifery
Vocational

Founded 1983.

5792 **PABLO BORBON MEMORIAL INSTITUTE OF TECHNOLOGY**
Rizal Avenue, Batangas City 4201
Cables: PBMIT, Batangas City
Telephone: 725-2138; 3138; 3091
President: Mariano Albayalde (1986-)

D. of Engineering
Head: Lucena D. Hernanadez; *staff* 36 (9)
D. of Teacher Education
Head: Antonia H. Bisa; *staff* 49
D. of Industrial Technology
Head: Porfirio C. Ligaya; *staff* – (6)
D. of Technical Education
Head: Igmidio C. Bisa; *staff* 32
Graduate S.
Dean: Leoncia P. Sulit; *staff* – (12)
Also high school.

Founded 1903 as school, acquired present status and title 1968. A State institution. Governing body: the Board of Trustees of which the Minister of Education, Culture and Sports is the Chairman.

Academic Year: June to April (June-November; December-April).

Admission Requirements: Graduation from high school and entrance examination.

Fees (Pesos): 20 per unit, per semester.

Languages of Instruction: English and Tagalog.

Degrees and Diplomas: Bachelor of–Science in Industrial Education, 4 yrs; Civil Engineering; Electrical Engineering; Mechanical Engineering, 5 yrs. Master of–Arts; Management, a further 2 yrs.

Library: 20,712 vols.

Publication: Graduate Research Journal.

Press or Publishing House: PBMIT Press.

Academic Staff, 1986-87:

Rank	Full-time	Part-time
Professors	15	4
Associate Professors	10	–
Assistant Professors	42	–
Instructors	90	8
Total	157	12

Student Enrolment, 1986-87:

	Men	Women	Total
Of the country	2999	977	3976

5793 **PAGLAUM STATE COLLEGE**
Talisay, Negro Occidental
Telephone: 57-13; 53-05
President: Sulpecio P. Cartera
Administrative Officer: George G. Agraviador

Science
Agriculture
Industrial Technology
Also elementary and high schools

Founded as school 1954, acquired present status and title 1983. A State institution.

Academic Year: June to April (June-October; November-April).

Admission Requirements: Graduation from high school and entrance examination.

Fees (Pesos): 8 per unit; Graduate, 20.

Languages of Instruction: English and Pilipino.

Degrees and Diplomas: Associate in Secretarial Science, 2 yrs. Bachelor of Science in–Industrial Education, B.S.I.E.; Elementary Education, B.S.E.E.D.; Industrial Technology, B.S.I.T; Commerce, B.S.C. Master in–Technology; Industrial Education; Education.

Publication: The Technopacers (biannually).

Academic Staff, 1986-87:

Rank	Full-time
Associate Professor	1
Assistant Professor	1
Instructors	29
Assistant Instructors	36
Teachers	78
Total	145

Student Enrolment, 1986-87: 3517.

5794 **PALAWAN NATIONAL AGRICULTURAL COLLEGE**
Aborlan, Palawan

Agriculture
Engineering
Arts
Education
Technical Sciences

Founded 1910 as a farm settlement school. Became college 1963. Governing bodies: the Board of Trustees of which the Minister of Education, Culture and Sports is Chairman; the Chairmen of the House and Senate Committees on Education, the Director of Public Schools, the President of the College, and the President of the Alumni Association. Some residential facilities for academic staff and students.

Academic Year: July to April (July-November; December-April).

Admission Requirements: Graduation from high school.

Language of Instruction: English.

Degrees and Diplomas: Bachelor of–Science in Agriculture, B.S.A.; Science in Agricultural Education, B.S.A.E.; Science in Home Economics, B.S.H.E., 4 yrs.

Library: Central Library.

Academic Staff: c. 30.

Student Enrolment: c. 600.

5795 **PALAWAN STATE COLLEGE**
Tiniguiban, Puerto Princesa City
Telephone: 2158
President: Paterno M. Bruselas (1986-90)
Vice-President: Teresita L. Salva

C. of Education
Dean: Avelina L. Romantico; *staff* 45 (2)
C. of Arts and Sciences
Dean: Erlinda D. San Juan *staff* 72 (3)
C. of Business Administration
Dean: Leoncita C. Navidad; *staff* 22 (1)
C. of Engineering
Dean: Eduardo A. Gadiano; *staff* 12 (3)
Graduate S.
Dean: Crispiniano R. Acosta; *staff* 4 (6)
Also elementary and high schools, and 4 Extramural Study Centres.

Founded as teachers' college 1972, acquired present status and title 1984. A State institution. Governing body: the Board of Trustees of which the Minister of Education, Culture and Sports is Chairman. Residential facilities for academic staff.

Academic Year: June to April (June-October; November-April).

Admission Requirements: Graduation from high school and entrance examination.

Fees (Pesos): 250 per year; Graduate, 30 per unit.

Languages of Instruction: English and Pilipino.

Degrees and Diplomas: Bachelor of–Arts; Arts in Education; Elementary Education; Secondary Education; Psychology; Biology; Zoology; Business Administration; Business Education, 4 yrs. Science in–Civil Engineering; Electrical Engineering; Mechanical Engineering, 5 yrs. Master of–Public Administration; Arts in Education; Management; Arts in Teaching, a further 2 yrs.

Library: Central Library, 449 vols.

Special Facilities (Museums, etc.): Palawan Studies Center.

Publications: The Pioneer (quarterly); The PSC Journal (annually).

Academic Staff, 1990:

Rank	Full-time	Part-time
Professors	5	–
Associate Professors	6	–
Assistant Professors	19	
Instructors	177	24
Total	184	24

Student Enrolment, 1990:

	Men	Women	Total
Of the country	1675	3480	5155

5796 **PALOMPON INSTITUTE OF TECHNOLOGY**
Palompon, Leyte
President: Gil R. Dagami (1986-92)
Registrar: Angelita F. Pajaron

D. of Marine Transportation
Chairman: Crisolgo A. Motril; *staff* 11 (2)
D. of Languages
Chairman: Delia T. Combista; *staff* 11
D. of Mathematics and Sciences
Chairman: Arcelito G. Tapere; *staff* 11
D. of Social Sciences
Chairman: Maxima O. Salvino; *staff* 7 (1)
D. of Industrial Technology and Education
Chairman: Albino B. Ayop; *staff* 21
D. of Home Technology
Chairman: Portia P. Moreno; *staff* 45
D. of Physical Education
Chairman: Tito L. Jorda; *staff* 6
D. of Research
Chairman: Antonio E. Reposar; *staff* 3
D. of Extension Education
Chairman: Presentacion Sevilla; *staff* 2 (7)
D. of Radio-Communication
Chairman: Jaime D. Combista; *staff* 5 (1)

Founded 1964 as school, acquired present status and title 1972. A State institution. Governing body: the Board of Trustees. Residential facilities for students.

Academic Year: June to April (June-October; November-April).

Admission Requirements: Graduation from high school and entrance examination.

Fees (Pesos): 438 per semester.

Languages of Instruction: English, Spanish and Pilipino.

Degrees and Diplomas: Bachelor of Science in–Marine Transportation; Industrial Education; Industrial Technology; Home Technology, 4yrs.

Library: Central Library, 7500 vols.

Academic Staff, 1990: c. 120
Student Enrolment, 1990: c. 1990

5797 **PAMPANGA AGRICULTURAL COLLEGE**
Magalang, Pampanga 2018

D. of Arts and Sciences
D. of Animal Husbandry
D. of Crop Science
D. of Forestry
D. of Technical Sciences
D. of Agriculture
D. of Fishery
D. of Education
D. of Research
Graduate S.
D. of Agricultural Business
D. of Engineering
D. of Home Economics
D. for Lifelong Education
Also high school.

Founded 1885 as agricultural experimental station, became college 1965 and acquired present status 1974. A State institution. Governing body: the Board of Trustees. Residential facilities for academic staff and students.

Academic Year: June to March (June-October; November-March).

Admission Requirements: Graduation from high school and entrance examination.

Language of Instruction: English.

Degrees and Diplomas: Bachelor of Science in–Agriculture, B.S.A.; Forestry, B.S.F.; Agricultural Education; Home Economics, B.S.H.E.; Agricultural Engineering, B.S.A.E.; Agri-Business, B.S.Ag.B.; Elementary Education, B.E.Ed.; Agricultural Economics, 4 yrs. Master of Science in Agriculture, B.S.A.; Agricultural Education, B.S.A.Ed.; Professional Studies, M.P.S., a further 2 yrs. Also Associate in Agricultural Technology, 2 yrs.

Library: c. 19,700 vols.

Special Facilities (Museums, etc.): College Museum.

Publications: Sinukuan Gazette (biannually); Research Journal (biannually).

Academic Staff: c. 120.

Student Enrolment: c. 1470.

5798 **PANAY STATE POLYTECHNIC COLLEGE**
Mambusao, Capiz 5706
President: Ernesto V. Botin (1981-)
Registrar: Pablo Espino

Agriculture (including Forestry and Fisheries)
Education
Technical Sciences

Founded 1980, incorporating Mambusao Agricultural and Technical College and Capiz Agricultural and Fishery School. A State institution. Governing body: the Board of Trustees of which the Minister of Education, Culture and Sports is Chairman. Governing body: the Board of Trustees of which the Minister of Education, Culture and Sports is Chairman. Residential facilities for academic staff and students. Residential facilities for academic staff and students.

Academic Year: June to March (June-October; November-March).

Admission Requirements: Graduation from high school and entrance examination.

Languages of Instruction: English and Pilipino.

Degrees and Diplomas: Associate in Agricultural Technology, A.A.T.; Fishery Technology, A.F.T., 2 yrs. Bachelor of Science in–Agriculture, B.S.A.; Agricultural Homemaking, B.S.A.H.; Agricultural Education, B.S.Ag.Ed.; Agricultural Economics, B.S.Ag.Econ.; Home Economics, B.S.H.E.; Agricultural Technology, B.A.T.; Fishery Technology, B.F.T.; Fishery, B.S.F.; Fishery Education, B.S.F.Ed.; Forestry, B.S.F., 4 yrs; Agricultural Engineering, 5 yrs. Master of Science, a further 2 yrs. Also qualification of Forest Ranger, 2 yrs.

Library: c. 44,500 vols.

Publications: Journal (biannually); The Farmer's Echo (biannually); Forum (biannually); The Green Thumb (biannually).

Academic Staff: c. 200.

Student Enrolment: c. 4110.

5799 **PHILIPPINE NORMAL COLLEGE**
Taft Avenue and Ayala Boulevard, Ermita
Telephone: 3-53-14
President: Edilberto P. Dagot

Arts and Sciences (including Mathematics)
Education
Engineering
Language Study Ce.
Child Study Ce.
Health Education Ce.
Special Education Ce.
Graduate S.
Branches at: Alicia, Cadiz City, Prosperidad.

Founded as normal school 1901, became college 1950. A State institution mainly financed by the government. Governing body: the Board of Trustees, of which the Minister of Education, Culture and Sports is Chairman. Some residential facilities for students.

Academic Year: July to April (July-November; November-April).

Admission Requirements: Graduation from high school and entrance examination.

Language of Instruction: English.

Degrees and Diplomas: Bachelor of Science in Elementary Education, B.S.E.E.; Bachelor of Science in Elementary Education (Major in Home Economics), 4 yrs. Master of Arts in Education, M.A., 5 yrs.

Library: 85,000 vols.

Special Facilities (Museums, etc.): Museum of Health.

Publications: The Torch; Newsette; Bulletin.

Academic Staff: c. 300.

Student Enrolment: c. 6620.

5800 **POLYTECHNIC STATE COLLEGE OF ANTIQUE**
Sibalom, Antique
Cables: PSCA, Sibalom, Antique
President: Godofredo E. Gallega (1984-90)
Administrative Officer: Dioscoro A. Tronzon

Industrial Education (including Arts Education, Vocational Education, and Business Management)
Also high school.

Founded 1954 as school of Arts and Trade, acquired present status and title 1982. A State institution. Governing body: the Board of Trustees of which the Minister of Education, Culture and Sports is Chairman. Governing body: the Board of Trustees of which the Minister of Education, Culture and Sports is Chairman. Residential facilities for academic staff and students. Residential facilities for academic staff and students.

Academic Year: June to March (June-October; November-March).

Admission Requirements: Graduation from high school and entrance examination.

Fees (Pesos): 7 per unit, per semester.

Languages of Instruction: English and Pilipino.

Degrees and Diplomas: Associate in Trade, 2 yrs. Bachelor of Science in–Practical Arts Education, B.S.P.A.Ed.; Industrial Education, B.S.I.E.; Business Management, B.B.M.; Secondary Education, B.S.E., 4 yrs. Master of Arts in Vocational Education.

Library: Central Library, 12,848 vols.

Publications: PSCA Weel (biannually); Research Journal (annually).

Academic Staff, 1986-87:

Rank	Full-time	Part-time
Professor	1	–
Associate Professor	1	–
Assistant Professors	5	2
Instructors	61	3
Teachers	15	3
Total	83	8

Student Enrolment, 1986-87:

	Men	Women	Total
Of the country	829	934	1763

5801 **QUIRINO STATE COLLEGE**
Bonifacio, Diffun, Quirino
President: Julian A. Alvarez (1987-92)
Administrative Assistant: Benjamin T. Julian

Agriculture (including Animal Husbandry)
Education

Home Technology
Graduate S.
Research and Extension D.
Also high school.

Founded 1963 as high school, acquired present status and title 1983. A State institution. Governing body: the Board of Trustees of which the Secretary of Education, Culture and Sports is Chairman. Residential facilities for academic staff and students.

Academic Year: June to March (June-October; November-March).

Admission Requirements: Graduation from high school and entrance examination.

Fees (Pesos): Graduate school, 52 per unit.

Languages of Instruction: English and Pilipino.

Degrees and Diplomas: Bachelor of–Agricultural Technology, B.A.T.; Agricultural Education, B.S.A.Ed.; Science in Agriculture, B.S.A.; Science in Home Technology, B.S.H.T., 4 yrs. Master of Arts in Education, M.A.Ed., a further 2 yrs. Also Diploma in Agricultural Technology, D.A.T., 2 yrs.

Publications: QSC Journal (semi-annually); the Ganano Breeze (biannually).

Academic Staff, 1989-90:

Rank	Full-time	Part-time
Professors	–	5
Associate Professors	1	–
Assistant Professors	4	–
Instructors	8	–
Teachers	9	–
Total	45	5

Student Enrolment, 1989-90:

	Men	Women	Total
Of the country	488	666	1154

5802 **RIZAL COLLEGE OF AGRICULTURE AND TECHNOLOGY**
Sampaloc, Tanay, Rizal
President: Heracleo D. Ladgrada
Registrar: Elsie C. Puño

C. of Education and Home Technology
Dean: Rosita Marquez; *staff* 21
C. of Agriculture
Dean: Almario P. Garcia; *staff* 12
C. of Arts and Science
Dean: Soledad S.D. Arada; *staff* 14
C.of Agricultural Engineering and Technology
Dean: Rodolfo G. Smanaiego; *staff* 5
Graduate S.
Dean: Milagros R. Niñonuevo; *staff* 5 (10)
D. of Research, Extension and Production

Founded 1959, reorganized into a State College (Chartered), 1984. Governing body: Board of Trustees.

Academic Year: June to March.

Admission Requirements: Graduation from high school and entrance examination.

Fees (Pesos): Tuition, 7 per unit, per semester.

Languages of Instruction: English and Pilipino.

Degrees and Diplomas: Bachelor of–Agriculture Technology; Elementary Education; Science in Education; Arts; Science, 4 yrs; Science in Agriculture Engineering, 5 yrs. Master of–Arts; Science; Public Administration; Science in Agriculture, a further 2 yrs. Also diplomas, 2 yrs.

Special Facilities (Museums, etc.): Arboretum

Academic Staff, 1990:

Rank	Full-time	Part-time
Professor	1	–
Associate Professors	4	–
Assistant Professors	9	–
Instructors	5	–
Teachers	23	–
Professorial Lecturers	5	–
Total	47	10

Student Enrolment, 1990:

	Men	Women	Total
Of the country	768	695	1463

5803 **RIZAL TECHNOLOGICAL COLLEGES**
Boni Avenue Mandaluyong Metro Manila 1501
Telephone: 79-24-20, 79-21-95; 79-23-06
President: Josefina V. Estolas

C. of Arts and Sciences
Dean (Acting): Rosalinda Leonardo *staff* 14 (4)
C. of Business Technology
Dean (Acting): Alonzo Ruzano; *staff* 46 (8)
C. of Engineering Technology
Dean (Acting): Antonio Villgas; *staff* 92 (2)
C. of Graduate S.
Dean (Acting): Clarita J. Javier; *staff* 2 (23)
D. of Non-Formal Education
Director (Acting): Norma T. Mendez; *staff* 6 (1)
Research and Development Ce.
Director (Acting): Jesus R.F. Tommes; *staff* 8
Also technical high school.

Founded 1969 as provincial college, acquired present status and title 1978. A State institution. Governing body: the Board of Trustees of which the Secretary of Education, Culture and Sports is Chairman.

Academic Year: June to March (June-October; November-March).

Admission Requirements: Graduation from high school and entrance examination.

Fees (Pesos): 66.10 per unit.

Languages of Instruction: English and Pilipino.

Degrees and Diplomas: Associate in–Electronics Technology; Electrical Technology; Mechanical Technology; Computer Technology, 3 yrs. Bachelor of–Arts; Business Technology; Architecture; Science in–Education; Technological Communication; Industrial Psychology, 4 yrs; Computer Engineering; Civil Engineering; Industrial Management Engineering; Mechanical Engineering; Electronics Communications Engineering; Electrical Engineering, 5 yrs. Master in–Technology Education; Business Technology; Public Administration; Engineering Technology, a further 3 yrs. Doctor of–Technology Education; Public Administration; Business Technology, 4 yrs.

Library: Central Library, 32,072 vols.

Publications: Techno-Post (biannually); The Quest (annually); The Pioneer (annually).

Academic Staff, 1990: c. 320 (30).

Student Enrolment, 1990: c. 6050 (Also 174 external students).

5804 **ROMBLON STATE COLLEGE**
Odiongan, Romblon 3211
President: Victorino L. Aguila (1983-)
Administrative Officer: Renato G. Solidum

Agriculture
Home Technology

Founded 1914 as farm school, became college 1962. Acquired present status and title 1983. A State institution. Governing body: the Board of Trustees of which the Minister of Education, Culture and Sports is Chairman. Residential facilities for academic staff and students.

Academic Year: June to April (June-October; November-April).

Admission Requirements: Graduation from high school and entrance examination.

Fees (Pesos): 6 per subject, per semester.

Languages of Instruction: English, Pilipino and Spanish.

Degrees and Diplomas: Bachelor of Science in–Agriculture; Agricultural Technology; Home Technology, 4 yrs.

Library: Central Library, *c.* 10,000 vols.

Publication: The Harrow (quarterly).

6423 **PAŃSTWOWA WYŻSZA SZKOLA FILMOWA, TELEWIZYJNA I TEATRALNA IM. LEONA SCHILLERA**

State College of Cinematography, Television, and Dramatic Art
ul. Targowa 61, 90-323 Łódź
Telex: 884380 FILM PL
Telephone: 74-39-43
Rektor: Henryk Kluba

D. of Film and Television Directing
Dean: Wojciech Has; *staff* 20 (4)
D. of Cinema
Dean: Jerzy Woźniak; *staff* 13 (18)
Acting D.
Dean; Jan Machulski; *staff* 24 (18)
Also Postgraduate Managing Department; Editing Courses; and Screenplay Writing Courses.

Founded 1948. A State institution under the jurisdiction of the Ministry of Culture and Art. Some residential facilities for students.

Academic Year: October to May (October-January; February-May).

Admission Requirements: Secondary school certificate.

Fees: None for Polish Students. For foreign students, US$ *c.* 8000 per annum.

Language of Instruction: Polish.

Degrees and Diplomas: Magister sztuki, 4 yrs.

Library: c. 30,000 vols.

Special Facilities (Museums, etc.): Art Gallery; Movie Studio; TV Studio; Theatre; Photography Studio; Film Production Centre.

Academic Staff, 1989-90: 37 (9).

Student Enrolment, 1989-90:

	Men	Women	Total
Of the country	126	58	184
Of other countries	24	8	32
Total	150	66	216*

*Also *c.* 76 external students.

Teacher Training

6424 **WYŻSZA SZKOŁA PEDAGOGICZNA**

College of Education
ul. Chodkiewicza 30, 85-084 Bydgoszcz
Telex: 0562573 WSP PL
Telephone: 41-32-03

F. of Education
F. of Humanities
F. of Mathematics and Technology
Also 22 departments.

Founded 1969 as teacher training college, acquired present status 1974. A State institution under the jurisdiction of the Ministry of National Education. Governing body: the Senate.

Academic Year: October to June (October-February; February-June).

Admission Requirements: Secondary school certificate and entrance examination.

Fees: None.

Language of Instruction: Polish.

Degrees and Diplomas: Magister, mgr., in all fields, 5 yrs.

Libraries: Central Library, *c.* 245,000 vols. Neophilological library, *c.* 30,000; Musical Education, *c.* 13,000.

Publications: Studies: Philology; Pedagogy; Psychology; Technology; Biology.

Press or Publishing House: Pedagogical Publishing House.

Academic Staff: c. 280.

Student Enrolment: c. 1650.

6425 **WYŻSZA SZKOŁA PEDAGOGICZNA**

Pedagogical University
Waszyngtona 4/8, 42-201 Częstochowa
Telex: 037261 PUNIV PL
Telephone: 470-64
Rektor: Edward Polanowski (1984-90)
Dyrektor Administracyjny: Aleksander Gogulski

F. of Humanities and Education
Dean: Julian Maliszewski; *staff* 250 (45)
F. of Mathematics and Natural Science
Dean: Andrzej Lisicki; *staff* 103 (7)
D. of Foreign Languages
Head: Andrzej Watroba; *staff* 17 (3)
D. of Physical Education
Head: Stanisław Kupczyk; *staff* 14
D. of Computer Sciences
Head: Alicja Podgórska; *staff* 6 (1)
Pedagogical I.
Director: Zygmunt Zimny; *staff* 121 (36)
I. of Polish Philology
Director: Edward Polanowski; *staff* 40 (3)
I. of Arts
Director: Leon Markiewicz; *staff* 89 (6)
I. of Chemistry
Director: Eugeniusz Gurgul; *staff* 30 (1)
I. of Physics
Director: Józef Świątok; *staff* 37 (2)
I. of Mathematics
Director: Czesław Ginalski; *staff* 33 (4)
Branch in Wieluń.

Founded 1971 as teacher training college, acquired present status 1973. A State institution under the jurisdiction of the Ministry of National Education. Governing body: the Senate. Residential facilities for academic staff and students.

Arrangements for co-operation with similar institutions in USSR, Germany, Czechoslovakia.

Academic Year: October to June (October-January; February-June).

Admission Requirements: Secondary school certificate and entrance examination.

Fees: None.

Language of Instruction: Polish.

Degrees and Diplomas: Magister, mgr., 5 yrs.

Library: Pedagogical University Library, 174,710 vols.

Special Facilities (Museums, etc.): Astronomical Observatory.

Publications: Research Report Papers, Series (c. 5 copies a year); Scientific and Didactic Books (c. 15 titles a year).

Press or Publishing House: Pedagogical University Publishing House.

Academic Staff, 1989-90:

Rank	Full-time	Part-time
Profesorowie	12	6
Docenci	30	7
Wykładowcy	92	12
Asystenci	250	30
Total	384	55

Student Enrolment, 1989-90:

	Men	Women	Total
Of the country	760	3061	3821

6426 **WYŻSZA SZKOŁA PEDAGOGICZNA**

College of Education
ul. Wesoła 56, 25-363 Kielce
Telex: 0613478 WSP PL
Rektor: Zdzisław Czarny (1984-87)
Dyrektor Administracyjny: Stanisław Musiał

F. of Education
F. of Liberal Arts
F. of Mathematics and Natural Sciences

Founded 1969 as teacher training college, acquired present status 1973. A State institution under the jurisdiction of the Ministry of National Education. Governing body: the Senate. Residential facilities for academic staff and students.

Arrangements for co-operation with: Pedagogická Fakulta, Nitra; University of Greifswald.

Academic Year: October to June (October-February; February-September).

Admission Requirements: Secondary school certificate and entrance examination.

Fees: None for Polish students.

Language of Instruction: Polish.

Degrees and Diplomas: Magister, mgr., 5 yrs.

Library: c. 245,000 vols.

Publication: Kieleckie Studia (quarterly).

Press or Publishing House: Publishing House.

Academic Staff: c. 440 (130).

Student Enrolment: c. 4000.

6427 **WYŻSZA SZKOŁA PEDAGOGICZNA**
College of Education
ul. Podchorążych 2, 30-084 Kraków
Telex: 0322 444 WSP PL
Telephone: 37-47-77
Rektor: Mieczysław Rozmus (1984-87)
Dyrektor Administracyjny: Jerzy Ziemiński

F. of Humanities
Dean: Czesław Majorek; *staff* 327 (34)
F. of Geography and Biology
Dean: Jan Rajman; *staff* 67 (9)
F. of Mathematics, Physics and Technical Education
Dean: Józef Tabor; *staff* 146 (11)
Also 19 institutes and departments.

Founded 1946 as teacher training college, acquired present status 1974. A State institution under the jurisdiction of the Ministry of National Education. Governing body: the Senate. Residential facilities for students in hostels.

Arrangements for co-operation with: Teacher Training College, Szeged; College of Education, Leipzig; College of Education, Dresden; Pedagogická Fakulta, Nitra; Stockholm Institute of Education; Ernst Moritz University of Greifswald; Kiev Education Institute; Free University of Brussels; King Alfred's College, Winchester.

Academic Year: October to June (October-February; February-June).

Admission Requirements: Secondary school certificate and entrance examination.

Fees: None for Polish students.

Languages of Instruction: Polish. Degrees and Dipomas: Magister, mgr., 5 yrs. Doktor, dr., by thesis. Dr.habil. (teaching qualification,university level) in Humanities, by thesis after doctorate.

Libraries: Central Library, 346,301 vols; libraries of the institutes, 183,051.

Publication: Rocznik Naukowo-Dydaktyczny (annually).

Press or Publishing House: Publishing House.

Academic Staff, 1986-87: 623 (54).

Student Enrolment, 1986-87:

	Men	Women	Total
Of the country	1078	2738	5882*

*Also 2066 external students.

6428 **WYŻSZA SZKOŁA PEDAGOGICZNA**
College of Education
ul. Żołnierska 14, 10-950 Olsztyn
Telex: 0526223 WSP PL
Telephone: 245-09

F. of Mathematics and Natural Sciences
F. of Education
F. of Arts (including Philology, Library Science, and Music)
D. of Foreign Languages
D. of Physical Education

Founded 1969 as teacher training college, acquired present status 1974. A State institution under the jurisdiction of the Ministry of National Education. Governing body: the Senate. Residential facilities for students.

Academic Year: October to September (October-February; February-September).

Admission Requirements: Secondary school certificate and entrance examination.

Fees: None.

Language of Instruction: Polish.

Degrees and Diplomas: Magister, mgr., 4 yrs.

Libraries: Central Library, *c.* 141,550 vols; department libraries, *c.* 40,700.

Special Facilities (Museums, etc.): Zoology Museum.

Academic Staff: *c.* 30 (30).

Student Enrolment: *c.* 1380 (Also *c.* 1390 external students).

6429 **WYŻSZA SZKOŁA PEDAGOGICZNA IM. POWSTAŃCÓW ŚLĄSKICH**
College of Education
ul. Oleska 48, 45 052 Opole
Telex: 0732230 WSP PL
Telephone: 358-41
Rektor: Stanisław Kochman (1984-90)
Dyrektor Administracyjny: Tadeusz Kampczyk

F. of Philology and History (including Education and Economics)
Dean: Z. Piasecki
F. of Mathematics, Physics and Chemistry
Dean: J. Pietrzykowski
I. of Polish Language and Literature
Director: M. Kaczmarek
I. of East Slavonic Studies
Director: A. Wieczorek
I. of English and American
Director: P. Ruszkiewicz; *staff* 17 (2)
I. of History
Director: J. Seredyka
Branch in Nysa.

Founded in Wrocław 1950 as teacher training college, moved to Opole 1954. Acquired present status 1974. A State institution under the jurisdiction of the Ministry of National Education. Governing bodies: the Faculty Councils; the Senate. Some residential facilities for academic staff and students.

Arrangements for co-operation with: College of Education, Potsdam; Pedagogická Fakulta, Hradec Králové; Institute of Education, Bielogorod; University of East Anglia, Norwich.

Academic Year: October to September (October-February; February-September).

Admission Requirements: Secondary school certificate.

Fees: None.

Languages of Instruction: Polish and Russian; also English, German, and Czech.

Degrees and Diplomas: Magister, mgr., 5 yrs. Doktor, a further 5-6 yrs.

Library: Central Library, department libraries, total, *c.* 358,200 vols.

Publication: Working Papers of the Institutes.

Press or Publishing House: Wydawnictwo Wyższej Szkoły Pedagogiczneh (The College Press).

Academic Staff: *c.* 230 (30).

Student Enrolment: *c.* 3000.

6430 **WYŻSZA SZKOŁA PEDAGOGICZNA**
Pedagogical University
ul. Turkienicza 24, 35-959 Rzeszów
Telex: 0633343 WSP PL
Telephone: 388-21
Fax: 324-22
Rektor: Marian Bobran (1986-90)

F. of Philology
Dean: Zbigniew Światłowski; *staff* 114 (12)
F. of Mathematics and Physics
Dean: Roman Ampel; *staff* 111 (21)
F. of Education and Social Sciences
Dean: Alojzy Zielecki; *staff* 193 (73)
I. of Physical Education and Sport
Foreign Languages I.
Research Ce.
Head: Andrzej Bylica; *staff* 5
Also affiliated college in Krosno.

Founded 1965 as teacher training college, acquired present status 1974. Governing body: the Senate. Residential facilities for 25 academic staff and 1360 students.

Arrangements for co-operation with the Universities of: Leipzig; Kosice; Colleges of Education in: Güstrow; Erfurt; Neunbrandenburg; Kalinigrad; Nyirygemaza; Drohobycz; Blagojewgrad; Politechnic in Lvov.

Academic Year: October to June (October-February; February-September).

Admission Requirements: Secondary school certificate and entrance examination.

Fees: None.

Language of Instruction: Polish.

Degrees and Diplomas: Magister, mgr., 5 yrs.

Library: Central Library, 348,000 vols.

Special Facilities (Museums, etc.): Astronomical Observatory.

Publication: Zeszyty Naukowe.

Academic Staff, 1989-90:

Rank	Full-time	Part-time
Profesorowie	15	8
Docenci	30	14
Adiunkci	121	29
Asystenci	252	55
Total	318	106

Student Enrolment, 1990:

	Men	Women	Total
Of the country	923	1969	2892*

*Also 1403 external students.

6431 **WYŻSZA SZKOŁA PEDAGOGICZNA**

College of Education

ul. Arciszewskiego 22a, 76-200 Słupsk

Telephone: 72-91

Rektor: Andrzej Czarnik (1978-87)

Dyrektor Administracyjny: Jan Szumski

F. of Humanities
Dean: Tomasz Szrubka; *staff* 59 (2)
F. of Mathematics and Natural Sciences
Dean: Ludwik Żmudziński; *staff* 82 (8)
F. of Education
Dean: Heynryk Stiller; *staff* 83 (19)
D. of Foreign Languages
D. of Physical Education

Founded as teacher training college 1969, acquired present status 1974. A State institution under the jurisdiction of the Ministry of National Education. Governing body: the Senate. Residential facilities for students.

Academic Year: October to September (October-February; February-September).

Admission Requirements: Secondary school certificate and entrance examination.

Fees: None.

Language of Instruction: Polish.

Degrees and Diplomas: Magister, mgr., 5 yrs.

Library: Central Library, 228,000 vols.

Publication: Faculty publications.

Academic Staff, 1986-87:

Rank	Full-time	Part-time
Profesorowie	16	1
Docenci	27	3
Adiunkci	88	9
Wykładowcy	70	20
Asystenci	50	–
Total	251	33

Student Enrolment, 1986-87:

	Men	Women	Total
Of the country	433	1334	1767*

*Also 1000 external students.

6432 **WYŻSZA SZKOŁA PEDAGOGIKI SPECJALNEJ IM. MARII GRZEGOZEWSKIEJ**

College of Special Education

ul. Szczęśliwicka 40, 02-353 Warszawa

Telephone: 22-16-31

Rektor: Karol Poznański (1984-87)

Dyrektor: Tadeusz Misiak

F. of Education (for the handicapped)

Founded 1922, acquired present status 1976. A State institution under the jurisdiction of the Ministry of National Education. Governing body: the Senate. Residential facilities for students in hostels.

Arrangements for co-operation with: Humboldt University of Berlin; University of Giessen; Charles University, Prague.

Academic Year: October to June (October-February; February-June).

Admission Requirements: Secondary school certificate and entrance examination.

Fees: None.

Language of Instruction: Polish.

Degrees and Diplomas: Magister, mgr., 5 yrs.

Library: 48,000 vols.

Special Facilities (Museums, etc.): College Museum M. Grzegożewskiej.

Academic Staff, 1986-87: 115 (70).

Student Enrolment, 1986-87: 1820 (Also 3278 external students).

6433 **WYŻSZA SZKOŁA PEDAGOGICZNA**

College of Education

Pl. Slowiański 6, 65-625 Zielona Góra

Telex: 0433467 WSP PL

Telephone: 635-20

Rektor: Kazimierz Bartkiewicz (1984-87)

Dyrektor Administracyjny: Stefan Bolinski

F. of Humanities
Dean: Joachim Benyskiewicz; *staff* 86 (23)
F. of Education
Dean: Maria Jackowicka; *staff* 94 (11)
F. of Mathematics, Physics, and Technology
Dean: Kazimierz Uździcki; *staff* 55 (9)
Also 16 institutes and departments.

Founded 1971 as teacher training school. Acquired present status 1973. A State institution under the jurisdiction of the Ministry of National Education. Governing body: the Senate. Residential facilities for 40 academic staff and 880 students.

Arrangements for co-operation with: College of Education, Potsdam; College of Education, Leipzig; College of Education, Dresden; Martin Luther University of Halle-Wittenberg; Pedagogicka Fakulta, Hradec Králové; Teacher Training College, Eger.

Academic Year: October to May (October-January; February-May).

Admission Requirements: Secondary school certificate and entrance examination.

Fees: None.

Language of Instruction: Polish.

Degrees and Diplomas: Magister, mgr., 5 yrs.

Libraries: Central Library, *c.* 25,000 vols; libraries of the institutes, *c.* 21,000.

Publications: Studia i Materiały; Dydaktyka Literatury.

Press or Publishing House: Wydawnictwo WSP.

Academic Staff, 1986-87:

Rank	Full-time	Part-time
Profesorowie	6	4
Docenci	32	13
Starsi wykładowcy/Wykładowcy	148	9
Nauczyciele	102	–
Total	288	38

Student Enrolment, 1986-87:

	Men	Women	Total
Of the country	651	1354	2005*

*Also 845 external students.

6434 **AKADEMIA WYCHOWANIA FIZYCZNEGO**

Academy of Physical Education

ul. Wiejska 1, 80-336 Gdańsk-Oliwa

Telex: 0512496 AWF PL

Telephone: 52-50-51

Rektor: Zdzisław Józefowicz (1987-90)

Dyrektor Administracyjny: Adam Goliger

Physical Education

Founded 1952 as school, became college 1969 and acquired present title 1981. A State institution under the jurisdiction of the Committee for Physical Culture and Sport. Governing body: the Senate. Residential facilities for students.

Arrangements for co-operation with: College of Education, Magdeburg; University of Kiel; University of Mosul; Institute of Physical Culture, Leningrad; University of Ancona.

Academic Year: October to June (October-February; February-June).

Admission Requirements: Secondary school certificate and entrance examination.

Fees: None for Polish students.

Language of Instruction: Polish.

Degrees and Diplomas: Magister, 4 yrs (5 yrs by correspondence).

Library: Central Library, 65,751 vols.

Publications: Zeszyty Naukowe (Scientific Papers); Zeszyty Metodyczne (Methodical Papers); Monografie (Monographs).

Press or Publishing House: Wydawnictwo Uczelniane AWF.

Academic Staff, 1989-90: 168 (19).
Student Enrolment, 1989-90:

	Men	Women	Total
Of the country	638	298	936*

*Also 492 students by correspondence.

6435 **WYŻSZA SZKOŁA WYCHOWANIA FIZYCZNEGO**
Academy of Physical Education
ul. Mikołowska 72a, 40-065 Katowice
Telex: 0315581 AWF PL
Telephone: 51-40-66
Rektor: Stanisław Socha
Dyrektor: Alfred Sosgórnik

Physical Education

Founded 1970 as college, acquired present title 1979. A State institution under the jurisdiction of the Committee for Physical Culture. Residential facilities for *c.* 250 students.

Academic Year: October to June (October-February; February-June).

Admission Requirements: Secondary school certificate and entrance examination.

Fees: None.

Language of Instruction: Polish.

Degrees and Diplomas: Magister, mgr., 4 yrs.

Library: 35,000 vols.

Publications: Rocznik Naukowy; Informacja Ekspresowa; Informatory przebiegu studiów.

Academic Staff, 1989-90: 59 (15).

Student Enrolment: c. 1450.

6436 **AKADEMIA WYCHOWANIA FIZYCZNEGO**
Academy of Physical Education
Al. Planu 6-letniego 62A, 31-571 Kraków
Telex: 0325235 AWF PL
Telephone: 48-50-06
Rektor: Adam Klimek (1981-87)
Dyrektor Administracyjny: Czesław Kołodziej

Physical Education

Also branches in Rzeszów and Kielce.

Founded 1927 as institute of the Jagiellonian University, became college 1950 and acquired present title 1973.A State institution under the jurisdiction of the Committee for Physical Culture and Sport. Governing body: the Senate. Some residential facilities for students.

Arrangements for co-operation with: University of Copenhagen; University of Paris; University of Milan; Catholic University, Nijmegen.

Academic Year: October to June (October-January; February-June).

Admission Requirements: Secondary school certificate and entrance examination.

Fees: None.

Language of Instruction: Polish.

Degrees and Diplomas: Magister, mgr., 4 yrs. Doktor by thesis.

Library: Central Library, 94,338 vols.

Special Facilities (Museums, etc.): Anatomy Museum.

Publication: Roczniki Naukowe (Scientific Papers, annually).

Academic Staff, 1986-87:

Rank	Full-time	Part-time
Profesorowie zwyczajni	1	–
Profesorowie nadzwyczajni	6	3
Docenci	16	5
Wykładowcy i Starsi wykładowcy	49	11
Adiunkci	70	5
Starsi asystenci	66	2
Asystenci	29	1
Lektorzy	5	2
Asystenci stażyści	11	–
Nauczyciele	1	2
Total	254	31

Student Enrolment, 1986-87:

	Men	Women	Total
Of the country	991	667	1658
Of other countries	20	4	24
Total	1011	671	1682*

*Also 698 external students.

6437 **AKADEMIA WYCHOWANIA FIZYCZNEGO**
Academy of Physical Education
ul. Marchlewskiego 27/39, 61-871 Poznań
Telex: 0413230 AWF PL
Telephone: 33-00-81
Rektor: Jerzy Matynia (1985-87)
Dyrektor Administracyjny: Zdzisław Kudła

F. of Physical Education

Dean: Sławomir Drozdowski; *staff* 135 (12)

F. of Tourism and Recreation

Dean: Jerzy Bogucki; *staff* 47 (5)

Branch at Gorzów Wielkopolski.

Founded 1919 as institute of the Uniwersytet im. Adama Mickiewicza w Poznaniu, became college 1950, acquired present title 1973. A State institution under the jurisdiction of the Committee for Physical Culture and Sport. Residential facilities for academic staff and students.

Academic Year: December to June (December-January; February-June).

Admission Requirements: Secondary school certificate and entrance examination.

Fees: None.

Language of Instruction: Polish.

Degrees and Diplomas: Magister, mgr., 4 yrs. Doktor by thesis.

Libraries: Central Library, *c.* 52,000 vols; Tourism and Recreation, 5400.

Publications: Roczniki Naukowe WSWF Poznań; Kronika WSWF Poznań.

Academic Staff, 1986-87: 290 (29).

Student Enrolment, 1986-87:

	Men	Women	Total
Of the country	1170	720	1890
Of other countries	7	1	8
Total	1177	721	1898

6438 **AKADEMIA WYCHOWANIA FIZYCZNEGO IM. K. ŚWIERCZEWSKIEGO**
Academy of Physical Education
ul. Marymoncka 34, Warszawa 45
Telex: 816213 AWF PL
Telephone: 34-08-13

Physical Education

Also branch at Biała Podlaska.

Founded 1929 as institute, started giving three-year course 1938 and acquired present status 1954. Since 1958 the academy has been authorized to award the degree of Doctor of Physical Education, and since 1966 the qualification of Dr.hab. A State institution under the jurisdiction of the Committee for Physical Culture. Residential facilities for some academic staff and for 80% of the students.

Academic Year: October to June (October-January; February-June).

Admission Requirements: Secondary school certificate and entrance examination.

Fees: None.

Language of Instruction: Polish.

Degrees and Diplomas: Magister, mgr.w.f., 4 yrs (5 by correspondence). Doktor by thesis. Dr.hab. (teaching qualification, university level), by thesis after doctorate.

Library: c. 75,000 vols.

Publication: Roczniki Naukowe (Scientific Papers).

Academic Staff: c. 180.

Student Enrolment: c. 800 (Also *c.* 450 external students).

6439 **AKADEMIA WYCHOWANIA FIZYCZNEGO**
Academy of Physical Education
Al. Padererewskiego 35, 51-612 Wrocław
Telex: 0712103 AWF PL
Telephone: 48-25-27
Rektor: Zbigniew Sadowski (1987-90)
Dyrektor Administracyjny: Andrzej Stachowski

Physical Education

Founded 1946 as an institute of the Uniwersytet Wrocławski, became college 1950 and acquired present title 1972. A State institution under the jurisdiction of the Committee for Youth and Physical Culture. Residential facilities for students.

Arrangements for co-operation with: Charles University, Prague; University of Oldenburg; University of Hanover; Kiev State Institute of Physical Culture; Republic Sport School, Kiev; State University of Zaporozhe; Dresden High School of Communication

Academic Year: October to June (October-February; February-June).

Admission Requirements: Secondary school certificate and entrance examination.

Fees: None.

Language of Instruction: Polish.

Degrees and Diplomas: Magister, mgr., 4 yrs. Doktor by thesis. Dr.hab.(teaching qualification, university level), by thesis after doctorate.

Library: Central Library, *c.* 60,000 vols.

Publications: Rozprawy Naukowe; Studia i Monografie; Zeszyty Naukowe WSWF (Scientific Papers).

Press or Publishing House: Press Section.

Academic Staff, 1990:

Rank	Full-time	Part-time
Profesorowie	11	–
Docenci	13	3
Wykładowcy	9	6
Starsi wykładowcy	22	14
Adiunkci	51	19
Starsi asystenci	57	14
Asystenci	20	4
Asystenci stażyści	22	–
Total	205	60

Student Enrolment, 1990:

	Men	Women	Total
Of the country	631	373	1004
Of other countries	6	2	8
Total	637	375	1012*

*Also 416 external students and students by correspondence.

6440 **WYŻSZA SZKOŁA MORSKA**

Merchant Marine Academy

ul. Czerwonych Kosynierów 83, 81-962 Gdynia

Telex: 054568 WSM PL

Telephone: 20-75-12

Fax: (48-58) 20-67-01

Rektor: Józef Lisowski (1989-90)

Dyrektor Administracyjny: Jolanta Ewertowska

F. of Navigation

Dean: Zdzisław Chuchla; *staff* 73 (13)

F. of Mechanical Engineering

Dean: Jerzy Jeszke; *staff* 60 (6)

F. of Electrical Engineering (including Computer Sciences and Radio Communication)

Dean: Jerzy Majewski; *staff* 68 (10)

F. of Maritime Administration

Dean: Piotr Przybytowski; *staff* 26 (3)

Also Officers Training College (for Polish and Foreign Officers).

Founded 1920 as school, acquired present status and title 1969. A State institution under the jurisdiction of the Office of Maritime Economy. Governing body: the Senate. Residential facilities for students.

Arrangements for co-operation with: College of Maritime Engineering, Warnemünde-Wustrow; College of Technology, Bremen; College of Technology, Bremerhaven; College of Marine Engineering, Leningrad; Southampton Institute of Higher Education.

Academic Year: October to June (October-February; February-June).

Admission Requirements: Secondary school certificate or foreign equivalent, and entrance examination.

Fees: None.

Language of Instruction: Polish.

Degrees and Diplomas: Diploma of Engineer, 4 ½ -5 yrs.

Library: 100,000 vols.

Special Facilities (Museums, etc.): Tradition Chamber.

Publications: Zeszyty Naukowe (Scientific Papers); Joint Proceedings.

Academic Staff, 1989-90:

Rank	Full-time	Part-time
Profesorowie	15	4
Docenci	26	12
Adiunkci	70	13
Starsi wykładowcy	88	13
Wykładowcy	20	2
Starsi asystenci	59	2
Asystenci	29	–
Total	307	46

Student Enrolment, 1989-90:

	Men	Women	Total
Of the country	1209	16	1219
Of other countries	32	–	32
Total	1235	16	1251*

*Also 240 external students.

6441 **WYŻSZA SZKOŁA MORSKA**

Marine Engineering College

ul. Wały Chrobrego 1, 70-500 Szczecin

Cables: Wuesem

Telex: 0422585 WSM PL

Telephone: 326-31

Rektor: Sławomir Hulanicki (1984-87)

Dyrektor Administracyjny: Bolesław Dudzic

F. of Mechanical Engineering

F. of Navigation (including Deep Sea Fishing)

Also 10 institutes.

Founded 1947 as school, acquired present status and title 1969. A State institution under the jurisdiction of the Officer of Maritime Economy. Governing body: the Senate. Residential facilities for academic staff and all students.

Arrangements for co-operation with the College of Maritime Engineering, Warnemünde-Wustrow.

Academic Year: October to June (October-January; February-June).

Admission Requirements: Secondary school certificate or foreign equivalent, and entrance examination. Women are not admitted.

Fees: None.

Language of Instruction: Polish.

Degrees and Diplomas: Diploma of Engineer, 5 yrs.

Libraries: Central Library, *c.* 85,000 vols; libraries of the institutes, 2000.

Publication: Zeszyty Naukowe WSM w Szczecinie (Scientific Papers).

Academic Staff: c. 200 (30).

PORTUGAL

Universities and University Institutions

Public Institutions

6442 ***UNIVERSIDADE DOS AÇORES**
University of the Azores
Rua da Mãe de Deus, 9502 Ponta Delgada Codex, S. Miguel, Açores
Telex: 82115 UNIPDL
Telephone: 26318; 27428

D. of History and Social Sciences
D. of Modern Languages and Literature
D. of Education
D. of Mathematics and Computer Sciences
D. of Earth Sciences
D. of Economics and Business Administration
D. of Ecology
D. of Agriculture (including Animal Husbandry) (Angra do Heroísmo)
D. of Oceanography and Fishery (Horta)

Founded 1976 as college, became a university 1980. An autonomous State institution under the jurisdiction of the Ministry of Education and Culture. Governing bodies: the Scientific Committee; the University Committee. Some residential facilities for academic staff and students.

Academic Year: October to July (October-March; March-July).

Admission Requirements: Secondary school certificate or recognized foreign equivalent, and entrance examination.

Language of Instruction: Portuguese.

Degrees and Diplomas: Bacharel, 3 yrs. Licenciado in–Modern Languages; History and Social Sciences; Mathematics and Design; Biology and Geology; Agriculture and Animal Husbandry; Economics, 4-5 yrs. Doutor, by examination and thesis following Licenciado.

Library: Documentation Centre, *c.* 88,540 vols.

Publications: Arquipélago (Series: Human Sciences; Natural Sciences) (biannually).

Academic Staff: c. 190.

Student Enrolment: c. 1060.

6443 **UNIVERSIDADE DO ALGARVE**
University of Algarve
Largo do Pé da Cruz 26, 8000 Faro
Telex: 56168 IPFARO P
Telephone: 29152
Reitor: Carlos Lloyd Braga (1986-)
Administrador: Maria Celeste do Patrocíno

Ut. of Horticulture and Fruit Production
Director: Ferdinando Reis Cunha; *staff* 14 (5)
Ut. of Biology and Fishery
Director: Sadat M. Xá Musavor; *staff* 14 (1)
Ut. of Business Administration
Director: José Manuel Monteiro da Silva; *staff* 13
Ut. of Exact Sciences
Director: Abílio Marques da Silva *staff* 10 (2)
Ut. of Social and Human Sciences
Director: Maria Teresa J. Gamito M. Arnaud; *staff* 7
Arab Studies Ce.
Head: José D. Garcia Domingues; *staff* 2
Ce. of Archaeology
Head: Teresa Júdice Gamito; *staff* 1

Founded 1979. An autonomous State institution under the jurisdiction of the Ministry of Education and Culture. Some residential facilities for academic staff.

Academic Year: October to July (October-February; March-July).

Admission Requirements: Secondary school certificate.

Fees (Escudos): 300 per course, per annum.

Language of Instruction: Portuguese.

Degrees and Diplomas: Licenciado in–Biology and Fishery; Horticulture and Fruit Production, 10 sem; Business Administration, 5 yrs.Doutor.

Library: 7,500 vols.

Publication: Newsletter (3 times a year).

Academic Staff, 1986-87:

Rank	Full-time	Part-time
Professores Catedráticos	3	–
Professores Associados	5	–
Professores Auxiliares	3	4
Assistentes	6	–
Assistentes Convidados	6	13
Assistentes Estagiários	24	–
Total	47	17

Student Enrolment, 1986-87:

	Men	Women	Total
Of the country	118	139	257

6444 **UNIVERSIDADE DE AVEIRO**
University of Aveiro
Rua Dr. Mário Sacramento, 62, 3800 Aveiro
Telex: 37373
Telephone: (034) 25085
Reitor: Joaquim Renato Ferreira de Araújo (1986-)
Administrador: Ivon Luis Martins Brandão

D. of Modern Languages and Culture
Head: Albino de Almeida Matos; *staff* 40
D. of Education
Head: Manuel Alte da Veiga; *staff* 17
D. of Mathematics
Head: Maria Beatriz Fernandes Matias; *staff* 25
D. of Physics
Head: Marília Fernandes Thomaz; *staff* 28
D. of Chemistry
Head: Antonio José V. Ferrer Correia; *staff* 27 (2)
D. of Earth Sciences
Head: A.A. Soares de Andrade; *staff* 32
D. of Biology
Head: Gustavo Cardoso Nunes Caldeira; *staff* 34
D. of Environmental Engineering
Head: Carlos Soares Borrego; *staff* 21 (6)
D. of Electronics and Telecommunications
Head: Dinis Gomes Magalhães dos Santos; *staff* 42
D. of Ceramics and Glass Technology
Head: Henrique M. Morais Diz; *staff* 20
D. of Didactics
Head: Eugénio Alte da Veiga; *staff* 23

Founded 1973, first students admitted 1975. A State institution under the jurisdiction of the Ministry of Education and Culture. Governing bodies: the Conselho da Universidade; the Conselho Administrativo. Residential facilities for academic staff and *c.* 200 students.

Arrangements for co-operation with the Universities of: Bremen; Louvain; Barcelona; Nancy; Illinois; Sheffield; Brussels; Lancaster; Essex; Strathclyde; Newcastle-upon-Tyne; Wales; Toulouse; Aberdeen; Leeds, Salamanca; Utrecht; Nebraska; Warwick; Pau; Sophia, Tokyo; Poitiers; Grenoble; Quebec, Trois-Rivières. King's College, London; University College, Cardiff.

Academic Year: October to July (October-February; March-July).

Admission Requirements: Secondary school certificate and entrance examination.

Fees (Escudos): 1500 per annum.

Language of Instruction: Portuguese.

Degrees and Diplomas: Licenciado in–Mathematics and Design; Physics and Chemistry; Biology and Geology; Modern Languages; Electronics and Telecommunications; Ceramics and Glass Technology; Environmental Engineering, 5 yrs. Degree of Pós-graduação (Mestrado) in–Geo-chemistry; Didactics; Psychology.

Library: Total, *c.* 45,000 vols.
Publications: Revista, Series A: Ciências da Educação; Boletim.
Academic Staff, 1986-87:

Rank	Full-time	Part-time
Professores Catedráticos	12	–
Professores Associados	23	1
Professores Auxiliares	32	3
Assistentes	93	9
Assistantes Estagiários	111	–
Monitores	15	–
Colaboradores	15	–
Investigadores	9	–
Total	310	13

Student Enrolment, 1986-87:

Of the country	2365
Of other countries	25
Total	2390

6445 **UNIVERSIDADE DA BEIRA INTERIOR**
Rua Marqués d'Avila e Bolama, 6200 Covilhã
Telex: 53733
Telephone: (75) 25141
Fax: (75) 26198
Reitor: Cândido Manuel Passos Morgado
Secretario Geral: Correia Pinheiro

D. of Textile Engineering
Head: José Mendes Lucas
D. of Business Administration
Head: João V. Oliveira Lisboa
D. of Mathematics
Head: Alvaro Manuel D. Nunes
D. of Civil Engineering
Head: Stephan Rosendahl
D. of Sociology, Inforamtion, and Social Sciences
Head: Moisés Adão L. Martins
D. of Chemical Engineering
Head: Isabel Almeida Ferra
D. of Physics
Head: Avelino H. Passos Morgado
D. of Paper Engineering
Head: Manuel José Santos Silva
D. of Electromechanical Engineering
Head: Luis Carlos C. Gonçalves
Computer Sciences Ce.
Head: José A. Pacheco Carvalho
Teaching and Learning Resource Ce. (C.R.E.A.)
Head: José de Almeida Geraldes
Study Ce. for Regional Development (C.E.D.R.)
Head: Felisberto M. Reigado
Study Ce. for Patrimony Protection (C.E.P.P.)
Head: Martin Höck

Founded 1973 as Instituto Politécnico da Covilhã. Became Instituto Universitário 1979 and acquired present title 1986. Governing bodies: the Assemblea; the Senado Universitário; the Conselho Administrativo. Residential facilities for students.

Arrangements for co-operation with: Universidade Federal do Maranhão; Universidade Federal do Parana; Universidad Politécnica de Barcelona; Universidad de Valladolid; Universidad Politécnica de Cataluña; Université de Haute-Alsace; Ecole française de Papeterie et des Industries graphiques de Grenoble; University of Clemson.

Academic Year: September to June (September-January; February-June).

Admission Requirements: Secondary school certificate and entrance examination.

Language of Instruction: Portuguese.

Degrees and Diplomas: Designer Diplomas. Licendiado, 5 yrs. Degree of Pós-graduação (Mestrado). Doutor.

Academic Staff, 1989-90:

Rank	Full-time	Part-time
Professores Catedráticos	2	8
Professores Associados	1	3
Professores Auxiliares	26	2
Assistentes	33	15
Assistentes Estagiários	69	–
Leitores	1	1
Monitores	7	–
Total	139	29

Student Enrolment, 1989-90:

	Men	Women	Total
Of the country	1032	985	1988
Of other countries	13	6	18
Total	1045	961	2006

6446 ***UNIVERSIDADE DE COIMBRA**
University of Coimbra
Paço das Escolas, 3000 Coimbra
Telex: 52273
Telephone: (39) 35410
Fax: (39) 25841
Electronic mail: @6a ciuc 2. uc. rccn. pt
Reitor: Rui de Alarcão (1982-94)
Secretário Geral: Carlos Luzio Vaz

F. of Arts
Director: João Roque; *staff* 206 (8)
F. of Law
Director: Orlando de Carvalho; *staff* 67
F. of Medicine (including Dentistry)
Director: Antônio Poiares Baptista; *staff* 105 (112)
F. of Science and Technology (including Computer Engineering and Architecture)
Director: José Nuno Dias Urbano; *staff* 439 (22)
F. of Pharmacy
Director: Adriano Barbosa de Sousa; *staff* 49 (7)
F. of Economics (including Sociology and Management)
Director: Henrique Soares Albergaria *staff* 60 (14)
F. of Psychology and Educational Studies
Director: Joaquim Ferreira Gomes; *staff* 53 (3)
Ce. for History of Society and Culture
Ce. for Classical and Humanities Studies
Ce. for Portuguese Literature
Ce. for Psychopedagogy
Interdisciplinary Ce. for Juridical and Economic Studies
Ce. for Ophthamology
Ce. for Gastroenterology
Also 10 research centres of the faculties of Pharmacy, and Science and Technology; University Teaching Hospital, Summer Course for foreign students and Annual Course of Portuguese Language and Culture, and studies abroadunder the ERASMUS programme.

Founded in Lisbon 1290, transferred to Coimbra 1308, returned to Lisbon during the 14th century, permanently established at Coimbra 1537. Reorganized 1772. Operated under the jurisdiction of the Ministry of Education andCulture. Governing bodies: the Assembleia; the Senado; the Conselho Administrativo; Conselho Social. Residential faculties for students.

Arrangements for co-operation with the Universities of: Grenoble II; Halle-Wittenberg; Illinois; Poitiers; Sheffield; Lvov; Eduardo Mondlane, Maputo; Salamanca; Fluminense; Praga; Minas Gerais; Caminas; São Paulo; Darmstadt; Utrecht; Nantes; Pernambuco; Konstanz; Rio de Janeiro (Catholic); Frankfurt.

Academic Year: October to July (October-February; March-July).

Admission Requirements: Secondary school certificate and entrance examination.

Fees (Escudos): 1200 per annum; Sciences and Technology, 150 per subject, per semester.

Language of Instruction: Portuguese.

Degrees and Diplomas: Licenciado in–Arts, 4 yrs; Science; Psychology; Pharmacy; Economics; Law, 5 yrs; Medicine, 6 yrs. Degree of Pós-graduação (Mestrado). Doutor, by examination and thesis following Licenciado.

Libraries: c. 1,417,940 vols; faculty libraries.

Special Facilities (Museums, etc.): Museums: Anthropology; Zoology; Botany; Mineralogy and Geology. Observatory.

Academic Staff, 1990-91:

Rank	Full-time	Part-time
Professores	243	23
Assistentes	582	194
Leitores	25	–
Total	850	217

Student Enrolment, 1990-91:

	Men
Of the country	15,237
Of other countries	599
Total	15,836

6447 **UNIVERSIDADE DE ÉVORA**

University of Évora

Largo dos Colegiais 2, 7001 Évora Codex

Telephone: (069) 25572/4

D. of Exact Sciences (Mathematics, Physics, and Chemistry)
D. of Natural Sciences
D. of Phytology
D. of Bionomics
D. of Environmental Planning
D. of Education
D. of Rural Engineering
D. of Animal Husbandry and Veterinary Medicine
D. of Arts
D. of Sociology
D. of Ecology
D. of Agricultural Economics
D. of Materials Technology
Sec. for Lifelong Education

Founded 1974, first students admitted 1975/76. A State institution operated under the jurisdiction of the Ministry of Education and Culture. Residential facilities for students.

Academic Year: September to July (September-February; February-July).

Admission Requirements: Secondary school certificate and entrance examination.

Language of Instruction: Portuguese.

Degrees and Diplomas: Licenciado, 5 yrs. Doutor, by examination and thesis following Licenciado. Also teaching qualification.

Library: c. 20,000 vols.

Academic Staff: c. 180.

Student Enrolment: c. 1600.

6448 **UNIVERSIDADE DE LISBOA**

University of Lisbon

Praça da Universidade, 1966 Lisboa Codex

Telephone: 76-76-24

Reitor: Virgilio A. Meira Soares

F. of Letters
F. of Law (including Economics and Political Science)
F. of Medicine
F. of Science (including Engineering)
F. of Pharmacy
D. of Psychology
I. of Geophysics

Also 5 affiliated institutes.

Founded 1911, but traces its history back to the university established in Lisbon in 1288 and subsequently transferred to Coimbra. A State institution under the jurisdiction of the Ministry of Education and Culture. Governing bodies: the Senado, composed of the Rector, the two Vice-Rectors, the deans of the faculties and representatives of the academic staff; the Assembleia geral; the Conselho Administrativo. Residential facilities for students.

Academic Year: October to July (October-February; March-July).

Admission Requirements: Secondary school certificate or foreign equivalent, and entrance examination.

Language of Instruction: Portuguese.

Degrees and Diplomas: Licenciado in–Classical Languages and Literature; Modern Languages and Literature; History; Geography; Philosophy; Law; Pharmacy; Psychology; Pure Mathematics; Applied Mathematics; Geographical Engineering; Physics; Chemistry; Geology; Biology, 4-5 yrs; Medicine, 6 yrs. Doutor, by examination and thesis following Licenciado. Diploma, curso professional de Farmácia, 3 yrs.

Library: Faculty libraries, c. 378,040 vols.

Special Facilities (Museums, etc.): Museums: Archaeology and Ethnology; Botany; Zoology and Anthropology; Mineralogy and Geology.

Publications: Anuário; Arquivos; Boletim; Revista da Faculdade de Letras; O Arqueólogo Português; Revista da Faculdade de Direito; Arquivo de Anatomia e Antropologia; Arquivo do Instituto Bacteriologico Câmara Pestana; Revista da Faculdade de Ciências; Anais do Instituto Geofisico; Portugalie Phisica; Portugaliae Revista de Biologia; Boletim da Faculdade de Farmácia; Estudos sobre a fauna portuguesa; Trabalhos do Instituto de Fisiologia.

Academic Staff: c. 880 (160).

Student Enrolment: c. 18,600.

6449 **UNIVERSIDADE DA MADEIRA**

Madeira University

Convento dos Jesuistas, Praça do Municipio, 9000, Funchal, Madeira

Telephone: 37609

Fax: 37143

Reitor: Raul Albuquerque Sardinha

Secrétaria Geral: Ana Isabel Cardoso

D. of Human Motivity (Physical Education and Sport)
Head: Fernando Ferreira; *staff* 10 (21)
D. of Computer Studies
Head: Rita Vasconcellos; *staff* 2 (24)
Ce. of Teacher Training
Head: Fernando Henriques *staff* 23 (8)

Founded 1982 as school, became university 1988. Governing body: the Comissão Instaladora.

Academic Year: October to June.

Admission Requirements: Secondary school certificate and entrance examination.

Fees (Escudos): c. 3000.

Language of Instruction: Portuguese.

Degrees and Diplomas: Licienciatura, 5 yrs. Degree of Pós-graduação (Mestrado), a further 2 yrs. Doutor.

Student Enrolment, 1990:

Men	Women	Total
40	88	128

6450 ***UNIVERSIDADE DO MINHO**

University of Minho

Largo do Paço, 4719 Braga Codex

Telex: 32135

Telephone: 612234

Fax: 77936

Reitor: Sérgio Machado dos Santos

Secretary-General: José Frederico Aguilar Monteiro

S. of Engineering (including Industrial Electronics, Polymer Engineering, Computer Sciences and Production and Systems)
Head: Mário Duarte Araújo; *staff* 129
S. of Sciences (including Earth Sciences)
Head: Maria Isabel Calado Ferreira; *staff* 101 (6)
I. of Social Sciences (including Sociology and Anthropology, and Social Communication)
Head: Manuel Silva Costa; *staff* 34 (5)
I. of Education
Head: José Ribeiro Dias; *staff* 44
S. of Economics and Management (including Political Science, Law and International Relations)
Head: Rui Neves da Costa Rodrigues; *staff* 39
Ut. for Lifelong Education
I. of Letters and Human Sciences (including Portuguese, French, English, and North-American Studies, and Philosophy and Culture)
Head: José Azevedo Ferreira; *staff* 38 (11)
Teacher Training Ce.
Head: João Formosinhó S. Simões; *staff* 32 (10)

Also 10 Research Centres of the Schools and Institution.

Founded 1974 with a structure based on a series of Scientific Pedagogical Units. A State institution under thejurisdiction of the Ministry of Education and Culture. Residential facilities for academic staff and students.

Academic Year: October to July (October-February; March-July).

Admission Requirements: Secondary school certificate or equivalent and entrance examination, or foreign equivalent recognized by the Ministry of Education.

Language of Instruction: Portuguese.

Degrees and Diplomas: Licenciado in–Management; Public Administration; International Relations, 4 yrs; Engineering, 5 yrs. Degree of Pós-graduação (Mestrado) in–Education; Computer Sciences; Textile Engineering, a further 2 yrs. Doutor, by examination and thesis following Licenciado. Also teaching qualifications.

Library: c. 59,423 vols.

Special Facilities (Museums, etc.): Museu da Casa Nogueira da Silva.

Publications: Folha Informativa (monthly); Revista Portuguesa de Educação; Factos e Ideias; Diacrítica; Fórum; Cadernos do Noroeste; Cadernos de Arqueologia.

Academic Staff: c. 520.

Student Enrolment: c. 5200.

6451 ***UNIVERSIDADE NOVA DE LISBOA**

New University of Lisbon

Praça do Príncipe Real 26, 1200 Lisboa

Telex: 44733 UNL RTR P

Telephone: 351-1-3467972

Fax: 351-1-3361924

Reitor: J.A. Esperança Pina (1982-)

Vice-Reitor: Manuel Pinto Barbosa

F. of Science and Technology (including Environmental Engineering, Industrial Production Engineering, Computer Sciences, and Physical and Material Engineering)

Director: Leopoldo Guimaraes; *staff* 299 (64)

F. of Social and Human Sciences (including Modern Literature and Language, History, Art History, Anthropology, Sociology, Philosophy, History of Ideas, Social Communication, Music, and Geography and Regional Planning)

Director: Adriano D. Rodrigues; *staff* 227 (37)

F. of Economics

Director: Diogo de Lucena; *staff* 63 (30)

F. of Medicine

Director: Nuno T. Cordeiro Ferreira; *staff* 80 (135)

I. of African Studies

Director: A. Mesquitela Lima

I. of Hygiene and Tropical Medicine

Director: L. Ferraz de Oliveira; *staff* 29 (11)

I. of Statistics and Information Management

Director: Manuel Villares

Founded 1973. Department structure replaced 1977 by faculties enjoying administrative autonomy. A State institution under the jurisdiction of the Ministry of Education. Governing bodies: the Assemblea; the Conselho Administrativo; the Senado. Residential facilities for students.

Arrangements for co-operation with: Universities of Paris I and X; University of São Paulo; Imperial Collegeof Science and Technology, London; University of Angola.

Academic Year: October to July (October-February; March-July).

Admission Requirements: Secondary school certificate or recognized foreign equivalent, and entrance examination.

Fees (Escudos): 1200 per annum.

Language of Instruction: Portuguese.

Degrees and Diplomas: Licenciado in–History; Sociology; Philosophy; Music; Modern Languages and Literature; Geography, 4 yrs; Computer Sciences; Physics; Mathematics; Geology; Environmental Engineering; Production Engineering; Social Communication; Economics, 5 yrs; Medicine, 6 yrs. Degree of Pos-graduaão (Mestrado), a further 2 yrs. Doutor, by examination and thesis. Also diplomas of specialization.

Library: Total, 79,188 vols.

Publications: University Yearbook; Guides of the Faculties; Annals of the Institute of Hygiene and Tropical Medicine.

Press or Publishing House: Printing Services.

Academic Staff, 1989-90:

Rank	Full-time	Part-time
Professores Catedráticos	66	4
Professores Associados	64	29
Professores Auxiliares	112	40
Assistentes	286	190
Assistentes Estagiários	53	–
Leitores	17	1
Monitores	5	1
Colaboradores e Investigadores	9	7
Total	612	265

Student Enrolment, 1989-90:

	Men	Women	Total
Of the country	2666	4187	6853

6452 **UNIVERSIDADE DO PORTO**

University of Porto

Rua D. Manuel II, 4003 Porto Codex

Telex: 23121 UNIPOR P

Telephone: 699519; 698477

Reitor: Alberto M. Amaral (1985-88)

F. of Science

F. of Medicine

F. of Engineering

F. of Architecture

F. of Letters

F. of Pharmacy

F. of Economics

F. of Psychology and Education

I. of Physical Education

I. of Biomedical Sciences

Ce. of Nutrition and Food Technology

I. of Anthropology

Botanical I.

I. of Geophysics (Observatory)

I. of Zoology (including Maritime Zoology)

Computer Ce.

Founded 1803 as Academia Real de Marinha e Comércio, incorporating Escola de Navegação e Pilotagem, established 1762 and Real Escola Naútica 1779. Became Academia Politécnica 1837 and combined 1911 with the Real Escola de Cirurgia, founded 1825, to become the Universidade do Porto. An autonomous State institution underthe jurisdiction of the Ministry of Education and Culture. Governing body: the Conselho Administrativo (Administrative Board). Some residential facilities for academic staff and students.

Arrangements for co-operation with: the Universities of–Bordeaux I and III; Angola; Santiago de Compostela; Paris VI and XI; Metz; Toulouse. State University of Virginia; Virginia Polytechnic Institute; Federal University of Ouro Prêto; State University of Londrino; Royal Institute of Technology, Stockholm.

Academic Year: October to July (October-February; March-July).

Admission Requirements: Secondary school certificate or equivalent and entrance examination, or foreign equivalent recognized by the Ministry of Education.

Language of Instruction: Portuguese.

Degrees and Diplomas: Licenciado in–Philosophy; Geography; History; Modern Languages and Literature, 4 yrs; Psychology; Engineering; Physical Education; Economics, 5 yrs; Medicine, 6 yrs. Degree of Pós-graduação (Mestrado). Doutor, by examination and thesis after Licenciado.

Library: Faculty libraries.

Special Facilities (Museums, etc.): Museums: Anthropology and Ethnology; Mineralogy and Geology; Zoology; Pathological Anatomy; Anatomy; Marine Museum; Historical Archaeology.

Publications: Boletims; faculty and institute publications.

Academic Staff: c. 960 (470).

Student Enrolment: c. 14,500.

6453 **UNIVERSIDADE TÉCNICA DE LISBOA**

Technical University of Lisbon
Alameda Santo António dos Capuchos 1, 1.100 Lisboa
Telex: 62067 UTL P
Telephone: 545434; 577569
Reitor: António Simões Lopes (1985-)
Administrador: Pedro Meireles

F. of Veterinary Medicine
Head: Tito Horácio Fernandes; *staff* 66 (12)
I. of Agronomy (including Forestry, Landscape Architecture, and Food Technology)
Head: José Carlos Dárgent da Albuquerque; *staff* 146 (11)
Higher I. of Economics and Management
President: Antônio Francisco Espinho Romão; *staff* 216 (123)
Higher Technical I. (including Engineering)
President: Diamantino Freitas Gomes Durão; *staff* 569 (135)
Higher I. of Social and Political Sciences
President: Óscar Soares Barata; *staff* 20 (65)
F. of Human Kinetics
President: Henrique Melo Barreiros; *staff* 98 (10)
F. of Architecture
Head: José Teodoro Faria Troufa Real; *staff* 100 (10)
Also 77 associated research Centres.

Founded 1930, incorporating 4 previously existing institutions founded between 1830 and 1911. Later, 3 other high schools were added. State institution under the jurisdiction of the Ministry of Education and Culture. Governing bodies: the University Senate; the University Assembly. Residential facilities for 474 students.

Arrangements for co-operation with: Technical University Madrid; University of Poitiers; University of Pau; University of Compiègne; University of Paris X; Federal University of Santa María; Federal University of Bahia; Federal University of Pará; Federal University of Maranhão; Federal University of Ceará; Federal University of Brasília; Federal University of Pernambuco; Federal University of Paraíba; Federal University of Rio de Janeiro; Pontifical Catholic University of Rio de Janeiro; University of São Paulo; Universidade de Angola; Universidade Eduardo Mondlane, Maputo; University of Seville; University of Orléans; Institut national polytechnique de Lorraine; Institut national de Sciences appliquées de Rennes; University of East Asia; Institut français du Pétrole; Technical University of Berlin; Massachusetts Institute of Technology; Federal University of Santa Catarina; University of Kyoto; University of Quebec; University of Arizona; State University of Rio de Janeiro; Universidade Estadual Paulista, São Paulo; State University of Campinas; Universityof Paris 7; University of Passau; University of Toronto.

Academic Year: October to July (October-February; March-July).

Admission Requirements: Secondary school certificate or recognized foreign equivalent, and entrance examination.

Fees (Escudos): 1200-1500 per annum.

Language of Instruction: Portuguese.

Degrees and Diplomas: Licenciado in–Public Administration; Anthropology; Social Communication; Social Service; International Relations, 4 yrs; Veterinary Medicine; Agronomy; Forestry; Landscape Architecture and Agroindustry; Economics; Civil Engineering; Electrical Engineering and Computer Sciences; Engineering Physics; Informatics and Computers; Material Sciences; Mining Engineering; Naval Construction Engineering; Chemical Engineering; Applied Mathematics and Computer Sciences; Industrial Production; Dance; Special Education and Rehabilitation; Physical Education; Ergonomy; Architecture, 5 yrs. Degree of Pógradução (Mestrado, Master) in–Animal Production; Tropical Veterinary Medicine; Vegetal Production; Agricultural Economics; Plant Protection; Economics; Applied Mathematics for Economics and Management; Management; Operations Research and Systems Engineering; Structural Engineering; Hydraulics and Water Resources; Mineralogy and Mining Planning; Electrical Engineering and Computer Sciences; Mechanical Engineering; Catalytic Chemistry; Biotechnology; Physics; Applied Mathematics; Materials Engineering; Political Sciences; International Relations; Anthropology; Sociology; Strategy; African Studies; Sciences of Education; Sports; Regional and Urban Planning; Food Science and Technology; Energy Planning, a further 2 yrs.

Library: School and Institute libraries. Total 251,866 vols.

Special Facilities (Museums, etc.): Geology Museum; Zoology Museum.

Publications: Revista of the Institute of Economics; Anais of the Institute of Agriculture; Ludens (4 times a year); Revista de Estudos Políticos e Sociais (quarterly); Revista of the Institute of Physical Education (quarterly); Guide of UTL (yearbook).

Academic Staff, 1989-90:

Rank	Full-time	Part-time
Professores Catedráticos	108	–
Professores Associados	131	–
Professores Auxiliares	210	3
Professores Convidados	29	74
Assistentes	356	–
Assistentes Convidados	92	288
Assistentes Estagiários	287	–
Leitores	2	1
Total	1215	366

Student Enrolment, 1989-90:

	Men	Women	Total
Of the country	8389	5386	13,775
Of other countries	377	141	518
Total	8766	5527	14,293

6454 **UNIVERSIDADE DE TRÁS-OS-MONTES E ALTO DOURO**

Quinta de Prados, 5001 Vila Real
Telex: 24436
Telephone: (0099) 25030/39
Reitor: Fernando Real (1980-)
Administrador: Francisco Miguel Rodrígues

D. of Biology
Head: Torres Pereira; *staff* 14
D. of Economics and Sociology
Head: Joaquim Lima Pereira; *staff* 8
D. of Forestry
Head: Antonio Lopes Gomes; *staff* 9
D. of Mathematics and Physics
Head: Luís Paulo M.M.M. Sampayo; *staff* 31
D. of Pathology and Animal Hygiene
Head: Horácio Manuel da Graça; *staff* 4
D. of Earth Sciences
Head: José Isidro S.F. Seita; *staff* 23
D. of Plant Protection
Head: Antonio Lopes Gomes; *staff* 4
D. of Crop Science and Rural Engineering
Head: Nuno Moreira; *staff* 13
D. of Animal Husbandry
Head: Joaquim Lima Pereira; *staff* 13
D. of Education
Head: Ribeiro Dias

Founded 1973 as Polytechnic, and admitted first students 1975. Became Instituto Universitario 1979 and acquired present status and title 1986. A State institution under the jurisdiction of the Ministry of Education and Universities. Residential facilities for students.

Arrangements for co-operation with the Universities of: Purdue; Wisconsin; Idaho; Adelaide; Georgia; Illinois;Wageningen.

Academic Year: October to June (October-January; March-June).

Admission Requirements: Secondary school certificate.

Fees (Escudos): 1300 per annum.

Language of Instruction: Portuguese.

Degrees and Diplomas: Licenciado in–Crop Production; Education; Forestry; Animal Husbandry, 5 yrs. Also 1st and 2nd yrs of Licenciado in Engineering; Economics. Doutor.

Library: Documentation Centre, *c.* 9,000 vols.

Special Facilities (Museums, etc.): Geology Museum.

Academic Staff, 1986-87:

Rank	Full-time
Professores Catedráticos	5
Professores Associados	7
Professores Auxiliares	8
Assistentes	75
Assistentes Estagiários	50
Total	145

Student Enrolment, 1986-87:

Of the country	1287
Of other countries	13
Total	1300

6455 **ESCOLA SUPERIOR DE MEDICINA DENTÁRIA**
Institute of Dentistry
Avenida Prof. Gama Pinto, 1600 Lisboa

Dentistry

6456 **ESCOLA SUPERIOR DE MEDICINA DENTÁRIA**
Institute of Dentistry
Rua Dr. Roberto Frias, 4200 Porto

Dentistry

6457 **INSTITUTO SUPERIOR DE CIÊNCIAS DO TRABALHO E DA EMPRESA**
Higher Institute of Management and Administration
Avenida das Forças Armadas, 1600 Lisboa 2
Telex: 62542
Telephone: 735050
Presidente: J. Manuel Prostes Fonseca

Business Administration
Sociology
Social Anthropology

Founded 1972.

Academic Year: October to July (October-February; March-July).

Admission Requirements: Secondary school certificate and entrance examination.

Fees (Escudos): 1200 per annum.

Language of Instruction: Portuguese.

Degrees and Diplomas: Licenciado, 4-5 yrs. Degree of Pós-graduação (Mestrado) (planned). Doutor, by examination and thesis after Licenciado.

Library: 18,000 vols.

Academic Staff, 1986-87: 32 (238).

Student Enrolment, 1986-87:

	Men	Women	Total
Of the country	1491	1240	2731
Of other countries	45	22	67
Total	1536	1262	2798

Private Establishments

6458 **UNIVERSIDADE AUTÓNOMA DE LISBOA LUÍS DE CAMÕES**
Luis de Camões Autonomous University of Lisbon
Rua Sta. Marta 56, 1100 Lisboa

D. of Law
D. of Business Administration
D. of Economics
D. of Arts

Founded 1986.

6459 **UNIVERSIDADE CATÓLICA PORTUGUESA**
Catholic University of Portugal
Palma de Cima, 1600 Lisboa 4
Telephone: 726-55-50
Reitor: J. Bacelar e Oliveira, S.J. (1984-88)

F. of Philosophy
Director: José Policarpo
F. of Theology
Director: José Policarpo
F. of Human Sciences (including Business Administration, Economics and Law)
Director: M.J. de Almeida Costa
F. of Philosophy (Braga)
Director: L. Craveiro da Silva, S.J.
I. of Theology (Braga)
Director: M. Isidro Alves
S. of Food Technology (Porto)
Director: A. Medina
Also Regional Centres in Viseu and Porto.

Founded 1967, recognized by the State 1971. A private institution. Governing body: the Conselho Superior (Board of Trustees).

Arrangements for co-operation with: Pontifical University of Maranhão; Catholic University of Louvain; University of East Asia, Macau.

Academic Year: October to July (October-March; April-July).

Admission Requirements: Secondary school certificate and entrance examination.

Fees (Escudos): 50,000-105,000 per annum; Graduate, 60,000-90,000.

Language of Instruction: Portuguese.

Degrees and Diplomas: Licenciado in–Philosophy; Human Sciences, Religious Sciences, 4 yrs; Theology; Economics; Law; Business Administration; Food Technology; Social Development, 5 yrs. Degree of Pós-graduação (Mestrado) in–Philosophy; Law; Theology, a further 2 yrs. Postgraduate Diploma in European Economy, 1 yr. Doctorates.

Libraries: Central Library, 200,000 vols; Philosophy (Braga), 100,000.

Publications: Didaskalia; Revista Portuguesa de Filosofia; Theologika; Economia; Direito e Justiça.

Academic Staff: c. 230.

Student Enrolment: c. 6200.

6460 **UNIVERSIDADE INTERNACIONAL**
International University
Estrada de Benfica 275, 1500 Lisboa

D. of Law
D. of Business Administration

Founded 1986.

6461 **UNIVERSIDADE LUSÍADA**
Rua da Junqueira 194, 1300 Lisboa

D. of Law
D. of History
D. of Business Administration
D. of Economics

Founded 1978 as Universidade Livre. Acquired present status and title 1986. A private institution.

6462 **UNIVERSIDADE PORTUCALENSE INFANTE D. HENRIQUE**
Rua Rodrigues de Freitas 349, 4000 Porto
Telex: 20091 UPORTU
Telephone: 568839
Fax: 572127
Reitor: Francisco da Costa Durão
Secretário Geral: Fernando Bayolo Pacheco de Amorim

D. of Law
Head: Alexandrino Melo e Silva; *staff* 13 (28)
D. of History
Head: Humberto Carlos Baquero Moreno; *staff* 20 (5)
D. of Business Administration
Head: Camilo Cimourdain de Oliveira; *staff* 5 (32)
D. of Economics
Head: Jaão Ruiz Almeida Garret; *staff* 4 (32)
D. of Mathematics
Head: Francisco da Costa Durão; *staff* 9 (18)
D. of Computer Sciences
Head: Jorge Reis Lima; *staff* 12 (54)
Extension D.
Head: Joaquim da Silva Cunha; *staff* 1 (3)
History Research I.
Head: Luis Antônio Oliveira Ramos; *staff* 3 (2)
Technical I. (in preparation)
Head: Alexandrino Melo e Silva
Juridical I. (in preparation)
Head: Alexandrino Melo eSilva
I. of Archaeology
Head: Eduardo Jorge Lopes da Silva
I. of Property Conservation and Restoration (in preparation)
Head: Albérto Mendonça Tavares
I. of Finance (in preparation)
Head: Rui José Conceição Nunes
I. of Informatics Systems Development
Head: Antônio Manuel A. L. Godinho; *staff* 3 (4)
Ce. for Economic Studies (in preparation)
Head: João Ruiz Almeida Garret
Ce. for Pure and Applied Mathematics
Head: Francisco da Costa Durão; *staff* 6 (12)

Ce. for Technology and Information Systems Research
Head: Jorge Reis Lima; *staff* 13 (21)
Ce. for European Studies (in preparation)
Head: João Ruiz Almeida Garrett
Ce. for African Studies
Head: Joaquim da Silva Cunha; *staff* 6 (10)
Ce. for Co-operative Studies
Head: Albérico Medonça Tavares; *staff* 2 (3)

Founded 1986. A private institution. Governing bodies: the Co-operative Direction; the General Assembly.

Arrangements for co-operation with the Universities of: Seville; Pais Basco; Santa Cecilia dos Bandeirantes, Santos; Minas Gerais.

Academic Year: October to July.

Admission Requirements: Secondary school certificate or equivalent and entrance examination.

Fees (Escudos): 180,000 per annum.

Degrees and Diplomas: Bacharel, 3 yrs. Licentiatura, 4-5 yrs. Degree of Pós-gradução (Mestrado), 4 yrs. Doctor, Ph.D., 6 yrs.

Library: 42,000 vols.

Publications: Revista de Ciências Históricas (annually); Revista do Centro de Estudos Africanos-Africana (biannually).

Academic Staff, 1990:

Rank	Full-time	Part-time
Professores Catedráticos	3	18
Professores Associados	3	11
Professores Auxiliares	10	31
Mestres	7	14
Assistentes	22	61
Assistentes Estagiários	10	25
Investigadores	1	5
Assistentes de Investigação	2	1
Técnicos	9	1
Total	67	167

Student Enrolment, 1989-90:

	Men	Women	Total
Of the country	1638	1773	3411

Other Institutions

Public Establishments

6463 **INSTITUTO POLITÉCNICO DE BEJA**
Technical Institute of Beja
Rua de Sto. António, 1-A, 7800 Beja

S. of Education
S. of Agriculture

6464 **INSTITUTO POLITÉCNICO DE BRAGANÇA**
Technical Institute of Bragança
Rua 1 de Dezembro 8, 5300 Bragança
Telex: 27750
Telephone: 23082
Presidente: Joaquim Lima Pereira

S. of Education
S. of Agriculture

Founded 1979. A State institution under the jurisdiction of the Ministry of Education and Culture.

Academic Year: October to June (October-February; March-June).

Admission Requirements: Secondary school certificate and entrance examination.

Fees (Escudos): Registration, 100; tuition, 1200 per annum.

Language of Instruction: Portuguese.

Degrees and Diplomas: Bacharel, 3 yrs.

Academic Staff, 1986-87: 33.

Student Enrolment, 1986-87:

	Men	Women	Total
Of the country	63	58	121

6465 **INSTITUTO POLITÉCNICO DE CASTELO BRANCO**
Technical Institute of Castelo Branco
Rua S. João de Deus 25, Apartado 119, 6000 Castelo Branco
Telex: 53901
Telephone: (072) 23394
Presidente: Vergilio Antônio Pinto de Andrade

S. of Agriculture (including Animal Husbandry and Forestry)
S. of Education

Founded 1979. A State institution under the jurisdiction of the Ministry of Education and Culture.

Academic Year: October to July (October-February; March-July).

Admission Requirements: Secondary school certificate and entrance examination.

Fees (Escudos): 600 per semester.

Language of Instruction: Portuguese.

Degrees and Diplomas: Bacharel, 3-4 yrs.

Library: 7710 vols.

Academic Staff, 1986-87: 42 (2).

Student Enrolment, 1986-87:

	Men	Women	Total
Of the country	162	100	262*

*Also 7 foreign students.

6466 **INSTITUTO POLITÉCNICO DO COIMBRA**
Technical Institue of Coimbra
Rua Pinheiro Chagas, 96, 2 3000 Coimbra

S. of Education
S. of Agriculture
ccountancy
Administration

6467 **INSTITUTO POLITÉCNICO DE FARO**
Technical Institute of Faro
Quinta da Penta, Estrada da Penta, Lote 8, 8000 Faro

S. of Education
S. of Technology and Administration
S. of Hotel Management

6468 **INSTITUTO POLITÉCNICO DA GUARDA**
Technical Institute of Guarda
Rua Comandante Salvador do Nascimento, 6300 Guarda
Telephone: 071-21364
Presidente: João Bento Raimundo

S. of Education
S. of Technology and Administration

Founded 1980. A State institution under the jurisdiction of the Ministry of Education and Culture.

Academic Year: October to July (October-February; March-July).

Admission Requirements: Secondary school certificate and entrance examination.

Fees (Escudos): 2000 per annum.

Language of Instruction: Portuguese.

Degrees and Diplomas: Bacharel, 3-4 yrs.

Academic Staff, 1986-87: 42.

Student Enrolment, 1986-87:

	Men	Women	Total
Of the country	14	46	60

6469 **INSTITUTO POLITÉCNICO DE LEIRIA**
Technical Institute of Leiria
Edifício Maringa Torre 2, 2 2400 Leiria
Telephone: (351-44) 34773
Fax: (351-44) 28097
Presidente: Antônio Ferreira Pereira de Melo
Administrador: Joaquim Gonçalves

S. of Education (ESEL)
President: Antônio V. de Azevedo; *staff* 46
S. of Administration and Technology (ESTG)
President: Emídio Faria; *staff* 13 (1)
S. of Art and Design (ESAD)
President: Antônio Jacinto Reis Vidigal; *staff* 8 (3)

Founded 1980. Governing body: the Comissão Istaladora.

Academic Year: September to July (September-February; March-July).

Admission Requirements: Secondary school certificate or equivalent and entrance examination.

Fees (Escudos): 1050 per semester.

Language of Instruction: Portuguese.

Degrees and Diplomas: Bacharel, 3 yrs. Licentiatura, 4 yrs.

Academic Staff, 1990:

Rank	Full-time	Part-time
Professores Adjuntos	24	–
Professores Assistentes	35	1
Encarregados de Trabalho	1	–
Total	60	1

Student Enrolment, 1990: 494.

6470 **INSTITUTO POLITÉCNICO DE LISBOA**

Technical Institute of Lisbon

Campo dos Mártires da Pátria 2, 1100 Lisboa

S. of Dance
S. of Education
S. of Music

6471 **INSTITUTO POLITÉCNICO DE PORTALEGRE**

Technical Institute of Portalegre

Praça da República, Apartado 125, 7301 Portalegre

S. of Education
S. of Technology and Administration

Founded 1980.

6472 **INSTITUTO POLITÉCNICO DO PORTO**

Technical Institute of Porto

Rua Dr. Roberto Frias, 4200 Porto

S. of Education
S. of Music
S. of Health Sciences

6473 **INSTITUTO POLITÉCNICO DE SANTAREM**

Technical Institute of Santarem

Largo de Seminário, 2000 Santarem

S. of Education
S. of Agriculture

6474 **INSTITUTO POLITÉCNICO DE SETÚBAL**

Technical Institute of Setubal

Largo dos Defensores da República 1, 2900 Setúbal

Telephone: 35301

Fax: 31110

Presidente: Júlio M. Montalvão e Silva

Administrador: Manuela Serra

S. of Technology
President: João Duarte Silva
S. of Education
President: Raul Carvalho

Founded 1979. A State institution.

Academic Year: October to July.

Admission Requirements: Secondary school certificate and entrance examination.

Language of Instruction: Portuguese.

Degrees and Diplomas: Bacharel, 3 yrs.

Student Enrolment, 1989-90: 360.

6475 **INSTITUTO POLITÉCNICO DE VIANA DO CASTELO**

Technical Institute of Viana do Castelo

Apartado 51, 4901 Viana do Castelo Codex

S. of Education
S. of Agriculture
S. of Technology
S. of Business Administration

6476 **INSTITUTO SUPERIOR POLITÉCNICO DE VISEU**

Higher Technical Institute of Viseu

Rua Francisco Alexandre Lobo 55, 3500 Viseu

Telephone: 032-25528

Presidente: João Pedro Barros (1985-)

S. of Education
S. of Technology

Founded 1980 as school, acquired present status and title 1985. A State institution under the jurisdiction of the Ministry of Education and Culture.

Academic Year: September to July (September-March; March-July).

Admission Requirements: Secondary school certificate.

Fees (Escudos): 1500 per annum.

Languages of Instruction: Portuguese. Degrees and diplomas: Bacharel, 3-4 yrs.

Library: 5372 vols.

Academic Staff, 1986-87: 32.

Student Enrolment, 1986-87:

	Men	Women	Total
Of the country	50	196	246
Of other countries	–	1	1
Total	50	197	247

6477 **INSTITUTO GREGORIANO DE LISBOA**

Gregorian Institute of Lisbon

Avenida 5 de Outubro 258, 1600 Lisboa

Telephone: 7930004

Organ, Choral Conducting, Gregorian Chant

Founded 1976. Governing body: the Comissão Instaladora.

Academic Year: October to July.

Admission Requirements: Secondary school certificate and entrance examination.

Language of Instruction: Portuguese.

Degrees and Diplomas: Bacharel, 3 yrs. Diploma Estudos Superiores Especializados, a further 2 yrs.

Publications: Revue Modus (annually); Musica Lusitaniae Sacra.

Press or Publishing House: Edition of the Instituto Gregoriano de Lisboa.

6478 **ESCOLA SUPERIOR DE BELAS-ARTES**

Institute of Arts

Largo da Academia Nacional de Belas-Artes, 1200 Lisboa

Telephone: 366148/9

Presidente: Conceição Ferreira (1976-87)

F. of Architecture
F. of Painting
F. of Sculpture
F. of Design

Founded 1836 as Royal Academy of Arts, became college 1911 and acquired present status 1986. A State institution.

Academic Year: October to July (October-December; January-April; April-July).

Admission Requirements: Secondary school certificate.

Fees (Escudos): 1200 per annum.

Language of Instruction: Portuguese.

Degrees and Diplomas: Licenciado, 5 yrs. Also teaching qualifications.

Library: 2000 vols.

Academic Staff, 1986-87: 58.

Student Enrolment, 1986-87:

	Men	Women	Total
Of the country	360	490	850
Of other countries	5	5	10
Total	365	495	860

6479 **ESCOLA SUPERIOR DE BELAS-ARTES**

Institute of Arts

Avenida Rodrigues de Freitás 265, 4000 Porto

F. of Painting
F. of Sculpture
F. of Design

Founded 1973.

6480 **INSTITUTO SUPERIOR DE ARTES PLÁSTICAS DA MADEIRA**

Higher Institute of Plastic Arts of Madeira
Rua da Carreira 56, 9000 Funchal, Madeira
Telephone: 26209
Presidente: António A. F. Coutinho Gorjão
Secretária Geral: Ana Paula C. N. Coelho de Oliveira

Painting, Sculpture, Design, Graphics

Founded 1955 as private academy, acquired present status and title 1977. A State institution.

Academic Year: October to September (October-February; February-June).

Admission Requirements: Secondary school certificate.

Language of Instruction: Portuguese.

Degrees and Diplomas: Bacharel, 3 yrs. Licenciado, 5 yrs.

Library: c. 5000 vols.

Special Facilities (Museums, etc.): Galeria de Exposições e Arquivo de Trabalhos Escolares do ISAPM.

Publications: Revista Espaço Arte (biannually); Boletim Anuário do ISAPM (annually).

Press or Publishing House: Serviço de Publicações do ISAPM (Oficina de Reprografia - off-set).

Academic Staff, 1989-90:

Rank	Full-time
Professores	3
Primeiros-Assistentes	6
Assistentes	3
Total	12

Student Enrolment, 1989-90:

	Men	Women	Total
Of the country	25	61	86

6481 **INSTITUTO SUPERIOR DE CONTABILIDADE E ADMINISTRAÇÃO**

Higher Institute of Accountancy and Administration
Rua João Mendonça 17, 3800 Aveiro

Accountancy
Administration

Founded 1976.

6482 **INSTITUTO SUPERIOR DE CONTABILIDADE E ADMINISTRAÇÃO**

Higher Institute of Accountancy and Administration
Rua Luis de Camoes, Quinta de São Jerónimo, 3000 Coimbra

Accountancy
Administration

Founded 1975.

6483 **INSTITUTO SUPERIOR DE CONTABILIDADE DEADMINISTRAÇÃO**

Higher Institute of Accountancy and Administration
Avenida Miguel Bombarda 20, 1000 Lisboa

Accountancy
Administration

Founded 1975.

6484 **INSTITUTO SUPERIOR DE CONTABILIDADE E ADMINISTRAÇÃO**

Higher Institute of Accountancy and Administration
Rua Entreparedes 48, 4000 Porto

Accountancy
Administration

Founded 1975.

6485 **INSTITUTO SUPERIOR DE ENGENHARIA**

Higher Institute of Engineering
Quinta da Nora, 3000 Coimbra

Engineering

Founded 1975.

6486 **INSTITUTO SUPERIOR DE ENGENHARIA**

Higher Institute of Engineering
Rua Conselheiro Emílio Navarro, 1900 Lisboa

Engineering

Founded 1975.

6487 **INSTITUTO SUPERIOR DE ENGENHARIA**

Higher Institute of Engineering
Rua de São Tomé, 4200 Porto

Engineering

Founded 1975.

Private Establishments

6488 **COOPERATIVA DE ENSINO SUPERIOR ARTÍSTICO, ARVORE I**

Cooperative of Advanced Studies in Arts, Arvore I
Rua Passeio das Virtudes 14, 4000 Porto

Founded 1986.

6489 **COOPERATIVA DE ENSINO SUPERIOR DE TÉCNICAS AVANÇADAS DE GESTÃO E INFORMÁTICA, ARVORE I**

Cooperative of Advanced Studies in Business Administration and Informatics, Arvore I
Campo dos Mártires da Pátria 67, 2 Dto., 1100 Lisboa

Business Administration
Informatics

Founded 1986.

6490 **ESCOLA SUPERIOR DE JORNALISMO**

Institute of Journalism
Rua do Melo 2, 4000 Porto

Journalism

Founded 1986.

6491 **INSTITUTO SUPERIOR DE ADMINISTRAÇÃO E GESTAÇÃO**

Higher Institute of Business Administration and Management
Avenida da Boavista 1043, 4100 Porto

Business Administration
Management

Founded 1986.

6492 **INSTITUTO SUPERIOR DE ASSISTENTES E INTÉRPRETES**

Higher Institute of Personal Assistants and Interpreters
Rua António Pedro 24, 4000 Porto
Telex: 20166 ISAI P
Telephone: (02) 316465
Director: Manuel Gomes da Torre

D. of Translation
Head: Manuel Gomes da Torre; *staff* 2 (28)
I. for Personal Assistants (Advanced Secretariats)
Head: Luciano Z. Moutinho Tajares; *staff* 2 (25)
I. of Tourism
Head: Raul Matos Fernandes; *staff* 2 (28)
I. of Management
Head: José Luís Alum Marinho; *staff* – (27)

Founded 1979. Officially recognized by the Ministry of Education to award degree 1986.

Academic Year: October to July (Ocobter-February; March-July).

Admission Requirements: Secondary school certificate and entrance examination.

Fees (Escudos): 200,000 per annum.

Language of Instruction: Portuguese.

Degrees and Diplomas: Bacharel, 3 yrs.

Academic Staff, 1989-90: 74.
Student Enrolment, 1989-90:

	Men	Women	Total
Of the country	75	349	424

493 **INSTITUTO SUPERIOR DE GESTÃO**
Higher Institute of Business Administration
Estrada da Ameixoeira 112/116, 1700 Lisboa

usiness Administration
Founded 1986.

494 **INSTITUTO SUPERIOR DE LÍNGUAS E ADMINISTRAÇÃO**
Higher Institute of Languages and Business Administration
Isla Sarl, 47 Pracas, Lisboa
Telex: 63501 ISLA P

Founded 1986.

495 **INSTITUTO SUPERIOR DE MATEMÁTICAS MODERNAS**
Higher Institute of Modern Mathematics
Rua das Flores 59, 1200 Lisboa

lodern Mathematics
Founded 1971.

496 **INSTITUTO DE NOVAS PROFISSÕES**
Institute of New Professions
Avenida Duque de Loulé 47, 1100 Lisboa
Telephone: 555319
Fax: 548501
Director: José Carlos Amado

). of Business Administration
:o-ordinator: Alfeu Pimentel Saraiva; *staff* – (42)
. of Public Relations and Advertising
:o-ordinator: América Ramalho; *staff* – (35)
. of Tourism
:o-ordinator: J. M. Carvalho Oliveira; *staff* – (30)
. of Business Administration
:o-ordinator: J. M. Carvalho Oliveira; *staff* – (15)

D. of Secretarial Studies
Co-ordinator: Maria do Carmo Rosarinho; *staff* 2 (22)
D. for Administrative Assistants
Co-ordinator: António Castro Serrão; *staff* – (24)

Founded 1964. A private institution recognized by the Ministry of Education.

Participates in the ERASMUS Programme with Dorset Institute.

Academic Year: October to June.

Admission Requirements: Secondary school certificate and entrance examination.

Fees (Escudos): 177,000 per annum.

Language of Instruction: Portuguese.

Degrees and Diplomas: Bacharel, 3 yrs. Degree of Pós-graduação, 2-5 yrs.

Publications: História da Filosofia do Direito e do Estado; Quanta Grão e Campos; Introdução à obra de Manuel de Oliveira; Tourism Education for the Early 21st Century - VIII World Congress of Waptt; L'Entreprise et l'Evolution moderne du Tourisme: Besoins et Prévisions en ce qui Concerne la Formation; Relations Publiques: Facteurde la Communication sociale; L'Entreprise; Sistema Nacional de Ensino.

Academic Staff, 1989-90: 135.
Student Enrolment, 1989-90:

	Men	Women	Total
Of the country	441	1111	1552
Of other countries	2	–	2
Total	443	1111	1554

6497 **INSTITUTO SUPERIOR POLITÉCNICO INTERNACIONAL**
International Higher Technical Institute
Estrada de Benfica 275, 1500 Lisboa

Business Administration
Social Welfare
Founded 1987.

6498 **INSTITUTO SUPERIOR DE PSICOLOGIA APLICADA**
Higher Institute of Applied Psychology
Rua Jardim do Tabaco 44, 1100 Lisboa

QATAR

6499 ***UNIVERSITY OF QATAR**

P.O. Box 2713, Doha
Cables: univqatar
Telex: 4630 UNVSTY DH
Telephone: (974) 832222
Fax: (974) 835111

President (Acting): Abdullah Juma Al-Kobaisi (1986-)
Secretary-General: Abdul Rahman Hassan Al-Ibrahim

F. of Education
Dean: Ahmed Khairy Kazem; *staff* 111 (4)
F. of Humanities and Social Sciences (including Arabic, Geography, History, Library Science, Social Work, Sociology, Philosophy, and English)
Dean: Maher Hassan Fahmy; *staff* 150 (1)
F. of Science (including Marine Sciences, Geology, Mathematics, Physics, Chemistry, Zoology, Botany, and Computer Sciences)
Dean: Mohamed Fathy Saoud; *staff* 111 (2)
F. of Islamic Studies
Dean: Yousef El-Qaradhawi; *staff* 59 (1)
F. of Engineering (including Chemical, Civil, Electrical and Mechanical Engineering)
Dean: Ismail Abdel Rahman Tag; *staff* 39
F. of Administrative Sciences and Economics
Dean: Ibrahim Mohamed Al-Subaie; *staff* 23
English Language Teaching Ut.
Director: Tassula Healey; *staff* 11
Environmental Studies Ut.
Head: Said Al-Haffar; *staff* 1
F. of Technical Education (including Computer Programming, Accountancy, Secretarial Studies, and Scientific and Educational Laboratory Studies)
Dean: Ahmed Al-Marakashi
Computer Ce.
Scientific and Applied Research Ce.
Director: Gabr Fadl Al-Noaimi; *staff* 12
Educational Research Ce.
Director: Monir Morsi; *staff* 5
Sirra and Sunna Research Ce.
Director: Yousef Al-Qaradhawi; *staff* 3
Documentation and Humanities Research Ce.
Director: Osman Sid Ahmed; *staff* 14 (25)

Founded 1973 as Faculties of Education, acquired present status and title 1977. A State institution with academic and financial autonomy. Financially supported by the government. Governing bodies: the University Council, composed of the President as Chairman, the Vice-President, the deans, 2 professors and 3 members from the private sector; the Higher Council of Education, with the Minister of Education as the University Consultative; the Board of Regents. Residential facilities for academic staff and students.

Arrangements for co-operation with the Universities of: Al-Azhar; Basrah; Al-Mustansiriyah; Mauritania.

Academic Year: September to June (September-January; February-June).

Admission Requirements: Secondary school certificate (Thanawiya Aama) or recognized foreign equivalent.

Fees: None.

Languages of Instruction: Arabic, and English in Faculty of Engineering.

Degrees and Diplomas: Bachelor of–Arts in Humanities and Education; Administrative Sciences and Economics; Science in Science; Acts in Islamic Studies, 4 yrs; Science in Engineering, 5 yrs. Postgraduate diplomas in Education and Certificate in Elementary Teaching. Diploma in–Library Science; Technical Education, 2-5 sem.

Library: Separate libraries for men and for women, 300,000 vols.

Special Facilities (Museums, etc.): Oceanographic Research Vessel, MV Mukhtabar Albihar; Educational Technology Centre.

Publications: Bulletin of the Faculty of Education; Bulletin of the Faculty of Humanities and Social Sciences; Bulletin of the Faculty of Islamic Studies; University of Qatar Science Bulletin; Journal of Administrative Sciences and Economics; Engineering Journal of Qatar University (all annually); Book of Abstracts (Engineering, biennially); Fruits of Knowledge (Public lectures, annually).

Academic Staff, 1989-90:

Rank	Full-time
Ustaz (Professor)	75
Ustaz Musa'id (Assistant Professors)	106
Mudarris (Lecturer)	129
Mudarris Musa'id (Assistant Lecturer)	74
Mauied (Graduate Assistant)	31
Others	89
Total	504

Student Enrolment, 1989-90:

	Men	Women	Total
Of the country	1000	3301	4301
Of other countries	637	699	1336
Total	1637	4000	5637

REUNION

6500 **UNIVERSITÉ DE LA RÉUNION**

15, Avenue René Cassin, 97489 Saint-Denis Cedex
Telex: 916645 RE
Telephone: (262) 29.45.45
Fax: (262) 29.17.00
Président: Michel Carayol
Secrétaire général: Jöelle Zampini

F. of Law, Economics, and Political Science
Dean: François Miclo
F. of Letters and Human Sciences
F. of Science
Dean: Jacques-Yves Conan
I. of Business Administration
Director: Michel Boyer
I. of Linguistics and Anthropology
Director: Christian Barat

Founded 1825 as Ecole de Jurisprudence, became Ecole de Droit 1926, Institut d'Etudes juridiques, politiques et économiques 1950, and Centre Universitaire 1971. Acquired present status and title as a full-functioning French University and title 1982. Governing body: the Conseil, comprising 41 members. Residential facilities for students.

Arrangements for co-operation with the Universities of: Bamberg; Madagascar; Mauritius; New South Wales.

Academic Year: September to June (September-December; February-June).

Admission Requirements: Secondary school certificate (baccalauréat) or equivalent and entrance examination.

Fees (Francs): 625 per annum.

Language of Instruction: French.

Degrees and Diplomas: Diplôme d'études universitaires générales (D.E.U.G.); Diplôme d'études universitaires scientifique (D.E.U.S.T.), 2 yrs.Licence, 1 yr after D.E.U.G. Licence en Droit, law, 4 yrs. Maîtrise, 4 yrs. Diplôme d'études supérieures spécialisées, (D.E.S.S.) 1 further yr.

Library: Service commun de la documentation, *c.* 7200 vols.

Academic Staff, 1989-90:

Rank	Full-time
Professeurs	31
Maîtres-Assistants/Maîtres de conférences	84
Assistants	23
Total	138

Student Enrolment, 1989-90:

Of the country	4306
Of other countries	273
Total	4579

6501 **MUSÉUM D'HISTOIRE NATURELLE**

Rue Poivre, 97400 Saint-Denis
Telephone: 20-02-19
Conservateur: M. Gruchet (1964-)

Natural History (Research)

Founded 1854. Attached to the Muséum national d'Histoire naturelle, Paris.

Library: c. 1690 vols.

ROMANIA*

Universities and Technical Universities

6502 ***UNIVERSITATEA DIN BUCUREŞTI**
University of Bucharest
64 bulevardul Gheorghe Gheorghiu-Dej, Sector 5, cod 70608 Bucureşti
Telephone: 14-57-44
Rector: Ion Ioviţ-Popescu (1984-88)
Secretarul Universităţii: Elena Ivan

F. of Mathematics
F. of Physics
F. of Biology, Geology and Geography
F. of Philology (Romanian Language and Literature, Foreign Languages and Literature)
F. of History and Philosophy
F. of Law
D. of Physical Education and Sport
I. of Mathematics
I. of Geography
I. of Linguistics
I. of Literary Theory and History
I. of History
I. of South-East European Studies
I. of Archaeology
I. of Thracian Studies
I. of Philosophy
I. of Juridical Research
Ce. for Sociological Research
Computer Ce.
Hydrobiological Research Ce. (Brăila)
Zoological and Biological Research Ce. (Sinaia)
Geographic Research Ce. (Orşova)
Geographic Research Ce. (Pătîrlagele)
Foreign Language Ce.

Founded 1694 by Prince Constantin Bassarab Brancovan as academy, established as university 1864, reorganized 1948. Present structure adopted 1977. A State institution responsible to the Ministry of Education. Governing bodies: the Academic Senate; the Academic Council. Residential facilities for *c.* 4000 students.

Arrangements for co-operation with *c.* 40 Universities throughout the world.

Academic Year: September to July (September-December; February-July).

Admission Requirements: Secondary school certificate and entrance examination.

Fees: None.

Language of Instruction: Romanian.

Degrees and Diplomas: Examen de Stat, Licentiat, 4-5 yrs, and dissertation. Doctorate, 3-5 yrs after State examination. Doctor docent (teaching qualification, university level), by thesis after doctorate. Also Diplom de Stat (teaching qualification, secondary level), 3 yrs.

Libraries: Central Library, 2.68 million vols; libraries of the faculties and institutes.

Special Facilities (Museums, etc.): University Museum; Grigore Antipa Natural History Museum.

Publications: Analele Universitaţii Bucureşti (10 annual series); Studii şi cercetări de geologie (annually); Studii şi cercetări geofizică (annually); Studii şi cercetări de geografie (annually); Revue roumaine de géologie (annually); Revue roumaine de géographie (annually); Revue roumaine de géophysique (annually); Revista de istorie si teorie literară (quarterly); Synthesis de literatură comparată (annually); Limba română (bimonthly); Studii şi cercetări lingvistice (bimonthly); Revista de filosofie (bimonthly); Revue roumaine de philosophie (quarterly); Revue roumaine de logique (quarterly); Studii şi cercetări juridice (quarterly); Revue des sciences sociales et juridiques (biannually); Studii şi cercetări de istorie veche şi arheologie (quarterly); Dacia (annually); Studii şi cercetări de numismatică (annually); Revue des études sud-est européennes (quarterly); Revista de istorie (monthly); Revue roumaine d'histoire (quarterly); Acta hortobotanica bucurestiensia.

Press or Publishing House: Centrual de multiplicare al Universitaţii Bucureşti.

Academic Staff, 1986-87: 894.

Student Enrolment, 1986-87:

	Men	Women	Total
Of the country	1888	3386	5274
Of other countries	212	115	327
Total	2100	3501	5601*

*Also 2206 external students.

6503 **UNIVERSITATEA DIN BRAŞOV**
University of Braşov
29, boulevard Gheorghe Gheorghiu-Dej, 2200 Braşov
Telex: 61381
Telephone: 4-15-80
Rector: Filofteia Negrutiu (1984-85)

F. of Mechanical Engineering
F. of Technology and Machine Engineering
F. of Forestry
F. of Wood Technology

Founded 1971 incorporating the Technical Institute of Braşov, founded 1956, and Institute of Education (1960). A State institution responsible to the Ministry of Education Governing body: the Senat. Residential facilities for students.

Academic Year: September to July (September-February; February-July).

Admission Requirements: Secondary school certificate and entrance examination.

Fees: None.

Language of Instruction: Romanian.

Degrees and Diplomas: Examen de Stat, Diploma de Inginer, 5 yrs. Licentiat, 4 yrs. Doctorat, a further 3-4 yrs. Also teaching qualification secondary level, 3 yrs and Diplôme de Technicien supérieur.

Libraries: Central Library, 630,000 vols; faculty libraries, *c.* 292,700.

Special Facilities (Museums, etc.): Forestry Museum. Herbarium; Dendrological Garden.

Publications: Travaux scientifiques series A–Mécanique et Technologie de la Construction des Machines: Mathématiques, Series B–Sylviculture et Industrie du Bois; Sciences naturelles; Physique-Chimie. Bulletins; Bibliographies.

Academic Staff, 1986-87: 601.

Student Enrolment: c. 10,520.

6504 **UNIVERSITATEA DIN CLUJ-NAPOCA**
University of Cluj-Napoca
Stradă Kogălniceanu 1, 3400 Cluj-Napoca
Telephone: 16101
Rector: Ionel Haiduc (1990-92)
Secretary-General: Cornel Iures

F. of Mathematics
Dean: Gheorghe Coman; *staff* 69
F. of Chemistry and Industrial Chemistry
Dean: Emil Cordos; *staff* 102
F. of Biology, Geography, and Geology
Dean: Iustinian Petrescu; *staff* 51

*Major changes have affected the higher education system of the country and individual institutions during the preparation of this edition. These are reflected as far as they have been communicated to IAU before 30 September 1990.

F. of History and Philosophy (including Ancient History, Medieval History, Modern History, Contemporary History, History of Philosophy and Logics, Sociology, Psychology, Politology, Philosophy, and Pedagogics)
Dean: Andrei Marga; *staff* 79
F. of Philology (including Romanian Language and General Linguistics, and Literature and Theory of Literature, Hungarian Language and Literature, Germanic, Romance and Slavonic Philology)
Dean: Liviu Petrescu; *staff* 140
F. of Law
Dean: Martian Niciu; *staff* 37
F. of Economics
Dean: Constantin Tulai; *staff* 91
I. of Physics
Dean: Vasile Crisan; *staff* 52
Computer Ce.
Director: Grigor Moldovan; *staff* 34
Also summer courses.

Founded 1959 by the unification of the Universitatea 'Victor-Babeş' 1919, and the Universitatea 'Bolyai' 1945. A State institution responsible to the Ministry of Education. Governing body: the Sénat, comprising 52 members. Residential facilities for *c.* 70% of the students.

Arrangements for co-operation with the Universities of: Geneva; Bruxelles; Tübingen; Cracow; Rouen.

Academic Year: September to June (September-January; February-June).

Admission Requirements: Secondary school certificate or equivalent, and entrance examination.

Fees: None.

Languages of Instruction: Romanian, Hungarian, and German.

Degrees and Diplomas: Examen de Stat, Licentiat, 4-5 yrs. Doctorate, 3-5 yrs after the State Examination and at least 2 yrs professional experience. Doctor docent, dr.doc. (teaching qualification, university level), by thesis after doctorate.Also Diploma de Stat (teaching qualification, secondary level), 3 yrs. Diploma of Sub-Inginer; Inginer.

Libraries: Central Library, 3,500,000 vols; 8 specialized libraries, *c.* 1,011,000.

Special Facilities (Museums, etc.): Museums: Botany; Zoology; Palaeontology; Mineralogy. Botanical Garden.

Publications: Studia Universitatis 'Babeş-Bolyai' (13 series); Contribuţii Botanice; Matematica.

Press or Publishing House: University Press.

Academic Staff, 1989-90:

Rank	Full-time
Profesori (Professors)	56
Conferenţiari (Associate Professors)	115
Lectori (Assistant Professors)	295
Asistenţi (Teaching Assistants)	160
Total	626

Student Enrolment, 1989-90:

	Men	Women	Total
Of the country	778	2229	3007
Of other countries	200	52	252
Total	978	2281	3259*

*Also 1530 external students.

6505 **UNIVERSITATEA DIN CRAIOVA**
University of Craiova
13 Str. Al. I Cuza, 1100 Craiova
Telephone: 14398
Rector: Nicola Tiberiu (1985-93)

F. of Natural Sciences
F. of Economics
F. of Philology and History
F. of Electrical Engineering
F. of Mechanical Engineering
F. of Agriculture (including Animal Husbandry and Horticulture)
F. of Medicine (including Pharmacy)
Also Agricultural Research Centres.

Founded 1966. A State institution responsible to the Ministry of Education. Financed by the State, also receives financial support for research from industry. Governing body: the Sénat. Residential facilities for 4259 students.

Arrangements for co-operation with the Universities of: Wrocław; Veliko-Turnovo; Skopje; Mérida; Kuopio.

Academic Year: September to July (September-January; February-July).

Admission Requirements: Secondary school certificate or equivalent, and entrance examination.

Fees: None.

Language of Instruction: Romanian.

Degrees and Diplomas: Examen de Stat, Licentiat in faculties of Natural Sciences; Economics; Philology, 4 yrs. Diplomas of Inginer in faculties of Electrical Engineering; Mechanical Engineering; Agriculture; Horticulture, 5 yrs; Medicine, 6 yrs. Doctorate, a further 3-5 yrs. Doctor docent, dr.doc. (teaching qualification, university level), by thesisafter doctorate. Also Diploma de Stat (teaching qualification, secondary level), 3 yrs.

Library: 661,608 vols.

Publications: Anale Universităţii; Mesaj Comunist (Scientific and Literary Revue).

Academic Staff, 1986-87: 812.

Student Enrolment, 1986-87:

	Men	Women	Total
Of the country	3716	3785	7501
Of other countries	538	103	641
Total	4254	3888	8142*

*Also 932 external students.

6506 **UNIVERSITATEA DIN GALAŢI**
University of Galaţi
Bulevardul Republicii 47, 6200 Galaţi
Telephone: (934) 14112
Rector: Mihai Jâşcanu (1990-94)

F. of Mechanical Engineering
Dean: Alexandru Epureanu; *staff* 113 (15)
F. of Food Technology and Fishery
Dean: Cornel Popa; *staff* 146 (4)
F. of Shipbuilding and Electrical Engineering
Head: Emil Ceangă; *staff* 49
F. of Metallurgy
Vice-Dean: Olga Mitoşeriu; *staff* 28 (15)
F. of Philology and Sciences
Head: Nicuşor Velican; *staff* 43 (12)
F. of Economics
Head: Emil Gavrilă; *staff* 53 (24)

Founded 1948 as Technical Institute. Acquired present status and title 1974. A State institution responsible to the Ministry of Education. Governing body: the Sénat. Residential facilities for students.

Arrangements in co-operation with: Institute of the Food Industry, Plovdiv; University of Rostock; Institute of Shipbuilding, Leningrad.

Academic Year: September to July (September-February; February-July).

Admission Requirements: Secondary school certificate and entrance examination.

Language of Instruction: Romanian.

Degrees and Diplomas: Examen de Stat, Diploma de Inginer, 5 yrs. Licentiat, 4 yrs. Doctorate, a further 3-4 yrs. Doctor docent (teaching qualification, university level), by thesis after doctorate. Diploma of Sub-Inginer, 3 yrs.

Library: Central Library, 415,000 vols.

Publication: Bulletin (annually) (8 series).

Academic Staff, 1989-90:

Rank	Full-time	Part-time
Profesori	45	–
Conferenţiari	88	–
Lectori	145	21
Asistenţi	154	49
Total	432	70

Student Enrolment, 1989-90:

	Men	Women	Total
Of the country	3417	3601	7018
Of other countries	19	–	19
Total	3436	3601	7037

6507 ***UNIVERSITATEA DIN IAŞI**
University of Iaşi
Calea 23 August 11, 6600 Iaşi
Telex: 022212
Telephone: 40559
Rector: Călin-Petru Ignat
Secrétar chef: Rodica Stegaru

F. of Mathematics
Dean: Aurel Răscanu; *staff* 58
F. of Physics
Dean: Mircea Sandulovicia; *staff* 42
F. of Biology
Dean: Constantin Pisică; *staff* 25
F. of Geography and Geology
Dean: Mihai Saramet; *staff* 33
F. of Law
Dean: Ştefan Rauschi; *staff* 16
F. of History
Dean: Ion Caprosu; *staff* 31
F. of Philosophy
Dean: Petru Ioan; *staff* 40
F. of Letters (including Romanian, English, French, German, Russian, Classic Language and Literature)
Dean: Dumitru Irimia; *staff* 104
F. of Economics
Dean: Dumitru Zait; *staff* 67
Computer Ce.
Director: Gh. Grigoraş; *staff* 37

Founded 1860, the university is a State institution responsible to the Ministry of Education. Governing body: the Sénat. Residential facilities for academic staff and students.

Arrangements for co-operation with the Universities of: Lublin; Jena; Freiburg; Greifswald.

Academic Year: September to July (September-February; February-June).

Admission Requirements: Secondary school certificate and entrance examination.

Fees: None.

Language of Instruction: Romanian.

Degrees and Diplomas: Examen de Stat, Licentiat, 4 yrs. Doctorate, a further 3-5 yrs. Doctor docent, dr.doc. (teaching qualification, university level), by thesis after doctorate. Also lower level qualifications, 3-5 yrs.

Libraries: Central Library; faculty libraries, total, 2,685,000 vols.

Special Facilities (Museums, etc.): Museums: National History; Palaeontology; Crystallography. Botanical Garden.

Publication: Annales scientifiques de l'Université.

Academic Staff, 1989-90:

Rank	Full-time
Profesori (Professors)	54
Conferenţiari (Senior Lecturers)	96
Lectori (Lecturers)	221
Asistenţi (Assistant Lecturers)	43
Total	416

Student Enrolment, 1989-90:

	Men	Women	Total
Of the country	1450	3116	4566
Of other countries	16	4	20
Total	1466	3120	4586*

*Also 2029 external students.

6508 **UNIVERSITATEA DIN TIMIŞOARA**

University of Timişoara
Bulevardul Vasile Pârvan 4, Timişoara III
Telephone: 128-05
Rector: Petru Onita (1984-88)
Secrétar chef: Gheorghe Velciov

F. of Natural Sciences
F. of Philology
F. of Economics

Founded 1948 as Institute of Education, became university 1962. A State institution, responsible to the Ministry of Education. Governing body: the Sénat, comprising 41 members. Residential facilities for students.

Academic Year: September to July (October-February; February-July).

Admission Requirements: Secondary school certificate and entrance examination.

Fees: None.

Language of Instruction: Romanian.

Degrees and Diplomas: Examen de Stat, Licentiat, 4-5 yrs. Doctorate, a further 3-5 yrs. Doctor docent, dr.doc. (teaching qualification, university level), by thesis after doctorate. Also Diploma de Stat (teaching qualification, secondary level), 3 yrs.

Library: Central Libary, 662,000 vols.

Publications: Anale Universitatii din Timişoara–Series: Mathematics; Philology; Physics and Chemistry; Economics and Social Science.

Academic Staff, 1986-87: 278.

Student Enrolment, 1986-87:

	Men	Women	Total
Of the country	402	979	1381
Of other countries	112	25	137
Total	514	1004	1518*

*Also 2670 external students.

6509 **UNIVERSITATEA TEHNICĂ**

Technical University
Calea Armatei Roşii 5, Oradea
Telephone: (991) 3-28-30

F. of Electrotechnical Engineering
; *staff* 28
F. of Mechanical Engineering
; *staff* 24
F. of Sciences
; *staff* 20

Founded 1963. Reorganized 1975 with one faculty. Became technical university 1990. A state institution responsible to the Ministry of Education. Residential facilities for students.

Academic Year: September to June (September-December; January-June).

Admission Requirements: Secondary school certificate.

Fees: None.

Language of Instruction: Romanian.

Degrees and Diplomas: University Diploma (engineering and teaching qualification), 5 yrs.

Library: c. 174,000 vols.

Special Facilities (Museums, etc.): 3 MW Geothermal Plant; Dendrological Park; Research Laboratory.

Publications: Scientific works (annually); Gaudeamus (monthly student publication).

Academic Staff, 1990: 72.

Student Enrolment, 1990: 1273.

6510 **INSTITUTUL POLITEHNIC DIN BUCUREŞTI**

Technical Institute of Bucharest
Splaiul Independenţei 313, 77206 Bucureşti 6
Telex: 10252 IPOLB
Telephone: 31-40-10/31-04-69
Rector: V. N. Constantinescu (1990-)
Secrétar şef: Dumitru Catrina

F. of Electrical Engineering
Head: Aurelian Crăciunescu; *staff* 192 (104)
F. of Automation and Computers
Head: Teodor Dănilă; *staff* 131 (105)
F. of Electronics and Telecommunications
Head: Marin Drăgulinescu; *staff* 175 (133)
F. of Mechanical Engineering
Head: Nicolae Apostolescu; *staff* 131 (106)
F. of Machine Engineering Equipment and Precision Mechanics
Head: Constantin Ispes; *staff* 116 (119)
F. of Agricultural Engineering
Head: Nicolae Enescu; *staff* 69 (30)
F. of Aerospace Construction
Head: Mihai Niţă; *staff* 74 (56)
F. of Metallurgy
Head: Emil Florian; *staff* 90 (61)
F. of Transport Engineering
Head: Eugen Negruş; *staff* 123 (99)
F. of Chemical Engineering
Head: Florin Badea; *staff* 126 (112)
F. of Energetics
Head: Cezar Ionescu; *staff* 105 (60)

Founded 1867 as Ecole des Ponts, Chaussées et Mines, reorganized 1881, became Ecole polytechnique de Bucarest 1920. Reorganized as Institut polytechnique de Bucarest 1948 and some faculties detached as separate institutions. Received present title 1965. A State institution responsible to the Ministry of Education. Governing body: the Rector, 4 Pro-Rectors, and the Sénat. Residential facilities for c. 13,200 students.

Arrangments for co-operation with Fachhochschule Darmstradt.

Academic Year: September to July (September-February; February-July).
Admission Requirements: Secondary school certificate and entrance examination.
Fees: None.
Language of Instruction: Romanian.
Degrees and Diplomas: Examen de Stat, Diploma de Inginer, 5 yrs. Doctorate, a further 3-4 yrs. Doctor docent (teaching qualification, university level), by thesis after doctorate. Also technical qualification, 4 yrs.
Libraries: Central Library, *c.* 1,350,000 vols; libraries of the 12 faculties.
Publication: Buletinul Institutului politehnic 'Gheorghe Gheorghiu-Dej' Bucureşti (in English, French, German and Russian).
Academic Staff, 1990:

Rank	Full-time	Part-time
Professors	112	–
Lecturers	827	10
Assistants	491	1026
Total	1430	1036

Student Enrolment, 1989-90:

	Men	Women	Total
Of the country	15,712	11,422	27,134
Of other countries	192	9	201
Total	15,904	11,431	27,335*

*Also 7639 evening students.

6511 **INSTITUTUL NAŢIONAL DE CHIMIE**
National Institute of Chemistry
Splaiul Independenţei 313, Bucureşti

F. of Chemical Technology
Founded 1977.

6512 **INSTITUTUL POLITEHNIC DIN CLUJ-NAPOCA**
Technical Institute of Cluj-Napoca
Stradă Emil Isac 15, 3400 Cluj-Napoca
Telex: 31352
Telephone: 34565
Rector: Horia Colan
Secrétar şef: Teodor Nilas

F. of Mechanical Engineering
Head: Mircea Cretu; *staff* 384
F. of Constructional Engineering
Head: Anton Ionescu; *staff* 193
F. of Electrical Engineering
Head: Victor Popescu; *staff* 186

Founded 1884 as an Ecole industrielle, became technical institute 1948. A State institution responsible to theMinistry of Education. Governing body: the Sénat. Residential facilities for students.
Academic Year: September to July (September-December; January-July).
Admission Requirements: Secondary school certificate and entrance examination.
Fees: None.
Language of Instruction: Romanian.
Degrees and Diplomas: Examen de Stat, Diploma de Inginer, 5 yrs. Doctorate, a further 3-4 yrs.
Library: Central Library, 642,000 vols.
Publication: Buletinul ştiinţific.
Academic Staff, 1989-90:

Rank	Full-time
Profesori universitari	32
Conferenţiari	66
Sefi de lucrăti (lectori)	204
Asistenţi	128
Total	430

Student Enrolment, 1989-90: 7840.

6513 **INSTITUTUL POLITEHNIC DIN IAŞI**
Technical Institute of Iaşi
Calea 23 August 22, 6600 Iaşi
Telex: 22216 IPOL
Telephone: 981-46577
Rector: Cameluţa Beldie (1984-88)

F. of Civil Engineering
F. of Industrial Chemistry
F. of Electrical Engineering
F. of Hydraulic Engineering
F. of Light Industries (including Textile Engineering)
F. of Mechanical Engineering
I. of Engineering (Bacău)
I. of Engineering (Suceava)

Founded 1937 incorporating former departments of electrical and chemical engineering of University of Iaşi, established 1912. A State institution responsible to the Ministry of Education. Residential facilities for academic staff and students.
Academic Year: September to July (September-February; February-July).
Admission Requirements: Secondary school certificate and entrance examination.
Fees: None.
Language of Instruction: Romanian.
Degrees and Diplomas: Examen de Stat, Licentiat, 4 yrs; Diploma de Inginer, 5 yrs. Doctorate, a further 3-4 yrs. Diploma of Sub-Inginer, 3 yrs.
Libraries: Central Library, 850,069 vols; libraries of the faculties, *c.* 620,000.
Publications: Bulletin (quarterly); Buletinul ştiinţific (annually).
Academic Staff, 1986-87: 1138 (120).
Student Enrolment, 1984-85:

	Men	Women	Total
Of the country	7210	6910	14,120
Of other countries	373	8	381
Total	7583	6918	14,501

6514 **INSTITUTUL POLITEHNIC DIN TIMIŞOARA**
Technical Institute of Timişoara
Bulevardul 30 decembrie 2, 1900 Timişoara
Rector: Coleta de Sabata (1981-88)

F. of Mechanical Engineering
F. of Electrical Engineering
F. of Chemical Technology
F. of Civil and Constructional Engineering
F. of Industrial Chemistry
F. of Agricultural Mechanization
I. of Engineering (Reşiţa)
I. of Engineering (Hunedoara)

Founded 1920, as school, became technical institute 1948. A State institution responsible to the Ministry of Education. Governing body: the Sénat. Residential facilities for students.
Arrangements for co-operation with: Technical University, Brno; Otto von Guericke Technical College of Magdeburg; University of Ljubljana.
Academic Year: September to July (September-January; February-July).
Admission Requirements: Secondary school certificate or equivalent, and entrance examination.
Fees: None.
Language of Instruction: Romanian.
Degrees and Diplomas: Examen de Stat, Diploma de Inginer, 5 yrs. Doctorate, 3-5 yrs after State Examination. Diploma of Sub-Inginer,3 yrs.
Library: 663,000 vols.
Publication: Buletinul ştiinţific (annually).
Press or Publishing House: Institute Press.
Academic Staff, 1986-87: 778.
Student Enrolment, 1986-87:

	Men	Women	Total
Of the country	7757	4219	11,976
Of other countries	310	11	321
Total	8067	4230	12,297

Other Institutions

Technical Education

6515 **INSTITUTUL DE CONSTRUCŢII DIN BUCUREŞTI**

Building Institute

Bulevardul Republicii 176, Sector 2, 73232 Bucureşti

Telephone: 42-42-00

Rector: Florea Chiriac (1984-88)

F. of Civil Industrial and Agricultural Engineering

F. of Building Engineering

F. of Railway and Highway Engineering

F. of Hydraulic Engineering

Founded 1948. Formerly part of Ecole des Ponts et Chaussées founded 1867 and transformed into Ecole polytechnique 1921. Responsible to the Ministry of Education. Governing body: the Sénat. Some residential facilities for students.

Arrangements for co-operation with the Technical Universities of: Gdansk; Szczecin; Leipzig; Dresden; Magdeburg; Berlin. University of Melbourne; Helsinki University of Technology; University of Palermo; Nagoya University; Chalmers University of Technology, Göteburg; University of Arizona; Polytechnical Institute, Leningrad; Institute of Civil Engineering, Tomsk.

Academic Year: September to July (September-February; February-July).

Admission Requirements: Secondary school certificate and entrance examination.

Fees: None.

Language of Instruction: Romanian.

Degrees and Diplomas: Examen de Stat, Diploma de Inginer, 5 yrs. Doctorate, 3-5 yrs after State Examination. Doctor docent, dr.doc. (teaching qualification, university level), by thesis after doctorate. Diploma of Sub-Inginer, 4 yrs (evening classes).

Libraries: Central Library; faculty libraries, total, *c.* 540,000 vols.

Publication: Buletinul ştiinţific (biannually).

Academic Staff, 1986-87: 481.

Student Enrolment, 1986-87:

	Men	Women	Total
Of the country	3245	2840	6085
Of other countries	299	13	312
Total	3544	2853	6397

6516 **INSTITUTUL DE ARCHITECTURĂ DIN BUCUREŞTI**

Institute of Architecture

Stradă Academiei 18-20, Sector 1, 70 109 Bucureşti

Telephone: 13-80-80

Rector: Cornel Dumitrescu (1981-89)

Architecture (including Town Planning)

Founded 1897 as school of architecture attached to the Ecole des Beaux-Arts, Bucharest. Became Faculty of Architecture of the Bucharest Polytechnic 1939 and faculty of Institute of Building Engineering 1948. Acquired present independent status 1952. A State institution responsible to the Ministry of Education. Residential facilities for *c.* 400 students.

Academic Year: September to July (September-January; February-July).

Admission Requirements: Secondary school certificate and entrance examination.

Fees: None.

Language of Instruction: Romanian.

Degrees and Diplomas: Examen de Stat, Diploma Architekt, 6 yrs. Doctorate, a further 2-4 yrs. Doctor docent (teaching qualification,university level), by thesis after doctorate.

Library: 200,000 vols.

Special Facilities (Museums, etc.): Building Materials Museum. Lapidarium.

Publication: Studii şi Proiecte (Studies and Projects).

Academic Staff, 1986-87: 100.

Student Enrolment, 1986-87:

	Men	Women	Total
Of the country	334	293	627
Of other countries	316	9	325
Total	650	302	952

6517 **INSTITUTUL DE MINE DIN PETROŞANI**

Mining Engineering Institute

Stradă Institutului 20, 2675 Petroşani

Telephone: 42580/1

Rector: Dumitru Fodor (1980-88)

F. of Mining Engineering

F. of Mining, Mechanical Engineering and Installations

Founded 1948 as Institut du Charbon, reorganized as institute 1952 incorporating former Institute of Mining atBrad. Bucharest Institute of Mining also incorporated 1957. Governing body: the Sénat. Responsible to the Ministry of Education. Some residential facilities for academic staff and students.

Academic Year: September to July (September-January; January-July).

Admission Requirements: Secondary school certificate and entrance examination.

Fees: None.

Language of Instruction: Romanian.

Degrees and Diplomas: Examen de Stat, Diploma de Inginer, 5 yrs. Doctorate, 3-5 yrs after State Examination. Also lower level technical qualification, 3 yrs.

Library: Central Library, 323,000 vols.

Publication: Lucrări ştiinţifice.

Academic Staff, 1986-87: 264 (90).

Student Enrolment, 1986-87:

	Men	Women	Total
Of the country	2839	1035	3874
Of other countries	3	–	3
Total	2842	1035	3877

6518 **INSTITUTUL DE PETROL ŞI GAZE**

Institute of Petroleum and Gas

Bulevardul Bucureşti 39, 2000 Ploeşti

Telephone: 73171

Rector: Niculae Macovei (1989-90)

Secrétar şef: Marin Mocanu

D. of Petroleum Refining and Petrochemistry

Dean: Ion Opris; *staff* 60 (10)

D. of Drilling and Production Engineering

Dean: Mihai-Pascu Coloja; *staff* 114 (10)

D. of Petrochemical and Petroleum Equipment

Dean: Emil Tocaci; *staff* 110 (25)

D. of Thermocatalytic Processes of Petroleum Cuts

Head: Constantin Ionescu; *staff* 5 (5)

D. of Petrochemical Technology

Head: Flavian Cuiban; *staff* 6 (2)

Founded 1973. Formerly part of Technical Institute of Bucharest. A State institution financed by the Ministry of Education. Governing body: the Sénat, comprising the Rector, Vice-Rectors, deans, vice-deans, students and research staff. Residential facilities for students.

Academic Year: September to July (September-December; January-July).

Admission Requirements: Secondary school certificate.

Fees: None.

Language of Instruction: Romanian.

Degrees and Diplomas: Examen de Stat, Diploma de Inginer, 5 yrs. Doctorate, a further 3-4 yrs.

Library: Central Library, 350,000 vols.

Special Facilities (Museums, etc.): Art Gallery; Movie Studio; Theatre Studio; Disco-Studio.

Publication: Buletinul (biannually).

Press or Publishing House: Institute Press.

Academic Staff, 1989-90: 284 (45).

Student Enrolment, 1989-90:

	Men
Of the country	3740
Of other countries	80
Total	3820*

*Also 1234 evening students.

Professional Education

6519 **INSTITUTUL AGRONOMIC DIN BUCUREŞTI**

Institute of Agriculture

Bulevardul Mărăşti 59, 71331 Bucureşti

Telephone: 18-39-55

Rector: Constantin Pintilie (1984-88)

F. of Agriculture (including Horticulture, Veterinary Medicine, Animal Husbandry and Land Development)

Founded 1852, became university institution 1921 and acquired present title 1948. A State institution. Governing bodies: the Sénat; the Faculty Councils. Residential facilities for 1730 students.

Academic Year: September to July (September-January; January-July).

Admission Requirements: Secondary school certificate and entrance examination.

Fees: None.

Language of Instruction: Romanian.

Degrees and Diplomas: Examen de Stat and professional titles in–Agriculture; Horticulture; Animal Husbandry, 4 yrs; Rural Engineering; Veterinary Medicine, 5 yrs. Doctorate, a further 3-4 yrs. Doctor docent (teaching qualification, university level), by thesis after doctorate.

Libraries: Central Library, total, 450,048 vols; Veterinary Medicine.

Publication: Lucrari ştiinţifice (annually).

Academic Staff, 1986-87: 293.

Student Enrolment, 1986-87:

	Men	Women	Total
Of the country	1057	1057	2114
Of other countries	36	9	45
Total	1093	1066	2159

6520 **INSTITUTUL AGRONOMIC DIN CLUJ-NAPOCA**

Institute of Agriculture

Stradă Mănăştur 3, 3400 Cluj-Napoca

Telephone: 18792

Rector: Alexandru Salontai (1984-88)

F. of Agriculture (including Horticulture, Animal Husbandry and Veterinary Medicine)

Founded 1869 as agricultural school, became institution of higher education 1906, faculty 1938 and institute 1948. Acquired present title 1958. A State institution. Governing body: the Sénat. Residential facilities for 646 students.

Academic Year: September to July (September-February; February-July).

Admission Requirements: Secondary school certificate and entrance examination.

Fees: None.

Language of Instruction: Romanian.

Degrees and Diplomas: Examen de Stat and professional titles in–Agriculture; Animal Husbandry; Veterinary Medicine, 5 yrs. Doctorate, a further 3-4 yrs.

Library: Central Library, 213,059 vols.

Special Facilities (Museums, etc.): Museums: Botany; Phytopathology; Anatomical.

Publication: Buletinul ştiinţifice (annually).

Academic Staff, 1986-87: 148.

Student Enrolment, 1986-87:

	Men	Women	Total
Of the country	634	342	976
Of other countries	38	9	47
Total	672	351	1023*

*Also 228 external students

6521 **INSTITUTUL AGRONOMIC DIN IAŞI**

Institute of Agriculture

Alec M. Sadoveanu 3, 6600 Iaşi

Telephone: 41601

Rector: Adrian Ionel (1984-88)

F. of Agriculture (including Horticulture, Veterinary Medicine, and Animal Husbandry)

Teaching Experimental Station

Founded 1912 as section of the University of Iaşi, became Faculty of Agriculture 1936, and separate State institution 1948. Residential facilities for 1150 students.

Academic Year: September to July (September-January; February-July).

Admission Requirements: Secondary school certificate and entrance examination.

Fees: None.

Language of Instruction: Romanian.

Degrees and Diplomas: Examen de Stat and professional titles in–Agriculture; Horticulture; Animal Husbandry; Veterinary Medicine, 5 yrs. Doctorate, a further 3-4 yrs. Doctor docent (teaching qualification university level), by thesis after doctorate.

Library: Central Library, 165,000 vols.

Publication: Buletinul ştiinţifice.

Academic Staff, 1986-87: 145.

Student Enrolment, 1986-87:

	Men	Women	Total
Of the country	486	479	965
Of other countries	13	1	14
Total	499	480	979*

*Also 345 external students.

6522 **INSTITUTUL AGRONOMIC DIN TIMIŞOARA**

Institute of Agriculture

Calea Aradului 119, 1900 Timişoara

Telephone: 43016

Rector: Ilie Duvlea (1980-88)

F. of Agriculture (including Veterinary Medicine and Animal Husbandry)

Ce. of Experimental Didactics

Founded 1945 as faculty of Technical Institute, Timişoara, became independent State institution 1948. A State institution. Governing body: the Sénat. Residential facilities for *c.* 1140 students.

Academic Year: September to July (September-January; February-July).

Admission Requirements: Secondary school certificate or foreign equivalent, and entrance examination.

Fees: None.

Language of Instruction: Romanian.

Degrees and Diplomas: Examen de Stat and professional titles in–Agriculture; Animal Husbandry, 4 yrs; Veterinary Medicine, 5 yrs. Doctorate, a further 3-4 yrs.

Library: 194,260 vols.

Publication: Lucrări ştiinţifice (annually).

Academic Staff, 1986-87: 122.

Student Enrolment, 1986-87:

	Men	Women	Total
Of the country	518	294	812
Of other countries	21	1	22
Total	539	295	834*

*Also 269 external students.

6523 **ACADEMIA DE STUDII ECONOMICE**

Academy of Economics

Piaţa Romană 6, 70167 Bucureşti

Telex: ASERO 11863

Telephone: 110610

Rector: Alexandru Puiu

F. of Industrial and Agricultural Economics

F. of Economic Cybernetics and Computer Sciences

F. of General Economics

F. of Commerce

F. of Accountancy and Finance

Founded 1913, a State institution. Governing body: the Sénat.

Academic Year: September to July (September-February, February-July).
Admission Requirements: Secondary school certificate and entrance examination.
Fees: None.
Language of Instruction: Romanian.
Degrees and Diplomas: Examen de Stat, Licentiat, 4 yrs. Doctorat.
Library: 1,260,000 vols.
Publication: Revue Teorie şi Practica Economica.
Academic Staff, 1986-87: 531.
Student Enrolment, 1986-87:

	Men	Women	Total
Of the country	2406	6014	8420
Of other countries	69	7	76
Total	2475	6021	8496

6524 **INSTITUTUL DE MEDICINA- SI FARMACIE**
Institute of Medicine and Pharmacy
Stradă Dionisie Lupu 37, 70183 Bucureşti
Telephone: 11-17-07
Rector: Ludovic Paun (1984-88)

F. of Medicine
F. of Pediatrics
F. of Dentistry
F. of Pharmacy
F. of Postgraduate Specialization

Founded as medical school 1857, became faculty of University of Bucharest 1869, detached as separate institute1948. A State institution.
Academic Year: September to July (September-February; February-July).
Admission Requirements: Competitive entrance examination following secondary school certificate.
Fees: None.
Language of Instruction: Romanian.
Degrees and Diplomas: Professional title of–Doctor in Medicine, Pediatrics, or Dentistry, or of Pharmacist, 6 yrs. Doctorate, a further 3-4 yrs.
Libraries: Central Library, *c.* 1,250,000 vols; faculty libraries.
Special Facilities (Museums, etc.): Anatomy Museum.
Publication: Medicinistul.
Academic Staff, 1986-87: 830.
Student Enrolment, 1986-87:

	Men	Women	Total
Of the country	1203	3077	4280
Of other countries	1454	399	1853
Total	2657	3476	6133

6525 **INSTITUTUL DE MEDICINA- SI FARMACIE**
Institute of Medicine and Pharmacy
Stradă I Mai 13, 3400 Cluj-Napoca
Telephone: 16585
Rector: Nicu George Ionescu (1984-92)

F. of Medicine
F. of Pharmacy and Dentistry

Founded 1775 as school, became faculty of medicine of the University of Cluj 1872. Detached and re-establishedas separate institution 1948. A State institution. Residential facilities for students.
Academic Year: October to June (October-February; February-June).
Admission Requirements: Competitive entrance examination following secondary school certificate or foreign equivalent.
Fees: None.
Language of Instruction: Romanian.
Degrees and Diplomas: Examen de Stat and professional qualifications, 6 yrs. Doctorates in Medicine or Pharmacy, a futher 3-4 yrs.
Library: 323,530 vols.
Special Facilities (Museums, etc.): Museum of the History of Medicine and Pharmacy.
Publication: Clujul Medical (quarterly).
Academic Staff, 1986-87: 460.
Student Enrolment, 1986-87:

	Men	Women	Total
Of the country	788	1408	2196
Of other countries	917	253	1170
Total	1705	1661	3366

6526 **INSTITUTUL DE MEDICINA- SI FARMACIE**
Institute of Medicine and Pharmacy
Stradă Universităţii 16, 6600 Iaşi
Telephone: 13845
Rector: Lorica Gavrilita (1981-88)

F. of Medicine (including Pediatrics)
F. of Dentistry (including Pharmacy)

Founded 1879, as faculty of 'Al. I. Cuza' University, detached as separate institution 1948. A State institution. Residential facilities for students.
Academic Year: September to July (September-January; February-July).
Admission Requirements: Competitive entrance examination following secondary school certificate or recognized foreign equivalent.
Fees: None.
Language of Instruction: Romanian.
Degrees and Diplomas: Professional titles in–Dentistry; Pharmacy, 5 yrs; Medicine, 6 yrs. Doctorate, a further 3-4 yrs.
Library: 359,827 vols.
Special Facilities (Museums, etc.): Anatomy Museum.
Publication: Revue Médico-Chirurgicale.
Academic Staff, 1986-87: 337.
Student Enrolment, 1986-87:

	Men	Women	Total
Of the country	339	1357	1696
Of other countries	1147	111	1258
Total	1486	1468	2954

6527 **INSTITUTUL DE MEDICINA- SI FARMACIE**
Institute of Medicine and Pharmacy
30 Stradă Gheorghe Marinescu, Tirgu-Mureş
Telephone: 15551

F. of Medicine
F. of Pharmacy
F. of Dentistry

Founded 1945, a State institution. Residential facilities for students.
Academic Year: September to June (September-December; January-June).
Admission Requirements: Competitive entrance examination following secondary school certificate.
Fees: None.
Languages of Instruction: Romanian and Hungarian.
Degrees and Diplomas: Professional titles in–Pharmacy, 5 yrs; Medicine, 6 yrs. Doctorates, a further 3-4 yrs.
Library: *c.* 202,170 vols.
Special Facilities (Museums, etc.): Anatomy Museum; History and Medicine Museum.
Publication: Medical Revue (biannually).
Academic Staff: *c.* 300.
Student Enrolment: *c.* 1800.

6528 **INSTITUTUL DE MEDICINA TIMIŞOARA**
Institute of Medicine
Piaţa 23 août, 1900 Timişoara
Telephone: 37612
Rector: Ba-canu S. Gheorgho (1979-88)

F. of Medicine and Dentistry (including Pediatrics)

Founded 1945, a State institution.
Academic Year: September to July (September-January; February-July).
Admission Requirements: Competitive entrance examination following secondary school certificate or recognized foreign equivalent.
Fees: None.
Language of Instruction: Romanian.
Degrees and Diplomas: Professional titles in–Medicine; Dentistry, 6 yrs. Doctorate.
Library: 301,260 vols.
Publication: Timişoara medicalia.

Academic Staff, 1986-87: 344.
Student Enrolment, 1986-87:

	Men	Women	Total
Of the country	447	1115	1562
Of other countries	1088	174	1262
Total	1535	1289	2824

6529 **ACADEMIA DE TEATRU ŞI FILM BUCUREŞTI**
Academy of Theatre and Film
Stradă Matei Voievod 75-77, Sector 2, 73224 Bucureşti VI
Telephone: 42-47-26
Rector: Victor Rebengiuc (1990-94)
Secrétar şef: Florian Potra

F. of Dramatic Art
Dean: Catalina Buzoianu
F. of Film
Dean: Stere Gulea

Founded 1864 as Conservatory of Music and Dramatic Art, acquired university status 1948 and present title 1954. A State institution responsible to the Ministry of Education. Governing body: the Sénat. Some residential facilities for students.

Academic Year: September to July (September-January; February-July).
Admission Requirements: Secondary school certificate and entrance examination.
Fees: None.
Language of Instruction: Romanian.
Degrees and Diplomas: Professional titles of–Actor; Theatre Director; Film Director; Director of Photography; Cameraman; Theatre and Film Critic, 4 yrs. Doctorate in History and Theory of Theatre or Film.
Library: 73,600 vols.
Academic Staff, 1990: 65 (38).
Student Enrolment, 1990-91:

	Men	Women	Total
Of the country	129	101	230
Of other countries	12	3	15
Total	141	104	245

6530 **INSTITUTUL DE TEATRU DIN TIRGU-MUREŞ**
Institute of Dramatic Art
Stradă Köteles Samuel 6, Tirgu-Mureş

F. of Dramatic Art (including Cinematography and Television)
Founded 1948.

6531 **INSTITUTUL DE ARTE PLASTICE DIN BUCUREŞTI**
Institute of Plastic Arts
Stradă General Budişteanu 19, 70744 Bucureşti
Telephone: 13-05-56
Rector: Ecaterina Teodorescu (1985-89)

F. of Plastic Arts
F. of Decorative Arts
I. of History of Arts

Founded 1864 as school, acquired present status and title 1950. A State institution. Residential facilities for students.

Academic Year: September to July (September-February; February-July).
Admission Requirements: Secondary school certificate and entrance examination.
Fees: None.
Language of Instruction: Romanian.
Degrees and Diplomas: State qualifications in various fields, 4 yrs. Doctorate in Museology.
Libraries: Central Library, 42,773 vols; History of Arts, 51,361.
Academic Staff, 1984-85: 63.
Student Enrolment, 1986-87:

	Men	Women	Total
Of the country	121	107	228
Of other countries	1	1	2
Total	122	108	230

6532 **INSTITUTUL DE ARTE PLASTICE DIN CLUJ-NAPOCA**
Institute of Plastic Arts
Piaţa Libertăţii 31, Cluj-Napoca
Telephone: 11577
Rector: Mircae Balau (1984-)

F. of Plastic Arts and Design

Founded 1864 as school of art, became academy 1931 and acquired present status and title 1950. A State institution. Some residential facilities for students.

Academic Year: October to June (October-February; February-May).
Admission Requirements: Secondary school certificate.
Fees: None.
Language of Instruction: Romanian.
Degrees and Diplomas: State qualifications in various fields, 4 yrs.
Library: 57,234 vols.
Academic Staff, 1986-87: 32.
Student Enrolment, 1986-87:

	Men	Women	Total
Of the country	68	44	112

6533 **ACADEMIA DE MUZICĂ DIN BUCUREŞTI**
The Bucharest Academy of Music
Stradă Stirbei Vodă 33, 79551 Bucureşti
Telephone: 14-26-10
Rector: Nicolae Beloiu (1990-)
Secrétar şef: Laurenţia Galiş

F. of Performing Music
Dean: Petre Lefterescu
F. of Composition, Musicology, Musical Pedagogy
Dean: Iosif Csire

Founded 1864. Reorganized 1948 as Conservatory of Music of university status. A State institution. Reorganized1990 as Academy of Music. Residential facilities for students.

Arrangemnts for co-operation with similar institutes in European countries planned from 1990.

Academic Year: September to July (September-February; February-July).
Admission Requirements: Secondary school certificate from a school of music and entrance examination.
Fees: None.
Language of Instruction: Romanian.
Degrees and Diplomas: Examen de diplomă, Licenţiat, 5 yrs.
Libraries: 207,810 vols; 11,500 records; 7100 tapes.
Publications: Studii de Muzicologie (Musicology Studies); Orfeu (Students Journal of Music).
Academic Staff, 1989-90: 93.
Student Enrolment, 1989-90:

	Men
Of the country	186
Of other countries	9
Total	195

6534 **ACADEMIA DE MUZICĂ DIN CLUJ**
Academy of Music
Stradă 23 August 25, 3400 Cluj-Napoca
Telephone: 15973
Rector: Alexandru Fărcaş (1990-)

F. of Composition and Musicology (Teachers of Music)
Dean: Florentin Mihăescu; *staff* 16 (5)
F. of Vocal and Instrumental Music
Dean: Liviu Ghitea; *staff* 35 (10)

Founded 1819 as School of Music. Became an Academy of Music and Dramatic Art 1919. Reorganized 1950 as Conservatory of Music of university status. A State institution. Acquired present title 1990. Governing body: the Sénat. Residential facilities for students at Cité universitaire.

Academic Year: October to July (October-January; February-July).
Admission Requirements: Secondary school certificate from a school of music or foreign equivalent, and entrance examination.
Fees: None.
Language of Instruction: Romanian.
Degrees and Diplomas: Examen de Stat, Licentiat, 4-5 yrs. Doctorate in Musicology.
Library: c. 157,505 vols.
Publication: Lucrari de muzicologie.

Academic Staff, 1989-90:

Rank	Full-time
Profesori	12
Conferenţiari	26
Lectori	12
Asisţenti	6
Total	56

Student Enrolment, 1989-90:

	Men	Women	Total
Of the country	54	65	119

6535 **CONSERVATORUL DE MUZICĂ DIN IAŞI**
Conservatory of Music
Stradă Cloşca 9, 6600 Iaşi
Telephone: 47246
Rector: Dan Hatmanu (1984-88)

F. of Music and Plastic Arts

Founded 1860 as school of Music and oratory. Reorganized 1949 as Conservatory of music of university status. AState institution. Residential facilities for students.

Academic Year: September to July (September-January; February-July).

Admission Requirements: Secondary school certificate from school of music, and entrance examination.

Fees: None.

Language of Instruction: Romanian.

Degrees and Diplomas: Examen de Stat, Licentiat, 4 yrs.

Library: 100,097 vols.

Publication: Musicology Writing (annually).

Academic Staff, 1986-87: 56.

Student Enrolment, 1986-87:

	Men	Women	Total
Of the country	175	109	284

6536 **INSTITUTUL DE SUBINGINERI**
Stradăa Mărăşeşti 157, 5500 Bacău
Telephone: 32673

F. of English and French (including Political Science and Education)
F. of Machine Engineering
F. of Physical Education

Founded 1961 as teacher training institution. Developed to incorporate fields of professional study. A State institution responsible to the Ministry of Education. Governing body: the Sénat. Residential facilities for students.

Academic Year: September to July (September-February; February-July).

Admission Requirements: Secondary school certificate and entrance examination.

Fees: None.

Language of Instruction: Romanian.

Degrees and Diplomas: Examen de Stat, Licentiat, in–English and French; Physical Education; Diploma de Sub-Inginer.

Library: Total, *c.* 127,030 vols.

Publication: Buletinul stiinţific (biennially).

Academic Staff: c. 100.

Student Enrolment: c. 1060.

6537 **INSTITUTUL DE SUBINGINERI**
Stradă Victor Babeş 65, Baia-Mare
Telephone: 15-43

F. of Philology
F. of Mathematics
F. of Natural Sciences

Founded 1961.

Academic Year: October to June (October-February; February-June).

Fees: None.

Language of Instruction: Romanian.

Degrees and Diplomas: Diploma de Stat (teaching qualification secondary level), 3 yrs.

Library: c. 25,000 vols.

Academic Staff: c. 100.

Student Enrolment: c. 450 (Also *c.* 400 external students).

6538 **INSTITUTUL DE SUBINGINERI**
Bulevardul V. I. Lenin 124, Constanţa

F. of Philology and History
F. of Mathematics and Physics
F. of Physics and Chemistry
F. of Natural Sciences
F. of Physical Education

Founded 1961.

Academic Year: October to June.

Admission Requirements: Secondary school certificate.

Fees: None.

Language of Instruction: Romanian.

6539 **INSTITUTUL DE SUBINGINERI**
Stradă Karl Marx 5, Hundedora

Founded 1972.

6540 **INSTITUTUL DE SUBINGINERI**
Stradă Draga 11, Piteşti
Telephone: 14305

F. of Philology
F. of Mathematics and Physics
F. of Natural Sciences
F. of Physical Education

Founded 1962.

Academic Year: October to August (October-February; February-July).

Admission Requirements: Secondary school certificate.

Fees: None.

Language of Instruction: Romanian.

Degrees and Diplomas: Diploma de Stat (teaching qualification, secondary level), 3 yrs.

Library: c. 50,000 vols.

Special Facilities (Museums, etc.): Museums: Zoology; Botany; Local Literature.

Publication: Juventus.

Academic Staff: c. 60.

Student Enrolment: c. 600.

6541 **INSTITUTUL DE INVĂŢĂMÎNT SUPERIOR REŞIŢA**
Piaţa Lenin 1-4, Reşita 1700
Telephone: 964-13901; 964-13601

Production Engineering

Founded 1971. Attached to the Technical Institute of Timişoara.

Academic Year: September to May (Septemmber-December; February-May).

Admission Requirements: Secondary school certificate.

Fees: None.

Language of Instruction: Romanian.

Degrees and Diplomas: Diplom de Stat, 4 ½-5 yrs.

Library: 40,100 vols.

Publication: Lucrările tehnico-ştiinţifice ale Institutului de Invăţămînt Superior din Reşiţa.

Academic Staff, 1990: 25 (36).

Student Enrolment, 1990:

	Men	Women	Total
Of the country	451	314	765

6542 **INSTITUTUL DE SUBINGINERI**
Bulevardul Victoriei 5-7, 2700 Sibiu
Telephone: 17989

F. of Mechanical Engineering
F. of Philology and History
S. of Law and Administration
Transylvania Research Ce.

Founded 1976. A State institution responsible to the Ministry of Education. Governing body: the Sénat. Residential facilities for students.

Academic Year: September to July (September-February; February-July).

Admission Requirements: Secondary school certificate and entrance examination.

Fees: None.

Language of Instruction: Romanian.

Degrees and Diplomas: Examen de Stat, Licentiat, 4-5 yrs. Diploma of Sub-Inginer, 3 yrs. Postgraduate diploma, 1 yr.

Library: Total, *c.* 967,470 vols.

Publication: Buletinul ştiinţific (annually).

Academic Staff: c. 150.

Student Enrolment: c. 1830 (Also *c.* 170 external students).

6543 **INSTITUTUL DE SUBINGINERI**
Institute of Higher Education
Stradă Emil Bodnăraş 1, Suceava
Telephone: 2366

F. of Philology
F. of Mathematics and Physics
F. of Physics and Chemistry
F. of Music
F. of History and Geography
F. of Physical Education

Founded 1963, a State institution responsible to the Ministry of Education. Residential facilities for students.

Academic Year: October to June (October-January; February-May).

Admission Requirements: Secondary school certificate.

Fees: None.

Language of Instruction: Romanian.

Degrees and Diplomas: Diploma de Stat (teaching qualification, secondary level), 3 yrs.

Library: c. 27,000 vols.

Academic Staff: c. 60.

Student Enrolment: c. 550 (Also c. 60 external students).

6544 **INSTITUTUL DE INVĂŢĂMÎNT SUPERIOR**
Stradă Nicolae Iorga I, Tîrgu-Mureş 4300
Telephone: 954-17275

F. of Engineering (including Mechanical Engineering, Automatization and Computer Studies, and Energetics)

Founded 1960.

Academic Year: October to June.

Admission Requirements: Secondary school certificate.

Fees: None.

Language of Instruction: Romanian.

Degrees and Diplomas: Diploma de Stat, Engineering, 5 yrs.

Library: 115,000 vols.

Publication: Buletin ştiinţific al institutului (annually).

Academic Staff, 1989-90:

Rank	Full-time	Part-time
Profesori	2	–
Conferenţiari	9	–
Sef lucrari	11	3
Total	22	3

Student Enrolment, 1989-90:

	Men	Women	Total
Of the country	305	126	431

6545 **INSTITUTUL DE EDUCAŢIE FIZICĂ ŞI SPORT**
Institute of Physical Education
Stradă Stefan Furtuna 140, Sector 6, Bucureşti
Telephone: 49.53.65
Rector: Elena Firea (1984-)

Physical Education (including Sports)

Founded 1922. A State institution. Residential faculties for students.

Academic Year: September to July (September-January; February-July).

Admission Requirements: Competitive entrance examination following secondary school certificate or equivalent.

Fees: None.

Language of Instruction: Romanian.

Degrees and Diplomas: Exam de Stat, Licentiat, 3 yrs.

Library: 153,200 vols.

Academic Staff, 1986-87: 84.

Student Enrolment, 1986-87:

	Men	Women	Total
Of the country	166	114	280
Of other countries	412	81	493
Total	578	195	773*

*Also 266 external students.

RWANDA

6546 ***UNIVERSITÉ NATIONALE DU RWANDA**
National University of Rwanda
B.P. 56, Butare
Telex: 22 605 BTE RW
Telephone: (250) 30302; 30271
Recteur: Maurice Ntahobari (1989-)
Secrétaire général: Charles Ntakirutinka

F. of Letters (including Philosophy) (Ruhengeri)
Dean: Baributsa Maniragaba; *staff* 38 (19)
F. of Applied Sciences
Dean: J. Baptiste Katabarwa; *staff* 11 (25)
F. of Science (Ruhengeri)
Dean: Cyprien Bishangara; *staff* 44
F. of Economics, Social Sciences and Management
Dean: Gaïtan Rusibane; *staff* 34 (11)
F. of Medicine
Dean: Séraphin Bararengana; *staff* 42 (8)
F. of Law
Dean: Charles Karinijabo; *staff* 11 (13)
F. of Agriculture (including Animal Husbandry)
Dean: Runyinta Barabwiriza; *staff* 19 (8)
F. of Education (Ruhengeri)
Dean: Eustache Munyantwali; *staff* 14 (13)
C. of Modern Technology (Ruhengeri)
Director: Cyprien Munyanshongore; *staff* 7
University Extension (Kigali)
Director: Athanase Sindikubwabo

Also University Hospital; University Laboratory; Fish Culture Station, Rwasave.

Founded 1963 as a national institution and its initial organization and direction entrusted to the Dominican Order, Province of St. Dominic, Canada. Reorganized 1976 and Institut pédagogique national incorporated 1981. Governing bodies: the Conseil universitaire, including a representative of the President of the Republic, the Minister of Education, the Rector, Vice-Rector and Deans; the Sénat académique. Residential facilities for academic staff and students.

Arrangements for co-operation with Universities in: Zaïre; Burundi; Tanzania; Kenya; Congo; Cameroon; Angola; Gabon; Central African Republic; Chad; Algeria; France; Belgium; Federal Republic of Germany; Netherlands; United Kingdom; USA; Canada.

Academic Year: October to June (October-December; January-March; April-June).

Admission Requirements: Secondary school certificate (Diplôme des Humanités complètes) or equivalent, or foreign equivalent.

Fees (Rwanda franc): Registration, 100 per annum; tuition, 4,000.

Language of Instruction: French.

Degrees and Diplomas: Baccalauréat in–Law, Sciences; Letters; Economics; Social Sciences; Human Biology; Management; Agriculture; Education; Nutrition; Public Health; Pharmacy, 2 yrs; Engineering, 3 yrs. Licence in–Law; Economics; Management; Social Sciences; Education; Science; Letters; Pharmacy, 4 yrs. Professional title of Ingénieur in–Agriculture; Civil Engineering; Electromechanical Engineering, 5 yrs. Doctorat en Médecine, 6 yrs.

Libraries: Central Library, 158,953 vols; Ruhengeri Campus, 51,000. Specialized libraries of the faculties.

Publications: Etudes Rwandaises (Séries: Sciences naturelles et appliquées; Lettres et Sciences humaines).

Academic Staff, 1989-90:

Rank	Full-time
Professeurs titulaires	13
Professeurs associés	25
Chargés de cours	80
Chargés de cours associés	81
Assistants	116
Total	315

Student Enrolment, 1989-90:

	Men	Women	Total
Of the country	1329	457	1786
Of other countries	87	13	100
Total	1416	470	1886

6547 **UNIVERSITÉ ADVENTISTE D'AFRIQUE CENTRALE**
B.P. 118, Gisenyi

F. of Theology
F. of Sciences
F. of Letters
F. of Education
F. of Education and Administration
Ce. for Technical Research and Applied Sciences

Founded 1984.

6548 **INSTITUT AFRICAIN ET MAURICIEN DE STATISTIQUES ET D'ÉCONOMIE APPLIQUÉE**
African and Mauritian Institute of Statistics and Applied Economy
B.P. 1109, Kigali
Telephone: 8.4989; 8.4889
Directeur: Idrissa Guira (1986-90)

D. of Statistics
Head: Kwadjovi Akpaka; *staff* 4
D. of Applied Economics
Head: Bonaventur Rwasangabo
D. of Mathematics
Head: Sourou Gérard Codja; *staff* 3

Founded 1975 by the Organisation Commune Africaine et Mauricienne (OCAM). Governing body: the Conseil d'administration, comprising Ministers, or their representatives, of ex OCAM Member States. Residential facilities for academic staff and students.

Arrangements for co-operation with: Ecole de Statistique d'Abidjan; Institut de Statistique, de Planification et d'Economie appliquée, Yaoundé.

Academic Year: October to July (October-December; January-April; May-July).

Admission Requirements: Competitive entrance examination following secondary school certificate (baccalauréat, séries scientifiques) or equivalent.

Fees (Rwanda franc): 80,000 per annum.

Language of Instruction: French.

Degrees and Diplomas: Diplôme d'Ingénieur des Travaux Statistiques (I.T.S.), 3 yrs.

Library: 6670 vols.

Academic Staff, 1989-90: 10.

Student Enrolment, 1979-90:

	Men	Women	Total
Of the country	17	3	20
Of other countries	51	1	52
Total	68	4	72

6549 **INSTITUT SUPÉRIEUR CATHOLIQUE DE PÉDAGOGIE APPLIQUÉE**
B.P. 37, Ruhengeri

Education

Founded 1986.

6550 **INSTITUT SUPÉRIEUR DES FINANCES PUBLIQUES**
B.P. 158, Kigali

Finance

Founded 1986.

6551 **ÉCOLE SUPÉRIEURE DE GESTION ET D'INFORMATIQUE (INSTITUT FIDÈLE)**

B.P. 210, Gisenyi
Telephone: 306
Directeur: Jacques Paquay (1986-)
Secrétaire général: Damien Muruho

Computer Sciences
Management
Secretarial Studies

Founded 1985.

Academic Year: October to June (October-January; February-June).

Admission Requirements: Secondary school certificate (baccalauréat).

Fees (Rwanda franc): 150,000 per annum; foreign students, 200,000.

Language of Instruction: French.

Degrees and Diplomas: Diplôme, 2 yrs.

Academic Staff, 1986-87: 8 (12).

Student Enrolment, 1986-87:

	Men	Women	Total
Of the country	57	28	85
Of other countries	3	2	5
Total	60	30	90

SAUDI ARABIA

Universities

6552 ***JAMIAT AL-MALIK SAUD**

King Saud University

P.O. Box 2454, Riyadh 11451

Telex: 201019 KSU SJ

Telephone: 467-0000

President: Mansoor Ibrahim Al-Turki (1979-)

Vice-President for Financial and Administrative Affairs: Hamoud Abdulaziz Al-Badr

Ce. of Arts
Dean: Abdulaziz Abdulatif El-Sheikh; *staff* 553
Ce. of Education
Dean: Ahmed Othman Al-Twigry; *staff* 269
Ce. of Education (Abha)
Dean: Adulatif Husein Farag; *staff* 123
Ce. of Agriculture
Dean: Khalid Abdulrahman Al-Hamoudy; *staff* 187
Ce. of Agriculture and Veterinary Medicine (Al-Gaseem)
Dean: Salih Nassar Al-Nassar; *staff* 44
Ce. of Pharmacy
Dean: Ibrahim Abdulrahman Al-Mishaal; *staff* 110
Ce. of Medicine
Dean: Faleh Zaid Al-Faleh; *staff* 255
Ce. of Dentistry
Dean: Saleh Hamzah Al-Sohhibany; *staff* 73
Ce. of Science
Dean: Ahmed Nasser Al-Mutib; *staff* 350
Ce. of Administration
Dean: Faiz Ibrahim Al-Habeeb; *staff* 210
Ce. of Business Administration and Economics (Al-Gaseem)
Dean: Sultan Mohammad Al-Sultan; *staff* 31
Ce. of Allied Medical Sciences (Nursing and Dietetics)
Dean: Abdulaziz Ali Al-Mashari; *staff* 73
Ce. of Engineering
Dean: Ali Abdulatif Al-Seif; *staff* 183
Ce. of Medicine (Abha)
Dean: Ghazi Abdulatif Gamgom *staff* 70
Ce. of Computer Sciences and Information
Dean: Dia-Lotfy Al-Khateeb; *staff* 38
Ce. of Planning Architecture and Planning
Dean: Mohamed Abdullah Al-Hussayen; *staff* 39
Arabic Language I.
Dean: Mahmood I. Seiny; *staff* 50
Ce. for Women
Dean: Hind Majeed Al-Khothaila
S. of Graduate Studies
Dean: Hussein Mohammed Alwi; *staff* 4
Ce. for Lifelong Education

Founded 1957 by Royal Decree. Colleges of Education and Engineering incorporated as faculty 1968. Governing bodies: the Supreme Council presided over the by Vice-Presidents; the University Council. Some residential facilities for academic staff and students.

Arrangements for co-operation with: Purdue University; University of Oklahoma City; University of Alabama; University of Illinois; University of Texas; Baylor University; University of Colorado; University of London; University of Toronto; University of Khartoum; National Tsing Hua University.

Academic Year: September to August (September-January; January-May; June-August).

Admission Requirements: Secondary school certificate or equivalent.

Fees: None.

Languages of Instruction: Arabic and English.

Degrees and Diplomas: Bachelor of–Arts; Arts in Education; Science; Science in Education; Science in Computer Sciences; Science in Administration; Science in Nursing; Science in Agriculture, 8 sem; Science in Engineering; Architecture; Planning; Dental Surgery, 10 sem; Medicine and Surgery, 6 yrs. Intermediate Teaching Diploma, 1 yr. Master, a further 2-4 yrs. Doctorate, Ph.D., 3-5 yrs. Postgraduate Diploma in Education, 1 yr.

Library: Total, 1,270,405 vols.

Special Facilities (Museums, etc.): Museums: Archaeology; Folklore; Zoology; Geology; Botany.

Press or Publishing House: University Press.

Academic Staff, 1986-87:

Rank	Full-time
Professors	249
Associate Professors	334
Assistant Professors	980
Lecturers	520
Demonstrators	56
Total	2644

Student Enrolment, 1986-87:

	Men	Women	Total
Of the country	17,057	4864	21,921
Of other countries	4161	1699	5860
Total	21,218	6563	27,781

6553 **JAMIAT AL-MALIK FAISAL**

King Faisal University

P.O. Box 380, El-Hasa

Telex: 81629 FAISAL S.J. AL-HASA

Telephone: 035800000

Fax: 5801243

President: Mohammed S. Al-Qahtani

Secretary-General (Acting): Saad A. Al-Barak

F. of Agriculture and Food Sciences
Dean: Fahed El-Mulhim; *staff* 143
F. of Medicine and Medical Sciences (including Nursing)
Dean: Kadi Makpoul; *staff* 236
F. of Architecture and Planning
Dean: Abdul Aziz Al-Saati; *staff* 112
F. of Veterinary Medicine and Animal Resources (Hofuf)
Dean: Suliman Al-Miman; *staff* 54
C. of Education (including Islamic Studies, Arabic Language, Foreign Languages, Social Studies, Chemistry, Biology, Mathematics, and History)
Dean: Saad Al-Hariegi; *staff* 148
C. of Administrative Science and Planning
Dean: Ibrahim Al-Turki; *staff* 50

Also 2 Colleges at Dammam, Veterinary Hospital, and University Hospital at Al-Khobar.

Founded 1974. A State institution under the jurisdiction of the Ministry of Higher Education. Governing bodies: the University Council; the Supreme Council. Residential facilities for academic staff and students.

Academic Year: September to June (September-January; February-June).

Admission Requirements: Secondary school certificate or foreign equivalent.

Fees: None.

Languages of Instruction: English and Arabic.

Library: In process of development.

Academic Staff, 1989-90:

Rank	Full-time
Professors	79
Associate Professors	110
Assistant Professors	228
Lecturers	102
Demonstrators	224
Total	743

Student Enrolment, 1989-90:

	Men	Women	Total
Of the country	2239	2345	4584
Of other countries	185	76	261
Total	2424	2421	4845

6554 **AL-JAMIAT AL ISLAMIAH**

Islamic University
P.O. Box 170, Medinah
Cables: Alislamia
Telex: 470022 ISLAMIA
Telephone: 24080

F. of Islamic Law (Shari'a)
F. of Islamic History
F. of Theology
F. of Sunna
F. of Arabic Language and Literature

Founded 1961 as an International Islamic foundation. Residential facilities for single students.

Admission Requirements: Secondary school certificate or equivalent.

Language of Instruction: Arabic.

Degrees and Diplomas: Bachelor of Art in Arabic and Islamic Studies. Also Master's degree and Doctorate.

Libraries: Central Library, *c.* 56,000 vols; libraries of the faculties, *c.* 100,000.

Publications: Magazine; Bulletin; Prospectus.

Academic Staff: c. 350.

Student Enrolment: c. 2740.

6555 **JAMIAT AL-IMAM MOHAMED IBN SAUD AL-ISLAMIAH**

Al-Imam Mohammad Ibn Saud Islamic University
P.O. Box 5701, Riyadh 11432
Cables: muhammadiah
Telex: 401166
Telephone: 4054448
Rector: Abdullah Ibn Abdulmohsin Al-Turki (1976-)
Secretary-General: Al'Ameen Al'Aam

F. of Islamic Law (Shari'a)
Dean: Abdulaziz Ben Abdurrahman Al Saeed; *staff* 43
F. of Arabic Language
Dean: Maeedh Ibn Musa'ed Aloufi; *staff* 54 (1)
F. of Fundamentals of the Religion
Dean: Faleh Ben Mohammad Al Saghir; *staff* 45 (3)
F. of Social Sciences
Dean: Nasser Ben Abdulaziz Al Dawood; *staff* 98 (3)
F. of Islamic D'awa and Communication
Dean: Zaid Ben Abdulkarim Al Zaid; *staff* 20
F. of Shari'a and Fundamentals of the Religion (Qassim)
Dean: Saleh Mohammad Al Hasan; *staff* 31
F. of Arabic and Social Sciences (Qassim)
Dean: Sulaiman Ben Hamad Al Oudah; *staff* 54 (1)
F. of Shari'a and Fundamentals of the Religion (in the South)
Dean: Abdullah Al Shaker Al Musleh; *staff* 38
F. of Arabic Language and Social Sciences (in the South)
Dean: Saad Ibn Hussain Othman; *staff* 51 (3)
F. of Shari'a and Islamic Studies (Al Ahsa)
Dean: Abdullah Al-Wahaiby; *staff* 56
Higher I. for the Islamic Call (Madinah Al Munawwarah)
Director: Mohammad Salem Ben Shadid Al'Oufi; *staff* 18
Higher I. of Judiciary (Postgraduate)
Director: Abdul Karim Ben Mohammad Al Lahem; *staff* 6
Deanery for Academic Research
Dean: Mohammad Ben Abdurrahman Al Rubai'; *staff* 2 (5)

Also 6 institutes for teaching Arabic and Islamic sciences in Japan, Indonesia, United Arab Emirates, Mauritania, Djibouti and USA.

Founded 1974, incorporating previously existing colleges and institutes. Governing body: the Supreme University Council.

Academic Year: September to May (September-December; January-May).

Admission Requirements: Secondary school certificate and examination in Arabic.

Fees: None.

Language of Instruction: Arabic.

Degrees and Diplomas: Bachelor 4 yrs. Master, 2-3 yrs. Doctorate (Ph.D.), 2-4 yrs. Diploma, 1-2 yrs.

Library: Central Library, 107,719 vols. Libraries of the faculties and higher institutes, 276,248.

Press or Publishing House: University Press.

Academic Staff, 1989-90: 761 (11).

Student Enrolment, 1989-90:

	Men	Women	Total
Of the country	10,940	2061	13,001
Of other countries	1034	98	1132
Total	11,974	2159	14,133

6556 **JAMAAH-TUL-MALIK FAHD LIL-BETROL WAL MA'ADIN**

King Fahd University of Petroleum and Minerals
Dhahran 31261
Cables: aljamaah
Telex: 801060 KFUPM SJ
Telephone: (3) 860-2000
Fax: (3) 860-3332; (3) 860-3306
Rector & Chief Executive Officer: Bakr Abdullah Bakr (1970-)
Secretary-General (Acting): Jasem M. Al-Ansari

C. of Sciences
Dean: Mohammad Zamel Al-Faer; *staff* 152
C. of Engineering Sciences and Applied Engineering
Dean: Fareed Mohammad Zedan; *staff* 142 (13)
C. of Environmental Design
Dean: Ibrahim Al-Shukri; *staff* 30
C. of Industrial Management
Dean: Mohammad Ibrahim Al-Twaijri; *staff* 40
C. of Computer Science and Engineering
Dean: Mohammad Ibrahim Al-Suwaiyel; *staff* 52
C. of Graduate Studies
Dean: Ala Hussain Al-Rabeh; *staff* 1
Data Processing Ce.
Director: Mohammad Abul-Hamaeyl; *staff* 74
English Language Ce.
Head: Roderick Wathen; *staff* 75
Research I.
Director: Abdallah Esa Al-Dabbagh; *staff* 342 (65)

Founded 1963 by Royal Decree. Acquired present title 1986. Administratively attached to the Ministry of HigherEducation, but enjoys internal autonomy. Financed by the government. Governing body: the Board, including Ministers of State, Council of Deans. Residential facilities for academic staff and students.

Arrangements for co-operation with: Friedrich Alexander Universität Erlangen-Nuerenberg; University of Manchester; Institute of Science and Technology, Manchester.

Academic Year: September to August (September-January; February-June; July-August).

Admission Requirements: Secondary school certificate (Tawjahiya) or equivalent, and entrance examination. Students from abroad considered on merit.

Language of Instruction: English.

Degrees and Diplomas: Bachelor of Science in–Engineering; Science; Environmental Design (Architecture); Industrial Management; Computer Science and Engineering, 5 yrs. Master of Science in–Architectural, Civil and Chemical Engineering; Chemistry; Computer Science; Construction Engineering and Management; Computer Engineering; City and Regional Planning; Electrical Engineering; Geology; Mechanical Engineering; Petroleum Engineering; Physics and Systems Engineering, a further 2-3 yrs. Doctor (Ph.D.) in–Civil, Chemical, Electrical, Mechanical and Petroleum Engineering; Chemistry; Mathematics, 5 yrs.

Library: 236,836 vols. Also microfilms, microfiches, monographs, etc. total, 813,634.

Special Facilities (Museums, etc.): Museums: Geology; Science.

Publications: Arabian Journal of Science and Engineering (quarterly); KFUPM News and Akhbar-al-Jamaah (weekly).

Press or Publishing House: KFUPM Press.

Academic Staff, 1989-90:

Rank	Full-time
Professors	37
Associate Professors	126
Assistant Professors	175
Lecturers	224
Graduate Assistants	57
Total	619

Student Enrolment, 1989-90:

	Men
Of the country	4032
Of other countries	642
Total	4674

6557 **JAMIAT AL-MALIK ABDUL-AZIZ**

King Abdul-Aziz University

P.O. Box 1540, Jeddah 21441

Cables: jameat abdulaziz

Telex: 601141 KAUNI SJ

Telephone: (687) 9033

President: Rida Mohamed Said Obeid (1984-)

Secretary-General: Hassan Abu Rukba

F. of Economics and Administration

Dean: Madani A. Alaki; *staff* 272

Ce. of Arts and Humanities (including Library Science and Journalism)

Dean: Solaiman M. Al-Ghannam; *staff* 298

Ce. of Science (including Computer Sciences)

Dean: Nabih Baashen; *staff* 246

Ce. of Engineering (including Architecture)

Dean: Fouad M. Ghazali; *staff* 257

Ce. of Marine Sciences

Dean: Musa Al-Amoudi; *staff* 33

Ce. of Meteorology and Environmental Studies

Dean: Omar Ali Sabbak; *staff* 29

Ce. of Medicine and Allied Sciences

Dean: Osama Subashki; *staff* 216

Ce. of Education (Medina)

Dean: Munir S. Khashkjy; *staff* 125

Ce. of Earth Sciences

Dean: Abdul Razzaq Bakar; *staff* 79

Computer Ce.

Director: Ahmed Abbas Adas

External D.

Dean: Mohammad Muslim Al-Raddadi

Founded 1967 as a private institution, acquired status as State university 1971. Governing bodies: the Supreme Council; the University Council. Residential facilities for academic staff and students.

Arrangements for co-operation with: Royal College of Medicine, Ireland; University of Texas; University of Virginia.

Academic Year: September to June (September-January; January-June).

Admission Requirements: Secondary school certificate or equivalent.

Fees: None.

Languages of Instruction: Arabic and English.

Degrees and Diplomas: Bachelor of–Science; Arts; Medicine. Also Master's degree and Doctorate. Special Diploma in Education.

Libraries: Central Library, 434,592 vols; libraries of the colleges.

Press or Publishing House: University Press.

Academic Staff, 1986-87:

Rank	Full-time
Professors	189
Associate Professors	273
Assistant Professors	549
Lecturers	246
Demonstrators	330
Total	1587

Student Enrolment, 1986-87:

	Men	Women	Total
Of the country	11,687	6142	17,829
Of other countries	2181	1483	3664
Total	13,868	7625	21,493*

*Also 6738 external students.

6558 **JAMIAT UMM AL-QURA**

Umm Al-Qura University

P.O. Box 407/715, Makkah

Telephone: (02) 5564770

F. of Islamic Law (Shari'a and Studies)

F. of Education

F. of Applied Sciences and Engineering

F. of D'awa and Usul al-Din

F. of English

F. of Education (Taif)

F. of Library Science (Taif)

Founded 1979, incorporating existing faculties of the King Abdul-Aziz University.

SENEGAL

6559 ***UNIVERSITÉ CHEIKH ANTA DIOP DE DAKAR**
University Cheikh Anta Diop of Dakar
B.P. 5005, Dakar-Fann
Cables: unndak sg
Telex: 51262 SG
Telephone: 25-05-30
Recteur: Souleymane Niang (1986-92)
Secrétaire général: Mbaye Niang

F. of Law and Economics
Dean: Moustafa Sourang; *staff* 82
F. of Medicine and Pharmacy (including Dentistry)
Dean: René Ndoye; *staff* 149
F. of Science
Dean: Hamet Seydi; *staff* 177
F. of Letters and Human Sciences
Dean: Aloyse Raymond Ndiaye; *staff* 117
I. of African Studies
I. of Social Pediatrics
Director: Mohamadou Fall
I. of Applied Tropical Medicine
Director: Omar Bao
S. of Sciences and Veterinary Medicine
Director: Alassane Séré
S. of Library Science and Documentation Studies
Director: Ousmane Sané; *staff* 14
Teacher Training S.
Director: Sega Seck Fall; *staff* 59
Applied Linguistics Ce.
Director: Cherif Mbodj; *staff* 8
Ce. of Information Sciences and Techniques
Director: Babacar Sine; *staff* 13
Psychopathological Research Ce.
Director: Babacar Diop
I. of French (for foreign students)
Director: Amadou Ly; *staff* 9
Mathematics Research I.
Director: Christian Sina Diatta
I. of Technology
Director: Souleymane Seck; *staff* 114
S. of Technical and Professional Teacher Training (E.N.S.E.T.P.)
Director: Amadou Lamine Dia; *staff* 3
I. for the Rights of Man and Peace
Director: Bakary Traore
I. of Health and Development
Director: Ibrahim Wone; *staff* 2
Fundamental I. of Black Africa
Director: Cheikh Anta Diop

Founded 1918 as Ecole de Médecine, became Institut des hautes Etudes 1950 and university by decree 1957. A State institution. Governing body: the Assemblée. Residential facilities for foreign academic staff and for some of the students.

Arrangements for co-operation with Universities in: Africa; France; Canada; Germany; Japan; USA.

Academic Year: October to July (October-February; March-July).

Admission Requirements: Secondary school certificate (baccalauréat) or recognized equivalent, and entrance examination.

Fees (Francs C.F.A.): 50,000 per annum for foreign students.

Language of Instruction: French.

Degrees and Diplomas: Letters and Human Sciences: Diplôme universitaire d'études littéraires (D.U.E.L.), 2 yrs; Licence, 1 further yr; Maîtrise, 1 yr after Licence. Doctorat (3e cycle), 2 yrs after Maîtrise. Medicine and Pharmacy: Diplôme de Pharmacien; Doctorat en Chirurgie dentaire, 5 yrs; Doctorat (3e cycle) en Sciences odontologiques, 7-8 yrs. Doctorat d'Etat en Médecine, 7 yrs. Doctorat d'Etat de Pharmacie, 8-9 yrs. Certificat in Psychiatry, 4 yrs after Doctor of Medicine. Doctorat d'Etat en Médecine vétérinaire, 6 yrs. Law and Economics: Diplôme d'études juridiques générales ou économiques générales, 2 yrs. Maîtrise–en Droit, law; ès Sciences économiques, 2 further yrs; Certificat d'études supérieures (C.E.S.) in Law or Economics, 1 yr after Maîtrise; Diplôme d'études approfondies (D.E.A.) in Law or Economics, 2 yrs after Maîtrise. Science: Diplôme universitaire d'études scientifiques (D.U.E.S.), 2 yrs; Licence, 1 yr after D.U.E.S.; Maîtrise, 1 yr after Licence; Diplôme d'études approfondies (D.E.A.), 2 yrs after Maîtrise. Also varioustechnical qualifications.

Libraries: c. 400,000 vols; faculty libraries.

Special Facilities (Museums, etc.): Ethnological Museum; Historical Museum; Marine Museum.

Publications: Annales africaines (Faculty of Law, annually); Bulletin et Mémoires de la Faculté de Médecine at Pharmacie (annually); Bulletin de la Société médicale d'Afrique noire de Langue française; Médecine d'Afrique noire; L'Enfant en Milieu tropical (monthly); Psychopathologie africaine; Annales de la Faculté des Sciences (annually); Revue de Géographie d'Afrique Occidentale (Faculty of Letters); Bulletin de l'Institut français d'Afrique noire; Notes africaines; Afrique médicale; Cancérologie tropicale (biannually).

Academic Staff, 1988-89:

Rank	Full-time
Professeurs/Maîtres de conférences	143
Chargés d'enseignement	21
Maîtres Assistants	163
Assistants	378
Total	705

Student Enrolment, 1988-89:

Of the country	12,881
Of other countries	1952
Total	14,833

6560 **ÉCOLE NATIONALE D'ADMINISTRATION ET DE LA MAGISTRATURE**
Rue Dial-Diop, Dakar
Telephone: 21-69-71; 22-58-25

Public Administration (including Diplomatic Studies, Economics, and Finance)
Magistrature

Founded 1960 and reorganized 1965. A State institution attached to the Office of the President of the Republic. Governing body: the Conseil de perfectionnement, including the Office of the President as Chairman, the Rector and deans of the faculties of law and letters of the University of Dakar, and representatives of various Ministries. Residential facilities for students.

Academic Year: November to July (November-February; March-July).

Admission Requirements: Competitive entrance examination open to serving civil servants, or Licence in law or economics or equivalent for entry to third year of study.

Fees: None.

Language of Instruction: French.

Degrees and Diplomas: Brevet, 3 yrs.

6561 **ÉCOLE POLYTECHNIQUE DE THIÈS**
B.P. 10, Thiès
Telex: 77108 EPTHIÈS
Telephone: 51-16-32; 51-15-48
Fax: 51-14-76
Commandant: Mamadou Seck
Secretary-General: Arona Diop

D. of Civil Engineering
Head: Massamba Diene
D. of Electro-Mechanical Engineering
Head: Ngor Sarr

Founded 1973. A State institution. Residential facilities for academic staff and students.

Arrangements for co-operation with: Ecole polytechnique de Montréal; Ecole polytechnique fédérale de Lausanne; Université de Liège; Faculté polytechnique de Mons.

Academic Year: October to July (October-February; February-July).

Admission Requirements: Secondary school certificate (baccalauréat) and entrance examination.

Fees: None.

Language of Instruction: French.

Degrees and Diplomas: Diplôme d'Ingénieur, 5 yrs.

Library: 13,200 vols.

Publication: Polythiès (annually).

Academic Staff, 1989-90: 24 (16).

Student Enrolment, 1989-90:

	Men	Women	Total
Of the country	55	6	61
Of other countries	86	–	86
Total	141	6	147

6562 **ÉCOLE NATIONALE D'ÉCONOMIE APPLIQUÉE**

Km 6, Route de Ouakam, Dakar-Fann
Telephone: 22-31-76

Applied Economics

Founded 1963. A State institution under the jurisdiction of the Ministry of Education. Governing body: the Conseil de perfectionnement. Residential facilities for academic staff and students.

Academic Year: January to December (January-July; July-December).

Admission Requirements: Secondary school certificate (baccalauréat) and entrance examination.

Language of Instruction: French.

Degrees and Diplomas: Diplômes, 2-3 yrs.

Library: c. 2500 vols.

Publication: Bulletin.

Academic Staff: c. 30.

Student Enrolment: c. 130.

6563 **ÉCOLE NORMALE SUPÉRIEURE D'ENSEIGNEMENT TECHNIQUE ET PROFESSIONNEL**

Cité Claudel Corniche Ouest, Dakar
Telephone: 21-76-69
Directeur: Amadou Lamine Dia (1980-)
Secrétaire général: Djibril Gueye

Teacher Training (Technical)

Founded 1979 as Ecole normale d'Enseignement technique masculin, and incorporated Ecole normale d'Enseignement technique féminin and Ecole nationale de Secrétariat. A State institution responsible to the Ministry of Education. Residential facilities for students.

Academic Year: October to July (October-December; January-March; April-June).

Admission Requirements: Secondary school certificate (baccalauréat) or recognized equivalent.

Fees (Francs C.F.A.): Registration, 600; tuition, 250,000 per annum.

Language of Instruction: French.

Degrees and Diplomas: Certificats d'Aptitude.

Library: 3,174 vols.

Academic Staff, 1986-87: 55 (11).

Student Enrolment, 1986-87:

	Men	Women	Total
Of the country	104	42	146
Of other countries	24	23	47
Total	128	65	193

6564 **CENTRE DE FORMATION PÉDAGOGIQUE SPÉCIALE**

B.P. 149, Ex-Base Aérienne, Thiès
Telephone: 51-13-82

Teacher Training

Founded 1968.

6565 **ÉCOLE NATIONALE DE FORMATION MARITIME**

Km. 4,5, Route de Rufisque
Telephone: 21-38-23

Maritime Studies

6566 **ÉCOLE NATIONALE D'HORTICULTURE**

Cambérène, Dakar-lie
Telephone: 21-78-21

Horticulture

6567 **ÉCOLE NATIONALE DE CADRES RURAUX**

B.P. 41, Bambey
Telephone: 58-63-60

Agriculture
Stockraising
Forestry

Founded 1960.

6568 **CENTRE DE FORMATION ET DE PERFECTIONNEMENT ADMINISTRATIFS**

Cité Hersent, rue de l'Est, Point E, Dakar-Fann
Telephone: 22-00-58

Administrative Studies

Founded 1965. A State institution under the jurisdiction of the Ministry of Education.

Academic Year: November to June (November-March; April-June).

Admission Requirements: Secondary school certificate (baccalauréat) and entrance examination.

Fees: None.

Language of Instruction: French.

Degrees and Diplomas: Diplôme, 2 yrs.

Library: c. 500 vols.

Academic Staff: c. – (80).

Student Enrolment: c. 160.

6569 **CENTRE AFRICAIN D'ÉTUDES SUPÉRIEURES EN GESTION**

72, boulevard de la République, Dakar
Telephone: 21-92-23; 21-92-54

Business Administration
Lifelong Education

Founded 1980. A State institution under the jurisdiction of the Ministry of Education. Governing body: the Conseil d'administration.

Academic Year: October to July.

Admission Requirements: University degree, and at least 3 yrs professional experience.

Fees: None.

Language of Instruction: French.

Degrees and Diplomas: Diplôme supérieur de Gestion des Entreprises (D.S.G.E.), 2 yrs.

Library: c. 10,000 vols.

Academic Staff: c. 10 (30).

Student Enrolment: c. 400.

6570 **ÉCOLE NATIONALE DES ASSISTANTS SOCIAUX ET ÉDUCATEURS SPÉCIALISÉS**

Km 4, Route de Ouakam, Dakar
Telephone: 23-07-70
Directeur: Lassana Kaba (1978-)
Secrétaire général: Cheikh Ben Ibrahima Sène

Social Work

Founded 1968. A State institution under the jurisdiction of the Ministry of Education.

Academic Year: October to July (October-February; March-July).

Admission Requirements: Secondary school certificate (baccalauréat) and entrance examination.

Fees: None.

Language of Instruction: French.

Degrees and Diplomas: Diplôme d'Etat, 3 yrs.

Library: 1,300 vols.

Academic Staff, 1986-87: 4 (83).

Student Enrolment, 1986-87:

	Men	Women	Total
Of the country	37	9	46
Of other countries	11	39	50
Total	48	48	96

6571 **ÉCOLE NATIONALE DES POSTES ET TÉLÉCOMMUNICATIONS**

Rue Ousmane Socé Diop, B.P. 6, Rufisque
Telephone: 36-00-29

Telecommunication Engineering

6572 **ÉCOLE MULTINATIONALE DE TÉLÉCOMMUNICATIONS**

Rue Ousmane Socé Diop, Rufisque
Telephone: 36-44-43

Telecommunication Engineering

Founded 1971.

6573 **ÉCOLE D'ARCHITECTURE ET D'URBANISME**

Dakar-Immeuble Seydou Nourou Tall, Dakar
Telephone: 22-39-81

Architecture
Town Planning

Founded 1963. A State institution under the jurisdiction of the Ministry of Culture.

Arrangements for co-operation with similar institutions in: France (Paris, Marseilles); Belgium (Brussels); Tunisia (Tunis).

Academic Year: October to July (November-February; February-July).

Admission Requirements: Secondary school certificate (baccalauréat) and entrance examination.

Language of Instruction: French.

Degrees and Diplomas: Certificat d'études d'Architecture (1er et 2ème cycles). Diplôme de Technicien supérieur en Architecture et en Urbanisme. Diplômes (D.P.L.G.).

Library: School Library.

Publication: Cahiers.

Academic Staff: c. 10 (40).

6574 **ÉCOLE NATIONALE DES BEAUX-ARTS**

124-126, Avenue A. Peytavin, Dakar
Telephone: 22-35-53

Fine Arts

Founded 1979.

6575 **ÉCOLE NORMALE SUPÉRIEURE D'ENSEIGNEMENT ARTISTIQUE**

124-126, Avenue A. Peytavin, Dakar
Telephone: 22-35-53

Teacher Training

Founded 1979.

6576 **CONSERVATOIRE NATIONAL DE MUSIQUE, DE DANSE ET D'ART DRAMATIQUE**

B.P. 3111, Dakar
Telephone: 212511

Music
Dance
Drama

Founded 1948 as school, acquired present status and title 1978. A State institution under the jurisdiction of the Ministry of Culture.

Academic Year: October to June.

Language of Instruction: French.

Degrees and Diplomas: Certificat d'Aptitude à l'Enseignement musical; Certificat supérieur d'Animation culturelle.

Academic Staff: c. 50 (30).

Student Enrolment: c. 300.

6577 **INSTITUT NATIONAL SUPÉRIEUR DE L'ÉDUCATION POPULAIRE ET DE SPORT**

Stade Iba Mar Diop, Dakar
Telephone: 21-33-84
Directeur: Gérard Diamé (1982-)

Education
Physical Education

Founded 1979. A State institution under the jurisdiction of the Ministry of Education.

Arrangements for co-operation with similar institutions in: Cameroon; Congo; Côte d'Ivoire; Canada.

Academic Year: October to July (October-February; March-July).

Admission Requirements: Secondary school certificate (baccalauréat) or recognized equivalent, and entrance examination.

Fees (Francs C.F.A.): 50,000 per annum.

Language of Instruction: French.

Degrees and Diplomas: Diplôme d'études universitaires générales (D.E.U.G.), 2 yrs. Licence, 1 further yr. Maîtrise, 1 yr after Licence. Certificat d'Aptitude au Professorat d'Education physique et sportive (C.A.P.E.P.S.), 1 yr afterMaîtrise. Also Certificat d'Inspecteur, 2 yrs after Maîtrise.

Library: Central Library.

Academic Staff, 1986-87: 12 (14).

Student Enrolment, 1986-87:

	Men	Women	Total
Of the country	91	5	96
Of other countries	7	4	11
Total	98	9	107

6578 **CENTRE DE PERFECTIONNEMENT EN LANGUE ANGLAISE**

Dakar

English

6579 **ÉCOLE NATIONALE DES DOUANES**

Avenue Carde, Rue René Ndiaye, Dakar
Telephone: 22-45-73

Customs and Excise

Founded 1970.

6580 **ÉCOLE NATIONALE DE POLICE ET DE LA FORMATION PERMANENTE**

Boulevard Habib Bourguiba, B.P. 5025, Dakar-Fann
Telephone: 22-28-18; 23-06-76

Police Studies

6581 **ÉCOLE INTER-ETATS DES SCIENCES ET DE MÉDECINE VÉTÉRINAIRES**

Dakar-Fann

Veterinary Medicine

6582 **INSTITUT NATIONAL D'ADMINISTRATION ET DE MAGISTRATURE**

Rue Dial-Diop, Dakar

Administration (including Legal Administration)

6583 **INSTITUT SÉNÉGALO-BRITANNIQUE D'ENSEIGNEMENT DE L'ANGLAIS**

B.P. 35, Rue du 18 juin, Dakar-Fann

English

SOMALIA

6584 ***JAAMACADDA UMMADDA SOOLAALIYEED**
Somali National University
P.O. Box 15, Mogadiscio
Telephone: 25035
President: Abdel Fareh Hassan (1987-)

F. of Law
F. of Economics
F. of Agriculture
F. of Education
F. of Veterinary Medicine
F. of Medicine
F. of Industrial Chemistry
F. of Geology
F. of Languages
F. of Journalism
F. of Engineering

Founded 1954 as institute of law, economics, and social sciences. Became Istituto Universitario della Somalia 1959, Università nazionale della Somalia 1970, and acquired present title 1979. A State institution.

Academic Year: July to June (July-December; January-June).

Admission Requirements: Secondary school certificate and entrance examination.

Languages of Instruction: Italian, English, and Arabic.

Degrees and Diplomas: Laurea, Doctor.

Academic Staff: c. 550.

Student Enrolment: c. 4650.

SOUTH AFRICA

Universities

6585 ***UNIVERSITY OF CAPE TOWN**

Private Bag, Rondebosch 7700
Telex: 57-22208
Telephone: 650-9111
Vice-Chancellor: Stuart John Saunders (1981-)
Registrar: Hugh Theodore Amoore

F. of Arts
Dean: R.H. Pheiffer; *staff* 126 (22)
F. of Commerce *staff* 86 (19)
F. of Education
Dean: I. de V. Heyns; *staff* 22 (5)
F. of Engineering
Dean: J.B. Martin; *staff* 62 (67)
F. of Fine Art and Architecture
Dean: J.W. Rabie; *staff* 44 (22)
F. of Law
Dean: Ernest Jackson Whitaker *staff* 26 (10)
F. of Medicine (including Pharmacy)
Dean: G. Dall; *staff* 525 (480)
F. of Music
; *staff* 29 (31)
F. of Science
Dean: V.C. Moran; *staff* 177 (59)
F. of Social Science and Humanities
Dean: I. Bunting; *staff* 100 (67)
Ce. for African Studies
Director: Ms M. Simons
Energy Research I.
Director: Ryszard Karol Dutkiewicz
I. of Child Health
Director: Hans de Villiers Heese
I. of Oceanography
Director: G.B. Brundit
I. of Marine Law
Director: D.G. Devine
I. of Criminology
Director: D. van Zyl Smit
I. for Advanced Studies in Philosophy
Director: Z.R. van Straaten
I. of Molecular Biology
Directors: C. von Holt;D.R. Woods
I. of Photogrammetry and Remote Sensing
Director: L.P. Adams
I. of African Ornithology
Director: W.R. Siegfried
Mining Research Ce. for Heart Disease and Immunology
Director: E.B. Dowdle
Ce. for Intergroup Studies (Race and Language)
Director: H.W. van der Merwe
Ce. for Extramural Studies
Director: Clive John Millar; *staff* 6
Also *c.* 20 Research Units and Groups.

Founded 1829 as college by local community, acquired official status 1873. Became university by Act of Parliament 1916 and granted Charter 1918. An autonomous institution receiving financial support (70%) from the State.Open to all who meet the academic requirements, regardless of colour, race, sex or religion. Governing bodies: the University Council, comprising 26 members, including 2 observers from the student body; the University Senate. Limited residential facilities for academic staff and for *c.* 2200 students.

Academic Year: February to December (February-April; April-June; July-September; September-December).

Admission Requirements: Matriculation Certificate or certificate of exemption issued by the Joint Matriculation Board.

Fees (Rand): Tuition, 2000-3000 per annum.

Language of Instruction: English.

Degrees and Diplomas: Bachelor of–Arts, B.A., in various fields; Science, B.Sc., in various fields; Business Science, B.Bus.Sc.; Library and Information Science, B.Bibl.; Commerce, B.Com.; Laws, Ll.B.; Social Science, B.Soc.Sc.; Primary Education, B.Prim.Ed.; Music, M.Mus., 3-5 yrs; Medicine and Surgery, M.B., Ch.B.; Architecture, B.Arch., 6 yrs. Bachelor with Honours (Hons.), in most fields, 1 further yr. Bachelor of Education, B.Ed., 1 yr after first degree. Master, in various fields, 1-2 further yrs. Doctorates, 1-2 yrs. Also undergraduate and postgraduate diplomas.

Library: J.W. Jagger Library, 7 branch libraries, total 761,000 vols.

Special Facilities (Museums, etc.): Herbarium; Irma Stern Museum (Fine Art Collection); Archaeological Museum; P.A. Wagner Museum (Mineralogical and Geological Specimens).

Publications: General and Faculty Prospectuses (annually); Mathematics Colloquium (annually); Research Report (annually); UCT News (8 times a year); Jagger Journal (annually); Acta Juridica (annually); Bolus Herbarium Contributions (annually); Oceanography Yearbook; Social Dynamics (biannually); Centre for African Studies Communications (annually); Studies in History of Cape Town (annually).

Academic Staff, 1986-87:

Rank	Full-time	Part-time
Professors	154	1
Associate Professors	121	–
Senior Lecturers	400	267
Lecturers	343	299
Assistant Lecturers	112	37
Others	73	178
Total	1203	782

Student Enrolment, 1986-87:

	Men	Women	Total
Of the country	7487	4901	12,388*

*Including 441 foreign students.

6586 **UNIVERSITY OF DURBAN-WESTVILLE**

Private Bag X54001, Durban 4000
Cables: Inkol
Telephone: (031) 82-1211
Rector: J.J.C. Greyling (1981-88)
Registrar (Administrative): G.E. Heystek

F. of Arts (including Political Science and Library Science)
Dean: S.S. Nadvi
F. of Commerce and Administration
Dean: F. Calitz
F. of Education
Dean: R.W. Jardine
F. of Engineering
Dean: A.M. Guthrie
F. of Health Sciences
Dean: D.K. Turnbull
F. of Law
Dean: W.A. Ramsden
F. of Science
Dean: A.L. du Preez
F. of Theology
Dean: N.A.C. Heuer
I. of Social and Economic Research
Director: J. Butler-Adam
Extension D.

Founded 1961 as university college under aegis of the University of South Africa, became university 1972. An autonomous institution receiving financial support from the State. Governing bodies: the University Council, comprising 20 members; the University Senate. Residential facilities for *c.* 1200 students.

Academic Year: January/February to December (January-April; April-June; July-December).

Admission Requirements: Matriculation Certificate or certificate of exemption issued by the Joint Matriculation Board.

Language of Instruction: English.

Degrees and Diplomas: Baccalaureus-Artium, B.A., in various fields; Scientia, B.Sc., in various fields; Commercii, B.Com.; Administrationis, B.Admin.; Iuris, B.Iuris; Legum, LL.B.; Bibliothecologiae, B.Bibl.; Musicae, B.Mus.; Paedagogiae, B,Paed.; Procurationis, B.Proc.; Theologiae, B.Theol.; Bachelor of–Dental Therapy; Oral Health; Business Science, B.Bus.Sc.; Engineering, B.Eng.; Accountancy, B.Acc.; Home Economics, B.Home Econ.; Pharmacy, B.Pharm.; Medical Science, B.Med.Sc.; Physiotherapy, B.Physio.; Optometry, B.Optom.; Speech and Hearing Therapy; Occupational Therapy, 3-4 yrs. Bachelor with Honours (Hons.), in most fields, 1 further yr. Master, a further 1-2 yrs. Doctorates, 1-2 yrs. Also undergraduate and postgraduate diplomas.

Library: c. 150,000 vols.

Special Facilities (Museums, etc.): Documentation Centre on Indian Culture and History.

Publications: University Journal (annually); Journal of the Faculty of Education (annually); The Column (2-3 times a year); Publications by the Staff.

Press or Publishing House: University of Durban-Westville Press.

Academic Staff: c. 340 (90).

Student Enrolment: c. 5000.

6587 **UNIVERSITY OF FORT HARE**

Private Bag X1314, Alice 5700, Ciskei
Telex: CX 242193
Telephone: 0404-32011

Rector and Vice-Chancellor (Acting): J.B. Gardner (1990-)
Registrar (Academic): G.G. Antrobus

F. of Theology
Dean: G. Thom; *staff* 7
F. of Law
Dean: J. Labuschagne; *staff* 12
F. of Arts
Dean: J.M. Els; *staff* 80 (2)
F. of Education
Dean: B.R.G. Lindeque; *staff* 24
F. of Science
Dean: J.R. Seretio; *staff* 74 (3)
F. of Economics
Dean: S.S. Human; *staff* 15
F. of Agriculture
Dean: F.J.C. Swanepoel; *staff* 39 (3)
D. of Nursing
Head: Mrs. L. Evertse; *staff* 9 (1)
D. for External Studies
Head: H. Antrobus; *staff* 1
D. of Agricultural and Rural Development
Director: A.O. de Lange; *staff* 10 (1)
Fort Hare I. of Management (FHIM)
Director: M. Kotze; *staff* 5 (1)
Ce. for Xhosa Literature
Director: G.T. Sirayi; *staff* 12
Academic Development Ce.
Director: A. Havenga; *staff* 12

Founded 1916 as South African Native College by the United Free Church of Scotland. Affiliated to Rhodes University 1951-59. Transferred to Department of Bantu Education 1960. Acquired present status and title 1970. Governing bodies: the University Council; the University Senate. Residential facilities for academic staff and students.

Academic Year: January to December (January-April; April-June; July-September; September-December).

Admission Requirements: Matriculation Certificate or certificate of exemption issued by the Joint Matriculation Board.

Fees (Rand): 5500-6000 per annum.

Language of Instruction: English.

Degrees and Diplomas: Baccalaureus-Artium, B.A., in various fields; Scientia, B.Sc., in various fields; Curationis, nursing, B.Cur.; Commercii, B.Comm; Iuris, B.Iuris; Legum, LL.B.; Paedagogiae, B.Paed.; Procurationis, B.Proc.; Theologiae, B.Theol. Bachelor with Honours (Hons.), in most fields, 1 further yr. Master, a further 1-2 yrs. Doctorates, 1-2yrs. Also undergraduate and postgraduate diplomas.

Library: Central Library (Howard Pimm collection of Africana).

Special Facilities (Museums, etc.): F.S. Malan Museum; De Beers Centenary Art Gallery.

Publications: Papers; Fort Harian (3 times a year).

Academic Staff, 1989:

Rank	Full-time	Part-time
Professors	38	1
Associate Professors	4	–
Senior Lecturers	70	2
Lecturers	86	5
Junior Lecturers	29	5
Total	227	13

Student Enrolment, 1989:

	Men	Women	Total
Of the country	2105	1916	4021
Of other countries	52	61	113
otal	2157	1977	4134*

*Also 795 external students and students by correspondence.

6588 **MEDICAL UNIVERSITY OF SOUTHERN AFRICA-MEDUNSA**

P.O. Medunsa 0204 Transvaal
Telex: 3-2580 SA
Telephone: (12) 529-4111
Fax: (12) 582323

Vice-Chancellor and Principal: L.T. Taljaard (1984-)
Chief Director: G.J. de Korte

F. of Medicine
Dean: T. Heyl; *staff* 205
F. of Dentistry
Dean: F.D. Verwayen; *staff* 40
F. of Veterinary Science
Dean: N.C. Owen; *staff* 39
F. of Basic Sciences
Dean: E.C. Zingu; *staff* 30

Founded 1976. An autonomous institution receiving financial support from the central government. Governing body: the University Council, comprising 28 members: the University Senate, comprising 81 members. Residential facilities for c. 1830 students.

Academic Year: January to November (January-May; May-November).

Admission Requirements: Matriculation Certificate or certificate of exemption issued by the Joint Matricultation Board.

Fees (Rand): c. 2800 per annum.

Language of Instruction: English.

Degrees and Diplomas: Bachelor of–Science (Medical), B.Sc.(Med); Science, B.Sc.; Nursing Education and Nursing Administration, B.Cur. (I and A), 3 yrs; Occupational Therapy, B.Occ.Ther.; Science in Dietetrics, B.Sc.(Diet); Science in Physiotherapy, B.Sc.(Physiotherapy), 4 yrs; Nursing Science and Art, B.Cur., 4 ½ yrs; Dental Surgery, B.Ch.D.; Medicine and Surgery, M.B., Ch.B.; Veterinary Medicine and Surgery, B.V.M.Ch., 6 yrs. Masters. Doctorates.

Library: Medunsa Library.

Academic Staff, 1990:

Rank	Full-time	Part-time
Professors	54	
Associate Professors	27	–
Senior Lecturers	96	–
Lecturers	134	113
Junior Lecturers	10	
Total	321	113

Student Enrolment, 1990:

	Men	Women	Total
Of the country	1245	720	1965
Of other countries	32	20	52
Total	1277	740	2017

6589 **UNIVERSITY OF NATAL**

King George V. Avenue, Durban 4001
Telephone: 63320

F. of Architecture and Allied Disciplines
F. of Arts
F. of Science
F. of Education
F. of Law
F. of Commerce

F. of Engineering (Durban only)
F. of Agriculture
F. of Medicine (for non-white students only) (Durban only)
F. of Social Sciences
Also 6 Associated Research Institutes.

Founded 1909 by Act of Parliament as university college, became independent university 1949. An autonomous institution with centres in Durban and Pietermaritzburg receiving financial support from the State. Governing bodies: the University Council; the University Senate. Residential facilities for *c.* 1960 students.

Academic Year: February to November.

Admission Requirements: Matriculation Certificate or certificate of exemption issued by the Joint Matriculation Board.

Language of Instruction: English.

Degrees and Diplomas: Bachelor of–Arts, B.A.; Agricultural Management, M.Agric.Mgt.; Science, B.Sc., in various fields; Commerce, B.Comm.; Social Science, B.Soc.Sc.; Accountancy, B.Acc.; Music, B.Mus.; Procurationis, B.Proc., 3-4 yrs; Architecture, B.Arch., 6 yrs; Medicine, M.B.Ch.B., 7 yrs. Bachelor with Honours (Hons.), in most fields, 1 further yr. Bachelor of Education, B.Ed., 1 yr after first degree. Bachelor of Laws, LL.B., 3 yrs after first degree. Master, in various fields, 1-2 further yrs. Doctorates, 1-2 yrs. Also postgraduate diplomas.

Library: Total, *c.* 338,000 vols.

Academic Staff: c. 820.

Student Enrolment: c. 9000.

6590 **NORTH UNIVERSITEIT VAN DIE NOORDE**
UNIVERSITY OF THE NORTH
Private Bag X1106, Sovenga 0727
Cables: unikol
Telex: 322798
Telephone: (01522) 43100

F. of Arts
F. of Social Sciences (including Nursing)
F. of Mathematics and Natural Sciences
F. of Law
F. of Economics and Administration
F. of Education
F. of Agriculture
F. of Theology
Branch at Qwaqwa.

Founded 1959 as college to serve the Tsonga, Sotho, Vedda, Xitsonga and Tswana communities. Acquired present status and title 1970. An autonomous institution receiving financial support from the State. Governing bodies: the University Council; the University Senate. Residential facilities for *c.* 30 men and *c.* 15 women students.

Academic Year: February to November (February-June; August-November).

Admission Requirements: Matriculation Certificate or certificate of exemption issued by the Joint Matriculation Board.

Language of Instruction: English.

Degrees and Diplomas: Baccalaureus-Curationis, B.Cur I et A; Rationis, B.R.; Iuris, B.Iuris; Procurationis, B.Proc.; Bachelor of–Arts, B.A.; Arts in Social Work, B.A. (S.W.); Library-Information Science, B.Bibl.; Science, B.Sc.; Pharmacy, B.Pharm.; Optometry, B.Optom.; Science in Medical Laboratory Sciences, B.Sc. (Med.Lab. Sci.); Commerce, B.Comm.; Administration, B.Admin.; Arts in Pedagogy, B.A. Paed.; Commerce in Pedagogy, B.Comm.Paed.; Agriculture in Pedagogy, B.Agric.Paed.; Theology, B.Th.; Agricultural Management, B.Agric.Admin.; Science in Agriculture, B.Sc.Agric., 3-4 yrs. Doctorates.

Library: c. 131,570 vols.

Academic Staff: c. 320.

Student Enrolment: c. 4180.

6591 **UNIVERSITEIT VAN DIE ORANJE-VRYSTAAT**
UNIVERSITY OF THE ORANGE FREE STATE
P.O. Box 339, Bloemfontein 9300
Telex: 52666
Telephone: (51) 401-9111
Fax: (51) 401-2117
Rektor en Vise-Kanselier: F.P. Retief
Vice-Rectors: C.D. Roode; E.G. Boonstra

F. of Arts (including Political Science)
Dean: A.H. Snyman; *staff* 130 (13)
F. of Natural Sciences (including Computer Sciences)
Dean: H.J. Potgieter; *staff* 131 (21)
F. of Social Sciences
Dean: R.A. Viljoen; *staff* 55 (4)
F. of Education
Dean: P.F. Theron; *staff* 32 (10)
F. of Commerce and Public Administration
Dean: W.J. Joubert; *staff* 41 (2)
F. of Law
Dean: D.W. Morkel; *staff* 23 (3)
F. of Agriculture (including Animal Husbandry)
Dean: J.C. Novello; *staff* 51
F. of Medicine (including Pharmacy)
Dean: G.M. Potgieter; *staff* 181 (61)
F. of Theology
Dean: P.C. Potgieter; *staff* 16 (3)

Founded 1855 by Sir George Grey and established as university college 1904, became university under present title 1950. An autonomous institution receiving financial support from the State. Governing bodies: the University Council; the University Senate. Residential facilities for maximum 3190 students in hostels.

Academic Year: February to December (February-March; April-June; July-September; October-December).

Admission Requirements: Matriculation Certificate or certificate of exemption issued by the Joint Matriculation Board.

Language of Instruction: Afrikaans. English (when applicable).

Degrees and Diplomas: Bachelor of–Arts, B.A., in various fields; Science, B.Sc., in various fields; Social Science, B.Soc.Sc.; Commerce, B.Com.; Personnel Guidance, B.P.L.; Administration, B.Admin.; Medical Science, B.Med.Sc.; Economics, B.Econ.; Agriculture, B.Agric.; Radiography, B.Rad.; Library Science, B.Bibl.; Accountancy, B. Compt.; Baccalaureus-Iuris, B.Iuris; Civilis Iuris, B.C.Iur.; Procurationis, B.Proc., 3-4 yrs; Architecture, B.Arch., 4 ½ yrs; Medicine and Surgery, M.B., Ch.B., 6 yrs. Bachelor with Honours (Hons.), in most fields, 1 further yr. Bachelor of Education, B.Ed., 1 yr after first degree. Bachelor of Theology, B.Th., 3 yrs after first degree. Bachelor of Laws, LL.B., 2-3 yrs after first degree. Master, in various fields, 1 further yr. Doctorates 1-2 yrs. Also postgraduate diplomas.

Library: Central Library, 436,341 vols.

Publications: Summary of Thesis and Essays, part 14; Acta Academica, part 13.

Press or Publishing House: University Press.

Academic Staff, 1989-90:

Rank	Full-time	Part-time
Professore	108	1
Mede-professore (Associate Professors)	8	–
Senior Lektore	171	10
Lektore	187	88
Junior Lektore	15	13
Total	489	112

Student Enrolment, 1989-90:

	Men	Women	Total
Of the country	4971	4168	9139
Of other countries	37	41	78
Total	5008	4209	9217

6592 **UNIVERSITEIT PORT ELIZABETH**
UNIVERSITY OF PORT ELIZABETH
P.O. Box 1600, Port Elizabeth 6000
Telex: 74-7342SA
Telephone: 5311-928
Fax: 5311-280
Principal and Vice-Chancellor: H.F. Redelinghuys (1985-)
Registrar (Academic): J. Coetzee

F. of Arts (including Music and Nursing)
Dean: J.M. Kirsten; *staff* 88
F. of Science
Dean: A. Goosen; *staff* 67
F. of Education
Dean: C.A. Taylor; *staff* 24 (9)
F. of Economics (including Architecture)
Dean: O.P.J. Immelman; *staff* 36 (7)
F. of Law
Dean: C. van Loggerenberg; *staff* 12 (2)

I. for Science and Mathematics Education
Director: D.J. Kriel; *staff* 1 (2)
I. for Planning Research
Director: E.T. Heath; *staff* 5
Uranium Chemistry Research Ut.
Director: J.G.H. du Preez; *staff* 1 (4)
Ce. for Continuing Education
Director: J. Erwee;; *staff* 12
I. for Coastal Research
Director: B.L. Robertson
Also 2 Teachers' Colleges.

Founded 1964 by Act of Parliament and financially supported by the State. Governing bodies: the University Council; the University Senate. Residential facilities for *c.* 1200 students.

Academic Year: February to November (February-June; July-November).

Admission Requirements: Matriculation Certificate or certificate of exemption issued by the Joint Matriculation Board.

Fees (Rand): *c.* 2100 per annum, according to degree; postgraduate: first year, 1750; subsequent years, 330.

Languages of Instruction: Afrikaans and English.

Degrees and Diplomas: Bachelor of–Architecture, 2 yrs. Baccalaureus–Artium, B.A.; Scientiae, B.Sc.; Commercii, B.Com.; Juris, B.Juris, 3 yrs; Artium (Educationis), B.A.(Ed); Musicae, B.Mus.; Musicae (Educationis), B.Mus.(Ed); Artium in Social Work, B.A.(S.W.); Curationis, B.Cur.; Pharmaciae, B.Pharm.; Primae Educationis, B.Prim.Ed.; Commercii (Educationis), B.Com.(Ed.); Commercii (Rationum), B.Com.(Rationum); Scienciae in Quantity Surveying, B.Sc (Q.S.); Procurationis, B.Proc., 4 rs; Scientiae in Building Management, B.Sc.(Bdg.Man.) 5 yrs. Baccalaureus with Honours (Hons.), in most fields, 1 further yr. Baccalaureus Educationis, B.Ed.; Baccalaueus Artium (Human Movement Science), B.A. (Human Movement Science), 1 yr after first degree. Baccalaureus Legum, LL.B., 2 yrs after first degree. Magister, in various fields, 1-2 further yrs. Doctor–Philosophiae, D.Philo; Litterarum, D.Litt.; Musicae, D.Mus.; Curationis, D.Cur.; Scientiae, D.Sc.; Educationis, D.Ed., 1-2 yrs. Also diplomas.

Library: Central Library, *c.* 300,000 vols.

Publications: Building Management Journal (annually); Labour Turnover in Port Elizabeth (annually); Obiter (annually); UPE Focus (biannually); Publications Series; Institute for Planning Research publications.

Academic Staff, 1990:

Rank	Full-time	Part-time
Professors	64	–
Associate Professors	12	–
Senior Lecturers	68	–
Lecturers	96	209
Junior Lecturers	14	–
Total	254	209

Student Enrolment, 1990:

	Men	Women	Total
Of the country	2075	1650	3725
Of other countries	35	40	75
Total	2110	1690	3800*

*Also 1100 part-time students.

6593 **POTCHEFSTROOMSE UNIVERSITEIT VIR CHRISTELIKE HOËR ONDERWYS**

Potchefstroom University for Christian Higher Education
Private Bag, Potchefstroom 2520, Transvaal
Cables: puk
Telex: 4-21363 SA
Telephone: 22112
Rektor en Vise-Kanselier: T. van der Walt

F. of Arts
Dean: L.A. Gouws
F. of Natural Sciences
Dean: P. van Eldik
F. of Engineering
Dean: R.C. Everson
F. of Pharmacy
Dean: A.P.G. Goossens
F. of Law
Dean: C.R. de Beer
F. of Theology
Dean: J.L. Helberg
F. of Education
Dean: J.J. de Wet
F. of Economics
Dean: J.J.D. Havenga
I. for Biokinetics
Director: G.L. Strydom
I. of Leisure Studies
Director: G.J.L. Scholtz
I. of Linguistic and Literary Research
Director: H.G.W. du Plessis
I. of Planning and Development
Director: J.L. Schutte
I. of Politics and African Studies
Director: C.J. Maritz
I. for the Provincial Press in South Africa
Director: A. Juyn
I. of Psychotherapy and Guidance
Director: P.E. van Jaarsveld
I. of Reformational Studies
Director: B.J. van der Walt
I. of Research in Children's Literature
Director: C.A. Lohann
I. of South African Music
Director: H.P.A. Coetzee
I. of Ecological Research
Director: J.J.P. van Wyk
I. of Petrochemical Research
Director: J.G. van Nierop
I. of Industrial Pharmacy
Director: A.P. Lotter
I. of Pedology
Director: H.J. von M. Harmse
I. of Physiological Research
Director: Jurg J. van der Walt
I. of Futures Studies
Director: C.H. Boshoff
I. of Management Development
Director: J.J.L. Coetzee; *staff* 6
I. of Manpower and Management Research
Director: P.C. Schutte
Bureau for Lifelong Education
Also 17 Constituent Bureaux and Units.

Founded 1869, became constitutent college of University of South Africa 1921, and by Act of Parliament became independent university 1951. An autonomous institution receiving financial support from the State. Governing bodies: the University Council, comprising 16 members; the University Senate. Residential facilities for students in 15 hostels.

Academic Year: February to December (February-April; April-June; July-December).

Admission Requirements: Matriculation Certificate or certificate of exemption issued by the Joint Matriculation Board.

Language of Instruction: Afrikaans.

Degrees and Diplomas: Baccalaureus-Artium, in various fields; Scientiae, in various fields; Commerce, B.Com.; Law, B.Jur.; Bibliothecologiae; Pharmaciae; in Engineering; Commercii; Accountancy; Primariae Educationis; Musicae; Procurationis, B.Proc., 3-4 yrs. Bachelor with Honours (Hons.), in most fields, 1 further yr. Bachelor of Education, B.Ed., 1 yr after first degree. Bachelor of Laws, LL.B., 2 yrs after first degree. Bachelor of Theology, Th.B., 4 yrs after B.A. Master, in various fields, 1-2 further yrs. Doctorates, 1-2 yrs. Also undergraduate and postgraduatediplomas.

Library: Ferdinand Postma Library, *c.* 500,000 vols.

Publications: Die PU-kaner (8 times a year); PU-kaner Skakelblad (3 times a year).

Academic Staff: c. 590.

Student Enrolment: c. 8000.

6594 **UNIVERSITEIT VAN PRETORIA**

University of Pretoria
Lynnwoodroad, Hillcrest, Pretoria 0083
Cables: puniv
Telex: 322723
Telephone: (012) 4209111
Fax: 432185
Electronic mail: uninet
Onderkanselier en Rektor: D.M. Joubert
Vise-Rektor: P. Smit

F. of Arts (Afrikaans, Fine Arts and History of Art, Drama, English, Criminology, Human Movement Science, Music, Semitic Languages Sociology, Philosophy, Anthropology and Archaeology, African Languages, Information Science, German, Greek, Latin, Social Work, French, Psychology, Speech Therapy and Audiology, History and Cultural History, andPolitical Science and International Politics)
Dean: W.C. Van Wyk; *staff* 216 (37)
F. of Science (Zoology, Landscape Architecture, Architecture, Entomology, Domestic Science and Dietetics, Computer Science, and Building Management)
Dean: N. Sauer; *staff* 184 (13)
F. of Agricultural Sciences
Dean: T. Erasmus; *staff* 56 (1)
F. of Law
Dean: D.J. Joubert; *staff* 33 (5)
F. of Theology A (Reformed Church of Africa)
Dean: J.P. Oberholzer; *staff* 13 (1)
F. of Theology B (Dutch Reformed Church)
Dean: W.S. Prinsloo; *staff* 16 (1)
F. of Economic and Management Sciences
Dean: J.J. Stadler; *staff* 115 (20)
F. of Veterinary Science
Dean: R.I. Coubrough; *staff* 83 (2)
F. of Education
Dean: M.J. Bondesio; *staff* 40 (2)
F. of Medicine (including Nursing, Pharmacy, and Obstetrics and Gynaecology)
Dean: J.V. Van Der Merwe; *staff* 465 (69)
F. of Dentistry
Dean: S.T. Zietsman; *staff* 73 (6)
F. of Engineerinig (Production and Systems, Electrical, Agricultural, Mechanical, Chemical, Mining Civil, and Material Science andMetallurgical Engineering; and Surveying and Town and Regional Planning)
Dean: Jag Malherbe; *staff* 133 (5)
I. for Strategic Studies
Director: M. Hough; *staff* 1 (1)
Sport Research and Training I.
Director: J.L. Botha; *staff* – (1)
I. of Chromatography
I. for Geological Research on the Bushvild Complex
Director: G. Von Gruenewaldt *staff* 5
Mammal Research I.
Director: J.D. Skinner; *staff* 6 (1)
Margaretha Mes I. for Seed Research
Director: H.A. van de Venter; *staff* 3 (1)
South African I. for Agricultural Extension
Director: G.H. Duvel; *staff* – (1)
I. for Missiological Research
Director: D. Crafford *staff* 1 (1)
Bureau for Economic Policy and Analysis
Director: BN.J. Schoeman; *staff* 2
Bureau for Financial Analysis
Director: A.P. Zevenbergen; *staff* 3 (1)
Hans Snyckers I. for the Study of Disease Phenomena Peculiar to Southern Africa
Director: W.J.H. Vermaak; *staff* – (1)
Glaxo I. for Clinical Pharmacology
Director: De K. Sommers; *staff* – (1)
Atomic Energy I. for Life Sciences
Director: I.C. Dormehl; *staff* 6 (1)
I. for Pathology
Director: I.W. Simpson; *staff* – (1)
Ce. for Stomatological Research
Director: W.J.C. coetzee; *staff* 2
Carl and Emily Fuchs I. for Micro-Electronics
Manager: W.R. Malan; *staff* 30
Also Extension after-hours tuition programme in Witbank.

Founded 1908 by Transvaal government, became separate university college 1910 and autonomous university 1930. Financially supported by the State. Governing bodies: the University Council, comprising 26 members; the University Senate. Residential facilities for 4339 students.

Arrangements for Joint Scientific Programmes with: Ben Gurion University, Israel; University of Chili.

Academic Year: January to November (January-June; July-November).

Admission Requirements: Matriculation Certificate or certificate of exemption issued by the Joint Matriculation Board.

Fees (Rand): 2890-4685 per annum; postgraduate, 1110-4660.

Languages of Instruction: Afrikaans (Faculty of Veterinary Science, Afrikaans and english).

Degrees and Diplomas: Bachelor of–Arts, B.A., in various fields; Science, B.Sc., in various fields; Commerce, B.Com.; Radiography, B.Rad.; Library and Information Science, B.Library Science; Logopedics and Audiology, B.Log.; Primary Education, B.Prim.Ed.; Music, B.Mus.; Home Economics, B.Hom Economics; Dietetics, B.Diet.; Administration, B.Admin.; Physiotherapy, B.Phys.T.; Occupational Therapy, B.Occ.Ther.; Pharmacy, B.Pharm.; Engineering, B.Eng.; Town and Regional Planning, B.Town & Reg.Plan.; Land Surveying, B.Land. Surv.; Landscape Architecture, B.L.; Baccalaureus-Legum Civilium, B.L.C.; Iuris, B.Iur.; Procurationis, B.Proc., Nursing, B.Cur. 3-4 yrs; Architecture, B.Arch.; Veterinary Science, B.V.Sc.; Dentistry, B.Ch.D., 5-5 ½ yrs; Medicine and Surgery, M.B.Ch.B., 6 yrs. Bachelor with Honours (Hons.), in most fields, 1 further yr. Bachelor of Education, B.Ed., 1 yr after first degree. Bachelor of Divinity, B.D., 3 yrs after B.A. Baccalaureus Legum, LL.B., 2 yrs after first degree. Master, invarious fields, 1-4 further yrs. Doctorates, 1 yr. Also undergraduate and postgraduate diplomas, 1-4 yrs.

Library: Total, *c.* 761,870 vols.

Special Facilities (Museums, etc.): Anton van Wouw House Museum; Van Tilburg Collection; University Art Collection.

Publications: Tukkiewerf (quarterly); Jaarverslag, Tukkievaria (10 a year); Perdiby (weekly students' newspaper); Pulikasies van die Universitiet van Pretoria/Nuwe reeks (Publications of ther University of Pretoria-New Series) (I) Research (annually); Ad-destinatum: Gedenkboek van die Universiteit van Pretoria, Opvoedkundige studies (Educational Studies, 3-4 issues annually); Openbare Fakultietslesings (irregular); Huldigingsbundels (irregular); trek (Students' magazine, annually); Kgwerano (irregular).

Academic Staff, 1990:

Rank	Full-time	Part-time
Dekane	9	3
Adjunk-Dekane	1	2
Professore/Hoofde	146	4
Professore	166	6
Buitengewoone Professore	1	20
Direkteur	3	5
Mede-Professore	155	4
Senior Lektore	358	36
Senior Dosente	–	18
Lektore	289	18
Junior Lektore	63	–
Dosente	3	340
Junior Dosents	–	76
Senior Navorsingsbeampte	32	2
Navorsingsbeampte	21	1
Assistent Navorsingsbeampte	11	2
Kliniese Dosente	4	4
Total	1262	541

Student Enrolment, 1990:

	Men	Women	Total
Of the country	13,419	9643	23,062
Of other countries	250	120	370
Total	13,669	9763	23,432*

*Also 5853 external students.

6595 **RANDSE AFRIKAANSE UNIVERSITEIT**

P.O. Box 524, Johannesburg 2000
Cables: rauniv
Telex: 4245426 SA
Telephone: (11) 489-2911
Fax: (11) 489-2191

Rektor en Vise-Kanselier: C.F. Crouse (1987-)
Registrar: H.J. Kruger

F. of Arts
Dean: P.M.S. von Staden; *staff* 115 (40)
F. of Education (including Nursing)
Dean: P.J. Maree; *staff* 40 (21)
F. of Engineering
Dean: P van der Merwe; *staff* 32 (17)
F. of Science (including Optometry)
Dean: G.H. de Swardt; *staff* 73 (38)

F. of Economics and Commerce
Dean: W. F. Rademeyer; *staff* 59 (38)
F. of Law
Dean: J.C. vd Walt; *staff* 21 (10)
I. for Child and Adult Guidance
Director: A.S. du Toit; *staff* 15 (13)
I. of American Studies
Director: C.F. Nöffke; *staff* 4
I. of Energy Studies
Director: D.J. Kotzé; *staff* 2
Ce. for the Study of Islam Science
Head: J.A. Naudé; *staff* 1 (1)
Bureau for Lifelong Education
Head: B.J. du Toit; *staff* 2
Also 2 Teachers' Colleges.

Founded 1966 by Act of Parliament, first students admitted 1968. Financially supported by the State. Governing bodies: the University Council; the University Senate. Residential facilities for 2205 students.

Academic Year: January to November (January-June; July-November).

Admission Requirements: Matriculation Certificate or certificate of exemption issued by the Joint Matriculation Board.

Fees (Rand): Undergraduate, 1369; Honours, 1180; postgraduate, 944.

Language of Instruction: Afrikaans.

Degrees and Diplomas: Bachelor of–Arts, B.A., in various fields; Science, B.Sc., in various fields; Commerce, B.Com., in various fields; Optometry, B.Optom.; Library Science, B.Bibl.; Primary Education, B.Prim.Ed.; Engineering, B.Eng., Baccalaureus Procurationis, B.Proc., 3-4 yrs; Nursing, B.Cur., 4 ½ yrs. Bachelor with Honours (Hons.) in most fields, 1 further yr. Bachelor of Education, B.Ed., 1 yr after first degree. Baccalaureus Legum, LL.B., 2 yrs after first degree. Master, in various fields, 1-2 further yrs. Higher Education Diploma, H.O.D., 4 yrs. Doctorates, 1-2 yrs. Postgraduate diplomas.

Library: 335,959 vols.

Special Facilities (Museums, etc.): Museums: Geology, Zoology and Anthropology. Art Collection.

Publications: Quarterly Econometric Forecast; USA Economy (monthly); Amerikaanse Oorsig (biannually); Midde-Ooste in die Nuus (biweekly); Journal for Islamic Studies (annually); Higher Education Bulletin (bimonthly); Aambeeld: OpinionMagazine (quarterly).

Academic Staff, 1988-89:

Rank	Full-time	Part-time
Professors	127	91
Associate Professors	39	24
Senior Lecturers	78	44
Lecturers	88	19
Junior Lecturers	1714	–
Total	349	178

Student Enrolment, 1988-89:

	Men	Women	Total
Of the country	4612	3898	8510

6596 **RHODES UNIVERSITY**

P.O. Box 94, Grahamstown, Cape Province 6140
Cables: rhodescol
Telex: 24-4219 SA
Telephone: (0461) 22023
Fax: (0461) 25049
Electronic mail: postmaster @ f4. n494. z5. fidonet. org
Vice-Chancellor: D.S. Henderson (1975-)
Registrar: K.S. Hunt

F. of Arts (Human Movement Studies, Anthropology, History, Geography, English, French, Afrikaans, African Languages, Classics, Politics, Music, Fine Art, Journalism, Linguistics, Philosophy, Psychology)
Dean: N.G. Whisson; *staff* 110
F. of Science
Dean: M.E. Brown; *staff* 74 (1)
F. of Law
Dean: J.A. Harker; *staff* 9
F. of Education
Dean: R. Tunmer; *staff* 13 (8)
F. of Commerce
Dean: P. van der Watt; *staff* 27 (8)
F. of Social Science
Dean: T.V.R. Beard; *staff* 10
F. of Divinity
Dean: B.P. Gaybba; *staff* 7
F. of Pharmacy
Dean: B. Potgieter; *staff* 16
I. of Social and Economic Research
I. for the Study of English in Africa
Director: L.S. Wright; *staff* 11
Leather Industries Research I.
Director: D.R. Cooper; *staff* 14
I. for Freshwater Studies
Director: J.O. Keeffe; *staff* 7
I. of Ichthyology
Director: M.N. Bruton; *staff* 13
Tick Research Ut.
Director: B.H. Fivaz; *staff* 2
English Dictionary Ut.
Editor (Acting): Mar P.M. Silva; *staff* 6 (1)
Also Division in East London (Accountancy, Economics, Commercial Law, Business Administration, History, and Psychology).

Founded 1904 as university college, became constituent college of the University of South Africa 1916 and incorporated as independent university 1951. An autonomous institution receiving financial support from the State. Governing bodies: the University Council; the Senate. Residential facilities for 1920 students.

Academic Year: February to December (February-April; April-June; July-September; September-December).

Admission Requirements: Matriculation Certificate or certificate of exemption issued by the Joint Matriculation Board.

Fees (Rand): 3200-3450; Honours, 2300-2850; Masters, 850-1150; Doctorate, 450-1150.

Language of Instruction: English.

Degrees and Diplomas: Bachelor of–Arts, B.A., in various fields; Bachelor of Arts (Human Movement Studies) B.A. (4 yrs); Science, B.Sc., in various fields; Journalism and Media Studies, B.Journ.; Commerce, B.Com.; Economics, B.Econ.; Social Science, B.Soc.Sc.; Fine Art, B.Fine Art; Music, B.Mus.; Theology, B.Th.; Primary Education, B.Prim.Ed.; Pharmacy, B.Pharm.; Bachelor with Honours (Hons.), in most fields, 1 further yr. Bachelor of Education, B.Ed., 1 yr after first degree. Bachelor of Laws, LL.B., 2 yrs after first degree. Bachelor of Divinity, B.D., 3 yrs after first degree. Master, in various fields, 1-2 further yrs. Doctorates, 2 yrs. Also undergraduate and postgraduate diplomas.

Libraries: Central Library, 300,000 vols; Cory Library for Historical Research.

Special Facilities (Museums, etc.): National English Literary Museum; Albany Museum; JLB Smith Institute of Ichthyology; Leather Industries Research Institute.

Publication: Rhodes Review (biannually).

Academic Staff, 1990:

Rank	Full-time	Part-time
Professors	56	–
Associate Professors	23	1
Senior Lecturers	72	1
Lecturers	105	8
Junior Lecturers	13	26
Total	269	36

Student Enrolment, 1990:

	Men	Women	Total
Of the country	1823	1550	3373
Of other countries	303	284	587
Total	2126	1834	3960

6597 **UNIVERSITEIT VAN SUID-AFRIKA**
UNIVERSITY OF SOUTH AFRICA

P.O. Box 392, Pretoria, Transvaal 0001
Telex: 350068 SA
Telephone: pretoria 429-3111
Fax: 429-3221
Principal and Vice-Chancellor: Jan Casper Gerhardus Janse van Vuuren (1989-)
Registrar (Academic and Student Affairs): M.H. Stockhoff

F. of Arts (including African Languages and Politics, Afrikaans, Arabic, Biblicial Studies, Classical Hebrew, Criminology, Economics, Education, English, French, Geography, German, Greek, History, History of Art, Industrial Psychology, International Politics, Italian, Islamic Studies, Judaica, Latin, Linguistics, Logic, Mathematics, Modern Hebrew, Municipal Government and Administration, Public Administration, Philosophy, Politics, Portuguese, Private Law, Psychology, Roman Law, Russian, Science of Religion, Socio-Cultural Anthropology, and Sociology)
Dean: F.A. Maritz; *staff* 502 (670)
F. of Economics and Management Sciences
Dean: J.A. Döckel; *staff* 273 (10)
F. of Law
Dean: W.J. Hosten; *staff* 91 (17)
F. of Science (including Astronomy, Computer Science, Information Systems, Microbiology, Operations Research, Psychology, Statistics, Zoology)
Dean: C.J.H. Schutte; *staff* 99 (7)
F. of Theology
Dean: J.J. Burden; *staff* 73 (10)
I. for Behavioural Sciences
Head: R.D. Griesel; *staff* 9 (2)
I. for Continuing Education
Head: N.C. van Ryneveld; *staff* 2 (2)
I. for Criminology
Head: G.T. du Preez; *staff* 2
I. of Educational Research
Head: C.P. Jansen; *staff* 3 (2)
I. for Foreign and Behavioural Sciences
Head: A.E.A.M. Thomashausen; *staff* 3 (4)
I. for Theological Research
Head: W. Vorster; *staff* 3 (7)
I. for Market Research
Head: P.A. Nel; *staff* 7 (1)
Also 3 branches in other cities.

Founded 1873 as University of Cape of Good Hope. Incorporated by Act of Parliament as the University of South Africa 1916. Since 1951 concerned only with external students for whom it provides tuition by correspondence. Governing bodies: the University Council, comprising 21 members; the University Senate.

Arrangements for co-operation with University of Namibia.

Academic Year: January to December.

Admission Requirements: Matriculation Certificate or certificate of exemption issued by the Joint Matriculation Board.

Fees (Rand): 300-900 per annum.

Languages of Instruction: English and Afrikaans.

Degrees and Diplomas: Bachelor of–Arts, B.A., in various fields; Science, B.Sc., in various fields; Commerce, B.Com.; Administration, B.Admin.; Theology, B.Th.; Music, B.Mus.; Diaconiology, B.Diac.; Primary Education, B.Prim.Ed.; Library Science, B.Bibl.; Accountancy, B.Compt.; Baccalaureus-Iuris, B.Iur.; Procurationis, B.Proc., 3-4 yrs. Bachelor with Honours (Hons.), in most fields, 1 further yr. Bachelor of Education, B.Ed., 1 yr after first degree. Baccalaureus Legum, LL.B., 2-4 yrs after first degree. Bachelor of Divinity, B.D., 3 yrs after B.A. Master, in various fields, 1-2 further yrs. Doctorates, 1-2 yrs. Also undergraduate and postgraduate diplomas.

Library: Central Library, 1,300,000 vols.

Special Facilities (Museums, etc.): Museums: Anthropology; Theology; Nursing Science. Art Gallery; Archives and Special Collection.

Publications: Africanus (annually); Ars Nova (annually); Codicillus (biannually); Communicatio (biannually); De Arte (biannually); Dynamica (annually); Educare (biannually); English Usage in South Africa (biannually); Kleio (annually); Politeia (biannually); Progressio (biannually); Mousaion (biannually); Musicus (biannually); Theologia Evangelica (3 times a year); Unisa English Studies (biannually); Unisa Psychologia (biannually).

Press or Publishing House: Department of Publishing Services.

Academic Staff, 1990:

Rank	Full-time	Part-time
Principal	1	–
Vice-Principals	3	–
Professors	232	–
Associate Professors	140	–
Senior Lecturers	408	–
Lecturers	298	–
Junior Lecturers	84	108
Academic Assistants	–	8
Total	1166	116

Student Enrolment, 1990:

	Men	Women	Total
Of the country	49,321	43,108	92,429
Of other countries	5876	6008	11,884
Total	55,197	49,116	104,313*

*All by correspondence.

6598 **UNIVERSITEIT VAN STELLENBOSCH**
University of Stellenbosch
Victoria Street, Stellenbosch, Cape Province 7600
Telex: 52-0383
Telephone: 2231-779111
Fax: 2231-774499
Rector and Vice-Chancellor Michiel J. de Vries (1979-)

F. of Arts
Dean: S.P. Cilliers; *staff* 180 (16)
F. of Science
Dean: C.A. Engelbrecht; *staff* 110
F. of Education
Dean: W.L. Nell; *staff* 60
F. of Agriculture
Dean: H.A. Louw; *staff* 48
F. of Law
Dean: C.G. van der Merwe; *staff* 15
F. of Theology
Dean: B.A. Müller; *staff* 10 (8)
F. of Commerce and Administration
Dean: S.M. Swart; *staff* 84 (1)
F. of Engineering
Dean: H.C. Viljoen; *staff* 83
F. of Medicine
Dean: H.P. Wassermann; *staff* 70 (9)
F. of Forestry
Dean: H.F. Vermaas; *staff* 12
F. of Dentistry
Dean: W.P. Dreyer; *staff* 62
F. of Military Science
Head: J.C. Kotzé
I. of Industrial Engineering
Director: R. Reinecke; *staff* 2
I. of Biotechnology
Director: H.J.J. van Vuuren; *staff* 3
I. of Electrical Engineering
Director: F.S. van der Merwe; *staff* 9
I. of Electronics
Director: J.J. de Plessis; *staff* 2
I. of Cartographical Analysis
Director: I.J. van der Merwe; *staff* 7
I. of Polymer Science
Director: R.D. Sanderson; *staff* 10 (4)
I. of Soviet Studies
Director: P.R. Nel; *staff* 4
I. of Civil Engineering
Director: R.J. du Preez; *staff* 8
I. of Language Teaching
; *staff* 12
I. of Sport and Movement Studies
Director: B.M. Wild; *staff* 3
I. of Theoretical Nuclear Physics
Director: C.A. Engelbrecht; *staff* 4 (1)
I. of Applied Business Sciences
Director: A.A. Archer; *staff* 14
I. of Applied Computer Sciences
Director: P. Teunisen; *staff* 8
I. of Mathematics and Science
Director: J.H. Nel; *staff* 3
Ce. for Molecular and Cellular Biology
Director: A.J. Bester; *staff* 29
Ce. for Robotics
Director: C.J. Fourie; *staff* 2
Buro for Chemical Engineering
Head: G.S. Harrison; *staff* 7
Buro for Economic Research
Head: O.D.J. Stuart; *staff* 14

Buro for Medical and Dental Education
Head: F.D. Terblanche; *staff* 15
Buro for Systems Engineering
Head: A. Schoonwinkel; *staff* 43
I. for Structural Engineering
Head: R.J. Du Preez; *staff* 2
I. for Futures Research
Head: P.H. Spies; *staff* 17
Research Ce. for Computer Applications on Language and Text of the Old Testament
Head: W.T. Claassen; *staff* 4 (4)
Also 9 Research Units.

Founded 1866 as college, incorporated as an independent university 1918. An autonomous institution receiving financial support from the State. Governing bodies: the University Council; the University Senate.

Academic Year: February to December (February-March; April-June; July-September; October-December).

Admission Requirements: Matriculation Certificate or certificate of exemption issued by the Joint Matriculation Board.

Language of Instruction: Afrikaans. Examinations may also be written in English.

Degrees and Diplomas: Bachelor of–Arts, B.A., in various fields; Science, B.Sc., in various fields; Drama, B.Dram.; Administration, B.Admin.; Agricultural Management, B.Agric.Management; Accounting, B.Accounting; Commerce, B.Com.; Economics, B.Econ.; Military Science, B.Milit.; Music, B.Mus.; Musical Education, B.Mus.Ed.; Librarianship, B.Lib.; Nursing, B.Nursing; Occupational Therapy, B.Occ.Ther.; Home Economics, B.Home.Ec.; Home Economics Education, B.HomeEc.Ed.; Park and Recreation Administration, B.Park&Recr.Admin.; Agricultural Education, B.Agric.Educn.; Primary Teaching, B.Prim.Teach.; Engineering, B.Eng., 3-4 yrs; Dentistry, B.Ch.D., 5 ½ yrs; Medicine and Surgery, M.B.Ch.B., 6 yrs. Bachelor with Honours (Hons.), in most fields, 1 further yr. Bachelor of Education, B.Ed., 1 yr after first degree. Bachelor of Laws, LL.B., 2 yrs after first degree. Bachelor of Theology, B.Th., 3 yrs after B.A. Master, in various fields, 1-2 further yrs. Doctorates. Also undergraduate and postgraduate diplomas.

Library: Total, 532,563 vols.

Special Facilities (Museums, etc.): Botanic Gardens; University Art Museum/Gallery.

Academic Staff, 1989:

Rank	Full-time
Professors	216
Associate Professors	47
Senior Lecturers	254
Lecturers	223
Junior Lecturers	38
Total	778

Student Enrolment, 1989:

	Men	Women	Total
Of the country	8282	5734	14,016*

*Also 490 external students.

6599 **UNIVERSITY OF VENDA**
Private Bag X2220, Sibasa, Republic of Venda
Telex: (15581) 331694
Telephone: (15581) 21071 9
Fax: (15581) 22045
Principal: P.W. du Plessis (1986-)
Registrar (Academic): N.J. de Beer

F. of Arts (Afrikaans and Nederlands, Anthropology, Biblical Studies, English, Geography, History, Music, Politicology, Psychology and Social Work)
Dean: E.K. Lukhaimane
F. of Business and Administration
Dean: F.J. van Jaarsveld
F. of Education
Dean: M.T. Flynn
F. of Law
Dean (Acting): B.K. Peckham
F. of Natural Science (including Nursing)
Dean: I.G. Gaigher; *staff* 15

Founded 1983. Governing body: the Board of Trustees. Residential facilities for academic staff and students.

Academic Year: January to December (January-April; April-July; July-September; September-December).

Admission Requirements: Matriculation Certificate or certificate of exemption issued by the Joint Matriculation Board.

Fees (Rand): 1160-1700 per annum.

Language of Instruction: English.

Degrees and Diplomas: Bachelor of–Arts, B.A., in various fields; Science, B.Sc., in various fields; Administration, B.Admin.; Agriculture, B.Agric.; Economics, B.Econ.; Commerce, B.Com.; Baccaleureus Iuris, B. Iuris, 3-4 yrs. Bachelor with Honours (Hons.), in most fields, 1 further yr. Bachelor of Education, B.Ed., 1 yr after first degree. Bachelot of Laws, LL.B., 2 yrs after first degree. Master, in various fields, 1-2 further yrs. Doctorates, 1-2 yrs. Also undergraduate and postgraduate diplomas.

Library: University of Venda Library.

Academic Staff, 1986-87:

Rank	Full-time	Part-time
Professors	28	–
Senior Lecturers	21	73
Junior Lecturers	11	–
Total	60	73

Student Enrolment, 1986-87:

	Men	Women	Total
Of the country	1893	673	2566

6600 **VISTA UNIVERSITEIT/VISTA UNIVERSITY (DECENTRALIZED CAMPUSES)**
Private Bag X634, Pretoria 0001
Telephone: (12) 322-8967
Fax: (12) 320-0528
Rector and Vice-Chancellor: S.W.B. Engelbrecht (1987-)
Registrar/Administration: Lubbe Anp

D. of Accountancy
Head (Acting): R.P. Voges; *staff* 11 (3)
D. of African Languages
Head: D.P. Lombard, *staff* 18 (2)
D. of Afrikaans
Head: E.A. Jooste; *staff* 11
D. of Business Economics
Head: A.P. du Plessis; *staff* 7 (2)
D. of Commercial Law
Head: P.J. Malan; *staff* 5 (2)
D. of Economics
Head: M. Levin; *staff* 8 (4)
D. of Education
Head: P.D.G. Steyn; *staff* 27 (2)
D. of English
Head: J.M. Leighton; *staff* 17
D. of Geography
Head: J.H. Reynhardt; *staff* 10 (2)
D. of History
Head: A.J. Fick; *staff* 14
D. of Mathematics and Statistics
Head: G.A.P. Heyman; *staff* 6 (2)
D. of Psychology
Head: C.N. Hoelson; *staff* 15 (2)
D. of Sociology
Head: M.E. Close; *staff* 11 (1)
Ce. for Further Training (for Teachers)
Head: H. Askes; *staff* 45 (6)
D. of Private Law
Head: J.C. Bekker
D. of Public Administration
Head: J.J.N. Cloete
D. of Public Law
Head: N.J.C. van den Berg
Ut. for Cognitive Studies
Director: G.N. Naude

Founded 1982. An urban university catering primarily to local Black matriculants at eight decentralized campuses: Pretoria (Mamelodi); Johannesburg (Soweto); Bloemfontein (Batho); Port Elizabeth (Zwide); East Land (Daverton); Vanderbiljpark (Sebokerg; Welkom, and Pretoria for Further Training. An autonomous institution receivingfinancial support from the State. Governing bodies: the University Council; the University Senate.

Academic Year: January to December (January-March; April-June; July-September; September-December).

Admission Requirements: Matriculation Certificate or certificate of exemption issued by the Joint Matriculation Board.
Fees (Rand): 1680 per annum.
Language of Instruction: English.
Degrees and Diplomas: Bachelor in–Arts, B.A., B.A.Ed., B.A.Hons.; Education, B.Ed.; Law, B.Jur. Master of–Arts; Commerce; Education. Doctor, Ph.D..
Academic Staff, 1989-90:

Rank	Full-time	Part-time
Professors	29	9
Associate Professors	8	3
Senior Lecturers	48	24
Lecturers	194	45
Junior Lecturers	35	25
Total	314	106

Student Enrolment, 1989-90:

	Men	Women	Total
Of the country	3450	2550	6000*

*Also 19,000 external students.

6601 **UNIVERSITEIT VAN WES-KAAPLAND**
UNIVERSITY OF THE WESTERN CAPE
Private Bag X17, Bellville 7530
Cables: unibell sa
Telex: SA 5226661
Telephone: (21) 9592911
Fax: (21) 9513627
Rector and Vice-Chancellor: G.J. Gerwel
Registrar: A.F. Daniels

F. of Arts (Afrikaans and Nederlands, Anthropology, Arabic, Biblical Studies, English, French, Geography and Environmental Studies, German, Hellenistic Greek, History, Human Movement Studies and Physical Education, Library and Information Science, Linguistics, Music, Semitics, Sociology, Xhosa)
Dean: S.G.M. Ridge; *staff* 136 (26)
F. of Law
Dean: P.C. Smit; *staff* 18 (11)
F. of Theology
Dean: G.D. Cloete; *staff* 12 (5)
F. of Economic and Management Sciences
Dean: W.J.L. Van Vuuren; *staff* 40 (13)
F. of Natural Sciences (including Computer Sciences, Dietetics, Earth Science, Pharmacology, Pharmaceutical Chemistry, Pharmaceutics, Statistics, Zoology)
Dean: B. Esterhuizen; *staff* 90 (29)
F. of Education
Dean: H. Ditterman; *staff* 45 (5)
F. of Dentistry
Dean: M.H. Moola; *staff* 48 (7)
F. of Community and Health Sciences
Dean: Mrs. S. Coetzee; *staff* 61 (4)
I. for Social Development
Director: P.J. Le Roux; *staff* 4
I. for Historical Research
; *staff* 4
I. for Counselling
Director: F.C.T. Sonn; *staff* 14
I. for Small Business Studies
Director: D.J. Visser; *staff* 3
Teaching Ce.
Director: A.J.L. Sinclair; *staff* 8
Ce. for Adult and Continuing Education
Director: Mrs S. Walters; *staff* 5 (5)
Gold Fields Science and Mathematics Research Ce.
Director: M.C. Nehl; *staff* 15
Research Ce.
Dean: R. Christie; *staff* 2

Founded 1960 as university college of the University of South Africa, became independent university 1984. An autonomous institution receiving financial support from the State. Governing bodies: the University Council; the University Senate. Residential facilities for *c.* 2400 students in hostels.
Academic Year: February to November (February-March; April-June; July-September; September-November).

Admission Requirements: Matriculation Certificate or certificate of exemption issued by the Joint Matriculation Board.
Languages of Instruction: English and Afrikaans.
Degrees and Diplomas: Baccalaureus-Artium, B.A., in various fields; Scientiae, B.Sc., in various fields; Administrationis, B.Admin.; Iurisprudence, B.Iuris.; Bibliothecologiae, B.Bibl.; Educationis, B.Ed.; Theologiae, B.Th.; Commercii, B.Comm.; Economicae, B.Econ.; Pharmaceuticae, B.Pharm.; Procurationis, B.Proc., 3-4 yrs; Curationis, nursing, B.Cur., 4 ½ yrs; Chirurgiae Dentium, B.Ch.D, 5 ½ yrs. Baccalaureus with Honours (Hons.), in most fields, 1 further yr. Baccalaureus Educationis, B.Ed., 1 yr after first degree. Baccalaureus Theologiae, B.Th., 3 yrs after first degree. Baccalaureus Legum, LL.B., 2 yrs after first degree. Master, in various fields, 1-2 further yrs. Doctorates. Also diplomas.
Libraries: Central Library; libraries of: Dentistry; Theology; Law; Africana.
Special Facilities (Museums, etc.): Cape Flats Nature Reserve.
Publications: Campus Bulletin; UWC News.
Press or Publishing House: Printing Department.
Academic Staff, 1990:

Rank	Full-time	Part-time
Professors	83	5
Associate Professors	11	–
Senior Lecturers	125	30
Lecturers	149	44
Junior Lecturers	64	26
Total	432	100

Student Enrolment, 1990:

	Men	Women	Total
Of the country	6873	5532	12,405

6602 **UNIVERSITY OF THE WITWATERSRAND**
1 Jan Smuts Avenue, Johannesburg 2001
Cables: uniwits
Telex: 42 27125
Telephone: 716-1111
Vice-Chancellor and Principal: Robert Charlton (1988-)
Registrar: K.W. Standenmacher

F. of Arts (including Library and Information Science)
Dean: N.G. Garson; *staff* 279 (50)
F. of Science
Dean: C.F. Cresswell; *staff* 270 (35)
F. of Medicine (including Nursing)
Dean: C. Rosendorff; *staff* 164 (48)
F. of Engineering
Dean: D. Glasser; *staff* 96 (25)
F. of Commerce
Dean: E. Kahn; *staff* 56 (4)
F. of Law
Dean: June D. Sinclaire; *staff* 42 (16)
F. of Dentistry
Dean: J.F. van Reenen; *staff* 21 (14)
F. of Architecture
Dean: P.D. Tyson; *staff* 31 (10)
F. of Education
Dean: D.J. Freer; *staff* 52 (11)
F. of Business Administration
Dean: G.S. Andrews; *staff* 23 (4)
African Studies I.
Director: C. van Onselen; *staff* 7
I. of Geophysical Research
Director: L.O. Nicolaysen; *staff* 14 (2)
I. for Palaeontological Research
Director: M.A. Raath; *staff* 4
I. of Portuguese Studies
Director: L.A. Leal; *staff* 4
Medical Research I.
Director: J. Metz
Dental Research I.
Director: P.E. Cleaton-Jones; *staff* 2
Ce. for Nuclear Sciences Research
Director: J.P.F. Sellschop; *staff* 15 (8)
Ce. for the Study of Medical Education
Director: J.R. Kriel; *staff* 3
Ce. for Continuing Education
Director: D.D. Russell; *staff* 15 (4)

Also 8 Research Units and pre-university school.

Founded 1896 as school of mines at Kimberley. Incorporated in Transvaal Technical Institute 1904, renamed South African School of Mines and Technology 1910. Became university college 1920 and university 1922. An autonomous institution receiving financial support from the State. Governing bodies: the University Council; the University Senate. Residential facilities for visiting academic staff and for students.

Arrangements for co-operation in research with Florida State University.

Academic Year: February to November (February-April; April-July; July-September; September-November).

Admission Requirements: Matriculation Certificate or certificate of exemption issued by the Joint Matriculation Board.

Fees (Rand): 2050-3300 per annum; postgraduate, *c.* 1000-3000.

Language of Instruction: English.

Degrees and Diplomas: Bachelor of–Arts, B.A., in various fields; Science, B.Sc., in various fields; Music, B.Mus.; Commerce, B.Com.; Pharmacy, B. Pharm.; Economic Science, B.Econ.Sc.; Primary Education, B.Prim.Ed.; Pharmacy,B.Pharm.; Baccalaureus Procurationis, B.Proc., 3-4 yrs; Architecture, B.Arch.; Accountancy, B.Acc., 5 yrs; Dental Science, 5 ½ yrs; Medicine and Surgery, M.B.B.Ch., 6 yrs. Bachelor with Honours (Hons.), in most fields, 1 further yr. Bachelor of Education, B.Ed., 1 yr after first degree. Bachelor of Laws, LL.B., 2-3 yrs after first degree. Master, in various fields, 1-2 further yrs. Doctorates, 1-2 yrs. Also undergraduate and postgraduate diplomas.

Library: Total, 876,000 vols.

Special Facilities (Museums, etc.): Adler Museum of the History of Medicine; Archaeology Museum; Bleloch Museum (Geology); Brebner Museum (Surgery); Robert Broom Museum (Sterkfontein Caves); Dental Museum; Hunterian Museum (Anatomy); Moss Herbarium; Museum of Obstetrics and Gynaecology; Palaeontology Museum; Social Anthropology Museum; Sutherland Strachan Museum (Pathology); Museum of Wireless, Radio and Electronics; Zoology Museum.

Publications: African Studies (biannually); English Studies in Africa (biannually); Palaeontologia Africana (annually).

Press or Publishing House: University Press.

Academic Staff, 1986-87:

Rank	Full-time	Part-time
Professors	158	24
Associate Professors	83	36
Senior Lecturers	207	45
Lecturers	265	118
Senior Tutors	52	10
Tutors and Junior Lecturers	104	34
Total	869	218

Student Enrolment, 1986-87:

Of the country	15,489
Of other countries	2534
Total	18,023

6603 **UNIVERSITEIT VAN ZULULAND/UNIVERSITY OF ZULULAND**

Private Bag X1001, Kwa-Dlangezwa 3886
Cables: unizul
Telex: 6-28081 SA
Telephone: (351) 93911
Fax: (351) 93735
Rector and Vice-Chancellor: A.C. Nkabinde (1978-89)
Registrar (Academic): E.W. Redelinghuys

F. of Arts
Dean: H.J. van Eetveldt; *staff* 102
F. of Education
Dean: P.C. Luthuli; *staff* 39
F. of Science
Dean: D.N. Boshoff; *staff* 46
F. of Commerce and Administration
Dean: P.S. Zondi; *staff* 5 (2)
F. of Law
Dean: C.A.M. Dlamini; *staff* 12
F. of Theology
Dean: M.C. Kitshoff; *staff* 12 (2)
Ce. of Nursing (Ngwalezane)
Head: Mrs T.G. Mashaba; *staff* 15
D. of Extramural Studies (Umlazi)
Vice-Rector: H.J. Dreyer; *staff* 22

Founded 1959 as university college for Zulu and Swazi students. Became university 1970. An autonomous institution receiving financial support from the State. Governing bodies: the University Council; the University Senate. Residential facilities for academic staff and students.

Academic Year: February to December (February-June; July-December).

Admission Requirements: Matriculation Certificate or certificate of exemption issued by the Joint Matriculation Board.

Fees (Rand): 195-355 per course.

Language of Instruction: English.

Degrees and Diplomas: Bachelor of–Arts, B.A., in various fields; Science, B.Sc., in various fields; Theology, B.Th.; Library Science, B.Bibl.; Commerce, B.Com.; Baccalaureus-Procurationis, B.Proc.; Iuris, B.Iuris; Paedagogiae, B.Paed., 3-4 yrs. Bachelor with Honours (Hons.), in most fields, 1 further yr. Bachelor of Education, B.Ed., 1 yr after first degree. Bachelor of Laws, LL.B., 2 yrs after first degree. Master, in various fields, 1-2 further yrs. Doctorates, 1-2 yrs. Also undergraduate and postgraduate diplomas.

Library: *c.* 95,000 vols.

Publications: Paedonomia (biannually); Journal of Psychology (biannually).

Academic Staff, 1990:

Rank	Full-time
Professors	50
Senior Lecturers	56
Lecturers	122
Junior Lecturers	22
Total	250

Student Enrolment, 1990:

	Men	Women	Total
Of the country	2619	2744	5353
Of other countries	2	3	5
Total	2621	2747	5358

Other Institutions

Technical Education

6604 **KAAPSE TECHNIKON/CAPE TECHNIKON**

Longmarket Street, P.O. Box 652, Cape Town 8000
Cables: teccom
Telex: 521666
Telephone: (21) 4616220
Fax: (21) 4617564
Rector: T.C. Shippey (1979-)
Registrar: J. van Zyl

S. of Applied Art
Head: S.A. Slack; *staff* 25
S. of Civil Engineering
Head: J.P. Bosman; *staff* 21
S. of Electrical Engineering
Head: N. Belme; *staff* 22
S. of Food and Clothing Technology
Head: J.L.H. Oosthuizen; *staff* 19
S. of Management
Head: A.J. Welgemoed; *staff* 47
S. of Business Informatics
Head: E.W. Pienaar; *staff* 37
S. of Architecture and Building
Head: L.R. Jocobson; *staff* 12
S. of Pharmacy
Head: D.L. Munday; *staff* 8
S. of Mechanical Engineering
Head: L.U. Engelbrecht; *staff* 25
S. of Life Sciences
Head: C.J. Leodolff; *staff* 33
S. of Physical Sciences
Head: M.B. Hanley; *staff* 23
S. of Secretarial Sciences
Head: J.P. Spencer; *staff* 22

S. of Teacher Training (Commerce)
Head: A.C. de W. Lagrange; *staff* 17
Bureau of Research and Development
Director: E.A. Liken; *staff* 3

Founded 1907 as college, acquired present status and title 1979. An autonomous institution receiving financialsupport from the State. Governing body: the Council. Residential facilities for students.

Academic Year: January to December (January-June; July-December).

Admission Requirements: Matriculation Certificate.

Fees (Rand): *c.* 2400 per annum.

Languages of Instruction: English and Afrikaans.

Degrees and Diplomas: National Diploma, 3 yrs. National Higher Diploma, NH.Dip., 4 yrs. Masters Diploma in Technology, M.Dip.Tech., 5 yrs. Laureatus in Technology, Laur.Tech., 6 yrs.

Library: Cape Technikon Library Services, 33,000 vols.

Academic Staff, 1989:

Rank	Full-time
Directors	15
Associate Directors	52
Senior Lecturers	77
Lecturers	176
Total	320

Student Enrolment, 1989:

Of the country	6374
Of other countries	44
Total	6418

6605 **TECHNIKON MANGOSUTHU**

P.O. Box 12363, Jacobs 4026, Natal
Telex: 621841
Telephone: (31) 907 1855
Fax: (31) 907 2892
Rector: Adolf Johannes Vos
Vice-Rector Administration: D.E. Jenkins

S. of Electrical Engineering
Director: G.A. Kruger; *staff* 19
S. of Health Sciences
Director: L.E. Oboldster; *staff* 10
S. of Mechanical Engineering
Director (Acting): B.K. Stewart; *staff* 7 (3)
S. of Chemical Engineering
Director: E.R. Schutte' *staff* 11
S. of Civil Engineering
Director (Acting): J.C. Landmer; *staff* 8 (1)
S. of Secretarial and Business Studies
Director: A. L. van Stoden; *staff* 14 (6)
S. of Public Administration
Director (Acting): J.W.W. Uys; *staff* 4 (5)
S. of Agriculture
Director: E.W. Haynes; *staff* 8

Founded 1979. Governing body: the Council. Residential facilities for academic staff and students.

Academic Year: January to December.

Admission Requirements: Matriculation Certificate.

Language of Instruction: English.

Library: 14,000 vols.

Academic Staff, 1990: 81 (15).

Student Enrolment, 1990:

	Men	Women	Total
Of the country	851	329	1180
Of other countries	146	40	186
Total	897	369	1366

6606 **TECHNIKON NATAL**

P.O. Box 953, Durban 4000
Cables: nattechnikon
Telex: 620187
Rector: A.L. du Preez (1983-)

S. of Applied Sciences
Chairman: D. Bird; *staff* 40 (3)
S. of Arts
Chairman: B.A. Dobie; *staff* 49 (16)
S. of Commerce
Chairman: C.A. Maggs; *staff* 41 (19)
S. of Design
Chairman: D.H. Staniland; *staff* 41 (12)
S. of Engineering (including Architecture)
Chairman: K.E. Tarbett; *staff* 24 (2)
S. of Life Sciences
Chairman: C.J. Jansen; *staff* 21 (8)

Founded 1907, acquired present title 1968. An autonomous institution receiving financial support from the State. Governing body: the Council. Residential facilities for 778 students.

Academic Year: January to December (January-June; July-December).

Admission Requirements: Matriculation Certificate or recognized equivalent.

Fees (Rand): 1300-1420 per annum.

Languages of Instruction: English and Afrikaans.

Degrees and Diplomas: National Diploma/Certificate, 3 yrs. National Higher Diploma, 4 yrs. National Diploma in Technology, 1 furtheryr. Laureatus in Technology, 6 yrs.

Library: Technikon Library.

Academic Staff, 1986-87:

Rank	Full-time	Part-time
Rector	1	–
Vice-Rectors	3	–
Directors	11	–
Associate Directors	46	–
Senior Lecturers	57	–
Lecturers	155	60
Total	273	60

Student Enrolment, 1986-87:

	Men	Women	Total
Of the country	2595	1790	4385
Of other countries	430	270	700
Total	3025	2060	5085

6607 **TECHNIKON NOORD-TRANSVAAL**
TECHNIKON NORTHERN TRANSVAAL

Private Bag X24, Soshunguve 0152

S. of Electrical Engineering
S. of Management and Administration
S. of Mechanical Engineers
S. of Medical Health Sciences
S. of Physical Sciences
S. of Secretarial Sciences
S. of Surveying
S. of Mining and Civil Engineering

Founded 1980.

6608 **TECHNIKON OVS/TECHNIKON OFS**

Private Bag X20539, Bloemfontein 9301
Telephone: 051-71003
Rector: J.J. Van Lill
Registrar: J.J. Hamman

Founded 1981. An autonomous institution receiving financial support from the State. Governing body: the Council. Residential facilities for students.

Academic Year: January to December (January-March; April-June; September-December).

Admission Requirements: Matriculation Certificate or recognized equivalent.

Fees (Rand): 180-780 per annum.

Languages of Instruction: English and Afrikaans.

Degrees and Diplomas: National Diploma, 3 yrs. National Higher Diploma, NH.Dip., 4 yrs. National Diploma in Technology, Dip.Tech., 5yrs. Laureatus in Technology, Laur.Tech., 6 yrs.

Academic Staff, 1986-87:

Rank	Full-time	Part-time
Directors	5	–
Heads of Departments	12	–
Senior Lecturers	7	–
Lecturers	49	51
Total	73	51

Student Enrolment, 1986-87:

	Men	Women	Total
Of the country	582	845	1427
Of other countries	4	9	13
Total	586	854	1440

6609 **TECHNIKON PENINSULAR/TECHNIKON SKIEREILAND**
Private Bag X3, Kasselsvlei 7533, Cape

S. of Applied Sciences
S. of Art and Design
S. of Business Studies
S. of Civil Engineering and Building
S. of Secretarial Sciences (including Computer Sciences)
S. of Teacher Training

6610 **PORT ELIZABETHSE TECHNIKON**
Private Bag X6011, Port Elizabeth 6000
Telex: 243051
Telephone: 041-533121

S. of Applied Sciences
S. of Art and Design
S. of Civil Engineering and Building
S. of Management
S. of Mechanical Engineering
S. of Electrical Engineering
S. of Pharmacy
S. of Communication and Secretarial Sciences

Founded 1882 as school of art, acquired present status and title 1979. A State institution. Residential facilities for 185 men and 172 women students.

Academic Year: January to December (January-June; July-December).

Admission Requirements: Senior Certificate or equivalent.

Languages of Instruction: English and Afrikaans.

Degrees and Diplomas: National Diploma, 3 yrs. National Higher Diploma, NH.Dip., 4 yrs. Masters Diploma in Technology, M.Dip.Tech., 5 yrs. Laureatus in Technology, Laur.Tech., 6 yrs.

Library: 17,000 vols.

Publication: Protechnida (quarterly).

Academic Staff: c. 150 (60).

Student Enrolment: c. 1780.

6611 **TECHNIKON PRETORIA**
420 Church Street East, Pretoria 0002

S. of Agricultural Sciences
S. of Art
S. of Biology
S. of Chemistry
S. of Civil Engineering
S. of Computer Sciences
S. of Electrical Engineering
S. of Food and Textile Technology
S. of Health Sciences
S. of Communication
S. of Management
S. of Mechanical Engineering
S. of Performing Arts
S. of Pharmacy
S. of Physical Sciences
S. of Secretarial Sciences

Founded 1968.

6612 **TECHNIKON RSA (DISTANCE TEACHING)**
Private Bag 6, Florida 1710
Telephone: (471) 2000
Fax: (471) 2134
Rector: Z. van Dyk (1980-)
Registrar: E.J. Kilpert

S. of Accountancy and Computer Data Processing
Director: W.F.C. Koekemoer; *staff* 18 (21)
S. of Management
Director: H. Uys; *staff* 18 (26)
S. of Natural Sciences
Director: D. Baird; *staff* 20 (31)
S. of Economic and Behavioural Sciences
Director: T.H. Augustyn; *staff* 19 (32)
S. of Government Administration
Director: J.C. Jacobs; *staff* 28 (53)
S. of Police Administration and Law
Director: J. Smit; *staff* 30 (110)

Founded 1980. Previously the External Studies Division of the Technikon Witwatersrand. An autonomous institution receiving financial support from the State. Governing bodies: the Council, comprising not more than 20 members; the Management Committee of the Council; the Academic Council.

Academic Year: January to December.

Admission Requirements: Matriculation Certificate or recognized equivalent.

Fees (Rand): 200 per subject, per annum.

Languages of Instruction: English and Afrikaans.

Degrees and Diplomas: National Diploma, 3 yrs. National Higher Diploma, NH.Dip., 4 yrs. National Diploma in Technology, N.Dip.Tech.,5 yrs.

Library: Technikon RSA Library, *c.* 5,000 vols.

Academic Staff, 1989-90:

Rank	Full-time	Part-time
Rector	1	–
Vice-Rectors	2	–
Directors	6	–
Associate Directors	11	–
Senior Lecturers	16	–
Lecturers	39	323
Total	75	323

Student Enrolment, 1989-90: c. 28,000 (by correspondence).

6613 **M.L. SULTAN TECHNIKON**
P.O. Box 1334, Durban 4000
Cables: sulkon
Telephone: (031) 316681
Rector: R. Soni (1987-90)
Registrar: R. Jagath

S. of Art and Design
Director: L.W. Cross; *staff* 19 (26)
S. of Applied Sciences
Director: D.H. Goodes; *staff* 15 (11)
S. of Building and Civil Engineering
Director: A.M.C. Loubser *staff* 21
S. of Hotel and Catering Administration
Director: B. Smith *staff* 17 (4)
S. of Electrical Engineering
Director (Acting): D.J. Grieve; *staff* 24
S. of Health Sciences
Director: D.J. Munn; *staff* 22 (6)
S. of Management, Administration and Computer Sciences
Director: D.D. Bhikha; *staff* 24 (69)
S. of Mechanical Engineering
Director: D.A. Lee; (14)
S. of Secretarial Studies, Communication and Languages
Director: G. Moodley; *staff* 22 (23)

Founded 1946 as college, acquired present status and title 1979. An autonomous institution receiving financialsupport from the State. Governing body: the Council. Residential facilities for students.

Academic Year: January to December (January-June; July-December).

Admission Requirements: Matriculation Certificate or recognized equivalent.

Fees (Rand): 500-970 per semester.

Language of Instruction: English.

Degrees and Diplomas: National Diploma, 3 yrs. National Higher Diploma, NH.Dip., 4 yrs. Masters Diploma in Technology, M.Dip.Tech., 5 yrs. Laureatus in Technology, Laur.Tech., 6 yrs.
Library: B.P. Patel Memorial Library, 20,000 vols.
Publications: Praktikon (annually); Newsletter (each semester).
Academic Staff, 1986-87:

Rank	Full-time	Part-time
Rector	1	–
Vice-Rector	1	–
Directors	9	–
Heads of Departments	23	–
Senior Lecturers	33	–
Lecturers	113	139
Total	180	139

Student Enrolment, 1986-87:

	Men	Women	Total
Of the country	2943	1461	4404
Of other countries	3	1	4
Total	2946	1462	4408

6614 **VAALDRIDHOEKSE TECHNIKON**
VAAL TRIANGLE TECHNIKON
Private Box X021, Vanderbijlpark 1900
Telex: 423199
Telephone: (016) 81-2141
Rector: I. Steyl (1972-90)
Registrar: J. de W. du Toit

S. of Applied Sciences
Director: H.A. du Plessis; *staff* 27 (8)
S. of Mechanical Engineering
Director: T.W. Engela; *staff* 33 (7)
S. of Electrical Engineering
Director: H. Mentz; *staff* 32 (10)
S. of Management and Administration
Director: H.J. Alberts; *staff* 26 (20)
S. of Art and Design
Director: B.E. Record; *staff* 11 (10)
S. of Food and Clothing Technology
Director: B.E. Record; *staff* 7 (6)

Founded 1966 as College, acquired present status and title 1979. An autonomous institution receiving financialsupport from the State. Governing body: the Council, comprising 15 members. Residential facilities for 750 students.
Academic Year: January to December (January-April; April-June; July-October; October-December).
Admission Requirements: Matriculation Certificate or recognized equivalent.
Fees (Rand): 750 per annum.
Languages of Instruction: English and Afrikaans.
Degrees and Diplomas: National diploma, 3 yrs. National Higher Diploma, NH.Dip., 4 yrs. National Diploma in Technology, N.Dip.Tech.,5 yrs. Laureatus in Technology, Laur.Tech., 6 yrs.
Academic Staff, 1986-87:

Rank	Full-time	Part-time
Rector	1	–
Vice-Rectors	2	–
Directors	6	–
Heads of Department	29	–
Senior Lecturers	30	–
Lecturers	81	61
Total	149	61

Student Enrolment, 1986-87:

	Men	Women	Total
Of the country	2601	1045	3646
Of other countries	8	–	8
Total	2609	1045	3654

6615 **TECHNIKON WITWATERSRAND**
P.O. Box 3293, Johannesburg 2000

S. of Computer Sciences
S. of Art and Design
S. of Biology
S. of Chemistry and Chemical Engineering
S. of Civil Engineering, Building and Architecture
S. of Electrical Engineering
S. of Health Service
S. of Hotel Management
S. of Languages and Communications
S. of Mechanical and Industrial Engineering
S. of Mining and Metallurgy
S. of Optometry
S. of Pharmacy
S. of Management
S. of Secretarial Sciences

Founded 1968.

Agricultural Education

6616 **LANDBOUKOLLEGE GLEN**
Glen College of Agriculture
Private Bag X01, Glen 9360
Telex: 267690
Telephone: 05214-2051
Director: T.E. Skinner (1979-)

Agriculture

Founded 1919 as school, acquired present status and title 1938. Under the supervision of the State Department of Agriculture. Residential facilities for students in hostels.
Academic Year: January to November (January-June; July-November).
Admission Requirements: Matriculation Certificate.
Fees (Rand): 1200 per annum.
Languages of Instruction: Afrikaans and English.
Degrees and Diplomas: Diploma, 2 yrs.
Academic Staff, 1986-87: 15.
Student Enrolment, 1986-87:

	Men	Women	Total
Of the country	132	8	140

6617 **CEDARA COLLEGE OF AGRICULTURE**
Pietermaritzburg 3200

6618 **FRUIT AND FRUIT TECHNOLOGY RESEARCH INSTITUTE**
Private Bag X5013, Stellenbosch 7600
Telex: 57-24147SA
Telephone: 02231-2001

Deciduous Fruits, Nuts, and Date Production

Founded 1937 as Western Province Fruit Research Station.

6619 **COLLEGE OF AGRICULTURE**
Grootfontein, Middelburg 5900

6620 **COLLEGE OF AGRICULTURE AND RESEARCH STATION**
Private Bag X804, Potchefstroom 2520

Nursing Education

6621 **CARINUS NURSING COLLEGE**
Private Bag, Rochester 7940Fax: (404) 6151

Nursing

Founded 1948. Affiliated to University of Cape Town 1985. Governing body: the Council. Residential facilities for students.
Academic Year: 44 weeks from 1 January.
Admission Requirements: Matricultation Certificate.
Fees (Rand): 7.50 per month.
Language of Instruction: English.
Degrees and Diplomas: Diplomas, 4 yrs.
Academic Staff, 1989-90: c. 59.
Student Enrolment, 1989-90: 350.

6622 **NICO MALAN-VERPLEGINGSKOLLEGE**
Nico Malan College of Nursing
Private Bag, Athlone 7760

6623 **OTTO DU PLESSIS VERPLEGINGSKOLLEGE**
Otto du Plessis Nursing College
Private Bag X7, P.O. Tygerberg, Cape Town 7505
Telephone: (938) 4118
Head: Miss J.M. Viljoen (1984-)
Senior Provincial Administration Clerk: Mrs. A.A. Rust

Nursing
Midwifery
Community Health
Post-Basic Courses

Founded 1959. Responsible to the Cape Provincial Administration and associated with the University of Stellenbosch. Residential facilities for students.

Academic Year: January to December.
Admission Requirements: Matriculation Certificate.
Fees (Rand): 360 per annum.
Language of Instruction: Afrikaans.
Degrees and Diplomas: Diplomas, 4 yrs.
Library: 3777 vols.
Academic Staff, 1989-90: 35.
Student Enrolment, 1989-90:

	Men	Women	Total
Of the country	1	348	349

6624 **SARLEH DOLLIE-VERPLEGINGSKOLLEGE**
Sarleh Dollie College of Nursing
Private Bag, Tygerberg 7505

6625 **SHARLEH CRIBB-VERPLEGINGSKOLLEGE**
Sharleh Cribb College of Nursing
Private Bag X6047, Port Elizabeth 6000

6626 **COLLEGE OF NURSING**
Lion Street, Welkom 9460

6627 **BOITEMELO-HOSPITAALKOLLEGE**
Boitemelo Hospital College
Private Bag, Kroonstad 9500

6628 **PEELONOMI HOSPITAL LECTURE UNIT**
Private Bag X20581, Bloemfontein 9300

6629 **VRYSTAAT-OPLEIDINGSKOLLEGE VIR VERPLEGING**
Free State College of Nursing
Private Bag X20598, Bloemfontein 9300

6630 **PRETORIA-KOLLEGE VIR VERPLEGING**
Pretoria College of Nursing
Private Bag X169, Pretoria 0001

6631 **B.G. ALEXANDER COLLEGE OF NURSING**
309 Smit Street, Hillbrow, Johannesburg 2001

6632 **WESKOPPIES-OPPLEIDINGSKOOL VIR VERPLEEGKUNDIGES**
Weskoppies Training School for Nurses
Private Bag X113, Pretoria 0001

6633 **WES-TRANSVAALSE VERPLEGINGSKOLLEGE**
Western Transvaal College of Nursing
Private Bag X14, Klerksdorp 2570

6634 **TARA, THE H. MOROSS TRAINING SCHOOL FOR NURSES**
Private Bag X7, Randburg 2125

6635 **TRAINING SCHOOL FOR NURSES**
No. 1 Military Hospital, Voortrekkerhoogte 0187

6636 **FRERE COLLEGE OF NURSING**
Private Bag 9023, East London 5201
Telephone: (431) 27350
Head: Miss P. Bellad-Ellis
Senior Administrative Officer: Mrs. E. du Toit

General Nursing
Midwifery
Community Nursing Science
Psychiatric Nursing Science
Natural and Social Sciences

Founded 1970. Responsible to the Cape Provincial Administration. Residential facilities for academic staff and students.

Academic Year: January to October.
Admission Requirements: Senior Certificate.
Fees (Rand): 90 per annum.
Languages of Instruction: English and Afrikaans.
Degrees and Diplomas: Diploma, in Nursing Science and Midwifery, 4 yrs.
Library: Frere College Resource Centre, *c.* 3000 vols.
Academic Staff, 1990: c. 26.
Student Enrolment, 1990:

	Men	Women	Total
Of the country	10	150	160

Teacher Training

6637 **BARKLY HOUSE COLLEGE OF EDUCATION**
Molteno Road, Claremont 7700
Telephone: (21) 617088
Head: Elizabeth W. Fullard (1986-)

Teacher Training (pre-primary level)

Founded 1946 as Training College. Acauired present status 1964 and title 1988. Residential facilities for 58 students.

Academic Year: January to December (January-March; April-June; July-September; October-December).
Admission Requirements: Matriculation Certificate.
Languages of Instruction: English and Afrikaans.
Degrees and Diplomas: Diplomas, 3-4 yrs.
Library: 12,000 vols.
Student Enrolment, 1990: 100 (women).

6638 **TEACHERS' COLLEGE**
Highbury Road, Mowbray, Cape Town 7700

6639 **TEACHERS' COLLEGE**
P.O. Box 102, Graaff-Reinet 6280

6640 **TEACHERS' COLLEGE**
Private Bag X649, Oudtshoorn 6620

6641 **TEACHERS' COLLEGE**
P.O. Box 311, Paarl 7620

6642 **DIE ONDERWYSKOLLEGE PORT ELIZABETH**
Port Elizabeth College of Education
Winchester Way, P.O. Box 364, Port Elizabeth 6000
Telephone: (41) 532177
Fax: (41) 532178
Rector: L.K. van der Walt
Registrar: Mrs. E.V. de Villiers

Teacher Training (primary level)

Founded 1973. Under the jurisdiction of the Cape Education Department and operating in collaboration with the University of Port Elizabeth.

Governing bodies: the Council, comprising members; the Senate. Residential facilities for *c.* 30 men and *c.* 110 women students.

Academic Year: January to November (January-March; April-June; July-September; October-November).

Admission Requirements: Matriculation Certificate, including the two official languages and one other matriculation subject on the Higher Grade.

Fees (Rand): 240 per annum.

Languages of Instruction: Afrikaans and English.

Degrees and Diplomas: Diplomas, 3-4 yrs.

Library: 50,000 vols.

Academic Staff, 1989-90: 15 (1).

Student Enrolment, 1990:

	Men	Women	Total
Of the country	32	152	184
Of other countries	–	1	1
Total	32	153	185

6643 **DENNEOORD COLLEGE**
Van Riebeeck Street, Stellenbosh 7600

6644 **TEACHERS' COLLEGE**
Van Riebeeck Street, Wellington 7655

6645 **OPLEIDINGSKOLLEGE ATHLONE**
Training College Athlone
1 Sanddrift Street, Paarl 7646

6646 **ATHLONE TRAINING CENTRE FOR PRE-PRIMARY TEACHERS**
1 Sanddrift Street, Paarl 7646

6647 **BECHET TRAINING COLLEGE**
P.O. Box 3746, Greyville 4023

6648 **BELLVILLE TRAINING COLLEGE**
Private Bag X8, Kasselsvlei 7533

6649 **DOWER TRAINING COLLEGE**
Private Bag 6059, Port Elizabeth 6000

6650 **ST. FRANCIS REMOTE CAMPUS**
Krombaai Road, Crawford 7700

6651 **PHATSIMANG COLLEGE OF EDUCATION**
Private Bag X50291, Homestead, Kimberley 8300

6652 **COLLEGE FOR CONTINUING EDUCATION**
Private Bag X49, Soshanguva 0152

6653 **KAGISANONG COLLEGE OF EDUCATION**
Private Bag X20523, Bloemfontein

6654 **RAND TRAINING COLLEGE**
Private Bag X6, Langlaagte 2102

6655 **OPLEIDINGSKOLLEGE ROGGEBAAI**
Training College Roggebaai
Prestwich Street, Cape Town 8001

6656 **SUID-KAAPLANDSE OPLEIDINGSKOLLEGE**
Southern Cape Training College
Private Bag X646, Oudtshoorn 6620

6657 **PENINSULA TECHNIKON**
Private Bag X3, Kasselsvlei 7533

6658 **BETHEL COLLEGE OF EDUCATION**
Bodenstein 2726

6659 **CAPE COLLEGE OF EDUCATION**
Private Bag X2041, Fort Beaufort 5720
Telephone: (0435) 31179
Rector: H.J.L. van Deventer (1982-)

Teacher Training (primary and secondary levels)

Founded 1981. A State institution under the jurisdiction of the Department of Education and Training. Residential facilities for students.

Academic Year: January to December (January-June; July-December).

Admission Requirements: Matriculation Certificate.

Fees (Rand): 380 per annum.

Language of Instruction: English.

Degrees and Diplomas: Diplomas, 3 yrs.

Library: College Library, *c.* 10,000 vols.

Academic Staff, 1986-87:

Rank	Full-time
Rector	1
Vice-Rector	1
Heads of Departments	9
Senior Lecturers	10
Lecturers	41
Total	62

Student Enrolment, 1986-87:

	Men	Women	Total
Of the country	224	576	800

6660 **EAST RAND COLLEGE OF EDUCATION**
Private Bag X52, Spings 1560
Telephone: 737-1306
Rector: B.G. Lubbe (1982-)

Teacher Training (primary and secondary levels and Technical)

Founded 1982. A State institution under the jurisdiction of the Department of Education and Training.

Academic Year: January to December (January-February; July-December).

Admission Requirements: Matriculation Certificate.

Fees (Rand): 160 per annum.

Language of Instruction: English.

Degrees and Diplomas: Diplomas, 3 yrs.

Library: College Library.

Academic Staff, 1986-87:

Rank	Full-time	Part-time
Rector	1	–
Vice-Rector	1	–
Heads of Departments	11	–
Senior Lecturers	12	–
Lecturers	27	11
Total	52	11

Student Enrolment, 1986-87:

	Men	Women	Total
Of the country	302	404	706

6661 **INDUMISO COLLEGE OF EDUCATION**
Private Bag 9077, Pietermaritzburg 3200

6662 **MPHOHADI COLLEGE OF EDUCATION**
Private Bag X66, Kroonstad 9500

6663 **SEBOKENG COLLEGE OF EDUCATION**
P.O. Box 3005, Three Rivers 1935
Telephone: (016) 337163
Rector: J.P. Redilinghuys (1982-)
Registrar: Mrs. S. van Heerden

Teacher Training (primary and secondary levels)
Founded 1976 as school, aquired present status and title 1982. A State institution under the jurisdiction of the Department of Education and Training.
Academic Year: January to December (January-June; July-December).
Admission Requirements: Matriculation Certificate.
Fees (Rand): 200 per annum.
Language of Instruction: English.
Degrees and Diplomas: Diplomas, 3 yrs.
Library: College Library, 20,000 vols.
Academic Staff, 1986-87: 50.
Student Enrolment, 1986-87:

	Men	Women	Total
Of the country	400	330	730

6664 **SOWETO COLLEGE OF EDUCATION**
Box 90064, Bertsham, Johannesburg 2013
Telephone: 933-1093

Teacher Training (primary and secondary levels)
Founded 1978, acquired present status and title 1980.
Academic Year: January to December (January-June; July-December).
Admission Requirements: Senior Certificate.
Language of Instruction: English.
Degrees and Diplomas: Diplomas, 3 yrs.
Academic Staff: c. 80.
Student Enrolment: c. 900.

6665 **TRANSVAAL COLLEGE OF EDUCATION**
Private Bag X11, Soshanguve 0152

6666 **HOXANE COLLEGE OF EDUCATION**
Private Bag, Hazy View 1242

6667 **TIVUNBENI COLLEGE OF EDUCATION**
Private Bag X1420, Letaba 0870
Telex: GIYANI
Telephone: 01523-4170/3

Teacher Training (secondary level)
Founded 1970 as school, acquired present status and title 1983. Under the jurisdiction of the Gazankulu Department of Education. Residential facilities for *c.* 360 men and *c.* 120 women students.
Academic Year: January to November (January-June; July-November).
Admission Requirements: Matriculation Certificate.
Languages of Instruction: English, Tsonga, and Afrikaans.
Degrees and Diplomas: Diplomas, 3 yrs.
Academic Staff: c. 50.
Student Enrolment: c. 600.

6668 **SPRINGFIELD COLLEGE OF EDUCATION**
Private Bag, Dormenton, Durban 4015

6669 **TRANSVAAL COLLEGE OF EDUCATION**
Private Bag X2, Laudium, 0037 Pretoria
Telephone: (12) 314-4011
Rector: H. Du B. Kemp
Registrar: L. Sarajooana

Teacher Training (primary and secondary levels)
Founded 1954 in Fordsburg, Johannesburg. Moved to present location 1982. Sole function to train Indian teachers for the Administrative House of Delegates, Department of Education and Culture. Under the supervision of theDepartment of Education and Culture (House of Delegates). Residential facilities for students.
Academic Year: January to December.
Admission Requirements: Matriculation Certificate.
Fees (Rand): 2400 per annum.
Languages of Instruction: English and Afrikaans.
Degrees and Diplomas: Diplomas, 4 yrs.
Student Enrolment, 1990:

	Men	Women	Total
Of the country	45	113	158

6670 **MGWENY COLLEGE OF EDUCATION**
Private Bag X1008, Kanyamazane 1214

6671 **NDEBELE COLLEGE OF EDUCATION**
Private Bag 4011, Siyabuswa 0472

6672 **AMANZIMTOTI ZULU COLLEGE OF EDUCATION**
P.O. Adams Mission 4100

6673 **APPELBOSCH COLLEGE OF EDUCATION**
Private Bag X202, Ozwatini 3476

6674 **ESIKHAWINI COLLEGE OF EDUCATION**
Private Bag X8520, Esikhawini 3887
Telephone: (0358) 63041
Rector: E.D. Gasa (1983-)

Teacher Training (secondary level)
Founded 1982. A State institution under the jurisdiction of the Department of Education and Training.
Academic Year: February to December (February-June; July-December).
Admission Requirements: Matriculation Certificate.
Language of Instruction: English.
Degrees and Diplomas: Diploma, 3 yrs.
Academic Staff, 1986-87: 9
Student Enrolment, 1986-87:

	Men	Women	Total
Of the country	316	325	641

6675 **ESHOWE COLLEGE OF EDUCATION**
Private Bag X503, Eshowe 3815
Telephone: 4213½
Rector: T.A. Smith (1981-)

Teacher Training (secondary level)
Founded 1958, acquired present status and title 1982. Under the jurisdiction of the Kwazulu Department of Education and Culture. Residential facilities for academic staff and students.
Academic Year: January to December (January-June; July-December).
Admission Requirements: Matriculation Certificate or certificate of exemption issued by the Joint Matriculation Board.
Fees (Rand): 565-702 per annum.
Language of Instruction: English, Afrikaans, Zulu.
Degrees and Diplomas: Diploma, 3 yrs.
Academic Staff, 1986-87:

Rank	Full-time	Part-time
Rector	1	–
Vice-Rector	1	–
Heads of Departments	7	–
Senior Lecturers	4	–
Lecturers	18	7
Total	31	7

Student Enrolment, 1986-87:

	Men	Women	Total
Of the country	268	219	487

6676 **MADADENI COLLEGE OF EDUCATION**
Madadeni

Teacher Training (primary level)
Founded 1970 as training school, acquired present status and title 1982. Under the jurisdiction of the Department of Education and Training and Kwazulu Education and Culture. Residential facilities for academic staff and students.
Academic Year: January to December (January-June; July-December).
Admission Requirements: Matriculation Certificate or certificate of exemption issued by the Joint Matriculation Board.
Languages of Instruction: English and Zulu.
Degrees and Diplomas: Diplomas, 3 yrs.
Library: c. 15,000 vols.
Publication: College Magazine (annually).
Academic Staff: c. 80.
Student Enrolment: c. 1020 (Also *c.* 100 external students).

6677 **MPUMALANGA COLLEGE OF EDUCATION**
Private Bag X1004, Hammersdale 3700

6678 **NTUZUMA COLLEGE OF EDUCATION**
Private Bag X2, Kwa Mashu 4360

6679 **UMBUMBULU COLLEGE OF EDUCATION**
Private Bag X12, Amanzimtati 4125

6680 **UMLAZI COLLEGE OF EDUCATION**
Private Bag X04, Isipingo 4110

6681 **DR. C.N. PHATUDI COLLEGE OF EDUCATION**
Private Bag X1020, Burgersfort 50

6682 **KWENA MOLOTO COLLEGE OF EDUCATION**
Private Bag X4015, Seshego 0742
Telephone: (1521) 921189
Rector: J.S. Engelbrecht
Registrar: M.S. Mamaregane

Teacher Training (primary and secondary level)
Academic Year: January to December (January-June; July-December).
Admission Requirements: Matriculation Certificate.
Fees (Rand): 250 per annum.
Language of Instruction: English.
Degrees and Diplomas: Diplomas, 3 yrs.
Academic Staff, 1990: 62.
Student Enrolment, 1990:

	Men	Women	Total
Of the country	400	410	810

6683 **MAMOKGALAKE CHUENE COLLEGE OF EDUCATION**
Private Bag X629, Groblersdal 0470

6684 **MOJADJI COLLEGE OF EDUCATION**
Private Bag X746, Duiwelskloof 00833

6685 **MOKOPANE COLLEGE OF EDUCATION**
Private Bag X601, Mahwelereng 0626

6686 **SEKHUKHUNE COLLEGE OF EDUCATION**
P.O. Lefalane 0741

6687 **SETOTOLWANE COLLEGE OF EDUCATION**
Private Bag X7372, Pietersburg 0700

Teacher Training (secondary level)
Founded 1904 as school, acquired present status and title 1982. Under the jurisdiction of the Lebowa Department of Education. Residential facilities for students.
Academic Year: February to November (February-June; August-November).
Admission Requirements: Senior Certificate.
Language of Instruction: English.
Degrees and Diplomas: Diploma, 3 yrs.
Academic Staff: c. 40.
Student Enrolment: c. 540.

6688 **DURBANSE ODERWYSKOLLEGE**
Durban College of Education
Queen Mary Avenue, Durban 4001

6689 **EDGEWOOD COLLEGE OF EDUCATION**
Private Bag X2001, Pinetown 3600
Telephone: (031) 7001455
Rector: A.L. Le Roux (1974-)
Registrar: N.L. Fort

Teacher Training (primary and secondary levels)
Founded 1966. A State institution under the jurisdiction of the Department of Education and Training. Residential facilities for students.
Academic Year: January to December (January-June; July-December).
Admission Requirements: Matriculation Certificate.
Fees (Rand): 900 per annum.
Language of Instruction: English.
Degrees and Diplomas: Diplomas 3 yrs. Bachelor of Primary Education (with University of Natal), 4 yrs.
Library: College Library.
Academic Staff, 1986-87:

Rank	Full-time
Rector	1
Vice-Rector	1
Heads of Departments	13
Senior Lecturers and Lecturers	61
Total	76

Student Enrolment, 1986-87:

	Men	Women	Total
Of the country	188	430	618*

*Also 88 external students.

6690 **NATAL COLLEGE OF EDUCATION**
NATALSE ONDERWYSKOLLEGE
Private Bag 9007, Pietermaritzburg 3200
Telephone: 54515
Rector: S.D. Wallace (1986-)

Teacher Training (primary level)
Founded 1912 as Natal Training College, amalgamated with Natal College of Education for Further Training (founded 1977) with present title 1986. Under the jurisdiction of the Natal Provincial Administration. Residential facilities for students.
Academic Year: January to December (January-April; April-July; July-September; October-December).
Admission Requirements: Senior Certificate or equivalent.
Fees (Rand): 900 per annum.
Languages of Instruction: English and Afrikaans.
Degrees and Diplomas: Higher Diploma in Education (for pre-primary and primary levels), 4 yrs.
Academic Staff, 1986-87:

Rank	Full-time
Rector	1
Vice-Rectors	2
Heads of Departments	8
Senior Lecturers	12
Lecturers	19
Total	42

Student Enrolment, 1986-87:

	Men	Women	Total
Of the country	87	564	651

6691 **COLLEGE OF EDUCATION FOR FURTHER TRAINING**
Private Bag 9007, Pietermaritzburg
Telephone: (0331) 58200

Teacher Training (primary level) (by correspondence)
Founded 1977 to assist primary teachers to improve their qualifications by correspondence. Under the jurisdiction of the Natal Provincial Administration.
Academic Year: January to November (January-March; April-June; July-November).
Admission Requirements: Teaching Diplomas or recognized foreign qualification.
Language of Instruction: English or Afrikaans.
Degrees and Diplomas: Diplomas, 2 yrs.
Academic Staff: c. 20.
Student Enrolment: c. 480 (by correspondence).

Other institutions

6692 **BLOEMFONTEINSE ONDERWYSKOLLEGE**
Bloemfontein College of Education
1 Park Road, Bloemfontein, Orange Free State 9301
Telephone: 47820/3
Rector: B. du P. Brink
Registrar: V. van Vuuren

Teacher Training (primary level)

Founded 1898 as normal school. Acquired present status and title 1965. Under the jurisdiction of the Department of Education and Culture. Governing bodies: the Senate; the Board. Some residential facilities for academic staff and students.

Academic Year: January to December (January-March; April-June; July-September; October-December).

Admission Requirements: Matriculation Certificate.

Fees (Rand): 700 per annum.

Languages of Instruction: Afrikaans and English.

Degrees and Diplomas: Diplomas, 3-4 yrs. Postgraduate diplomas in Education, 1 yr. Degree, 4 yrs. Bachelor (in collaboration with UOFS).

Library: Visser Library, *c.* 56,000 vols.

Academic Staff, 1990: 49 (4).

Student Enrolment, 1990:

	Men	Women	Total
Of the country	53	205	258*

*Also 93 external students.

Other Institutions

6693 **BONAMELO COLLEGE OF EDUCATION**
Private Bag X849, Witsieshoek 9870

6694 **SEFIKENG COLLEGE OF EDUCATION**
Private Bag X827, Witsieshoek 9870

6695 **TSHIYA COLLEGE OF EDUCATION**
TSHIYA ONDERWYSKOLLEGE
Private Bag X809, Witsieshoek 9870
Telephone: 533½
Rector: V.M. Botha
Registrar: M. Mochunoane

Teacher Training (primary and secondary levels)

Founded 1982. A State institution under the jurisdiction of the Qwagwa Department of Education. Residential facilities for academic staff and 480 students.

Academic Year: January to December (January-March; April-June; July-September; September-December).

Admission Requirements: Matriculation Certificate.

Fees (Rand): 200 per annum.

Languages of Instruction: English, Afrikaans and Southern Sotho.

Degrees and Diplomas: Diplomas, 3 yrs.

Library: College Library, *c.* 9000 vols.

Academic Staff, 1986-87:

Rank	Full-time
Heads of Departments	8
Senior Lecturers	12
Lecturers	42
Total	62

Student Enrolment, 1986-87:

	Men	Women	Total
Of the country	390	399	789

6696 **ONDERWYSKOLLEGE GOUDSTAD**
Private Bag X27, Auckland Park, Johannesburg
Telephone: (011) 726-3200

Teacher Training

6697 **JOHANNESBURG COLLEGE OF EDUCATION**
17 Hoofd Street, Braamfontein 2001

6698 **ONDERWYSKOLLEGE POTCHEFSTROOM**
Cr. Borcherd and Hoffman Streets, Potchefstroom 2520

6699 **ONDERWYSKOLLEGE PRETORIA**
Pretoria College of Education (Afrikaans-medium)
Private Bag X382, Pretoria 0001

6700 **PRETORIA COLLEGE OF EDUCATION**
Private Bag X380, Pretoria 0001
Telephone: 325-1431
Rector: R.M. Yule (1985-)
Registrar: F. Wolmarens

Teacher Training (primary and secondary levels)

Founded 1980. A State institution affiliated to the University of South Africa.

Academic Year: January to November (January-June; August-October).

Admission Requirements: Matriculation Certificate.

Fees (Rand): 250 per annum.

Language of Instruction: English.

Degrees and Diplomas: Diplomas, 3 yrs. Bachelor in Primary Education, 4 yrs.

Student Enrolment, 1986-87:

	Men	Women	Total
Of the country	112	403	515

6701 **HEBRON COLLEGE OF EDUCATION**
Private Bag X1084, Garankuwa 0208

6702 **MORTELE COLLEGE OF EDUCATION**
Private Bag X376, Makapanstad 0404

6703 **STRYDOM COLLEGE OF EDUCATION**
Private Bag X217, Seloshesha 9785

6704 **TAUNG COLLEGE OF EDUCATION**
Private Bag X03, Pudimoe 8581

6705 **TLABANE COLLEGE OF EDUCATION**
Private Bag X2003, Tlabane 0305

6706 **LENNON SEBE COLLEGE OF EDUCATION**
P.O. Box 685, King Williams Town 5600

6707 **DR. W. B. RUBANASE COLLEGE OF EDUCATION**
Private Bag X140, Mdantsane 5219

6708 **MASIBULELE COLLEGE OF EDUCATION**
Private Bag X338, Whittlesea 5360

6709 **MAKHADO COLLEGE OF EDUCATION**
Private Bag X1004, Dzanani

6710 **TSHISIMANI COLLEGE OF EDUCATION**
Private Bag X1302, Tshakhuma

6711 **VENDA COLLEGE OF EDUCATION**
Private Bag X2269, Sibasa

6712 **ARTHUR TSENGIWE TEACHERS' TRAINING COLLEGE**
P.O. Box 2, Cala

6713 **BENSONVALE TEACHERS' TRAINING COLLEGE**
P.O. Bensonvale, Hershel

6714 **BUTTERWORTH TEACHERS' TRAINING COLLEGE**
P.O. Butterworth

6715 **CIOIRA TEACHERS' TRAINING COLLEGE**
Private Bag X5034, Umtata

6716 **CLARKEBURY TEACHERS' TRAINING COLLEGE**
Clarkebury

6717 **MALUTI TEACHERS' TRAINING COLLEGE**
P.O. Box 87, Matatiele

6718 **MOUNT ARTHUR TEACHERS' TRAINING COLLEGE**
Private Bag X123, Lady Frere

6719 **SHAWBURY TEACHERS' TRAINING COLLEGE**
Qumbu

6720 **SIGCAU TEACHERS' TRAINING COLLEGE**
Private Bag X514, Flagstaff

SPAIN

Universities

6721 **UNIVERSIDAD DE ALCALÁ DE HENARES**
University of Alcalá de Henares
Plaza de San Diego, s/n, 28801 Alcalá de Henares Madrid
Telex: 23896
Telephone: (34-1) 8890400
Fax: (34-1) 8890667
Rector: Manuel Gala (1986-90)
Vice-Rector (International Relations): Luis Beltrán

F. of Science
Dean: Fernando Jordán de Urries y Senante
F. of Economics and Business Administration
Dean: Diego Azqueta
F. of Law
Dean: Luis García-San Miguel
F. of Pharmacy
Dean: Vicente Vilas
F. of Philosophy and Letters
Dean: María Dolores Cabañas
F. of Medicine
Dean: Antonio López
S. of Telecommunication Engineering
Director: Ricardo García
S. of Teachers' Training
Director: José María Sánchez
Undergraduate C. (Madrid)
Director: Luis Rodríguez
C. of Nursing (Guadalajara)
Director: María Carmen Hernández
C. of Education (Guadalajara)
Director: Fernando Laborda
Ce. of European Studies
Director: Carlos Molina
Ce. of American Studies
Director: Angel Berenguer
Hispanic-American Ce. of Industrial Relations (Madrid)
Director: José Manuel Almansa
Modern Languages Ce.
Director: Francisco Moreno
Also 33 departments of the faculties.

Founded 1499 by Cardenal Cisneros, reorganized 1977, incorporating previously existing faculties of the University of Madrid. An autonomous institution receiving financial aid from the Government. Governing body: the Junta de Gobierno.

Arrangements for co-operation with institutions of higher education in: Argentina; Colombia; Germany; Hungary;Italy; Mexico; Poland; Switzerland; USA; USSR.

Academic Year: October to June (October-December; January-March; April-June).

Admission Requirements: Secondary school certificate (bachiller) and pre-university examination (madurez).

Language of Instruction: Spanish.

Degrees and Diplomas: Licenciado in all faculties, 5 yrs, except Medicine, 6 yrs. Doctorate, a further 2 yrs by thesis.

Library: Total *c.* 120,000 vols.

Academic Staff: c. 430.

Student Enrolment: c. 10,115.

6722 **UNIVERSIDAD DE ALICANTE**
University of Alicante
San Vicente del Raspeig, Alicante
Telex: 66616
Telephone: (965) 66150
Fax: 5668-867
Rector: Ramoń Martín-Mateo
Secretario General: Juan José Díaz

F. of Science
Dean: Mario Pardo Casado; *staff* 38 (1)
F. of Philosophy and Letters
Dean: Antonio Ramas Hidalgo; *staff* 62
F. of Medicine
Dean: Emilio Balaguer; *staff* 56 (41)
F. of Law
Dean: Joaquin Martínez Valla; *staff* 34 (5)
F. of Economics and Management
Dean: Carlos Barciele López; *staff* 22
Ce. of Optics
; *staff* 5
Ce. of Education
Director: Angel Herrera Blanco; *staff* 48 (3)
Ce. of Nursing
Director: Pilar Hernández Sánchez; *staff* 13
Ce. of Management
Director: Adolfo Posacas García; *staff* 18 (2)
I. of Geography
Director: Antonio Gil; *staff* 8
I. of Biology
Director: Antonio Estevez Rubio
I. of Sociology
Director: Benjamin Ottera
Ce. of Industrial Medicine
Director: Juan Batista Martí Lloret
Ce. of Social Work
Director: Jesús D. Martínez
Ce. of Statistics
Director: Marco Antonio López Cerdá

Founded 1968 as college, acquired present status and title 1979. An autonomous institution receiving financialaid from the government. Governing bodies: the Claustro; the Junta de Gobierno; the Consejo.

Arrangements for co-operation with: East Anglia University; Sheffield City Polytecnic.

Academic Year: October to June (October-December; January-March; April-June).

Admission Requirements: Secondary school certificate (bachiller) and pre-university examination (madurez), or entrance examination foradults.

Fees (Pesetas): 35,000-45,000 per annum.

Language of Instruction: Spanish.

Degrees and Diplomas: Diplomado, 3 yrs. Licenciado, 5 yrs; Medicine, 6 yrs. Doctorates.

Library: Faculty and College libraries.

Publications: Mediterranea (Ecology) (annually); Campus (4 times a year).

Academic Staff, 1989-90: 320.

Student Enrolment, 1989-90:

	Men	Women	Total
Of the country	6069	8207	14,276

6723 ***UNIVERSITAT DE BARCELONA**
University of Barcelona
Gran Via de les Corts Catalanes 585, 08007 Barcelona
Telephone: (93) 318-42-66
Fax: (93) 3025947
Rector: Josep Bricall (1986-)
Gerente: Josep Roig Marti

D. of Human and Social Sciences
Chairman: Gabriel Oliver
F. of Philosophy
Dean: Antonio Alegre
F. of Geography and History
Dean: Salvador Claramunt
F. of Philology
Dean: Pedro Juan Quetglás
F. of Fine Arts
Dean: Miquel Quilez
D. of Law, Economics, and Social Sciences
Chairman: Albert Josep Biayna
F. of Law
Dean: Joaquin Tornos
F. of Economics and Business Administration
Dean: Fernando Casado
Ce. of Business Administration
Dean: Joaquin Fernández
Ce. of Business Administration (Vich)
D. of Experimental Sciences and Mathematics
Chairman: Enric Isidre Canela
F. of Biology
Dean: Francesc Carmona
F. of Chemistry
Dean: Enrique Pedroso
F. of Physics
Dean: Pere Setglar
F. of Mathematics
Dean: Josep Maria Font
F. of Geology
Dean: Francesc Calvet
D. of Health Sciences
Chairman: Jorge Domingo
F. of Medicine
Dean: Francisco Navarro
F. of Pharmacy
Dean: Joan Bosch
F. of Dentistry
Dean: Cosme Gay
F. of Psychology
Dean: Maria del Carmen Triado
Ce. of Nursing
Director: Rosa Blasco
Ce. of Podology
Director: Virginia Nobel
D. of Educational Sciences
Chairman: Josep Maria Rotger
F. of Educational Sciences
Dean: Miquel Martinez
Ce. of Education
Director: Remedios Romanos
F. of Law (Lérida)
Dean: Maria Teresa Areces
F. of Philosophy and Letters (Lérida)
Dean: Joan Vilagrasa
F. of Medicine (Lérida)
Dean: Manuel Rubio
F. of Philosophy and Letters (Campo de Tarragona)
Dean: Santiago Roquer
F. of Chemistry (Campo de Tarragona)
Dean: Francesc Xavier Rius
F. of Medicine (Campo de Tarragona)
Dean: Jose Maria Tomas
Ce. of Education (Campo de Tarragona)
Director: Saturnino Gimeno
Ce. of Business Administration (Campo de Tarragona)
Director: Antonio Terceño
Ce. of Oenology (Campo de Tarragona)
Director: Lluis Maria Arola
Undergraduate C.
Ce. of Nursing (Barcelona (3), Tarragona, Tortosa, Lleida)
Ce. of Business Administration (Vic)
Ce. of Education (Vic)
Ce. of Social Work (Barcelona (2), Tarragona, Lleida)
F. of Physical Education
I. of Education (ICE)
Director: Ignacio Vila
I. of Archaeology and Prehistory
Director: Ana Maria Rauret
I. of Criminology
Director: José Maria Escribá
I. of Regional Economics
Director: Juan M. de la Torre
I. of Hellenic Studies
Director: Josep Alsina
I. of Pharmacy
Director: Josep M. Suñer
I. of Medieval History
Director: Manuel Riu

Founded 1450 under the authority of Alfonso V and confirmed by Papal Bull. The university was established in Cervera by Philip V. By 1873 this institution was transferred to Barcelona and the University of Barcelona was formally re-established as a State institution under the jurisdiction of the Ministry of Education and Science. Reorganized 1985 as an autonomous institution under the jurisdiction of the Generalitat of Catalonia and financially supported by the State and the Generalitat. Governing bodies: the Claustro General; the Junta de Gobierno (Administrative Board), comprising the Rector, the deans of the faculties, the Vice-Rectors, the Secretary-General, the Presidents of Divisions, the Gerente, and representatives of the academic and administrative staff and students. Some residential facilities for academic staff and students in Colegios Mayores.

Arrangements for co-operation with the Universities of: Montpellier; Tufts, Massachusetts; Chile (Pontifical); Chihuahua; Paris-Sorbonne; Leningrad; León, Nicaragua; Laval, Québec; Georgetown, Washington; Sciences sociales de Toulouse; Fribourg; Litoral, Santa Fe; California, Berkeley; Camerino; Grenoble III; Damascus; Nicaragua (Autónoma); Oran; Illinois; Savoie, Chambéry; Toulouse III; Southampton; Bordeaux I; Internacional Menéndez y Pelayo; Técnica de Lisboa; Tecnica di Firenze; Paris; Johns Hopkins; Siena.Ecole normale supérieure de Saint-Cloud; Pushkin Institute of Russian, Moscow; Hochschule für bildende Künste Braunschweig; Cambridge Crystallographic Data Centre; Pädagogischen Hochschule Ludwigsburg; Ecole des hautes Etudes en Sciences sociales, Paris; Dorset Institute, Bournemouth. Participates in the ERASMUS programme.

Academic Year: October to May (October-December; January-March; April-May).

Admission Requirements: Secondary school certificate (bachiller) and pre-university examination (madurez), or entrance examination foradults.

Fees (Pesetas): 40,300-62,000 per annum.

Languages of Instruction: Catalán and Spanish.

Degrees and Diplomas: Diplomado, 3 yrs. Licenciado in all faculties, 5 yrs, except Medicine, 6 yrs. Doctorates, by thesis.

Libraries: General Library, *c.* 630,625 vols; Art, 9632; Philology, 123,345; Philosophy, 42,603; Geography and History, 101,083; Law, *c.* 114,953; Economics, 121,575; Business, 33,843; Biology, 29,144; Physics and Chemistry, 31,246; Geology, 15,259; Mathematics, 13,915; Pharmacy, 12,065; Nursing, 5812; Medicine, 150,918; Dentistry, 741; Psychology, 17,988; Education, 45,414; Pedagogy, 42,794. Lérida, 30,578; Tarragona/Reus, 39,865.

Special Facilities (Museums, etc.): Zoology Museum; Pinacoteca; Museo de Criminología

Publications: Anuario de Filología; Logos (Barcelona); Boletín del Instituto de Estudios Helénicos; Publicacions de la Universitat de Barcelona; Cuadernos de Arqueologia; Temes Monogràfics Bioestadistica; Ciencia-Industria Farmacéutica; Índice Histórico Español; Studium opthalmologium; Fossilia Folia Botánica Miscellanea; Boletin de Estratigrafía (Barcelona); Revista de Geografía; Boletín Americanista; Revista d'Art (Departamento Historia del Arte); Traza y Boza (Medieval); Trabajos de Antropología; Archivos de Pediatría; Anuario de Psicologia; Revista del Departamento de Psiquiatría; Cuadernos de Economía; Cuadernos de Información Económica; Publicacions del Departament de Psicología; Convivium (Barcelona); Universitas Tarraconensis; Geo-crítica; Archivos Españoles de Medicina Interna; Revista del Seminario de la Cátedra de Patología Médica de Barcelona; Collectanea Mathematica; Pedralbes; Historia y Fuente Oral; Temps d'Educació.

Press or Publishing House: Servei d'Informació i Publicacions.

Academic Staff, 1988-89:

Rank	Full-time	Part-time
Catedráticos Eméritos	–	22
Catedráticos Universidad	281	53
Catedráticos Escuela	50	4
Profesores Titulares Universidad	1079	158
Profesores Titulares Escuela	249	14
Profesores Asociados Universidad	471	536
Profesores Asociados Escuela	63	57
Profesores Asociados Extranjeros	7	–
Profesores Ayudantes Universidad	281	–
Profesores Ayudantes Escuela	8	–
Total	2489	844

Student Enrolment, 1988-89:

	Men	Women	Total
Of the country	31,934	47,645	79,579
Of other countries	–	–	882
Total	31,934	47,645	80,461*

*Also 105 external students.

6724 ***UNIVERSITAT AUTÒNOMA DE BARCELONA**

Autonomous University of Barcelona
Campus Universitario de Bellaterra, 08193 Bellaterra
Telex: 52040
Telephone: (93) 5811000
Fax: (93) 5812000
Rector: Josep M. Vallès Casadevall
Secretario General: Enric Cassany Cels

F. of Medicine
Dean: Jaume Guàrdia Massó; *staff* 73 (392)
F. of Philosophy and Letters (including Art and Education)
Dean: José Martínez Gázquez; *staff* 192 (21)
F. of Science
Dean: Manuel Castellet Solanas; *staff* 289 (19)
F. of Economics and Business Administration
Dean: Joan Montllor Serrats; *staff* 91 (30)
F. of Law
Dean: Isidre Molas Batllori; *staff* 52 (37)
F. of Information Sciences
Dean: Mar Fontcuberta Balaguer; *staff* 83 (37)
F. of Veterinary Medicine
Dean: Margarita Arboix i Arzo; *staff* 84 (12)
F. of Political Sciences and Sociology
Dean: Joan Botella Corral; *staff* 39 (3)
F. of Psychology
Dean: Ignacio Morgado Bernal; *staff* 59 (3)
Undergraduate Ce. (Sciences, Law, Philosophy, Philology, History, Geography, Education) (Gerona)
Director: Josep Nadal Farreras; *staff* 90 (15)
Ce. of Education (Pre-school, Sciences, Social Sciences, Philology) (Bellaterra)
Director: Jaume Botey Vallès; *staff* 116 (20)
Ce. of Education (Pre-school, Sciences, Social Sciences, Philology) (Gerona)
Director: Josep Torrellas Vendrell; *staff* 34 (10)
Ce. of Education (Sciences, Social Sciences, Philology) (Lérida)
Director: Maria Rubies Garrofé
Ce. of Business Administration (Sabadell)
Director: Lina Sanou Vilarrodona; *staff* 25 (11)
Ce. of Business Administration (Gerona)
Director: Luis Pérez Herrero; *staff* 34 (10)
Ce. of Translation and Interpretation
Director: Sean Golden; *staff* 50 (4)
Ce. of Computer Sciences (Sabadell)
Director: Jordi Roig de Sárate; *staff* 20 (3)
Ce. of Nursing (Barcelona, Gerona, Vich, Manresa, Santa Coloma de Gramanet)
I. of Musicology Research
Director: Francesc Bonamusa Gaspà
I. of Education Sciences
Director: Teresa Eulalia Isern; *staff* 16 (2)
I. of Biology
Director: Claudi M. Cuchillo Foix
I. of Medieval Studies
Director: José M. Domene Ruiz

Also schools and institutes attached to the various faculties, and attached private School of Computer Sciences at Santa Coloma de Gramanet (Barcelona).

Founded 1968 by decree of the government and following the publication of a White Paper on education. Financedby the State. Governing bodies: the Junta de Gobierno (Administrative Board), including the Rector, and the deans and directors of the faculties and institutes, and representatives of the academic staff, administrative body, and students; the Claustro. Residential facilities for academic staff.

Participates in the ERASMUS programme.

Academic Year: October to June (October-December; January-Easter; Easter-June).

Admission Requirements: Secondary school certificate (bachiller) and pre-university examination (madurez), or entrance examination foradults.

Fees (Pesetas): 41,050-58,150 per annum.

Language of Instruction: Spanish.

Degrees and Diplomas: Diplomado, 3 yrs. Licenciado, a further 2 yrs; Medicine, a further 3 yrs. Doctorate, a further 2 yrs by thesis.

Library: Total, *c.* 200,000 vols.

Publications: Cuadernos de Psicología; Documentos d'Análisi Urbana; Documentos d'Análisi Metológica en Geografía; Administración Pública; Publicaciones de Matemáticas; Publicaciones de Geologia; Avances en Terapéutica.

Academic Staff, 1989-90: 1353 (629).

Student Enrolment, 1989-90: 34,993.

6725 **UNIVERSIDAD DE CÁDIZ**

University of Cádiz
C/Ancha 16, Cádiz
Telex: 76197
Telephone: (956) 22-47-10
Rector: José Luis Romero Palanco (1986-90)
Secretaria General: Sara Acuña Guirola

F. of Science
F. of Medicine
F. of Philosophy and Letters
F. of Law (Jérez de la Frontera)
Undergraduate Ce. (Law) (Jérez de la Frontera)
Undergraduate Ce. (Chemistry, Philosophy and Letters)
Ce. of Business Administration
Ce. of Education
Ce. of Engineering (Technical)
Ce. of Nursing (Jérez de la Frontera)
Ce. of Education (La Linea de la Concepción)
Ce. of Business Administration (Jérez de la Frontera)
Ce. of Engineering (Technical) (Algeciras)

Founded 1979.

Academic Year: September to June.

Admission Requirements: Secondary school certificate (bachiller) and pre-university examination (madurez), or entrance examination forstudents over 25 yrs.

Fees (Pesetas): 35,000-50,000 per annum.

Language of Instruction: Spanish.

Degrees and Diplomas: Diplomado, 3 yrs. Licenciado, 5 yrs. Medicine, 6 yrs. Doctorates, by thesis.

Academic Staff: *c.* 640.

Student Enrolment: *c.* 8400.

6726 ***UNIVERSIDAD DE CANTABRIA**

University of Cantabria
Avenida de los Castros s/n, 39005 Santander
Telex: 35861 EDUCI E
Telephone: (34) (42) 201222
Fax: (34) (42) 201183
Rector: José Maria Ureña Francés
Secretaria General: Beatriz Arizaga

F. of Science
F. of Medicine
Dean: Juan A. García-Porrero
F. of Philosophy and Letters
Dean: Alfonso Moure Romanillo
F. of Law (Cantabria)
Dean: Luís Martin Rebollo

F. of Economics and Business Administration
Dean: José Maria Sarabia Alzaga
S. of Civil Engineering (Highways, Canals and Ports, Technical)
Director: Federico Gutiérrez-Solana
Politechnic S. of Engineering
Director: Ignacio Eguiluz Morán
S. of Marine Studies
Director: Emilio Eguía López
Ce. of Education
Director: Demetrio Cascón Martínez
Ce. of Mining Engineering
Director: Eliseo Fernández Espina
Ce. of Nursing
Director: Juan J. Jordá Catalá
Ce. of Education (Torrelavega)
Director: Jesús Flórez Beledo
Ce. of Labour Relations
Director: Gabriel García Becedas
I. of Educational Sciences
Director: Fernando Guerra López
I. of Animal Husbandry
I. of Prehistory
Also 23 Departments. Spanish courses for foreigners at Laredo.

Founded 1972, as University of Santander, incorporating a school of civil engineering and a faculty of science established 1967 and 1968 as branch campuses of the University of Valladolid. Acquired present title 1984. A State institution under the jurisdiction of the Ministry of Education and Science. Governing bodies: the Claustro; the Junta de Gobierno; the Consejo Social. Residential facilities for students.

Arrangements for co-operation with the Universities of: Guayaquil, Ecuador; California, Berkeley; Wisconsin-Madison; Belgrano; North Carolina; North Carolina State; Salta, Argentina; Peru (Católica); Le Havre; Rouen; Exeter; Miami; Valle, Colombia. Participates in the SANTANDER Group.

Academic Year: October to July (October-February; February-July).

Admission Requirements: Secondary school certificate (bachiller) and pre-university examination (madurez), or entrance examination forstudents over 25 years.

Language of Instruction: Spanish.

Degrees and Diplomas: Licenciado in–Science; Law; Letters, 5 yrs. Engineering; Medicine, 6 yrs. Professional title of Ingeniero Técnico Superior de Caminos, Canales y Puertos. Diplomado. Doctorates.

Library: Total, 200,000.

Special Facilities (Museums, etc.): Museo de las Comarcas de Santillana.

Press or Publishing House: Servicio de Publicaciones.

Academic Staff, 1988-89:

Rank	
Catedráticos	68
Profesores Titulares	200
Otros Profesores	341
Total	609

Student Enrolment, 1988-89: 9487.

6727 ***UNIVERSIDAD DE CASTILLA-LA MANCHA**
Calle Paloma 9, 1307 Ciudad Real
Rector: Luis Arroyo (1988-)

F. of Chemistry
Dean: Enrique Diez Barra
F. of Philosophy and Letters
Dean: Félix Pillet Capdepón
F. of Law (Albacete)
Dean: Luis Arroyo Zapatero
F. of Fine Arts (Cuenca)
Dean: Florencio Garrido Ramos
Undergraduate Ce. (Law, Letters) (Cuenca)
Director: Gregorio Robles Morchón
Undergraduate Ce. (Law, Economics, Letters, and Chemistry) (Toledo)
Director: Daniel Poyán Diaz
Ce. of Agricultural Engineering (Technical)
Ce. of Industrial Engineering (Technical) (Albacete)
Ce. of Architecture (Technical) (Cuenca)
Ce. of Agricultural Engineering
Ce. of Education
Ce. of Industrial Engineering (Albacete, Almadén)
Ce. of Agricultural Engineering (Albacete)
Ce. of Forestry (Albacete)
Ce. of Computer Sciences (Albacete)
Ce. of Education (Albacete, Cuenca, Guadalajara, Toledo)
Ce. of Nursing (Albacete, Cuenca, Guadalajara)
Ce. of Mining (Almadén)
Ce. of Electrical Engineering (Toledo)

Founded 1982.

Academic Year: October to June (October-March; March-June).

Admission Requirements: Secondary school certificate (bachiller) and pre-university examination (madurez).

Language of Instruction: Spanish.

Degrees and Diplomas: Diplomado, 3 yrs. Licenciado, 5 yrs. Professional title of Ingeniero Técnico, 3 yrs.

Academic Staff, 1986-87: 320.

Student Enrolment, 1986-87: 6185.

6728 **UNIVERSIDAD POLITÉCNICA DE CATALUÑA**
Technical University of Cataluña
Avenida Dr. Gregorio Marañón s/n, Barcelona 26
Telex: 52.821
Telephone: (93) 249-38-04
Rector: Gabriel Ferrate Pascual (1978-)

F. of Computer Sciences
F. of Economics
F. of Business Administration
S. of Architecture
S. of Architecture (El Vallés)
S. of Industrial Engineering
S. of Industrial Engineering (Tarrasa)
S. of Telecommunication Engineering
S. of Highway Engineering
S. of Agricultural Engineering (Lérida)
I. of Education
I. of Textile Research
I. of Petrochemistry
Computer Ce.
I. of Transport Research
I. of Cybernetics
I. of Energetics
Ce. of Architecture (Technical)
Ce. of Industrial Engineering (Technical) (Tarrasa)
Ce. of Industrial Engineering (Technical) (Vilanueva y Geltrú)
Polytechnic Ce. (Manresa)
Polytechnic Ce. (Gerona)
Ce. of Agricultural Engineering (Technical) (Lérida)
Ce. of Optometry (Tarrasa)
Ce. of Agricultural Engineering (Technical)
Ce. of Industrial Engineering (Technical)
Ce. of Knitting and Weaving
Ce. of Telecommunication Engineering (Technical) (Vilanueva y Geltrú)
Ce. of Industrial Engineering (Technical) (Igualada)
Ce. of Industrial Engineering (Technical) (Tarragona)

Founded 1968 as Polytechnic Institute, became University 1973, incorporating Escuela Técnica Superior de Arquitectura, founded 1870; Escuela Técnica Superior de Ingenieros Industriales (1851); Escuela Técnica Superior de Ingenieros Industriales, Tarrasa (1904). A State institution under the jurisdiction of the Ministry of Education and Science. Governing bodies: the Junta de Gobierno, comprising 50 members; the Claustro General, comprising 500 members.

Academic Year: October to July (October-February; February-July).

Admission Requirements: Secondary school certificate (bachiller) or foreign equivalent recognized by the Ministry of Education and Science, and pre-university examination (madurez). Entrance examination for students over 25.

Library: Total, *c.* 78,610.

Publications: Revista Técnica; Qüestió (quarterly); Cuadernos de Ingeniería (3 times a year).

Academic Staff: c. 1670.
Student Enrolment: c. 16,500.

6729 ***UNIVERSIDAD PONTIFICIA COMILLAS**
Pontifical University Comillas
Alberto Aguilera 23, 28015 Madrid
Telex: 34-1 2486569 G3
Telephone: (1) 734-39-50
Fax: (1) 734-45-570
Rector: Guillermo Rodriguez-Izquierdo Gavala (1984-90)
Secretario General: Ricardo Lobato García

F. of Theology
Dean: José Joaquín Alemany Briz
F. of Canon Law
Dean: José María Urteaga Embil
F. of Philosophy and Letters
Dean: Luis López-Yarto Elizalde
F. of Economics and Business Administration
Dean: Antonio Arroyo Rodríguez
F. of Law
Dean: Manuel Gallego Díaz
S. of Engineering
Director: Luis García Pascual
Ce. of Social Work
Director: Adolfo Fernández Díaz Nava
I. of Business Management
Director: Carlos Bornillos García
I. of Home and Family Life
Director: Marciano Vidal
I. of Modern Languages
Director: Christopher Waddington
Ce. of Industrial Engineering (Technical)
Director: Luis García Pascual
Ce. for Lifelong Education
Director: Juan Manuel Cobo Suero
Ce. of Computer Sciences
Director: Mateo Camps Llufríu
Ce. of Nursing
Director: Calixto Plumed Moreno
I. for Technological Research
Director: José Ignacio Pérez Arriaga
Research I. on Liberalism
Director: Enrique Menéndez Ureña

Also Research Institutes and Centres of Theology at: Valladolid, Las Palmas, Logroño, Ciudad Real, Colmenar Veijo (Madrid), Córdoba, and Tagaste (Madrid).

Founded 1892 by Pope Leo XIII. Acquired present status 1901. The administrative and academic direction of the institution is entrusted to the Society of Jesus. Reorganized 1935. Transferred from Santander to Madrid 1960. The degrees and diplomas of the institution are recognized by the State which, under the 1946 convention withthe Vatican, also provides some financial support. Governing bodies: the Senado, comprising 60 members; the Junta de Gobierno, comprising 20 members. Residential facilities for c. 50 students.

Academic Year: October to June (October-December; January-April; April-June).

Admission Requirements: Secondary school certificate (bachiller) and pre-university examination (madurez).

Fees (Pesetas): 95,387-547,975 per annum.

Language of Instruction: Spanish.

Degrees and Diplomas: Diplomado in–Theology (Baccalauria); Industrial Engineering; Social Work; Computer Sciences; Nursing, 3 yrs. Licenciado or Professional titles in–Philosophy and Letters; Theology; Canon Law; Economics and Business Administration; Law, 5 yrs; Engineering, 6 yrs. Doctorado, a further 2 yrs. Also Graduate Diploma in Business Management, 2 yrs.

Library: Total, 400,000 vols.

Publications: Miscellanea Comillas; Pensamiento; Estudios Eclesiásticos; Revistas (Law and Economics, and Management); Anales (Mechanical and Electrical Engineering).

Academic Staff, 1989-90:

Rank	Full-time	Part-time
Ordinarios	46	39
Agregados	28	12
Adjuntos	41	14
Colaboradores	93	701
Ayudantes	12	68
Maestros de Taller	1	1
Total	221	835

Student Enrolment, 1989-90:

	Men	Women	Total
Of the country	8535	5293	13,828*

*Also 356 foreign students.

6730 ***UNIVERSIDAD DE CÓRDOBA**
University of Córdoba
Alfonso XIII, 13, 14071 Córdoba
Telex: 76561 EDUCIE
Telephone: (957) 473125
Fax: (957) 485452
Rector: Amador Jover Moyano (1984-)
Secretario General: Rafael Ayuzo Muñoz

F. of Veterinary Medicine
Dean: Félix Infante Miranda
S. of Agricultural Engineering (Technical)
Director: José Ignacio Cubero Salmerón
F. of Medicine
Dean: Manuel Casal Román
F. of Science
Dean: Eugenio Domínguez Vilches
F. of Philosophy and Letters
Dean: Antonio López Ontiveros
F. of Law
Dean: Juan Ignacio Font Galán
Politechnic C.
Director: Luis Ballesteros Olmo
C. of Mining (Bélmez)
Director: Rafael Hernando Luna
C. of Education
Director: Anastasio Villanueva Sepulveda
S. of Nursing
Director: Manuel Vaquero Avellán
I. of Education
Director: Carmen Bach Piella
F. of Economics and Business (E.T.E.A.)
Director: Antonio Rodero Franganillo
C. of Education 'Sagrado Corazón'
Director: Juan Bautista Aparicio Macarro
C. of Business Studies
Director: Augusto Gómez Cabrera

Also 45 departments of the various faculties.

Founded 1972 and incorporating a number of previously existing faculties and schools, the oldest of which, Veterinary Medicine, was established in 1847. An autonomous institution receiving financial aid from the government. Governing body: the Claustro Universitario.

Academic Year: October to June.

Admission Requirements: Secondary school certificate (bachiller) and entrance examination.

Language of Instruction: Spanish.

Degrees and Diplomas: Licenciado in–Philosophy and Letters; Science, 5 yrs; Veterinary Medicine, 5 yrs and dissertation. Professional titles in–Agriculture; Nursing, 5 yrs; Medicine, 6 yrs. Doctorate in Veterinary Medicine, by thesis.

Academic Staff: c. 800.
Student Enrolment: c. 10,000.

6731 ***UNIVERSIDAD DE DEUSTO**
University of Deusto
Avenida de las Universidades, Apartado 1, 48080 Bilbao
Telephone: (94) 4-45-31-00
Rector: Jesús María Eguiluz Ortuzar, S.J. (1986-)
Secretario General: José Ramón Scheifler Amezaga

F. of Law
Dean: Ernesto Martínez Díaz de Guereñu; *staff* 42 (41)

F. of Philosophy and Arts
Dean: Fernando García de Cortazar; *staff* 68 (14)
F. of Theology
Dean: Isidro María Sans Benguria; *staff* 23 (6)
F. of Economics and Business Administration
Dean: Antonio Freije Uriarte; *staff* 16 (38)
F. of Economics and Business Administration (San Sebastián)
Dean: Francisco José Olarte Marín; *staff* 8 (25)
F. of Political Science and Sociology
Dean: Antonio Yabar Maisterrena; *staff* 23 (10)
F. of Philosophy and Education
Dean: Manuel Marroquín Pérez; *staff* 42 (7)
F. of Computer Sciences
Dean: Máximo Llaguno Ellacuria; *staff* 25 (14)
International I. of Business Administration
Director: Antonio Freije Uriarte
I. of Education
Director: Roberto Pascual Pacheco; *staff* 4
I. of Modern Languages
Director: Winfried Arnold; *staff* 20 (5)
I. of Religious Studies
Director: Isidro María Sans Benguria
I. of Pastoral Studies
Director: Félix Meler Simón; *staff* 4
I. of Basque Studies
Director: Francisco Altuna Bengoechea
I. of European Studies
Director: Nicolás María Mariscal Berastegui; *staff* 4
S. of Juridical Studies
Director: José Guerra San Martín
S. of Tourism
Director: Jesús Terán Corrales
I. of Co-operative Studies
Director: Dionisio Aranzadi Telleria

Founded 1886 as school by the Society of Jesus, acquired present status 1963. Faculty of Theology of Oña (Burgos) incorporated 1964. Degrees and diplomas recognized under the terms of a convention between the Holy See and the government of Spain. Financed by the Church and government. Governing bodies: the Patronato Universitario; the Consejo de Dirección; the Consejo Académico. Residential facilities for *c.* 310 students.

Academic Year: October to June (October-December; January-March; April-June).

Admission Requirements: Secondary school certificate (bachiller), and pre-university examination (madurez). Provision may be made for the recognition of foreign qualifications.

Fees (Pesetas): Tuition, 180,000 per annum.

Language of Instruction: Spanish.

Degrees and Diplomas: Diplomado in–Tourism; Secretarial Studies, 3 yrs. Licenciado in–Law; Political Science and Sociology; Economics and Business Administration; Philosophy and Letters; Philosophy and Education, 5 yrs; Theology, 6 yrs. Professional titles in–Translation; Interpretation; Programming; Computing. Doctorate in–Law; Philosophy and Letters; Theology, at least one year following Licenciado and thesis.

Libraries: Central Library, *c.* 125,000 vols; European Studies library; Basque Studies library.

Publications: Estudios de Deusto; Boletín de Estudios Económicos; Revista de Letras; Revista de Información General.

Academic Staff, 1986-87: c. 600.

Student Enrolment, 1986-87:

	Men	Women	Total
Of the country	5824	8736	14,560

6732 ***UNIVERSIDAD NACIONAL DE EDUCACIÓN A DISTANCIA**

National University for Distance Education
Ciudad Universitaria, 28040 Madrid
Telex: 45256
Telephone: (91) 5493600
Rector: Mariano Artés Gómez (1987-)
Secretario General: Enrique Cartera Montenegro

F. of Law
Dean: Santiago Sánchez González; *staff* 43 (54)
F. of Economics and Business Administration
Dean: Rafael Castejón Montijano; *staff* 39 (45)
F. of Philosophy and Education
Dean: Federico Gómez y Rodríguez de Castro; *staff* 69 (35)
F. of Sciences
Dean: Idlefonso Yáñez de Diego; *staff* 98
F. of Psychology
Dean: Santiago Segovia; *staff* 66
F. of Philology
Dean: Jenaro Costa Rodríguez; *staff* 80
F. of Geography and History
Dean: Jesús Viñuales; *staff* 78
Ce. of Industrial Engineering (Technical)
Director: Miguel Angel Sebastian; *staff* 50 (17)
I. of Educational Sciences
Director: Eustaquio Martín; *staff* 10

Study Centres at: Albacete, Alcira, Algeciras, Almería, Ávila, Baleares, Ibiza, Menorca, Barbastro, Barcelona, Burgos, Cádiz, Calatayud, Cantabria, Cartagena, Castellón, Cervera, Ceuta, Ciudad Real, Cuenca, Denia, Elche, Fuerzas Armadas, Gerona, Huelva, Jaén, La Palma, La Rioja, Las Palmas, Lanzarote, Madrid, Málaga, Melilla, Mérida, Navarra, Palencia, Ponferrada, Pontevedra, Santa Cruz de la Palma, Santander, Segovia, Soria, Talavera de la Reina, Teruel, Tortosa, Vergara, Vitoria. Also Universidad Laboral at: Córdoba, Gijón, La Coruña, Sevilla, Tenerife, Valencia, Zamora.

Founded 1972 by decree to give access to higher education to those who, by reason of their place of residence, work or other obligations, are unable to attend university. First students admitted 1973. Based in Madrid, the university has 52 regional centres throughout the country. The degrees and diplomas awarded enjoy the same status as those awarded by existing State universities. Governing bodies: the Junta de Gobierno, comprising 40 members; the Claustro, conprising 240 members (60% professors, 40% students and administrators).

Arrangements for co-operation with: The National Open University, Caracas; University of Brasília; Universidad Distrital 'Francisco José de Caldas', Bogotá; Universidad Autónoma de Sinaloa; Universidad Boliviana;Universidad de Guayaquil.

Academic Year: October to July (October-December; January-March; April-July).

Admission Requirements: Secondary school certificate (bachiller). Entrance examination for adults over 25.

Fees (Pesetas): Tuition, *c.* 35,300-50,000 per annum; Direct Access Courses, 20,000.

Language of Instruction: Spanish.

Degrees and Diplomas: Licenciado, in all fields, 5 yrs. Doctorate, by thesis, a further 2 yrs.

Libraries: Central Library; specialized libraries.

Publication: Revista a distancia (bimonthly).

Press or Publishing House: UNED Press.

Academic Staff, 1989-90:

Rank	Total
Catedráticos	97
Profesores Titulares	421
Profesores Asociados	115
Ayudantes	104
Total	737

Student Enrolment, 1989-90:

	Men	Women	Total
Of the country	56,421	51,362	107,783

6733 ***UNIVERSIDAD DE EXTREMADURA**

University of Extremadura
Avenida Elvas s/n, Badajoz
Telex: 28638
Telephone: (924) 236958
Rector: Antonio Sánchez Misiego (1984-)

F. of Law (Cáceres)
Dean: Jaime Pérez-Llantada y Gutiérrez
F. of Philosophy and Letters (Cáceres)
Dean: Bonifacio Palacios Martín
F. of Veterinary Medicine (Cáceres)
Dean: Ignacio Navarrete López-Cózar
F. of Medicine
Dean: José María Vinagre Velasco
F. of Science
Dean: Cristobal Valenzuela Calahorro
F. of Economics and Business Administration
Dean: José María Viani López-Sallaberry
Ce. of Industrial Engineering (Technical)
Ce. of Agricultural Engineering (Technical)

Ce. of Business Administration
Polytechnic Ce. (Cáceres)
Polytechnic Ce. (Mérida)
Ce. of Nursing
Ce. of Nursing (Mérida)
Ce. of Nursing (D. Benito)
Ce. of Nursing (Cáceres)
Ce. of Nursing (International Ce.) (Cáceres)
Ce. of Nursing (Plasencia)
Ce. of Business Administration (Cáceres)
Ce. of Business Administration (Plasencia)
Ce. of Agricultural Engineering (Technical) (Almendralejo)
Ce. of Education
Ce. of Education (Cáceres)
Ce. of Education (Almendralejo)

Founded 1973, incorporating previously existing faculties and schools of the Universities of Seville and Salamanca. An autonomous institution receiving financial aid from the government. Governing bodies: the Junta de Gobierno; the Claustro.

Academic Year: October to June (October-December; January-March; April-June).

Admission Requirements: Secondary school certificate (bachiller) and pre-university examination (madurez).

Language of Instruction: Spanish.

Degrees and Diplomas: Diplomado, 3 yrs. Licenciado in–Philosophy and Letters; Law; Science, 5 yrs; Medicine, 6 yrs. Professional title of Ingeniero Técnico, 3 yrs. Doctorados.

Library: Libraries of the faculties and schools, total, 124,545 vols.

Publications: Anuario de la Facultad de Derecho; Revista Norba de la Facultad de Filosofía y Letras.

Academic Staff: c. 600.

Student Enrolment: c. 11,300.

6734 ***UNIVERSIDAD DE GRANADA**

University of Granada
Hospital Real, Avenida del Hospicio s/n, Granada
Telephone: (958) 278400
Rector: José Vida Soria

F. of Law (including Political Science)
F. of Medicine
F. of Pharmacy
F. of Philosophy and Letters
F. of Science
F. of Fine Arts
Undergraduate Ce. (Science, Philosophy and Letters) (Almería)
Undergraduate Ce. (Science, Philosophy and Letters) (Jaén)
Ce. of Business Administration
Ce. of Translation and Interpretation
Ce. of Nursing
Ce. of Library Science
Ce. of Business Administration (Almería)
Ce. of Business Administration (Melilla)
Ce. of Business Administration (Jaén)
Ce. of Architecture (Technical)
Ce. of Engineering (Technical) (Jaén)
Ce. of Engineering (Technical) (Linares)
Ce. of Education
Ce. of Education (Almería)
Ce. of Education (Ceuta)
Ce. of Education (Jaén)
Ce. of Education (Melilla)

Founded 1531 by Papal Bull of Clement VII, Carlos V having previously created the Colegio de Lógica, Filosofía e Teología e Canones in 1526. The university is operated under the jurisdiction of the State and is financed by the government. Governing bodies: the Junta de Gobierno, composed of the Rector, the Vice-Rectors, the deans of the faculties, representatives of the academic staff, a representative of the student body, and the Secretary-General; the Patronato. Some residential facilities for students.

Academic Year: October to July (October-December; January-April; April-June).

Admission Requirements: Secondary school certificate (bachiller) or foreign equivalent recognized by the Ministry of Education and Science, and pre-university examination (madurez), or entrance examination for adults.

Language of Instruction: Spanish.

Degrees and Diplomas: Licenciado in–Law; Science; Philosophy and Letters; Pharmacy, 5 yrs; Medicine, 6 yrs. Doctorate in–Law; Science; Medicine; Pharmacy; Letters, a further 2 yrs and thesis.

Libraries: General Library, c. 78,610 vols; faculty libraries, Law, c. 62,580; Letters, c. 57,680; Medicine, c. 17,770; Science, c. 15,240; Pharmacy, c. 13,540.

Publications: Boletín; Anales del Desarrollo; Ars Farmacéutica; Cuadernos de Geología; Cuadernos Hispánicos de Historia de la Medicina y la Ciencia; Actualidad Obstétrico-Ginecológica.

Academic Staff: c. 950 (320).

Student Enrolment: c. 35,000.

6735 **UNIVERSIDAD HISPANOAMERICANA 'SANTA MARÍA DE LA RÁBIDA'**

Hispano-American University of 'Santa María de la Rábida'
Huelva

Founded 1943.

6736 **UNIVERSIDAD INTERNACIONAL 'MENÉNDEZ PELAYO'**

International University 'Menéndez Pelayo'
Amador de los Ríos 1, Madrid 4
Telephone: 27-26-50
Rector: Raúl Morodo Leoncio

D. of Comparative Politics (Research)
D. of Economics and Energy Resources (Research)
D. of Development and Social Change (Research)
D. of Humanities (Research)
D. of European Community Law (Research)
D. of Experimental Science (Research)
D. of Social History (Research)
D. of Art and Communication (Research)
I. of Educational Research
P. for Foreign Students

Founded 1932 as Universidad Internacional de Santander by the Ministry of Education. Acquired present title 1945. Reorganized 1980. An autonomous institution responsible to the Ministry of Education and Science.

Degrees and Diplomas: Certificates of aptitude and proficiency in Spanish Language and Literature and Spanish History. Diploma in Hispanic Studies. Doctorates.

Library: 15,000 vols. (in Santander).

Academic Staff: c. 700.

Student Enrolment: c. 6000.

6737 **UNIVERSIDAD INTERNACIONAL 'PÉREZ GALDÓS'**

International University 'Pérez Galdós'
Las Palmas de Gran Canaria

Founded 1962.

6738 ***UNIVERSIDAD DE LAS ISLAS BALEARES**

University of the Balearic Islands
Miguel de los Santos Oliver 2, 0771 Palma de Mallorca
Telex: 69121
Telephone: (971) 295200
Rector: Nadal Batle Nicolau (1982-88)
Secretario General: Alejandro Onsalo Orfila

F. of Philosophy and Letters
Dean: Camilo José Cela Conde; *staff* 64 (10)
F. of Science
Dean: Andres Palou Oliver; *staff* 71 (2)
F. of Law
Dean: Francisco Astarloa Villena; *staff* 26 (8)
Ce. of Business Administration and Computer Sciences
Director: Teresa Riera Madurell; *staff* 25 (9)
Ce. of Education (Baleares)
Director: Baltasar Bibiloni Llabres; *staff* 44 (2)
Ce. of Education
Director: Baltasar Bibiloni Llabres; *staff* 44 (2)
Ce. of Nursing
Director: Misericordia Ramon Juanpere; *staff* 7 (24)

Founded 1978 and tracing its history to the 15th century and to the former Universidad de Palma. Incorporating faculties and colleges previously part of the Universidad Autónoma of Barcelona. A State institution under the jurisdiction of the Ministry of Education and Science. Governing bodies: the Claustro Universitario; the Junta de Gobierno.

Arrangements for co-operation with the Universities of: Aix-Marseilles I; London; Sheffield; Cuyo.

Academic Year: October to June (October-December; January-March; April-June).

Admission Requirements: Secondary school certificate (bachiller) and pre-university examination (madurez), or entrance examination foradults.

Fees (Pesetas): 35,000-50,000 per annum.

Languages of Instruction: Castellano and Catalán.

Degrees and Diplomas: Diplomado, 3 yrs. Licenciado in all faculties, 5 yrs. Doctorates, by thesis, a further 2 yrs.

Library: Total, 135,000 vols.

Publications: Mayurca; Cuadernos de la Facultad de Derecho (Law); Caligrama (biannually).

Press or Publishing House: Servicio de Publicaciones.

Academic Staff, 1986-87:

Rank	Full-time	Part-time
Catedráticos	49	3
Profesores Titulares	92	6
Profesores Contratados	102	17
Total	243	26

Student Enrolment, 1986-87:

	Men	Women	Total
Of the country	3015	3776	6791
Of other countries	21	23	44
Total	3036	3799	6835

6739 **UNIVERSIDAD DE LA LAGUNA**

University of La Laguna

La Laguna, Tenerife, Canarias

Telex: 93137 EDUCI E

Telephone: (922) 25-81-19

Rector: José C.A. Betencour

F. of Law
F. of Chemistry
F. of Philology
F. of Medicine and Surgery
F. of Mathematics
F. of Biology
F. of Pharmacy
F. of Economics and Business Administration
F. of Fine Arts
F. of Geography and History
F. of Philosophy and Education
I. of Education
I. of Astrophysics
I. of Linguistics
I. of Organic Chemistry
I. of Regional Development
I. of Political and Social Sciences
I. of Business Administration
Ce. of Business Administration (Santa Cruz de Tenerife)
Ce. of Business Administration (Las Palmas)
Ce. of Nursing (including Midwifery)
Ce. of Nursing
Ce. of Nursing (Las Palmas)
Ce. of Education
Ce. of Education (Las Palmas)
Ce. of Education (Santa Cruz de Tenerife)

Founded 18th century, reorganized 1927. A State institution. Governing bodies: the Claustro Universitario; the Junta de Gobierno. Some residential facilities for students.

Academic Year: October to June.

Admission Requirements: Secondary school certificate (bachiller) or foreign equivalent recognized by the Ministry of Education and Science, and pre-university examination (madurez).

Language of Instruction: Spanish.

Degrees and Diplomas: Licenciado in all faculties, 5 yrs; Medicine and Surgery, 6 yrs. Diploma, 3 yrs. Doctorado. Teaching diploma.

Libraries: University Library, *c.* 47,300 vols; also faculty libraries.

Publications: Revista de Historia Canaria; Revista de Filología; Anales.

Academic Staff: c. 1060.

Student Enrolment: c. 18,050.

6740 **UNIVERSIDAD DE LAS PALMAS DE GRAN CANARIA**

University of Las Palmas

Alfonso XIII, 2, 35003 Las Palmas, Canarias

Telex: 95238

Telephone: (928) 362000

Fax: (928) 380926

S. of Architecture
S. of Industrial Engineering
Head: Juan Ortega Saavedra
Polytechnic Ce.
Head: José María de la Portilla Fernández
C. of Informatics
Head: José Rafael Pérez
F. of Informatics
Head: Roberto Moreno Díaz
Ce. of Architecture
Head: Joaquín Casariego Ramírez
Ce. for Marine Sciences
Head: José Joaquín Hernández Brito
I. for Physical Education
Head: José Hernández Moreno
S. of Telecommunication Engineering (Technical)
Head: Dutaro Nuñez Ordoñez
C. of Business Studies
Head: Rafael Esparza Machín
C. of Nursing
Head: Rafael Vallespín Maitero
C. of Technical Engineering (Telecommunications)
Head: Eduardo Rovaris Rameros
C. of Translation and Interpretation
Head: Isabel Pascua Febles
C. of Education
Head: Julio Machargo Salvador
F. of Veterinary Medicine
Head: Carlos Manuel Ruis de Galarreta Hernández

Founded 1979, incorporating previously existing schools. A State institution under the jurisdiction of the Ministry of Education and Science.

Arrangements for co-operation with: University College of London; Technical University of Cracow; National Institute of Technology, Quito.

Academic Year: October to June (October-December; January-March; April-July).

Admission Requirements: Secondary school certificate (bachiller) or recognized foreign equivalent, and pre-university examination (madurez).

Language of Instruction: Spanish.

Degrees and Diplomas: Diplomado in Computer Sciences, 3 yrs. Licenciado in Marine Sciences. Professional titles of–Ingeniero Técnico, 3 yrs; Ingeniero Industrial; Arquitecto, 6 yrs. Doctorates, by thesis, a further 2-3 yrs.

Academic Staff: c. 190 (130).

Student Enrolment: c. 3130.

6741 **UNIVERSIDAD DE LEÓN**

University of León

Carretera de Santander s/n, León

Telephone: (987) 240451

Rector: Andres Suárez y Suárez

F. of Biology
F. of Veterinary Medicine
F. of Law
F. of Philosophy and Letters
Undergraduate Ce. (Philosophy and Letters, Law)
Ce. of Business Administration
Ce. of Nursing
Ce. of Social Work
Ce. of Engineering (Technical)
Ce. of Education
Ce. of Education (Ponferrada)

Founded 1979.

Academic Staff: c. 390.

Student Enrolment: c. 7000.

6742 ***UNIVERSIDAD COMPLUTENSE DE MADRID**
Complutense University of Madrid
Isaac Peral s/n, 28040 Madrid
Telex: 22459
Telephone: (34-1) 5490244
Fax: (34-1) 2438643
Rector: Gustavo Villapalos (1987-94)
Secretario General: Teodoro González-Ballesteros

F. of Philosophy and Education Sciences (including Methodology and Psychology)
Dean: M. Maceiras; *staff* 147
F. of Geography and History
Dean: J. Portela; *staff* 261
F. of Philology (Spanish, Roman, Latin, French, Iitalian, German, British, and Greek Philology, Arabic and Islamic Studies, Hebrew, Slavic)
Dean: J. Sánchez-Lobato; *staff* 271
F. of Mathematics
Dean: J. Ferrera; *staff* 139
F. of Physics
Dean: F. Sánchez-Quesada; *staff* 161
F. of Chemistry
Dean: M.A. Alario; *staff* 217
F. of Geology
Dean: M. Doval; *staff* 93
F. of Biology
Dean: R. Hernández; *staff* 198
F. of Law
Dean: J. Iturmendi; *staff* 355
F. of Medicine
Dean: V. Moya; *staff* 998
F. of Pharmacy
Dean: B. del Castillo; *staff* 216
F. of Veterinary Medicine
Dean: G. Suárez; *staff* 228
F. of Economics and Business Administration
Dean: C. Berzosa; *staff* 368
F. of Political and Social Sciences
Dean: J.L. Paniagua; *staff* 258
F. of Information and Communication Sciences
Dean: J. Fernández; *staff* 252
F. of Psychology
Dean: J.M. Arredondo; *staff* 145
F. of Arts
Dean: R. Garceran; *staff* 109
F. of Odontology
Dean: J.P. Moreno; *staff* 113
Undergraduate C. (4) (Philology, Geography and History, Psychology, Chemistry, Biology, Medicine, Pharmacy, Law, Economics and Business, Information Sciences)
S. of Statistics
Director: B. Hernández; *staff* 55
S. of Business Administration
Director: S. Piñe
S. of Optometry
Director: G. Rico; *staff* 55
S. of Nursing, Physiotherapy, and Podology
Director: J. Beneit; *staff* 57
S. of Social Work
Director: A. Palafox; *staff* 40
S. of Education (4) (primary level)
Director: A. Moreno; *staff* 113
S. for the Development of Teaching Ces.
Head: E. Pujals; *staff* 23
I. of Environmental Sciences
Head: Carlos Vicente Córdoba
I. of Embriology
Head: Juan Jimenez Collado
I. of Applied Magnetism
Head: Antonio Hernando Grande
I. of Forensic Anatomy
Head: Modesto Martínez Piñeiro
I. of Astronomy and Geodesy
Head: Ricardo Viera Diaz
European Documentation Ce.
Head: Manuel Pérez González

Also 7 Teaching Hospitals, Summer Courses in Escorial and Almeria, and courses for foreign students (SpanishLanguage and Literature).

The origins of the Universidad Complutense of Madrid go back seven centuries, when King Sancho IV ('The Brave') of Castile founded a study centre in Alcalá de Henares. Given the status of university 1499, under the patronage of Cardinal Jimenez de Cisneros, and authorized by Papal Bull of Pope Alexander VI. Studies began 1508-1509. Transferred permanently to Madrid 1836, and renamed Central University of Madrid. Original name returnedto it by statute 1970. A State institution under the jurisdiction of the Ministry of Education and Science. Governing bodies: the Junta de Gobierno, comprising 6 members, including the Rector, the Vice-Rector, deans, directors, representatives of the professors, students and administrators; the Claustro Universitario. Residential facilities for students in 7 Colegios Mayores.

Arrangements for 85 international co-operation agreements with other universities, for exchange programmes, joint research projects, and academic and scientific co-operation. Bilateral agreements renewed periodically.

Academic Year: October to June (October-February; February-June).

Admission Requirements: Secondary school certificate (bachiller) or foreign equivalent recognized by the Ministry of Education and Science, examination orientation, and entrance examination.

Fees (Pesetas): *c.* 50,000-70,000.

Language of Instruction: Spanish.

Degrees and Diplomas: Licenciado in all faculties, 5 yrs, except Medicine, 6 yrs. Doctorate by thesis, a further 3-4 yrs. Other degrees: Master, a further 2 yrs. Titles of Especialista, 1 further yr; Experto , a further 1-2 sems.

Libraries: University Library, *c.* 600,000 vols; also faculty, school, and college libraries.

Special Facilities (Museums, etc.): Complutense Museum; Botanical Garden.

Publications: Revista de la Universidad de Madrid (several issues per year); Guia de la Universidad Complutense (annually); Memoria de la Universidad Complutense (annually); Gaceta Complutense (monthly); Summer Courses of Complutense (annually).

Press or Publishing House: Editorial de la Universidad Complutense. Servicio de Publicaciones.

Academic Staff, 1988-89:

Rank	Full-time	Part-time
Catedráticos (Full Professors)	523	78
Profesores Titulares (Associate Professors)	1978	160
Profesores Asociados (Visiting Professors)	–	1202
Ayudantes (Assistants)	1023	–
Total	3524	1440

Student Enrolment, 1988-89: 129,000

6743 **UNIVERSIDAD AUTÓNOMA DE MADRID**
Autonomous University of Madrid
Ciudad Universitaria de Cantoblanco, 28049 Madrid
Telex: 27810-EDUCI E
Telephone: (91) 734-01-00
Rector: Cayetano López Martinez

F. of Philosophy and Letters
F. of Law
Dean: Antonio Remiro Brotons
F. of Science
Dean: Fernando Agullo López
F. of Medicine
Dean: Andres Cerdan Vallejo
F. of Economics and Business Administration
Dean: Juan Carlos García-Bermejo Ochoa
F. of Psychology
Undergraduate Ce. (Science, Economics and Business Administration) (Cuenca)
Undergraduate C. (Law, Philosophy and Letters) (Cuenca)
Undergraduate Ce. (Medicine) (Cuenca)
Ce. of Education
Ce. of Education (Cuenca)
Ce. of Education (Segovia)
Also 26 institutes.

Founded 1968 by government decree and following the publication of a White Paper on Education. Financed by theMinistry of Education and Science. Governing bodies: the Claustro Universitario; the Junta de Gobierno.

Arrangements for co-operation with the Universities of: Boston; Warsaw; Tours; Mexico (Autonomous); Sofia; Sassari; Al Mustansiriyah.

Academic Year: October to July (October-December; January-April; April-July).

Admission Requirements: Secondary school certificate (bachiller) and pre-university examination (madurez), or entrance examination foradults.

Language of Instruction: Spanish.

Degrees and Diplomas: Licenciado in all faculties, 5 yrs, except Medicine, 6 yrs. Doctorate, by thesis.

Library: c. 78,340 vols.

Special Facilities (Museums, etc.): Museo de Artes y Tradiciones Populares; Museo de Mineralogía.

Publications: Revista de la Universidad 'Cantoblanco'; Revista Museo de Artes Populares; Boletín Informativo.

Press or Publishing House: Servicio de Publicaciones de la Universidad Autónoma de Madrid.

Academic Staff: c. 800 (390).

Student Enrolment: c. 25,700.

6744 ***UNIVERSIDAD POLITÉCNICA DE MADRID**

Technical University of Madrid

Avenida Ramiro de Maeztu s/n, Ciudad Universitaria, 28040 Madrid

Telex: 23780 UPMAD E

Telephone: (91) 254-50-00

Rector: Rafael Portaencasa Baeza (1980-)

Secretario General: José Manuel Herrero Marzal

F. of Computer Sciences
Director: Luis Malé Hernández; *staff* 62 (73)
S. of Architecture
Director: Emilio Larrodera López; *staff* 100 (211)
S. of Aeronautical Engineering
Director: Julio González Bernaldo de Quirós; *staff* 68 (76)
S. of Agricultural Engineering
Director: Manuel Arroyo Varela; *staff* 163 (86)
S. of Civil Engineering
Director: José Antonio Torroja Cavanillas; *staff* 60 (196)
S. of Industrial Engineering
Director: Fernando Aldana Mayor; *staff* 152 (134)
S. of Mining
Director: Francisco Michavila Pitarch; *staff* 77 (60)
S. of Marine Engineering
Director: Alejandro Mira Monerris; *staff* 30 (56)
S. of Telecommunications
Director: Juan Enrique Page de la Vega; *staff* 140 (77)
S. of Forestry Engineering
Director: Rodolfo Carretera Carrero; *staff* 84 (37)
I. of Education
I. of Aerial Surveying
I. of Environmental Sciences
I. of New Energy Resources
I. of Solar Energy
I. of Control Systems
I. of Teledetection
Undergraduate Ce. (Architecture)
Ce. of Aeronautical Engineering (Technical)
Director: Ángel Barcela Herreros; *staff* 34 (69)
Ce. of Agricultural Engineering (Technical)
Director: Fernando Ruiz García; *staff* 40 (36)
Ce. of Agricultural Engineering (Technical) (Ciudad Real)
Ce. of Architecture (Technical)
Director: Miguel Oliver Alemary; *staff* 58 (67)
Ce. of Forestry (Technical)
Director: Adolfo Rupérez Cuellar; *staff* 16 (35)
Ce. of Industrial Engineering (Technical)
Director: José Francisco Carballido Quesada; *staff* 54 (91)
Ce. of Civil Engineering (Technical)
Director: Román Ferreras Fernández; *staff* 25 (63)
Ce. of Mining (Technical) (Almadén)
Ce. of Telecommunication Engineering (Technical)
Director: Arturo Martínez de Tejada; *staff* 64 (51)
Ce. of Surveying (Technical)
Director: Fernando Martín Asín; *staff* 29 (9)
Ce. of Computer Sciences (Technical)
Director: Maria Araceti Lorenzo Prieto; *staff* 35 (40)
Ce. of Agricultural Engineering (Technical) (Villaba)
Ce. of Industrial Engineering (Technical) (Toledo)
Ce. of Industrial Engineering (Technical) (Almadén)
Ce. of Telecommunication Engineering (Technical) (Alcalá de Henares)
I. of Physical Education

Founded 1972 incorporating previously existing schools. A State institution under the jurisdiction of the Ministry of Education and Science. Governing bodies: the Junta de Gobierno; the Junta de Centro; the Consejo Social. Residential facilities for students.

Arrangements for co-operation with over 50 universities in North and South America and Europe.

Academic Year: October to June (October-February; February-June).

Admission Requirements: Secondary school certificate (bachiller) and pre-university examination (madurez). Entrance examination for students over 25 yrs.

Fees (Pesetas): 50,000 per annum.

Language of Instruction: Spanish.

Degrees and Diplomas: Diplomado in Computer Sciences, 3 yrs. Licenciado, 6 yrs. Professional titles of–Arquitecto Técnico; Ingeniero Técnico, 3 yrs; Ingeniero; Arquitecto, 6 yrs. Doctorates, by thesis, a further 2 yrs.

Library: Total, c. 85,000 vols.

Special Facilities (Museums, etc.): Geological Museum.

Academic Staff, 1986-87:

Rank	Full-time	Part-time
Catedráticos	268	71
Profesores Titulares	583	190
Profesores Encargados de Curso	753	17
Total	1604	278

Student Enrolment, 1986-87:

	Men	Women	Total
Of the country	37,000	2000	39,000
Of other countries	900	100	1000
Total	37,900	2100	40,000

6745 **UNIVERSIDAD DE MÁLAGA**

University of Málaga

Plaza del Ejido, Málaga 52

Telephone: (952) 2550

F. of Science
F. of Economics and Business Administration
F. of Philosophy and Letters
F. of Medicine
F. of Law
Ce. of Business Administration
Ce. of Computer Sciences
Ce. of Nursing
Ce. of Nursing (Ronda)
Ce. of Engineering (Technical)
Ce. of Education
Ce. of Education (Antequera)

Founded 1972, a State institution under the jurisdiction of the Ministry of Education and Science. Governing body: the Junta de Gobierno.

Academic Year: October to June (October-December; January-March; April-June).

Admission Requirements: Secondary school certificate (bachiller) and pre-university examination (madurez).

Language of Instruction: Spanish.

Degrees and Diplomas: Diplomado in–Business Administration; Industrial Engineering, 3 yrs. Licenciado in–Law; Economics; Business Administration; Medicine; Chemistry; Mathematics, 5 yrs. Doctorate. Also Teaching diploma.

Library: Central Library.

Academic Staff: c. 285 (170).

Student Enrolment: c. 15,800.

6746 **UNIVERSIDAD DE MURCIA**

University of Murcia

Calle Santo Cristo, 1 Murcia

Telex: 67058

Telephone: (968) 249200

F. of Law

F. of Philosophy and Education
F. of Science
F. of Medicine
F. of Economics and Business Administration
F. of Veterinary Medicine
Ce. of Computer Sciences
Ce. of Nursing
Ce. of Nursing (Cartagena)
Ce. of Business Administration
Ce. of Business Administration (Cartagena)
Ce. of Engineering (Technical) (Cartagena)
Ce. of Education

Founded 1915, a State institution under the jurisdiction of the Ministry of Education and Science. Governing body: the Junta de Gobierno, comprising the Rector as president, deans of the faculties, Administrator, Interventor,Secretary-General, and a representative of the Student Association. Some residential facilities for students.

Academic Year: October to June (October-December; January-March; April-June).

Admission Requirements: Secondary school certificate (bachiller) and pre-university examination (madurez).

Language of Instruction: Spanish.

Degrees and Diplomas: Diplomado in Business Administration. Licenciado in all faculties, 5 yrs, except Medicine, 6 yrs. Doctorate bythesis.

Libraries: c. 27,300 vols; specialized libraries, *c.* 21,660.

Publication: Anales de la Universidad de Murcia.

Academic Staff: c. 800.

Student Enrolment: c. 14,000.

6747 ***UNIVERSIDAD DE NAVARRA**

University of Navarra
Campus Universitario, 31080 Pamplona
Telex: 37917 UNAV E
Telephone: (3448) 252700
Fax: (3448) 173650
Electronic mail: unav
Rector: Alfonso Nieto (1979-91)
Secretario General: Jaime Nubiola

F. of Law
Dean: José Antonio Doral; *staff* 40 (45)
F. of Philosophy and Letters (including Philology, Psychology, Archaeology, Geography and History, and Education)
Dean: Rafael Alvira; *staff* 130 (35)
F. of Canon Law
Dean: Carmelo de Diego; *staff* 34 (12)
F. of Medicine
Dean: Jesús Vázquez; *staff* 147 (98)
F. of Pharmacy
Dean: Pilar Fernández Otero; *staff* 61 (13)
F. of Science
Dean: Rafael Jordana; *staff* 76 (15)
F. of Theology
Dean: José Luis Illanes; *staff* 60 (10)
F. of Journalism
Dean: Manuel Casado; *staff* 40 (12)
F. of Economics and Management
Dean: Miguel Alfonso Martínez-Echevarria
F. of Philosophy (Ecclesiastic Studies)
Dean: Mariano Artigas; *staff* 20 (28)
S. of Industrial Engineering Technology
Director: José María Bastero; *staff* 42 (25)
S. of Architecture
Director: Leopoldo Gil Nebot; *staff* 60 (19)
I. of Education
Director: David Isaacs; *staff* 4
I. of Liberal Arts
I. of Secretarial Studies and Administration
Director: Ana Ledesma; *staff* – (24)
I. of Business Administration
Director: Carlos Cavallé; *staff* 71 (30)
I. of Spanish Language and Culture (for foreign students)
Director: Ángel Raimundo Fernández
I. of Church History
Director: José Orlandis
I. of Modern Languages
Director: José Dawid; *staff* 6
I. of Applied Sciences
Director: Rafael Jordana
Ce. of Nursing (including Midwifery)
Director: Ana Carmen Marcuello
S. of Library Science
Director: Nuria Orpi
S. of Laboratory Technology
Director: Salvador Valdés
S. of Internal Medicine
Director: Jesús Prieto
Physiology Research Ce.
Director: Francisco Ponz
European Documentation Ce.
Director: Miguel Alfonso Martínez-Echevarria
Research Ce. of Applied Pharmacobiology
Director: Antonio Monge
L. of Building Research
Director: Javier Lahuerta
Ce. of Social Responsibility of Private Enterprise
Director: Alejandro Llano
Ce. of Industrial Research (Guipúzcoa)
Director: José María Bastero
Computer Technology Ce.
Director: Ignacio Coupeau
I. of Science for the Family
Director: Pedro J. Viladrich
Research Ce. of Modern History
Director: Valentín Vázquez de Prada
Professional S. of Legal Practice
Director: Faustino Cordón

Founded 1952 as Estudio General de Navarra by Opus Dei, recognized as Catholic university by decree of the Holy See 1960. Degrees granted equivalence with State degrees 1962. A private autonomous institution. Governing body: the Junta de Gobierno (Administrative Board), including the Rector as Chairman, Vice-Rectors, Secretary-General, Administrator-General, manager deans of the faculties, institutes, and schools and representatives of the students. Financially supported by Association of Friends of the University of Navarra, and by tuition fees anddonations. Residential facilities for students in ten Colegios Mayores.

Arrangements for co-operation with: Kyoto University of Foreign Studies; Harvard Graduate School of Business Administration; University of Columbia; University of Piura (Perú); University of La Sabana, Colombia; Universidad Iberoamericana de Postgrado; Universidad Nacional de Cuyo, Mendoza; University of Tamkang; Università degli Studi 'G. D'Annunzio', Chieti; Universidad Panamericana, México; Universidad Católica de Chile.

Academic Year: October to June (October-December; January-March; March-June).

Admission Requirements: Secondary school certificate (bachiller) or recognized foreign equivalent, and pre-university examination (madurez).

Fees (Pesetas): 167,000-270,000 per annum; foreign students, US$ 1605-2596.

Language of Instruction: Spanish.

Degrees and Diplomas: Diplomado in–Applied Chemistry; Dietetics and Human Nutrition; Nursing; Secretarial and Administrative Studies, 3 yrs. Bachiller in–Liberal Arts; Science, 3 yrs; Theology, 5 yrs. Licenciado in–Canon Law, 2 yrs; Biology; Economics and Management; Education; Geography and History; Law; Pharmacy; Philology; Philosophy; Public Communication, 5 yrs; Medicine, 6 yrs. Master in–Biotechnology; Business Administration; Business Law; Liberal Arts; Medicaments Research and Development; Physical and Mechanical Metallurgy, 2 yrs. Professional titles of–Arquitecto; Ingeniero Industrial, 6 yrs. Doctorate, by thesis, in–Canon Law; Theology, 1 further yr; Business Administration, 3 yrs; all other fields, a further 2 yrs.

Library: Total, 550,000 vols.

Special Facilities (Museums, etc.): Zoological Museum.

Publications: Revista de Medicina (quarterly); Ius Canonicum (biannually); Nuestro Tiempo (monthly); Scripta Theologica (quarterly); Redacción (quarterly); Anuario Filosófico (biannually); Persona y Derecho (biannually); Europe Today (monthly); Revista de Edificación (biannually); Comunicación y Sociedad (quarterly); Revista Española de Fisiologiia (quarterly); RILCE (biannually); Allergologie et Immunopathologie (bimonthly).

Press or Publishing House: Ediciones Universidad de Navarra S.A. Servicio de Publicaciones de la Universidad de Navarra, S.A.

Academic Staff, 1989-90:

Rank	Full-time	Part-time
Profesores Ordinarios	136	–
Profesores Agregados	68	–
Profesores Adjuntos	225	–
Profesores Encargados Interinos de Curso	65	–
Ayudantes y Otros	302	–
Profesores Extraordinarios	–	47
Profesores Asociados	–	266
Profesores Visitantes	–	48
Total	796	361

Student Enrolment, 1985-86:

Men	Women	Total
7683	7658	15,341

6748 ***UNIVERSIDAD DE OVIEDO**
University of Oviedo
San Francisco 1-3-5, Oviedo
Telex: 87322
Telephone: (985) 21-98-85
Rector: Alberto Marcos Vallaure (1984-)

F. of Medicine (including Pharmacy)
Dean: Juan Sebastián López Arranz
F. of Philosophy and Education
Dean: Modesto Berciano Villalibre
F. of Law
Dean: Juan I. Sánchez Rodríguez
F. of Economics and Business Administration
Dean: Emilio Costa Reparaz
F. of Philology
Dean: Aurora Aragón Fernández
F. of Geography and History
Dean: David Ruiz González
F. of Chemistry
Dean: Julio Rodríguez Fernández
F. of Biology
Dean: Ricardo Anadón Alvarez
F. of Geology
Dean: Luis Guillermo Corretgé Castañón
S. of Industrial Engineering
Director: Mariano Rodríguez-Avial Llardent
S. of Mining
Director: Alfonso Hevia Cangas
I. of Education
I. of Management
Ce. of Mining (Technical)
Ce. of Business Administration (Gijón)
Ce. of Business Administration (Oviedo)
Ce. of Industrial Engineering (Technical)
Ce. of Nursing
Ce. of Education
Ce. of Computer Sciences
Ce. of Computer Sciences (Gijón)

Founded 1604 as university by Royal Charter, previously approved by Papal Bull. Instruction commenced 1608. The university is a State institution under the jurisdiction of the Ministry of Education and Science. Governing bodies: the Patronato; the Claustro General; the Junta de Gobierno. Residential facilities for students in 3 Colegios Mayores.

Arrangements for co-operation with: University of Bochum; University of Rennes II; University of Chile; University of Toulouse I; Ecole supérieure de Commerce et d'Administration d'Entreprise, Poitiers. Mexican Universities.

Academic Year: October to June (October-December; January-March; April-June).

Admission Requirements: Secondary school certificate (bachiller) or foreign equivalent recognized by the Ministry of Education and Science, and pre-university examination (madurez).

Language of Instruction: Spanish.

Degrees and Diplomas: Diplomado in–Business Administration; Nursing; Education; Mining; Industrial Engineering; Computer Sciences. Licenciado in–Philosophy and Education; Philology; Geography and History; Chemistry; Biology; Geology; Law; Economics and Business Administration, 5 yrs; Medicine, 6 yrs. Professional titles of–Ingeniero Técnico, various fields, 3 yrs; Ingeniero–de Minas; Industrial, 6 yrs. Doctorado, a further 2 yrs.

Libraries: Central Library, *c.* 420,000 vols; specialized libraries.

Publications: Breviora Geológica Astúrica; Trabajos de Geología; Revista de Biología; Revista de Minas; Archivos de la Facultad de Medicina.

Press or Publishing House: Servicio de Publicaciones.

Academic Staff: c. 1300.

Student Enrolment: c. 22,800.

6749 ***UNIVERSIDAD DEL PAÍS VASCO/EUSKAL HERRIKO UNIBERTSITATEA**
Basque University
Apartado 1397, 48080 Bilbao (Vizcaya)
Telex: 32098 EDUCI E
Telephone: (34-4) 464-77-00
Fax: (34-4) 464-7446
Rector: Emilio Barberá Guillem (1986-90)
Secretario General: Javier Hualde Sánchez

F. of Economics and Business Administration (Bilbao)
Dean: Javier Corcuera Atienza; *staff* 108 (35)
F. of Science (Bilbao)
Dean: José A. Madariaga Zamacona; *staff* 200 (2)
F. of Medicine and Dentistry (Bilbao)
Dean: Ramón Cisterna Cáncer
F. of Chemistry (San Sebastián)
Dean: Alberto González Guerrero; *staff* 63 (3)
F. of Law (San Sebastián)
Dean: Jacinto Gil Rodríguez
F. of Computer Sciences (San Sebastián)
Dean: Javier Torrealdea Folgado; *staff* 55 (7)
F. of Fine Arts (Bilbao)
Dean: Paloma Rodríguez Escudero Sánchez; *staff* 63 (3)
F. of Information Services (Bilbao)
Dean: Celestino del Arenal Moyúa; *staff* 70 (9)
F. of Philology, Geography and History (Vitoria)
Dean: Francisco Goenago Mendizábal
F. of Philosophy and Education (San Sebastián)
Dean: Enrique Echeburúa Odiozola; *staff* 130 (10)
S. of Industrial Engineering and Telecommunications (Bilbao)
Director: Ricardo Alvarez Isasi; *staff* 127 (55)
S. of Architecture (San Sebastián)
Director: Luis D. León Vigiola; *staff* 6 (41)
Undergraduate Ce. (Vitoria)
Ce. of Business Administration (Bilbao)
Director: Miguel Grau Abas; *staff* 29 (33)
Ce. of Nursing (Bilbao)
Director: Ana Pascual Pérez
Ce. of Engineering (Technical) (Bilbao)
Director: Ernesto Martínez Sagarzazu
Ce. of Business Administration (San Sebastián)
Director: José Alvarez López
Ce. of Engineering (Technical) (San Sebastián)
Director: Ricardo Echeparen Zugasti
Ce. of Engineering (Technical) (Vitoria)
Director: Alberto Martínez de Aragon
Ce. of Mining Engineering (Bilbao)
Director: Antonio Bengoechea Larraz
Ce. of Education (Bilbao)
Director: Angeles Echevarría Martínez
Ce. of Education (San Sebastián)
Director: Inés Sanz Lerma; *staff* 62
Ce. of Education (Vitoria)
Director: Pedro María González Pueyes
Ce. of International Law (Vitoria)
Ce. for Lifelong Education
I. of Criminology
Director: Antonio Beristain Ipiña
I. of Public Economics
Director: Juan Ursutia Elejalde
I. of Epidemiology and Heart Disease Prevention
Director: Julio Grao Rodríguez
I. of Educational Sciences
Director: Julio Grao Rodríguez

Also affiliated centres at: Oñate, Eskoriaza, Mundragón, Derio, Eibar, and San Sebastián, and institutesattached to the various faculties.

Founded 1968 as Universidad de Bilbao. Reorganized under present title 1980. An autonomous institution receiving financial aid from the Ministry of Education and Science. Governing bodies: the Consejo Social; the Claustro Universitario; the Junta de Gobierno. Some residential facilities for academic staff and students.

Arrangements for co-operation with the Universities of: Pau; Łódź. Rosario, Reno, Nevada. Universidad Centroamericana 'José Simeón Cañas', San Salvador.

Academic Year: October to June (October-December; December-March; March-June).

Admission Requirements: Secondary school certificate (bachiller) and pre-university examination (madurez), or entrance examination foradults.

Fees (Pesetas): 35,000-50,000.

Languages of Instruction: Spanish and Basque.

Degrees and Diplomas: Diplomado, 3 yrs. Licenciado in all fields, 5 yrs, except Technical Engineering, 4 yrs; Medicine; Architecture, 6 yrs. Doctorates by thesis. Teaching diploma, 3 yrs.

Library: Central Library, 34,490 vols.

Publications: Recursos Cientificos y Lineas de Investigación; Revista 'Ereiton'.

Academic Staff, 1986-87: 2150.

Student Enrolment, 1986-87: 41,294.

6750 ***UNIVERSIDAD DE SALAMANCA**

University of Salamanca

Patio de Escuelas 1, 37008 Salamanca

Telex: 26828 EDUCI E

Telephone: (923) 214518

Fax: (923) 214937

Rector: Julio Fermoso García

Secretario General: Ángel Sánchez Blanco

F. of Philology
Dean: Concepción Vázquez de Benito
F. of Geography and History
Dean: Angel Rodríguez Sánchez
F. of Philosophy and Educational Sciences
Dean: Eugenio Garrido Martin
F. of Law
Dean: Benjamín González Alonso
F. of Fine Arts
Dean: Rafael Sánchez-Carralero López
F. of Science
Dean: Pedro L. Garcia Pérez
F. of Chemistry
Dean: Eladio J. Martin Mateos
F. of Biology
Dean: Gregorio Nicolás Rodrigo
F. of Medicine
Dean: José I. Paz Bouza
F. of Pharmacy
Dean: Juan M. Cachaza Silverio
F. of Economic Sciences
Dean: Pablo Muñoz Gallego
Ce. of Business Administration
Director: Angel Martín Simón
Ce. of Nursing
Director: José M. Martín García
Ce. of Social Work
Director: José Ortega Esteban
Ce. of Library Science
Director: Santiago González Gómez
Ce. of Education (Zamora)
Director: José Rodríguez Pimentel
Ce. of Education (Ávila)
Director: José L. Astudillo Terradillos
Ce. of Education (Ávila)
Director: Serafin de Tapia Sánchez
Ce. of Social Graduates
Director: Agustín Sánchez de Vega
Ce. of Industrial Engineering (Technical)
Director: Félix Redondo Quintela
Ce. of Industrial Engineering
Director: Jaime Samto Domingo Santillana
I. of Educational Sciences
Director: Carlos Schramm

Also University Hospital and International Courses.

Founded in 1218. A State institution under the jurisdiction of the Ministry of Education and Science. Governing bodies: the Junta de Gobierno; the Claustro Universitario. Residential facilities for academic staff and students.

Arrangements for co-operation with the Universities of: Coimbra; Clermont-Fernand I; Caen; Würzburg; Prague (Charles); Iberoamericana.

Academic Year: October to June (October-December; January-March; April-June).

Admission Requirements: Secondary school certificate (bachiller) and pre-university examination (madurez).

Fees (Pesetas): 40,000-60,000 per annum.

Language of Instruction: Spanish.

Degrees and Diplomas: Licenciado, 5 yrs; Medicine, 6 yrs. Professional titles. Doctorate in all faculties.

Libraries: Central Library, *c.* 190,000 vols; faculty libraries, *c.* 50,500.

Publications: Acta Salmanticensia, 4 series; Cuadernos de Historia de la Medicina Española; Anales de Medicina; Zephyrus; Minos; Cuadernos de la Cátedra de Miguel de Unamuno; Theses et Studia Philologica Salmanticensia; Memoria Académica; Guia de los Cursos.

Press or Publishing House: Ediciones Universidad de Salamanca.

Academic Staff, 1989-90:

Rank	Full-time	Part-time
Catedráticos	220	10
Titulares	768	19
Colaboradores	264	–
Ayudantes	–	382
Encargados de Curso	–	13
Otros	4	2
Total	1256	426

Student Enrolment, 1989-90:

	Men	Women	Total
Of the country	9860	15,212	25,072
Of other countries	115	103	218
Total	9975	15,315	25,290*

*Also 25,290 by correspondence.

6751 **UNIVERSIDAD PONTIFICIA DE SALAMANCA**

Pontifical University of Salamanca

Compñia 5, 37008 Salamanca

Telephone: (923) 215209

Fax: (923) 213450

Rector: José Manuel Sánchcz (1990-)

Secretario General: Marceliano Arranz Rodrigo

F. of Theology
Dean: J. Román Flecha Andrés; *staff* 19 (11)
F. of Canon Law
Dean: J. Luis Acebal Luján; *staff* 6 (2)
F. of Philosophy
Dean: Alfonso Pérez de Laborda; *staff* 8 (10)
F. of Trilingual Biblical Philology
Dean: José Droz Retz; *staff* 5 (6)
F. of Education
Dean: Vicente Faubell Zapata; *staff* 8 (14)
F. of Psychology
Dean: Ma. Francisca Martín; *staff* 14 (12)
F. of Political and Social Sciences
Dean: Vicente Pereña; *staff* 8 (14)
F. of Informatic Sciences
Dean: Ma. Teresa Aubach; *staff* 14 (15)
I. of Pastoral Studies
Director: Juan Martin Velasco; *staff* 6 (10)
S. of Speech Studies
Director: Jesús Málaga G.; *staff* 10 (15)
S. of Language Psychology
Director: Jusús Málaga G.; *staff* 12 (16)
I. of Catechetical Studies
Director: Antonio Cañizares; *staff* 8 (12)
S. of Family Studies
Director: Dionisio Borobio; *staff* 8 (14)
S. of Education (Teaching Training for Adult Education)
Director: Manuel Fernández Pellitero

I. of European Studies of Human Rights
Director: Alfonso Ortega; *staff* 8 (20)
I. of Infant Clinical Psychology
Director: Luis Jiménez Díaz; *staff* 8 (12)
I. of Spanish Language and Culture
Director: Mercedes de Iande; *staff* 6 (15)
Ce. for Oriental and Ecumenical Studies
Director: Adolfo González Montes; *staff* 2 (2)
I. of History of Theology
Director: Antonio Garcia Y Garcia; *staff* 2
I. of Biblical Archaeology
Director: Florentino Diez Fernández; *staff* 3 (4)

Founded in 1940 as Pontifical University, thus reviving the Ecclesiastical Faculties of the University of Salamanca, founded in the 12th century, which were suppressed in the 19th century. The university is operated under the patronage of the Hispanic Episcopate and the jurisdiction of an Episcopal Commission, the President of which is the Cardinal Archbishop of Madrid. In compliance with the Apostolic Constitution, Deus scientiarum Dominus, the university is entitled to award degrees. These are given civil recognition under the terms of the Concordat of 1953 and 1962. The institution receives financial support from the Church, and from public and private bodies and individuals. Governing bodies: the Claustro Universitario; the Junta de Gobierno; the Patronato. Residential facilities in Colegio Mayor.

Arrangements for co-operation with Universities of: Jerusalem; Buenos Aires; Tel-Aviv; Montevideo; Washington;Würzburg; Louvain.

Academic Year: October to June (October-December; January-March; April-June).

Admission Requirements: Secondary school certificate (bachiller) and pre-university examination (madurez).

Language of Instruction: Spanish. (Also Latin in Theological faculties).

Degrees and Diplomas: Bachiller in Theology, 3 yrs. Licenciado in Theology, 5 yrs. Doctorate in–Law; Philosophy; Philology; Education; Psychology; social and Political Science, by thesis, a further 2 yrs. Diplomado in institutes, centres, and schools, 3 yrs.

Libraries: University Library, *c.* 15,000 vols; specialized libraries.

Publications: Salmanticensis; Helmantica; Diálogo Ecuménico; Colectanea de Jurisprudencia Canónica; Cuadernos Salmantinos de Filosofía; Cuadernos de Familia.

Academic Staff, 1989-90: 190 (210).
Student Enrolment, 1989-90: 4550.

6752 ***UNIVERSIDAD DE SANTIAGO DE COMPOSTELA**
University of Santiago de Compostela
Palacio de San Jerónimo, Plaza de España, Santiago de Compostela La Coruña
Telex: 86.013
Telephone: (981) 58-38-00
Rector: Carlos Pajares Vales (1986-90)
Secretario General: Florencio Arce Vázquez

F. of Philosophy and Education
Dean: José Barreiro Barreiro
F. of Biology
Dean: Dario Díaz Cosin
F. of Economics and Business Administration
Dean: Luis Caramés Vieitez
F. of Law
Dean: José Gómez Segade
F. of Pharmacy
Dean: José Andrés Cañadell
F. of Philology
Dean: Jesús Pena Seijas
F. of Physics
Dean: José Rivas Rey
F. of Geography and History
Dean: Ramón Villares Paz
F. of Mathematics
Dean: José Masa Vázquez
F. of Medicine
Dean: Jesús Otero Costas
F. of Chemistry
Dean: Ricardo Riguera Vega
F. of Veterinary Medicine (Lugo)
Dean: Luis de la Cruz Palomino
S. of Architecture
S. of Industrial Engineering
Director: Enrique Mandado Pérez
S. of Telecommunications
I. of Criminology
I. of Education
I. of Galician Language
I. of Regional Studies and Development
Undergraduate Ce. (Biology, Economics, Education, Psychology, Philologym Chemistry) (La Coruña)
Director: José Armesto Barberto
Undergraduate C . (Biology, Philology, Mathematics, Chemistry) (Lugo)
Director: José Estevez Cabanes
Undergraduate Ce. (Biology, Education, Psychology, Pharmacy, Geography and History, Chemistry) (Orense)
Director: Teresa Iglesias Randulfe
Undergraduate Ce. (Biology, Philology, Chemistry, Economics and Business Administration) (Vigo)
Director: Anselmo Seone Pampín Montenegro
Ce. of Architecture (Technical)
Director: Juan Pérez Valcarcel
Ce. of Agricultural Engineering (Technical) (Lugo)
Ce. of Marine Engineering (Technical) (El Ferrol)
Director: Ramón de Vicente Vázquez
Ce. of Industrial Engineering (Technical) (Vigo)
Ce. of Nursing
Director: Victoria Fernández Varela
Ce. of Education
Director: Angel González Fernández
Ce. of Business Administration
Director: Maria Luisa Fernanda Abreu
Ce. of Education (La Coruña)
Ce. of Education (Lugo)
Ce. of Education (Orense)
Ce. of Education (Pontevedra)

Founded 1495 as Colegio de Estudiantes by Lope Gómez de Marzoa. Became Estudio Gramática 1501. Approved by Papal Bull of Julian II 1504, and Papal Bull of Clement VII 1526, became university by Papal Bull of Pius V 1566. A State institution under the jurisdiction of the Ministry of Education and Science. Governing bodies: the Claustro Universitario; the Junta de Gobierno. Some residential facilities for academic staff and students in 7 Colegios Mayores and 1 Residencia Universitaria.

Arrangements for co-operation with Universities in Europe and U.S.A.

Academic Year: October to June (October-December; January-March; April-June).

Admission Requirements: Secondary school certificate (bachiller) and pre-university examination (madurez).

Fees (Pesetas): 40,000 per annum.

Languages of Instruction: Spanish and Gallego.

Degrees and Diplomas: Diplomado in–Nursing; Management Studies; Education, 3 yrs. Titles of–Arquitecto; Técnico; Ingeniero Técnico, 3 yrs. Licenciado, in all fields, 5 yrs; Medicine, 6 yrs. Professional titles of– Arquitecto; IngenieroIndustrial, 6 yrs. Doctorates, a further 3-5 yrs. Teaching qualification, 3 yrs.

Library: Central Library, 113,304 vols.

Special Facilities (Museums, etc.): Natural History Museum.

Publication: Acta Científica Compostellana.

Academic Staff, 1986-87: 1570.

Student Enrolment, 1986-87:

Of the country	38,769
Of other countries	2110
Total	40,879

6753 **UNIVERSIDAD DE SEVILLA**
University of Seville
Calle San Fernando 4, Sevilla
Telephone: (954) 218600
Rector: Guillermo Jimenez Sánchez

F. of Philosophy and Education
F. of Economics and Business Administration
F. of Science
F. of Law
F. of Fine Arts
F. of Medicine
F. of Geography and History

F. of Philology
F. of Biology
F. of Pharmacy
F. of Physics
F. of Mathematics
F. of Chemistry
F. of Geology (La Rábida)
Undergraduate Ce. (Palos de la Frontera)
Ce. of Business Administration
Ce. of Architecture (Technical)
Ce. of Engineering (Technical)
Ce. of Nursing
Ce. of Nursing (Huelva)
Ce. of Nursing (La Rábida)
Ce. of Engineering (Technical) (La Rábida)
Ce. of Education
Ce. of Education (Huelva)

Founded end of 15th century as Colegio Mayor. Recognized by Papal Bull 1505 and authorized to confer degrees. Officially became university 1551. A State institution under the jurisdiction of the Ministry of Education andScience. Residential facilities for students.

Academic Year: October to May.

Admission Requirements: Secondary school certificate (bachiller) and pre-university examination (madurez).

Language of Instruction: Spanish.

Degrees and Diplomas: Diplomado in Business Administration, 4 yrs. Licenciado, 5 yrs, except Medicine, 6 yrs. Professional titles in–Architecture; Industrial Engineering; Agriculture, 5 yrs. Doctorates by thesis. Also postgraduate Certificates of specialization in Medicine.

Libraries: University Library, *c.* 101,000 vols; Philosophy and Letters, *c.* 55,840; Law, *c.* 43,000; Science, *c.* 4300; Medicine (Sevilla), *c.* 2600.

Publication: Anales de la Universidad Hispalense.

Academic Staff: c. 1550.

Student Enrolment: c. 34,000.

6754 **UNIVERSIDAD DE VALENCIA**

University of Valencia
Calle Nave 2, Valencia 3
Telephone: (96) 3217380

F. of Law
F. of Physics
F. of Science (Alicante)
F. of Medicine
F. of Psychology
F. of Philosophy and Education
F. of Philosophy and Letters (Alicante)
F. of Economics and Business Administration
F. of Geography and History (including Archaeology)
F. of Philology
F. of Chemistry
F. of Mathematics
F. of Biology
F. of Pharmacy
Undergraduate Ce. (Pharmacy, Law)
Undergraduate Ce. (Castellón de la Plana)
Ce. of Business Administration
Ce. of Physiotherapy
Ce. of Nursing
Ce. of Nursing (Castellón de la Plana)
Ce. of Education
Ce. of Education (Castellón de la Plana)
Ce. of Education (Cheste)

Founded 1500 as a university and recognized by Papal Bull in succession to previous institutions established in the 13th and 14th centuries. A State institution under the jurisdiction of the Ministry of Education and Science.

Academic Year: October to June.

Admission Requirements: Secondary school certificate (bachiller) and pre-university examination (madurez). Provision may be made for the recognition of foreign qualifications.

Language of Instruction: Spanish.

Degrees and Diplomas: Diplomado, 3 yrs. Licenciado in–Law; Philology; Geography and History; Pharmacy; Economics; Mathematics; Biology; Physics; Chemistry; Philosophy; Medicine, 5 yrs. Doctorates, a further 2 yrs.

Libraries: University Library, *c.* 27,190 vols; also faculty libraries, total, *c.* 131,780.

Publications: Anales de la Universidad de Valencia; Anuario de la Facultad de Medicina.

Academic Staff: c. 1570.

Student Enrolment: c. 40,750.

6755 ***UNIVERSIDAD POLITÉCNICA DE VALENCIA**

Polytechnic University of Valencia
Camino de Vera s/n, 46071 Valencia
Telex: 62808 UPVA E
Telephone: (96) 360-36-00; 387-70-00
Fax: (96) 360-42-08
Rector: Justo Nieto Nieto (1989-94)
Secretario General: Luis Segura Gomis

S. of Agriculture
Director: Baldomero Segura García del Rio
S. of Architecture
Director: Bernardo Perepérez Ventura
S. of Civil Engineering (Highways, Canals, and Ports)
Director: Pedro Fuster García
S. of Industrial Engineering
Director: Eliseo Gómez-Senent Martínez
S. of Telecommunication
Director: José-Luis Marín Galán
F. of Computer Sciences
Dean: Vicente Hernández García
F. of Fine Arts
Dean: Facundo Tomás Ferre
I. of Hydrology
Director: Juan José Alonso Pascual
I. of Biomechanics
Director: Pedro Vera Luna
I. of Education
Director: Vicente San Onofre Morales
I. of Construction
Director: Vicente Sifre Martínez
Ce. of Architecture (Technical)
Director: José Luis Montalva Conesa
Ce. of Industrial Engineering (Technical)
Director: Enrique Ballester Sarría
Ce. of Industrial Engineering (Technical) (Alcoy)
Director: Roberto García Payá
Ce. of Agricultural Engineering (Technical)
Director: Juan Julia Igual
Ce. of Agricultural Engineering (Technical) (Orihuela)
Director: Miguel Angel Martínez Cañadas
Ce. of Technical Studies (Architecture, Computer Sciences, Public Works)
Director: Miguel Louis Cereceda
Ce. of Computer Sciences
Director: Pedro Blesa Pons
Ce. of Topography and Public Works
Director: Manuel Chueca Pazos

Founded 1968 incorporating four existing Escuelas Técnicas. Became university 1971. A State institution under the jurisdiction of the Ministry of Education and Science. Governing bodies: the Claustro General, comprising 519 members; the Junta de Gobierno, comprising 75 members; the Consejo Social, comprising 16 members. Residential facilities for academic staff and students in Colegios Mayores.

Arrangements for co-operation with: University of Quindio; National Technical University of Callao; Federal University of Uberlândia; Swiss Federal Institute of Technology.

Academic Year: October to June (October-February; February-June).

Admission Requirements: Secondary school certificate (bachiller) or recognized foreign equivalent, and pre-university examination (madurez).

Fees (Pesetas): 50,000 per annum.

Language of Instruction: Spanish.

Degrees and Diplomas: Diplomado in Computer Sciences, 3 yrs. Licenciado, 6 yrs. Titles of–Ingeniero Técnico; Arquitecto Técnico, 3 yrs. Professional titles of–Arquitecto; Ingeniero, in–Agriculture; Civil Engineering; Industrial Engineering, 6 yrs. Doctorates, by thesis, a further 2 yrs.

Libraries: Central Library, 60,000 vols; department libraries.

Special Facilities (Museums, etc.): Toy Museum.

Publications: Agora (every 2 weeks); Apunta (weekly).

Press or Publishing House: Servicio de Publicaciones.

Academic Staff, 1986-87: 999.
Student Enrolment, 1986-87: 13,799.

6756 **UNIVERSIDAD DE VALLADOLID**
University of Valladolid
Plaza Santa Cruz 8, 47002 Valladolid
Telex: 26357
Telephone: (983) 264000
Rector: Fernando Tejerina García (1984-90)
Secretario General: Jesús María Palomares Ibañez

F. of Law
Dean: Avelino García Villarejo; *staff* 83 (35)
F. of Science
Dean: Santiago López González; *staff* 168 (72)
F. of Arts and Philology
Dean: Basilio Calderón Calderón; *staff* 161 (77)
F. of Medicine
Dean: Enrique Barbosa Ayucar; *staff* 93 (89)
F. of Economics and Business Administration
Dean: Juan Hernangómez; *staff* 90 (49)
F. of Law
Dean: Carlos Vattier; *staff* 23
S. of Architecture
Director: Ramón Rodríguez Llera; *staff* 40 (58)
S. of Industrial Engineering
Director: Cesáreo Hernández Iglesias; *staff* 70 (49)
Undergraduate Ce. (Science, Philosophy and Letters) (Burgos)
Director: Juan J. García González; *staff* 47 (14)
Ce. of Business Administration
Director: Angel Arenal Vega; *staff* 34 (10)
Ce. of Industrial Engineering (Technical)
Director: Ángel Reboto Hernández; *staff* 107 (35)
Ce. of Nursing
Director: Mercedes Rafael Santamaria; *staff* 13 (21)
Ce. of Business Administration (Burgos)
Director: José M. Villanueva Sáiz; *staff* 9 (7)
Ce. of Industrial Engineering (Technical) (Burgos)
Director: José Ramón Novoa Suárez; *staff* 74 (31)
Ce. of Agricultural Engineering (Technical) (Palencia)
Director: Manuel Betagón Baeza; *staff* 40 (19)
Ce. of Education
Director: María Castañar Dominguez Garrido; *staff* 74 (14)
Ce. of Education (Burgos)
Director: Fernando Esteban Ruiz; *staff* 42 (7)
Ce. of Education (Palencia)
Director: Enrique Delgado Huertos; *staff* 39 (10)
Ce. of Education (Soria)
Director: José A. Tejero Hernández; *staff* 27 (6)
I. of Educational Sciences
Director: Luis V. Díaz Martin; *staff* 10 (2)
I. of Atmosphere Studies
Director: José Casanova Colás
Also 5 affiliated colleges.

Founded 1293 and recognized by Pope Clement VI in 1346. Endowed and granted special privileges by the Kings of Spain. Reorganized as a State university in the 19th century. The university is a State institution under thejurisdiction of the Ministry of Education and Science. Some residential facilities for academic staff and students.

Arrangements in co-operation with the Universities of: Bradford; Clermont-Ferrand; Lille III; Ghent; Saarbrücken; Jerusalem; Mexico; Pau; Orleans; Angers; Toulouse; Wrocław; Puerto Rico; Aarhus; Kosova; Venezuela; Argentina; Uruguay; Santo Domingo; Beira; Coimbra; Iowa; Iberamericana.

Academic Year: October to July (October-February; April-July; July-December; January-March).

Admission Requirements: Secondary school certificate (bachiller) and pre-university examination (madurez).

Language of Instruction: Spanish.

Degrees and Diplomas: Diplomado. Licenciado in all faculties, 5 yrs, except Medicine, 6 yrs. Doctorate by thesis.

Library: c. 300,000 vols.

Special Facilities (Museums, etc.): Natural Sciences Museum.

Academic Staff, 1989-90:

Rank	Full-time	Part-time
Catedráticos	140	21
Titulares	407	50
Contratados	600	130
Total	1147	201

Student Enrolment, 1989-90:

	Men	Women	Total
Of the country	17,602	18,854	36,456

6757 ***UNIVERSIDAD DE ZARAGOZA**
University of Saragossa
Plaza de San Francisco s/n, 50009 Zaragoza
Telex: 58064 EDUCI E
Telephone: (976) 354100
Rector: Vicente Camarena Badia (1986-90)
Secretario General: Rosa Ruiz

F. of Arts
Dean: Guillermo Redondo; *staff* 70 (18)
F. of Law
Dean: Manuel Ramírez; *staff* 170 (15)
F. of Science
Dean: Justiniano Aporta; *staff* 175 (20)
F. of Economics and Business Administration
Dean: José Antonio Biescas; *staff* 60 (10)
F. of Medicine
Dean: Manuel Bueno; *staff* 115 (320)
F. of Veterinary Medicine
Dean: Emilio Manrique; *staff* 110 (10)
F. of Engineering
Director: Manuel Silva; *staff* 70 (25)
Undergraduate C. (Philosophy and Letters, Medicine) (Huesca)
Director: Micaela Muñoz; *staff* – (40)
Undergraduate Ce. (Science, Philosophy and Letters) (Logroño)
Director: Carmelo Cunchillos; *staff* – (51)
Undergraduate Ce. (Science, Philosophy and Letters) (Teruel)
Director: Guillermo Pérez; *staff* – (25)
Ce. of Business Administration
Director: Jorge Infante; *staff* 17 (17)
Ce. of Engineering (Technical)
Director: Jesús Madre; *staff* 32 (37)
Politechnic Ce.
Director: José A. Alba; *staff* 14 (16)
Ce. of Nursing
Director: Santiago Pellejero; *staff* 1 (20)
Ce. of Business Administration (Logroño)
Director: Pablo Arrieta; *staff* 8 (12)
Ce. of Business Administration (Pamplona)
Director: Luis Gallego; *staff* 17 (14)
Ce. of Education
Director: Antonio Valero; *staff* 51 (17)
Ce. of Education (Huesca)
Director: José Nassarre; *staff* 25 (9)
Ce. of Education (Logroño)
Director: Fabian González; *staff* 20 (16)
Ce. of Education (Pamplona)
Director: Pilar Abós; *staff* 33 (25)
Ce. of Education (Soria)
Director: Josè Blasco
Ce. of Social Studies
Director: Enrique Gastón
I. of Educational Sciences
Director: Agustín Ubieto; *staff* 2 (5)
I. of Languages
Director: Ignacio Vazquez; *staff* – (27)

Founded 1474 as Universitas magistrorum, recognized by Papal Bull. Established 1542 with Papal recognition 1555 and formally recognized as University 1583. Reorganized 1807 and 1971. Became an autonomous institution under the jurisdiction of the Ministry of Education and Science 1983. Governing bodies: the Junta de Gobierno; the Juntas de Facultades, including deans, professors and students; the Junta del Centro Politécnico Superior; the Claustro Universitario; the Consejo Social. Residential facilities for students.

Arrangements for co-operation with the Universities of: Pau; Bordeaux I; Toulouse III; Aix-Marseille; Trieste; Lille; Morelos (State); Paderborn;

Rosario; Pernambuco; Copenhagen; Bordeaux III; Paris; Montpellier; Toulouse I, II; Tours; Lyon II; Paris IV; Milan; Trieste; Rome; Managua; Warsaw; Lancaster; Liverpool; Manchester; Glasgow; Salford; Paderborn; Clausthal; Minsk; Leningrad; Moscow; Nottingham.

Academic Year: October to June (October-December; January-March; March-June).

Admission Requirements: Secondary school certificate (bachiller) and pre-university examination (madurez). Entrance examination for students over 25 yrs.

Fees (Pesetas): 41,050-58,150 per annum.

Language of Instruction: Spanish.

Degrees and Diplomas: Diplomado, 3 yrs. Licenciado in all faculties, 5 yrs, except Medicine, 6 yrs. Doctorate by thesis, a further 2-4 yrs.

Libraries: Central Library, 102,000 vols; Law, 74,000; Medicine, 8000; Science, 24,000; Economics, 20,000; Philosophy andLetters, 100,000; Veterinary Medicine, 12,000.

Publication: Tornavoz (quarterly).

Academic Staff, 1989-90:

Rank	Full-time
Catedráticos	171
Titulares	912
Maestros de Taller	12
Asociados	681
Ayudantes	190
Eméritos	10
Otros	22
Total	2018

Student Enrolment, 1989-90:

	Men	Women	Total
Of the country	17,387	19,237	36,624
Of other countries	125	53	178
Total	17,512	19,290	36,802

Also 31 Colegios Universitarios (1st cycle)

Other Institutions

Private Institutions

6759 **ACADEMIA UNIVERSITARIA DE DERECHO**

Burgos

Law

Founded 1956.

6760 **ESCUELA SUPERIOR DE ADMINISTRACIÓN Y DIRECCIÓN DE EMPRESAS (ESCADE)**

Avenida de Pedralbes 60-62, 08034 Barcelona

Cables: esade

Telex: 98286

Telephone: (34-3) 203-78-00

Fax: (34-3) 204-81-05

Director: Jaime Filella (1988-92)

Secretario General: Carlos M. Tomás

D. of Business Administration (including Social Sciences and Economics)

Dean: Lluís M. Pugés; *staff* 96 (264)

Language S.

Director: P. Mills

Also executive programmes in Madrid.

Founded 1958. A private institution recognized by the Ministry of Education and Science. Attached to the University of Cataluña 1985. Governing body: the Board of Trustees.

Arrangements for student exchanges with: Ecole des hautes Etudes commerciales, Paris; Graduate School of Business, New York University; McGill University; University of Cologne; Stockholm School of Economics; Libera Università di Economia e Commercio 'Luigi Bocconi', Milano; Brandeis University.

Academic Year: October to June (October-December; January-March; April-June).

Admission Requirements: Secondary school certificate (bachiller) and pre-university examination (madurez), or equivalent.

Fees (Pesetas): 550,000-1,500,000 per annum.

Language of Instruction: Spanish.

Degrees and Diplomas: Diplomas, 1-2 yrs. Licenciado y Master en Ciencias empresariales, 5 yrs. Master en Dirección y Administración de Empresas, 2-3 yrs. Diploma in Executive Studies, 1 yr. combined BBA-MBA Programme (Licenciado en Ciencias empresariales y MBA), 5 yrs. MBA degree, 2 yrs full-time or 3 yrs part-time. Also certificates.

Library: 50,000 vols.

Publication: Colección ESADE de Estudios de la Empresa.

Academic Staff, 1989-90:

Rank	Full-time	Part-time
Profesores	78	39
Ayudantes y Auxiliares de Prácticas	–	104
Profesores de Idiomas	18	45
Profesores colaboradores	–	76
Total	96	264

Student Enrolment, 1989-90:

	Men	Women	Total
Of the country	1786	543	2329
Of other countries	101	28	129
Total	1887	571	2458

6761 **ESCUELA SUPERIOR DE TÉCNICA EMPRESARIAL AGRÍCOLA**

Apartado 439, Córdoba

Telephone: (957) 29-61-33

Agricultural Administration

Business Administration

Founded 1964. A private institution recognized by the Ministry of Education and Science.

Academic Year: October to June (October-December; January-Easter; Easter-June).

Admission Requirements: Secondary school certificate (bachiller) and pre-university examination (madurez).

Language of Instruction: Spanish.

Degrees and Diplomas: Licenciado en Ciencias empresariales (agraria), 5 yrs.

Library: c. 9300 vols.

Academic Staff: c. 30.

Student Enrolment: c. 430.

6762 **ESCUELA SUPERIOR DE RELACIONES PÚBLICAS**

Barcelona

Public Relations

Founded 1969.

6763 **ESTUDIO SUPERIOR**

Lérida

6764 **ESTUDIOS UNIVERSITARIOS Y TÉCNICOS DE GUIPÚZXOA**

Paseo del Urumea-Mundáiz, 20012 San Sebastián

Telephone: 27-31-00

Rector: Juan Plazaola Artola

Secretario General: Jesús Arbunies Avalos

F. of Economics and Business Administration

Dean: Francisco Olarte Marín; *staff* 3 (1)

F. of Philosophy and Letters

Dean: José Ángel Asunce Arrieta; *staff* 5

S. of Tourism

Director: José María Pérez de Arenaza

Founded 1956 as Escuela Superior Técnica Empresarial, acquired present title 1960. A private institution attached to the University of Deusto. Recognized by the Ministry of Education 1963. Governing body: the Junta de Gobierno.

Academic Year: October to June (October-January; February-June).

Admission Requirements: Secondary school certificate (bachiller) and pre-university examination (madurez).

Fees (Pesetas): Tuition, 129,500.

Languages of Instruction: Spanish and Basque.

Degrees and Diplomas: Licenciado, 5 yrs. Magister in Business Administration. Doctorates. Also Diplomas.

Library: c. 45,000 vols.

Publications: Estudios Empresariales; Revista 'Mundáiz'.

Academic Staff, 1986-87:

Rank	Full-time	Part-time
Catedráticos	5	3
Titulares	4	–
Profesores Encargados	18	73
Total	27	76

Student Enrolment, 1986-87:

	Men	Women	Total
Of the country	1069	1207	2276

6765 **FACULTAD DE CIENCIAS ECONÓMICAS Y EMPRESARIALES**

Paseo de Mundáiz 50, 20012 San Sebastián
Telephone: 43-27-31-00
Fax: 43-29-26-35
Decano: José M. Echeverria (1984-97)

Business Technology

Founded 1956 as school, attached to the University of Deusto 1979. A private independent institution.

Participation in the ERASMUS programme with similar institutions in: United Kingdom; France; Belgium; Netherlands; Germany; Denmark.

Academic Year: October to June (October-February; February-June).

Admission Requirements: Secondary school certificate (bachiller) and pre-university examination (madurez).

Fees (Pesetas): Registration, 40,000; tuition, 171,500.

Language of Instruction: Spanish.

Degrees and Diplomas: Licenciado en Ciencias Econômicas y Empresariales, 5 yrs. Master en Gestion de Empresas (MBA). Doctorado en Ciencias Econômicas y Empresariales.

Library: c. 40,000 vols.

Publication: Estudios Empresariales (quarterly).

Academic Staff: c. 30 (30).

Student Enrolment: c. 900.

6766 **INSTITUTO CATÓLICO DE ARTES E INDUSTRIAS**

Calle de Alberto Aguilera 23, Madrid 15

6767 **INSTITUTO CATÓLICO DE DIRECCIÓN DE EMPRESAS**

23 Calle Alberto Aguilera, Madrid

Business Administration

6768 **INSTITUTO QUÍMICO DE SARRIÁ**

08017 Barcelona
Telephone: (34-3) 203-89-00
Fax: (34-3) 205-62-65
Director: Miguel Gassiot Matas
Secretario general: M. Luisa Espasa Sempere

D. of Chemometrics
Director: Werner Bek Knoeller; *staff* 8
D. of Chemical Engineering
Director: Alberto Barrera Berro; *staff* 6
D. of Analytical Chemistry
Director: Luis Victori Companys; *staff* 5
D. of Organic Chemistry
Director: Pedro Victory Arnal; *staff* 4

Founded 1916 by the Society of Jesus. A private institution recognized by the State 1965. Attached to Autonomous University of Barcelona 1972. Became an Associated Center of the Consejo Superior de Investigaciones Científicas 1987. Governing body: the Board of Directors.

Arrangements for co-operation with the Universities of: Porto; Montpellier; Gloningen; Geneva; Tromsö; Wärzburg; Vienna; Glasgow; Reading; Keele; Limerick; Wrocław (Agricultural); Columbia; Michigan; Detroit; Wayne State; Georgetown; California; Berkeley; Miami; Mexico; Alberta; Chile (Catholic); Concepción, Chile; Misiones; Litoral, Santa Fe; Bolivia; Ecuador (Catholic). Also with many research institutions, schools and centres.

Academic Year: October to June (October-January; February-June).

Admission Requirements: Secondary school certificate (bachiller) and pre-university examination (madurez). Provision may be made for the recognition of foreign qualifications.

Languages of Instruction: Spanish and Catalán.

Degrees and Diplomas: Professional title of Ingeniero Químico, 6 yrs. Doctorate by thesis, a further 3-4 yrs.

Library: 35,316 vols.

Publications: Afinidad; Boletín Académico.

Academic Staff, 1988-89: c. 100.

Student Enrolment, 1988-89:

	Men	Women	Total
Of the country	448	274	722
Of other countries	16	9	25
Total	464	283	747

SUDAN

Universities

6769 ***GAMA'AT EL KHARTOUM**
University of Khartoum
P.O. Box 321, Khartoum
Cables: Gamaa
Telephone: 75100
Vice-Chancellor: Omar Beleil

F. of Agriculture
F. of Arts (including Geography and Philosophy)
F. of Economic and Social Studies
F. of Engineering and Architecture
F. of Law
F. of Medicine (including Dentistry)
F. of Pharmacy
F. of Science
F. of Veterinary Science
F. of Education
S. of Extramural Studies
S. of Mathematics
I. of African and Asian Studies
Building Research Station
Research Ut. (Sudanese Studies)
Hydrobiological Research Ut.
Arid Zone Research Ut.
Computer Ce.
Development Studies and Research Ce.

Founded 1951 as University College of Khartoum incorporating Gordon Memorial College, established 1902, and the Kitchener School of Medicine, established 1924. Became university 1956. An autonomous institution financed by the State. Governing bodies: the University Council, comprising 29 members; the Academic Senate, composed entirely of members of the academic staff. Residential facilities for academic staff and students.

Academic Year: July to April (July-September; October-December; January-March).

Admission Requirements: Secondary school certificate.

Languages of Instruction: English. Arabic in Departments of Islamic Law, of Islamic History, and of Arabic.

Degrees and Diplomas: Bachelor of Arts, B.A.; general, 4 yrs; Honours, 5 yrs. Bachelor of Science, B.Sc.; general, in Social Studies; Economics; Business Administration; Social Anthropology; Political Science; Accountancy; Statistics; Economics and Social Studies, 4 yrs; Honours, 5 yrs. Engineering, 4 yrs; Agriculture, Honours, 4 yrs; Architecture, 5 yrs. Bachelor of Laws (Civil), 3 yrs; (Islamic), 4 yrs. Bachelor of Pharmacy, B.Pharm., 5 yrs; Bachelor of Veterinary Science, B.V.Sc., 5 yrs. Bachelor of Medicine, M.B., B.S., 6 yrs. Master and Doctor in all faculties.Also postgraduate diplomas.

Libraries: Main Library, *c.* 300,000 vols; Engineering and Architecture, *c.* 8500; Medicine and Pharmacy, *c.* 9000; Agriculture and Veterinary Science, *c.* 28,000; Law, *c.* 5000.

Special Facilities (Museums, etc.): Natural History Museum.

Publications: Gazette (three times a year); Research Committee Report (annually).

Academic Staff: c. 680.

Student Enrolment: c. 14,000.

6770 **CAIRO UNIVERSITY, KHARTOUM BRANCH**
P.O. Box 1055, Khartoum
Telephone: 80055

F. of Arts (including Sociology)
Dean: Mohamed Rushdy Hassan
F. of Commerce
Dean: Mohamad Zaki Al Messir
F. of Law
Dean: Hussein Yehia
F. of Science
Dean: Ahmad Amer
I. of Statistics

Founded 1955 by Decree, became independent 1959. The institution is financed by Cairo University. Residential facilities for academic staff and students from outside Khartoum.

Academic Year: August to April (August-November; December-April).

Admission Requirements: Egyptian, Sudanese, or Cambridge school certificate, or equivalent.

Fees: None.

Degrees and Diplomas: Bachelor of–Arts; Commerce; Law; Science, 4 yrs. Master of–Arts; Commerce, a further 2 yrs. Doctor, Ph.D., in–Law; Commerce; Arts.

Library: c. 63,000 vols.

Academic Staff: c. 120.

Student Enrolment: c. 20,000.

6771 ***UNIVERSITY OF GEZIRA**
P.O. Box 20, Wad Medani
Telephone: 2605
Vice-Chancellor: Omer Hassan Goha

F. of Agricultural Sciences
F. of Medical Sciences
F. of Science and Technology
F. of Economics and Rural Development
Also preparatory college.

Founded 1975. An autonomous State institution. Governing bodies: the Council, comprising 29 members; the Senate, of 13 members. Residential facilities for academic staff and students.

Academic Year: October to June (October-January; February-June).

Admission Requirements: Secondary school certificate.

Language of Instruction: English.

Degrees and Diplomas: Bachelor of Science in–Economics, B.Sc. (Econ.); Agriculture, B.Sc. (Agric.); Technology, B.Sc. (Tech.), 5 yrs; Bachelor of Medicine and Surgery, M.B.N., B.Ch., 6 yrs. Master of–Science, M.Sc.; Philosophy, M.Phil. Doctor of Philosophy, Ph.D.

Library: c. 7500 vols.

Academic Staff: c. 150.

Student Enrolment: c. 810.

6772 ***UNIVERSITY OF JUBA**
P.O. Box 321, Juba
Cables: Juvarsity Juba
Telephone: 2114
Vice-Chancellor: Abdel-Aal Abdullah Osman

Ce. of Natural Resources (Biological and Physical Sciences, Agriculture, Forestry and Veterinary Medicine)
Ce. of Social and Environmental Studies (including Humanities and Economic and Social Studies)
Ce. of Medicine
Ce. of Education
Ce. of Adult Education

Founded 1975. Accepted first students in 1977. An autonomous State institution. Governing bodies: the University Council; the Senate. Residential facilities for academic staff and students.

Academic Year: September to July (September-December; April-July).

Admission Requirements: Secondary school certificate or foreign equivalent.

Fees: None.

Language of Instruction: English.

Degrees and Diplomas: Bachelor of–Arts, B.A.; Science, B.Sc., 4 yrs; Honours, 5 yrs. Also diploma, 3 yrs.

Library: c. 6000 vols.

Publication: Juvarsity (monthly).

Academic Staff: c. 130.
Student Enrolment: c. 640.

6773 ***OMDURMAN ISLAMIC UNIVERSITY**
P.O. Box 381, Omdurman
Telephone: 54220
Vice-Chancellor (Acting): Al-Tahir Ahmed Abdul Gadir

F. of Islamic Studies
Dean (Acting): Al-Tahir Al-Dirdiri
F. of Islamic Law (Shari'a and Social Studies)
Dean: Ahmed Al-Khatim Abdulla
F. of Arts
Dean: Babikir Al-Amin Al-Dirdiri
Girls' Ce.
Extramural Ut.
Head: Tagel Sir Al-Iraqi

Founded 1912 as Islamic Institute, became college 1924 and university 1965. Acquired present status 1975. A State institution under the jurisdiction of and financially supported by the National Council for Higher Education. Governing bodies: the University Council; the Senate; the Faculty Boards. Residential facilities for *c.* 1500 students.

Academic Year: July to April (July-November; December-April).
Admission Requirements: Secondary school certificate or recognized equivalent.
Language of Instruction: Arabic.
Degrees and Diplomas: Bachelor of Arts, B.A., Law, LL.B.; Science, B.Sc., 4 yrs. Master of Arts, M.A., a further 2-3 yrs. Degree of Doctor of Philosophy, Ph.D., 3 yrs. Also Diplomas in–Education; Islamic Economics, 1 yr.
Libraries: Central Library, *c.* 90,000 vols; Girls College, *c.* 10,000.
Publication: Journals of the Faculties.
Press or Publishing House: The University Press.
Academic Staff, 1986-87:

Rank	Full-time
Professors	8
Assistant Professors	13
Lecturers	94
Teaching Assistants	80
Total	195

Student Enrolment, 1986-87:

	Men	Women	Total
Of the country	2845	790	3635
Of other countries	121	70	191
Total	2966	860	3826

6774 **AHFAD UNIVERSITY FOR WOMEN**
P.O. Box 167, Omdurman
Telephone: 53363
President: Yusuf Badri

S. of Family Science
Head: Amna Rahama; *staff* 15 (9)
S. of Psychology and Pre-School Education
Head: Sid Ahmed Mahmud; *staff* 18 (5)
S. of Organizational Management
Head: Amna Badri; *staff* 9 (9)
S. of Rural Development and Extension

Founded 1907 as primary school, became high school 1955 and university college 1966. Acquired present status and title 1985. A private institution receiving 50% financial aid from the government. Governing bodies: the Board of Trustees; the Council; the Academic Board. Someresidential facilities for academic staff and students.

Arrangements for co-operation with Iowa State University.
Academic Year: August to April (August-December; January-April).
Admission Requirements: Secondary school certificate or equivalent.
Fees (Pounds): 1500 per annum.
Degrees and Diplomas: Bachelor, 4 yrs.
Library: 35,000 vols.
Publications: Ahfad Journal; Women and Change (biannually).
Academic Staff, 1986-87:

Rank	Full-time	Part-time
Professors	3	1
Associate Professors	2	2
Assistant Professors	1	20
Lecturers	15	–
Teaching Assistants	11	–
Total	32	23

Student Enrolment, 1986-87:

	Women
Of the country	878
Of other countries	24
Total	902

Other Institutions

Technical Education

6775 **KHARTOUM POLYTECHNIC**
P.O. Box 407, Khartoum
Telephone: 78508

Ce. of Engineering
Ce. of Commerce (including Secretarial Studies)
Ce. of Agriculture
Ce. of Fine and Applied Arts
Ce. of Further Education
Also 3 affiliated colleges.

Founded 1950 as Khartoum Technical Institute. Became Khartoum Polytechnic 1967 and acquired present status 1975 with the incorporation of previously existing higher technical institutes and specialized colleges. An autonomous institution financed by the central government. Residential facilities for academic staff and students.

Academic Year: July to March (July-September; September-December; January-March).
Admission Requirements: Secondary school certificate or equivalent.
Fees: None.
Language of Instruction: English.
Degrees and Diplomas: Diploma, 3-4 yrs. Also Certificates, 2 yrs.
Library: Reference Library, *c.* 19,470 vols.
Student Enrolment: c. 1630 (Also *c.* 1900 part-time students).

6776 **ABU HARAZ COLLEGE OF AGRICULTURE AND NATURAL RESOURCES**
Abu Haraz

Founded 1976.

6777 **ABU NAAMA COLLEGE OF AGRICULTURE AND NATURAL RESOURCES**
Abu Naama

Founded 1976.

6778 **MECHANICAL ENGINEERING COLLEGE**
P.O. Box 26, Atbara
Rector: El Fadil Adam Abdella
Registrar: Hassan Mohed Omen

D. of Power Technology
Head: Hashim Ahmed Ali; *staff* 5 (2)
D. of Engineering Science
Head: Abdel Moniem Awad El Kaim; *staff* 8
D. of Production
Head: Hassan El Bashin El Agab; *staff* 7

Founded 1973. Governing body: the Council. Residential facilities for foreign students.

Arrangements for co-operation with Leeds Polytechnic.
Academic Year: October to July.
Admission Requirements: Secondary school certificate or equivalent.
Fees (Pounds): 500; foreign students, 17,000.
Language of Instruction: English.
Student Enrolment: 40.

6779 **SCHOOL FOR TECHNICAL OPTICIANS**
Eye Hospital, Khartoum

Founded 1954.

6780 **TELECOMMUNICATION TRAINING CENTRE**
Khartoum South

Telecommunication Engineering

Founded 1903 as school, acquired present status 1969.

6781 **WAD EL MAGBOUL INSTITUTE FOR RURAL WATER TECHNICIANS**
Rural Water Corporation, P.O. Box 381, Khartoum
Cables: Rewina
Telephone: 893561

Drilling Technology and Surveying

Founded 1962 as Training Centre, acquired present title and status 1975. Under the jurisdiction of the Rural Water Corporation of the Ministry of Energy and Mining. Receives some financial support from the United NationsDevelopment Programme. Governing body: the Administration Council. Residential facilities for academic staff and students.

Academic Year: September to May (September-January; January-June).
Admission Requirements: Secondary school certificate.
Fees: None.
Language of Instruction: English.
Degrees and Diplomas: Diplomas, 3 yrs. Also Certificates.
Academic Staff: c. 30.
Student Enrolment: c. 100 (Men).

Professional Education

6782 **POLICE COLLEGE AND INSTITUTES**
P.O. Box 1416, Khartoum-Buri
Cables: Polischool
Telephone: 80109; 77205

Police Studies

Founded 1937 as school, acquired present status 1958. Reorganized 1980 and divided into 3 institutes. A State institution. Residential facilities.

Academic Year: July to June.
Admission Requirements: Secondary school certificate.
Fees: None.
Languages of Instruction: Arabic and English.
Degrees and Diplomas: Duration of studies, 3 yrs.
Special Facilities (Museums, etc.): Museum of Criminology.
Publication: Sudan Police Journal.
Academic Staff: c. 20.
Student Enrolment: c. 350.

6783 **COLLEGE FOR PRISON OFFICERS**
P.O. Box 1703, Khartoum
Cables: Tadrib
Telephone: 71013

Prison Management

Founded 1950 as a school, became College 1960. A State institution under the jurisdiction of the Ministry of the Interior. Residential facilities for staff and students.

Academic Year: April to April (April-May; July-April).
Admission Requirements: Secondary school certificate and entrance examination.
Fees: None.
Languages of Instruction: Arabic and English.
Degrees and Diplomas: Diploma, 2 yrs.
Library: c. 3000 vols.
Student Enrolment, 1984-85: 85.

6784 **FOREST RANGERS' COLLEGE**
P.O. Box 12, Khartoum

Forest Preservation

Founded 1946.

6785 **HIGHER INSTITUTE OF RADIOGRAPHY AND RADIOTHERAPY**
P.O. Box 1908, Khartoum
Telephone: 71818

Radiography
Radiotherapy

Founded 1933 as school, became institute of a joint project between the Sudan Government and WHO 1970. A Stateinstitution under the jurisdiction of the National Council for Higher Education. Residential facilities for students.

Academic Year: December to November (December-May; July-November).
Admission Requirements: Secondary school certificate.
Fees: None.
Language of Instruction: English.
Degrees and Diplomas: Diploma, 3 yrs.
Academic Staff: c. 30.
Student Enrolment: c. 130.

6786 **INSTITUTE OF MUSIC AND DRAMA**
P.O. Box 80, El Mourada, Omdurman

Music and Drama

Founded 1969 as Institute of Music, Drama and Folklore, acquired present title 1976. A State institution underthe jurisdiction of the Ministry of Culture and Information. Residential facilities for academic staff and students.

Academic Year: January to November (January-April; July-November).
Admission Requirements: Secondary school certificate or equivalent, and entrance audition.
Language of Instruction: Arabic.
Degrees and Diplomas: Diploma in–Drama, 4 yrs; Music, 5 yrs. Certificates in Drama and Music, 4 yrs.
Library: Institute Library.
Academic Staff: c. 15.
Student Enrolment: c. 180.

6787 **KHARTOUM NURSING COLLEGE**
P.O. Box 1063, Khartoum
Telephone: 72865

Nursing

Founded 1956.
Degrees and Diplomas: Diploma, 3 yrs.

6788 **SCHOOL OF HYGIENE**
P.O. Box 205, Khartoum
Telephone: 72890
Dean: Awad Abuzeid Mukhtar
Registrar: Mohamed Ali El Haj

Hygiene (including Environmental Health, Nutrition and Food Hygiene, Applied Health Sciences, and Biostatistics and Epidemiology)

Founded 1933. A State institution. Governing bodies: the Board of Directors; the Academic Council. Residential facilities for students.

Academic Year: July to April (July-October; October-February; March-April).
Admission Requirements: Secondary school certificate or equivalent.
Fees: None.
Language of Instruction: English.
Degrees and Diplomas: Diploma, 3 yrs.
Special Facilities (Museums, etc.): Graphic Museum.
Academic Staff: c. 5.
Student Enrolment, 1990:

Of the country	70
Of other countries	10
Total	80

Teacher Training

6789 **HIGHER INSTITUTE FOR PHYSICAL EDUCATION**
P.O. Box 12, Khartoum South
Telephone: 42331; 43231

Physical Education

Founded 1969. A State institution. Residential facilities for academic staff and students.

Academic Year: September to April (September-December; January-April).

Admission Requirements: Secondary school certificate.

Fees: None.

Language of Instruction: Arabic.

Degrees and Diplomas: Diploma, 4 yrs.

Academic Staff: c. 20.

Student Enrolment: c. 70.

SURINAME

6790 **ANTON DE KOM UNIVERSITETI VAN SURINAME**

University of Suriname
Leysweg 26, Paramaribo
Cables: Unisur
Telex: ADEKUS 311 SN
Telephone: 60410

F. of Medicine
Dean: B. Oostburg; *staff* 7 (31)
F. of Social Sciences (including Law and Economics)
Dean: E. Azimullah; *staff* 29 (35)
F. of Technology (including Agriculture, Forestry, Animal Husbandry and Mining)
Dean: E. Naarendorp; *staff* 27 (36)
Also 3 Research Institutes.

Founded 1968 incorporating School of Medicine, founded 1882, and School of Law, 1948. Reorganized 1983. Under the supervision of the Ministry of Education, Sciences and Culture. Governing body: the Board of Governors.

Arrangements for co-operation with the Free University of Brussels.

Academic Year: October to August (October-March; April-August).

Admission Requirements: Secondary school certificate or recognized foreign equivalent.

Fees: Tuition, none.

Languages of Instruction: Dutch and English.

Degrees and Diplomas: Bachelor of Science, 4 yrs. Master, a further 1 ½ yrs. Doctor of Medicine.

Libraries: Central Libraries, 60,000 vols; Medicine, 14,000.

Publications: Surinaams Juristenblad (quarterly); Surinaams Medisch Bulletin (quarterly); Sociaal-Economisch Tijdschrift (biannually).

Academic Staff, 1986-87:

Rank	Full-time	Part-time
Lector	2	11
Hoofddocent	27	42
Algemeen docent	18	20
Adjunct Wetenschappelijk medewerker	17	12
Gastdocent	–	2
Total	63	87

Student Enrolment, 1986-87:

	Men	Women	Total
Of the country	770	557	1327
Of other countries	3	3	6
Total	773	560	1333

SWEDEN

Universities

6791 **UNIVERSITETET I GÖTEBORG**
University of Göteborg
Vasaparken, 41124 Göteborg
Telephone: (31) 631000
Fax: (31) 634660
Rektor: Jan S. Nilsson (1986-92)
Universitetsdirektör: Christina Stendahl

F. of Medicine
Dean: Tore Scherstén
F. of Odontology
Dean: Jan Lindhe
F. of Arts and Fine Arts
Deans: Lars Lindvall; Jan Ling
F. of Social Sciences
Dean: Björn Hettne
F. of Mathematics and Natural Sciences
Dean: Ingvar Lindgren

Founded 1954 by the merging of what was then the Gothenburg College (founded as a private college 1891) and the Gothenburg Medical College. Gothenburg School of Economics incorporated 1971. Reorganized 1977 under national higher education reform, incorporating the School of Pre-School Education, the School of Journalism, the College of Music, SIHUS (the College of Nursing), the School of Social Work and Public Administration, the College of Speech and Drama, SÄMUS (the School of Music Education), and the Valand College of Art. Responsible to the Universitetshögskoleämbetet-UHÄ (National Board of Universities and Colleges). Governing body: the Universitetsstyrelsen (University Board), including the Rector, representatives of the academic staff, of administrative staff, and of students, and non-university members. Some residential facilities for students.

Academic Year: September to June (September-January; January-June).

Admission Requirements: Secondary school certificate or foreign equivalent, or age at least 25 yrs with 4 yrs work experience and a documented good knowledge of English.

Fees: None.

Language of Instruction: Swedish.

Degrees and Diplomas: Högskoleexamen or Filosofie Kandidatexamen, national certificate, or professional qualification, corresponding to 6-8 sem full-time study in most fields; Medicine, 11 sem. Licentiate in Philosophy, 2 yrs postgraduate study. Dortor of Philosophy, 4 yrs postgraduate studies. Also shorter courses, 1-3 sem.

Libraries: Central Library, *c.* 2,300,000 vols; Biomedical library, *c.* 276,000; Economics, *c.* 112,000; Education *c.* 74,000; Botany, *c.* 54,000.

Special Facilities (Museums, etc.): Museums: Biology; Classical Archaeology.

Publications: Acta Universitatis Gothoburgensis; Acta Bibliotecae Universitatis Gothoburgensis; New Literature on Women (quarterly bibliography); department publications.

Academic Staff, 1989-90:

Rank	Full-time
Professorer	173
Högskolelektorer	332
Högskoleadjunkter	277
Utländska lektorer	6
Forskarassistenter	117
Forskare	35
Forskningsassistenter	77
Klinisk lärare	37
Läsare i odont. ämne	19
Total	1073

Student Enrolment, 1985-86:

	Men	Women	Total
Of the country	8155	13,885	22,040

6792 **UNIVERSITETET I LINKÖPING**
Linköping University
581-83 Linköping
Telex: 509 66 UNLIN
Telephone: (13) 281000
Fax: (13) 282525
Rektor: Sven Erlander (1983-)
Förvaltningschef: Ingrid Cassel

F. of Fine Arts and Sciences (including Education)
Dean: Ulla Riis
F. of Medicine (including Pharmacy, Pharmacology)
Dean: Per Bjurulf
D. of Theme Research (Child Studies, Health and Society, Communication Studies, Technology and Social Change, and Water in the Environment and Society)
Dean: Lars Ingelstam
I. of Technology (Management and Economics, Production Economics, Mathematics, Computer and Information Science, Physics and Measuremant Technology, Electrical Engineering, Mechanical Engineering, and Biomedical Engineering)
Dean: Hasse Odenõ
Audio-visual Ce.
Director: Curt Karlssan
Computer Ce.
D. of Teacher Training
Head: Stellan Boozon-Johansson
National Computer Ce.
Head: Lars Eldén
D. of In-Service Education of Teaching Staff
Director: Lennart Berggren

Founded 1967 as branch of University of Stockholm, acquired university status and title of Linköpings Högskola 1970, and present title 1975. Reorganized 1977 under national higher education reform, incorporating former School of Education founded 1970. Responsible to the Universitetshögskoleämbetet-UHÄ (National Board of Universities and Colleges). Governing body: the Universitetsstyrelsen (University Board), including the Rector, representatives of the academic staff, of administrative staff, and of students, and non-university members. Residential facilities for students.

Arrangements for exchange programmes with Germany, France, United Kingdom, United States, Spain, Switzerland.

Academic Year: September to June (September-January; January-June).

Admission Requirements: Secondary school certificate or foreign equivalent, or age at least 25 yrs with 4 yrs work experience and knowledge of English.

Fees: None.

Language of Instruction: Swedish.

Degrees and Diplomas: Högskoleexamen, national certificate, or professional qualification, corresponding to 6-8 sem full-time study in most fields; Medicine, 11 sem. Also shorter courses, 2-5 sem. Doctorates, a further 4 yrs after degree.

Library: *c.* 165,000 vols.

Special Facilities (Museums, etc.): Science Centre.

Academic Staff, 1990: 2000.

Student Enrolment, 1990: 10,400.

6793 ***LUNDS UNIVERSITET**
Lund University
P.O. Box 117, 221-00 Lund
Telex: 33533 LUNIVER S
Telephone: 46 (46) 107000
Fax: 46 (46) 104715
Rektor: Håkan Westling (1989-93)
Universitetsdirektör: Peter Honeth

F. of Humanities (Theikigy, History and Philosophy, Langueges)

F. of Law
Dean: Gunnar Bramstång
F. of Medicine (including Physiotherapy)
Dean: Sven-Erik Bergentz
F. of Arts
Dean: Göran Rystad
F. of Social Sciences (including Social Work and Public Administration)
Dean: Olof Wärneryd
F. of Mathematics and Natural Sciences
Dean: Bengt E.Y. Svensson
F. of Dentistry (Malmö)
Dean: Per-Olof Glantz
F. of Technology and Engineering
Dean: Skotte Mårtensson
F. of Education (Malmö)
Rector: Gunnar Bergendal
F. of Music and Theatre (Malmö)
Rector: Håkan Lundström
Ce. for Women Studies and Women Researchers
P. for East and South-East Asian Studies
P. for Middle East and North Africa Studies
Electron Accelerator L.
Wallenberg L. (Medicine and Natural Sciences Research I.)
Raoul Wallenberg I. for Human Rights and Humanitarian Law
I. for Research in Economics and Management
Habitat and Development Studies Committee
Also research departments and schools of the faculties, and 2 Teaching Hospitals.

Founded 1666 to assure the rapid swedenization of the newly conquered Danish provinces. Lund Institute of Technology incorporated 1969 as faculty. The State assumed financial responsibility in the 19th century. Reorganized 1977 under national higher education reform, incorporating 5 previously existing institutions in Lund and Malmö founded between 1909 and 1962. Responsible to the Universitetshögskole-ämbetet-UHÄ (National Board of Universities and Colleges). Governing body: Universitetsstyrelsen (University Board), including the Rector, representatives of the academic staff, of administrative staff, and of students, and non-university members. Some residential facilities for visiting academic staff.

Arrangements for co-operation with numerous institutions, including: University of California; University of Sussex; University of Braunschweig; Washington State University; University of Dar es Salaam; Swiss Federal Institute of Technology; Academy of Medicine, Warsaw; University of Kiel; University of Toulouse; University of Greifswald; Chulalongkorn University, Bangkok; University of Tasmania; Zhejian University; Khartoum University.

Academic Year: September to June (September-January; January-June).

Admission Requirements: Secondary school certificate or foreign equivalent, or age at least 25 yrs with 4 yrs work experience and knowledge of English.

Fees: None.

Language of Instruction: Swedish. Some courses given in English.

Degrees and Diplomas: Högskoleexamen, national certificate, or professional qualification, corresponding to 6 sem full-time study in most fields; Medicine, 11 sem. Ämneslärarexamen, Master, of–Science; Laws; Arts; Fine Arts, at least 8sem. Also shorter courses, 2-5 sem. Doctorates, a further 4 yrs after degree.

Library: University Library, *c.* 3,500,000 vols.

Special Facilities (Museums, etc.): Arkivmuseet; Antikmuseet; Historiska Museet; Zoologiska Museet; Botaniska trädgården; Lunds Konstmuseum.

Publications: Lunds Universitets Årsskrift (annual); Lundaforskare föreläser (annually); Scripta Academica.

Press or Publishing House: Lund University Press.

Academic Staff, 1990:

Rank	Full-time
Professors and Lecturers	1060
Teachers and Researchers	1500
Technical and Administrative Staff	2140
Others	310
Total	5010

Student Enrolment, 1990: 25,400 (Including 750 foreign students).

6794 ***STOCKHOLMS UNIVERSITET**
University of Stockholm
Universitetsvägen 10, 106 91 Stockholm
Cables: University Stockholm
Telex: 8105199
Telephone: (08) 16-20-00
Fax: (8) 15-36-93
Rektor: Inge Jonsson (1988-94)
Universitetsdirektör: Rune Lindquist

F. of Humanities
D. of Ancient Culture and Society/Classical Archaeology and Ancient History
Head: Lennart Palmqvist; *staff* 2 (3)
D. of Archaeology
Head: Åke Hyenstrand; *staff* 8 (4)
D. of Philosophy
Head: Lars Bergström; *staff* 8 (9)
I. of Ethnology
Head: Mats Hellspong; *staff* 3 (4)
D. of History
Head: Göran Dahlbäck; *staff* 10 (2)
D. of Journalism and Communication
Head: Thorbjörn Lindskog; *staff* 12 (12)
D. of History of Art
Head: Thomas Hall; *staff* 12
D. of the History of Literature
Head: Magnus Röhl; *staff* 15 (5)
D. of Musicology
Head: Holger Larsen; *staff* 2 (1)
D. of Comparative Religion
Head: Louise Bäckman; *staff* 3
D. of Theatre and Cinema Arts
Head: Willmar Sauter; *staff* 8 (5)
D. of English
Head: Magnus Ljung; *staff* 16 (1)
D. of Finnish
Head: Erling Wande; *staff* 6 (1)
D. of Classicial Languages
Head: Jan Öberg; *staff* 10
D. of Linguistics
Head: Peter af Trampe; *staff* 18 (4)
D. of Scandinavian Languages
Head: Inger Larsson; *staff* 15 (1)
D. of Oriental Languages
Head: Torbjörn Lodén; *staff* 12 (2)
D. of Romance Languages
Head: Gunnel Engwall; *staff* 13 (11)
D. of Slavic and Baltic Languages
Head: Lars Stensland; *staff* 8 (6)
D. of Swedish
Head: Björn Julén
D. of German
Head: Lars-Olof Nyhlén; *staff* 10 (2)
F. of Law
D. of Law
Head: Claes Peterson; *staff* 44 (7)
F. of Social Sciences
D. of Computer and Systems Sciences
Head: Tord Dahl; *staff* 36 (1)
D. of Economic History
Head: Ronny Pettersson; *staff* 7 (6)
D. of Business Administration
Head: Olle Högberg; *staff* 22 (23)
Ut. of Informatics and Systems Science
Head: Kjell Samuelsson; *staff* 1
I. for International Economic Studies
Head: Assar Lindbeck; *staff* 14
I. of International Education
Head: Ingemar Fägerlind; *staff* 7
D. of Criminology
Head: Knut Sveri; *staff* 1 (3)
D. of Human Geography
Head: Ulf Sporrong; *staff* 9 (2)
D. of Economics
Head: Tomas Restad; *staff* 20
D. of Education
Head: Arvid Löfberg; *staff* 18 (4)

D. of Psychology
Head: Lars Nystedt; *staff* 36 (6)
D. of Social Anthropology
Head: Ulf Hannerz; *staff* 12 (5)
S. of Social Work
Head: Thomas Lindstein; *staff* 29 (8)
D. of Sociology
Head: Peter Hedström; *staff* 29 (3)
D. of Statistics
Head: Per Dahmström; *staff* 11 (1)
D. of Political Science
Head: Olof Ruin; *staff* 24 (3)
F. of Natural Sciences
D. of Astronomy (Stockholm Observatory)
Head: Claes Fransson; *staff* 8 (4)
D. of Physics
Head: Ulf Wahlgren; *staff* 13 (8)
D. of Mathematics
Head: Gudrun Brattström; *staff* 32
D. of Meteorology
Head: Ulla Hammarstrand; *staff* 19
D. of Analytical Chemistry
Head: Björn Josefsson; *staff* 6 (1)
D. of Biochemistry
Head: Bertil Andersson; *staff* 18 (3)
D. of Physical, Inorganic and Structural Chemistry
Head: Peder Kierkegaard; *staff* 30 (3)
D. of Organic Chemistry
Head: Bertil Erbing; *staff* 10 (1)
D. of Biophysics
Head: Anders Ehrenberg; *staff* 9 (2)
D. of Basic Biology Education
Head: Margareta Ohné; *staff* 1
D. of Botany
Head: Jan-Erik Tillberg; *staff* 12 (5)
D. of Genetics
Head: Ulf Ranung; *staff* 4
D. of Population Genetics
Head: Bert Bolin; *staff* 1
D. of Geology and Geochemistry
Head: Lennart Sjöberg; *staff* 22
D. of Quaternary Research
Head: Lars Brunnberg; *staff* 5
D. of Microbiology
Head: Leif Isaksson; *staff* 8 (1)
D. of Molecular Biology
Head: Britt-Marie Sjöberg; *staff* 2
D. of Physical Geography
Head: Leif Wastenson; *staff* 23
Ut. for Neurochemistry and Neurotoxicology
Head: Edith Heilbronn; *staff* 4
D. of Radiobiology
Head: Gunnar Ahnström; *staff* 7
Wenner-Gren I.
Head: Barbara Cannon; *staff* 20 (1)
D. of Zoology
Head: Björn Ganning; *staff* 17 (4)
D. of System Ecology and Natural Resources
Head: Bengt-Owe Jansson; Erik Arrhenius; *staff* 3
Ce. for Baltic Studies
Head: Aleksander Loit; *staff* 1 (1)
Ce. for the Study of Child Culture
Head: Gunnar Berefelt; *staff* 1
Ce. for Research in International Migration and Ethnic Relations
Head: Thomas Hammar; *staff* 4
Ce. for Women Research Workers
Head: Anita Dahlberg; *staff* 2
Ce. for Pacific Asia Studies
Director: Bert Edström; *staff* 1
I. for English-Speaking Students (IES)
Head: Bengt Sundelius; *staff* 16
I. of Latin American Studies
Head: Weine Karlsson; *staff* 2
Stockholm Ce. for Marine Research
Director: Kurt Boström; *staff* 1
Swedish I. for Social Research
Head: Eskil Wadensjö; *staff* 12 (2)
Ut. for Sign Language Interpretation
Head: Kenneth Hyltenstam; *staff* 5
I. for Interpretation and Translation Studies
Head: Gunnar Lemhagen; *staff* 1
Ce. for Research on Bilingualism
Head: Kenneth Hyltenstam; *staff* 5 (1)
Wallenberg L. (including Environmental Chemistry, Organic Chemistry, Genetic and Cellular Toxicology)
Head: Carl-Axel Wachtmeister; *staff* 5
Also field stations: Askö (Marine Ecology); Tarfala (Glaciology and Mountain); Tjärnö (Marine Biology); Tovetorp (Ethology); Tullbotorp (Botany).

Founded 1877 as a private institution for higher education, became State university 1960. Reorganized 1977 under national higher education reform. Responsible to the Universitetshögskoleämbetet-UHÄ (National Board of Universities and Colleges). Governing body: the Universitetsstyrelsen (University Board), including the Rector, representatives of the academic staff, of administrative staff, and of students, and of public interests.

Arrangements for exchange of researchers and students with: Eötvös Loránd University, Budapest; University of Warsaw; Tokyo University; Beijing University; Yanbian University; Chinese Academy of Social Sciences; Åbo Academy; Leningrad State University; University of Riga; University of Dohto.

Academic Year: August to June (August-January; January-June).

Admission Requirements: Secondary school certificate or foreign equivalent, or age at least 25 yrs with 4 yrs work experience and knowledge of English. Admission to all programmes and courses is restricted.

Fees (Krona): 140-180 per term.

Language of Instruction: Swedish.

Degrees and Diplomas: Högskoleexamen, national certificate, or professional qualification, corresponding to 6-8 sem full-time study in most fields. Also shorter courses, 2-5 sem. Doctorates, a further 4 yrs after degree.

Library: Law, Humanities, Social Sciences, and Natural Sciences, total, 2,300 m. of which 800,000 are to be found in different department libraries.

Special Facilities (Museums, etc.): Stockholm Observatory; Bergius Botanic Garden.

Publication: Acta Universitatis Stockholmiensis.

Academic Staff, 1988-89:

Rank	Full-time
Untenured Professors	9
Professors	148
Teachers and Research Workers	949
Research Associates	161
Assistant Lecturers, Assistants	167
Doctoral Students	140
Total	1574

Student Enrolment, 1989-90:

Men	Women	Total
11,000	15,000	26,000

6795 ***UMEÅ UNIVERSITET**
Umeå University
901-87 Umeå
Telex: 54005 UNIVUME
Telephone: (90) 16-50-00
Fax: (90) 16-54-88
Rektor: Lars Beckman (1973-89)
Universitetsdirektör: Dan Brändstrom

F. of Dentistry
Dean: Bo Bergman; *staff* 66 (63)
F. of Medicine
Dean: Sven Dahlgren; *staff* 167 (155)
F. of Mathematics and Natural Sciences
Dean: Arne Claesson; *staff* 178 (119)
F. of Social Sciences
Dean: Sigbrit Franke-Wikberg; *staff* 180 (145)
F. of Arts
Dean: Karl-Johan Danell; *staff* 80 (47)
Sec. for Education
Head: Åke G. Svensson; *staff* 147 (28)
D. of Population Studies
Director: Nils Häggström
Computer Ce.
Ce. for Arctic Cultural Research
Ce. for Regional Science Research

Kiruna Geophysical I.

Founded 1965, incorporating School of Dentistry, founded 1956, and Medical School, founded 1959. Reorganized 1977 under national higher education reform, incorporating 4 previously existing schools of education. Responsible to the Universitetshögskoleämbetet-UHÄ (National Board of Universities and Colleges). Governing body: the Universitetsstyrelsen (University Board), including the Rector, representatives of the academic staff, of administrative staff, of students, and non-university members. Residential facilities for students include 3500 rooms and flats.

Arrangements for co-operation with: University of Würzburg; York University, Toronto; University of Hawaii; Saint David's University College, Lampeter.

Academic Year: September to June (September-January; January-June).

Admission Requirements: Secondary school certificate or foreign equivalent, or age at least 25 yrs with 4 yrs work experience and knowledge of English.

Fees: None.

Language of Instruction: Swedish.

Degrees and Diplomas: Högskoleexamen, national certificate, or professional qualification, corresponding to 6-8 sem full-time study in most fields; Medicine, 11 sem. Also shorter courses, 2-5 sem. Doctorates, a further 4 yrs after degree. Master's degree for foreign students.

Library: c. 600,000 vols.

Special Facilities (Museums, etc.): Picture Museum.

Publication: Acta Universitatis Umensis.

Academic Staff, 1986-87:

Rank	Full-time
Professorer	120
Högskolelektorer	270
Forskarassistenter	70
Others	515
Total	905

Student Enrolment, 1986-87:

	Men	Women	Total
Of the country	3390	3660	7050
Of other countries	380	130	510
Total	3770	3790	7560*

*Also 600 external students.

6796 ***UPPSALA UNIVERSITET**

Uppsala University

P.O. Box 256, 751 05 Uppsala

Telex: 76024 UNIVUPS S

Telephone: 46-18-155400

Fax: 46-18-11853

Rektor: Stig Strömholm (1989-95)

Universitetsdirektör: Johnny Andersson

F. of Theology
Dean: Ragnar Holte
F. of Law
Dean: Per-Henrik Lindblom
F. of Medicine
Dean: Hans Ulfendahl
F. of Pharmacy
Dean: Lennart Paalzow
F. of Arts
Dean: Carl-Göran Andrae
F. of Social Sciences
Dean: Leif Lewin
F. of Science
Dean: Sven Kullander

Founded 1477, reorganized 1595. Reorganized 1977 under national higher education reform, incorporating former School of Education founded 1965. Responsible to the Universitets- och högskoleämbetet-UHÄ (National Board of Universities and Colleges). Governing body: the Konsistorium (The University Board), comprising 15 members including the Rector as Chairman, 3 representatives from the faculties, 8 representing the Society, and 3 students. Some residential facilities for students.

Arrangements for c. 40 exchange agreements with Scandinavian universities; c. 30 discipline based exchange agreements with universities outside Scandinavia; c. 15 general exchange agreements with universities outside Scandinavia.

Academic Year: September to June (September-January; January-June).

Admission Requirements: Secondary school certificate or foreign equivalent, or age at least 25 yrs with 4 yrs work experience and knowledge of English.

Fees: None.

Languages of Instruction: Swedish and some English.

Degrees and Diplomas: Högskoleexamen, filosofie kandidatexamen, national certificate, or professional qualification, corresponding to 6-8 sem full-time study in most fields; Medicine, 11 sem. Master of–Science; Arts; Social Science, a further 3 sem. Licentiatexamen, 2 yrs postgraduate study. Doktorsexamen a further 4 yrs after degree.

Libraries: University Library, c. 2,000,000 vols; libraries of the faculties and centres, 530,000.

Special Facilities (Museums, etc.): Botanic Museum and Garden; The Coin Cabinet; Zoological Museum; Gustavianum (Archaeology).

Publication: Acta Universitatis Upsaliensis.

Press or Publishing House: Uppsala University Press.

Academic Staff, 1990:

Rank	Full-time
Professorer (Professors)	246
Högskolelektorer (Associate Professors)	599
Högskoleadjunkter (Junior Lecturers)	291
Forskningsassistent (Junior Research Fellows)	168
Forskningsassistent (Research Assistants)	478
Total	1782

Student Enrolment, 1988:

Men	Women	Total
8300	8700	17,000

Other University Institutions

Göteborg Region

6797 **CHALMERS TEKNISKA HÖGSKOLA**

Chalmers University of Technology

41296 Göteborg

Telex: 27556 CHALAD S

Telephone: (31) 72-10-00

Fax: (31) 72-38-72

Rektor: Anders Sjöberg (1989-)

Förvaltningschef: Folke Hjalmers

S. of Mathematical Sciences
Dean: Axel Ruhe
S. of Physics and Engineering Physics
Dean: Björn Jonson
S. of Chemical Engineering
Dean: Nils-Herman Schöön
S. of Electrical and Computer Engineering
Dean: Erik Kohlberg
S. of Mechanical Engineering and Vehicle Engineering
Dean: Bo Appelqvist
S. of Civil Engineering
Dean: Sten Bengtsson
S. of Architecture
Dean: Björn Linn
C. of Applied Engineering and Maritime Studies
Dean: Erland Hultin
Ce. of Medical Engineering
Head: Robert Magnusson
Ce. for Materials Science
Head: Claes-Göran Granqvist
Ce. for Applied Mathematics
Head: Axel Ruhe
Ce. for Environmental Studies
Head: Jan Stefenson
Ce. for Built-up Areas Environment Studies
Head: Lars Stackell
Ce. for Marine Research and Technology
Head: K. Gösta Eriksson
Ce. for Computer Calculations
Head: Nils-Erik Wiberg
Ce. for the History of Technology
Head: Jan Hutt

Ce. for Industrial Engineering and Management
Head: Ulf Karlsson
Chalmers Innovation Ce.
Head: Torkel Wallmark
Ce. for Computer Science and Engineering
Head: Robert Magnusson
Ce. for Biotechnology
Head: Gunnar Björsell
Ce. for Semiconductors and Microelectronics
Head: Olof Engström
Ce. for Man, Technology and Society
Head: Anders Ulfvarsson
Ce. for Combustion Research
Head: Erik Olsson
Ce. for Biotechnology
Head: Christina Högfors
Ce. for Transport and Traffic
Head: Bertil Aldman

Founded 1829 as school following a bequest by William Chalmers in 1811, became university of technology 1937. Reorganized 1977 under higher education reform. A State university responsible to the Universitetshögskoleämbetet-UHÄ (National Board of Universities and Colleges). Governing body: the Universitetsstyrelsen (University Board).

Arrangments for co-operation with Imperial College, London; University of Strathclyde; Université Compiègne; University of Waterloo, Canada; Technische Universität Wien; Ecole Polytechnique, Lausanne; Rheinisch-Westfälische Technische Hochschule, Aachen; Ecole national supérieur de Toulouse.

Academic Year: August to June.

Admission Requirements: Secondary school certificate or foreign equivalent, or age at least 25 yrs with 4 yrs work experience and knowledge of English.

Fees: None.

Language of Instruction: Swedish.

Degrees and Diplomas: Master of–Science in Engineering; in Architecture, 4 ½ yrs. Licenciate of Engineering, 2 yrs after Master. Ph.D., a further 6 yrs.

Library: c. 300,100 vols.

Special Facilities (Museums, etc.): Onsala Space Observatory at Råö.

Publications: Forskarutbildning; Kursplaner; Kurskatalog; Utbildning av civilingenjörer och arkitekter; Annual Report; Chalmers Forskarför (Hearings).

Academic Staff, 1989:

Rank	Full-time
Ordinarie professurer	88
Extra professurer	14
Extra docenter	4
Forskarassistenter	58
Högskolelektorer	187
Högskoleadjunkter	82
Assistenter, doktorandtjänster	302
Forskningsassistenter/forskare	238
Total	973

Student Enrolment, 1989: c. 6000.

6798 **HÖGSKOLAN I BORÅS**

Borås College
Box 874, 500 15 Borås
Telephone: (33) 16-40-00
Rektor: Nils-Bertil Faxén (1978-90)

S. of Library and Information Science
Head: Lars Seldén; *staff* 17 (10)
D. of Economics and Social Studies
Head: Göran Lundin; *staff* 12 (1)
D. of Textile and Clothing Manufacturing
Dean: Anders Ericson; *staff* 2 (4)
D. of Economics and Social Studies
Head: Göran Lundin; *staff* 12 (1)

Founded 1977 following national reform of higher education and incorporating previously existing institutions.Responsible to the Universitetshögskoleämbetet-UHÄ (National Board of Universities and Colleges). Governing body: the Högskolestyrelsen (College Board), composed of representatives of the academic staff, non-academic staff, representatives of the student body and representatives of public life.

Arrangements for co-operation with: Gustavus Adolphus College; Nankato State University, Minnesota.

Academic Year: September to June (August-January; January-June).

Admission Requirements: Secondary school certificate or foreign equivalent, or age at least 25 yrs with 4 yrs work experience and knowledge of English.

Fees: None.

Language of Instruction: Swedish.

Degrees and Diplomas: Diplomas and Certificates, 2 yrs.

Library: c. 120,000 vols.

Academic Staff, 1986-87:

Rank	Full-time	Part-time
Universitetslektorer	9	1
Lektorer	22	14
Total	31	15

Student Enrolment, 1986-87:

	Men	Women	Total
Of the country	1200	800	2000
Of other countries	5	5	10
Total	1205	805	2010

6799 **HÖGSKOLAN I KARLSTAD**

University of Karlstad
Box 9501, 650 09 Karlstad
Telephone: (54) 83-80-00
Rektor: Lennart Andersson

D. of Modern Languages
Head: Birgitta Berglund-Nilsson; *staff* 10 (10)
D. of Natural Sciences
Head: Torbjörn Wiklund; *staff* 20 (10)
D. of Mathematics, Statistics, and Computer Sciences
Head: Stig Håkangård; *staff* 15 (10)
D. of Education and Psychology
Head: Mats Eriksson; *staff* 15 (10)
D. of Economics (including Business Administration)
Head: Charlie Karlsson; *staff* 27 (5)
D. of Music, Art, and Physical Education
Head: Bertil Wivhammer; *staff* 15 (10)
D. of Swedish
Head: Sten-Olof Ullstrom; *staff* 11 (6)
D. of Social Sciences (including Commercial Law and Political Science)
Head: Karl-Erik Sammeli; *staff* 38 (11)
D. of Teaching Methods
Head: Kent Åsenlöf; *staff* 18 (4)
D. of Engineering Technology
Dean: Bernt Landstrom; *staff* 20 (10)
Ce. for Technical Research
Head: Claes Helgesson; *staff* 1 (1)
Ce. for Service Research
Head: Bo Edvardsson; *staff* 4 (7)
Ce. for Gender Studies
Head: Lena Olsson; *staff* 1 (1)

Founded 1977, following national reform of higher education and incorporating former Karlstad branch of Gothenburg University, and the School of Education, founded 1843. Responsible to the Universitetshögskoleämbetet-UHÄ (National Board of Universities and Colleges). Governing body: the Högskolestyrelsen (College Board).

Arrangements for co-operation with: University of Hull; University of Caen; Augustana College; Gustavas Adolphus College.

Academic Year: September to June (September-January; January-June).

Admission Requirements: Secondary school certificate or foreign equivalent, or age at least 25 yrs with 4 yrs work experience and knowledge of English.

Fees: None.

Language of Instruction: Swedish.

Degrees and Diplomas: Bachelor of–Science; Arts. Master of–Science; Education. Teaching diplomas, 2-4 yrs.

Library: c. 150,000 vols.

Publication: Anslaget.

Academic Staff, 1989-90:

Rank	Full-time	Part-time
Professor	1	6
Docenter	8	5
Lektorer	65	35
Adjunkter	100	25
Total	174	71

Student Enrolment, 1989-90:

Of the country	4200
Of other countries	100
Total	4300

6800 **HÖGSKOLAN I SKÖVDE**

Skövde College
Box 408, 54128 Skövde
Telephone: 46-500-77600
Fax: 46-500-16325
Electronic mail: E-mail:jonas@his.se
Rektor: Lars-Erik Johansson (1983-96)
Kanslichef: Ted Hullberg

D. of Economics and Business Administration
Head: Kjell Nilsson; *staff* 9 (20)
D. of Electronics and Computer Technology
Head: Hans Johansson; *staff* 8 (5)
D. of Computer Sciences
Head: Stig Emanuelsson; *staff* 8 (10)
D. of Arts, Languages and Media
Head: Ingalill Söderqvist; *staff* 3 (15)
D. of Cultural and Communication Studies
Head: Ingalill Söderqvist; *staff* 1 (3)
Ce. for Continuing Education (for Teachers)
Head: Kurt Båchstrôm; *staff* 1 (15)

Founded 1977 under national higher education reform. Acquired present status 1983. Responsible to the Universitetshögskoleämbetet-UHÄ (National Board of Universities and Colleges).

Academic Year: September to June (September-January; January-June).

Admission Requirements: Secondary school certificate or foreign equivalent, or age at least 25 yrs with 4 yrs work experience and knowledge of English.

Fees: None.

Language of Instruction: Swedish.

Degrees and Diplomas: Högskoleexamen, national certificate, or professional qualifications, 2-4 yrs.

Library: 40,000 vols.

Publications: Reports; Papers.

Academic Staff, 1989-90: 29 (68).

Student Enrolment, 1989-90:

	Men	Women	Total
Of the country	841	719	1560

Linköping Region

6801 **HÖGSKOLAN I JÖNKÖPING**

Jönköping College
Gjuterigatan 23-25, 55111 Jönköping
Telephone: (036) 16-51-60

D. of Education and Psychology
D. of Languages and Literature (Swedish, German, and English)
D. of Economics and Social Studies
D. of Science
D. of Art, Music, and Physical Education

Founded 1977, following national reform of higher education and incorporating former Schools of Education. Responsible to the Universitetshögskoleämbetet-UHÄ (National Board of Universities and Colleges).

Lund Region

6802 **HÖGSKOLAN I HALMSTAD**

Halmstad College
Box 7014, 300 07 Halmstad
Telephone: (035) 37800

6803 **HÖGSKOLAN I KALMAR**

University College of Kalmar
Box 905, 391-29 Kalmar
Telephone: 0480-97500
Fax: 0480-18298
Vice-Chancellor: Dan Isacson

Merchant Maritime A.
Head: Eric Björkman
D. of Technology
Head: Göran Lundgren
D. of Natural Science and Technology
Head: Ulf Lidman
D. of Teacher Training
Head: Stellan Ranebo
D. of Social Science
Head: Leif Rytting
D. Fojo (in-service training for journalists)
Head: Annelie Ewers
I. of Tourism and Economic Research
Head: Anders Steene
Design Ce.
Head: Dan Isacson

Founded 1877 as a Teacher Training College. Reorganized 1977 according to the National Higher Education Act.

Arrangements for student and lecturer exchange with the United Kingdom and a project with Poland in the environmental sector.

Academic Year: August to June (August-January; January-June).

Admission Requirements: Secondary school certificate or foreign equivalent, or age at least 25 yrs with 4 yrs work experience and knowledge of English.

Fees: None.

Language of Instruction: Swedish.

Degrees and Diplomas: Högskoleexamen, national certificate, or professional qualifications, 1-3 yrs.

Library: College Library.

Publication: Rostadskriften.

Academic Staff, 1990: 120.

Student Enrolment, 1990: 2500.

6804 **HÖGSKOLAN I KRISTIANSTAD**

Kristianstad College
Box 59, 291 21 Kristianstad
Telephone: (044) 11-56-45
Rektor: Kaj Björk (1989-95)
Avdelningsdirektor: Lars Lindahl

D. of Education and Psychology
Head: Bengt Selghed; *staff* 28
D. of Literature and Communication Studies
Head: Lars-Erik Gavelman; *staff* 28
D. of Natural and Technical Sciences
Head: Britt Lindahl; *staff* 16
D. of Economics and Social Sciences
Head: Agneta Erfors; *staff* 18
D. of Civil, Electrical and Mechanical Engineering
Head: Helena Sjolander; *staff* 5

Founded 1947 as School of Education. Reorganized 1977 under national reform of higher education. Responsible to the Universitetshögskoleämbetet-UHÄ (National Board of Universities and Colleges).

Academic Year: August to June (August-December; January-June).

Admission Requirements: Secondary school certificate or foreign equivalent, or age at least 25 yrs with 4 yrs work experience and knowledge of English.

Fees: None.

Language of Instruction: Swedish.

Degrees and Diplomas: Teaching qualifications, 2-3 yrs. Bachelor of Science in Business Administration and Economics, university certificate in Engineering, 2 yrs.

Library: 70,000 vols.

Academic Staff, 1986-87: 75 (350).

Student Enrolment, 1986-87: 2350.

6805 **HÖGSKOLAN I VÄXJÖ**

Växjö College
Box 5053, 350 05 Växjö
Telephone: (470) 810-00
Rektor: Hans Wieslander (1977-89)

D. of Behavioural Sciences
D. of Economic and Business Administration
D. of Mathematics, Statistics, and Computer Sciences
D. of Educational Methodology
D. of Modern Languages
D. of Swedish, Comparative Literature and Communication
D. of Art, Music, and Sport
D. of Social Sciences and History
D. of Natural Sciences

Founded 1977 following the national reform of higher education, incorporating former branch of Lund University at Växjö and School of Education. Responsible to the Universitetshögskoleämbetet-UHÄ (National Board of Universities and Colleges). Governing body: the Högskolestyrelsen (College Board). Residential facilities for students.

Arrangements for co-operation with: Gustavus Adolphus College, Minnesota; Augustana College, Ohio; University of Wisconsin.

Academic Year: September to June (September-January; January-June).

Admission Requirements: Secondary school certificate or foreign equivalent, or age at least 25 yrs with 4 yrs work experience and knowledge of English.

Fees: None.

Language of Instruction: Swedish.

Degrees and Diplomas: Högskoleexamen, national certificate, or professional qualification, 3 yrs.

Library: c. 85,000 vols.

Academic Staff: c. 80 (10).

Student Enrolment: c. 3500.

Stockholm Region

6806 **KUNGLIGA TEKNISKA HÖGSKOLAN**

The Royal Institute of Technology
100 44 Stockholm
Cables: technology
Telex: 103 89 KTHB STOCKHOLM
Telephone: 468-79 06000
President: Gunnar Brodin (1981-87)
Högskoledirektör: Jan Nygren

S. of Physics
Dean: Bengt Nagel; *staff* 131 (59)
S. of Mechanical Engineering
Dean: Bo Lindström; *staff* 247 (57)
S. of Applied Mechanics and Vehicle Technology
Dean: Berhl Storåkers; *staff* 110 (28)
S. of Electrical Engineering
Dean: Erling Dahlberg; *staff* 285 (65)
S. of Civil Engineering
Dean: Sven Kinnunen; *staff* 108 (51)
S. of Chemical Engineering
Dean: Folke Ingman; *staff* 322 (73)
S. of Metallurgy and Materials Technology
Dean: Lars-Ingvar Staffansson; *staff* 135 (31)
S. of Architecture
Dean: Igor Dergalin; *staff* 94 (52)
S. of Surveying
Dean: Gert Knutsson; *staff* 95 (45)
S. of Computer Sciences and Engineering
Dean: Lars-Erik Thorelli; *staff* 100 (50)
Microwave I. Foundation
I. of Optical Research
I. of Production Engineering Research
I. of Technical Audiology
Ce. for Design and Production Technology
Computer Ce.
Ce. for Materials Technology
Head: Hans Åström
Ce. for Environmental Sciences
Head: Per Olof Persson

Founded 1827 as institute, reorganized as a university and became Royal Institute 1876. Reorganized 1977 under national higher education reform. Responsible to the Universitetshögskoleämbetet-UHÄ (National Board of Universities and Colleges). Governing body: the Styrelsen (Board).

Arrangements for co-operation with c. 15 foreign universities, including: University of Tokyo; Massachusetts Institute of Technology.

Academic Year: August to June (August-December; January-June).

Admission Requirements: Secondary school certificate or foreign equivalent, or age at least 25 yrs with 4 yrs work experience and knowledge of English.

Fees: Tuition, none.

Language of Instruction: Swedish.

Degrees and Diplomas: Professional qualifications (M.Sc.) corresponding to 4 ½ yrs study. Licentiate of Technology, 2 yrs postgraduate study. Doctor of Philosophy, Ph.D., a further 4 yrs.

Library: Institute Library, c. 500,000 vols.

Publication: Scientific Reports.

Academic Staff, 1986-87:

Rank	Full-time	Part-time
Professor	113	–
Extra professor	16	1
Adjungerad professor	–	37
Högskolelektorer	160	30
Högskoleadjunkter	51	12
Forskarassistenter	17	–
Forskare	226	–
Forskningsingenjörer	370	46
Total	953	126

Student Enrolment, 1986-87:

	Men	Women	Total
Of the country	6600	1600	8200*

*Also 600 external students.

6807 **KAROLINSKA INSTITUTET**

Karolinska Institute
Solnavägen 1, 104 01 Stockholm 60
Cables: Karolinst
Telephone: (08) 34-05-60

F. of Medicine
F. of Dentistry
S. of Physiotherapy
S. of Speech Theraphy
S. of Psychotherapy

Founded 1810. Kungliga Tandläkarhögskolan i Stockholm (Royal Dental School) incorporated 1964. Reorganized 1977 under national higher education reform. A State institution of university rank responsible to the Universitetshögskoleämbetet-UHÄ (National Board of Universities and Colleges).

Academic Year: August to June (August-January; January-June).

Admission Requirements: Secondary school certificate or foreign equivalent, or age at least 25 yrs with 4 yrs work experience and knowledge of English.

Fees: None.

Language of Instruction: Swedish.

Degrees and Diplomas: Professional qualifications in Medicine corresponding to 11 sem full-time study, and in Dentistry to 9 sem, followed by 1 yr internship. Doctorates, a further 4 yrs.

Library: c. 250,000 vols.

Special Facilities (Museums, etc.): Medical History Museum.

Publications: Karolinska institutets katalog över lärere och administration; Meddelanden från Centrala Förvaltningen; Undervisningskatalog (Teaching plan for students); Forskarutbildningskatalog (Teaching plan for research students).

Academic Staff: c. 880.

Student Enrolment: c. 4300.

6808 **HÖGSKOLAN FÖR LÄRARUTBILDNING I STOCKHOLM**

Stockholm Institute of Education
Box 34 103, 100 26 Stockholm
Telephone: (08) 221680

Education
Physical Education

Nursing
Music
Art

Founded 1977 following national reform of higher education, incorporating former College of Physical Education, founded 1959, School of Education (1956), Institute of Nursing and other previously existing teacher training institutions. Responsible to the Universitetshögskoleämbetet-UHÄ (National Board of Universities and Colleges). Governing body: the Styrelsen (Board).

Academic Year: August to June (August-December; January-June).

Admission Requirements: Secondary school certificate or foreign equivalent, or age at least 25 yrs with 4 yrs work experience and knowledge of English.

Fees: None.

Language of Instruction: Swedish.

Degrees and Diplomas: Teaching qualifications, 2-4 yrs. Doctorate, a further 4 yrs. Also Diploma in Special Education.

Library: Total, *c.* 135,000 vols.

Academic Staff: c. 700.

Student Enrolment: c. 5000.

6809 **HANDELSHÖGSKOLAN I STOCKHOLM**

Stockholm School of Economics
Sveavägen 65, 113 83 Stockholm
Cables: Schoolecon
Telex: 16514
Telephone: (8) 736-90-00
Fax: (8) 31-81-86
Electronic mail: admacl@sehhs.bitnet
Rektor: Staffan Burenstam Linder
Högskoledirektör: Rolf Linné

D. of Economics
Head: Lars Bergman; *staff* 24
D. of Business Administration
Head: Sven-Erik Sjöstrand; *staff* 115
D. of International Economics and Geography
Head: Mats Lundahl; *staff* 25
D. of Law
Head: Gunnar Karnell; *staff* 10
D. of Statistical Economics
Head: Anders Westlund; *staff* 20
Professional Communication Skills Ut.
Director: Sean Gaffney; *staff* 8
D. of Finance
Head: Bertil Näslund; *staff* 20
Economic Research I.
Director: Lars-Gunnar Mattsson
I. of International Business
Director: Jan-Erik Vahlne; *staff* 25
I. of Management of Innovation and Technology
Director: Bengt Stymne
Marketing Techniques C.
Director: Göran Liljegren
Computer D.
Stockholm I. of Soviet and East European Economics
Director: Anders Åslund; *staff* 8
Also Executive Training Division.

Founded 1909 by Royal Statute. A private institution of university rank subject to public control. Financiallysupported by the government (10%) and donations and other sources of income (90%). Governing body: the Board of Directors.

Arrangments for co-operation with Universities, including: California, Los Angeles; Minnesota; Michigan, Ann Arbor; McGill; Western Ontario; Keio. Participates in the NORDPLUS programme and PIM-Member.

Academic Year: August to June (August-December; January-June).

Admission Requirements: Secondary school certificate or foreign equivalent, or age at least 25 yrs with 4 yrs work experience and knowledge of English.

Fees: None.

Language of Instruction: Swedish.

Degrees and Diplomas: Professional title of Civilekonom, 3 yrs. Ekonomie doctor, a further 4 yrs.

Library: c. 180,000 vols.

Publications: List Econ; Ekonomisk dokumentation.

Academic Staff, 1990:

Rank	Full-time
Professorer	30
Docenter	10
Doktorer	20
Teachers/Researchers	100
Total	160

Student Enrolment, 1990:

	Men	Women	Total
Of the country	1150	450	1600

6810 **DRAMATISKA INSTITUTET**

Institute of Dramatic Arts
Box 27090, 102 51 Stockholm
Cables: draminst. stockholm
Telephone: (8) 665-13-00
Fax: (8) 665-14-84
Rektor: Janos Hersko

Dramatic Arts (including Cinema, Television, and Radio)

Founded 1969. Reorganized 1977 under national higher education reform. Responsible to the Universitetshögskoleämbetet-UHÄ (National Board of Universities and Colleges). Governing body: the Styrelsen (Board).

Academic Year: August to May.

Admission Requirements: Secondary school certificate or foreign equivalent, or age at least 25 yrs with 4 yrs work experience.

Fees: None.

Language of Instruction: Swedish.

Degrees and Diplomas: Diplomas, 2-3 yrs.

Academic Staff: c. 60.

Student Enrolment, 1990:

	Men	Women	Total
Of the country	30	32	62
Of other countries	4	2	6
Total	34	34	68

6811 **GRAFISKA INSTITUTET OCH INSTITUTET FÖR HÖGRE KOMMUNIKATIONS-OCH REKLAMUTBILDNING**

Institute of Graphic Art, Communication and Advertising
Valhallavägen 191F, Box 27094, 102 51 Stockholm
Telephone: (8-660) 02-24
Fax: (8-660) 56-05
Vice-Chancellor: Chris Ottander (1977-)

Graphic Art
Communication
Advertising
Marketing

Founded 1943. Reorganized 1977 under national higher education reform.

Academic Year: September to August (September-December; January-May; May-August).

Admission Requirements: University degree and at least 1 year vocational experience within field or 5 years of vocational career.

Fees: None.

Language of Instruction: Swedish.

Degrees and Diplomas: University Certificate.

Student Enrolment, 1986-87:

	Men	Women	Total
Of the country	90	56	146
Of other countries	3	1	4
Total	93	57	150*

*Also 500 external students.

6812 **KONSTFACKSKOLAN**

The National College of Art, Craft and Design
Box 27 116, 102 52 Stockholm
Telephone: (46-8) 667-95-50
Fax: (46-8) 783-05-63

D. of Textile Art and Design
Head: Veronica Nygren; *staff* – (8)
D. of Environmental Art
Head: Leif Andersson; *staff* – (6)
D. of Sculpture
Head: Vassil Simittchiev; *staff* – (4)

D. of Ceramics and Glass
Head: Oiva Toikka; *staff* – (4)
D. of Interior Architecture
Head: Andrejs Legradine; *staff* – (9)
D. of Metal Crafts
Head: Gudmund Elvestad; *staff* – (4)
D. of Graphic Design and Illustration
Head: H. LIndström; *staff* – (4)
Photographic A.
Head: Jan Fridlund; *staff* – (2)
D. of Art Education
Head: Masse Hansson; *staff* – (16)
D. of Industrial Design
Head: Lars Lalerstedt; *staff* – (5)
D. of Colour and Form
Head: Costa Wessel; *staff* – (25)

Founded 1844 as school, acquired present status and title 1945. Responsible to the Universitetshögskoleämbetet-UHÄ (National Board of Universities and Colleges, NBVC). Governing body: the Styrelsen (Board), comprising 13 members.

Arrangements for the regular interchange of studednts and graduates with: U.S.A., Finland, and the United Kingdom.

Academic Year: August to June (August-January; January-June).

Admission Requirements: Selection based on proven artistic ability, following Grundskola.

Fees: None.

Language of Instruction: Swedish.

Degrees and Diplomas: Diploma, 4 yrs.

Library: c. 50,000 vols.

Academic Staff, 1990: c. 170.

Student Enrolment, 1990: c. 500 (Including 10-20 foreign students).

6813 **KONSTHÖGSKOLAN**
College of Fine Arts
Fredsgatan 12, 111 52 Stockholm
Telephone: (8) 614-40-00
Fax: (8) 21-13-39
Rektor: Olle Kåks (1987-93)

S. of Painting
S. of Sculpture
S. of Graphic Arts
S. of Art Education
S. of Architecture
S. of Modern Art History
S. of Materials

Founded 1735 as Royal Academy Art School. Acquired present status and title 1978. Responsible to the Universitetshögskoleämbetet-UHÄ (National Board of Universities and Colleges). Governing body: the Styrelsen (Board).

Academic Year: September to June (September-December; January-June).

Admission Requirements: Selection based on proven artistic ability. Architecture: Professional title and at least 1 yr practical experience.

Fees: None.

Language of Instruction: Swedish.

Degrees and Diplomas: Bachelor of Arts in Fine Arts, 5 yrs. Diplomas.

Publications: Catalogue; Timetable.

Academic Staff: c. 40.

Student Enrolment, 1990: 207.

6814 **MUSIKHÖGSKOLAN I STOCKHOLM**
The State College of Music in Stockholm
Valhallavägen 103-109, 115 31 Stockholm
Telephone: (8) 663-11-90
Fax: (8) 664-14-24
Rektor: Gunnar Bucht (1987-)
Avdelningschef: Wilhelm Jentzen

Music Performance and Teaching
Ce. for Research in Music Education
Head: Lennart Reimers; *staff* 3 (3)

Founded 1771 as Royal Academy and School of Music, became Royal Academy of Music 1940 and State College 1971. Responsible to the Universitetshögskoleämbetet-UHÄ (National Board of Universities and Colleges).

Academic Year: August to June (August-January; January-June).

Admission Requirements: Secondary school certificate and entrance examinations.

Fees: None.

Language of Instruction: Swedish.

Degrees and Diplomas: Diplomas, 4-6 yrs.

Library: c. 3000 vols.

Academic Staff, 1990:

Rank	Full-time	Part-time
Professorer	4	–
Lektorer	62	54
Lärare	–	97
Ackompanjatörer	3	4
Total	69	155

Student Enrolment, 1990:

	Men	Women	Total
Of the country	340	289	629
Of other countries	3	2	5
Total	343	291	634

6815 **DANSHÖGSKOLAN**
College of Dance
Box 27043, 102 51 Stockholm
Telephone: (08) 651100
Rektor: Lena Malmsjö (1976-90)

Dance
Choreography
Mime

Founded 1963 as Institute of Choreography, became school 1970, acquired present status and title 1978. A State institution responsible to the Universitetshögskoleämbetet-UHÄ (National Board of Universities and Colleges). Governing body: the Styrelsen (Board), composed of 11 members.

Academic Year: August to June (August-December; January-June).

Admission Requirements: Secondary school certificate or foreign equivalent, evidence of artistic ability and audition.

Fees: None.

Language of Instruction: Swedish.

Degrees and Diplomas: Högskoleexamen, national certificate, 3 yrs.

Academic Staff, 1986-87: 8 (c. 60).

Student Enrolment, 1986-87:

	Men	Women	Total
Of the country	8	51	59
Of other countries	5	6	11
Total	13	57	70

6816 **MUSIKDRAMATISKA SKOLAN I STOCKHOLM**
Music Drama School
Strandvägen 82, 115 27 Stockholm
Telephone: (08) 62-61-81

Music Drama

Founded in 18th century, acquired present status and title 1968. A State institution responsible to the Universitetshögskoleämbetet-UHÄ (National Board of Universities and Colleges). Governing body: the Styrelsen (Board).

Academic Year: September to June (September-December; January-June).

Admission Requirements: Secondary school certificate or equivalent, and evidence of musical ability. Minimum age for admission, 20 years.

Fees: None.

Degrees and Diplomas: Diplomas, 3 yrs.

Academic Staff: c. 5 (30).

Student Enrolment: c. 30.

6817 **TEATERHÖGSKOLAN I STOCKHOLM**
School of Scenic Design
Box 200 44, 104 60 Stockholm
Telephone: (8) 41-21-60

Scenic Design

Degrees and Diplomas: Diplomas, 3 ½ yrs.

Umeå Region

6818 **HÖGSKOLAN I LULEÅ**

Luleå University

Högskolemrådet, Porsön, 951 87 Luleå

Telex: 80447 LUHS

Telephone: (920) 910-00

Fax: (920) 972-88

Rektor: Torbjörn Hedberg (1979-91)

Högskoledirektör: Staffan Sarbäck

S. of Engineering (including Mechanical, Civil, Computer and Industrial Engineering; Environmental Planning and Design)

Dean: Lennart Elfgren; *staff* 275

S. of Education

Dean: Stig Johansson; *staff* 50

S. of Music

Head: Lars Lindberg; *staff* 30

S. of Business

Dean: Håkan Myrlund; *staff* 35

Also branches in: Skellefteå, Piteå, and Kiruna. Courses for foreign students.

Founded 1971. Reorganized 1977 under national higher education reform and incorporating former College of Education founded 1907. College of Music affiliated 1978. Responsible to the Universitets-högskoleämbetet-UHÄ (National Board of Universities and Colleges). Governing body: the University Board. Residential facilities for students.

Arrangements for exchange co-operation with: Beijing University of Iron and Stell Technology; Central South University of Technology, Changsha; Colorado School of Mines; Institut national polytechnique de Lorraine, Nancy; Lakehead University; Academy of Mining and Metallurgy, Cracow; Technische Universität Clausthal; University of Strathclyde; Technische Universität Hamburg-Harburg.

Academic Year: August to June (August-January; January-June).

Admission Requirements: Secondary school certificate or foreign equivalent, or age at least 25 yrs with 4 yrs work experience and knowledge of English.

Fees: None.

Language of Instruction: Swedish.

Degrees and Diplomas: Certificate, 2-2 ½ yrs. Bachelor, 3-3 ½ yrs. Master, 4 yrs. Licentiate in Engineering, a further 2 yrs. Ph.D., a further 2 yrs.

Library: Luleå University Library, 150,000 vols.

Special Facilities (Museums, etc.): House of Technology.

Publications: Research and Technical Reports, Teknik i norr (7 times a year); Annual Reports.

Academic Staff, 1990:

Rank	Full-time
Professorer	26
Adjungerade professorer	11
Högskolelektorer	67
Högskoleadjunkter	148
Forskare	20
1 forskningsingenjörer	50
Forskningsingenjörer	68
Total	390

Student Enrolment, 1990:

Of the country	3200
Of other countries	350
Total	3550*

*Also 860 external students and students by correspondence.

6819 **HÖGSKOLAN I SUNDSVALL/HÄRNÖSAND**

Sundsvall/Härnösand College

Box 860, 85124 Sundsvall

Telephone: (4660) 154260

Rektor: Ola Román (1977-89)

D. of Technology

Head: Lennart Bergström; *staff* 25

D. of Technology (Härnösand)

Head: Hans Erik Carlsson; *staff* 15

D. of Social Sciences

Head: Leif Lindefeldt; *staff* 25

S. of Education

Head: Inger Axelsson; *staff* 50

Founded 1977 following national reform of higher education and incorporating previously existing institutions.Responsible to the Universitetshögskoleämbetet-UHÄ (National Board of Universities and Colleges).

Academic Year: September to May (September-December; January-May).

Admission Requirements: Secondary school certificate or foreign equivalent, or age at least 25 yrs with 4 yrs work experience and knowledge of English.

Language of Instruction: Swedish.

Academic Staff: c. 100.

Student Enrolment, 1986-87: 2000.

6820 **HÖGSKOLAN I ÖSTERSUND**

Östersund College

Box 373, 83125 Östersund

Rektor: Stefan Hammarqvist (1981-87)

Administration

Social Work

Systems Analysis

Tourism

Human Resources Development

Founded 1971. Reorganized 1977 under national higher education reform. Responsible to the Universitetshögskoleämbetet-UHÄ (National Board of Universities and Colleges).

Academic Year: August to June.

Admission Requirements: Secondary school certificate or foreign equivalent, or age at least 25 yrs with 4 yrs work experience and knowledge of English.

Fees: None.

Language of Instruction: Swedish.

Degrees and Diplomas: Högskoleexamen, national certificate, or professional qualifications, 2-3 ½ yrs.

Academic Staff: c. 50.

Student Enrolment: c. 870 (Also c. 170 external students).

Uppsala Region

6821 **SVERIGES LANTBRUKSUNIVERSITET**

Swedish University of Agricultural Sciences

750 07 Uppsala

Telephone: (18) 67-10-00; 16-90-00

Fax: (18) 30-03-37

Rektor: Mårten Carlsson

Universitetsdirektör: Görel Oscarsson

F. of Agriculture (including Horticulture)

Head: Jan Persson

F. of Forestry

Head: Per-Ove Bäckström

F. of Veterinary Medicine

Head: Jan Luthman

I. of Veterinary Medicine

Head: Göran Hugosson

Founded 1975 as University of Agriculture, Forestry, and Veterinary Medicine, incorporating previously existing Colleges of Agriculture, founded 1849, Forestry (1828), and Veterinary Medicine (1775). Acquired present title 1977. The University has its main centre at Ultuna, Uppsala and others at Alnarp/Lund, Skara, Garpenberg/Skinnskatteberg, and Umeå. A State institution under the jurisdiction of the Ministry of Agriculture. Governing body: the Universitetsstyrelsen (University Board). Residential facilities for academic staff and students.

Participates in the NORDPLUS, COMETT, STEP, etc. programmes.

Academic Year: September to June (September-January; January-June).

Admission Requirements: Secondary school certificate. (Avgångsbetyg 2 or 3 yrs course at a Gymnasium).

Fees: None.

Languages of Instruction: Swedish and English.

Degrees and Diplomas: Master of Science, 4 ½-5 ½ yrs. University Certificate, 1-1 ½ yrs. Doctorates, a further 4 yrs.

Library: Library Ultuna, c. 250,000 vols.

Special Facilities (Museums, etc.): Museums: Agriculture (Alnarp); Forestry (Garpenberg); Veterinary Medicine (Skara). Research Information Centre.

Publications: The Swedish Journal of Agricultural Research (quarterly); Annual Report of the Royal Veterinary College; Studia Forestalia Suecica.

Academic Staff, 1989: 1253.

Student Enrolment, 1989:

Of the country	2400
Of other countries	165
Total	2565*

*Including *c.* 50% women students.

6822 **HÖGSKOLAN I ESKILSTUNA/VÄSTERÅS**
Eskilstuna/Västerås College
Box 11, 721 03 Västerås
Telephone: (21) 127920

6823 **HÖGSKOLAN I FALUN/BORLÄNGE**
Falun/Borlänge College
Box 2004, 791 02 Falun
Telephone: (23) 81900

Sec. for Technology and Mathematics
Sec. for Administration, Economics and Social Studies
Sec. for Educational Sciences

Founded 1977, following national reform of higher education, incorporating former School of Education founded 1968. Responsible to the Universitetshögskoleämbetet-UHÄ (National Board of Universities and Colleges). Governing body: the Styrelsen (Board).

Academic Year: August to June (August-November; November-June).

Admission Requirements: Secondary school certificate or foreign equivalent, or age at least 25 yrs with 4 yrs work experience and knowledge of English.

Fees: None.

Language of Instruction: Swedish.

Degrees and Diplomas: Högskoleexamen, national certificate, or professional qualification, 1 ½-2 yrs.

Library: c. 40,000 vols.

Publication: Högskoleinformatören (biannually).

Academic Staff: c. 30 (40).

Student Enrolment: c. 1090.

6824 **HÖGSKOLAN I GÄVLE/SANDVIKEN**
Gävle/Sandviken College
Box 6952, 800 06 Gävle
Telephone: (26) 64-85-00
Fax: (26) 64-86-86
President: Birgitta Stymme (1989-)

D. of Education for Teaching Professions
Head: Alvat Wallinder
D. of Education for Administration and Economic Professions
Head: Lars-Torsten Eriksson
D. for Education for Technical Professions
D. for Education for Information, Communication and Cultural Professions
Head: Siv Näsman

Founded 1977 following national reform of higher education, incorporating former School of Education founded 1946. Responsible to the Universitetshögskoleämbetet-UHÄ (National Board of Universities and Colleges). Governing body: the Styrelsen (Board). Residential facilities for *c.* 30 students.

Academic Year: August to June (August-January; January-June).

Admission Requirements: Secondary school certificate or foreign equivalent, or age at least 25 yrs with 4 yrs work experience and knowledge of English.

Fees: None.

Language of Instruction: Swedish.

Academic Staff, 1990: c. 70.

Student Enrolment, 1990: c. 2000.

6825 **HÖGSKOLAN I ÖREBRO**
University College of Örebro
Box 923, 701 30 Örebro
Telephone: (19) 30-10-00
Fax: (19) 33-01-30
Rektor: Ingemar Lind (1990-)

D. of Systems Analysis
Head: Åke Holmen; *staff* 15
D. of Business Economics
Head: Claes Hultman; *staff* 19
D. of Pre-school and Leisure Education
Head: C. Lindman; *staff* 40 (10)
D. of Physical Education
Head: Stewe Persson; *staff* 25 (5)
D. of Humanities (including Nordic Languages, History and Literature)
Head: Turrd Stromberg; *staff* 14 (5)
D. of Law
Head: Mikael Schnürer; *staff* 9 (3)
D. of Technology
Head: B. Johansson; *staff* 10 (3)
D. of Modern Languages
Head: Kurt Johansson; *staff* 9 (4)
D. of Music
Head: Anita Nilsson; *staff* 20 (30)
D. of Political Science and Administration
Head: Erok Amnå; *staff* 15 (5)
D. of Education and Psychology
Head: Tomas Berggren; *staff* 20 (5)
D. of Psychology, Education and Economics
Head: Walter Stervander; *staff* 9 (2)
D. of Social Work
Head: H. Soydan; *staff* 9 (3)
D. of Sociology
Head: Bernt Johansson; *staff* 16 (5)
Ce. for Urban and Housing Policy
Head: Ingemar Erlander; *staff* – (12)

Founded 1977, following national reform of higher education and incorporating previously existing institutions. Responsible to the Universitetshögskoleämbetet-UHÄ (National Board of Universities and Colleges). Governing body: the Högskolestyrellsen (Senate).

Arrangements for co-operation with the Universities of: Łódź; Stirling; Bristol; Missouri.

Academic Year: September to June (September-December; January-June).

Admission Requirements: Secondary school certificate or foreign equivalent, or age at least 25 yrs with 4 yrs work experience and knowledge of English.

Fees: None.

Language of Instruction: Swedish.

Library: c. 150,000 vols.

Publication: Prospects (in Swedish).

Academic Staff, 1989-90: 200 (50).

Student Enrolment, 1989-90: 4500.

SWITZERLAND

Universities and Technical Universities

6826 **UNIVERSITÄT BASEL**
University of Basle
Petersplatz 1, 4051 Basel
Telephone: 25-73-73
Rektor: Karl Pestalozzi (1990-)
Adjunkt: Mathias Stauffacher

F. of Theology (Protestant)
Dean: Ernst Jenni; *staff* 8 (8)
F. of Law
Dean: Detlef Krauss; *staff* – (17)
F. of Medicine (including Dentistry)
Dean: OtmarGratzl; *staff* 37 (224)
F. of Philosophy and History (including Economics and Social Sciences)
Dean: Jürgen Von Ungern-Sternberg; *staff* 51 (122)
F. of Philosophy and Natural Sciences (including Pharmacy)
Dean: Martin Frey; *staff* 70 (115)
I. of Physical Education
I of Remedial Education and Psychology
I. of Tropical Medicine
I. of Gerontology
Teachers Seminar
Computer Ce

Founded 1460 under the authority of Papal Bull of Pius II. Since 1830 under the jurisdiction of the Canton of Basle. Financed by the Canton of Basle. Governing bodies: the Kuratel, composed of 5 members elected by the Canton; the Regenz, including the Rector, deans, other members of the academic staff, and students, and one member of the administration. Residential facilities for *c.* 300 students.

Academic Year: October to June (October-February; April-June).

Admission Requirements: Secondary school certificate (Maturitätszeugnis) or recognized foreign equivalent.

Fees (Francs): 260 per semester.

Language of Instruction: German.

Degrees and Diplomas: Lizentiat der–Rechte, lic.jur., law; Sozialwissenschaften, lic.rer.pol., economics and social sciences; Philosophie, lic.phil., philosophy; Theology. Diplomas in–Medicine; Mathematics; Physics; Assurance; Chemistry; Pharmacy; Zoology; Earth Sciences; Geography. Doctorates in–Theology; Law; Medicine; Dentistry; Natural Sciences; Philosophy; Political Science.

Library: Total, *c.* 2,500,000 vols.

Special Facilities (Museums, etc.): Museums: Art; History; Natural Science; Pharmacy; Ethnology; Anatomy; Palaeontology.

Publications: Basler Universitätsreden; Akademische Vorträge; Theologische Zeitschrift; Basler Studien zur Rechtswissenschaft; Schriftenreihen des Instituts für Internationales Recht, Sozialwissenschaften, angewandte wirtschaftsforschung; Uni Nova; Basler Beiträge zur Ethnologie und Geographie.

Academic Staff, 1986-87:

Rank	Full-time	Part-time
Ordentliche Professoren	121	4
Ausserordentliche Professoren	38	138
Gastdozenten	–	21
Ehrendozenten	–	9
Privatdozenten	13	217
Lektoren	2	97
Total	174	486

Student Enrolment, 1986-87:

	Men	Women	Total
Of the country	4310	2366	6676*

* Including 376 foreign students.

6827 **UNIVERSITÄT BERN**
University of Berne
Hochschulstrasse 4, 3012 Bern
Telephone: (31) 65-81-11
Rektor: Andreas Ludi (1990-)

F. of Protestant Theology
Dean: Walter Dietrich
F. of Catholic Theology
Dean: Herwig Aldenhoven
F. of Law and Economics
Dean: Bruno Huwiler
F. of Medicine
Dean: Georg Eisner
F. of Veterinary Medicine
Dean: Urs Schatzmann
F. of Philosophy (Languages and History)
Dean: August Flammer
F. of Science (Natural Sciences)
Dean: Eberhardt Schmidt
Teacher Training S.
President: Kurt Egger

Founded 1528 as school, became academy in 18th century and university 1834. Financed by the Canton of Berne and since 1966 also substantially by the federal government. Governing bodies: the Akademischer Senat, composed of the Rector, all professors, and certain other members of the academic staff; the Senatausschuss (Committee of the Senate), composed of the Rector, the Pro-Rector, the Rector-designate,the deans, a representative of each faculty, and the Secretary. Residential facilities for *c.* 150 students.

Academic Year: October to July (October-March; April-July).

Admission Requirements: Secondary school certificate (Maturitätszeugnis) or equivalent.

Fees (Francs): 250 per semester.

Language of Instruction: German.

Degrees and Diplomas: Lizentiat in all faculties, 4-5 yrs. Doktor, 5-6 yrs. Doctor of Medicine, 6-7 yrs. State examination and titles–Notar Fürsprecher, law; Pfarrer, theology; Arzt, medicine; Gymnasiallehrer, teaching qualification, secondary level.

Libraries: University and Public Library; libraies of the Faculties.

Publication: Vorlesungsverzeichnis.

Academic Staff: c. 770.

Student Enrolment, 1989-90:

Men	Women	Total
6000	3500	9500

6828 ***UNIVERSITÉ DE FRIBOURG**
University of Fribourg
Miséricorde, 1700 Fribourg
Telephone: (037) 21-91-11
Recteur: Hans Meier (1991-95)
Administrateur: Hans-E. Brülhart

F. of Theology (Catholic)
Dean: Servais Pinckaers; *staff* 22 (65)
F. of Law, Social Sciences, and Economics
Dean: Louis Bosshart; *staff* 20 (91)
F. of Letters (including Liberal Arts and Education)
Dean: Evandro Agazzi; *staff* 36 (227)
F. of Sciences (including Pre-clinical Medicine)
Dean: Lother Schellenberg; *staff* 11 (190)
I. of Moral Theology
Director: Adrian Holderegger
I. of Pastoral Theology
Directors: Léo Karrer; M. Donzé
I. of Oecumenical Studies
Director: Guido Vergauwen

I. of Missiology
Director: Richard Friedli
I. of Economics and Social Sciences
Director: Florian-H. Fleck
I. of Automation Research
Director: Jürg Kohlas
I. of Ecclesiastical Law
Director: Louis Carlen
International I. of Social and Political Sciences
Director: Otfried Höffe
I. of Education
Directors: Fritz Oser
I. of Orthopaedic Education
Directors: Jean-Luc Lambert; Urs Haeberlin
I. of Physical Education
Director: Frédéric Sottas
I. of Psychology
Director: Jean Retschitzki
I. of Eastern European Studies
Director: Guido Küng
I. of Mediaeval Studies
I. of Journalism and Social Communication
Director: Louis Bosshart
English I.
French I.
Director: Yves Giraud; *staff* 8
German I.
Director: Günter Schneider; *staff* 7

Founded 1889, including faculties of law and letters. Faculty of theology established 1890, and science 1895. The university is Catholic and international in character. Created by the Canton of Fribourg, it is a State responsibility and receives financial support from the Catholic population of Switzerland under the convention of 1949. Governing bodies: the Rectorat, comprising the Rector, 3 Vice-Rectors, and the Administrator; the Sénat, composed of 8 representatives of the State authorities, and 16 representatives of the University.

Arrangements for co-operation with Catholic Universities in: France; Italy; USA; Federal Republic of Germany. Also co-operation with the Universities of: Kent; Canterbury; Strasbourg; Barcelona; Tübingen; Linz. Centre universitaire de Luxembourg.

Academic Year: October to July (October-March; April-July).

Admission Requirements: Secondary school certificate (baccalauréat or maturité fédérale) or recognized foreign equivalent.

Fees (Francs): Registration, 73; tuition, 230 per semester; foreign students, 350.

Languages of Instruction: French and German.

Degrees and Diplomas: Licence in–Law; Economics and Social Sciences; Letters; Social Service; Psychology; Natural Sciences; Physical Education, 8 sem; Theology, 10 sem. Diplôme in–Theology; Commercial Teaching; Automation; Journalism; Social Service; Psychology; Social and Political Sciences; Biochemistry; Biology; Chemistry; Geology; Geography; Mathematics; Mineralogy; Physics. Doctorate in–Theology; Law; Economics and Social Sciences; Letters; Mathematics; Natural Sciences. Teaching qualification (secondary level).

Library: University and Cantonal Library, more than 1,500,000 vols.

Special Facilities (Museums, etc.): Museum of Art and History; Museum of Natural History.

Academic Staff, 1989-90:

Rank	Full-time	Part-time
Professeurs ordinaires et extraordinaires	96	3
Professeurs associés	32	4
Professeurs auxiliaires, Chargés de cours	1	198
Maîtres-Assistants	42	17
Assistants	211	128
Total	382	350

Student Enrolment, 1989-90:

	Men	Women	Total
Of the country	2541	1978	4519
Of other countries	1436	505	1941
Total	3977	2483	6460

6829 ***UNIVERSITÉ DE GENÈVE**
University of Geneva
24, rue du Général-Dufour, 1211 Genève 4
Telex: UNICH 423801
Telephone: (22) 7-05-71-11
Recteur: Jean-Claude Favez
Directeur administratif: Claude Bossy
Secrétaire général: André Vifian

F. of Science
Dean: Jean-Pierre Imhof; *staff* 637
F. of Letters (including Archaeology)
Dean: André Hurst; *staff* 271
F. of Economics and Social Sciences
Dean: Peter Tschopp; *staff* 233
F. of Law (including Forensic Medicine)
Dean: Alfred Dufour; *staff* 129
F. of Medicine (including Dentistry)
Dean: Antoine Cuendet; *staff* 667
F. of Theology (Protestant)
Dean: Jean-Marc Chappuis; *staff* 26
F. of Psychology and Education
Dean: Edouard Bayer; *staff* 249
S. of Architecture
President: Pierre Golinelli; *staff* 77
S. of Translation and Interpretation
President: Marguerite Wieser; *staff* 128
S. of Physical Education
Director: Olivier Jeanneret
I. of International Studies
Director: Lucius Caflisch
I. for Oecumenical Studies
Director: Karl H. Hertz; *staff* 4 (1)
I. of International Management
Director: Juan Rada
S. of French Language and Culture
Director: Georges Meid; *staff* 16
I. of European Studies
President: Henri Schamm
I. of Development Studies
Director: Jacques Forster
Ce. for Oecumenical Studies
Director: Adriaan Geense
U. for Mature Students
President: Aloys Werner

Founded 1559 as Schola Genevensis by Calvin, established as university 1873. The university is an official institution operated under the supervision of the Department of Public Education and is financed by the State. Governing bodies: the Rectorat, composed of the Rector, Vice-Rectors, administrative director and general secretary; the Collège des Recteurs et Doyens, composed of the Rectorat and the deans; the Sénat, composed of all professors; the Conseil, comprising 27 members, including representatives of the academic and administrative staff and of students.

Academic Year: October to July (October-March; April-July).

Admission Requirements: Secondary school certificate (baccalauréat) or equivalent.

Fees (Francs): Tuition, 710-1110 per annum.

Language of Instruction: French.

Degrees and Diplomas: Licence in–Mathematics; Biochemistry; Chemistry and Physics; Chemistry; Biology; Geography; Natural Sciences; Geology; Letters (History, Philosophy, Languages); Modern History; History of Arts; Social Sciences (various fields); Sociology; Economics; Law; Political Science; Medical Sciences; Dentistry; Theology Education; Psychology, *c.* 6-8 sem. Doctorate in–Mathematical Sciences; Mathematical Statistics; Astronomy; Physics; Chemistry; Geology and Mineralogy; Biology; Biochemistry; Anthropology; Pharmacy; Letters; Philosophy; Social Sciences; Economics; Political Science; Law; Medicine; Dentistry; Medical Biology; Theology; Theology, mention 'oecumenical'; Education; Psychology. Diplôme fédéral (State qualification) de–Médecin; Médecin-Dentiste; Médecin-Spécialiste. Professional titles of–Ingénieur géologue; Informaticien; Ingénieur chimiste; Pharmacien; Physicien, physics; Chimiste, analytic chemistry; Architecte; Traducteur; Interprète; Interprètede conférence;Maître de gymnastique. Professional qualifications in–Child Psychology; Education Studies. Certificate of specialization in–Astrophysics; Chemistry; Statistical Geology; Molecular Biology; Photobiology; Human Ecology; Poetic Phonetics; Genetic Psychology; Education; Computer Translation; Terminology; Oecumenical Studies; Administration; Social Politics.

Libraries: University and Public Library, *c.* 1,660,000 vols; faculty libraries, *c.* 941,000.

Publications: Programme annuel des cours; Dies Academicus; Guide de l'Etudiant; Règlements et Plans d'Etudes des diverses Facultés; Catalogue des publications de l'Université; Catalogue des programmes de recherche.

Academic Staff, 1986-87:

Rank	Full-time
Corps professoral (professeurs ordinaires,extraordinarires, honoraires, invités, associés, assistants, chargés de cours)	790
Collaborateurs de l'enseignement et de la recherche	1650
Total	2440

Student Enrolment, 1986-87:

	Men	Women	Total
Of the country	4266	4424	8690
Of other countries	1005	1214	2209
Total	5271	5638	10,909

6830 ***UNIVERSITÉ DE LAUSANNE**

University of Lausanne

Dorigny, 1015 Lausanne

Telex: 455110 UNIL

Telephone: (21) 602-11-11

Fax: (21) 692-42-97

Recteur: Pierre Ducrey (1987-95)

Directeur administratif: Christian Pilloud

F. of Theology (Protestant)

Dean: Daniel Marguerat; *staff* 9 (11)

F. of Law

Dean: Pierre-Robert Gilliéron; *staff* 18 (27)

F. of Medicine

Dean: Jean-Jacques Livio; *staff* 146 (115)

F. of Letters

Dean: Claude Bérard; *staff* 59 (100)

F. of Science

Dean: Jean-Claude Bünzli; *staff* 82 (63)

F. of Political and Social Sciences

Dean: Rémy Droz; *staff* 24 (40)

S. of Commercial Studies

Dean: Olivier Blanc; *staff* 25 (34)

S. of Modern French

Director: René Richterich; *staff* 7 (24)

S. of Pharmacy

Director: Bernard Testa; *staff* 7 (14)

I. of Criminology and Police Science

Director: Pierre-André Margot; *staff* 4

I. of Public Administration

Director: Raimund E. Germann; *staff* 6 (6)

Founded 1537 as Académie de Lausanne, a theological seminary. Became university in 1890 when a faculty of medicine was added to the four existing faculties. The university is a self-governing institution under the administrative and financial control of the Cantonal authorities. Governing bodies: the Sénat; the Rectorat. Residential facilities for *c.* 350 students.

Arrangements for co-operation with the: Universities of Dijon; University of Niamey; Wrocław; Dakar; Malawi;Leningrad; Beijing; Kent; Uppsala.

Academic Year: October to June (October-March; April-June).

Admission Requirements: Secondary school certificate (baccalauréat or maturité) or recognized equivalent.

Fees (Francs): 280-460 per semester, according to field of study; foreign students, 480-660.

Language of Instruction: French.

Degrees and Diplomas: Licence in–Letters (university degree); Law; Theology; Religious Sciences; Psychology; Economics; Actuarial Sciences, Social Sciences; Sociology; Political Science; Psycho-pedagogy, 6 sem; Letters (State degree); Natural Sciences; Chemistry; Mathematics; Physics, 8 sem; Medical Doctor (foreign students only), 12 sem. Diplôme and title of– Chemist; Biologist; Geologist; Physicist; Doctor; Mathematician; and Pharmacist (for foreign students only), 8 sem. Doctorates in–Theology; Law; Social Sciences; Political Science; Sociology; Psychology; Actuarial Sciences; Education; Economics and Commercial Sciences; Criminology; Letters; Medicine (for Swiss students); Science; Pharmacy. Also certificate and diploma in French studies and criminology.

Libraries: Bibliothèque cantonale et universitaire, *c.* 1,600,000 vols; bibliothèque centrale universitaire, *c.* 500,000.

Special Facilities (Museums, etc.): Musées d'instituts (Sciences).

Publications: Uni-Lausanne (3 times a year); Communications (monthly); Memento (weekly); Publications de l'Université; Dies Academicus.

Academic Staff, 1989-90:

Rank	Full-time	Part-time
Professeurs ordinaires	208	6
Professeurs extraordinaires	–	37
Professeurs associés	44	34
Professeurs assistants	4	3
Privat-docents	–	102
Maîtres-Assistants	20	25
Agrégés	25	83
Lecteurs	5	11
Professeurs invités	–	39
Suppléants	21	94
Total	327	434

Student Enrolment, 1989-90:

	Men	Women	Total
Of the country	2793	2451	5244
Of other countries	894	847	1741
Total	3687	3298	6985

6831 **UNIVERSITÉ DE NEUCHÂTEL**

University of Neuchâtel

Avenue du ler-Mars 26, 2000 Neuchâtel

Telephone: (38) 25-38-51

Fax: (38) 25-18-32

Recteur: Remy Scheurer (1987-91)

Secrétaire général: Pierre Barraud

F. of Letters (including Psychology)

Dean: Bernard Py; *staff* 33 (46)

F. of Science

Dean: Claude Mermod; *staff* 37 (58)

F. of Law and Economics

Dean: Claude Jeanrenaud; *staff* 23 (20)

F. of Theology (Protestant)

Dean: Martin Rose; *staff* 6 (3)

I. of Sociology and Political Science

Director: François Hainard

I. of Ethnology

Director: Pierre Centlivres

I. of History

Director: Philippe Marguerat

I. of Physics

Director: Eric Jeannet

I. of Botany

Director: Erhard Stulz

I. of Geography

Director: Frédéric Chiffelle

I. of Zoology

Director: André Aeschlimann

I. of Geology

Director: Bernard Kübler

I. of Chemistry

Director: Claus Bernauer

I. of Microtechnology

Director: René Daendliker

I. of Structural Metallurgy

Director: Willy Form

I. of Mathematics

Director: Hans Nageli

I. of Linguistics

Directors: Claude Sandoz; C. Rubattel

Ce. for Applied Linguistics

Directors: René Jeanneret; B. Py

Ce. for Hydrogeology

Director: F. Zwahlen

Ce. for Franco-Swiss Studies

Directors: Louis-Edouard Roulet; R. Scheurer; Philippe Henry; Philippe Marguerat

Ce. for Dialectology and the Study of Regional French

Director: Pierre Knecht

Semiological Research Ce.
Director: Jean-Blaise Grize
Computer Ce.
Director: Randoald Corfu
U. for Mature Students
Director: René Jeanneret
Theology Research I.
Director: Pierre Bühler
L. of Language and Spoken Word Processing (Letters)
Director: François Grosjean

Founded 1838 as academy, became university 1909. Operated under the control of the Cantonal authorities. Governing bodies: the Conseil rectoral; the Conseil de l'Université; the Sénat. Some residential facilities for students.

Special arrangements for co-operation with the Universities of: Besançon; Compiègne; Perugia; Paris IV (Sorbonne); Iaşi; Centre universitaire de Luxembourg.

Academic Year: October to June (October-March; April-June).

Admission Requirements: Secondary school certificate (baccalauréat or maturité) or recognized equivalent.

Fees (Francs): 130-730 per annum; foreign students, 1130.

Language of Instruction: French.

Degrees and Diplomas: Licence in–Law, 6 sem; Letters; Science; Economics; Political Science; Social Sciences; Industrial Psychology; Theology, 7-10 sem. Diplôme in–French, 4 sem; Speech Therapy; Actuarial Sciences, 6-7 sem; Physics; Chemical Engineering; Electro-Physics; Metallurgy; Geology, 8 sem; Psychology, 10 sem. Doctorate in– Letters; Science; Economics; Political Science; Social Sciences; Theology, 2-3 yrs after Licence or Diplôme. Also certificate in Journalism; theology, 6 sem.

Libraries: Central Library; faculty and institute libraries, total 300,000 vols.

Special Facilities (Museums, etc.): Museums: Ethnology; Archaeology; Natural History; Art and History.

Publications: Publications de l'Université; Publications des Facultés; Recueil de Travaux des Instituts.

Academic Staff, 1989-90: *c.* 270.

Student Enrolment, 1989-90: *c.* 2380.

6832 ***UNIVERSITÄT ZÜRICH**

University of Zürich
Rämistrasse 71, 8006 Zürich
Telex: UNIZH 817260
Telephone: (1) 257-1111
Rektor: Hans Heinrich Schmid (1988-92)
Sekretär: Hanspeter Meister

F. of Theology (Protestant)
Dean: Hans Ruh; *staff* 13 (8)
F. of Law and Economics
Dean: Walter Haller; *staff* 56 (31)
F. of Medicine (including Dentistry)
Dean: Paul Kleihues; *staff* 94 (212)
F. of Veterinary Medicine
Dean: Friedrich Untermann; *staff* 22 (14)
F. of Philosophy I (Letters)
Dean: Harald Burger; *staff* 96 (70)
F. of Philosophy II (Sciences)
Dean: Georges Wagnière; *staff* 75 (61)
U. for Mature Students
Also *c.* 150 institutes, colleges, and clinics.

Founded 1523 by Ulrich Zwingli as a school. Became university by public vote 1833. Governing bodies: the Akademischer Senat; the Senatausschuss (Committee of the Senate), composed of the Rector, the former Rector, the deans, a representative of the Privatdozenten, and the Aktuar (recorder).

Academic Year: October to July (October-April; April-July).

Admission Requirements: Secondary school certificate (Maturitätszeugnis) or recognized equivalent.

Fees (Francs): 200 per semester.

Language of Instruction: German.

Degrees and Diplomas: Lizentiat in–Philosophy; Law; Economics; Theology; Medicine; Dentistry; Veterinary Medicine, 6-8 sem. Doktor, a further 2 sem. Doktor in Natural Sciences, 4-5 yrs; Doktor in Medicine, at least 7 yrs. Diploma in Natural Sciences, 4 yrs.

Library: *c.* 1,400,000 vols.

Special Facilities (Museums, etc.): Museums: Anthropology; Archaeology; Ethnology; Zoology; Palaeontology; Medicine. Botanical Garden and Museum.

Academic Staff, 1990:

Rank	Full-time	Part-time
Ordinarius	254	–
Extraordinarius	92	–
Assistenzprofessoren	16	–
Titularprofessoren	–	178
Privatdozenten	–	232
Others	–	973
Total	362	1383

Student Enrolment, 1990:

	Men	Women	Total
Of the country	10,631	7985	18,616
Of other countries	1164	780	1944
Total	11,795	8765	20,560

6833 ***ÉCOLE POLYTECHNIQUE FÉDÉRALE DE LAUSANNE**

Federal Institute of Technology of Lausanne
CE 0- Ecublens, 1015 Lausanne
Cables: epfl
Telex: 254478 DPFV CH
Telephone: (21) 693-11-11
Fax: (21) 693-21-24
Président: Bernard Vittoz (1978-)
Secrétaire général: Pierre-F. Pittet

D. of Rural Engineering
D. of Civil Engineering
D. of Mechanical Engineering (including Microtechnics)
D. of Microtechnics
D. of Physics
D. of Electrical Engineering
D. of Computer Science
D. of Chemistry
D. of Mathematics
D. of Architecture
D. of Materials Testing
Ce. for Plasma Research
Head: Francis Troyon
Computer Ce.
Director: Michel Reymond
I. of Metallurgy
Head: Willy Benoit
D. of Special Mathematics
Director: Philippe Kindler
I. of Microscopy Electronics
Director: Philippe Buffat
D. of Education and Didactics
Director: Marcel Goldschmid
Language Ce.
Also 81 departments, postgraduate institutes and laboratories.

Founded 1853 as a private school, became part of the Faculty of Science in University of Lausanne 1890, and an autonomous institute attached to the University 1946. Acquired present status as federal institution 1969. Financed by the federal government. Governing bodies: the Conférence des Chefs de départements; the Conseil des Maîtres. Some residential facilities for students.

Arrangements for co-operation with: Carnegie Mellon Institute of Technology, Pittsburgh; University of Tokyo; Universidad de Valle, Cali; Universidad F. Sta. Maria, Valparaiso; Ecole polytechnique, Thiès; Xian Jiaotong University; Institut des Ponts et Chaussées, Paris; Institut Polytechnique, Toulouse; Institut national des Sciences appliquées, Lyon; Lund University; Linköping Institute of Technology; Iowa State University; Georgia Institute of Technology; Université du Québec; University of Waterloo; Ecole nationale supérieure de Grenoble.

Academic Year: October to June (October-February; April-June).

Admission Requirements: Secondary school certificate (baccalauréat) or equivalent.

Fees (Francs): 480 per semester; foreign students, 580 per semester.

Language of Instruction: French.

Degrees and Diplomas: Diplôme–d'Ingénieur (in various fields); 4 yrs and 4 months; d'Architecte, 4 yrs and 5 months. Docteur ès Sciences techniques, Docteur ès Sciences, a further 3-5 yrs.

Libraries: 280,000 vols; libraries of the departments, total, 71,000.

Publications: 'Etudes et Professions' (annually); Rapport d'Activité (annually); Polyrama; Rapport scientifique (annually).

Press or Publishing House: Presses Polytechniques Romandes.

Academic Staff, 1989-90:

Rank	Full-time
Professeurs	131
1ers Assistants and assistants	800
Collaborateurs scientifiques	748
Total	1679

Student Enrolment, 1989-90:

	Men	Women	Total
Of the country	2109	362	2471
Of other countries	853	193	1046
Total	2962	555	3517

6834 ***EIDGENÖSSISCHE TECHNISCHE HOCHSCHULE ZÜRICH ÉCOLE POLYTECHNIQUE FÉDÉRALE ZURICH POLITECNICO FEDERALE SVIZZERO ZURIGO**

Swiss Federal Institute of Technology
Rämistrasse 101, ETH-Zentrum, 8092 Zürich
Telex: 817 379 EHHG CH
Telephone: (1) 256-22-11
Fax: (1) 252-01-92
Präsident: Hans Bühlmann
Rektor: Hans von Gunten
Generalsekretär: Hans-Rudolf Denzler

D. of Architecture (including Town Planning)
Head: Franz Oswald
D. of Civil Engineering
Head: Karl Dietrich
D. of Mechanical Engineering
Head: Max Anliker
D. of Electrical Engineering
Head: George Moschytz
D. of Computer Sciences
Head: Peter Läuchli
D. of Materials Science
Head: Hans Böhni
D. of Chemistry (including Metallurgical Chemistry)
Head: Werner Richarz
D. of Pharmacy
Head: Otto Sticher
D. of Forestry
Head: Hans Sticher
D. of Agriculture
Head: Jürg Solms
D. of Rural Engineering and Surveying
Head: Hans-Gert Kahl
D. of Mathematics and Physics
D. of Natural Sciences
Head: Karl Bättig
D. of Liberal Studies (History, Philosophy, Languages, Law, and Economics)
Head: Roland Ris
Also 83 institutes, laboratories, 29 chairs, and several experimental stations.

Founded 1855 as the only institution of higher education directly responsible to the federal (central) government, which appoints the Schweizerischer Schulrat, the governing body of the institute. The Rector is elected by the body of the professors, and the heads by the professors of their divisions. Financed by the government.

Academic Year: October to July (October-February; April-July).

Admission Requirements: Secondary school certificate (Maturitätszeugnis) or recognized equivalent, or entrance examination.

Fees (Francs): 400 per semester, foreign students, 500.

Languages of Instruction: German and some French.

Degrees and Diplomas: Diplomas in–Architecture; Civil Engineering; Mechanical Engineering; Electrical Engineering; Computer Sciences; Materials Sciences; Chemical Engineering; Chemistry; Food Engineering; Pharmacy; Forestry; Agriculture; Rural Engineering; Surveying; Mathematics; Physics; Natural Sciences, 4 yrs. Doctorat, by thesis after diploma in–Technical Sciences; Mathematical Sciences; Natural Sciences.

Libraries: Central Library, *c.* 3,100,000 vols; also division and laboratory libraries.

Special Facilities (Museums, etc.): Museums: Geology, Mineralogy-Petrography; Entomology; Graphic Arts; Botany.

Publications: ETH–Bulletin (7 times a year); ETHZ–Annual Report; Report on ETHZ–Research (every 3 years); publications ofthe institutes.

Press or Publishing House: Verlag der Fachvereine.

Academic Staff, 1986: 276.

Student Enrolment, 1986-87:

	Men	Women	Total
Of the country	7471	1526	8997
Of other countries	1034	234	1268
Total	8505	1760	10,265

6835 **HOCHSCHULE ST. GALLEN FÜR WIRTSCHAFTS RECHTS-UND SOZIALWISSENSCHAFTEN**

University of St. Gallen for Business Administration, Economics, Law and Social Sciences
Dufourstrasse 50, 9000 St. Gallen
Telephone: (71) 30-21-11
Fax: (71) 22-83-55
Rektor: Rolf Dubs
Verwaltungsdirektor: Franz Hagmann

D. of Business Administration
Head: Rolf Wunderer
D. of Economics and Economic Geography
Head: Alex Keel
D. of Law
Head: Ivo Schwander
D. of Cultural Sciences (including Philosophy, Languages and History)
Head: Felix Philipp Ingold
Ce. for Futurology
Head: Hans-Georg Graf
Also 21 specialized institutes.

Founded 1898. An autonomous institution mainly financed by the city and Canton of Saint Gall and by the 'Bund'. Governing bodies: the Hochschulrat (Council), comprising 11 members; the Senat.

Academic Year: April to March (April-July; October-March).

Admission Requirements: Secondary school certificate (Maturitätszeugnis), or foreign equivalent and entrance examination.

Language of Instruction: German.

Degrees and Diplomas: Lizentiat in–Economics and Business Administration, lic.oec.; Public Administration, lic.rer.publ.; Law, lic. iur., 8 sem. Teacher of Commercial Subjects, mag.oec., 9 sem. Lizentiat in Informatics, lic.oec.inform, 8 sem. Doctorate in–Economics and Business Administration, Dr.oec.; Public Administration, Dr.rer.publ.; Law, Dr.iur., 10 sem and thesis.

Libraries: Central Library, *c.* 100,000 vols; institute libraries.

Publications: Vorlesungsverzeichnis; Rektoratsbericht; Hochschulnachrichten; HSG Information; Öffentliches Programm; Aula-Vorträge; Informationsbroschüre; Weiterbildungsbroschüre.

Press or Publishing House: Presse-und Informationsstelle.

Academic Staff: c. 60 (270).

Student Enrolment, 1990:

	Men	Women	Total
Of the country	2650	550	3200
Of other countries	650	150	800
Total	3300	700	4000

SYRIA

Universities

6836 ***GAMI'T DIMAŠQ**
University of Damascus
Damascus
Telex: HAMAK 411971
Telephone: 215100/1-6; 221003; 219604
President: Ziad Shwaiki (1981-)
Secretary-General: Fayez Tnbaji

F. of Letters (Arabic, English, French, History, Geography, Philosophy and Social Studies, Journalism, Librarianship)
Dean: Hamed Khalil; *staff* 341 (53)
F. of Law
Dean: Aziz Shokri; *staff* 56 (22)
F. of Economics and Commerce
Dean: Aref Dalila; *staff* 77 (8)
F. of Science
Dean: Ghadir Zayzafoon; *staff* 303 (40)
F. of Medicine
Dean: Adnan Souman; *staff* 284 (53)
F. of Dentistry
Dean: Adnan Massassati; *staff* 164 (102)
F. of Pharmacy
Dean: Abdul Ghani Ma' Al-Bared; *staff* 113 (61)
F. of Engineering (Civil)
Dean: Mahmoud Wardeh; *staff* 162 (17)
F. of Mechanical and Electrical Engineering
Dean: Nazih Abu Saleh; *staff* 259 (23)
F. of Education
Dean: Mahmoud Al-Sauued; *staff* 71 (12)
F. of Islamic Studies (including Islamic Law)
Dean: Ibrahim Salkini; *staff* 19 (16)
F. of Fine Arts
Dean: Kjaled Almaz; *staff* 65 (5)
F. of Agriculture (including Horticulture and Animal Husbandry)
Dean: Mahmoud Yasin; *staff* 135 (33)
S. of Nursing
Dean: Heyyam Al-Rayyes: *staff* 39
F. of Architecture
Dean: Talal Uqeili; *staff* 65 (1)

Also 7 intermediate institutes; Children's Hospital, Maternity Hospital, Dental Clinics, Al-Mowassaa Hospital,Al-Assad Teaching Hospital, Open Heart Centre, Nuclear Medical Centre, Intensive Care Centre.

Founded 1903 in Damascus as medical institute. Institute of Law founded in Beirut 1912, both re-established in Damascus 1919, and Arabic replaced Turkish as medium of instruction. Merged to become the Syrian University 1923. New faculties established 1946 and Technological Institute incorporated as faculty 1972. Present title adopted 1958. A State institution reponsible to the Ministry of Higher Education. Governing body: the University Council, composed of the Rector as Chairman, 2 Vice-Rectors, the deans of the faculties, and representatives of the Ministry of Higher Education and Student's Union. Residential facilities for 9805 students in hostels.

Academic Year: September to May (September-December; February-May).

Admission Requirements: Secondary school certificate or equivalent.

Fees: None.

Language of Instruction: Arabic.

Degrees and Diplomas: Licentiate of–Letters; Law; Islamic Law; Science; Commerce; Fine Arts; Agriculture, 4 yrs; Pharmacy and Pharmaceutical Chemistry; Engineering; Architecture; Mechanical and Electrical Engineering, 5 yrs. Master of–Economics; Agriculture; Architecture; Letters; Commerce; Education; Law; Pharmacy; Medicine; Dentistry; Science; Engineering. Doctor of–Dental Surgery, 5 yrs; Medicine, 6 yrs. Master, 3 yrs. Doctor in Letters, Economics, Agriculture, Pharmacy; Medicine and Dentistry; Sciences; Electrical and Mechanical Engineering; Law. General Diploma in Education; Special Diploma in–Education; Law; Economics, 1 yr.

Libraries: Central Library, *c.* 51,380 vols; libraries of the faculties, *c.* 71,080.

Publications: Aljami'a Journal; Historical Studies; Damascus University Bulletin; Statistical Abstract.

Press or Publishing House: Damascus University Press, Damascus, Syria.

Academic Staff, 1989-90:

Rank	Full-time	Part-time
Professors	344	–
Assistant Professors	160	–
Lecturers	355	446
Instructors	992	–
Technical Assistants	312	–
Total	2163	446

Student Enrolment, 1989-90:

	Men	Women	Total
Of the country	45,847	26,274	72,121
Of other countries	5427	3627	9054
Total	51,274	29,901	81,175

6837 **UNIVERSITY OF ALEPPO**
Aleppo
Telex: ALUNIV 331018 SY
Telephone: 236130
President: Mohammed Ali Hourieh (1979-90)
Secretary-General: Abdul Rahman Zkert

F. of Medicine (including Pharmacology)
Dean: Mounzer Barakat; *staff* 45 (75)
F. of Economics
Dean: Ahmad Ashkar; *staff* 41 (8)
F. of Letters (Arabic, English, French)
Dean: Ahmad Hebbo; *staff* 67 (96)
F. of Agriculture I (including Animal Husbandry)
Dean: Jum'a Ibraheem; *staff* 88 (20)
F. of Agriculture II
Dean: Mhuieddeen Qairawani; *staff* 5 (12)
F. of Science
Dean: Mahmoud Karroum; *staff* 141 (68)
F. of Dentistry
Dean: Zuhair Tarazi; *staff* 56 (60)
F. of Law
Dean: M. Sa'eed Farhoud; *staff* 16 (19)
F. of Civil Engineering
Dean: Sameh Djazmati; *staff* 31 (78)
F. of Architecture
Dean: Abdul-Ghani Al-Shihabi; *staff* 15 (80)
F. of Mechanical Engineering
Dean: Salman Sagbini; *staff* 19 (62)
F. of Electrical Engineering
Dean: Michel Hallaq; *staff* 33 (62)
I. for the History of Arabic Science
Director: Khaled Maghout; *staff* 3 (7)
Agriculture Research Ce.
Director: Fawzi Khayali; *staff* 3 (9)
S. of Nursing
Director: Nizar Akil
Computer Ce.
Director: Omar Farouk Azrak; *staff* 10
English Language Advisory Ce.
Director: Giyath Barakat; *staff* 12
French Language Advisory Ce.
Director: Kitty Salem; *staff* – (6)
Russian Language Teaching Ce.
Head: Kamal Abdul-Ralman; *staff* – (2)

Audio-visual Ce.
Director: Lailya Akkad; *staff* 2 ()
Professional Work Ut. (Engineering, Chemistry, Physics, Agriculture, and Economics)

Founded 1946 as Faculty of Engineering of Damascus University. Became university 1960. The university is a State institution responsible to the Ministry of Higher Education. Governing body: the University Senate, composed of the Rector, 2 Vice-Rectors, the deans of the faculties, a professor representing the academic staff, 3 students representing the Student Union, a representative of the Ministry of Higher Education and the University's Secretary-General. Residential facilities for academic staff and students.

Arrangements for co-operation with the Universities of: Warsaw; Sarajevo; Karl Marx-Stadt (Technical); Lyon II; Leeds; Strathclyde; Liverpool; Erevan; Prague; Gödöllö; Aden.

Academic Year: September to June (September-February; February-June).

Admission Requirements: Secondary school certificate (baccalauréat) or recognized equivalent.

Fees (Lira): 82-132.

Language of Instruction: Arabic.

Degrees and Diplomas: Bachelor, 4 yrs; Engineering; Dentistry; Agriculture, 5 yrs; Medicine, 6 yrs. Diploma of Graduate Study, 1-2 yrs; Special Diploma, 1 yr. Master, 3 yrs. Doctorate, at least 2 yrs.

Library: Total, 230,000 vols.

Publications: Journal for the History of Arabic Science (biannually); Newsletter of the Institute for the History of Arabic Science (seasonal); Adiyat Halab (annually); Research Journal (monthly).

Academic Staff, 1989-90: 1810.

Student Enrolment, 1989-90:

	Men	Women	Total
Of the country	34,567	14,190	48,257
Of other countries	1742	239	1981
Total	36,309	14,479	50,738

6838 ***GAMI'T ALBA'ATH**

Al-Baath University
P.O. Box 77, Homs
Telex: 441133
Telephone: 31440
President: Abdul Majid Cheikh Hussein (1979-88)
Secretary-General: Kassem Hammoud

F. of Arts and Humanities (Arabic and English)
Dean: Rodwan Kodmani; *staff* 14 (31)
F. of Dentistry
Dean: Salim Abokwaider; *staff* 7 (58)
F. of Veterinary Medicine
Dean: Tamer Haddad; *staff* 44 (15)
F. of Science
Dean: Akram Bazboz; *staff* 41 (14)
F. of Chemical and Petroleum Engineering
Dean: Mohamed Al-Shaar; *staff* 71 (8)
F. of Civil Engineering and Architecture
Dean: Ibrahim Matoi; *staff* 10 (125)
F. of Architecture
Dean: Hussam Barakat; *staff* 15 (17)
Also an Intermediate Institutes of Engineering and Veterinary Medicine.

Founded 1979 incorporating the Institute of Chemical and Petroleum Engineering, founded 1973 and the Faculty of Veterinary Medicine (Homs) of the University of Aleppo. A State institution responsible to the Ministry of Higher Education. Governing body: the Council. Residential facilities for academic staff and 1300 students.

Arrangements for co-operation with: Heriot-Watt University; Technical University of Bratislava; Sheffield University.

Academic Year: September to July (September-January; February-June).

Admission Requirements: Secondary school certificate.

Fees (Lira): *c.* 200.

Language of Instruction: Arabic.

Degrees and Diplomas: Bachelor of Arts, 4-5 yrs. Master, a further 2 yrs. Doctor, Ph.D., 3 yrs.

Library: Total, 35,700 vols.

Publication: Research Journal (biannually).

Academic Staff, 1989-90:

Rank	Full-time	Part-time
Professors	37	16
Assistant Professors	45	24
Lecturers	106	228
Total	188	268

Student Enrolment, 1989-90:

	Men	Women	Total
Of the country	6916	5446	12,362
Of other countries	304	293	597
Total	7220	5739	12,959

6839 ***GAMI'T TISHREEN**

Tishreen University Lattakia
Baghdad Street, Lattakia
Telex: TIUNIV 451084 SY
Telephone: 36311
President: Khaled Hallaje
Secretary-General: Najat Othman

F. of Sciences
Dean: Muhamad Al-Haushi; *staff* 50 (179)
F. of Agriculture
Dean: Ahmad Jalloul; *staff* 62 (65)
F. of Arts and Humanities
Dean: Najeib Ghazaoui; *staff* 28 (106)
F. of Civil Engineering
Dean: George Dagher; *staff* 22 (79)
F. of Electrical and Mechanical Engineering
Dean: Abdallah Said; *staff* 24 (111)
F. of Medicine
Dean: Zuhair Hallaj; *staff* 40 (171)
F. of Dentistry
Dean: Hassan Naser Al Din; *staff* 1 (16)
F. of Architecture
Dean: Nuhad Abdullah; *staff* 1 (16)
F. of Economics
Dean: Ibrahim Al-Ali; *staff* 4 (27)
I. of Engineering
Director: Ghassan Younes
I. of Medicine
Director: Ali Hassan
I. of Commerce
Director: Ahmed Mansour
I. of Languages
Director: Najeib Ghazaoui
S. of Nursing
Director: Moustafa Menlla
Marine Research Ce.
Director: Abed Alltif Yousef
Computer Ce.

Founded 1971 as Lattakia University, acquired present title 1976. A State institution responsible to the Ministry of Higher Education. Governing body: the University Council. Residential facilities for academic staff and students.

Arrangements for co-operation with other Universities including: Rostock; Grenoble; Paris 6; Bordeaux; Strathclyde; Sheffield; Patras.

Academic Year: September to May (October-January; January-May).

Admission Requirements: Secondary school certificate (baccalauréat) or equivalent.

Language of Instruction: Arabic.

Degrees and Diplomas: Bachelor of–Arts; Science; Economics, 4 yrs; Science in Engineering, various fields; Agriculture; 5 yrs. Master of–Arts, 1 further yr; Medicine, 3-4 yrs. Doctor, Ph.D., in Arabic Literature, a further 2 yrs. Doctor of–Dentistry; Medicine, 5-6 yrs.

Library: Total, *c.* 31,349 vols.

Publication: University Journal.

Academic Staff, 1989: c. 230.

Student Enrolment, 1989: c. 17,770.

6840 **HIGHER INSTITUTE OF POLITICAL SCIENCES**
Al-Tall, Damascus
Telephone: 741110
Director: Akram Al-Ahmar
Secretary: Ghazi Al-Saadi

D. of Political Studies
Head: Hassan Abu Hamoud; *staff* 7
D. of International Relations
Head: Majed Shadoud
D. of Economics and Administration
Head: Yousef Jazzan; *staff* 7

Founded 1976. Administed by the Ministry of Higher Education. Residential facilities for academic staff and students.

Academic Year: September to May (September-December; January-May).

Admission Requirements: Secondary school certificate.

Fees (Lira): 130 per annum.

Language of Instruction: Arabic.

Degrees and Diplomas: Diplomas (planned).

Library: c. 15,000 vols.

Academic Staff, 1989-90: 23.

Student Enrolment, 1989-90:

Men	Women	Total
412	46	458

TAIWAN

Universities and Colleges

National Institutions

6841 ***NATIONAL CENTRAL UNIVERSITY**
Chung-Li 32054
Telephone: (034) 427151/9
President: Chuan-Tao Yu (1982-)
Secretary-General: An-Chih Yang

C. of Liberal Arts
Dean: Hu-Hsiang Fung; *staff* 65 (7)
C. of Science (including Astronomy and Optical Science)
Dean: Chieh-Hou Yang; *staff* 84 (12)
C. of Engineering
Dean: Zuu-Chang Hong; *staff* 71 (24)
S. of Management (including Industrial Economics)
Dean: Chi Schive; *staff* 20 (6)
Ce. for Space and Remote Sensing Research
Director: Jer-Jiunn Chen; *staff* 13
Computer Ce.
Director: L.M. Tseng; *staff* 14

Founded 1968 and incorporating Institute of Geophysics founded 1962, as re-establishment of National Central University, founded in Nanking 1915 and closed 1949. A State institution financed by the government. Residential facilities for academic staff and students.

Arrangements for co-operation with the Universities of: Alabama; Boston. Georgia Institute of Technology.

Academic Year: August to July (August-January; February-July).

Admission Requirements: Graduation from high school and entrance examination.

Fees (New Taiwan $): 9000 per semester.

Languages of Instruction: Chinese and English.

Degrees and Diplomas: Bachelor of–Arts; Science; Management; Engineering, 4 yrs. Master, a further 2 yrs. Doctorate, Ph.D.

Library: Central Library, *c.* 200,000 vols.

Publication: Research Summaries.

Academic Staff, 1986-87: 264.

Student Enrolment, 1986-87:

	Men	Women	Total
Of the country	2015	750	2765

6842 **NATIONAL CHENG KUNG UNIVERSITY**
Ta-Hsueh Road, Tainan 700
Telephone: (6) 2361111
Fax: (6) 2368660
President: Jer Ru Maa (1988-)
Secretary-General: San-Yuan Tsai

C. of Liberal Arts
Dean: Joseph C. Yen; *staff* 119 (16)
C. of Sciences
Dean: Yuh-Jia Li; *staff* 158 (8)
C. of Engineering
Dean: Ke-Yang Li; *staff* 521 (71)
C. of Management
Dean: Shuei-Shen Liu; *staff* 95 (27)
C. of Medicine (including Pharmacy)
Dean: Kun-Yen Huang; *staff* 168 (25)
Vocational Technical S. (evening courses)
Director: Jin-Shyong Chen; *staff* 60 (50)
Evening S. (Liberal Arts, Management Science, Sciences and Engineering)
Director: Shih-Chung Li; *staff* – (300)
Also 26 Graduate Schools; Affiliated Hospital; and Aeronautics and Astronautics Experimental Field.

Founded 1931 by Japanese government as Tainan Higher Technical School. Became Taiwan Provincial College of Engineering, a State institution 1946, and provincial university 1956. Acquired present status and title 1971. Governing bodies: the University Council; the Executive Council; the Instruction Council. Residential facilities for academic staff and 5000 students.

Arrangements for co-operation with: University of Kentucky; University of Southern California; University of California, Los Angeles; George Washington University; University of Oklahoma; University of Missouri-Rolla; University of Tennessee; University of Alaska; University of Arizona; Purdue University; San Jose State University; Kyung Hee University; Choon-nam National University; Rhenish-Westphalian Technical University, Aachen; Technical University of Hanover; Johann Wolfgang Goethe University of Frankfurt; Technical University of Munich; Abadan Institute of Technology; University of Nantes; University of Delaware; University of Cincinnati; San Diego State University; Technische Hochschule Darmstadt; Southern Illinois University at Carbondale.

Academic Year: August to July (August-January; February-July).

Admission Requirements: Applicants must be graduates or under-graduates of accredited universities or Colleges or senior high school graduates from friendly countries.

Fees (New Taiwan $): Tuition, 6100-9000 per semester.

Languages of Instruction: Chinese and English.

Degrees and Diplomas: Bachelor of–Arts; Science; Medicine, 4 yrs. Master of Science, a further 2-4 yrs and thesis. Doctorate, Ph.D., at least 2 further yrs.

Libraries: Main Library, 255,174 vols; 32 libraries of the departments.

Special Facilities (Museums, etc.): Cultural Museum.

Publications: Cheng Kung Journal (annually); Cheng Kung News (monthly).

Press or Publishing House: Press Department.

Academic Staff, 1989-90:

Rank	Full-time	Part-time
Professors	201	46
Associate Professors	346	52
Instructors	222	57
Assistants	171	–
Total	940	155

Student Enrolment, 1989-90:

	Men	Women	Total
Of the country	7836	3301	11,137
Of other countries	723	175	898
Total	8559	3476	12,035*

*Also 2057 external students.

6843 **NATIONAL CHENGCHI UNIVERSITY**
64, Chih-nan road, Sec. II, Taipei City
Cables: Nccu
Telephone: (2) 939-8335
Fax: (2) 939-8043
President: King-Yuh Chang (1989-)

Ce. of Law
Dean: Chih Jen Gene; *staff* 144 (99)
Ce. of Liberal Arts and Science
Dean: Shou-nan Wang; *staff* 133 (47)
Ce. of Commerce
Dean: Ting-wang Cheng; *staff* 84 (70)
Ce. for Public and Business Administration
Director: Jun-Shu Chang; *staff* 21
Ce. of Communication Studies
Dean: Chin-heng Yen; *staff* 33 (28)
C. of Foreign Languages
Dean: Burt Ling King; *staff* 71 (34)
Computer Ce.
Director: Jinann; *staff* 10

Foreign Language Ce.
Director: Fun Feng; *staff* 15 (7)
Ce. of Election Study
Director: Yih-Yan Chen; *staff* 2
I. of International Relations
Director: Bih-jaw Lin; *staff* 15
Also 23 Graduate Schools.

Founded 1927 as Special School for the Training of Administrative Personnel, became Central Institute of Political Sciences 1929 and university 1945. Suspended 1949 and re-established in Taiwan 1954 by the Ministry of Education. A State institution. Governing body: the Executive Council. Some residential facilities for academic staff and students.

Arrangements for co-operation with move than 20 institutions of higher education in: USA; Korea; Federal Republic of Germany; Israel; Saudi Arabia; South Africa.

Academic Year: August to July (August-January; February-July).

Admission Requirements: Graduation from high school, or recognized foreign equivalent, and entrance examination.

Fees (New Taiwan $): 6980-9080 per semester.

Languages of Instruction: Chinese and English.

Degrees and Diplomas: Bachelor, in all Departments, 4 yrs. Master, a further 2 yrs and thesis. Doctorate, Ph.D., 4-8 yrs.

Libraries: Central Library, *c.* 457,957 vols; Social Science Material Centre, *c.* 467,900; Library of Institute of International Relations, *c.* 57,724; Library of Centre for Public and Business Administration Education, *c.* 80,798.

Publications: The National Chengchi University News; National Chengchi University Legal Essays; Journalistic Studies; East Asia Quarterly; America Monthly Mainland China Studies; Issues and Studies (Spanish, Chinese, Japonese, English, and French editions).

Academic Staff, 1989-90:

Rank	Full-time	Part-time
Professors	165	116
Associate Professors	184	91
Instructors	80	70
Assistants	99	–
Total	528	277

Student Enrolment, 1989-90:

	Men	Women	Total
Of the country	3534	4709	8243
Of other countries	100	20	120
Total	3634	4729	8363

6844 NATIONAL CHIAO TUNG UNIVERSITY-COLLEGE OF ENGINEERING

1001 Ta Hsueh Road, Hsinchu
Cables: Chiaota Hsinchu
Telephone: (35) 712121

I. of Electronics
I. of Management Science
I. of Computer Sciences
I. of Transport Engineering
I. of Applied Mathematics

Founded 1957 as Institute of Electronics, a graduate school of the former National Chiao Tung University. Undergraduate departments opened 1964. Became College of Engineering 1967. A State institution. Residential facilities for academic staff and students.

Academic Year: August to July (August-January; February-June).

Admission Requirements: Graduation from high school and entrance examination.

Language of Instruction: Chinese.

Degrees and Diplomas: Bachelor of–Engineering; Business Administration, 4 yrs. Master, a further 2 yrs. Doctorate, Ph.D., 3-5 yrs.

Library: *c.* 100,000 vols.

Academic Staff: *c.* 350.

Student Enrolment: *c.* 4000.

6845 NATIONAL CHUNG HSING UNIVERSITY

250 Kuokuang Road, Taichung 400
Cables: 6593 Taichung, Taiwan
Telephone: (42) 873-181

C. of Agriculture (including Forestry, Animal Husbandry, and Veterinary Medicine)
C. of Law and Commerce
C. of Science and Engineering
C. of Liberal Arts
Night S. of Law and Commerce
Night S. of Liberal Arts and Business Administration
Data Processing Ce. (Taipei)
Audio-visual Ce.
Computer Ce.
Also 16 research institutes
graduate studies.

Founded 1919 as Academy of Agriculture and Forestry, became part of Japanese Taihoku Imperial University 1928, transferred to Taichung as independent institution 1942, re-established as State institution 1945 and became Provincial College of Agriculture 1946 and university 1961. Acquired present title 1971. Governing bodies: the University Council; the Executive Council. Residential facilities for *c.* 80 academic staff and *c.* 3600 students.

Academic Year: August to July (August-January; February-July).

Admission Requirements: Graduation from secondary school or recognized foreign equivalent, and entrance examination.

Languages of Instruction: Chinese and English.

Degrees and Diplomas: Bachelor in all fields, 4-5 yrs. Master, a further 2-4 yrs. Doctorate, Ph.D., at least 2 further yrs.

Libraries: Central Library, *c.* 207,050 vols; Law and Commerce branch library, *c.* 130,000.

Publications: Journal of Agriculture and Forestry; Journal of Law and Commerce; Journal of Science and Engineering; Journal of Literature and History; Review of Statistics; Bulletin of Botanical Research; Bulletin of the Experimental Forest; Economics Studies.

Press or Publishing House: Chung Hsing University Press Division; Taipei College of Law and Commerce Press Division.

Academic Staff: *c.* 930.

Student Enrolment: *c.* 10,050.

6846 NATIONAL COLLEGE OF PHYSICAL EDUCATION

250 Wen Hua 1st Road, Kweishan 3333, Taoyuan

Founded 1987.

6847 NATIONAL OPEN UNIVERSITY

172 Chung Cheng Road, Lu Chow, Taipei County

Founded 1986.

6848 NATIONAL TAIWAN NORMAL UNIVERSITY

162 East Hoping Road, Section 1, Taipei 10610
Telephone: (2) 362-5101/5
Fax: (2) 392-2784
President: Shang-yung Liang (1984-)
Secretary-General: Chang-nien Yang

C. of Education
Dean: Yung-hwa Chen
C. of Arts
Dean: Chou Ho
C. of Science
Dean: Chin-yih Wu
C. of Fine and Applied Arts
Dean: Shiow-chung Liang
In-service Teachers' Education Ce.
Director: Shang-yung Liang
Extension D.
Dean: Po-chang Chen
Also 19 research institutes, graduate studies and junior and senior high schools.

Founded 1946 as Taiwan Provincial Teachers' College. Acquired university status 1955 as the only university devoted to the training of secondary school teachers. A State institution responsible to the Ministry of Education. Governing bodies: the University Council; the Executive Council. Residential facilities for academic staff and students.

Arrangements for co-operation with: University of Wisconsin; Pennsylvania State University; San Francisco State University; University of Missouri; University of North Colorado; Iowa State University; Keimyung University; Chung Nan University; Chung-Ang University; Sung Kyun Kwan University; Hankuk University.

Academic Year: August to July (September-January; February-June).

Admission Requirements: Graduation from senior high school or recognized foreign equivalent, and entrance examination.

Language of Instruction: Chinese.

Degrees and Diplomas: Bachelor of–Education; Arts; Science, 4 yrs and 1 yr teaching practice. Master of–Education; Arts, at least a further 2 yrs and thesis. Doctorate, Ph.D., 2-6 further yrs and dissertation.

Library: Central Library and branch libraries, 700,233 vols.

Publications: Bulletin of National Taiwan Normal University; Bulletin of Institute of Educational Research; Bulletin of Research Institute of Chinese Literature; Abstract of Chinese Educational Literature.

Academic Staff, 1986-87:

Rank	Full-time	Part-time
Professors	286	125
Associate Professors	224	76
Instructors	167	72
Assistants	128	13
Total	805	286

Student Enrolment, 1986-87:

	Men	Women	Total
Of the country	3390	4539	7929
Of other countries	51	43	94
Total	3441	4582	8023

6849 **NATIONAL TAIWAN UNIVERSITY**

Sec. 4, Roosevelt Road 1, Taipei
Telephone: (2) 3510231
President: Chen Sun (1984-)
Secretary-General: Chen-kang Peng

C. of Liberal Arts (including Archaeology, Anthropology, and Library Science)
Dean: Yen Chu
C. of Science
Dean: Kuang-hsiung Kuo
C. of Law (including Political Science, Economics, Business Administration, and Sociology)
Dean: Song-shi Yuan
C. of Medicine (including Dentistry, Pharmacy, and Nursing)
Dean: Czan-siung Yang
C. of Engineering
Dean: Chun-tsung Wang
C. of Agriculture (including Forestry, Veterinary Medicine and Animal Husbandry)
Dean: Yuan-chi Su
Computer Ce.
Director: Te-son Kuo
Language Ce.
Director: Chen-lai Lu
Evening D.
Director: Hugh S.C. Chen
Also 53 Graduate Institutes.

Founded 1945, replacing Taihoku Imperial University founded by the Japanese Government in 1928. A State institution. Residential facilities for academic staff and students.

Academic Year: August to June (September-January; February-June).

Admission Requirements: Graduation from senior high school or foreign equivalent, and entrance examination.

Fees (New Taiwan $): 2910-3780.

Language of Instruction: Chinese.

Degrees and Diplomas: Bachelor of–Arts; Science; Law, 4 yrs; Medicine, 7 yrs. Master, a further 2-3 yrs. Doctorate, Ph.D., 3-5 yrs.

Library: Main Library, libraries of the colleges and departments, total *c.* 1,600,000 vols.

Special Facilities (Museums, etc.): Museum of Anthrolpology.

Publications: Bulletins of the Colleges and Departments; Chinese Paleography; Acta Geologica Taiwanica; Acta Botanica Taiwanica; Acta Oceanographica Taiwanica; Acta Zoologica Taiwanica; Journal of Social Science; Journal of Sociology; Bulletin of the College of Engineering; Monographs of the College of Agriculture; Memoirs of the College of Medicine; Civil Engineering Studies.

Academic Staff, 1986-87:

Rank	Full-time	Part-time
Professors	679	291
Associate Professors	489	159
Instructors	249	143
Assistants	254	–
Total	1671	593

Student Enrolment, 1986-87:

	Men	Women	Total
Of the country	8801	5463	14,264
Of other countries	1460	809	2269
Total	10,261	6272	16,533

6850 **NATIONAL TSING HUA UNIVERSITY**

101, Sec. 2, Kuang-Fu Road, Hsinchu City 30043
Cables: Tsinghua Telefax: 886-035-710776
Telephone: (35) 714155
President: Kao-Wen Mao (1981-)
Dean for Academic Affairs: Yee-Yen Lee

C. of Science
Dean: Chun-Shan Shen
C. of Engineering
Dean: R.C.T. Lee
C. of Nuclear Science
Dean: Derling Tseng
C. of Humanities and Social Sciences
Dean: Yih-Yuan Li
I. of Linguistics
Computer Ce.
Director: Ching-Tsai Pan
Also 17 Graduate Institutes.

Founded 1911 as college, became university 1925. Closed 1949 and re-established 1955. A State institution. Residential facilities for academic staff and students.

Academic Year: August to July (August-January; February-July).

Admission Requirements: Graduation from senior high school and entrance examination.

Fees (New Taiwan $): 5530-7740.

Language of Instruction: Chinese.

Degrees and Diplomas: Bachelor of–Arts; Science, 4 yrs. Master of Science, 2-4 yrs. Doctorate, Ph.D., 3-6 yrs.

Library: Central Library, *c.* 207,000 vols.

Publication: Tsing Hua Journal.

Academic Staff, 1986-87:

Rank	Full-time	Part-time
Professors	147	26
Associate Professors	150	43
Instructors	40	28
Assistants	12	–
Total	349	97

Student Enrolment, 1986-87:

	Men	Women	Total
Of the country	2934	680	3614

6851 **NATIONAL INSTITUTE OF THE ARTS**

172 Chung Cheng Road, Lou-Chou, Taipei County 24702
Telephone: 2821331
Fax: 2832131
President: You-Yu Bao (1982-90)
Secretary-General: Te-Sheng Wang

Graduate S. of Theatre
Head: Stan SHen-Chuan Lai; *staff* 6
Graduate S. of Music
Head: Chu-Wey Liu; *staff* – (3)
D. of Music
Head: Chu-Wey Liu; *staff* 24 (44)
D. of Fine Arts
Head: Chi-man Lai; *staff* 16 (20)
D. of Theatre
Head: Stan Sheng-chuan Lai; *staff* 20 (8)
D. of Dance
Head: Yun-yu Wang; *staff* 18 (13)

Traditional Arts Research Ce.
Head: Te-Sheng Wang; *staff* 3

Founded 1982. A State institution. Governing body: the Executive Council. Some residential facilities for academic staff and for students.

Academic Year: September to June (September-January; February-June).

Admission Requirements: Graduation from high school and entrance examination.

Fees (New Taiwan $): 7500 per semester.

Language of Instruction: Chinese.

Degrees and Diplomas: Bachelor of Fine Arts, 5 yrs. Master, a further 2-3 yrs.

Library: c. 68,600 vols.

Publication: Arts Review (annually).

Academic Staff, 1989-90: c. 108 (89).

Student Enrolment, 1989-90:

Men	Women	Total
214	387	601

6852 **NATIONAL TAIWAN INSTITUTE OF TECHNOLOGY**

Section 4, 43 Keelung Road, Taipei
Telephone: (02) 7333141/9
Fax: 8862-7331044
President: Yen-Ping Shi (1980-)
Director, Secretariate: Yu-Kwan Lee

Graduate S.
Director: Shun-Tyan Chen; *staff* 1
D. of Industrial Management
Chairman: Sheng-Lin Chang; *staff* 25 (17)
D. of Electronics Engineering
Chairman: Jean-Lien Cheng; *staff* 42 (8)
D. of Mechanical Engineering
Chairman: Tien-Shou Lei; *staff* 38 (10)
D. of Textile Engineering
Chairman: J.Y. Lee; *staff* 11 (10)
D. of Construction Engineering
Chairman: Shi-Shuenn Chen; *staff* 27 (7)
D. of Chemical Engineering
Chairman: Yi-Hsu Ju; *staff* 28 (6)
D. of Electrical Engineering
Chairman: Chang-Huan Liu; *staff* 25 (12)
D. of Business Administration
Chairman: Shen-Lin Chang; *staff* 10 (3)
D. of Information Management
Chairman: Cheng-Fu Yang; *staff* 4 (5)
D. of Humanities
Chairman: Fu-Chuang Hsu; *staff* 27 (60)
Construction Technology Ce.
Head: Yung-Hsiang Cheng; *staff* 13
Automation and Control System Ce. (including Graduate School Engineering)
Head: Shun-Tyan Shen; *staff* 1
Materials Research Ce.
Head: Cherng-Yuan Sun; *staff* 1
Ce. for Research in Technological and Vocational Education
Director: Sheng-Hsiung Hsu; *staff* 3
Computer Ce.
Continuing Education P.

Founded 1974 as State institution. Residential facilities for academic staff and students.

Academic Year: September to June (September-January; February-June).

Admission Requirements: Graduation from high school and entrance examination.

Fees (New Taiwan $): Undergraduate, 3700 per semester.

Language of Instruction: Chinese.

Degrees and Diplomas: Bachelor of Science in Engineering, 2-4 yrs. Master of Science, a further 2-4 yrs. Doctorate, Ph.D.

Library: 200,000 vols.

Special Facilities (Museums, etc.): Laboratory and Workshops.

Academic Staff, 1988-90:

Rank	Full-time	Part-time
Professors	39	19
Assistant Professors	109	47
Instructor	36	9
Total	185	75

Student Enrolment, 1989: 4499.

6853 **NATIONAL TAIWAN COLLEGE OF MARINE SCIENCE AND TECHNOLOGY**

2 Pei-Nien Road, Keelung
Telephone: (032) 622192
President: Sen-Shyong Jeng (1981-)
Dean of Academic Affairs: Chung-Ren Chou

D. of Marine Transportation
Chairman: Tai-Shen Lee; *staff* 13 (2)
D. of Marine Engineering
Chairman: K.Y. Wu; *staff* 11 (3)
D. of Nautical Technology
Chairman: Tai-Shen Lee; *staff* 6
D. of Marine Engineering and Technology
Chairman: Tai-Zen Su; *staff* 6
D. of Fisheries
Chairman: Chuan-Hung Ho; *staff* 14 (8)
D. of Fish Processing
Chairman: Bonnie Sun Pan; *staff* 14 (12)
D. of Shipping and Transport Management
Chairman: Younger Wu; *staff* 15 (8)
D. of River and Harbour Engineering
Chairman: Chung-Ren Chou; *staff* 14 (3)
D. of Naval Architecture
Chairman: Wei-Hui Wang; *staff* 11 (9)
D. of Oceanography
Chairman: Hsien-Wei Li; *staff* 10 (8)
D. of Electronics
Chairman: Fu-Sheng Lu; *staff* 14 (3)
D. of Aquaculture
Chairman: Ching-Fong Chang; *staff* 12 (7)
I. of Marine Science
Chairman: Lie-Hsyang Lin; *staff* 3 (4)
Law of the Sea I.
In-Service Training P. for Seafarers
Evening S.

Founded 1953 as junior college, became senior college 1964, and acquired present status and title 1979. Financed by and under the jurisdiction of the Ministry of Education. Residential facilities for academic staff and students.

Arrangements for co-operation with: Nagasaki University; Busan Fisheries College.

Academic Year: August to July (August-January; February-July).

Admission Requirements: Graduation from high school and entrance examination.

Fees (New Taiwan $): 6000-8000 per semester.

Language of Instruction: Chinese.

Degrees and Diplomas: Bachelor of–Business Administration; Science, 4-5 yrs. Master of–Science; Arts, a further 2 yrs. Doctorate, Ph.D., 3 yrs.

Library: Central Library, *c.* 90,000 vols.

Publications: College Journal; department publications.

Academic Staff, 1986-87:

Rank	Full-time	Part-time
Professors	45	28
Associate Professors	49	34
Lecturers	45	28
Assistants	59	–
Total	198	90

Student Enrolment, 1986-87:

	Men	Women	Total
Of the country	2210	788	2998
Of other countries	1	–	1
Total	2211	788	2999

6854 **NATIONAL YANG MING MEDICAL COLLEGE**

155 Li-Nong Street, Section 2, Shih-Pai, Taipei 11221
Telephone: (2) 821-2301
Fax: (2) 826-4051

S. of Medicine (including Pharmacy)
Dean: Benjamin N. Chiang; *staff* 246 (49)
S. of Dentistry
Dean: Chao-Chang Chan; *staff* 24 (49)
S. of Medical Technology
Dean: Fu-wy Chen; *staff* 10 (17)

Graduate I. of Neurosciences
Director: Jiann-wu Wei; *staff* 5 (4)
Graduate I. of Microbiology and Immunology
Director: Szechen Lo; *staff* 11 (18)
Graduate I. of Biochemistry
Director: Yan-hwa Wu Lee; *staff* 8 (8)
Graduate I. of Biomedical Engineering
Director: Tsair Koo; *staff* 8 (8)
Graduate I. of Physiology
Director: Shyi-gang Wang; *staff* 5 (5)
Graduate I. of Pharmacology
Director: Samuel Hing-hun Chan; *staff* 5 (9)
Graduate I. of Public Health
Director: Chung-fu LLan; *staff* 3 (19)
Graduate I. of Clinical Medicine
Director: Benjamin N. Chiang; *staff* 4 (17)
Graduate I. of Anatomical Sciences
Director: Shyh-chang Sheu; *staff* 7 (3)
Graudate I. of Genetics
Director: Kuang-dong Wu; *staff* 3 (13)

Founded 1975. A State institution. Residential facilities for academic staff and students.

Academic Year: August to July (September-January; February-June).

Admission Requirements: Graduation from high school and entrance examination.

Languages of Instruction: Chinese and English.

Degrees and Diplomas: Bachelor of–Medical Technology, 4 yrs; Dentistry, 6 yrs; Medicine, 7 yrs. Master of Science, a further 2 yrs.Doctorate (Ph.D.) in–Microbiology and Immunology; Biochemistry; Clinical Medicine, 2-6 yrs.

Library: Central Library, *c.* 58,300 vols.

Publication: Scientific Papers (300 per year).

Academic Staff, 1990:

Rank	Full-time	Part-time
Professors	33	22
Associate Professors	55	82
Lecturers	63	259
Teaching Assistants	95	314
Total	246	677

Student Enrolment, 1990:

	Men	Women	Total
Of the country	1198	572	1770

6855 **KAOHSIUNG NORMAL UNIVERSITY**
116 Ho-ping First Road, Kaohsiung 800
Telephone: (07) 751-7161/8
Fax: (07) 721-1857
President: Shou-Shan Chang
Secretary-General: Yi-Hsiang

D. of Chinese
Chairperson: Chung-Lin Wong; *staff* 27 (2)
D. of English
Chairperson: Cecilia Sun; *staff* 24 (9)
D. of Mathematics
Chairperson: Wu-Nan Chou; *staff* 22 (1)
D. of Industrial Arts Education
Chairperson: Sheng-Kun Chen; *staff* 24 (8)
D. of Physics
Chairperson: Shiung-Ho Chiang; *staff* 13
D. of Education
Chairperson: Sheng-Chuan Lin; *staff* 24 (3)
D. of Chemistry
Chairperson: Ching-Yang Chou; *staff* 14
Graduate S. of Chinese Literature and Language
Director: Ju-Lian Chow; *staff* 8 (3)
Graduate S. of Education
Director: Jaw-Woei Chiou; *staff* 7 (1)
D. of Extension Studies
Director: Shen-Der Wang
Graduate S. of English Education
Director: Ching-Chi Chen; *staff* 4 (4)
Graduate S. of Mathematics Education
Special Education Ce.
Director: Bao-Shan Lin; *staff* 2
Computer Ce.
Director: Shin-Gia Kuo; *staff* 5
Audio-visual Education Ce.
Director: Yung-Ko Shang; *staff* 3
Also high school.

Founded 1969 as Provincial College, became National College 1980, and acquired present National University status 1989. Residential facilities for academic staff and students.

Arrangements for co-operation with 8 colleges in the U.S.A..

Academic Year: August to July (August-January; February-June).

Admission Requirements: Graduation from high school and entrance examination.

Fees: None.

Language of Instruction: Chinese.

Degrees and Diplomas: Bachelor of–Arts; Education; Science, 5 yrs. Master of Education; Arts; Science, a further 2-4 yrs.

Library: c. 410,859 vols.

Publications: University Research Journal (annually); Campus News (every two weeks); University Journal (quarterly).

Academic Staff, 1990:

Rank	Full-time	Part-time
Professors	39	13
Associate Professors	67	11
Instructors	38	11
Assistants	46	–
Total	190	35

Student Enrolment, 1990:

	Men
Of the country	1427
Of other countries	9
Total	1436*

*Also 1717 external students.

6856 **NATIONAL SUN YAT-SEN UNIVERSITY**
Taipei

Founded 1980.

6857 **NATIONAL TAIWAN COLLEGE OF EDUCATION**
Changhua City 50058
Telephone: (047) 232105
President: William Hsieh-chi Yeh (1983-89)
Dean of Academic Affairs: Ing-chyi Su

D. of Guidance and Counselling
Chairman: Chia-sing Peng; *staff* 28 (2)
D. of Language Education
Chairman: Leslie Tong; *staff* 12 (2)
D. of Special Education
Chairman: Grace Bao-guey Lin; *staff* 11 (6)
D. of Industrial Education
Chairman: Cheng-feng Chi; *staff* 28 (12)
D. of Business Education
Chairman: Puyet Sun; *staff* 14 (4)
D. of Mathematics
Chairman: Chun-shen Chen; *staff* 15 (3)
D. of Physics
Chairman: Chorng-jee Guo; *staff* 15 (3)
D. of Biology
Chairman: Chang-tien Tsai; *staff* 12 (2)
D. of Chemistry
Chairman: Jenn-lin Lin; *staff* 15 (1)
I. of In-service Training for Teachers
Head: Sen-ke Sang; *staff* – (67)
Also 2 Graduate Schools and 1 affiliated Vocational Industrial School.

Founded 1971 as Provincial College, acquired present status and title 1980. Residential facilities for academic staff and 1842 students.

Academic Year: August to July (September-January; February-June).

Admission Requirements: Graduation from high school and entrance examination.

Fees (New Taiwan $): 5589-7799 per semester.

Language of Instruction: Chinese.

Degrees and Diplomas: Bachelor of–Education (Guidance and special Education), 3 yrs; Science; Education, 4 yrs. Master, a further 2-4 yrs.

Library: c. 110,000 vols.

Publications: Journal (annually); Studies in Language Education (annually); Journal of Industrial Education (annually); Journal of Special Education (annually); Business Education (quarterly).

Academic Staff, 1986-87:

Rank	Full-time	Part-time
Professors	46	3
Associate Professors	48	9
Instructors	43	23
Assistants	37	–
Total	174	37

Student Enrolment, 1986-87:

	Men	Women	Total
Of the country	1745	1258	3003

6858 **TAIWAN PROVINCIAL CHIAYI TEACHERS' COLLEGE**

151 Lin-sen East Road, Chiayi
Telephone: (5) 270442-4
Fax: (5) 2763316
President: Kwo-Yann Hwang

D. of Elementary Education
D. of Literature and Language Education
D. of Social Studies Education
D. of Mathematics and Science Education
D. of Early Childhood Education

Founded 1957 as Normal School, became Taiwan Teachers' College 1966 and acquired present status and title 1987. Residential facilities for students.

Academic Year: August to June (August to January; February-June).
Language of Instruction: Chinese.
Degrees and Diplomas: Bachelor, 4 yrs.
Publication: Journal (annually).
Academic Staff, 1989-90: 108 (12).
Student Enrolment, 1989-90:

Men	Women	Total
886	1203	2089

6859 **TAIWAN PROVINCIAL HSINCHU NORMAL COLLEGE**

521 Nan Dah Road, Hsin-chu
Telephone: (35) 213132
Fax: (35) 231380
President: Frank Ping-Yu Yen
Director: Jason Chang

D. of Elementary Education
Chairman: Kuei-Chieh Liu; *staff* 29 (11)
D. of Languages and Literature
Chairman: Chou-Loong Lee; *staff* 18 (1)
D. of Mathematics and Science
Chairman: Jae-Tien Shoung; *staff* 16 (3)
D. of Social Studies
Chairman: Cheng-Tien Shen; *staff* 8 (12)
D. of Fine Arts and Crafts
Chairman: Shian-Pin Fan; *staff* 16 (8)
P. of Liberal Arts Education
P. of Evening Courses (for elementary teachers)
Special Education Ce.
Director: Shwu-Mey Wu; *staff* 1 (4)
Early Childhood Education Ce.
Director: Lily Chiang; *staff* 2

Founded 1940 as Normal School. Became Junior Teachers College 1965, and acquired present status and title 1987. Residential facilities for academic staff and students.

Arrangements for co-operation with: Shippensburg University; Millersville University; Bloomsburg University; Georgia Southwestern College; Northern Colorado University.

Academic Year: September to June (September-January; February-June).
Admission Requirements: Graduation from high school and entrance examination.
Fees: None.
Language of Instruction: Chinese.
Degrees and Diplomas: Bachelor of Education, B.Ed., 4 yrs.
Library: 109,500 vols.
Special Facilities (Museums, etc.): Music Hall; Fine Arts Exhibition Hall.
Press or Publishing House: Hsinchu Teachers College Publication Division.
Academic Staff, 1990: 110 (38).
Student Enrolment, 1990:

	Men	Women	Total
Of the country	395	561	956

6860 **TAIWAN PROVINCIAL HUALIEN NORMAL COLLEGE**

123 Hua-Hsi, Hualien
Founded 1947. Acquired present status 1987.

6861 **TAIWAN PROVINCIAL PINGTUNG NORMAL COLLEGE**

1Lin Sen Road, Pingtung
Founded 1940. Acquired present status 1987.

6862 **TAIWAN PROVINCIAL TAICHUNG NORMAL COLLEGE**

140 Min-shen Road, Taichung
Founded 1923. Acquired present status 1987.

6863 **TAIWAN PROVINCIAL TAICHUNG NORMAL COLLEGE**

140 Min-shen Road, Taichung
Founded 1923. Acquired present status 1987.

6864 **TAIWAN PROVINCIAL TAINAN TEACHERS' COLLEGE**

17 Su Lin Street, Tainan
Founded 1898. Acquired present status 1987.

6865 **TAIWAN PROVINCIAL TAIPEI TEACHERS' COLLEGE**

17 Su Lin Street, Tainan
Founded 1898. Acquired present status 1987.

6866 **TAIWAN PROVINCIAL TAIPEI TEACHERS' COLLEGE**

134 Sec. 2, Ho Ping East Road, Taipei
Founded 1896. Acquired present status 1987.

6867 **TAIWAN PROVINCIAL TAITUNG TEACHERS' COLLEGE**

684, Sec 1,Chunghua Road, Taitung
Founded 1848. Acquired present status 1987.

6868 **TAIPEI MUNICIPAL TEACHERS' COLLEGE**

1 Ai Kuo West Road, Taipei
Founded 1945. Acquired present status 1987.

Private Institutions

6869 **CHANG GUNG MEDICAL COLLEGE**

259 Wen-Hua First Rood, Kweishian, Taoyuan
Telephone: (886-3) 328-1200
Fax: (886-3) 328-3031
Chancellor: Delon Wu
Secretary-General: J.T. Shih

S. of Medicine
Dean: Tseng-Tong Tuo; *staff* 104 (74)
S. of Medical Technology
Dean: Tson Z Liu; *staff* 2 (17)
S. of Nursing
Dean: Sheuan Lee; *staff* 4 (20)
Also Teaching Hospital; Chang Gung Memorial Hospital.

Founded 1987. A private institution under the jurisdiction of the Ministry of Education. Governing body: the Board of Directors. Residential facilities for academic staff and students.

Arrangements for co-operation with Texas A and M University.

Academic Year: September to June (September-January; February-June).
Admission Requirements: Graduation from high school or recognized equivalent, and entrance examination.

Fees (New Taiwan $): 32,569-40,009 per term.
Language of Instruction: Chinese.
Degrees and Diplomas: Bachelor in all fields, 4-7 yrs.
Library: 14,000 vols.
Academic Staff, 1990:

Rank	Full-time	Part-time
Professors	24	8
Associate Professors	36	10
Lecturers	42	56
Assistants	8	–
Total	110	74

Student Enrolment, 1990:

	Men	Women	Total
Of the country	180	111	291

6870 **CHINA MEDICAL COLLEGE**
91 Hsieh Shih Road, Taichung
Telephone: (04) 2317153

S. of Medicine
S. of Chinese Medicine
S. of Pharmacy
S. of Public Health
S. of Dentistry
S. of Nursing
S. of Medical Technology

Founded 1958. A private institution under the jursidiction of the Ministry of Education. Residential facilities for academic staff and students.
Academic Year: August to June (August-January; February-June).
Admission Requirements: Graduation from high school or recognized equivalent, and entrance examination.
Language of Instruction: Chinese.
Degrees and Diplomas: Bachelor in all fields. Master.
Library: Chinese Medicine Library, 48,260 vols.
Academic Staff: c. 140 (210).
Student Enrolment: c. 3660.

6871 **CHUNG SHAN MEDICAL AND DENTAL COLLEGE**
No. 113, 2 sec. Tachien Street, Taichung
Telephone: (04) 252 6190/3

S. of Medicine
S. of Dentistry
S. of Nursing
S. of Medical Technology
S. of Nutrition

Founded 1960. Acquired present status and title 1977. A private institution under the jurisdiction of the Ministry of Education.
Arrangements for co-operation with: Tokyo Medical College; Gifu Dental College; Nippon Dental University.
Academic Year: September to June (September-January; February-June).
Admission Requirements: Graduation from high school and entrance examination.
Language of Instruction: Chinese.
Degrees and Diplomas: Bachelor.
Library: c. 20,000 vols.
Academic Staff: c. 130 (70).
Student Enrolment: c. 2260.

6872 **CHUNG YUAN CHRISTIAN UNIVERSITY**
Chung-Li, Tao Yuan Hsien 32023
Telephone: (3) 4563171
Fax: (3) 4563160
President: Shiu-Hau Yin
Secretary-General: Peter Tsao

C. of Science (including Psychology)
Dean: Being-Tau Chung
C. of Engineering (including Architecture)
Dean: Samuel H.S. Wang
C. of Business Administration (including Accountancy)
Dean: Samuel K.c. Chang
Evening D.
Dean: Yih-Fong chang
Computer Ce.
Dean: Tsai-Ming Hsieh

Founded 1955 as a private Christian College of science and engineering recognized by the Ministry of Education. Acquired present status and title 1980. Governing body: the Board of Trustees. Residential facilities for academic staff and students.
Arangements for co-operation with: Adamson University; Mississippi State University; Cleveland State University; University of Wyoming.
Academic Year: August to July (August-January; February-July).
Admission Requirements: Graduation from high school and entrance examination.
Language of Instruction: Chinese.
Degrees and Diplomas: Bachelor of–Science; Business Administration, 4 yrs; Science in Architecture, 5 yrs. Master, a further 2 yrs.Doctorate, Ph.D., 2-6 yrs.
Library: Central Library, *c.* 120,000 vols.
Special Facilities (Museums, etc.): Chung-Cheng Hall.
Publication: Chung Yuan Journal.
Academic Staff, 1989:

Rank	Full-time	Part-time
Prefessors	45	45
Associate Professors	105	126
Instructors	71	179
Teaching Assistants	106	14
Total	327	364

Student Enrolment, 1989:

	Men	Women	Total
Of the country	5086	2803	7889

6873 **UNIVERSITY OF CHINESE CULTURE**
Hwakang, Yang Ming Shan, Taipei 11114
Telephone: 861-0511
Fax: 861-053
President: Louis J.W. Jeng

C. of Letters
Dean: Sung Shee; *staff* 52 (155)
C. of Journalism and Communicate
Dean: Paul H.C. Wang; *staff* 28 (64)
C. of Science
Dean: Yin Fuh; *staff* 135 (142)
C. of Engineering (including Computer Sciences and Architecture and Urban Planning)
Dean: Yin Fuh
C. of Business Administration
Dean: Tsai-Mei Lin; *staff* 47 (64)
C. of Agriculture (including Animal Husbandry, Food and Nutrition)
Dean: David Wu; *staff* 43 (130)
C. of Arts
Dean: Pan-Li Chuang; *staff* 58 (89)
C. of Foreign Languages (Japanese, Korean, Russian, English, French, and German)
Dean: Yueh-lun Soong; *staff* 87 (82)
Graduate S. (24 Graduate Institutes)
Evening D.

Founded 1962 as a private college, became University 1980. Residential facilities for academic staff and students.
Academic Year: September to June (September-January; February-June).
Admission Requirements: Graduation from high school or foreign equivalent, and entrance examination.
Language of Instruction: Chinese.
Degrees and Diplomas: Bachelor of–Arts; Science, 4 yrs. Master of–Arts; Science, a further 2 yrs. Doctorates, at least 3 yrs.
Library: Total, *c.* 380,000 vols.
Special Facilities (Museums, etc.): Cultural Museum.

Publications: Chinese Culture (quarterly); Beautiful China (monthly); Sino-America Relations (quarterly, in English); Hwa Kang Journal (annually, in Chinese).

Press or Publishing House: Chinese Culture University Press.

Academic Staff, 1989-90:

Rank	Full-time	Part-time
Professors	112	267
Vice-Professors	154	330
Instructors	155	583
Teacher Assistants	122	44
Total	543	1224

Student Enrolment, 1989-90:

	Men	Women	Total
Of the country	7860	5702	13,562
Of other countries	18	11	29
Total	7878	5713	13,591

6874 **FENG CHIA UNIVERSITY**

100 Wenhua Road, Hsituan, Taichung
Telephone: 2522250/9
Fax: 04-2549517

President: Ted C. Yang (1988-)
Secretary-General: Pei-Kuei Kung

C. of Engineering (including Architecture)
Dean: Chung-Kuang Su; *staff* 187 (204)
C. of Business Administration (including International Trade, Banking and Insurance, Statistics, and Economics)
Dean: Han-Chu Liu; *staff* 99 (137)
C. of Management Studies
Dean: Chien Han; *staff* 34 (45)
C. of Science
Dean: Hsiang-Lai Kung; *staff* 41 (22)
Graduate S. of Textile Engineering
Director: Ching-An Lin
Graduate S. of Insurance
Director: Hsien-Cheng Tsang
Graduate S. of Automatic Control Engineering
Director: Jia-Ming Shyu
Graduate S. of Economics
Director: Chun-Chih Liu
Graduate S. of Chemical Engineering
Director: Te-Chang Wu
Graduate S. of Mechanical Engineering
Director: Chao-Yin Hsiao
Graduate S. of Information Engineering
Director: Hao-Jung Lo
Graduate S. of Civil and Hydraulic Engineering
Director: Tzu-Chiang Jan
Graduate S. of Applied Mathematics
Director: Yuan-An How
Graduate S. of Chinese Literature
Director: Jui-Kun Tai
Also 7 special departments for overseas Chinese students.

Founded 1961 as a private college recognized by the Ministry of Education. Became university 1980. Governing body: the Board of Trustees. Some residential facilities for academic staff and students.

Arrangements for co-operation with Universities and institutions of higher education in USA, Belgium, and other countries.

Academic Year: September to June (September-January; February-June).

Admission Requirements: Graduation from high school and entrance examination.

Fees (New Taiwan $): Total, 26,188 per semester.

Languages of Instruction: Chinese and English.

Degrees and Diplomas: Bachelor of–Engineering; Commerce; Law, 4 yrs; Architecture, 5 yrs. Master of–Science; Business Administration. Doctorate, Ph.D.

Library: Main Library, *c.* 300,000 vols.

Publications: Feng Chia Journal; college magazines.

Academic Staff, 1990:

Rank	Full-time	Part-time
Professors	63	133
Associate Professsors	135	170
Instructors	167	296
Teaching Assistants	135	4
Total	500	603

Student Enrolment, 1990:

Men	Women	Total
11,459	5862	17,321

6875 **FU JEN CATHOLIC UNIVERSITY**

Hsin-chuang, Taipei, Hsein 242
Telephone: (86-2) 903-1100/19
Fax: (86-2) 9035524

President: Archbishop Stanislaus Lokuang
Secretary-General: Augustine Wang Chen-Juei

C. of Arts and Letters (including Library Science)
C. of Science and Engineering
Dean: Peter Chou Shan-Shing; *staff* 109 (101)
C. of Foreign Languages
Dean: José Ramón Alvarez; *staff* 68 (66)
C. of Law
Dean: Matthew Yuan, S.J.; *staff* 52 (114)
C. of Business Administration (including Economics)
Dean: Frank Yao Chia-Chi, S.J.; *staff* 79 (144)
C. of Theology
Ce. for Mandarin Language
Director: Patrick Hogan, S.V.D.; *staff* 20 (14)
I. of East Asia Spiritual Studies
D. of Evening Studies
Director: Joseph Lü; *staff* 5 (315)
C. of Liberal Arts
Dean: Aloysius Chang; *staff* 100 (143)
C. of Fine Arts
Dean: Andrew Tsien; *staff* 27 (82)
Also 11 Graduate Schools.

Founded 1963 as re-establishment of university founded in Peking in 1925 under sponsorship of Benedictine Archabbey of St. Vincent, U.S.A., and for which administrative responsibility was transferred to the Society of the Divine Word in 1933, closed 1950. The university is a private institution operated under the jurisdiction of the Ministry of Education and administered jointly by the Chinese diocesan clergy, secular clergy, members ofthe Society of the Divine Word, and of the Society of Jesus. Governing body: the Board of Trustees. Residential facilities for students.

Arrangements for co-operation with: San Francisco State University; Iowa State University; Catholic Universityof America.

Academic Year: September to June (September-January; February-June).

Admission Requirements: Graduation from high school and entrance examination.

Languages of Instruction: Chinese and English.

Degrees and Diplomas: Bachelor of–Arts; Science; Laws, 4 yrs. Master of–Science; Arts; Business Administration; Engineering, a further 2 yrs. Doctorate, Ph.D.

Libraries: Liberal Arts; Social Sciences; Natural Sciences: total, *c.* 360,000.

Publications: Studies; Economic Journal; Law Journal; Philosophy Journal; Theologica Collectanea; Social Prospective.

Press or Publishing House: Fu Jen Press.

Academic Staff, 1990: 561 (1012).

Student Enrolment, 1990:

	Men	Women	Total
Of the country	7304	8627	15,931

6876 **KAOHSIUNG MEDICAL COLLEGE**

100 Shih-Chuan 1st Road, Kaohsiung City
Cables: Kaomedco
Telephone: 3121101/10

S. of Medicine
S. of Dentistry
S. of Pharmacy
S. of Nursing
S. of Technology for Medical Sciences
Graduate I. of Medicine

Graduate I. of Pharmacy

Founded 1954, the college is a private institution under the jurisdiction of the Ministry of Education. Governing body: the Board of Trustees. Some residential facilities for students.

Arrangements for co-operation with University of Arkansas.

Academic Year: August to July (September-January; February-June).

Admission Requirements: Graduation from high school or equivalent, and entrance examination.

Languages of Instruction: Chinese and English.

Degrees and Diplomas: Bachelor of–Science in Pharmacy; Science in Nursing; Science in Technology for Medical Sciences, 4 yrs; Dentistry, 6 yrs; Medicine, 7 yrs. Master of Science. Doctorate, Ph.D.

Library: c. 40,000 vols.

Publications: Abstracts of Theses; Bulletin.

Academic Staff: c. 250 (80).

Student Enrolment: c. 2740.

6877 **PROVIDENCE COLLEGE OF ARTS AND SCIENCES**

200 Chung Chi Road, Sa Lu, Taichung Hsien

Telephone: 245108/9

D. of Chinese Literature
D of Western Language and Literature
D. of Business Administration
D. of Mathematics
D. of Chemistry
D. of Nutrition and Food Technology
D. of Information Sciences
Evening S.

Founded 1957 by the Providence Sisters in China as Junior College of English Language. Acquired present status1963. A private institution under the jurisdiction of the Ministry of Education. Governing body: the Board of Trustees, composed of 15 members, including bishops, priests, and sisters. Residential facilities for single academic staff and for students.

Academic Year: August to July (August-January; February-July).

Admission Requirements: Graduation from high school and entrance examination.

Languages of Instruction: Chinese and English.

Degrees and Diplomas: Bachelor of–Arts; Science, 4 yrs.

Library: c. 74,880 vols.

Publications: Pechoes; Yi Yuan; Ching Wan Lan Tzu; Lin Yin; Ts'ai Hung Zyu; department publications.

Academic Staff: c. 120 (190).

Student Enrolment: c. 3040.

6878 **SOOCHOW UNIVERSITY**

70 Lin-Hsi Road, Wai-Shuang-Hsi, Taipei 111

Telephone: (02) 881-2873

C. of Arts (including Chinese Literature, Foreign Languages and Literature, and Political Science)
C. of Science
C. of Law
C. of Commerce (including Economics, Business Mathematics, and Computer Sciences)
Graduate S. of Chinese Literature
Graduate S. of Law
Graduate S. of Economics
Graduate S. of Accountancy
Extension D.
Evening S.

Founded 1900 in Soochow and received Charter from State of Tennessee. Supported by the Methodist Episcopal Church, South. Closed 1949 and re-established in Taipei 1950. Acquired present status and title 1954. A private institution operated under the supervision of the Ministry of Education. Governing body: the Board of Trustees. Residential facilities for some academic staff and for c. 1600 students.

Academic Year: September to June (September-January; February-June).

Admission Requirements: Graduation from high school and entrance examination.

Languages of Instruction: Chinese and English.

Degrees and Diplomas: Bachelor of Arts, B.A., in–Chinese; Foreign Languages and Literature; Political Science; Economics, 4 yrs; Bachelor of–Commerce, B.Comm.; Science, B.S., 4 yrs; Law, LL.B., 5 yrs. Master of–Law; Arts; Commerce, a further 2-3 yrs. Doctorate, Ph.D., in–Chinese; Economics; Law, a further 3-4 yrs.

Libraries: Central Library, 120,000 vols; Law, c. 20,000.

Publications: Soochow Journal of Literature and Social Studies (annually); Journal of Social and Political Sciences; Law Journal; Journal of Chinese Art History; Journal of Mathematics and Natural Sciences.

Academic Staff: c. 330 (340).

Student Enrolment: c. 9030.

6879 **TAIPEI MEDICAL COLLEGE**

250 Wu Hsing Street, Taipei 105

Telephone: (02) 707-3102

S. of Medicine
S. of Dentistry
S. of Pharmacy
S. of Medical Technology
S. of Nursing
S. of Nutrition and Health Sciences
Night S. of Pharmacy

Founded 1960, the college is a private institution under the jurisdiction of the Ministry of Education. Governing body: the Board of Directors, comprising 11 members.

Academic Year: August to July (August-January; February-July).

Admission Requirements: Graduation from senior high school or equivalent, or foreign equivalent, and entrance examination.

Languages of Instruction: Chinese and English.

Degrees and Diplomas: Bachelor of–Science in Pharmacy; Science in Nursing; Science in Medical Technology; Science in Nutrition and Health, 4 yrs; Dentistry, 6 yrs; Medicine, 7 yrs.

Library: c. 40,000 vols.

Publications: Bulletin (annually); Catalogue Taipei Medical College (monthly); Newsletter (monthly).

Academic Staff: c. 150 (160).

Student Enrolment: c. 3060.

6880 **TAMKANG UNIVERSITY**

151, Yingchuan Road, Taipei Hsien 251

Telephone: 6212106/10

C. of Liberal Arts (including Chinese and Western Languages and) Literature
C. of Science
C. of Engineering (including Architecture and Computer Sciences)
C. of Commerce
C. of Management
S. of Graduate Studies
Ce. for Area Studies
D. of Public Service
Evening C.

Founded 1950 as junior college of English, became College of Arts and Sciences 1958, and university 1980. Governing body: the Board of Trustees.

Academic Year: August to July (August-January; February-July).

Admission Requirements: Graduation from high school and entrance examination.

Languages of Instruction: Chinese and English.

Degrees and Diplomas: Bachelor of–Arts; Science; Business, 4-5 yrs. Master, a further 2-3 yrs. Doctorate in–Chemistry; Management.

Library: c. 300,000 vols.

Publications: Tamkang Review; Tamkang Mathematics Journal; Journal of Educational Media Science (quarterly); Policy Analysisand Information (biannually).

Press or Publishing House: The Tamkang University Press.

Academic Staff: c. 1500.

Student Enrolment: c. 17,150.

6881 **TATUNG COLLEGES OF TECHNOLOGY**

40 Chung-shan N. Road, Sec. III, Taipei 104

Telex: 11348 TATUNG

Telephone: (02) 592-5252

D. of Mechanical Engineering
D. of Electrical Engineering
D. of Business Administration
D. of Industrial Design
D. of Chemical Engineering
Graduate S. of Electrical Engineering
Graduate S. of Mechanical Engineering

Graduate S. of Business Administration

Founded 1943 as a private vocational school of industry, junior college added 1956. Acquired present status 1963. The institution maintains close co-operation with Tatung Engineering Company. Governing body: the Board of Directors. Some residential facilities for students.

Academic Year: August to July (August-January; February-July).

Admission Requirements: Graduation from high school and entrance examination.

Languages of Instruction: Chinese and English.

Degrees and Diplomas: Bachelor of Science in–Mechanical Engineering; Electrical Engineering; Business Administration; Chemical Engineering; Industrial Design, 4 yrs (5 yrs for night school). Master of– Science; Business Administration, a further 2 yrs.

Library: Institute Library, *c.* 105,100 vols.

Special Facilities (Museums, etc.): Science Museum.

Publication: Tatung Journal.

Academic Staff: c. 270 (110).

Student Enrolment: c. 1200.

6882 **TUNGHAI UNIVERSITY**

Taichung 400
Telephone: (4) 3590827
Fax: (4) 3590361
President: Ko-Wang Mei (1978-)
Chief Secretary: Chi-An Chuang

C. of Arts (including Chinese Literature, Foreign Languages and Literature, History, Philosophy, Music, Fine Arts)
; *staff* 132 (100)

C. of Science
Dean: Wan-Cheng Hsieh; *staff* 113 (48)

C. of Agriculture (including Animal Husbandry, Food Science, and Landscape Architecture)
Dean: Tsung-Hsiung Shih; *staff* 36 (15)

C. of Engineering (including Architecture, Chemical Engineering, Industrial Engineering, Industrial Design)
; *staff* 55 (23)

C. of Management
Dean: Ying-Wu Li; *staff* 68 (37)

C. of Law
Dean: Chi-Jen Feng; *staff* 83 (98)

Ce. for Chinese Language (for foreign students)
Director: I-Chien Fung; *staff* 9 (10)

Evening D.
Director: Shan-Lien Sun; *staff* – (323)

Environmental Research Ce.
Director: Lien-Tsai Jao; *staff* 7 (8)

Environmental Planning and Landscape Reseach ce.
Director: Cheng Tsao; *staff* 10

Also Branch in Taipei.

Founded 1955, the first private university in Taiwan, with the active support of the United Board for Christian Higher Education in Asia. Governing body: the Board of Directors, comprising 15 members, representing Chinese and Western leaders in business, educationand government. Residential facilities for academic staff and students.

Arrangements for co-operation with *c.* 30 universities and institutions of higher education, mainly in USA, Canada, United Kingdom, Japan, and Korea.

Academic Year: September to June (September-January; February-June).

Admission Requirements: Graduation from recognized senior high school or school of equivalent standing, and entrance examination.

Fees (New Taiwan $): 20,720-24,570 per semester.

Languages of Instruction: Chinese and English.

Degrees and Diplomas: Bachelor. Master. Doctorate, Ph.D..

Library: c. 295,870 vols.

Special Facilities (Museums, etc.): Christian Activity Building; Auditorium; Experimental Farm; Landscape Garden.

Publications: Tunghai Journal; Tunghai News; Tunghai Culture Monthly.

Press or Publishing House: Tunghai University Press.

Academic Staff, 1989:

Rank	Full-time	Part-time
Professors	100	47
Associate Professors	147	82
Lecturers	110	192
Instructors	22	12
Teaching Assistants	143	41
Total	522	379

Student Enrolment, 1989:

	Men	Women	Total
Of the country	4576	3744	8320
Of other countries	19	6	25
Total	4595	3750	8345

Also 50 Junior Colleges

THAILAND

Universities and University Institutions

State Institutions

6884 **MAHAVITAYALAI CHIANG MAI**

Chiang Mai University

Hua Kaew Road, Muang District, Chiang Mai 50002

Telex: 43553 UNICHIM TH

Telephone: (6653) 221699

Fax: (6653) 217143

Rector: Kasem Watanachai

F. of Humanities
Dean: Wattana Suksamai; *staff* 180 (25)
F. of Social Sciences (including Accountancy, Economics, Political Science, and Business Administration)
Dean: Chakrapand Wongburanavart; *staff* 127 (3)
F. of Science
Dean: Tavisakdi Ramingwong; *staff* 212 (12)
F. of Education
Dean: Prasit Malumpong; *staff* 136 (29)
F. of Medicine
Dean: Tejatat Tejaser; *staff* 337 (166)
F. of Dentistry
Dean: Tharong Chat-Vthai; *staff* 64 (30)
F. of Nursing
Dean: Wichit Srisuphan; *staff* 116 (77)
F. of Pharmacy
Dean: Pachprink Sangdee; *staff* 53 (31)
F. of Medical Technology
F. of Agriculture (including Animal Husbandry)
Dean: Nakorn Na Lampang; *staff* 122
F. of Engineering
Dean: Norkun Sittiphong; *staff* 83 (7)
F. of Associated Medical Sciences
Dean: Sanong Changarasamee; *staff* 61 (182)
F. of Fine Arts
Dean: Anam Chankhunthod; *staff* 19 (16)
Graduate S.
Dean: Viboon Rattanapanone; *staff* 18
I. for Science and Technology Research and Development
Director: Thiraphat Vilarthong; *staff* 5
Research I. for Health Sciences
Director: Chirasak Khamboonruang; *staff* 45
Social Research I.
Director: Chayan Vaddhanaphuti; *staff* 14

Founded 1964. A State institution responsible to the Ministry of University Affairs. Governing body: the University Council, consisting of the Prime Minister as Chairman, the Rector, the Vice-Rector, the deans and honorary members. Some residential facilities for academic staff and students.

Arrangements for co-operation with: La Trobe University; Western Australian College of Advanced Education; Katholieke Universiteit Leuven; Faculteit Voor Vergelijkende Godsdienstwetenschappen; Ryerson Polytechnical Institute; University of Victoria; University of Passau; Johann Wolfgang Goethe University; Nippon Medical School; Saikei University; University of Ryukyus; Kyoto Seika University; Kinki University; Mie Univrsity; Nagasaki University; Pasan University; International Rice Research Institute; Uppsala University; University of Minnesota, Duluth; California State University, Long Beach; University of Wisconsin, Madison; Colorado State University; University of California; University of Illinois at Chicago; George Peabody College for Teachers at Vanderbilt University; Louisana State University; Oregon State University; Indiana University.

Academic Year: June to May (June-October; November-March; April-May).

Admission Requirements: Secondary school certificate (Mathayom Suksa 5) or equivalent, and entrance examination.

Fees (Baht): 10 per credit; maximum 21 credits.

Language of Instruction: Thai.

Degrees and Diplomas: Bachelor of–Arts, B.A.; Engineering, B.Eng.; Science, B.S., in various fields, 4 yrs. Doctor of–Dental Surgery, D.D.S.; Medicine, M.D., 6 yrs.

Library: c. 1,600,000 vols.

Publication: Chiangmai University (monthly).

Academic Staff: c. 1450.

Student Enrolment, 1989-90:

	Men	Women	Total
Of the country	4983	5381	10364

6885 ***CHULALONGKORN MAHAVITAYALAI**

Chulalongkorn University

Phyathai Road, Bangkok 10500

Telephone: 215 0880/5

Atikarnbodi (Rector): Kasem Suwanakul (1977-89)

Rong-Atikarnbodi (Vice-Rector for Administrative Affairs): Amphon Namatra

F. of Arts
Dean: Duangduen Suwattee; *staff* 176 (66)
F. of Architecture
Dean: Chalerm Sootjarit; *staff* 67 (25)
F. of Commerce and Accountancy
Dean: Suthi Ekhahitanonda; *staff* 124 (33)
F. of Dentistry
Dean: Punni Soaksawasdi; *staff* 153 (22)
F. of Economics
Dean: Pairoj Vongvipanond; *staff* 70
F. of Education
Dean: Anan Attachoo; *staff* 385 (65)
F. of Engineering
Dean: Tavee Lertpanyavit; *staff* 219 (28)
F. of Law
Dean: Prasit Kovilaikool; *staff* 36 (28)
F. of Medicine
Dean: Charas Suwanwela; *staff* 377 (389)
F. of Pharmacy
Dean: Boonardt Saisorn; *staff* 115 (21)
F. of Political Science
Dean: Kramol Tongdhamachart; *staff* 65 (36)
F. of Science
Dean: Kamchad Mongkolkul; *staff* 360 (51)
F. of Veterinary Science
Dean: Rabin Ruttanaphani; *staff* 67 (31)
F. of Mass Communication and Public Relations
Dean: Surapone Virulrak; *staff* 48 (8)
F. of Fine and Applied Arts
Dean: Songkoon Atthakor; *staff* 21 (24)
Graduate S.
Dean: Thavron Vajrabhaja; *staff* 2 (12)
I. of Population Studies
Director: Nibhon Debevalya; *staff* 14
I. of Social Research
Director: Warin Wonghanchao
I. of Health Research
Director: Nikorn Dusitsin; *staff* 28
I. of Environmental Research
Director: Surin Setamanit; *staff* 2
Language I.
Director: Khun Kanda Thammongkol; *staff* 95 (6)
Thai Studies P.
Director: Pensri Dukee
Computer Ce.
C. of Nursing (including Midwifery)

S. of Analytical Chemistry
D. for Lifelong Education
Director: Paitoon Pongsabutra

Founded 1902 as Royal Pages' School, became civil service college 1911 and university 1916. A State institution responsible to the Ministry of University Affairs. Governing bodies: the University Council; the Faculty Senate. Residential facilities for academic staff and women students.

Academic Year: June to March (June-October; November-March).

Admission Requirements: Secondary school certificate (Mathayom Suksa 5) or recognized equivalent, and entrance examination.

Fees (Baht): 35 per credit per semester; Graduate School, 200.

Language of Instruction: Thai.

Degrees and Diplomas: Diplomas in–Education; Architecture, 3 yrs. Bachelor of–Arts; Education; Accountancy; Business Administration; Arts in Sociology; Arts in Political Science; Engineering; Communication Arts; Science in Animal Science; Economics; Science; Science in Basic Medical Science; Science in Statistics; Science in Medical Technology; Science in Medical Science; Laws, 4 yrs; Architecture; Fine and Applied Arts; Science in Pharmacy; Industrial Design, 5 yrs. Master of–Education; Communication; Arts; Architecture; Laws; Political Science; Economics; Engineering; Accountancy; Business Administration; Science in Statistics; Science in Pharmacy; Dentistry; Urban Planning; Science, a further 2 yrs. Doctor of–Dental Surgery; Medicine; Engineering; Philosophy (Political Science); Veterinary Medicine, 6 yrs. Doctorate in Education and Arts, Ph.D. (in Thai), 4-10 sem. Also postgraduatediplomas of specialization.

Libraries: Central Library, 192,472 vols; faculty libraries: Education, 62,310; Commerce and Accountancy, *c.* 10,300; Medicine, *c.* 31,560; Dentistry, *c.* 3660; Political Science, *c.* 20,090; Engineering, *c.* 28,650; Architecture, *c.* 5500; Veterinary Science, *c.* 10,680; Pharmacy, *c.* 7180; Science, *c.* 24,400; Arts, *c.* 23,450; Mass Communication,*c.* 7950; Law, *c.* 8820; Economics, *c.* 4500; Thailand Information Centre, *c.* 28,500.

Publications: Journal of Education (bimonthly); Journal of Social Science (quarterly); Journal of Architecture (annually); Journal of Veterinary Medicine (quarterly); Journal of Graduate School (biennially); Journal of Communication Arts (bimonthly); Research Journal (annually); Newsletter (weekly); 'Pra Kearw', Students' Handbook (annually); University Bulletin (biennially); Journal of Medical Science (quarterly); Journal of Pharmaceutical Sciences (bimonthly); Engineering Pamphlet (quarterly); Journal of Arts (annually); 'The Student' (monthly); Journal of Laws (every 4 months); Business Review (quarterly); Economic Review (biannually); Academic Resources Journal (biannually); Dental Journal (quarterly); Journal of Language Teaching and Learning in Thailand.

Press or Publishing House: Chulalongkorn University Press.

Academic Staff, 1986-87:

Rank	Full-time
Sastracharn (Professors)	99
Rong-Sastracharn (Associate Professors)	639
Poochuay Sastracharn (Assistant Professors)	902
Acharn (Lecturers)	761
Total	2401

Student Enrolment, 1986-87:

	Men	Women	Total
Of the country	6786	6514	13,300
Of other countries	32	3	35
Total	6788	6517	13,305

6886 **MAHAVITAYALAI KASETSART**

Kasetsart University
50 Phaholyothin Road, Bangkhen, Bangkok 10900
Cables: Unikase 10900
Telephone: 5790113
Atikarnbodi (Rector): Sutharm Areekul (1986-88)
Rong-Atikarnbodi (Vice-Rector for Administrative Affairs): Charan Chantalakhana

F. of Agriculture (including Animal Husbandry, Food Technology and Horticulture)
Dean: Somsak Vangnai; *staff* 247 (17)
F. of Forestry
Dean: Somsak Sukwong; *staff* 62 (5)
F. of Economics and Business Administration
Dean: Chamien Boonma; *staff* 125 (62)
F. of Fishery
Dean: Wit Tarnchanalukit; *staff* 40 (12)
F. of Veterinary Science
Dean Pirom Srivoranat; *staff* 69 (55)
F. of Engineering
Dean Boonsom Suwachirat; *staff* 105 (21)
F. of Agro-Industrial Technology
Dean Tasanee Sorasuchart; *staff* 31 (2)
F. of Humanities (including Library Science)
Dean: Singthong Pornnikom; *staff* 82 (34)
F. of Science
Dean: Sookpracha Vachananda; *staff* 211 (15)
F. of Education (including Physical Education)
Dean Yupa Veravaidhaya; *staff* 307 (69)
F. of Social Science
Dean: Nipon Kantasewi; *staff* 59 (30)
Graduate S.
Dean Yongyut Chiemchaisri; *staff* 795 (129)
Food Research and Development I.
Director: Bulan Phittakpol; *staff* 94
Swine Research and Production Training Ce.
Director: Somchai Chanswang; *staff* 5
Biological Pest Control Research Ce.
Director: Banpot Napompeth; *staff* 6
Corn and Sorghum Research Ce.
Director: Rachain Thiraporn; *staff* 20
Extention D.
Director: Boontham Chitanan; *staff* 80

Founded 1917 as school, became agricultural college 1928 and university 1943. Responsible to the Ministry of University Affairs. Governing body: the University Council, comprising 32 members. Some residential facilities for academic staff and 4700 students.

Arrangements for co-operation with: Nagoya Daigaku; Kyoto Daigaku; University of Illinois; Oregon State University; Virginia Polytechnic Institute and State University; State University of New York at Syracuse; Massey University; Mississippi State University; University of Rhode Island; University of Georgia; University of Alberta; Huazhong Agricultural University; South China Agricultural University.

Academic Year: June to March (June-October; November-March).

Admission Requirements: Secondary school certificate (Mathayom Suksa 5) or recognized equivalent, and entrance examination.

Fees (Baht): Tuition, 200-500; Graduate School, 800-1000.

Language of Instruction: Thai.

Degrees and Diplomas: Bachelor of–Arts, B.A.; Science, B.Sc.; Engineering, B.Eng.; Education, B.Ed., 4 yrs. Master of–Arts, M.A.; Education, M.Ed., Agriculture; Teaching, M.A.T.; Science, M.Sc.; Business Administration, M.B.A.; Engineering, M.Eng.; Home Economics, M.H.E., a further 2 yrs. Doctor of Veterinary Medicine, D.V.M., 6 yrs. Doctorate, Ph.D., 3 yrs.

Libraries: Central Library, 102,742 vols; faculty libraries, *c.* 234,063.

Publications: Animal Production (quarterly); Kasetsart Research Reports (annually); Journals; Kasetsart Technical Bulletin.

Academic Staff, 1986-87:

Rank	Full-time	Part-time
Sastracharn (Professors)	13	–
Rong-Sastracharn (Associate Professors)	174	–
Poochuay Sastracharn (Assistant Professors)	495	451
Acharn (Lecturers)	688	–
Total	1370	1821

Student Enrolment, 1986-87:

	Men	Women	Total
Of the country	6622	4461	11,083
Of other countries	4	–	4
Total	6626	4461	11,087

6887 **KHON KAEN UNIVERSITY**

123 Friendship Highway, Khon Kaen 40002
Telex: 55303 UNIKHON TH
Telephone: (43) 241333-44
President: Nopadol Tongsopit
Vice-President for Administration: Rangari Nantasarn

F. of Agriculture
Dean: Tawisuk Santawisuk; *staff* 123
F. of Engineering (including Civil, Electrical, Mechanical, Agricultural, Industrial, Environmental, and Chemical Engineering)
Dean: Prinya Chindaprasirt; *staff* 111

F. of Education
Dean: Kaewta Kanewan; *staff* 216
F. of Science
Dean: Srisumon Sitathani; *staff* 151
F. of Nursing
Dean: Kalaya Paranaari; *staff* 103
F. of Medicine
Dean: Pisit Sanpitak; *staff* 354
F. of Humanities and Social Sciences (including Foreign Languages, Library Science, Social Science, Thai and Literature, and Sociology and Anthropology)
Dean: Charin Paorohita; *staff* 89
F. of Associated Medical Sciences
Dean: Nettachaleo Sanpitak; *staff* 59
F. of Public Health
Dean: Chalermdes Vudhikamraksa; *staff* 30
F. of Dentistry
Dean: Pratip Pentunvamit; *staff* 45
F. of Pharmaceutical Sciences
Dean: Sumon Sakonchai; *staff* 27
F. of Technology (including Biotechnology, Geotechnology, and Food Technology)
Dean: Tipvanna Ngarmsak; *staff* 29
F. of Veterinary Science
Dean: Cherdchai Ratanasathakul; *staff* 24
F. of Architecture
Dean: Dhiti Hengrasamee; *staff* 10
Research and Development I.
Director: Krasae Chanawong
Instructional Resources Ce.
Director: Aphai Prakobpol
Computer Ce.
Director: Boonsong Watanakij
Also Ubonrachathani College (Agriculture, Engineering, and Basic Studies).

Founded 1964. A State institution responsible to the Ministry of University Affairs. Governing body: the University Council. Residential facilities for academic staff and students.

Arrangements for co-operation with the University of the Ryukyues; Sage University; University of Heidelberg; Auburn University; University of Texas; Iowa State University; Case Western Reserve University; Central Luzon State University; Ben-Gurion University of the Negev.

Academic Year: June to March (June-October; November-March).

Admission Requirements: Secondary school certificate (Mathayom 6) and entrance examination.

Fees (Baht): 30 per credit.

Language of Instruction: Thai.

Degrees and Diplomas: Bachelor of–Sciences in Architecture; Agriculture; Engineering; Education; Arts; Arts and Sciences in Nursing; Science in Medical Technology; Technology; Science in Public Health, 4 yrs; Science in Pharmacy, 5 yrs. Master of–Education; Science; Engineering, a further 2 yrs. Doctor of–Medicine; Dental Surgery, 6 yrs.

Library: Instruction Resource Centre, *c.*109,690 vols.

Special Facilities (Museums, etc.): Esarn Cultural Centre.

Publication: Faculty publications.

Academic Staff, 1990:

Rank	Full-time
Professors	42
Lecturers	672
Assistant Professors	481
Associate Professors	204
Total	1361

Student Enrolment, 1990:

	Men	Women	Total
Of the country	3528	3224	6752*

*Also 2 external students.

6888 *KING MONGKUT'S INSTITUTE OF TECHNOLOGY LADKRABANG

Chalongkrung Road, Ladkrabang District, Bangkok 10520
Telex: 84967 INSMONG TH
Telephone: (662) 3269157; 3269964
Fax: (662) 3267333
Rector: Kosol Petchsuwan (1986-)
Vice-Rector for Administration: Wilaiwan Wonyodpun

F. of Architecture
Dean: Pisit Viriyavadhana; *staff* 124 (25)
F. of Engineering
Dean: Birasak Varasundharosoth; *staff* 180 (26)
F. of Industrial Education
Dean: Khunying Wanida Dhupatemiya; *staff* 64 (19)
F. of Agricultural Technology
Dean: Warlardej Chantrasorn; *staff* 118 (30)
F. of Science (including Applied Physics, Industrial Chemistry, Biotechnology, Applied Statistics, and Applied Mathematics)
Dean: Suwan Kusamran; *staff* 67 (30)
S. of Graduate Studies
Dean: Supachai Ratanopas; *staff* 5
Computer Research and Service Ce.
Director: Pairash Thajchayapong; *staff* 29
Electronics Research Ce.
Head: Somkiat Supadech; *staff* 10 (2)
Also Research Centre at Chumphon Province.

Founded 1960 as College of Telecommunications, became one of the three campuses of King Mongjut's Institute of Technology 1971. Acquired present university status 1986. A State institution responsible to the Ministry of University Affairs. Governing body: the Council, comprising 16 members. Residential facilities for academic staff and 50 men and 50 women students.

Arrangements for co-operation with the Universities of: Tokai; Pittsburgh State; Leuven (Catholic); Budapest (Technical); Hebrew, Jerusalem.

Academic Year: June to March (June-October; November-March).

Admission Requirements: Secondary school certificate (Mathoyom 6) or equivalent, and entrance examination.

Fees (Baht): *c.* 1500 per semester.

Language of Instruction: Thai.

Degrees and Diplomas: Bachelor, 2-5 yrs. Master, a further 2 yrs. Doctorate in Engineering, 2 yrs after Master.

Library: Central Library and libraries of the faculties, total, 200,000 vols.

Publications: Ladkrabang Engineering Journal (bimonthly); Portfolio (F. of Architecture (quarterly); King Mongkut's Agricultural Journal (3 issues per annum); Journal of Faculty of Industrial Education; Journal of Faculty of Science; CRSC Bulletins KMITL (bimonthly).

Academic Staff, 1990:

Rank	Full-time
Professors	2
Associate Professors	26
Assistant Professors	109
Lecturers	268
Scientists/Academic Assistants	61
Total	466

Student Enrolment, 1990:

	Men	Women	Total
Of the country	3779	1128	4907

6889 KING MONGKUT'S INSTITUTE OF TECHNOLOGY NORTH BANGKOK

1518 Pibulsongkram Road, Bang Sue, Bangkok 10800
Telephone: (662) 5858541/8
Fax: (662) 5874350
President: Chana Kasipar

F. of Engineering
Dean: Suthi Aksornkitti; *staff* 172
F. of Industrial Education and Science
Dean: Terawuit Boonyasopon; *staff* 155
F. of Applied Science
Dean: Wimolyut Warnasawang
I. of Technical Education Development
Director: Sobsan Utakrit; *staff* 67
C. of Industrial Technology
Director: Samreung Rusmivisva; *staff* 208
Graduate S.
Dean: Suporn Panrat-Isra; *staff* 10
Also 4 Research studies (spark erosion parameters, moulds and dyes, plastic extruder set construction).

Founded 1960 as Technical Institute, became one of the three campuses of King Mongkut's Institute of Technology 1971. Acquired present university status 1986. A State institution responsible to the Ministry of UniversityAffairs.

Academic Year: June to March (June-October; November-March).

Admission Requirements: Secondary school certificate (Mathoyom 6) or equivalent, and entrance examination.

Fees (Baht): 1820-2200 per semester; graduate, 2700.

Language of Instruction: Thai.

Degrees and Diplomas: Bachelor, 2-5 yrs. Master, a further 2 yrs. Doctorate in Engineering, 2 yrs after Master.

Library: Central Library, 40,000 vols.

Publications: KMIT News Bulletin; KMIT Journal; Engineering Journal; Applied Science Journal; Thesis Journal; Graduate School Journal; Library Journal (monthly); Newsweek; Bridge (weekly).

Press or Publishing House: KMIT Press.

Academic Staff, 1990:

Rank	Full-time
Lecturers	265
Assistant Professors	72
Associate Professors	26
Total	263

Student Enrolment, 1988: 6081.

6890 ***KING MONGKUT'S INSTITUTE OF TECHNOLOGY THONBURI**

Tambon Bangmod, Ratburana, Bangkok 10140

F. of Engineering

F. of Industrial Education and Science

F. of Power Engineering and Materials

Founded 1960 as Technical Institute, became one of the three campuses of King Mongkut's Institute of Technology 1971. Acquired present university status 1986. A State institution responsible to the Ministry of UniversityAffairs.

Academic Year: June to March (June-October; November-March).

Admission Requirements: Secondary school certificate (Mathoyom 6) or equivalent, and entrance examination.

Language of Instruction: Thai.

Degrees and Diplomas: Bachelor, 2-5 yrs. Master, a further 2 yrs. Doctorate in Engineering, 2 yrs after Master.

6891 **MAEJO INSTITUTE OF AGRICULTURAL TECHNOLOGY**

Sansai-Prao Road, Sansai District, Chiang Mai 50290

Cables: insmajo

Telex: 43553 UNICHIM TH

Telephone: (53-244) 858/60

Fax: (53-244) 861

President: Anon Tiangtrong (1989-92)

Registrar: Prasarn Wongmaneeroong

F. of Agricultural Production

Dean: Nipon Chaimongkol; *staff* 67

F. of Agricultural Business

Dean: Vichai Tanvatanagul; *staff* 60

Graduate S.

Chairman: Arnon Tiangtrong; *staff* 60

Office of Agricultural Research and Extension

Director: Thongchai Tong-uthaisri; *staff* 10

Also Chumporn Training Station.

Founded 1934 as school, attached to Kasetsart University as preparatory school 1939. Became a Vocational School under the jurisdiction of the Ministry of Education 1948, and college 1958. Reorganized 1975 as degree-granting institution. Responsible to the Ministry of University Affairs. Governing body: the University Council, comprising 27 members. Residential facilities for academic staff and *c.* 1800 students.

Arrangements for co-operation with: Catholic University of Leuven; State University of Gent; Ehime University;Kyushu Tokai University; University of Alberta.

Academic Year: June to March (June-October; November-March).

Admission Requirements: Certificate in Vocational Agriculture (for two-year curriculum); Diploma in Technical Agriculture (for two-year curriculum).

Fees (Baht): 25 per credit; graduate, 200.

Language of Instruction: Thai.

Degrees and Diplomas: Bachelor of Agricultural Technology, 2-4 yrs. Master, 1 ½-2 yrs.

Library: 37,575 vols.

Publications: Journal of Agricultural Research and Extension; Journal of Agricultural Extension and Development (quarterly);Institute Bulletin (weekly).

Academic Staff, 1990:

Rank	Full-time
Associate Professors	13
Assistant Professors	55
Instructors	67
Total	135

Student Enrolment, 1990:

	Men	Women	Total
Of the country	1320	449	1769

6892 **MAHAVITAYALAI MAHIDOL**

Mahidol University

198/2 Trok Wat Saowakhon, Bang Yikan, Bangkok 10700

Cables: unimahi

Telex: 84770 UNIMAHI TH

Telephone: (662) 433-7110

Fax: (662) 433-7083

President: Natth Bhamarapravati (1979-)

F. of Medicine (Siriraj Hospital)

Dean: Pradit Chareonthaitawee; *staff* 550

F. of Public Health

Dean: Debhanom Muangman; *staff* 155

F. of Medical Technology

Dean: Pimpan Leangphibul; *staff* 61

F. of Tropical Medicine

Dean: Santasiri Sornmani; *staff* 76

F. of Science

Dean: Pairote Prempree; *staff* 220

F. of Medicine (Ramathibodi Hospital)

Dean: Athasit Vejjajiva; *staff* 417

F. of Dentistry

Dean: Nisa Chearapongse; *staff* 112

F. of Pharmacy

Dean: Pranee Jaiarj; *staff* 93

F. of Social Sciences and Humanities

Dean: Santhat Sirmsri; *staff* 70

F. of Nursing

Dean: Tassana Boontong; *staff* 176

F. of Environment and Resource Studies

Dean: Thanakorn Uan-on; *staff* 17

F. of Graduate Studies

Dean: Monthree Chulasamaya; *staff* 65

F. of Engineering

Dean (Acting): Thanakorn Uan-On

I. for Population and Social Research

Director: Apichat Chamratrithirong; *staff* 21

I. of Nutrition

Director: Sakorn Dhanamitta; *staff* 6

I. of Language and Culture for Rural Development

Director: Poonpit Amatyakul; *staff* 11

I. of Sciences and Technology for Development

Director: Serene Piboonniyom; *staff* 9

ASEAN I. for Health Development

Director: Krasae Chanawongse; *staff* 26

Computer Ce.

Director: Supachai Tongwongsan; *staff* 27

National Laboratory Animal Ce.

Director: Pradon Chatikavanij; *staff* 17

Also International Students Degree Programme.

Founded 1889 as school, amalgamated with Chulalongkorn University 1917. Became degree conferring institution 1929. Separated from Chulalongkorn University 1943 to form University of Medical Sciences. Acquired present title 1969. Responsible to the Ministry of University Affairs. Governing body: the University Council. Residential facilities for academic staff and students.

Academic Year: May to February (May-September; October-February).

Admission Requirements: Secondary school certificate (Mathayom Suksa 5) and entrance examination.

Fees (Baht): Tuition, 50-100 per credit.

Languages of Instruction: Thai and English.

Degrees and Diplomas: Bachelor of–Science, B.Sc., in various fields, including Public Health; Medical Technology; Radiological Technology; Nursing; Pysiotherapy; Engineering; Biology; Chemistry; Biotechnology; Physics, 4 yrs. Pharmacy, 5 yrs. Master of Arts, M.A.; Education, M.Ed.;

Science, M.Sc., 2 yrs after Bachelor. Doctor of Medicine, M.D.; Dental Surgery, D.D.S., 6 yrs. Doctor of Science, D.Sc., 3 yrs after Bachelor. Master in–Pubic Health, M.P.H.; Primary Health Care Management, M.P.H.M.; Science in Clinical Tropical Medicine, M.Sc.Clin.Trop.Med., 1 yr after M.D.. Doctorate, Ph.D., 2 yrs after Master. Diploma in–Tropical Medicine and Hygiene, D.T.M.&H., 6 months after M.D.; Clinical Science, 1 yr after M.D.

Library: Central Library and 15 specialized libraries, total, *c.* 300,000 vols.

Special Facilities (Museums, etc.): Congdon's Anatomical Museum; Prehistoric Museum.

Publications: Bulletins and Journals of the Faculties; Annual Research Abstracts.

Academic Staff, 1988:

Rank	Full-time
Sastracharn (Professors)	108
Rong-Sastracharn (Associate Professors)	463
Poochuay Sastracharn (Assistant Professors)	847
Acharn (Instructors)	637
Total	2055

Student Enrolment, 1988-89:

	Men	Women	Total
Of the country	4211	5323	9534
Of other countries	79	32	111
Total	4290	5355	9645

6893 **NATIONAL INSTITUTE OF DEVELOPMENT ADMINISTRATION**

Sukhapibal 2 Road, Bangkok 10240
Cables: insnida bangkok 10240
Telex: NIDA BANGKOK 10240
Telephone: (662) 377-7400/9; 377-9660/9
Fax: (662) 375-8802
Atikarnbodi (Rector): Somsakdi Xuto
Vice Rector for Academic Affairs and Registrar: Thiraphong Vikitset

S. of Public Administration
Dean: Uthai Laohavichien; *staff* 29 (3)
S. of Business Administration
Dean: Singha Chiamsiri; *staff* 22 (11)
S. of Development Economics
Dean: Prasit Tongyingsiri; *staff* 22 (2)
S. of Applied Statistics
Dean: Prachoom Suwattee; *staff* 21 (13)
Development Administration Research Ce.
Training Ce.
Director: Chartchai Na Chiangmai; *staff* 12
Language Ce.
Director: Piangchai Bundharat; *staff* 14 (2)
Research Ce.
Director: Jamlong Atikul; *staff* 9
Information Systems Education Ce.
Director: Chamaiporn Chatsiri; *staff* 5
Graduate P. in Social Development
Director: Tang-on Munjaiton; *staff* 16 (1)

Founded 1955 as Institute of Public Administration attached to Thammasat University. Became separate and acquired present title and status 1966 with support of the Ford Foundation and Midwest Consortium for International Activities (Indiana, Illinois, Wisconsin, and Michigan State Universities). A State institution for postgraduate studies responsible to the Ministry of University Affairs. Governing body: the Council.

Arrangements for co-operation with: Indiana University; University of Tennessee.

Academic Year: June to May (June-October; Novembmer-March; April-May).

Admission Requirements: B.A. or equivalent degree and entrance examination.

Fees (Baht): Master, 13,000 per annum; Doctorat, 30,000 (foreign students, 100,000).

Language of Instruction: Thai.

Degrees and Diplomas: Master of–Public Administration, M.P.A.; Business Administration, M.B.A.; Science in Development Economics; Arts in Social Development; Science in Applied Statistics, 2 yrs. Doctorate, Ph.D in–Development Administration; Population and Development.

Library: Development Document Centre, 157,450 vols.

Special Facilities (Museums, etc.): Audiovisual and Public Relation Centre.

Publication: Thai Journal of Development Administration (quarterly).

Academic Staff, 1990:

Rank	Full-time
Professors	11
Associate Professors	51
Assistant Professors	46
Instructors	54
Total	162

Student Enrolment, 1990: 2214 (Including 876 Women).

6894 **MAHAWITTAYALAI SONGKLANAGARIND**

Prince of Songkhla University
P.O. Box 102, Hat Yai, 90110 Songkhla
Telex: 62168 UNISONG TH (HAT YAI); 61311 UNISONG TH (PATTANI)
Telephone: (74-23) 5800 (Hat Yai); (73) 34-9111 (Pattani)
Fax: (74-23) 1376 (Hat Yai); (73) 348519 (Pattani)
President: Phasook Kullavanij (1985-)
Vice-President: Siripongse Sribhibhadh

F. of Science (including Foreign Languages, Pharmacology, and Physiology)
Dean: Methi Sunbhanich; *staff* 213
F. of Engineering
Dean: Weerapant Musigasarn; *staff* 94
F. of Education
Dean: Swai Liamkaew; *staff* 106
F. of Humanities and Social Sciences
Dean: Manoh Yaden; *staff* 94
F. of Management Sciences
Dean: Thawee Dhanatrakul; *staff* 55
F. of Natural Resources
Dean: Prasert Chitapong; *staff* 94
F. of Pharmacy
Dean: Samardh Angsusingh; *staff* 35
F. of Nursing
Dean: Duangvadee Sunkhobol; *staff* 104
F. of Dentistry
Dean: Pramuk Chitchumnong; *staff* 45
F. of Science and Technology
Dean: Padoonyot Duangmala; *staff* 58
F. of Medicine
Dean: Tada Yipintsoi; *staff* 131
Graduate S.
Dean: Kan Chantrapromma
Extension D.
Director: Charmnarn Pratoomsindh; *staff* 27
Computer Ce.

Also Hospital, University's Demonstration School and College of Islami Studies, Centre of Educational Technology, Mae Khri Agricultural Centre Tepa Agricultural Centre, Klong Hoi-Kong Agricultural Centre.

Founded 1968. A State institution responsible to the Ministry of University Affairs. Governing body: the University Council, comprising 1(members. Residential facilities for academic staff and students. Residential facilities for academic staff and 3790 students.

Arrangements for co-operation with: University of Western Australia University of Missouri; California State Universityy of Long Beach; Uppsala University; University of Malaya; University of Sains Malaysia; University of Rhode Island.

Academic Year: June to May (June-October; October-March; March May).

Admission Requirements: Secondary school certificate (Mathayom Suksa 6) or equivalent, and entrance examination.

Fees (Baht): 1610 per semester.

Language of Instruction: Thai.

Degrees and Diplomas: Bachelor of–Science; Arts; Science in Education Arts in Education; Nursing; Public Administration; Business, 4 yrs; Pharmacy, 5 yrs. Master of–Arts; Science; Engineering; Business Administration; Public Administration, a further 1-2 yrs. Doctor of–Medicine; Dental Surgery, 6 yrs. Also Certificates, 1-2 yrs.

Library: Total, 233,414 vols.

Special Facilities (Museums, etc.): Southern Studies Museum (Pattani Campus); University Radio Station; Jana Nutrition and Rural Development Centre; Tepa Educational Park.

Publications: Songklanakarin Journal of Science and Technology (quarterly); Journal of Management Sciences (biannually); Song-klanagarind Medical Journal (quarterly); Rusamilae Journal (quarterly); Engineering Journal (biannually).

Academic Staff, 1988-89:

Rank	Full-time
Sastracharn (Professors)	3
Rong-Sastracharn (Associate Professors)	57
Poochuay Sastracharn (Assistant Professors)	257
Acharn (Lecturers)	784
Total	1101

Student Enrolment, 1988-89:

	Men	Women	Total
Of the country	3094	3698	6792

6895 **RAMKHAMHAENG UNIVERSITY (OPEN UNIVERSITY)**

Ramkhamhaeng Road, Huamark, Bangkapi, Bangkok 10240

Telephone: 3180917

Atikarnbodi (Rector): Thamnoon Soparatana

F. of Law
F. of Business Administration
F. of Humanities (including Library Science)
F. of Education
F. of Science
F. of Political Science
F. of Economics

Study Centres in: Chiangmai, Phitsanuloke, Nakhon Sawan, Khon Kaen, Ubon Rachathani, Nakhon Rachasima, Udon Thani, Nakhon Sithammarat, and Songkha.

Founded 1971 as an open admissions university. Distance teaching by radio and television introduced 1977 and Study Centres set up in the provinces. A State institution responsible to the Ministry of University Affairs. Governing body: the Council.

Arrangements for co-operation with: University of Pittsburgh; City University of New York; Southern Illinois University; University of Surrey.

Academic Year: June to March (June-October; November-March).

Admission Requirements: Secondary school certificate (Mathayom 6). Class II civil servants with Mathayom Suksa 3.

Language of Instruction: Thai.

Degrees and Diplomas: Bachelor of–Science; Arts in–Law; Business Administration; Humanities; Education; Political Science; Economics. Master of Arts in–Economics; Education; Humanities. Also Diplomas of specialization.

Library: Central Library, *c.* 126,750 vols.

Publications: Bulletin; Periodical.

Academic Staff: c. 740 (50).

Student Enrolment: c. 410,000.

6896 **SILPAKORN UNIVERSITY**

Tha Phra Palace Campus, Na Phralan Road, Bangkok 10200

Telex: UNISILP

Telephone: (662) 2215869

Fax: (662) 2257258

President: Khaisri Dri-Aroon

F. of Painting, Sculpture and Graphic Arts
Dean: Surasak Chareonwong; *staff* 25 (10)
F. of Architecture
Dean: Trungjai Buranasomphob; *staff* 38 (11)
F. of Decorative Arts
Dean: Niran Krairiksh; *staff* 44 (35)
F. of Archaeology
Dean: Poot Veraprasert; *staff* 53 (18)
F. of Arts
Dean: Pensiri Charoenpote; *staff* 105 (24)
F. of Education
Dean: Surapol Payomyam; *staff* 94 (15)
F. of Science
Dean: Somkiat Thadnaniti; *staff* 98 (40)
F. of Pharmamcy
Dean: Sinchai Kokitichai; *staff* 27 (75)
Graduate S.
Dean: Somjate Waiyakarn
Art I.
Head: Nonthivath Chandhanapalin
Research and Development I.
Head: Naruemitr Sodsuk
I. of Western Thai Culture
Head: Vipha Khongkanan
Computer Ce.
Head: Rujira Pipitpochanakarn

Founded 1934 as School of Fine Arts, acquired present status and title 1943. A State institution responsible to the Ministry of University Affairs. Governing body: the University Council. Residential facilities for academic staff and students.

Arrangements for co-operation with the Universities of: Missouri-Columbia; Monash; Tasmania; Sydney; Paris III; Clakamus Community College.

Academic Year: June to March (June-October; November-March).

Admission Requirements: Secondary school certificate (Mathayom 6) or equivalent, and entrance examination.

Fees (Baht): 5000-6000 per annum; Graduate Studies, 8000-16,000.

Language of Instruction: Thai.

Degrees and Diplomas: Bachelor of–Decorative Arts; Arts, B.A.; Education, B.Ed.; Science, B.Sc., 4 yrs; Science in Pharmacy; Architecture, B.Arch.; Fine Arts, B.F.A., 5 yrs. Also diplomas, 3 yrs. Master, a further 2 yrs.

Library: 240,000 vols.

Special Facilities (Museums, etc.): University Art Gallery.

Publications: Journal (biannually); Bulletin (annually); Documents of the Institutional Research Centre.

Academic Staff, 1988-89:

Rank	Full-time	Part-time
Sastracharn (Professors)	5	–
Rong-Sastracharn (Associate Professors)	52	–
Poochuary Sastracharn (Assistant Professors)	184	–
Archarn (Lecturers)	226	–
Others	–	217
Total	467	217

Student Enrolment, 1988-89:

	Men	Women	Total
Of the country	1331	2037	3368

6897 **MAHAVITAYALAI SRI NAKHARINWIROT**

Sri Nakharinwirot University

Sukumvit Soi 23, Bangkok 10110

Telephone: 2580310

F. of Education
F. of Science
F. of Social Sciences
F. of Humanities
F. of Physical Education and Hygiene
F. of Nursing
F. of Graduate Studies
Research I. of Behavioural Sciences
I. of Southern Thai Studies
Bureau of Education of Psychology

Campuses at: Pathumwan, Bangkaen, Palasuksa, Bangsaen, Pitsanuloke, Songkla, Mahasarakam.

Founded 1954 as college, acquired university status 1974. Responsible to the Ministry of University Affairs. Governing body: the Council.

Academic Year: June to March (June-October; November-March).

Admission Requirements: Secondary school certificate.

Language of Instruction: Thai.

Degrees and Diplomas: Bachelor of–Education, B.Ed.; Arts, B.A.; Science, B.Sc., 4 yrs. Master of Education, M.Ed., a further 2 yrs.Doctor of Education, Ed.D., a further 3 yrs. Also Certificate of Specialization, 1 yr.

Library: Central Library, *c.* 100,000 vols.

Special Facilities (Museums, etc.): Sea Animals Museum.

Academic Staff: c. 2760.
Student Enrolment: c. 22,000.

6898 ***SUKHOTHAI THAMMATHIRAT OPEN UNIVERSITY**
Chaengwattana Road, Bangpood, Pakkred, Nonthaburi 11120
Cables: Unisuko Th
Telex: 72353 UNISUKO TH
Telephone: (573) 5730030/3
Fax: (662) 5735890
President: Iam Chaya-Ngam
Vice-President for Academic Affairs: Tong-In Wangsotorn

S. of Educational Studies (including Early Childhood Education, Elementary Education, Thai, Social Studies, Mathematics, Educational Administration, Guidance, and Non-Formal Education)
Chairman: Preecha Kampirapakorn; *staff* 46
S. of Liberal Arts (including Thai Studies, and Information Science)
Chairman: Chutima Sacchanond; *staff* 24
S. of Management Science
Chairman: Thanachai Yomchinda; *staff* 37
S. of Law
Chairman: Wisan Pantuna; *staff* 33
S. of Economics
Chairman: Winai Ussivakul; *staff* 14
S. of Health Science
Chairman: Kanya Kanchanaburanonta; *staff* 21
S. of Home Economics
Chairman: Tasanee Limsuwan; *staff* 19
S. of Agriculture Extension and Co-operatives
Chairman: Ladda Bhisalbutra; *staff* 20
S. of Political Science
Chairman: Jumpol Nimpanich; *staff* 11
S. of Communication Arts
Chairman: Chao-rat Cherdchai; *staff* 18
Also local and regional study centers located throughout the Kingdom.

Founded 1978 by Royal Decree as an open admissions State institution under the supervision of the Ministry of University Affairs. First students admitted December 1980. Distance education system using multi-media teaching/learning packages-printed materials, video and audio-cassettes, radio, television, and tutorial sessions at the local and regional study centres, creating a home-based study programme. Governing bodies: the University Council; the Academic Senate.

Arrangements for academic staff exchange with the University of Minnesota.

Academic Year: July to April (July to October; December-April).

Admission Requirements: Secondary school certificate (Mathayom Suksa 5) or equivalent.

Fees (Baht): Registration, 150; tuition, 200 per course; educational materials, 200 per course.

Language of Instruction: Thai.

Degrees and Diplomas: Bachelor of Arts, 2-4 yrs. Certificate of Achievement, 1-2 yrs.

Library: Office of Documentation and Information, 50,000 vols.

Special Facilities (Museums, etc.): Educational Broadcasting Production Centre; Lecture Theatre; Training Centre.

Publication: Never Too Far (distance education newsletter distributed worldwide)(biannually).

Press or Publishing House: Sukhothai Thammathirat Open University Press (STOU Press).

Academic Staff, 1989-90:

Rank	Full-time
Professors	3
Associate Professors	69
Assistant Professors	70
Instructors	153
Total	295

Student Enrolment, 1988-89:

	Men	Women	Total
Of the country	67,752	67,187	134,939

6899 ***MAHAVITAYALAI THAMMASAT**
Thammasat University
Prachan Road, Bangkok 10200
Telex: 72132 TAMSAT TH
Telephone: (662) 221-6171/80
Fax: (662) 221-8099
Atikarnbodi (President): Krirkkiat Phipatseritham (1988-91)
Rong-Atikarnbodi (Vice-President for Administrative Affairs): Tiphya Binsri

F. of Law
Dean: Prathan Watanavanich; *staff* 52 (119)
F. of Commerce and Accountancy
Dean: Yupha Kanchanadul; *staff* 91 (30)
F. of Economics
Dean: Supote Chun-Anantathum; *staff* 80 (2)
F. of Social Administration
Dean: Nipa S. Tumornsoontorn; *staff* 40 (80)
F. of Liberal Arts (including Psychology, Library Science, History, Philosophy, Linguistics, English, English Language and Literature, French, Thai, Japanese, Drama, Geography, Chinese, German, and Russian)
Dean: Wongchan Pinainitisatra; *staff* 164 (270)
F. of Journalism and Mass Communication
Dean: Boonrak Boonyaketamala; *staff* 39 (58)
F. of Sociology and Anthropology
Dean: Sumitr Pitiphat; *staff* 28 (40)
F. of Science and Technology (including Environmental Science, Health Science, Rural Technology, Agricultural Technology, Computer Science, Mathematics, and Statistics)
Dean (Acting): Prajot Thammakorn; *staff* 71 (4)
F. of Political Science
Dean: Surachai Sirikrai; *staff* 44 (4)
F. of Engineering (including Electrical and Industrial)
Dean: Naksitte Coovattanachai
Graduate S.
Dean: Piboon Limprapat
Graduate Volunteers' Ce.
Director: Chantaluck Na Pombejra; *staff* 30
I. for Continuing Education and Social Service
Director: Varakorn Samakoses; *staff* 8
Thai Khadi Research I.
Director: Xat Kichtham; *staff* 32
Human Resources I.
Director: Chira Hongladarom; *staff* 18
I. of East Asian Studies
Director: Chulacheeb Chinwanno; *staff* 31
Language I.
Director: Seri Wongmonta; *staff* 19
Ce. of Information Processing and Education and Development
Director: Thanet Norabhoompipat; *staff* 67
Also Hospital, and Special Study Programme on 'Buddhism and Thai society', Economics Master Degree Programme, Marketing Master Degree Programme (all in English).

Founded 1934 as the University of Moral and Political Sciences, offering courses leading to Bachelor of Law. Considerably expanded 1949 and renamed 1952. Responsible to the Ministry of University Affairs. Governing body: the University Council, comprising 10 members and 13 ex-officio members. Residential facilities for academic staff and students.

Arrangements for co-operation with the Universities of: Aix-Marseilles; Northern Illinois; York; Chuo; Hitotsubashi; Hosei; Kanagawa; Keio; Soka; Ryukyus; Waseda; Hiroshima; Tokyo.

Academic Year: June to March (June-October; November-March).

Admission Requirements: Secondary school certificate (Mathayom Suksa 5) or equivalent, and entrance examination.

Fees (Baht): Total, 15,000 per annum.

Language of Instruction: Thai.

Degrees and Diplomas: Bachelor of Arts, B.A., in–Mathematics; Philosophy; Drama; Statistics; Psychology; Library Science; History; Linguistics; Literature; Foreign Languages; Economics; Journalism and Mass Communication; Political Science, 4 yrs. Bachelor of–Laws, LL.B.; Business Administration; Social Work; Environmental Science; Health Science; Computer Sciences, 4 yrs. Master, a further 2 yrs. Also a postgraduate diploma in Volunteering.

Libraries: Central Library, 14,035 vols; faculty libraries, c. 146,630.

Publications: Weekly Newsletter; Yoon Thong (annually); Faculty Journals; Newsletter; Thai Japanese Studies (quarterly).

Press or Publishing House: University Press.

Academic Staff, 1989-90:

Rank	Full-time
Sastracharn (Professors)	12
Rong-Sastracharn (Associate Professors)	149
Poochuay Sastracharn(Assistant Professors)	220
Acharn (Lecturers)	244
Total	625

Student Enrolment, 1989-90:

	Men	Women	Total
Of the country	5421	7813	13,267
Of other countries	6	7	13
Total	5430	7850	13,280

Private Institutions

6900 **BANGKOK UNIVERSITY**
40/4 Rama 4 Road, Phra Khanong, Bangkok 10110
Telephone: 24901-41
President: Charoen Kanthawongs (1962-)
Vice-President for Academic Affairs: Thanu Kulachol

S. of Accountancy
Dean: Mathana Santiwat; *staff* 61 (28)
S. of Business Administration (including Secretarial Science)
Dean: Sakol Bhusiri; *staff* 91 (54)
S. of Communication Arts
Dean: Laksana Satswedin; *staff* 50 (17)
S. of Economics
Dean: Quanchai Aungtrakul; *staff* 10 (18)
S. of Humanities
Dean: Apiwat Watanangura; *staff* 134 (44)
S. of Law
Dean: Ampharat Visessmit; *staff* 6 (19)
S. of Computer Sciences
Dean: Somchit Wongtiraumnoy; *staff* 5 (10)
Graduate S. of Business Administration
Dean: Suphong Limtanakool; *staff* 14 (12)
Evening S.
Head: Smarn Songprasit; *staff* 158 (101)

Founded 1962 as Polytechnic Institute, became Bangkok College 1962 and acquired present university status and title 1984. A private institution under the supervision of the Ministry of University Affairs. Governing body: the Board of Trustees.

Arrangements for co-operation with the Universities of: Farleigh Dickinson; Hawaii; Ohio; Southern Illinois.

Academic Year: June to March (June-October; November-March).

Admission Requirements: Secondary school certificate (Mathayom 6) or equivalent, and entrance examination.

Languages of Instruction: Thai and English.

Degrees and Diplomas: Bachelor of–Business Administration; Arts in Communication; Science in Accountancy; Economics; Arts; Law; Science in Computer Sciences, 4 yrs. Master in Business Administration, a further 2 yrs.

Library: c. 60,000 vols.

Publications: B.U. News (monthly); Newsletter (monthly, in English); Executive Journal (quarterly).

Academic Staff, 1986-87: 727 (200).

Student Enrolment, 1986-87:

	Men	Women	Total
Of the country	4401	6294	10,695
Of other countries	4	–	4
Total	4405	6294	10,699

6901 **DHURAKIJPUNDIT UNIVERSITY**
University of Business Sciences
110 Prachachuen Road, Bangkhen, Bangkok 10210
Telephone: 5800050
Fax: 5899606
President: Sawai Sudhipitak (1968-)
Vice President for Administrative Affairs: Lertlak S. Burusphat

F. of Administration
Dean: Pannarai Sanvichein; *staff* 34 (60)
F. of Accountancy
Dean: Vanvipa Thapvongse; *staff* 16 (12)
F. of Economics
Dean: Pote Panyatig; *staff* 15 (14)
F. of Law
Dean: Somchai Sapvanich; *staff* 15 (42)
F. of Humanities
Dean: Lertpovn Panasakul; *staff* 68 (35)
F. of Communication Arts
Dean: Lertlak S. Burusphat; *staff* 8 (30)
Office of Research and Planning
Head: Muangtong Khamanee; *staff* 9 (10)

Founded 1968, recognized by the Ministry of University Affairs as a private university, equal in standard and academic quality to State Universities, 1984. The University has 3 campuses. Governing body: the University Council, comprising 13 members.

Academic Year: June to June (June-October; November-March; April-June).

Admission Requirements: Secondary school certificate or equivalent, and entrance examination.

Fees (Baht): 320 per credit; graduate, 1500.

Languages of Instruction: Thai and some English.

Degrees and Diplomas: Bachelor, 4 yrs. Master, a further 2 yrs.

Library: Library and Information Centre, 82,023 vols.

Special Facilities (Museums, etc.): Cultural Centre for Art and Culture Promotion.

Publication: Sudhi Paritat Journal (every 4 months).

Press or Publishing House: Educational Media Service Department.

Academic Staff, 1989:

Rank	Full-time	Part-time
Professors	4	14
Associate Professors	3	9
Assistant Professors	15	11
Lecturers	14	159
Total	36	193

Student Enrolment, 1989:

	Men	Women	Total
Of the country	2694	5068	7762*

*Also 1619 everning students.

6902 **PAYAP UNIVERSITY**
48/5 Huay Kaew Road, LPO 101, Chiang Mai 50000
Cables: papayuniv
Telephone: (53) 24-12-55
Fax: (53) 24-19-83
President: Amnuay Tapingkae (1977-)

F. of Humanities
Dean: Cheewin Insaeng *staff* 47 (29)
F. of Science
Dean: Duangduen Poocharoen; *staff* 22 (5)
F. of Social Sciences
Dean: Narong Prachadetsuwat; *staff* 14 (9)
F. of Nursing (including Midwifery)
Dean: Jarunee Tammacoon; *staff* 21 (59)
F. of Theology
Dean: William Yoder; *staff* 16 (2)
F. of Business Administration
Dean: Wanna Supakul; *staff* 29 (9)
F. of Accountancy and Finance
Dean: Manit Pabut; *staff* 14 (3)
Christian Communication I.
Director: Alan Eubank
Research Development Ce.
Director: Prasert Bhandhachat

Founded 1974 as college by the Church of Christ in Thailand. Acquired present title 1984. A private institution under the supervision of the Ministry of University Affairs. Governing body: the Board of Trustees, comprising 14 members. Residential facilities for theological academic staff and for theological students and student nurses.

Arrangements for co-operation with the Universities of: Northern Illinois; Puget Sound; International Christian, Tokyo. Whitworth College, Spokane.

Academic Year: May to March (May-October; November-March).

Admission Requirements: Secondary school certificate (Mathayom Suksa 6) or equivalent, and entrance examination.

Fees (Baht): 5000-6000 per semester.
Languages of Instruction: Thai and English.
Degrees and Diplomas: Bachelor of–Arts; Science; Theology; Business Administration, 4 yrs; Science in Nursing, 5 yrs. Also Diploma in–Nursing and Public Health; Theology, 3 yrs and Certificate in Midwifery, 6 months. Master of Divinity, a further 2-3 yrs.
Library: Central Library, *c.* 53,803 vols.
Academic Staff, 1986-87: 239 (116).
Student Enrolment, 1986-87: 3141.

6903 **MAHAWITTHAYALAI SIAM**
Siam University
235 Phetkasem Road, Phasicharoen, Bangkok 10160
Telephone: (662) 467-0456
Fax: (662) 457-3982
President: Pornchai Mongkhonvanit (1984-)
Vice-President for Academic Affairs: Vichian Saensophone

F. of Liberal Arts (Hotel Management and Tourism, English Business Communication)
Dean: Sarat Bunyaratpan; *staff* 35 (11)
F. of Business Administration
Dean (Acting): Pornchai Mongkhonvanit; *staff* 62 (29)
Graduate S.
Dean (Acting): Adisai Korvattana; *staff* 9 (8)
Research Ce.
Director: Kamol Janlekha; *staff* 5
Extension Ce.
Language Ce.

Founded 1965 as Siam Technical College. Acquired present status and title 1986. Governing body: the Board of Trustees.
Arrangements for co-operation with the University of Bridgeport; Northrop University; California State University, Long Beach; Mercy College.
Academic Year: June to February (June-October; October-February).
Admission Requirements: Secondary school certificate (Mathayom 6, Mathayom Suksa 5) or equivalent.
Fees (Baht): 6500-21,000 per semester.
Languages of Instruction: Thai and English.
Degrees and Diplomas: Bachelor of–Business Administration; Laws; Accountancy; Engineering;, Communication Arts, 4 yrs. Master of–Arts (Communication Arts); Engineering (Engineering Management), a further 2 yrs.
Library: Central Library, *c.* 60,000 vols.
Special Facilities (Museums, etc.): University Culture Centre; Multi-Media Resources Centre.
Publication: Siam University Newsletter.
Academic Staff, 1986-87:

Rank	Full-time	Part-time
Professors	2	8
Associate Professors	1	10
Assistant Professors	1	20
Instructors	170	36
Total	174	74

Student Enrolment, 1988-89: 7911.

6904 **VITAYALAI SRIPATUM**
Sripatum University
161 Phahonyotin Road, Bangkhen, Bangkok 10900
Telephone: 5791746
President: Prasit Sundarotok (1980-)
Registrar: Napha Triwong

F. of Business Administration (including Accountancy)
Dean: Rutchaneeporn Pookayaporn; *staff* 28 (37)
F. of Law
Dean: Padung Padamasankni; *staff* 3O (38)
Polytechnic F.
Dean: Prasert Pholdi; *staff* 58 (22)

Founded 197O as Thaisuriya College. A private institution under the supervision of the Ministry of University Affairs.
Academic Year: June to March (June-October; November-March).
Admission Requirements: Secondary school certificate, grades 12 or 13 and entrance examination.
Fees (Baht): 3500-4500 per semester.
Language of Instruction: Thai.
Degrees and Diplomas: Bachelor of–Law; Management; Banking, 4 yrs. Also Diplomas, 2 yrs.
Libraries: Central Library, 30,000 vols; Law, 2500.
Academic Staff, 1986-87: – (3)
Student Enrolment: c. 160 (Men).

6905 **UNIVERSITY OF THE THAI CHAMBER OF COMMERCE**
126/1 Vipavadee Rangsit Road, Samsen Nai, Phayathai, Bangkok 10400
Telephone: 276-1040
Fax: 276-2126
President: Patchai Bunnag (1974-)
Registrar: Vanvimol Sontornsawat

F. of Accountancy
Dean: Pornpun Ekpaopun; *staff* 35 (47)
F. of Business Administration
Dean: Anek Solgosoom; *staff* 59 (54)
F. of Economics
Dean: Somporn Jennapar; *staff* 49 (28)
F. of Human Sciences (English for Business Administration, English Literature, Thai Language for Communication, Japanese)
Dean: Sunee Dhanasarnsombat; *staff* 93 (35)
F. of Science (including Applied Statistics, and Computer Science)
Dean: Anek Pungpholpool; *staff* 59 (43)
F. of Communication Arts
; *staff* 10 (25)
F. of Engineering
; *staff* 6 (15)
S. of Graduate Studies
; *staff* 4 (89)
Research Ce
Dean: Chatchai Bunnag; *staff* 3 (1)

Founded 1970. A non-profit, private institution.
the Board of Trustees; the Administration Board.
Academic Year: June to May (June-September; November-January; March-May).
Admission Requirements: Secondary school certificate (Mathayom 6, Mathayom sukan 5) or equivalent.
Fees (Baht): 280 per credit.
Degrees and Diplomas: Bachelor, 4 yrs. Master, a further 2 yrs.
Library: Central Library, 75,000 vols.
Publication: Journal (quarterly).

6906 ***ASIAN INSTITUTE OF TECHNOLOGY**
P.O. Box 2754, Bangkok 10501
Cables: ait Bangkok
Telex: 84276 TH
Telephone: 5290100/13
President: Alastair M. North (1983-93)
Academic Secretary: Emilie A. Ketudat

D. of Agricultural and Food Technology
Chairman: Sarath Ilangantileke *staff* 15 (3)
D. of Computer Technology
Chairman: H.N. Phien; *staff* 6 (5)
D. of Energy Technology
Chairman: J.C Mora; *staff* 8 (3)
D. of Human Settlements Development
Chairman: K.S. Yap; *staff* 12 (2)
D. of Environmental Engineering
Chairman: S. Vigneswaran; *staff* 8 (3)
D. of Geotechnical and Transport Engineeering
Chairman: Y. Honjo; *staff* 11
D. of Industrial Engineering and Management
Chairman: P. Vrat; *staff* 9 (1)
D. of Structural Engineering and Construction
Chairman: Worsak K. N.;E9 (1)
D. of Water Resources Engineering
Chairman: A. Das Gupta; *staff* 5 (4)
Language Ce.
Director: David R. Hall; *staff* 7
Regional Computer Ce.
Director: Charson C.
Asian Disaster Preparedness Ce.
Director: A.O. Ward
Continuing Education Ce.
Director: Nicanor C. Austriaco

Regional Research and Development Ce.
Director: Prida T.
S. of Management
Director: G. Hirsch; *staff* 8
Telecommunications Project
Director: A.B. Sharma; *staff* 1
Agricultural Land and Water Development P.
Co-ordinator: G.N. Paudyal; *staff* 6 (2)
Interdisciplinary Natural Resources Development Management P.
Co-ordinator: J. Lukens; *staff* 7 (2)

Founded by SEATO 1959, became independent 1967. A private autonomous postgraduate institution governed by an international Board of Trustees comprising not less than 9 nor more than 60 members. The Institute admits students from Asian countries and the members of its academic staff come from more than 20 countries in Asia, Australasia, Europe, and North America. Governing bodies: the Board Trustees; compring 50 members, including academic, diplomatic, government, NGO, private sector, and international representation. Residential facilities for academic staff and students.

Academic Year: September to August (September-December; January-April; May-August).

Admission Requirements: Degree of Bachelor or equivalent.

Fees (US$): 3100 per annum.

Language of Instruction: English.

Degrees and Diplomas: Diploma, 2-3 sem. Master of–Engineering, M.Eng.; Science, M.Sc., 5 sem. Doctor of–Engineering, D.Eng.; Technical Science, 9 sem after Master.

Library: 190,000 vols.

Publications: Research Summary (annually); Review (quarterly); Annual Report.

Academic Staff, 1990:

Rank	Full-time	Part-time
Professors	24	–
Associate Professors	52	–
Assistant Professors	23	–
Instructors	1	–
Visiting/Associated Faculty	15	26
Total	115	26

Student Enrolment, 1990: 789.

Other Institutions

Technical Education

6907 **RAJAMANGALA INSTITUTE OF TECHNOLOGY**
339 Samsen Road, Thewes, Bangkok 10300
Telephone: (662) 2800436
Fax: (662) 2800435
President (Atikarnbodi): Tamnoon Ridtimani (1989-)
Registrar: Surapong Em-udom

F. of Agriculture (including Animal Husbandry, Fishing, and Food Science and Technology) (Bangphra)
Dean: Winit Chotsawang; *staff* 67
F. of Agriculture (Nakhon Si Thannarat)
Dean: Treephol Johjit; *staff* 15
F. of Engineering Technology
Dean: Chanchai Siriwat; *staff* 59
F. of Business Administration
Dean: Thongchai Lawan; *staff* 50
F. of Home Economics
Dean: Wimol Patanapichai; *staff* 36
F. of Fine Arts
Dean: Saowanit Sangwichien; *staff* 33
F. of Drama and Music
Dean: Pranee Samranwongse
F. of Liberal Arts
Dean: Prapasri Amornsin; *staff* 39
F. of Education
Dean: Muchelin Kittipong; *staff* 25
Agricultural Research and Training Ce. (Lampang)
Director: Sa-Ard Phothipan; *staff* 22
Agricultural Research Ce. (Sakon Nakhon)
Director: Pian Charnsuebsri
Garment Industry Research and Training Ce.

Founded 1975, incorporating previously existing technical institutes and colleges, The Institute has the legalstatus of a Department of the Ministry of Education. The Institute has 29 campuses. Governing body: the Council. Residential facilities for academic staff and students.

Arrangements for co-operation with institutions in: USA; Europe; Australia; Asia.

Academic Year: June to March (June-October; November-March).

Admission Requirements: Secondary school certificate (Mathayom Suksa 3 or 6), ninth or twelfth grade, and entrance examination.

Fees (Baht): Registration, 250; tuition, 50 per credit.

Language of Instruction: Thai.

Degrees and Diplomas: Bachelor, 2 yrs. Diploma, 2 yrs. Certificate, 3 yrs.

Library: Faculty and Campus libraries.

Special Facilities (Museums, etc.): Broadcasting Station.

Publication: Journal (quarterly).

Press or Publishing House: Bangkok Technical Press.

Academic Staff, 1990:

Rank	Full-time
Sastrajarn (Professors)	2
Rong-Sastrajarn (Associate Professors)	15
Phu-chuay Sastrajarn (Assistant Professors)	77
Lecturers	3555
Total	3649

Student Enrolment, 1990:

	Men	Women	Total
Of the country	32,397	23,952	56,349

Teacher Training

6908 **AYUTTHAYA TEACHERS' COLLEGE**
Ayuttaya 13000

Teacher Training
Founded 1936.

6909 **BANSOMDET CHAO PHEAYA TEACHERS' COLLEGE**
Thonburi Bangkok 10600

Teacher Training
Founded 1923.

6910 **BURIRAM TEACHERS' COLLEGE**
Buriram 31000

Teacher Training
Founded 1930.

6911 **CHACHOENGSAO TEACHERS' COLLEGE**
Chachoengsao 24000

Teacher Training
Founded 1940.

6912 **CHANDARAKASEM TEACHERS' COLLEGE**
Bangkhen, Bangkok 10900

Teacher Training
Founded 1941.

6913 **CHIANGMAI TEACHERS' COLLEGE**
Chiangmai 50000

Teacher Training
Founded 1924.

6914 **CHIANGRAI TEACHERS' COLLEGE**
Phahonyotin Road, Ban Du, Umphur Muang, Chiangrai 57000
Telephone: 311713

F. of Humanities and Social Sciences
F. of Education
F. of Sciences (including Physical Education, Home Economics, and Agriculture)

In-Service Training P.

Founded 1973. A State institution under the supervision of the Ministry of Education. Residential facilities for academic staff and students.

Academic Year: June to March (June-October; November-March).

Admission Requirements: Secondary school certificate (Mathayom 6) and entrance examination.

Language of Instruction: Thai.

Degrees and Diplomas: Bachelor of Education, 2-4 yrs. Also Higher Certificate of Education, 2 yrs.

Library: c. 22,940 vols.

Academic Staff: c. 150.

Student Enrolment: c. 1780.

6915 **KAMPHAENGPET TEACHERS' COLLEGE**

Kamphaengpet 62000

Teacher Training

Founded 1973.

6916 **KANCHANABURI TEACHERS' COLLEGE**

Kanchanaburi 71000

Telephone: (34) 511683

Fax: (34) 511683

President: Paisarn Kraisit

Vice-President: Karn Kunason

F. of Education

Dean: Padung Ampornmuni; *staff* 30

F. of Humanities and Social Sciences

Dean: Cherdchai Duangpamorn; *staff* 35

F. of Science and Technology

Dean: Samran Kwankue; *staff* 36

F. of Management Sciences

Dean: Prateep Klaisuban; *staff* 36

Ce. for Research and Educational Service

Director: Supatra Tantiwanich; *staff* 11

Ce. for Arts and Culture

Director: Worawut Suwannnarit; *staff* 12

Language Ce.

Director: Somjate Kanjana; *staff* 5

Founded 1973. Governing body: the Board of Trustees, compring the President, 4 Vice-Presidents, deans of the faculties, 6 directors, 10 faculty representatives, and 10 external distinguished scholars. Residential facilities for academic staff and students.

Academic Year: February to October (June-September; October-February).

Admission Requirements: Secondary school certificate (Mathoyom suksa 6) and extrance examination.

Fees (Baht): 20 per credit, per semester.

Language of Instruction: Thai.

Degrees and Diplomas: Bachelor of–Education; Liberal Arts; Sciences, 4 yrs. Associate Degree, 2 yrs.

Library: Central Library, 43,646 vols.

Special Facilities (Museums, etc.): Arts and Cultural Centre.

Publications: Kwae Yai (annually); Newsletter (Weekly).

Academic Staff, 1990: 230.

Student Enrolment, 1990:

	Men	Women	Total
Of the country	265	666	931*

*Also 1143 external students.

6917 **LAMPANG TEACHERS' COLLEGE**

Lampang 52000

Teacher Training

Founded 1972.

6918 **LOEI TEACHERS' COLLEGE**

Loei 42000

Teacher Training

Founded 1973.

6919 **MAHASARAKHAM TEACHERS' COLLEGE**

Mahasarakham 44000

Telephone: (43) 711452

F. of Education

F. of Humanities and Social Sciences

F. of Sciences (including Home Economics, Industrial Arts, and Agriculture)

F. of Management Sciences

Extension D.

Founded 1930 as agricultural teacher training school, became college 1962. Reorganized 1984 to include furtherfields of study. A State institution under the supervision of the Ministry of Education. Residential facilities for academic staff and students.

Academic Year: June to March (June-October; November-March).

Admission Requirements: Secondary school certificate (Mathayom 6).

Language of Instruction: Thai.

Degrees and Diplomas: Bachelor, 4 yrs.

Library: Central Library, 50,000 vols.

Academic Staff: c. 200.

Student Enrolment: c. 2690 (Also c. 2310 external students).

6920 **MUBAN CHOMBUNG TEACHERS' COLLEGE**

Ratchaburli 70150

Teacher Training

Founded 1954.

6921 **TAWARAWADI UNITED COLLEGES (NAKHON PATHOM TEACHERS' COLLEGE)**

Nakornpatham 73000

Telephone: 241019

President: Worachai Yaowapanee (1986-)

F. of Education

Dean: Bandon Supithi; *staff* 65

F. of Humanities and Social Sciences

Dean: Sa-ard Leardhiran; *staff* 79

F. of Sciences and Technology (including Home Economics, Health Sciences, Industrial Arts, and Agriculture)

Dean: Supoch Impermpol; *staff* 60

F. of Management Sciences

Dean: Rawang Nedphokaew; *staff* 20

Founded 1936. Reorganized 1984 to include further fields of study. A State institution under the supervision of the Ministry of Education. Residential facilities for academic staff and 600 students.

Academic Year: June to March (June-October; November-March).

Admission Requirements: Secondary school certificate (Mathayom 6) and entrance examination.

Fees (Baht): 65 per unit.

Language of Instruction: Thai.

Degrees and Diplomas: Bachelor of–Education; Arts; Science, 4 yrs.

Library: Central Library, 69,170 vols.

Academic Staff, 1986-87:

Rank	Full-time
Rong-Sastracharn (Associate Professor)	1
Poochuay Sastracharn (Assistant Professors)	24
Acharn (Instructors)	200
Total	225

Student Enrolment, 1986-87:

	Men	Women	Total
Of the country	897	1668	2565

6922 **NAKHON RATCHASIMA TEACHERS' COLLEGE**

Nakhon Ratchasima 30000

Telephone: 242158

F. of Education

F. of Humanities and Social Sciences (including Law and Political Science)

F. of Sciences and Technology (including Home Economics, Health Sciences, Industrial Arts, and Agriculture)

F. of Management Sciences

In-Service Training P.

Founded 1913 as school, became college 1959. Reorganized 1984 to include further fields of study. A State institution under the supervision of the Ministry of Education. Residential facilities for academic staff and students.

Academic Year: June to March (June-October; November-March).

Admission Requirements: Secondary school certificate (Mathayom 6) and entrance examination.

Language of Instruction: Thai.

Degrees and Diplomas: Bachelor of Education, 4 yrs. Also Higher Certificate of Education, 2 yrs.

Library: Central Library, *c.* 100,000 vols.
Academic Staff: c. 200.
Student Enrolment: c. 1990.

6923 **NAKHONSAWAN TEACHERS' COLLEGE**
Nakhonsawan 60000

Teacher Training
Founded 1922.

6924 **NAKHON SI THAMMARAT TEACHERS' COLLEGE**
Nakhon Si Thammarat 80289
Telephone: 356544
Rector: Prasert Chariyanukul (1984-87)
Rector: Samboon Chantwee

F. of Education
Dean: Chumsak Indrarak; *staff* 38
F. of Humanities and Social Sciences
Dean: Thakoeng Phanthakoengamorn; *staff* 60
F. of Science (including Home Economics, Physical Education, and Agriculture)
Dean: Vichien Kaewboonsong *staff* 58
F. of Management Sciences
Dean: Chaow Tabtimtong; *staff* 14
In-Service Training P.

Founded 1957 as school, became college 1969. Reorganized 1984 to include further fields of study. A State institution under the supervision of the Ministry of Education. Residential facilities for academic staff and students.

Academic Year: June to March (June-October; November-March).
Admission Requirements: Secondary school certificate (Mathayom 6) and entrance examination.
Fees (Baht): 2000-4000 per annum.
Language of Instruction: Thai.
Degrees and Diplomas: Degrees and diplomas: Bachelor of–Education; Liberal Arts; Sciences, 4 yrs.
Library: Central Library, 80,788.
Special Facilities (Museums, etc.): Anthropology Museum.
Academic Staff, 1986-87: 182.
Student Enrolment, 1986-87:

	Men	Women	Total
Of the country	416	852	1268*

*Also 1350 external students.

6925 **PHETCHABOON TEACHERS' COLLEGE**
Phetchaboon 67000

Teacher Training
Founded 1973.

6926 **PHETCHABURI TEACHERS' COLLEGE**
Phetchaburi 76000

Teacher Training
Founded 1926.

6927 **PHETCHABURIWITHAYALONGKORN TEACHERS' COLLEGE**
Klongluan, Pathum Thani 13180
Cables: Petchburi T.C. Thind 13180
Telephone: 5168226; 5168220

F. of Education
F. of Sciences (including Physical Education, Agriculture, and Home Economics)
F. of Sociology and Humanities

Founded 1932 as school, acquired present status and title 1970. A State institution under the supervision of the Ministry of Education. Residential facilities for academic staff and students.

Academic Year: June to March (June-October; November-March).
Admission Requirements: Secondary school certificate (Mathayom 6).
Language of Instruction: Thai.
Degrees and Diplomas: Bachelor of Education, 4 yrs. Also Higher Certificate of Education, 2 yrs.
Library: c. 63,200 vols.
Special Facilities (Museums, etc.): Thai Culture Museum.
Publication: Pancha Nakorn (quarterly journal).
Academic Staff: c. 10.
Student Enrolment: c. 1970.

6928 **PHIBUNSONGKRAM TEACHERS' COLLEGE**
Pitsanuloke 65000

Teacher Training
Founded 1923.

6929 **PHUKET TEACHERS' COLLEGE**
Phuket 83000

Teacher Training
Founded 1972.

6930 **PRANAKORN TEACHERS' COLLEGE**
Bangkhen, Bangkok 10900

Teacher Training
Founded 1892.

6931 **RAMBHAI BARNI COLLEGE**
Raksakchamool Street, Chanthaburi 22000
Telephone: 311534
Rector: Kosin Rangsayapan
Secretary-General Banchob Wongpipatpong

F. of Education
Dean: Navin Rungros; *staff* 31
F. of Humanities and Social Sciences
Dean: Latthi Nongnueng; *staff* 41 (2)
F. of Agriculture and Industry
Dean: WorawanSangkaew; *staff* 11 (2)
F. of Sciences and Technology
Dean: BangkonNilrak; *staff* 34
F. of Management Sciences
Dean: Chaiyot Polwatna; *staff* 13
Demonstration S.
Dean: Wandee Sukthitiphat; *staff* 4
Research and Educational Extension Ce.
Director: Pichai Saranrom; *staff* 8
Cultural and Arts Ce.
Director: Supwat Aimoch; *staff* 12

Founded 1972. Residential facilities for academic staffs and students.

Academic Year: March to November (June-October; November-March).
Admission Requirements: Secondary school certificate (Mathoyom 6) and entrance examination.
Fees (Baht): 20 per credit.
Language of Instruction: Thai.
Degrees and Diplomas: Bachelor of–Art; Education; Science, 4 yrs.
Library: Central Library, 10,000 vols.
Special Facilities (Museums, etc.): The Queen's House; The Cultural Centre.
Academic Staff, 1990: 130
Student Enrolment, 1990:

	Men	Women	Total
Of the country	68	303	371
Of other countries	200	500	700
Total	268	803	1071

6932 **SAKONNAKHON TEACHERS' COLLEGE**
Sakonnakhon 47000

Teacher Training
Founded 1964.

6933 **SONGKHLA TEACHERS' COLLEGE**
Songkhla 90000

Teacher Training
Founded 1919.

6934 **SUANDUSIT TEACHERS' COLLEGE**
Dusit 10300
Telephone: 241-0769

F. of Humanities and Social Sciences
D. of Science (including Home Economics and Physical Education)

F. of Education

Founded as homecraft secondary school 1934, became teachers' college 1960. A State institution for women underthe supervision of the Ministry of Education.

Academic Year: June to March (June-October; November-March).

Admission Requirements: Secondary school certificate (Mathayom Suksa 5) or equivalent, and entrance examination.

Language of Instruction: Thai.

Degrees and Diplomas: Bachelor of Education, 4 yrs. Also Higher Certificate of Education, 2 yrs.

Library: c. 100,000 vols.

Publications: Information (each semester); Student's Handbook (annually).

Academic Staff: c. 260.

Student Enrolment: c. 1820.

6935 **SUANSUNANTHA TEACHERS' COLLEGE**

Dusit 10300

Teacher Training

Founded 1937.

6936 **SURATTHANI TEACHERS' COLLEGE**

Suratthani 84000

Telephone: (77)272466

Fax: (77)272967

Rector: Satit Kaewchoeu

Head: Wilart Muangnoy

F. of Education

Assistant Professor: Somsak Chobtrong; *staff* 36

F. of Science and Technology

Lecturer: Wisan Srimahawaroe; *staff* 35 (2)

F. of Humanities and Social Studies

Lecturer: Kosum Apakappakun; *staff* 42

F. of Management Science

Lecturer: Kungwon Iamsamang; *staff* 13 (8)

Research Ce. for Planning and Development

Associated Professor: Somkiat Tansakun; *staff* 1 (4)

Cultural Ce.

Lecturer: Samruay Keekhanon; *staff* 1 (10)

Also Chumporn Inservice Training Centre

Founded 1973 as teacher training institution. Acquired present status 1985. Governing body: the Board. Residential facilities for academic staff and students.

Joint programmes with Saskatchewan Institute of Applied Science and Technology, Canada.

Academic Year: June to March (June-October; November-March).

Admission Requirements: Secondary school certificate and entrance examination.

Fees (Baht): 900-1150 per semester.

Language of Instruction: Thai.

Degrees and Diplomas: Bachelor, 4 yrs. Also Diploma, 2 yrs.

Library: Central Library.

Publication: Srivichaya (twice a year).

Academic Staff, 1989:

Rank	Full-time
Associated Professor	3
Assistant Professor	24
Total	27

Student Enrolment, 1989:

	Men	Women	Total
Of the country	1057	1811	2868

6937 **SURIN TEACHERS' COLLEGE**

Surin 32000

Teacher Training

Founded 1973.

6938 **THEPSATRI TEACHERS' COLLEGE**

Narai Road, Muang District, Lopburi 32000

Telephone: 411029

President: Thong Runcharoen (1986-89)

F. of Education

Dean: Chairat Tipsapapkool; *staff* 49

F. of Humanities and Social Sciences (including Law and Political Science)

Head: Kanok Tosurat; *staff* 75

F. of Science (including Home Economics, Health Sciences, Industrial Arts, and Agriculture)

Dean: Chitrakarn Ekamolkool; *staff* 51

F. of Management Sciences

Dean: Somporn Puangpet; *staff* 10

Founded 1921. A State institution under the supervision of the Ministry of Education. Residential facilities for academic staff and students.

Academic Year: June to March (June-October; November-March).

Admission Requirements: Secondary school certificate (Mathayom 6) and entrance examination.

Fees (Baht): 1000 per semester.

Language of Instruction: Thai.

Degrees and Diplomas: Bachelor of–Education; Art; Science, 4 yrs.

Library: Central Library, 60,000 vols.

Academic Staff, 1986-87:

Rank	Full-time
Rong-Sastracharn (Associate Professors)	4
Poochuay Sastracharn (Assistant Professors)	15
Acharn (Instructors)	148
Total	167

Student Enrolment, 1986-87:

	Men	Women	Total
Of the country	419	1013	1432

6939 **THONBURI TEACHERS' COLLEGE**

Thonburi, Bangkok 10600

Teacher Training

Founded 1953.

6940 **UBONRACHATANI TEACHERS' COLLEGE**

162 Changsanit, Ubonrachatani 34000

Telephone: (45) 254471

Fax: (45) 44111

President: Poonna Pula

Vice-President: Surasak Lekhawatana

F. of Education

Dean: Prachoom Pongpan; *staff* 46

F. of Humanities and Social Sciences

Dean: Pimpa Nitisak; *staff* 49 (1)

F. of Science and Technology

Dean: Ukol Lamaichin *staff* 41

F. of Agriculture and Industry (including Animal Husbandry)

Dean: Wztaya Kangsantza; *staff* 8

F. of Management Science

Dean Ruangwit Ketsuwan *staff* 9

Research Ce. and Education Service

; *staff* 5

Founded 1958. Governing body: the Board of Trustees. Residential facilities for academic staff and students.

Academic Year: June to May (June-October; November-March; March-May).

Admission Requirements: Secondary school certificate (Mathayom 6) or equivalent and entrance examination.

Fees (Baht): 1500 per semester.

Language of Instruction: Thai.

Degrees and Diplomas: Associate Degree. Bachelor, 2-4 yrs.

Libraries: Central Library; libraries of the faculties and departments.

Special Facilities (Museums, etc.): Cultural Centre.

Academic Staff, 1990: 171.

Student Enrolment, 1990:

	Men	Women	Total
Of the country	655	985	1640

6941 **UDONTHANI TEACHERS' COLLEGE**

Udonthani 41000

Teacher Training

Founded 1923.

6942 **UNITED COLLEGES OF BUDDHACHINNARAT**
Nakhonsawan 60000
Telephone: 222-341
President: Hom Klayanonda (1979-87)

F. of Education
Dean: Kudtiya Kantawong
F. of Sciences and Technology (including Home Economics, Agriculture, Physical Education, and Health Science)
Dean: Dwittaya Wachabundit
F. of Humanities and Social Sciences
Dean: Sanoe Bootpradit
F. of Management Sciences
Dean: Dusit Phutrakoon

Founded 1922 as agricultural teacher training school, became college 1968, and acquired present title 1986. A State institution under the supervision of the Ministry of Education. Residential facilities for academic staff and students.

Academic Year: June to March (June-October; November-March).

Admission Requirements: Secondary school certificate (Mathayom 6) and entrance examination.

Fees (Baht): 20 per credit.

Language of Instruction: Thai.

Degrees and Diplomas: Bachelor of–Education; Arts, 4 yrs.

Library: Central Library, 100,000 cols.

Academic Staff, 1986-87: 184.

Student Enrolment, 1986-87: 1127.

6943 **UNITED COLLEGES RATTANAKOSIN BANSOMDEJ**
Issaraparb Road, Bangkok 106001
Telephone: 4666662/4
President: Surabandh Yanthong (1985-89)

F. of Education
Dean: Orasa Prachnakorn; *staff* 68
F. of Humanities and Social Sciences (including Law and Political Science)
Dean Charan Khumnan; *staff* 94
F. of Sciences and Technology (including Home Economics, Health Sciences, Industrial Arts, and Agriculture)
Dean Cha-em Saithong; *staff* 62
F. of Management Sciences
Dean Suraphol Teeraratanapan; *staff* 9
In-Service Training P.

Founded 1896 as school, became college 1958. Acquired present title 1986. A State institution under the supervision of the Ministry of Education. Residential facilities for academic staff.

Academic Year: June to March (June-October; November-March).

Admission Requirements: Secondary school certificate (Mathayom 6) and entrance examination.

Fees (Baht): *c.* 1200 per semester.

Language of Instruction: Thai.

Degrees and Diplomas: Bachelor of–Education; Science; Liberal Arts, 4 yrs.

Library: Central Library, 92,472 vols.

Academic Staff, 1986-87:

Rank	Full-time
Rong-Sastracharn (Associate Professors)	216
Poochuay Sastracharn (Associate Professors)	21
Acharn (Instructors)	5
Total	242

Student Enrolment, 1986-87:

	Men	Women	Total
Of the country	801	1124	1925

6944 **UTTARADIT TEACHERS' COLLEGE**
Uttaradit 53000

Teacher Training

Founded 1936.

6945 **YALA TEACHERS' COLLEGE**
Amphur Maung, Yala 95000
Telephone: (73) 21-2443

F. of Education
F. of Humanities and Social Sciences
F. of Science

Founded as vocational school 1934, became teachers' college 1953. Reorganized 1984 to include further fields of study. A State institution under the supervision of the Ministry of Education. Governing body: the Board. Residential facilities for academic staff and students.

Arrangements for co-operation with Washington State University.

Academic Year: June to March (June-October; November-March).

Admission Requirements: Secondary school certificate (Mathayom 6).

Language of Instruction: Thai.

Degrees and Diplomas: Bachelor of Education 2-4 yrs. Also Higher Certificate of Education, 2-4 yrs.

Library: c. 75,350 vols.

Academic Staff: c. 150.

Student Enrolment: c. 4150.

Private Institutions

6946 **ASSUMPTION BUSINESS ADMINISTRATION COLLEGE**
682 Mu 11, Muban Seri, Ramkamhaeng Soi 24, Huamark, Bangkok 10240
Telex: 87468 ABACTH
Telephone: 3141446; 3140456

F. of Business Administration
D. of Management
D. of Marketing
D. of Finance and Banking
D. of Accountancy
D. of Computer Sciences
D. of Business Economics
D. of English Language
D. of General Studies
Graduate S.
P. for Lifelong Education

Founded 1969, acquired present title 1972. A private institution under the supervision of the Brothers of Saint Gabriel and recognized by the Ministry of University Affairs. Governing body: the Board of Trustees.

Arrangements for co-operation with: University of Santa Clara; California State University; De La Salle University.

Academic Year: June to March (June-October; November-March).

Admission Requirements: Secondary school certificate (Mathayom 6) or equivalent, and entrance examination.

Language of Instruction: English.

Degrees and Diplomas: Bachelor of Business Administration, B.B.A., 4 yrs. Degree of Master, a further 2 yrs.

Library: c. 17,000 vols.

Publications: Journal (quarterly in English); Vintage (annually); Newsletter (every three months).

Press or Publishing House: The ABAC Press.

Academic Staff: c. 70 (100).

Student Enrolment: c. 3730.

6947 **BUNDIT PHITSANULOK COLLEGE**
601 Phraongkhaw Road, Muang District, Phitsanulok 65000

F. of Law
F. of Business Administration

Founded 1986.

6948 **BUNDIT SAKONNAKHON COLLEGE**
5O/11 Tambon Thatnaweng, Muang District, Sakonnakhon 47000

F. of Agriculture

Founded 1983.

6949 **CHRISTIAN COLLEGE**
124 Silom Road, Bangkok 10500
Telephone: 2332506
President: Khun Odom Subhatri (1985-87)
Registrar: Thanaporn Saripong

F. of Nursing
Dean: Pornpun Tinnabal; *staff* 19 (70)

Founded 1983. A private institution under the supervision of the Ministry of University Affairs.

Academic Year: June to March (June-October; November-March).

Admission Requirements: Secondary school certificate (Mathayom 6).

Fees (Baht): 12,000 per annum.
Language of Instruction: Thai.
Degrees and Diplomas: Bachelor of Science in Nursing, 4 yrs.
Academic Staff, 1986-87: 19 (70).
Student Enrolment, 1986-87: 110 (Women).

6950 **HUA CHIEW COLLEGE**
Soi Anantanak-Soi, Bangkok 10100
Telephone: 2231280
President: Kunnikar Tanprasert (1985-88)

F. of Nursing and Midwifery

Founded 1981. A private institution under the supervision of the Ministry of University Affairs.
Academic Year: June to March (June-October; November-March).
Admission Requirements: Secondary school certificate (Mathayom 6).
Fees (Baht): 300-350 per unit.
Language of Instruction: Thai.
Degrees and Diplomas: Bachelor, 4 yrs.
Academic Staff, 1986-87: 36.
Student Enrolment, 1986-87: 190 (Women).

6951 **INSTITUTE OF SOCIAL TECHNOLOGY**
43/1111 Raminthra Road, Bangkhen, Bangkok 10220

F. of Business Administration
F. of Economics
F. of Liberal Arts
Graduate S.

Founded 197O.

6952 **KASEMBUNDIT COLLEGE**
99/101 Soi Akhanay Phatanakarn Road Bangkok 10250

F. of Law
F. of Business Administration
F. of Engineering
F. of Communication Arts

Founded 1987.

6953 **MISSION COLLEGE**
430 Phitsanulok Road, Dusit, Bangkok 10300

F. of Nursing

Founded 1986.

6954 **NORTHEAST COLLEGE**
200 Mitraphab Road, Muang District, Khon Kaen 40000

F. of Business Administration

Founded 1988.

6955 **PHAKKLANG COLLEGE**
932/1 Moo 9, Asia Road, Tambon Nakhonsawantok, Muang District, Nakhonsawan 60000

F. of Business Administration

Founded 1986.

6956 **RANGSIT COLLEGE**
Tambon Lakhok, Muang District, Pathumyhani 12000

F. of Business Administration
F. of Education

Founded 1984.

6957 **SAENGTHAM COLLEGE**
½0 Moo, 4 Petkasem Road, Sampran, Nakhon Pathom 73100

Sec. of Basic Studies
F. of Divinity
F. of Humanities

Founded 1975 as a college of education within the Catholic Lux Mundi Seminary. A private institution recognized by the Ministry of Education. Financially supported by tuition fees and Church donations. Governing body: the Board of Administration. Residential facilities for academic staff and students.
Academic Year: June to March (June-October; November-March).
Admission Requirements: Secondary school certificate (Mathayom Suksa 5) or equivalent.
Language of Instruction: Thai.
Degrees and Diplomas: Bachelor of–Arts, B.A. (Philosophy); Divinity, B.D. (Theology), 4 yrs.
Library: c. 6000 vols.
Publication: Saengtham Papitasna (quarterly review).
Academic Staff: c. 10 (20).
Student Enrolment: c. 160 (Men).

6958 **SAINT LOUIS NURSING COLLEGE**
215 South Sathorn Road, Yannawa, Bangkok 10120

F. of Business Administration

Founded 1985.

6959 **SIAM BUNDIT COLLEGE**
Ronachaicharynyut Road, Muang District, Roi Et 45000

F. of Business Administration

Founded 1985.

6960 **SOUTH-EAST ASIA COLLEGE**
19/1 Phetkasem Road, Nong-Khaem, Bangkok 10160

F. of Business Administration
F. of Industrial Technology
F. of Engineering
Graduate S.

Founded 1973.

6961 **SRI-ESARN COLLEGE**
Maha Sarakam-Kosumpisai Road, Maha Sarakam 44000

F. of Arts
F. of Business Administration
F. of Science
F. of Law
F. of Economics
F. of Agriculture
Ce. for Culture
Ce. for Research

Founded 1979.

6962 **SRISOPHON COLLEGE**
103 Sithammasoke Road, Muang District, Nakhon Si Thaarat 80000

F. of Business Administration
F. of Economics

Founded 1984.

6963 **VONGCHAVALITKUL COLLEGE**
199 Mu 6, Tombon Banko, Nakhorn Ratchasima 30000

F. of Business Administration
F. of Law
F. of Economics

Founded 1984.

6964 **YONOK COLLEGE**
303 Phaholyothin Road, Lampang 52000
Telephone: (54) 222-155
Fax: (54) 223-284
President: Nirund Jivasantikarn
Secretary-General: Suwah Trimanaphan

S. of Business
Dean: Cheawcharn Wichitphan
S. of Communications
Dean: U-Larn Naungjamnong; *staff* 3 (2)
D. of English
Chairman: Modecai Abromowitz; *staff* 10
Research I.
Head: Kiatkajorn Chaisangsookhum; *staff* – (3)
Arts and Culture I.
Head: Sakdi Rattanachai; *staff* 3
Southeast Asia I. of Uplands Development
Head: Stan Matthew; *staff* 1 (1)

Founded 1988. A non-profit college supervised by the Yonok Foundation chartered by Ministry of University Affairs. Governing body: the Board of Governors. Residential facilities for academic staff and 200 students.

Arrangements for co-operation with Baylor University.

Academic Year: June to May (June-October; November-March; April-May).

Admission Requirements: Secondary school certificate or equivalent.

Fees (Baht): 200 per semester hour.

Languages of Instruction: Thai and English.

Degrees and Diplomas: Bachelor.

Library: Yonok Library.

Special Facilities (Museums, etc.): Yonok Museum.

Academic Staff, 1989-90: 28 (2).

Student Enrolment, 1989-90:

	Men	Women	Total
Of the country	31	115	146

TOGO

6965 ***UNIVERSITÉ DU BÉNIN**

University of Bénin
B.P. 1515, Lomé
Telex: UBTO 5258
Telephone: 21-35-00
Recteur: Komlavi Fofoli Seddoh

F. of Letters (History, Geography, Philosophy, English, Modern Letters, Linguistic, French)
Dean: Issa Takassi; *staff* 97 (35)
S. of Administration and Law
Dean: M. Pocanam; *staff* 22 (36)
S. of Economics and Management
Dean: Mavor Agbodan; *staff* 22 (23)
S. of Sciences
Dean: K. Kekeh; *staff* 66 (7)
F. of Medicine
Dean: Kessie; *staff* 40 (1)
S. for Medical Assistants
Director: A. Agbetra; *staff* 1 (62)
S. of Agriculture (including Animal Husbandry)
Director: Kpakote; *staff* 21
S. of Industrial and Civil Engineering
Director: K. Koulekey; *staff* 22 (11)
I. of Education
Director: B. Gbikpi; *staff* 19 (29)
I. of Health Technology
Director: K. Dogba; *staff* 9 (14)
I. of Management Technology
Director: T. Gogue; *staff* 4 (41)
S. of Secretarial Studies
Director: Mme. Seddoh; *staff* 5 (8)

Founded 1970 replacing former Centre d'Enseignement supérieur, established 1962 with sections in Dahomey and Togo under an agreement between the governments of the two countries and government of France. A State institution enjoying academic and financial autonomy. Governing bodies: the Grand Conseil; the Conseil de l'Université. Some residential facilities for students.

Arrangements for co-operation with: Université de Sherbrooke; Institut polytechnique de Montréal; University of North Carolina; Université René Descartes (Paris V); Universités de Lille; Université Paris-Val de Marne (Paris XII); Université de Poitiers; University of Lagos; University of Cape Coast; Universidade Federal de Bahia; Universidade de Brasília; Universidade Estudual Paulista Julio de Mesquita Filho, São Paulo; Université libre de Bruxelles; Free University of Berlin.

Academic Year: October to June (October-December; January-March; April-June).

Admission Requirements: Secondary school certificate (baccalauréat) or equivalent, or special entrance examination.

Language of Instruction: French.

Degrees and Diplomas: Diplôme universitaire d'études scientifiques (D.U.E.S.); Diplôme universitaire d'études générales (D.U.E.G.); Diplôme universitaire d'études littéraires (D.U.E.L.), 2 yrs; Licence–ès Lettres; ès Sciences; ès Sciences de l'Education en Droit, law; ès Sciences économiques, 3 yrs; Maîtrise, 1 yr after Licence. Diplôme d'Ingenieur agronome, 5 yrs; Diplôme–d'Ingenieur d'exécution; d'Assistant médical, 3 yrs. Doctorat de 3e cycle. Doctorat d'Ingenieur, 3 yrs. Doctorat en Médecine, 7 yrs. Also Capacité en Droit, 2 yrs.

Library: c. 40,000 vols: libraries of the schools.

Publication: Annales de l'Université du Bénin.

Press or Publishing House: Presses de l'Université du Bénin.

Academic Staff, 1989:

Rank	Full-time
Professors	9
Associate Professors	21
Senior Lecturers	91
Lecturers	127
Total	248

Student Enrolment, 1990:

	Men	Women	Total
Of the country	6248	816	7055
Of other countries	460	212	672
Total	6699	1028	7727

6966 **ÉCOLE AFRICAINE ET MAURICIENNE D'ARCHITECTURE ET D'URBANISME**

B.P. 2067, Lomé
Telex: MINEDUC 5322
Telephone: 21-62-53
Directeur: Nassirou Ayeva

Architecture and Town Planning

Founded 1975 by the Organisation de la Coopération Africaine et Malgache (OCAM). Financially supported by Member States of OCAM. Governing body: the Conseil d'administration. Residential facilities for academic staff and students.

Arrangements for co-operation with the Universities of: Aix-Marseille; Paris VIII.

Academic Year: September to June (September-January; January-June).

Admission Requirements: Secondary school certificate (baccalauréat) and entrance examination.

Fees (Francs CFA): 3,200,000 per annum.

Language of Instruction: French.

Degrees and Diplomas: Diplôme–d'Architecte; d'Urbaniste, 5 yrs.

Library: c. 1050 vols.

Publication: Les villes précoloniales en Afrique tropicale.

Academic Staff, 1986-87: 7 (31).

Student Enrolment, 1986-87:

	Men	Women	Total
Of the country	76	2	78
Of other countries	11	–	11
Total	87	2	89

6967 **ÉCOLE NORMALE SUPÉRIEURE**

B.P. 7, Atakpame

Teacher Training (French, English, History, Geography, Physics, Chemistry, Mathematics, Natural Sciences)

Founded 1968.

6968 **INSTITUT NATIONAL DE LA JEUNESSE ET DES SPORTS**

B.P. 7176, Lomé

Founded 1976.

TUNISIA

University Institutions

6969 ***UNIVERSITÉ DES LETTRES, DES ARTS ET DES SCIENCES HUMAINES (TUNIS I)**

29, rue Asdrubel, Lafayette, 1002 Tunis
Telex: MINSUP 13870 TN
Président: Abdelkader Mehiri (1988-)
Secrétaire général: Hassine Aleya

F. of Human and Social Sciences (Arabic, French, English, History, Geography, Philosophy, Psychology, Sociology)
Dean: Hassouna Mzabi; *staff* 147 (54)
F. of Letters (Mannouba)
Dean: Béchir Lamine; *staff* 218 (18)
I. of Modern Languages
Director: Kacem Ben Hamza; *staff* 151 (83)
I. of Press and Information
Director: Moncef Chennoufi; *staff* 34 (45)
I. of Documentation
Director: Khelifa Chater; *staff* 8 (42)
I. of Education and Further Education
Director: Mehdi Abdeljaoued
Ce. of Economic and Social Research (CERES)
Director: Abdelwaheb Bouhdiba
National Ce. of Scientific Documentation (C.N.U.D.S.I.)
Director: Fatma Chammam

Founded 1960, incorporating Ez-Zitouna Islamic University, the Institut des hautes Etudes established in 1945, and other existing institutions of higher education. The University, which is composed of faculties and professional schools, operates under the authority of the Ministry of Higher Education and Scientific Research. Governing body: the Councils of the University and its constituent faculties and schools.

Arrangements for co-operation with institutions and universities in: Algeria, Belgium, France, Morocco, Switzerland, USSR, Italy, Spain, U.S.A.

Academic Year: October to June (October-February; February-June).

Admission Requirements: Secondary school certificate (baccalauréat) or foreign equivalent.

Languages of Instruction: Arabic and French.

Degrees and Diplomas: Licence–en Droit, law; en Sciences économiques; en Théologie; en Journalisme; Religious Sciences, 4 yrs. Diplôme universitaire d'études–scientifiques (D.U.E.S.); littéraires (D.U.E.L.), 2 yrs. Diplôme in–Commerce; Education, 4 yrs; Engineering, 4-6 yrs; Architecture and Town Planning, 7 yrs. Certificates–d'Aptitude au Journalisme; de Capacité en Droit, law; de Capacité en Sciences économiques, 2 yrs. Maîtrise de–Sciences; Lettres, 4 yrs. Diplôme d'études approfondies (D.E.A.) en Sciences, 1-2 yrs after Maîtrise. Doctorat (3e cycle)–ès Lettres; ès Sciences. Doctorat d'Etat en Langue et Littérature arabes. Diplôme de Technicien supérieur en Sciences économiques et de Gestion, 2 yrs after Licence. Doctorat en Médecine, 6 yrs.

Library: Total, *c.* 186,000 vols.

Publications: Cahiers de Tunisie (quarterly); Annales de l'Université de Tunis (in Arabic); Revue des Sciences sociales; Revue de Droit; Revue des Sciences.

Academic Staff, 1989-90: c. 4100 (1450).

Student Enrolment, 1989-90: c. 29,570.

6970 **UNIVERSITÉ DES SCIENCES, DES TECHNIQUES ET DE MÉDECINE (TUNIS II)**

29, rue Asdrubal, 1002 le Belvédére, Tunis
Telephone: (1) 789-312
Fax: (1) 789-312
Président: Mohamed Amara
Secrétaire général: Mustapha Ouerghemmi

F. of Mathematics, Physics and Natural Sciences
Dean: Houcine Chebli; *staff* 326 (47)
F. of Medicine (including Pharmacy)
Dean: Abdelaziz Ghachem; *staff* 472 (32)
I. of Art (including Architecture and Town Planning)
Director: Mustapha Tlili; *staff* 99 (21)
I. of Scientific and Technical Research
Director: Larbi Bouguerra; *staff* 73
Preparatory S. of Engineering (Nabeul)
Director: Moncef Chekir; *staff* 47 (17)
I. of Agriculture
Director: Abderazak Daaloul; *staff* 95 (35)
I. of Forestry (Tabarka)
Director: Brahim Hasnaoui; *staff* 13 (3)
S. of Engineering
Director: Mustapha Besbes; *staff* 142 (31)
S. of Information Sciences
Director: Mohamed Ben Ahmed; *staff* 26 (7)
S. of Technical Studies
Director: Slaheddine Gherissi; *staff* 131 (24)
S. of Education (Bizerte)
Director: Jemaiel Ben Brahim; *staff* 74 (14)
S. of Veterinary Medicine (Sidi Thabet)
Director: Mohamed Kilani; *staff* 35 (26)
S. of Physical Education (Kassar-Said)
Director: Taoufik Haouet; *staff* 60 (2)
S. of Agriculture (Mateur)
Director: Ridha Bargaqui; *staff* 20 (15)
S. of Agriculture (Mograne)
Director: Habib Amamou; *staff* 24 (27)
S.of Agriculture (Kef)
Director: Amor El Yahiaqui; *staff* 12 (17)
S. of Rural Engineerinig (Medjez El-Bab)
Director: Salem Laour; *staff* 28 (52)
S. of Telecommunications Engineering
Director: Tahar Belakhdar
S. of Civil Aviation and Metereology (Borj El-Amri)
Director: Slaheddine Guiza; *staff* 31
S. of Food Industries
Director: Bouraoui Regaya; *staff* 18 (15)
I. of Nutrition and Food Technology
Director: Zouheir Kallel; *staff* 25
Ce. for Computer Sciences
Director: Mohamed Jaoua

Founded 1988 from exisiting faculties.

Arrangements for co-operation with the Universities of: Cadi Ayadh, Marrakech; Ottawa; Laval; Oran.

Languages of Instruction: French and Arabic.

Degrees and Diplomas: Diplôme d'études universitaires scientifiques (D.E.U.S.) Dipôme d'Ingénieur. Diplôme d'études approfondies (D.E.A.) Maîtrise. Doctorat du 3ème cycle. Doctorat d'Etat.

Student Enrolment, 1989-1990:

	Men	Women	Total
Of the country	7722	4884	12,606
Of other countries	346	82	428
Total	8068	4966	13,034

6971 **UNIVERSITÉ DE DROIT, D'ECONOMIE ET DE GESTION (TUNIS III)**

B.P. 106, Tunis
Président: Chedlu Bouzakoura

F. of Law and Political Science
F. of Economics (including Management)
F. of Juridical Studies, and Political and Social Sciences
I. of Manangement
I. of Commerce and Hotel Administration
I. of Commerce (Carthage)
Ce. for Research and Publicity

6972 **UNIVERSITÉ DE MONASTIR (CENTRE)**
Monastir

F. of Science and Technology
Dean: Khelifa Harzallah; *staff* 128
F. of Law (Sousse)
Dean: Bechir Tekkari
F. of Letters and Human Sciences (Kairouan)
Dean: Hedi Sioud; *staff* 41 (7)
F. of Medicine
Dean: Habib B. Farhat
F. of Pharmacy
Dean: Moncef Jeddi
F. of Dentistry
Dean: Moncef Jeddi
F. of Medicine (Sousse)
Dean: Mohsen Jeddi
I. of Textile Technology (Ksar Helal)
Director: Mohamed Ghorsane
S. of Education (Sousse)
Director: Farouk Ammar Amor

6973 **UNIVERSITÉ DE SFAX (SUD)**
Route de l'Aereport km 1, Sfax
Telephone: (4) 40-678
Fax: (4) 40-913
Président: Mohamed Hédi Ktari
Secrétaire général: Mohsen Ben Mansour

F. of Economics and Management
Dean: Slma Zouari Bouattour; *staff* 120
F. of Medicine
Dean: Mokhtar Jeddi Habib; *staff* 80
I. of Engineering (Gabès)
Director: Slah Rhomdane; *staff* 30
I. of Industrial and Mining Engineering (Gafsa)
Director: Saied Laatar; *staff* 25
S. of Engineering
Director: Youssef Mlik; *staff* 165
S. of Engineering (Gabès)
Director: Mohieddine Alaoui *staff* 100
F. of Sciences
Dean: Mansour Salem; *staff* 60
F. of Letters and Human Sciences
Dean: Fathi Triki; *staff* 30
F. of Law
Dean: Néji Baccouche; *staff* 20
Ce. of Biotechnology
Director: Radhouane Ellouz; *staff* 15

Arrangements for co-operation with institutions in: Mauritania, Morocoo, Algeria, Libya, France, Belgium, Italy, Egypt, Saudi Arabia.

Academic Year: September to July (September-January; February-July).

Admission Requirements: Secondary school certificate (baccalauréat).

Languages of Instruction: French and Arabic.

Degrees and Diplomas: Brevet de Technicien supérieur, 2 yrs. Diplômes d'Ingénieur, 4-6 yrs. Maîtrise. Doctoret en Médecine, 7 yrs.

Student Enrolment, 1989-90:

	Men	Women	Total
Of the country	5760	3135	8895

6974 **UNIVERSITÉ ISLAMIQUE EZ-ZITOUNA**
Rue Asrubal, Tunis
Président: Touhami Negra

I. of Religious Sciences
I. of Theology

6975 **ÉCOLE DE LA MARINE MARCHANDE**
12, rue Abd Ibn Zoubeir, Sousse
Telephone: 032236

Marine Engineering
Founded 1968.

6976 **ÉCOLE NATIONALE D'ADMINISTRATION**
24, Avenue du Docteur Calmette, Mutuelleville, Tunis

Administration
Founded 1949.

6977 **ÉCOLE NATIONALE DES CADRES DE LA JEUNESSE**
2050 Bir-El-Bey
Telephone: (1) 290-080; 224
Directeur: Mohamed Hedi Aissa (1985-)

Teacher Training

Founded 1966. A State institution under the jurisdiction of the Ministry of Youth and Sport. Residential facilities for academic staff and students.

Academic Year: October to June (October-February; February-June).

Admission Requirements: Secondary school certificate (baccalauréat) and entrance examination.

Fees (Dinars): 2500 per annum.

Languages of Instruction: Arabic and French, and English.

Degrees and Diplomas: Diplôme, 20 months.

Library: c. 5000 vols.

Academic Staff, 1986-87: 12 (23).

Student Enrolment, 1986-87:

	Men	Women	Total
Of the country	101	26	127
Of other countries	3	–	3
Total	104	26	130

6978 **ÉCOLE SUPÉRIEURE D'HORTICULTURE**
Chott Mariem, Sousse
Telephone: 0369059

Horticulture

6979 **INSTITUT DES RÉGIONS ARIDES**
Médenine
Telephone: 05 40661

6980 **INSTITUT NATIONAL D'ANIMATION CULTURELLE**
Tunis

6981 **INSTITUT SUPÉRIEUR D'ART DRAMATIQUE**
2, rue Danton, 1002 Tunis
Telephone: 780-158
Directeur: Ali Belarbi (1983-89)

Drama

Founded as Centre 1969, acquired present status and title 1981. *Academic Staff, 1986-87:* 16 (3).

Student Enrolment, 1986-87:

	Men	Women	Total
Of the country	35	15	50
Of other countries	1	–	1
Total	36	15	51

6982 **INSTITUT SUPÉRIEUR DE MUSIQUE**
20 avenue de Paris, Tunis
Directeur: Mahmoud Guettat (1982-)

Arabic Music
Musicology

Founded 1982. Under the jurisdiction of the Ministry of Culture.

Academic Year: September to June (September-February; March-June).

Admission Requirements: Secondary school certificate (baccalauréat) and aptitude test.

Language of Instruction: Arabic.

Degrees and Diplomas: Diplôme universitaire des Etudes musicales (D.U.E.M.), 2 yrs. Maîtrise de Musique, a further 2 yrs.

Academic Staff, 1986-87: 11 (12).

Student Enrolment, 1986-87:

	Men	Women	Total
Of the country	52	13	65

TURKEY

Universities and Technical Universities

6983 **AKDENIZ ÜNIVERSITESI**
Akdeniz University
Antalya
Telephone: (90 311) 25-841

F. of Agriculture
F. of Arts and Sciences
F. of Engineering (Isparta)
F. of Medicine
I. of Medical Sciences
I. of Science
I. of Social Sciences
C. of Education (Burdur)
S. of Fishery (Egridir)
S. of Tourism and Hotel Management
Also Colleges of Vocational Education at: Burdur and Isparta.

Founded 1982, incorporating the Antalya Medical Faculty of the University of Ankara. An autonomous State institution.

Academic Staff: c. 270.
Student Enrolment: c. 4630.

6984 **ANADOLU ÜNIVERSITESI**
Anadolu University
Yunus Emr Kampüsu, Eskisehir
Telex: 35147
Telephone: 50581

F. of Architecture and Engineering
Dean: Musa Şenel; *staff* 152 (1)
F. of Medicine
Dean: Ismail Bağcilar; *staff* 234 (8)
F. of Pharmacy
Dean: Ihsan Sarikardaşoğlu; *staff* 31
F. of Economics and Administration
Dean: Aykut Herekman; *staff* 85
F. of Arts and Sciences
Dean: Ercan Güvan; *staff* 96
F. of Education
Dean: Doğan Bayar; *staff* 62
F. of Open Education
Dean: Semih Büker; *staff* 76
S. of Administration (Kütahya)
Director: Riza Aşikoğlu; *staff* 15
S. of Finance and Accountancy (Afyon)
Director: Halim Sözbilir; *staff* 18
S. of Applied Fine Arts
Director: Engin Ataç; *staff* 14
S. of Aviation
Director: Ahmet Nuri Yüksel
Graduate I. of Social Sciences
Director: Fazil Tekin; *staff* 1
Graduate S. of Science
Director: Rüstem Kaya
Metallurgical Research I.
Director: Macit Yaman
Graduate I. of Medical Sciences
Director: Hüseyin Sarniç
Ce. for Hearing Impaired Children
Director: Umran Tüfekçioğlu
Medicinal Plants Research Ce.
Director: K. Hüsnü Can Başer
Also Colleges of Vocational Education at: Afyon, Bilecik, and Bolvadin.

Founded 1973. Reorganized 1982 following higher education reform and incorporating Academy of Economics and Commercial Sciences, founded 1958, and Academy of Engineering and Architecture(1968). An autonomous State institution. Residential facilities for academic staff and students.

Academic Year: October to July (October-February; March-July).

Admission Requirements: Secondary school certificate (graduation from lycée) or recognized foreign equivalent, and entrance examination.

Languages of Instruction: Turkish and English.

Degrees and Diplomas: Lisans, Bachelor, 4 yrs. Doctorate, a further 4 yrs. Doctor of Medicine, 6 yrs. Master, a further 2 yrs.

Library: Total 47,681 vols.

Publication: Faculty Journals (quarterly).

Press or Publishing House: University Press Centre.

Academic Staff, 1986-87:

Rank	Full-time	Part-time
Profesör (Professors)	45	2
Doçent (Associate Professors)	105	7
Ogretim Görevlisi (Assistant Professors)	145	–
Asistan (Assistants)	315	–
Okutman (Instructors)	41	–
Lecturers	75	–
Total	726	9

Student Enrolment, 1986-87:

	Men	Women	Total
Of the country	8994	4076	13,070
Of other countries	47	14	61
Total	9041	4090	13,131

6985 ***ANKARA ÜNIVERSITESI**
Ankara University
Tandoğan Meydani, Ankara 06100
Telex: TR IRB 42045
Telephone: (41) 223-43-61
Fax: (41) 223-63-70
Rektör: Nekdet Serin
Genel Sekreter: aypar Altinel

F. of Letters (Ancient Languages and Cultures, Anthropology, Archeology and History of Art, Drama, Eastern Languages and Literatures, Geography, History, Library Science, Philosophy, Psychology, Sociology, Turkish Language and Literature, Western Languages)
Dean: Rüçhan Arik; *staff* 258
F. of Pharmacy
Dean: Eriş Asil; *staff* 90
F. of Educational sciences
Dean: Ömer Kürkçüoğlu; *staff* 85
F. of Science (including Astronomy and Space Sciences)
Dean: Aral Olcay; *staff* 316
F. of Law
Dean: Özcan K. Çlobican; *staff* 92 (5)
F. of Political Science (including Economics, International Relations, and Business Administration)
Dean: Güney Devrez; *staff* 114
F. of Medicine
Dean: Hayati Ekmen; *staff* 758 (54)
F. of Divinity
Dean: Meliha Anbarcioğlu; *staff* 69
F. of Veterinary Medicine (including Animal Husbandry)
Dean: Ferruh Dinçer; *staff* 116
F. of Agriculture (including Dairy Technology, Fisheries, Landscape Architecture, and Horticulture)
Dean: I. Akif Kansu; *staff* 319
F. of Dentistry
Dean: Ali Zaimoğlu; *staff* 100

C. of Home Economics
Director: Didar Eser; *staff* 21
C. of Journalism and Mass Communication
Director: Oya Tokgöz; *staff* 28
S. of Jurisprudence
Director: Ramazan Aslan
Graduate S. of Social Sciences
Director: Mualla Öncel; *staff* 24
I. of Turkish Republic History
Director: Hasan Köni; *staff* 23
Graduate S. of Medical Sciences
Director: Fahri Bölükbaşi; *staff* 21
Graduate S. of Natural and Applied Sciences
Director: Burhan Kacar; *staff* 29
I. of Forensic Medicine
Director: Ibrahim Tunali; *staff* 9
D. of Physical Education and Sport
D. of Fine Arts
D. of Foreign Language
D. of Turkish Language
Turkish Language Teaching Ce.
Atatürk's Principles Applied Research Ce.
Head: Hasan Köni
Biotechnology Applied Research Ce.
Head: Tuncer Özdamar
Cardiology applied Research Ce.
Head: Türkan Gürol
Education-Rehabilitation Applied Research Ce.
Head: Efser Kerimoğlu
Environmental Problems Applied Research Ce.
European Communities Applied Research Ce.
Foreign Languages Teaching and Applied Ce.
Gastroenterology Applied Research Ce.
Mediterranean Applied Research Ce.
Oncology Applied Research Ce.
Ottoman History Applied Research Ce.
Pediatric Hematology and Oncology Applied Research Ce.
Journalism and Communication Applied Research Ce.
Turkish Geography Applied Research Ce.
Psychiatric Crisis Applied Research Ce.
Also Technical Training Colleges at: Çankiri, Kastamonu, Başkent and Kirikkale.

Founded 1946 as a State university incorporating former faculties of law, letters, science, and medicine, established during the period 1925-43. The faculties of veterinary science and agriculture became part of the university in 1948 and the faculty of political science in 1950. Reorganized 1982 following higher education reform. An autonomous State institution. Governing body: the University Administrative Board, comprising the Rector, deans, and 3 professors, the University Senate. Some residential facilities for students in state dormitories.

Arangmetns for co-operation with the Universities of: Tanta; Soka; Bamberg; Passau; Gödöllö (Agricultural); Zagreb; Berlin (Free); Roma; Trunity; Warsaw; Edinburgh; Tunis III; Aleppo (Syria); Chile; Charles; Prague.

Academic Year: October to June (October-January; February-June).

Admission Requirements: Secondary school certificate (graduation from lycée) or recognized foreign equivalent, and entrance examination.

Fees (Lira): 40,000-200,000.

Language of Instruction: Turkish.

Degrees and Diplomas: Lisans, Bachelor, in–Letters; Pharmacy; Education; Science; Law; Political Science; Journalism and Mass Communication, 4 yrs; Divinity; Dentistry; Veterinary Science, 5 yrs; Medicine, 6 yrs. Mühendislik, Bachelor of Science, in–Chemistry; Physics; Geology; Agriculture, 4 yrs. Yüksek Lisans, Master of Arts or Science, 2 yrs after Lisans. Specialist in–Veterinary Medicine; Agriculture, 2 yrs after Lisans; Medicine, 8 yrs. Doktora, at least 2-4 yrs after Lisans. Doçentlik, 4 yrs after Doktora. Profesörlak, 5-7 yrs after Doçentlik. Teaching qualifications. Also Technical Training diplomas, 2 yrs.

Library: Central Library and faculty libraries, 645,000 vols.

Special Facilities (Museums, etc.): Ankara Üniversitesi Ahlatlibel Observatorium; Herbarium and Fauna Collection.

Publication: Journals of the Faculties.

Press or Publishing House: Ankara Üniversitesi Basimevi.

Academic Staff, 1990:

Rank	Full-time	Part-time
Profesör (Professors)	223	59
Doçent (Associate Professors)	390	–
Yardmici Doçent (Assistant Professors)	373	–
Araştirma Görevlisi (Research Assistants)	1344	–
Okutman (Instructors)	233	–
Total	2622	59

Student Enrolment, 1990:

	Men	Women	Total
Of the country	19,182	12,452	31,634
Of other countries	361	165	526
Total	19,543	12,617	32,160

6986 ***ATATÜRK ÜNIVERSITESI**

Atatürk University

Atatürk Üniverstesi Rektörlüğü, Erzurum 25170
Telephone: (90-11) 11209
Fax: (90-11) 17140
Rektör: Hurşit Ertuğrul
Genel Sekreter: Ekrem Kfarakişoğullari

F. of Dentistry
Dean: Muzaffer Kürkçüoğlu; *staff* 36
F. of Veterinary Medicine
Dean: Necdet Leloğlu; *staff* 35
F. of Law (Ersincan)
Dean: Şakir Bayindir; *staff* 12
F. of Arts and Sciences (including Chemistry, Geography, History, Turkish Language and Literature, Philosophy, English, French, German,Archaeology, Arabic and Persion Languages and Literature)
Dean: Ahmet Çakir; *staff* 187
F. of Medicine
Dean: Sabahat Kot; *staff* 259 (4)
F. of Agriculture (including Animal Husbandry and Horticulture)
Dean: Abdüsselam Ergene; *staff* 124
F. of Teology
Dean: Emrullah Yüksel; *staff* 53
F. of Education
Dean: Şerif Aktaş; *staff* 121
F. of Economics and Business Administration
Dean: Talat Güllap; *staff* 52
F. of Engineering (Chemistry)
Dean: Erol Oral; *staff* 62
Teachers Training C. (Ağri)
Director: Selahattin Salman; *staff* 18
C. of Vocational Training (Erzincan)
Director: Şakir Bayindir; *staff* 21
Teachers Training C. (Erzincan)
Director: Necati Fahri Taş; *staff* 22
C. of Nursing
Director: Sacide Gazilerli; *staff* 15
Graduate S. of Science
Director: Metin Balci; *staff* 11
Graduate S. of Social Sciences
Director: Halûk Ipekten; *staff* 16
Graduate S. of Health
Director: Arif Özel; *staff* 14
I. of Turkish Republic History
Director: Ramiz Banoğlu; *staff* – (4)
Environmental Conservation Studies Ce.
Director: Orhan Özbay; *staff* 1
Earthquake Research Ce.
Director: Salih Bayraktutan; *staff* 5
European Community Research Ce.
Director: Tayyar Ayyildiz; *staff* 4
Ibrahm Hakki Research Ce.
Director: Abdülkuddüs Bingöl; *staff* 6
Computer Sciences Application and Research Ce.
Director: Fatin Sezgin; *staff* 15

Founded 1955. Reorganized 1982 following higher education reform. An autonomous State institution. Governing bodies: the Executive Committee; the Senate. Residential facilities for 650 academic staff and dormitories for 9000 students.

Academic Year: October to June (October-February; March-June).

Admission Requirements: Secondary school certificate (graduation from lycée) or recognized foreign equivalent, and entrance examination.

Fees (Lira): 40,000-200,000 per annum.

Language of Instruction: Turkish.

Degrees and Diplomas: Lisans, Bachelor, 4 yrs. Bachelor of Science, 2-3 yrs. Yüksek Lisans, Master, a further 2 yrs. Doctorate, a further 4 yrs. Doctor of Medicine, 6 yrs.

Libraries: Central Library, *c.* 215,000 vols; faculty libraries.

Publications: Medical Bulletin (quarterly); Agricultural Review; Economics and Management; Journal of Arts and Sciences.

Press or Publishing House: Atatürk Üniversitesi Basimevi.

Academic Staff, 1990:

Rank	Full-time
Profesör (Professors)	123
Doçent (Associate Professors)	63
Yrd. Doçent Dr. (Assistant Professors)	129
Oğretim Görevlisi (Lecturers)	160
Okutman (Instructors)	111
Uzman-Araştirma Görevlisi (Research Assistant)	592
Total	1178

Student Enrolment, 1990: 14,515.

6987 **BILKENT ÜNIVERSITESI**

Bilkent University

P.O. Box 8, 06572 Maltepe, Ankara

Telex: 42999 TCSM TR

Telephone: 664040

Rector: Mithat Coruh

Vice-President for Academic Affairs: Ozay Oral

F. of Engineering
Dean: Özay Oral; *staff* 40

F. of Music and Fine Arts
Dean: Altan Günalp; *staff* 5

F. of Arts and Sciences (English Language and Literature, American Culture and Literature, Archaeology, and Art History)
Dean: Bülent R. Bozkurt; *staff* 2 (5)

S. of Foreign Languages (English, French, German)
; *staff* 14 (1)

F. of Fine Arts
Dean (Acting): Bulent Özguç

F. of Economics and Adminisciences
Dean: Subidey Togan

S. of Graduate Studies

Computer Ce.

Science and Engineering Research Ce.

D. of World Systems and Economics

Also College of Vocational Training.

Founded 1984 by the Hacettepe University Foundation, Medical Centre foundation, and Child Health Institute Foundation. A private institution. Governing bodies: the Board of Trustees; the Senate. Residential facilities for academic staff and students.

Academic Year: October to June (October-January; February-June).

Admission Requirements: Secondary school certificate (graduation from lycée) or recognized equivalent, and entrance examination.

Fees (US$): 4000 per annum.

Degrees and Diplomas: Lisans. Bachelor of Arts or Science, 4 yrs. Yüksek Lisans, Master of Arts or Science, 1 yr after Bachelor. Doctorate.

Library: Central Library, 10,000 vols.

Academic Staff, 1989: c. 350.

Student Enrolment, 1989: c. 4500 (Also 120 external students).

6988 ***BOĞAZIÇI ÜNIVERSITESI**

Boğaziçi University

80815 Bebek Istanbul

Telex: 26411 BOUN TR

Telephone: 163-15-00/60 Ex

Rektor: Ergün Toğrol

F. of Economic and Administrative Sciences
Dean: Ahmet N. Koc; *staff* 72 (25)

F. of Engineering
Dean: Z. Ilsen Önsan; *staff* 143 (33)

F. of Arts and Sciences (including Foreign Language Teaching)
Dean: Murat Dikmen; *staff* 140 (21)

F. of Education
Dean: Hikmet Sebuktekin; *staff* 30

S. of Foreign Languages (English)
Director: Muazzez Yazici; *staff* 102 (5)

I. of Turkish Republic History
Director: Yüsel Inel; *staff* 20 (4)

I. of Environment Sciences
Director: Yüksel Inel; *staff* 20 (4)

I. of Biomedical Engineering
Director: Sabih Tansal; *staff* 13 (5)

I. of Earthquake Research and Observatory
Director: Muammer Dizer; *staff* 10

Graduate I. of Science and Engineering
Director: Murat Dikman; *staff* 10

Graduate I. of Social Sciences
Director: Ahmet N. Koç; *staff* 7 (10)

Also College of Vocational Education.

Founded 1863 as Robert College, a private institution, under charter from the State of New York. Became Turkish State University with present title 1971. Reorganized 1982 following higher education reform. Governing bodies: the Council; the Senate. Some residential facilities for academic staff and students.

Academic Year: October to June (October-January; February-June).

Admission Requirements: Secondary school certificate (graduation from lycée) or recognized equivalent, and entrance examination.

Fees (Lira): 80,000-84,000 per annum; foreign students, 480,000-1,560,-000.

Language of Instruction: English.

Degrees and Diplomas: Associate, Degrees, 2 yrs. Lisans, Bachelor, of Arts or Science, 4 yrs. Mühendislik Unvani, Bachelor of Science, in various fields, 4 yrs. Yüksek Lisans, Master of Arts or Science; Yüksek Mühendislik Unvani, Master of Science in Engineering, 1 yr after Bachelor. Doktora, at least 2-4 yrs after Lisans. Teaching qualifications.

Library: Central Library, 211,001 vols.

Special Facilities (Museums, etc.): Cultural Heritage Museum.

Publications: Journals of: Engineering; Sciences; Humanities; Social Sciences.

Press or Publishing House: Yayim Işleri Şube Müdürlüğü.

Academic Staff, 1989-90:

Rank	Full-time	Part-time
Profesör (Professors)	101	40
Doçent (Associate Professors)	63	11
Yardmici Doçent (Assistants)	52	1
Oğretim Görevlisi (Assistant Professors)	114	73
Uzman (Specialists)	25	–
Okutman (Instructors)	56	–
Araştirma Görevlisi (Researchers)	229	–
Total	640	125

Student Enrolment, 1989-90:

	Men	Women	Total
Of the country	4761	3593	8354
Of other countries	316	143	459
Total	5077	3736	8813

6989 ***ÇUKUROVA ÜNIVERSITESI**

Çukurova University

Adana

Telex: 62934 - 62935

Telephone: (90 71) 13 75 52

Fax: (90 71) 14 37 94

Rektor: Mithat Ozsan

Genel Sekreter: Adnan Tibet

F. of Administrative Sciences and Economics
Dean: Kadir Tuan

F. of Agriculture (including Animal Husbandry)
Dean: Osman Tekinet

F. of Medicine
Dean: Emia V. Eikoçak

F. of Science and Letters
Dean: Yusuf Ünlü

F. of Engineering and Architecture
Dean: Azziz Ertunč

F. of Education (English and German Languages)
Dean: Vural Ülkü

Natural and Applied Science I.
Director: Ural Dinç
I. of Social Sciences
Director: Nejat Erk
I. of Health Sciences
Chairperson: Güneş Yüzdğir
D. of Foreign Languages
Dean: Özder Etmekçi
S. of Fisheries (Adana)
Director: Ercan Saruhan
S. of Teacher Training (Adana)
Director: Adil Türkoğlu
S. of Teacher Training (Matay)
Computer Ce.
Also Colleges of Vocational Education at: Mersin, Ceyhan, Osmaniye, Antakya, and Iskenderun, and Training and Research Hospital at Balcali.

Founded 1969 as college of agriculture, became university 1973. Reorganized 1982 following higher education reform. An autonomous State institution. Governing body: the Senate, the University Executive Council. Residential facilities for academic staff and 2464 men and 1318 women students.

Arrangements for co-operation with: University of Hohenheim; University of Bordeaux II; University of Southampton.

Academic Year: October to May (October-January; February-May).

Admission Requirements: Secondary school certificate (graduation from lycée) and entrance examination.

Fees (Lira): 40,000-200,000 per annum.

Languages of Instruction: Turkish and English.

Degrees and Diplomas: Lisans, Bachelor, 4 yrs. Yüksek Lisans, Master, a further 2 yrs. Doctor of Medicine, 6 yrs. Doctorate, Ph.D., 4-5 yrs after Lisans. Also Vocational College Diplomas, 2 yrs.

Library: c. 25,000 vols.

Special Facilities (Museums, etc.): Arts and Culture Centre.

Publication: Faculty journals (4 issues per year).

Press or Publishing House: University Press.

Academic Staff, 1990:

Rank	Full-time	Part-time
Professors	128	27
Associate Professors	107	–
Assistant Professors	88	–
Total	323	27

Student Enrolment, 1988-1990:

	Men	Women	Total
Of the country	9974	4612	14,586
Of other countries	172	32	204
Total	10,196	4644	14,790

6990 **CUMHURIYET ÜNIVERSITESI**

Cumhuriyet University
Sivas
Telex: 15167
Telephone: 13023
Rektor: Muvaffak Akman (1982-92)
Genel Sekretar: Ateş Güdüllüoğlu

F. of Medicine
Dean: Ali Gökalp; *staff* 216
F. of Arts and Sciences (including Chemistry, Biology, French Language nd Literature, Sociology, Mathematics and Turkish Language)
Dean: Bünyamin Özbay; *staff* 120
F. of Engineering (including Mineralogy and Petrography)
Dean: Ali Öztürk; *staff* 53
F. of Agriculture
Dean: Emin Tuğay; *staff* 54
S. of Nursing
Director: Meliha Atalay; *staff* 18
I. of Medical Sciences
Director: Atilla Atalay; *staff* 3
I. of Sciences
Director: Ibrahim Gümüssuyu; *staff* 2
I. of Social Sciences
Director: Vahap Sag; *staff* 1
D. of Turkish Republic History
Head: Ali Erkul; *staff* 5
D. of Turkish Language
Head: Nazim Hikmet; *staff* 5
D. of Foreign Languages
Head: Sedat Torel; *staff* 19
D. of Fine Arts
Head: Zeki Tutkun; *staff* 5
D. of Physical Education and Sports
Head: Mustafa Dülger; *staff* 6
Also Colleges of Vocational Education at: Sivas, Tokat, and Divriği.

Founded 1973 as university faculty of medicine. Reorganized as university 1982 following higher education reform. An autonomous State institution. Governing body: the Senate. Residential facilities for academic staff and 1200 students.

Academic Year: October to September (October-February; February-September).

Admission Requirements: Secondary school certificate (graduation from lycée).

Fees (Lira): 10,000-100,000 per annum.

Language of Instruction: Turkish.

Degrees and Diplomas: Lisans, Bachelor, 4 yrs. Yüksek Lisans, Master, a further 1-2 yrs. Doctor of Medicine, 6 yrs. Doctorate, Ph.D. Diploma in Nursing. Also Vocational College diplomas.

Library: Central Library, c. 10,000 vols.

Publications: Medical Journal; Social Sciences Journal; Sciences Journal (all biannually).

Academic Staff, 1989-90:

Rank	Full-time
Profesör (Professors)	36
Doçent (Associate Professors)	35
Oğretim Görevlisi (Assistant Professors)	63
Uzman (Specialists)	24
Okutman (Instructors)	87
Araştirma Görevlisi (Researchers)	283
Öğretim Görevlisi (Lecturers)	75
Total	603

Student Enrolment, 1989-90:

	Men	Women	Total
Of the country	144	62	206

6991 ***DICLE ÜNIVERSITESI**

Dicle University
Diyarbakir
Telephone: 18725
Fax: 17825

F. of Medicine
Dean: Omer Mete; *staff* 225 (6)
F. of Dentistry
Dean: Mustaga Ülgen; *staff* 14
F. of Law
Dean: Aydin Zeukliler; *staff* 15
F. of Arts and Sciences
Dean: Mustafa Özcan; *staff* 70
F. of Engineering and Architecture
Dean: Erkan Öngel; *staff* 10
F. of Agriculture
Dean: İhsan Özkaynak; *staff* 29
F. of Education
Dean: Faruk İnce; *staff* 86
C. of Nursing
Director: Hüseyin Yalçinkaya
I. of Sciences
Director: Turhan Özden
I. of Health Sciences
Director: Güneri Eriem
I. of Social Sciences
Director: Sacit Akçay
Also Colleges of Vocational Education at: Diyarbakir, Batman, and Sanliurfa.

Founded 1966 as Faculty of Medicine attached to the University of Ankara, detached and re-established with Faculty of Science as University of Diyarbakir 1973. Reorganized and acquired present title 1982 following highereducation reform. An autonomous State institution. Governing body: the Senate. Residential facilities for academic staff and students.

Academic Year: October to May (October-January; February-May).

Admission Requirements: Secondary school certficate (graduation from lycée) and entrance examination.

Fees: None.

Language of Instruction: Turkish.

Degrees and Diplomas: Lisans, Bachelor, 4 yrs; Dentistry, 5 yrs. Doctor of Medicine, 6 yrs. Doctorate, Ph.D. Also Diplomas.

Libraries: Central Library, *c.* 28,000 vols; faculty libraries.

Publication: Faculty publications.

Press or Publishing House: University Press.

Academic Staff, 1986-87:

Rank	Full-time	Part-time
Profesör (Professors)	11	2
Doçent (Associate Professors)	28	4
Yardmici Doçent (Assistants)	57	–
Oğretim Görevlisi (Assistant Professors)	100	–
Uzman (Specialists)	17	–
Okutman (Instructors)	53	–
Araştirma Görevlisi (Researchers)	286	–
Total	552	6

Student Enrolment, 1986-87:

Men	Women	Total
5260	1868	7128

6992 **DOKUZ EYLÜL ÜNIVERSITESI**

Dokuz Eylül University

Cumhuriyet Bul. 144, Izmir 35210

Telephone: (90 51) 21-40-80

Fax: (51) 22-09-78

F. of Medicine
Dean: Abdullah Kenanoğlu; *staff* 144 (14)
F. of Education (including Foreign Languages and Physical Education)
Dean: Adnan Gülerman; *staff* 159
F. of Engineering (Denizli)
Dean: Mustafa Demirsoy; *staff* 36
F. of Fine Arts
Dean: Akin Süel; *staff* 51
F. of Law
Dean: Seyfullah Edis; *staff* 19 (1)
F. of Theology
Dean: Ethem Ruhi Fiğlali; *staff* 54
F. of Economics and Administration
Dean: Atilla Sezgin; *staff* 120 (2)
F. of Engineering and Architecture
Dean: Şafak Uzsoy; *staff* 228
S. of Justice
Director: Seyfullah Edis; *staff* 15
S. of Tourism and Hotel Administration
Dean: Alp Timur; *staff* 20
S. of Education (Demirci)
Director: Ibrahim Özkan; *staff* 14
S. of Education (Denizli)
Director: Erdogan Kuruş; *staff* 16
S. of Finance and Accountancy (Manisa)
Director: Hüseyin Karkayali; *staff* 24
S. of Business Administration (Mugla)
Director: Sitki Karahan; *staff* 20
I. of Marine Sciences
Director: Erol Izdar; *staff* 13
I. of Basic Sciences
Director: Cevdet Öğüt
I. of Health Sciences
Director: Melahat Okuyan
I. of Social Sciences
Director: Sadik Acar
I. of Turkish Republic History
Director: Ergun Aybars; *staff* 12
Conservatory
Director: Necati Gedikli; *staff* 46
Also College of Vocational Education.

Founded 1982, incorporating previously existing institutions together with some faculties of the Aegean University. An autonomous State institution. Residential facilities for students.

Arrangements for co-operation with: University of Hamburg; University of Hanover; University of Stuttgart; Miami University (Marine Science).

Academic Year: October to July (October-February; March-July).

Admission Requirements: Secondary school certificate (graduation from lycée) or recognized equivalent, and entrance examination.

Fees (Lira): 40,000-100,000 per annum.

Language of Instruction: Turkish.

Degrees and Diplomas: Lisans, Bachelor, 4 yrs; Doctor of Medicine, 6 yrs. Yüsek Lisans, Master, a further 2 yrs. Doctorates.

Library: Central Library, 150,000 vols.

Publication: Faculty Reviews.

Academic Staff, 1986-87:

Rank	Full-time	Part-time
Profesör (Professors)	37	9
Doçent (Associate Professors)	110	10
Yardmici doçent (Assistants)	143	–
Okutman (Instructors)	82	–
Araştirma Görevlisi (Researchers)	362	–
Lecturers	300	–
Total	1034	19

Student Enrolment, 1986-87:

	Men	Women	Total
Of the country	14,146	8226	22,372
Of other countries	258	64	322
Total	14,404	8290	22,694

6993 ***EGE ÜNIVERSITESI**

Aegean University

Bornova, Izmir 35040 (Rectorate)

Telephone: 180110

Fax: 182867

Rektor: Sermet Akgü

Genel Sekreter: Abdürrahim Incekara

F. of Medicine
Dean: Ilhan Vidinel; *staff* 577 (64)
F. of Agriculture (including Horticulture, Landscape Architecture, and Animal Husbandry)
Dean: Ibrahim Karaca; *staff* 234
F. of Science (including Astronomy and Space Sciences, and Statistics)
Dean: İsmet Ertaş; *staff* 180
F. of Dentistry
Dean: Berran Öztürk; *staff* 91 (11)
F. of Letters (Sociology, Psychology, Education, Archaeology and History of Art, Philosophy, Turkish Language and Literature, History, Geography, and Western Languages and Literatures)
Dean: Gönul Öney; *staff* 126
F. of Engineering (Food Engineering, Textile Engineering, and Computer Sciences and Engineering)
Dean: Temel Çakaloz; *staff* 202
F. of Pharmacy
Dean: Aysen Karan; *staff* 60
I. of Social Sciences
Director: Ismail Aka; *staff* 7
I. of Science
Director: Feridun Topaloğlu; *staff* 1
I. of Health Sciences
Director: Necmettin Zeybek
I. of Solar Energy
Director: Gürbüz Atatündüz; *staff* 8
I. of Nuclear Sciences
Director: Selman Kinaçi; *staff* 13
S. of Water Production
Director: Atilla G. Alpbaz; *staff* 21 (1)
S. of Press and Publication Studies
Director: Özcan Özal; *staff* 23
S. of Nursing
Director: Inci Erefe; *staff* 36
Conservatory of Turkish Music
Director: Refet Saygili; *staff* 10
S. of Professional Studies
Director: Mehmet Dokuzogüz
S. of Health Technology
Director: Yilmaz Şenyilmaz
D. of Foreign Languages
Director: Reşit Küçükboyaci; *staff* 77
D. of Turkish Republic History
Director: Tuncer Baykara; *staff* 11

D. of Turkish Language
Director: Fikret Türkmen; *staff* 22
D. of Physical Fitness and Education
Director: Asli Özer; *staff* 20
Also Schools of Vocational Education at Alaşehir, Çeşre, and Uşak.

Founded 1955 as an autonomous State institution. Several private colleges of higher education incorporated 1971. Reorganized 1982 following higher education reform. Financially supported by the government. Governing bodies: the Senate; the Board of Administration. Residential facilities for academic staff and students.

Arrangements for co-operation with: Rhenish-Westphalen Technical University, Aachen; University of the Saar; Justus Liebig University, Giessen; University of Reading; California State University; University of Pennsylvania; Miami University; University of Catania; Université d'Aix-Marseille; State University Centre of Antwerp; University of Siegen; University of Groningen; Technische Hochschule Carolo-Wilhemina zu Braunschweig. Also participates in the EARN and BITNET European Academic and Research Network.

Academic Year: October to June (October-January; March-June).

Admission Requirements: Secondary school certificate (graduation from lycée) or recognized foreign equivalent, and entrance examination.

Fees (Lira): 40,000-260,000.

Languages of Instruction: Turkish and some English.

Degrees and Diplomas: Lisans, Bachelor, in–Science; Engineering; Agricultural Engineering; Letters; Pharmacy, 4 yrs. Yüksek Lisans, Master, of–Arts; Science, a further 1-2 yrs. Doctorate, 2-4 yrs after Lisans. Doctor of–Dental Surgery, 5yrs; Medicine, 6 yrs.

Libraries: Central Library, *c.* 25,000 vols; faculty libraries, *c.* 225,000.

Special Facilities (Museums, etc.): Museum of Natural History; Ege University Observatory; Botanical Garden and Herbarium.

Publication: Journals of the Faculties.

Press or Publishing House: Central University Publishing Press.

Academic Staff, 1989-90:

Rank	Full-time
Profesör (Professors)	399
Doçent (Associate Professors)	170
Yardmici Doçent (Assistants Professors)	84
Öğretim Görevlisi (Senior Lecturers)	60
Uzman (Specialists)	51
Okutman (Instructors)	108
Araştirma Görevlisi (Researchers)	847
Total	1719

Student Enrolment, 1989-90:

	Men	Women	Total
Of the country	8384	8525	16,909
Of other countries	301	107	408
Total	8685	8632	17,317

6994 **ERCIYES ÜNIVERSITESI**

Erciyes University
Talas Yolu, Kayseri
Telephone: (90 351) 218-11
Fax: (90-351) 174931
Rektor: Naci Kinacioğlu (1978-)
Genel Sekreter: Veli Kiliç

F. of Arts and Sciences
Dean: Mehmet Doğan; *staff* 86
F. of Medicine
Dean: Semih Baskan; *staff* 308 (1)
F. of Engineering
Dean: Aksel Öztürk; *staff* 72
F. of Theology
Dean: Ünver Günay; *staff* 51
F. of Business Administration and Management
Dean: Mustafa Saatçi; *staff* 34
I. of Social Sciences
Director: Ahmet Uğur
I. of Health Sciences
Director: Ahmet Bilge
I. of Natural Sciences
Director: Bekir Sami Yilbaş
I. of Tourism
Director: Mustafa Saatçi; *staff* 6
Also Colleges of Vocational Education at Kayseri and Yozgat.

Founded 1978 as Kayseri University, incorporating the Institute of Islamic Studies, founded 1956 and the Gevher Nesibe Faculty of Medicine of Hacettepe University. Reorganized 1982 following higher education reform and acquired present title. An autonomous State institution.

Academic Year: October to July (October-February; February-July).

Admission Requirements: Secondary school certificate (graduation from lycée) and entrance examination.

Language of Instruction: Turkish.

Degrees and Diplomas: Lisans, Bachelor, in all fields, 4 yrs. Doktora of Medicine, 6 yrs. Also Vocational College diplomas, 2 yrs.

Library: 19,000 vols.

Academic Staff, 1989-90:

Rank	Full-time	Part-time
Profesör (Professors)	49	–
Doçent (Associate Professors)	63	1
Yardmici doçent (Assistants)	64	–
Oğretim Görevlisi (Assistant Professors)	76	–
Uzman (Specialists)	26	–
Okutman (Instructors)	71	–
Araştirma Görevlisi (Researchers)	313	–
Çevirici	1	–
Eğitim-Öğretim Planlamasi	1	–
Total	663	1

Student Enrolment, 1989-90:

	Men	Women	Total
Of the country	5116	1682	7098

6995 **FIRAT ÜNIVERSITESI**

Firat University
Elâziğ
Telex: 64538
Telephone: (90 811) 17930

F. of Arts and Sciences
F. of Engineering
F. of Medicine
F. of Technical Education
F. of Veterinary Science
I. of Medical Sciences
I. of Science
I. of Social Sciences

Founded 1975, incorporating the Faculty of Veterinary Medicine of the University of Ankara. Reorganized 1982 following higher education reform and incorporating the Academy of Engineering and Architecture, founded 1967. An autonomous State institution. Governing body: the Senate. Residential facilities for academic staff and *c.* 800 men and *c.* 50 women students.

Academic Year: October to June (October-February; March-June).

Admission Requirements: Secondary school certificate (graduation from lycée) and entrance examination.

Language of Instruction: Turkish.

Degrees and Diplomas: Lisans, Bachelor. Doktora, at least 2-4 yrs after Lisans. Doçentlik, 4 yrs after Doktora. Profesörlak, 5-7yrs after Doçentlik.

Libraries: Central Library; faculty libraries.

Academic Staff: c. 290.

Student Enrolment: c. 2420.

6996 **GAZI ÜNIVERSITESI**

Gazi University
Besevler, Ankara
Telex: 44002 GURI TR
Telephone: (90-4) 213-4244
Fax: (90-4) 221-3200
Rektör: Necat Tüzün
Genel Sekreter: Satilmiş Erdal

F. of Architecture and Engineering
Dean: Yücel Ercan; *staff* 192 (2)
F. of Arts and Sciences (Statistics, Mathematics, Physics, Biology, Chemistry, Turkish Language and Literature, History, Philosophy)
Dean: Rasih Demirci; *staff* 152
F. of Dentistry
Dean: Köksal Baloş; *staff* 78

F. of Economics and Administrative Sciences
Dean: Turgut Önen; *staff* 194
F. of Education
Dean: Reşat Genç; *staff* 342
F. of Medicine
Dean: Enver Hasanoğlu; *staff* 343 (3)
F. of Pharmacy
Dean: Ningur Noyanalpan; *staff* 68
F. of Technical Education
Dean: Ramazan Özen; *staff* 159
F. of Vocational Education
Dean: Remzi Örten; *staff* 190
I. of Accident Research and Prevention
Director: Neşet H. Gökok; *staff* 8
I. of Medical Sciences
Director: Turgut Imir; *staff* 20
I. of Science
Director: Sümer Şahin; *staff* 14
I. of Social Sciences
Dean: Kaya Türker; *staff* 19
C. of Art Education
Director: Recep Kanit; *staff* 28
C. of Art Education (for Women)
Director: Zeynep Polat; *staff* 39
C. of Education
Director: Reşat Genç; *staff* 6
C. of Education (Bolu)
Director: Faruk Kadri Serengil; *staff* 30
C. of Education (Kastamonu)
Director: Mustafa Eski; *staff* 27
C. of Education (Kirşehir)
Director: Ibrahim Arslanoğlu; *staff* 23
C. of Press and Publication-Broadcasting
Director: Ahmet Bican Ercilasun; *staff* 21
F. of Economics and Administrative Sciences (Bolu)
Dean: Yahya Kemal Kaya; *staff* 32
Energy-Environmental Systems and Industrial Rehabilitation Research Ce.
Haci Bektaş-I Veli Research Ce.
Ce. of Turkish Republic History
Accounting Application and Research Ce.
Also Colleges of Vocational Education at: Bolu, Kirsehir and Yozgat.

Founded 1982, incorporating the Gazi Teachers' College, Ankara, founded 1926, and the Ankara Academy of Economic and Commercial Sciences (1955). An autonomous State institution. Residential facilities for students.

Academic Year: October to June (October-January; March-June).

Admission Requirements: Secondary school certificate (graduation from lycée) and entrance examination.

Fees (Lira): 30,000-200,000 per annum.

Language of Instruction: Turkish.

Degrees and Diplomas: Lisans, Bachelor, 4 yrs. Yüksek Lisans, Master, a further 2 yrs. Doctorate, Ph.D., a further 2 yrs.

Library: Central Library, 55,890 vols.

Special Facilities (Museums, etc.): Concert Hall, Theatre, Art and Handicraft Galleries.

Publications: Monthly News Bulletin; Periodical Scientific Newletters of the Faculties.

Press or Publishing House: Publishing House of the College of Press and Publication Broadcasting.

Academic Staff, 1990:

Rank	Full-time
Profesör	185
Doçent	115
Yrd. Doçent	299
Öğrt. Görevlisi	653
Arş. Görevlisi	716
Uzman	46
Okutman	145
Total	2159

Student Enrolment, 1990:

	Men	Women	Total
Of the country	17,526	12,759	30,285
Of other countries	281	116	397
Total	17,807	12,875	30,682

6997 ***HACETTEPE ÜNIVERSITESI**
Hacettepe University
Hacettepe Parki, Ankara
Telex: 42232
Telephone: 211-94-42

F. of Medicine
Dean: Doğan Taner; *staff* 620 (37)
F. of Pharmacy
Dean: Atilla Hincal; *staff* 64
F. of Dentistry
Dean: Aytekin Bilge; *staff* 80 (6)
F. of Administrative Sciences and Economics (Beytepe)
Dean: Turgut Tan; *staff* 37
F. of Education (including Foreign Languages) (Beytepe)
Dean: Rifat Önsoy; *staff* 74
F. of Engineering (including Earth Sciences) (Beytepe)
Dean: Yavuz Erkan; *staff* 242
F. of Fine Arts (Beytepe)
Dean: Gülsen Canli; *staff* 37
F. of Letters (including Library Science, Psychology, and Archaeology) (Beytepe)
Dean: Emel Doğramaci; *staff* 143
F. of Science (including Statistics) (Beytepe)
Dean: Okyay Alpaut; *staff* 108
F. of Engineering (Zonguldak)
Dean: Necati Erşen; *staff* 67
S. of Nursing
Director: Eren Kum; *staff* 38
S. of Home Economics
Director: Şule Bilir; *staff* 28
S. of Physical Therapy and Rehabilitation
Director: Candan Algun; *staff* 20
S. of Health Administration
Director: Erkmen Böke; *staff* 17
S. of Food Technology and Nutrition
Director: Ayse Baysal; *staff* 23
S. of Social Services
Director: Sema Kut; *staff* 23
I. of Health Sciences
Director: E. Ferhan Tezcan; *staff* 19
I. of Population Studies
Director: Ergül Tunçbilek; *staff* 12
I. of Child Health
Director: Namik Çevik; *staff* 51
I. of Oncology
Director: Turan Kutkam; *staff* 6
S. of Music (Ankara State Conservatory) (Beytepe)
Director: Ersin Onay; *staff* 18
S. of Vocational Technology (Beytepe)
Director: Oktay Beşkardeş; *staff* 11
S. of Foreign Languages (Beytepe)
Director: Himmet Umunç; *staff* 166
I. of Psychiatry and Neurology
Director: Aykut Erbengi; *staff* 3
I. of Sciences
Director: Acar Işin; *staff* 18
I. of Nuclear Science (Beytepe)
Director: Dinçer Ülkü; *staff* 19
I. of Social Sciences (Beytepe)
Director: Tugrul Çubuku; *staff* 23
I. of Turkish Republic History (Beytepe)
Director: Abdurrahman Çayci; *staff* 21
Also Colleges of Vocational Education at: Ankara, Eregli, and Zonguldak.

Founded 1206 as Çifte Medreseler (Twin Colleges) for medicine and liberal arts in Kayseri, which continued until the beginning of the 20th century. New university charter and present title granted 1967. Beytepe Campus, outside the city, founded 1969, is the site for all faculties except Medicine and allied fields. Reorganized 1982 following higher education reform with a third campus in Zonguldak. An autonomous State institution financed mainly by the government. Governing bodies: the University Executive Committee, comprising the Rector, former Rector, deans of the faculties, and directors of the schools; the Senate, comprising the members of the Executive Committee and two members elected from each faculty. Residential facilities for students.

Arrangements for co-operation with: Ohio State University; University of Giessen; College of Education, Reutlingen.

Academic Year: October to July (October-February; February-July).

Admission Requirements: Secondary school certificate (graduation from lycée) and entrance examination.

Fees (Lira): 40,000-100,000 per annum.

Languages of Instruction: Turkish and English.

Degrees and Diplomas: Lisans, Bachelor, in all fields, 4 yrs. Yüksek Lisans, Master, 1-2 yrs after Lisans. Doktora of–Medicine, 6yrs. Philosophy, Ph.D. Teaching qualifications. Also Vocational College diplomas, 2 yrs.

Libraries: Central Library, 110,000 vols; Beytepe Campus, 126,000.

Publications: Edebiyat Fakultesi Dergisi (Journal of the Faculty of Letters) (biannually); Hacettepe Medical Journal (3 times a year); Journal of Earth Sciences; Sosyal Hizmetler Yuksekokulu Dergisi (Journal of the School of Social Science) (3 times a year); Iktisadi ve Idari Bilimler Fakultesi Dergisi (Journal of the Faculty of Administrative Sciences and Economics) (biannually).

Press or Publishing House: Hacettepe Press and Publishing Centre.

Academic Staff, 1986-87:

Rank	Full-time	Part-time
Profesör (Professors)	147	29
Doçent (Associate Professors)	258	16
Yardmici Doçent (Assistants)	224	–
Oğretim Görevlisi (Assistant Professors)	254	–
Uzman (Specialists)	87	–
Okutman (Instructors)	208	–
Araştirma Görevlisi (Researchers)	940	–
Total	2120	45

Student Enrolment, 1986-87:

	Men	Women	Total
Of the country	11,345	9327	20,672
Of other countries	362	269	631
Total	11,707	9596	21,303

6998 **INÖNÜ ÜNIVERSITESI**

Inönü University

Malatya 44069

Telex: 6140

Telephone: (90 821) 21871

F. of Arts and Sciences
Dean: Bakir Çetinkaya; *staff* 71
F. of Education (including Modern Turkish Language)
Dean: F. Halide Dolu; *staff* 17 (1)
F. of Economics and Administration
Dean: Naim Akman; *staff* 24
I. of Science
Director: Esnef Yüksel; *staff* 13
I. of Social Sciences
Director: Naim Akman; *staff* 13
I. of Turkish Republic History
Head: Halide Dolu; *staff* 4
Also Colleges of Vocational Education at Malatya and Adiyaman.

Founded 1975. Reorganized 1982 following higher education reform. An autonomous State institution. Governing bodies: the Council; the Senate. Residential facilities for academic staff and 852 students.

Academic Year: October to June (October-February; March-June).

Admission Requirements: Secondary school certificate (graduation from lycée) or recognized equivalent, and entrance examination.

Fees (Lira): 40,000-70,000 per annum.

Language of Instruction: Turkish.

Degrees and Diplomas: Lisans, Bachelor, 4 yrs; Yüsek Lisans, Master, 1-2 yrs after Lisans. Doctorate 2-4 yrs. Also Vocational College Diplomas, 2 yrs.

Library: Central Library, 14,523 vols.

Publication: Bulletin.

Press or Publishing House: University Press.

Academic Staff, 1986-87:

Rank	Full-time
Profesör (Professors)	10
Doçent (Associate Professors)	7
Yardmici Doçent (Assistants)	22
Oğretim Görevlisi (Assistant Professors)	25
Uzman (Specialists)	6
Okutman (Instructors)	26
Araştirma Görevlisi (Researchers)	70
Total	166

Student Enrolment, 1986-87:

	Men	Women	Total
Of the country	1424	524	1948
Of other countries	3	2	5
Total	1427	526	1953

6999 ***ISTANBUL UNIVERSITESI**

Istanbul University

Beyazit, Istanbul 34452

Telex: 22062 ISUR TR

Telephone: (901) 522 4200

Fax: (901) 520 54 73

Rektör: Cim'i Demiroğlu (1987-92)

Genel Sekreter: Fuat Çelebioğlu

F. of Medicine
Dean: Korkmaz Altuğ; *staff* 662 (89)
F. of Law
Dean: Ilhan Akin; *staff* 123 (20)
F. of Letters
Dean: Nurhan Atasoy; *staff* 236
F. of Science
Dean: Kâmuran Avcioğlu; *staff* 142
F. of Economics
Dean: Akin Ilkin; *staff* 161 (1)
F. of Forestry
Dean: Hasan Çanakçi; *staff* 85 (1)
F. of Pharmacy
Dean: Gültekin Sunam; *staff* 79 (1)
F. of Dentistry
Dean: Peter Sandalli; *staff* 111 (13)
F. of Medicine (Cerrahpaşa)
Dean: Faruk Yenel; *staff* 667 (74)
F. of Engineering
Dean: Ergür Tütüncüoğlu; *staff* 139
F. of Business Administration
Dean: Fuat Çelebioğlu; *staff* 95 (8)
F. of Veterinary Science
Dean: Erkan Artan; *staff* 105
F. of Political Science (including International Law)
Dean: Cumhur Ferman; *staff* 42
C. of Nursing
Director: Perihan Velioğlu; *staff* 43
C. of Journalism
Director: Tayfun Akgüner; *staff* 13
C. of Marine Products
Director: Ismet Baran; *staff* 30
I. of Cardiology
Director: Cem'i Demiroğlu; *staff* 21
I. of Social Sciences
Director: Işil Akbaygil; *staff* 38
I. of Natural Sciences
Director: Ergür Tütüncüoğlu; *staff* 15
I. of Health Sciences (Medicine, Dentistry, Pharmacy, Nursing, Veterinary Medicine)
Director: Sevim Büyükdevrim; *staff* 17
I. of Child Health
Director: Olcay Neyzi; *staff* 18
I. of Forensic Medicine
Director: Sevil Atasoy; *staff* 11
I. of Oncology
Director: Nijad Bilge; *staff* 15
I. of Marine Sciences and Geography
Director: Selâmi Gözenç; *staff* 12

I. of Turkish Republic History
Director: Cem'i Demiroğlu; *staff* 3
S. of Tobacco Specialist Education
Director: Sedat Ayanoğlu; *staff* 9
S. of Para-Legal Education
Director: Vecdi Aral; *staff* 3
Conservatory
Director: Ova Sünder; *staff* 140
S. of Health Services
Director: Turgay Atasü; *staff* 3
S. of Social Sciences
Director: Erol Uçdal; *staff* 8
S. of Technical Sciences
Director: Ergür Tütüncüoğlu
Problems of Women Research and Application Ce.
Director: Neclâ Arat
C. of Prenatal Diagnosis Research and Application
Director: Memnune Yykscl
C. of Public Health Research and Application
Director: Turhan Akinci
C. of Physiotherapy and Rehabilitation Research and Application
Director: Güzin Dilşen
C. of Cardiology Research and Application
Director: Cem'i Demiroğlu
C. of Pediatric Health Research and Application
Director: Olcay Neyzi
C. of Oncological Research, Application and Education
Director: Nijad Bilge
C. of Medical Ecology and Hydroclimatology
Director: Nurten Özer
C. of Traditional Medicine Research and Application
Director: Bayhan Çubukçu
Edirne Ce. for Southeast Europe Research and Application
C. of International University Relationships Research and Application
Director: Bener Karakartal
Political Sciences Research and Application C.
Director: Cumhur Ferman
Ophtalmological Diseases and Cornea Transplantation Research and Application C.
Director: Celal Erçikan
C. of Music Research and Application
C. of Environmental Problems Research and Application
Director: Fikret Baykut
Research and Development Co-ordination Ce.
Director: Cuma Bayat
C. of Experimental Medical Research and Application
Director: A. Sevim Büyükdevrim
C. of Neurological Sciences Research and Application
Director: Cengiz Kuday
C. of Bronchology Research and Application
Director: Seyhan Çelikoğlu
C. of Genetic Teratology Research and Application
Director: Asim Cenani
Family Planning and Infertility Research and Application C.
Director: Halim Hattat
C. of Behçet's Disease Research and Application
Director: Hasan Yasici
Postgraduate Research and Application C.
Director: Akin Ilkin
C. of Biomedical Engineering Research and Application
Director: Ergür Tütüncüoğlu
C. of Hepatopancreatobiliary System Diseases Research and Application
D. of Medical Biology (Cerrahpaşa)
D. of Physiotherapy and Rehabilitation

Founded 1453 following the conquest of Istanbul by the Turks. The Faculty of Medicine was established 1827, and the Darülfünun for teaching the positive sciences 1863. Reorganized 1924 as a secular institution and again in 1933. Under the law of 1946 and 1973 the universities were guaranteed administrative and academic independence and financial autonomy. Reorganized 1982 following the higher education reform. Governing bodies: the Senate; the Executive Council.

Academic Year: November to June (November-February; March-June).

Admission Requirements: Secondary school certificate (graduation from lycée) or equivalent recognized by Ministry of Education, and entrance examination.

Fees (Lira): 40,000-200,000 per annum.

Language of Instruction: Turkish.

Degrees and Diplomas: Lisans, Bachelor, in all fields, 4 yrs. Yüksek Lisans, Master, a further 2-4 yrs. Doctorate, a further 2-4 yrs.

Libraries: Central Library, 400,000 vols; faculty libraries, 744,000.

Special Facilities (Museums, etc.): Zoology Museum. Botanical Garden; Conference Halls.

Publications: Bülteni (biannually); Faculty Reviews and Periodicals.

Press or Publishing House: Main Printing House and Film Centre; Faculty of Letters Printing House; Faculty of Science Printing House.

Academic Staff, 1989-90:

Rank	Full-time	Part-time
Profesör (Professors)	684	203
Doçent (Assistant Professors)	364	4
Yardimçi Doçent (Associate Professors)	177	–
Research Fellows, Lecturers, Assistants	1976	–
Total	3201	207

Student Enrolment, 1989-90:

	Men	Women	Total
Total	27,230	20,135	47,365

7000 ***ISTANBUL TEKNIK ÜNIVERSITESI**
Technical University of Istanbul
Ayazağa, Istanbul
Telex: 28186 ITÜ TR
Telephone: 176-30-30

F. of Civil Engineering
Dean: Hasan Boduroglu; *staff* 191
F. of Engineering (Sakarya)
Dean: Inal Seçkin; *staff* 101
F. of Architecture (including Urban and Regional Planning)
Dean: Gündüz Atalik; *staff* 124
F. of Mechanical Engineering
Dean: Yaşar Özemir; *staff* 134 (1)
F. of Aerospace Engineering
Dean: Cengiz Dökmeci; *staff* 41
F. of Electrical Engineering and Electronics
Dean: Duran Leblebici; *staff* 155 (2)
F. of Mining Engineering
Dean: Erdoğan Yüzer; *staff* 87
F. of Arts and Sciences
Dean: Cevdet Aydoğan; *staff* 142 (1)
F. of Marine Architecture
Dean: Reşat Baykal; *staff* 45
F. of Chemical Engineering and Metallurgy
Dean: Özer Bekaroğlu; *staff* 83
F. of Management Studies
Dean: Mustafa Gediktaş; *staff* 54 (2)
I. of Nuclear Energy
Director: Ertuğrul Yazgan; *staff* 18
I. of Sciences and Technology
Director: Kemal Sarioğlu
I. of Social Sciences
Director: Nilüfer Ağat
D. of Turkish Republic History
Director: Cahit Özgür; *staff* 96
D. of Fine Arts
Director: Mehmet Şener Küçukdoğlu; *staff* 11
D. of Physical Education
Director: Yalçin Aköz; *staff* 17
Conservatory
Also 9 Research Centres and Colleges of Vocational Education at: Düzce and Sakarya.

Founded 1944 replacing the former School of Engineering, the history of which can be traced back to 1773. Reorganized 1982 following higher education reform. An autonomous State institution. Governing bodies: the Senate; the Executive Council.

Academic Year: October to June (October-January; March-June).

Admission Requirements: Secondary school certificate (graduation from lycée) or recognized equivalent, and entrance examination.

Fees (Lira): 130,000 per annum, 650,000 foreign students.

Language of Instruction: Turkish.

Degrees and Diplomas: Lisans, Bachelor, in–Engineering; Architecture; Arts and Sciences; Music, 4 yrs. Yüsek Lisans, Master, a further 1 ½-2 yrs. Doctorate, Ph.D..

Library: Central Library, 250,000 vols.

Special Facilities (Museums, etc.): Museum of Mineralogy; Museum of History of Science and Technology.

Publications: Bulletin (biannually, in English); Magazine (bimonthly, in Turkish); News from Istanbul Technical University (every three months, in Turkish).

Press or Publishing House: I.T.U. Central Publishing House.

Academic Staff, 1989-90:

Rank	Full-time	Part-time
Profesör (Professors)	301	4
Doçent (Associate Professors)	198	1
Yardmici Doçent (Assistants)	141	–
Oğretim Görevlisi (Assistant Professors)	151	–
Uzman (Instructors)	52	–
Okutman (Lecturers)	108	–
Araştirma Görevlisi (Researchers)	707	–
Total	1658	5

Student Enrolment, 1989-90:

	Men	Women	Total
Of the country	15,164	4790	19,954
Of other countries	341	74	415
Total	15,505	4864	20,369

7001 ***KARADENIZ ÜNIVERSITESI**

Karadeniz University

Trabzon

Telex: 067-83110

Telephone: (90 031) 169-20

F. of Architecture and Engineering

Dean: Aybar Ertepinar; *staff* 189

F. of Medicine

Dean: Aydin Inal; *staff* 117

F. of Science and Letters

Dean: Mustafa Ascaner; *staff* 88

F. of Forestry

Dean: Akut Ikizler; *staff* 62

F. of Education

Dean: Mehmet Ali Kisakürek; *staff* 65

F. of Economics and Administration

Dean: Cinar Atay; *staff* 28

I. of Natural and Applied Sciences

Director: Omer Alptekin; *staff* 3

I. of Social Sciences

Director: Ersan Bocutoğlu; *staff* 1

I. of Health Sciences

Director: Recep Bingol

S. of Marine Sciences and Technology (Sürmene)

Director: Salih Celikkale; *staff* 16

Also Colleges of Vocational Education at Giresun, Gümüshane, Sürmene, Ordu, and Rize.

Founded 1963 as Karadeniz Teknik Üniversitesi. Reorganized and acquired present title 1982 following higher education reform. An autonomous State institution. Governing bodies: the Senate; the Administrative Board. Residential facilities for academic staff and *c.* 4000 students.

Academic Year: October to June (October-January; March-June).

Admission Requirements: Secondary school certificate (graduation from lycée) and entrance examination.

Fees (Lira): 40,000-100,000 per annum.

Language of Instruction: Turkish.

Degrees and Diplomas: Mühendis, Bachelor in Engineering, 4 yrs. Lisans, Bachelor, in Science, 4 yrs. Yüksek Mühendis Mimar in Architecture, Master, a further 2 yrs. Doctor of Medicine, 6 yrs. Doctorate, Ph.D..

Libraries: Central Library, 60,982 vols; faculty libraries, *c.* 10,000.

Special Facilities (Museums, etc.): Geology Museum.

Publications: Bulletin (Architecture) (annually); Journal of the Faculty of Forestry (biannually); Journal of Basic Sciences(quarterly).

Press or Publishing House: University Publishing House (Karadeniz Üniversitesi Basimexi).

Academic Staff, 1986-87:

Rank	Full-time
Profesör (Professors)	32
Doçent (Associate Professors)	96
Yardmici Doçent (Assistants)	282
Oğretim Görevlisi (Assistant Professors)	76
Uzman (Specialists)	17
Okutman (Instructors)	128
Lecturers	49
Total	680

Student Enrolment, 1986-87:

	Men	Women	Total
Of the country	7291	2364	9655

7002 **MARMARA ÜNIVERSITESI**

Marmara University

Sultanahmet, Istanbul

Telex: 29051 ITX TR

Telephone: 526-11-67

Fax: 528-16-64

Rektor: Orhan Oğuz (1982-90)

Genel Sekretar: Yahya Adiyaman

F. of Arts and Sciences (including Chemistry, Mathematics, HIstory, Turkish Language and Literature, Archives)

Dean: Hakki Dursun Yildiz; *staff* 99

F. of Law

Dean: Ergun Önen; *staff* 76 (1)

F. of Education (including Physical Education)

Dean: Coşkun Alptekin; *staff* 249

F. of Technical Education

Dean: A. Sait Sevgener; *staff* 122 (1)

F. of Administrative Economics and Sciences

Dean: Ömer Faruk Batirel; *staff* 249 (5)

F. of Dentistry

Dean: Ilhan Çuhadaroğlu; *staff* 64

F. of Pharmacy

Dean: Cemil Senvar; *staff* 58

F. of Medicine

Dean: Atif Akdas; *staff* 98

F. of Engineering

Dean: Ahmet Serpil; *staff* 13 (6)

F. of Theology

Dean: Salih Tuğ; *staff* 104

F. of Fine Arts

Dean: Mustafa Aslier; *staff* 140

I. of Social Sciences

Director: Adnan Tezel; *staff* 27

I. of Medical Sciences

Director: Tevfik Akoğlu *staff* 17

I. of Graduate Studies in Sciences

Director: Cemil Şenvar; *staff* 4

I. for European Community Studies

Director: Haluk Kabaalioğlu; *staff* 4

I. of Banking and Insurance

Director: Ilhan Uludag; *staff* 4

S. of Journalism

Director: Ismet Giritli; *staff* 46

Also 4 Schools of Vocational Education.

Founded 1883 as college of commerce, became Academy of Economics and Commercial Sciences 1959. Reorganized as university 1982 following higher education reform. An autonomous State institution. Governing body: the University Council. Residential facilities for academic staff and woman students.

Arrangements for co-operation with institutions, including: Penn State-Harrisburg, Western Michigan University; A&M Texas; Manchester University; University of Nice; University of Grenoble; Munster University; Karlsruhe University; University of Priština; Technical University of Aachen.

Academic Year: October to June (October-January; March-June).

Admission Requirements: Secondary school certificate (graduation from lycée).

Languages of Instruction: Turkish and English.

Degrees and Diplomas: Lisans, Bachelor, in all fields, 4 yrs. Yüksek Lisans, Master, a further 2 yrs. Doctor of Medicine, 6 yrs. Doctorate, Ph.D.; LL.D., 4 yrs after Lisans.

Libraries: Central Library, 15,000 vols; libraries of the departments.

Special Facilities (Museums, etc.): Movie Studio; Art Gallery.

Publications: Marmaranin Sesi (monthly Bulletin); Journal of Economics and Administrative Sciences (annually); Journal of Pharmacy (annually).

Press or Publishing House: Printing Office of Technical Education Faculty.

Academic Staff, 1989-90: 1452 (18).

Student Enrolment, 1989-90:

	Men	Women	Total
Of the country			
Of other countries	252	115	367
	10,990	7896	18,886
Total	11,242	8011	19,253

7003 **MIMAR SINAN ÜNIVERSITESI**

Mimar Sinan University

Findikli-Istanbul

Telex: 26439 TS TV TR

Telephone: 145-00-00; 145-87-60

F. of Architecture

F. of Fine Arts

F. of Arts and Sciences (including Statistics)

Graduate I. of Social Sciences

Graduate I. of Technological Sciences

S. of Music (State Conservatory of Music)

Also 5 Research Centres.

Founded 1883 as college of fine arts, became academy 1926 and State Academy of Fine Arts 1969. Reorganized as university 1982 following higher education reform. An autonomous State institution. Governing body: the Senate.

Academic Year: October to June (October-January; March-June).

Admission Requirements: Secondary school certificate (graduation from lycée) and entrance examination.

Language of Instruction: Turkish.

Degrees and Diplomas: Lisans, Bachelor, 4-6 yrs. Yüksek Lisans, Master, a further 2-4 yrs. Doctorate, a further 4-8 yrs.

Library: Total, *c.* 62,500 vols.

Special Facilities (Museums, etc.): State Museum of Painting and Sculpture.

Publication: Bilingual Bulletin (monthly).

Press or Publishing House: Mimar Sinan Üniversitesi Matbaa Müdürlügü.

Academic Staff: c. 250 (110).

Student Enrolment: c. 2770.

7004 ***ONDUKUZ MAYIS ÜNIVERSITESI**

Ondokuz Mayis University

Samsun 55139

Telex: 82022 SOM TR

Telephone: (90 36) 110460

Fax: 119766

Electronic mail: TROMO

Rektor: Mehmet Sağlam

Genel Sekreter: Nazim Alkan

F. of Agriculture (including Animal Husbandry, Horticulture, and Food Technology:)

Dean: Fahrettin Tosun; *staff* 45

F. of Medicine (including Basic Medical Sciences, Medical Sciences, Surgical Sciences)

Dean: Ercihan Güney; *staff* 178 (9)

F. of Education

Dean: Bayram Kodaman; *staff* 96

F. of Science and Letters (including Physics, Chemistry, Biology, Mathematics, Statistics, Environmental Engineering)

Dean: Fevzi Köksal; *staff* 76

F. of Theology

Dean: Ekrem Sarikcioğlu *staff* 31

Ce. of Fishery

Director: Muammmer Erdem; *staff* 14

S. of Education (Amasya)

Director: Hikmet Develi; *staff* 12

S. of Education (Samsum)

Director: Nuri Kuruoğlu; *staff* 8

I. of Medical Sciences

Director: Cafer Marangoz; *staff* 3

I. of Sciences

Director: Fevzi Köksal; *staff* 8

I. of Social Sciences

Director: Bilal Dindar; *staff* 13

C. of Health Services

Director: Kuddusi Cengiz; *staff* 5

Junior College

Director: Ömer Çekelez; *staff* 19

Surgical Research Ce.

Director: Kamuran Erk

Also Colleges of Vocational Education at Amasya and Corum and junior college.

Founded 1975. Reorganized 1982 following higher education reform. An autonomous State institution. Governing body: the Senate. Residential facilities for 179 academic staff and 3826 students.

Academic Year: October to June (October-February; March-June).

Admission Requirements: Diploma of high school.

Fees (Lira): 40,000-200,000 per annum.

Language of Instruction: Turkish.

Degrees and Diplomas: Lisans, Bachelor, in all fields 4 yrs. Yüksek Lisans, Master, a further 2 yrs. Doctor of Medicine, 6 yrs. Doctorate Ph.D. Also Vocation College diplomas, 2 yrs.

Library: Central library, *c.* 60,000 vols.

Publication: Faculty Journals.

Press or Publishing House: University Printing Office.

Academic Staff, 1989-90:

Rank	Full-time	Part-time
Profesör (Professors)	63	9
Doçent (Associate Professors)	43	–
Oğretim Görevlisi (Assistant Professors)	125	–
Araştirma Görevlisi (Researchers)/Okutman (Instructors)/Lecturers	261	49
Total	492	58

Student Enrolment, 1989-90:

	Men	Women	Total
Of the country	5173	3007	8180

7005 **ORTA DOGU TEKNIK ÜNIVERSITESI**

Middle East Technical University

Inönü Bulvaru, Ankara 06531

Telex: 42761 ODTK TR

Telephone: (90 41) 223 71 00

Fax: (90-41) 223 30 54

Rektor: Saatçioğlu (1988-)

Genel Sekreter: Hüseyin Ateş

F. of Economics and Administration

Dean: Muhan Soysal; *staff* 64

F. of Architecture

Dean: Rüştü Yüce; *staff* 87

F. of Arts and Sciences

Dean: Dilhan Eryurt; *staff* 300

F. of Education (including Foreign Languages and Physical Education)

Dean: Kemal Güçlüol; *staff* 62

F. of Engineering

Dean: Süha Sevük; *staff* 528

S. of Natural and Applied Sciences

Director: Alpay Ankara; *staff* 12

S. of Social Sciences

Director: Sabri Koç; *staff* 16

S. of Foreign Languages

Director: Abdurrahman Çiçek; *staff* 173

S. of Marine Sciences (Erdemliçel)

Director: Umit Ünlüata; *staff* 28

Founded 1956 as a State institution and planned and developed by the government of Turkey with the co-operation of the United Nations and Unesco. Acquired present autonomous status 1959. Reorganized 1982 following higher education reform. Using English as the principal medium of instruction, the institution is intended to provide facilities for study and research for students from Turkey and other countries of the Middle East. Financialsupport provided by the Turkish government and private foundations. Governing bodies: the Board of Trustees; the University Council. Residential facilities for some academic staff and *c.* 4300 students.

Academic Year: October to July (October-January; March-July).

Admission Requirements: Secondary school certificate (graduation from lycée) or recognized foreign equivalent, and entrance examination.

Fees (Lira): 4000 per semester.

Language of Instruction: English.

Degrees and Diplomas: Bachelor of Arts in Education. Bachelor of Science, B.S., in–Management; Political Science and Public Administration; Economics; Statistics; Mathematics; Physics; Chemistry; Psychology and Sociology; Chemical Engineering; Electrical Engineering; Mechanical Engineering; Mining Engineering; Geological Engineering; Petroleum Engineering; Environmental Engineering; Computer Electrical Engineering; Education; Civil Engineering; Industrial Engineering; Metallurgical Engineering; Bachelor of–Architecture, B.Arch.; City Planning, B.C.P., 4 yrs. Master of–Science, in various fields; Architecture; Business Administration; City Planning, a further 2 yrs. Doctorate, Ph.D. Also teaching certificate, 4 yrs.

Library: *c.* 349,157 vols.

Special Facilities (Museums, etc.): Museum of Archaeology.

Publications: Journal of Pure and Applied Sciences (3 times a year); Studies in Development; Journal of the Faculty of Architecture; Journal of Applied Research; Metu News Bulletin (4 times a year).

Academic Staff, 1989-90:

Rank	Full-time
Profesör (Professors)	210
Doçent (Associate Professors)	231
Oğretim Görevlisi (Assistant Professors)	203
Asistan (Assistants)	728
Okutman (Lecturers)	215
Uzman (Specialists)	51
Total	1638

Student Enrolment, 1989-90:

	Men	Women	Total
Of the country	11,723	6006	17,729
Of other countries	1106	303	1409
Total	12,829	6309	19,138*

*Also 2617 external students.

7006 **SELÇUK ÜNIVERSITESI**

Selçuk University

Meram Yeni Yol, Konya

Telephone: (90 331) 20991

Rektor: Halil Cin

Genel Sekretar: Rifat Karaman

F. of Agriculture
Dean: Fethi Bayrakli; *staff* 55
F. of Architecture and Engineering
Dean: Nizamettin Armagan; *staff* 129
F. of Arts and Sciences (including Chemistry, Mathematics, Physics, Arabic Language and Literature, Archaeology and Art, History, English, German, French, Turkish and Urdu Languages and Literatures, and Sociology)
Dean: Nadir Doğan; *staff* 138
F. of Education
Dean: Saim Sakaoŭ; *staff* 137
F. of Law
Dean: Süleyman Arslan; *staff* 25
F. of Medicine
Dean: Ibrain Erkul; *staff* 202
F. of Theology
Dean: Orham Karmiş; *staff* 56
F. of Veterinary Science
Dean: Hümeyra Özgen; *staff* 70
F. of Dentistry
Dean: Timur Esener; *staff* 21
F. of Economics and Administrative Sciences (Konya)
Dean: Şehabettin Yiğitbaşi; *staff* 11
F. of Economics and Administrative Sciences (Nigde)
Dean: Eyüp Aktepe; *staff* 7
I. of Medical Sciences
Director: Yüksel Tatkan
I. of Science
Director: O. Cenap Tekinşen
I. of Social Sciences
Director: Önder Göçkün
C. of Art (for women)
Director: H. Örcün Bariştа
C. of Education (Nigde)

Also Colleges of Vocational Education at Konya, Nigde, Beyşehir, Seydişehir, Karaman, Aksaray, and Akşehir

Founded 1975. Reorganized 1982 following higher education reform. An autonomous State institution. Governing body: the University Senate. Residential facilities for Academic staff and students.

Arrangement for co-operation with Rouen University of France.

Academic Year: October to June (October-January; February-July).

Admission Requirements: Secondary school certificate (graduation from lycée) and entrance examination.

Fees (Lira): 40,000-200,000 per term.

Language of Instruction: Turkish.

Degrees and Diplomas: Lisans, Bachelor, 4 yrs. Yüksek Lisans, Master, a further 2 yrs. Doctor of–Medicine; Veterinary Medicine, 6yrs.

Libraries: Central Library; Faculty libraries.

Publication: Faculty periodicals.

Press or Publishing House: University Publishing House.

Academic Staff, 1990:

Rank	Full-time
Profesor (Professors)	92
Doĉent (Associate Professors)	63
Yardmici Doçent	154
Lecturers (Assistants)	380
Uzman (Specialists)	25
Araştirma Grevlisi (Research Assistants)	395
Total	1109

Student Enrolment, 1990:

	Men	Women	Total
Of the country	2535	6172	8707
Of other countries	31	29	60
Total	2566	6201	8767

7007 **TRAKYA ÜNIVERSITESI**

Trakya University

22030 Edirne

Telephone: (90-181) 122-59

Fax: (90-181) 13694

Rektor: Ahmet Karademz (1982-92)

Genel Sekreter: Önder Kormaz

F. of Agriculture (Tekirdag)
Dean: Cemil Cangir; *staff* 49
F. of Architecture and Engineering
Dean: Mehmet Işcan; *staff* 40
F. of Sciences and Letters
Dean: Cemil Karadeniz; *staff* 65
F. of Medicine (including Pharmacy)
Dean: Osman Şengönül
C. of Health Services (Edirne)
Director: Recep Mesut
I. of Social Sciences
Director: Necmettin Hacieminoğlu
I. of Sciences
Director: Cengiz Kurtonur
I. of Health Sciences
Director: Recep Mesut
I. of Education (Edirne)
Director: Abdullah Aras
C. of Education (Canakkale)
Director: Hasan Çebi

Also Colleges of Vocational Education at: Edirne, Canakkale, Kirklareli, Çorlu, Keşan, and Tekirdağ

Founded 1982, incorporating the Edirne Faculty of Medicine of University of Istanbul and the Edirne Academy ofArchitecture and Engineering, founded 1977. An autonomous State institution. Governing body: the Senate. Residential facilities for academic staff and 806 women and 2400 men students.

Academic Year: October to June (October-January; February-June).

Admission Requirements: Secondary school certificate (graduation from lycée) and entrance examination.

Fees (Lira): 40,000-130,000 per annum.

Language of Instruction: Turkish.

Degrees and Diplomas: Lisans, Bachelor, 4 yrs. Yüksek Lisans, Master, a further 1-2 yrs. Doctor of Medicine, 6 yrs. Doktora, Ph.D., a further 2-3 yrs.

Academic Staff, 1989-90:

Rank	Full-time
Profesör	38
Doçent	37
Yrd. Doçent	40
Araştirma Görevlisi	198
Uzman	20
Okutman	53
Ögretim Görevlisi	113
Total	499

Student Enrolment, 1989-90: 12,178.

7008 ***ULUDAG ÜNIVERSITESI**

Uludag University

Görkle Kampusü, 16384 Görükle, Bursa

Telex: 32225 BUNR.TR

Telephone: (90-24) 147550-51-52-53

Fax: (90-24) 148050

Rektor: Nihat Balkir (1978-92)

Genel Sekreter: Suna Gökirnak

F. of Agriculture
Dean: Nevzat Yürür; *staff* 48
F. of Medicine
Dean: Ayhan Kizil; *staff* 266 (15)
F. of Education (including Turkish and Foreign Languages)
Dean: Ulviye Özer; *staff* 73
F. of Science and Letters
Dean: Cihan Özmutlu; *staff* 41
F. of Economics and Administration Sciences
Dean: Yüksel Işyar; *staff* 73
F. of Theology
Dean: Emir Tekin Altingaş; *staff* 32
F. of Engineering
Dean: Fatih C. Babalik; *staff* 51
F. of Veterinary Science
Dean: Turgut Özgüden; *staff* 44
F. of Education (Balikesir)
Dean: Orhan A. Sekendiz; *staff* 58
F. of Engineering (Balikesir)
Dean: Asim Yücel; *staff* 30
I. of Sciences
Principal: Cihan Özmutlu; *staff* 99
I. of Social Sciences
Principal: Yüksel Işyar; *staff* 64
I. of Health Sciences
Principal: Şermin Baker; *staff* 33
C. of Tourism and Hotel Management (Balikesir)
Principal: Necdet Hacioğlu; *staff* 7
C. of Teacher Training
Principal: Alaeddin Kaya; *staff* 11
D. of Turkish Republic History
Director: Şermin Paker; *staff* 9
D. of Turkish Language
Director: Halis Ertürk; *staff* 9
D. of Fine Arts
Director: Şermin Paker; *staff* 3
D. of Foreign Languages
Director: Tuncer Tokol; *staff* 67
D. of Physical Education
Director: Bahattin Kovanci; *staff* 16
Also 3 Schools of Vocational Education.

Founded 1975 as Bursa Üniversitesi, incorporating the Bursa Faculty of Medicine of the University of Istanbul and the Bursa Academy of Economic and Commercial Sciences. Reorganized and acquired present title 1982 following higher education reform. An autonomous State institution. Residential facilities for students.

Participates in European CRE Co-operation Programme.

Academic Year: September to June (September-February; February-June).

Admission Requirements: Secondary school certificate (graduation from lycée) or recognized equivalent, and entrance examination.

Fees (Lira): Turkish students, 40,000-200,000; foreign students, 540,000-1,200,000.

Language of Instruction: Turkish.

Degrees and Diplomas: Lisans, Bachelor, 4 yrs. Yüksek Lisans, Master, a further 2 yrs. Doctor of–Veterinary Medicine, 5 yrs. Doctorate.

Library: Library of the faculties of Medicine and Economics, Social Sciences and Engineering, total, *c.* 130,000 vols.

Publications: Medical Periodicals (quarterly); Periodicals of Veterinary and Social Sciences (biannually).

Press or Publishing House: University Publishing House.

Academic Staff, 1989-90:

Rank	Full-time	Part-time
Profesör (Professors)	134	15
Doçent (Associate Professors)	90	–
Yardmici Doçent (Assistants)	94	–
Oğretim Görevlisi (Assistant Professors)	182	–
Uzman (Specialists)	25	–
Okutman (Instructors)	104	–
Araştirma Görevlisi (Researchers)	451	–
Total	1080	15

Student Enrolment, 1989-90:

	Men	Women	Total
Of the country	12,026	6547	18,573
Of other countries	191	45	236
Total	12,217	6592	18,809

7009 **YILDIZ ÜNIVERSITESI**

Yildiz University

Yildiz, Istanbul

Telex: 26837 IYU TR

Telephone: 161-02-20

F. of Architecture
Dean: Refik Şenvardar; *staff* 100 (2)
F. of Engineering (including Computer Sciences)
Dean: Kenen Suer; *staff* 400
F. of Science and Literature
Dean: Fahri User; *staff* 150
F. of Engineering (Kocaeli)
Dean: Attila Ataman
I. of Social Sciences
Director: İlker Birdal; *staff* 8
I. of Sciences
Director: Turgut Uzel; *staff* 11
Also College of Vocational Education at Izmit.

Founded 1911 as school of engineering, became technical college 1937 and State Academy of Engineering and Architecture 1969. Reorganized as university 1982 following higher education reform. An autonomous State institution. Governing body: the Senate.

Academic Year: October to July (October-January; February-July).

Admission Requirements: Secondary school certificate (graduation from lycée) and entrance examination.

Fees (Lira): 70,000 per annum; foreign students, 350,000.

Language of Instruction: Turkish.

Degrees and Diplomas: Lisans, Bachelor of Science, in–Engineering; Architecture, 4 yrs. Yüksek Lisans, Master of Science, a further 2 yrs. Doctorate.

Library: 45,000 vols.

Publication: Periodical.

Press or Publishing House: Yildiz Üniversitesi Matbaasi.

Academic Staff, 1986-87:

Rank	Full-time	Part-time
Profesör (Professors)	200	2
Doçent (Associate Professors)	350	–
Araştirma Görevsli (Researchers)	198	–
Total	750	2

Student Enrolment, 1986-87:

	Men	Women	Total
Of the country	12,069	2371	14,440
Of other countries	–	–	240
Total	12,069	2371	14,680

7010 ***YÜZÜNCÜ YIL ÜNIVERSITESI**

Yüzüncü Yil (Centennial) University

Yüzüncü Yil Üniversitesi Kampüsü, Van

Cables: üniversite-van

Telephone: (9-615) 1010

Fax: (9-615) 1009

Rektor: Nihat Baysu

Genel Sekreter: Salih Mercan

F. of Sciences and Literature (including Food Technology)
Dean (Acting): Nurhan AkyÜz; *staff* 127
F. of Veterinary Medicine
Dean: Hayati Çamaş; *staff* 46
F. of Agriculture (including Animal Husbandry)
Dean: S. Mehmet Şen; *staff* 60 (1)
I. of Social Sciences
Director: Erel Günel
I. of Sciences (including Zootechnology)
Director: Yusuf Vanli
S. of Education (including Turkish Language and Literature)
Director: Yilmaz Önay; *staff* 9
D. of Physical Education
Co-ordinator: Ataman Güre
D. of Fine Arts
Co-ordinatör: Yusuf Vanli
D. of Turkish Republic History
Co-ordinator: Haatu Çamaş
D. of Turkish Language
Co-ordinator: Muzaffer Akkuş
D. of Carpets
Co-ordinator: Münevver Ünsal
Also Colleges of Vocational Education at Tatvan and Hakkari.

Founded 1982. An autonomous State institution. Governing bodies: the Executive Board; the Senate. Residential facilities for academic staff and students.

Academic Year: October to July (October-January; March-July).

Admission Requirements: Secondary school certificate (graduation from lycée) and entrance examination.

Fees (Lira): 100,000-150,000 per annum.

Language of Instruction: Turkish.

Degrees and Diplomas: Lisans, Bachelor, 4 yrs. Yüksek Lisans, Master, a further 1-2 yrs. Also teaching qualifications.

Library: c. 30,000 vols.

Academic Staff, 1989-90:

Rank	Full-time
Profesör (Professors)	8
Doçent (Associate Professors)	6
Oğretim Görevlisi (Assistant Professors)	30
Yardmici Doçent (Assistants)	266
Total	310

Student Enrolment, 1989-90:

	Men	Women	Total
Of the country	1798	398	2196

UNION OF SOVIET SOCIALIST REPUBLICS*

Universities

7011 ***ALTAJSKIJ GOSUDARSTVENNYJ UNIVERSITET**
Altai State University
Ul. Dimitrova 66, 656099 Barnaul 99, Rossiskaja SFSR

F. of History and Philology
F. of Economics
F. of Law
F. of Physics and Mathematics
F. of Chemistry and Biology
D. for Correspondence Courses

Founded 1973. Placed under the authority of the Union-Republic State Committee for Public Education. Financed by the State. Governing bodies: the Rector and Pro-Rectors; the Academic Council.

Academic Year: September to July.

Admission Requirements: Competitive entrance examination following general or special secondary school certificate.

Fees: None.

Degrees and Diplomas: Diploma of Specialist in a particular field of study, 5 yrs. Kandidat nauk, Candidate of the Sciences, a further 3 yrs and thesis. Doktor nauk, by thesis after Kandidat.

Student Enrolment: c. 1500 (Also *c.* 1600 evening and correspondence students).

7012 ***AZERBAJDŽANSKIJ ORDENA TRUDOVOGO KRASNOGO ZNAMENI GOSUDARSTVENNYJ UNIVERSITET IM. S. M. KIROVA**
Azerbaijan State University
Ul. P. Lumumby 23, 370073 Baku Azerbajdžanskaja SSR
Rektor: A.A. Bakir-Zade

F. of History
F. of Philology
F. of Journalism
F. of Oriental Studies (including Interpretation)
F. of Library Science
F. of Law
F. of Economics
F. of Mathematics and Applied Mathematics
F. of Physics
F. of Chemistry
F. of Biology
F. of Geology and Geography
F. for Correspondence Courses
D. for Evening Studies

Founded 1920 with two faculties, and gradually extended to the present ten. Placed under the authority of the Union-Republic State Committee for Public Education. Financed by the State. Governing bodies: the Rector and Pro-Rectors; the Academic Council; the Faculty Councils. Residential facilities for staff and students.

Academic Year: September to July.

Admission Requirements: Competitive entrance examination following general or special secondary school certificate.

Fees: None.

Languages of Instruction: Azerbaijan and Russian.

Degrees and Diplomas: Diploma of Specialist in a particular field of study, 5 yrs; Kandidat nauk, Candidate of the Sciences, a further 3 yrs and thesis. Doktor nauk, Doctor of the Sciences, by thesis after Kandidat.

Library: c. 1,000,000 vols.

Special Facilities (Museums, etc.): Museums: Biology; Minerals.

Publications: Učënye Zapiski (scientific papers) (4 series); Za Leninskoe Vospitanie (university journal).

Academic Staff: c. 600.

Student Enrolment: c. 6200 (Also *c.* 7000 evening and correspondence students).

7013 **BAŠKIRSKIJ GOSUDARSTVENNYJ UNIVERSITET IM. 40-LETIJA OKTJABRJA**
Bashkir State University
Ul. Frunze 32, 450074 Ufa, Baškirskaja ASSR
Cables: Bašgosuniversitet
Telephone: 2-63-70

F. of History
F. of Philology
F. of Mathematics
F. of Physics
F. of Geography
F. of Biology
F. of Chemistry
F. of Foreign Languages
F. of Law
D. for Evening Studies
D. for Correspondence Courses

Founded 1957. Placed under the authority of the Union-Republic State Committee for Public Education. Financed by the State. Governing bodies: the Rector and Pro-Rectors; the Academic Council.

Academic Year: September to July (September-January; January-July).

Admission Requirements: Competitive entrance examination following general or special secondary school certificate.

Fees: None.

Languages of Instruction: Russian, Bashkir, and Tatar.

Degrees and Diplomas: Diploma of Specialist in a particular field of study, 5 yrs. Kandidat nauk, Candidate of the Sciences, a further 3 yrs and thesis. Doktor nauk, by thesis after Kandidat.

Student Enrolment: c. 3650 (Also *c.* 4650 evening and correspondence students).

7014 ***BELORUSSKIJ ORDENA TRUDOVOGO KRASNOGO ZNAMENI GOSUDARSTVENNYJ UNIVERSITET IM. V.I. LENINA**
Belorussian State University
Leninskij prosp. 4, 220080 Minsk, Belorusskaja SSR
Rektor: L.I. Kiselevskij

F. of History
F. of Philology
F. of Journalism
F. of Law
F. of Mathematics
F. of Applied Mathematics
F. of Physics
F. of Chemistry
F. of Biology
F. of Geography
F. for Correspondence Courses
Applied Physics Research I.
D. for Evening Studies

Founded 1921. Almost completely destroyed during Second World War. Reconstruction started 1945. Placed under the authority of the Union-Republic State Committee for Public Education. Financed by the State. Governing bodies: the Rector and Pro-Rectors; the Academic Council.

Academic Year: September to July.

Fees: None.

Languages of Instruction: Russian and Belorussian.

*Major changes have affected the higher education system of the country and individual institutions during the preparation of this edition. These are reflected as far as they have been communicated to IAU before 30 September 1990.

Degrees and Diplomas: Diploma of Specialist in a particular field of study, 5 yrs. Kandidat nauk, Candidate of the Sciences, a further 3 yrs and thesis. Doktor nauk, Doctor of the Sciences, by thesis after Kandidat.

Libraries: Main Library, *c.* 1,000,000 vols; Philology library; Law library.

Special Facilities (Museums, etc.): Museums: History; Numismatics; Zoology; Geology.

Academic Staff: c. 1600.

Student Enrolment: c. 10,000 (Also *c.* 8000 evening and correspondence students).

7015 **ČEČENO-INGUŠSKIJ GOSUDARSTVENNYJ UNIVERSITET IM L.N. TOLSTOGO**

Checheno-Ingush State University

U. Šeripova 32, 364907 Groznyj, Čečeno-Ingušskaja ASSR

Telephone: 23-40-89

Rektor: Victor Khan-Kalik

Vice-Rektor: Inal Loov

F. of Philology (including Russian Literature and Language, Chechen and Ingoosh Language and Literature, Acting and Journalism)
Dean: Firuza Ozdoyeva; *staff* 60 (10)
F. of History
Dean: Aslanbek Hasbulatov; *staff* 30
F. of Economics
Dean: Taimaz Abubakarov; *staff* 15 (4)
F. of Biology and Chemistry
Dean: Ukhum-Ali Magomedbekov; *staff* 34 (10)
F. of Geography
Dean: Varvara Bokova; *staff* 17 (4)
F. of Physics
Dean: Raikom Dadashev; *staff* 27 (4)
F. of Mathematics
Dean: Hamzat Murdayev; *staff* 40 (6)
F. of Romance and Germanic Philology
Dean: Maya Ryaschina; *staff* 28 (3)
D. for Evening Studies
Dean: Ayub Mankiev
D. for Medical Treatment
Dean: Bulat Visaitov
D. for Correspondence Courses
Dean: Ibrahim Israilov
All-Union Ce. for Problems of Psychological Communication
Dean: Victor Kan-Kalic; *staff* 10 (4)
L. of Plants
Dean: Galushko Anatoly; *staff* 6 (14)
L. of Physical and Chemical Research of Mercury
Dean: Ibragimov Khamzat; *staff* 10 (12)
L. of Radiomeasurements
Dean: Kasakov Anatoly; *staff* 8 (20)

Founded 1972. Placed under the authority of the Union-Republic State Committee for Public Education. Financed by the State. Governing body: the University Council. Residential facilities for students.

Arrangements for co-operation with Sofia University and Semmelweis Medical University.

Academic Year: September to July.

Admission Requirements: Competitive entrance examination following general or special secondary school certificate.

Fees: None.

Language of Instruction: Russian.

Degrees and Diplomas: Diploma of Specialist in a particular field of study. Kandidat nauk, Candidate of the Sciences, a further 3 yrs and thesis. Doktor nauk, by thesis after Kandidat.

Library: University Scientific Library, *c.* 800,000 vols.

Special Facilities (Museums, etc.): Literary Museum; Alpinarium; Mountainous Geographic Research Station.

Publications: Collections of Scientific Papers: History; Russian and Vainakh Philology; Romance and Germanic Philology; Physics; Mathematics (annually).

Press or Publishing House: Press House affiliated to Rostov University Publishing House.

Academic Staff, 1990:

Rank	Full-time	Part-time
Professors	26	1
Readers	133	6
Senior Teachers	54	15
Assistants	113	41
Total	326	63

Student Enrolment, 1990:

	Men	Women	Total
Of the country	602	2206	2808*

*Also 2789 evening and correspondence students.

7016 **ČELJABINSKIJ GOSUDARSTVENNYJ UNIVERSITET**

Chelyabinsk State University

Ul. Br. Kashirinyh, 129, 454136 Celjabinsk 136, Rossiskaja SFSR

Telephone: 42-09-25

Rektor: V.D. Batukhtin

Vice-Rektor: S.V. Matveev

F. of History
Dean: N.B. Zibulsky; *staff* 249 (400)
F. of Physics
Dean: V.K. Pershin; *staff* 200
F. of Philology
Dean: T.J. Shishmarenkova; *staff* 340
F. of Mathematics
Dean: V.I. Ukhobotov; *staff* 440
F. of Economics
Dean: A.V. Emurgnov; *staff* 300 (200)
F. of Physics and Technics
Dean: B.I. Tambovzev; *staff* 300

Founded 1976, a State institution. Placed under the authority of the Union-Republic State Committee for PublicEducation. Financed by the State. Governing bodies: the Rector and Pro-Rectors; the Academic Council.

Academic Year: September to July.

Admission Requirements: Competitive entrance examination following general or special secondary school certificate.

Fees: None.

Degrees and Diplomas: Diploma of Specialist in a particular field of study, 5 yrs. Kandidat nauk, Candidate of the Sciences, a further 3 yrs and thesis. Doktor nauk, by thesis after Kandidat.

Special Facilities (Museums, etc.): Museum of Archaeology.

Academic Staff, 1990:

Rank	Full-time	Part-time
Professors	17	8
Assistant Professors	120	16
Assistants	100	–
Total	237	24

Student Enrolment, 1990:

	Men	Women	Total
Of the country	200	250	450

7017 **ČERNOVICKIJ ORDENA TRUDOVOGO KRASNOGO ZNAMENI GOSUDARSTVENNYJ UNIVERSITET**

Chernovtsy State University

Ul. Kocjubinskogo 2, 274012 Černovcy, Ukrainskaja SSR

F. of History
F. of Philology
F. of Mathematics
F. of Physics
F. of Chemistry
F. of Biology
F. of Geography
F. of Foreign Languages
D. for Evening Studies
D. for Correspondence Courses

Founded 1875. Placed under the authority of the Union-Republic State Committee for Public Education. Financed by the State. Governing bodies: the Rector and Pro-Rectors; the Academic Council.

Academic Year: September to July.

Admission Requirements: Competitive entrance examination following general or special secondary school certificate.

Fees: None.

Degrees and Diplomas: Diploma of Specialist in a particular field of study, 5 yrs. Kandidat nauk, Candidate of the Sciences, a further 3 yrs and thesis. Doktor nauk, by thesis after Kandidat.

Student Enrolment: c. 3550. (Also *c.* 6500 evening and correspondence students).

7018 **ČHUVAŠSKIJ GOSUDARSTVENNYJ UNIVERSITET IM. I.N. UL'JANOVA**

Chuvash State University

Moskovskij prosp. 15, 428015 Čeboksary, Rossiskaja SFSR

Telex: 158125 OPYT

Telephone: 24-11-67; 24-87-65

Rektor: Sidorov Pyotr Alexsandrovich (1981-90)

Vice-Rektor: Terentiev Aleksej Grigoryevich

F. of Electrical Engineering

F. of History and Philology

F. of Medicine

F. of Economics

F. of Chemistry

F. of Industrial Electrification

F. of Physics and Mathematics

F. of General Technology (correspondence courses)

D. for General Evening Studies

D. for Correspondence Courses

Founded 1969. Placed under the authority of Union-Republic State Committee for Public Education. Financed by the State. Governing bodies: the Rector and Pro-Rectors; the Academic Council.

Academic Year: September to July.

Admission Requirements: Competitive entrance examination following general or special secondary school certificate.

Fees: None.

Degrees and Diplomas: Diploma of Specialist in a particular field of study, 5 yrs. Kandidat nauk, Candidate of the Sciences, a further 3 yrs and thesis. Doktor nauk, by thesis after Kandidat.

Student Enrolment: c. 5000 (Also *c.* 3600 evening and correspondence students).

7019 **DAGESTANSKIJ ORDENA DRUŽBY NARODOV GOSUDARSTVENNYJ UNIVERSITET IM. V.I. LENINA**

Dagestan State University

Sovetskaja ul. 8, 367025 Mahačkala, Dagestanskaja ASSR

Telephone: 7-29-50

F. of History

F. of Philosophy

F. of Physics

F. of Mathematics

F. of Chemistry

F. of Biology

F. of Foreign Languages

F. of Economics

F. of Law

F. of Commerce

D. for Evening Studies

D. for Correspondence Courses

Founded 1957. Placed under the authority of the Union-Republic State Committee for Public Education. Financed by the State. Governing bodies: the Rector and Pro-Rectors; the Academic Council.

Academic Year: September to July.

Admission Requirements: Competitive entrance examination following general or special secondary school certificate.

Fees: None.

Degrees and Diplomas: Diploma of Specialist in a particular field of study, 5 yrs. Kandidat nauk, Candidate of the Sciences, a further 3 yrs and thesis. Doktor nauk, by thesis after Kandidat.

Academic Staff: c. 200.

Student Enrolment: c. 3750 (Also *c.* 3100 evening and correspondence students).

7020 **DAL'NEVOSTOČNYJ GOSUDARSTVENNYJ UNIVERSITET**

Far East State University

Ul. Suhanova 8, 690600 Vladivostok, Prinorskaga Kraja, GSP Rossiskaja SFSR

Telex: 213218 FESU SU

Telephone: 5-72-00; 2-12-80; 2-47-00

Fax: 5-72-00

Rektor: Vladimir Ivanovich Kurzlov (1990-)

F. of Philology (Russian and English)

Dean: L.P. Bondarenko; *staff* 62

F. of Oriental Studies

Dean: V.L. Larin; *staff* 67

F. of Journalism

Dean: I.A. Galkina; *staff* 15

F. of History

Dean: R.M. Samigulin; *staff* 24

F. of Law

Dean: S.D. Knyazev; *staff* 72

F. of Mathematics

Dean: V.B. Osipov; *staff* 64

F. of Physics

Dean: V.N. Savchenko; *staff* 41

F. of Geophysics

Dean: G.V. Svinukhov; *staff* 46

F. of Chemistry

Dean: G.Ya. Zolotar; *staff* 35

F. of Biology and Soil Science

Dean: O.I. Belogurov; *staff* 42

Research I. of Physics and Technics

D. for Evening Studies

Head: E.V. Nadtochi

D. for Correspondence Courses

Head: E.V. Nadtochi

Also International Department, Courses of Russian Language for Foreign Students and Commercial Bureau.

Founded 1923. Placed under the authority of the Union-Republic State Committee for Public Education. Financed by the State. Governing bodies: the Rector and Pro-Rectors; the Academic Council. Residential facilities for 2366 students.

Arrangements for inter-university co-operation with: Harbin University; Heilongjing University; Hanyeng University; Kyungnam University; Hokkaido Tokai University; University of Maryland, Asian Division; University of Alaska; Washington State University; California State University; University of Virginia; University of Alaska Fairbanks; University of Hawaii; Kingston Polytechnic Institute.

Academic Year: September to July.

Admission Requirements: Competitive entrance examination following general or special secondary school certificate.

Fees: None.

Language of Instruction: Russian.

Degrees and Diplomas: Diploma of Specialist in a particular field of study, 5 yrs. Kandidat nauk, Candidate of the Sciences, a further 3 yrs and thesis. Doktor nauk, by thesis after Kandidat.

Library: Scientific Library, 500,000 vols.

Special Facilities (Museums, etc.): Museum of Zoology; Museum of Archaeology.

Publication: Far East University Press.

Academic Staff, 1990:

Rank	Full-time
Academicians	5
Professors	32
Associate Professors	215
Senior Teachers	287
Assistants	175
Total	714

Student Enrolment, 1990:

	Men	Women	Total
Of the country	1443	2725	4168*

*Also 3494 external students and students by correspondence.

7021 **DNEPROPETROVSKIJ ORDENA TRUDOVOGO KRASNOGO ZNAMENI GOSUDARSTVENNYJ UNIVERSITET IM. 300-LETIJA VOSSOEDINENIJAUKRAINY S ROSSIEJ**

Dniepropetrovsk State University

Prosp. Gagarina 72, 320625 Dnepropetrovsk 10, Ukrainskaja SSR

Telephone: 3-16-71

F. of History
F. of Philosophy
F. of Mathematics and Applied Mathematics
F. of Physics
F. of Physics and Technology
F. of Chemistry
F. of Biology
F. of Economics
F. of Radio-Physics
F. of General Studies
D. for Evening Studies

Founded 1919. Placed under the authority of the Union-Republic State Committee for Public Education. Financed by the State. Governing bodies: the Rector and Pro-Rectors; the Academic Council.

Academic Year: September to July.

Admission Requirements: Competitive entrance examination following general or special secondary school certificate.

Fees: None.

Degrees and Diplomas: Diploma of Specialist in a particular field of study, 5 yrs. Kandidat nauk, Candidate of the Sciences, a further 3 yrs and thesis. Doktor nauk, by thesis after Kandidat.

Student Enrolment: c. 6800 (Also c. 5660 evening and correspondence students).

7022 **DONECKIJ GOSUDARSTVENNYJ UNIVERSITET**

Donets State University

Universitetskaja ul. 24, 340055 Doneck, Ukrainskaja SSR

Telephone: 33-00-28

F. of Law
F. of History
F. of Philology
F. of Languages
F. of Physics
F. of Mathematics
F. of Chemistry
F. of Biology
F. of Economics
D. for Evening Studies
D. for Correspondence Courses

Founded 1965. Placed under the authority of the Union-Republic State Committee for Public Education. Financed by the State. Governing bodies: the Rector and Pro-Rectors; the Academic Council.

Academic Year: September to July.

Admission Requirements: Competitive entrance examination following general or special secondary school certificate.

Fees: None.

Degrees and Diplomas: Diploma of Specialist in a particular field of study, 5 yrs. Kandidat nauk, Candidate of the Sciences, a further 3 yrs and thesis. Doktor nauk, by thesis after Kandidat.

Student Enrolment: c. 5200 (Also c. 6100 evening and correspondence students).

7023 ***EREVANSKIJ ORDENA TRUDOVOGO KRASNOGO ZNAMENI GOSUDARSTVENNYJ UNIVERSITET**

Erevan State University

CUl. Mravjana 1, 375049 Erevan, Armjanskaja SSR

Telephone: 55-46-29

Rektor: S.A. Ambartsoumjan (1977-)

F. of History
F. of Philology
F. of Oriental Languages and Literature
F. of Law
F. of Mathematics
F. of Applied Mathematics
F. of Physics
F. of Chemistry
F. of Biology
F. of Geology
F. of Geography
F. of Radio-Physics and Electronics
F. of Russian Language and Literature
F. for Improving Qualifications of Academic Staff
D. for Correspondence Courses
D. for Evening Studies

Founded 1920. Placed under the authority of the Union-Republic State Committee for Public Education. Financed by the State. Governing bodies: the Rector and Pro-Rectors; the Academic Council. Residential facilities for academic staff and students.

Academic Year: September to June (September-January; February-June).

Admission Requirements: Competitive entrance examination following general or special secondary school certificate.

Fees: None.

Languages of Instruction: Armenian and Russian.

Degrees and Diplomas: Professional titles and diplomas of Specialist in a particular field of study, 5 yrs. Kandidat nauk, Candidateof the Sciences, a further 3 yrs and thesis. Doktor nauk, by thesis after Kandidat.

Library: University Library, c. 1,600,000 vols.

Special Facilities (Museums, etc.): Museums: History; Geology.

Publications: Scientific Notes; Herald of the University; Young Scientific Worker; Erevan University; Students' Scientific Notes.

Academic Staff: c. 800.

Student Enrolment: c. 8000.

7024 **GOMEL'SKIJ GOSUDARSTVENNYJ UNIVERSITET**

Gomel' State University

Ul. Sovetskaja 104, 246699 Gomel', Belorusskaja SSR

Telephone: 57-11-15

F. of History and Philology
F. of Mathematics and Applied Mathematics
F. of Physics
F. of Biology and Soil Science
F. of Geology
F. of Economics
F. of Physical Education
D. for Evening Studies
D. for Correspondence Courses

Founded 1970. Placed under the authority of the Union-Republic State Committee for Public Education. Financed by the State. Governing bodies: the Rector and Pro-Rectors; the Academic Council. Residential facilities for academic staff and students.

Academic Year: September to July (September-February; February-July).

Admission Requirements: Competitive entrance examination following general or special secondary school certificate.

Fees: None.

Languages of Instruction: Russian and Belorussian.

Degrees and Diplomas: Diploma of Specialist in a particular field of study, 5 yrs. Kandidat nauk, Candidate of the Sciences, a further 3 yrs and thesis. Doktor nauk, by thesis after Kandidat.

Library: c. 600,000 vols.

Academic Staff: c. 500.

Student Enrolment: c. 4000 (Also c. 3250 external students).

7025 **GOR'KOVSKIJ ORDENA TRUDOVOGO KRASNOGO ZNAMENI GOSUDARSTVENNYJ UNIVERSITET IM. N. I. LOVAČEVKOGO**

Gorky State University

Prosp. Gagarina 23, 603600 Gor'kij, Rossiskaja SFSR

Telephone: 65-64-71

F. of History and Philology
F. of Mathematics and Applied Mathematics
F. of Computer Science and Cybernetics
F. of Physics
F. of Radio-Physics
F. of Chemistry
F. of Biology
F. of Industrial Economics
D. for Evening Studies
D. for Correspondence Courses

Founded 1920. Placed under the authority of the Union-Republic State Committee for Public Education. Financed by the State. Governing bodies: the Rector and Pro-Rectors; the Academic Council.

Academic Year: September to June (September-January; February-June).

Admission Requirements: Competitive entrance examination following general or special secondary school certificate.

Fees: None.

Language of Instruction: Russian.

Degrees and Diplomas: Diploma of Specialist in a particular field of study, 5 yrs. Kandidat nauk, Candidate of the Sciences, a further 3 yrs and thesis. Doktor nauk, by thesis after Kandidat.

Library: c. 1,800,000 vols.

Special Facilities (Museums, etc.): Zoology Museum..

Publication: Scientific Transactions.

Academic Staff: c. 660.

Student Enrolment: c. 6500 (Also c. 4000 evening and correspondence students).

7026 **GRODNENSKIJ GOSUDARSTVENNYJ UNIVERSITET**

Grodno State University

Ul. Ozesko 22, 230023 Grodno, Belorusskaja SSR

Telephone: 7-01-73

F. of History and Philology
F. of Languages
F. of Mathematics
F. of Law
F. of Physics

Founded 1978. Placed under the authority of the Union-Republic State Committee for Public Education. Financed by the State. Governing bodies: the Rector and Pro-Rectors; the Academic Council.

Academic Year: September to July.

Admission Requirements: Competitive entrance examination following general or special secondary school certificate.

Fees: None.

Degrees and Diplomas: Diploma of Specialist in a particular field of study, 5 yrs. Kandidat nauk, Candidate of the Sciences, a further 3 yrs and thesis. Doktor nauk, by thesis after Kandidat.

7027 ***HAR'KOVSKIJ ORDENA TRUDOVOGO KRASNOGO ZNAMENI I ORDENA DRUŽBY NARODOV GOSUDARSTVENNYJ UNIVERSITET IM. A.M. GOR'KOGO**

Kharkov State University

Pl. Dzeržinskogo 4, 310077 Har'kov, Ukrainskaja SSR

Telephone: 45-73-75

Rektor: Ivan E. Tarapov

F. of History
Dean: Julian I. Zhuravskij
F. of Mathematics and Mechanics
Dean: Oleg V. Uvarov
F. of Physics
Dean: Victor V. Vorobjev
F. of Chemistry
Dean: Igor K. Ishchenko
F. of Biology
Dean: Vasily I. Glushchenko
F. of Geology and Geography
Dean: Victor N. Gorstka
F. of Economics
Dean: Ivan E. Tkachenko
F. of Foreign Languages (and Interpretation)
Dean: Jury K. Chuchko
F. of Philology
Dean: Leonid G. Avksentjev
F. of Radio-Physics
Dean: Vasily A. Svich
F. of Technical Physics
Dean: Vladimir I. Lapshin
I. of Chemical Research
Director: Oleg A. Ponomarev
I. of Biological Research
Director: Victor V. Lemeshko
Preparatory F. for Foreign Students
Dean: Victor A. Shalajev
D. for Evening Studies
D. for Correspondence Courses

Founded 1805. Developed considerably after 1917 and served as a basis for the creation of a number of other institutions of higher education. The university is placed under the authority of the USSR State Committee for Public Education. Financed by the State. Governing bodies: the Rektor and Pro-Rektors; the Academic Council. Residential facilities for students in hostels.

Arrangements for co-operation with: University of Maine; Universisty of Southern Maine; University of Cincinnati; Xavier Jesuit University; University of California, Hayward; University of Wisconsin, Green Bay; Dickinson State University; Southeastern Massachusetts University; Georgia College; University of Beirut; University of Oran; University of Bath; University of Poznan; University of Košice; University of Constantina; Universityof Rostock; University of Lille III; University of Cairo; University of Sarajevo; University of San Marcos.

Academic Year: September to July (September-January; February-July).

Admission Requirements: Competitive entrance examinations.

Fees: None.

Languages of Instruction: Russian and Ukrainian.

Degrees and Diplomas: Diploma of Specialist in a particular field of study, 5 yrs. Kandidat nauk, Candidate of the Sciences, a further 3 yrs and thesis. Doktor nauk, Doctor of the Sciences, by thesis after Kandidat.

Libraries: Central Scientific Library, c. 3,500,000 vols; Institute of Chemical Research, c. 15,000; Institute of Biological Research, c. 20,000; Observatory, c. 1000.

Special Facilities (Museums, etc.): Museums: Darwinism; Archaeology; Mineralogy; University History.

Publications: Vestnik Har'kovskogo Universiteta (Kharkov University Herald); Transactions of the Physical Department of the Faculty of Physics and other series.

Academic Staff, 1989-90:

Rank	Full-time
Professors, Doctors of Sciences	94
Assistant Professors, Candidates of Science	540
Lecturers	356
Total	990

Student Enrolment, 1989-90:

Of the country	11,000
Of other countries	900
Total	11,900*

*Also 5000 evening and correspondence students.

7028 ***IRKUTSKIJ GOSUDARSTVENNYJ UNIVERSITET IM. A. A. ŽDANOVA**

Irkutsk State University

Ul. K. Marksa 1, 664003 Irkutsk 3, Rossiskaja SFSR

Telephone: 4-44-30

Rektor: P. Yu. Kozlov

F. of Philology (including Mongolian Studies)
F. of Law
F. of History
F. of Mathematics
F. of Physics
F. of Chemistry
F. of Biology and Soil Science
F. of Geology
F. of Geography

D. for Evening Studies
D. for Correspondence Courses
I. of Physical and Chemical Research
I. of Biological and Geographical Research
Observatory
Botanical Garden Biological Station 'Angara'
Biological Station 'Baikal'

Founded 1918 with two faculties; law, and history and philology. Underwent a number of transformations. New faculties were established, some of which were again detached from the university to form separate institutions. The university is placed under the authority of the Union-Republic State Committee for Public Education. Financed by the State. Governing body: the Rector and Pro-Rectors, the Academic Council and the Faculty Councils.

Academic Year: September to July (September-January; February-July).

Admission Requirements: Competitive entrance examination following general or special secondary school certificate.

Fees: None.

Language of Instruction: Russian.

Degrees and Diplomas: Diploma of Specialist in a particular field of study, 5 yrs. Kandidat nauk, Candidate of the Sciences, a further 3 yrs and thesis. Doktor nauk, by thesis after Kandidat.

Libraries: Naučnaja biblioteka (science), *c.* 1,500,000 vols; Učebnaja biblioteka (textbooks and teaching material), *c.* 180,000.

Special Facilities (Museums, etc.): Baikal Museum; Zoology Museum; Herbarium of Eastern Siberia.

Publications: Trudy Irkutskogo Gosudarstvennogo Universiteta (transactions); Isvestija Biologo-Geografičeskogo Naučno-Issledovatel'skogo Instituta (Bulletin of the Research Institute for Biology and Geography); Isvestija Fisiko-Himičeskogo Naučno-Issledovatel'skogo Instituta (Bulletin of the Research Institute for Physics and Chemistry); Trudy Naučnoj Biblioteki (Transactions of the Scientific Library); Irkutskij Universitet.

Student Enrolment: c. 5600 (Also *c.* 4300 evening and correspondence students).

7029 **IVANOVSKIJ GOSUDARSTVENNYJ UNIVERSITET IM. PERVOGO V ROSSII IVANOVO-VOZNESENSKOGO OBŠČEGORODSKOGO SOVETA RABOCIH DEPUTATOV**

Ivanovo State University

Ul. Ermaka 39, 153377 Ivanovo, Rossiskaja SFSR

Telephone: 4-02-16

F. of History
F. of Law
F. of Philology
F. of Romance and Germanic Philology
F. of Mathematics
F. of Physics
F. of Biology and Chemistry
F. of Economics
D. for Evening Studies
D. for Correspondence Courses

Founded 1974. Placed under the authority of the Union-Republic State Committee for Public Education. Financed by the State. Governing bodies: the Rector and Pro-Rectors; the Academic Council

Academic Year: September to July.

Admission Requirements: Competitive entrance examination following general or special secondary school certificate.

Fees: None.

Degrees and Diplomas: Diploma of Specialist in a particular field of study, 5 yrs. Kandidat nauk, Candidate of the Sciences, a further 3 yrs and thesis. Doktor nauk, by thesis after Kandidat.

Student Enrolment: c. 2400 (Also *c.* 2800 evening and correspondence students).

7030 **JAKUTSKIJ ORDENA DRUŽBY NORODOV GOSUDARSTVENNYJ UNIVERSITET**

Yakutsk State University

Ul. Belinskogo 58, 677891 Jakutsk, Rossiskaja SFSR

Telephone: 4-38-22

Rektor: Andreev Vasiliy Sergeyevitch

Vice-Rektor: Sivtsey Innokentiy Semyenovitch

F. of History and Law
Dean: N.A. Gogolev; *staff* 31 (16)

F. of Foreign Languages (English, French, German Languages and Literature)
Dean: S.N. Barashkova; *staff* 28 (3)

F. of Physics
Dean: I.S. Kychkin; *staff* 49 (6)

F. of Mathematics
Dean: I.Y. Yegorov; *staff* 58 (19)

F. of Biology and Geography
Dean: V.N. Vinokurov; *staff* 46 (18)

F. of Agriculture (including Veterinary Medicine and Animal Husbandry)

F. of Medicine
Dean: A.S. Grigoyev; *staff* 74 (11)

F. of Engineering and Technology
Dean: V.V. Filippov *staff* 59 (29)

F. of Geology and Surveying
Dean: R.M. Scryabin; *staff* 45 (10)

F. of Philology
Dean: A.A. Burtsev; *staff* 58 (1)

F. of Teacher Training
Dean: I.I. Savvinov

D. of Evening Studies

D. for Correspondence Courses
Dean: I.I. Yegorov

Agricultural Station

Cinema L.

Scientific Research D.
Dean: V.R. Kuzmin

Founded 1934 as teacher training institute, became university in 1956. Placed under the authority of the Union-Republic State Committee for Public Education. Financed by the State. Governing bodies: the Rector and Pro-Rectors; the Academic Council. Residential facilities for academic staff and students.

Academic Year: September to July (September-February; February-July).

Admission Requirements: Competitive entrance examination following general or special secondary school certificate.

Fees: None.

Language of Instruction: Russian.

Degrees and Diplomas: Diploma of Specialist in a particular field of study, 5 yrs. Kandidat nauk, Candidate of the Sciences, a further 3 yrs and thesis. Doktor nauk, by thesis after Kandidat.

Library: Central Library, *c.* 215,000 vols.

Special Facilities (Museums, etc.): Museums: Human Anatomy; Legal Medicine; Domestic Animals' Anatomy; Geology and Zoology; Archaeology. Picture Gallery.

Publication: Učënye Zapiski (scientific papers).

Press or Publishing House: Editorial-Publishing Department.

Academic Staff, 1990: 605.

Student Enrolment, 1990:

	Men	Women	Total
Of the country	1900	2854	4754*

*Also 2562 correspondence students.

7031 **JAROSLAVSKIJ GOSUDARSTVENNYJ UNIVERSITET**

Yaroslavl State University

Sovetskaja ul. 14, Centr, 150000 Jaroslavl', Rossiskaja SFSR

Telephone: 4-02-16

F. of Physics
F. of Mathematics
F. of Economics
F. of Psychology and Biology
F. of History and Law
D. for Evening Studies

Founded 1970. Placed under the authority of the Union-Republic State Committee for Public Education. Financed by the State. Governing bodies: the Rector and Pro-Rectors; the Academic Council.

Academic Year: September to July.

Admission Requirements: Competitive entrance examination following general or special secondary school certificate.

Fees: None.

Degrees and Diplomas: Diploma of Specialist in a particular field of study, 5 yrs. Kandidat nauk, Candidate of the Sciences, a further 3 yrs and thesis. Doktor nauk, by thesis after Kandidat.

Student Enrolment: c. 2200 (Also *c.* 300 evening and correspondence students).

7032 **KABARDINO-BALKARSKIJ ORDENA DRUŽNY NARODOV GOSUDARSTVENNYJ UNIVERSITET**

Kabardino-Balkarsk State University

Ul. Černyševskogo 173, 360004 Nal'čik, Kabardino-Balkarskaja ASSR

Telephone: 2-52-54

F. of History and Philology
F. of Physics
F. of Mathematics
F. of Agriculture
F. of Chemistry and Biology
F. of Engineering and Technology
F. of Medicine
F. of Physical Education
F. of Romance and German Philology
F. of Agriculture
F. of Economics and Computer Sciences
D. for Evening Studies
D. for Correspondence Courses

Founded 1957 on the basis of a pedagogical institute, established 1932. Placed under the authority of Union-Republic State Committee for Public Education. Financed by the State. Governing body: the Rector and Pro-Rectors, and the Academic Council. Residential facilities for academic staff and students.

Academic Year: September to June (September-January; February-June).

Admission Requirements: Competitive entrance examination following general or special secondary school certificate.

Fees: None.

Language of Instruction: Russian.

Degrees and Diplomas: Diploma of Specialist in a particular field of study, 5 yrs. Kandidat nauk, Candidate of the Sciences, a further 3 yrs and thesis. Doktor nauk, by thesis after Kandidat.

Library: c. 200,000 vols.

Publication: Scientific Transactions.

Student Enrolment: c. 5000 (Also c. 4000 evening and correspondence students).

7033 **KALININGRADSKIJ GOSUDARSTVENNYJ UNIVERSITET**

Kaliningrad State University

Al. Nevsky St. 14, 236041 Kaliningrad, Rossiskaja SSR

Telex: PAVLIN 262 217

Telephone: 3-49-41

Rector: Medvedev Nikoliy Andreevitch

F. of History and Philology
Dean: G.P. Zhidkov
F. of Physics
Dean: A.I. Ivanov
F. of Mathematics
Dean: V.S. Malakhovsky
F. of Law
Dean: V.P. Nazhimov
F. of Chemistry
Dean: V.A. Funtikov
F. of Biology
Dean: N.P. Birukov

Founded 1967. Placed under the authority of the Union-Republic State Committee for Public Education. Financed by the State. Governing bodies: the Rector and Pro-Rectors; the Academic Council. Residential facilities for academic staff and students.

Academic Year: September to July.

Admission Requirements: Competitive entrance examination following general or special secondary school certificate.

Fees: None.

Language of Instruction: Russian.

Degrees and Diplomas: Diploma of Specialist in a particular field of study, 5 yrs. Kandidat nauk, Candidate of the Sciences, a further 3 yrs and thesis. Doktor nauk, by thesis after Kandidat.

Library: Central Library, 470,000 vols.

Special Facilities (Museums, etc.): Museum of I. Kant.

Publication: Journal.

Student Enrolment: c. 2800.

7034 **KALININSKIJ GOSUDARSTVENNYJ UNIVERSITET**

Kalinin State University

Ul. Željabova 33, 170013 Kalinin, Rossiskaja SFSR

Telephone: 3-15-50

F. of Mathematics
F. of Physics
F. of Chemistry and Biology
F. of Philology
F. of Romance and Germanic Philology
F. of History
F. of Economics
F. of Law
D. for Evening Studies
D. for Correspondence Courses

Founded 1971. Placed under the authority of the Union-Republic State Committee for Public Education. Financed by the State. Governing bodies: the Rector and Pro-Rectors; the Academic Council.

Academic Year: September to July.

Admission Requirements: Competitive entrance examination following general or special secondary school certificate.

Fees: None.

Degrees and Diplomas: Diploma of Specialist in a particular field of study, 5 yrs. Kandidat nauk, Candidate of the Sciences, a further 3 yrs and thesis. Doktor nauk, by thesis after Kandidat.

Student Enrolment: c. 3200 (Also c. 4000 evening and correspondence students).

7035 **KALMYCKIJ GOSUDARSTVENNYJ UNIVERSITET**

Kalmyk State University

Ul. Puškina 11, 358000 Elista, Rossiskaja SFRS

Telephone: 2-50-60

F. of Philology
F. of Physics and Mathematics
F. of Biology
F. of Agriculture
D. for Correspondence Courses

Founded 1970. Placed under the authority of the Union-Republic State Committee for Public Education. Financed by the State. Governing bodies: the Rector and Pro-Rectors; the Academic Council.

Academic Year: September to July.

Admission Requirements: Competitive entrance examination following general or special secondary school certificate.

Fees: None.

Degrees and Diplomas: Diploma of Specialist in a particular field of study, 5 yrs. Kandidat nauk, Candidate of the Sciences a further 3 yrs and thesis. Doktor nauk, by thesis after Kandidat.

Student Enrolment: c. 2300 (Also c. 2400 evening and correspondence students).

7036 **KARAGANDINSKIJ GOSUDARSTVENNYJ UNIVERSITET**

Karaganda State University

Universitetskaja ul. 28, 470074 Karaganda, Kazahskaja SSR

Telephone: 74-49-50

F. of History
F. of Philology
F. of Physics
F. of Mathematics
F. of Biology
F. of Chemistry
F. of Economics
F. of Law
D. for Evening Courses
D. for Correspondence Courses

Founded 1972. Placed under the authority of the Union-Republic State Committee for Public Education. Financed by the State. Governing bodies: the Rector and Pro-Rectors; the Academic Council.

Academic Year: September to July.

Admission Requirements: Competitive entrance examination following general or special secondary school certificate.

Fees: None.

Degrees and Diplomas: Diploma of specialist in a particular field of study, 5 yrs. Kandidat nauk, Candidate of the Sciences, a further 3 yrs and thesis. Doktor nauk, by thesis after Kandidat.

Student Enrolment: c. 3200 (Also c. 2600 evening and correspondence students).

7037 ***KAZAHSKIJ ORDENA TRUDOVOGO KRASNOGO ZNAMENI GOSUDARSTVENNYJ UNIVERSITET IM. S.M. KIROVA**

Kazakh State University

Ul. Timiryazeva 46, 480121 Alma-Ata, Kazakskaja SSR

Telephone: 62-41-42

Rector: U.A. Dzholdasbekov (1970-)

F. of Biology
F. of Geography
F. of Mathematics
F. of Mechanics and Applied Mathematics
F. of Physics
F. of Chemistry
F. of History
F. of Journalism
F. of Philosophy and Economics
F. of Law
F. of Philology
F. for Evening Studies
F. for Correspondence Courses
Also 13 Research Laboratories.

Founded 1934. Placed under the authority of the Union-Republic State Committee for Public Education. Financed by the State. Governing bodies: the Rector and Pro-Rectors; the Academic Council. Residential facilities for more than 3000 academic staff and students.

Arrangements for co-operation with: University of Rostock.

Academic Year: September to July (September-January; February-June).

Admission Requirements: Competitive entrance examination following general or special secondary school certificate.

Fees: None.

Languages of Instruction: Russian and Kazakh.

Degrees and Diplomas: Diploma of Specialist in a particular field of study, 5 yrs. Kandidat nauk, Candidate of the Sciences, a further 3 yrs and thesis. Doktor nauk, by thesis after Kandidat.

Library: Total, 1,500,000 vols.

Special Facilities (Museums, etc.): Museums: Zoology; Botany; Archaeology.

Publication: Scientific publications (annually).

Academic Staff: c. 1000 (50).

Student Enrolment: c. 13,000.

7038 ***KAZANSKIJ ORDENA TRUDOVOGO KRASNOGO ZNAMENI ORDENA LENINA GOSUDARSTVENNYJ UNIVERSITET IM. V.I. UL'JANOVA LENINA**

Kazan State University

Ul. Lenina 18, 320008 Kazan', Rossiskaja SFSR

Telephone: 32-88-75

Rektor: A.I. Konovalov (1979-)

F. of History and Philology (including Journalism)
Dean: Florid Agzamov
F. of Law
Dean: Alexander Ryabov
F. of Mathematics, and Applied Mathematics, and Cybernetics
Dean: Vladimir Vishnevski
F. of Physics
Dean: Alexander Maklakov
F. of Chemistry
Dean: Irina Konovalova
F. of Biology and Soil Science
Dean: Anatoli Golubev
F. of Geology
Dean: Rid Tuhvatullin
F. of Geography
Dean: Yuri Perevedentsev
D. for Evening Studies
D. for Correspondence Courses

Founded 1804. Placed under the authority of the Union-Republic State Committee for Public Education. Financed by the State. Governing bodies: the Rector and Pro-Rectors; the Academic Council.

Academic Year: September to July.

Admission Requirements: Competitive entrance examination following general or special secondary school certificate.

Fees: None.

Language of Instruction: Russian.

Degrees and Diplomas: Diploma of Specialist in a particular field of study, 5 yrs. Kandidat nauk, Candidate of the Sciences, a further 3 yrs and thesis. Doktor nauk, by thesis after Kandidat.

Library: c. 4,700,000 vols.

Special Facilities (Museums, etc.): Museums: History; Zoology; Geology; Ethnography.

Publications: Izvestia Vuzov; Matematica.

Student Enrolment, 1986-87:

Of the country	7437
Of other countries	300
Total	7737

7039 **KEMEROVSKIJ GOSUDARSTVENNYJ UNIVERSITET**

Kemerovo State University

Krasnaja ul. 6, 650043 Kemerovo, Rossiskaja SFSR

Telex: 133141 SLAVA SU

Telephone: 23-12-26

Rektor: Yu.A. Zakharov

Utchenyi Secretar: V.S. Laricheva

F. of Economics
Dean: T.V. Zemlaynskaya; *staff* 45 (4)
F. of Philology
Dean: E.A. Surkov; *staff* 46 (6)
F. of Romance and Germanic Languages and Literature
Dean: T.M. Voloschuk; *staff* 47
F. of History
Dean: Yu.L. Govorov; *staff* 52 (7)
F. of Mathematics
Dean: V.B. Kim; *staff* 105 (4)
F. of Physics
Dean: Yu.N. Zguravlev; *staff* 57 (12)
F. of Chemistry
Dean: Yu.N. Safonov; *staff* 83 (10)
F. of Biology
Dean: G.V. Efremova; *staff* 69 (7)
F. of Law
Dean: B.Ya. Blyachman; *staff* 46
F. of Qualification Improvement
Dean: V.I. Belkov; *staff* 21 (18)
F. of Professional Orientation
Dean: Yu.I. Kyzylasov; *staff* 30 (25)
D. for Correspondence Courses
Dean: A.P. Baturin; *staff* 30 (24)
Lifelong Education Ce.
Head: C.I. Shulikov; *staff* 340 (90)
Scientific Research Ce.
Head: M.S. Lantzman; *staff* 160 (200)
Research I. of Solid State Physics and Chemistry
Head: Yu.A. Zakharov; *staff* 120 (70)
Research L. of Computers
Head: N.N. Kozik; *staff* 30 (10)
Research Ce. of Physiology of Human Beings
Head: E.M. Kazin; *staff* 40 (40)
Research L. of Youth Sociology
Head: B.G. Proshkin; A.M. Shpak; *staff* 19 (30)
Research L. of Siberian Archaeology
Head: A.I. Martynov; *staff* 40 (50)
L. of Siberian Dialects
Head: L.A. Araeva; *staff* 12 (10)
Research L. of Higher School Pedagogy
Heads: B.P. Nevzorov; N.E. Kasatkina; *staff* 13 (7)
Research L. of Humanitarian and Social Sociology
Head: S.M. Ryabykh; *staff* 35 (40)

Founded 1974. Placed under the authority of the Union-Republic State Committee for Public Education. Financed by the State. Governing bodies: the Rector and Pro-Rectors; the Academic Council. Residential facilities for 2900 students.

Joint programmes with: Institute of Archaeology (Academy of Science, Bulgaria); Institute of Mathematics (Academy of Science, Hungary); Dresden University. Lakehead University; Laurentian University; Lock-Haven University, USA; Liaoning University, China; Marie Haps Institute, Belgium; Berlin University (planned programmes).

Academic Year: September to July.

Admission Requirements: Competitive entrance examination following general or special secondary school certificate.

Fees: None.

Language of Instruction: Russian.

Degrees and Diplomas: Diploma of Specialist in a particular field of study, 5 yrs. Kandidat nauk, Candidate of the Sciences, a further 3 yrs and thesis. Doktor nauk, by thesis after Kandidat.

Library: Scientific Library, 700,000 vols.

Special Facilities (Museums, etc.): Archaeological Museum; Zoology Museum; History of Kuzbass Party Organization Museum. Astronomy Complex; University Radio System; University TV System.

Press or Publishing House: Kemerovo Branch of the Publishing House of Tomsk University.

Academic Staff, 1990:

Rank	Full-time
Professor	21
Dotzent	197
Starchyi prepodavatel	137
Assistent	137
Naychnyi sotrudnik	141
Sotrudnik	1180
Total	1813

Student Enrolment, 1990:

	Men	Women	Total
Of the country	925	2602	3527*

*Also 2741 external and correspondence students.

7040 ***KIEVSKIJ ORDENA LENINA I ORDENA OKTJABRASKOJ REVOLJUCII GOSUDARSTVENNYJ UNIVERSITET IM. T.G. SEVČENKO**

Kiev T.G. Shevchenko State University

Vladimirskaja ul. 64, 252601 Kiev 17, Ukrainskaja SSR

Telephone: 226-54-77

Fax: 224-61-66

Rektor: V.V. Skopenko (1985-)

F. of Philology
Dean: P.P. Kononenko; *staff* 106 (28)
F. of History
Dean: A.I. Slusarenko; *staff* 115 (5)
F. of Philosophy
Dean: N.F. Taranenko; *staff* 152 (20)
F. of Law
Dean: V.I. Goncharenko; *staff* 93 (30)
F. of Economics
Dean: V.P. Nesterenko; *staff* 82 (10)
F. of Romance and German Philology
Dean: O.E. Semenets; *staff* 189 (20)
F. of Journalism
Dean: A.Z. Moskalenko; *staff* 42 (72)
F. of International Relations and Law
Dean: A.S. Philipenko; *staff* 142 (12)
F. of Mathematics and Applied Mathematics
Dean: N.A. Perestiuk; *staff* 87 (25)
F. of Cybernetics (Computer Science)
Dean: O.K. Zakusilo; *staff* 94 (30)
F. of Physics
Dean: L.A. Bulavin; *staff* 92 (10)
F. of Radio-Physics
Dean: N.G. Nahodkin; *staff* 75 (35)
F. of Chemistry
Dean: V.V. Suhan; *staff* 67 (4)
F. of Biology
Dean: N.N. Musienko
F. of Geography
Dean: N.N. Padun; *staff* 54 (12)
F. of Geology
Dean: V.S. Shabatin; *staff* 49 (52)
F. of History
Dean: A.I. Slusarenko; *staff* 115 (5)
F. of Chemistry
Dean: V.V. Suhan; *staff* 67 (4)
Preparatory F. for Foreign Students
Dean: I.I. Nikolayenko; *staff* 75
Observatory
Director: V.V. Telnuk-Adamchuk; *staff* 50 (20)
Calculus Ce.
Head: V.I. Zamkovoi
D. of Physical Training
Head: V.B. Zinchenko; *staff* 42 (10)
D. for Evening Studies
D. for Correspondence Courses
I. of International Relations
Director: V.G. Butkevich; *staff* 221 (12)
Research I. of Physiology
Director: A.I. Masjuk; *staff* 150
Refresher I. for Teachers of Social Sciences
Director: V.I. Korolev; *staff* 44 (36)

Founded 1834. Placed under the authority of Union State Committee for Public Education and Ukrainian Ministry of Post-Secondary and Secondary Specialized Education. Financed by the State. Governing bodies: the Rector and Pro-Rectors; the Academic Council. Residential facilities for academic staff and students.

Arrangements for co-operation with 20 foreign institutions.

Academic Year: September to June (September-January; February-June).

Admission Requirements: Competitive entrance examination following general or special secondary school certificate or equivalent.

Fees: None.

Languages of Instruction: Ukrainian and Russian.

Degrees and Diplomas: Diploma of Specialist in a particular field of study, 5 yrs. Kandidat nauk, Candidate of the Sciences, a further 3 yrs and thesis. Doktor nauk, by thesis after Kandidat.

Libraries: Scientific Library, 3,400,000 vols; Specialized libraries, 130,000.

Special Facilities (Museums, etc.): Museums: Botany; Zoology; Geology; Mineral; Petrography; History of the University. Observatory; Botanical Garden.

Publications: Vestnik Kievskogo Universiteta (bulletin, several series); Collections of scientific works; Kijevskij Universitetet (newspaper).

Press or Publishing House: 'Vishcha skola'; 'Lybid'.

Academic Staff, 1989-90:

Rank	Full-time
Academicians	7
Doctors of Science (Professors)	234
Assistant Professors	1300
Others	2200
Total	3741

Student Enrolment, 1989-90:

Of the country	10,591
Of other countries	1632
Total	12,223*

*Also 2408 evening course students and 5184 students by correspondence.

7041 ***KIRGIZSKIJ ORDENA TRUDOVOGO KRASNOGO ZNAMENI GOSUDARSTVENNYJ UNIVERSITET IM 50-LETIJA SSSR**

Kirghiz State University

Ul. Frunze 537, 720024 Frunze 24 Kirgizskaja SSR

Telephone: 26-26-34

F. of History
F. of Law
F. of Philology
F. of Economics
F. of Finance
F. of Mathematics and Applied Mathematics
F. of Physics
F. of Geography
F. of Biology
F. of Foreign Languages
F. of Chemistry
D. for Evening Studies
D. for Correspondence Courses

Founded 1951. Placed under the authority of the Union-Republic State Committee for Public Education. Financed by the State. Governing bodies: the Rector and Pro-Rectors; the Academic Council.

Academic Year: September to July.

Admission Requirements: Competitive entrance examination following general or special secondary school certificate.

Fees: None.

Degrees and Diplomas: Diploma of Specialist in a particular field of study, 5 yrs. Kandidat nauk, Candidate of the Sciences, a further 3 yrs and thesis. Doktor nauk, by thesis after Kandidat.

Student Enrolment: c. 7300 (Also c. 5600 evening and correspondence students).

7042 ***KIŠINEVSKIJ ORDENA TRUDOVOGO KRASNOGO ZNAMENI GOSUDARSTVENNYJ UNIVERSITET IM. V.I. LENINA**

Kishinev State University

Sadovaja ul. 60, 277003 Kišinev, Moldavskaja SSR

Telex: 163645

Telephone: 24-00-41

Rektor: B.E. Mel'nik

F. of Mathematics and Cybernetics
F. of Physics
F. of Chemistry
F. of Biology and Soil Science
F. of History
F. of Economics and Commerce
F. of Law
F. of Journalism
F. of Philology
F. of Library Science
F. of Foreign Languages
Computer C.
D. for Correspondence Courses

Founded 1946. Placed under the authority of the Union-Republic State Committee for Public Education. Financed by the State. Governing bodies: the Rector and Pro-Rectors; the Academic Council. Residential facilities for students.

Arrangements for co-operation with: 'Al. I. Cuza' University, Iaşi; University of Plovdiv.

Academic Year: September to July (September-January; February-July).

Admission Requirements: Competitive examination following general or special secondary school certificate.

Fees: None.

Languages of Instruction: Moldavian and Russian.

Degrees and Diplomas: Diploma of Specialist in a particular field of study, 5 yrs. Kandidat nauk, Candidate of the Sciences, a further 3 yrs and thesis. Doktor nauk, by thesis after Kandidat.

Library: 2,260,000 vols.

Special Facilities (Museums, etc.): Natural History Museum.

Publication: Journal (weekly).

Academic Staff, 1986-87: c. 800.

Student Enrolment, 1986-87:

	Men	Women	Total
Of the country	2222	4446	6668
Of other countries	506	231	737
Total	2728	4677	7405*

*Also 5032 external students.

7043 **KRASNOJARSKIJ GOSUDARSTVENNYJ UNIVERSITET**

Krasnoyarsk State University

Prosp. Svobodnyj 79, 660062 Krasnojarsk 62, Rossiskaja SFSR

Telephone: 25-45-03

F. of Law
F. of Mathematics
F. of Physics
F. of Biology and Chemistry
D. for Evening Studies
D. for Correspondence Courses

Founded 1970. Placed under the authority of the Union-Republic State Committee for Public Education. Financed by the State. Governing bodies: the Rector and Pro-Rectors; the Academic Council.

Academic Year: September to July.

Admission Requirements: Competitive entrance examination following general or special secondary school certificate.

Fees: None.

Degrees and Diplomas: Diploma of Specialist in a particular field of study, 5 yrs. Kandidat nauk, Candidate of the Sciences, a further 3 yrs and thesis. Doktor nauk, by thesis after Kandidat.

Student Enrolment: c. 1750 (Also c. 1400 evening and correspondence students).

7044 **KUBANSKIJ GOSUDARSTVENNYJ UNIVERSITET**

Kuban State University

Ul. Karla Libknehta 149, 350751 Krasnodar Kraevoj, Rossiskaja SFSR

Telephone: 33-75-37

F. of Philology
F. of History
F. of Mathematics
F. of Physics
F. of Biology
F. of Chemistry
F. of Geography
F. of Romance and Germanic Philology
F. of Law
F. of Economics
F. of Art and Graphic Art
D. for Evening Studies
D. for Correspondence Courses

Founded 1970. Placed under the authority of the Union-Republic State Committee for Public Education. Financed by the State. Governing bodies: the Rector and Pro-Rectors; the Academic Council.

Academic Year: September to July.

Admission Requirements: Competitive entrance examination following general or special secondary school certificate.

Fees: None.

Degrees and Diplomas: Diploma of Specialist in a particular field of study, 5 yrs. Kandidat nauk, Candidate of the Sciences, a further 3 yrs and thesis. Doktor nauk, by thesis after Kandidat.

Student Enrolment: c. 4300 (Also c. 6000 evening and correspondence students).

7045 **KUJBYŠEVSKIJ GOSUDARSTVENNYJ UNIVERSITET**

Kuybshev State University

Ul. Akademika Pavlova 1, 443086 Kujbyšev oblastnoj 86, Rossiskaja SFSR

Telephone: 34-54-02

F. of Philology
F. of History
F. of Law
F. of Mathematics and Applied Mathematics
F. of Physics
F. of Chemistry and Biology
D. for Evening Studies
D. for Correspondence Courses

Founded 1970. Placed under the authority of the Union-Republic State Committee for Public Education. Financed by the State. Governing bodies: the Rector and Pro-Rectors; the Academic Council.

Academic Year: September to July.

Admission Requirements: Competitive entrance examination following general or special secondary school certificate.

Fees: None.

Degrees and Diplomas: Diploma of Specialist in a particular field of study, 5 yrs. Kandidat nauk, Candidate of the Sciences, a further 3 yrs and thesis. Doktor nauk, by thesis after Kandidat.

Student Enrolment: c. 2100 (Also c. 200 evening and correspondence students).

7046 ***LATVIJSKIJ ORDENA TRUDOVOGO KRASNOGO ZNAMENI GOSUDARSTVENNYJ UNIVERSITET IM. PETRA STUČKI**

Latvian State University

Bul. Rajnisa 19, 226098 Riga, Latvijskaja SSR

Telephone: 22-29-76

Rektor: Juris Zakis (1970-)

F. of Philology
F. of Pedagogics
F. of History and Philosophy
F. of Foreign Languages
F. of Geography
F. of Law
F. of Finance and Trade
F. of Chemistry
F. of Physics and Mathematics
F. of Biology
F. of Economics
I. of Solid State Physics
Computer Ce.

Spectroscopy Research L.
Observatory
Botanical Garden
L. for Physiological Development of Plants
D. for Evening Studies
D. for Correspondence Courses

Founded 1919. Placed under the authority of the Ministries of Higher and Specialized Secondary Education of the Republic and of the Union. Financed by the State. Governing bodies: the Rector and Pro-Rectors; the Academic Council. Residential facilities for students.

Arrangements for co-operation with Universities in: German Democratic Republic; Poland; Czechoslovakia; Italy;Syria.

Academic Year: September to July (September-January; February-June).

Admission Requirements: Competitive entrance examination following general or special secondary school certificate.

Fees: None.

Languages of Instruction: Latvian and Russian.

Degrees and Diplomas: Diploma of Specialist in a particular field of study, 5 yrs. Kandidat nauk, Candidate of the Sciences, a further 3 yrs and thesis. Doktor nauk, by thesis after Kandidat.

Library: *c.* 2,000,000.

Special Facilities (Museums, etc.): History of the University Museum; Zoology Museum.

Publication: Scientific Transactions.

Academic Staff: *c.* 1150.

Student Enrolment: *c.* 20,000.

7047 ***LENINGRADSKIJ GOSUDARSTVENNYJ UNIVERSITET**

Leningrad State University

Universitetskaja nab. 7/9, 199164 Leningrad V-164, Rossiskaja SFSR

Telephone: 218-76-31

Rektor: Stanislav P. Merkur'yev (1986-)

F. of History
F. of Philology
F. of Oriental Studies
F. of Philosophy
F. of Psychology
F. of Law
F. of Economics
F. of Mathematics and Mechanics
F. of Applied Mathematics
F. of Physics
F. of Chemistry
F. of Biology and Soil Science
F. of Geology
F. of Geography
F. of Journalism
D. of Interpretation
D. for Evening Studies
D. for Correspondence Courses
I. of Mathematical and Applied Mathematical Research
Astronomic Observatory
I. of Physical Research
I. of Chemical Research
I. of Geographical and Economic Research
I. of Biological Research
I. of Physiological Research
I. of Geological Research

Founded 1819 by Alexander I as the University of St. Petersburg. Evacuated to Saratov during World War II. Buildings heavily damaged during blockade of Leningrad, now completely restored. Placed under the authority of the Ministries of Higher and Specialized Secondary Education of the Republic and of the Union. Financed by the State. Governing bodies: the Rector and Pro-Rectors; the Academic Council; the Faculty Councils. Residential facilities for students.

Arrangements for co-operation with: Karl-Marx-Universität, Leipzig; Eötvös Loránd Tudományegyetem, Budapest; Ceské vysoké učeni technické v Praze; Sveučilište u Zagrebu; Universidad de Oriente (Cuba); Viên Dai hoc Hô Chi Minh ville; Uniwersytet Wrocławski im Bolesława Bieruta; Universitatea din Cluj-Napoca; Turun Yliopisto; Universität Hamburg; Carleton University; Freie Universität Berlin; Universitetet i Stockholm; Universitat de Barcelona; Osaka Daigaku; Université de Conakry; University of Khartoum.

Academic Year: September to July (September-January; February-July).

Admission Requirements: Competitive entrance examination following general or special secondary school certificate.

Fees: None.

Language of Instruction: Russian.

Degrees and Diplomas: Diploma of Specialist in a particular field of study, 5 yrs. Kandidat nauk, Candidate of the Sciences, a further 3 yrs and thesis. Doktor nauk, by thesis after Kandidat.

Library: Gor'kij Scientific Library, *c.* 5m. vols.

Special Facilities (Museums, etc.): Mendeleyev Museum; General University Museum; Botanical Garden.

Publication: Vestnik Leningradskogo Universiteta (bulletin, several series).

Press or Publishing House: University Press.

Academic Staff: *c.* 4000.

Student Enrolment: *c.* 15,000 (Also *c.* 8000 evening and correspondence students).

7048 **L'VOVSKIJ ORDENA LENINA GOSUDARSTVENNYJ UNIVERSITET IM. IVANA FRANKO**

L'vov State University

Universitetskaja ul. 1, 290602 L'vov, Ukrainskaja SSR

Telephone: 72-20-68

F. of History
F. of Philology
F. of Journalism
F. of Law
F. of Economics
F. of Mathematics
F. of Mechanics and Applied Mathematics
F. of Physics
F. of Chemistry
F. of Geology
F. of Biology
F. of Geography
F. of Foreign Languages
D. for Correspondence Courses
D. for Evening Studies
Astronomical Observatory
Magnetics Station
Mountain Biological Station
Radio-Biological L.
L. of Geo-Chemical and Radio Metrical Prospection

Founded 1661; closed 1805; reopened 1817 as a German-speaking university; destroyed 1848 during bombardment of L'vov and closed until 1851. Teaching in Polish and Ukrainian authorized 1871. Became a Polish university in 1919; reorganized in 1939 when the Western territories of the Ukraine became part of the Soviet Union. Placed under the authority of the Union-Republic State Committee for Public Education. Financed by the State. Governing bodies: the Rector and Pro-Rectors; the Academic Council.

Academic Year: September to July (September-January; February-July).

Admission Requirements: Competitive entrance examination following general or special secondary school certificate, with knowledge of one foreign language (English, French, or German).

Fees: None.

Language of Instruction: Ukrainian.

Degrees and Diplomas: Diploma of Specialist in a particular field of study, 5 yrs. Kandidat nauk, Candidate of the Sciences, a further 3 yrs and thesis. Doctor nauk, by thesis after Kandidat.

Library: Central Library, *c.* 1,300,000 vols.

Special Facilities (Museums, etc.): Museums: Zoology; Mineralogy; Geology; Numismatics.

Publications: Transactions of the Social Science Department (Problems of Philosophy, Problems of Political Economy, Problems of History of the C.P.S.U.); Papers of the L'vov University, historical series (Problems of History of the USSR, Problems of the People's Democracies, Problems of General History); Problems of Slavonic Linguistics; Literary Criticism; Problems of Russian Linguistics; Problems of Ukrainian Linguistics; Problems of Journalism; Transactions of the Faculty of Modern Languages; Papers of L'vov University, legal series; Geographical Collection; Mineralogical Collection; Geological Collection; Papers of the L'vov University, geological series; Papers of the L'vov University, chemical series; Papers of the L'vov University, biological series; Physical Collection; Mathematical Sciences. Theory and Applications.

Student Enrolment: c. 6500 (Also *c.* 6000 evening and correspondence students).

7049 **MARIJSKIJ GOSUDARSTVENNYJ UNIVERSITET**

Mari State University

pl. Lenina 1, 424001 Yoshkar-Ola, Marijskaja ASSR

Telephone: 6-32-16

Rektor: Ivshin Victor Pavlovich (1985-)

Prorektor: Chemodanov Victor Ivanovich

F. of History and Philology
Dean: A.N. Chimaev; *staff* 41
F. of Physics and Mathematics
Dean: V.P. Yagodarov; *staff* 30
F. of Biology and Chemistry
Dean: M.G. Grigorjev; *staff* 67
F. of Agriculture
Dean: A.I. Perevozchikov; *staff* 40
F. of Economy
Dean: L.A. Kochergin; *staff* 25
D. for Correspondence Courses
Also 3 Research Laboratories.

Founded 1972. Placed under the authority of the Ministries of Higher and Specialized Secondary Education of the Republic and of the Union. Financed by the State. Governing bodies: the Rector and Pro-Rectors; the Academic Council. Residential facilities for students.

Academic Year: September to July.

Admission Requirements: Competitive entrance examination following general or special secondary school certificate.

Fees: None.

Language of Instruction: Russian.

Degrees and Diplomas: Diploma of Specialist in a particular field of study, 5 yrs. Kandidat nauk, Candidate of the Sciences, a further 3 yrs and thesis. Doktor nauk, by thesis after Kandidat.

Library: 470,000 vols.

Special Facilities (Museums, etc.): Zoological Museum; Archaeological Museum; Museum of the History of the University; Agrobiostation.

Academic Staff, 1990:

Rank	Full-time
Professors	6
Readers	83
Senior Lecturers	94
Assistant Lecturers	47
Total	230

Student Enrolment, 1990:

	Men	Women	Total
Of the country	633	1372	2005*

*Also 1534 evening and correspondence students.

7050 **MORDOVSKIJ ORDENA DRUŽBY NARODOV GOSUDARSTVENNYJ UNIVERSITET IM. N.P. OGAREVA**

Mordovian State University

Bol'ševistskaja ul. 68, 430000 Saransk, Mordovskoj ASSR

Telephone: 4-45-63

F. of History and Geography
F. of Philology
F. of Foreign Languages
F. of Mathematics
F. of Physics
F. of Chemistry
F. of Biology
F. of Electronics and Automation
F. of Building Engineering
F. of Lighting Engineering
F. of Economics
F. of Mechanization of Agriculture
F. of Agriculture
F. of Medicine
D. for Evening Studies
D. for Correspondence Courses

Founded 1957. Placed under the authority of the Union-Republic State Committee for Public Education. Financed by the State. Governing bodies: the Rector and Pro-Rectors; the Academic Council.

Academic Year: September to July.

Admission Requirements: Competitive entrance examination following general or special secondary school certificate.

Fees: None.

Degrees and Diplomas: Diploma of Specialist in a particular field of study, 5 yrs. Kandidat nauk, Candidate of the Sciences, a further 3 yrs and thesis. Doktor nauk, by thesis after Kandidat.

Student Enrolment: c. 7000 (Also 9500 evening and correspondence students).

7051 ***MOSKOVSKIJ ORDENA LENINA I ORDENA I ORDENA OKTJABR'SKOI REVOLJUCII TRUDOVOGO KRASNOGO ZNAMENI GOSUDARSTVENNYJ UNIVERSITET IM. M.V. LOMONOSOVA**

Moscow State University

Leninskije Gory, 117234 Moskva V-234, Rossiskaja SFSR

Telephone: 139-53-40

Rektor: A. Logunov

F. of Physics
F. of Computer Mathematics and Cybernetics
F. of Chemistry
F. of Mathematics and Mechanics
F. of Biology and Soil Science
F. of Geography
F. of Geology
F. of History
F. of Philology
F. of Law
F. of Philosophy
F. of Economics
F. of Journalism
F. of Psychology
D. for Evening Studies
D. for Correspondence Courses
I. of Asian and African Studies
I. of Mechanics (Research)
I. of Nuclear Physics (Research)
I. of Astronomy

Founded 1755 by M.V. Lomonosov. Played an essential part in Russian cultural life, notably by founding a number of institutions of secondary and higher education. Expanded considerably after the October Revolution and developed steadily through a number of transformations. In recent years the science faculties were transferred to new buildings on the Lenin Hills. Placed under the authority of the Union-Republic State Committee for Public Education. Financed by the State. Governing bodies: the Rector and Pro-Rectors; the Academic Council. Residential facilities for academic staff and students.

Arrangements for co-operation with: University of Warsaw; Humboldt University of Berlin; Comenius University, Bratislava; Charles University, Prague; University of Budapest; University of Bucharest; University of Belgrade; University of Havana; University of Sofia; University of Mongolia; University of Cairo; Australian National University; Waseda University; Tokai University, Tokyo; University of the Republic, Montevideo. Also arrangements for co-operation with many other universities in Australia, Canada, Denmark, France, Japan, United Kingdom, United States, and in countries of Asia, Africa, and Latin America.

Academic Year: September to July (September-January; February-July).

Admission Requirements: Entrance examination following general or special secondary school certificate.

Fees: None.

Language of Instruction: Russian.

Degrees and Diplomas: Diploma of Specialist in a particular field of study, 5 yrs. Kandidat nauk, Candidate of the Sciences, a further 3 yrs and thesis. Doktor nauk, by thesis after Kandidat.

Library: A.M. Gorki Scientific Library, *c.* 6,600,000 vols.

Special Facilities (Museums, etc.): Museums: Zoology; Soil Science; History of the University; Anthropology.

Publication: Vestnik Moskovskogo Universiteta (various series).

Academic Staff: c. 8000.

Student Enrolment: c. 30,000.

7052 ***NOVOSIBIRSKIJ ORDENA TRUDOVOGO KRASNOGO ZNAMENI GOSUDARSTVENNYJ UNIVERSITET IM. LENINSKOGO KOMSOMOLA**

Novosibirsk State University

Ul. Pirogova 2, 630090 Novosibirsk 90, Rossiskaja SFSR

Telex: 133 146 TEVUS SU

Telephone: 35-62-44

Fax: (383-2) 35-26-53

Rektor: Y.L. Ershov (1985-)

Prorektor: V.N. Vragov

F. of Mathematics and Applied Mathematics
Dean: A.V. Kašihov; *staff* 22 (190)
F. of Physics
Dean: N.S. Dikanskij; *staff* 16 (90)
F. of Natural Sciences
Dean: N.M. Bažin; *staff* 33 (28)
F. of Geology and Geophysics
Dean: V.A. Solovjev; *staff* 5 (27)
F. of Humanities
Dean: L.G. Panin; *staff* 22 (9)
F. of Economics
Dean: G.M. Mkrtojan; *staff* 19 (50)
I. of Qualification
Director: I.A. Moletotov; *staff* 8 (8)
Scientific-Study Ce.
Director: A.A. Nikitin; *staff* 50 (71)
Sub D. for Science and Research
Head: A.M. Tumajkin; *staff* 502 (910)
KASSI-External Economic Association (Courses of Russian for Foreign Students)
Director: S.R. Sverohkov; *staff* 10 (55)

Founded 1959. Placed under the authority of the Union-Republic State Committee for Public Education. Financed by the State. Governing bodies: the Rector and Pro-Rectors; the Academic Council. Residential facilities for academic staff and students.

Arrangements for co-operation with: Stanford University; Oldenburg University; Torun University; Milan University; Sofia University.

Academic Year: September to June (September-January; February-June).

Admission Requirements: Competitive entrance examination following general or special secondary school certificate.

Fees: None.

Language of Instruction: Russian.

Degrees and Diplomas: Diploma of Specialist in a particular field of study, 5 yrs. Kandidat nauk, Candidate of the Sciences, a further 3 yrs and thesis. Doktor nauk, by thesis after Kandidat.

Library: 650,000 vols.

Special Facilities (Museums, etc.): Geological Museum.

Publication: Scientific Publications.

Academic Staff, 1990: 465.

Student Enrolment, 1990:

	Men	Women	Total
Of the country	2750	1450	4200

7053 **NUKUSSKIJ GOSUDARSTVENNYJ UNIVERSITET IM. T.G. ŠEVČENKO**

Nukus State University

Ul. Universitetskaja 1, 742012 Nukus, Uzbekskaja SSR

Telephone: 2-42-58

F. of Languages
F. of History
F. of Romance and Germanic Philology
F. of Natural Sciences
F. of Agriculture
F. of Economics

A State institution. Placed under the authority of the Union-Republic State Committee for Public Education. Financed by the State. Governing bodies: the Rector and Pro-Rectors; the Academic Council.

Academic Year: September to July.

Admission Requirements: Competitive entrance examination following general or special secondary school certificate.

Fees: None.

Degrees and Diplomas: Diploma of Specialist in a particular field of study, 5 yrs. Kandidat nauk, Candidate of the Sciences, a further 3 yrs and thesis. Doktor nauk, by thesis after Kandidat.

7054 **ODESSKIJ ORDENA TRUDOVOGO KRASNOGO ZNAMENI GOSUDARSTVENNYJ UNIVERSITET IM. I.I. MEČNIKOVA**

Odessa State University

Ul. Petra Velikogo 2, 270057 Odessa, Ukrainskaja SSR

Telephone: 23-58-13

F. of History
F. of Law
F. of Philology
F. of Romance and Germanic Philology
F. of Mathematics and Applied Mathematics
F. of Physics
F. of Chemistry
F. of Biology
F. of Geology and Geography
D. for Evening Studies
D. for Correspondence Courses

Founded 1807. Placed under the authority of the Union-Republic State Committee for Public Education. Financed by the State. Governing bodies: the Rector and Pro-Rectors; the Academic Council.

Academic Year: September to July.

Admission Requirements: Competitive entrance examination following general or special secondary school certificate.

Fees: None.

Degrees and Diplomas: Diploma of Specialist in a particular field of study, 5 yrs. Kandidat nauk, Candidate of the Sciences, a further 3 yrs and thesis. Doktor nauk, by thesis after Kandidat.

Student Enrolment: c. 4850 (Also *c.* 6300 evening and correspondence students).

7055 **OMSKIJ GOSUDARSTVENNYJ UNIVERSITET**

Omsk State University

Prosp Mira 55a, 644077 Omsk 77, Rossiskaja SFSR

Telephone: 64-17-01

F. of Philology
F. of History
F. of Mathematics
F. of Chemistry
F. of Humanities
F. of Physics
D. for Correspondence Courses

Founded 1974. Placed under the authority of the Union-Republic State Committee for Public Education. Financed by the State. Governing bodies: the Rector and Pro-Rectors; the Academic Council.

Academic Year: September to July.

Admission Requirements: Competitive entrance examination following general or special secondary school certificate.

Fees: None.

Degrees and Diplomas: Diploma of Specialist in a particular field of study, 5 yrs. Kandidat nauk, Candidate of the Sciences, a further 3 yrs and thesis. Doktor nauk, by thesis after Kandidat.

Student Enrolment: c. 800 (Also *c.* 50 evening and correspondence students).

7056 **PERMSKIJ ORDENA TRUDOVOGO KRASNOGO ZNAMENI GOSUDARSTVENNYJ UNIVERSITET IM. A.M. GOR'KOGO**

Perm State University

Ul. Bukireva 15, 614600 Perm', Rossiskaja SFSR

Telephone: 33-38-10

F. of History
F. of Philology
F. of Law
F. of Economics
F. of Mathematics and Applied Mathematics
F. of Physics
F. of Chemistry
F. of Biology
F. of Geology
F. of Geography
D. for Evening Studies
D. for Correspondence Courses

Founded 1817. Placed under the jurisdiction of the Union-Republic State Committee for Public Education. Financed by the State. Governing bodies: the Rector, the Pro-Rectors; the Academic Council.

Academic Year: September to July.

Admission Requirements: Competitive entrance examination following general or special secondary school certificate.

Fees: None.

Degrees and Diplomas: Diploma of Specialist in a particular field of study, 5 yrs. Kandidat nauk, Candidate of the Sciences, a further 3 yrs and thesis. Doktor nauk, by thesis after Kandidat.

Academic Staff: c. 350.

Student Enrolment: c. 5200 (Also c. 5150 evening and correspondence students).

7057 **PETROZAVODSKIJ GOSUDARSTVENNYJ UNIVERSITET IM. O.V. KUUSINENA**

Petrozavodsk State University

Pr. Lenina 33, 185640 Petrozavodsk, Rossiskaja SFSR

Telephone: 7-17-91

F. of History and Philology

F. of Physics and Mathematics

F. of Biology

F. of Agriculture

F. of Forestry and Wood Technology

F. of Medicine

F. of Building Construction

F. of General Technology (correspondence and evening courses)

D. for Correspondence Courses

Founded 1940 with four faculties, some of which were later reorganized or replaced by others in order to adapt the structure of the university to the particular needs of the country. Especially in the fields of agriculture, forestry, and geological prospection, it trains specialists who under the prevalent Soviet pattern would normally have been trained in specialized institutions. Placed under the authority of the Union-Republic State Committee for Public Education. Financed by the State. Governing bodies: the Rector and Pro-Rectors; the Academic Council. Some residential facilities for students.

Academic Year: September to July (September-January; February-July).

Admission Requirements: Competitive entrance examination following general or special secondary school certificate.

Fees: None.

Degrees and Diplomas: Diploma of Specialist in a particular field of study, 5 yrs. Kandidat nauk, Candidate of the Sciences, by thesis. Doktor nauk, by thesis after Kandidat.

Library: c. 160,000 vols.

Special Facilities (Museums, etc.): Geology Museum; Geo-Botany Museum.

Publication: Učënye Zapiski Petrozavodskogo Gosudarstvennogo Universiteta (scientific transactions).

Student Enrolment: c. 4300 (Also c. 300 evening and correspondence students).

7058 ***ROSTOVSKIJ ORDENA TRUDOVOGO KRASNOGO ZNAMENI GOSUDARSTVENNYJ UNIVERSITET IM. M.A. SUSLOVA**

Rostov State University

Ul. Fridriha Engel'sa 105 344711, Rostov-na-Donu GSP-11, Rossiskaja SFSR

Telephone: 66-32-31

Rektor: J.V.A. Ždanov

F. of Philology

Dean: N.V. Zaburova; *staff* 64 (51)

F. of History

Dean: V.E. Maksimenko; *staff* 43 (7)

F. of Mathematics and Applied Mathematics

Dean: A.V. Belokon'; *staff* 109 (42)

F. of Law

Dean: A.A. Puškarenko; *staff* 38 (15)

F. of Physics

Dean: L.M. Rabkin; *staff* 74 (7)

F. of Chemistry

Dean: T.G. Lupejko; *staff* 55 (12)

F. of Biology and Soil Science

Dean: O.G. Čarojan; *staff* 50 (9)

F. of Geology and Geography

Dean: A.N. Reznikov; *staff* 57 (4)

F. of Economics

Dean: V.C. Zolotarev; *staff* 39 (13)

F. of Philosophy

Dean: V.P. Kohanovskij; *staff* 54 (34)

D. for Evening Studies

D. for Correspondence Courses

Founded 1915. Placed under the authority of the Union-Republic State Committee for Public Education. Financed by the State. Governing bodies: the Rector and Pro-Rectors; the Academic Council.

Arrangements for co-operation with Universities in: Poland; Yugoslavia.

Academic Year: September to July.

Admission Requirements: Competitive entrance examination following general or special secondary school certificate.

Fees: None.

Degrees and Diplomas: Diploma of Specialist in a particular field of study, 5 yrs. Kandidat nauk, Candidate of the Sciences, a further 3 yrs and thesis. Doktor nauk, by thesis after Kandidat.

Library: Central Library, 2,200,000 vols.

Special Facilities (Museums, etc.): Museums: Biology; Geology; History.

Publications: Journal (weekly); 'Izvestiya SKNC' (quarterly).

Press or Publishing House: University Press.

Academic Staff: c. 900.

Student Enrolment: c. 10,000.

7059 **SAMARKANDSKIJ ORDENA TRUDOVOGO KRASNOGO ZNAMENI GOSUDARSTVENNYJ UNIVERSITET IM. ALIŠERA NAVOI**

Samarkand State University

Bul. Gor'kogo 15, 703004 Samarkand, Uzbekskaja SSR

Telephone: 5-26-26

Rektor: Alimov Shavkat Arifdjanovich (1985-)

F. of Law

Dean: Nazarov Karim

F. of History

Dean: Fayziyev Assad

F. of Geography

Dean: Umarov Mardon

F. of Uzbek and Tadjcic Philology

Dean: Valikhodjayev Batir

F. of Foreign Languages

Dean: Nusharov Melikul Makhmadovich

F. of Mechanics and Mathematics

Dean: Yarmukhamedov Sharof

F. of Physics

Dean: Amanov Shavkat

F. of Chemistry

Dean: Khamrakulov Timur Kurbanovich

F. of Biology

Dean: Lakhanov Djabbar

D. for Evening Studies

D. for Correspondence Courses

Founded 1927 as State pedagogical institute. Became a State academy 1927 and university 1933. Placed under theauthority of the Union-Republic State Committee for Public Education. Financed by the State. Governing bodies: the Rector and Pro-Rectors; the Academic Council. Residential facilities for students.

Academic Year: September to July (September-January; February-July).

Admission Requirements: Competitive entrance examination following general or special secondary school certificate.

Fees: None.

Languages of Instruction: Uzbek, Tajik, and Russian.

Degrees and Diplomas: Diploma of Specialist in a particular field of study, 5 yrs. Kandidat nauk, Candidate of the Sciences, a further 3 yrs and thesis. Doktor nauk, by thesis after Kandidat.

Library: c. 2,220,000 vols.

Special Facilities (Museums, etc.): Darwin Biology Museum; Geography and Palaeontology; Physics; History.

Publication: Works of the Samarkand State University (daily).

Press or Publishing House: University Press.

Academic Staff: c. 600

Student Enrolment: c. 5000 (Also c. 5000 evening and correspondence students).

7060 **SARATOVSKIJ ORDENA TRUDOVOGO KRASNOGO ZNAMENI GOSUDARSTVENNYJ UNIVERSITET IM. N.G. ČERNYŠEVSKOGO**

Saratov State University

Astrahanskaja ul. 83, 410071 Saratov, Rossijskaja SFSR

Telephone: 2-16-96

Rektor: A.M. Bogomolov

F. of History
Dean: Parfenov Igor' Danilovič
F. of Philology
Dean: Prozorov Valerij Vladimirovič
F. of Mechanics and Mathematics
Dean: Privalov Andrej Andreevič
F. of Physics
Dean: Berezin Valentin Ivanovič
F. of Chemistry
Dean: Černova Rimma Kuz'minična
F. of Biology
Dean: Šljahtin Gennadij Viktorovič
F. of Geography
Dean: Poljanskaja Elena Aleksandrovna
F. of Geology
Dean: Ignatov Boris Fedorovič
Chair of Philosophy
Chair of Political Economy
Chair of Political Sciences
Chair of Sociology
Chair of Pedagogy
Chair of Physical Training and Sport
Chair of German Language
Chair of English and French Languages
D. for Evening Studies
D. for Correspondence Courses

Founded 1909. Placed under the authority of the Ministry of Specialized Higher and Secondary Education. Financed by the State. Governing bodies: the Rector and Pro-Rectors; the Academic Council.

Academic Year: September to July.

Admission Requirements: Competitive entrance examination following general or special secondary school certificate.

Fees: None.

Degrees and Diplomas: Diploma of Specialist in a particular field of study, 5 yrs. Kandidat nauk, Candidate of the Sciences, a further 3 yrs and thesis. Doktor nauk, by thesis after Kandidat.

Academic Staff, 1990:

Rank	Full-time
Professor	74
Docent	321
Staršij prepodavatel'	58
Prepodavatel'	3
Assistent	15
Total	471

Student Enrolment, 1990:

	Men	Women	Total
Of the country	2263	3340	5603*

*Also 4250 external students.

7061 **SEVERO-OSETINSKIJ GOSUDARSTVENNYJ UNIVERSITET IM K.L. HETAGUROVA**

North Osetin State University

Ul. Batutina 46, 362000 Ordžonikidze, Rossiskaja SFSR

Telephone: 3-98-24

F. of Physics and Mathematics
F. of Philology
F. of Chemistry and Biology
F. of History
F. of Foreign Languages
F. of Law
F. of Economics
F. of Physical Education
D. for Evening Studies
D. for Correspondence Courses

Founded 1970. Placed under the authority of the Union-Republic State Committee for Public Education. Financed by the State. Governing bodies: the Rector and Pro-Rectors; the Academic Council. Residential facilities for students.

Academic Year: September to July (September-December; February-July).

Admission Requirements: Competitive entrance examination following general or special secondary school certificate.

Fees: None.

Languages of Instruction: Ossetic and Russian.

Degrees and Diplomas: Diploma of Specialist in a particular field of study, 5 yrs; Physical Education, 4 yrs. Kandidat nauk, Candidate of the Sciences, a further 3 yrs and thesis. Doktor nauk, by thesis after Kandidat.

Library: Scientific Library, *c.* 670,000 vols.

Special Facilities (Museums, etc.): Zoology Museum; Geology Museum.

Academic Staff: c. 400.

Student Enrolment: c. 3500 (Also *c.* 3200 external students).

7062 **SIMFEROPOL'SKIJ GOSUDARSTVENNYJ UNIVERSITET IM. M.V. FRUNZE**

Simferopol State University

Ul. Jaltinskaja 4, 333036 Simferopol', Ukrainskaja SSR

Telephone: 3-22-80

F. of History
F. of Philology
F. of Romance and Germanic Philology
F. of Geography
F. of Natural Sciences
F. of Physics
F. of Mathematics
D. for Evening Studies
D. for Correspondence Courses

Founded 1972. Placed under the authority of the Union-Republic State Committee for Public Education. Financed by the State. Governing bodies: the Rector and Pro-Rectors; the Academic Council.

Academic Year: September to July.

Admission Requirements: Competitive entrance examination following general or special secondary certificate.

Fees: None.

Degrees and Diplomas: Diploma of Specialist in a particular field of study, 5 yrs. Kandidat nauk, Candidate of the Sciences, a further 3 yrs and thesis. Doktor nauk, by thesis after Kandidat.

Student Enrolment: c. 3500 (Also *c.* 2500 evening and correspondence students).

7063 **SUHUMSKIJ GOSUDARSTVENNYJ UNIVERSITET IM. A.M. GOR'KOGO**

Suhumi State University

Ul. Cereteli 9, 384900 Suhumi, Abhazskaja ASSR

Telephone: 2-43-74

Rektor: Aleko A. Gvaramia (1988-)

Prorektors: M. Labakhua; O. Domenia

D. of Commerce
D. of Law
D. of Philology
Dean: Sh. Aristava; *staff* 48 (18)
D. of Foreign Languages
Dean: Sh. Aristava; *staff* 24 (11)
D. of History and Law
Dean: S. Sharia; *staff* 53 (47)
D. of Mathematics
Dean: L. Karba; *staff* 33 (9)
D. of Physics
Dean: L. Karba; *staff* 29 (7)
D. of Biology
Dean: R. Ninua; *staff* 20 (27)
D. of Geography
Dean: R. Ninya; *staff* 15 (12)
D. of Pedagogy
Dean: V. Sakhokia; *staff* 24 (13)
D. of Economics
Dean: I. Feizba; *staff* 26 (12)
Research Sec.
Head: A. Omanadže; *staff* 46 (82)

Founded 1932. Until 1979 called Sukhumi State Teacher Training College named after A.M. Gorky. Reorganized 1979 into Abkhazian State University, in accordance with the Resolution of Council of Ministers of

USSR and Ministry of Education. The University is subordinate to the Ministry of People's Education of Georgia. Governing bodies: the Rector's Council; the University Council; the University Academic Council; the Faculty Academic Councils. Residential facilities for academic staff and students.

Academic Year: September to July (September-December; February-May).

Admission Requirements: Competitive entrance examination following general or special secondary school certificate.

Fees: None.

Languages of Instruction: Abkhazian, Georgian and Russian.

Degrees and Diplomas: Diploma of Specialist in a particular field of study, 5 yrs.

Library: Main Library, 600,000 vols.

Special Facilities (Museums, etc.): Experimental Biological Garden; Greenhouse; Health Centre.

Publication: Staff Research Works (annually).

Academic Staff, 1990:

Rank	Full-time	Part-time
Profesores	26	6
Profesores asistentes	72	36
Kandidates nauk	118	20
Staršyj prepodavotel	38	53
Asistentes	17	41
Total	271	156

Student Enrolment, 1990:

	Men	Women	Total
Of the country	1568	1432	3000*

*Also 1900 external and correspondence students.

7064 **SYKTYVKARSKIJ GOSUDARSTVENNYJ UNIVERSITET IM. 50-LETIJA SSSR**

Syktyvkar State University

Oktjabr'skij prosp. 55, 167001 Syktyvkar, Komi ASSR

Telephone: 3-68-20

F. of History and Philology
F. of Physics and Mathematics
F. of Chemistry and Biology
F. of Economics
D. for Evening Studies
D. for Correspondence Courses

Founded 1972. Placed under the authority of the Union-Republic State Committee for Public Education. Financed by the State. Governing bodies: the Rector and Pro-Rectors; the Academic Council. Residential facilities for academic staff and students.

Academic Year: September to July (September-January; February-July).

Admission Requirements: Competitive entrance examination following general or special secondary school certificate.

Fees: None.

Language of Instruction: Russian.

Degrees and Diplomas: Diploma of Specialist in a particular field of study, 5 yrs. Kandidat nauk, Candidate of the Sciences, a further 3 yrs and thesis. Doktor nauk, by thesis after Kandidat.

Library: c. 200,000 vols.

Special Facilities (Museums, etc.): Zoology Museum; Archaeology Museum.

Academic Staff: c. 170.

Student Enrolment: c. 1700 (Also c. 250 external students).

7065 ***TADŽIKSKIJ GOSUDARSTVENNYJ UNIVERSITET IM. V.I. LENINA**

Tajik State University

Prosp. Lenina 17, 734025 Dušanbe, Tadžikskaja SSR

Telephone: 23-37-98

Rektor: F.T. Tahirov

F. of History
Dean: Niez Mirzoevich Mirzoev; *staff* 46
F. of Tajik Philology
Dean: Ibrahim K. Usmonov; *staff* 47
F. of Accountancy and Economics
Dean: M. Zarifov; *staff* 42
F. of Finance and Credit
Dean: M. Isomatov; *staff* 29
F. of Russian Language and Literature
Dean: Anton Antonovich Gorbachevskii; *staff* 35
F. of Oriental Languages
Dean: Komil Musofirovich Musofirov; *staff* 31
F. of Law
Dean: Oinihol Bobonazarovna Bobonazarova; *staff* 39
F. of Economics and Planning
Dean: Chulsara Babaevna Bobosadikova; *staff* 46
F. of Physics
Dean: Fateh Khalikovich Khakimov; *staff* 43
F. of Mathematics and Applied Mathematics
Dean: Harif Malikovich Malikov; *staff* 81
F. of Chemistry
Dean: Zuhuridin Nurievich Yousupov; *staff* 39
F. of Biology
Dean: Habib Muradovich Cafarov; *staff* 34
F. of Geology
Dean: Abdulhak Radjabovich Faiziev; *staff* 23
D. for Evening Studies
Dean: Abduladjon Oripovich Oripov
D. for Correspondence Courses
Dean: Abduladjon Oripovich Oripov
Research D. of Radiochemistry of Rare and Scattered Elements
Head: B.O. Khamidov
Research L. for Physics of Polymer Strength
Head: D.S. Saidov
Research L. for Automated Teaching Systems
Head: K.Ya. Radjabov
Research L. of Introduction and Acclimatization of Plants
Head: K.N. Nimadjanova
Research D. of Problems of Co-ordinating Chemistry and Ecology
Head: M.M. Mansurov
Research L. of Peptids
Head: Sh.Kh. Khalikov
Research Group on Biotechnology
Head: M.M. Jakubova
Research L. of Fermentology
Head: M.A. Babadjanova
Research L. of Sociological Studies
Head: Sh.Kh. Khasanova
Research L. of Archaeology, Ethnography and Folklore of Tajikistan
Head: A.D. Babaev
Information and Computer Ce.
Head: N.M. Mansurov

Founded 1948 with two faculties. Placed under the authority of the Union-Republic State Committee for Public Education which determine the budget, decide on staff and student numbers, and provide general, scientific, andmethodological direction. Governing bodies: the Rector and Pro-Rectors; the Academic Council.

Academic Year: September to July (September-January; February-July).

Fees: None.

Languages of Instruction: Russian and Tajik.

Degrees and Diplomas: Diploma of Specialist in a particular field of study, 5 yrs. Kandidat nauk, Candidate of the Sciences, a further 3 yrs and thesis. Doktor nauk, by thesis after Kandidat.

Library: 980,423 vols.

Publications: Učёnye Zapiski (scholarly papers: series of Historical, Natural, Physical and Mathematical, Economic, Philosophical Sciences); Vestnik Tajikeskogo Gosuniversiteta.

Student Enrolment, 1989-90: 12,498 (Including 2046 evening students, and 3686 students by correspondence).

7066 ***TARTU ÜLIKOOL**

Tartu Univeristy

Ülikooli 18, 202400 Tartu, Estonskaja SSR

Telex: 173243 TAUN SU

Telephone: (7-01434) 34866

Fax: (7-01434) 35440

Rektor: Jüri Kärner (1988-93)

F. of History (including Defectology, Psychology, and Sociology)
Dean: Helmut Piirimäe; *staff* 44 (6)
F. of Philology (Estonian, English, French, German, Russian, Language, Literature and Journalism)
Dean: Jüri Valge; *staff* 143 (7)
F. of Physics and Chemistry
Dean: Henn Voolaid; *staff* 58 (10)

F. of Mathematics
Dean: Ivar-Igor Saarniit; *staff* 53 (5)
F. of Biology and Geography
Dean: Aadu Loog; *staff* 38 (11)
F. of Law
Dean: Inge Orgo; *staff* 29 (6)
F. of Economics
Dean: Mart Sõrg; *staff* 47 (1)
F. of Medicine
Dean: Lembit Allikmets; *staff* 215 (10)
F. of Physical Education
Dean: Mati Pääsuke; *staff* 56 (2)
D. for Correspondence Courses
Head: Valter Haamer
Computer Ce.
Head: Jüri Tapfer; *staff* 42
I. of General and Molecular Pathology
Director: Aavo-Valdur Mikelsaar
Estonian Ce. (Tallinn)
Director: Toomas-Andres Sulling
Also 40 research laboratories and centres in science and medicine.

Founded 1802 as Universitas Dorpantensis by Alexander I, with German as the language of instruction but tracing its origins to the Academy founded by Gustav II Adolphus of Sweden in 1632. German was replaced by Russian in 1893, when the University was renamed Universitas Iurievensis. Became the University of Tartu after World War I. It later served as a basis for the foundation of the Academy of Sciences of the Estonian SSSR Governing bodies: the Rector and Pro-Rectors; the Academic Council; the Faculty Councils. Residential facilities for *c.* 3200 students.

Arrangements for co-operation with *c.* 30 universities and research institutions: joint research programmes, interchange of students and lecturers, etc.

Academic Year: September to July (September-January; February-July).

Admission Requirements: Secondary school certificate (Keskkooli Lõputunnislus) and entrance examination (Sisseastumiseksamid).

Fees: None.

Language of Instruction: Estonian, Russian.

Degrees and Diplomas: Diploma of Specialist in a particular field of study, 5 yrs. Candidate of the Sciences, by thesis, a further 3-4 yrs. Doctor of the Sciences (D.Sc.), by thesis after Candidate.

Libraries: Research Library, *c.* 4,200,000 vols; *c.* 80 Chair libraries and library of the Faculty of History and Philology, *c.* 253,000; other libraries, *c.* 83,000.

Special Facilities (Museums, etc.): Museums: Classical; Zoology and Geology; History of Tartu University. Botanical Gardens.

Publications: Transactions; Scandinavian Studies; in specialized series.

Press or Publishing House: Tartu University Publishing Department.

Academic Staff, 1990: 830.

Student Enrolment, 1990:

	Men	Women	Total
Of the country	2091	3465	5556*

*Also 2200 students by correspondence.

7067 ***TAŠKENTSKIJ ORDENA TRUDOVOGO KRASNOGO ZNAMENI GOSUDARSTVENNYJ UNIVERSITET IM. V.I. LENINA**
Tashkent State University
Universitetskaja ul. Vuzgorodok, 700095 Taškent, Uzbekskaja SSR
Telephone: 40-02-24

F. of History
F. of Philology
F. of Journalism
F. of Romance and Germanic Philology
F. of Oriental Studies
F. of Law
F. of Mathematics
F. of Applied Mathematics
F. of Physics
F. of Chemistry
F. of Biology and Soil Science
F. of Geology
F. of Geography
D. for Evening Studies
D. for Correspondence Courses

Founded 1920. Placed under the authority of the Union-Republic State Committee for Public Education. Financed by the State. Governing bodies: the Rector and Pro-Rectors; the Academic Council.

Academic Year: September to July.

Admission Requirements: Competitive entrance examination following general or special secondary school certificate.

Fees: None.

Degrees and Diplomas: Diploma of Specialist in a particular field of study, 5 yrs. Kandidat nauk, Candidate of the Sciences, a further 3 yrs and thesis. Doktor nauk, by thesis after Kandidat.

Student Enrolment: *c.* 8500 (Also *c.* 8000 evening and correspondence students).

7068 ***TBILISSKIJ ORDENA TRUDOVOGO KRASNOGO ZNAMENI GOSUDARSTVENNYJ UNIVERSITET**
Tbilisi State University
Prosp. Čavčavadz 1, 380028 Tbilisi, Gruzinskaja SSR
Telephone: 31-47-92
Rektor: Vazha M. Okudjava

F. of History
F. of Philology
F. of Journalism
F. of Philosophy and Psychology
F. of West European Languages and Literature
F. of Law
F. of Economics
F. of Cybernetics and Applied Mathematics
F. of Physics
F. of Mathematics and Mechanics
F. of Chemistry
F. of Biology
F. of Geology and Geography
F. of Oriental Studies
F. of Industrial and Trade Economics
F. of Business Economics
Applied Mathematics Research I.
D. for Evening Studies
D. for Correspondence Courses

Founded 1918. Placed under the authority of the Union-Republic State Committee for Public Education. Financed by the State. Governing body: the Rector and Pro-Rectors, and the Academic Council.

Academic Year: September to June (September-February; February-June).

Admission Requirements: Competitive entrance examination following general or special secondary school certificate.

Fees: None.

Languages of Instruction: Georgian and Russian.

Degrees and Diplomas: Diploma of Specialist in a particular field of study, 5 yrs. Kandidat nauk, Candidate of the Sciences, a further 3 yrs and thesis. Doktor nauk, by thesis after Kandidat.

Libraries: Scientific Library, *c.* 2,500,000 vols; faculty libraries.

Special Facilities (Museums, etc.): Museums: Geography; Palaeontology; Geology; Mineralogy; Petrography; History; Biology.

Publications: Scientific Works (Series A and B); The Young Journalist (Magazine); The First Ray (Anthology).

Academic Staff: *c.* 1500.

Student Enrolment: *c.* 14,500.

7069 ***TJUMENSKIJ GOSUDARSTVENNYJ UNIVERSITET**
Tyumen State University
Ul. Semakov 10, 625000 Tyumen 3, Rossiskaja SFSR
Telephone: (345) 26-19-30
Rektor: Alexei I. Ivandaev (1987-90)
Registrar: Zheleznova Lubov'a

F. of Philology
Dean: Natalia V. Khromova; *staff* 44 (3)
F. of Romance and Germanic Philology
Dean: Ludmila S. Makarova; *staff* 52 (1)
F. of Physics
Dean: Victor P. Lebedev; *staff* 19 (6)
F. of Chemistry
Dean: Vladimir V. Kiselev; *staff* 20 (8)
F. of Economics
Dean: Murry A. Budyanskiy; *staff* 34 (11)
F. of Geography
Dean: Olga V. Soromotina; *staff* 21 (1)

F. of History
Dean: Konstantin M. Gur'ev; *staff* 21 (1)
F. of Biology
Dean: Margarita F. Melnikova; *staff* 24 (7)
F. of Mathematics
Dean: Alexandre N. Degtev; *staff* 37 (3)
F. of Law
Dean: Osvald I. Klots; *staff* 19 (5)
D. for Evening Studies
D. for Correspondence Courses
Scientific Research Ce.
Head: Yuriy Volkov

Founded 1973. Placed under the authority of the Union-Republic State Committee for Public Education. Financed by the State. Governing bodies: the Rector and Pro-Rectors; the Academic Council. Residential facilities for students.

Joint research programme with Bulgarian Institute of Sociology. Arrangements for co-operation with: LaurentianUniversity; Lakehead University; Université Franch-Conté, Besançon; Harbin Shipbuilding Institute.

Academic Year: September to June (September-January; February-June).

Admission Requirements: Competitive entrance examination following general or special secondary school certificate.

Fees: None.

Language of Instruction: Russian.

Degrees and Diplomas: Diploma of Specialist in a particular field of study, 5 yrs. Kandidat nauk, Candidate of the Sciences, a further 3 yrs and thesis. Doktor nauk, by thesis after Kandidat.

Library: University Library, 739,000 vols.

Special Facilities (Museums, etc.): Biological Museum; Archaeology Museum.

Academic Staff, 1990:

Rank	Full-time
Professors	16
Readers	102
Senior Lecturers	140
Assistants	92
Total	350

Student Enrolment, 1990: 3274 (Also 2654 external students).

7070 TOMSKIJ ORDENA OKTJABR'SKOJ REVOLJUCII I ORDENA TRUDOVOGO KRASNOGO ZNAMENI GOSUDARSTVENNYJ UNIVERSITET IMV.V. KUJBYŠEVA

Tomsk State University
Prosp. Lenina 36, 634010 Tomsk 10, Rossiskaja SFSR
Telephone: 3-30-60

F. of History
F. of Philology
F. of Law
F. of Economics
F. of Mathematics and Mechanics
F. of Applied Mathematics
F. of Physics
F. of Radio-Physics
F. of Physics and Technology
F. of Chemistry
F. of Biology and Soil Science
F. of Geology and Geography
D. for Evening Studies
D. for Correspondence Courses

Founded 1888. Placed under the authority of the Ministries of Higher and Specialized Secondary Education of the Republic and of the Union. Financed by the State. Governing bodies: the Rector and Pro-Rectors; the Academic Council.

Academic Year: September to July.

Admission Requirements: Competitive entrance examination following general or special secondary school certificate.

Fees: None.

Degrees and Diplomas: Diploma of Specialist in a particular field of study, 5 yrs. Kandidat nauk, Candidate of the Sciences, a further 3 yrs and thesis. Doktor nauk, by thesis after Kandidat.

Student Enrolment: c. 5600 (Also *c.* 2200 evening and correspondence students).

7071 *TURKMENSKIJ ORDENA TRUDOVOGO KRASNOGO ZNAMENI GOSUDARSTVENNYJ UNIVERSITET IM. M. GOR'KOGO

Turkmen State University
Prosp. Lenina 31, 744014 Ašhaabad, Turkmenskaja SSR
Telephone: 5-11-59
Rektor: O.N. Muradov

F. of Economics
F. of History
F. of Law
F. of Turkmen Philology
F. of Russian Philology
F. of Mathematics
F. of Physics
F. of Biology and Geography
F. of Physical Education
F. of Foreign Languages
F. for Evening Studies
D. for Correspondence Courses

Founded 1950. Placed under the authority of the Union-Republic State Committee for Public Education. Financed by the State. Governing bodies: the Rector and Pro-Rectors; the Academic Council.

Academic Year: September to July.

Admission Requirements: Competitive entrance examination following general or special secondary school certificate.

Fees: None.

Degrees and Diplomas: Diploma of Specialist in a particular field of study, 5 yrs. Kandidat nauk, Candidate of the Sciences, a further 3 yrs and thesis. Doktor nauk, by thesis after Kandidat.

Student Enrolment: c. 6300 (Also *c.* 5000 evening and correspondence students).

7072 UDMURSKIJ GOSUDARSTVENNYJ UNIVERSITET IM. 50-LETIJA SSSR

Udmurtsk State University
Krasnogerojskaja ul. 71, 426037 Ustinov, Udmurskaja ASSR
Telephone: 75-59-33

F. of History
F. of Philology
F. of Physics and Mathematics
F. of Biology and Chemistry
F. of Economics and Law
F. of Romance and Germanic Philology
F. of Art and Graphic Art
F. of Physical Education
D. for Correspondence Courses

A State university placed under the authority of the Union-Republic State Committee for Public Education. Financed by the State. Governing bodies: the Rector and Pro-Rectors; the Academic Council.

Academic Year: September to July.

Admission Requirements: Competitive entrance examination following general or special secondary school certificate.

Fees: None.

Degrees and Diplomas: Diploma of Specialist in a particular field of study, 5 yrs. Kandidat nauk, Candidate of the Sciences, a further 3 yrs and thesis. Doktor nauk, by thesis after Kandidat.

Student Enrolment: c. 3500 (Also *c.* 2600 evening and correspondence students).

7073 *UNIVERSITET DRUŽBY NARODOV IM. PATRISA LUMUMBY

Patrice Lumumba People's Friendship University
Ordžonikidze, Dom 3, Moskva V-302, Rossiskaja SFSR
Telephone: 234-00-11
Rektor: V.F. Stanis

F. of Engineering
F. of Physics, Mathematics and Natural Sciences
F. of Medicine
F. of Economics and Law
F. of Agriculture
F. of History and Philology
Preparatory F.
F. of Russian Language Teaching

Founded 1960. Open mainly to students from developing countries but including *c.* 25 per cent Russian students. The degrees and diplomas are the same as those awarded by other Soviet universities. Financed by the State and by organizations which took part in the foundation of the university. Placed under the authority of the Union-Republic State Committee for Public Education. Governing bodies: the Rector and Pro-Rectors; the University Council, including student representatives. Residential facilities for all students.

Academic Year: September to July.

Admission Requirements: The General Certificate of Education, Advanced Level or equivalent.

Fees: None.

Language of Instruction: Russian.

Degrees and Diplomas: Diploma of Specialist (Master's Degree) in a particular field of study, 5 yrs; Medicine, 6 yrs; Agriculture, 4-5 yrs. Kandidat nauk, Candidate of the Sciences, a further 3 yrs and thesis. Doktor nauk, by thesis after Kandidat.

Library: Scientific Library of the University, *c.* 1,300,000 vols.

Special Facilities (Museums, etc.): Museums: History of the University; Anatomy; Geology.

Publications: Series: Trudy Universiteta; 'Drúzba'; Friendship.

Academic Staff: c. 2000.

Student Enrolment: c. 8000.

7074 **URAL'SKIJ ORDENA TRUDOVOGO KRASNOGO ZNAMENI GOSUDARSTVENNYJ UNIVERSITET IM. A.M. GOR'KOGO**

Ural State University

Prosp. Lenina 51, 620083 Sverdlovsk K-83, Rossiskaja SFSR

Telephone: 55-73-94; 55-75-12

Rektor: Parigori E. Suetin

Prorektor: George R. Zmanovski

F. of History
Dean: Valeri I. Mikhailenko; *staff* 51 (12)
F. of Philosophy
Dean: Vyacheslav V. Skorobogatski; *staff* 56 (19)
F. of Philology
Dean: Valentin V. Blazhes; *staff* 51 (11)
F. of Journalism
Dean: Boris N. Lozovskii; *staff* 26 (3)
F. of Mathematics and Applied Mathematics
Dean: Vitali P. Prokopev; *staff* 77 (22)
F. of Physics
Dean: Khalid M. Bikkin; *staff* 55 (15)
F. of Chemistry
Dean: Alexander A. Vshivkov; *staff* 28 (5)
F. of Biology
Dean: Nikolai N. Firsov; *staff* 26 (4)
F. of Economy
Dean: Anatoli V. Grebenkin; *staff* 15 (7)
D. for Evening Studies
D. for Correspondence Courses
Printing Shop for Training Journalists
Head: Maria I. Vavylenko; *staff* 20
Graduate S. of Statesmanship
Head; Natalya V. Loskytova; *staff* 2
I. of Physics and Applied Mathematics
Head: Leonid P. Zverev; *staff* 198 (54)
I. of Russian Culture
Head: Rydolph G. Pikhoya; *staff* 50 (5)
L. of Biorecultivation of Industrially Destroyed Lands
Head: Sergei V. Komov; *staff* 18

Founded 1920 by Lenin and Gorky. Placed under the authority of the Union-Republic State Committee for Public Education. Financed by the State. Governing bodies: the Rector and Pro-Rectors; the Academic Council. Residential facilities for academic staff and students.

Arrangements for co-operation with Charles University, Prague.

Academic Year: September to July (September-January; February-July).

Admission Requirements: Competitive entrance examination following general or special secondary school certificate or equivalent foreign qualifications.

Fees: None.

Language of Instruction: Russian.

Degrees and Diplomas: Diploma of Specialist in a particular field of study, 5 yrs. Kandidat nauk, Candidate of the Sciences, a further 3 yrs and thesis. Doktor nauk, by thesis after Kandidat.

Library: c. 400,000 vols. Scientific Library, department of rare books.

Special Facilities (Museums, etc.): Museums: Zoology; Botany; Early Printed Russian Books. Botanical Garden. Visual Observation Station for Artificial Satellites.

Publication: Periodical Scientific Bulletin.

Press or Publishing House: Publishing and Press House.

Academic Staff, 1990: 463 (19).

Student Enrolment, 1990: 7095 (Also 2905 external students).

7075 **UŽGORODSKIJ GOSUDARSTVENNYJ UNIVERSITET**

Uzhgorod State University

Ul. M. Gor'kogo 46, 294000 Užgorod, Ukrainskaja SSR

Telephone: 3-42-02

F. of History
F. of Romance and German Philology
F. of Mathematics
F. of Physics
F. of Chemistry
F. of Biology
F. of Medicine
F. of General Technological Studies
D. for Evening Studies
D. for Correspondence Courses

Founded 1945 as the first institution of higher education established after the reunion of Trans-Carpathia with the Ukraine. Received considerable assistance from other institutions in the Soviet Union, especially the Universities of Moscow, Kiev, and Kharkov. Postgraduate studies (aspirantura) since 1953. Placed under the authority of the Union-Republic State Committee for Public Education. Financed by the State. Governing bodies: the Rector and Pro-Rectors; the Academic Council. Residential facilities for academic staff and hostels for students.

Academic Year: September to July (September-January; February-July).

Admission Requirements: Competitive entrance examination following general or special secondary school certificate.

Fees: None.

Language of Instruction: Ukrainian.

Degrees and Diplomas: Diploma of Specialist in a particular field of study, 5 yrs, except Medicine, 6 yrs. Kandidat nauk, Candidate of the Sciences, a further 3 yrs and thesis. Doktor nauk, by thesis after Kandidat.

Library: c. 300,000 vols.

Special Facilities (Museums, etc.): Museums: Zoology; Anatomy. Botanical Garden.

Publication: Naučnye Zapiski Užgorodskogo Universiteta (Scientific Papers).

Student Enrolment: c. 4200 (Also *c.* 6500 evening and correspondence students).

7076 ***VIL'NJUSSKIJ ORDENA TRUDOVOGO KRASNOGO ZNAMENI I ORDENA DRUŽBY NARODOV GOSUDARSTVENNYJ UNIVERSITET IM. V. KAPSUKASA**

Vilnius V. Kapsukas State University

Universiteto 3, 232734 Vil'njus, Litovskaja SSR

Cables: Vilnius Vaiva

Telex: 261128 VA'VA

Telephone: 623-779

Rektor: Jonas Kubilius (1958-)

Registrar: Irena Rageliene

F. of Physics
Dean: Antanas Bandzaitis; *staff* 68
F. of Mathematics and Applied Mathematics
Dean: Vytautas Merkys; *staff* 80 (7)
F. of Chemistry
Dean: Algimantas Levinskas; *staff* 36
F. of Natural Sciences (Biology, Geography, and Geology)
Dean: Rimvydas Tarvydas; *staff* 57 (4)
F. of Medicine
Dean: Albertas Svičiulis; *staff* 185 (6)
F. of History (including Journalism, Library Science, and Psychology)
Dean: Vytautas Lesčius; *staff* 83 (6)
F. of Philology
Dean: Aleksas Girdenis; *staff* 231 (4)
F. of Law
Dean: Pranas Rasimaričius; *staff* 59 (4)
F. of Commerce
Dean: Bronius Čereška; *staff* 30 (4)

F. of Economics, Cybernetics, and Finance
Dean: Jonas Mackevičius; *staff* 79 (8)
F. of Industrial Economics
Dean: Vytautas Grigoras; *staff* 49 (3)
F. of Evening Studies (Kaunas)
Dean: Algirdas Šalčius; *staff* 66 (1)
Computer Ce.
Director: Algimantas Malickas; *staff* 355
F. of Medical In-Service Training
Dean: Petras Visockas; *staff* 48
F. for Refresher Courses
Dean: Vygantas Nekrašas; *staff* 5
D. for Evening Studies
D. for Correspondence Courses

Founded 1579 as Academica and Universitas Vilnensis with two faculties: philosophy and theology. Reorganized 1781 and again 1803 as the Imperial University of Vilnius. Closed by Tsarist government 1832 when faculties of medicine and theology became separate academies. Reopened 1919. Closed during German occupation 1943. Placed under the authority of the Union-Republic State Committee for Public Education. Financed by the State. Governing bodies: the Rector and Pro-Rectors; the Academic Council. Residential facilities for academic staff and students.

Arrangements for co-operation with: Ernst-Moritz-Arndt-Universität, Greifswald; Kossuth Lajos University, Debrecen; Charles University, Prague; Jagiellonian University, Cracow; Academy of Medicine, Erfurt; Johann Wolfgang Goethe University, Frankfurt; Marien Ngouabi University, Brazzaville; Addis Ababa University.

Academic Year: September to July (September-January; February-July).

Admission Requirements: Entrance examination following general or special secondary school certificate, or foreign equivalent.

Fees: None.

Language of Instruction: Lithuanian.

Degrees and Diplomas: Diploma of Higher Education, 4-6 yrs. Kandidat nauk, Candidate of the Sciences, in–Physics and Mathematics; Geology and Mineralogy; History; Philosophy; Education; Philology; Medicine by thesis. Doktor nauk in–Physics and Mathematics; History; Philology; Medicine, by thesis.

Library: Scientific University Library and specialized departments libraries, with a total of *c.* 4,500,000 vols.

Special Facilities (Museums, etc.): Museum of Science.

Publications: Scientific Proceedings; Tarybinis Studentas (weekly).

Academic Staff, 1986-87:

Rank	Full-time	Part-time
Professors	130	16
Associate Professors	675	37
Lecturers, Assistants	409	8
Total	1214	61

Student Enrolment, 1986-87:

	Men	Women	Total
Of the country	1701	6106	7807
Of other countries	2	6	8
Total	1703	6112	7815*

*Also 2266 evening and 5212 correspondence students.

7077 **VOLGOGRADSKIJ GOSUDARSTVENNYJ UNIVERSITET**
Volgograd State University
2ja Prodol'naja ul. 20, 400062 Volgograd 62, Rossiskaja SFSR
Telephone: 43-81-24

D. of Russian Language and Literature
D. of Romance and German Language and Literature
D. of History
D. of Mathematics
D. of Physics

A State university placed under the authority of the Union-Republic State Committee for Public Education. Financed by the State. Governing bodies: the Rector and Pro-Rectors; the Academic Council.

Academic Year: September to July.

Admission Requirements: Competitive entrance examination following general or special secondary school certificate.

Fees: None.

Degrees and Diplomas: Diploma of Specialist in a particular field of study, 5 yrs. Kandidat nauk, Candidate of the Sciences, a further 3 yrs and thesis. Doktor nauk, by thesis after Kandidat.

7078 **VORONEŽSKIJ ORDENA LENINA GOSUDARSTVENNYJ UNIVERSITET IM. LENINSKOGO KOMSOMOLA**
Voronezh State University
Universitetskaja pl. 1, 294693 Voronež, Rossiskaja SFSR
Telephone: 5-29-83

F. of History
F. of Philology
F. of Romance and Germanic Languages
F. of Economics
F. of Law
F. of Mathematics and Applied Mathematics
F. of Physics
F. of Chemistry
F. of Biology and Soil Science
F. of Geology
F. of Geography
D. for Evening Studies
D. for Correspondence Courses

Founded 1919. Placed under the authority of the Union-Republic State Committee for Public Education. Financed by the State. Governing bodies: the Rector and Pro-Rectors; the Academic Council.

Academic Year: September to July.

Admission Requirements: Competitive entrance examination following general or special secondary school certificate.

Fees: None.

Degrees and Diplomas: Diplomas of Specialist in a particular field of study, 5 yrs. Kandidat nauk, Candidate of the Sciences, a further 3 yrs and thesis. Doktor nauk, by thesis after Kandidat.

Student Enrolment: *c.* 6700 (Also *c.* 6500 evening and correspondence students).

7079 **ZAPOROŽSKIS GOSUDARSTVENNYS UNIVERSITET**
ul. Žukovskogo 66, 220600 Zaporoze, Ukrainskaja SSR
Telephone: 64-45-46

F. of Philology
F. of Foreign Languages
F. of History
F. of Physics and Mathematics
F. of Physical Education

Other Institutions

Polytechnical, Industrial and Factory Institutes

Polytechnical

7080 **AZERBAJDŽANSKIJ POLITEHNIČESKIJ INSTITUT IM. Č. IL'DRYMA**
Azerbaijan Polytechnical Institute
Pr. Narimanova 25, 370602 Baku, Azerbajdžanskaja SSR
Telephone: 38-33-43
Rektor: Sadikhov Ali Adayat (1964-)
Secretary-General: Mekhtieva Zemfira

F. of Mechanical Engineering
Dean: R.N. Makhmudov
F. of Metallurgical Engineering
Dean: B.U. Oirasov
F. of Radio Engineering
Dean: Ch.A. Efendier
F. of Motor Transport
Dean: K. Togiev
F. of Robot Engineering
Dean: R.J. Ali-zade
F. of Automation and Computer Technology
Dean: H.J. Bayramov
F. of Electrical Engineering
Dean: J.Y. Mamedov
F. of Machine Building
F. of Evening Studies
Bioengineering L.
Head: E. Babaev

Automatization of Machine and Mechanisms, and Robot Design
Head: R.J. Ali-zade
L. for Polymer Materials
Branch I. (Kirovabad)
Academic Year: September to July.
Admission Requirements: Competitive entrance examination following general or special secondary school certificate.
Degrees and Diplomas: Diploma of Specialist in relevant fields, 5 yrs.

7081 **ALTAJSKIJ POLITEHNIČESKIJ INSTITUT IM. I. I. POLZUNOVA**
Altai Polytechnical Institute
Pr. Lenina 46, 656099 Barnaul 99, Rossiskaja SFSR

F. of Mechanical Engineering
F. of Agricultural, Automobile, and Tractor Engineering
F. of Chemical Technology
F. of Construction Engineering
F. of Correspondence Courses
Several D. for Evening Studies
Academic Year: September to July.
Admission Requirements: Competitive entrance examination following general or special secondary school certificate.
Degrees and Diplomas: Diploma of Specialist in relevant fields, 5 yrs.

7082 **BELORUSSKIJ ORDENA TRUDOVOGO KRASNOGO ZNAMENI POLITEHNIČESKIJ INSTITUT**
Belorussian Polytechnical Institute
Leninskij Prosp. 65, 220027 Minsk, Belorusskaja SSR

F. of Machine Engineering
F. of Mechanical Engineering
F. of Automobile and Tractor Engineering
F. of Energetics
F. of Radio-Technology
F. of Chemical Engineering
F. of Architecture
F. of Construction Engineering
F. of Hydraulic and Highway Engineering
F. of Peat Technology
F. of Engineering Economics
F. of Teacher Training (Engineering)
F. of General Technical Studies (Evening Studies)
F. for Correspondence Courses
F. for Evening Studies (Žodino)
Branch I. (Gomel)
Academic Year: September to July.
Admission Requirements: Competitive entrance examination following general or special secondary school certificate.
Degrees and Diplomas: Diploma of Specialist in relevant fields, 5 yrs.
Student Enrolment: c. 1350 (Also *c.* 9500 evening and correspondence courses).

7083 **ČELJABINSKIJ POLITEHNIČESKIJ INSTITUT IM. LENINSKOGO KOMSOMOLA**
Chelyabinsk Polytechnical Institute
Pr. Lenina 76, 454044 Čeljabinsk 44, Rossiskaja SFSR

F. of Metallurgical Engineering
F. of Mechanical Engineering
F. of Automated Mechanical Engineering
F. of Automobile and Tractor Engineering
F. of Engine Construction
F. of Energetics
F. of Precision Engineering
F. of Construction Engineering
F. for Evening Studies (Mechanical Engineering)
F. for Evening Studies (Energetics)
F. for Evening Studies (Construction Engineering)
F. for Correspondence Studies (Machine Engineering)
F. for Correspondence Studies (Electric Power Supply)
F. for Evening Studies (Čeljjabinsk Tractor Factory)
F. for Evening Studies (Čeljabinsk Metal Factory)
F. for Evening Studies (Miass)
F. for Evening and Correspondence Studies (Zlatoust)
D. for Evening Studies (Kopeisk)
D. for Evening Studies (Kyshtym)
D. for Evening Studies (Novijzlatoust)
Academic Year: September to July.
Admission Requirements: Competitive entrance examination following general or special secondary school certificate.
Degrees and Diplomas: Diploma of Specialist in relevant fields, 5 yrs.
Student Enrolment: c. 12,000 (Also *c.* 9000 evening and correspondence students).

7084 **ČITINSKIJ POLITEHNIČESKIJ INSTITUT**
Čita Polytechnical Institute
Ul. Aleczavodskaya 30, 672039 Čita, Rossiskaja SFSR
Telephone: 64393
Rektor: Boris Ivanovich Kostylev
Prorektor: Lev Petrovich Kulinich

F. of Machine Engineering
Dean: V.V. Grushev; *staff* 33 (6)
F. of Mechanical Engineering
Dean: V.N. Danilenko; *staff* 50 (10)
F. of Energetics
Dean: V.A. Tapkhayev; *staff* 86 (12)
F. of Mining Engineering
Dean: P.B. Avdeyev; *staff* 50 (10)
F. of Construction Engineering
Dean: Y.M. Kon; *staff* 49 (9)
D. for Evening Studies
Head: M.M. Philippov; *staff* 30
D. for Correspondence Courses
Head: V.A. Byvaly; *staff* 35
Research Ce.
Head: V.F. Kusin; *staff* 60
Branch I. (Krasnokamensk)
Founded 1966 as a Branch of Irkutsk Polytechnical Institute. Acquired present title 1974. Governing body: the Senate, comprising 100 members. Residential facilities for students.
Arrangments for co-operation with Beijing University.
Academic Year: September to June.
Admission Requirements: Competitive entrance examination following general or special secondary school certificate.
Fees: None.
Degrees and Diplomas: Diploma of Specialist in relevant fields, 5 yrs.
Library: Central Library, 272,898 vols.
Special Facilities (Museums, etc.): Museum of Minerals.
Publication: Institute's Collection of Papers (annually).
Academic Staff, 1990:

Rank	Full-time
Professors	9
Assistant Professors	135
Teaching Staff	225
Total	369

Student Enrolment, 1990:

	Men	Women	Total
Of the country	1820	780	2600*

*Also 32 external students and 900 students by correspondence.

7085 **DAGESTANSKIJ POLITEHNIČESKIJ INSTITUT**
Dagestan Polytechnical Institute
Prosp. Kalinina 70, 367024 Mahačkala, Dagestanskaja ASSR

F. of Mechanical Engineering
F. of Precision Engineering
F. of Technology
F. of Construction Engineering
F. of Hydraulic Engineering
F. for Evening Studies
D. for Correspondence Courses
Academic Year: September to July.
Admission Requirements: Competitive entrance examination following general or special secondary school certificate.
Degrees and Diplomas: Diploma of Specialist in relevant fields, 5 yrs.

7086 **DAL'NEVOSTOČNYJ ORDENA TRUDOVOGO KRASNOGO ZNAMENI POLITEHNIČESKIJ INSTITUT IM. V. V. KUIJBYSĚVA**
Far East Polytechnical Institute
Puškinskaja ul. 10, Centre GSP, 690600 Vladivostok, Rossiskaja SFSR

F. of Geology and Prospecting
F. of Mining Engineering
F. of Mechanical Engineering
F. of Electrical Engineering
F. of Radio Engineering
F. of Construction Engineering
F. of Hydraulic Engineering
F. of Shipbuilding Engineering
F. for Evening Studies
F. for Correspondence Courses

Academic Year: September to July.

Admission Requirements: Competitive entrance examination following general or special secondary school certificate.

Degrees and Diplomas: Diploma of Specialist in relevant fields, 5 yrs.

7087 **DONECKIJ ORDENA TRUDOVOGO KRASNOGO ZNAMENI POLITEHNIČESKIJ INSTITUT**

Donets Polytechnical Institute

Ul. Artema 58, 340066 Doneck, Ukrainskaja SSR

F. of Mining Engineering
F. of Geology and Surveying
F. of Mining Technology and Electrification
F. of Mechanical Engineering
F. of Metallurgical Engineering
F. of Computer Technology and Automation
F. of Energetics
F. of Chemical Engineering
F. of Engineering Economics
F. for Evening Studies
F. for Correspondence Courses
Branch I. (Gorlovok)
Branch I. (Krasnoarmeisk)

Academic Year: September to July.

Admission Requirements: Competitive entrance examination following general or special secondary school certificate.

Degrees and Diplomas: Diploma of Specialist in relevant fields, 5 yrs.

7088 **EREVANSKIJ ORDENA TRUDOVOGO KRASNOGO ZNAMENI POLITEHNIČESKIJ INSTITUT IM. KARLA MARSKA**

Erevan Polytechnical Institute

Ul. Terjana 105, 375009 Erevan, Armjanskaja SSR

Telephone: 59-85-55

F. of Mechanical and Machine Engineering
F. of Electrical Engineering
F. of Energetics
F. of Cybernetics (Automation, and Computer Technology)
F. of Radio Engineering
F. of Chemical Engineering
F. of Construction Engineering
F. of Mining Engineering and Metallurgy
F. for Correspondence Courses
D. for Evening Studies
Branch I. (Kirobakan)
Branch I. (Leninakan)

Academic Year: September to July.

Admission Requirements: Competitive entrance examination following general or special secondary school certificate.

Degrees and Diplomas: Diploma of Specialist in relevant fields, 5 yrs.

Student Enrolment: *c.* 14,500 (Also *c.* 5300 evening and correspondence students).

7089 **FERGANSKIJ POLITEHNIČESKIJ INSTITUT**

Fergansk Polytechnical Institute

Ferganskaja Ul. 86, Kirgili 1, 712022 Fergana, Uzbekskaja SSR

Telephone: 2-13-33

Engineering (various fields)
D. for Evening Studies
D. for Correspondence Courses

Academic Year: September to July.

Admission Requirements: Competitive entrance examination following general or special secondary school certificate.

Degrees and Diplomas: Diploma of Specialist in relevant fields, 5 yrs.

7090 **FRUNZENSKIJ POLITEHNIČESKIJ INSTITUT**

Frunze Polytechnical Institute

Pr. Mira 66, 720057 Frunze, Kirgizskaja SSR

Telephone: 42-14-62

F. of Mining Engineering
F. of Mechanical Engineering
F. of Food Technology
F. of Architecture and Construction Engineering
F. of Engineering Economics
F. of Energetics
F. of General Technical Studies (Osha)
F. of General Technical Studies (GES Osha)
F. of Evening Studies
F. for Correspondence Courses

Academic Year: September to July.

Admission Requirements: Competitive entrance examination following general or special secondary school certificate.

Degrees and Diplomas: Diploma of Specialist in relevant fields, 5 yrs.

7091 **GOMEL'SKIJ POLITEHNIČESKIJ INSTITUT**

Gomel Polytechnical Institute

Prosp. Oktjabrja 48, 246746 Gomel, Belorusskaja SSR

Telephone: 48-16-00

Rektor: Albert Shaginyan

Prorektor: Stanislav Sarelo

F. of Electrical Engineering
F. of Machine Engineering
Dean: Anton Akulich; *staff* 69 (21)
F. of Mechanical Engineering and Technology
Dean: Vladimir Rusov; *staff* 63 (26)
F. of Automation and Computer
F. of Automation and Electromechanics
Dean: Leonid Evminov; *staff* 114 (39)
Scientific Research D.
Dean: Victor Ken'ko; *staff* 46 (138)

Founded 1981, previously part of the Byelorussian Polytechnic. Governing body: the Scientific Council and the Rectorate. Residential facilities for academic staff and students.

Academic Year: September to June (September-January; February-June).

Admission Requirements: Competitive entrance examination following general or special secondary school certificate.

Fees: None.

Degrees and Diplomas: Diploma of Specialist in relevant fields, 5 yrs.

Library: 270,000 vols.

Academic Staff, 1990:

Rank	Full-time	Part-time
Professors	7	3
Assistant Professors	123	22
Instructors	118	63
Total	248	88

Student Enrolment, 1990: 3040 (Also 570 external students).

7092 **GOR'KOVSKIJ ORDENA TRUDOVOGO KRASNOGO ZNAMENI POLITEHNIČESKIJ INSTITUT IM A.A. ŽDANOVA**

Gorki Polytechnical Institute

Ul. K. Minina 24, 603600 Gor'kij, Rossiskaja SFSR

Telephone: 36-73-43

F. of Machine Engineering
F. of Mechanical Engineering
F. of Electrical Engineering
F. of Radio Engineering
F. of Metallurgical Engineering
F. of Shipbuilding Engineering
F. of Chemical Engineering
F. of Physical Technology
F. for Evening Studies (Radio Engineering)
F. for Evening Studies (Automobile Engineering)
F. for Evening Studies (Machine Engineering)
F. for Evening Studies (Chemical Engineering)
F. for Correspondence Courses

Academic Year: September to July.

Admission Requirements: Competitive entrance examination following general or special secondary school certificate.

Degrees and Diplomas: Diploma of Specialist in relevant fields, 5 yrs.
Student Enrolment: c. 8300 (Also *c.* 7000 evening and correspondence students).

7093 **GRUZINSKIJ ORDENA LENINA I ORDENA TRUDOVOGO KRASNOGO ZNAMENI POLITEHNIČESKIJ INSTITUT IM. V.I. LENINA**
Georgian Polytechnical Institute
Ul. Lenina 77, 380075 Tbilisi 75, Gruzinskaja SSR
Telephone: 36-65-05

F. of Geology
F. of Mining Engineering F. of Energetics
F. of Construction Engineering
F. of Chemical and Food Technology
F. of Mechanical and Machine Engineering
F. of Metallurgical Engineering
F. of Automobile Engineering
F. of Communications Technology and Electronics
F. of Hydraulic and Sanitary Engineering
F. of Light Industrial Engineering
F. of Automation and Computer Technology
F. of Applied Physics
F. of Transport Engineering
F. of Architecture
F. of Evening Studies
F. for Correspondence Courses
Branch I. (Kutaisi)

Founded 1922 as faculty of the Georgian State University, acquired present status 1959.
Academic Year: September to July (September-January; February-July).
Admission Requirements: Competitive entrance examination following general or special secondary school certificate or diploma from technical school.
Degrees and Diplomas: Diploma, *c.* 5 yrs, 6 yrs in Architecture.
Student Enrolment: c. 23,000.

7094 **HABAROVSKIJ POLITEHNIČESKIJ INSTITUT**
Habarovsk Polytechnical Institute
Tihookeanskaja Ul. 136, 680035 Habarovsk Kraevoj 35, Rossiskaja SFSR
Cables: habarovsk-35, polytechnical institute
Telephone: 35-83-18
Rektor: Victor K. Bulgakov
Prorektor: Vitaly V. Shkutko

F. of Mechanical Engineering
Dean: Vladimir M. Davydov; *staff* 81 (9)
F. of Highway Engineering
Dean: Apolinary I. Yarmolinsky; *staff* 45 (8)
F. of Automobile Engineering
Dean: Alexander V. Feigin; *staff* 75 (7)
F. of Construction Engineering
Dean: Vladimir N. Antonets; *staff* 120 (20)
F. of Engineering Economics
Dean: Victor G. Trunin; *staff* 75 (37)
F. of Forestry, Wood Technology and Chemical Engineering
Dean: Gennady F. Khramtsov; *staff* 80 (10)
F. of Electronic Technology
Dean: Constantin T. Pazyuk; *staff* 41 (55)
F. for Evening Studies
Dean: Dinatoly A. Dodonov; *staff* 50
F. for Correspondence Courses (Engineering)
Dean: Yury I. Kulikov; *staff* 60
F. for Correspondence Courses (Construction Engineering)
Dean: Sergey G. Lysak; *staff* 40
Research Ce.
Head: Anatoly P. Ulashkin; *staff* 120 (450)
Ecology Ce.
Head: Mikhail N. Shevtsov; *staff* 20 (15)
Hydrodynamics and Geophysics Research L.
Head: Konstantin A. Chehonin; *staff* 10 (15)
L. of Microscopic Particle Systems
Head: Victor A. Knyr; *staff* 5 (6)

Founded 1958. Governing body: the Council of Scientists. Residential facilities for academic staff and students.
Arrangements for co-operation with Harbin Polytechnical Institute.
Academic Year: September to July.

Admission Requirements: Competitive entrance examination following general or special secondary school certificate.
Fees: None.
Language of Instruction: Russian.
Degrees and Diplomas: Diploma of Specialist in relevant fields, 5 yrs.
Library: 1,200,000 vols.
Academic Staff, 1990: 332.
Student Enrolment, 1990:

	Men	Women	Total
Of the country	3400	2400	5800*

*Also 3600 external students.

7095 **HAR'KOVSKIJ ORDENA LENINA I ORDENA OKTJABR'SKOJ REVOLJUCII POLITEHNIČESKIJ INSTITUT IM. V.I. LENINA**
Kharkov Polytechnical Institute
Ul. Frunze 21, 310002 Har'kov, Ukrainskaja SSR
Telephone: 47-80-68

F. of Mechanical and Metallurgical Engineering
F. of Machine Engineering
F. of Energetics
F. of Automobile and Tractor Engineering
F. of Electrical Engineering
F. of Electrical Power Production
F. of Physics (Physics of Metals)
F. of Automation and Computer Technology
F. of Radio-Technology
F. of Inorganic Chemical Technology
F. of Chemical Engineering
F. of Applied Physics
F. of General Technical Studies
F. for Evening Studies
Several F. for Correspondence Courses
Branch I. (Rubeznoe)
Branch I. (Sumy)

Academic Year: September to July.
Admission Requirements: Competitive entrance examination following general or special secondary school certificate.
Degrees and Diplomas: Diploma of Specialist in relevant fields, 5 yrs.
Student Enrolment: c. 11,500 (Also *c.* 9000 evening and correspon-dence students).

7096 **IRKUTSKIJ ORDENA TRUDOVOGO KRASNOGO ZHAMENI POLITEHNIČESKIJ INSTITUT**
Irkutsk Polytechnical Institute
Ul. Lermontova 83, 664028 Irkutsk 28, Rossiskaja SFSR
Cables: poisk 202
Telex: 133153 INST SU
Telephone: 43-16-12
Rektor: S.B. Leono

D. of Mining
Head: D.F. Mahno
D. of Geological Prospective
Head: A.J. Davwdenko; *staff* 65
D. of Metallurgy
Head: V.M. Salov; *staff* 68
D. of Automechanics
Head: I.V. Gorbunov; *staff* 85
D. of Aviation
Head: V.A. Yushin; *staff* 86
D. of Machine Building
Head: V.V. Nagaev; *staff* 76
D. of Architecture and Civil Engineering
Head: V.G. Temnikov; *staff* 104
D. of Sanitary Engineering
Head: V.D. Kazanov; *staff* 51
D. of Power Engineering
Head: A.S. Zhdanov; *staff* 166
D. of Cybernetics
Head: S.V. Bakhvalov; *staff* 48
D. of Chemical Engineering
Head: A.L.Volkov; *staff* 48

Founded 1930. Formerly Siberian Mining Institute. Reorganized as Polytechnic 1960.

Arrangements for co-operation with: Polytechnic of Mongolia; Freiberg Mining Academy; Warsaw Polytechnic; Geological University of Beijing (China).

Academic Year: September to July.

Admission Requirements: Competitive entrance examination following general or special secondary school certificate.

Degrees and Diplomas: Diploma of Specialist in relevant fields, 5 yrs.

Library: 1,215,000 vols.

Publications: ORE Dressing; Geological Survey; Search and Prospecting for Useful Mineral Resources; Dynamics of Vibroactive Systems.

Student Enrolment: *c.* 11,000 (Also *c.* 7700 evening and correspondence students).

7097 **KALININSKIJ ORDENA TRUDOVOGO KRASNOGO ZNAMENI POLITEHNIČESKIJ INSTITUT**

Kalinin Polytechnical Institute

Pervomaijskaja nab. 22, 170035 Kalinin, Rossiskaja SFSR

Telex: ZNANIE - 159

Telephone: 1-63-35

Rektor: V.A. Mironov

F. of Mechanical Technology

Dean: V.I. Goryachev; *staff* 300 (7)

F. of Civil Engineering

Dean: Yu.I. Sedov; *staff* 185 (3)

F. of Automated Control Systems

Dean: G.A. Dmitriev; *staff* 237 (4)

F. for Evening Studies

Dean: N.N. Sokolov

F. for Correspondence Courses

Dean: S.D. Semeenkov

Inter-Branch F. for Qualification Increase of Executive and National Economy Specialists

Dean: Yu.A. Yanov

Preparatory F. for Foreigners and S. of Russian Language

Dean: E.N. Konoplyov; *staff* 60

Computer Ce.

Also 5 Research Laboratories.

Founded 1922 as Moscow Peat Institute. Acquired present title 1965. Governing bodies: the Council; the Faculty Council.

Arrangements for co-operation with Oulu University.

Academic Year: September to June (September-January; January-June).

Admission Requirements: Competitive entrance examination following general or special secondary school certificate.

Fees: None. Foreign students, US$ 2300-6500 per annum.

Degrees and Diplomas: Diploma of Specialist in relevant fields, 5 yrs. Candidate of the Sciences, a further 3 yrs. Doktor of the Sciences, 3 yrs.

Library: 714,529 vols.

Special Facilities (Museums, etc.): Museum of the Institute's History.

Publication: The Research Proceedings (annually).

Press or Publishing House: Editorial Publishing Department.

Academic Staff, 1989: 1921.

Student Enrolment, 1989: 4697.

7098 **KAMSKIJ POLITEHNIČESKIJ INSTITUT**

Kamskij Polytechnical Institute

Prosp. Mira 68/19, 423810 Naberežnye Čelny, Rossiskaja SFSR

Telephone: 53-73-96

Rektor: Sadykov Insor Hadievič

F. of Machine Engineering

Dean: Ahmetšin Almaz Harisovič

F. of Motor and Tractor Technology

Dean: Rumjancev Valerij Vladimirovič

D. for Evening Studies

Founded 1980.

Academic Year: September to July.

Admission Requirements: Competitive entrance examination following general or special secondary school certificate.

Fees: None.

Degrees and Diplomas: Diploma of Specialist in relevant fields, 5 yrs.

Library: 200,000 vols.

Academic Staff, 1990: 258.

Student Enrolment, 1990: 4097.

7099 **KARAGANDINSKIJ ORDENA TRUDOVOGO KRASNOGO ZNAMENI POLITEHNIČESKIJ INSTITUT**

Karaganda Polytechnical Institute

Bul'var Mira 56, 470041 Karaganda, Kazahskaja SSR

Telephone: 54-77-87

F. of Mining Engineering

F. of Mining Electrification and Automation

F. of Mechanical Engineering

F. of Automobile Engineering

F. of Construction Engineering

F. of General Technical Studies

F. for Evening Studies (Balkhash)

F. for Evening Studies (Dyezkazgan)

F. of Great Technical Studies (Kokchetovsk)

D. for Evening Studies

Academic Year: September to July.

Admission Requirements: Competitive entrance examination following general or special secondary school certificate.

Degrees and Diplomas: Diploma of Specialist in relevant fields, 5 yrs.

7100 **KAUNO POLITECHNIKOS INSTITUTAS**

Kaunas Polytechnic Institute

73, Donelaicio, 233006 Kaunas, Lietuva

Telephone: 20-26-40

Fax: 20-26-40

Rector: Vladislavas Domarkas

Deputy Rector for Administration: Domas Vilkys

F. of Automation Engineering

Dean: J. Daunoras; *staff* 60 (6)

F. of Power Engineering

Dean: A. Navickas; *staff* 58 (4)

F. of Chemical Engineering

Dean: K. Sasnauskas; *staff* 87 (2)

F. of Industrial Economics

Dean: B. Martinkus; *staff* 102 (18)

F. of Light Industry Engineering

F. of Machine Building Engineering

Dean: R. Banevicius; *staff* 105 (9)

F. of Mechanical Engineering

Dean: P. Svencianas; *staff* 78 (7)

F. of Radio Engineering

Dean: S. Mickunas; *staff* 127 (4)

F. of Civil Engineering

Dean: M. Malakauskas; *staff* 45 (6)

F. of Computer Engineering

Dean: J. Matickas; *staff* 114 (8)

Research D.

Deputy Rector: Y. Krisciunas; *staff* 582 (54)

D. of Humanities

; *staff* 207 (11)

Computer Ce.

Director: J. Puodzius; *staff* 270 (9)

D. for Correspondence Courses

Deputy Rector: J. Palaima

Vibration Technology Research Ce.

Ultrasound Technology Research Ce:

Head: V. Domarkas; *staff* 95

Packing Technology Research Ce.

Head: B. Ruogalvis; *staff* 91

Also Faculties in: Vilnius, Klaipeda, Siauliai, Panevezys.

Founded 1920, became Lithuanian State University 1922, and Kaunas State University 1940. Technical Department detached and re-established under present title 1950. A State institution. Governing body: the Council, comprising 103 members. Residential facilities for 80% of day students.

Arrangements for co-operation with Universities in: Poland, Bulgaria, Hungary, Germany, Czechoslovakia.

Academic Year: September to July (September-February, February-July).

Admission Requirements: Entrance examination following general or special secondary school certificate.

Fees: None.

Languages of Instruction: Lithuanian and Russian.

Degrees and Diplomas: Diploma of Specialist in a particular field, 5 yrs. Kandidat nauk, Candidate of the Sciences, a further 3 yrs and thesis. Doktor nauk, by thesis after Kandidat.

Library: *c.* 2,200,000.

Special Facilities (Museums, etc.): University History Museum.

Publications: Chemistry and Chemical Technology (annually); Electrotechnics (annually); Radiotechnics (biannually); Ultrasound, ISSN 0369-6367 (annually); Vibrotechnics ISSN 0233-9293 (quarterly); Technology of Textile and Leather (annually).

Academic Staff, 1990:

Rank	Full-timez	Part-time
Profesorius (Professors)	61	2
Docentas (Assistant Professors)	555	13
Vyr dest. (Senior Lecturers)	251	35
Asistentas (Assistants)	232	58
Total	1099	98

Student Enrolment, 1990:

	Men	Women	Total
Of the country	6043	3220	9263*

*Also 1437 students by correspondence and 2128 students of evening studies.

7101 **KAZAHSKIJ ORDENA TRUDOVOGO KRASNOGO ZNAMENI POLITEHNIČESKIJ INSTITUT IM. V.I. LENINA**

Kazakh Polytechnical Institute

Ul. Stapaeva 22, 480013 Alma-Ata, Kazahskaja SSR

Telex: 251315 ISTOK

Telephone: 679001

Rektor: Rakishev Bayan Rakishevich

F. of Geology and Prospecting
Dean: Nusipov Yergali Nusipovich; *staff* 63
F. of Hydrogeology and Prospecting Engineering
Dean: Musanov Alken Musanovich; *staff* 77
F. of Mining Engineering
Dean: Tsekhovoi Alexei Filippovich; *staff* 90
F. of Petroleum Engineering
Dean: Zholtayev Geroi Zholtayevich; *staff* 89
F. of Metallurgical Engineering
Dean: Sadykov Zhanarystan Sadykovich; *staff* 106
F. of Mechanical Engineering
Dean: Yesyrev Pavel Georgievich; *staff* 122
F. of Automatic Machinery and Control Systems
Dean: Asaubayev Kanat Shaikhanovich; *staff* 99
F. of Electronic Computer Technology
Dean: Sarypbekov Zhaksybek Sarypbekovich; *staff* 116
F. of General Technical Studies (Shevchenko)
Dean: Bozhanov Yesbergen Tokshalykovich; *staff* 71
F. of General Technical Studies (Zyryanovsk)
Dean: Amirkhanov Zaur Sirazhivich; *staff* 13
F. of General Technical Studies (Ustkamenogorsk)
Dean: Zhaglov Vladimir Stepanovich; *staff* 30
Branch I. (Guriev)
Dean: Serikov Tuleush Paudenvich; *staff* 64
Branch I. (Karatau)
Dean: Nurlybayev; *staff* 85
Research D. (Mining Engineering, Metallurgical Engineering, Automatic Machinery and Computer Technology, Mechanical Engineering, Geology, Petroleum Geology, Geophysics)
Dean: Luganov Vladimir Alexeevich; *staff* 327 (370)

Founded 1934 as Kazakh Mining and Metallurgical Institute. Reorganized into a polytechnic 1960. Acquired present title 1984. Governing bodies: the Board, comprising 134 members; the Academic Council (67).

Academic Year: September to June (September-January; February-June).

Admission Requirements: Competitive entrance examination following general or special secondary school certificate.

Languages of Instruction: Kazakh and Russian.

Degrees and Diplomas: Diploma of Engineer in relevant fields, 5 yrs. Diploma of Candidate of the Sciences, in relevant fieldes.

Library: 1,300,000 vols.

Special Facilities (Museums, etc.): Mineralogical Museum; Museum of Battle and Labour Glory.

Academic Staff, 1990: 1023 (10).

Student Enrolment, 1989-90:

Men	Women	Total
11,896	6168	18,064*

*Also 2268 evening students and 6823 students by correspoondence.

7102 **KHARKOVSKIJ INZHENERNO-PEDAGOGICHESKIJ INSTITUTE**

Kharkov Engineering Pedagogics Institute

Universitetskaja ul. 16, 310003 Har'kov, Ukrainskaja SSR

Telephone: 22-43-03

Rektor: Stanislav Feodorovitch Artyuh (1958-)

Prorektor: Kruk Nikolai Petrovitch

F. of Technical Mechanical Technology
Dean: Yuri Mikhailov; *staff* 52 (6)
F. of Power Engineering
Dean: Allexander Alex Kutchava; *staff* 70 (15)
F. of General Technical Studies
F. of General Technical Studies (Artemovsk)
F. of General Technical Studies (Konstantinovka)
F. of General Technical Studies (Slavjansk)
F. of Machine Building
Dean: Victor Timofeev. Akimov; *staff* 65 (6)
F. of Chemical Technological
Dean: Vasily Ivan Potrashkov; *staff* 69 (8)
F. of Electrical Mechanics
Dean: Vladimir Petr. Solyanik; *staff* 69 (8)
Several F. for Correspondence Courses
D. for Evening Studies
L. of Assembly Processes
Head: Mark Konstant. Kravtsov; *staff* 50 (20)
Polymer Electrochemistry L.
Dean: Vasily Danilov. Besugly; *staff* 8 (8)
Surface Metal Physics L.
Dean: Anatoly Maximov. Shkilko; *staff* 5 (5)
Special Design-Technological Bureau 'Armplast'
Dean: Stanislav Feodor. Artyuh; *staff* 50 (25)

Founded 1958 as the Ukranian Correspondence Polytechnic Institute. Acquired present status and title 1990. Under the authority of the Ministry of Higher Education of the UkSSR. Governing body: the Scientific Council. Residential facilities for 1220 students in hostels.

Arrangements for co-operation with: Cracow Mining and Metallurgy Academy; Dresden Technical University; Inner-Mongolian Agricultural and Cattle-Breeding Institute.

Academic Year: September to July.

Admission Requirements: Competitive entrance examination following general or special secondary school certificate.

Fees: None.

Languages of Instruction: Russian and Ukrainian.

Degrees and Diplomas: Diploma of Specialist in relevant fields, 5 yrs.

Library: Central Library, 900,000 vols.

Publication: Republican Scientific (Technical Articles Collection 'Hoisting Equipment') (annually).

Academic Staff, 1990:

Rank	Full-time	Part-time
Professors	20	5
Assistant Professors	260	21
Total	280	26

Student Enrolment, 1990:

	Men	Women	Total
Of the country	380	720	1100*

*Also 6240 students by correspondence.

7103 **KIEVSKIJ ORDENA LENINA POLITEHNIČESKIJ INSTITUT IM. 50-LETIJA VELIKOJ OKTJABR'SKOJ SOCIALISTIČESKOJ REVOLJUCCII**

Kiev Polytechnical Institute

prosp. Pobedy 37, 252056 Kiev, Ukrainskaja SSR

Telephone: 441-93-03

F. of Mechanical Engineering
F. of Machine Engineering
F. of Precision Engineering
F. of Electro-Energetics
F. of Automation and Electronic Equipment
F. of Electrification and Automation of Mining
F. of Thermo-Energetics
F. of Chemical Engineering (Machines)
F. of Chemical Engineering (Technology)
F. of Radio Engineering
F. of Radio Electronics
F. of Electro-Acoustics

F. of General Technical Studies
F. for Evening Studies
F. of General Technical Studies (Žitomir)
Branch I. (Vinnitz)
Branch I. (Chernigov)
Academic Year: September to July.
Admission Requirements: Competitive entrance examination following general or special secondary school certificate.
Degrees and Diplomas: Diploma of Specialist in relevant fields, 5 yrs.
Student Enrolment: *c.* 15,300 (Also *c.* 10,300 evening and correspondence students).

7104 **KIROVSKIJ POLITEHNIČESKIJ INSTITUT**
Kirov Polytechnical Institute
Ul. Komuny 36, 610023 Kirov 23, Rossiskaja SFSR
Telephone: 2-65-71
F. of Automation and Computer Technology
F. of Electrical Engineering
F. of Machine Engineering
F. of Chemical Engineering
F. of General Technical Studies
D. for Evening Studies
D. for Correspondence Courses
Academic Year: September to July.
Admission Requirements: Competitive entrance examination following general or special secondary school certificate.
Degrees and Diplomas: Diploma of Specialist in relevant fields, 5 yrs.

7105 **KIŠINEVSKIJ POLITEHNIČESKIJ INSTITUT IM. S.G. LAZO**
Kishinev Polytechnical Institute
Prosp. Lenina 168, 277612 Kišinev, Moldavskaja SSR
Telephone: 44-13-00
F. of Energetics
F. of Electrophysics
F. of Mechanical Engineering
F. of Food Technology
F. of Construction Engineering
F. of Engineering Economics
D. for Evening Studies
D. for Correspondence Courses
Academic Year: September to July.
Admission Requirements: Competitive entrance examination following general or special secondary school certificate.
Degrees and Diplomas: Diploma of Specialist in relevant fields, 5 yrs.

7106 **KOMSOMOL'SKIJ-NA-AMURE POLITEHNIČESKIJ INSTITUT**
Komsomol'sk-na-Amure Polytechnical Institute
Prosp. Lenina 27, 681013 Komsomol'sk-na-Amure Habarovskogo Kraja, Rossiskaja SFSR
Telephone: 3-22-53
F. of Machine Engineering (day and evening courses)
F. of Shipbuilding Engineering (day and eveningcourses)
F. of Aeronautical Engineering (day and evening courses)
F. of Construction Engineering (day and evening courses)
F. for Correspondence Courses
Academic Year: September to July.
Admission Requirements: Competitive entrance examination following general or special secondary school certificate.
Degrees and Diplomas: Diploma of Specialist in relevant fields, 5 yrs.

7107 **KRASNODARSKIJ ORDENA TRUDOVOGO KRASNOGO ZNAMENI POLITEHNIČESKIJ INSTITUT**
Krasnodar Polytechnical Institute
Krasnaja ul. 135, 350006 Krasnodar 6, Rossiskaja SFSR
Telephone: 55-16-24
F. of Energetics
F. of Mechanical and Machine Engineering
F. of Construction Engineering
F. of Chemical Technology
F. of Engineering Economics
F. of Farinaceous Food Technology
F. of General Technical Studies
F. of General Technical Studies (Novorossisk)
F. of General Technical Studies (Sochi)
F. for Evening Studies
F. for Correspondence Courses
Branch I. (Armair)
Academic Year: September to July.
Admission Requirements: Competitive entrance examination following general or special secondary school certificate.
Degrees and Diplomas: Diploma of Specialist in relevant fields, 5 yrs.
Student Enrolment: *c.* 6550 (Also *c.* 8700 evening and correspondence students).

7108 **KRASNOJARSKIJ POLITEHNIČESKIJ INSTITUT**
Krasnojarsk Polytechnical Institute
Ul. Kirenskogo 26, 660074 Krasnojarsk 74, Rossiskaja SFSR
Telephone: 5-23-94
F. of Mechanical Engineering
F. of Machine Engineering
F. of Automobile Engineering
F. of Construction Engineering
F. of Thermo-Energetic Engineering
F. of Electrical Engineering
F. of Radio Engineering
F. of General Technical Studies
F. for Evening Studies
F. for Correspondence Courses
Branch I. (Abakan)
Academic Year: September to July.
Admission Requirements: Competitive entrance examination following general or special secondary school certificate.
Degrees and Diplomas: Diploma of Specialist in relevant fields, 5 yrs.
Student Enrolment: *c.* 9300 (Also *c.* 6150 evening and correspondence students).

7109 **KUJBYŠEVSKIJ ORDENA TRUDOVOGO KRASNOGO ZNAMENI POLITEHNIČESKIJ INSTITUT IM. V.V. KUJBYŠEVA**
Kuybyshev Polytechnical Institute
Galaktionovskaja ul. 141, 443010 Kujbyšev obl., Rossiskaja SFSR
Telephone: 32-42-36
F. of Mechanical Engineering
F. of Petroleum Engineering
F. of Oil Processing
F. of Thermo-Energetic Engineering
F. of Electrical Engineering
F. of Automation and Measurement Technology
F. of Chemical Engineering
F. of Engineering Technology
F. of General Technical Studies (Otradnyy)
F. for Evening Studies (Novo-Kuybyshev)
F. for Correspondence Courses
D. for Evening Studies
Branch I. (Syzran)
Academic Year: September to July.
Admission Requirements: Competitive entrance examination following general or special secondary school certificate.
Degrees and Diplomas: Diploma of Specialist in relevant fields, 5 yrs.

7110 **KURSKIJ POLITEHNIČESKIJ INSTITUT**
Kursk Polytechnical Institute
Ul. 50-letija Oktjabrja 94, 305039 Kursk, Rossiskaja SFSR
Telephone: 2-57-43
F. of Precision Engineering (Computer)
F. of Machine Engineering
F. of Mechanical Technology (Textiles)
F. of General Technical Studies
F. for Evening Studies
Academic Year: September to July.
Admission Requirements: Competitive entrance examination following general or special secondary school certificate.
Degrees and Diplomas: Diploma of Specialist in relevant fields, 5 yrs.

7111 **KUTAISSKIJ POLITEHNICESKIJ INSTITUT IM. N.I. MUSHELISHVILI**

Kutaisi Polytechnical Institute

Pr. Molodezhi, 98, 384014 Kutaisi, Georgian SSR

Telephone: 3-40-27 Teletype: 02 160 158 format

Rektor: Archil A. Kostava

F. of Humanitarian Sciences (History of Georgia, Political Economy, Georgian Language amnd Literature and History of Culture, Philosophy, Social-Political History, Economics of Production and Organization)

Dean: Amiran O. Nicoleishvili; *staff* 80 (56)

General Technical F.

Dean: David M. Lekveishvili; *staff* 122 (41)

F. of Automechanics

Dean: Grigol M. Chitaia; *staff* 41 (64)

Machine Building and Technological Process Automatization

Dean: Grigol G. Chelidze; *staff* 49 (38)

F. of Food Industry and Chemical Technology

Dean: Omar V. Zivzivadze; *staff* 31 (47)

F. of Technology and Equipment of Light Industry

Dean: Zinaida A. Vadachkoria; *staff* 37 (60)

F. for Evening and Correspondence Courses

Dean: Otar Sh. Sesikashvili

Problemic Scientific Research L. (Cosmophysical Research)

Head: Teimauaz G. Adeishvili; *staff* 12 (8)

Knitting Technology and Textile Materials Scientific Research Ce.

Head: Adesealom V. Mamulashvili; *staff* 8 (7)

L. of Textile Industry Major Processes

Head: George B. Jokharidze; *staff* 3 (3)

Scientific Technical Ce. of Youth

Head: Iuri A. Iazikovi; *staff* 1 (7)

Regional Ce. of Environmental Ecology Research

Head: Jemali M. Metreveli; *staff* 50 (30)

Computer Ce.

Founded 1974. Acquired present title 1977. Governing body: the Council, comprising 28 members. Residential faciliteis for 200 students.

Arrangments for co-operation with: Dresden Technical University; Dresden Transpoort School; Gorvaldovo Technical Institute; Plovdiv Institute of Food Industry.

Academic Year: September to July (September-February; February-July).

Admission Requirements: Competitive entrance examination following general or special secondary school certificate.

Languages of Instruction: Georgian and Russian.

Degrees and Diplomas: Diploma of Specialist in relevant fields, 5 yrs.

Library: 148,000 vols.

Academic Staff, 1990:

Rank	Full-time
Professors	9
Assistant Professors	102
Chief Teachers	92
Assistants	157
Total	360

Student Enrolment, 1990:

	Men	Women	Total
Of the country	4077	2350	6427*

*Also 146 students by correspondences.

7112 **KUZBASSKIJ POLITEHNIČESKIJ INSTITUT**

Kuzbass Polytechnical Institute

Vessennjaja ul. 28, 650026 Kemerovo 26, Rossiskaja SFSR

Telephone: 23-33-23

F. of Mining Engineering

F. of Pit Construction

F. of Engineering Economics

F. of Electrification of Mining

F. of Chemical Engineering

F. for Evening Studies

F. for Correspondence Courses

Academic Year: September to July.

Admission Requirements: Competitive entrance examination following general or special secondary school certificate.

Degrees and Diplomas: Diploma of Specialist in relevant fields, 5 yrs.

7113 ***LENINGRADSKIJ ORDENA LENINA POLITEHNIČESKIJ INSTITUT IM. M.I. KALININA**

Leningrad Polytechnical Institute

Politehnič-eskaja ul. 29, 195251 Leningrad K-251, Rossiskaja SFSR

Telex: 121803 ODRA

Telephone: 247-21-31

Rektor: Yu. S. Vasiliev (1983-)

F. of Hydraulic Engineering

F. of Electrical Engineering

F. of Energetics and Power Engineering

F. of Mechanical and Machine Engineering

F. of Physical Mechanics

F. of Physical Metallurgy

F. of Engineering Economics

F. of Radio Engineering

F. of Technical Cybernetics

F. for Evening Studies

F. for Correspondence Courses

Branch I. (Pskov)

Founded 1899.

Arrangements for co-operation with: Technische Universität Dresden; České vysoké učeni technické v Praze; Universidad de Oriente; Viên Dai hoc Hô Chi Minh ville; Kim Chaek University of Technology; Yarmouk University; Beijing Polytechnical University; Universität Hannover; Technische Universität Graz.

Academic Year: September to July.

Admission Requirements: Competitive entrance examination following general or special secondary school certificate.

Fees: None.

Language of Instruction: Russian.

Degrees and Diplomas: Diploma of Specialist in relevant fields, 5 yrs. Kandidat nauk, Candidate of the Sciences, a further 3 yrs andthesis. Doktor nauk, by thesis after Kandidat.

Library: c. 2,500,000 vols.

Special Facilities (Museums, etc.): History Museum; Technology Museum.

Academic Staff, 1986-87 c. 1800.:

Student Enrolment, 1986-87 c. 22,000.:

7114 **LIPECKIJ POLITEHNIČESKIJ INSTITUT**

Lipetsk Polytechnical Institute

Ul. Zegelja 1, 398662 Lipeck, Rossiskaja SFSR

Telephone: 24-13-09

F. of Metallurgical Engineering

F. of Machine Engineering

F. of Mechanical Engineering

F. of Construction Engineering

F. of Electrical Engineering

F. of Transport Engineering

F. for Evening Studies

Academic Year: September to July.

Admission Requirements: Competitive entrance examination following general or special secondary school certificate.

Degrees and Diplomas: Diploma of Specialist in relevant fields, 5 yrs.

7115 **L'VOVSKIJ ORDENA LENINA POLITEHNIČESKIJ INSTITUT IM. LENINSKOGO KOMSOMOLA**

L'vov Polytechnical Institute

Ul. Mira 12, 290646 L'vov, Ukrainskaja SSR

Telephone: 72-47-33

F. of Surveying

F. of Mechanical Engineering

F. of Machine Engineering

F. of Energetics

F. of Thermo-Energetic Engineering

F. of Electrical Engineering

F. of Engineering Economics

F. of Radio Engineering

F. of Automation Engineering

F. of Electrophysics

F. of Chemical Engineering

F. of Organic Chemistry Technology

F. of Architecture

F. of Construction Engineering

F. of General Technical Studies

F. of General Technical Studies (Dragobych)
F. of General Technical Studies (Lutsk)
F. of General Technical Studies (Novovolynsk)
F. for Evening Studies
F. for Correspondence Courses
Branch I. (Ternopol)

Academic Year: September to July.

Admission Requirements: Competitive entrance examination following general or special secondary school certificate.

Degrees and Diplomas: Diploma of Specialist in relevant fields, 5 yrs.

Student Enrolment: c. 13,000 (Also *c.* 11,500 evening and correspondence students).

7116 **MARIJSKIJ ORDENA DRUZBY NARODOV POLITEHNIČESKIJ INSTITUT IM. A.M. GOR'KOGO**

Mariysk Polytechnical Institute
Pl. Lenina 3, 424024 Joškar-Ola, Marijskoj ASSR
Telephone: 5-59-77
Rektor: G.S. Oshepkov (1988-93)
Prorektor: V.M. Golovatjuk

F. of Forestry Engineering
Dean: A.N. Chemodanov; *staff* 56
F. of Construction Engineering
Dean: A.V. Piliagin; *staff* 70
F. of Engineering Economics
Dean: V.L. Pozdeev; *staff* 35
F. of Forestry
Dean: M.M. Kotov; *staff* 34
F. of Mechanical Engineering
Dean: V.V. Loginov; *staff* 80
F. of Radio Engineering
Dean: A.N. Zaharov; *staff* 77
F. of Land Reclamation and Road Building
Dean: P.N. Butin; *staff* 14
F. of Designing and Production of Radio Equipment
Dean: M.A. Oditsov; *staff* 18
F. of Correspondence Courses
D. for Evening Studies

Founded 1932 as Volga Region Forest Engineering Institute. Acquired present title 1968. Under the authority ofthe Ministry of Higher Education of the Russian Soviet Federative Socialist Republic (RSFSR). Governing bodies: the Council; the Academic Council.

Academic Year: September to July.

Admission Requirements: Competitive entrance examination following general or special secondary school certificate.

Fees: None.

Language of Instruction: Russian.

Degrees and Diplomas: Diploma of Engineer, 5 yrs. Diploma of Candidate of the Sciences, a further 3 yrs.

Library: Scientific-technical Library, *c.* 900,000 vols.

Special Facilities (Museums, etc.): Institute History Museum. Biological Garden.

Academic Staff, 1989:

Rank	Full-time
Professor (Professors)	10
Dotsent (Assistant Professors)	238
Starshij prepodavatel (Senior Instructors)	150
Docent (Assistants)	143
Total	541

Student Enrolment, 1990:

	Men	Women	Total
0f the country	2800	1510	4310

7117 **NOVGORODSKIJ POLITEHNIČESKIJ INSTITUT**

Novgorod Polytechnical Institute
Leningradskaja ul. 41, 173003 Novgorod, Rossiskaja SFSR
Telephone: 7-72-44

F. of Radio Engineering
F. of Electro-Mechanical Engineering
F. of Mechanical Technical Technology
F. for Evening Studies
F. for Correspondence Courses

Founded 1973. Placed under the authority of the Union-Republic State Committee for Public Education. Governing bodies: the Rector and Pro-Rectors; the Academic Council. Some residential accommodation for students.

Academic Year: September to July (September-December; February-June).

Admission Requirements: Competitive entrance examination following general or special secondary school certificate.

Language of Instruction: Russian.

Degrees and Diplomas: Diploma of Specialist in relevant fields, 5 yrs.

Library: c. 250,000 vols.

Academic Staff: c. 1500.

Student Enrolment: c. 1500 (Also *c.* 500 external students).

7118 **NOVOČERKASSKIJ ORDENA TRUDOVOGO KRASNOGO ZNAMENI POLITEHNIČESKIJ INSTITUT IM. SERGO ORDŽONIKIDZE**

Novocherkassk Polytechnical Institute
Ul. Prosveščenija 132, 346400 Novočerkassk GSP-1, Rossiskaja SFSR
Telephone: 55-7-79

F. of Mining and Geology
F. of Mechanization and Mining Automation
F. of Energetics
F. of Electrical Engineering
F. of Chemical Engineering
F. of Construction Engineering
F. for Evening Studies
F. for Correspondence Courses
Branch I (Shakhty)

Founded 1907. Placed under the authority of the Union Republic State Committee for Public Education.

Academic Year: September to July (September-February; February-July).

Admission Requirements: Competitive entrance examination following general or special secondary school certificate.

Fees: None.

Language of Instruction: Russian.

Degrees and Diplomas: Diploma of Specialist in relevant fields, 5 yrs. Kandidat nauk, Candidate of the Sciences, in–Technology; Geology and Mineralogy; Chemical Engineering, a further 3 yrs and thesis. Doktor nauk, in Chemical Engineering, by thesis after Kandidat.

Library: c. 2,300,000 vols.

Special Facilities (Museums, etc.): Mineralogy Museum; Palaeontology Museum.

Academic Staff: c. 1350.

Student Enrolment: c. 12,000 (Also *c.* 6080 external students).

7119 **NOVOPOLOCKIJ POLITEHNIČESKIJ INSTITUT IM. LENINSKOGO KOMSOMOLA BELORUSSII**

Novopolock Polytechnical Institute
Ul. Blokhina 29, 211440 Novopolock, Vitebskoj obl., Belorusskaja SSR
Telex: 252169 VESNASU
Telephone: 5-20-12
Fax: 5-82-75
Rektor: Ernest M. Babenko
Vicerektor: Leonid S. Turishchev

F. of Machine Building
Dean: Gennadii M. Makarenko; *staff* 53 (42)
F. of Technology
Dean: Sergei I. Khoroshka; *staff* 32 (20)
F. of Building
Dean: Fyodor F. Yasko; *staff* 43 (18)
F. of Sanitary Engineering
Dean: Victor V. Lapin; *staff* 52 (41)
F. of Geodesy
Dean: Vladimir P. Podshivalov; *staff* 45 (14)
F. of Radio Engineering
Dean: Arkadii F. Oskin; *staff* 57 (22)
F. of Extramural Studies
Dean: Victor S. Sartanov
Scientific Research D.
Dean: Vladimir K. Lipsky; *staff* 150 (400)

Founded 1968 as Branch of the Byelorussian Technological Institute. Acquired present title 1974. Under the authority of the BSSR Ministry of Public Education. Governing body: the Academic Councils. Residential facilities for academic staff and students.

Academic Year: September to July.

Admission Requirements: Competitive entrance examination following general or special secondary school certificate.

Fees: None. Foreign students, US$ 2500 per annum.

Language of Instruction: Russian.

Degrees and Diplomas: Diploma of Engineer, 5 yrs. Diploma of Candidate of the Sciences, a further 3 yrs.

Library: Main Library, 549,234 vols.

Special Facilities (Museums, etc.): Experimental Workshops; Geodetic Polygon.

Academic Staff, 1990:

Rank	Full-time	Part-time
Professors and Doctors	132	19
Teachers and Instructors	150	138
Total	282	157

Student Enrolment, 1990:

	Men	Women	Total
Of the country	1500	870	2370
Of other countries	170	5	175
Total	1670	875	2545*

*Also 950 external students and students by correspondence.

7120 **ODESSKIJ ORDENA TRUDOVOGO KRASNOGO ZNAMENI POLITEHNIČESKIJ INSTITUT**

Odessa Polytechnical Institute

Prosp. T. G. Ševčenko 1, 270044 Odessa, Ukrainskaja SSR

Telephone: 22-19-92

F. of Mechanical Engineering
F. of Machine Engineering
F. of Thermo-Energetic Engineering
F. of Thermo-Energy Production
F. of Electrical Engineering
F. of Radio Engineering
F. of Automation and Computer Technology
F. of Chemical Engineering
F. of Engineering Economics
F. of General Technical Studies
F. for Evening Studies

Academic Year: September to July.

Admission Requirements: Competitive entrance examination following general or special secondary school certificate.

Degrees and Diplomas: Diploma of Specialist in relevant fields, 5 yrs.

7121 **OMSKIJ POLITECHNIČESKIJ INSTITUT**

Omsk Polytechnical Institute

Prosp. Mira 11, 644050 Omsk 50, Rossiskaja SFSR

Telephone: 65-35-37

F. of Mechanical Engineering
F. of Refrigeration Engineering
F. of Automation Engineering
F. of Machine Engineering
F. of Printing Engineering
F. of Radio Engineering
F. of General Technical Studies
F. for Evening Studies (several)

Academic Year: September to July.

Admission Requirements: Competitive entrance examination following general or special secondary school certificate.

Degrees and Diplomas: Diploma of Specialist in relevant fields, 5 yrs.

7122 **ORENBURGSKIJ POLITEHNIČESKIJ INSTITUT**

Orenburg Polytechnical Institute

Prosp. Popedy 13, 460352 Orenburg, Rossiskaja SFSR

Telephone: 7-67-70

F. of Mechanical Engineering
F. of Electrical Engineering
F. of Construction Engineering

Academic Year: September to July.

Admission Requirements: Competitive entrance examination following general or special secondary school certificate.

Degrees and Diplomas: Diploma of Specialist in relevant fields, 5 yrs.

7123 **PENZENSKIJ POLITEHNIČESKIJ INSTITUT**

Penza Polytechnical Institute

Krasnaja ul. 40, 440017 Penza, Rossiskaja SFSR

Telephone: 69-84-12

F. of Machine Engineering
F. of Mechanical Engineering
F. of Precision Engineering
F. of Automation and Data Processing
F. of Radio Engineering and Computer Technology
F. for Evening Studies
F. for Correspondence Courses

Academic Year: September to July.

Admission Requirements: Competitive entrance examination following general or special secondary school certificate.

Degrees and Diplomas: Diploma of Specialist in relevant fields, 5 yrs.

7124 **PERMSKIJ POLITEHNIČESKIJ INSTITUT**

Perm Polytechnical Institute

Komsomol'skij Prosp. 29a, 616600 Perm' GSP-45, Rossiskaja SFSR

Telephone: 32-63-60

F. of Mining Engineering
F. of Electrical Engineering
F. of Mechanical Engineering
F. of Machine Engineering
F. of Aeronautical Engineering
F. of Construction Engineering
F. of Chemical Engineering
F. of Chemical Engineering (Kirovsk)
F. of General Technical Studies
F. of General Technical Studies (Berezniki)
F. of General Technical Studies (Lys'va)
F. for Correspondence Courses (Mining)
F. for Correspondence Courses (General Technology)
D. for Evening Studies

Academic Year: September to July.

Admission Requirements: Competitive entrance examination following general or special secondary school certificate.

Degrees and Diplomas: Diploma of Specialist in relevant fields, 5 yrs.

7125 **RIŽSKIJ ORDENA TRUDOVOGO KRASNOGO ZNAMENI POLITEHNIČESKIJ INSTITUT IM. A.JA. PELJŠE**

Riga Polytechnical Institute

Ul. Lenina 1, 226355 Riga, Latvijskaja SSR

Telephone: 22-58-85

F. of Construction Engineering
F. of Radio Engineering and Communications
F. of Automation and Computer Technology
F. of Mechanical and Machine Engineering
F. of Electrical Engineering and Energetics
F. of Precision and Automation Engineering
F. of Engineering Economics
F. of Chemical Engineering
F. of General Technical Studies
F. of General Technical Studies (Daugavpils)
F. of General Technical Studies (Liepája)
F. for Correspondence Courses
F. for Evening Studies

Founded 1862. Residential facilities for students.

Arrangements for co-operation with the Czech Technical University in Prague.

Academic Year: September to July.

Admission Requirements: Competitive entrance examination following general or special secondary school certificate.

Languages of Instruction: Latvian and Russian.

Degrees and Diplomas: Diploma of Specialist in relevant fields, 5 yrs; Architecture, 6 yrs.

Library: c. 650,000 vols.

7126 **SARATOVSKIJ ORDENA TRUDOVOGO KRASNOGO ZNAMENI POLITEHNIČESKIJ INSTITUT**

Saratov Polytechnical Institute

Politehničeskaja ul. 77, 410016 Saratov 16, Rossiskaja SFSR

Telephone: 25-73-11

F. of Machine Engineering
F. of Electronics and Precision Engineering

F. of Energetics
F. of Automobile Engineering
F. of Construction Engineering
F. of Highway Engineering
F. of General Technical Studies (Balakov)
F. of General Technical Studies (Engels)
F. for Correspondence Courses (Precision Engineering and Energetics)
F. for Correspondence Courses (Construction Engineering)
D. for Evening Studies

Academic Year: September to July.

Admission Requirements: Competitive entrance examination following general or special secondary school certificate.

Degrees and Diplomas: Diploma of Specialist in relevant fields, 5 yrs.

Student Enrolment: c. 9680 (Also *c.* 6950 evening and correspondence students).

7127 **SEVERO-ZAPADNYJ ZAOČNYJ POLITEHNIČESKIJ INSTITUT**
Northwestern Correspondence Polytechnical Institute
Ul. Halturina 5, 191065 Leningrad D-41, Rossiskaja SFSR
Telephone: 312-07-92

F. of Energetics and Automation
F. of Chemical Engineering and Metallurgy
F. of Precision and Machine Engineering
F. of Mechanical Engineering
F. of Technical Cybernetics (Computer Technology)
F. of Radio Engineering
F. of General Technical Studies (Kronstadt)
F. for Evening Studies (Užorsk)
D. for Evening Studies
Branch I. (Cherepovets)
Branch I. (Vologda)

Academic Year: September to July.

Admission Requirements: Competitive entrance examination following general or special secondary school certificate.

Degrees and Diplomas: Diploma of Specialist in relevant fields, 6 yrs.

7128 **STAVROPOL'SKIJ POLITEHNIČESKIJ INSTITUT**
Stavropol Polytechnical Institute
Pr. Kulakova 2, 355038 Stavropol', Rossiskaja SFSR
Telephone: 6-32-86
Rektor: Boris Mikhailovich Sinel'nikov (1987-)

F. of Food Technology
Dean: Sergei Vyacheslavovich Vasilisin *staff* 64
F. of Mechanical Engineering and Energetics
Dean: Eugeni Alekceevich Chebotaryov *staff* 118
F. of Power Engineering and Electronics
Dean: Alexandr Il'chenko; *staff* 85
F. of Engineering Economics and Computer-aided Manufacturing
Dean: Georgi Alexandrovich Khodzhayev; *staff* 76
F. of Automobile Engineering
Dean: Victor Ivanovich Kozhevnikov; *staff* 64
F. of Civil and Industrial Engineering
Dean: Eugeni Dmitrievich Basov; *staff* 55
D. for Correspondence Courses
Research Ce.
Head: Aleksandr Petrovich Baev; *staff* 130
Also branches at Cherkessk, Pyatigorsk, and Nevinnomyssk

Founded 1971. Governing body: the Academic Council. Residential facilities for students.

Academic Year: September to July (September-January; February-July).

Admission Requirements: Competitive entrance examination following general or special secondary school certificate.

Degrees and Diplomas: Diploma of Engineer, 5 yrs. Candidate of the Sciences, a further 3 yrs.

Library: Central Library, 492,932 vols.

Academic Staff, 1990:

Rank	Full-time
Professors	22
Dotcents	311
Assistents	232
Total	565

Student Enrolment, 1990:

	Men	Women	Total
Of the country	5167	3443	8610

7129 **TADŽIKSKIJ POLITEHNIČESKIJ INSTITUT**
Tadjik Polytechnical Institute
Pr. Kujbyševa 10a, 734042 Dušanbe, Tadžikskaja SSR
Telephone: 22-40-22
Rektor: Anuar Vahobovich Vahobov

F. of Energetics
F. of Mechanical Engineering
F. of Construction Engineering
F. of Architecture
D. for Evening Studies
D. for Correspondence Courses

Founded 1956. Residential facilities for academic staff and students.

Arrangements for co-operation with institutions in: Afghanistan; Bulgaria; Germany.

Academic Year: September to July.

Admission Requirements: Competitive entrance examination following general or special secondary school certificate.

Fees (Roubles): 4000 per annum.

Languages of Instruction: Tajik, and Russian.

Degrees and Diplomas: Diploma of Engineer, 5 yrs.

Library: 1,000,000 vols.

Academic Staff, 1990: 530.

Student Enrolment, 1990: 7298.

7130 **TALLINA TEHNIKAÜLIKOOL**
Tallinn Technical University
Ehitajate tee 5, 200108 Tallinn, Estonia
Telex: 173101 STJUT SU
Telephone: 53-72-58
Fax: 142/53-24-46
Rektor: Boris Tamm (1976-)
Učonyj Sekretar (Scientific Secretary): Vilvl Russ

F. of Power Engineering
Dean: Olev Tapupere; *staff* 56 (4)
F. of Control Engineering
Dean: Jean Vôrk; *staff* 60 (8)
F. of Mechanical Engineering
Dean: Mihkel Pikner; *staff* 60 (1)
F. of Chemical Engineering
Dean: Tiit Kaps; *staff* 48 (7)
F. of Civil Engineering
Dean: Kaldo Hääl; *staff* 67 (7)
F. of Economics
Dean: Jaak Tamberg; *staff* 121 (25)
F. of General Studies
Dean: Ahto Lõhmus; *staff* 164 (2)
F. for Evening Studies
Dean: Felix Angelstök
F. for Correspondence Courses
Dean: Ants Virkus
Scientific Research D.
Dean: Jüri Tanner; *staff* 594
D. of Adult Computer Education
Dean: Toomas Mikli *staff* 11 (20)
F. of Continuing Education (Engineering)
Dean: Juüri Vanaveski; *staff* 1 (45)
Also 27 Research Laboratories.

Founded as private technical school 1918, became State institution 1920, acquired university status 1936 and present title 1941. Residential facilities for *c.* 2300 students.

Arrangements for co-operation with: Budapest University of Technology; Eindhoven University of Technology; Dresden University of Technology; Helsinki University of Technology; Royal Institute of Technology,

Sweden; Tampere University of Technology; Lappenranta University of Technology.

Academic Year: August to June (August to mid-January; January to June).

Admission Requirements: Secondary school certificate and entrance examination.

Fees: None.

Languages of Instruction: Estonian and Russian.

Degrees and Diplomas: Diploma of Specialist in relevant fields, 5 yrs. Kandidat nauk, Candidate of the Sciences, a further 3 yrs andthesis. Doktor nauk, by thesis after Kandidat.

Library: 870,000 vols.

Special Facilities (Museums, etc.): Museum of Tallinn Technical University.

Publication: Transactions (20-25 issues per annum).

Press or Publishing House: Tallinn Technical University Press.

Academic Staff, 1990:

Rank	Full-time	Part-time
Professors	46	10
Associate Professors	348	13
Senior Lecturers	141	36
Assistants	115	7
Total	650	66

Student Enrolment, 1990:

	Men	Women	Total
Of the country	4552	1968	6520*

*Also 2326 external students.

7131 **TAŠKENTSKIJ ORDENA DRUŽBY NARODOV POLITEHNIČESKIJ INSTITUT IM. A. BIRUNI**

Tashkent Polytechnical Institute

Ul. Navoi 13, 700011 Taškent, Uzbekskaja SSR

Telephone: 41-13-12

F. of Geology and Prospecting
F. of Mining Engineering and Metallurgy
F. of Mechanical Engineering
F. of Aeronautical Engineering
F. of Energetics
F. of Automation Engineering
F. of Chemical Engineering
F. of Architecture
F. of Construction Engineering
F. of General Technical Studies (Buhara)
D. for Evening Studies
D. for Evening Studies (Chirchik)
D. for Correspondence Courses
Branch I. (Almalik)
Branch I. (Angren)
Branch I. (Navoi)

Academic Year: September to July.

Admission Requirements: Competitive entrance examination following general or special secondary school certificate.

Degrees and Diplomas: Diploma of Specialist in relevant fields, 5 yrs.

Student Enrolment: 14,000 (Also *c.* 18,000 evening and correspondence students).

7132 **TOL'JATINSKIJ POLITEHNIČESKIJ INSTITUT**

Togliatti Polytechnical Institute

Belorusskaja ul. 14, 445667 Tol'jatti, Kubjševskoj obl., Rossiskaja SFSR

Telephone: 23-41-25

F. of Electrotechnical Engineering
Dean: Nemcev Aleksandr Dmitrievič
F. of Automobile Engineering
Dean: Skutniev Vasilij Mihajlovič
F. of Building Technology
Dean: Nikišev Valerij Aleksandrovič
F. of Civil Engineering
Dean: Loginov Jurij Nikolaevič
Technological F.
Dean: Masakov Vasilij Vasil'evič
D. for Evening Courses

Academic Year: September to July.

Admission Requirements: Competitive entrance examination following general or special secondary school certificate.

Degrees and Diplomas: Diploma of Specialist in relevant fields, 5 yrs.

7133 **TOMSKIJ ORDENA OKTABR'SKOJ REVOLJUCII I ORDENA TRUDOVOGO KRASNOGO ZNAMENI POLITEHNIČESKIJ INSTITUT IM. S.M. KIROVA**

Tomsk Polytechnical Institute

Pr. Lenina 30, 634004 Tomsk 4, Rossiskaja SFSR

Telex: 128184 TEMA

Telephone: 49-24-17

Rektor: Yu.P. Poholkov

Vicerektor: B.V. Sjomkin

F. of Geology and Prospecting
Dean: B.I. Spiridonov; *staff* 87
F. of Machine Engineering
Dean: R.I. Dedjuh; *staff* 96
F. of Thermo-Energetics
Dean: S.A. Beljaev; *staff* 89
F. of Electrical Power Production
Dean: V.V. Litvak; *staff* 79
F. of Electrophysics
Dean: V.K. Zukov; *staff* 79
F. of Chemical Engineering
Dean: V.D. Filimonov; *staff* 107
F. of Applied Physics
Dean: G.N. Kolpakov; *staff* 90
F. of Automation and Electromechanics
Dean: R.F. Bekishev; *staff* 171
F. of Machine Building for Plants (Yurga)
F. of Automation and Computer Technology
Dean: A.N. Osokin; *staff* 121
F. of Mechanics and Machine Building
Dean: V.T.Fedko; *staff* 19
F. for Evening Studies
Dean: V.I. Napjokov
F. for Correspondence Courses
Dean: V.I. Brilin
Nuclear Physics Research I.
Dean: Yu.P. Usov; *staff* 650
Introscopy Research I.
Dean: V.L. Chahlov; *staff* 460
High-Voltages Research I.
Dean: V.J. Ushakov; *staff* 350
Cybernetic Ce.
Dean: V.Z. Jampolsky; *staff* 20

Founded 1896 as Institute. Acquired present title 1944. Under the authority of the RCFSR Ministry of Higher Education. Governing body: the Council. Residential facilities for students in 14 hostels.

Academic Year: September to June (September-January; February-June).

Admission Requirements: Competitive entrance examination following general or special secondary school certificate.

Language of Instruction: Russian.

Degrees and Diplomas: Diploma of Specialist in relevant fields, 5 yrs.

Library: Obruchev Scientific Technical Library, 3m. vols.

Special Facilities (Museums, etc.): Kirov Museum; Institute History Museum.

Press or Publishing House: Publishing Department.

Academic Staff, 1990:

Rank	Full-time
Professor	63
Kandidat nauk	766
Starshij prepodavatel	214
Asistent	104
Total	1147

Student Enrolment, 1989:

	Men	Women	Total
Of the country	1200	1300	2500*

*Also 3900 external students.

7134 **TUL'SKIJ ORDENA TRUDOVOGO KRASNOGO ZNAMENI POLITEHNIČESKIJ INSTITUT**

Tula Polytechnical Institute
Pr. Lenina 92, 300600 Tula, Rossiskaja SFSR
Telex: 253310 NAUKA
Telephone: 25-83-62
Rektor: E.M. Sokolov (1979-)
ProREKTOR po mezdunarodnim kontaktam (Deputy Rector for International Relations): V.S. Kutepov

F. of Automation Engineering
Dean: V.G. Orlov; *staff* 96 (13)
F. of Mechanical Engineering
Dean: V.G. Grigorovich; *staff* 112 (7)
F. of Metal Processing Technology
Dean: A.P. Nikiforov; *staff* 80 (5)
F. of Machine Engineering
Dean: V.V. Lubimov; *staff* 75 (7)
F. of Heavy Industrial Engineering
Dean: G.G. Dubensky; *staff* 95
F. of Mining Engineering
Dean: E.I. Zakharov; *staff* 116 (9)
F. of Cybernetics (Automation and Computer Technology)
Dean: V.S. Karpov; *staff* 83 (13)
F. of Construction Engineering
Dean: M.E. Hazanov; *staff* 149 (7)
F. for Evening Studies (Machine Engineering)
Dean: A.A. Kuznetsov
F. for Economic Studies
Dean: V.I. Abramov; *staff* 70 (7)
F. for Foreign Students
Dean: V.M. Samokhvalov
Undergraduate D.
Dean: G.A. Matveev
F. for Evening Studies (Polytechnic)
Dean: L.N. Shmaralov
F. for Correspondence Courses
Dean: A.F. Simankin
Mining Machines L.
Director: V.A. Brener; *staff* 10 (19)
Machine Building Technologies L.
Director: S.A. Yamnikov; *staff* 11 (23)
Metal Science L.
Director: S.A. Golovin; *staff* 16 (18)
Electrochemical Technologies L.
Director: V.V.Lubimov; *staff* 23 (34)

Also contract courses of Russian Culture and Religion for foreign citizens.

Founded 1935. Under the authority of the Ministry of Higher and Secondary Education of the Russian Federal Republic. Governing body: the Council. Residential facilities for academic staff and students in 12 hostels.

Arrangements for co-operation with: Transport and Communication Institute, Zilina; Higher Machine Electro-Technical Institute, Plovdiv.

Academic Year: September to July.

Admission Requirements: Competitive entrance examination following general or special secondary school certificate.

Fees: None. US$ 4000, for foreign students.

Language of Instruction: Russian.

Degrees and Diplomas: Diploma of Specialist in relevant fields, 5 yrs.

Library: c. 1 M. vols.

Special Facilities (Museums, etc.): Construction and Maintenance Workshops: Experimental Laboratory.

Press or Publishing House: Editing Department, Printing Arts Department.

Academic Staff, 1990:

Rank	Full-time	Part-time
Professors	52	6
Assistant Professors	512	41
Senior Tutors	79	12
Tutors	461	16
Total	1104	75

Student Enrolment, 1989-90:

	Men	Women	Total
Of the country	6970	5030	12,000
Of other countries	236	26	262
Total	7206	5056	12,262*

*Also 1430 external students.

7135 **TURKMENSKIJ POLITEHNIČESKIJ INSTITUT**

Turkmen Polytechnical Institute
Ul. Kotovskogo 1, 744025 Ašhabad 8, Turkmenskaja SSR
Telephone: 9-37-10

F. of Construction Engineering
F. of Municipal Engineering
F. of Oil Technology
F. of Mechanical Engineering and Energetics
F. of Chemical Engineering
D. for Evening Studies
D. for Correspondence Courses

Academic Year: September to July.

Admission Requirements: Competitive entrance examination following general or special secondary school certificate.

Degrees and Diplomas: Diploma of Specialist in relevant fields, 5 yrs.

7136 **UL'JANOVSKIJ POLITEHNIČESKIJ INSTITUT**

Ul'janovsk Polytechnical Institute
Ul. L'va Tolstogo 42, 432700 Ul'Janovsk, Rossiskaja SFSR
Telephone: 1-24-83

F. of Mechanical Engineering
F. of Radio Engineering
F. of Energetics
F. of Light Industrial Engineering
F. for Evening Studies
F. for Correspondence Courses

Academic Year: September to July.

Admission Requirements: Competitive entrance examination following general or special secondary school certificate.

Degrees and Diplomas: Diploma of Specialist in relevant fields, 5 yrs.

7137 **URAL'SKIJ ORDENA TRUDOVOGO KRASNOGO ZNAMENI POLITEHNIČESKIJ INSTITUT IM. S.M. KIROVA**

Ural Polytechnical Institute
Mir, 19, 620002 Sverdlovsk K2, RSFSR
Telex: 221438 JASHMA
Telephone: 440362
Rektor: S.S. Naboichenko (1986-)
Senior Proreklor: V.S. Kortov

F. of Metallurgical Engineering
Dean: Yu.N. Ovchinnikov; *staff* 167 (10)
F. of Mechanical Engineering
Dean: G.L. Baranov; *staff* 130 (1)
F. of Electrical Engineering
Dean: F.N. Sarapulov; *staff* 98 (5)
F. of Heat Power Engineering
Dean: Z.N. Kutyavin; *staff* 140 (2)
F. of Radio Engineering
Dean: A.V. Blochin; *staff* 140 (15)
F. of Chemical Technology
Dean: A.I. Mattern; *staff* 74 (6)
F. of Silicate Technology
Dean: N.F. Koknaev; *staff* 32
F. of Construction Engineering
Dean: F.F. Tamplon; *staff* 118 (5)
F. of Economics
Dean: L.A. Konovalov; *staff* 73 (12)
F. of Physico-Engineering
Dean: A.R. Bektov; *staff* 110 (17)
F. of Engineering (5) (Sverdloovsk)
Branch I. (Nizhnii Tagil)
F. for Evening Studies (2)
Head: V.N. Kichigin
F. for Correspondence Courses (3)
Computer Ce.

Also 29 Research Centres.

Founded 1920. Under the authority of the Ministry of Higher Education of the Russian Federation. Governing bodies: the Academic Council; the Faculty Academic Councils, comprising 10 members. Residential facilities for 5588 students in hostels.

Arrangements for co-operation with: Mongolian Polytechnical Institute; Chuntsin University; College of Mechanical and Electrical Engineering, Plzen; Institute of Mechanical and Electrical Engineering, Bulgaria.

Academic Year: September to July (September-January; February-July).

Admission Requirements: Competitive entrance examination following general or special secondary school certificate.

Fees: None.

Language of Instruction: Russian.

Degrees and Diplomas: Diploma of Specialist in relevant fields, 5 yrs. Candidate of the Sciences, a further 3-4 yrs. Doktor nauk, a further 5-7 yrs.

Libraries: Central Library, 1,533,000 vols. Nizhni-Tagil library, 156,800; Engineering faculty libraries (Sverdlovsk region), 134,800; Institute libraries, 2,108,600.

Special Facilities (Museums, etc.): Institute History Museum; Television Centre.

Publications: Publishing office which issues teaching and support materials and Intercollege Proceedings (annually): Physico-chemical Investigations of Metallurgical Processes; Heat Treatment and Physics of Metals; Forming and Shaping of Metals, Theory of Metallurgical and Mining Machines; Chemistry of Solid Body; Radiation-simulated Phenomena in Solid Bodies.

Academic Staff, 1990:

Rank	Full-time	Part-time
Professors	98	22
Assistant Professors	716	27
Senior Research Associates	118	16
Others	1577	65
Total	2509	130

Student Enrolment, 1990:

Of the country	13,700
Of other countries (Mongolia)	300
Total	14,000*

*Also 11,000 external students.

7138 **YAROSLAVSKIJ POLITEHNICHESKIJ INSTITUT**
Yaroslavl Polytechnic Institute
Moskovskij Pr.88, 150053 Yaroslavl, Rossiskaja SFSR
Telex: 217296 VUZ
Telephone: 44-15-19
Rektor: Yuri A. Moskvichev (1986-)

F. of Applied Chemistry
Dean: Mikhail P. Chagin; *staff* 119 (3)
F. of Machine Engineering and Instrumentation
Dean: Nikolai P. Shanin; *staff* 99 (3)
F. of Multi-Vehicular Engineering
Dean: Alexander V. Zharov; *staff* 136 (8)
F. of Construction Engineering
Dean: Valery I. Firago; *staff* 110 (18)
F. for Evening Studies I (1-4 years of study)
Dean: Stanislav P. Shevyakov
F. for Evening Studies II (5-6 years of study)
Dean: Igor V. Budny
D. of Science and Research
Dean: Vyacheslav N. Sedorov; *staff* 411 (506)

Founded 1944 as Technological Institute of the Rubber Industry. Acquired present title 1973. Governing body: the General Board. Residential facilities for students.

Arrangements for co-operation with: Institute of Chemical Technology, Burgas; Agricultural Academy of Bydgoszcz; Czech Technical University of Prague; Higher School of Technology, Radom.

Academic Year: September to July.

Admission Requirements: Competitive entrance examination following general or special secondary school certificate.

Fees: None.

Language of Instruction: Russian.

Degrees and Diplomas: Diploma of Specialist in relevant fields, 5 yrs. Candidate of the Sciences, a further 3-4 yrs.

Library: Total, 800,000 vols.

Special Facilities (Museums, etc.): Polytechnic History Museum.

Publications: Chemistry and Oil Chemistry; Proceedings of Scientific Conferences.

Press or Publishing House: Publishing House.

Academic Staff, 1989-90:

Rank	Full-time	Part-time
Professors	20	2
Dotzent (Assistant Professors)	231	10
Starshil Prepodavatel (Lecturers)	120	11
Prepodavatel (Assistant Lecturers)	93	9
Total	464	32

Student Enrolment, 1989-90:

	Men	Women	Total
Of the country	2372	1344	3716*

*Also 211 external students.

7139 **VINNICKIJ POLITEHNIČESKIJ INSTITUT**
Vinnitsa Polytechnical Institute
Khmelnitskoye schausse, 95, 286021 Vinnitsa, Ukrainskaja SSR
Telephone: 2-57-18
Rektor: Mokin Boris Ivanovich

F. of Machine Engineering
Dean: Victor B. Petrov; *staff* 68
F. of Automation and Microelectronics
Dean: Vasiliy M. Kichak; *staff* 57
F. of Radio Engineering
Dean: Yu V. Krushevsky; *staff* 43
F. of Energetics
Dean: David B. Nalbandyan; *staff* 66
F. of Construction Engineering
Dean: G.S. Ratushnyak; *staff* 61 (2)
F. of Fundamental Engineering, and Practical Science
Dean: V.L. Karpenko; *staff* 166 (1)
F. of Social Sciences and Humanities
Dean: V.G. Balitsky; *staff* 128 (3)
F. of Computer Technology
Dean: A.N. Melnikov; *staff* 61
D. for Evening Studies
Research Ce.
Prorector: S.J. Tkachenko
Also 11 Research Centres and Laboratories.

Founded 1974. Governing body: the Academic Board, comprising 106 members.

Arrangements for co-operation with Technical University of Munich.

Academic Year: September to June (September-January; February-June).

Admission Requirements: Competitive entrance examination following general or special secondary school certificate.

Languages of Instruction: Ukrainian and Russian.

Degrees and Diplomas: Diploma of Engineer in relevant fields, 4-5 yrs.

Library: 676,000 vols.

Academic Staff, 1990:

Rank	Full-time	Part-time
Professors	30	–
Assistant Professors	278	–
Senior Teachers	125	6
Teachers	217	–
Total	650	6

Student Enrolment, 1990:

	Men	Women	Total
Of the country	5700	2040	7740
Of other countries	520	40	560
Total	6220	2080	8300*

*Also 1970 students by correspondence and 870 evening students.

7140 **VLADIMIRSKIJ POLITEHNICESKIJ INSTITUT**
Vladimir Polytechnical Institute
Ul. Gor'kogo 87, 600026 Vladimir, Rossiskaja SFSR
Telex: 412528 STAL
Telephone: 3-33-58
Rektor: Aleksey G. Sergeev (1988-)

F. of Mechanical Engineering
Dean: Igor V. Gavrilin; *staff* 141 (17)
F. of Automobile Transport
Dean: Yuriy V. Bashenov; *staff* 95 (11)
F. of Radio Engineering
Dean: Lyudmila Sushkova; *staff* 86 (10)

F. of Technical Cybernetics
Dean: Aleksandr N. Ponomarev; *staff* 73 (9)
F. of Chemical Engineering
Dean: Eduard P. Sisoev; *staff* 98 (12)
F. of Construction Engineering
Dean: Ivan I. Shishov; *staff* 75 (9)
F. for Foreign Students
Dean: Sergeiy V. Poliakov; *staff* 36 (2)
F. for Evening Studies (Radio and Instrument Making)
Dean: Oleg R. Nikitin
F. for Evening Studies (Construction Engineering)
Dean: Valeriy P. Barishnikov
F. for Evening Studies (Mechanical Engineering)
Dean: Valdimir I. Usenko
F. for Correspondence Courses
Dean: Konstantin F. Sokov
Scientific Research Ce.
Head: Lev M. Samsonov; *staff* 179 (743)
Also Branches in Kovrov and Murom.

Founded 1958 as branch of one of the Moscow Institutes. Became independent 1964. Under the authorities of the Ministry of Higher and Secondary Specialized Education of the RSFSR. Governing bodies: the Rector Office; the Institute Council.

Arrangements for co-operation with institutions in: Czechoslovakia, Poland, Bulgaria, USA.

Academic Year: September to July.

Admission Requirements: Competitive entrance examination following general or special secondary school certificate.

Language of Instruction: Russian.

Degrees and Diplomas: Diploma of Specialist in relevant fields, 5 yrs.

Special Facilities (Museums, etc.): Institute History Museum.

Publication: Polytechnic (weekly).

Academic Staff, 1990:

Rank	Full-time	Part-time
Professors	27	4
Assistant Professors	470	31
Senior Teachers	71	4
Junior Teachers	226	47
Total	794	86

Student Enrolment, 1990:

	Men	Women	Total
Of the country	5938	3959	9897
Of other countries	331	20	351
Total	6269	3979	10,248*

*Also 990 external students.

7141 **VOLGOGRADSKIJ ORDENA TRUDOVOGO KRASNOGO ZNAMENI POLITEHNIČESKIJ INSTITUT**
Volgograd Polytechnical Institute
Prosp. im. V.I. Lenina 28, 400066 Volgograd 66, Rossiskaja SFSR
Telephone: 34-22-92

F. of Machine Engineering
F. of Automobile and Tractor Engineering
F. of Metallurgy (Foundry Technology)
F. of Chemical Engineering
F. for Evening Studies (Mechanical Engineering)
F. for Evening Studies (Chemical Engineering)
F. for Evening Studies (Volžckom)
F. for Correspondence Courses

Academic Year: September to July.

Admission Requirements: Competitive entrance examination following general or special secondary school certificate.

Degrees and Diplomas: Diploma of Specialist in relevant fields, 5 yrs.

7142 **VOLOGODSKIJ POLITEHNIČESKIJ INSTITUT**
Vologda Polytechnical Institute
Ul. Vorošilova 3, 160600 Vologda, Rossiskaja SFSR
Telephone: 2-46-45

F. of Electro-Energetics
F. of Machine Engineering and Technology
F. of Civil and Construction Engineering
F. for Evening Studies
F. for Correspondence Courses

Academic Year: July to September.

Admission Requirements: Competitive entrance examination following general or special secondary school certificate.

7143 **VORONEŽSKIJ POLITEHNIČESKIJ INSTITUT**
Voronezh Polytechnical Institute
Moskovskij prosp. 14, 394026 Voronež, Rossiskaja SFSR
Telephone: 16-40-67

F. of Mechanical Engineering
F. of Aeronautical Engineering
F. of Applied Physics
F. of Radio Engineering
F. of Electrical Engineering
F. for Evening Studies (Mechanical and Machine Engineering)
F. for Evening Studies (Radio Engineering)
F. for Correspondence Courses

Academic Year: September to July.

Admission Requirements: Competitive entrance examination following general or special secondary school certificate.

Degrees and Diplomas: Diploma of Specialist in relevant fields, 5 yrs.

7144 **VSESOJUZNYJ ORDENA TRUDOVOGO KRASNOGO ZNAMENI ZAOČNYJ POLITEHNIČESKIJ INSTITUT**
All-Union Correspondence Polytechnical Institute
Ul. Pavla Korčagina 22, 129805 Moskva, Rossiskaja SFSR
Telephone: 283-77-58

F. of Mining Engineering
F. of Petroleum Engineering
F. of Metallurgical Engineering
F. of Machine Engineering
F. of Automobile and Tractor Engineering
F. of Chemical Engineering
F. of Energetics
F. of Electrophysics
F. of Construction Engineering
F. of Engineering Economics
D. for Evening Studies
Also Branches at Orsk, Kolomen, Gubkin, Magadan, Podol'sk, Riazan.

Academic Year: September to July.

Admission Requirements: Competitive entrance examination following general or special secondary school certificate.

Degrees and Diplomas: Diploma of Specialist in relevant fields, 5 yrs.

Industrial

7145 **BRATSKIJ INDUSTRIAL'NYJ INSTITUT**
Bratsk Industrial Institute
Ul. Makarenko 40, 665709 Bratsk 9, Rossiskaja SFSR
Telephone: 7-22-14

F. of Energy Technology
F. of Mechanical Engineering
F. of Forestry Technology
F. of Construction Engineering
F. for Evening Studies
F. for Correspondence Courses

Academic Year: September to July.

Admission Requirements: Competitive entrance examination following general or special secondary school certificate.

Degrees and Diplomas: Diploma of Specialist in relevant fields, 5 yrs.

7146 **DNEPRODZERŽINSKIJ ORDENA TRUDOVOGO KRASNOGO ZNAMENI INDUSTRIAL'NYJ INSTITUT IM. ARSENIČEVA**
Dneprodzerzhinsk Industrial Institute
Dnepropetrovskaja Ul. 2, 322618 Dneprodzeržinsk, Ukrainskaja SSR
Telephone: 3-21-23

F. of Metallurgy
F. of Technology
F. of General Technical Studies
F. for Evening Studies

Academic Year: September to July.

Admission Requirements: Competitive entrance examination following general or special secondary school certificate. Special selection for workers in these fields.
Degrees and Diplomas: Diploma of Specialist in relevant fields, 5 yrs.

7147 **HERSONSKIJ INDUSTRIAL'NIJ INSTITUT**
Kherson Industrial Institute
Bereslavskoe šosse 24, 325008 Herson, Ukrainskaja SSR
Telephone: 5-47-11

F. of Machine Engineering and Automation
F. of Mechanical Engineering
F. of Textile Technology
F. of Technology
F. of Economics
F. for Evening Studies
Academic Year: September to July.
Admission Requirements: Competitive entrance examination following general or special secondary school certificate.
Degrees and Diplomas: Diploma of Specialist in relevant fields, 5 yrs.

7148 **KRAMATORSKIJ INDUSTRIAL'NYJ INSTITUT**
Kramatorsk Industrial Institute
Ul. Škadinova 76, 343916 Kramatorsk, Ukrainskaja SSR
Telephone: 5-90-97

F. of Mechanical Engineering
F. of Automation Engineering
F. of Metallurgical Engineering
F. of General Technical Studies
D. for Evening Studies
Academic Year: September to July.
Admission Requirements: Competitive entrance examination following general or special secondary school certificate.
Degrees and Diplomas: Diploma of Specialist in relevant fields, 5 yrs.

7149 **PAVLODARSKIJ INDUSTRIAL'NYJ INSTITUT**
Pavlodarsk Industrial Institute
Ul. Sverdlova 63, 637003 Pavlodar, Kazahskaja SSR
Telephone: 2-76-42

F. of Mechanical Engineering
F. of Machine Engineering
F. of Energetics
F. of Construction Engineering
F. of General Technical Studies (Ermak)
F. of General Technical Studies (Ekinbastuz)
D. for Evening Studies
D. for Correspondence Courses
Academic Year: September to July.
Admission Requirements: Competitive entrance examination following general or special secondary school certificate.
Degrees and Diplomas: Diploma of Specialist in relevant fields, 5 yrs.

7150 **RUDNENSKIJ INDUSTRIAL'NYJ INSTITUT**
Rudnyj Industrial Institute
Ul. 50-let Oktjabrja 38, 459120 Rudnyj, Kazahskaja SSR
Telephone: 3-52-53

Mining and Civil Engineering
Academic Year: September to July.
Admission Requirements: Competitive entrance examination following general or special secondary school certificate.
Degrees and Diplomas: Diploma of Specialist in relevant fields, 5 yrs.

7151 **SVERDLOVSKIJ INŽENERNO-PEDAGOGIČESKIJ INSTITUT**
Ul. Masinostroitelej 11, 620012 Sverdlovsk, Rossiskaja SFSR

7152 **TJUMENSKIJ INDUSTRIAL'NYJ INSTITUT IM. LENINSKOGO KOMSOMOLA**
Tjumen Industrial Institute
Ul. Volodarskogo 38, 625036 Tjumen', Rossiskaja SFSR
Telephone: 6-55-91

F. of Geology and Prospecting
F. of Petroleum and Gas Exploitation
F. of Engineering Economics
F. of Transport Engineering (including Transport of Petroleum and Gas)
F. of Mechanical Engineering
F. of Light Engineering
F. of Electrical Engineering
F. of Chemical Engineering
F. for Evening Studies
F. for Correspondence Courses
Academic Year: September to July.
Admission Requirements: Competitive entrance examination following general or special secondary school certificate.
Degrees and Diplomas: Diploma of Specialist in relevant fields, 5 yrs.

7153 **UHTINSKIJ INDUSTRIAL'NYJ INSTITUT**
Ukhtinsk Industrial Institute
Pervomajskaja ul. 13, 169400 Uhta, Rossiskaja SFSR
Telephone: 5-37-80

F. of Geology
F. of Petroleum and Gas Engineering
F. of Construction Engineering
F. of Forestry Technology
F. for Evening Studies
D. for Correspondence Courses
Academic Year: September to July.
Admission Requirements: Competitive entrance examination following general or special secondary school certificate.
Degrees and Diplomas: Diploma of Specialist in relevant fields, 5 yrs.

7154 **ZAPOROŽSKIJ INDUSTRIAL'NYJ INSTITUT**
Zaporozhskij Industrial Institute
Pr. Lenina 226, 330600 Zaporož'e, Ukrainskaja SSR
Telephone: 2-72-21

F. of Energy Technology
F. of Physics and Meteorology
F. of Construction Engineering
Academic Year: September to July.
Admission Requirements: Competitive entrance examination following general or special secondary school certificate.
Degrees and Diplomas: Diploma of Specialist in relevant fields, 5 yrs.

Factory

7155 **ZAVOD-VTUZ PRI KARAGANDINSKOM METALLURGIČESKOM KOMBINATE**
Metallurgy Factory Institute
Pr. Lenina 34, 472300 Temir-Tau, Kazahskaja SSR
Telephone: 3-54-02

F. of Chemical and Metallurgical Engineering
F. of Economics
F. for Evening Studies
Academic Year: September to July.
Admission Requirements: Competitive entrance examination following general or special secondary school certificate. Special selection for workers in these fields.
Degrees and Diplomas: Diploma of Specialist in relevant fields, 5 yrs.

7156 **ZVOD-VTUZ PRI NORIL'SKOM GORNO-METTALLURGIČESKOM KOMBINATE IM. A.P. ZAVENJAGINA**
Ul. 50 let Oktjabrja 7, 663310 Norilsk
Telephone: 6-38-61

7157 **LENINGRADSKY INSTITUT MASHINOSTROYENIJA**
Leningrad Institute of Machine Building
Poljustrovskij prosp. 14, 195108 Leningrad K-108, Rossiskaja SFSR
Telex: 121425
Telephone: 540-01-54
Fax: 5425058, Teletype: 322166 turbo
Rektor: Michael A. Martynov (1988-)
Proректор: Oleg C. Zavjalov

F. of Machine Engineering
Dean: Lev N. Petrov
F. of Turbine Engineering
DEan: Igor A. Bogov

F. of Nuclear Power Engineering
Dean: Vladimir B. Yurcovsky
F. for Evening Studies
Dean: Vadim P. Sinelnicov
Special D. for Modern Technology
Head: Evgeniy M. Dedicov
F. of Postgraduate Education
Dean: George A. Sauridi
Research D.
Head: Yuri A. Derzhavetz

Founded 1930.

Academic Year: September to July.

Admission Requirements: Competitive entrance examination following general or special secondary school certificate. Special selection for workers in these fields.

Language of Instruction: Russian.

Degrees and Diplomas: Diploma of Specialist in relevant fields, 6 yrs.

Library: 150,000 vols.

Academic Staff, 1990: 230 (50).

Student Enrolment, 1990:

	Men	women	Total
Total	2400	700	3100

7158 **ZAVOD-VTUZ PRI MOSKOVSKOM DVAŽDY ORDENA LENINA I ORDENA TRUDOVOGO KRASNOGO ZNAMENI AVTOMOBIL'NOM ZAVODEIM. I.A. LIHAČEVA**

Automobile Factory Institute

Avtozavodskaja ul. 16, 109068 Moskva, Rossiskaja SFSR
Telephone: 275-52-37

F. of Mechanical Engineering
F. of Automobile Engineering
F. of Evening Studies

Academic Year: September to July.

Admission Requirements: Competitive entrance examination following general or special secondary school certificate. Special selection for workers in these fields.

Degrees and Diplomas: Diploma of Specialist in relevant fields, 5 yrs.

7159 **PENZENSKIJ ZAVOD-VTUZ NA PRAVAH FILIALA PRNZENSKOGO POLITEHNIČESKOGO INSTITUTA**

Factory Institute

Pr. Baĭdukova 1o, 440039 Penza, Rossiskaja SFSR
Telephone: 32-63-60

F. of Electronic Computer Engineering
F. of Machine Tool and Precision Engineering
D. for Evening Studies

Academic Year: September to July.

Admission Requirements: Competitive entrance examination following general or special secondary school certificate. Special selection for workers in these fields.

Degrees and Diplomas: Diploma of Specialist in relevant fields, 5 yrs.

Institutes of Energetics and Electrical Engineering

7160 **ALMA-ATINSKIJ ENERGETIČESKIJ INSTITUT**

Alma-Ata Power Engineering Institute

Ul. Kosmonavtov 126, 480013 Alma-Ata, Kazahskaja SSP
Telex: 251232
Telephone: 67-57-40
Fax: 73272636634
Rektor: Alexander Fyodorovich Bogotyrev

F. of Electro-Energetics
Dean: Marat Kanafyovich Dusebayev' *staff* 87
F. of Radio Engineering and Communication
Dean: Vladimir Leonidovich Goncharov; *staff* 44
F. of Thermal Energetics
Dean: Ernest Akimovich Serikov; *staff* 145
F. of Electro-Mechanical Engineering
Dean: Suleyman Abdualievich Bugubayev; *staff* 56

D. for Evening Studies
Dean: Bahtiyar Dauletovich Dauletov
D. for Correspondence Courses
Dean; Leonid Ardamovich Rogozovsky
Research D.
Head: Evgeniy Vitalievich Malyshevsky; *staff* 350

Founded 1975. Previously part of Kazakh Polytechnical Institute. Governing body: the Academic Council. Residential facilities for students.

Arrangements for co-operation with: Institute of Mechanical and Electrical Engineering, Sofia; Institute of Mining and Metallurgy, Ostrava.

Academic Year: September to July.

Admission Requirements: Competitive entrance examination following general or special secondary school certificate.

Fees: None.

Languages of Instruction: Russian and Kazakh.

Degrees and Diplomas: Diploma of Specialist in relevant fields, 5 yrs.

Library: c. 309,597 vols.

Academic Staff, 1990: 329.

Student Enrolment, 1990: 4716.

7161 **IVANOVSKIJ ORDENA 'ZNAK POČETA' ENERGETIČESKIJ INSTITUT IM. V.I. LENINA**

Institute of Energetics

Rabfakovskaja ul. 34, 153548 Ivanovo, Rossiskaja SFSR
Telephone: 48-97-10

F. of Thermo-Energetics
F. of Industrial Thermo-Energetics
F. of Electrical Energetics
F. of Electrical Engineering
F. for Evening Studies
F. for Correspondence Courses

Academic Year: September to July.

Admission Requirements: Competitive entrance examination following general or special secondary school certificate.

Degrees and Diplomas: Diploma of Specialist in relevant fields, 5 yrs.

7162 **LENINGRADSKIJ ORDENA LENINA I ORDENA OKTJABR'SKOJ REVOLUCII ELEKTROTEHNIČESKIJ INSTITUT IM. V.I. UL'JANOVA LENINA**

Institute of Electrical Engineering

Ul. Prof. Popova 5, 197022 Leningrad P-22, Rossiskaja SFSR
Telephone: 234-89-05

F. of Radio Engineering
F. of Automation and Computer Technology
F. of Electrification and Automation
F. of Marine Radio Technology
F. of Electronic Engineering
F. of Electro-Physics
F. for Evening Studies (Automation)
F. for Evening Studies (Radio Electronics)
Branch I. (Novgorod)

Academic Year: September to July.

Admission Requirements: Competitive entrance examination following general or special secondary school certificate.

Degrees and Diplomas: Diploma of Specialist in relevant fields, 5 yrs.

7163 ***MOSKOVSKIJ ORDENA LENINA I ORDENA OKTJABR'SKOJ REVOLJUCII ENERGETIČESKIJ INSTITUT**

Institute of Energetics

Krasnokazarmennaja ul. 14, 105835 Moskva E-250, Rossiskaja SFSR
Telephone: 362-72-31
Rector: I.M. Arlov

F. of Machine Construction
F. of Thermo-Energetics
F. of Industrial Energetics
F. of Electrical Energetics
F. of Electrical Power Engineering
F. of Electrical Engineering
F. of Electronic Engineering
F. of Automation and Computer Technology
F. of Radio Engineering
F. of Electrification and Automation of Transport and Industry
Several F. for Evening Studies
Branch I. (Kazani)

Branch I. (Smolensk)
Academic Year: September to July.
Admission Requirements: Competitive entrance examination following general or special secondary school certificate.
Degrees and Diplomas: Diploma of Specialist in relevant fields, 5 yrs.

7164 **NOVOSIBIRSKIJ ELEKTROTEHNIČESKIJ INSTITUT**
Institute of Electrical Engineering
Pr. Karla Marksa 20, 630092 Novosibirsk, Rossiskaja SFSR
Telephone: 46-35-87

F. of Radio Engineering
F. of Automation and Computer Technology
F. of Automated Control Systems
F. of Electrical Physics
F. of Electronic Engineering
F. of Electrical Engineering
F. of Electrical Energetics
F. of Machine Construction
F. of Electro-Technical Assembly
F. of Aircraft Engineering
D. for Evening Studies
D. for Correspondence Courses
Academic Year: September to July.
Admission Requirements: Competitive entrance examination following general or special secondary school certificate.
Degrees and Diplomas: Diploma of Specialist in relevant fields, 5 yrs.

Institutes of Geology, Mining, Petroleum, and Metallurgical Engineering

Geology, Mining, and Petroleum Engineering

7165 **AZERBAJDŽANSKIJ ORDENA TRUDOVOGO KRASNOGO ZNAMENI INSTITUT NEFTI I HIMII IM. M. AZIZBEKOVA**
Institute of Petroleum Technology and Chemistry
Pr. Lenina 20, 307061 Baku, Azerbajdžanskaja SSR
Telephone: 93-83-85

F. of Geology and Prospecting
F. of Chemical Engineering
F. of Petroleum Production (Oil and Gas)
F. of Mechanical Engineering
F. of Energetics
F. of Automation of Production Processing
F. of Engineering Economics
D. for Evening Studies
D. for Correspondence Courses
Branch I. (Sumgaita)
Academic Year: September to July.
Admission Requirements: Competitive entrance examination following general or special secondary school certificate.
Degrees and Diplomas: Diploma of Specialist in relevant fields, 5 yrs.

7166 **DNEPROPETROVSKIJ ORDENA TRUDOVOGO KRASNOGO ZNAMENI GORNYJ INSTITUT IM. ARTEMA**
Institute of Mining
Pr. Karla Marksa 19, 320600 Dnepropetrovsk, Ukrainskaja SSR
Telephone: 45-43-44

F. of Geology and Prospecting
F. of Mining Engineering
F. of Electro-Mechanical Engineering
F. of Mechanical and Machine Engineering
F. of Mine Shaft Construction
F. of General Technical Studies (Aleksandra)
F. for Correspondence Courses
D. for Evening Studies
Academic Year: September to July.
Admission Requirements: Competitive entrance examination following general or special secondary school certificate.
Degrees and Diplomas: Diploma of Specialist in relevant fields, 5 yrs.

7167 **GROZENSKIJ ORDENA TRUDOVOGO KRASNOGO ZNAMENI NEFTJANOJ INSTITUT IM. AKAD. M.D. MILLIONŠ ČIKOVA**
Institute of Petroleum Technology
Pl. Revolucii 21, 364902 Groznyj GSP-2, Rossiskaja SFSR
Telephone: 2-21-65

F. of Geology and Prospecting
F. of Petroleum Production (Oil and Gas)
F. of Petroleum Technology
F. of Mechanical Engineering
F. of Construction Engineering
F. of Engineering Economics
D. for Correspondence Courses
D. for Evening Studies
Academic Year: September to July.
Admission Requirements: Competitive entrance examination following general or special secondary school certificate.
Degrees and Diplomas: Diploma of Specialist in relevant fields, 5 yrs.

7168 **IVANO-FRANKOVSKIJ INSTITUT NEFTI I GAZA**
Institute of Petroleum and Gas Technology
Karpatskaja Ul. 15, 284018 Ivano-Frankovsk, Ukrainskaja SSR
Telephone: 4-22-18

F. of Geology and Prospecting
F. of Petroleum Production
F. of Automation and Economics
F. of Mechanical Engineering
F. of General Technical Studies
D. for Evening Studies
D. for Correspondence Courses
Academic Year: September to July.
Admission Requirements: Competitive entrance examination following general or special secondary school certificate.
Degrees and Diplomas: Diploma of Specialist in relevant fields, 5 yrs.

7169 **KRIVOROŽSKIJ ORDENA TRUDOVOGO KRASNOGO ZNAMENI GORNORUDNYJ INSTITUT**
Institute of Mining
Ul. XXII Parts'ezda 11, 324030 Krivoj Rog, Dnepropetrovskoj obl., Ukrainskaja SSR
Telephone: 71-46-04

F. of Surveying and Mine Shaft Construction
F. of Geology and Prospecting
F. of Mining Engineering
F. of Electrical Engineering
F. of Mechanical and Machine Engineering
F. of Construction Engineering
F. of General Technical Studies
F. for Evening Studies
Academic Year: September to July.
Admission Requirements: Competitive entrance examination following general or special secondary school certificate.
Degrees and Diplomas: Diploma of Specialist in relevant fields, 5 yrs.

7170 **LENINGRADSKIJ ORDENA LENINA, ORDENA OKTJABR'SKOJ REVOLJUCII I ORDENA TRUDOVOGO KRASNOGO ZNAMENI GORNYJ INSTITUT IM. G.V. PLEHANOVA**
Institute of Mining
Vasil'evskij ostrov, 21-ia linija 2, 199026 Leningrad B-26, Rossiskaja SFSR
Telephone: 218-82-01

F. of Geology and Prospecting
F. of Mining Engineering
F. of Mine Shaft Construction
F. of Engineering Economics
F. of Geophysics
F. of Electrical Engineering
F. of Surveying
F. of Metallurgy
F. for Evening Studies
F. for Correspondence Courses
Branch I. (Vorkut)
Academic Year: September to July.
Admission Requirements: Competitive entrance examination following general or special secondary school certificate.

Degrees and Diplomas: Diploma of Specialist in relevant fields, 5 yrs.

7171 **MOSKOVSKIJ ORDENA TRUDOVOGO KRASNOGO ZNAMENI GEOLOGORAZVEDOČNYJ INSTITUT IM. SERGO ORDŽONIKIDZE**

Institute of Geology and Prospecting

Korp. Z Prosp. K. Marksa 18, 103912 Moskva GSP-3, Rossiskaja SFSR

Telephone: 203-21-58

F. of Geology and Prospecting
F. of Geophysics
F. of Hydro-Geology
F. of Prospecting and Extraction Techniques
F. for Evening Studies

Academic Year: September to July.

Admission Requirements: Competitive entrance examination following general or special secondary school certificate.

Degrees and Diplomas: Diploma of Specialist in relevant fields, 5 yrs.

7172 **MOSKOVSKIJ ORDENA TRUDOVOGO KRASNOGO ZNAMENI GORNYJ INSTITUT**

Institute of Mining

Leninskij prosp. 6, 117049 Moskva M-49, Rossiskaja SFSR

Telephone: 236-96-10

F. of Coal Mining
F. of Mining of Mineral and Non-Mineral Deposits
F. of Mining and Engineering
F. of Automation and Electrification
F. of Applied Physics
D. for Evening Studies
D. for Correspondence Courses

Academic Year: September to July.

Admission Requirements: Competitive entrance examination following general or special secondary school certificate.

Degrees and Diplomas: Diploma of Specialist in relevant fields, 5 yrs.

7173 **MOSKOVSKIJ ORDENA OKTJABR'SKOJ REVOLJUCII I ORDENA TRUDOVOGO KRASNOGO ZNAMENI NEFTII GAZA IM. I.M. GUBKINA**

Institute of Petroleum and Gas Technology

Leninskij pr. 65, 117296 Moskva B-296, Rossiskaja SFSR

Telephone: 130-92-73

F. of Geology, Geophysics and Geo-chemistry
F. of Gas and Petroleum Production
F. of Automation and Computer Technology
F. of Mechanical Engineering
F. of Chemical Engineering
F. of Engineering Economics
F. for Evening Studies
F. for Evening Studies (Al'metevsk, Nebit Dag, Leninogorsk, Krasnobodsk)
F. for Correspondence Courses

Academic Year: September to July.

Admission Requirements: Competitive entrance examination following general or special secondary school certificate.

Degrees and Diplomas: Diploma of Specialist in relevant fields, 5 yrs.

7174 **SVERDLOVSKIJ ORDENA TRUDOVOGO KRASNOGO ZNAMENI GORNYJ INSTITUT IM. V.V. VAHRUŠEVA**

Institute of Mining

Ul. Kujbyševa 30, 620219 Sverdlovsk, Rossiskaja SFSR

Telephone: 29-31-43

F. of Geology and Prospecting
F. of Geophysics
F. of Mining Engineering
F. of Mechanical Engineering
F. for Evening Studies
F. for Correspondence Courses

Academic Year: September to July.

Admission Requirements: Competitive entrance examination following general or special secondary school certificate.

Degrees and Diplomas: Diploma of Specialist in relevant fields, 5 yrs.

7175 **UFIMSKIJ NEFTJANOJ INSTITUT**

Institute of Petroleum Technology

Ul. Kosmonavtov 1, 450062 Ufa 62, Baškirskaja SSR

Telephone: 25-24-00

F. of Petroleum Production
F. of Engineering Economics
F. of Mechanical Engineering
F. of Construction Engineering
F. of Chemical Engineering
F. of Automation
F. of Production Processes
F. of General Technical Studies
F. for Evening Studies
F. for Evening Studies (Salavat, Oktrabrysk)
F. for Correspondence Courses

Academic Year: September to July.

Admission Requirements: Competitive entrance examination following general or special secondary school certificate.

Degrees and Diplomas: Diploma of Specialist in relevant fields, 5 yrs.

Metallurgical Engineering

7176 **DNEPROPETROVSKIJ ORDENA TRUDOVOGO KRASNOGO ZNAMENI METALLURGIČESKIJ INSTITUT IM. L.I. BREŽNEVA**

Institute of Metallurgy

Prosp. Gagarina 4, 320095 Dnepropetrovsk, Ukrainskaja SSR

Telephone: 45-31-56

F. of Metallurgy
F. of Mechanical and Power Engineering
F. of Metal Processing
F. of Chemical Engineering
F. of Engineering Economics
F. of General Technical Studies
F. for Evening Studies
F. for Evening Studies (Krivoi Rog)
Branch I. (Zaporož)

Academic Year: September to July.

Admission Requirements: Competitive entrance examination following general or special secondary school certificate.

Degrees and Diplomas: Diploma of Specialist in relevant fields, 5 yrs.

7177 **KOMMUNARSKIJ GORNO-METALLURGIČESKIJ INSTITUT**

Institute of Mining and Metallurgy

Pr. Lenina 16, 349104 Kommunarsk Vorošilovgradskoj obl., Ukrainskaja SSR

Telephone: 2-01-61

F. of Mining Engineering
F. of Electrification and Automation
F. of Metallurgy
F. of Automation of Production Processes
F. of Electrical Machine Engineering
F. of Construction Engineering
F. of Economics
F. of General Technical Studies
D. for Evening Studies
Branch I. (Kadievka)

Academic Year: September to July.

Admission Requirements: Competitive entrance examination following general or special secondary school certificate.

Degrees and Diplomas: Diploma of Specialist in relevant fields, 5 yrs.

7178 **KRASNOJARSKIJ ORDENA TRUDOVOGO KRASNOGO ZNAMENI INSTITUT CVETNYH METALLOV IM. M.I. KALININA**

Institute of Non-Ferrous Metals

Vuzovskij per. 3, 660025 Krasnojarsk 25, Rossiskaja SFSR

Telephone: 34-77-92

F. of Mining Engineering
F. of Metallurgy
F. of Electro-Mechanical Engineering
F. of Metal Processing
F. for Evening Studies

F. for Correspondence Courses
Academic Year: September to July.
Admission Requirements: Competitive entrance examination following general or special secondary school certificate.
Degrees and Diplomas: Diploma of Specialist in relevant fields, 5 yrs.

7179 **MAGNITOGORSKIJ ORDENA TRUDOVOGO KRASNOGO ZNAMENI GORNO-METALLURGIČESKIJ INSTITUT IM. G.I. NOSOVA**
Institute of Mining and Metallurgy
Pr. V.I. Lenina 38, 455000 Magnitogorsk Celjabinskj obl., Rossiskaja SFSR
Telephone: 2-12-87

F. of Energetics
F. of Mining Engineering
F. of Metallurgy
F. of Construction Engineering
F. of Technology
F. of Mechanical Engineering
F. for Evening Studies (2)
F. for Evening Studies (Beloreck)
F. for Correspondence Courses
Academic Year: September to July.
Admission Requirements: Competitive entrance examination following general or special secondary school certificate.
Degrees and Diplomas: Diploma of Specialist in relevant fields, 5 yrs.

7180 **MOSKOVSKIJ ORDENA OKTJABR'SKOJ REVOLJUCII I ORDENA TRUDOVOGO KRASNOGO ZNAMENI INSTITUT STALI I SPLAVOV**
Institute of Steel and Alloys Technology
Leninskij pr. 4, 117936-GSP Moskva 49, Rossiskaja SFSR
Telephone: 236-99-64

F. of Ferrous Metals and Alloys
F. of Physical Chemistry
F. of Semi-Conductors
F. of Non-Ferrous and Rare Metals
F. for Evening Studies
Academic Year: September to July.
Admission Requirements: Competitive entrance examination following general or special secondary school certificate.
Degrees and Diplomas: Diploma of Specialist in relevant fields, 5 yrs.

7181 **MOSKOVSKIJ ORDENA TRUDOVOGO KRASNOGO ZNAMENI VECERNIJ METALLURGIČESKIJ INSTITUT**
Institute of Metallurgy
Lefortovskij Val 26, 111250 Moskva E-250, Rossiskaja SFSR
Telephone: 361-13-75

F. of Metallurgy
F. of Technology
F. of General Technical Studies
Also seveal Branch Institues.
Academic Year: September to July.
Admission Requirements: Competitive entrance examination following general or special secondary school certificate.
Degrees and Diplomas: Diploma of Specialist in relevant fields, 5 yrs.

7182 **SEVERO-KAVKAZSKIJ ORDENA DRUŽBY NARODOV GORNO-METALLURGIČESKIJ INSTITUT**
Institute of Mining and Metallurgy
Ul. Kosmonavta Nikolaeva 44, 362004 Ordžonikidze, Severo-Osetinskaja ASSR
Telephone: 3-93-79

F. of Mining Geology
F. of Electronic Engineering
F. of Electro-Mechanical Engineering
F. of Metallurgy
F. of Construction Engineering
F. of General Technical Studies (Piatigorsk)
F. for Evening Studies
F. for Correspondence Courses
Academic Year: September to July.
Admission Requirements: Competitive entrance examination following general or special secondary school certificate.
Degrees and Diplomas: Diploma of Specialist in relevant fields, 5 yrs.

7183 **SIBIRSKIJ ORDENA TRUDOVOGO KRASNOGO ZNAMENI METALLURGIČESKIJ INSTITUT IM. SERGO ORDŽONIKIDZE**
Institute of Metallurgy
Prosp. Kirova 42, 654053 Novo-Kuzneck, Kemerovskoj obl., Rossiskaja SFSR
Telephone: 46-47-47

F. of Mining Engineering
F. of Metallurgy
F. of Electro-Metallurgy
F. of Metal Processing
F. of Mechanical Engineering
F. of Technology
F. of Construction Engineering
F. for Evening Studies (2)
F. for Evening Studies (Prokop'evsk)
D. for Correspondence Courses
Academic Year: September to July.
Admission Requirements: Competitive entrance examination following general or special secondary school certificate.
Degrees and Diplomas: Diploma of Specialist in relevant fields, 5 yrs.

7184 **ŽDANOVSKIJ METALLURGIČESKIJ INSTITUT**
Institute of Metallurgy
Pr. Respubliki 7, 341000 Ždanov Doneckoj obl., Ukrainskaja SSR
Telephone: 34-30-97

F. of Metallurgy
F. of Mechanical and Machine Engineering
F. of Metal Processing
F. of Technology
F. of General Technical Studies
F. for Evening Studies
Academic Year: September to July.
Admission Requirements: Competitive entrance examination following general or special secondary school certificate.
Degrees and Diplomas: Diploma of Specialist in relevant fields, 5 yrs.

Institutes of Machine and Mechanical Engineering

Machine, Machine Tool, and Precision Engineering

7185 **BRJANSKIJ ORDENA 'ZNAK POČOTA' INSTITUT TRANSPORTNOGO MAŠINOSTROENIJA**
Institute of Transport Machines
Bul'var 50-let Oktjabrja 7, 241035 Brjansk, Rossiskaja SFSR
Telephone: 5-07-59

F. of Transport Machines
F. of Power Machines (Turbine and Internal Combustion)
F. of Foundry Engineering and Welding
F. of Mechanical Engineering
F. for Evening Studies
F. for Correspondence Courses
Academic Year: September to July.
Admission Requirements: Competitive entrance examination following general or special secondary school certificate.
Degrees and Diplomas: Diploma of Specialist in relevant fields, 5 yrs.

7186 **IŽEVSKIJ MEHANIČESKIJ INSTITUT**
Studenčeskaja ul. 7, 426069 Iževsk, Udmurtskoj ASSR
Telephone: 23-83-50

7187 **KIROVOGRADSKIJ INSTITUT SEL'SKOHOZJAJSTVENNOGO MAŠINOSTROENIJA**
Institute of Agricultural Engineering
Pr. Pravdy 70a, 316017 Kirovograd, Ukrainskaja SSR
Telephone: 9-34-64

F. of Agricultural Engineering
F. of Mechanical and Machine Engineering
F. of Maintenance Technology
D. of Evening Studies
Academic Year: September to July.

Admission Requirements: Competitive entrance examination following general or special secondary school certificate.
Degrees and Diplomas: Diploma of Specialist in relevant fields, 5 yrs.

7188 **KURGANSKIJ MAŠINOSTROITEL'NYJ INSTITUT**
Institute of Machine Construction
Pl. Lenina, 640669 Kurgan obl., Rossiskaja SFSR
Telephone: 2-34-22

F. of Mechanical Engineering
F. of Automobile and Tractor Engineering
F. of Engineering Economics
F. for Evening Studies
F. for Correspondence Courses
Academic Year: September to July.
Admission Requirements: Competitive entrance examination following general or special secondary school certificate.
Degrees and Diplomas: Diploma of Specialist in relevant fields, 5 yrs.

7189 **LENINGRADSKIJ ORDENA TRUDOVOGO KRASNOGO ZNAMENI INSTITUT TOČNOJ MEHANIKI I OPTIKI**
Institute of Precision and Optical Engineering
Sablinskaja ul. 14, 197401 Leningrad, Rossiskaja SFSR
Telephone: 238-43-96

F. of Precision Engineering
F. of Optical Engineering
F. of Optical Electronic Engineering
F. for Evening Studies
Academic Year: September to July.
Admission Requirements: Competitive entrance examination following general or special secondary school certificate.
Degrees and Diplomas: Diploma of Specialist in relevant fields, 5 yrs.

7190 **LENINGRADSKIJ ORDENA LENINA I ORDENA KRASNOGO ZNAMENI MEHANIČESKIJ INSTITUT IM. MARŠALA SOVETSKOGO SOJUZA USTINOVA D.F.**
Institute of Mechanical Engineering
1-ja Krasnoarmejskaja ul. ½1, 198005 Leningrad L-5, Rossiskaja SFSR
Telephone: 292-23-47

F. of Machine Engineering
F. of Mechanical Engineering
F. of Apparatus Construction
F. for Evening Studies
Academic Year: September to July.
Admission Requirements: Competitive entrance examination following general or special secondary school certificate.
Degrees and Diplomas: Diploma of Specialist in relevant fields, 5 yrs.

7191 **MOGILEVSKIJ MASHINOSTROITEL'NYJ INSTITUT**
Institute of Machine Engineering
Ul. Lenina 70, 212005 Mogilev, Belorusskaja SSR
Telephone: 5-63-30
Rektor: V. I. Hodyrev

F. of Mechanical Engineering
Dean: R.V. Shadooroe; *staff* 64 (32)
F. of Machine Engineering
Dean: A.N. Maksimenko; *staff* 66 (35)
F. of Electrical Engineering
Dean: V.M. Belokon; *staff* 91 (42)
F. of Transport Engineering
Dean: B.B. Borisov; *staff* 94 (41)
F. for Study with Foreign Students
Dean: J.V. Surovegin
F. for Correspondence Courses
Dean: E.B. Atmanaky
Scientific Research Ce.
Head: V.P. Belsky; *staff* 118 (202)
Also 2 Scientific-Technical Co-operatives for Research Development.
Founded 1961. Governing bodies: the Scientific Council; the Council. Residential facilities for academic staff and students.
Arrangements for Academic Exchange Programme with Portland State University. Also co-operation with: Instituteof Mechanical and Electrical Engineering, Gabrovo; College of Engineering, Koszalin.
Academic Year: September to July.
Admission Requirements: Competitive entrance examination following general or special secondary school certificate.
Language of Instruction: Russian.
Degrees and Diplomas: Diploma of Specialist in relevant fields, 5 yrs.
Library: 600,000 vols.
Special Facilities (Museums, etc.): Historical Museum; Video Club.
Academic Staff, 1990: 352 (18).
Student Enrolment, 1990:

	Men	Women	Total
Of the country	2175	668	2843
Of other countries	104	–	104
Total	2279	668	2947*

*Also 1335 students by correspondence.

7192 **MOSKOVSKIJ AVTOMEHANIČESKIJ INSTITUT**
Institute of Automobile Engineering
B. Semenovskaja ul. 38, 105023 Moskva E-23, Rossiskaja SFSR
Telephone: 369-28-32

F. of Tractor and Automobile Engineering
F. of Automobile and Tractor Motors
F. of Production Technology and Automation
F. of Metal Processing Technology
F. for Evening Studies (3)
Academic Year: September to July.
Admission Requirements: Competitive entrance examination following general or special secondary school certificate.
Degrees and Diplomas: Diploma of Specialist in relevant fields, 5 yrs.

7193 **MOSKOVSKIJ INSTITUT ELEKTRONNOGO MAŠINOSTROENIJA**
Institute of Electronic Engineering
B. Vuzovskij per. 3, 109028 Moskva, Rossiskaja SFSR
Telephone: 297-90-89

F. of Semi-Conductors and Vacuum Tubes
F. of Automation and Computer Technology
F. of Applied Mathematics
F. of Radio Engineering
F. for Evening Studies (2)
Academic Year: September to July.
Admission Requirements: Competitive entrance examination following general or special secondary school certificate.
Degrees and Diplomas: Diploma of Specialist in relevant fields, 5 yrs.

7194 **MOSKOVSKIJ ORDENA TRUDOVOGO KRASNOGO ZNAMENI STANKOINSTRUMENTAL'NYJ INSTITUT**
Institute of Machine Tool Engineering
Vadkovskij per. 3-a, 101472 Moskva GSP, Rossiskaja SFSR
Telephone: 289-43-15

F. of Precision Engineering
F. of Machine Tool Engineering
F. of Machine Technology
F. of Metal Processing Automation
F. for Evening Studies
Academic Year: September to July.
Admission Requirements: Competitive entrance examination following general or special secondary school certificate.
Degrees and Diplomas: Diploma of Specialist in relevant fields, 5 yrs.

7195 **MOSKOVSKOE ORDENA LENINA I ORDENA OKTJABR'SKOJ REVOLJUCII I ORDENA TRUDOVOGO KRASNOGO ZNAMENI VYSŠEE TEHNIČESKOE UČILIŠČE IM. N.E. BAUMANA**
Institute of Mechanical Engineering
2-ja Baumanskaja ul. 5, 107005 Moskva B-5, Rossiskaja SFSR
Telephone: 267-05-41

F. of Automation and Mechanization of Production
F. of Energetics (including Internal Combustion Engines and Turbines)
F. of Transport Engineering
F. of Precision Engineering
F. of Machine Construction
F. for Evening Studies
Branch I. (Kaluga)
Academic Year: September to July.

Admission Requirements: Competitive entrance examination following general or special secondary school certificate.

Degrees and Diplomas: Diploma of Specialist in relevant fields, 5 yrs.

7196 **ROSTOVSKIJ-NA-DONU ORDENA TRUDOVOGO KRASNOGO ZNAMENI INSTITUT SEL'SKOHOZJAJSTVENNEGO MAŠINOSTROENIJA**

Institute of Agricultural Engineering

Pl. Gagarina 1, 344708 Rostov-na-Donu, Rossiskaja SFSR

Telephone: 38-15-66

F. of Agricultural Engineering
F. of Machine Engineering
F. of Precision Engineering and Automation
F. of Metal Processing
F. of Foundry Technology
F. for Evening Studies (2)
F. for Correspondence Courses

Academic Year: September to July.

Admission Requirements: Competitive entrance examination following general or special secondary school certificate.

Degrees and Diplomas: Diploma of Specialist in relevant fields, 5 yrs.

7197 **SEVASTOPOL'SKIJ PRIBOROSTROITEL'NYJ INSTITUT**

Institute of Precision Engineering

Studgorodok, 335053 Sevastopol', Ukrainskaja SSR

Telephone: 24-14-24

F. of Automation and Computer Technology
F. of Radio Engineering
F. of Machine and Precision Engineering F. of Mechanical Engineering (Shipbuilding)
F. of General Technical Studies (Kerchi)
D. for Evening Studies
Branch I. (Simferopol)

Academic Year: September to July.

Admission Requirements: Competitive entrance examination following general or special secondary school certificate.

Degrees and Diplomas: Diploma of Specialist in relevant fields, 5 yrs.

7198 **VOROŠILOVGRADSKIJ MAŠINOSTROITEL'NYJ INSTITUT**

Institute of Machine Engineering

Kvartal Molodežnij 20a, 348034 Vorošilovgrad, Ukrainskaja SSR

Telephone: 6-23-90

F. of Mechanical Engineering
F. of Metallurgical Engineering
F. of Transport Machines
F. of Electrical Machines
F. of Automation
F. of Economics
F. of General Technical Studies
F. of General Technical Studies (Krasnodar)
D. for Evening Studies

Academic Year: September to July.

Admission Requirements: Competitive entrance examination following general or special secondary school certificate.

Degrees and Diplomas: Diploma of Specialist in relevant fields, 5 yrs.

7199 **VSESOJUZNYJ ZAOČNYJ MAŠINOSTROITEL'NYJ INSTITUT**

Correspondence Institute of Machine Engineering

Ul. Stromynka 20, 107076 Moskva 5-ja, Rossiskaja SFSR

Telephone: 268-55-19

F. of Mechanization and Automation of Metallurgical Processes
F. of Automation of Machine Engineering
F. of Precision Engineering
F. of Transport and Motor Engineering
F. of General Technical Studies
D. for Evening Studies
Branch I. (Orel)
Branch I. (Murom)
Branch I. (Elektrostali)

Academic Year: September to July.

Admission Requirements: Competitive entrance examination following general or special secondary school certificate.

Degrees and Diplomas: Diploma of Specialist in relevant fields, 5 yrs.

7200 **ZAPOROŽSKII ORDENA 'ZNAK POCOTA' MAŠINOSTROITEL'NYJ INSTITUT IM. V.J. ČUBARJA**

Institute of Machine Engineering

Ul. Žukovskogo 64, 330063 Zaporože, Ukrainskaja SSR

Telephone: 64-25-06

F. of Machine Engineering
F. of Electrical Engineering
F. of Automobile Engineering
F. of Mechanical Engineering and Metallurgy
F. of Electronic Engineering
F. of General Technical Studies
D. for Evening Studies

Academic Year: September to July.

Admission Requirements: Competitive entrance examination following general or special secondary school certificate.

Degrees and Diplomas: Diploma of Specialist in relevant fields, 5 yrs.

Chemico-Mechanical Engineering

7201 **MOSKOVSKIJ ORDENA TRUDOVOGO KRASNOGO ZNAMENI INSTITUT HIMIČESKOGO MASINOSTROENIJA**

Institute of Chemical Engineering

Ul. Karla Marksa 21/4, 107884 Moskva B-66, Rossiskaja SFSR

Telephone: 261-49-61

F. of Inorganic Chemical Processes
F. of Organic Chemical Processes
F. of Chemical Machines
F. of Chemical Apparatus
F. of Cybernetics and Automation
F. for Evening Studies

Academic Year: September to July.

Admission Requirements: Competitive entrance examination following general or special secondary school certificate.

Degrees and Diplomas: Diploma of Specialist in relevant fields, 5 yrs.

7202 **TAMBOVSKIJ INSTITUT HIMEČESKOGO MAŠINOSTROENIJA**

Institute of Chemical Engineering

Leningradskaja Ul. 1, 392620 Tambov, Rossiskaja SFSR

Telephone: 2-10-19

F. of Technology
F. of Machine Engineering
F. of Mechanical Engineering
F. of Automation
F. of General Technical Studies
F. for Evening Studies
D. for Correspondence Courses

Academic Year: September to July.

Admission Requirements: Competitive entrance examination following general or special secondary school certificate.

Degrees and Diplomas: Diploma of Specialist in relevant fields, 5 yrs.

Shipbuilding Engineering

7203 **LENINGRADSKIJ ORDENA LENINA KORABLESTROITEL'NYJ INSTITUT**

Institute of Shipbuilding

Locmanskaja ul. 3, 190008 Leningrad F-8, Rossiskaja SFSR

Telephone: 216-22-82

F. of Shipbuilding
F. of Marine Engines
F. of Marine Equipment
F. of Engineering Economics
F. for Evening Studies
F. for Correspondence Courses

Academic Year: September to July.

Admission Requirements: Competitive entrance examination following general or special secondary school certificate.

Degrees and Diplomas: Diploma of Specialist in relevant fields, 5 yrs.

7204 **NIKOLAEVSKIJ ORDENA TRUDOVOGO KRASNOGO ZNAMENI KORABLESTROITEL'NYJ INSTITUT IM. ADMIRALA S.O. MAKOROVA**

Institute of Shipbuilding

Ul. Geroev Stalingrada 5, 327001 Nikolaev, Ukrainskaja SSR

Telephone: 35-91-48

F. of Shipbuilding
F. of Marine Engines
F. of Electrical Equipment
D. for Evening Studies
Branch I. (Herson)

Academic Year: September to July.

Admission Requirements: Competitive entrance examination following general or special secondary school certificate.

Degrees and Diplomas: Diploma of Specialist in relevant fields, 5 yrs.

Aeronautical Engineering

7205 **ANDROPOVSKJI AVIACIONNYJ TEHNOLOGIČESKIJ INSTITUT**

Institute of Aviation Technology

Ul. Puśhkina 2, 152934 Andropov, Rossiskaja SFSR

Telephone: 2-82-07

F. of Aeronautical Engineering
F. of Aviation Metallurgy
F. of Radio Engineering
F. of Evening Studies

Academic Year: Septembér to July.

Admission Requirements: Competitive entrance examination following general or special secondary school certificate.

Degrees and Diplomas: Diploma of Specialist in relevant fields, 5 yrs.

7206 **HAR'KOVSKIJ ORDENA LENINA AVIACIONNYJ INSTITUT IM. N.E. ZUKOVSKOGO**

Institute of Aviation Engineering

Ul. Čkalova 17, 310084 Har'kov, Ukrainskaja SSR

Telephone: 44-23-13

F. of Aircraft Construction
F. of Aircraft Engine Construction
F. of Radio Engineering
F. for Evening Studies

Academic Year: September to July.

Admission Requirements: Competitive entrance examination following general or special secondary school certificate.

Degrees and Diplomas: Diploma of Specialist in relevant fields, 5 yrs.

7207 **KAZANSKIJ ORDENA TRUDOVOGO KRASNOGO ZNAMENI I ORDENA DRUŽBY NARODOV AVIACIONNYJ INSTITUT IM. A.N. TUPOLEVA**

Institute of Aviation Engineering

Ul. Karla Marksa 10, 420084 Kazan', Rossiskaja SFSR

Telephone: 39-71-14

F. of Aircraft Construction
F. of Aircraft Engine Construction
F. of Automobile and Tractor Engineering
F. of Radio Engineering
F. of Computer Technology and Control Systems
F. for General Technical Studies (evening courses)

Academic Year: September to July.

Admission Requirements: Competitive entrance examination following general or special secondary school certificate.

Degrees and Diplomas: Diploma of Specialist in relevant fields, 5 yrs.

7208 **KUJBYŠEVSKIJ ORDENA TRUDOVOGO KRAŠNOGO ZNAMENI AVIACIONNYJ INSTITUT IM. AKADAMIKA S.P. KOROLEVA**

Institute of Aviation Engineering

Molodogvardejskaja ul. 151, 443001 Kujbyšev, Rossiskaja SFSR

Telephone: 32-26-06

F. of Aircraft Construction
F. of Aircraft Engine Construction
F. of Exploitation of Aircraft
F. of Metal Processing
F. of Construction and Technology of Radio Equipment
F. for Evening Studies

Academic Year: September to July.

Admission Requirements: Competitive entrance examination following general or special secondary school certificate.

Degrees and Diplomas: Diploma of Specialist in relevant fields, 5 yrs.

7209 **LENINGRADSKIJ INSTITUT AVIACIONNOGO PRIBOROSTROENIJA**

Institute of Aeronautical Instrument Construction

Ul. Gercena 67, 190000 Leningrad, Rossiskaja SFSR

Telephone: 312-21-07

F. of Aeronautical Instrument Construction
F. of Radio Engineering
F. of Electromechanical Equipment
F. of Electronics and Computer Technology
F. for Evening Studies
F. for Correspondence Courses

Academic Year: September to July.

Admission Requirements: Competitive entrance examination following general or special secondary school certificate.

Degrees and Diplomas: Diploma of Specialist in relevant fields, 5 yrs.

7210 **MOSKOVSKIJ AVIACIONNYJ TEHNOLOGIČESKIJ INSTITUT IM. K.E. CIOLKOVSKOGO**

Institute of Aviation Technology

Ul. Petrovka 27, 103767 Moskva K-31, Rossiskaja SFSR

Telephone: 221-20-17

F. of Aeronautical Engineering
F. of Aircraft Technology (Metallurgy)
F. of Radio Equipment
F. for Evening Studies
Branch I. (Stupino)

Academic Year: September to July.

Admission Requirements: Competitive entrance examination following general or special secondary school certificate.

Degrees and Diplomas: Diploma of Specialist in relevant fields, 5 yrs.

7211 **MOSKOVSKIJ ORDENA LENINA I ORDENA OKTJABR'SKOJ REVOLJUCII AVIACIONNYJ INSTITUT IM. SERGO ORDŻONIKIDZE**

Institute of Aviation Engineering

Volokolamskoe Šosse 4, 125871 Moskva, A-80 Rossiskaja SFSR

Telephone: 158-13-73

F. of Aircraft Construction
F. of Aircraft Installations
F. of Aircraft Engine Construction
F. of Aeroplane and Helicopter Construction
F. of Automatic Aircraft Control Systems
F. of Radio Engineering
F. of Economics and Organization of Aircraft Production
F. for Evening Studies.

Academic Year: September to July.

Admission Requirements: Competitive entrance examination following general or special secondary school certificate.

Degrees and Diplomas: Diploma of Specialist in relevant fields, 5 yrs.

7212 **UFIMSKIJ ORDENA LENINA AVIACIONNYJ INSTITUT IM. SERGO ORDŽONIKIDZE**

Institute of Aviation Engineering

Ul. Karla Marksa 12, 450025 Ufa 25, Baškirskaja ASSR

Telephone: 22-63-07

F. of Aircraft Engine Construction
F. of Electromechanics
F. of Mechanical Technology
F. of Engineering Economics
F. for Evening Studies
F. for Correspondence Courses

Academic Year: September to July.

Admission Requirements: Competitive entrance examination following general or special secondary school certificate.

Degrees and Diplomas: Diploma of Specialist in relevant fields, 5 yrs.

Printing Technology

7213 **MOSKOVSKIJ POLIGRAFIČESKIJ INSTITUT**
Institute of Printing Technology
Ul. Prjanišnikova 2a, 127550 Moskva A8, Rossiskaja SFSR
Telephone: 216-14-70

F. of Printing Machine Construction
F. of Printing Processes
F. of Engineering Economics
F. of Graphic Art and Design
F. of Editing and Publishing
D. for Evening Studies
D. for Correspondence Courses
Branch I. (Leningrad)

Academic Year: September to July.
Admission Requirements: Competitive entrance examination following general or special secondary school certificate.
Degrees and Diplomas: Diploma of Specialist in relevant fields, 5 yrs.

7214 **UKRAINSKIJ POLIGRAFIČESKIJ INSTITUT IM. IVANA FEDOROVA**
Institute of Printing Technology
Ul. Podgolosko 19, 290006 L'vov, Ukrainskaja SSR
Telephone: 22-78-62

F. of Printing Machine Construction
F. of Printing Processes
F. of Engineering Economics
F. of General Technical Studies
F. for Correspondence Courses
F. for Evening Studies (Kiev)
D. for Evening Studies

Academic Year: September to July.
Admission Requirements: Competitive entrance examination following general or special secondary school certificate.
Degrees and Diplomas: Diploma of Specialist in relevant fields, 5 yrs.

Cinematograph Engineering

7215 **LENINGRADSKIJ INSTITUT KINOINŽENEROV**
Institute of Cinematograph Technology
Ul. Pravdy 13, 191126 Leningrad F-126, Rossiskaja SFSR
Telephone: 215-73-23

F. of Electrical Technology (Sound Engineering)
F. of Mechanical Technology (Cameras and Equipment)
F. of Chemical Technology (Photographic Materials)
F. for Correspondence Courses (Moscow)
D. for Correspondence Courses

Academic Year: September to July.
Admission Requirements: Competitive entrance examination following general or special secondary school certificate.
Degrees and Diplomas: Diploma of Specialist in relevant fields, 5 yrs.

Institutes of Electronics, Electrical Equipment and Automation

7216 **HAR'KOVSKIJ ORDENA TRUDOVOGO KRASNOGO ZNAMENI INSTITUT RADIOELEKTRONIKI IM. AKAD. M.K. JANKELJA**
Institute of Radio Electronics
Pr. Lenina 14, 310141 Har'kov, Ukrainskaja SSR
Telephone: 43-30-53

F. of Automated Control Systems
F. of Radio Engineering
F. of Electronics
F. of Computer Technology
F. of General Technical Studies
D. for Evening Studies

Academic Year: September to July.
Admission Requirements: Competitive entrance examination following general or special secondary school certificate.
Degrees and Diplomas: Diploma of Specialist in relevant fields, 5 yrs.

7217 **MOSKOVSKIJ ORDENA TRUDOVOGO KRASNOGO ZNAMENI FISIKO-TEHNIČESKIJ INSTITUT**
Physico-Technical Institute
Institutskij per 9, Dolgoprudnyj, 171700 Moskovskaja obl., Rossiskaja SFSR
Telephone: 408-48-00

F. of Radio Engineering and Cybernetics
F. of General and Applied Physics
F. of Aerophysics and Cosmic Research
F. of Molecular and Chemical Physics
F. of Physical and Quantum Electronics
F. of Aeronautical Technology
F. of Applied Mathematics

Academic Year: September to July.
Admission Requirements: Competitive entrance examination following general or special secondary school certificate.
Degrees and Diplomas: Diploma of Specialist in relevant fields, 5 yrs.

7218 **MOSKOVSKIJ ORDENA TRUDOVOGO KRASNOGO ZNAMENI INŽENERNO-FIZIČESKIJ INSTITUT**
Institute of Physics and Engineering
Kaširskoe Šosse 31, 114509 Moskva M-409, Rossiskaja SFSR
Telephone: 324-84-17

F. of Experimental and Theoretical Physics
F. of Energetics
F. of Electronics and Automation
F. of Computer Electronics
F. of Advanced Physics
D. for Evening Studies
Branch I. (Obninsk)

Academic Year: September to July.
Admission Requirements: Competitive entrance examination following general or special secondary school certificate.
Degrees and Diplomas: Diploma of Specialist in relevant fields, 5 yrs.

7219 **MOSKOVSKIJ ORDENA TRUDOVOGO KRASNOGO ZNAMENI INSTITUT ELEKTRONNOJ TEHNIKI**
Institute of Radio Electronics and Electronic Technology
St. Krjukovo Oktjabr'skoj Ž.d, Zelenograd, 103498 Moskva K-498, Zelenograd, Rossiskaja SFSR
Telephone: 531-44-41

F. of Physical Engineering
F. of Physical Chemistry
F. of Micro Equipment and Cybernetics
F. of Electronic Machines
D. for Evening Studies

Academic Year: September to July.
Admission Requirements: Competitive entrance examination following general or special secondary school certificate.
Degrees and Diplomas: Diploma of Specialist in relevant fields, 5 yrs.

7220 **MOSKOVSKIJ INSTITUT RADIOTEHNIKI ELEKTRONIKI I AVTOMATIKI**
Institute of Radio Electronics and Electronic Technology
Pr. Vernadskogo 78, 117454 Moskva V454, Rossiskaja SFSR
Telephone: 433-04-55

F. of Automated Control Systems
F. of Electrical Equipment and Measurement Technology
F. of Radio Equipment Construction
F. for Evening Studies (Radio Engineering)
F. for Evening Studies (Automation and Computer Technology)
F. for Evening Studies (Electronics)
F. for Correspondence Courses
Branch I. (Dubna)

Academic Year: September to July.
Admission Requirements: Competitive entrance examination following general or special secondary school certificate.
Degrees and Diplomas: Diploma of Specialist in relevant fields, 5 yrs.

7221 **OBNINSKIJ INSTITUT ATOMNOJ ENERGETIKI**
Ul. Zolio-Kjuri 1, 249020 Obninsk Kalužskoj obl., Rossiskaja SFSR

7222 **TOMSKIJ INSTITUT AVTOMATIZIROVANNYH SISTEM UPRAVLENIJA I RADIOELEKTRONIKI**
Institute of Automated Control Systems and Radio Electronics
Prosp. Lenina 40, 634050 Tomsk 50, Rossiskaja SFSR
Telephone: 2-32-27

F. of Radio Engineering
F. of Equipment Construction
F. of Electronic Technology and Automation
F. for Evening Studies
F. for Correspondence Courses

Academic Year: September to July.
Admission Requirements: Competitive entrance examination following general or special secondary school certificate.
Degrees and Diplomas: Diploma of Specialist in relevant fields, 5 yrs.

Institutes of Radio Engineering and Telecommunications

Radio Engineering

7223 **MINSKIJ RADIOTEHNIČESKIJ INSTITUT**
Institute of Radio Technology
Ul. Petrucja Brovki 6, 220069 Minsk, Belorusskaja SSR
Telephone: 32-32-35

F. of Radio Engineering
F. of Automation and Computer Technology
F. for Evening Studies

Academic Year: September to July.
Admission Requirements: Competitive entrance examination following general or special secondary school certificate.
Degrees and Diplomas: Diploma of Specialist in relevant fields, 5 yrs.

7224 **RJAZANSKIJ RADIOTEHNIČESKIJ INSTITUT**
Institute of Radio Technology
Ul. Gagarine 59/1, 390024 Rjazan' 24, Rossiskaja SFSR
Telephone: 72-24-45

F. of Radio Equipment Construction
F. of Radio Engineering
F. of Electronics
F. of Automation and Remote Control
F. of Automated Control Systems
F. for Evening Studies

Academic Year: September to July.
Admission Requirements: Competitive entrance examination following general or special secondary school certificate.
Degrees and Diplomas: Diploma of Specialist in relevant fields, 5 yrs.

7225 **TAGANROGSKIJ RADIOTEHNIČESKIJ INSTITUT IM. V.D. KAKMYKOVA**
Institute of Radio Technology
Ul. Čehova 22, 347915 Taganrog 15, Rossiskaja SFSR
Telephone: 6-49-22

F. of Radio Engineering
F. of Radio Electronics
F. of Automation and Computer Technology
F. for Evening Studies
F. for Correspondence Courses

Academic Year: September to July.
Admission Requirements: Competitive entrance examination following general or special secondary school certificate.
Degrees and Diplomas: Diploma of Specialist in relevant fields, 5 yrs.

Telecommunications

7226 **KUJBYŠEVSKIJ ELEKTROTEHNIČESKIJ INSTITUT SVJAZI**
Institute of Telecommunications
Ul. L'va Tolstogo 23, 443099 Kujbyšev obl. 99, Rossiskaja SFSR
Telephone: 33-38-56

F. of Radio Communications and Broadcasting
F. of Automatic Telecommunications
F. of Multi-Channel Telecommunications
D. for Correspondence Courses

Academic Year: September to July.
Admission Requirements: Competitive entrance examination following general or special secondary school certificate.
Degrees and Diplomas: Diploma of Specialist in relevant fields, 5 yrs.

7227 **LENINGRADSKIJ ELEKTROTEHNIČESKIJ INSTITUT SVJAZI IM. PROF. M.A. BONČ-BRUEVIČA**
Institute of Telecommunications
Nab. Reki Mojka 61, 191065 Leningrad D-65, Rossiskaja SFSR
Telephone: 211-60-87

F. of Radio Technology
F. of Radio Equipment Construction
F. of Radio Communications and Broadcasting
F. of Automatic Telecommunications
F. of Multi-Channel Telecommunications
F. for Evening Studies
F. for Correspondence Courses

Academic Year: September to July.
Admission Requirements: Competitive entrance examination following general or special secondary school certificate.
Degrees and Diplomas: Diploma of Specialist in relevant fields, 5 yrs.

7228 **MOSKOVSKIJ ORDENA TRUDOVOGO KRASNOGO ZNAMENELEKTROTEHNIČESKIJ INSTITUT SVJAZI**
Institute of Telecommunications
Aviamotornaja ul. 8, 111024 Moskva E-24, Rossiskaja SFSR
Telephone: 274-27-62

F. of Radio Communications and Broadcasting
F. of Automation, Tele-Mechanics and Electronics
F. of Automatic Telecommunications
F. of Multi-Channel Telecommunications
F. of Telecommunications Installations
F. of Engineering Economics
F. for Evening Studies

Academic Year: September to July.
Admission Requirements: Competitive entrance examination following general or special secondary school certificate.
Degrees and Diplomas: Diploma of Specialist in relevant fields, 5 yrs.

7229 **NOVOSIBIRSKIJ ELEKTROTEHNIČESKIJ INSTITUT SVJAZI IM. N.D. PSURČEVA**
Institute of Telecommunications
Ul. Kirova 86, 630125 Novosibirsk 8, Rossiskaja SFSR
Telephone: 66-10-38

F. of Radio Communications and Broadcasting
F. of Automatic Telecommunications
F. of Multi-Channel Telecommunications
F. of Engineering Economics
F. for Correspondence Courses
Branch I. (Habarovsk)

Academic Year: September to July.
Admission Requirements: Competitive entrance examination following general or special secondary school certificate.
Degrees and Diplomas: Diploma of Specialist in relevant fields, 5 yrs.

7230 **ODESSKIJ ELEKTROTEHNIČESKIJ INSTITUT SVJAZI IM. A.S. POPOVA**
Institute of Telecommunications
Ul. Čeljuskincev ⅓, 270021 Odessa 20, Ukrainskaja SSR
Telephone: 3-22-44

F. of Radio Communications and Broadcasting
F. of Automatic Telecommunications
F. of Multi-Channel Telecommunications
F. of General Technical Studies
F. for Correspondence Courses (2)
F. for Evening Studies

Academic Year: September to July.
Admission Requirements: Competitive entrance examination following general or special secondary school certificate.
Degrees and Diplomas: Diploma of Specialist in relevant fields, 5 yrs.

7231 **TAŠKENTSKIJ ELEKTROTEHNIČESKIJ INSTITUT SVJAZI**

Institute of Telecommunications

Ul. Engel'sa 108, 700000 Taškent, Uzbekskaja SSR

Telephone: 35-09-34

F. of Radio Communications and Broadcasting
F. of Automatic Telecommunications
F. of Multi-Channel Telecommunications
D. for Evening Courses
D. for Correspondence Courses

Academic Year: September to July.

Admission Requirements: Competitive entrance examination following general or special secondary school certificate.

Degrees and Diplomas: Diploma of Specialist in relevant fields, 5 yrs.

7232 **VSESOJUZNYJ ZAOČNYJ ELEKTROTEHNIČESKIJ INSTITUT SVJAZI**

Correspondence Institute of Telecommunications

U. Narodnogo Opolčenija 32, 123855 Moskva D-423, Rossiskaja SFSR

Telephone: 194-92-65

F. of Radio Communications and Broadcasting
F. of Automatic and Multi-Channel Telecommunications
F. of Engineering Economics
Branch I. (Minsk)
Branch I. (Tbilisi)

Academic Year: September to July.

Admission Requirements: Competitive entrance examination following general or special secondary school certificate.

Degrees and Diplomas: Diploma of Specialist in relevant fields, 5 yrs.

Institutes of Chemical Engineering

7233 **BELORUSSKIJ ORDENA TRUDOVOGO KRASNOGO ZNAMENI TEHNOLOGICESKIJ INSTITUT IM. S.M. KIROVA**

Institute of Technology

Ul. Sverdlova 13a, 220630 Minsk, Belorusskaja SSR

Telephone: 26-14-32

Rektor: Zarskij Ivan Mihajlovič

F. of Forestry Engineering
Dean: Vyrko Nikolaj Pavlocič
F. of Forestry
Dean: Rožkov Leonid Nikolaevič
F. of Wood Technology
F. of Organic Chemical Technology
Dean: Polujanaovič Vladimir Jakovlevič
F. of Chemical Technology and Techniques
Dean: Hves'ko Gennadij Mihajlovič
F. for Correspondence Courses
D. for Evening Studies
Branch I. (Novopolotsk)

Founded 1930.

Arrangements for co-operation with Warsaw Agricultural University.

Academic Year: September to July.

Admission Requirements: Competitive entrance examination following general or special secondary school certificate.

Languages of Instruction: Russian and Byelorussian.

Degrees and Diplomas: Diploma of Specialist in relevant fields, 5 yrs. Kandidat nauk, Candidates of the Sciences, a further 3 yrs.

Library: 923,000 vols.

Academic Staff, 1990: 486 (127).

Student Enrolment, 1990:

	Men	Women	Total
Of the country	3297	2328	5625
Of other countries	184	7	191
Total	3481	2335	5816*

*Also 1333 external and correspondence students.

7234 **DNEPROPETROVSKIJ ORDENA TRUDOVOGO KRASNOGO ZNAMENI HIMIKO-TEHNOLOGIČESKIJ INSTITUT IM. F.E. DZERŽINSKOGO**

Institute of Chemical Technology

Prosp. Gagarina 8, 320640 Dnepropetrovsk, Ukrainskaja SSR

Telephone: 45-32-91

F. of Inorganic Chemical Technology
F. of Organic Chemical Technology
F. of Silicate Technology
F. of High Molecular Compound Technology
F. of Mechanical Engineering
F. for Evening Studies

Academic Year: September to July.

Admission Requirements: Competitive entrance examination following general or special secondary school certificate.

Degrees and Diplomas: Diploma of Specialist in relevant fields, 5 yrs.

7235 **IVANOVSKIJ ORDENA TRUDOVOGO KRASNOGO ZNAMENI HIMIKO-TEHNOLOGIČESKIJ INSTITUT**

Institute of Chemical Technology

Prosp. F. Engel'sa 7, 153460 Ivanovo, Rossiskaja SFSR

Telephone: 2-92-41

F. of Inorganic Chemical Technology
F. of Organic Chemical Technology
F. of Silicate Technology
F. of Mechanical Engineering
F. for Correspondence Courses
D. for Evening Studies

Academic Year: September to July.

Admission Requirements: Competitive entrance examination following general or special secondary school certificate.

Degrees and Diplomas: Diploma of Specialist in relevant fields.

7236 **KAZAHSKIJ HIMIKO-TEHNOLOGIČESKIJ INSTITUT**

Institute of Chemical Technology

Kommunističeskij prosp. 5, 486018 Čimkent, Kazahskaja SSR

Telephone: 3-64-12

F. of Inorganic Chemical Technology
F. of Organic Chemical Technology
F. of Silicate Technology
F. of Mechanical Engineering
F. of Construction Engineering
F. for Evening Studies
D. for Correspondence Courses

Academic Year: September to July.

Admission Requirements: Competitive entrance examination following general or special secondary school certificate.

Degrees and Diplomas: Diploma of Specialist in relevant fields, 5 yrs.

7237 **KAZANSKIJ ORDENA TRUDOVOGO KRASNOGO ZNAMENI HIMIKO-TEHNOLOGIČESKIJ INSTITUT IM. S.M. KIROVA**

Institute of Chemical Technology

Ul. Karla Marksa 68, 420015 Kazan', Rossiskaja SFSR

Telephone: 32-38-18

F. of Chemical Engineering
F. of Polymer Technology
F. of Refrigeration and Automation Technology
F. of Technology
F. of Mechanical Engineering
F. of Petroleum Technology
F. for Evening Studies (2)
F. for Correspondence Courses (2)
F. for Evening Studies (Nižne-Kamsk)

Academic Year: September to July.

Admission Requirements: Competitive entrance examination following general or special secondary school certificate.

Degrees and Diplomas: Diploma of Specialist in relevant fields, 5 yrs.

7238 **LENINGRADSKIJ ORDENA TRUDOVOGO KRASNOGO ZNAMENI ORDENA OKTJABR'SKOJ REVOLJUCII I TEHNOLOGIČESKIJ INSTITUTIM. LENSOVETA**

Institute of Technology

Zargorodnyj prosp. 19, 198013 Leningrad, Rossiskaja SFSR

Telephone: 292-13-12

F. of Chemistry
F. of Physical Chemistry
F. of Silicate and Inorganic Chemical Technology
F. of Mathematics and Mechanics (Machines and Apparatus)
F. of Organic Chemical Technology
F. of Cybernetics
F. of Engineering
F. of Engineering Technology
F. of Physical Chemistry Engineering
F. of Chemical Technology Engineering
F. for Evening Studies

Academic Year: September to July.

Admission Requirements: Competitive entrance examination following general or special secondary school certificate.

Degrees and Diplomas: Diploma of Specialist in relevant fields, 5 yrs.

7239 **MOSKOVSKIJ ORDENA TRUDOVOGO KRASNOGO ZNAMENI INSTITUT TONKOJ HIMIČESKOJ TEHNOLOGII IM. M.V. LOMONOSOVA**

M.V. Lomonosov Institute of Fine Chemical Technology

prosp. Vernadskogo 86, 117571 Moskva, Rossiskaja SFSR

Telephone: 437-35-27

Rektor: V.S. Timofeev (1989-)

Secretary-General: A.S. Perfilyeva

F. of Chemistry and Technology of Rare Elements and Materials for Electronics
Dean: D.V. Drobot; *staff* 350
F. of Chemistry and Technology of Polymers
Dean: E.E. Potapov; *staff* 290
F. of Biotechnology and Organic Synthesis
Dean: A.F. Mironov; *staff* 400
F. for Evening Studies
Dean: S.P. Naumenkov
Ce. for Biotechnology
Head: I.A. Vasilenko; *staff* 12
Ce. for Metallurgy of Sintered Materials
Head: S.S. Kiparisov; *staff* 4
Ce. for Rubber Chemistry and Physics
Head: E.E. Potapov; *staff* 8

Founded 1930.

Arrangements for co-operation with: Nottinghan University; University of Strasbourg; Gumboldt University, Berlin; Institute of Chemical Technology, Burgos.

Academic Year: September to July.

Admission Requirements: Competitive entrance examination following general or special secondary school certificate.

Language of Instruction: Russian.

Degrees and Diplomas: Diploma of Specialist in relevant fields, 5 yrs.

Library: Library, 230,000 vols.

Academic Staff, 1990:

Rank	Full-time
Professors	60
Lecturers	140
Assistants/Instructors	190
Researchers	650
Total	1040

Student Enrolment, 1990:

	Men	Women	Total
Of the country	800	1950	2750
Of other countries	200	50	250
Total	1000	2000	3000

7240 **MOSKOVSKIJ ORDENA LENINA I ORDENA TRUDOVOGO KRASNOGO ZNAMENI HIMIKO-TEHNOLOGIČESKIJ INSTITUT IM. D.I. MENDELEEVA**

Institute of Chemical Technology

Mijusskaja pl. 9, 125820 GSP Moskva A-47, Rossiskaja SFSR

Telephone: 258-85-20

F. of Organic Chemical Technology
F. of Inorganic Chemical Technology
F. of Fuel Technology
F. of Silicate Technology
F. of Chemical Engineering Technology
F. of Physical Chemistry (Radioactive Substances and Isotopes)
F. for Evening Studies
Branch I. (Novomoskovsk)

Founded 1920.

Admission Requirements: Competitive entrance examination following general or special secondary school certificate.

Degrees and Diplomas: Professional title of Engineer in Chemical Technology. Candidate of–Chemical Sciences; Technical Sciences, bythesis. Doctor of–Chemical Sciences; Technical Sciences, by thesis after Candidate.

7241 **VORONEŽSKIJ TEHNOLOGIČESKIJ INSTITUT**

Institute of Technology

Prosp. Revoljucii 19, 394017 Voronež, Rossiskaja SFSR

Telephone: 1-09-16

F. of Food Technology
F. of Meat and Dairy Produce Technology
F. of Mechanical Engineering
F. of Chemical Engineering
D. for Evening Studies
D. for Correspondence Courses

Academic Year: September to July.

Admission Requirements: Competitive entrance examination following general or special secondary school certificate.

Degrees and Diplomas: Diploma of Specialist in relevant fields, 5 yrs.

Institutes of Forestry, Wood, Cellulose and Paper Technology

7242 **ARHANGEL'SKIJ ORDENA TRUDOVOGO KRASNOGO ZNAMENI LESOTEHNIČESKIJ INSTITUT IM. V.V. KUJBYŠEVA**

Institute of Forestry and Wood Technology

Nab. im. V.I. Lenina 17, 163007 Arhangel'sk, Rossiskaja SFSR

Telephone: 49-159

F. of Forestry
F. of Forestry Management
F. of Forestry Engineering
F. of Wood Technology
F. of Industrial Thermo-Dynamics
F. of Chemical Engineering
F. of Industrial and Civil Engineering
F. of General Technical Studies (Kotlas)
F. for Evening Studies
F. for Correspondence Courses

Academic Year: September to July.

Admission Requirements: Competitive entrance examination following general or special secondary school certificate.

Degrees and Diplomas: Diploma of Specialist in relevant fields, 5 yrs.

7243 **BRJANSKIJ ORDENA TRUDOVOGO KRASNOGO ZNAMENI TEHNOLOGIČESKIJ INSTITUT**

Institute of Technology

Ul. Stanke Dimitrova 3, 241037 Brjansk obl., Rossiskaja SFSR

Telephone: 119-12

F. of Forestry
F. of Forestry Engineering
F. of Wood Technology
F. of Construction Engineering
F. of General Technical Studies
D. for Evening Studies

D. for Correspondence Courses
Academic Year: September to July.
Admission Requirements: Competitive entrance examination following general or special secondary school certificate.
Degrees and Diplomas: Diploma of Specialist in relevant fields, 5 yrs.

7244 **LENINGRADSKAJA ORDENA LENINA LESOTEHNIČESKAJA AKADEMIJA IM. S.M. KIROVA**
Academy of Forestry and Wood Technology
Institutskij per. 5, 194018 Leningrad K-18, Rossiskaja SFSR
Cables: Leningrad Lesnoakademija
Telephone: 224-04-41

F. of Forestry
F. of Forestry Management
F. of Forestry Mechanics
F. of Wood Technology
F. of Chemical Engineering
F. of Engineering Economics
F. for Evening Studies
F. for Correspondence Courses
Timber Processing Research I.
Forestry Exploitation Research I.
Branch I. (Syktyvkar)
Founded 1803 as institute, became academy 1929. Residential facilities for academic staff and students.
Admission Requirements: Competitive entrance examination following general or special secondary school certificate.
Fees: None.
Degrees and Diplomas: Diploma of Specialist in relevant fields, 5 yrs. Kandidat nauk, Candidate of the Sciences, Doctor of the Sciences.
Libraries: Central Library, *c.* 1,200,000 vols; specialized libraries.
Special Facilities (Museums, etc.): Museums: Entomology; Animal Biology; Forestry.
Publication: Scientific Transactions.
Academic Staff: c. 1000.
Student Enrolment: c. 5600 (Also *c.* 6800 external students and students by correspondence).

7245 **LENINGRADSKIJ ORDENA TRUDOVOGO KRASNOGO ZNAMENI TEHNOLOGIČESKIJ INSTITUT CELLJULOZNO-BUMAŽNOJ PROMYŠLENNOSTI**
Institute of Cellulose and Paper Technology
Ul. Ivana Černyh 4, 198092 Leningrad, Rossiskaja SFSR
Telephone: 186-56-39

F. of Paper Technology (including Recycling)
F. of Mechanical Engineering
F. of Engineering Economics
F. of Thermo-Energetics
D. for Evening Studies
D. for Correspondence Courses
Academic Year: September to July.
Admission Requirements: Competitive entrance examination following general or special secondary school certificate.
Degrees and Diplomas: Diploma of Specialist in relevant fields, 5 yrs.

7246 **L'VOVSKIJ LESOTEHNIČESKIJ INSTITUT**
Institute of Forestry and Wood Technology
Ul. Puškina 103, 290032 L'vov, Ukrainskaja SSR
Telephone: 35-24-11

F. of Forestry
F. of Forestry Management
F. of Engineering Economics
F. of Forestry Engineering
F. of Wood Technology
F. for Correspondence Courses
D. for Evening Studies
Academic Year: September to July.
Admission Requirements: Competitive entrance examination following general or special secondary school certificate.
Degrees and Diplomas: Diploma of Specialist in relevant fields, 5 yrs.

7247 **MOSKOVSKIJ LESOTEHNIČESKIJ INSTITUT**
Institute of Forestry and Wood Technology
Pervaja Institutskaja ul. 1, 141001 Mytišči 1 Moskovskaja obl., Rossiskaja SFSR
Telephone: 582-45-78

F. of Electronics and Computer Technology
F. of Automation (Cellulose and Paper Production)
F. of Automation (Wood Technology)
F. of Automation (Timber Industry)
F. of Automation (Plastics)
F. of Forestry Management (including Urban Afforestation)
F. for Correspondence Courses
F. for Evening Studies
Academic Year: September to July.
Admission Requirements: Competitive entrance examination following general or special secondary school certificate.
Degrees and Diplomas: Diploma of Specialist in relevant fields, 5 yrs.

7248 **SIBIRSKIJ ORDENA TRUDOVOGO KRASNOGO ZNAMENI TEHNOLOGIČESKIJ INSTITUT**
Institute of Technology
Prosp. Mira 82, 660649 Krasnojarsk Kraevoj 49, Rossiskaja SFSR
Telephone: 27-99-96

F. of Forestry Engineering
F. of Forestry
F. of Mechanical Engineering
F. of Wood Technology
F. of Chemical Technology
F. of Engineering Economics
F. for Evening Studies
F. for Correspondence Courses
Academic Year: September to July.
Admission Requirements: Competitive entrance examination following general or special secondary school certificate.
Degrees and Diplomas: Diploma of Specialist in relevant fields, 5 yrs.

7249 **URAL'SKIJ ORDENA TRUDOVOGO KRASNOGO ZNAMENI LESOTEHNIČESKIJ INSTITUT IM. LENINSKOGO KOMSOMOLA**
Institute of Forestry and Wood Technology
Sibirskij trakt 37, 620032 Sverdlovsk B-32, Rossiskaja SFSR
Telephone: 24-23-77

F. of Forestry
F. of Forestry Management
F. of Forestry Engineering
F. of Wood Technology
F. of Chemical Technology
F. of Engineering Economics
F. for Correspondence Courses
Academic Year: September to July.
Admission Requirements: Competitive entrance examination following general or special secondary school certificate.
Degrees and Diplomas: Diploma of Specialist in relevant fields, 5 yrs.

7250 **VORONEŽSKIJ ORDENA DRUZBY NARODOV LESOTEHNIČESKIJ INSTITUT**
Institute of Forestry and Wood Technology
Ul. Timirjazeva 8, 394613 Voronež, Rossiskaja SFSR
Telephone: 56-41-08

F. of Forestry
F. of Forestry Management
F. of Forestry Engineering
F. of Wood Technology
F. for Correspondence Courses
Academic Year: September to July.
Admission Requirements: Competitive entrance examination following general or special secondary school certificate.
Degrees and Diplomas: Diploma of Specialist in relevant fields, 5 yrs.

Institutes of Food Industries

Food Industries

7251 **BUHARSKIJ TEHNOLOGIČESKIJ INSTITUT PIŠČEVOJ I LEGKOJ PROMYŠLENNOSTI**
Institute of Light Engineering and Food Technology
Prosp. Leninskogo Komsomola 15, 705017 Buhara, Uzbekskaja SSR
Telephone: 3-04-02

Food Technology
Light Engineering

Academic Year: September to July.
Admission Requirements: Competitive entrance examination following general or special secondary school certificate.
Degrees and Diplomas: Diploma of Specialist in relevant fields, 5 yrs.

7252 **DŽAMBULSKIJ TEHNOLOGIČESKIJ INSTITUT LEGKOJ I PIŠČEVOJ PROMYŠLENNOSTI**
Institute of Light Engineering and Food Technology
Kommunističeskaja Ul. 58, 484030 Džambul, Kazahskaja SSR
Telephone: 4-38-81

F. of Food Technology
F. of Light Industry Technology
F. of Mechanical Engineering
F. of Engineering Economics
D. for Evening Studies
D. for Correspondence Courses
Branch I. (Alma-Ata)
Branch I. (Semipalatinsk)

Academic Year: September to July.
Admission Requirements: Competitive entrance examination following general or special secondary school certificate.
Degrees and Diplomas: Diploma of Specialist in relevant fields, 5 yrs.

7253 **KEMEROVSKIJ TEHNOLOGIČESKIJ INSTITUT PIŠČEVOJ PROMYŠLENNOSTI**
Institute of Food Technology
Bul'var Stroitelej 47, 650060 Kemerovo, Rossiskaja SFSR
Telephone: 51-13-43

F. of Technology (Food Products)
F. of Mechanical Engineering
D. for Correspondence Courses

Founded 1972. Governing bodies: the Rector and Pro-Rectors; the Academic Council, comprising 27 members.
Academic Year: September to July (September-January; February-July).
Admission Requirements: Competitive entrance examination following general or special secondary school certificate.
Fees: None.
Language of Instruction: Russian.
Degrees and Diplomas: Diploma of Specialist in relevant fields, 5 yrs.
Library: *c.* 171,000 vols.
Academic Staff: *c.* 250.
Student Enrolment: *c.* 3000 (Also *c.* 900 external students).

7254 **KIEVSKIJ ORDENA TRUDOVOGO KRASNOGO ZNAMENI TEHNOLOGIČESKIJ INSTITUT PIŠČEVOJ PROMYŠLENNOSTI**
Institute of Food Technology
Vladimirskaja ul. 68, 252017 Kiev, Ukrainskaja SSR
Telephone: 220-64-00

F. of Sugar Technology
F. of Fermentation Technology (Microbiology and Vitamins)
F. of Farinaceous Food Technology
F. of Mechanical Engineering
F. of Thermo-Dynamics and Automation of Food Processing
F. of Meat and Dairy Produce Technology
F. of Engineering Economics
F. of General Technical Studies
F. for Evening Studies

Academic Year: September to July.
Admission Requirements: Competitive entrance examination following general or special secondary school certificate.
Degrees and Diplomas: Diploma of Specialist in relevant fields, 5 yrs.

7255 **KIROVABADSKIJ TEHNOLOGIČESKIJ INSTITUT**
Institute of Technology
Pos. Kiraz, Kirovabad, Azerbajdžandkaja SSR

D. of Food Technology
D. of Light Industry Engineering
D. for Evening Studies
D. for Correspondence Courses

Academic Year: September to July.
Admission Requirements: Competitive entrance examination following general or special secondary school certificate.
Degrees and Diplomas: Diploma of Specialist in relevant fields, 5 yrs.

7256 **LENINGRADSKIJ ORDENA TRUDOVOGO KRASNOGO ZNAMENI TEHNOLOGIČESKIJ INSTITUT HOLODIL'NOJ PROMYŠLENNOSTI**
Institute of Refrigeration Technology
Ul. Lomonosova 9, 191002 Leningrad, Rossiskaja SFSR
Telephone: 219-89-36

F. of Refrigeration Engineering
F. of Mechanical Engineering
F. of Technology (Food Conservation)
F. for Evening Studies
F. for Correspondence Courses

Academic Year: September to July.
Admission Requirements: Competitive entrance examination following general or special secondary school certificate.
Degrees and Diplomas: Diploma of Specialist in relevant fields, 5 yrs.

7257 **MOGILEVSKIJ TEHNOLOGIČESKIJ INSTITUT**
Institute of Technology
Prosp. Šmidta 3, 212027 Mogilev, Belorusskaja SSR
Telephone: 4-33-30

Food Technology

Academic Year: September to July.
Admission Requirements: Competitive entrance examination following general or special secondary school certificate.
Degrees and Diplomas: Diploma of Specialist in relevant fields, 5 yrs.

7258 **MOSKOVSKIJ ORDENA TRUDOVOGO KRASNOGO ZNAMENI TEHNOLOGIČESKIJ INSTITUT MJASNOJ I MOLOČNOJ PROMYSLENNOSTI**
Institute of the Meat and Dairy Industries
Ul. Talalihina 33, 109818 Moskva Ž-29, Rossiskaja SFSR
Telephone: 271-63-36

F. of Technology (Meat and Dairy Produce)
F. of Mechanical Engineering
F. of Engineering Economics
F. of Veterinary Science
F. for Evening Studies
D. for Correspondence Courses

Academic Year: September to July.
Admission Requirements: Competitive entrance examination following general or special secondary school certificate.
Degrees and Diplomas: Diploma of Specialist in relevant fields, 5 yrs.

7259 **MOSKOVSKIJ TRUDOVOGO KRASNOGO ZNAMENI TEHNOLOGIČESKIJ INSTITUT PIŠČEVOJ PROMYSLENNOSTI**
Institute of Food Technology
Volokolamskoe Šosse 11, 125080 Moskva A-80, Rossiskaja SFSR
Telephone: 158-71-84

F. of Grain Processing and Storage
F. of Food Production
F. of Mechanical Engineering
F. of Engineering Economics
F. for Evening Studies

Academic Year: September to July.
Admission Requirements: Competitive entrance examination following general or special secondary school certificate.

7260 **ODESSKIJ TEHNOLOGIČESKIJ INSTITUT PIŠČEVOJ PROMYŠLENNOSTI IM. M.V. LOMONOSOVA**
Institute of Food Technology
Ul. Sverdlova 112, 270039 Odessa, Ukrainskaja SSR
Telephone: 25-32-84

F. of Grain Processing and Storage
F. of Mechanical Engineering
F. of Meat and Dairy Produce Technology
F. of Food Conservation (including Wine)
F. of Automation Technology
F. of Engineering Economics
F. for Evening Studies
Branch I. (Herson)

Academic Year: September to July.

Admission Requirements: Competitive entrance examination following general or special secondary school certificate.

Degrees and Diplomas: Diploma of Specialist in relevant fields, 5 yrs.

7261 **ODESSKIJ TEHNOLOGIČESKIJ INSTITUT HOLODIL'NOJ PROMYŠLENNOSTI**
Institute of Refrigeration Technology
Ul. Petra Velikogo 1/3, 270000 Odessa, Ukrainskaja SSR
Telephone: 23-22-20

F. of Low Temperature Technology
F. of Thermo-Physics
F. of Refrigeration Engineering
F. of General Technical Studies (3)
F. for Evening Studies

Academic Year: September to July.

Admission Requirements: Competitive entrance examination following general or special secondary school certificate.

Degrees and Diplomas: Diploma of Specialist in relevant fields, 5 yrs.

7262 **SEMIPALATINSKIJ TEHNOLOGIČESKIJ INSTITUT MJASNOJ I MOLOČNOJ PROMYŠLENNOSTI**
Institute of Meat and Dairy Industries
Ul. Glinki 49, 490150 Semipalatinsk, Kazahskaja SSR
Telephone: 5-07-80

F. of Mechanical Engineering
F. of Meat Technology
F. for Evening Studies
F. for Correspondence Courses

Academic Year: September to July.

Admission Requirements: Competitive entrance examination following general or special secondary school certificate.

Degrees and Diplomas: Diploma of Specialist in relevant fields, 5 yrs.

7263 **VOSTOČNO-SIBIRSKIJ TEHNOLOGIČESKIJ INSTITUT**
Institute of Technology
Ul. Smolina 26, 670000 Ulan-Ude, Burjatskaja ASSR
Telephone: 53-49

F. of Technology (Leather, Fur, and Cereals)
F. of Meat and Dairy Produce Technology
F. of Mechanical Engineering
F. of Construction Engineering
F. of Electrical Engineering
F. for Correspondence Courses
D. for Evening Studies

Academic Year: September to July.

Admission Requirements: Competitive entrance examination following general or special secondary school certificate.

Degrees and Diplomas: Diploma of Specialist in relevant fields, 5 yrs.

7264 **VSESOJUZNYJ ZAOČNYJ INSTITUT PIŠČEVOJ PROMYŠLENNOSTI**
Correspondence Institute of Food Technology
Ul. Čkalova 73, 109803 Moskva Z-4, Rossiskaja SFSR
Telephone: 297-51-97

F. of Food Production
F. of Food Technology (Farinaceous)
F. of Grain Technology
F. of Mechanical Engineering
F. of Fishery Technology
F. of Engineering Economics
F. of Economics of Agricultural Products F. of General Technical Studies
D. for Evening Studies
Branch I (Krasnojarsk)

Academic Year: September to July.

Admission Requirements: Competitive entrance examination following general or special secondary school certificate.

Degrees and Diplomas: Diploma of Specialist in relevant fields, 5 yrs.

Fishery Industries

7265 **ASTRAHANSKIJ TEHNIČESKIJ INSTITUT RYBNOJ PROMYŠLENNOSTI I HOZJAJSTVA**
Institute of the Fish Industry
Ul. Tatiščeva 16, 414025 Astrahan', Rossiskaja SFSR
Telephone: 2-09-02

F. of Technology (Fish Products)
F. of Fishery
F. of Mechanical Engineering (Refrigeration)
F. of Fishery Industries
F. of Marine Engineering
F. for Evening Studies
F. for Correspondence Courses

Academic Year: September to July.

Admission Requirements: Competitive entrance examination following general or special secondary school certificate.

Degrees and Diplomas: Diploma of Specialist in relevant fields, 5 yrs.

7266 **DAL'NEVOSTOČNYJ TEHNIČESKIJ INSTITUT RYBNOJ PROMYŠLENNOSTI I HOZJAJSTVA**
Institute of the Fish Industry
Lugovaja ul. 526, 690636 Vladivostok, Rossiskaja SFSR
Telephone: 9-53-06

F. of Food Technology
F. of Technology (Fish Products)
F. of Mechanical Engineering
F. of Navigation
F. of Fishery Economics
F. for Evening Studies
F. for Correspondence Courses
Branch I. (Petropavlosk-na-Kamčatke)

Academic Year: September to July.

Admission Requirements: Competitive entrance examination following general or special secondary school certificate.

Degrees and Diplomas: Diploma of Specialist in relevant fields, 5 yrs.

7267 **KALININGRADSKIJ TEHNIČESKIJ INSTITUT RYBNOJ PROMYŠLENNOSTI I HOZJAJSTVA**
Institute of the Fish Industry
Sovetskij prosp. 1, 236000 Kaliningrad Oblastnoj, Rossiskaja SFSR
Telephone: 2-62-91

F. of Industrial Fishery
F. of Technology (Fish Products)
F. of Ichthyology
F. of Shipbuilding
F. of Mechanical Engineering
F. of Engineering Economics
F. for Evening Studies
D. for Correspondence Courses
D. for Correspondence Courses (Riga)

Academic Year: September to July.

Admission Requirements: Competitive entrance examination following general or special secondary school certificate.

Degrees and Diplomas: Diploma of Specialist in relevant fields, 5 yrs.

Institutes of Textile and Light Engineering

7268 **BLAGOVEŠČENSKIJ TEHNOLOGIČESKIJ INSTITUT**
Institute of Technology
Ignat'evskoe Šosse 21, 675007 Blagoveščensk Amurskoj obl., Rossiskaja SFSR
Telephone: 5-41-16

Light and Textile Engineering

Academic Year: September to July.

Admission Requirements: Competitive entrance examination following general or special secondary school certificate.

Degrees and Diplomas: Diploma of Specialist in relevant fields, 5 yrs.

7269 **DAL'NEVOSTOČNYJ TEHNOLOGIČESKIJ INSTITUT BYTOVOGO OBSLUŽIVANIJA**
Institute of Light Industrial Technology
Ul. Gogolja 41, 690600 Vladivostok, Rossiskaja SFSR
Telephone: 5-72-21

F. of Technology
F. of Engineering Economics
F. for Correspondence Courses

Academic Year: September to July.

Admission Requirements: Competitive entrance examination following general or special secondary school certificate.

Degrees and Diplomas: Diploma of Specialist in relevant fields, 5 yrs.

7270 **HMEL'NICKIJ TEHNOLOGIČESKIJ INSTITUT BYTOVOGO OBSLUŽIVANIJA**
Institute of Light Industrial Technology
Institutskaja ul. 11, 280016 Hmel'nickij, Ukrainskaja SSR
Telephone: 2-37-55

F. of Mechanical Engineering
F. of Technology
D. for Evening Studies

Academic Year: September to July.

Admission Requirements: Competitive entrance examination following general or special secondary school certificate.

Degrees and Diplomas: Diploma of Specialist in relevant fields, 5 yrs.

7271 **IVANOVSKIJ ORDENA TRUDOVOGO KRASNOGO ZNAMENI TEKSTIL'NYJ INSTITUT IM. M.V. FRUNZE**
Institute of Textile Technology
Prosp. F. Engel'sa 21, 153475 Ivanovo, Rossiskaja SFSR
Telephone: 4-90-46 ext. 5-73

F. of Textile Technology
F. of Mechanical Engineering
F. for Evening Studies
F. for Correspondence Courses

Academic Year: September to July.

Admission Requirements: Competitive entrance examination following general or special secondary school certificate.

Degrees and Diplomas: Diploma of Specialist in relevant fields, 5 yrs.

7272 **KIEVSKIJ TEHNOLOGIČESKIJ INSTITUT LEGKOJ PROMYŠLENNOSTI**
Institute of Light Industrial Technology
Ul. Nemiroviča-Dančenko 2, 252601 Kiev 11, Ukrainskaja SSR
Telephone: 97-75-12

F. of Clothing Technology
F. of Knitting Technology
F. of Leather Technology
F. of Chemical Technology
F. of Mechanical Engineering
F. of Engineering Economics
F. of General Technical Studies
F. for Evening Studies

Academic Year: September to July.

Admission Requirements: Competitive entrance examination following general or special secondary school certificate.

Degrees and Diplomas: Diploma of Specialist in relevant fields, 5 yrs.

7273 **KOSTROMSKOJ ORDENA TRUDOVOGO KRASNOGO ZNAMENI TEHNOLOGIČESKIJ INSTITUT**
Institute of Technology
Ul. Dzeržinskogo 17, 156021 Kostroma, Rossiskaja SFSR
Telephone: 7-79-60

F. of Mechanical Technology
F. of Technology (Natural and Chemical Fibres)
F. of Forestry and Wood Technology
F. of Mechanical Engineering
F. of Engineering Economics
F. for Correspondence Courses
D. for Evening Studies

Academic Year: September to July.

Admission Requirements: Competitive entrance examination following general or special secondary school certificate.

Degrees and Diplomas: Diploma of Specialist in relevant fields, 5 yrs.

7274 **LENINGRADSKIJ ORDENA TRUDOVOGO KRASNOGO ZNAMENI INSTITUT TEKSTIL'NOJ I LEGKOJ PROMYŠLENNOSTI IM. S.M. KIROVA**
Institute of Textile and Light Industrial Technology
Ul. Gercena 18, 181065 Leningrad D-65, Rossiskaja SFSR
Telephone: 315-07-47

F. of Textile Technology
F. of Leather Technology
F. of Clothing Technology
F. of Mechanical Engineering
F. of Chemical Technology
F. of Engineering Economics
F. for Evening Studies
F. for Correspondence Courses

Academic Year: September to July.

Admission Requirements: Competitive entrance examination following general or special secondary school certificate.

Degrees and Diplomas: Diploma of Specialist in relevant fields, 5 yrs.

7275 **MOSKOVSKIJ ORDENA TRUDOVOGO KRASNOGO ZNAMENI TEKSTIL'NYJ INSTITUT IM. A.N. KOSYGINA**
Institute of Textile Technology
Kalužskaja ul. 1, 117918 Moskva, Rossiskaja SFSR
Telephone: 234-28-90

F. of Mechanical Engineering (Textiles)
F. of Machine Engineering
F. of Automation and Mechanization
F. of Chemical Technology
F. of Applied Arts
F. of Engineering Economics
F. for Evening Studies

Academic Year: September to July.

Admission Requirements: Competitive entrance examination following general or special secondary school certificate.

Degrees and Diplomas: Diploma of Specialist in relevant fields, 5 yrs.

7276 **MOSKOVSKIJ TEHNOLOGIČESKIJ INSTITUT**
Institute of Technology
Glavnaja ul. 99, Pos. Cerkizovo, Puškinskij rajon, 141220 Moskovskaja obl., Rossiskaja SFSR
Telephone: 184-63-03 ext. 4-40

F. of Chemical Technology (Textiles)
F. of Applied Art
F. of Wood Technology
F. of Mechanical Engineering
F. of Engineering Economics
D. for Correspondence Courses
D. for Evening Studies
Branch I. (Leningrad)

Academic Year: September to July.

Admission Requirements: Competitive entrance examination following general or special secondary school certificate.

Degrees and Diplomas: Diploma of Specialist in relevant fields, 5 yrs.

7277 **MOSKOVSKIJ ORDENA TRUDOVOGO KRASNOGO ZNAMENI TEHNOLOGIČESKIJ INSTITUT LEGKOJ PROMYŠLENNOSTI**
Institute of Light Industrial Technology
Ul. Osipenko 33, 113035 Moskva M35, Rossiskaja SFSR
Telephone: 231-31-48

F. of Chemical Technology (Leather)
F. of Textile and Leather Technology
F. of Mechanical Engineering
F. for Evening Studies
Branch I. (Novosibirsk)

Academic Year: September to July.

Admission Requirements: Competitive entrance examination following general or special secondary school certificate.

Degrees and Diplomas: Diploma of Specialist in relevant fields, 5 yrs.

7278 **OMSKIJ TEHNOLOGIČESKIJ INSTITUT BYTOVOGO OBSLUZIVANIJA**
Institute of Light Industrial Technology
Krasnogvardeiskaja ul. 9, 640099 Omsk, Rossiskaja SFSR
Telephone: 24-16-93

F. of Engineering Economics
F. of Textile Technology

Academic Year: September to July.

Admission Requirements: Competitive entrance examination following general or special secondary school certificate.

Degrees and Diplomas: Diploma of Specialist in relevant fields, 5 yrs.

7279 **ŠAHTÍNSKIJ TEHNOLOGIČESKIJ INSTITUT BYTOVO OBSLUŽIVANIJA**
Technological Institute of Public Services
Ul. Ševčenko 147, 346500 Šahty, Rostov Region PSFSR
Telex: TELETAJP 8836 'KVANT'
Telephone: 2-71-46
Rektor: Viktor Alekseevič Romanov (1969-)

F. of Mechanical Engineering
Dean: Vladimir Mih. Fetisov; *staff* 69 (6)
F. of Engineering Economics
Dean: Anatolij Stepanovič Burjakov; *staff* 72 (8)
D. of Correspondence Courses
Head: V.T. Prohorov; *staff* 91 (2)

Founded 1969. Under the Ministevstva Bytovogo Obsluživania. Residential facilities for 1300 students.

Academic Year: September to July.

Admission Requirements: Competitive entrance examination following general or special secondary school certificate.

Fees: None.

Language of Instruction: Russian.

Degrees and Diplomas: Diploma of Specialist in relevant fields, 5 yrs.

Library: 400,000 vols.

F1989-90

Rank	Full-time	Part-time
Professors	6	–
Assistant Professors	117	16
Instructors	67	–
Assistants	98	–
Total	288	16

Student Enrolment, 1989-90: 2063 (Also 2708 correspondence students).

7280 **TAŠKENTSKIJ ORDENA DRUŽBY NARODOV INSTITUT TEKSTIL'NOJ I LEGKOJ PROMYŠLENNOSTI**
Institute of Textile Technology
Ul. Gorbunova 5, 700100 Taškent, Uzbekskaja SSR
Telephone: 53-06-06

F. of Textile Machines
F. of Clothing Technology
F. of Chemical Technology
F. of Engineering Economics
D. for Evening Studies
D. for Correspondence Courses

Academic Year: September to July.

Admission Requirements: Competitive entrance examination following general or special secondary school certificate.

Degrees and Diplomas: Diploma of Specialist in relevant fields, 5 yrs.

7281 **VITEBSKIJ TEHNOLOGIČESKIJ INSTITUT LEGKOJ PROMYŠLENNOSTI**
Institute of Light Industrial Technology
Moskovskij prosp. 72, 210028 Vitebsk, Belorusskaja SSR
Telephone: 5-72-34

F. of Mechanical Engineering
F. of Textile and Leather Technology
F. of Engineering Economics
F. for Evening Studies
F. for Correspondence Courses

Academic Year: September to July.

Admission Requirements: Competitive entrance examination following general or special secondary school certificate.

Degrees and Diplomas: Diploma of Specialist in relevant fields, 5 yrs.

7282 **VSESOJUZNYJ ZAOČNYJ INSTITUT TEKSTIL'NOJ I LEGKOJ PROMYŠLENNOSTI**
Correspondence Institute of Textile and Light Industrial Technology
Ul. Norodnogo Opolčenija 38, Korp. 2, 123298 Moskva, Rossiskaja SFSR
Telephone: 943-63-62

F. of Textile Technology
F. of Light Engineering (Leather Technology)
F. of Chemical Technology
F. of Mechanical Engineering
F. of Engineering Economics
Branch I (Barnaul)
Branch I. (Omsk)

Academic Year: September to July.

Admission Requirements: Competitive entrance examination following general or special secondary school certificate.

Degrees and Diplomas: Diploma of Specialist in relevant fields, 5 yrs.

Institutes of Architecture and Civil Engineering

Architecture

7283 **MOSKOVSKIJ ORDENA TRUDOVOGO KRASNOGO ZNAMENI ARHITEKTURNYJ INSTITUT**
Institute of Architecture
Ul. Rozhdestvenka, 11, 103754-GSP Moskva K-31, Rossijskaja SFSR
Telephone: 824-79-90
Fax: (85) 8211240
Rektor: Alexander P. Kudryavtsev (1987-)

F. of General Studies
Dean: Valdimir A. Smirnov; *staff* 176 (30)
F. of Civil Architecture and Engineering (Basic Studies)
Dean: Vladimir A. Plishkin; *staff* 94 (30)
F. of Specialized Studies
Dean: Victor P. Klimanov; *staff* 109 (30)
F. for Evening Studies
Dean: Anatoly I. Matveenko; *staff* 172
Scientific Projecting Ce.
Head: Vladimir A. Sharapov; *staff* 60 (70)

Also Refresher Courses for Teachers, Town Planners, and Specialists.

Founded 1920. Acquired present title 1933. Governing bodies: the Council; the Academic Council. Residential facilities for students in hostel.

Academic Year: September to July.

Admission Requirements: Competitive entrance examination following general or special secondary school certificate.

Fees: None.

Language of Instruction: Russian.

Degrees and Diplomas: Diploma of Architect, 6 yrs. Master (for foreign students), 6 yrs. Candidate of Architecture, a further 3 yrs.Ph.D. (for foreign postgraduates), a further 3 yrs. Doctor of Architecture, a further 3 yrs.

Library: 400,000 vols.

Special Facilities (Museums, etc.): Moscow School of Architecture; Art Gallery.

Publication: Collection of Diploma Designs (annually).

Academic Staff, 1989-90: 399 (220).
Student Enrolment, 1989-90:

	Men	Women	Total
Of the country	183	177	360
Of other countries	30	5	35
Total	213	182	395

7284 **SVERDLOVSKIJ ARHITEKTURNYJ INSTITUT**
Institute of Architecture
Ul. Karla Libknehta 23, 620219 Sverdlovsk GSP-1089, Rossiskaja SFSR
Telephone: 51-80-45

F. of General Studies
F. of Industrial Architecture and Design
F. of Urban Architecture and Planning

Academic Year: September to July.
Admission Requirements: Competitive entrance examination following general or special secondary school certificate.
Degrees and Diplomas: Diploma of Specialist in relevant fields, 5 yrs.

7285 **ALMA-ATINSKIJ ARHITEKTURNO-STROITEL'NYJ INSTITUT**
Institute of Civil Engineering
Ul. Obručeva 28, 480123 Alma-Ata, Kazahskaja SSR
Telephone: 49-46-11

F. of Architecture
F. of Construction Engineering
F. of Hydraulic Engineering
F. of Construction Engineering (including Town Planning)
D. for Evening Studies
D. for Correspondence Courses

Academic Year: September to July.
Admission Requirements: Competitive entrance examination following general or special secondary school certificate.
Degrees and Diplomas: Diploma of Specialist in relevant fields, 5 yrs.

Civil Engineering

7286 **BAKINSKIJ INŽENERNO-STROITEL'NYJ INSTITUT**
Institute of Civil Engineering
Ul. Krylova 13, 370073 Baku, Azerbajdžanskaja SSR
Telephone: 38-33-96

F. of Architecture
F. of Construction Engineering
F. of Transport Engineering
F. of Hydraulic Engineering
F. of Sanitary Engineering
D. for Evening Studies
D. for Correspondence Courses

Academic Year: September to July.
Admission Requirements: Competitive entrance examination following general or special secondary school certificate.
Degrees and Diplomas: Diploma of Specialist in relevant fields, 5 yrs.

7287 **BELGORODSKIJ TEHNOLOGIČESKIJ INSTITUT STROITEL'NYJ MATERIALOV IM. I.A. GRIŠMANOVA**
Institute of Construction Materials
Ul. Kostjukova 46, 308012 Belgorod, Rossiskaja SFSR
Telephone: 5-41-03

F. of Chemical Engineering
F. of Mechanical Engineering
F. of Building Technology
F. for Evening Studies

Academic Year: September to July.
Admission Requirements: Competitive entrance examination following general or special secondary school certificate.

7288 **BRESTSKIJ INŽENERNO-STROITEL'NYJ INSTITUT**
Institute of Civil Engineering
Moskovskaja ul. 267, 220017 Brest, Belorusskaja SSR
Telephone: 2-40-84

F. of Construction Engineering
F. of Architecture
F. of Agricultural Construction Engineering
F. of Hydraulic Engineering
D. for Evening Studies

Academic Year: September to July.
Admission Requirements: Competitive entrance examination following general or special secondary school certificate.
Degrees and Diplomas: Diploma of Specialist in relevant fields, 5 yrs.

7289 **CELINOGRADSKIJ INŽENERNO-STROITEL'NYJ INSTITUT**
Institute of Civil Engineering
Ul. Ciolkovskogo 2, 473021 Celinograd, Kazahskaja SSR
Telephone: 4-29-53

F. of Civil Engineering
F. of Mechanical Engineering (Automobile Transport)
D. for Evening Studies
D. for Correspondence Courses

Academic Year: September to July.
Admission Requirements: Competitive entrance examination following general or special secondary school certificate.
Degrees and Diplomas: Diploma of Specialist in relevant fields, 5 yrs.

7290 **DNEPROPETROVSKIJ INŽENERNO-STROITEL'NYJ INSTITUT**
Institute of Civil Engineering
Ul. Černyševskogo 24-a, 320600 Dnepropetrovsk, Ukrainskaja SSR
Telephone: 46-73-57

F. of Construction Engineering
F. of Construction Technology (Building Materials)
F. of Mechanical Engineering
F. of Agricultural Building and Architecture
F. of General Technical Studies
F. for Evening Studies

Academic Year: September to July.
Admission Requirements: Competitive entrance examination following general or special secondary school certificate.
Degrees and Diplomas: Diploma of Specialist in relevant fields, 5 yrs.

7291 **GOR'KOVSKIJ ORDENA TRUDOVOGO KRASNOGO ZNAMENI INŽENERNO-STROITEL'NYJ INSTITUT IM. V.P. ČKALOVA**
Institute of Civil Engineering
Krasnoflotskaja ul. 65, 603000 Gor'kij, Rossiskaja SFSR
Telephone: 34-02-01

F. of Architecture
F. of Construction Engineering
F. of Sanitary Engineering
F. of Hydraulic Engineering
F. for Correspondence Courses
D. for Evening Studies

Academic Year: September to July.
Admission Requirements: Competitive entrance examination following general or special secondary school certificate.
Degrees and Diplomas: Diploma of Specialist in relevant fields, 5 yrs.

7292 **HAR'KOVSKIJ INSTITUT INŽENEROV KOMMUNAL'NOGO STROITEL'STVA**
Institute of Town Planning
Ul. Revoljucii 12, 310002 Har'kov, Ukrainskaja SSR
Telephone: 47-00-88

F. of Construction Engineering (including Town Planning)
F. of Urban Transport (Electric)
F. of Engineering Economics
D. for Evening Studies

Academic Year: September to July.
Admission Requirements: Competitive entrance examination following general or special secondary school certificate.
Degrees and Diplomas: Diploma of Specialist in relevant fields, 5 yrs.

7293 **HAR'KOVSKIJ INŽENERNO-STROITEL'NYJ INSTITUT**
Institute of Civil Engineering
Sumskaja ul. 40, 310002 Har'kov, Ukrainskaja SSR
Telephone: 40-29-19

F. of Construction Engineering
F. of Electrical Urban Transport
F. of Engineering Economics
F. of Sanitary Engineering
F. for Evening Studies
Academic Year: September to July.
Admission Requirements: Competitive entrance examination following general or special secondary school certificate.
Degrees and Diplomas: Diploma of Specialist in relevant fields, 5 yrs.

7294 **IVANOVSKIJ INŽENERNO-STROITEL'NYJ INSTITUT**
Institute of Civil Engineering
Krasnych Zor ul., 153547 Ivanovo, Rossiskaja SFSR
Telephone: 2-31-62

F. of Construction Engineering
F. of Construction Technology (Building Materials)
F. for Evening Studies
F. for Correspondence Courses
Academic Year: September to July.
Admission Requirements: Competitive entrance examination following general or special secondary school certificate.
Degrees and Diplomas: Diploma of Specialist in relevant fields, 5 yrs.

7295 **KAZANSKIJ INŽENERNO-STROITEL'NYJ INSTITUT**
Institute of Civil Engineering
Zelenaja ul. 1, 420043 Kazan' 43, Rossiskaja SFSR
Telephone: 37-72-40

F. of Architecture and Construction Engineering
F. of Industrial and Civil Engineering
F. of Building Technology
F. of Building Engineering
F. of Highway Engineering
F. of Sanitary Engineering
F. of General Technical Studies
F. of General Technical Studies (Bugul'me)
F. of General Technical Studies (Naberežnie Celni)
F. for Evening Studies
F. for Correspondence Courses
Academic Year: September to July.
Admission Requirements: Competitive entrance examination following general or special secondary school certificate.
Degrees and Diplomas: Diploma of Specialist in relevant fields, 5 yrs.

7296 **KIEVSKIJ ORDENA TRUDOVOGO KRASNOGO ZNAMENI INŽENERNO-STROITEL'NYJ INSTITUT**
Institute of Civil Engineering
Vozduhoflotskij prosp. 31, 252180 Kiev, Ukrainskaja SSR
Telephone: 267-71-20

F. of Architecture
F. of Construction Engineering
F. of Automation of Building Production
F. of Building Technology
F. of Urban Construction and Planning
F. of Sanitary Engineering
F. of General Technical Studies
F. of General Technical Studies (Cherkassah)
F. for Evening Studies
F. for Correspondence Courses
Academic Year: September to July.
Admission Requirements: Competitive entrance examination following general or special secondary school certificate.
Degrees and Diplomas: Diploma of Specialist in relevant fields, 5 yrs.

7297 **KRASNOJARSKIJ INŽENERNO-STROITEL'NYJ INSTITUT**
Institute of Civil Engineering
Prosp. Svobodnyj 82, 660062 Krasnojarsk, Rossiskaja SFSR
Telephone: 25-66-69

D. of Architecture
D. of Civil and Industrial Engineering
D. of Urban Construction and Planning
D. of Sanitary Engineering
Academic Year: September to July.
Admission Requirements: Competitive entrance examination following general or special secondary school certificate.
Degrees and Diplomas: Diploma of Specialist in relevant fields, 5 yrs.

7298 **KUJBYŠEVSKIJ ORDENA 'ZNAK POČOTÁ' INŽENERNO-STROITEL'NYJ INSTITUT IM. A.I. MIKOJANA**
Institute of Civil Engineering
Molodogvardejskaja ul. 194, 443644 Kujbyšev obl., Rossiskaja SFSR
Telephone: 33-97-77

F. of Agriculture
F. of Industrial and Civil Engineering
F. of Sanitary Engineering
F. of Hydraulic Engineering
F. for Evening Studies
F. for Correspondence Courses
Academic Year: September to July.
Admission Requirements: Competitive entrance examination following general or special secondary school certificate.
Degrees and Diplomas: Diploma of Specialist in relevant fields, 5 yrs.

7299 **MAKEEVSKIJ INŽENERNO-STROITEL'NYJ INSTITUT**
Institute of Civil Engineering
Pos. Dzeržinskogo, 339023 Makeevka Donečkoj obl., Ukrainskaja SSR
Telephone: 90-29-38

F. of Construction Engineering
F. of Sanitary Engineering
F. of General Technical Studies
F. for Evening Studies
Academic Year: September to July.
Admission Requirements: Competitive entrance examination following general or special secondary school certificate.
Degrees and Diplomas: Diploma of Specialist in relevant fields, 5 yrs.

7300 **MOSKOVSKIJ ORDENA TRUDOVOGO KRASNOGO ZNAMENI INŽENERNO-STROITEL'NYJ INSTITUT IM. V.V. KUJBYŠEVA**
Institute of Civil Engineering
Jaroslavskoe Šosse 26, 127337 Moskva Z-114, Rossiskaja SFSR
Telephone: 183-48-10

F. of Industrial and Civil Engineering
F. of Heat Engineering
F. of Hydraulic Engineering
F. of Heating Technology
F. of Construction Technology (Building Materials)
F. of Water Supply Engineering
F. of Urban Construction
F. of Mechanical Engineering
F. of Automated Control Systems
D. for Evening Studies
Academic Year: September to July.
Admission Requirements: Competitive entrance examination following general or special secondary school certificate.
Degrees and Diplomas: Diploma of Specialist in relevant fields, 5 yrs.

7301 **NOVOSIBIRSKIJ ORDENA TRUDOVOGO KRASNOGO ZNAMENI INŽENERNO-STROITEL'NYJ INSTITUT IM. V.V. KUJBYŠEVA**
Institute of Civil Engineering
Leningradskaja ul. 113, 630008 Novosibirsk 8, Rossiskaja SFSR
Telephone: 66-42-95

F. of Architecture
F. of Hydraulic Engineering
F. of Construction Engineering
F. of Building Economics
F. for Evening Studies
F. for Correspondence Courses
Academic Year: September to July.
Admission Requirements: Competitive entrance examination following general or special secondary school certificate.
Degrees and Diplomas: Diploma of Specialist in relevant fields, 5 yrs.

7302 **ODESSKIJ INŽENERNO-STROITEL'NYJ INSTITUT**
Institute of Civil Engineering
Ul. Didrihsona 4, 270029 Odessa, Ukrainskaja SSR
Telephone: 23-33-42

F. of Architecture
F. of Construction Engineering
F. of Hydraulic Engineering
F. of Construction Technology (Building Materials)
F. of Sanitary Engineering
F. of Civil Engineering (Nitiolaev)
F. of General Technical Studies
F. for Evening Studies

Academic Year: September to July.
Admission Requirements: Competitive entrance examination following general or special secondary school certificate.
Degrees and Diplomas: Diploma of Specialist in relevant fields, 5 yrs.

7303 **PENZENSKIJ INŽENERNO-STROITEL'NYJ INSTITUT**
Institute of Civil Engineering
Ul. G. Titova 28, 440028 Penza, Rossiskaja SFSR
Telephone: 62-05-03

F. of Construction Engineering
F. of Construction Technology (Building Materials)
F. of Sanitary Engineering
D. for Evening Studies
D. for Correspondence Courses

Academic Year: September to July.
Admission Requirements: Competitive entrance examination following general or special secondary school certificate.
Degrees and Diplomas: Diploma of Specialist in relevant fields, 5 yrs.

7304 **POLTAVSKIJ INŽENERNO-STROITEL'NYJ INSTITUT**
Institute of Civil Engineering
Pervomajskij prosp. 24, 314601 Poltava, Ukrainskaja SSR
Telephone: 7-33-27

F. of Architecture
F. of Industrial and Civil Engineering
F. of Sanitary Engineering
F. of General Technical Studies
F. for Evening Studies

Academic Year: September to July.
Admission Requirements: Competitive entrance examination following general or special secondary school certificate.
Degrees and Diplomas: Diploma of Specialist in relevant fields, 5 yrs.

7305 **ROSTOVSKIJ INŽENERNO-STROITEL'NYJ INSTITUT**
Institute of Civil Engineering
Socialističeskaja ul. 162, 344022 Rostov-na-Donu GSP-2, Rossiskaja SFSR
Telephone: 65-02-05

F. of Construction Engineering
F. of Architecture
F. of Sanitary Engineering
F. of Highway Engineering
F. of Construction Technology (Building Materials)
F. for Evening Studies
F. for Correspondence Courses

Academic Year: September to July.
Admission Requirements: Competitive entrance examination following general or special secondary school certificate.
Degrees and Diplomas: Diploma of Specialist in relevant fields, 5 yrs.

7306 **SAMARKANDSKIJ ARHITEKTURNO-STROITEL'NYJ INSTITUT IM. M.U. ULUGBEKA**
Institute of Architecture and Civil Engineering
Ul. Ljaljazar 70, 703047 Samarkand, Uzbekskaja SSR
Telephone: 3-20-25

F. of Architecture
F. of Construction Engineering
F. of Economics
D. for Evening Studies
D. for Correspondence Courses

Academic Year: September to July.
Admission Requirements: Competitive entrance examination following general or special secondary school certificate.
Degrees and Diplomas: Diploma of Specialist in relevant fields, 5 yrs.

7307 **LENINGRADSKIJ ORDENA TRUDOVOGO KRASNOGO ZNAMENI I ORDENA OKTJABR'SKOJ REVOLJUCII INŽENERNO-STROITEL'NYJ INSTITUT**
Institute of Civil Engineering
2-ja Krasnoarmejskaja ul. 4, 198005 Leningrad, Rossiskaja SFSR
Telephone: 292-20-26

F. of Construction Engineering
F. of Architecture
F. of Sanitary Engineering
F. of Mechanical Engineering
F. of Highway Engineering
F. for Evening Studies
F. for Correspondence Courses

Academic Year: September to July.
Admission Requirements: Competitive entrance examination following general or special secondary school certificate.
Degrees and Diplomas: Diploma of Specialist in relevant fields, 5 yrs.

7308 **TJUMENSKIJ INŽENERNO-STROITEL'NYJ INSTITUT**
Institute of Civil Engineering
Ul. Lunačarskogo 2, 625001 Tjumen, Rossiskaja SFSR
Telephone: 3-45-31

F. of Construction Engineering
F. of Highway Engineering
D. for Evening Studies
D. for Correspondence Courses

Academic Year: September to July.
Admission Requirements: Competitive entrance examination following general or special secondary school certificate.
Degrees and Diplomas: Diploma of Specialist in relevant fields, 5 yrs.

7309 **TOMSKIJ INŽENERNO-STROITEL'NYJ INSTITUT**
Institute of Civil Engineering
Soljanaja pl. 2, 634003 Tomsk 3, Rossiskaja SFSR
Telephone: 5-39-30

F. of Construction Engineering
F. of Mechanical Engineering
F. of Highway Engineering
F. of Technology (Building Materials)
D. for Evening Studies
D. for Correspondence Courses

Academic Year: September to July.
Admission Requirements: Competitive entrance examination following general or special secondary school certificate.
Degrees and Diplomas: Diploma of Specialist in relevant fields, 5 yrs.

7310 **UST'-KAMENOGORSKIJ STROITEL'NO-DOROŽNYJ INSTITUT**
Institute of Civil Engineering
Studgorodok, 492034 Ust'-Kamenogorsk, Kazahskaja SSR
Telephone: 44-63-54

F. of Construction Engineering
F. of Highway Engineering
F. of Automobile Engineering F. of Architecture
F. of Architecture
F. of Water Supply Engineering
F. of Engineering Economics
D. for Evening Studies
D. of General Technical Studies (Zyrjanovsk)
D. of General Technical Studies (Semipalatinsk)
D. for Correspondence Courses

Academic Year: September to July.
Admission Requirements: Competitive entrance examination following general or special secondary school certificate.
Degrees and Diplomas: Diploma of Specialist in relevant fields, 5 yrs.

7311 **VIL'NJUSSKIJ INŽENERNO-STROITEL'NYJ INSTITUT**
Institute of Civil Engineering
Ul. Sauletekio 11, 232054 Vil'njus, Litovskaja SSR
Telephone: 74-72-52
Rektor: Aleksandro Čyras Aleksandras (1969-)

F. of Architecture
F. of Construction
F. of Urban Construction
F. of Mechanical Technology
F. of Automation

Founded 1956 as branch of Kaunas Polytechnical Institute. Became separate institution with present title 1969. Governing bodies: the Rector and Pro-Rectors; the Academic Heads; the Academic Council. Residential facilities for academic staff and students.

Academic Year: September to July (September-January; February-July).

Admission Requirements: Competitive entrance examination following general or special secondary school certificate.

Fees: None.

Language of Instruction: Lithuanian.

Degrees and Diplomas: Diploma of Specialist in relevant fields, 5 yrs.

Library: Central Library, *c.* 1,000,000 vols.

Special Facilities (Museums, etc.): History Museum.

Publications: Transactions of a Lithuanian Mechanical Society (annually); Reinforced Concrete Structures (annually); Proceedings in Geodesy (annually); Construction Management (annually); Urban Development and Regional Planning (annually).

Academic Staff, 1986-87: 816.

Student Enrolment, 1986-87:

	Men	Women	Total
Of the country	2965	1214	4179

7312 **VOLGOGRADSKIJ INŽENERNO-STROITEL'NYJ INSTITUT**
Institute of Civil Engineering
Akademičeskaja ul. 1, 400074 Volgograd, Rossiskaja SFSR
Telephone: 44-13-72

F. of Construction Engineering
F. of Sanitary Engineering
F. of Highway Engineering
F. for Evening Studies
F. for Evening Studies (Volžsk)
D. for Correspondence Courses

Academic Year: September to July.

Admission Requirements: Competitive entrance examination following general or special secondary school certificate.

Degrees and Diplomas: Diploma of Specialist in relevant fields, 5 yrs.

7313 **VORONEŽSKIJ ORDENA TRUDOVOGO KRASNOGO ZNAMENI INŽENERNO-STROITEL'NYJ INSTITUT**
Institute of Civil Engineering
Ul. 20-letija Oktjabrja 84, 394680 Voronež, Rossiskaja SFSR
Telephone: 7-52-68

F. of Construction Engineering
F. of Construction Technology (Building Materials)
F. of Sanitary Engineering
F. of Mechanical Engineering
F. of Highway Engineering
F. of Engineering Economics
F. for Correspondence Courses
F. for Evening Studies

Academic Year: September to July.

Admission Requirements: Competitive entrance examination following general or special secondary school certificate.

Degrees and Diplomas: Diploma of Specialist in relevant fields, 5 yrs.

7314 **VSESOJUNYJ ZAOČNYJ INŽENERNO-STROITEL'NYJ INSTITUT**
Correspondence Institute of Civil Engineering
Srednjaja Kalitnikovskaja ul. 30, 109807 Moskva, Rossiskaja SFSR

F. of Industrial and Civil Engineering (2)
F. of Architecture
F. of Technology (Building Materials)
F. of Mechanical Engineering
F. of Highway Engineering
F. of Sanitary Engineering
F. of Urban Construction and Planning
F. of Engineering Economics
F. of General Technical Studies
F. for Evening Studies (2)
Branch I. (Alma-Ata)

Academic Year: September to July.

Admission Requirements: Competitive entrance examination following general or special secondary school certificate.

Degrees and Diplomas: Diploma of Specialist in relevant fields, 5 yrs.

Institutes of Surveying and Cartography

7315 **MOSKOVSKIJ ORDENA LENINA INSTITUT INŽENEROV GEODEZII, AEROFOTOS'EMKI I KARTOGRAFI**
Institute of Surveying, Aerial Photography and Cartography
Gorohovskij per. 4, 103064 Moskva K-64, Rossiskaja SFSR
Telephone: 261-40-44

F. of Surveying
F. of Aerial Photographic Surveying
F. of Optical Mechanics
F. of Cartography
F. for Correspondence Studies
D. for Evening Studies

Academic Year: September to July.

Admission Requirements: Competitive entrance examination following general or special secondary school certificate.

Degrees and Diplomas: Diploma of Specialist in relevant fields, 5 yrs.

7316 **NOVOSIBIRSKIJ ORDENA 'ZNAK POČETA' INSTITUT INŽENEROV GEODEZII, AEROFOTOS'EMKI I KARTOGRAFI**
Institute of Surveying, Aerial Photography and Cartography
Ul. Plahotnogo 10, 630108 Novosibirsk 108, Rossiskaja SFSR
Telephone: 43-37-01

F. of Surveying
F. of Aerial Photographic Surveying
F. of Optics
F. for Correspondence Courses

Academic Year: September to July.

Admission Requirements: Competitive entrance examination following general or special secondary school certificate.

Degrees and Diplomas: Diploma of Specialist in relevant fields, 5 yrs.

Institutes of Hydrology and Meteorology

7317 **LENINGRADSKIJ GIDROMETEOROLOGIČESKIJ INSTITUT**
Institute of Meteorology and Hydrology
Malo-Ohtinskij pr. 98, 195196 Leningrad K-196, Rossiskaja SFSR
Cables: Gidrometvuz
Telephone: 22-49-83

F. of Meteorology
F. of Hydrology
F. of Oceanography
D. for Correspondence Courses
Computer Ce.
Air-Sea Research I.
Aeronautical Meteorology Research I.
Submarine Research I.

Founded in Moscow 1930, transferred to Leningrad 1944. Residential facilities for students.

Admission Requirements: September to July (September-January; February-July).

Admission Requirements: Competitive entrance examination following general or special secondary school certificate.

Fees: None.

Language of Instruction: Russian.

Degrees and Diplomas: Diploma of Specialist in relevant fields, 5 yrs.

Library: *c.* 140,000 vols.

Publication: Transactions.

7318 **ODESSKIJ GIDROMETEOROLOGIČESKIJ INSTITUT**
Institute of Meteorology and Hydrology
Ul. Lwowskaja 15, 270016 Odessa, Ukrainskaja SSR
Cables: Odessa, Gidromet
Telephone: 22-49-83

F. of Meteorology
F. of Hydrology
F. for Correspondence Courses

Founded 1933.

Academic Year: September to June (September-January; February-June).

Admission Requirements: Competitive entrance examination following general or special secondary school certificate.

Fees: None.

Languages of Instruction: Ukrainian and Russian.

Degrees and Diplomas: Diploma of Specialist in relevant fields, 5 yrs.

Institutes of Agriculture

Agriculture

7319 **ALTAJSKIJ SEL'SKOHOZJAJSTVENNYJ INSTITUT**
Institute of Agriculture
Krasnoarmejskij pr. 98, 656099 Barnaul, Rossiskaja SFSR
Telephone: 5-45-35

Agriculture (including Animal Husbandry and Veterinary Science)
Also correspondence courses.

Academic Year: September to July.

Admission Requirements: Competitive entrance examination following general or special secondary school certificate.

Degrees and Diplomas: Diploma of Specialist in relevant fields, 5 yrs.

7320 **ANDIŽANSKIJ INSTITUT HLOPKOVODSTVA**
Cotton Institute
Selo Kuigan-Jar, Andižanskogo r-na, 711520 Andižanskaja obl., Uzbekskaja SSR
Telephone: 4-54-34

Agriculture
Also correspondence courses.

Academic Year: September to July.

Admission Requirements: Competitive entrance examination following general or special secondary school certificate.

Degrees and Diplomas: Diploma of Specialist in relevant fields, 5 yrs.

7321 **ARMJANSKIJ ORDENA 'ZNAK POČETA' SEL'SKOHOZJAJSTVENNYJ INSTITUT**
Institute of Agriculture
Ul. Terjana 74, 375009 Erevan, Armjanskaja SSR
Telephone: 52-45-41

Agriculture (including Horticulture, Viticulture, and Food Processing)
Also correspondence courses.

Academic Year: September to July.

Admission Requirements: Competitive entrance examination following general or special secondary school certificate.

Degrees and Diplomas: Diploma of Specialist in relevant fields, 5 yrs.

7322 **AZERBAJDŽANSKIJ ORDENA 'ZNAK POČETA' SEL'SKOHOZJAJSTVENNYJ INSTITUT IM. S. AGAMALILY**
Institute of Agriculture
Ul. Azizbekova 262, 374700 Kirovabad, Azerbajdžanskaja SSR
Telephone: 2-10-64

Agriculture (including Horticulture, Viticulture, Animal Husbandry, Veterinary Science, and Sericulture)
Also correspondence courses.

Academic Year: September to July.

Admission Requirements: Competitive entrance examination following general or special secondary school certificate.

Degrees and Diplomas: Diploma of Specialist in relevant fields, 5 yrs.

7323 **BAŽIRSKIJ ORDENA TRUDOVOGO KRASNOGO ZNAMENI SEL'SKOHOZJAJSTVENNYJ INSTITUT**
Institute of Agriculture
Ul. 50-letija Oktjabrja 34, 450089 Ufa, Rossiskaja SFSR
Telephone: 22-90-40

Agriculture (including Animal Husbandry and Veterinary Science)
Also correspondence courses.

Academic Year: September to July.

Admission Requirements: Competitive entrance examination following general or special secondary school certificate.

Degrees and Diplomas: Diploma of Specialist in relevant fields, 5 yrs.

7324 **BELGORODSKIJ SEL'SKOHOZJAJSTVENNYJ INSTITUT**
Institute of Agriculture
Ul. Vavilova 24, Pos. Majskij, Belgorodskij r-n, 309103 Belgorodskaja obl., Rossiskaja SFSR
Telephone: 204-15

Agriculture (including Animal Husbandry and Veterinary Science)
Also correspondence courses.

Academic Year: September to July.

Admission Requirements: Competitive entrance examination following general or special secondary school certificate.

Degrees and Diplomas: Diploma of Specialist in relevant fields, 5 yrs.

7325 **BELOCERKOVSKIJ SEL'SKOHOZJAJSTVENNYJ INSTITUT IM P.L. POGREBNJAKA**
Institute of Agriculture
M. Svobody 8/1, 256400 Belaja Cerkov' Kievskoj obl., Ukrainskaja SSR
Telephone: 5-12-88

Agriculture (including Animal Husbandry and Veterinary Science)
Also correspondence courses.

Academic Year: September to July.

Admission Requirements: Competitive entrance examination following general or special secondary school certificate.

Degrees and Diplomas: Diploma of Specialist in relevant fields, 5 yrs.

7326 **BELORUSSKAJA ORDENA OKTJABR'SKOJ REVOLJUCII I ORDENA TRUDOVOGO KRASNOGO ZNAMENI SEL'SKOHOZJAJSTVENNAJA AKADEMIJA**
Academy of Agriculture
213410 Gor'ki Mogilevskoj obl., Belorusskaja SSR
Telephone: 2-15-45

Agriculture (including Horticulture, Viticulture, and Animal Husbandry)
Also correspondence courses.

Academic Year: September to July.

Admission Requirements: Competitive entrance examination following general or special secondary school certificate.

Degrees and Diplomas: Diploma of Specialist in relevant fields, 5 yrs.

7327 **BLAGOVEŠČENSKIJ SEL'SKOHOZJAJSTVENNYJ INSTITUT**
Institute of Agriculture
Politehničeskaja ul. 86, 675005 Blagoveščensk, Amurskoj obl., Rossiskaja SFSR
Telephone: 2-32-06

Agriculture (including Animal Husbandry, and Veterinary Science)
Also correspondence courses.

Academic Year: September to July.

Admission Requirements: Competitive entrance examination following general or special secondary school certificate.

Degrees and Diplomas: Diploma of Specialist in relevant fields, 5 yrs.

7328 **BRJANSKIJ SEL'SKOHOZJAJSTVENNYJ INSTITUT**
Institute of Agriculture
Pos. Kokino, Vygoniceskij r-n, 243365 Brjanskaja obl., Rossiskaja SFSR
Telephone: 69-37-21

Agriculture (including Animal Husbandry)
Also correspondence courses.

Academic Year: September to July.

Admission Requirements: Competitive entrance examination following general or special secondary school certificate.

Degrees and Diplomas: Diploma of Specialist in relevant fields, 5 yrs.

7329 **BURJATSKIJ SEL'SKOHOZJAJSTVENNYJ INSTITUT**
Institute of Agriculture
Ul. Puškina 8, 670020 Ulan-Ude, Burjatskaja ASSR
Cables: Sel'hozinstitut
Telephone: 2-40-11

Agriculture (including Veterinary Science and Animal Husbandry)

Also correspondence courses.

Founded 1935, acquired present status 1960.

Academic Year: September to July.

Admission Requirements: Competitive entrance examination following general or special secondary school certificate.

Degrees and Diplomas: Professional qualifications in–Veterinary Science, 10 sem; Animal Husbandry, 9 sem; Building Engineering; Meat Technology; Leather and Fur Technology, 11 sem.

7330 **CELINOGRADSKIJ SEL'SKOHOZJAJSTVENNYJ INSTITUT**
Institute of Agriculture
Prosp. Pobedy 116, 473012 Celinograd, Kazahskaja SSR
Telephone: 2-50-56

Agriculture (including Animal Husbandry)

Branch I. (Kustanaisk)

Also correspondence courses.

Founded 1958.

Academic Year: September to July (November-February; February-March).

Admission Requirements: Competitive entrance examination following general or special secondary school certificate.

Degrees and Diplomas: Diplomas in–Scientific Agriculture; Surveying Engineering; Mechanical Engineering; Economic Accountancy; Agricultural Economics.

7331 **ČUVAŠKIJ SEL'SKOHOZJAJSTVENNYJ INSTITUT**
Institute of Agriculture
Ul. Karla Marksa 29, 428000 Čeboksary, Čuvaškaja SSR

Agriculture (including Animal Husbandry)

Also correspondence courses.

Academic Year: September to July.

Admission Requirements: Competitive entrance examination follow-ing general or special secondary school certificate.

Degrees and Diplomas: Diploma of Specialist in relevant fields, 5 yrs.

7332 **DAGESTANSKIJ ORDENA DRUŽBY NARODOV SEL'SKOHOZJAJSTVENNYJ INSTITUT**
Institute of Agriculture
Ul. M. Gadžieva 180, 367032 Mahačkala, Dagestanskaja 180 ASSR
Telephone: 7-25-25

Agriculture (including Animal Husbandry, Veterinary Science, Horticulture, and Viticulture)

Also correspondence courses.

Academic Year: September to July.

Admission Requirements: Competitive entrance examination following general or special secondary school certificate.

Degrees and Diplomas: Diploma of Specialist in relevant fields, 5 yrs.

7333 **DNEPROPETROVSKIJ ORDENA TRUDOVOGO KRASNOGO ZNAMENI SEL'SKOHOZJAJSTVENNYJ INSTITUT**
Institute of Agriculture
Ul. Vorošilova 25, 320638 Dnepropetrovsk, Ukrainskaja SSR
Telephone: 44-81-32

Agriculture (including Animal Husbandry and Veterinary Science)

Also correspondence courses.

Academic Year: September to July.

Admission Requirements: Competitive entrance examination following general or special secondary school certificate.

Degrees and Diplomas: Diploma of Specialist in relevant fields, 5 yrs.

7334 **DONSKOJ ORDENA TRUDOVOGO KRASNOGO ZANEMNI SEL'SKOHOZJAJSTVENNYJ INSTITUT**
Institute of Agriculture
346493 St. Persijanovka Rostovskoj obl. Rossiskaja SFSR
Telephone: 9-36-25

Agriculture (including Animal Husbandry and Veterinary Science)

Also correspondence courses.

Academic Year: September to July.

Admission Requirements: Competitive entrance examination following general or special secondary school certificate.

Degrees and Diplomas: Diploma of Specialist in relevant fields, 5 yrs.

7335 **ESTONSKAJA SEL'SKOHOZJAJSTVENNAJA AKADEMIJA**
Academy of Agriculture
Ul. Rija 12, 202400 Tartu, Estonskaja SSR
Telephone: 7-55-97

Agriculture (including Animal Husbandry, Veterinary Science, Forestry, and Food Technology)

Also correspondence courses.

Founded 1951.

Academic Year: September to July.

Admission Requirements: Competitive entrance examination following general or special secondary school certificate or diploma from technical school.

Degrees and Diplomas: Professional titles in–Agriculture; Agricultural Economics; Animal Husbandry, 10 sem; Veterinary Science; Agricultural Engineering; Mechanical Engineering; Forestry Engineering; Hydro-Technology; Land Reclamation, 11 sem. Also Teaching certificate, 10 sem.

7336 **GOR'KOVSKIJ SEL'SKOHOZJAJSTVENNYJ INSTITUT**
Institute of Agriculture
Prosp. Gagarina 97, 603078 Gor'kij, Rossiskaja SFSR
Telephone: 65-34-60

Agriculture (including Animal Husbandry and Veterinary Science)

Also correspondence courses.

Academic Year: September to July.

Admission Requirements: Competitive entrance examination following general or special secondary school certificate.

Degrees and Diplomas: Diploma of Specialist in relevant fields, 5 yrs.

7337 **GORSKIJ SEL'SKOHOZJAJSTVENNYJ INSTITUT**
Institute of Agriculture
Ul. Kirova 37, 362040 Ordžonikidze, Severo Osetinskaja ASSR
Telephone: 3-23-04

Agriculture (including Animal Husbandry and Veterinary Science)

Also correspondence courses.

Academic Year: September to July.

Admission Requirements: Competitive entrance examination following general or special secondary school certificate.

Degrees and Diplomas: Diploma of Specialist in relevant fields, 5 yrs.

7338 **GRODNENSKIJ SEL'SKOHOZJAJSTVENNYJ INSTITUT**
Institute of Agriculture
Ul. Tereškovoij 28, 230600 Grodno, Belorusskaja SSR
Telephone: 7-01-68

Agriculture (including Animal Husbandry)

Also correspondence courses.

Founded 1951.

Academic Year: September to July.

Admission Requirements: Competitive entrance examination following general or special secondary school certificate.

Degrees and Diplomas: Diploma of Specialist in relevant fields, 5 yrs.

7339 **GRUZINSKIJ INSTITUT SUBTROPIČESKOGO HOZJAJSTVA**
Institute of Agriculture
Kelasuri, 384904 Suhumi, Gruzinskaja SSR
Telephone: 3-38-69

D. of Sub-Tropical Agriculture
D. of Sub-Tropical Agricultural Technology
D. of Mechanization of Sub-Tropical Agriculture

Also correspondence courses.

Founded 1952 as institute of agriculture in Kutaisi, adopted present name 1959. Placed under the authority of the Ministries of Agriculture and Higher and Specialized Secondary Education of the Republic. Residential facilities for students.

Academic Year: September to July (September-February; February-June).

Admission Requirements: Competitive entrance examination following general or special secondary school certificate.

Fees: None.

Languages of Instruction: Russian and Georgian.

Degrees and Diplomas: Diplomas of Specialist in relevant fields, 4 yrs and 10 months–5 yrs and 4 months according to faculty. Kandidat nauk, Candidate of the Sciences, a further 3 yrs and thesis.

Library: Scientific Library, *c.* 165,000 vols.

Publication: Trudy instituta (Transactions of the Institute).

Academic Staff: c. 180.

Student Enrolment: c. 900 (Also *c.* 4500 external students).

7340 **GRUZINSKIJ ORDENA TRUDOVOGO KRASNOGO ZNAMENI SEL'SKOHOZJAJSTVENNYJ INSTITUT**

Institute of Agriculture

13-j Kilometr Voenno-Gruzinskoj Dorogi, 380031 Tbilisi, Digomi Gruzinskaja SSR

Telephone: 51-47-63

Agriculture (including Horticulture, Viticulture, Forestry, abd Sericulture)

Also correspondence courses.

Academic Year: September to July.

Admission Requirements: Competitive entrance examination following general or special secondary school certificate.

Degrees and Diplomas: Diploma of Specialist in relevant fields, 5 yrs.

7341 **HAR'KOVSKIJ ORDENA TRUDOVOGO KRASNOGO ZNAMENI SEL'SKOHOZJAJSTVENNYJ INSTITUT IM. V.V. DOKUČAEVA**

Institute of Agriculture

p/o 'Kommunist-1', 312131 Har'kov, Ukrainskaja SSR

Telephone: 93-71-46

Agriculture

Also correspondence courses.

Academic Year: September to July.

Admission Requirements: Competitive entrance examination following general or special secondary school certificate.

Degrees and Diplomas: Diploma of Specialist in relevant fields, 5 yrs.

7342 **HERSONSKIJ ORDENA TRUDOVOGO KRASNOGO ZNAMENI SEL'SKOHOZJAJSTVENNYJ INSTITUT IM. A.D. CJURUPY**

Institute of Agriculture

Ul. Rosa Luxemburg 23, 325006 Herson 6, Ukrainskaja SSR

Telephone: 2-64-71

F. of Agriculture (including Animal Husbandry)

Research Ce.

F. of Professional Retraining

D. for Correspondence Courses

Founded 1874 as school, became university institution 1910. Financed by the Ministry of Agriculture. Governing bodies: the Rector and Pro-Rectors; the Council.

Academic Year: October to July (October-January; February-July).

Admission Requirements: Competitive entrance examination following general or special secondary school certificate.

Fees: None.

Language of Instruction: Russian.

Degrees and Diplomas: Diploma of Specialist in relevant fields, 5 yrs. Candidate of Agricultural Sciences, a further 3 yrs.

Library: c. 288,020 vols.

Special Facilities (Museums, etc.): History of the Institute.

Publication: Annual Transactions.

Academic Staff: c. 200.

Student Enrolment: c. 500.

7343 **IRKUTSKIJ ORDENA DRUŽBY NARODOV SEL'SKOHOZJAJSTVENNYJ INSTITUT**

Institute of Agriculture

Pos. Molodežnyj, 664038 Irkutsk, Rossiskaja SFSR

Telephone: 39-13-30

Agriculture (including Animal Husbandry)

Also correspondence courses.

Academic Year: September to July.

Admission Requirements: Competitive entrance examination following general or special secondary school certificate.

Degrees and Diplomas: Diploma of Specialist in relevant fields, 5 yrs.

7344 **IVANOVSKIJ SEL'SKOHOZJAJSTVENNYJ INSTITUT**

Institute of Agriculture

Sovetskaja ul. 45, 153467 Ivanovo, Rossiskaja SFSR

Telephone: 2-81-44

Agriculture (including Animal Husbandry and Veterinary Science)

Also correspondence courses.

Academic Year: September to July.

Admission Requirements: Competitive entrance examination following general or special secondary school certificate.

Degrees and Diplomas: Diploma of Specialist in relevant fields, 5 yrs.

7345 **IŽEVSKIJ SEL'SKOHOZJAJSTVENNYJ INSTITUT**

Institute of Agriculture

Ul. Kirova 16, 426018 Iževsk, Udmurtskoj ASSR

Telephone: 3-16-28

7346 **JAKUTSKIJ SEL'SKOHOZJAJSTVENNYJ INSTITUT**

Institute of Agriculture

Ul. P. Morozova 2, 677891 Jakutsk, Rossiskaja SFSR

Telephone: 2-23-20

Agriculture (including Animal Husbandry)

Also correspondence courses.

Academic Year: September to July.

Admission Requirements: Competitive entrance examination following general or special secondary school certificate.

Degrees and Diplomas: Diploma of Specialist in relevant fields, 5 yrs.

7347 **KALININSKIJ SEL'SKOHOZJAJSTVENNYJ INSTITUT**

Institute of Agriculture

p/o Saharovo, 171314 Kalinin, Rossiskaja SFSR

Telephone: 39-92-32

Agriculture (including Animal Husbandry)

Academic Year: September to July.

Admission Requirements: Competitive entrance examination following general or special secondary school certificate.

Degrees and Diplomas: Diploma of Specialist in relevant fields, 5 yrs.

7348 **KAMENEC-PODOL'SKIJ SEL'SKOHOZJAJSTVENNYJ INSTITUT**

Institute of Agricultur

Ul. Ševčenko 13, 281900 Kamenec-Podol'skij Chmielnickoj, Drainskaja SSR

Telephone: 52-18

Agriculture (including Animal Husbandry)

Also correspondence courses.

Academic Year: September to July.

Admission Requirements: Competitive entrance examination following general or special secondary school certificate.

Degrees and Diplomas: Diploma of Specialist in relevant fields, 5 yrs.

7349 **KAZAHSKIJ ORDENA TRUDOVOGO KRASNOGO ZNAMENI SEL'SKOHOZJAJSTVENNYJ INSTITUT**

Institute of Agriculture

Prosp. Abaja 8, 480021 Alma-Ata, Kazahskaja SSR

Telephone: 61-30-14

Agriculture (including Forestry and Horticulture)

Also correspondence courses.

Academic Year: September to July.

Admission Requirements: Competitive entrance examination following general or special secondary school certificate.

Degrees and Diplomas: Diploma of Specialist in relevant fields, 5 yrs.

7350 **KAZANSKIJ ORDENA 'ZNAK POČOTA' SEL'SKOHOZJAJSTVENNYJ INSTITUT IM. GOR'KOGO**
Institute of Agriculture
Ul. Karla Marksa 65, 420015 Kazan' 15, Rossiskaja SFSR
Telephone: 2-88-82

Agriculture

Also correspondence courses.

Academic Year: September to July.

Admission Requirements: Competitive entrance examination following general or special secondary school certificate.

Degrees and Diplomas: Diploma of Specialist in relevant fields, 5 yrs.

7351 **KIRGIZKIJ ORDENA 'ZNAK POČETA' SEL'SKOHOZJAJSTVENNYJ INSTITUT IM. K.I. SKRJABINA**
Institute of Agriculture
Kommunističeskaja ul. 68, 720453 Frunze, Kirgizskaja SSR
Telephone: 4-54-11

Agriculture (including Animal Husbandry and Veterinary Science)

Also correspondence courses.

Academic Year: September to July.

Admission Requirements: Competitive entrance examination following general or special secondary school certificate.

Degrees and Diplomas: Diploma of Specialist in relevant fields, 5 yrs.

7352 **KIROVSKIJ SEL'SKOHOZJAJSTVENNYJ INSTITUT**
Institute of Agriculture
Oktjabr'skij prosp. 133, 610039 Kirov obl., Ukrainskaja SSR
Telephone: 2-97-19

Agriculture (including Animal Husbandry and Veterinary Science)

Also correspondence courses.

Academic Year: September to July.

Admission Requirements: Competitive entrance examination following general or special secondary school certificate.

Degrees and Diplomas: Diploma of Specialist in relevant fields, 5 yrs.

7353 **KIŠINEVSKIJ ORDENA TRUDOVOGO KRASNOGO ZNAMENI SEL'SKOHOZJAJSTVENNYJ INSTITUT IM. M.V. FRUNZE**
Institute of Agriculture
Ul. Gribova 44, 277049 Kišnev, Moldavskaja SSR
Cables: Sel'hozinstitut
Telephone: 2-14-43

Agriculture (including Animal Husbandry, Horticulture, and Viticulture)

Also correspondence courses.

Founded 1940.

Academic Year: September to July.

Admission Requirements: Competitive entrance examination following general or special secondary school certificate or recognized equivalent.

Degrees and Diplomas: Professional titles in–Agriculture; Agricultural Economics, 4 yrs 10 months; Agricultural Engineering, 5 yrs 4 months.

7354 **KOSTROMSKOJ SEL'SKOHOZJAJSTVENNYJ INSTITUT**
Institute of Agriculture
p/o Karavaevo, 157930 Kostroma, Rossiskaja SFSR
Telephone: 4-12-63

Agriculture (including Animal Husbandry)

Also correspondence courses.

Academic Year: September to July.

Admission Requirements: Competitive entrance examination following general or special secondary school certificate.

Degrees and Diplomas: Diploma of Specialist in relevant fields, 5 yrs.

7355 **KRASNOJARSKIJ SEL'SKOHOZJAJSTVENNYJ INSTITUT**
Institute of Agriculture
Pr. Mira 88, 660607 Krasnojarsk, Rossiskaja SFSR
Telephone: 7-36-09

Agriculture (including Animal Husbandry)

Also correspondence courses.

Academic Year: September to July.

Admission Requirements: Competitive entrance examination following general or special secondary school certificate.

Degrees and Diplomas: Diploma of Specialist in relevant fields, 5 yrs.

7356 **KRYMSKIJ ORDENA 'ZNAK POČETA' SEL'SKOHOZJAJSTVENNYJ INSTITUT IM. M.I. KALININA**
Institute of Agriculture
Vuzgorodok, 333030 Simferopol' Krymskoj obl., 30, Rossiskaja SFSR
Telephone: 2-72-67

Agriculture (including Horticulture and Viticulture)

Also correspondence courses.

Academic Year: September to July.

Admission Requirements: Competitive entrance examination following general or special secondary school certificate.

Degrees and Diplomas: Diploma of Specialist in relevant fields, 5 yrs.

7357 **KUBANSKIJ ORDENA TRUDOVOGO KRASNOGO ZNAMENI SEL'SKOHOZJAJSTVENNYJ INSTITUT**
Institute of Agriculture
Ul. Kalinina 13, 350044 Krasnodar 44, Rossiskaja SFSR
Telephone: 52-31-46

Agriculture (including Horticulture, Viticulture, and Animal Husbandry)

Also correspondence courses.

Founded 1918.

Academic Year: September to July.

Admission Requirements: Competitive entrance examination following general or special secondary school certificate or diploma from a technical school.

Degrees and Diplomas: Diplomas in–Agriculture; Animal Husbandry; Accountancy and Economics, 9 sem; Agricultural Engineering, 10 sem.

7358 **KUJBYŠEVSKIJ SEL'SKOHOZJAJSTVENNYJ INSTITUT**
Institute of Agriculture
Pos. Ustj-Kineljskij, 446400 Kinel', Kujbyševskoj obl., Rossiskaja SFSR

Agriculture (including Animal Husbandry)

Also correspondence courses.

Academic Year: September to July.

Admission Requirements: Competitive entrance examination following general or special secondary school certificate.

Degrees and Diplomas: Diploma of Specialist in relevant fields, 5 yrs.

7359 **KURGANSKIJ SEL'SKOHOZJAJSTVENNYJ INSTITUT**
Institute of Agriculture
Ul. Kujbyševa 55, 640018 Kurgan obl., Rossiskaja SFSR
Telephone: 2-14-21

Agriculture (including Animal Husbandry)

Also correspondence courses.

Academic Year: September to July.

Admission Requirements: Competitive entrance examination following general or special secondary school certificate.

Degrees and Diplomas: Diploma of Specialist in relevant fields, 5 yrs.

7360 **KURSKIJ SEL'SKOHOZJAJSTVENNYJ INSTITUT IM. PROF. I.I. IVANOVA**
Institute of Agriculture
Ul. Karla Marksa 70, 305034 Kursk, Rossiskaja SFSR
Cables: Kursk Al
Telephone: 4-12-21

Agriculture (including Animal Husbandry and Veterinary Science)

Also correspondence courses.

Founded 1956.

Academic Year: September to July (September-December; February-July).

Admission Requirements: Competitive entrance examination following general or special secondary school certificate.

Degrees and Diplomas: Diploma of Specialist in relevant fields, 5 yrs.

7361 **KUSTANAJSKIJ SEL'SKOHOZJAJSTVENNYJ INSTITUT**
Institute of Agriculture
Ul. Sverdlova 119, 458011 Kustanaj, Kazahskaja SSR
Telephone: 5-12-23

Agriculture (including Animal Husbandry)

Also correspondence courses.

Academic Year: September to July.

Admission Requirements: Competitive entrance examination following general or special secondary school certificate.

Degrees and Diplomas: Diploma of Specialist in relevant fields, 5 yrs.

7362 **LATVIJSKAJA ORDENA TRUDOVOGO KRASNOGO ZNAMENI SEL'SKOHOZJAJSTVENNAJA AKADEMIJA**

Academy of Agriculture

Ul. Lenina 2, 229600 Elgava, Latvijskaja SSR

Cables: Akademija

Telephone: 2-25-84

D. of Agriculture
D. of Animal Husbandry D. of Veterinary Science
D. of Mechanization of Agriculture
D. of Irrigation and Rural Planning
D. of Forestry
D. of Food Technology
D. for Evening Courses
D. of Further Training (by correspondence)

Founded 1863 as Department of Agriculture of the Riga Polytechnical School. Present title adopted 1944. Under the authority of the Ministry of Agriculture of the USSR. Governed by the Rector and the Academic Council. Residential facilities for academic staff and students.

Academic Year: September to August (September-March; March-August).

Admission Requirements: Competitive entrance examination following general or special secondary school certificate.

Fees: None.

Languages of Instruction: Latvian and Russian.

Degrees and Diplomas: Professional qualifications, 5 yrs. Kandidat nauk, Candidate of the Sciences, a further 3 yrs. Doktor nauk, bythesis after Kandidat.

Library: c. 300,000 vols.

Special Facilities (Museums, etc.): Soil Science and Geology; Anatomy; Zoology.

Publication: Transactions of the Latvian Academy of Agriculture.

Academic Staff: c. 350.

Student Enrolment: c. 2800 (Also c. 2800 external students).

7363 **LENINGRADSKIJ ORDENA TRUDOVOGO KRASNOGO ZNAMENI SEL'SKOHOZJAJSTVENNYJ INSTITUT**

Institute of Agriculture

Leningradskoje šosse 2, 188620 Puškin Leningradskoj obl., Rossiskaja SFSR

Agriculture (including Horticulture, Viticulture, and Animal Husbandry)
Branch I. (Novgorod)

Also correspondence courses.

Academic Year: September to July.

Admission Requirements: Competitive entrance examination following general or special secondary school certificate.

Degrees and Diplomas: Diploma of Specialist in relevant fields, 5 yrs.

7364 **LIETUVOS ŽEMĖS UKIO AKADEMIJA**

Agricultural Academy of Lithuania

Campus, 234324 Kaunas, Lietuva

Telephone: 29-65-00

Rektor: Rimantas Urbonas

Head, Foreign Relations Department: Markas Zingeris

F. of Agronomy
Dean: Vyt. Slapakauskas; *staff* 75 (8)
F. of Forestry
Dean: Pr. Džiaukštas; *staff* 12 (6)
F. of Economics
Dean: J. Vaibauskas; *staff* 58 (6)
F. of Electrification
Dean: E. Cerškus; *staff* 29 (2)
F. of Land Reclamation
Dean: A. Kusta; *staff* 72 (4)
F. of Mechanics
Dean: Vl. Janulevičius; *staff* 4 (4)
Working Conditions Improvement L.
Head: Gv. Kazlauskas; *staff* 11 (2)
Forest Monitoring L.
Head: R. Juknys; *staff* 21 (13)
Horticulture Produce Storing Research L.
Head: Vl. Vilimas; *staff* 12 (6)
Fodder Chemization Effectiveness Research L.
Head: Pr.P. Janulis; *staff* 13 (8)

Also aid courses for foreign students. Experimental Farm.

Founded 1924. Under the jurisdiction of the Ministry of Agriculture of Lithuania. Governing body: the Senate, comprising 100 representatives of academic staff and students. Residential facilities for students.

Arrangements for co-operation with Academies of Agriculture, Wrocław and Olsztyn.

Academic Year: September to July.

Admission Requirements: Competitive entrance examination following general or special secondary school certificate.

Fees: None.

Languages of Instruction: Lithuanian and Russian.

Degrees and Diplomas: Diploma of Specialist in relevant fields, 5 yrs.

Library: Library of Agricultural Academy of Lithuania, 568,478 vols.

Special Facilities (Museums, etc.): Academy Museum.

Publication: Annual Faculty Research Papers.

Press or Publishing House: Typography of Academy of Agriculture.

Academic Staff, 1989-90:

Rank	Full-time	Part-time
Profesoriai	18	8
Docentai	195	6
Vyr. déstytojai	89	2
Déstytojai	40	17
Asistentai	115	2
Total	457	35

Student Enrolment, 1989-90:

	Men	Women	Total
Of the country	1016	2313	3329
Of other countries	18	6	24
Total	1034	2319	3353*

*Also 3823 external students.

7365 **L'VOVSKIJ SEL'SKOHOZJAJSTVENNYJ INSTITUT**

Institute of Agriculture

292040 Nesterskogo r-na Dubljany, L'vovskoj obl., Ukrainskaja SSR

Telephone: 79-33-45

Agriculture

Also correspondence courses.

Academic Year: September to July.

Admission Requirements: Competitive entrance examination following general or special secondary school certificate.

Degrees and Diplomas: Diploma of Specialist in relevant fields, 5 yrs.

7366 ***MOSKOVSKAJA ORDENA LENINA I ORDENA TRUDOVOGO KRASNOGO ZNAMENI SEL'SKOHOZJAJSTVENNAJA AKADEMIJA IM. K.A. TIMIRJAZEVA**

Academy of Agriculture

Ul. Timirjazevskaja 49, 127550 Moskva, Rossiskaja SFSR

Telephone: 216-04-80

Rektor: M.I. Sinyukov

F. of Agronomy
F. of Economics and Organization of Agriculture
F. of Animal Husbandry
F. of Horticulture and Viticulture
F. of Agricultural Chemistry and Soil Science
F. of Education (Agriculture)
S. of Agricultural Retraining
F. of Professional Retraining
Branches in Smolensk and Yaroslavl.

Founded 1865 as College of Agriculture and Forestry, reorganized 1917 and 1933. Residential facilities for academic staff and students.

Arrangements for co-operation with similar institutions in: Bulgaria; Czechoslovakia; German Democratic Republic; Hungary; Poland.

Academic Year: September to June (September-January; February-June).

Admission Requirements: Competitive entrance examination following general or special secondary school certificate.

Fees: None.

Language of Instruction: Russian.

Degrees and Diplomas: Diploma of Specialist in relevant fields, 5 yrs. Kandidat nauk, Candidate of the Sciences, a further 3 yrs andthesis. Doktor nauk, by thesis after Kandidat.

Library: c. 900,000 vols.
Special Facilities (Museums, etc.): Museums: Animal Husbandry; Horse Breeding; Soil Science; Entomology; Zoology; Geology; Anatomy of Farm Animals. Memorial Museum.
Academic Staff: c. 550.
Student Enrolment: c. 4500.

7367 **NOVGORODSKIJ SEL'SKOHOZJAJSTVENNYJ INSTITUT**
Pskovskaja ul. 3, 173015 Novgorod, Rossiskaja SFSR
Telephone: 7-03-82

7368 **NOVOSIBIRSKIJ SEL'SKOHOZJAJSTVENNYJ INSTITUT**
Institute of Agriculture
Ul. Dobroljubova 160, 630039 Novosibirsk 39, Rossiskaja SFSR
Telephone: 67-39-22

Agriculture (including Animal Husbandry and Veterinary Science)
Also correspondence courses.
Academic Year: September to July.
Admission Requirements: Competitive entrance examination following general or special secondary school certificate.
Degrees and Diplomas: Diploma of Specialist in relevant fields, 5 yrs.

7369 **ODESSKIJ SEL'SKOHOZJAJSTVENNYJ INSTITUT**
Institute of Agriculture
Ul. Sverdlova 99, 270039 Odessa 39, Ukrainskaja SSR
Telephone: 22-37-23

Agriculture (including Horticulture, Veterinary Science, Viticulture, and Animal Husbandry)
Also correspondence courses.
Academic Year: September to July.
Admission Requirements: Competitive entrance examination following general or special secondary school certificate.
Degrees and Diplomas: Diploma of Specialist in relevant fields, 5 yrs.

7370 **OMSKIJ ORDENA LENINA SEL'SKOHOZJAJSTVENNYJ INSTITUT IM. S.M. KIROVA**
Institute of Agriculture
Sibakovskaja ul. 4, 644008 Omsk 8, Rossiskaja SFSR
Telephone: 22-56-90

Agriculture (including Horticulture and Viticulture, Animal Husbandry, Irrigation, Food Technology, and Surveying)
Also correspondence courses.
Academic Year: September to July.
Admission Requirements: Competitive entrance examination following general or special secondary school certificate.
Degrees and Diplomas: Diploma of Specialist in relevant fields, 5 yrs.

7371 **ORENBURGSKIJ ORDENA TRUDOVOGO KRASNOGO ZNAMENI SEL'SKOHOZJAJSTVENNYJ INSTITUT**
Institute of Agriculture
Ul. Čeljuskincev 18, 460795 Orenburg, Ukrainskaja SSR
Cables: Sel'hozinstitut
Telephone: 7-52-30

D. of Agriculture
D. of Agricultural Economics
D. of Agricultural Engineering
D. of Veterinary Medicine
D. of Animal Husbandry
D. for Correspondence Courses
Founded 1930. Responsible to the Ministry of Agriculture. Residential facilities for academic staff and students.
Academic Year: September to July (September-January; February-July).
Admission Requirements: Competitive entrance examination following general or special secondary school certificate.
Fees: None.
Language of Instruction: Russian.
Degrees and Diplomas: Diploma of Specialist in relevant fields, 5 yrs.
Library: c. 300,000 vols.
Special Facilities (Museums, etc.): Museums: Zoology; Anatomy; Pathology; Parasitology.
Publication: Trudy Orenburgskogo sel'skohozjajstvennogo instituta.

Academic Staff: c. 300.
Student Enrolment: c. 2200 (Also c. 3000 external students).

7372 **ORLOVSKIJ SEL'SKOHOZJAJSTVENNYJ INSTITUT**
Institute of Agriculture
Razgradskaja ul. 17, 302033 Orel, Rossiskaja SFSR
Telephone: 6-29-15

Agriculture (including Animal Husbandry)
Also correspondence courses.
Academic Year: September to July.
Admission Requirements: Competitive entrance examination following general or special secondary school certificate.
Degrees and Diplomas: Diploma of Specialist in relevant fields, 5 yrs.

7373 **PENZENSKIJ SEL'SKOHOZJAJSTVENNYJ INSTITUT**
Institute of Agriculture
Botaničeskaja ul. 30, 440014 Penza, Rossiskaja SFSR
Telephone: 69-08-59

Agriculture (including Animal Husbandry)
Also correspondence courses.
Academic Year: September to July.
Admission Requirements: Competitive entrance examination following general or special secondary school certificate.
Degrees and Diplomas: Diploma of Specialist in relevant fields, 5 yrs.

7374 **PERMSKIJ GOSUDARSTVENNYJ SEL'SKOHOZJAJSTVENNYJ INSTITUT IM. AKAD. D.N. PRJANIŠNIKOVA**
Institute of Agriculture
Kommunističeskaja ul. 23, 614600 Perm' GSP-165, Rossiskaja SFSR
Telephone: 32-93-93

Agriculture (including Animal Husbandry, Horticulture and Viticulture)
Also correspondence courses.
Academic Year: September to July.
Admission Requirements: Competitive entrance examination following general or special secondary school certificate.
Degrees and Diplomas: Diploma of Specialist in relevant fields, 5 yrs.

7375 **PLODOOVOŠČNOJ INSTITUT IM. I.V. MIČURINA**
Institute of Horticulture
Ul. Internacional'naja 101, 393740 Mičurinsk Tambovskaja obl., Rossiskaja SFSR
Telephone: 9-01-61

Agriculture (including Horticulture, Viticulture and Animal Husbandry)
Also correspondence courses.
Founded 1930.
Academic Year: September to July (September-January; February-July).
Admission Requirements: Competitive entrance examination following general or special secondary school certificate.
Degrees and Diplomas: Diploma of Specialist in relevant fields, 5 yrs.

7376 **POLTAVSKIJ ORDENA TRUDOVOGO KRASNOGO ZNAMENI SEL'SKOHOZJAJSTVENNYJ INSTITUT**
Institute of Agriculture
Ul. Skovorody 1/3, 314003 Poltava, Ukrainskaja SSR
Telephone: 7-34-46

Agriculture (including Animal Husbandry)
Also correspondence courses.
Academic Year: September to July.
Admission Requirements: Competitive entrance examination following general or special secondary school certificate.
Degrees and Diplomas: Diploma of Specialist in relevant fields, 5 yrs.

7377 **PRIMORSKIJ SEL'SKOHOZJAJSTVENNYJ INSTITUT**
Institute of Agriculture
Bljuhera pr. 44, Primorskogo kraja, 692510 Ussurijsk Kraja 10, Rossiskaja SFSR
Telephone: 2-93-90

Agriculture (including Animal Husbandry and Forestry)
Also correspondence courses.
Academic Year: September to July.
Admission Requirements: Competitive entrance examination following general or special secondary school certificate.

Degrees and Diplomas: Diploma of Specialist in relevant fields, 5 yrs.

7378 **RJAZANSKIJ SEL'SKOHOZJAJSTVENNYJ INSTITUT IM. PROF. P.A. KOSTYČEVA**

Institute of Agriculture

Ul. Lenina 53, 390000 Rjazan', Rossiskaja SFSR

Telephone: 7-49-64

Agriculture (including Animal Husbandry)

Also correspondence courses.

Academic Year: September to July.

Admission Requirements: Competitive entrance examination following general or special secondary school certificate.

Degrees and Diplomas: Diploma of Specialist in relevant fields, 5 yrs.

7379 **SAMARKANDSKIJ ORDENA 'ZNAK POČETA' SEL'SKOHOZJAJSTVENNYJ INSTITUT IM. V.V. KUJBYŠEVA**

Institute of Agriculture

Ul. Karla Marksa 77, 703003 Samarkand, Uzbekskaja SSR

Telephone: 4-33-20

Agriculture (including Animal Husbandry and Veterinary Science)

Also correspondence courses.

Academic Year: September to July.

Admission Requirements: Competitive entrance examination following general or special secondary school certificate.

Degrees and Diplomas: Diploma of Specialist in relevant fields, 5 yrs.

7380 **SARATOVSKIJ SEL'SKOHOZJAJSTVENNYJ INSTITUT IM. AKAD. N.I. VAVILOVA**

Institute of Agriculture

Pl. Revoljucii 1, 410601 Saratov, Rossiskaja SFSR

Telephone: 2-16-28

Agriculture (including Forestry)

Also correspondence courses.

Academic Year: September to July.

Admission Requirements: Competitive entrance examination following general or special secondary school certificate.

Degrees and Diplomas: Diploma of Specialist in relevant fields, 5 yrs.

7381 **STAVROPOL'SKIJ ORDENA TRUDOVOGO KRASNOGO ZNAMENI SEL'SKOHOZJAJSTVENNYJ INSTITUT**

Institute of Agriculture

Zootehničeskij per. 10, 355014 Stravropol', Rossiskaja SFSR

Telephone: 5-18-11

Agriculture (including Animal Husbandry, Veterinary Science, and Sericulture)

Also correspondence courses.

Academic Year: September to July.

Admission Requirements: Competitive entrance examination following general or special secondary school certificate.

Degrees and Diplomas: Diploma of Specialist in relevant fields, 5 yrs.

7382 **SVERDLOVSKIJ SEL'SKOHOZJAJSTVENNYJ INSTITUT**

Institute of Agriculture

Ul. Karla Libknehta 42, 620219 Sverdlovsk GSP-219, Rossiskaja SFSR

Telephone: 51-33-63

Agriculture (including Animal Husbandry and Veterinary Science)

Also correspondence courses.

Academic Year: September to July.

Admission Requirements: Competitive entrance examination following general or special secondary school certificate.

Degrees and Diplomas: Diploma of Specialist in relevant fields, 5 yrs.

7383 **TADZIKSKIJ ORDENA 'ZNAK POČETA' SEL'SKOHOZJAJSTVENNYJ INSTITUT**

Institute of Agriculture

Prosp. V.I. Lenina 146, 734056 Dušanbe, Tadžikskaja SSR

Telephone: 24-53-41

Agriculture (including Animal Husbandry)

Also correspondence courses.

Academic Year: September to July.

Admission Requirements: Competitive entrance examination following general or special secondary school certificate.

Degrees and Diplomas: Diploma of Specialist in relevant fields, 5 yrs.

7384 **TAŠKENTSKIJ ORDENA DRUZBY NARODOV SEL'SKOHOZJAJSTVENNYJ INSTITUT**

Institute of Agriculture

Sel'hozinstitut, 700183 Taškent, Uzbekskaja SSR

Telephone: 33-46-85

Agriculture (including Horticulture, Viticulture, and Sericulture)

Also correspondence courses.

Academic Year: September to July.

Admission Requirements: Competitive entrance examination following general or special secondary school certificate.

Degrees and Diplomas: Diploma of Specialist in relevant fields, 5 yrs.

7385 **TJUMENSKIJ SEL'SKOHOZJAJSTVENNYJ INSTITUT**

Institute of Agriculture

Ul. Respubliki 7, 625003 Tjumen', Rossiskaja SFSR

Telephone: 6-16-43

Agriculture (including Animal Husbandry)

Also correspondence courses.

Academic Year: September to July.

Admission Requirements: Competitive entrance examination following general or special secondary school certificate.

Degrees and Diplomas: Diploma of Specialist in relevant fields, 5 yrs.

7386 **TURKMENSKIJ ORDENA 'ZNAK POČETA' SEL'SKOHOZJAJSTVENNYJ INSTITUT IM. M.I. KALININA**

Institute of Agriculture

Pervomajskaja ul. 62, 744000 GSP Ašhabad 12, Turkmenskaja SSR

Telephone: 4-25-22

Agriculture (including Animal Husbandry, Sericulture, Veterinary Science, Horticulture, and Viticulture)

Also evening and correspondence courses.

Academic Year: September to July.

Admission Requirements: Competitive entrance examination following general or special secondary school certificate.

Degrees and Diplomas: Diploma of Specialist in relevant fields, 5 yrs.

7387 **UKRAINSKAJA ORDENA TRUDOVOGO KRASNOGO ZNAMENI SEL'SKOHOZJAJSTVENNYJA AKADEMIA**

Academy of Agriculture

Ul. Geroev Oborony 15, 252041 Kiev, Ukrainskaja SSR

Telephone: 63-51-75

Agriculture (including Forestry, Animal Husbandry, and Veterinary Science)

Also correspondence courses.

Academic Year: September to July.

Admission Requirements: Competitive entrance examination following general or special secondary school certificate.

Degrees and Diplomas: Diploma of Specialist in relevant fields, 5 yrs.

7388 **UL'JANOVSKIJ SEL'SKOHOZJAJSTVENNYJ INSTITUT**

Institute of Agriculture

Bul. Novyj Venec 1, 432601 Ul'janovsk, Rossiskaja SFSR

Telephone: 1-42-72

Agriculture (including Animal Husbandry and Veterinary Science)

Also correspondence courses.

Academic Year: September to July.

Admission Requirements: Competitive entrance examination following general or special secondary school certificate.

Degrees and Diplomas: Diploma of Specialist in relevant fields, 5 yrs.

7389 **UMANSKIJ ORDENA TRUDOVOGO KRASNOGO ZNAMENI SEL'SKOHOZJAJSTVENNYJ INSTITUT IM. A.M. GOR'KOGO**

Institute of Agriculture

p/o 'Sofievka', 258900 Uman' Cerkasskoj obl., Ukrainskaja SSR

Telex: 147414

Telephone: 5-33-65, 5-22-02

Rektor: Alexander Zdorovtsov (1975-94)

Secretary-General: Margarette Nikonets

F. of Agronomy

Dean: Nicolai Nedvyga; *staff* 118 (3)

F. of Fruit and Vegetable Growing
Dean: Larisa Obihod; *staff* 89 (4)
F. of Economics
Dean: Vladinir Marchenko; *staff* 73 (4)
Research D.
Head: Anatoly Krasnoshtan; *staff* 36 (56)
L. of Orchard Soil Management
Head: Peter Kopytko; *staff* 17
Biotechnology L.
Head: Yuri Mishkurov; *staff* 5 (1)
Also correspondence refresher and preparatory courses.

Founded 1844. Under the supervision of the State Food Committee of the USSR Council of Ministers. Residential facilities for students in hostels.

Arrangements for co-operation with: Academic of Agriculture, Poznań; Academy of Technology and Agriculture, Bydgoszcz; University of California, Davies.

Academic Year: September to July (September-December; February-July).

Admission Requirements: Competitive entrance examination following general or special secondary school certificate.

Languages of Instruction: Ukrainian and/or Russian.

Degrees and Diplomas: Diploma of Specialist in relevant fields, 4-5 yrs.

Library: 200,000 vols.

Academic Staff, 1990:

Rank	Full-time	Part-time
Professors	9	2
Assistant Professors	73	1
Head Lecturers	37	–
Lecturers	35	3
Assistants	30	–
Total	184	6

Student Enrolment, 1990:

	Men	Women	Total
Of the country	814	665	1479*

*Also 1793 external students.

7390 **VELIKOLUKSKIJ SEL'SKOHOZJAJSTVENNYJ INSTITUT**
Institute of Agriculture
Pl. Lenina 1, 182100 Velikie Luki Pskovskoj obl., Rossiskaja SFSR
Telephone: 3-26-71

Agriculture (including Animal Husbandry)

Founded 1957.

Academic Year: September to July (September-January; February-July).

Admission Requirements: Competitive entrance examination following general or special secondary school certificate.

Fees: None.

Language of Instruction: Russian.

Degrees and Diplomas: Diploma of Specialist in relevant fields, 5 yrs.

Academic Staff: c. 130.

Student Enrolment: c. 350 (Also *c.* 1300 external students).

7391 **VOLGOGRADSKIJ SEL'SKOHOZJAJSTVENNYJ INSTITUT**
Institute of Agriculture
Institutskaja ul. 8, 400041 Volgograd, Rossiskaja SFSR
Telephone: 43-08-45

Agriculture (including Animal Husbandry)
Also correspondence courses.

Founded 1944.

Academic Year: September to July (September-February; February-July).

Admission Requirements: Competitive entrance examination following general or special secondary school certificate.

Degrees and Diplomas: Professional titles in–Agriculture; Economics; Animal Husbandry; Agricultural Engineering; Agricultural Electrical Engineering, 5 yrs.

7392 **VORONEŽSKIJ SEL'SKOHOZJAJSTVENNYJ INSTITUT IM. AKAD. D. GLINKI**
Institute of Agriculture
Ul. Mičurina 1, 394612 Voronež 12, Rossiskaja SFSR
Telephone: 6-40-18

Agriculture (including Rural Planning, Veterinary Science, and Animal Husbandry)
Also correspondence courses.

Academic Year: September to July.

Admission Requirements: Competitive entrance examination following general or special secondary school certificate.

Degrees and Diplomas: Diploma of Specialist in relevant fields, 5 yrs.

7393 **VOROŠILOVGRADSKIJ SEL'SKOHOZJAJSTVENNYJ INSTITUT**
Institute of Agriculture
348008 Vorošilovgrad 78, Ukrainskaja SSR
Telephone: 5-20-40

Agriculture (including Animal Husbandry)
Also correspondence courses.

Academic Year: September to July.

Admission Requirements: Competitive entrance examination following general or special secondary school certificate.

Degrees and Diplomas: Diploma of Specialist in relevant fields, 5 yrs.

7394 **VSESOJUZNYJ ORDENA 'ZNAK POČETA' SEL'SKOHOZJAJSTVENNYJ INSTITUT ZAOČNOGO OBRAZOVANIJA**
Correspondence Institute of Agriculture
143900 Balašiha Moskovskoj obl. 8, Rossiskaja SFSR
Telephone: 521-24-56

Agriculture (including Horticulture, Viticulture, and Animal Husbandry)

7395 **ZAPADNO-KAZAHSTANSKIJ SEL'SKOHOZJAJSTVENNYJ INSTITUT**
Institute of Agriculture
Gorodok SHI, 417025 Ural'sk, Kazahskaja SSR
Telephone: 2-19-30

Agriculture (including Animal Husbandry and Veterinary Science)
Also correspondence courses.

Academic Year: September to July.

Admission Requirements: Competitive entrance examination following general or special secondary school certificate.

Degrees and Diplomas: Diploma of Specialist in relevant fields, 5 yrs.

7396 **ŽITOMIRSKIJ SEL'SKOHOZJAJSTVENNYJ INSTITUT**
Institute of Agriculture
Ul. 50-letija Oktjabrja 9, 262001 Žitomir, Ukrainskaja SSR
Telephone: 7-44-71

Agriculture
Also correspondence courses.

Academic Year: September to July.

Admission Requirements: Competitive entrance examination following general or special secondary school certificate.

Degrees and Diplomas: Diploma of Specialist in relevant fields, 5 yrs.

Animal Husbandry and Veterinary Science

7397 **ALMA-ATINSKIJ ORDENA TRUDOVOGO KRASNOGO ZNAMENI ZOOVETERINARNYJ INSTITUT**
Institute of Veterinary Science and Animal Husbandry
Prosp. Abaja 28, 480047 Alma-Ata 28, Kazahskaja SSR
Telephone: 62-78-94

Veterinary Science
Animal Husbandry
Also correspondence courses.

Academic Year: September to July.

Admission Requirements: Competitive entrance examination following general or special secondary school certificate.

Degrees and Diplomas: Diploma of Specialist in relevant fields, 5 yrs.

7398 **EREVANSKIJ ORDENA 'ZNAK POČETA' ZOOTECHNIČESKOVETERINARNYJ INSTITUT**
Institute of Veterinary Science and Animal Husbandry
Ul. Nalbandjana 128, 375025 Erevan, Armjanskaja SSR
Telephone: 56-13-42

D. of Animal Husbandry
D. of Veterinary Science
D. of Dairy Produce Technology

D. for Correspondence Courses
Founded 1928. Responsible to the Ministry of Agriculture. Residential facilities for academic staff and students.
Academic Year: September to July (September-January; January-July).
Admission Requirements: Competitive entrance examination following general or special secondary school certificate.
Fees: None.
Languages of Instruction: Armenian and Russian.
Degrees and Diplomas: Diploma of Specialist in relevant fields, 5 yrs.
Library: c. 200,000 vols.
Special Facilities (Museums, etc.): Zoo-anatomical Museum.
Publication: Scientific Publications.
Academic Staff: c. 240.
Student Enrolment: c. 2500 (Also c. 1250 external students).

7399 **GRUZINSKIJ ORDENA 'ZNAK POČETA' ZOOVETERINARNYJ UČEBNO-ISSLEDOVATEL'SKIJ INSTITUT**
Institute of Veterinary Science and Animal Husbandry
Krcanisi, 383107 Tbilisi, Gruzinskaja SSR
Telephone: 72-37-52

Veterinary Science
Animal Husbandry
Also correspondence courses.
Academic Year: September to July.
Admission Requirements: Competitive entrance examination following general or special secondary school certificate.
Degrees and Diplomas: Diploma of Specialist in relevant fields, 5 yrs.

7400 **HAR'KOVSKIJ ZOOVETERINARYNJ INSTITUT IM. N.M. BORISENKO**
Institute of Veterinary Science and Animal Husbandry
p/o 'Malaja Danilovka', Dergačerskij r-n, 312050 Har'kovskaja obl., Ukrainskaja SSR
Telephone: 32-00-03

Veterinary Science
Animal Husbandry
Also correspondence courses.
Academic Year: September to July.
Admission Requirements: Competitive entrance examination following general or special secondary school certificate.
Degrees and Diplomas: Diploma of Specialist in relevant fields, 5 yrs.

7401 **KAZANSKIJ ORDENA LENINA VETERINARNYJ INSTITUT IM. N.E. BAUMANA**
Institute of Veterinary Science
Ul. Sibirskij trakt, 420074 Kazan', Rossiskaja SFSR
Telephone: 4-19-75

Veterinary Science
Animal Husbandry
Also correspondence courses.
Academic Year: September to July.
Admission Requirements: Competitive entrance examination following general or special secondary school certificate.
Degrees and Diplomas: Diploma of Specialist in relevant fields, 5 yrs.

7402 **LENINGRADSKIJ VETERINARNYJ INSTITUT**
Institute of Veterinary Science
Moskovskij prosp. 112, 196006 Leningrad, Rossiskaja SFSR
Telephone: 298-36-31

F. of Veterinary Science
Also correspondence courses.
Founded 1919. Responsible to the Ministry of Agriculture. Residential facilities for academic staff and students.
Academic Year: September to July (September-February; February-July).
Admission Requirements: Competitive entrance examination following general or special secondary school certificate.
Fees: None.
Language of Instruction: Russian.
Degrees and Diplomas: Doctor of Veterinary Medicine, Dr.Vet. Med., 5 yrs. Candidate of Veterinary Science, Cand.Vet.Sc., 3 yrs. Doctor of Veterinary Sciences, Dr.Vet.Sc., by thesis.
Library: c. 200,000 vols.
Special Facilities (Museums, etc.): Musuems: Pathological Anatomy; Animal Husbandry and Poultry Breeding; Veterinary Food Control.
Publication: Institute periodical (annually).
Academic Staff: c. 150.
Student Enrolment: c. 1000 (Also c. 550 external students).

7403 **LITOVSKAJA VETERINARNAJA AKADEMIJA**
Academy of Veterinary Science
Ul. L. Adomausko 18, 233022 Kaunas, Litovskaja SSR
Telephone: 6-03-83

Veterinary Science
Animal Husbandry
Also correspondence courses.
Academic Year: September to July.
Admission Requirements: Competitive entrance examination following general or special secondary school certificate.
Degrees and Diplomas: Diploma of Specialist in relevant fields, 5 yrs.

7404 **L'VOVSKIJ ORDENA TRUDOVOGO KRASNOGO ZNAMENI ZOOVETERINARNYJ INSTITUT**
Institute of Veterinary Science and Animal Husbandry
Pekarskaja ul. 50, 290601 L'vov, Ukrainskaja SSR
Telephone: 72-30-23

Veterinary Science
Animal Husbandry
Also correspondence courses.
Academic Year: September to July.
Admission Requirements: Competitive entrance examination following general or special secondary school certificate.
Degrees and Diplomas: Diploma of Specialist in relevant fields, 5 yrs.

7405 **MOSKOVSKAJA ORDENA TRUDOVOGO KRASNOGO ZNAMENI VETERINARNAJA AKADEMIJA IM. K.I. SKRJABINA**
Academy of Veterinary Science
Ul. Akad. K.I. Skrjabina 23, 109472 Moskva, Rossiskaja SFSR
Telephone: 377-65-01

Veterinary Science
Animal Husbandry
Commerce
Also correspondence courses.
Founded 1920 as institute, acquired present status 1948.
Academic Year: September to July (September-February; March-July).
Admission Requirements: Competitive entrance examination following general or special secondary school certificate.
Degrees and Diplomas: Professional titles of–Učyony Zootechnik, animal husbandry; Učyony Tavaroved, food production, 10 sem; Veteri-nary Vrač, 11-12 sem; Prepodavatel Tehnikuma (teaching qualification, technical level), 13 sem.

7406 **OMSKIJ GOSUDARSTVENNYJ VETERINARNYJ INSTITUT**
Institute of Veterinary Science
Oktjabrskaja ul. 92, 664007 Omsk, Rossiskaja SFSR
Telephone: 22-06-83

Veterinary Science
Also correspondence courses.
Academic Year: September to July.
Admission Requirements: Competitive entrance examination following general or special secondary school certificate.
Degrees and Diplomas: Diploma of Specialist in relevant fields, 5 yrs.

7407 **SARATOVSKIJ ZOOVETERINARNYJ INSTITUT**
Institute of Veterinary Science and Animal Husbandry
B. Sadovaja ul. 220, 410810 Saratov, Rossiskaja SFSR
Telephone: 2-33-09

Veterinary Science
Animal Husbandry
Also correspondence courses.
Academic Year: September to July.
Admission Requirements: Competitive entrance examination following general or special secondary school certificate.
Degrees and Diplomas: Diploma of Specialist in relevant fields, 5 yrs.

7408 **SEMIPALATINSKIJ ZOOVETERINARNYJ INSTITUT**
Institute of Veterinary Science and Animal Husbandry
Ul. Urickogo 17, 490050 Semipalatinsk1, Kazahskaja SSR
Telephone: 2-39-12

Veterinary Science
Animal Husbandry
Also correspondence courses.
Academic Year: September to July.
Admission Requirements: Competitive entrance examination following general or special secondary school certificate.
Degrees and Diplomas: Diploma of Specialist in relevant fields, 5 yrs.

7409 **TROICKIJ VETERINARNYJ INSTITUT**
Institute of Veterinary Science
Ul. Gagarina 13, 457100 Troick Čeljabinskoj obl., Rossiskaja SFSR
Telephone: 2-00-10

Veterinary Science
Animal Husbandry
Also correspondence courses.
Academic Year: September to July.
Admission Requirements: Competitive entrance examination following general or special secondary school certificate.
Degrees and Diplomas: Diploma of Specialist in relevant fields, 5 yrs.

7410 **VITEBSKIJ ORDENA 'ZNAK POČETA' VETERINARNYJ INSTITUT IM. OKTJABR'SKOJ REVOLJUCII**
Institute of Veterinary Science
Ul. 1-ja Dovatora 7/11, 210619 Vitebsk, Belorusskaja SSR
Telephone: 4-20-43

Veterinary Science
Animal Husbandry
Also correspondence courses.
Academic Year: September to July.
Admission Requirements: Competitive entrance examination following general or special secondary school certificate.
Degrees and Diplomas: Diploma of Specialist in relevant fields, 5 yrs.

7411 **VOLOGODSKIJ MOLOČNYJ INSTITUT**
Institute of Dairy Farming
Ul. Šmidta 2, 160901 Vologodskaja obl., Rossiskaja SFSR
Telephone: 9-37-30

Dairy Produce Technology
Animal Husbandry
Agriculture
Also correspondence courses.
Academic Year: September to July.
Admission Requirements: Competitive entrance examination following general or special secondary school certificate.
Degrees and Diplomas: Diploma of Specialist in relevant fields, 5 yrs.

Mechanization and Electrification

7412 **AZOVO-ČERNOMORSKIJ INSTITUT MEHANIZACII SEL'SKOGO HOZJAJSTVA**
Institute of Mechanization of Agriculture
Ul. Lenina 21, 347720 Zernograd Rostovskoj obl., Rossiskaja SSFSR
Telephone: 9-17-43

Mechanization of Agriculture
Also correspondence courses.
Academic Year: September to July.
Admission Requirements: Competitive entrance examination following general or special secondary school certificate.
Degrees and Diplomas: Diploma of Specialist in relevant fields, 5 yrs.

7413 **BELORUSSKIJ INSTITUT MEHANIZACII SEL'SKOGO HOZJAJSTVA**
Institute of Mechanization of Agriculture
Leninskij prosp. 99, 220608 Minsk, Belorusskaja SSR
Telephone: 64-61-91

Mechanization of Agriculture
Also correspondence courses.
Academic Year: September to July.
Admission Requirements: Competitive entrance examination following general or special secondary school certificate.
Degrees and Diplomas: Diploma of Specialist in relevant fields, 5 yrs.

7414 **ČELJABINSKIJ ORDENA TRUDOVOGO KRASNOGO ZNAMENI INSTITUT MEHANIZACII I ELEKTRIFIKACII SEL'SKOGO HOZJAJSTVA**
Institute of Mechanization and Electrification of Agriculture
Prosp. Lenina 75, 454080 Čeljabinsk, Rossiskaja SFSR
Telephone: 33-13-74

Mechanization and Electrification of Agriculture
Also correspondence courses.
Academic Year: September to July.
Admission Requirements: Competitive entrance examination following general or special secondary school certificate.
Degrees and Diplomas: Diploma of Specialist in relevant fields, 5 yrs.

7415 **HAR'KOVSKIJ INSTITUT MEHANIZACII I ELEKTRIFIKACII SEL'SKOGO HOZJAJSTVA**
Institute of Mechanization and Electrification of Agriculture
Artema ul. 44, 310078 Har'kov, Ukrainskaja SSR
Telephone: 22-37-86

Mechanization and Electrification of Agriculture
Also correspondence courses.
Academic Year: September to July.
Admission Requirements: Competitive entrance examination following general or special secondary school certificate.
Degrees and Diplomas: Diploma of Specialist in relevant fields, 5 yrs.

7416 **MELITOPOL'SKIJ ORDENA TRUDOVOGO KRASNOGO ZNAMENI INSTITUT MEHANIZACII SEL'SKOGO HOZJAJSTVA**
Institute of Mechanization of Agriculture
Prosp. B. Hmel'nickogo 18, 332315 Melitopol' Zaporožskoj obl, Ukrainskaja SSR
Telex: 337807
Telephone: 64-61-91, 2-24-11
Rektor: Nikoai Kryzhachkivsky (1987-)
Secretary-General: Lina Emelyanova

F. of Mechanization of Agriculture
Dean: Khusnizaman Mukhametshin; *staff* 170
F. for Electrification and Automation of Agriculture
Dean: Boris Zaitzev; *staff* 145
F. for Correspondence Courses
Dean: Nikolai Kudinov

Founded 1932. Under the supervision of the USSR Committee for Education/Food and Provision Commission. Governing bodies: the Council, comprising 105 members; the Council of the Scientists, comprising 30 members.
Arrangements for co-operation with Agricultural University of Wrocław.
Academic Year: October to June (October-January; February-June).
Admission Requirements: Competitive entrance examination following general or special secondary school certificate.
Fees: None.
Language of Instruction: Russian.
Degrees and Diplomas: Diploma of Specialist in relevant fields, 5 yrs. Master, a further 2-3 yrs; II. Sc., a further 2-3 yrs.
Library: 362,000 vols.
Special Facilities (Museums, etc.): Training and Experimental Farm at Uchkhoz.
Academic Staff, 1989-90:

Professors	8
Dotsent	93
Starshy prepodavatel	55
Assistent	159
Total	315

Student Enrolment, 1989-90:

	Men	Women	Total
Of the country	2084	208	2292*

*Also 2200 students by correspondence.

7417 **MOSKOVSKIJ ORDENA TRUDOVOGO KRASNOGO ZNAMENI INSTITUT INŽENEROV SEL'SKOHOZJAJSTVENNOGO PROIZVODSTVA IM. V.P. GORJAČKINA**

Institute of Agricultural Production

Timirjazevskaja ul. 58, 127550 Moskva, Rossiskaja SFSR

Telephone: 216-36-40

Mechanization of Agriculture
Electrification of Agriculture

Also correspondence courses.

Academic Year: September to July.

Admission Requirements: Competitive entrance examination following general or special secondary school certificate.

Degrees and Diplomas: Diploma of Specialist in relevant fields, 5 yrs.

7418 **SARATOVSKIJ ORDENA 'ZNAK POČETA' INSTITUT MEHANIZACII SEL'SKOGO HOZJAJSTVA IM. M.I. KALININA**

Institute of Mechanization of Agriculture

Sovetskaja ul. 60, 410740 Saratov, Rossiskaja SFSR

Telephone: 2-37-66

Mechanization of Agriculture

Also correspondence courses.

Academic Year: September to July.

Admission Requirements: Competitive entrance examination following general or special secondary school certificate.

Degrees and Diplomas: Diploma of Specialist in relevant fields, 5 yrs.

Irrigation and Land Improvement

7419 **DŽAMBULSKIJ GIDROMELIORATIVNO-STROITEL'NYJ INSTITUT**

Institute of Water Utilization

Kommunističeskaja ul. 62, 484039 Džambul', Kazahskaja SSR

Telephone: 4-36-51

Irrigation and Hydraulic Engineering
Civil and Industrial Engineering

Also correspondence courses.

Academic Year: September to July.

Admission Requirements: Competitive entrance examination following general or special secondary school certificate.

Degrees and Diplomas: Diploma of Specialist in relevant fields, 5 yrs.

7420 **KABARDINO-BALKARSKIJ AGROMELIORATIVNYJ INSTITUT**

Institute of Land Utilization

Ul. Tolstogo 185, 360004 Nal'čik, Kabardino-Balkarskaja ASSR

Telephone: 2-23-50

Agriculture (including Veterinary Science)
Irrigation and Hydraulic Engineering

Also correspondence courses.

Academic Year: September to July.

Admission Requirements: Competitive entrance examination following general or special secondary school certificate.

Degrees and Diplomas: Diploma of Specialist in relevant fields, 5 yrs.

7421 **MOSKOVSKIJ ORDENA TRUDOVOGO KRASNOGO ZNAMENI GIDROMELIORATIVNYJ INSTITUT**

Institute of Water Utilization

Ul. Prjanišnikova 19, 127550 Moskva Moskovskij, Rossiskaja SFSR

Telephone: 216-29-62

Irrigation and Hydraulic Engineering
Hydro-electrification

Also correspondence courses.

Academic Year: September to July.

Admission Requirements: Competitive entrance examination following general or special secondary school certificate.

Degrees and Diplomas: Diploma of Specialist in relevant fields, 5 yrs.

7422 **MOSKOVSKIJ ORDENA TRUDOVOGO KRASNOGO ZNAMENI INSTITUT INŽENEROV ZEMLEUSTROJSTVA**

Institute of Rural Planning

Ul. Kazakova 15, 103064 Moskva, Rossiskaja SFSR

Telephone: 261-31-46

Rural Planning (including Architecture and Surveying)

Also correspondence courses.

Academic Year: September to July.

Admission Requirements: Competitive entrance examination following general or special secondary school certificate.

Degrees and Diplomas: Diploma of Specialist in relevant fields, 5 yrs.

7423 **NOVOCERKASSKIJ ORDENA 'ZNAK POČETA' INŽENERNO-MELIORATIVNYJ INSTITUT**

Institute of Water and Land Utilization

Puškinskaja ul. 111, 346409 Novočerkassk, Rossiskaja SFSR

Telephone: 5-35-33

Irrigation
Hydro-mechanization
Forestry

Also correspondence courses.

Academic Year: September to July.

Admission Requirements: Competitive entrance examination following general or special secondary school certificate.

Degrees and Diplomas: Diploma of Specialist in relevant fields, 5 yrs.

7424 **TAŠKENTSKIJ ORDENA TRUDOVOGO KRASNOGO ZNAMENI INSTITUT INŽENEROV IRRIGACII I MEHANIZACII SEL'SKOGO HOZJAJSTVA**

Institute of Irrigation and Mechanization of Agriculture

Ul. Kary Nijazova 39, 700000 Taškent, Uzbekskaja SSR

Telephone: 33-46-85

Mechanization and Electrification of Agriculture
Irrigation and Hydro-mechanization
Rural Planning

Also correspondence courses.

Academic Year: September to July.

Admission Requirements: Competitive entrance examination following general or special secondary school certificate.

Degrees and Diplomas: Diploma of Specialist in relevant fields, 5 yrs.

7425 **UKRAINSKIJ ORDENA DRUŽBY NARODOV INSTITUT INŽENEROV VODNOGO HOZJAJSTVA**

Institute of Water Utilization

Leninskaja ul. 11, 266000 Rovno, Ukrainskaja SSR

Telephone: 2-10-86

F. of Irrigation and Water Utilization
F. of Planning and Water Utilization Systems
F. of Peat Technology
F. of Hydro-mechanization
F. of Hydraulic Engineering
F. of Civil Engineering
F. of General Technical Studies
F. of Correspondence Courses
D. for Evening Studies

Academic Year: September to July.

Admission Requirements: Competitive entrance examination following general or special secondary school certificate.

Degrees and Diplomas: Diploma of Specialist in relevant fields, 5 yrs.

Institutes of Transport and Telecommunications

Rail Transport

7426 **ALMA-ATINSKIJ INSTITUT INŽENEROV ŽELEZNODOROŽNOGO TRANSPORTA**

Institute of Railway Engineering

Ul. Sevcenko 97, 480012 Alma-Ata, Kazahskaja SSR

Telephone: 68-55-07

Railway Engineering

Academic Year: September to July.

Admission Requirements: Competitive entrance examination following general or special secondary school certificate.
Degrees and Diplomas: Diploma of Specialist in relevant fields, 5 yrs.

7427 **BELORUSSKIJ INSTITUT INŽENEROV ŽELEZNODOROŽNOGO TRANSPORTA**
Institute of Railway Engineering
Ul. Kirova 34, 246653 Gomel', Belorusskaja SSR
Cables: Beliizt
Telephone: 21-29-68

F. of Mechanical Engineering
F. of Electrical Engineering
F. of Industrial and Civil Engineering
F. of Railway Operation
F. of Construction Engineering (Railways)
F. for Evening Studies
F. for Correspondence Courses
Founded 1954.
Academic Year: September to July.
Admission Requirements: Competitive entrance examination following general or special secondary school certificate.
Degrees and Diplomas: Diploma of Specialist in relevant fields, 5 yrs.

7428 **DNEPROPETROVSKIJ ORDENA TRUDOVOGO KRASNOGO ZNAMENI INSTITUT INŽENEROV ŽELEZNODOROŽNOGO TRANSPORTA IM.M.I. KALININA**
Institute of Railway Engineering
Ul. Akademika Lazarjana 2, 320629 GSP Dnepropetrovsk 10, Ukrainskaja SSR
Cables: Diit
Telephone: 3-13-12

F. of Mechanical Engineering
F. of Electrification of Rail Transport
F. of Computer Technology
F. of Railway Operation
F. of Construction Engineering (Railways)
F. of Bridge and Tunnel Construction
F. of Industrial and Civil Engineering
F. of General Technical Studies
F. for Evening Studies
F. for Correspondence Courses
Founded 1930.
Academic Year: September to July.
Admission Requirements: Competitive entrance examination following general or special secondary school certificate.
Degrees and Diplomas: Diploma of Specialist in relevant fields, 5 yrs.

7429 **HABAROVSKIJ INSTITUT INŽENEROV ŽELEZNODOROŽNOGO TRANSPORTA**
Institute of Railway Engineering
Ul. Seryševa 47, 680056 Habarovsk 5, Rossiskaja SFSR
Cables: Habiižt
Telephone: 34-30-76

F. of Mechanical Engineering
F. of Electrification of Rail Transport
F. of Automation and Telecommunications
F. of Railway Operation
F. of Railway Construction
F. of Construction Engineering
F. for Correspondence Courses
D. for Evening Studies
Branch I. (Čita)
Founded 1937.
Academic Year: September to July.
Admission Requirements: Competitive entrance examination following general or special secondary school certificate.
Degrees and Diplomas: Diploma of Specialist in relevant fields, 5 yrs.

7430 **HAR'KOVSKIJ INSTITUT INŽENEROV ŽELEZNODOROŽNOGO TRANSPORTA IM. S.M. KIROVA**
Institute of Railway Engineering
Pl. Fejerbaha 7, 310050 Har'kov' 50, Ukrainskaja SSR
Cables: Hiit
Telephone: 22-22-82

F. of Mechanical Engineering
F. of Railway Construction
F. of Railway Operation
F. of Automation and Telecommunications
F. of Economics
F. for Evening Studies
F. for Correspondence Courses
Branch I. (Kiev)
Branch I. (Donets)
Founded 1930.
Academic Year: September to July.
Admission Requirements: Competitive entrance examination following general or special secondary school certificate.
Degrees and Diplomas: Diploma of Specialist in relevant fields, 5 yrs.

7431 **IRKUTSKIJ INSTITUT INŽENEROV ŽELEZNODOROŽNOGO TRANSPORTA**
Institute of Railway Engineering
Ul. Cernyševskogo 15, 664074 Irkutsk, Rossiskaja SFSR
Telephone: 6-08-37

Railway Engineering
Academic Year: September to July.
Admission Requirements: Competitive entrance examination following general or special secondary school certificate.
Degrees and Diplomas: Diploma of Specialist in relevant fields, 5 yrs.

7432 **KUJBYŠEVSKIJ INSTITUT INŽENEROV ŽELEZNODOROŽNOGO TRANSPORTA**
Institute of Railway Engineering
Pervyj Bezymjannyj per. 18, 443066 Kujbyšev 9, Rossiskaja SFSR
Telephone: 39-49-48

Railway Engineering
Academic Year: September to July.
Admission Requirements: Competitive entrance examination following general or special secondary school certificate.
Degrees and Diplomas: Diploma of Specialist in relevant fields, 5 yrs.

7433 **LENINGRADSKIJ ORDENA LENINA I ORDENA OKTJABR'SKOJ REVOLJUCII INSTITUT INŽENEROV ŽELEZNODOROŽNOGO TRANSPORTA IM. AKADEMIKA V.N. OBRAZCOVA**
Institute of Railway Engineering
Moskovskij pr. 9, 190031 Leningrad, Rossiskaja SFSR
Cables: Liižt
Telephone: 310-25-21

F. of Construction Engineering (Railways)
F. of Bridge and Tunnel Construction
F. of Electrification of Rail Transport
F. of Mechanical Engineering
F. of Railway Operation
F. of Electro-Technology
F. for Evening Studies
F. for Correspondence Courses
Branch I. (Velikie Luki)
Branch I. (Riga)
Founded 1809.
Academic Year: September to July.
Admission Requirements: Competitive entrance examination following general or special secondary school certificate.
Degrees and Diplomas: Diploma of Specialist in relevant fields, 5 yrs.

7434 **MOSKOVSKIJ ORDENA LENINA I ORDENA TRUDOVOGO KRASNOGO ZNAMENI INSTITUT INŽENEROV ŽELEZNODOROŽNOGO TRANSPORTA**

Institute of Railway Engineering
Ul. Obrazcova 15, 103055 Moskva, Rossiskaja SFSR
Cables: Moskva Miit
Telephone: 281-31-77

F. of Railway Operation
F. of Electrification of Rail Transport
F. of Mechanical Engineering
F. of Railway Construction
F. of Construction Engineering
F. of Bridge and Tunnel Engineering
F. of Energetics
F. of Engineering Economics
F. of Automation and Computer Technology
F. for Evening Studies

Founded 1896. Residential facilities for academic staff and students.

Arrangements for co-operation with: College of Transport and Communications, Dresden; College of Transport Engineering, Žilina. Exchange of students with: Technical University, Brno; Institute of Mechanical and Electrical Engineering, Sofia.

Academic Year: September to June (September-January; February-June).

Admission Requirements: Competitive entrance examination following general or special secondary school certificate.

Fees: None.

Language of Instruction: Russian.

Degrees and Diplomas: Diploma of Specialist in relevant fields, 5 yrs.

Library: c. 930,000 vols.

Publication: Trudy instituta (Transactions of the Institute).

Academic Staff: c. 700.

Student Enrolment: c. 10,600.

7435 **NOVOSIBIRSKIJ ORDENA TRUDOVOGO KRASNOGO ZNAMENI INSTITUT INŽENEROV ŽELEZNODOROŽNOGO TRANSPORTA**

Institute of Railway Engineering
Ul. Dusi Koval'čuk 191, 630023 Novosibirsk 23, Rossiskaja SFSR
Cables: Niižt
Telephone: 21-75-45

F. of Bridge and Tunnel Construction
F. of Construction Engineering
F. of Railway Construction
F. of Railway Construction Machines
F. of Railway Operation
F. of Rail Transport Economics
F. for Evening Studies
F. for Correspondence Courses

Founded 1932.

Academic Year: September to July.

Admission Requirements: Competitive entrance examination following general or special secondary school certificate.

Degrees and Diplomas: Diploma of Specialist in relevant fields, 5 yrs.

7436 **OMSKIJ INSTITUT INŽENEROV ŽELEZNODOROŽNOGO TRANSPORTA**

Institute of Railway Engineering
Pr. Karla Marksa 35, 644010 Omsk, Rossiskaja SFSR
Cables: Omiit
Telephone: 3-42-19

F. of Mechanical Engineering
F. of Electro-Technology
F. of Automation and Telemechanical Technology
F. of Electrification of Transport
F. for Correspondence Courses
F. for Evening Studies
Branch I. (Celinograd)

Founded 1930.

Academic Year: September to July.

Admission Requirements: Competitive entrance examination following general or special secondary school certificate.

Degrees and Diplomas: Diploma of Specialist in relevant fields, 5 yrs.

7437 **ROSTOVSKIJ ORDENA TRUDOVOGO KRASNOGO ZNAMENI INSTITUT INŽENEROV ŽELEZNODOROŽNOGO TRANSPORTA**

Institute of Railway Engineering
Pl. Nordnogo opolčenija 2, 344017 Rostov-na-Donu 17, Rossiskaja SFSR
Cables: Riižt
Telephone: 31-36-83

F. of Mechanical Engineering
F. of Energetics
F. of Railway Operation
F. of Electrification of Rail Transport
F. of Railway Construction Engineering
F. for Evening Studies
F. for Correspondence Courses
Branch I. (Baku)

Founded 1929.

Academic Year: September to July.

Admission Requirements: Competitive entrance examination following general or special secondary school certificate.

Degrees and Diplomas: Diploma of Specialist in relevant fields, 5 yrs.

7438 **TAŠKENTSKIJ ORDENA TRUDOVOGO KRASNOGO ZNAMENI INSTITUT INŽENEROV ŽELEZNODOROŽNOGO TRANSPORTA**

Institute of Railway Engineering
Oboronnaja ul. 1, 700045 Taškent L-45, Uzbekskaja SSR
Cables: Tašiit
Telephone: 91-14-40

F. of Railway Construction
F. of Construction Engineering
F. of Mechanical Engineering
F. of Automation and Telecommunications
F. of Railway Operation
F. of Rail Transport Economics
F. for Evening Studies
F. for Correspondence Courses
Branch I. (Alma-Ata)
Branch I. (Ašhabad)

Founded 1931.

Academic Year: September to July.

Admission Requirements: Competitive entrance examination following general or special secondary school certificate.

Degrees and Diplomas: Diploma of Specialist in relevant fields, 5 yrs.

7439 **URAL'SKIJ ELEKTROMEHANIČESKIJ INSTITUT INŽENEROV ŽELEZNODOROŽNOGO TRANSPORTA IM. JA.M. SVERDLOVA**

Electro-Mechanical Institute of Railway Engineering
Ul. Kolmogorova 66, 620079 Sverdlovsk 79, Rossiskaja SFSR
Cables: Upemiit
Telephone: 58-30-36

F. of Electro-Mechanical Engineering
F. of Mechanical Engineering
F. of Construction Engineering
F. of Railway Operation
F. of Electro-Technology
F. for Correspondence Courses
D. for Evening Studies
Branch I. (Čeljabinsk)

Founded 1956.

Academic Year: September to July.

Admission Requirements: Competitive entrance examination following general or special secondary school certificate.

Degrees and Diplomas: Diploma of Specialist in relevant fields, 5 yrs.

7440 **VSESOJUZNYJ ZAOCHNYJ INSTITUT INŽENEROV ŽELEZNODOROŽNOGO TRANSPORTA**

Correspondence Institute of Railway Engineering
Chasovaja ul. 22/2, 125808 GSP-47 Moskva, Rossiskaja SFSR
Telephone: 262-21-32
Rektor: A.T. Demchenko (1985-)
Vice-Chancellor: V.G. Mitzkevich

F. of Mechanical Engineering
; *staff* 38 (21)

F. of Electrical Engineering
; *staff* 53
F. of Electrification of Rail Transport
; *staff* 14 (30)
F. of Railway Operation
; *staff* 20 (32)
F. of Construction Engineering (Railways)
; *staff* 41 (24)
F. of Engineering Economics
; *staff* 24 (22)
F. of General Technical Studies
; *staff* 114 (34)

Also Branches at Gorky, Voronezs, and Jaroslavl, and Faculties at Saratov and Smolensk, and 4 Research Branch Laboratories.

Founded 1951. Residential facilities for students in hostel.

Academic Year: September to July.

Admission Requirements: Competitive entrance examination following general or special secondary school certificate.

Fees: None.

Language of Instruction: Russian.

Degrees and Diplomas: Diploma of Specialist in relevant fields, 6 yrs.

Library: Technical Library, 550,000 vols.

Special Facilities (Museums, etc.): Institute Museum.

Press or Publishing House: Publishing House.

Academic Staff, 1990: 246 (141).

Student Enrolment, 1990: 12,000 (all by correspondence).

Maritime Transport

7441 **DAL'NEVOSTOČNOE VYSŠEE INŽENERNOE MORSKOE UČILIŠČE IM. ADM. G.I. NEVEL'SKOGO**
College of Marine Engineering
Verhnjaja Portovaja ul. 50-a, 690059 Vladivostok 59, Rossiskaja SFSR
Telephone: 2-49-58

F. of Navigation
F. of Marine Engineering
F. of Electrical Engineering
F. for Correspondence Courses

Academic Year: September to July.

Admission Requirements: Competitive entrance examination following general or special secondary school certificate.

Degrees and Diplomas: Diploma of Specialist in relevant fields, 5 yrs.

7442 **KALININGRADSKOE VYSŠEE INŽENERNOE MORSKOE UČILIŠČE**
College of Marine Engineering
Ul. Molodežnaja 6, 236029 Kaliningrad Oblastnoj, Rossiskaja SFSR
Telephone: 2-72-04

F. of Navigation
F. of Marine Engineering
F. of Radio Technology

Academic Year: September to July.

Admission Requirements: Competitive entrance examination following general or special secondary school certificate.

Degrees and Diplomas: Diploma of Specialist in relevant fields, 5 yrs.

7443 **LENINGRADSKOE ORDENA OKTJABR'SKOJ REVOLJUCII VYSŠEE INŽENERNOE MORSKOE UČILIŠČE IM. ADMIRALA S.O.MAKAROVA**
College of Marine Engineering
Kosaja Linija 15-a, Vassil'evskij Ostrov, 199026 Leningrad, Rossiskaja SFSR
Telephone: 14-19-34

F. of Arctic Oceanography and Meteorology
F. of Navigation
F. of Marine Engineering
F. of Radio Technology
F. of Electrical Engineering
F. for Correspondence Courses
Branch I. (Archangel)

Academic Year: September to July.

Admission Requirements: Competitive entrance examination following general or special secondary school certificate.

Degrees and Diplomas: Diploma of Specialist in relevant fields, 5 yrs.

7444 **MURMANSKOE VYSŠEE INŽENERNOE MORSKOE UČILIŠČE IM. LENINSKOGO KOMSOMOLA**
College of Marine Engineering
Sportivnaja ul. 13/6, 183778 Murmansk, Rossiskaja SFSR
Telephone: 6-20-51

F. of Navigation
F. of Marine Engineering
F. of Electrical Engineering
F. for Correspondence Courses

Academic Year: September to July.

Admission Requirements: Competitive entrance examination following general or special secondary school certificate.

Degrees and Diplomas: Diploma of Specialist in relevant fields, 5 yrs.

7445 **NOVOROSSIJSKOE VYSŠEE INŽENERNOE MORSKOE UČILIŠČE**
College of Marine Engineering
Prosp. Lenina 93, 353918 Novorossijsk 18, Rossiskaja SFSR
Telephone: 6-45-45

F. of Marine Engineering
F. for Correspondence Courses

Academic Year: September to July.

Admission Requirements: Competitive entrance examination following general or special secondary school certificate.

Degrees and Diplomas: Diploma of Specialist in relevant fields, 5 yrs.

7446 **ODESSKIJ ORDENA TRUDOVOGO KRASNOGO ZNAMENI INSTITUT INŽENEROV MORSKOGO FLOTA**
Institute of Maritime Transport Engineering
Ul. Mečnikova 34, 270029 Odessa, Ukrainskaja SSR
Telephone: 3-35-28

F. of Hydraulics and Port Engineering
F. of Shipbuilding
F. of Marine Engineering
F. of Ship Operation
F. of Engineering Economics
F. of Mechanization of Ports
F. for Evening Studies (3)
F. for Correspondence Courses (2)

Academic Year: September to July.

Admission Requirements: Competitive entrance examination following general or special secondary school certificate.

Degrees and Diplomas: Diploma of Specialist in relevant fields, 5 yrs.

7447 **ODESSKOE VYSŠEE INŽENERNOE MORSKOE UČILIŠČE IM. LENINSKOGO KOMSOMOLA**
College of Marine Engineering
Ul. Didrihsona 8, 270029 Odessa 29, Ukrainskaja SSR
Telephone: 3-40-88

F. of Navigation
F. of Electrical Engineering
F. of Marine Engineering
F. of Automation
F. for Correspondence Courses (3)

Academic Year: September to July.

Admission Requirements: Competitive entrance examination following general or special secondary school certificate.

Degrees and Diplomas: Diploma of Specialist in relevant fields, 5 yrs.

7448 **PETROPAVLOVSK-KAMČATSKOE VYSŠEE INŽENERNOE MORSKOE UČILIŠČE**
Ul. Ključevskaja 35, 683023 Petropavlovsk-Kamčatskij

Inland Water Transport

7449 **GOR'KOVSKIJ ORDENA TRUDOVOGO KRASNOGO ZNAMENI INSTITUT INŽENEROV VODNOGO TRANSPORTA**
Institute of River Transport Engineering
Ul. Nesterova 5, 603005 Gor'kij, Rossiskaja SFSR
Telephone: 36-17-56

F. of Marine Engineering
F. of Economics
F. of Navigation

F. of Ship Operation
F. for Correspondence Courses (5)
Founded 1930.
Academic Year: September to July.
Admission Requirements: Competitive entrance examination following general or special secondary school certificate.
Degrees and Diplomas: Diploma of Specialist in relevant fields.

7450 **LENINGRADSKIJ ORDENA TRUDOVOGO KRASNOGO ZNAMENI INSTITUT VODNOGO TRANSPORTA**
Institute of River and Maritime Transport
Dvinskaja ul. 5/7, 198035 Leningrad, Rossiskaja SFSR
Telephone: 251-12-21

F. of Waterways and Ports
F. of Marine Engineering
F. of Electrical Engineering
F. of Port Equipment and Mechanization
F. of Engineering Economics
F. for Correspondence Courses
Branch I. (Moscow)
Academic Year: September to July.
Admission Requirements: Competitive entrance examination following general or special secondary school certificate.
Degrees and Diplomas: Diploma of Specialist in relevant fields, 5 yrs.

7451 **MOSKOVSKIJ INSTITUT INŽENEROV VODNOGO TRANSPORTA**
Institute of River Transport Engineering
Ul. Rečnikov 16, 115407 Moskva, Rossiskaja SFSR
Telephone: 116-30-88
Rektor: N.P. Garanin
Prorektor: M.M. Golomazov

F. of Mechanical Engineering
Dean: A.R. Belousov
F. of Ship Operation
Dean: V.V. Nevolin
F. of Engineering Economics
Dean: N.T. Perepech
F. of Port Facilities and Cargo-Handling Equipment
Dean: W. Kareev
F. of Qualification Improvement
F. for Correspondence Courses
Prorektor: S.P. Davydov
Science Research Sect.
Head: V.I.. Dudacov
Founded 1980. Under the authority of the Ministry of River Fleet of RSFSR.
Arrangements for co-operation with similar Institutions in: China, Vietnam, and Czechoslovakia.
Academic Year: September to June (September-January; February-June).
Admission Requirements: Competitive entrance examination following general or special secondary school certificate.
Language of Instruction: Russian.
Degrees and Diplomas: Diploma of Specialist in relevant fields, 5-8 yrs.
Library: Central Library.
Publication: Proceedings (annually).
Academic Staff, 1990: 195.
Student Enrolment, 1990: 3000.

7452 **NOVOSIBIRSKIJ INSTITUT INŽENEROV VODNOGO TRANSPORTA**
Institute of River Transport Engineering
Ul. Ščetinkina 33, 630099 Novosibirsk, Rossiskaja SFSR
Telephone: 22-64-68

F. of Waterways and Ports
F. of Navigation and Transport
F. of Marine Engineering
F. of Electrical Engineering
F. for Correspondence Courses (3)
Academic Year: September to July.
Admission Requirements: Competitive entrance examination following general or special secondary school certificate.
Degrees and Diplomas: Diploma of Specialist in relevant fields, 5 yrs.

Civil Aviation

7453 **AKTJUBINSKOE VYSŠEE LETNOE UČILIŠČE GRAŽDANSKOJ AVIACII**
Institute of Civil Aviation
Ul. Maldagulovoj, 463024 Aktjubinsk, Rossiskaja SFSR
Telephone: 4-07-33

Civil Air Transport Operation
Academic Year: September to July.
Admission Requirements: Competitive entrance examination following general or special secondary school certificate.
Degrees and Diplomas: Diploma of Specialist in relevant fields, 5 yrs.

7454 **KIEVSKIJ ORDENA TRUDOVOGO KRASNOGO ZNAMENI INSTITUT INŽENEROV GRAŽDANSKOJ AVIACII IM. 60-LETJA SSSR**
Institute of Civil Aviation
Prosp. Kosmonavta Komorova 1, 252058 Kiev, Ukrainskaja SSR
Telephone: 43-31-41

F. of Mechanical Engineering
F. of Electrical Engineering
F. of Radio Technology
F. of Automation and Computer Technology
F. of Airport Operation
F. of Engineering Economics
F. of Aviation Fuels and Lubricants
F. for Correspondence Courses (3)
Academic Year: September to July.
Admission Requirements: Competitive entrance examination following general or special secondary school certificate.
Degrees and Diplomas: Diploma of Specialist in relevant fields, 5 yrs.

7455 **KIROVOGRADSKOE VYSŠEE LETNOJE UČILIŠČE GRAŽDANSKOJ AVIACII**
Institute of Civil Aviation
Ul. Dobrovoljskovo 1, 316005 Kirovograd Oblastnoj, Ukrainskaja SSSR
Telephone: 2-38-64

F. of Air Transport Operation
F. of Aerial Navigation
Academic Year: September to July.
Admission Requirements: Competitive entrance examination following general or special secondary school certificate.
Degrees and Diplomas: Diploma of Specialist in relevant fields, 5 yrs.

7456 **MOSKOVSKIJ INSTITUT INŽENEROV GRAŽDANSKOJ AVIACII**
Institute of Civil Aviation
Kronštadskij bul. 20, 125838 Moskva, Rossiskaja SFSR
Telephone: 452-59-76

F. of Mechanical Engineering
F. of Electro-Radio Automation
F. for Correspondence Courses
Academic Year: September to July.
Admission Requirements: Competitive entrance examination following general or special secondary school certificate.
Degrees and Diplomas: Diploma of Specialist in relevant fields, 5 yrs.

7457 **ORDENA LENINA AKADEMIJA GRAŽDANSKOJ AVIACII**
Institute of Civil Aviation
Ul. Pilotov 38, 196210 Leningrad, Rossiskaja SFSR
Telephone: 291-28-43

F. of Aerial Navigation
Academic Year: September to July.
Admission Requirements: Competitive entrance examination following general or special secondary school certificate.
Degrees and Diplomas: Diploma of Specialist, 5 yrs.

7458 **RIŽSKIJ KRASNOZNAMENNYJ INSTITUT INŽENEROV GRAŽDANSKOJ AVIACII IM. LENINSKOGO KOMSOMOLA**
Institute of Civil Aviation
Ul. Lomonosova 1, 226019 Riga, Latvijskaja SSR
Telephone: 24-21-97

F. of Mechanical Engineering
F. of Electrical Engineering
F. of Radio Technology
F. of Automation and Computer Technology
F. of Engineering Economics

Academic Year: September to July.

Admission Requirements: Competitive entrance examination following general or special secondary school certificate.

Degrees and Diplomas: Diploma of Specialist in relevant fields, 5 yrs.

Highway Engineering

7459 **HAR'KOVSKIJ AVTOMOBIL'NO-DOROŽNYJ INSTITUT IM. KOMSOMOLA UKRAINY**
Institute of Highway Engineering
Ul. Petrovskogo 25, 310078 Har'kov, Ukrainskaja SSR
Telephone: 42-30-29

F. of Highway Engineering
F. of Highway Construction Machines
F. of Automobile Transport Engineering
F. of Engineering Economics
F. of General Technical Studies
F. for Evening Studies

Academic Year: September to July.

Admission Requirements: Competitive entrance examination following general or special secondary school certificate.

Degrees and Diplomas: Diploma of Specialist in relevant fields, 5 yrs.

7460 **KIEVSKIJ AVTOMOBIL'NO-DOROŽNYJ INSTITUT IM. 6O-LETIJA VELIKOJ OKTJABR'SKOJ SOCIALISTIČESKOJ REVOLJUCII**
Institute of Highway Engineering
Ul. Suvorova 1, 252601 Kiev, Ukrainskaja SSR
Telephone: 93-82-03

F. of Highway Engineering
F. of Mechanical Engineering
F. of Automobile Transport Engineering
F. of Engineering Economics
F. of General Technical Studies
F. for Evening Studies

Academic Year: September to July.

Admission Requirements: Competitive entrance examination following general or special secondary school certificate.

Degrees and Diplomas: Diploma of Specialist in relevant fields, 5 yrs.

7461 **MOSKOVSKIJ ORDENA TRUDOVOGO KRASNOGO ZNAMENI AVTOMOBIL'NO-DOROŽNYJ INSTITUT**
Institute of Highway Engineering
Leningradskij prosp. 64, 125319 Moskva A-319, Rossiskaja SFSR
Telephone: 155-01-04

F. of Highway Engineering
F. of Airport Construction and Operation
F. of Hydraulic Control Systems
F. of Automobile Transport
F. of Highway Construction Machines
F. of Mechanical Constructions
F. of Economics and Organization of Automobile Transport
F. for Evening Studies

Founded 1930.

Academic Year: September to July.

Admission Requirements: Entrance examination following general or special secondary school certificate.

Fees: None.

Language of Instruction: Russian.

Degrees and Diplomas: Professional titles in–Transport Engineering; Civil Engineering; Mechanical Engineering. Kandidat nauk, Candidate of the Sciences, a further 3 yrs and thesis. Doktor nauk, by thesis after Kandidat.

Publication: Scientific Papers.

7462 **SIBIRSKIJ ORDENA TRUDOVOGO KRASNOGO ZNAMENI AVTOMOBIL'NO-DOROŽNYJ INSTITUT IM. V.V. KUJBYŠEVA**
Institute of Highway Engineering
Prosp. Mira 5, 644080 Omsk, Rossiskaja SFSR
Telephone: 65-98-81

F. of Highway Engineering
F. of Industrial and Civil Engineering
F. of Highway Construction Machines
F. of Automobile Transport
F. for Evening Studies
F. for Correspondence Courses

Academic Year: September to July.

Admission Requirements: Competitive entrance examination following general or special secondary school certificate.

Degrees and Diplomas: Diploma of Specialist in relevant fields, 5 yrs.

7463 **TAŠKENTSKIJ AVTOMOBIL'NO-DOROŽNYJ INSTITUT**
Institute of Highway Engineering
Ul. Karla Marksa 32, 700047-GSP Taškent, Uzbekskaja SSR
Telephone: 33-08-27

Highway Engineering
D. for Evening Studies
D. for Correspondence Courses

Academic Year: September to July.

Admission Requirements: Competitive entrance examination following general or special secondary school certificate.

Degrees and Diplomas: Diploma of Specialist in relevant fields, 5 yrs.

Institutes of Economics

Political Economics

7464 **ALMA-ATINSKIJ INSTITUT NARODNOGO HOZJAJSTVA**
Institute of Economics
Ul. Džandosova 55, 480035 Alma-Ata, Kazahskaja SSR

F. of Economics and Economic Planning
F. of Accountancy
F. of Finance
D. for Correspondence Courses
Branch I. (Čimkent, Aktjubinsk, and Karagand)

Academic Year: September to July.

Admission Requirements: Competitive entrance examination following general or special secondary school certificate.

Degrees and Diplomas: Diploma of Specialist in relevant fields, 5 yrs.

7465 **AŠHABADSKIJ INSTITUT NARODNOGO HOZJAJSTVA**
Institute of Economics
Ul. Hudajberdyeva 46, 744004 Ašhabad, Turkmenskaja SSR

F. of Economics and Economic Planning
F. of Accountancy
F. of Trade Economics
D. for Correspondence Courses

Academic Year: September to July.

Admission Requirements: Competitive entrance examination following general or special secondary school certificate.

Degrees and Diplomas: Diploma of Specialist in relevant fields, 5 yrs.

7466 **BAKINSKIJ FILIAL' LENINGRADSKOGO FINANSOVO-EKONOMIČESKOGO INSTITUT**
Institute of Economics
Ul. Kommunističeskaja 6, 370000 Baku, Azerbajdžanskaja SSR

F. of Commerce
F. of Accountancy
F. of Industrial Economics

F. of Finance and Statistics
F. of Economic Planning
F. of Trade Economics
D. for Evening Studies
D. for Correspondence Courses

Academic Year: September to July.

Admission Requirements: Competitive entrance examination following general or special secondary school certificate.

Degrees and Diplomas: Diploma of Specialist in relevant fields, 5 yrs.

7467 **BELORUSSKIJ ORDENA TRUDOVOGO KRASNOGO ZNAMENI GOSUDARSTVENNYJ INSTITUT NARODNOGO HOZJAJSTVA IM. V.V. KUJBYŠEVA**

Institute of Economics

Partizanskij prosp. 26, 220672 Minsk 110, Belorusskaja SSR

F. of Economic Planning
F. of Industrial Economics
F. of Accountancy
F. of Trade Economics
F. of Finance
F. of Evening Studies
F. for Correspondence Courses

Academic Year: September to July.

Admission Requirements: Competitive entrance examination following general or special secondary school certificate.

Degrees and Diplomas: Diploma of Specialist in relevant fields, 5 yrs.

7468 **EREVANSKIJ INSTITUT NARODNOGO HOZJAJSTVA**

Institute of Economics

Ul. Abovjana 52, 375025 Erevan, Armjanskaja SSR

Economics

Academic Year: September to July.

Admission Requirements: Competitive entrance examination following general or special secondary school certificate.

Degrees and Diplomas: Diploma of Specialist in relevant fields, 5 yrs.

7469 **GORIJSKIJ EKONOMIČESKIJ INSTITUT**

Institute of Economics

Prosp. Čavčavadze 57, 383500 Gori, Georgia SSSR

7470 **HABAROVSKIJ INSTITUT NARODNOGO HOZJAJSTVA**

Institute of Economics

Ul. Tihookeanskaja 134, 680049 Habarovsk 35, Rossiskaja SFSR

F. of Economic Planning
F. of Accountancy
F. for Evening Studies
F. for Correspondence Courses

Academic Year: September to July.

Admission Requirements: Competitive entrance examination following general or special secondary school certificate.

Degrees and Diplomas: Diploma of Specialist in relevant fields, 5 yrs.

7471 **IRKUTSKIJ INSTITUT NARODNOGO HOZJAJSTVA**

Institute of Finance and Economics

Ul. V.I. Lenina 11, 664003 Irkutsk 3, Rossiskaja SFSR

F. of Finance and Economics
F. of Economic Planning
F. of Economics of Machine and Automobile Transport Engineering
F. of Economics of Mining and Civil Engineering
F. for Correspondence Courses
D. for Evening Studies

Academic Year: September to July.

Admission Requirements: Competitive entrance examination following general or special secondary school certificate.

Degrees and Diplomas: Diploma of Specialist in relevant fields, 5 yrs.

7472 **KIEVSKIJ INSTITUT NARODNOGO HOZJAJSTVA IM. D.S. KOROTČENKO**

Institute of Economics

prosp. Pobeby 54/1, 252057 Kiev, Ukrainskaja SSR

F. of Economic Planning
F. of Labour and Industrial Economics
F. of Agricultural Economic Planning
F. of Accountancy
F. of Finance and Economics
F. of Data Processing
F. for Evening Studies
D. for Correspondence Courses

Academic Year: September to July.

Admission Requirements: Competitive entrance examination following general or special secondary school certificate.

Degrees and Diplomas: Diploma of Specialist in relevant fields, 5 yrs.

7473 **KUJBYŠEVSKIJ ORDENA 'ZNAK POČETA' PLANOVYJ INSTITUT**

Institute of Planning

Ul. Sovetskoj Armii 141, 443090 Kujbyšev obl. 90, Rossiskaja SFSR

F. of Industrial Economics
F. of Economic Planning
F. of Agricultural Economic Planning
F. of Accountancy
F. for Evening Studies
F. for Correspondence Courses
Branch I. (Ulianovsk)

Academic Year: September to July.

Admission Requirements: Competitive entrance examination following general or special secondary school certificate.

Degrees and Diplomas: Diploma of Specialist in relevant fields, 5 yrs.

7474 **MOSKOVSKIJ INSTITUT NARODNOGO HOZJAJSTVA IM. G.V. PLEHANOVA**

Institute of National Economy

Stremjannyj per. 28, 113230 Moskva M-54, Rossiskaja SFSR

Telephone: 236-30-70

Rektor: Vidjapin Vitalij Ivanovič

F. of Planning and Economics
Dean: Gretčenko Anatolij Ivanovič; *staff* 71 (2)
F. of Commerce
Dean: Galanov Vladimir Aleksandrovič; *staff* 69 (14)
F. of Commerce and Economics
Dean: Tjurmin Anatolij Mihaijlovija; *staff* 88 (14)
F. of Economics of the National Economy Branches
Dean: Egorov Anatolij Jur'evič; *staff* 57 (4)
Education, Scientific, and Industrial Ce. (including F. of Economic Cybernetics)
Dean: Eremeev German Aleksandrovič; *staff* 115 (20)
Commodity Research Ce.
Dean: Samarin Valerij Ivanovič; *staff* 74 (7)
Engineering and Technology Ce.
Dean: Lajko Mihail Jur'evič; *staff* 90 (15)
F. for Correspondence Courses
D. for Evening Studies

Founded 1907.

Arrangements for institutions in: Hungary (1); Poland (3); Bulgaria (2); Czechoslovakia (1); Germany (2); Netherlands (2); Finland (1); Austria (1); USA (1); France (1); People's Republic of Chine (1).

Academic Year: September to July.

Admission Requirements: Competitive entrance examination following general or special secondary school certificate.

Degrees and Diplomas: Diploma of Specialist in relevant fields, 5 yrs.

Library: 1,000,000 vols.

Academic Staff, 1989-90: 349.

Student Enrolment, 1989-90: 4908.

7475 **MOSKOVSKIJ ORDENA TRUDOVOGO KRASNOGO ZNAMENI EKONOMIKO-STATISTIČESKIJ INSTITUT**

Institute of Economic Statistics

Nežinskaja ul. 7, 119517 Moskva G-517, Rossiskaja SFSR

F. of Economics and Statistics
F. of Economic Cybernetics
F. of Mechanization and Automation of Accountancy
F. for Correspondence Courses
D. for Evening Studies

Academic Year: September to July.

Admission Requirements: Competitive entrance examination following general or special secondary school certificate.

Degrees and Diplomas: Diploma of Specialist in relevant fields, 5 yrs.

7476 **NOVOSIBIRSKIJ INSTITUT NARODNOGO HOZJAJSTVA**
Institute of Economics
Ul. Kamenskaja 56, 630070 Novosibirsk 70, Rossiskaja SFSR
F. of General Economics
F. of Accountancy
F. for Evening Studies
D. for Correspondence Courses
Academic Year: September to July.
Admission Requirements: Competitive entrance examination following general or special secondary school certificate.
Degrees and Diplomas: Diploma of Specialist in relevant fields, 5 yrs.

7477 **ODESSKIJ INSTITUT NARODNOGO HOZJAJSTVA**
Institute of Economics
Ul. Sovetskoj Armii 8, 270100 Odessa, Ukrainskaja SSR
F. of Credit Economics
F. of Finance
F. of Economic Planning
F. of Labour Economics
F. of Accountancy
F. for Evening Studies
F. for Correspondence Courses
Academic Year: September to July.
Admission Requirements: Competitive entrance examination following general or special secondary school certificate.
Degrees and Diplomas: Diploma of Specialist in relevant fields, 5 yrs.

7478 **ROSTOVSKIJ-NA-DONU ORDENA 'ZNAK POČETA' INSTITUT NARODNOGO HOZJAJSTVA**
Institute of Economics
Ul. Fridriha Engel'sa 69, 344708 Rostov-na-Donu, Rossiskaja SFSR
F. of Industrial Economics
F. of Finance
F. of Agricultural Economics
F. of Data Processing
F. for Correspondence Courses
D. for Evening Studies
Academic Year: September to July.
Admission Requirements: Competitive entrance examination following general or special secondary school certificate.
Degrees and Diplomas: Diploma of Specialist in relevant fields, 5 yrs.

7479 **SARATOVSKIJ ORDENA 'ZNAK POČETA' EKONOMIČESKIJ INSTITUT**
Institute of Economics
Ul. Radyščeva 89, 410760 Saratov, Rossiskaja SFSR
F. of Industrial Economics
F. of Agricultural Economics
F. of Credit Economics
F. of Accountancy
F. for Correspondence Courses
D. for Evening Studies
Academic Year: September to July.
Admission Requirements: Competitive entrance examination following general or special secondary school certificate.
Degrees and Diplomas: Diploma of Specialist in relevant fields, 5 yrs.

7480 **SVERDLOVSKIJ INSTITUT NARODNOGO HOZJAJSTVA**
Institute of Economics
Ul. 8 Marta 62, 620001 Sverdlovsk, Rossiskaja SFSR
F. of General Economics
F. of Economic Planning
F. of Accountancy
F. of Commerce
F. of Technology (Food Production and Catering)
F. for Evening Studies
F. for Correspondence Courses
Academic Year: September to July.
Admission Requirements: Competitive entrance examination following general or special secondary school certificate.
Degrees and Diplomas: Diploma of Specialist in relevant fields, 5 yrs.

7481 **TAŠKENTSKIJ ORDENA DRUZBY NARODOV INSTITUT NARODNOGO HOZJAJSTVA**
Institute of Economics
Ul. Almazar 183, 700063 Taškent 63, Uzbekskaja SSR
F. of Economic Planning
F. of Trade Economics
F. of Agricultural Economics
F. of Finance
F. of Accountancy
F. of Economic Cybernetics
F. for Correspondence Courses
D. for Evening Studies
Academic Year: September to July.
Admission Requirements: Competitive entrance examination following general or special secondary school certificate.
Degrees and Diplomas: Diploma of Specialist in relevant fields, 5 yrs.

Engineering Economics

7482 **HAR'KOVSKIJ INŽENERNO-EKONOMIČESKIJ INSTITUT**
Institute of Industrial Organization and Economics
Prosp. Lenina 9a, 310141 Har'kov, Ukrainskaja SSR
F. of Machine Engineering Economics
F. of Chemical Engineering Economics
F. of Metallurgical Engineering Economics
F. of Economic Data Processing
F. of Economics (Accountancy)
F. for Correspondence Courses
F. for Evening Studies
Academic Year: September to July.
Admission Requirements: Competitive entrance examination following general or special secondary school certificate.
Degrees and Diplomas: Diploma of Specialist in relevant fields, 5 yrs.

7483 **LENINGRADSKIJ ORDENA 'ZNAK POČETA' INŽENERNO-EKONOMIČESKIJ INSTITUT IM. PAL'MIRO TOL'JATTI**
Institute of Industrial Organization and Economics
Ul. Marata 27, 191002 Leningrad, Rossiskaja SFSR
F. of Machine Engineering Economics
F. of Civil Engineering and Town Planning Economics
F. of Chemical Engineering Economics
F. of Automatic Control of Production
F. of Energetics Economics
D. for Evening Studies
D. for Correspondence Courses
Academic Year: September to July.
Admission Requirements: Competitive entrance examination following general or special secondary school certificate.
Degrees and Diplomas: Diploma of Specialist in relevant fields, 5 yrs.

7484 **MOSKOVSKIJ ORDENA TRUDOVOGO KRASNOGO ZNAMENI INSTITUT UPRAVLENIJA IM. SERGO ORDŽONIKIDZE**
Institute of Industrial Organization and Economics
Podsosenskij per. 20, 109542 Moskva a, Rossiskaja SFSR
F. of Machine Engineering Economics
F. of Chemical and Metallurgical Economics
F. of Energetics Economics
F. of Automobile and Air Transport Economics
F. of Civil Engineering and Urban Management Economics
F. of Economic Cybernetics
F. for Correspondence Courses
D. for Evening Studies
Academic Year: September to July.
Admission Requirements: Competitive entrance examination following general or special secondary school certificate.
Degrees and Diplomas: Diploma of Specialist in relevant fields, 5 yrs.

Commerce

7485 **BELGORODSKIJ KOOPERATIVNYJ INSTITUT**
Institute of Co-operative Commerce
Sadovaja Ul. 116a, 308023 Belgorod, Rossiskaja SFSR
F. of Trade Economics
F. of Economics
D. for Correspondence Courses
Academic Year: September to July.
Admission Requirements: Competitive entrance examination following general or special secondary school certificate.
Degrees and Diplomas: Diploma of Specialist in relevant fields, 5 yrs.

7486 **DAL'NEVOSTOČNYJ INSTITUT SOVETSKOJ TORGOVLI**
Institute of Commerce
Okeanskij prosp. 19, 690600 Vladivostok Centr. GSP, Rossiskaja SFSR
F. of Trade Economics
F. of Marketing
F. of Food Technology (Catering)
D. for Evening Studies
D. for Correspondence Courses
Academic Year: September to July.
Admission Requirements: Competitive entrance examination following general or special secondary school certificate.
Degrees and Diplomas: Diploma of Specialist in relevant fields, 5 yrs.

7487 **DONECKIJ INSTITUT SOVETSKOJ TORGOVLI**
Institute of Commerce
Ul. Ščorsa 31, 340050 Doneck 50, Ukrainskaja SSR
Telephone: 93-18-14
Rektor: Philippov Vladimir Michailovitch
Vicerektor: Daniely Cajan Gajdovitch
F. of Commodities
Deans: Bashirov Islam Halidovitch; Onosov Nikolaj Maztveevitch; *staff* 690 (1172)
F. of Accounting Economics
Deans: Coval Gennady VAsiljetich; Stapanov Evgeny Michailovitch; *staff* 832 (861)
F. of Trade Economics
Deans: Colomiytchov Vitaly Petrovitch; *staff* 301 (680)
F. of Technology
Deans: Corshunocva Anna Phedorovna; *staff* 444 (79)
F. of Mechanical Technology
Deans: Datjkov Vladimir Pankratovitch; *staff* 261 (399)
Computer Ce.
Scientific Research Sec.
Head: Shelegeda Bella Grigorjevna; *staff* 12 (3)
D. for Evening Studies
D. for Correspondence Courses
Branch I. (Zaporože, Simferopol', and Krivoij Rog)
Founded 1920. Under the authority of the Trade Ministry of the Ukranian Socialist Soviet Republic. Governing body: the Learned Council. Residential facilities for academic staff and students.
Academic Year: September to July.
Admission Requirements: Competitive entrance examination following general or special secondary school certificate.
Fees: None.
Language of Instruction: Russian.
Degrees and Diplomas: Diploma of Specialist in relevant fields, 5 yrs.
Library: Scientific Library, 600,000 vols.
Special Facilities (Museums, etc.): History of the Institute Museum.
Publication: Trade and Public Catering in New Economic Conditions.
Academic Staff, 1990: 358 (8).
Student Enrolment, 1990:

	Men	Women	Total
Of the countries	542	1986	2528
Of other countries	117	74	191
Total	659	260	2719*

*Also 3910 students by correspondence.

7488 **GOMEL'SKIJ KOOPERATIVNYJ INSTITUT**
Institute of Co-operative Commerce
Prosp. Oktjabrja 52a, 246029 Gomel', Belorusskaja SSR
F. of Trade Economics
F. of Economics
D. for Correspondence Courses
Academic Year: September to July.
Admission Requirements: Competitive entrance examination following general or special secondary school certificate.
Degrees and Diplomas: Diploma of Specialist in relevant fields, 5 yrs.

7489 **HAR'KOVSKIJ INSTITUT OBŠČESTVENNOGO PITANIJA**
Institute of Catering
Kločovskaja ul. 333, 310051 Har'kov 51, Ukrainskaja SSR
F. of Economics
F. of Food Technology (Catering)
D. for Evening Studies
D. for Correspondence Courses
Academic Year: September to July.
Admission Requirements: Competitive entrance examination following general or special secondary school certificate.
Degrees and Diplomas: Diploma of Specialist in relevant fields, 5 yrs.

7490 **KARAGANDISKIJ KOOPERATIVNYIJ INSTITUT**
Institute of Co-operative Commerce
Ul. Akademičeskaja 9, 470017 Karaganda, Kazahskaja SSR
F. of Economics
F. of Accountancy
F. for Correspondence Courses
Branch I. (Alma-Ata)
Academic Year: September to July.
Admission Requirements: Competitive entrance examination following general or special secondary school certificate.
Degrees and Diplomas: Diploma of Specialist in relevant fields, 5 yrs.

7491 **KIEVSKIJ TORGOVO-EKONOMIČESKIJ INSTITUT**
Institute of Commerce
Ul. Kioto 19, 252156 Kiev, Ukrainskaja SSR
F. of Economics
F. of Trade
F. of Food Technology (Catering)
D. for Evening and Correspondence Studies
Branch I. (Vinnic, Odessa, Černovec)
Academic Year: September to July.
Admission Requirements: Competitive entrance examination following general or special secondary school certificate.
Degrees and Diplomas: Diploma of Specialist in relevant fields, 5 yrs.

7492 **LENINGRADSKIJ ORDENA TRUDOVOGO KRASNOGO ZNAMENI INSTITUT SOVETSKOJ TORGOVLI IM. F. ENGEL'SA**
Institute of Commerce
Novorossijskaja ul. 50, 194018 Leningrad, Rossiskaja SFSR
F. of Trade Economics
F. of Accountancy
F. of Marketing
F. of Food Technology (Catering)
D. for Evening and Correspondence Studies
Academic Year: September to July.
Admission Requirements: Competitive entrance examination following general or special secondary school certificate.
Degrees and Diplomas: Diploma of Specialist in relevant fields, 5 yrs.

7493 **L'VOVSKIJ TORGOVO-EKONOMIČESKIJ INSTITUT**
Institute of Commerce
Ul. Čkalova 10, 290008 L'vov, Ukrainskaja SSR
F. of Economics
F. of Marketing
F. for Correspondence Courses
Branch I. (Poltava)
Academic Year: September to July.
Admission Requirements: Competitive entrance examination following general or special secondary school certificate.
Degrees and Diplomas: Diploma of Specialist in relevant fields, 5 yrs.

7494 **MOSKOVSKIJ ORDENA DRUZBY NARODOV KOOPERATIVNYJ INSTITUT**
Institute of Co-operative Commerce
Ul. Very Vološinoj 12, 141006 Mytišči, Moskva obl., Rossiskaja SFSR
F. of Economics
F. of Trade
F. for Correspondence Courses
Also 7 branches.
Academic Year: September to July.
Admission Requirements: Competitive entrance examination following general or special secondary school certificate.
Degrees and Diplomas: Diploma of Specialist in relevant fields, 5 yrs.

7495 **NOVOSIBIRSKIJ INSTITUT SOVETSKOJ KOOPERATIVNOJ TORGOVLI**
Institute of Co-operative Commerce
Prosp. Karla Marksa 26, 630087 Novosibirsk, Rossiskaja SFSR
F. of Economics
F. of Marketing
F. of Food Technology (Catering)
F. for Correspondence Courses
Academic Year: September to July.
Admission Requirements: Competitive entrance examination following general or special secondary school certificate.
Degrees and Diplomas: Diploma of Specialist in relevant fields, 5 yrs.

7496 **POLTAVSKIJ KOOPERATIVNYJ INSTITUT**
Institute of Co-operative Commerce
Ul. Kovalja 3, 314601 Poltava, Ukrainskaja SSR
Co-operative Commerce
Academic Year: September to July.
Admission Requirements: Competitive entrance examination following general or special secondary school certificate.
Degrees and Diplomas: Diploma of Specialist in relevant fields, 5 yrs.

7497 **SAMARKANDSKIJ ORDENA DRUZBY NARODOV KOOPERATIVNYJ INSTITUT IM. V.V. KUJBYŠEVA**
Institute of Co-operative Commerce
Kommunističeskaja ul. 41, 703000 Samarkand, Uzbekskaja SSR
F. of Marketing
F. of Food Technology (Catering)
F. for Correspondence Studies (2)
Branch I. (Tashkent)
Academic Year: September to July.
Admission Requirements: Competitive entrance examination following general or special secondary school certificate.
Degrees and Diplomas: Diploma of Specialist in relevant fields, 5 yrs.

7498 **ZAOČNYJ INSTITUT SOVETSKOJ TORGOVLI**
Correspondence Institute of Commerce
Smol'naja ul. 36, 125445 Moskva A-252, Rossiskaja SFSR
F. of Trade Economics
F. of Accountancy
F. of Food Product Marketing
F. of Industrial Marketing
Also 13 branches.

Finance

7499 **KAZANSKIJ ORDENA 'ZNAK POČETA' FINANSOVO-EKONOMIČESKIJ INSTITUT IM. V.V. KUJBYŠEVA**
Institute of Finance and Economics
Ul. Butlerova 4, 420012 Kazan', Rossiskaja SFSR
F. of Finance and Credit
F. of Industrial Planning
F. of Accountancy
F. for Correspondence Courses
D. for Evening Studies
Academic Year: September to July.
Admission Requirements: Competitive entrance examination following general or special secondary school certificate.
Degrees and Diplomas: Diploma of Specialist in relevant fields, 5 yrs.

7500 **LENINGRADSKIJ ORDENA TRUDOVOGO KRASNOGO ZNAMENI FINANSOVO-EKONOMIČESKIJ INSTITUT IM. N.A. VOZNESENSKOGO**
Institute of Finance and Economics
Kanal Griboedova 30/32, 191023 Leningrad, Rossiskaja SFSR
F. of Finance
F. of Economic Planning
F. of Supply Planning
F. of Labour Economics
F. of Accountancy
F. for Evening Studies
F. for Correspondence Courses
Academic Year: September to July.
Admission Requirements: Competitive entrance examination following general or special secondary school certificate.
Degrees and Diplomas: Diploma of Specialist in relevant fields, 5 yrs.

7501 **MOSKOVSKIJ FINANSOVYJ INSTITUT**
Institute of Finance
Ul. Kibal'čiča 1, 129848 Moskva I-64, Rossiskaja SFSR
F. of Finance
F. of Credit Economics
F. of International Economic Relations
F. of Accountancy
F. for Evening Studies
Academic Year: September to July.
Admission Requirements: Competitive entrance examination following general or special secondary school certificate.
Degrees and Diplomas: Diploma of Specialist in relevant fields, 5 yrs.

7502 **TERNOPOL'SKIJ FINANSOVO-EKONOMIČESKIJ INSTITUT**
Institute of Finance
Pl. Pobedy 3, 282004 Ternopol', Ukrainskaja SSR
F. of Finance
F. of Accountancy
D. for Evening Studies
D. for Correspondence Courses
Academic Year: September to July.
Admission Requirements: Competitive entrance examination following general or special secondary school certificate.
Degrees and Diplomas: Diploma of Specialist in relevant fields, 5 yrs.

7503 **VSESOJUZNYJ ORDENA 'ZNAK POČETA' ZAOČNYJ FINANSOVO-EKONOMIČESKIJ INSTITUT**
Correspondence Institute of Finance and Economics
Ul. Oleko Dundiča 23, 121108 Moskva G-108, Rossiskaja SFSR
F. of General Economics
F. of Industrial Economics
F. of Finance and Credit
F. of Accountancy
Also 20 branches.

Institutes of Law

7504 **HAR'KOVSKIJ ORDENA TRUDOVOGO KRASNOGO ZNAMENI JURIDIČESKIJ INSTITUT IM. F.E. DZERŽINSKOGO**
Institute of Law
Puškinskaja ul. 77, 310024 Har'kov, Ukrainskaja SSR
Law
Also evening and correspondence courses.
Academic Year: September to July.
Admission Requirements: Competitive entrance examination following general or special secondary school certificate.
Degrees and Diplomas: Professional title in Law.

7505 **SARATOVSKIJ ORDENA 'ZNAK POČETA' JURIDIČESKIJ INSTITUT IM. D.I. KURSKOGO**
Institute of Law
Ul. Černyševskogo 104, 410720 Saratov, Rossiskaja SFSR

Law
Also evening and correspondence courses.
Admission Requirements: Competitive entrance examination following general or special secondary school certificate.
Degrees and Diplomas: Diploma of Specialist in relevants fields, 5 yrs.

7506 **SVERDLOVSKIJ ORDENA TRUDOVOGO KRASNOGO ZNAMENI JURIDIČESKIJ INSTITUT IM. R.A. RUDENKO**
Institute of Law
Ul. Komsomol'skaja 21, 620066 Sverdlovsk GSP-1038, Rossiskaja SFSR
Law
Also evening and correspondence courses.
Academic Year: September to July.
Admission Requirements: Competitive entrance examination following general or special secondary school certificate.
Degrees and Diplomas: Professional title in Law.

7507 **VSESOJUZNYJ JURIDIČESKIJ ZAOČNYJ INSTITUT**
Correspondence Institute of Law
Starokiročnyj per. 13, 107005 Moskva, Rossiskaja SFSR
Law
Also 7 branches.
Academic Year: September to July.
Admission Requirements: Competitive entrance examination following general or special secondary school certificate.
Degrees and Diplomas: Professional title in Law.

Institutes of Medicine

Medicine

7508 **AKTJUBINSKIJ GOSUDARSTVENNYJ MEDICINSKIJ INSTITUT**
State Institute of Medicine
Ul. Lenina 52, 463000 Aktjubinsk, Rossiskaja SFSR
Medicine (including Pediatrics)
Academic Year: September to July.
Admission Requirements: Competitive entrance examination following general or special secondary school certificate.
Degrees and Diplomas: Professional title in Medicine, 6 yrs.

7509 **ALMA-ATINSKIJ ORDENA TRUDOVOGO KRASNOGO ZNAMENI GOSUDARSTVENNYJ MEDICINSKIJ INSTITUT**
State Institute of Medicine
Ul. Komsomol'skaja 88, 480012 Alma-Ata, Kazahskaja SSR
Medicine (including Pediatrics, Dentistry, and Pharmacy)
Academic Year: September to July.
Admission Requirements: Competitive entrance examination following general or special secondary school certificate.
Degrees and Diplomas: Professional title in relevant fields, 5-6 yrs.

7510 **ALTAJSKIJ GOSUDARSTVENNYJ MEDICINSKIJ INSTITUT IM. LENINSKOGO KOMSOMOLA**
State Institute of Medicine
Prosp. Lenina 40, 656099 Barnaul, Rossiskaja SFSR
Medicine (including Pediatrics)
Academic Year: September to July.
Admission Requirements: Competitive entrance examination following general or special secondary school certificate.
Degrees and Diplomas: Professional title in Medicine, 6 yrs.

7511 **ANDIŽANSKIJ GOSUDARSTVENNYJ MEDICINSKIJ INSTITUT IM. M.I. KALININA**
State Institute of Medicine
Pr. Navoi 136, 710000 Andižan, Uzbekskaja SSR
Medicine
Academic Year: September to July.
Admission Requirements: Competitive entrance examination following general or special secondary school certificate.
Degrees and Diplomas: Professional title in Medicine, 6 yrs.

7512 **ARHANGEL'SKIJ ORDENA TRUDOVOGO KRASNOGO ZNAMENI GOSUDARSTVENNYJ MEDICINSKIJ INSTITUT**
State Institute of Medicine
Pr. Vinogradova 51, 163061 Arhangel'sk, Rossiskaja SFSR
Medicine (including Dentistry)
Academic Year: September to July.
Admission Requirements: Competitive entrance examination following general or special secondary school certificate.
Degrees and Diplomas: Professional title in relevant fields, 5-6 yrs.

7513 **ASTRAHANSKIJ GOSUDARSTVENNYJ MEDICINSKIJ INSTITUT IM. A.V. LUNAČARSKOGO**
State Institute of Medicine
Ul. Mečnikova 20, 414000 Astrahan', Rossiskaja SFSR
Medicine (including Pediatrics)
Academic Year: September to July.
Admission Requirements: Competitive entrance examination following general or special secondary school certificate.
Degrees and Diplomas: Professional title in Medicine, 6 yrs.

7514 **AZERBAJDŽANSKIJ ORDENA TRUDOVOGO KRASNOGO ZNAMENI GOSUDARSTVENNYJ MEDICINSKIJ INSTITUT IM. N. NARIMANOVA**
State Institute of Medicine
Ul. Bakihanova 23, 370022 Baku 22, Azerbajdžanskaja SSR
Medicine (including Pediatrics, Hygiene, Pharmacy, and Dentistry)
Also evening courses.
Academic Year: September to July.
Admission Requirements: Competitive entrance examination following general or special secondary school certificate.
Degrees and Diplomas: Professional title in relevant fields, 5-6 yrs.

7515 **BAŠKIRSKIJ GOSUDARSTVENNYJ MEDICINSKIJ INSTITUT IM. 15-LETIJA VLKSM**
State Institute of Medicine
Ul. Frunze 47, 450025 Ufa, Rossiskaja SFSR
Medicine (including Pediatrics and Hygiene)
Also evening courses.
Academic Year: September to July.
Admission Requirements: Competitive entrance examination following general or special secondary school certificate.
Degrees and Diplomas: Professional title in relevant fields.

7516 **BLAGOVEŠČENSKIJ GOSUDARSTVENNYJ MEDICINSKIJ INSTITUT**
State Institute of Medicine
Ul. Gor'kogo 95, 675006 Blagoveščensk Amurskoj obl., Rossiskaja SFSR
Medicine
Academic Year: September to July.
Admission Requirements: Competitive entrance examination following general or special secondary school certificate.
Degrees and Diplomas: Professional title in Medicine, 6 yrs.

7517 **CELINOGRADSKIJ MEDICINSKIJ INSTITUT**
Institute of Medicine
Prosp. Mira 51a, 473013 Celinograd, Kazahskaja SSR
Medicine (including Pediatrics)
Academic Year: September to July.
Admission Requirements: Competitive entrance examination following general or special secondary school certificate.
Degrees and Diplomas: Professional title in Medicine, 6 yrs.

7518 **ČELJABINSKIJ GOSUDARSTVENNYJ MEDICINSKIJ INSTITUT**
State Institute of Medicine
Ul. Vorovskogo 64, 454092 Čeljabinsk, Rossiskaja SFSR
Medicine (including Pediatrics)
Academic Year: September to July.
Admission Requirements: Competitive entrance examination following general or special secondary school certificate.
Degrees and Diplomas: Professional title in relevant fields, 5-6 yrs.

7519 **ČERNOVICKIJ GOSUDARSTVENNYJ MEDICINSKIJ INSTITUT**

State Institute of Medicine

Teatral'naja pl. 2, 274000 Černovcy, Ukrainskaja SSR

Medicine

Academic Year: September to July.

Admission Requirements: Competitive entrance examination following general or special secondary school certificate.

Degrees and Diplomas: Professional title in Medicine, 6 yrs.

7520 **ČITINSKIJ GOSUDARSTVENNYJ MEDICINSKIJ INSTITUT**

State Institute of Medicine

Ul. Gor'kogo 39a, 672090 Čita, Rossiskaja SFSR

Medicine (including Dentistry)

Academic Year: September to July.

Admission Requirements: Competitive entrance examination following general or special secondary school certificate.

Degrees and Diplomas: Professional title in relevant fields, 5-6 yrs.

7521 **DAGESTANSKIJ ORDENA DRUŽBY NARODOV GOSUDARSTVENNYJ MEDICINSKIJ INSTITUT**

State Institute of Medicine

Pl. Lenina 6, 367025 Mahačkala, Dagestanskaja ASSR

Medicine (including Dentistry and Pediatrics)

Also evening classes.

Academic Year: September to July.

Admission Requirements: Competitive entrance examination following general or special secondary school certificate.

Degrees and Diplomas: Professional title in relevant fields, 5-6 yrs.

7522 **DNEPROPETROVSKIJ ORDENA TRUDOVOGO KRASNOGO ZNAMENI MEDICINSKIJ INSTITUT**

State Institute of Medicine

Ul. Dzeržinskogo 9, 320044 Dnepropetrovsk, Ukrainskaja SSR

Medicine (including Pediatrics, Hygiene and Dentistry)

Also evening courses.

Academic Year: September to July.

Admission Requirements: Competitive entrance examination following general or special secondary school certificate.

Degrees and Diplomas: Professional title in relevant fields, 5-6 yrs.

7523 **DONECKIJ GOSUDARSTVENNYJ MEDICINSKIJ INSTITUT IM. MAKSIMA GOR'KOGO**

State Institute of Medicine

Prosp. Il'iča 16, 340098 Doneck, Ukrainskaja SSR

Medicine (including Pediatrics, Hygiene and Dentistry)

Also evening courses.

Academic Year: September to July.

Admission Requirements: Competitive entrance examination following general or special secondary school certificate.

Degrees and Diplomas: Professional title in relevant fields, 5-6 yrs.

7524 **EREVANSKIJ ORDENA TRUDOVOGO KRASNOGO ZNAMENI GOSUDARSTVENNYJ MEDICINSKIJ INSTITUT**

State Institute of Medicine

Ul. Kirova 2, 375025 Erevan 25, Armjanskaja SSR

Medicine (including Hygiene, Pediatrics and Dentistry)

Academic Year: September to July.

Admission Requirements: Competitive entrance examination following general or special secondary school certificate.

Degrees and Diplomas: Professional title in relevant fields, 5-6 yrs.

7525 **GOR'KOVSKIJ GOSUDARSTVENNYJ MEDICINSKIJ INSTITUT IM. S.M. KIROVA**

State Institute of Medicine

Pl. Minina i Požarskogo 10/1, 603005 Gor'kij, Rossiskaja SFSR

Medicine (including Pediatrics and Hygiene)

Academic Year: September to July.

Admission Requirements: Competitive entrance examination following general or special secondary school certificate.

Degrees and Diplomas: Professional title in relevant fields, 5-6 yrs.

7526 **GRODNENSKIJ GOSUDARSTVENNYJ MEDICINSKIJ INSTITUT**

State Institute of Medicine

Ul. Gorkogo 80, 230015 Grodno, Belorusskaja SSR

Medicine (including Pediatrics)

Academic Year: September to July.

Admission Requirements: Competitive entrance examination following general or special secondary school certificate.

Degrees and Diplomas: Professional title in Medicine, 6 yrs.

7527 **HABAROVSKIJ ORDENA TRUDOVOGO KRASNOGO ZNAMENI GOSUDARSTVENNYJ MEDICINSKIJ INSTITUT**

State Institute of Medicine

Ul. Karla Marksa 35, 680000 Habarovsk, Rossiskaja SFSR

Medicine (including Pediatrics and Pharmacy)

Academic Year: September to July.

Admission Requirements: Competitive entrance examination following general or special secondary school certificate.

Degrees and Diplomas: Professional title in relevant fields, 5-6 yrs.

7528 **HAR'KOVSKIJ MEDICINSKIJ INSTITUT**

Institute of Medicine

Prosp. V.I. Lenina 4, 310022 Har'kov, Ukrainskaja SSR

Medicine (including Pediatrics and Hygiene)

Academic Year: September to July.

Admission Requirements: Competitive entrance examination following general or special secondary school certificate.

Degrees and Diplomas: Professional title in relevant fields, 5-6 yrs.

7529 **IRKUTSKIJ GOSUDARSTVENNYJ MEDICINSKIJ INSTITUT**

State Institute of Medicine

Ul. Krasnogo Vosstanija 1, 664003 Irkutsk, Rossiskaja SFSR

Medicine (including Hygiene, Pharmacy and Dentistry)

Also evening courses.

Academic Year: September to July.

Admission Requirements: Competitive entrance examination following general or special secondary school certificate.

Degrees and Diplomas: Professional title in relevant fields, 5-6 yrs.

7530 **IVANO-FRANKOVSKIJ MEDICINSKIJ INSTITUT**

State Institute of Medicine

Galickaja ul. 2, 284000 Ivano-Frankovsk, Ukrainskaja SSR

Medicine (including Dentistry)

Academic Year: September to July.

Admission Requirements: Competitive entrance examination following general or special secondary school certificate.

Degrees and Diplomas: Professional title in relevant fields, 5-6 yrs.

7531 **IVANOVSKIJ GOSUDARSTVENNYJ MEDICINSKIJ INSTITUT IM. A.S. BUBNOVA**

State Institute of Medicine

Ul. F. Engel'sa 8, 153462 Ivanovo, Rossiskaja SFSR

Medicine (including Pediatrics)

Academic Year: September to July.

Admission Requirements: Competitive entrance examination following general or special secondary school certificate.

Degrees and Diplomas: Professional title in relevant fields, 5-6 yrs.

7532 **IŽEVSKIJ ORDENA DRUŽBY NARODOV GOSUDARSTVENNYJ MEDICINSKIJ INSTITUT**

State Institute of Medicine

Ul. Revoljucionnaja 199, 426034 Iževsk, Udmurtskoj ASSR

7533 **JAROSLVASKIJ GOSUDARSTVENNYJ MEDICINSKIJ INSTITUT**

State Institute of Medicine

Revoljucionnaja ul. 5, 150000 Jaroslavl', Rossiskaja SFSR

Medicine (including Dentistry and Pediatrics)

Academic Year: September to July.

Admission Requirements: Competitive entrance examination following general or special secondary school certificate.

Degrees and Diplomas: Professional title in relevant fields, 5-6 yrs.

7534 **KALININSKIJ GOSUDARSTVENNYJ MEDICINSKIJ INSTITUT**

State Institute of Medicine

Sovetskaja ul. 4, 170642 Kalinin, Rossiskaja SFSR

Medicine (including Dentistry)

Academic Year: September to July.

Admission Requirements: Competitive entrance examination following general or special secondary school certificate.

Degrees and Diplomas: Professional title in relevant fields, 5-6 yrs.

7535 **KARAGANDINSKIJ GOSUDARSTVENNYJ MEDICINSKIJ INSTITUT**

State Institute of Medicine

Ul. Gogolja 40, 470061 Karaganda, Kazahskaja SSR

Medicine (including Hygiene, Pediatrics and Dentistry)

Academic Year: September to July.

Admission Requirements: Competitive entrance examination following general or special secondary school certificate.

Degrees and Diplomas: Professional title in relevant fields, 5-6 yrs.

7536 **KAUNASSKIJ GOSUDARSTVENNYJ MEDICINSKIJ INSTITUT**

State Institute of Medicine

Ul. Mickevičiaus 9, 233683 Kaunas, Litovskaja SSR

Telephone: 2-61-10

Medicine (including Dentistry, Pharmacy, Pediatrics and Hygiene)

Founded 1950. Financed by the State.

Academic Year: September to June (September-January; February-July).

Admission Requirements: Competitive entrance examination following general or special secondary school certificate.

Fees: None.

Languages of Instruction: Lithuanian and Russian.

Degrees and Diplomas: Professional titles in–Medicine; Pharmacy; Dentistry, 5-6 yrs. Also Candidate and Doctorate.

Library: c. 530,000 vols.

Special Facilities (Museums, etc.): Museums: Anatomy; Pathological Anatomy.

Publication: Institute Proceedings.

Academic Staff: c. 360.

Student Enrolment: c. 3100.

7537 **KAZANSKIJ ORDENA TRUDOVOGO KRASNOGO ZNAMENI GOSUDARSTVENNYJ MEDICINSKIJ INSTITUT IM. S.V. KURAŠOVA**

State Institute of Medicine

Ul. Butlerova 49, 420012 Kazan' 12, Rossiskaja SFSR

Telephone: 36-06-52

Rektor: N.H. Amirov

Vicerektor: A.P. Pigalov

F. of Medicine
Dean: A.L. Zephirov

F. of Pediatrics
Dean: O.I. Pikuda

F. of Hygiene
Dean: V.M. Andreyev

F. of Dentistry
Dean: I.M. Andreyev

F. of Pharmacy
Dean: V.A. Shukin

Preparatory D.
Dean: Sh. B. Phaizullin

Central Research I.
Head: R.H. Ahmetzyanov

Founded 1814 as medical faculty of Kazan University. Acquired present status and title 1930.

Academic Year: September to June.

Admission Requirements: Competitive entrance examination following general or special secondary school certificate.

Fees: None.

Language of Instruction: Russian.

Degrees and Diplomas: Professional title in relevant fields, 5-6 yrs. Doktor nauk, Doctor of the Sciences, a further 5-6 yrs.

Library: 578,177 vols.

Special Facilities (Museums, etc.): Institute History Museum.

Publication: Kazan Medical Journal (bimonthly).

Academic Staff, 1990: 471 (36).

Student Enrolment, 1990:

	Men	Women	Total
Of the country	1866	2901	4867*

*Also 6 external students.

7538 **KEMEROVSKIJ GOSUDARSTVENNYJ MEDICINSKIJ INSTITUT**

State Institute of Medicine

Ul. Varošilova 22a, 650029 Kemerovo obl., Rossiskaja SFSR

Medicine (including Dentistry, Hygiene, Pediatrics and Pharmacy)

Academic Year: September to July.

Admission Requirements: Competitive entrance examination following general or special secondary school certificate.

Degrees and Diplomas: Professional title in relevant fields, 5-6 yrs.

7539 **KIEVSKIJ ORDENA TRUDOVOGO KRASNOGO ZNAMENI MEDICINSKIJ INSTITUT IM. AKAD. A.A. BOGOMOL'CA**

Institute of Medicine

Bul. Tarasa Ševčenko 13, 252004 Kiev, Ukrainskaja SSR

Medicine (including Pediatrics, Dentistry and Hygiene)

Also evening courses.

Academic Year: September to July.

Admission Requirements: Competitive entrance examination following general or special secondary school certificate.

Degrees and Diplomas: Professional title in relevant fields, 5-6 yrs.

7540 **KIRGIZSKIJ GOSUDARSTVENNYJ MEDICINSKIJ INSTITUT**

State Institute of Medicine

Ul. 50 let Oktjabrja 92, 720061 Frunze, Kirgizskaja SSR

Medicine (including Hygiene, Pediatrics, Dentistry and Pharmacy)

Academic Year: September to July.

Admission Requirements: Competitive entrance examination following general or special secondary school certificate.

Degrees and Diplomas: Professional title in relevant fields, 5-6 yrs.

7541 **KIŠINEVSKIJ GOSUDARSTVENNYJ MEDICINSKIJ INSTITUT**

State Institute of Medicine

Prosp. Lenina 165, 277017 Kišinev, Moldavskaja SSR

Medicine (including Pediatrics, Dentistry, Hygiene and Pharmacy)

Academic Year: September to July.

Admission Requirements: Competitive entrance examination following general or special secondary school certificate.

Degrees and Diplomas: Professional title in relevant fields, 5-6 yrs.

7542 **KRASNOJARSKIJ GOSUDARSTVENNYJ MEDICINSKIJ INSTITUT**

State Institute of Medicine

Ul. Partizana Železnjaka 1, 660022 Krasnojarsk, Rossiskaja SFSR

Medicine (including Pediatrics and Dentistry)

Also evening courses.

Academic Year: September to July.

Admission Requirements: Competitive entrance examination following general or special secondary school certificate.

Degrees and Diplomas: Professional title in relevant fields, 5-6 yrs.

7543 **KRYMSKIJ ORDENA TRUDOVOGO KRASNOGO ZNAMENI MEDICINSKIJ INSTITUT**

Institute of Medicine

Bul. Lenina 5/7, 333670 Simferopol', Rossiskaja SFSR

Medicine (including Pediatrics)

Academic Year: September to July.

Admission Requirements: Competitive entrance examination following general or special secondary school certificate.

Degrees and Diplomas: Professional title in relevant fields, 5-6 yrs.

7544 **KUBANSKIJ GOSUDARSTVENNYJ MEDICINSKIJ INSTITUT IM. KRASNOJ ARMII**

State Institute of Medicine

Ul. Sedina 4, 350603 Krasnodar, Rossiskaja SFSR

Medicine (including Dentistry and Pediatrics)

Academic Year: September to July.

Admission Requirements: Competitive entrance examination following general or special secondary school certificate.

Degrees and Diplomas: Professional title in relevant fields, 5-6 yrs.

7545 **KUJBYŠEVSKIJ MEDICINSKIJ INSTITUT IM. D.I. UL'JANOVA**

Institute of Medicine

Čapaevskaja ul. 89, 443099 Kujbyšev obl., Rossiskaja SFSR

Medicine (including Dentistry, Pediatrics and Pharmacy)

Academic Year: September to July.

Admission Requirements: Competitive entrance examination following general or special secondary school certificate.

Degrees and Diplomas: Professional title in Medicine, 6 yrs.

7546 **KURSKIJ GOSUDARSTVENNYJ MEDICINSKIJ INSTITUT**

State Institute of Medicine

Ul. Karla Marksa 3, 305033 Kursk, Rossiskaja SFSR

Medicine (including Pharmacy)

Academic Year: September to July.

Admission Requirements: Competitive entrance examination following general or special secondary school certificate.

Degrees and Diplomas: Professional title in Medicine, 6 yrs.

7547 **1-J LENINGRADSKIJ ORDENA TRUDOVOGO KRASNOGO ZNAMENI MEDICINSKIJ INSTITUT IM. AKAD. I.P. PAVLOVA**

Institute of Medicine

Ul. L'va Tolstogo 6/8, 197089 Leningrad P-89, Rossiskaja SFSR

Telephone: V-289-62

Medicine (including Dentistry)

Academic Year: September to July (September-January; February-July).

Admission Requirements: Competitive entrance examination following general or special secondary school certificate.

Degrees and Diplomas: Professional titles–in Dentistry, 5 yrs; General Medicine, 6 yrs.

7548 **LENINGRADSKIJ ORDENA TRUDOVOGO KRASNOGO ZNAMENI PEDIATRIČESKIJ MEDICINSKIJ INSTITUT**

Institute of Pediatrics

Litovskaja ul. 2, 194100 Leningrad K-100, Rossiskaja SFSR

Pediatrics

Academic Year: September to July.

Admission Requirements: Competitive entrance examination following general or special secondary school certificate.

Degrees and Diplomas: Professional title in Pediatrics.

7549 **LENINGRADSKIJ SANITARNO-GIGIENIČESKIJ MEDICINSKIJ INSTITUT**

Institute of Medicine and Hygiene

Piskarevskij prosp. 47, 195067 Leningrad, Rossiskaja SFSR

Medicine and Hygiene

Also evening courses.

Academic Year: September to July.

Admission Requirements: Competitive entrance examination following general or special secondary school certificate.

Degrees and Diplomas: Professional title in relevant fields, 5-6 yrs.

7550 **L'VOVSKIJ ORDENA DRUŽBY NARODOV MEDICINSKIJ INSTITUT**

State Institute of Medicine

Pekarskaja ul. 69, 290010 L'vov, Ukrainskaja SSR

Medicine (including Dentistry, Pediatrics, and Pharmacy and Hygiene)

Academic Year: September to July.

Admission Requirements: Competitive entrance examination following general or special secondary school certificate.

Degrees and Diplomas: Professional title in relevant fields, 5-6 yrs.

7551 **MINSKIJ ORDENA TRUDOVOGO KRASNOGO ZNAMENI GOSUDARSTVENNYJ MEDICINSKIJ INSTITUT**

State Institute of Medicine

Prosp. Dzeržinskogo, 220798 Minsk, Belorusskaja SSR

Medicine (including Dentistry, Pediatrics and Hygiene)

Academic Year: September to July.

Admission Requirements: Competitive entrance examination following general or special secondary school certificate.

Degrees and Diplomas: Professional title in relevant fields, 5-6 yrs.

7552 ***1-J MOSKOVSKIJ ORDENA LENINA I ORDENA TRUDOVOGO KRASNOGO ZNAMENI MEDICINSKIJ INSTITUT IM. I.M. SEČENOVA**

Institute of Medicine

2/6 Pirogovskaja ul., 119435 Moskva, Rossiskaja SFSR

Cables: Moscow 881, B. Pirogovskaya, 2/6

Telephone: 248-05-53

Rektor: Michail Paltsev

F. of Medicine I
F. of Medicine II
F. of Hygiene
F. of Pharmacy
Evening D. of Advanced Training (Pharmacy)
D. of Advanced Teachers' Training
Central Scientific Research L.
L. of Radiobiology
L. of Radiation Defence
L. of Anaesthesiology
L. of Brain Biochemistry

Founded 1755 as faculty of medicine of the University of Moscow. Became institute 1930. Under the authority ofthe Union-Republic State Committee for Public Education. Some residential facilities for students.

Arrangements for co-operation with: Charles University, Prague; Semmelweis Medical University; Academy of Medicine, Erfurt.

Academic Year: September to July (September-January; February-July).

Admission Requirements: Competitive entrance examination following general or special secondary school certificate.

Fees: None.

Language of Instruction: Russian.

Degrees and Diplomas: Professional title in relevant fields, 5-6 yrs. Kandidat nauk, Candidate of the Sciences, a further 3 yrs. Doktor nauk, by thesis after Kandidat.

Library: c. 1,000,000 vols.

Special Facilities (Museums, etc.): Museums: Normal Anatomy; Pathological Anatomy; Operative Surgery and Topographical Anatomy; General Hygiene; Skin and Venereal Diseases; Biology; Histology; Physiology, etc.

Publication: Scientific Papers 'Sa Meditsinskiye Kadry'.

Academic Staff, 1986-87: c. 1050.

Student Enrolment, 1986-87:

	Men	Women	Total
Of the country	2244	6339	8583
Of other countries	234	191	425
Total	2478	6530	9008

7553 **2-J MOSKOVSKIJ ORDENA LENINA GOSUDARSTVENNYJ MEDICINSKIJ INSTITUT IM. N.I. PIROGOVA**

State Institute of Medicine

Ul. Ostrovitjanova 1, 117437 Moskva G-435, Rossiskaja SFSR

Medicine (including Pediatrics, Biophysics and Biochemistry)

Also evening courses.

Academic Year: September to July.

Admission Requirements: Competitive entrance examination following general or special secondary school certificate.

Degrees and Diplomas: Professional title in relevant fields, 5-6 yrs.

7554 **NOVOSIBIRSKIJ MEDICINSKIJ INSTITUT**

Institute of Medicine

Krasnyj prosp. 52, 630091 Novosibirsk, Rossiskaja SFSR

Medicine (including Pediatrics and Dentistry)

Academic Year: September to July.

Admission Requirements: Competitive entrance examination following general or special secondary school certificate.

Degrees and Diplomas: Professional title in Medicine, 6 yrs.

7555 **ODESSKIJ MEDICINSKIJ INSTITUT IM. N.I. PIROGOVA**
Institute of Medicine
Narimana Narimanova, per.2, 270100 Odessa, Ukrainskaja SSR
Medicine (including Pediatrics and Dentistry)
Academic Year: September to July.
Admission Requirements: Competitive entrance examination following general or special secondary school certificate.
Degrees and Diplomas: Professional title in relevant fields, 5-6 yrs.

7556 **OMSKIJ ORDENA TRUDOVOGO KRASNOGO ZNAMENI GOSUDARSTVENNYJ MEDICINSKIJ INSTITUT IM. M.I. KALININA**
State Institute of Medicine
Ul. V.I. Lenina 12, 644099 Omsk, Rossiskaja SFSR
Medicine (including Pediatrics, Dentistry and Hygiene)
Academic Year: September to July.
Admission Requirements: Competitive entrance examination following general or special secondary school certificate.
Degrees and Diplomas: Professional title in relevant fields, 5-6 yrs.

7557 **ORENBURGSKIJ GOSUDARSTVENNYJ MEDICINSKIJ INSTITUT**
State Institute of Medicine
Sovetskaja ul. 6, 460834 Orenburg, Rossiskaja SFSR
Medicine (including Pediatrics)
Academic Year: September to July.
Admission Requirements: Competitive entrance examination following general or special secondary school certificate.
Degrees and Diplomas: Professional title in Medicine, 6 yrs.

7558 **PERMSKIJ GOSUDARSTVENNYJ MEDICINSKIJ INSTITUT**
State Institute of Medicine
Ul. Kujbyševa 39, 614600 Perm', GSP 186 Rossiskaja SFSR
Medicine (including Dentistry and Hygiene)
Academic Year: September to July.
Admission Requirements: Competitive entrance examination following general or special secondary school certificate.
Degrees and Diplomas: Professional title in relevant fields, 5-6 yrs.

7559 **RIŽSKIJ MEDICINSKIJ INSTITUT**
Institute of Medicine
Bul. Padomju 12, 226352 Riga, Latvijskaja SSR
Medicine (including Dentistry, Pharmacy, and Pediatrics)
Academic Year: September to July.
Admission Requirements: Competitive entrance examination following general or special secondary school certificate.
Degrees and Diplomas: Professional title in relevant fields, 5-6 yrs.

7560 **RJAZANSKIJ MEDICINSKIJ INSTITUT IM. AKAD. I.P. PAVLOVA**
Institute of Medicine
Ul. Majakovskogo 105, 390000 Rjazan', Rossiskaja SFSR
Medicine (including Hygiene and Pharmacy)
Academic Year: September to July.
Admission Requirements: Competitive entrance examination following general or special secondary school certificate.
Degrees and Diplomas: Professional title in Medicine, 6 yrs.

7561 **ROSTOVSKIJ ORDENA DRUŽBY NARODOV MEDICINSKIJ INSTITUT**
Institute of Medicine
Nahičevanskij per. 29, 344718 Rostov-na-Donu, Rossiskaja SFSR
Medicine (including Pediatrics and Hygiene)
Academic Year: September to July.
Admission Requirements: Competitive entrance examination following general or special secondary school certificate.
Degrees and Diplomas: Professional title in relevant fields, 5-6 yrs.

7562 **SAMARKANDSKIJ ORDENA DRUŽBY NARODOV GOSUDARSTVENNYJ MEDICINSKIJ INSTITUT IM. AKAD. I.P. PAVLOVA**
State Institute of Medicine
Ul. Frunze 18, 703000 Samarkand, Uzbekskaja SSR
Medicine (including Pediatrics)
Academic Year: September to July.
Admission Requirements: Competitive entrance examination following general or special secondary school certificate.
Degrees and Diplomas: Professional title in relevant fields, 5-6 yrs.

7563 **SARATOVSKIJ ORDENA TRUDOVOGO KRASNOGO ZNAMENI GOSUDARSTVENNYJ MEDICINSKIJ INSTITUT**
State Institute of Medicine
Ul. 20-Letija VLKSM 112, 410601 Saratov, Rossiskaja SFSR
Medicine (including Pediatrics)
Academic Year: September to July.
Admission Requirements: Competitive entrance examination following general or special secondary school certificate.
Degrees and Diplomas: Professional title in relevant fields, 5-6 yrs.

7564 **SEMIPALATINSKIJ GOSUDARSTVENNYJ MEDICINSKIJ INSTITUT**
State Institute of Medicine
Ul. Sovetskaja 103, 490050 Semipalatinsk, Kazahskaja SSR
Medicine (including Pediatrics)
Academic Year: September to July.
Admission Requirements: Competitive entrance examination following general or special secondary school certificate.
Degrees and Diplomas: Professional title in Medicine, 6 yrs.

7565 **SEVERO-OSETINKSKIJ GOSUDARSTVENNYJ MEDICINSKIJ INSTITUT**
State Institute of Medicine
Puškinskaja ul. 10, 362025 Ordžonikidze, Rossiskaja SFSR
Medicine (including Pediatrics)
Academic Year: September to July.
Admission Requirements: Competitive entrance examination following general or special secondary school certificate.
Degrees and Diplomas: Professional title in relevant fields, 5-6 yrs.

7566 **SMOLENSKIJ GOSUDARSTVENNYJ MEDICINSKIJ INSTITUT**
State Institute of Medicine
Ul. Glinki 3, 214000 Smolensk, Rossiskaja SFSR
Medicine (including Dentistry and Pediatrics)
Academic Year: September to July.
Admission Requirements: Competitive entrance examination following general or special secondary school certificate.
Degrees and Diplomas: Professional title in relevant fields, 5-6 yrs.

7567 **SREDNEAZIATSKIJ MEDICINSKIJ PEDIATRIČESKIJ INSTITUT**
Institute of Pediatrics
Ul. Čermet 103, 700140 Taškent, Uzbekskaja SSR
Pediatrics
Academic Year: September to July.
Admission Requirements: Competitive entrance examination following general or special secondary school certificate.
Degrees and Diplomas: Professional title, 6 yrs.

7568 **STAVROPOL'SKIJ GOSUDARSTVENNYJ MEDICINSKIJ INSTITUT**
State Institute of Medicine
Ul. Mira 310, 355024 Stavropol' Kraevoj, Rossiskaja SFSR
Medicine (including Dentistry and Pediatrics)
Academic Year: September to July.
Admission Requirements: Competitive entrance examination following general or special secondary school certificate.
Degrees and Diplomas: Professional title in relevant fields, 5-6 yrs.

7569 **SVERDLOVSKIJ ORDENA TRUDOVOGO KRASNOGO ZNAMENI GOSUDARSTVENNYJ MEDICINSKIJ INSTITUT**

State Institute of Medicine

Ul. Repina 3, 620119 Sverdlovsk 28, Rossiskaja SFSR

Medicine (including Pediatrics, Hygiene and Dentistry)

Academic Year: September to July.

Admission Requirements: Competitive entrance examination following general or special secondary school certificate.

Degrees and Diplomas: Professional title in relevant fields, 5-6 yrs.

7570 **TADŽIKSKIJ GOSUDARSTVENNYJ MEDICINSKIJ INSTITUT IM. ABUALI IBN-SINY (AVICENNY)**

State Institute of Medicine

Prosp. V.I. Lenina 139, 734003 Dušanbe, Tadžikskaja SSR

Medicine (including Pediatrics, Dentistry and Pharmacy)

Academic Year: September to July.

Admission Requirements: Competitive entrance examination following general or special secondary school certificate.

Degrees and Diplomas: Professional title in relevant fields, 5-6 yrs.

7571 **TAŠKENTSKIJ ORDENA TRUDOVOGO KRASNOGO ZNAMENI GOSUDARSTVENNYJ MEDICINSKIJ INSTITUT**

State Institute of Medicine

Ul. Karla Marksa 103, 700033 Taškent, Uzbekskaja SSR

Medicine (including Dentistry and Hygiene)

Academic Year: September to July.

Admission Requirements: Competitive entrance examination following general or special secondary school certificate.

Degrees and Diplomas: Professional title in relevant fields, 5-6 yrs.

7572 **TBILISSKIJ ORDENA TRUDOVOGO KRASNOGO ZNAMENI GOSUDARSTVENNYJ MEDICINSKIJ INSTITUT**

State Institute of Medicine

Prosp. V. Pšavela 33, 380077 Tbilisi 77, Gruzinskaja SSR

Telephone: 99-90-09

Medicine (including Pediatrics, Pharmacy, Dentistry and Hygiene)

Research L.

Founded 1918 as medical department of Tbilisi University, acquired present status 1930. Under the authority ofthe Ministry of Public Health of the Georgian Republic. Residential facilities for students.

Academic Year: September to June (September-January; February-June).

Admission Requirements: Competitive entrance examination following general or special secondary school certificate.

Fees: None.

Languages of Instruction: Georgian and Russian.

Degrees and Diplomas: Professional title in relevant fields, 5-6 yrs. Candidate of–Biological Sciences; Medical Sciences; Pharmaceutical Sciences, a further 3-5 yrs. Doctor, by thesis after candidate.

Library: Central Library, *c.* 300,000 vols.

Publications: Trudi Tbilisskogo Meditsinskogo Instituta (Proceedings); Nauchnie Raboti Studentov (Students' Scientific Works).

Academic Staff: c. 400.

Student Enrolment: c. 3500.

7573 **TERNOPOL'SKIJ MEDICINSKIJ INSTITUT**

State Institute of Medicine

Pl. Svobodny 6, 282001 Ternopol', Ukrainskaja SSR

Telephone: 6-31

Medicine

Founded 1957.

Academic Year: September to July (September-February; February-July).

Admission Requirements: Competitive entrance examination following general or special secondary school certificate or diploma of secondary medical education.

Degrees and Diplomas: Professional titles in–Medicine; Therapeutic Medicine, 6 yrs.

7574 **TJUMENSKIJ GOSUDARSTVENNYJ MEDICINSKIJ INSTITUT**

State Institute of Medicine

Odesskaja ul. 52, 625023 Tjumen', Ukrainskaja SSR

Medicine (including Pharmacy)

Academic Year: September to July.

Admission Requirements: Competitive entrance examination following general or special secondary school certificate.

Degrees and Diplomas: Professional title in relevant fields, 5-6 yrs.

7575 **TOMSKIJ ORDENA TRUDOVOGO KRASNOGO ZNAMENI GOSUDARSTVENNYJ MEDICINSKIJ INSTITUT**

State Institute of Medicine

Moskovskij trakt 2, 634050 Tomsk, Rossiskaja SFSR

Medicine (including Pharmacy, Pediatrics, Biophysics and Biochemistry)

Academic Year: September to July.

Admission Requirements: Competitive entrance examination following general or special secondary school certificate.

Degrees and Diplomas: Professional title in relevant fields, 5-6 yrs.

7576 **TURKMENSKIJ ORDENA DRUŽBY NARODOV GOSUDARSTVENNYJ MEDICINSKIJ INSTITUT**

State Institute of Medicine

Ul. Šaumjana 58, 744000 Ašhabad GSP-19, Turkmenskaja SSR

Medicine (including Dentistry and Pediatrics)

Academic Year: September to July.

Admission Requirements: Competitive entrance examination following general or special secondary school certificate.

Degrees and Diplomas: Professional title in relevant fields, 5-6 yrs.

7577 **USTINOVSKIJ ORDENA DRUŽBY NORODOV GOSUDARSTVENNYJ MEDICINSKIJ INSTITUT**

Revoljucionnaja ul. 199, 426034 Ustinov, Rossiskaja SFSR

7578 **VINNICKIJ ORDENA 'ZNAK POČETA' MEDICINSKIJ INSTITUT IM. AKAD. N.I. PIROGOVA**

Institute of Medicine

Ul. Pirogova 54, 286018 Vinnica, Ukrainskaja SSR

Medicine (including Pediatrics)

Academic Year: September to July.

Admission Requirements: Competitive entrance examination following general or special secondary school certificate.

Degrees and Diplomas: Professional title in Medicine, 6 yrs.

7579 **VITEBSKIJ ORDENA DRUŽBY NARODOV MEDICINSKIJ INSTITUT**

Institute of Medicine

Prosp. Frunze 27, 210023 Vitebsk, Belorusskaja SSR

Medicine (including Pharmacy)

Academic Year: September to July.

Admission Requirements: Competitive entrance examination following general or special secondary school certificate.

Degrees and Diplomas: Professional title in relevant fields, 5-6 yrs.

7580 **VLADIVOSTOKSKIJ MEDICINSKIJ INSTITUT**

Institute of Medicine

Prosp. Ostrjakova 2, 690600 Vladivostok, Rossiskaja SFSR

Medicine (including Hygiene and Pediatrics)

Academic Year: September to July.

Admission Requirements: Competitive entrance examination following general or special secondary school certificate.

Degrees and Diplomas: Professional title in relevant fields, 5-6 yrs.

7581 **VOLGOGRADSKIJ MEDICINSKIJ INSTITUT**

Institute of Medicine

Pl. Pavših Borcov 1, 400066 Volgograd 2, Rossiskaja SFSR

Medicine (including Dentistry and Pediatrics)

Founded 1935.

Academic Year: September to July (September-January; February-July).

Admission Requirements: Competitive entrance examination following general or special secondary school certificate.

Degrees and Diplomas: Professional titles in–Dentistry, 5 yrs; Medicine, 6 yrs.

7582 **VORONEŽSKIJ GOSUDARSTVENNYJ MEDICINSKIJ INSTITUT IM. N.N. BURDENKO**
State Institute of Medicine
Studenčeskaja ul. 10, 394622 Voronež, Rossiskaja SFSR

Medicine (including Pediatrics and Dentistry)

Academic Year: September to July.

Admission Requirements: Competitive entrance examination following general or special secondary school certificate.

Degrees and Diplomas: Professional title in relevant fields, 5-6 yrs.

7583 **VOROŠILOVGRADSKIJ MEDICINSKIJ INSTITUT**
State Institute of Medicine
Ul. 50-let Oborony Luganska, 348045 Vorošilovgrad, Ukrainskaja SSR

Medicine (including Pediatrics)

Academic Year: September to July.

Admission Requirements: Competitive entrance examination following general or special secondary school certificate.

Degrees and Diplomas: Professional title in Medicine, 6 yrs.

7584 **ZAPOROŽSKIJ MEDICINSKIJ INSTITUT**
State Institute of Medicine
Ul. Majakovskogo 26, 330074 Zaporože, Ukrainskaja SSR

Medicine (including Pharmacy and Pediatrics)

Academic Year: September to July.

Admission Requirements: Competitive entrance examination following general or special secondary school certificate.

Degrees and Diplomas: Professional title in relevant fields, 5-6 yrs.

Dentistry

7585 **MOSKOVSKIJ ORDENA TRUDOVOGO KRASNOGO ZNAMENI MEDICINSKIJ STOMATOLOGIČESKIJ INSTITUT IM. N.A. SEMAŠKO**
Institute of Dentistry
Delegatskaja ul. 20, 103473 Moskva, Rossiskaja SFSR
Telephone: D1-76-46

Dentistry

Also evening courses.

Founded 1923 as research institute, became teaching institute 1935.

Academic Year: September to July (September-January; February-July).

Admission Requirements: Competitive entrance examination following general or special secondary school certificate.

Degrees and Diplomas: Professional title in Dentistry, 5 yrs.

7586 **POLTAVSKIJ MEDICINSKIJ-STOMATOLOGIČESKIJ INSTITUT**
Institute of Dentistry
Ul. Ševčenko 23, 314024 Poltava, Ukrainskaja SSR

Dentistry

Also evening courses.

Academic Year: September to July.

Admission Requirements: Competitive entrance examination following general or special secondary school certificate.

Degrees and Diplomas: Professional title in Dentistry, 5yrs.

Pharmacy

7587 **HABAROVSKIJ GOSUDARSTVENNYJ FARMACEVTIČESKIJ INSTITUT**
State Institute of Pharmacy
Ul. K. Marksa 30, 680000 Habarovsk, Rossiskaja SFSR

Pharmacy

Academic Year: September to July.

Admission Requirements: Competitive entrance examination following general or special secondary school certificate.

Degrees and Diplomas: Professional title in Pharmacy, 5 yrs.

7588 **HAR'KOVSKIJ FARMACEVTIČESKIJ INSTITUT**
State Institute of Pharmacy
Puškinskaja ul. 53, 310024 Har'kov 24, Ukrainskaja SSR
Telephone: 470164
Rektor: Valentin Petrovich Chernjkh

F. of Pharmacy

Dean: Victor Gridasow

Founded 1921. Residential facilities for students in 3 hostels.

Academic Year: September to July.

Admission Requirements: Competitive entrance examination following general or special secondary school certificate.

Fees: None.

Languages of Instruction: Russian and Ukrainian.

Degrees and Diplomas: Professional title in Pharmacy, 5 yrs.

Library: 5000 vols.

Academic Staff, 1990:

Rank	Full-time
Professors	21
Assistant Professors	91
Senior Teachers	44
Teachers	75
Total	231

Student Enrolment, 1990: 1967.

7589 **LENINGRADSKIJ HIMIKO-FARMACEVTIČESKIJ INSTITUT**
Institute of Pharmacy
Ul. Professora Popova 14, 197022, Leningrad, Rossiskaja SFSR

Pharmacy (including Perfume Technology)

Also evening courses.

Academic Year: September to July.

Admission Requirements: Competitive entrance examination following general or special secondary school certificate.

Degrees and Diplomas: Professional title in relevant fields, 5 yrs.

7590 **PERMSKIJ FARMACEVTIČESKIJ INSTITUT**
Institute of Pharmacy
Ul. Lenina 48, 614600 Perm' GSP-277, Rossiskaja SFSR

Pharmacy

Also evening courses.

Academic Year: September to July.

Admission Requirements: Competitive entrance examination following general or special secondary school certificate.

Degrees and Diplomas: Professional title in Pharmacy, 5 yrs.

7591 **PJATIGORSKIJ FARMACEVTIČESKIJ INSTITUT**
Institute of Pharmacy
Prosp. Kalinina 11, 357533 Pjatigorsk, Stavropol'skogo Kraja Rossiskaja SFSR

Pharmacy

Academic Year: September to July.

Admission Requirements: Competitive entrance examination following general or special secondary school certificate.

Degrees and Diplomas: Professional title in Pharmacy, 5 yrs.

7592 **TAŠKENTSKIJ FARMACEVTIČESKIJ INSTITUT**
Institute of Pharmacy
Ul. Kafanova 35, 700015 Taškent, Uzbekskaja SSR

Pharmacy

Academic Year: September to July.

Admission Requirements: Competitive entrance examination following general or special secondary school certificate.

Degrees and Diplomas: Professional title in Pharmacy, 5 yrs.

Conservatories and Institutes of Dramatic and Fine Arts

7593 **ALMA-ATINSKAJA GOSUDARSTVENNAJA KONSERVATORIJA IM. KURMANGAZY**

State Conservatory

Ul. Kirova 136, 480091 Alma-Ata, Kazahskaja SSR

Music

Academic Year: September to July.

Admission Requirements: Competitive entrance examination following general or special secondary school certificate.

Degrees and Diplomas: Diploma of Specialist in relevant fields, 5 yrs.

7594 **ASTRAHANSKAJA GOSUDARSTVENNAJA KONSERVATORIJA**

State Conservatory

Sovetskaja ul. 23, 414000 Astrahan', Rossiskaja SFSR

Music

Academic Year: September to July.

Admission Requirements: Competitive entrance examination following general or special secondary school certificate.

Degrees and Diplomas: Diploma of Specialist in relevant fields, 5 yrs.

7595 **AZERBAJDŽANSKAJA ORDENA TRUDOVOGO KRASNOGO ZNAMENI GOSUDARSTVENNAJA KONSERVATORIJA IM. UZEIRA GADŽIBEKOVA**

State Conservatory

Ul. G. Dimitrova 98, 370014 Baku, Azerbajdžanskaja SSR

Music

Academic Year: September to July.

Admission Requirements: Competitive entrance examination following general or special secondary school certificate.

Degrees and Diplomas: Diploma of Specialist in relevant fields, 5 yrs.

7596 **BELORUSSKAJA ORDENA DRUŽBY NARODOV GOSUDARSTVENNAJA KONSERVATORIJA IM. A.V. LUNAČARSKOGO**

State Conservatory

Internacional'naja ul. 30, 220303 Minsk, Belorusskaja SSR

Music

Academic Year: September to July.

Admission Requirements: Competitive entrance examination following general or special secondary school certificate.

Degrees and Diplomas: Diploma of Specialist in relevant fields, 5 yrs.

7597 **DAL'NEVOSTOČNYJ PEDAGOGIČESKIJ INSTITUT ISKUSSTV**

Far-Eastern Pedagogical Institute Arts

Ul. 1 Maja 3, 690600 Vladivostok, Rossiskaja SFSR

Telephone: 2-49-22

Rektor: Veniamin Alekseyevich Goncharenko

Prorektor: Gennady Yakovlevich Nizovsky G

F. of Music

Dean: Felix Ginelevich Kalman; *staff* 76 (27)

F. of Dramatic Art

Dean: German Konstantinovich Rogov; *staff* 15 (6)

F. of Painting

Dean: Arkady Yakovlevich Malkin; *staff* 8 (4)

Founded 1962.

Academic Year: September to July (September-January; February-June).

Admission Requirements: Competitive entrance examination following general or special secondary school certificate.

Fees: None.

Language of Instruction: Russian.

Degrees and Diplomas: Diploma of Specialist in relevant fields, 4-6 yrs.

Academic Staff, 1990:

Rank	Full-time	Part-time
Professors	4	–
Associate Professors	30	3
Assistant Professors	28	–
Instructors	41	40
Total	103	43

Student Enrolment, 1990:

Men	Women	Total
142	308	450*

*Also 165 students by correspondence.

7598 **DONECKIJ GOSUDARSTVENNYJ MUZYKAL'NO-PEDAGOGIČESKIJ INSTITUT IM. S.S. PROKOFIEVA**

Institute of Music and Pedagogics

Ul. Artema 44, 340086 Doneck, Ukrainskaja SSR

Telephone: 938122

Rektor: Viktor Leonidovich (1986-)

Vicerektor: Alexander Alexandrovich Glazunov

F. of Music

F. of Performing Arts

Head: Alexander U. Vitovsky

Orchestral F.

Head: Alexander I. Shevchenko

Founded 1968. Under the authority of the Ministry of Culture of the Ukrain SR. Residential facilities for students.

Academic Year: September to June (September-January; February-June).

Admission Requirements: Competitive entrance examination following general or special secondary school certificate.

Fees: None.

Language of Instruction: Russian.

Degrees and Diplomas: Diploma of Specialist in relevant fields, 5 yrs.

Special Facilities (Museums, etc.): The Institute Museum.

Student Enrolment, 1990:

	Men	Women	Total
Of the country	149	255	404*

*Also 162 external students.

7599 **EREVANSKAJA ORDENA TRUDOVOGO KRASNOGO ZNAMENI GOSUDARSTVENNAJA KONSERVATORIJA IM. KOMITASA**

State Conservatory

Ul. Sajat-Novy 1a, 375009 Erevan 9, Armjanskaja SSR

Music

Academic Year: September to July.

Admission Requirements: Competitive entrance examination following general or special secondary school certificate.

Degrees and Diplomas: Diploma of Specialist in relevant fields, 5 yrs.

7600 **GOR'KOVSKAJA GOSUDARSTVENNAJA KONSERVATORIJA IM. M.I. GLINKI**

State Conservatory

Ul. Piskunova 40, 603600 Gor'kij, Rossiskaja SFSR

Music

Academic Year: September to July.

Admission Requirements: Competitive entrance examination following general or special secondary school certificate.

Degrees and Diplomas: Diploma of Specialist in relevant fields, 5 yrs.

7601 **GOSUDARSTVENNAJA KONSERVATORIJA LATVIKSKOJ SSR IM. JA. VITOLA**

Latvian State Conservatory

Ul. Krišjaņa Baroņa 1, 226050 Riga, Latvijskaja SSR

Telephone: 22-86-84

Music

Founded 1919. Governing body: the Rector and Pro-Rectors; the Academic Council.

Academic Year: September to July (September-January; February-July).

Admission Requirements: Competitive entrance examination following general or special secondary school certificate or equivalent.

Fees: None.

Languages of Instruction: Latvian and Russian.

Degrees and Diplomas: Diploma of Specialist in a particular field, 5 yrs.

Libraries: Central Library, *c.* 180,000 vols and scores; *c.* 25,000 recordings.
Academic Staff: c. 150.
Student Enrolment: c. 500 (Also *c.* 200 external students).

7602 **LIETUVOS KONSERVATORIJA**
Lithuanian Conservatory
Prosp. Geomino 42, 232000 Vilnius, Lietuvos Respublika
Telephone: 612691
Rektor: V. Lavrusas (1983-)
Vicerektor: J. Antanavicius

F. of Piano and Musicology
Dean: E. Ignatonis; *staff* 144 (30)
Orchestral F.
Dean: V. Leimontas; *staff* 74 (19)
F. of Choral and Orchestral Conducting, and Dramatic Art
Dean: O. Palekiene; *staff* 101 (31)
F. of Music (Kaunas)
Dean: R. Čepinskas; *staff* 18 (16)
L. of Folk Music Research
Head: D. Račlūnaite *staff* 7
L. of Music Theory
Head: R. Gaidamavičiūte; *staff* 5

Founded 1933. Acquired present title 1990. Governing body: the Council.
Arrangements for co-operation with Salzburg (Austria) Hochschule für Musik 'Mozarteum'.
Academic Year: September to July.
Admission Requirements: Competitive entrance examination following general or special secondary school certificate.
Language of Instruction: Lithuanian. Special subjects, Lithuanian, Russian, Polish, German, English.
Degrees and Diplomas: Diploma of Specialist in relevant fields, 5 yrs. Doktor nauk, 3 yrs. Master (for Musicologists).
Libraries: Two libraries, total, 420,000 vols; 25,000 records; 9000 tapes.
Publication: Menotyra (Science of Art, annually).
Academic Staff, 1990:

Rank	Full-time	Part-time
Professors	40	–
Assistant Professors	90	2
Others	197	78
Total	327	80

Student Enrolment, 1990:

	Men	Women	Total
Of the country	332	368	700
Of other countries	9	12	21
Total	341	380	721*

*Also 232 external students.

7603 **GOSUDARSTVENNYJ MUZYKAL'NO-PEDAGOGIČESKIJ INSTITUT IM. GNESINYH**
Gnesinz State Musical-Pedagogical Institute
Ul. Vorovskogo 3⅓6, 121069 Moskva G-69, Rossiskaja SFSR
Telephone: 29-15-54
Rektor: Sergey Kolobkov

Music
L. of Folk Music
Head: Margarite Yengovatova; *staff* 5 (4)
L. of Musical Informatic and Modern Methods of Teaching
Head: Boris Talalay; *staff* 8 (2)

Founded 1944 by the Gnesinz family.
Arrangements for joint research with Bulgaria, Poland, Yugoslavia, and exchanges with Finland.
Academic Year: September to July.
Admission Requirements: Competitive entrance examination following general or special secondary school certificate.
Language of Instruction: Russian.
Degrees and Diplomas: Diploma of Specialist in relevant fields, 5 yrs.
Library: central Library, 236,409 vols.
Special Facilities (Museums, etc.): E.F. Gnesinz Memorial Museum.
Publication: Scientific Papers.
Press or Publishing House: Publishing House.

Academic Staff, 1990:

Rank	Full-time	Part-time
Professors	35	3
Assistant Professors	79	12
Instructor	152	52
Total	266	67

Student Enrolment, 1990:

	Men	Women	Total
Of the country	368	443	811
Of other countries	53	12	65
Total	421	455	876*

*Also 605 external students.

7604 **HAR'KOVSKIJ GOSUDARSTVENNYJ INSTITUT ISKUSSTV IM. I.P. KOTLJAREVSKOGO**
State Institute of Arts
Pl. Sovetskoj Ukrainy 11/13, 310003 Har'kov, Ukrainskaja SSR

Music
Dramatic Art
Academic Year: September to July.
Admission Requirements: Competitive entrance examination following general or special secondary school certificate.
Degrees and Diplomas: Diploma of Specialist in relevant fields, 5 yrs.

7605 **KAZANSKAJA GOSUDARSTVENNAJA KONSERVATORIJA**
State Conservatory
B. Krasnaja Ul. 38, 420015 Kazan' 15, Rossiskaja SFSR

Music
Academic Year: September to July.
Admission Requirements: Competitive entrance examination following general or special secondary school certificate.
Degrees and Diplomas: Diploma of Specialist in relevant fields, 5 yrs.

7606 **KIEVSKAJA ORDENA LENINA GOSUDARSTVENNAJA KONSERVATORIJA IM. P.I. ČAJKOVSKOGO**
State Conservatory
Ul. Karla Marksa ⅓, 252001 Kiev, Ukrainskaja SSR

Music
Academic Year: September to July.
Admission Requirements: Competitive entrance examination following general or special secondary school certificate.
Degrees and Diplomas: Diploma of Specialist in relevant fields, 5 yrs.

7607 **KIRGIZSKIJ GOSUDARSTVENNYJ INSTITUT ISKUSSTV IM. B. BEJŠENALIEVOJ**
State Institute of Arts
Ul. Džantoševa 115, 720460 Frunze 5, Kirgizskaja SSR

Music
Academic Year: September to July.
Admission Requirements: Competitive entrance examination following general or special secondary school certificate.
Degrees and Diplomas: Diploma of Specialist in relevant fields, 5 yrs.

7608 **KRASNOJARSKIJ GOSUDARSTVENNYJ INSTITUT ISKUSSTV**
State Institute of Arts
Prosp. Mira 98, 660049 Krasnojarsk, Rossiskaja SFSR

Music
Also evening studies.
Academic Year: September to July.
Admission Requirements: Competitive entrance examination following general or special secondary school certificate.
Degrees and Diplomas: Diploma of Specialist in relevant fields, 5 yrs.

7609 **LENINGRADSKAJA ORDENA LENINA GOSUDARSTVENNAJA KONSERVATORIJA IM. N.A. RIMSKOGO-KORSAKOVA**
State Conservatory
Teatral'naja pl. 3, 190000 Centr. Leningrad, Rossiskaja SFSR

Music

Academic Year: September to July.

Admission Requirements: Competitive entrance examination following general or special secondary school certificate.

Degrees and Diplomas: Diploma of Specialist in relevant fields, 5 yrs.

7610 **L'VOVSKAJA GOSUDARSTVENNAJA KONSERVATORIJA IM. N.V. LYSENKO**

State Conservatory

Ul. St. Bojko 5, 290005 L'vov, Ukrainskaja SSR

Music

Academic Year: September to July.

Admission Requirements: Competitive entrance examination following general or special secondary school certificate.

Degrees and Diplomas: Diploma of Specialist in relevant fields, 5 yrs.

7611 **MOLDAVSKAJA GOSUDARSTVENNYJ KONSERVATORIJA**

Institute of Arts

Sadovaja ul. 87, 277014 Kišinev, Moldavskaja SSR

Music

Academic Year: September to July.

Admission Requirements: Competitive entrance examination following general or special secondary school certificate.

Degrees and Diplomas: Diploma of Specialist in relevant fields, 5 yrs.

7612 **MOLDAVSKAJA GOSUDARSTVENNYJ INSTITUT ISKUSSTV**

Ul. Sadovaja 85, 277014 Kišinev, Moldavskaja SSR

7613 **MOSKOVSKAJA DVAŽDY ORDENA LENINA GOSUDARSTVENNAJA KONSERVATORIJA IM. P.I. ČAJKOVSKOGO**

State Conservatory

Ul. Gercena 13, 103009 Moskva K-9, Rossiskaja SFSR

Music

Academic Year: September to July.

Admission Requirements: Competitive entrance examination following general or special secondary school certificate.

Degrees and Diplomas: Diploma of Specialist in relevant fields, 5 yrs.

7614 **NOVOSIBIRSKAJA GOSUDARSTVENNAJA KONSERVATORIJA IM. M.I. GLINKI**

State Conservatory

Sovetskaja ul. 31, 630099 Novosibirsk 99, Rossiskaja SFSR

Music

Academic Year: September to July.

Admission Requirements: Competitive entrance examination following general or special secondary school certificate.

Degrees and Diplomas: Diploma of Specialist in relevant fields, 5 yrs.

7615 **ODESSKAJA GOSUDARSTVENNAJA KONSERVATORIJA IM. A.V. NEŽDANOVOJ**

State Conservatory

Ul. Ostrovidova 63, 270000 Odessa, Ukrainskaja SSR

Music

Academic Year: September to July.

Admission Requirements: Competitive entrance examination following general or special secondary school certificate.

Degrees and Diplomas: Diploma of Specialist in relevant fields, 5 yrs.

7616 **ROSTOVSKIJ MUZYKAL'NO-PEDAGOGIČESKIJ INSTITUT**

Institute of Music and Pedagogics

Budennovskij prosp. 23, 344007 Rostov-na-Donu, Rossiskaja SFSR

Telephone: 663451

Rektor: Alexandr Stepanovich Danilov

Prorektor: Vladimir Mikhailovich

Music (Musicology, Composition, Vocal, Piano, Orchestral, Choral Conducting, Folk Instruments)

Founded 1967. Under the authority of the Ministry of Culture of the RSFSR. Residential facilities for acadimic staff and students.

Arrangements for co-operation with: Royal Scottish Academy of Music; University of Dortmend.

Academic Year: September to July (September-January; February-June).

Admission Requirements: Competitive entrance examination following general or special secondary school certificate.

Fees: None.

Language of Instruction: Russian.

Degrees and Diplomas: Diploma of Specialist in relevant fields, 5 yrs.

Library: 193,587 vols.

Academic Staff, 1990: 142.

Student Enrolment, 1990:

	Men	Women	Total
Of the country	166	340	506

7617 **SARATOVSKA GOSUDARSTVENNAJA KONSERVATORIJA IM. L.V. SOBINOVA**

State Conservatory

Prosp. Kirova 1, 410730 Saratov, Rossiskaja SFSR

Music

Academic Year: September to July.

Admission Requirements: Competitive entrance examination following general or special secondary school certificate.

Degrees and Diplomas: Diploma of Specialist in relevant fields, 5 yrs.

7618 **TADŽIKSKIJ GOSUDARSTVENNYJ INSTITUT ISKUSSTV IM. M. TURSYN-ZADE**

Ul. Ždanova 73a, 734032 Dušanbe, Tadžikskaja SSR

7619 **TALLINSKAJA GOSUDARSTVENNAJA KONSERVATORIJA**

State Conservatory

Bul'var Vabaduse 130, 200015 Tallin, Estonskaja SSR

Music

Academic Year: September to July.

Admission Requirements: Competitive entrance examination following general or special secondary school certificate.

Degrees and Diplomas: Diploma of Specialist in relevant fields, 5 yrs.

7620 **TAŠKENTSKAJA GOSUDARSTVENNAJA KONSERVATORIJA IM. M. AŠRAFI**

State Conservatory

Puškinskaja ul. 31, 700000 Taškent, Uzbekskaja SSR

Music

Academic Year: September to July.

Admission Requirements: Competitive entrance examination following general or special secondary school certificate.

Degrees and Diplomas: Diploma of Specialist in relevant fields, 5 yrs.

7621 **TBILISSKAJA GOSUDARSTVENNAJA KONSERVATORIJA IM. V. SARADŽIŠVILI**

State Conservatory

Ul. Griboedova 8, 380004 Tbilisi 4, Gruzinskaja SSR

Music

Academic Year: September to July.

Admission Requirements: Competitive entrance examination following general or special secondary school certificate.

Degrees and Diplomas: Diploma of Specialist in relevant fields, 5 yrs.

7622 **TURKMENSKIJ GOSUDARSTVENNYJ PEDAGOGIČESKIJ INSTITUT ISKUSSTV**

State Pedagogical Institute of Arts

Prosp. V.I. Lenina 3, 744007 Ašhabad, Turkmenskaja SSR

Music

Academic Year: September to July.

Admission Requirements: Competitive entrance examination following general or special secondary school certificate.

Degrees and Diplomas: Diploma of Specialist in relevant fields, 5 yrs.

7623 **UFIMKSKIJ GOSUDARSTVENNYJ INSTITUT ISKUSSTV**

State Institute of Arts

Ul. Lenina 14, 450093 Ufa, Rossiskaja SFSR

Music

Dramatic Art

Academic Year: September to July.

Admission Requirements: Competitive entrance examination following general or special secondary school certificate.

Degrees and Diplomas: Diploma of Specialist in relevant fields, 5 yrs.

7624 **URAL'SKAJA ORDENA TRUDOVOGO KRASNOGO ZNAMENI OSUDARSTVENNAJA KONSERVATORIJA IM. M.P. MUSORGSKOGO**

State Conservatory

Prosp. Lenina 26, 620014 Sverdlovsk, Rossiskaja SFSR

Music

Academic Year: September to July.

Admission Requirements: Competitive entrance examination following general or special secondary school certificate.

Degrees and Diplomas: Diploma of Specialist in relevant fields, 5 yrs.

7625 **VORONEŽSKIJ GOSUDARSTVENNYJ INSTITUT ISKUSSTV**

State Institute of Arts

Berezovaja Rošča 54, 394043 Voronež, Rossiskaja SFSR

Music

Dramatic Art

Academic Year: September to July.

Admission Requirements: Competitive entrance examination following general or special secondary school certificate.

Degrees and Diplomas: Diploma of Specialist in relevant fields, 5 yrs.

Institutes of Dramatic Art and Cinematography

7626 **ALMA-ATINSKIJ GOSUDARSTVENNYJ TEATRAL'NO-HUDOŽESTVENNYJ INSTITUT**

Institute of Dramatic Art

Sovetskaja ul. 28, 480100 Alma-Ata, Kazahskaja SSR

Dramatic Art

Academic Year: September to July.

Admission Requirements: Competitive entrance examination following general or special secondary school certificate.

Degrees and Diplomas: Diploma of Specialist in relevant fields, 5 yrs.

7627 **AZERBAJDŽANSKIJ GOSUDARSTVENNYJ INSTITUT ISKUSSTV IM. M.A. ALIEVA**

Institute of Arts

Ul. Karganova 13, 370000 Baku, Azerbajdžanskaja SSR

Dramatic Art

Fine Arts

Academic Year: September to July.

Admission Requirements: Competitive entrance examination following general or special secondary school certificate.

Degrees and Diplomas: Diploma of Specialist in relevant fields, 5 yrs.

7628 **BELORUSSKIJ GOSUDARSTVENNYJ TEATRAL'NO-HUDOŽESTVENNYJ INSTITUT**

Institute of Dramatic and Fine Arts

Leninskij prosp. 81, 220012 Minsk, Belorusskaja SSR

F. of Dramatic Art

F. of Fine Art

Academic Year: September to July.

Admission Requirements: Competitive entrance examination following general or special secondary school certificate.

Degrees and Diplomas: Diploma of Specialist in relevant fields, 5 yrs.

7629 **GOSUDARSTVENNYJ ORDENA TRUDOVOGO KRASNOGO ZNAMENI I ORDENA DRUŽBY NARODOV INSTITUT TEATRAL'NOGO ISKUSSTVAI2M. A.V. LUNAČARSKOGO**

Institute of Dramatic Art

Sobinovskij per. 6, 103009 Moskva K-9, Rossiskaja SFSR

Dramatic Art

Academic Year: September to July.

Admission Requirements: Competitive entrance examination following general or special secondary school certificate.

Degrees and Diplomas: Diploma of Specialist in relevant fields, 5 yrs.

7630 **GOSUDARSTVENNYJ INSTITUT TEATRAL'NOGO ISKUSSTVA IM. I.K. KARPENKO-KAROGO**

Institute of Dramatic Art

Ul. Jaroslavov Val 40, 252034 Kiev, Ukrainskaja SSR

Dramatic Art

Academic Year: September to July.

Admission Requirements: Competitive entrance examination following general or special secondary school certificate.

Degrees and Diplomas: Diploma of Specialist in relevant fields, 5 yrs.

7631 **GRUZINSKIJ GOSUDARSTVENNYJ TEATRAL'NYJ INSTITUT IM. Š. RUSTAVELI**

Theatre Institute

Prosp. Rustaveli 17, 380004 Tbilisi, Gruzinskaja SSR

Dramatic Art

Academic Year: September to July.

Admission Requirements: Competitive entrance examination following general or special secondary school certificate.

Degrees and Diplomas: Diploma of Specialist in relevant fields, 5 yrs.

7632 **LENINGRADSKIJ GOSUDARSTVENNYJ INSTITUT TEATRA, MUZYKI I KINEMATOGRAFII IM. N.K. CERKASOVA**

Theatre, Music and Cinema Institute

Mohovaja ul. 34, 192028 Leningrad D-28, Rossiskaja SFSR

Dramatic Art

Music

Cinema

Academic Year: September to July.

Admission Requirements: Competitive entrance examination following general or special secondary school certificate.

Degrees and Diplomas: Diploma of Specialist in relevant fields, 5 yrs.

7633 **SKOLA-STUDIJA (VUZ) IM. V.I. NEMIROVIČA-DANČENKO PRI MHAT SSSR IM. M. GOR'KOGO**

Studio School

Ul. Gor'kogo 6, str. 7, 103009 Moskva K-9, Rossiskaja SFSR

Dramatic Art

Academic Year: September to July.

Admission Requirements: Competitive entrance examination following general or special secondary school certificate.

Degrees and Diplomas: Diploma of Specialist in relevant fields, 5 yrs.

7634 **SVERDLOVSKIJ GOSUDARSTVENNYJ TEATRALJNYJ INSTITUT**

Ul. Kitibknehta 38, 620151 Sverdlovsk, Rossiskaja SFSR

7635 **TAŠKENTSKIJ GOSUDARSTVENNYJ TEATRAL'NO-HUDOŽESTVENNYJ INSTITUT IM. A.N. OSTROVSKOGO**

Institute of Dramatic and Fine Arts

Ul. Germana Lopatina 77, 700031 Taškent 31, Uzbekskaja SSR

Drama

Fine Arts

Academic Year: September to July.

Admission Requirements: Competitive entrance examination following general or special secondary school certificate.

Degrees and Diplomas: Diploma of Specialist in relevant fields, 5 yrs.

7636 **TEATRAL'NOE UČILIŠČE (VUZ) IM. M.S. ŠČEPKINA PRI GOSUDARSTVENNOM ORDENA LENINA I ORDENA OKTJABR'SKOJ REVOLJUCII AKADEMIČESKOM MALOM TEATRE SSR**

College of Drama

Pušečnaja ul. 2/6, 103012 Moskva, Rossiskaja SFSR

Dramatic Art (Theatre and Cinema)

Academic Year: September to July.

Admission Requirements: Competitive entrance examination following general or special secondary school certificate.
Degrees and Diplomas: Diploma of Specialist in relevant fields, 5 yrs.

7637 **TEATRAL'NOE UČILIŠČE (VUZ) IM. B.V. ŠČUKINA PRI GOSUDARSTVENNOM ORDENA LENINA I ORDENA TRUDOVOGO KRASNOGO ZNAMENI TEATRE IM. E. VAHTANGOVA**
College of Drama
Ul. Vahtangova 12a, 121002 Moskva G-2, Rossiskaja SFSR
Dramatic Art (Theatre and Cinema)
Academic Year: September to July.
Admission Requirements: Competitive entrance examination following general or special secondary school certificate.
Degrees and Diplomas: Diploma of Specialist in relevant fields, 5 yrs.

7638 **TEATRAL'NOE UČILIŠČE (VUZ) PRI JAROSLAVSKOM GOSUDARSTVENNOM AKADEMIČESKOM TEATRE IM. F.G. VOLKOVA**
College of Drama
Pervomajskaja ul. 43, 150000 Jaroslavl', Rossiskaja SFSR
Dramatic Art (Theatre and Cinema)
Academic Year: September to July.
Admission Requirements: Competitive entrance examination following general or special secondary school certificate.
Degrees and Diplomas: Diploma of Specialist in relevant fields, 5 yrs.

7639 **VSESOJUZNYJ ORDENA TRUDOVOGO KRASNOGO ZNAMENI GOSUDARSTVENNYJ INSTITUT KINEMATOGRAFII**
All-Union Institute of Cinematography
Ul. Vil'gel'ma Pika 3, 129226 Moskva I-226, Rossiskaja SFSR
F. of Scenario Studies
F. of Directing
F. of Cinematography
F. of Fine Art
F. of Cinematographic Art
F. of Economics
Academic Year: September to July.
Admission Requirements: Competitive entrance examination following general or special secondary school certificate.
Degrees and Diplomas: Diploma of Specialist in relevant fields, 5 yrs.

Institutes of Fine and Applied Arts

Fine and Applied Arts

7640 **GOSUDARSTVENNAJA AKADEMIJA HUDOŽESTV LATVIJSKOJ SSR IM. TEODORA ZAL'KALNA**
Academy of Arts
Bul'var Kommunarov 13, 226185 Riga, Latvijskaja SSR
Telephone: 33-22-02
Decorative and Applied Arts
Founded 1919.
Academic Year: October to July (October-January; February-June; June-July).
Admission Requirements: Competitive entrance examination following general or special secondary school certificate.
Language of Instruction: Latvian.
Degrees and Diplomas: Diploma of Specialist in relevant fields, 5 yrs. Kandidat nauk, Candidate of the Sciences, a further 3 yrs. Doktor nauk, by thesis after Kandidat.
Library: 65,000 vols.
Academic Staff: c. 120.
Student Enrolment: c. 450 (Also c. 120 external students).

7641 **GOSUDARSTVENNYJ HUDOŽESTVENNYJ INSTITUT LITOVSKOJ SSR**
Institute of Art
Ul. Tiesos 6, 232600 Vilnius, Litovskaja SSR
Cables: Ritmas
Telephone: 2-10-12; 2-29-92
Decorative and Applied Arts
Founded 1951 and incorporating former Vilmius and Kaunas Institutes of Arts, established 1920-22 and tracing their origins to the 16th century.
Academic Year: October to June (October-January; February-June).
Admission Requirements: Competitive entrance examination following general or special secondary school certificate.
Fees: None.
Language of Instruction: Lithuanian.
Degrees and Diplomas: Diploma of Specialist in relevant fields, 5 yrs.
Academic Staff: c. 110.

7642 **GOSUDARSTVENNYJ HUDOŽESTVENNYJ INSTITUT ESTONSKOJ SSR**
Institute of Art
Tartuskoe Šosse 1, 200104 Tallin, Estonskaja SSR
F. of Fine and Applied Arts
F. of Architecture
Academic Year: September to July.
Admission Requirements: Competitive entrance examination following general or special secondary school certificate.
Degrees and Diplomas: Diploma of Specialist in relevant fields, 5 yrs.

7643 **EREVANSKIJ GOSUDARSTVENNYJ HUDOŽESTVENNO-TEATRAL'NYJ INSTITUT**
Art and Theatre Institute
Ul. Isaakjana 36, 375009 Erevan, Armjanskaja SSR
Fine, Applied and Dramatic Arts
Academic Year: September to July.
Admission Requirements: Competitive entrance examination following general or special secondary school certificate.
Degrees and Diplomas: Diploma of Specialist in relevant fields, 5 yrs.

7644 **HAR'KOVSKIJ GOSUDARSTVENNYJ HUDOŽESTVENNO-PROMYŠLENNYJ INSTITUT**
Institute of Industrial Art
Krasnoznamennaja ul. 8, 310002 Har'kov, Ukrainskaja SSR
F. of Interior Design and Equipment
F. of Industrial Art
Academic Year: September to July.
Admission Requirements: Competitive entrance examination following general or special secondary school certificate.
Degrees and Diplomas: Diploma of Specialist in relevant fields, 5 yrs.

7645 **KIEVSKIJ GOSUDARSTVENNYJ HUDOŽESTVENNYJ INSTITUT**
Institute of Art
Ul. Smirnova-Lastočkina 20, 252053 Kiev 53, Ukrainskaja SSR
Fine and Applied Arts, Architecture
Academic Year: September to July.
Admission Requirements: Competitive entrance examination following general or special secondary school certificate.
Degrees and Diplomas: Diploma of Specialist in relevant fields, 5 yrs.

7646 **KRASNOJARSKIJ GOSUDARSTVENNYJ HUDOŽESTVENNYJ INSTITUT**
pr. Mira 98, 660049 Krasnojarsk, Rossiskaja SFSR

7647 **L'VOVSKIJ GOSUDARSTVENNYJ INSTITUT PRIKLADNOGO I DEKORATIVNOGO ISKUSSTVA**
Institute of Applied and Decorative Art
Ul. Gončarova 38, 290011 L'vov, Ukrainskaja SSR
Decorative and Applied Art
Academic Year: September to July.
Admission Requirements: Competitive entrance examination following general or special secondary school certificate.
Degrees and Diplomas: Diploma of Specialist in relevant fields, 5 yrs.

7648 **MOSKOVSKIJ GOSUDARSTVENNYJ INSTITUT ŽIVOPISI, SKULPTURY I HUDOŽESTVENNOJ PEDAGOGIKI**

Suščevskij val 73, Kor 2, 129272 Moskva, Rossiskaja SFSR

7649 **MOSKOVSKIJ ORDENA TRUDOVOGO KRASNOGO ZNAMENI GOSUDARSTVENNYJ HUDOŽESTVENNYJ INSTITUT IM. V.I. SURIKOVA**

Institute of Art

Tovariščeckij nep. 30, 109004 Moskva Ž-4, Rossiskaja SFSR

Fine and Graphic Arts

Academic Year: September to July.

Admission Requirements: Competitive entrance examination following general or special secondary school certificate.

Degrees and Diplomas: Diploma of Specialist in relevant fields, 5 yrs.

7650 **ORDENA TRUDOVOGO KRASNOGO ZNAMENI INSTITUT ŽIVOPISI SKUL'PTURY I ARHITEKTURY IM. I.E. REPINA**

Institute of Art, Sculpture, and Architecture

Universitetskaja nab. 17, 199034 Leningrad V-34, Rossiskaja SFSR

Fine and Applied Arts, Architecture

Academic Year: September to July.

Admission Requirements: Competitive entrance examination following general or special secondary school certificate.

Degrees and Diplomas: Diploma of Specialist in relevant fields, 5 yrs.

7651 **TBILISSKAJA ORDENA TRUDOVOGO KRASNOGO ZNAMENI GOSUDARSTVENNAJA AKADEMIJA HUDOŽESTV**

Academy of Arts

Ul. Griboedova 22, 380008 Tbilisi, Gruzinskaja SSR

Fine and Applied Arts, Architecture

Academic Year: September to July.

Admission Requirements: Competitive entrance examination following general or special secondary school certificate.

Degrees and Diplomas: Diploma of Specialist in relevant fields, 5 yrs.

Architecture and Industrial Art

7652 **LENINGRADSKOE VYSŠEE HUDOŽESTVENNOPROMYŠLENNOE UČILIŠČE IM. V.I. MUHINOJ**

Institute of Industrial Art

Soljanoj per. 13, 192028 Leningrad, Rossiskaja SFSR

F. of Industrial Art
F. of Interior Decoration
F. of Applied and Monumental Art
F. for Evening Studies

Academic Year: September to July.

Admission Requirements: Competitive entrance examination following general or special secondary school certificate.

Degrees and Diplomas: Diploma of Specialist in relevant fields, 5 yrs.

7653 **MOSKOVSKOE VYSŠEE HUDOŽESTVENNOPROMYŠLENNOE UČILIŠČE**

Institute of Industrial Art

Volokolamskoe Šosse 9, 125080 Moskva, Rossiskaja SFSR

F. of Industrial Design
F. of Interior Decoration
F. of Monumental, Decorative, and Applied Art
D. for Evening Studies

Academic Year: September to July.

Admission Requirements: Competitive entrance examination following general or special secondary school certificate.

Degrees and Diplomas: Diploma of Specialist in relevant fields, 5 yrs.

Pedagogical Institutes

7654 ***MOSKOVSKIJ ORDENA LENINA I ORDENA TRUDOVOGO KRASNOGO ZNAMENI GOSUDARSTVENNYJ PEDAGOGIČESKIJ INSTITUT IM. V .I. LENINA**

Moscow State Pedagogical Institute

Malaya Pirogovskaja ul. 1, 119435 Moskva, Rossiskaja SFSR

Telephone: 246-01-23

Fax: 248-01-62

Rektor: Victor L. Matrosov (1986-)

Prorektor: Michail L. Rocionov

F. of Physics
Dean: Yual N. Pashin; *staff* 69 (20)
F. of Mathematics
Dean: Michail M. Bunyaev; *staff* 84 (49)
F. of Biology and Chemistry
Dean: Gliya M. Vashchenko; *staff* 82 (12)
F. of Geography
Dean: Galina A. Tsvetkova; *staff* 57 (3)
F. of Chemistry
Dean: Tatyana N. Romashina; *staff* 30 (4)
F. of History
Dean: Rostislav M. Vedensky; *staff* 55 (15)
F. of Russian Language and Literature
Dean: Oksana Yu. Bogdanuva; *staff* 157 (17)
F. of Foreign Language
Dean: Yuliya F. Gureva; *staff* 145 (8)
F. of Primary School Education
Dean: Valentina V. Danilova; *staff* 63 (5)
F. of Music and Singing
Dean: Igor P. Kulasov; *staff* 90 (14)
F. of Graphic Arts
Dean: Valery I. Zhog; *staff* 64 (2)
F. of Pedagogics and Psychology
Dean: Vitaly A. Slastenin; *staff* 34 (14)
F. of Education of the Handicapped
Dean: Evgueny V. Oganesian; *staff* 58 (24)
F. of Industrial Pedagogy
Dean: Vladimiz A. Ivanov; *staff* 43 (2)
F. of Pre-school Education
Dean: Ludmila V. Pozdnyak; *staff* 35 (12)
F. for the Improvement of Public School Administration
Dean: Tatyana I. Shamova
F. for the Improvement of College Teaching
Dean: Michail L. Levitshy
Preparatory D.
Dean: Elena I. Yurchenko

Also 7 research laboratories.

Founded 1872 as Moscow Higher Women's Courses. Previously part of the former Second Moscow State University, founded 1917. A State institution responsible to the Union-Republic State Committee for Public Education. Residential facilities for academic staff and *c.* 4000 students.

Arrangements for co-operation with: Institute of Education, Leipzig; University of Plovdiv; Kossuth Lajos University, Debrecen; Palacký University, Olomouc; Hanoi Institute of Education; Humboldt University, Berlin; Peking Normal University, Havana Institute of Education, Blagoevgrad; Institute of Special Pedagogics, Budapest;University of Surrey, Guildford.

Academic Year: September to July (September-January; February-June).

Admission Requirements: Competitive entrance examination following general or special secondary school certificate.

Fees: None.

Language of Instruction: Russian.

Degrees and Diplomas: Diploma of Specialist in relevant fields of teaching or education, 5 yrs. Kandidat nauk, Candidate of the Sciences, a further 3 yrs and thesis. Doktor nauk by thesis after Kandidat. Also teaching qualification primary level, 4 yrs. For foreign students, MA courses.

Libraries: Central Library, *c.* 1,300,000 vols; libraries of the faculties.

Special Facilities (Museums, etc.): 2 Agro-Biological Stations; Observatory.

Publications: Collection of Scientific Works (annually); 'Leninetz' (weekly).

Press or Publishing House: Publishing House 'Prometheus'.

Academic Staff, 1989-90:

Rank	Full-time	Part-time
Professors	176	61
Dozents	454	46
Senior Teachers	176	40
Assistants	260	34
Total	1066	181

Student Enrolment, 1989-90:

	Men	Women	Total
Of the country	2174	8421	10,595
Of other countries	275	413	688
Total	2449	8834	11,283

Also 187 other institutes of education and 21 institutes of physical education.

Foreign Languages

7656 ***MOSKOVSKIJ GOSUDARSTVENNYJ PEDAGOGIČESKIJ INSTITUT INOSTRANNYH JAZYKOV IM. MORISA TOREZA**

Moscow State Institute of Foreign Languages

Metrostoevskaja ul. 38, 119034 Moskva G-34, Rossiskaja SFSR

Cables: Metrostroevskaja 38, Moskva

Telephone: 245-02-00; 245-32-03

Rektor: I.I. Haleevo (1986-)

F. of Interpretation (English, German, French, Spanish, and Italian)

Dean: Inna P. Krylova; *staff* 127 (28)

F. of English Language

Dean: G.U. Strelkova; *staff* 115 (5)

F. of German Language

Dean: B.T. Kossov; *staff* 46 (7)

F. of French Language

Dean: M.M. Boldyreva; *staff* 43 (4)

D. for Evening Studies

D. for Correspondence Courses

Founded 1930 as Institute of Modern Languages. A State institution responsible to the Union-Republic State Committee for Public Education. Residential facilities for 550 students.

Arrangements for co-operation with Martin Luther University of Halle-Wittenberg.

Academic Year: September to July (September-January; February-July).

Admission Requirements: Competitive entrance examination following general or special secondary school certificate.

Language of Instruction: Russian.

Degrees and Diplomas: Diploma of Specialist in relevant fields, 5 yrs. Kandidat nauk, Candidate of the Sciences, a further 3 yrs andthesis. Doktor nauk by thesis after Kandidat.

Library: c. 560,000 vols.

Special Facilities (Museums, etc.): M. Toreza Museum.

Publication: Journal.

Press or Publishing House: Publishing section of the Institute.

Academic Staff, 1986-87: c. 700.

Student Enrolment, 1986-87: c. 4000.

Also 11 other institutes of foreign languages and 21 institutes of cultural, literary and historical studies.

UNITED ARAB EMIRATES

7658 ***JAMEAT ALEMARAT AL ARABIA AL MUTAHEDA**

United Arab Emirates University
P.O. Box 15551, Al-Ain
Telex: 33521 JAMEAH EM
Telephone: (9713) 642500
Fax: (9713) 645277
Vice-Chancellor (Acting): Ezzat M. Khairy (1990-)
Secretary-General: Shabi M. Al Marzooqi

F. of Arts (Islamic Studies, Arabic Language and Literature, History and Archeology, Geography, Social Work, Philosophy, Foreign Languages, Mass Communication)
Dean: Mohammad I. Howar; *staff* 102 (10)
F. of Science (Mathematics and Computer Sciences, Physics, Chemistry, Biological Sciences, Geology)
Dean: Ezzat M. Khairy; *staff* 96 (8)
F. of Education (Kindergarten (for women), Primary, Home Economics (for women))
Dean: Mohi El-Din Touq; *staff* 48 (4)
F. of Economics and Administrative Sciences
Dean: Anim Fuad El Durghamy; *staff* 65 (4)
F. of Law and Shari'a (Islamic Law)
Dean: Mohsen Khalil; *staff* 27
F. of Agricultural Sciences (including Animal Husbandry)
Dean: Abdul Rahman Al-Saghir; *staff* 17 (2)
F. of Engineering (including Civil, Chemical and Petroleum, Electrical and Mechanical Engineering, Interior Architecture (women),Architectural Engineering, Electronic Engineering (women))
Dean: Awad S. Al-Hakeem; *staff* 53 (5)
F. of Medicine and Health Sciences
Dean: Blain McA. Ledingham; *staff* 27
Ce. Educational and Psychological Research, Development, and Services
Director: Abdullah H.Z. Al Kaylani; *staff* 5 (1)
History and Folklore Research Ce.
Director: Mohamed A. Al Mutawa; *staff* 3 (2)
Desert and Marine Environmental Research Ce.
Director: Mohamed Hadi Amiri; *staff* 12 (3)
Ce. for Administrative, Financial, and Economics Research
Director: Mohamed Hamid Selim; *staff* 4 (2)
Remote Sensing Ce.
Director: Mohamed Adel Ahmed Yehia; *staff* 1 (4)
Technology and Energy Research Ce.
Director: Yahya Hassan Hamid; *staff* 3 (2)
The Language Ce.
Director: Ahmed Babiker El Tahir; *staff* 23

Also Tutoral External Studies based at the UAE University Campus with branches at Abu Dhabi, Dubai, Sharjah, Ajman, Umm Al Quwain, Fujairah, and Ras Al Khaima.

Founded 1976 by Presidential Decree. Admitted first students 1977. A State institution enjoying independence in academic administration and financial matters. Financed by the government. Governing bodies: the University Council; the Scientific and Educational Affairs Council. Residential facilities for academic staff and students.

Arrangements for co-operation with the Midwest Universities Consortium for International Activities, Inc. (MUCIA), Columbus, Ohio (for training and qualifying Teaching Assistant's and other University personnel).

Academic Year: September to July (September-January; January-May; June-July).

Admission Requirements: Secondary school certificate (Shahadat Al-Thanawich Al Amah).

Fees: None.

Languages of Instruction: Arabic and English.

Degrees and Diplomas: Bachelor, 4 yrs. Will later also award Master's degrees and Doctorates.

Libraries: Total, 133,555 (in Arabic); 65,409 (in other languages).

Special Facilities (Museums, etc.): Natural History Museum. Movie Studio; Experimental Farm.

Publication: Faculty Journals (annually).

Press or Publishing House: UAE University Press.

Academic Staff, 1989-90:

Rank	Full-time
Professors	93
Assistant Professors	122
Instructors	128
Lecturers	245
Total	588

Student Enrolment, 1989-90:

	Men	Women	Total
Of the country	2338	5557	7895
Of other countries	248	320	568
Total	2586	5877	8463*

*Also 735 external students.

URUGUAY

7659 ***UNIVERSIDAD MAYOR DE LA REPÚBLICA ORIENTAL DEL URUGUAY**
University of the Republic
Avenida 18 de Julio 1968, Montevideo
Cables: Udelar
Telex: 222238
Telephone: 40-92-01/05

F. of Agriculture (including Stockraising and Forestry)
F. of Architecture
F. of Economics and Administration
F. of Law and Social Sciences
F. of Engineering
F. of Medicine
F. of Veterinary Medicine
F. of Dentistry
F. of Chemistry
F. of Humanities and Science
S. of Library Science
S. of Psychology
S. of Social Service

Founded 1833 by law and inaugurated 1849 by decree as the Universidad de la República. The university is an autonomous State institution financed by the central government. Governing body: the Consejo Directivo Central.

Academic Year: March to November (March-June; July-November).
Admission Requirements: Secondary school certificate (bachillerato).
Fees: None.
Language of Instruction: Spanish.
Degrees and Diplomas: Licenciado in–Administration; Economics; Biology; Singing; Musicology; History; Letters; Philosophy; Literature; Linguistics; Geography; Astronomy; Physics; Mathematics; Anthropology; Oceanography; Meteorology; Geology; Education; Music, 4-5 yrs. Professional titles of–Bibliotecólogo, 3 yrs; Agrimensor, surveying; Ingeniero agrónomo; Sociólogo; Psicólogo; Asistente social; Contador público, accountancy; Químico; Químico farmacéutico; Economista, 4-5 yrs; Escribano público, public registrar; Arquitecto, 6 yrs; Ingeniero, various fields, 5-6 yrs. Doctorates in–Law and Social Sciences; Dentistry; Pharmacy; Economics; Administration; Chemistry; Veterinary Science; Medicine. Also diplomas of specialization in Medicine.
Libraries: Faculty libraries, *c.* 299,000 vols; Medicine, 500,000.
Special Facilities (Museums, etc.): Museum of Plastic Arts.
Academic Staff: c. – (3240).
Student Enrolment: c. 35,310

7660 **UNIVERSIDAD DEL TRABAJO**
Technical University of Uruguay
Calle San Salvador 1674, Montevideo
Cables: Enind
Telephone: 4-50-94; 4-42-69

D. of Agriculture
D. of Industrial Engineering
D. of Applied Arts
D. of Commerce and Administration
D. of Education (Vocational)
D. of Educational Planning
D. of Educational Research (Vocational)

Also 8 institutes in the provinces affiliated to the university: Dairy Produce; Forestry; Veterinary Science; Mechanical and Electrical Engineering; Civil Engineering; Marine Engineering; Viticulture; Teacher Training (technical); Teacher Training (agricultural).

Founded 1942 incorporating former National School of Arts and Crafts. A State institution responsible to the Ministry of Education. Governing body: the Consejo Directivo. Residential facilities for students in the schools of agriculture.

Academic Year: March to November.
Admission Requirements: Secondary school certificate (bachillerato).
Fees: None.
Language of Instruction: Spanish.
Degrees and Diplomas: Technical qualifications in various fields, 4 yrs.
Library: c. 14,000 vols.
Special Facilities (Museums, etc.): Historical Museum.
Academic Staff: c. 4500.
Student Enrolment: c. 50,000.

7661 **UNIVERSIDAD CATÓLICA DEL URUGUAY 'DÁMASO A. LARRAÑAGA'**
Avenida 8 de Octubre 2738, Montevideo
Telephone: 80-35-15
Fax: 80-27-17
Rector: Joé Squadroni S.J. (1985-89)
Secretario General: Fernando Sorondo Bataller

F. of Philosophy and Letters
F. of Human Sciences and Theology (including Psychology and Computer Technology)
F. of Social Sciences and Economics (including Business Administration and Social Communication)
F. of Law
I. of Religious Sciences
I. of Juridical Sciences
I. of Philosophy and Ethics
I. of Social Sciences

Founded 1954 as Institute of Philosophy, Science and Letters, acquired present status and title 1984. Governing body: the Consejo Directivo.

Arrangements for co-operation with: Universidad Pontificia Comillas, Madrid; Catholic University of Louvain; Catholic University of Leuven; Universidad del Salvador, Argentina; Universidad de Santiago del Estero, Argentina; Pontifícia Universidade Católica de Porto Alegre; Universidade Federal de Porto Alegre; Universidad Católica de Chile; Instituto Superior de Arte y Ciencias Sociales, Chile; University of Minnesota; University of Loyola; University of Nebraska; University of Michigan.

Academic Year: March to November (March-July; August-November).
Admission Requirements: Secondary school certificate (bachillerato).
Fees (Nuevo Peso): 1,574,000.
Language of Instruction: Spanish.
Degrees and Diplomas: Licenciado, 4-5 yrs. Professional title of Técnico, 3 yrs.
Library: 25,000 vols.
Special Facilities (Museums, etc.): Radio Studio; Video Studio.
Publication: Estudios (quarterly).
Academic Staff, 1989-90:

Rank	Full-time
Profesores Titulares	28
Profesores Agregados	41
Profesores Adjuntos	172
Profesores Asistentes	21
Profesores Ayudantes	5
Profesores I	12
Total	279

Student Enrolment, 1989-90:

	Men	Women	Total
Of the country	426	625	1051
Of other countries	30	26	56
Total	456	651	1107*

*Also 2760 external students.

7662 **INSTITUTO DE ESTUDIOS SUPERIORES**
Constituyente 1711, Montevideo

D. of Philology
D. of Phonetics
D. of Music
D. of Geography and Geomorphology
D. of Palaeontology

D. of Geology
D. of Medical Climatology
D. of Mathematics
S. of Education

Founded 1930. A private institution receiving financial assistance from the Ministry of Education and municipal authorities.

Academic Year: April to October.

Admission Requirements: Secondary school certificate (bachillerato).

Fees: None.

Language of Instruction: Spanish.

Degrees and Diplomas: Teaching certificate, secondary level, 4 yrs.

Library: c. 2000 vols.

Academic Staff: c. – (110).

Student Enrolment: c. 50.

VENEZUELA

Universities

7663 **UNIVERSIDAD DE LOS ANDES**
University of the Andes
Avenida 3, Independencia, Mérida
Telex: 74137 ULAMEVE
Telephone: 520011
Rector: Pedro Angel Rincón Gutiérrez (1984-88)
Secretario General: Nestor López Rodríguez

F. of Law and Political Science
Dean: Andrés Eloy León Rojas; *staff* 75 (18)
F. of Medicine (including Nursing)
Dean: Freddy Rangel; *staff* 343 (205)
F. of Dentistry
Dean: Francisco Riva Martinez; *staff* 67 (6)
F. of Pharmacy
Dean: Luis González M.; *staff* 122 (10)
F. of Engineering
Dean: Felipe Pachano R.; *staff* 207 (34)
F. of Forestry
Dean: Guido Ochoa; *staff* 98 (5)
F. of Humanities and Education
Dean: Julio Cesar Tallaferro; *staff* 223 (6)
F. of Economics (including Business Administration)
Dean: Jacobo Latuff; *staff* 137 (21)
F. of Architecture
Dean: Bernardo Moncada C.; *staff* 86 (24)
F. of Science

Branches at Táchira and Trujillo. Also 14 institutes and centres of the faculties.

Founded 1785 as Seminario de San Buenaventura, authorized to award degrees 1806. Raised to full university rank 1810. Became a secular institution 1832. An autonomous State institution. Governing bodies: the Claustro Universitario; the Consejo Universitario, comprising the Rector, 2 Vice-Rectors, Secretary-General, deans of the faculties, and representatives of the students, of the graduates, and of the Ministry of Education. Residential facilities for academic staff and students.

Academic Year: January to December (January-June; July-December).

Admission Requirements: Secondary school certificate (bachillerato) and entrance examination.

Fees (Bolívares): Tuition, none.

Language of Instruction: Spanish.

Degrees and Diplomas: Licenciado in–History; Physics; Chemistry; Biology; Mathematics; Nutrition and Dietetics; Letters; Education; Bioanalysis; Nursing; Statistics; Administration; Accountancy; Political Science, 5 yrs. Professional titles in–Law; Dentistry; Pharmacy; Geography; Civil Engineering; Electrical Engineering; Chemical Engineering; Mechanical Engineering; Systems Engineering; Forestry Engineering; Economics; Geology; Architecture, 5 yrs; Medicine and Surgery, 6 yrs. Degree of Magister. Doctorates. Also title of Técnico superior, 3 yrs.

Libraries: Central Library, *c.* 44,000; faculty libraries, total, *c.* 220,617.

Special Facilities (Museums, etc.): Archaeology Museum.

Publications: Revistas and Anuarios of each faculty; Derecho y Reforma Agraria (annually); Actual (Cultura); Azul Magazine.

Academic Staff, 1986-87: 1909 (830).

Student Enrolment, 1986-87: 35,118.

7664 **UNIVERSIDAD DE CARABOBO**
University of Carabobo
Avenida Bolivar 125, Apartado postal 129, Valencia, Carabobo
Telex: 41478 UCRVLV
Telephone: (41) 215044
Rector: Gustavo Hidalgo V. (1988-92)

F. of Health Sciences (Medicine, Dentistry, Nursing)
F. of Engineering (Industrial, Electrical, Chemical and Mechanical)
F. of Economic and Social Sciences (including Business Administration)
F. of Education
D. of Postgraduate Studies
I. of Comparative Law
I. of Applied Mathematics
I. of Industrial Development
Ce. for Forensic Medicine
I. of Criminological Research
Ce. for Planning and Economic Development

Founded 1833 as National College, first courses started 1840. Became Federal College 1883. Status of university from 1892 to 1904 when the institution was attached to the Central University of Venezuela as schoolof law. Re-established 1958 as national university financed by the State. Governing body: the Consejo Universitario, comprising the Rector, Vice-Rectors, Secretary, deans, representatives of the Ministry of Education, 3 students, and 5 representatives from professional life.

Academic Year: January to December (January-June; July-December).

Admission Requirements: Secondary school certificate (bachillerato) or recognized equivalent.

Language of Instruction: Spanish.

Degrees and Diplomas: Licenciado in–Nursing, 4 yrs; Chemistry; Bioanalysis; Administration; Accountancy; Education; Industrial Relations, 5 yrs. Professional titles in–Law; Medicine; Economics; Engineering (various fields); Dentistry, 5-6 yrs. Degree of Magister in–Administration; Education; Industrial Relations; Mathematics. Doctorates in–Law; Medicine.

Libraries: Faculty libraries: Economics and Social Science, *c.* 29,000 vols; Education, *c.* 19,000; Law, *c.* 26,500; Engineering, *c.* 32,000; Health Sciences, *c.* 39,000; Postgraduate, *c.* 1900.

Publications: Gaceta Universitaria (quarterly); Poesia (monthly); Polqemica (biannually); Vigenete (monthly); Revista dela Facultad de Derecho (annually); Anuario del Instituto de Derecho Comparado; Separata (biannually).

Academic Staff: *c.* 2430.

Student Enrolment: *c.* 41,360.

7665 **UNIVERSIDAD CATÓLICA ANDRÉS BELLO**
La Vega, Montalbán, Caracas 102
Telephone: 47-5111

F. of Economics and Social Sciences
F. of Law
F. of Humanities and Education (including Psychology)
F. of Engineering
S. of Civil Engineering
S. of Industrial Engineering
S. of Philosophy
S. of Law
S. of Letters
S. of Education
S. of Business Administration and Accountancy
S. of Social Sciences
S. of Economics
S. of Psychology
S. of Social Communication
I. of Economic Research
Historical Research I.
Ce. of Literary Research
Ce. of Indigenous Languages
Ce. of Comparative Religions
Ce. of Legal Research

Founded 1953 as a private Catholic university of the Venezuelan episcopate and its direction entrusted to the Society of Jesus. Independent of the government. Financially supported by tuition fees (80%) and donations (20%). Governing body: the Consejo Universitario, presided over by the Rector and composed of the 2 Vice-Rectors, the Secretary-General, and the deans of the faculties.

Academic Year: October to July (October-January; February-June).

Admission Requirements: Secondary school certificate (bachillerato) or equivalent, and entrance examination.

Language of Instruction: Spanish.
Degrees and Diplomas: Licenciado in–Philosophy; Letters; Education; Psychology; Commercial Administration; Accountancy; Sociology; Industrial Relations; Social Communications, 5 yrs. Professional titles of–Abogado, law; Ingeniero civil; Ingeniero industrial; Economista, 5 yrs. Doctorates in–Law; Economics; Letters; Psychology, by thesis.
Library: Total, *c.* 195,000 vols.
Publications: Journal of the Faculty of Law (biannually); Journal of Montalbán (annually); Journal of Industrial and Labour Relations (biannually); Carta al Egresado (4 times a year).
Academic Staff: c. 80 (510).
Student Enrolment: c. 9200 (including *c.* 52% Women).

7666 **UNIVERSIDAD CATÓLICA DEL TÁCHIRA**
Apartado 366, San Cristóbal (Táchira)
Telex: 76499
Telephone: 430510; 43080

F. of Law
F. of Economics and Social Sciences
F. of Humanities and Education
F. of Religious Sciences

Founded 1962 as branch of Universidad Católica 'Andrés Bello', became independent 1982. A private institution.
Academic Year: October to September (October-February; March-September).
Admission Requirements: Secondary school certificate (bachillerato) and entrance examination.
Language of Instruction: Spanish.
Degrees and Diplomas: Licenciado in–Commercial Administration; Accountancy; Education, 5 yrs. Professional title of Abogado, law, 5yrs. Also title of Técnico superior en Educación Pre-escolar, 5 sem.
Library: c. 28,000 vols.
Publication: Paramillo (Revista anual de Ciencias Sociales).
Academic Staff: c. 30 (140).
Student Enrolment: c. 3220.

7667 **UNIVERSIDAD CATÓLICA 'CECILIO ACOSTA'**
Urb. La Paz, Etapa II, Edif. Sede Instituto Niños Cantores del Zulia, Maracaibo
Rector: Montiel Troconis (1988-92)

F. of Education and Social Communication
F. of Humanities and Social Sciences
F. of Fine Arts
S. of Education
S. of Social Communication
S. of Philosophy
S. of Plastic Arts

Founded 1983.

7668 ***UNIVERSIDAD CENTRAL DE VENEZUELA**
Central University of Venezuela
Ciudad Universitaria, Los Chaguaramas, Caracas
Telephone: 619811 (30 lines)
Rector: Edmundo Chirinos

F. of Architecture
F. of Political Science and Law
F. of Agriculture
F. of Science
F. of Veterinary Science
F. of Medicine
F. of Economics and Social Sciences
F. of Pharmacy
F. of Education and Humanities
F. of Engineering
F. of Dentistry
D. of Lifelong Education
Open University P.

Also 37 schools of the different faculties.

Founded 1696 as seminary, authorized to award degrees 1722, and became Royal and Pontifical University 1725. An autonomous State institution. Governing body: the Consejo Universitario, presided over by the Rector and composed of the Vice-Rectors, the Secretary-General, the deans of the faculties, a representative of the Ministry of Education, and 3 representatives of the student body.
Academic Year: January to December (January-June; July-December).
Admission Requirements: Secondary school certificate (bachillerato) and entrance examination.
Language of Instruction: Spanish.
Degrees and Diplomas: Licenciado in–Bioanalysis; Journalism; Library Studies; Social Work, 4 yrs; Biology; Physics; Mathematics; Chemistry; Geography; Meteorology; Cartography; Psychology; Business Administration; Computer Sciences; International Studies; Political Science; Philosophy; Letters; History; Education; Accountancy; Statistics, 5 yrs. Professional titles of–Agrimensor, surveying; Técnico en Trabajo social; Economista; Estadígrafo; Actuario; Farmacéutico; Hidrometeorologista; Ingeniero civil; Ingeniero geodesta, surveying; Ingeniero electricista; Ingeniero mecánico; Ingeniero químico; Ingeniero de Petróleo; Ingeniero metalúrgico; Ingeniero de Minas; Geólogo; Ingeniero agrónomo, agriculture; Arquitecto; Abogado, law; Médico cirujano; Médico veterinario; Odontólogo; Sociólogo; Antropólogo. Doctorates by thesis in–Dentistry; Pharmacy; Veterinary Medicine; Law; Economics; Sociology; Anthropology; Medicine; Philosophy; Letters; History; Education; Psychology.
Libraries: Central Library, *c.* 300,000 vols; faculty libraries, *c.* 259,580; Experimental Medicine Library.
Special Facilities (Museums, etc.): Museum of Education.
Academic Staff: c. 6990.
Student Enrolment: c. 52,070.

7669 **UNIVERSIDAD CENTRO OCCIDENTAL 'LISANDRO ALVAREDO'**
Carrera 19 entre Calle 8 y 9, Barquisimeto (Lara)
Telephone: (051) 513551; 514916; 510397
Rector: Carlos Zapata Escalona (1982-86)

S. of Medicine
S. of Agriculture
S. of Veterinary Science
S. of Administration (including Accountancy)
S. of Science
S. of Engineering
I. of Oenology Research
Extension D.

Founded 1962, the university is an autonomous State institution. Governing body: the Consejo Universitario, presided over by the Rector and comprised of 2 Vice-Rectors, the Secretary-General,the directors of the schools, a representative of the graduates and of the Ministry of Education.
Arrangements for co-operation with: University of Georgia; Oklahoma State University.
Academic Year: March to February (March-September; October-February).
Admission Requirements: Secondary school certificate (bachillerato) or recognized foreign equivalent, and entrance examination.
Language of Instruction: Spanish.
Degrees and Diplomas: Licenciado in–Commercial Administration; Accountancy; Computer Sciences; Mathematics, 5 yrs. Professional titles of–Analista de Sistemas; Técnicos municipales; Técnicos en Cooperativismo; Ingeniero agrónomo, agriculture; Médico veterinario; Ingeniero civil, 5 yrs. Médico cirujano, 6 yrs.
Libraries: Central Library, *c.* 26,230 vols; school libraries.
Publications: Boletín; Temas Universitarios; Tarea Común.
Academic Staff: c. 620 (200).
Student Enrolment: c. 13,170.

7670 **UNIVERSIDAD JOSÉ MARÍA VARGAS**
Avenida Sucre Torre Sur, piso 4, Los Dos Caminos, Caracas

F. of Administration
F. of Architecture and Plastic Arts
F. of Education
F. of Engineering

Founded 1983.

7671 **UNIVERSIDAD METROPOLITANA**
Distribuidor Universidad, Autopista Petare-Guarenas (La Urbina)
Apartado Postal 76819, Caracas 107
Cables: Unimet
Telephone: 2395622
Rector: Rodolfo Moleiro (1976-)

F. of Science and Arts
F. of Economics and Social Sciences
F. of Engineering

Founded 1965, opened 1970. A private institution. Governing bodies:

the Consejo Superior; the Consejo Académico.

Arrangements for co-operation with the University of Cornell.

Academic Year: October to July (October-February; March-July; August-September).

Admission Requirements: Secondary school certificate (bachillerato) and entrance examination.

Language of Instruction: Spanish.

Degrees and Diplomas: Licenciado in–Modern Languages; Administration, 5 yrs. Professional titles of–Ingeniero-mecánico; -químico; -eléctrico; -de Sistemas; -civil, 5 yrs; Ingeniero superior técnico in Pre-School Education, 3 yrs.

Library: c. 30,000 vols.

Academic Staff: c. 70 (220).

Student Enrolment: c. 3800.

7672 **UNIVERSIDAD NACIONAL ABIERTA**

National Open University

Avenida Los Calvani (antes Av. Gamboa No.18), San Bernardino, Caracas 1010

Telex: 26111

Telephone: (2) 574-13-22

Fax: (2) 574-3086

Rector: Gustavo Luis Carrera

Secretario: Milton Granados P.

Area of Mathematics

Co-ordinator: José Ramón Ortiz; *staff* 58

Area of Engineering (Industial and Systems Engineering)

Co-ordinator: Adalberto González; *staff* 37

Area of Education

Co-ordinator: Maruja Rivero de García; *staff* 137

Area of Administration (including Business Administration and Accountancy)

Co-ordinator: Santiago Cuadra; *staff* 60

Founded 1975, first students admitted 1977. Offers studies in 21 local centres in the different regions. Governing bodies: the Consejo Superior; the Consejo Directivo.

Academic Year: January to September (January-May; June-September).

Admission Requirements: Secondary school certificate (bachillerato).

Fees (Bolivares): 8723 per annum.

Language of Instruction: Spanish.

Degrees and Diplomas: Licenciado, 5 yrs. Magister, a further 2 yrs.

Library: Central Library, 53,535 vols.

Publications: Una Opinion; Una Document; Informe de Investigaciones ; Fondo Editorial Una (all biannually).

Academic Staff, 1990: 547.

Student Enrolment, 1990: 28,669.

7673 **UNIVERSIDAD NACIONAL EXPERIMENTAL DE LA COSTA ORIENTAL DEL LARGO DE MARACAIBO**

Maracaibo (Zulia)

Founded 1982.

7674 **UNIVERSIDAD NACIONAL EXPERIMENTAL 'FRANCISCO DE MIRANDA'**

Calle Norte, Edf. Rosalla, Coro (Falcón)

Telex: 56184 UFM

D. of Medicine

D. of Industrial Engineering

D. of Agriculture

D. of Veterinary Medicine

D. of Civil Engineering

Founded 1977. First students (of Medicine) admitted 1979. A State institution.

Academic Year: January to December (February-June; July-December).

Admission Requirements: Secondary school certificate (bachillerato).

Language of Instruction: Spanish.

Degrees and Diplomas: Professional titles of–Técnico superior, 2 ½ yrs; Ingeniero–civil; –industrial; –agrónomo; Médico veterinario, 5 yrs; Médico general, 6 yrs.

Library: Central Library, *c.* 50,000 vols.

Special Facilities (Museums, etc.): Museo: del Hombre; de Cerámica Colonial y Moderna; del Arte; de Ciencias y Tecnología.

Publications: Cultura Falconiana (quarterly); Hoja Universitaria; Gaceta Universitaria.

Academic Staff: c. 110.

Student Enrolment: c. 1000.

7675 **UNIVERSIDAD NACIONAL EXPERIMENTAL DE GUAYANA**

Edif. General de Seguros, Av. Las Américas, Puerto Ordaz (Bolívar)

Telex: 86543

Telephone: (086) 227931

Fax: (086) 225673

Rector: Aline Lampe Joubert

Secretario: Ingrid Hernández Mantellini

Introductory Course

Dean: Giesla Pinedo; *staff* 34 (3)

S. of Professional Studies

Dean: Magaly de Illaramendy; *staff* 11 (3)

S. of Forestry Industry

Director: Paussolino Martinez; *staff* 11 (3)

S. of Education

Director: Eddy Orozco; *staff* 8 (7)

S. of Industrial Engineering

Director: Douglas Ocando; *staff* 6 (1)

S. of Computer Engineering

Director: Angel Tarazona; *staff* 10 (14)

S. of Business Administration and Public Accounting

Director: Noel Rodríguez; *staff* 23 (6)

Institutional Projects P.

Director: Antonio Montes; *staff* 5

D. of Postgraduate Courses

Dean: Daniel Bermúdez; *staff* 5 (8)

Technological Research D.

Dean: Aixa Viera; *staff* 5

Educational Research D.

Dean: Luis D'Aubeter; *staff* 4

Anthropological Research D.

Dean: Mercedes Mandé; *staff* 1

Founded 1982. Acquired present status 1986. Governing bodies: Management University Council; the Consejo de Gerencia Universitaria; the Consejo Superior.

Academic Year: March to February.

Admission Requirements: Secondary school certificate (bachillerato).

Fees: None.

Language of Instruction: Spanish.

Degrees and Diplomas: Licenciado, 5 yrs. Magister, a further 2 yrs. Also title of Técnico superior, 3 yrs.

Library: Central Library, 8000 vols.

Publications: Gaceta Universitaria (3 per annum); Siglo XXI, (a periodical publication on culture); Science and Technologes Review (biannually).

Academic Staff, 1990:

Rank	Full-time	Part-time
Profesores Titulares	4	1
Profesores Asociados	3	–
Profesores Agregados	12	1
Profesores Asistentes	37	6
Profesores Instructores	80	29
Total	136	37

Student Enrolment, 1990:

	Men	Women	Total
Of the country	600	874	1474
Of other countries	37	45	82
Total	637	919	1556

7676 **UNIVERSIDAD NACIONAL EXPERIMENTAL DE LOS LLANOS CENTRALES 'ROMULO GALLEGOS'**

Avenida Los Llanos, San Juan de los Morros

Telephone: (046) 37596

Rector: Sebastián Viale-Rigo

D. of Agricultural and Animal Sciences (including Forestry)

D. of Health Sciences

Founded 1977. A State institution.

Arrangements for co-operation with the Ben-Gurion University of the Negev.

Academic Year: February to January (February-July; August-February).

Admission Requirements: Secondary school certificate (bachillerato) and entrance examination.

Language of Instruction: Spanish.

Degrees and Diplomas: Licenciado in Nursing, 5 yrs. Professional titles of–Ingeniero; Odontólogo, 5 yrs.

Library: Centro de Información y Documentación, 40,000 vols.
Publications: Boletín; Gazeta.
Academic Staff: c. 80.
Student Enrolment: c. 430.

7677 **UNIVERSIDAD NACIONAL EXPERIMENTAL DE LOS LLANOS OCCIENTALES 'EZEQUIEL ZAMORA'**
Apartado 19, Llano Alto-Barinas (Barinas)
Telex: 73171 VENEZ-V
Telephone: (073) 41201

P. of Agriculture
P. of Animal Husbandry
P. of Natural Resources
P. of Agricultural Economics
P. of Rural Social Development
P. of Agricultural Engineering
P. of Agro-Industrial Engineering
Extension D.

Founded 1975. A State institution financially supported by the government. Governing body: the Executive Board, comprising 5 members.
Academic Year: February to December (February-June; August-December)
Admission Requirements: Secondary school certificate (bachillerato).
Language of Instruction: Spanish.
Degrees and Diplomas: Licenciado in–Social Development; Regional Planning, 5 yrs. Professional title of–Ingeniero agrónomo; Ingeniero de Conservación; Zootecnista; Ingeniero Agro-Industrial, 5 yrs.
Library: Central Library, *c.* 20,000 vols.
Academic Staff: c. 250.
Student Enrolment: c. 1990.

7678 **UNIVERSIDAD NACIONAL EXPERIMENTAL 'RAFAEL MARÍA BARALT'**
Calle El Rosario, Cabimas-Dtto., Bolívar (Zulia)

Education
Social Sciences

7679 **UNIVERSIDAD NACIONAL EXPERIMENTAL DEL TÁCHIRA**
Apartado 436, Paramillo, San Cristóbal (Táchira)
Telex: 76196
Telephone: (076) 59056; 59292

S. of Industrial Engineering
S. of Mechanical Engineering
S. of Agricultural Engineering
S. of Animal Husbandry
Ce. for Regional Studies
Ce. for Lifelong Education

Founded 1974. A State institution. Governing body: the Consejo Universitario. Some residential facilities for academic staff and students.
Admission Requirements: Secondary school certificate (bachillerato) or equivalent, and entrance examination.
Language of Instruction: Spanish.
Degrees and Diplomas: Professional titles of–Ingeniero; Zootecnista, 5 yrs.
Library: c. 71,840 vols.
Publications: Boletín Bibliográfico; Gaceta (quarterly); Divulga (biannually); Vocero Universitario (quarterly); Cuadernos; Aleph Subcero; Matemáticas.
Academic Staff: c. 290.
Student Enrolment: c. 2670.

7680 **UNIVERSIDAD DE ORIENTE**
Apartado postal 245, Cumaná (Sucre)
Cables: Univorient
Telephone: (093) 23366
Rector: Pedro Augusto Beauperthuy

S. of Business Administration
S. of Sciences
S. of Education
S. of Social Sciences
S. of Agricultural Engineering (Monagas)
S. of Animal Husbandry (Monagas)
S. of Geology and Mining (Bolívar)
S. of Medicine (Bolívar)
S. of Engineering (Electrical, Industrial, Mechanical, Petroleum, Chemical) (Anzoátequi)
S. of Administration (Sucre)
S. of Science (Sucre)
S. of Education (Sucre)
S. of Social Studies (Sucre)
D. of Basic Studies
D. of Basic Studies (Bolívar)
I. of Oceanography

Founded 1958, the university is an autonomous State institution. Governing bodies: the Consejo Consultivo; the Junta Universitaria.
Academic Year: January to December (January-July; August-November).
Admission Requirements: Secondary school certificate (bachillerato) or recognized foreign equivalent.
Language of Instruction: Spanish.
Degrees and Diplomas: Licenciado in–Biology; Chemistry; Physics; Mathematics; Education; Business Administration; Sociology; English, 4-5 yrs. Professional titles of–Sociólogo, 4 yrs; Ingeniero (in various fields); Zootecnista, 5 yrs; Médico cirujano, 6 yrs.
Libraries: Central Library, *c.* 12,000 vols; branch libraries, *c.* 33,000.
Special Facilities (Museums, etc.): Museum of Oceanography.
Publications: Boletín del Instituto Oceanográfico; Revista de Sociología.
Academic Staff: c. 1260.
Student Enrolment: c. 21,020.

7681 **UNIVERSIDAD PEDAGÓGICA EXPERIMENTAL LIBERTADOR**
Avenida Sucre, Parque del Oeste, Caracas 1010
Telephone: 887511
Fax: 7556456
Rectora: Duilia Govea de Carpio

Education Research
I. of Teacher Training (5)
Extension D.

Founded 1983. Co-ordinates five major institutes of teacher training (Instituto Universitario Pedagógico). (see under Teacher Training).

7682 **UNIVERSIDAD RAFAEL URDANETA**
Rafael Urdaneta University
Lado Noro-oeste de la Rinconada Country Club. Apartado Correos 614, Maracaibo (Zulia)
Telephone: (061) 71751
Rector: Eloy Párraga Villamarin (1984-88)
Vice-Rector Académico: J. L. García Díaz

F. of Engineering
Dean: Fernando Urdaneta; *staff* 62 (59)
F. of Agriculture (Animal Husbandry)
Dean: Rómulo Rincón A.; *staff* 9 (22)
F. of Political Science and Administration (including Psychology)
Dean: José Luis Mendez La Fuente; *staff* 47 (50)
C. of Basic Studies
Co-ordinator: Eglé García de Fuenmayor; *staff* 24 (6)
Ce. for Lifelong Education

Founded 1973, first courses started 1976. A private institution recognized by the government. Financially supported by tuition fees and donations. Governing body: the Consejo Académico, comprising the Rector, 3 Vice-Rectors, the Secretary, and the deans of the faculties.
Academic Year: September to July (September-February; February-June).
Admission Requirements: Secondary school certificate (bachillerato) or equivalent, and entrance examination.
Fees (Bolívares): 6000 per semester.
Language of Instruction: Spanish
Degrees and Diplomas: Licenciado and Professional title of Ingeniero in all fields, 5 yrs. Degree of Maestría.
Library: Total, 73,000 vols.
Publication: Boletín (bimonthly).

Academic Staff, 1986-87:

Rank	Full-time	Part-time
Profesores Titulares	2	1
Profesores Asociados	8	2
Profesores Agregados	20	6
Profesores Asistentes	52	19
Profesores Instructores	–	4
Contratados	60	100
Total	142	132

Student Enrolment, 1986-87:

	Men	Women	Total
Of the country	1401	1333	2734

7683 **UNIVERSIDAD SANTA MARÍA**
Avenida Páez, Frente Plaza Madariaga, El Paraíso, Caracas
Telephone: 41-55-96

F. of Law
S. of Economics
S. of Administration and Accountancy
S. of Law
S. of Pharmacy
S. of Civil Engineering

Founded 1953 as a private institution.
Academic Year: September to July.
Language of Instruction: Spanish.
Degrees and Diplomas: Licenciado in–Administration; Accountancy, 5 yrs. Professional titles of–Abogado, law; Economista; Farmacéutico; Ingeniero civil, 5 yrs.
Academic Staff: c. 250.
Student Enrolment: c. 3500.

7684 **UNIVERSIDAD SIMÓN BOLÍVAR**
Apartado postal 80659, Caracas 1080
Telex: 21910 SUBVE
Telephone: 962-1101; 1201

D. of Physics and Mathematics
D. of Social Sciences and Humanities (including Design and Town Planning)
D. of Biological Sciences
D. of Engineering, Architecture and Technology (Litoral)
D. of Social Sciences (including Tourism) (Litoral)
Ce. for Correspondence Courses
Extension D.
Ce. for Lifelong Education
Also 7 Research Institutes.

Founded 1967 as a State experimental university, first courses started 1970. Governing bodies: the Consejo Directivo Universitario; the Consejo Académico; the Consejo Superior Universitario.

Arrangements for co-operation with: University of Paris III; Autonomous University of Barcelona; Technical University of Madrid; Universidad Externado de Colombia; University of the Andes.

Academic Year: September to July (September-December; January-April; April-July).
Admission Requirements: Secondary school certificate (bachillerato) or equivalent, and entrance examination.
Language of Instruction: Spanish.
Degrees and Diplomas: Licenciado in–Mathematics; Chemistry; Physics; Biology, 5 yrs. Professional titles of–Ingeniero (various fields), 5 yrs; Arquitecto, 6 yrs. Also diplomas of specialization and degree of Magister and Doctorate.
Library: Central Library, *c.* 75,000 vols.
Special Facilities (Museums, etc.): Colonial Imagery Museum.
Publications: Argos (quarterly); Revista Venezolana de Filosofia (quarterly).
Press or Publishing House: Editorial Equinoccio.
Academic Staff: c. 350 (30).
Student Enrolment: c. 6000.

7685 ***UNIVERSIDAD SIMÓN RODRÍGUEZ**
Avenida José María Vargas, Sante Fé Norte, Caracas 10181
Telephone: 979-10-22
Rector: Elizabeth Y. de Caldera

Education
Social Sciences
Engineering

Founded 1974. A State institution.
Degrees and Diplomas: Licenciado, 4 yrs.
Academic Staff: c. 420.
Student Enrolment: c. 13,610.

7686 **UNIVERSIDAD DEL SUR DEL LAGO**
Maracaibo (Zulia)

Agriculture
Marine Sciences
Education
Branches in: La Feria; El Vigia; Caja Seca; and Sabana de Mendoza.
Founded 1982. A private institution.

7687 **UNIVERSIDAD TECNOLÓGICA DEL CENTRO**
Via Areguita, Apartado 1620, Valencia (Carabobo)
Telephone: (45) 718088
Fax: (45) 718045
Rector: César Peña Vigas
Secretario General: Héctor Manuel Tamayo

Area of Mechanical Engineering
Head: José F. Torrealba
Area of Electrical Engineering
Head: Juan Carlos Gazman
Area of Information Engineering (Computer Science)
Head: Enrique Daboin
Area of Business Administration (including Accountancy)
Head: Tamara Colmenares
Area of Institutional Projects (Energy, Food, Water as Resource)
Head: Teinaldo Plaz

Founded 1979. A non-profit private institution. Governing body: the Consejo Superior.
Academic Year: September to July (September-December; January-April; May-July).
Admission Requirements: Secondary school certificate (bachillerato).
Fees (Bolivares): 7500.
Language of Instruction: Spanish.
Degrees and Diplomas: Title of Técnico superior, 3 yrs. Licenciado; Professional title of Ingeniero (in various fields), 5 yrs.
Library: 4500 vols.
Student Enrolment, 1990:

Men	Women	Total
521	595	1116

7688 **UNIVERSIDAD DEL ZULIA**
University of Zulia
Apartado postal 526, Maracaibo 4011 (Zulia)
Telex: 62172
Telephone: (061) 517697
Rector: José Ferrer (1984-)
Secretario: Robinson Aguirre

F. of Agriculture
Dean: José Urdaneta; *staff* 124 (11)
F. of Architecture
Dean: Nancy Avila de Montero; *staff* 93 (17)
F. of Veterinary Science
Dean: Heli S. Colina; *staff* 100 (10)
F. of Law
Dean: Idamis García Cedeño; *staff* 106 (53)
F. of Economics and Social Sciences (including Accountancy and Business Administration)
Dean: Gerónomo Tudares; *staff* 362 (51)
F. of Humanities and Education (including Journalism)
Dean: Dario Durán C.; *staff* 362 (51)
F. of Engineering
Dean: Antonio Cova; *staff* 381 (78)
F. of Medicine (including Nursing)
Dean: Dianela de Avila; *staff* 409 (221)
F. of Dentistry
Dean: María Ferrer de Sánchez; *staff* 89 (13)
F. of Science
Dean: José Finol; *staff* 372 (11)

Founded 1891, reorganized 1904 and 1946. The university is an official autonomous institution under the jurisdiction of the federal government.

Governing bodies: the Consejo Universitario, presided over by the Rector and including the Vice-Rector, the Secretary, the deans of the faculties, a representative from the Ministry of Education, and 3 representatives of the student body;the Consejos de Facultad. Some residential facilities for students.

Arrangements for co-operation with the Universities of: Texas at Austin; Georgia; Illinois; Oklahoma; Budapest(Technical); Nicaragua; Bucharest.

Academic Year: January to December (January-June; July-December).

Admission Requirements: Secondary school certificate (bachillerato) and entrance examination.

Fees (Bolívares): 100-500 per semester.

Language of Instruction: Spanish.

Degrees and Diplomas: Licenciado in–Education; Journalism; Letters; Philosophy; Business Administration; Bioanalysis; Nursing; Dietetics; Biology; Chemistry; Mathematics; Physics; Social Communication; Social Work; Accountancy, 5 yrs. Professional titles of–Abogado, law; Ingeniero civil; Ingeniero de Petróleo; Ingeniero geodesta; Ingeniero electricista; Ingeniero mecánico; Ingeniero quimico; Ingeniero industrial; Odontólogo; Arquitecto; Economista; Médico veterinario; Ingeniero agrónomo; Sociólogo, 5 yrs; Médico cirujano, 6 yrs. Degree of Magister and diplomas of specialization. Doctorates in–Law; Dentistry; Medicine.

Libraries: Central Library, 57,282 vols; faculty libraries, 215,636.

Publications: Revista de la Universidad (annually); Periódico de la Universidad (monthly); Revistas of the Faculties; Revista Ciencias (quarterly); Opción (quarterly); Revista Capítulo Criminológico (annually).

Press or Publishing House: Editorial de la Universidad del Zulia.

Academic Staff, 1986-87:

Rank	Full-time	Part-time
Profesores Titulares	1125	52
Profesores Asociados	61	44
Profesores Agregados	564	92
Profesores Asistentes	375	146
Instructores	55	52
Otros	123	28
Total	2303	434

Student Enrolment, 1986-87: 55,998.

Other Institutions

Technical Education

7689 **INSTITUTO UNIVERSITARIO POLITÉCNICO**

Parque Tecnológico Coroahuaico, Barquisimeto (Lara)
Cables: Polinal
Telephone: 051-422965

D. of Electrical Engineering
D. of Mechanical Engineering
D. of Chemical Engineering
D. of Metallurgy
D. of Electronics
D. of Basic Studies
D. of Industrial Training
Learning Resources Ce. (including Audio-visual Ce.)

Founded 1962 with assistance from the United Nations Development Programme. A State institution responsible tothe Ministry of Education.

Academic Year: March to March (March-July; January-March).

Admission Requirements: Secondary school certificate (bachillerato) or recognized foreign equivalent, and entrance examination.

Language of Instruction: Spanish.

Degrees and Diplomas: Professional titles and Ingeniero, 5 yrs. Maestría in Mathematics.

Library: c. 6000 vols.

Publication: Boletín (monthly).

Academic Staff: c. 190.

Student Enrolment: c. 3500.

7690 **INSTITUTO UNIVERSITARIO POLITÉCNICO 'LUIS CABALLERO MEJÍAS'**

Avenida Francisco Solano Cruce, Sabana Grande, Caracas

D. of Mechanical Engineering

D. of Instrument Technology
D. of Construction Engineering
D. of Industrial Engineering
D. of Systems Technology

Founded 1974. A State institution.

Degrees and Diplomas: Professional titles, 3-5 yrs.

7691 **INSTITUTO UNIVERSITARIO POLITÉCNICO DE LAS FUERZAS ARMADAS**

Base Aérea La Carlota, Caracas
Telephone: 355022

D. of Civil Engineering
D. of Electronics
D. of Electrical Engineering
D. of Aeronautical Engineering
D. of Chemical Engineering
D. of Marine Engineering

Founded 1974. A State institution.

7692 **INSTITUTO UNIVERSITARIO POLITÉCNICO EXPERIMENTAL DE GUAYANA**

Cuidad Guayana, Puerto Ordaz (Bolívar)
Cables: Poliguayana
Telephone: 086-391045

D. of Mechanical Engineering
D. of Electrical Engineering
D. of Metallurgy
D. of Basic Studies

Founded 1971 with the assistance of Unesco. A State institution responsible to the Ministry of Education.

Academic Year: January to November (January-May; August-November).

Admission Requirements: Secondary school certificate (bachillerato) and entrance examination.

Language of Instruction: Spanish.

Degrees and Diplomas: Diploma of Ingeniero (in a particular field), 5 yrs.

Library: c. 5000 vols.

Publications: Información; Boletín; Periódico.

Academic Staff: c. 30.

7693 **INSTITUTO UNIVERSITARIO DE TECHNOLOGÍA REGIÓN CAPITAL**

Apartado 40347, Caracas 1040-A
Telephone: 691881

D. of Business Administration (including Economics and Statistics)
D. of Civil Engineering
D. of Chemistry
D. of Chemical Engineering
D. of Mechanical Engineering
D. of Metallurgy
D. of Computer Sciences
D. of Electrical Engineering
Preparatory D.

Founded 1971. A State institution.

Arrangements for co-operation with the Universities of: Rennes; Pau; Grenoble; Tübingen. Institut Polytechnique de Montréal.

Academic Year: September to July.

Admission Requirements: Secondary school certificate (bachillerato) and entrance examination.

Language of Instruction: Spanish.

Degrees and Diplomas: Professional title of Técnico superior, 2-3 yrs.

Library: c. 15,300 vols.

Academic Staff: c. 200.

Student Enrolment: c. 1110

7694 **INSTITUTO UNIVERSITARIO DE TECNOLOGÍA 'ANTONIO JOSÉ DE SUCRE'**

Avenida Mohedano La Castellana, Altamira, Caracas
Telephone: 32-20-24

S. of Administration and Commerce
S. of Design (including Architecture and Urban Planning)
S. of Graphic Technology and Civil Engineering

Founded 1972. A private institution recognized by the State.

Degrees and Diplomas: Professional title of Técnico superior, 6 sem.

7695 **ESCUELA NACIONAL DE ADMINISTRACIÓN Y HACIENDA PÚBLICA**

Avenida Urdaneta, Edificio Central, Esquina Las Ibarras, Caracas
Telephone: 81-89-82

Public Administration and Finance

Founded 1944 as a training course in taxation, acquired present status and title 1977, incorporating the former Escuela Nacional de Administración Pública. A State institution under the jurisdiction of the Ministriesof Finance and Education and financed by the government. Governing bodies: the Consejo Académico, comprising 6 members; the Consejo Directivo, comprising 8 members.

Academic Year: January to December (January-June; July-December).

Admission Requirements: Secondary school certificate (bachillerato) and entrance examination.

Language of Instruction: Spanish.

Degrees and Diplomas: Licenciado en–Ciencias Fiscales en Rentas; Ciencias Fiscales en Finanzas Públicas, 5 yrs. Professional title of Técnico Superior Hacendista in Rent and Customs. Maestría en Administración Pública.

Library: Central Library, *c.* 10,000 vols.

Publication: Revista (monthly).

Academic Staff: c. 20 (340).

Student Enrolment: c. 760.

7696 **ESCUELA UNIVERSITARIO DE TECNOLOGIÁ 'RODOLFO LOERO ARISMENDI'**

Avenida Caurimare, Colinas de Bello Monte 2424, Caracas

Industrial Chemistry
Hydrology
Industrial Administration

Founded 1978. A State institution.

7697 **ESCUELA UNIVERSITARIO DE TECNOLOGÍA 'ALONSO GAMERO'**

Avenida Independencia, Parque Los Orumos, Coro (Falcón)
Cables: I.U.T.C. 7429-7517
Telephone: 59338; 59669

D. of Business Administration
D. of Chemistry
D. of Mechanical Engineering
D. of Agriculture and Animal Husbandry
D. of Civil Engineering
D. of Instrument Technology
D. of Basic Studies

Founded 1972, admitted first students 1979. A State institution. Governing body: the Consejo Académico.

Academic Year: January to December (January-June; July-December).

Admission Requirements: Secondary school certificate (bachillerato).

Language of Instruction: Spanish.

Degrees and Diplomas: Professional title of Técnico superior, 3 yrs.

Publications: Folia (biannually); Bulletin (weekly).

Academic Staff: c. 140 (40).

7698 **INSTITUTO UNIVERSITARIO DE TECNOLOGÍA DE CUMANÁ**

Carretera Cumaná-Cumanacoa Km. 4, Cumaná
Telex: 93165
Telephone: (093) 62901

Electrical Engineering
Chemistry
Applied Biology
Agriculture and Food Technology

Founded 1974 by Corporiente (East Regional Development Corporation). A State institution.

Academic Year: February to January.

Admission Requirements: Secondary school certificate (bachillerato) and entrance examination.

Language of Instruction: Spanish.

Degrees and Diplomas: Professional title of Técnico superior, 2-3 yrs.

Library: c. 8200 vols.

7699 **INSTITUTO UNIVERSITARIO DE TECNOLOGÍA DE EJIDO**

Via Manzano Baja, Ejido (Mérida)

Engineering (including Architecture)
Agriculture
Marine Technology

Founded 1981.

7700 **INSTITUTO UNIVERSITARIO DE TECNOLOGÍA DE EL TIGRE**

Carretera El Tigre, Via Ciudad Bolívar, El Tigre (Anzoategui)

Mechanical Engineering
Chemistry
Agriculture
Administration

Founded 1977. A State institution.

7701 **INSTITUTO UNIVERSITARIO DE TECNOLOGÍA ISAAC NEWTON**

Avenida Constitución Edif Alayon Plaza, Maracay (Aragua)

Engineering (including Architecture)
Social Sciences

Founded 1983. A private institution.

7702 **INSTITUTO UNIVERSITARIO DE LOS LLANOS**

Valle de La Pascua Urb, Guamachal

Agriculture
Stockraising
Agricultural Administration

Founded 1973. A State institution.

Degrees and Diplomas: Professional title of Técnico superior, 2 ½ yrs.

7703 **INSTITUTO UNIVERSITARIO EXPERIMENTAL DE TECNOLOGÍA DE LA VICTORIA**

Zona Industrial Soco, Avenida Ricaurte Frente a Maviplanca, La Victoria (Aragua)
Telex: 44130
Telephone: (044) 24723; 24878

D. of Electrical Engineering
D. of Mechanical Engineering

Founded 1976. A State institution.

Academic Year: September to July (September-December; January-March; April-July).

Admission Requirements: Secondary school certificate (bachillerato) and entrance examination.

Language of Instruction: Spanish.

Degrees and Diplomas: Professional title of Técnico superior, 2 yrs.

Library: c. 3900 vols.

Academic Staff: c. 60.

Student Enrolment: c. 370.

7704 **INSTITUTO UNIVERSITARIO DE TECNOLOGÍA DEL MAR**

Fundación La Salle, Punta de Piedras, Margarita (Nueva Esparta)

Marine Technology
Fishery Technology

Founded 1977. A State institution.

7705 **INSTITUTO UNIVERSITARIO DE TECNOLOGÍA PTO. CABELLO**

Avenida Bolívar 31-7, Rancho Grande, Puerto Cabello (Carabobo)

Mechanical Engineering
Metallurgy

Founded 1976. A State institution.

7706 **INSTITUTO UNIVERSITARIO DE TECNOLOGÍA AGRO-INDUSTRIAL**

Apartado 261, La Concordia, San Cristóbal (Táchira)
Telephone: (076) 26290

D. of Basic Studies
D. of Agriculture
D. of Food Technology

D. of Electrical Engineering

Founded 1972 by the Táchira Education Foundation. A State institution.

Academic Year: February to December (February-July; September-December).

Admission Requirements: Secondary school certificate (bachillerato) or equivalent.

Language of Instruction: Spanish.

Degrees and Diplomas: Professional titles of Técnico superior–en Agronomía; en Tecnología de Alimentos; en Electrónica, 3 yrs.

Library: Central Library, *c.* 17,000 vols.

Academic Staff: c. 145 (30).

Student Enrolment: c. 840.

7707 **INSTITUTO UNIVERSITARIO DE TECNOLOGÍA**

Avenida Alberto Ravell, Cruce con Avenida José Antonio Paez, San Felipe (Yaracuy)

D. of Agriculture
D. of Food Technology
D. of Stockraising
D. of Nutrition

Founded 1974.

Degrees and Diplomas: Professional title of Técnico superior, 2 ½ yrs.

7708 **INSTITUTO UNIVERSITARIO DE TECNOLOGÍA INDUSTRIAL**

Local del Colegio La Salle, Avenida La Salle, Urbanización Guaparo, Valencia (Carabobo)

Industrial Engineering
Architecture

Founded 1978.

7709 **INSTITUTO UNIVERSITARIO DE TECNOLOGÍA INDUSTRIAL**

Colegio Tirso de Molina, Avenida Cristóbal Rojas c/c Humboldt, San Bernardino, Caracas

Engineering (including Architecture)

Founded 1978.

7710 **INSTITUTO UNIVERSITARIO DE TECNOLOGÍA DE VALENCIA**

Urb. El Trigal, Calle Gual. 92-98, Valencia (Carabobo)

Chemistry
Electrical Engineering

Founded 1976.

7711 **INSTITUTO UNIVERSITARIO DE TECNOLOGÍA DE VENEZUELA**

Avenida Universidad, Edif. La Metropolitana, Caracas

Founded 1983.

7712 **INSTITUTO UNIVERSITARIO DE TECNOLOGÍA DEL ESTADO TRUJILLO**

Avenida Caracas, Edif. 'El Tiempo' Local 3, Valera (Trujillo)

Civil Engineering

Founded 1978. A State institution.

Professional Education

7713 **COLEGIO UNIVERSITARIO 'FERMÍN TORO'**

Carrera 29 No. 20-27, Barquisimeto (Lara)
Telephone: (051) 510304

D. of Basic Studies
D. of Social Sciences
D. of Natural Sciences
D. of Mathematics
D. of Education
D. of Business Administration

Founded 1975. A State institution. Governing bodies: the Consejo Directivo; the Consejo Académico.

Academic Year: February-January (February-July; September-January).

Admission Requirements: Secondary school certificate (bachillerato).

Language of Instruction: Spanish.

Degrees and Diplomas: Professional title of Técnico superior, 3 yrs.

Library: Central Library, *c.* 12,000 vols.

Academic Staff: c. 5 (70).

Student Enrolment: c. 2300.

7714 **COLEGIO UNIVERSITARIO JEAN PIAGET**

Avenida Principal, Qta. La Lomita Urbanización Los Guayabitos, Baruta

Psychopedagogy

Founded 1975. A private institution.

7715 **COLEGIO UNIVERSITARIO DE CABIMAS**

Calle la Estrella 117, Sector Ampara, Cabimas

Mechanical Engineering
Electrical Engineering
Petroleum Technology
Instrument Technology

Founded 1976. A State institution.

7716 **COLEGIO UNIVERSITARIO DE CARACAS**

Avenida Libertador Cruce con Calle Caicara Urbanización Los Cedros, Caracas
Telephone: 72-29-29

Administration
Education

Founded 1971. A State institution.

Degrees and Diplomas: Professional title of Técnio superior, 3yrs.

7717 **COLEGIO UNIVERSITARIO 'FRANCICSO DE MIRANDA'**

Esquina de Mijares, Caracas 1010
Telephone: 814351

Basic Studies
Administration
Education

Founded 1974. A State institution.

Academic Year: October to July (October-March; March-July).

Admission Requirements: Secondary school certificate (bachillerato).

Language of Instruction: Spanish.

Degrees and Diplomas: Professional title of Técnico superior, 3 yrs.

Library: 92,000 vols.

Publications: Boletín (monthly); Boletín bibliográfico (biannually).

Academic Staff: c. 120

Student Enrolment, 1984-85 3317.:

7718 **COLEGIO UNIVERSITARIO INAPSI**

Avenida El Bosque Quinta, 'Malalila',La Florida, Caracas

Psychopedagogy

7719 **COLEGIO UNIVERSITARIO MONSEÑOR DE TALAVERAAV**

Avenida Eugenio Mendoza, Cruce Los Granados, La Castellana, Caracas 1070
Telephone: 32-13-11

Education (Primary and for the Handicapped)
Administration

Founded 1969 as Institute of Psychopedagogy, acquired present status and title 1975. A State institution.

Academic Year: January to December (January-May; June-August; August-December).

Admission Requirements: Secondary school certificate (bachillerato).

Language of Instruction: Spanish.

Degrees and Diplomas: Professional title of Técnico superior, 3 yrs.

Library: c. 3000 vols.

Academic Staff: c. 60

Student Enrolment: c. 720.

7720 **COLEGIO UNIVERSITARIO DE REHABILITACIÓN**

Calle La Guayanita, Bella Vista, Caracas 102
Telephone: 49-47-60/9

Occupational Therapy
Kinetics

Physiotherapy
Orthopaedics

Founded 1959 as school, acquired present status and title 1975. Attached to the Central University of Venezuela. A State institution forming part of the Instituto Venezolano de Seguros Sociales.

Academic Year: October to July (October-March; March-July).

Admission Requirements: Secondary school certificate (bachillerato). Foreign students may be considered for admission on basis of previous study in field of Occupational Therapy or Physiotherapy.

Language of Instruction: Spanish.

Degrees and Diplomas: Professional title of Técnico superior de Rehabilitación, 2 yrs.

Library: c. 450 vols.

Publication: Boletín Informativo.

Academic Staff: c. 10 (20).

Student Enrolment: c. 100.

7721 **COLEGIO UNIVERSITARIO DE CARÚPANO**
Via El Pilar, Apartado 680, alle de Canchunchú, Carúpano (Sucre)

Administration
Education
Marine Technology
Agriculture
Fishery

Founded 1973. A State institution. Governing body: the Consejo Académico.

Academic Year: January to December (January-June; September-December).

Admission Requirements: Secondary school certificate (bachillerato).

Language of Instruction: Spanish.

Degrees and Diplomas: Professional title of Técnico superior, 3 yrs.

Libraries: Central Library, c. 13,400 vols; Naval Technology, c. 400.

Academic Staff: c. 150 (20).

Student Enrolment: c. 700.

7722 **COLEGIO UNIVERSITARIO DE LA REGIÓN CAPITAL**
Avenida Los Pinos, Los Teques (Miranda)

Administration
Education

Founded 1971. A State institution.

Admission Requirements: Professional title of Técnico superior, 3 yrs.

7723 **COLEGIO UNIVERSITARIO DE MARACAIBO**
Calle 79 H con Avenida 85, Urb. La Floresta, Sector La Limpia, Maracaibo (Zulia)
Telephone: 54-99-94
Director: Guillermo Bravo (1979-82)
Sub-Director Administrativo: Luis Carrillo

Industrial Processing
Metallurgy
Geology and Mining
Agriculture and Animal Husbandry

Founded 1974. A State institution. Governing body: the Consejo Académico.

Academic Year: January to December (January-May; July-December)

Admission Requirements: Secondary school certificate (bachillerato).

Language of Instruction: Spanish.

Degrees and Diplomas: Professional title of Técnico superior, 3 yrs.

Academic Staff: c. 150 (90).

Student Enrolment: c. 2400 (Also c. 270 external students)

7724 **COLEGIO UNIVERSITARIO 'DR. RAFAEL BELLOSO CHACÍN'**
Calle 77 Esquina Avenida 3H, Edf. Universal, Maracaibo (Zulia)
Telephone: 911252-911352
Director: Oscar Belloso Medina

Computer Sciences
Business Administration
Marketing
Administration

Founded 1982. A private institution.

Academic Year: September to July (September-March; March-July).

Admission Requirements: Secondary school certificate (bachillerato).

Fees (Bolívares): 5000 per semester.

Language of Instruction: Spanish.

Degrees and Diplomas: Professional title of Técnico superior, 3 yrs.

Academic Staff, 1986-87:

Rank	Full-time
Asociado	1
Agregados	17
Asistentes	25
Instructores	35
Total	78

Student Enrolment, 1986-87::

	Men	Women	Total
Of the country	713	632	1345
Of other countries	20	15	35
Total	733	647	1380

7725 **COLEGIO UNIVERSITARIO DE PSICOPEDAGOGÍA**
Avenida San Gabriel 45, Urb El Avila, Centro Alta Florida y Country Club, Caracas
Telephone: 74-19-94

Psychopedagogy

Founded 1971, recognized by the government 1977. A private institution. Governing bodies: the Consejo Directivo; the Consejo Académico.

Academic Year: September to July (September-March; March-July).

Admission Requirements: Secondary school certificate (bachillerato).

Language of Instruction: Spanish.

Degrees and Diplomas: Professional title of Técnico superior en Psicopedagogía, 3 yrs.

Library: c. 1000 vols.

Academic Staff: c. 10 (30)

Student Enrolment: c. 200.

7726 **INSTITUTO UNIVERSITARIO DE BANCA Y FINANZAS**
Edf. Insbanca, Mijares a Santa Capilla, Caracas

Banking and Finance

Founded 1978. A private institution.

7727 **INSTITUTO UNIVERSITARIO JESÚS E. LOSSADA**
Edif. Sede Del IUJEL, Calle 78, 17-129 Maracaibo (Zulia)

Social Sciences

Founded 1982. A private institution.

7728 **INSTITUTO UNIVERSITARIO DE MERCADOTECNÍA**
Edificio Cediaz, Planta Principal, Avenida Casanova, Caracas

Marketing

Founded 1973. A private institution.

Degrees and Diplomas: Professional title of Técnico superior, 2 ½ yrs.

7729 **INSTITUTO UNIVERSITARIO 'NUEVA ESPARTA'**
Reducto a Glorieta, Caracas

D. of Computer Sciences
D. of Engineering
D. of Tourism

Founded 1975. A private institution.

Degrees and Diplomas: Professional title of Técnico superior, 5-6 sem.

7730 **INSTITUTO DE NUEVAS PROFESIONES**
Avenida Romulo Gallegos, Caracas
Telephone: 74-57-78

D. of Tourism
D. of International Commerce
D. of Journalism

Founded 1974. A private institution.

Degrees and Diplomas: Professional title of Técnico superior, 6 sem.

7731 **INSTITUTO UNIVERSITARIO TECNOLÓGICO 'PEDRO EMILIO COLL'**
Avenida 17 (Baralt) 72-18, Maracaibo (Zulia)

Social Sciences

Founded 1982. A private institution.

7732 **INSTITUTO UNIVERSITARIO DE RELACIONES PÚBLICAS**
Altagracia a Mijares, Edificio Edoval, Caracas
Telephone: 81-82-35

Public Relations

Founded as a private institution 1964, acquired present status and title 1972. A State institution under the jurisdiction of the Ministry of Education. Governing body: the Consejo Académico.

Academic Year: September to July (September-January; February-July).

Admission Requirements: Secondary school certificate (bachillerato) and entrance examination.

Language of Instruction: Spanish.

Degrees and Diplomas: Title of Técnico superior en Relaciones públicas, 2 yrs.

Library: c. 1030 vols.

Academic Staff: c. 20.

Student Enrolment: c. 160.

7733 **INSTITUTO UNIVERSITARIO DE SEGUROS**
Qta. Guayamure, Avenida Los Chaguaramos, La Florida, Caracas

Marine Insurance

Founded 1972. A private institution.

Degrees and Diplomas: Professional title of Técnico superior en Seguros mercantiles, 3 yrs.

7734 **INSTITUTO UNIVERSITARIO TECNOLÓGICO DE SEGURIDAD INDUSTRIAL**
Institute of Industrial Safety
Apartado 2242, Los Arales, Via San Diego, Valencia (Carabobo)
Telephone: (041) 377353
Director: Juan Sánchez Riquelme (1982-)

Industrial Safety

Fire Prevention

Founded 1979. A private institution.

Academic Year: January to December (January-May; August-December).

Admission Requirements: Secondary school certificate (bachillerato) and entrance examination.

Fees (Bolívares): 3000 per semester.

Language of Instruction: Spanish.

Degrees and Diplomas: Professional title of Técnico superior, 3-4 yrs.

Library: 2000 vols.

Academic Staff, 1986-87 5 (33).:

Student Enrolment, 1986-87:

	Men	Women	Total
Of the country	156	39	195

7735 **INSTITUTO UNIVERSITARIO YMCA 'LOPE MENDOZA'**
Edf. YMCA, 5To. Piso, Avenida Guicaipuro, San Bernardino, Caracas 1011, D.F.
Telephone: (02) 520891
Fax: 520391
Director: Domingo J. Padilla R.
Secretario General: Martin García

F. of Recreation
Dean: Joel Torres; *staff* 6 (10)

F. of Tourism
Dean: Edgar Muñoz; *staff* 6 (6)

Founded 1983. A private institution. Governing body: the Consejo Superior (Board of Trustees).

Academic Year: February to January (February-July; September-January).

Admission Requirements: Secondary school certificate (bachillerato).

Fees (Bolívares): 8000 per semester.

Language of Instruction: Spanish.

Degrees and Diplomas: Title of Técnicos Superior, 3 yrs.

Teacher Training

7736 **INSTITUTO UNIVERSITARIO PEDAGÓGICO EXPERIMENTAL**
Avenida Vargas, Barquisimeto (Lara)
Telephone: 411800

D. of Modern Languages

D. of Mathematics

D. of Social Sciences (History and Geography)

D. of Experimental Sciences (including Physical Education)

D. of Pedagogics

D. of Technical Education

Founded 1959 as a State institution. Under the co-ordination the Universidad Pedagógica Experimental Libertador. Governing body: the Consejo Académico, comprising the Director, Deputy Director, and the Heads of Departments.

Academic Year: October to July (September-February; March-July).

Admission Requirements: Secondary school certificate (bachillerato).

Language of Instruction: Spanish.

Degrees and Diplomas: Professional title of Profesor de Educación Secundaria, Normal o Técnica (teaching qualifications, secondary level), 4 yrs.

Library: Central Library, *c.* 36,660 vols.

Special Facilities (Museums, etc.): Museum of Taxidermy.

Publication: Expresión (weekly).

Academic Staff: c. 250 (70).

Student Enrolment: c. 4700.

7737 **INSTITUTO UNIVERSITARIO 'AVEPANE'**
Avenida San Juan Bosco 57-15, Entre Avenida 9 y 10, Altamira, Caracas
Telephone: 261-7651
Director: Victoria Heredia de Hernández

Teacher Training (For the Handicapped)

Founded 1971. A private institution.

Academic Year: September to July (September-February; March-July).

Admission Requirements: Secondary school certificate (bachillerato) and entrance examination.

Fees (Bolívares): 2300 per semester.

Language of Instruction: Spanish.

Degrees and Diplomas: Teacher Training diploma (Specialist), 3 yrs.

Academic Staff, 1986-87: 9 (49).

Student Enrolment, 1986-87:

	Men	Women	Total
Of the country	11	434	445
Of other countries	1	30	31
Total	12	464	476

7738 **INSTITUTO UNIVERSITARIO PEDAGÓGICO DE CARACAS**
Avenida Páez, El Paraíso, Caracas
Telephone: 41-61-31
President: José Lorenzo Pérez (1986-89)

D. of Biology and Chemistry
Head: Jesús Rojas; *staff* 4 (11)

D. of Art
Head: Herminia Rivero; *staff* 18 (7)

D. of Spanish Literature and Latin
Head: Olivia Carmona; *staff* 35 (6)

D. of Earth Sciences
Head: Carlos Suárez Ruiz; *staff* 13 (2)

D. of Special Education
Head: Elisa Harting; *staff* 16 (29)

D. of Geography and History
Head: Morela Jiménez; *staff* 31 (8)

D. of Physical Education
Head: Emma Labrador; *staff* 26 (16)

D. of Modern Languages
Head: Roberto Jiménez; *staff* 43 (6)

D. of Mathematics and Physics
Head: Tomás Albero Ramírez; *staff* 47 (16)

D. of Education
Head: Esteban Sánchez; *staff* 78 (22)

D. of Teacher Training
Head: Hilda Guerra; *staff* 43 (2)

D. of Educational Technology
Head: Nelly Sánchez; *staff* 22 (3)

Founded 1936 as college, acquired present status and title 1948. A State institution under the co-ordination of the Universidad Pedagógica Experimental Libertador.

Academic Year: September to July (September-February; March-June).

Admission Requirements: Secondary school certificate (bachillerato) or equivalent, and entrance examination for certain departments.

Language of Instruction: Spanish.

Degrees and Diplomas: Teaching qualifications, secondary level, 5 yrs. Master in Education, a further 2 yrs.

Library: Central Library, *c.* 120,000 vols.

Academic Staff: *c.* 420.

Student Enrolment, 1986-87:

	Men	Women	Total
Of the country	1863	4974	6837

7739 **INSTITUTO UNIVERSITARIO PEDAGÓGICO 'MONSEÑOR RAFAEL ARÍAS BLANCO'**

Sector UD-5 Detras del Bloque 23, Caricuao, Caracas

Teacher Training (Engineering)

A private institution.

7740 **INSTITUTO VENEZOLANO DE AUDICIÓN Y LENGUAJE**

Urb. El Rosal, Caracas

Telephone: 33-63-77

Speech Training and Therapy (for the handicapped)

Founded 1974. A private institution.

Degrees and Diplomas: Professional titles of–Terapista del Lenguaje; Maestro de Niños sordos, 3 yrs.

7741 **INSTITUTO UNIVERSITARIO PEDAGÓGICO EXPERIMENTAL 'J.M. SISO MARTÍNEZ'**

Calle 8 Mod I, La Urbina, Estado Miranda

Directora: Adela Muñoz

Teacher Training (Industrial, Integral Education, Mathematics, Natural Sciences, Social Sciences)

Founded 1976. A State institution. Under the co-ordination of the Universidad Pedagógica Experimental Libertador.

Academic Year: September to July.

Admission Requirements: Secondary school certificate (bachillerato).

Language of Instruction: Spanish.

Degrees and Diplomas: Teacher Training diploma (Specialist), 3 yrs. Master, a further 2 yrs.

Academic Staff, 1989-90: 155.

Student Enrolment, 1989-90: *c.* 3800.

7742 **INSTITUTO UNIVERSITARIO PEDAGÓGICO EXPERIMENTAL 'RAFAEL ALBERTO ESCOBAR LARA'**

Apartado 288, Avenida Principal Las Delicias, Maracay 2102A (Aragua)

Telephone: (043) 411361

Director: Luis Abdelnour (1984-87)

D. of Mathematics
D. of Physics
D. of Chemistry
D. of Biology
D. of Spanish
D. of Physical Education
D. of English
D. of Social Sciences

Founded 1971. A State institution under the co-ordination of the Universidad Pedagógico Experimental Libertador. Governing body: the Consejo Académico.

Academic Year: April to January (April-July; September-January).

Admission Requirements: Secondary school certificate (bachillerato) and entrance examination.

Language of Instruction: Spanish.

Degrees and Diplomas: Technical or teaching qualifications, 3 yrs.

Library: Rafael Alberto Escobar Lara, *c.* 22,030 vols.

Publications: Mensaje (biannually; Boletín Informativo Post-grado (quarterly); Pertigas (biannually); Paradigma (biannually).

Academic Staff: *c.* 260 (70)

Student Enrolment: *c.* 4020

7743 **INSTITUTO UNIVERSITARIO PEDAGÓGICO EXPERIMENTAL**

Maturín (Monagas)

Telephone: (091) 39895

Teacher Training (Sciences and Engineering)

Founded 1971. A State institution under the co-ordination of the Universidad Pedagógica Experimental Libertador.

Degrees and Diplomas: Professional title of Profesor, 4 yrs.

VIET NAM
(Socialist Republic of)

Universities

7744 ***TRÙONG DAI HOC TÔNG HOP HÀNÔI**

University of Hanoi

23, boulevard Lê-thauh-Toñ, Hànôi

Telephone: 3222

Rector: Phan Hun Dat

F. of Mathematics

F. of Physics

F. of Chemistry

F. of Biology

F. of Geology and Geography

F. of Literature and Philology

F. of History

F. of Vietnamese Language (for foreign students)

Founded 1956. The university is a State institution, government financed. Governing bodies: the Rector and 4 pro-rectors; the university and faculty councils. Some residential facilities for academic staff and for two-thirds of the student body.

Academic Year: September to July (September-February; February-July).

Admission Requirements: Competitive entrance examination following secondary school certificate.

Fees: None.

Language of Instruction: Vietnamese.

Degrees and Diplomas: Diplomas, 4 or 5 yrs.

Libraries: University Library, *c.* 62,000 vols; faculty libraries with a total of *c.* 85,000.

Special Facilities (Museums, etc.): Animal Biology Museum.

Academic Staff: *c.* 150.

Student Enrolment: *c.* 1500.

7745 **VIÊN DAI HOC HÔ CHÍ MINH VILLE**

University of Ho Chi Minh City

3, Công-Trùong Chien-Sĩ, Hô Chí Minh ville

Telephone: 90-396

F. of Letters and Human Sciences

F. of Exact and Natural Sciences

Founded 1954, originally part of the university founded in Hanoi 1917. A State institution. Residential facilities for some students.

Academic Year: October to June (October-January; February-June).

Admission Requirements: Competitive entrance examination following secondary school certificate.

Language of Instruction: Vietnamese.

Degrees and Diplomas: Diplomas, 5 yrs.

Libraries: Faculty libraries: Science, *c.* 6000; Letters, *c.* 20,000; Education, *c.* 14,000.

Special Facilities (Museums, etc.): Zoology Museum; Geology Museum.

Academic Staff: *c.* 400 (300).

Student Enrolment: *c.* 25,000.

7746 **VIEN DAI HOC HUÊ**

University of Huê

3, le Loi, Huê

Telephone: 2256

F. of Letters

F. of Science

F. of Law and Economics

Founded 1957 as a State institution. Governing body: the Council. Residential facilities for academic staff and students.

Academic Year: November to July.

Admission Requirements: Secondary school certificate, and competitive entrance examination.

Language of Instruction: Vietnamese.

Library: Central Library, *c.* 30,000 vols.

Academic Staff: *c.* 160 (310).

Student Enrolment: *c.* 6400.

7747 **TRÙONG DAI HOC CÂN-THÔ**

University of Can-Tho

30 Thang 4 Street, Can-Tho (Hau Giang Province)

Telex: 812539 MEKYNO VT

Telephone: 20237,21262

Rektor: Tran Phuoc Duong (1989-92)

Vice-Rector: Le The Dong

F. of Mathematics and Physics

Dean: Nguyen Thanh Dao; *staff* 58

F. of Chemistry and Biology

Dean: Tran Son; *staff* 58

F. of Letters (Linguistics, Vietnamese Literature, Foreign Literature)

Dean: Nyuyen Hoa Bang; *staff* 36

F. of Foreign Languages (French, English, Russian)

Dean: Huynh Trung Tin; *staff* 60

F. of History and Geography

dean: Vu Thi Nhu Y; *staff* 32

F. of Agriculture

Dean: Tran Thuong Tuan; *staff* 91

F. of Irrigation Engineering

Dean: Le Quang Minh; *staff* 26

F. of Food Processing Technology

Dean: Bui Huu Thuan; *staff* 24

F. of Animal Husbandry and Veterinary Medicine

Dean: Chau Ba Loc

F. of Fishery

Dean: Nguyen Anh Tuan; *staff* 55

F. of Agricultural Economics

Dean: Dam Ho Cau; *staff* 15

F. of Agricultural Engineering

Dean: Vu Quang Thanh; *staff* 50 (3)

F. of Medicine

Dean: Pham Truong Minh; *staff* 159

D. of Leninist Marxism

Chairman: Chau Van Luc; *staff* 29

D. of Educational Psychology

Chairman: Tran Van Chin; *staff* 18

D of Physical Training and Sports

Director: Bui Dinh Trong; *staff* 7

Biological Nitrogen Research Ce.

Director: Tran Phuoc Duong; *staff* 30 (15)

Mekong Delta Farming System Research and Development Ce.

Director: Vo Tong Xuan; *staff* 23

Renewable Engineering Research Ce.

Director: Do Ngoc Quynh; *staff* 14

Hoa An Acid Sulfate Soil Experiment Station

Director: Nguyen Minh Quang; *staff* 13

Computer Ce.

Director: Vo Van Chin; *staff* 27

Also faculties of Economics and Technology at: Hâu Giang, Tiên Giang, Cuu Long, Angiang.

Founded 1966 as school of agriculture, acquired present status and title 1975. A State institution under the jurisdiction of the Ministry of Higher Education. Residential facilities for academic staff and students.

Arrangements for co-operation with: Agricultural University, Wageningen; University of Paris XI; University ofHawaii; University of Wisconsin-Madison; Michigan State University.

Academic Year: September to July (September-February; February-July).

Admission Requirements: Competitive entrance examination following secondary school certificate or foreign equivalent.

Fees: None.

Language of Instruction: Vietnamese.

Degrees and Diplomas: Bachelor, 4-5 yrs; Medicine, 6 yrs. Doctorat du 3e cycle, 3 yrs. Medical Doctor, 6 yrs.

Libraries: Central Library, *c.* 150,000 vols; library of Faculty of Medicine.

Publication: Annual Reports.

Academic Staff, 1989-90:

Rank	Full-time	Part-time
Professors	3	20
Lecturers	88	–
Instructors	675	–
Total	766	20

Student Enrolment, 1989-90:

	Men	Women	Total
Of the country	2421	1363	3684
Of other countries	7	–	7
Total	2428	1363	3691

7748 **TRUÒNG DAI HOC BÁCH KHOA HÀNÔI**

Technical University of Hanoi

Hà-nôi

Telephone: 52771; 53746

F. of Building Engineering
F. of Electrical Engineering
F. of Electronics
F. of Industrial Chemistry
F. of Food Technology
F. of Metallurgy
F. of Industrial Thermodynamics
F. of Textile Engineering
F. of Industrial Management
F. of Physics and Mathematics
I. of Applied Mechanics and Physics
Audio-visual Language Ce.
Ce. for Lifelong Education

Founded 1956. A State institution.

Academic Year: August to July (August-January; February-July).

Admission Requirements: Competitive entrance examination following secondary school certificate.

Language of Instruction: Vietnamese.

Degrees and Diplomas: Diplôme d'Ingénieur, 5 yrs. Docteur-Ingénieur. Diplomas of specialization.

Library: *c.* 600,000 vols.

Publication: Sciences et Techniques (quarterly).

Press or Publishing House: University Press.

Academic Staff: *c.* 700 (190).

Student Enrolment: *c.* 5250 (Also *c.* 2500 external students).

7749 **TRUÒNG DAI HOC BÁCH KHOA THÀNH PHÔ HÒ CHÍ MINH**

Ho Chi Minh City Polytechnic

268, rue Lý Thuòng Kiêt, Q. 10, Hò Chí Minh ville

Telex: 8555 DHBK HCM

Telephone: 52442

Rector: Truòng Minh Vê

Vice-Rector (Administration): Tràn Thanh Kỳ

S. of Mechanical Engineering
Head: Hò Dăc Tho; *staff* 64
S. of Electrical Engineering
Head: Nguyen Dúc Phong; *staff* 82
S. of Chemistry Engineering
Head: Pham văn Bôn; *staff* 39
S. of Civil Engineering
Head: Lê Bá Lùong; *staff* 46
S. of Applied Geology
Head: Hoàng Trong Mai; *staff* 22
S. of Basic Sciences
Head: Nguyen Canh; *staff* 70
F. for Correspondence Courses
S. of Water Resources Engineering
Head: Tràn Minh Quang; *staff* 44
S. of In-Service Training
Head: Tràn Chan Chinh; *staff* 2
Computer Ce.
Head: Nguyen văn Thòng
Ce. for Essential Oils and Pharmaceuticals
Head: Võ thi Ngoc Tùoi
Ce. for Thermal Power and Renewable Energy
Head: Tràn Thanh Kỳ
Ce. for New Materials
Head: Pham Pho
Abrasive Powder Ce.
Head: Nguyen thi Hoè
Silicate Materials Ce.
Head: Nguyen Kim Trúc
Polymer and Plastic Ce.
Head: Nguyen Hũu Nieu
Water Supply and Environmemtal Samitation Ce.
Head: Lâm Minh Triet
Ce. for Foreign Languages
Head: Nhan Cam Hoa

Also Courses for Cambodian students; Laboratory of the School of Engineering; Study Abroad Programmes (with financial assistance of foreign universities).

Founded 1957 as Centre national technique de Phu-Tho Saïgon. Acquired present status and title 1976. A Stateinstitution. Governing bodies: the Rectoral Board; the Council. Residential facilities for academic staff and students.

Arrangements for co-operation with: Leningrad Ploytechnic Institute; Ploytechnic Institute of Grenoble; Agricultural University of Wageningen; Delft University of Technology; Slovak Technical University of Bratislava; Technical University of Wrocław; Polytechnic of Central London; University of Tokyo; Asian Institute of Technology (Bangkok); University of New South Wales.

Academic Year: September to June (September-January; February-July).

Admission Requirements: Competitive entrance examination following secondary school certificate.

Fees: None.

Language of Instruction: Vietnamese.

Degrees and Diplomas: Diplôme d'Ingénieur, 5 yrs. Docteur-Ingénieur, a further 3 yrs. Master, a further 2 yrs.

Libraries: 39,017 vols (4304 in Vietnamese; 11,044 in English and French; 23,669 in Russian).

Academic Staff, 1990: 485.

Student Enrolment, 1990: 7047.

7750 **DAI HOC HÀNÔI**

Hanoi University of Health Sciences

rue Truong Tu, secteur Dong Da, Hânôi

Telephone: 43 790

Rector: Hoang Dinh Cau

Medicine (including Dentistry, Traditional Medicine, and Paediatrics)

Founded 1902 as Faculty of Medicine, became School 1963 and acquired present status and title 1986. A State institution under the jurisdiction of the Ministry of Health. Residential facilities for *c.* 2000 students.

Arrangements for co-operation with the Universities of: Strasbourg; Rostock. Institute of Medicine, Moscow.

Academic Year: September to July (September-February; March-July).

Admission Requirements: Competitive entrance examination following secondary school certificate.

Language of Instruction: Vietnamese.

Degrees and Diplomas: Docteur en Médecine, 6 yrs. Diplomas of specialization, 2 yrs. Candidat ès Sciences médicales, 4 yrs. Docteur ès Sciences médicales.

Library: University Library.

Academic Staff, 1986-87:

Rank	Full-time	Part-time
Professeurs	12	–
Professeurs associés	36	–
Enseignants	451	354
Techniciens	232	–
Administrateurs	227	–
Autres	94	–
Total	1042	354

Student Enrolment, 1986-87:

	Men	Women	Total
Of the country	1535	1044	2579
Of other countries	4	–	4
Total	1539	1044	2583

7751 **TRUÒNG DAI HOC SU PHAM KỸ THUAT**
University of Technical Education
1 Hoang Dieu, Thu Duc, Hô Chí Minh ville
Telephone: 98641
Rector: Nguyên Ngoc Canh (1978-)
Secretary-General: Bui Huy Huynh

D. of Mechanical Engineering
Head: Nguyên Duc Nam
D. of Electrical Engineering
Head: Nguyên Du Xung
D. of Agriculture (including Animal Husbandry)
Head: Hoang Dinh Sôn
D. of Basic Technology
Head: Bui Xuán Liêm
D. of Family Economics
Head: Pham Thi van Anh
D. of Applied Sciences
Head: Dinh Xuan Loc
D. of Education
Head: Do Huu Hao
D. for Lifelong Education
Head: Hoang Cong Khuong

Founded 1962 as part of the Technical University, acquired present status and title 1976. A State institution.

Arrangements for co-operation with Ecole normale supérieure de l'Enseignement technique de Cachan.

Academic Year: September to July (September-January; January-July).

Admission Requirements: Competitive entrance examination following secondary school certificate.

Language of Instruction: Vietnamese.

Degrees and Diplomas: Diplôme d'Ingénieur, 5 yrs. Candidat ès Sciences.

Library: University Library.

Publication: Pédagogie technique (quarterly).

Academic Staff, 1986-87: 430.

Student Enrolment, 1986-87:

	Men	Women	Total
Of the country	1500	500	2000
Of other countries	6	–	6
Total	1506	500	2006

Other Institutions

Technical Education

7752 **TRÙONG CAO DANG MY THUÂT CÔNG NGHIÊP**
Hànôi

Industrial Art

Founded 1966.

7753 **TRÙONG DAI HOC GIAO-THÔNG VÂN TAI**
College of Transport and Communications
Hànôi
Telephone: 43311
Director: Do Doãn Hai (1982-)

F. of Construction Engineering
Head: Nguyên Quang Chiêu; *staff* 65 (10)
F. of Mechanical and Electrical Engineering
Head: Nguyên van Hop; *staff* 86 (15)
F. of Transport and Economics
Head: Nguyên Viêt Yên; *staff* 46 (5)
F. of Basic Sciences
Head: Nguyên Xuân Luu; *staff* 99
F. for Distance Education
Head: Lê Dúc Trân; *staff* 12 (70)

Founded 1902 as school, acquired present status and title 1962. A State institution. Residential facilities for *c.* 200 academic staff and *c.* 1600 students.

Arrangements for co-operation with: Institute of Railway Engineering, Moscow; College of Transport and Communications, Dresden; Institut national des Sciences appliquées, Lyon; Ecole nationale des Ponts et Chaussées,Paris.

Academic Year: August to June (August-December; December-July).

Admission Requirements: Competitive entrance examination following secondary school certificate.

Fees: None.

Language of Instruction: Vietnamese.

Degrees and Diplomas: Diplôme d'Ingénieur, 5 yrs. Docteur ès Sciences techniques.

Library: c. 120,000 vols.

Publication: Revue Scientifique et Technique (quarterly).

Press or Publishing House: University Press.

Academic Staff, 1986-87: 352 (31).

Student Enrolment, 1986-87:

	Men	Women	Total
Of the country	1532	97	1629
Of other countries	24	–	24
Total	1556	97	1653*

*Also 1033 external students.

7754 **TRÙONG DAI HOC XÂY DUNG**
Hànôi

Constructional Engineering

Founded 1966.

7755 **TRÙONG DAI HOC THUY LOI**
Institute of Hydraulic Engineering
Hànôi
Telephone: 2201

F. of Hydraulic Engineering
F. of Electrical Engineering

Also technical secondary school.

Founded 1947 as school, became institute 1959, acquired present status 1960.

Academic Year: September to July.

Admission Requirements: Secondary school certificate or equivalent.

Degrees and Diplomas: Diploma, 5 yrs.

Academic Staff: c. 250.

Student Enrolment: c. 3500 (of which *c.* 3000 at technical secondary school).

7756 **TRÙONG DAI HOC MÓ VÂ DIA CHÂT**
Institute of Mining and Geology
Hànôi

Mining
Geology
Surveying

Founded 1966.

7757 **TRÙONG DAI HOC CO DIÊN**
Institute of Mechanical and Electrical Engineering
Hànôi

Mechanical Engineering

Electrical Engineering

7758 **TRÙONG DAI HOC CÔNG NGHIÊP NHE**
Institute of Light Industry
Hànôi

Light Industry

7759 **ÉCOLE SUPÉRIEURE POLYTECHNIQUE**
Da Nang

Engineering

7760 **ÉCOLE SUPÉRIEURE DE FORMATION DES TECHNICIENS ET CHERCHEURS**
Dalat

Training of Technicians
Training of Research Workers

Professional Education

7761 **TRÙONG DAI HOC NÔNG NGHIÊP I**
Institute of Agriculture I
Hànôi

F. of Agriculture
F. of Animal Husbandry and Veterinary Medicine
F. of Agricultural Engineering
Founded 1956.

7762 **TRÙONG DAI HOC NÔNG NGHIÊP II**
Institute of Agriculture II
Hànôi

F. of Agriculture
F. of Animal Husbandry and Veterinary Medicine
F. of Agricultural Engineering

7763 **TRÙONG CAO DANG MY THUÂT**
College of Fine Arts
Hànôi

F. of Painting
F. of Decorative Arts
F. of Sculpture
Founded 1957.

7764 **TRÙONG CAN BÔ THUONG NGHIÊP TRUNG UONG**
Hànôi

Commerce
Founded 1965.

7765 **TRÙONG CAN BÔ NGOAI THUONG**
College of International Commerce
Hànôi

F. of Foreign Affairs
F. of External Commerce
Founded 1962.

7766 **TRÙONG DAI HOC KINH TÊ KÊ HOACH**
College of Economics and Finance
Hànôi

F. of Industrial Economics
F. of Agricultural Economics
F. of Labour Economics
F. of Planning
F. of Statistics
Founded 1958.

7767 **TRÙONG CÁN BÔ-TAI CHINH KÊ TOÁN NGÂN HÂNG TRUNG UONG**
College of Finance, Accountancy and Banking
Hànôi

F. of Finance
F. of Accountancy
F. of Banking
Founded 1963.

7768 **NHAC VIÊN HÀNÔI**
Conservatoire of Hanoi
Ô Cha Duà, Hànôi
Cables: Nhacviên Hànôi
Telephone: 54969

Music
Founded 1956. Responsible to the Ministry of Culture and Information. Some residential facilities for students from outside Hanoi.
Academic Year: September to June (September-January; February-June).
Admission Requirements: Secondary school certificate.
Language of Instruction: Vietnamese.
Degrees and Diplomas: Diplôme, 5 yrs.
Academic Staff: c. 120.
Student Enrolment: c. 700.

7769 **TRÙONG DAI HOC DUOC**
College of Pharmacy
13 Lô thanh Tông Street, Hànôi
Telephone: 54539
Dean: Nguyên Thanh Do

Pharmacy
Founded 1961. A State institution under the jurisdiction of the Ministry of Health. Residential facilities for academic staff and students.
Arrangements for co-operation with similar institutions in USSR and Universities of Leiden and Groningen.
Academic Year: September to June.
Admission Requirements: Secondary school certificate.
Language of Instruction: Vietnamese.
Degrees and Diplomas: Professional titles. Docteur en Pharmacie.
Library: 20,000 vols.
Academic Staff, 1986-87: 160 (36).
Student Enrolment, 1984-85:

	Men	Women	Total
Of the country	448	321	769
Of other countries	5	7	12
Total	453	328	781*

*Also 122 external students.

7770 **TRÙONG DAI HOC THÚY SÁN**
School of Fishery
Hànôi

Fishery
Founded 1966.

7771 **TRÙONG DAI HOC LÂM NGHIÊP**
College of Forestry
Hànôi

Forestry
Wood Technology
Founded 1961.

7772 **ÉCOLE SUPÉRIEURE D'AGRICULTURE**
45, Cuóng Dê, Hô Chí Minh ville

S. of Agriculture
S. of Forestry
S. of Stockraising (including Veterinary Medicine)
D. of Fishery
D. of Teacher Training (Agriculture)
Experimental Farm
Founded 1959, became College 1964. A State institution. Residential facilities for academic staff and *c.* 1000 students.
Academic Year: November to July (November-February; March-July).
Admission Requirements: Secondary school certificate and entrance examination.
Language of Instruction: Vietnamese.
Degrees and Diplomas: Professional titles, 4 yrs.
Library: c. 5100 vols.

Academic Staff: c. 80 (90).
Student Enrolment: c. 21,100.

7773 **ÉCOLE SUPÉRIEURE D'ARCHITECTURE**
Hô Chí Minh ville

Architecture

7774 **ÉCOLE SUPÉRIEURE DE MÉDECINE-PHARMACIE**
Hô Chí Minh ville

Medicine
Pharmacy

7775 **ÉCOLE SUPÉRIEURE DE MÉDECINE**
Huê

Medicine

7776 **ÉCOLE SUPÉRIEURE DE FORMATION DES CADRES**
Tay Nguyen

Professional Education (for Ethnic Minorities)
In process of development.

Teacher Training

7777 **TRÙONG DAI HOC SU PHAM HÀNÔI I**
Hanoi Institute of Education I
Hànôi

F. of Letters
F. of Foreign Languages
F. of Mathematics
F. of Chemistry and Biology
Founded 1956.

7778 **TRÙONG DAI HOC SU PHAM HÀNÔI II**
10z /x/F110z /NAHanoi Institute of Education II
Hànôi

F. of Mathematics
F. of Physical Education
F. of Chemistry
F. of Biology
F. of Agricultural Technology

7779 **TRÙONG DAI HOC SU PHAM VIÊT BÁC**
Viêt Bác Institute of Education
Viêt Bác

F. of Mathematics
F. of Physics
F. of Chemistry
F. of Biology
F. of Letters F. of History
F. of Geography
Founded 1966.

7780 **TRÙONG DAI HOC SU PHAM VINH**
Vinh Institute of Education
Vinh

F. of Letters
F. of Mathematics
F. of Physics and Chemistry
F. of Biology
F. of History
Founded 1959.

7781 **TRÙONG CAN BÔ THÊ DUC THÊ THAO TRUNG UONG**
College of Physical Education and Sport
Bac-ninh

Physical Education
Sport
Founded 1962.

7782 **TRÙONG DAI HOC SU PHAM NGOAI NGU**
College for Foreign Language Teachers
Hànôi

Foreign Languages (Russian, Chinese, English and French)

7783 **TRÙONG DAI HOC NGOAI NGU**
College of Foreign Languages
Hànôi
Telephone: 43269
Directeur: Trùong Dong San

Foreign Languages (Russian, Chinese, English and French)
Founded 1967.
Academic Year: September to June (September-January; February-June).
Admission Requirements: Competitive entrance examination following secondary school certificate.
Language of Instruction: Vietnamese.
Degrees and Diplomas: Diplôme.
Library: 116,240 vols.
Academic Staff, 1986-87: 365.
Student Enrolment, 1986-87:

	Men	Women	Total
Of the country	285	1495	1780*

*Also 92 foreign students.

7784 **TRÙONG DAI HOC SU PHAM**
223 Nguyên Tri Phuong, Hô Chí Minh ville

F. of Mathematics
F. of Physics
F. of Chemistry
F. of Biology
F. of Letters
F. of History
F. of Geography
F. of Languages
Founded 1970.

7785 **TRÙONG DAI HOC SU PHAM**
Huê

F. of Mathematics
F. of Physics
F. of Chemistry
F. of Biology
F. of Letters
F. of History
F. of Geography
F. of Languages

YEMEN ARAB REPUBLIC

7786 ***GAM'AT SANA'A**

Sana'a University
P.O. Box 1247, Sana'a
Telephone: 200514
President: Abdul Aziz S. Al Maghaleh

F. of Science
F. of Arts
F. of Law and Islamic Law (Shari'a)
F. of Commerce and Economics
F. of Education
F. of Medicine
F. of Engineering
Ce. of Languages

Founded 1970. A State institution. The Minister of Education acts as President of the university. Financed by the State and by the government of Kuwait which covers salaries for academic staff and capital expenditure on buildings and equipment. Governing bodies: the University Council; the Faculty Councils. Residential facilities for academic staff and students.

Academic Year: September to June.

Admission Requirements: Secondary school certificate.

Fees: None for Yemeni students.

Languages of Instruction: Arabic and English.

Degrees and Diplomas: Bachelor of–Arts; Science; Law; Commerce, 4 yrs. Degree of Master in preparation.

Libraries: Central Library, *c.* 14,880 vols (in Arabic); *c.* 21,750 (in foreign languages); Yemeni Studies Centre library.

Academic Staff: c. 330.

Student Enrolment: c. 3520 (Also *c.* 600 external students).

YEMEN
(People's Democratic Republic)

7787 **UNIVERSITY OF ADEN**
P.O. Box 7039, Al-Mansoor
Telephone: 82434
Rector: Salim Omer Bukair

F. of Education
F. of Agriculture
F. of Economics and Administration
F. of Medicine
F. of Technology
F. of Law

F. of Education (Aden, Mukalla, Zingibar)

Founded 1975 and incorporating colleges founded between 1970 and 1973.

Academic Year: September to June.

Admission Requirements: Secondary school certificate.

Languages of Instruction: Arabic and English.

Degrees and Diplomas: Bachelor of Arts or Science. Others in preparation.

Academic Staff: c. 470.

Student Enrolment: c. 4800.

YUGOSLAVIA

Universities

7788 **UNIVERZITET 'DJURO PUCAR STARI' U BANJALUCI**

University of Banja Luka

Trg palih boraca br. 2, 78000 Banjaluka

Telephone: (78) 35018

Rektor: Rajko Kuzmanović (1988-90)

Generalni sekretar: Fuad Balić

F. of Law
Dean: Vjekoslav Vidović; *staff* 25 (11)
F. of Economics
Dean: Šerkija Berberović *staff* 31 (14)
F. of Electrical Engineering
Dean: Sedat Širbegović *staff* 31 (10)
F. of Mechanical Engineering
Dean: Raliko Zriuć *staff* 29 (18)
F. of Technology
Dean: Mirko Kuleč; *staff* 33 (32)
F. of Medicine
Dean: Mustafa Sefić; *staff* 66 (114)
Pedagogical A.
Dean: Mićo Stojanović; *staff* 21 (6)
S. of Mechanical Engineering:
Dean: Jusuf Čaaušević; *staff* 12 (6)
I. of History
Director: Galib Šljivo; *staff* 5 (12)
I. of Economics
Director: Duško Jakšić; *staff* 14
I. of Work Protection
Director: Slobodan Damjanović; *staff* 10 (6)
I. of Materials Technology
Director: Rajak Srdan; *staff* 6
I. of Scientific Research Work (UNICEP Company)
Director: Mesud Smajlagić; *staff* 10
Professional Electronics I. (Rudi Čajavec Company)
Director: Vito Rakić; *staff* 357
Machine Tool Factory Development I. (Jelšingrad Company)
Director: Redšep Jelačić; *staff* 8
I. of Agriculture (Bojanska Krajina Company)
Director: Jovo Stojůć; *staff* 7
I. of Economics and Development Entreprise (Bosanska Krajina Company)
Director: Ranko Predojević; *staff* 7
Also Medical Faculty Centre.

Founded 1975 and incorporating faculties formerly attached to the University of Sarajevo. A voluntary self-governing association of faculties, schools, and institutes financed by the Republic of Bosnia and Herzegovina. Governing bodies: the University Assembly; the Executive Board. Residential facilities for academic staff and students.

Arrangements for co-operation with: University of Silesia; University of Ostrava; Selăčuk University, Turkey; University of Halle-Wittenberg.

Academic Year: September to August (September-February; February-August).

Admission Requirements: Secondary school certificate.

Fees: None.

Language of Instruction: Serbo-Croat.

Degrees and Diplomas: First Degree, 2-3 yrs. Second Degree, 4-5 yrs. Third Degree or specialization, up to a further 2 yrs. Also doctorates.

Library: National and University Library, 300,000 vols.

Publications: Bulletin (quarterly); Survey of Lectures (annually).

Press or Publishing House: NGRO 'Glas' Balijaluka.

Academic Staff, 1989-90:

Rank	Full-time	Part-time
Redovni profesori (Professors)	36	20
Vanredni profesori (Associate Professors)	39	20
Docenti (Assistant Professors)	45	20
Predavači (Lecturers)	21	14
Asistenti (Assistants)	102	82
Stručni saradnik	–	86
Total	243	242

Student Enrolment, 1989-90:

Of the country	6851
Of other countries	189
Total	7040*

*Also 2380 external students.

7789 ***UNIVERZITET U BEOGRADU**

University of Belgrade

Studentski trg broj 1, 11000 Beograd 6

Telephone: (011) 635-153; 637-405

Rektor: Zoran M. Pjanić (1985-87)

Generalni sekretar: Dragiša Stijović

F. of Architecture (including Town Planning)
Dean: Aleksander Stjepanović; *staff* 79 (1)
F. of Veterinary Medicine
Dean: Nemanja Ševković; *staff* 153
F. of Civil Engineering
Dean: Milorad Ivković; *staff* 152 (42)
F. of Economics
Dean: Lazar Pejić; *staff* 124 (6)
F. of Electrical Engineering
Dean: Gojko Muždeka; *staff* 139 (59)
F. of Mechanical Engineering
Dean: Ivan Kolendić; *staff* 230 (24)
F. of Medicine
Dean: Jovan Mićić; *staff* 671 (2)
F. of Agriculture
Dean: Živorad Gajić; *staff* 255 (71)
F. of Law
Dean: Živomir Djordjević; *staff* 94
F. of Natural Sciences and Mathematics
Dean: Jovo Jarić; *staff* 359 (7)
F. of Mining and Geology
Dean: Dragoljub Djokić; *staff* 161 (22)
F. of Technology (Bor)
Dean: Živan Živković; *staff* 70 (31)
F. of Transport Engineering
Dean: Slobodan Lazović; *staff* 110 (18)
F. of Dentistry
Dean: Miodrag Kosovčević; *staff* 187 (29)
F. of Technology and Metallurgy
Dean: Jovan Mičić; *staff* 189
F. of Pharmacy
Dean: Miloš Aleksić; *staff* 108 (7)
F. of Philosophy (including Education, Archaeology, History and Sociology)
Dean: Dragoljub Živojinović; *staff* 179 (12)
F. of Physical Education
Dean: Jovan Petrović; *staff* 66 (2)
F. of Philology
Dean: Ljubomir Mihailović; *staff* 203 (2)
F. of Forestry
Dean: Olga Mijanović; *staff* 128 (2)
F. of Political Science
Dean: Radoš Smiljković; *staff* 70
F. of Organizational Sciences
Dean: Jovo Todorović; *staff* 64 (9)

F. of Defectology
Dean: Aleksandar Djordić; *staff* 45 (12)
F. of National Defence
Dean: Nikola Ivančević; *staff* 25 (18)
I. of Biological Research
Director: Divna Trajković; *staff* 86
I. of Nuclear Research
Director: Djordje Jović; *staff* 508
I. of Social Sciences
Director: Vladimir Goati; *staff* 34
Physics Research I.
Director: Radovan Atanasijević; *staff* 41
I. of Chemistry, Technology, and Metallurgy
Director: Aleksandar Djordjević; *staff* 134
I. of Nuclear Energy (Applied to Agriculture)
Director: Ratimir Cmiljanić; *staff* 79
Ce. for Multidisciplinary Studies
International U. Ce. for Social Sciences
Ce. for Marxism

Founded 1808 as school, became lyceum 1838, became college with faculties of philosophy, law, and technology 1863. Acquired university status 1905. In 1960 the faculties established in Novi Sad were detached and became the University of Novi Sad; in 1965 faculties established in Niš were detached and became University of Niš; in 1969 the faculties established in Priština formed the University of Priština; in 1974 those in Titograd formed the University of Titograd; in 1976 those in Kragujevac formed the University of Kragujevac. The university is a voluntary self-governing association of faculties and institutes. Financed by the federal government. Governing bodies: the University Assembly; the University Council, on which the Federal Government is represented; and the Administrative Board, and the Councils and Administrative Boards of the faculties. Some residential facilities for academic staff and for 12,000 students.

Arrangements for co-operation with 34 foreign institutions of higher education.

Academic Year: October to September (October-February; February-September).

Admission Requirements: Secondary school certificate or equivalent, or 4 yrs practical work and entrance examination.

Fees: None.

Language of Instruction: Serbo-Croat.

Degrees and Diplomas: First Degree, 2-3 yrs. Second Degree, 4-5 yrs. Third Degree or specialization, up to a further 2 yrs. Also doctorate, Ph.D.

Library: Svetozar Marković Library (University Library), 1,500,000 vols.

Publications: Pregled predavanja; Bilten; Univerzitetski glasnik; Gledišta; Dijalektika.

Academic Staff, 1986-87:

Rank	Full-time	Part-time
Redovni profesori (Professors)	935	99
Vanredni profesori (Associate Professors)	1256	142
Asistenti (Assistants)	1670	135
Total	3861	376

Student Enrolment, 1986-87:

	Men	Women	Total
Of the country	26,918	26,761	53,679
Of other countries	2249	735	2984
Total	29,167	27,496	56,663

7790 **UNIVERZITET U BITOLI**

University of Bitola
Bulevar 'I-vi Maj' bb, 97000 Bitola
Telephone: (097) 23-788; 23-192
Rektor: Dame Nestorovski

F. of Economics
F. of Technology
F. of Tourism
F. of Law
S. of Agriculture
A. of Education
I. of Tobacco Research
I. of Hydrobiology
I. of Ancient Slavic Culture

Founded 1979, incorporating previously existing institutions in the Southwest Macedonian Region founded between 1935 and 1977. An independent self-governing institution financed by the Republic of Macedonia. Governing bodies: the University Assembly; the University Council.

Academic Year: October to June (October-February; February-June).

Admission Requirements: Secondary school certificate.

Fees: None.

Languages of Instruction: Macedonian and Serbo-Croat.

Degrees and Diplomas: First Degree, 2 yrs. Second Degree, 4 yrs. Third Degree or specialization in Economics, up to a further 2 yrs.Also doctorate.

Library: c. 160,000 vols.

Academic Staff: c. 100 (50).

Student Enrolment: c. 9140.

7791 **UNIVERZITET 'SVETOZAR MARKOVIĆ' U KRAGUJEVCU**

University of Kragujevac
Trg Avnoja 1, 34 000 Kragujevac
Telephone: (34) 65-424
Fax: (34) 64-500
Rektor: Ilija Rosić (1988-)
Generalni sekretar: Miroslav Mijailović

F. of Mechanical Engineering
Dean: Milun Babić; *staff* 44 (10)
F. of Economics
Dean: Ljubica Simaković; *staff* 46
F. of Natural Sciences and Mathematics
Dean: Stanimir Konstantinović; *staff* 73 (33)
F. of Law
Dean: BBranko Marković; *staff* 33 (7)
F. of Medicine
Dean: Ivan Andjelković; *staff* 65 (8)
F. of Agriculture (Čačku)
Dean: Zivota Jestrocić; *staff* 30 (19)
Technical F. (Čačku)
Dean: Dragan Golubović; *staff* 33 (43)
Mechanical Engineering (Kraljevo)
Dean: RankoRakanović; *staff* 23 (1)
Fruit Research I. (Čačak)
Director: Miljojko Ranković; *staff* 20
Small Grains I.
Director: Dragoljub Maksimović; *staff* 21

Founded 1976. An independent self-governing institution financed by the Republic of Serbia. Governing bodies: the University Assembly; the University Council. Residential facilities for 500 students.

Arrangements for co-operation with the Universities of: Cracow (Technical); Dresden (Technical); Poznań; Western Illinois; Moscow. Institute of Economics, Sofia; Institute of Agriculture, Plovdiv.

Academic Year: October to June (October-January; February-June).

Admission Requirements: Secondary school certificate or recognized equivalent, and entrance examination.

Fees (US $): Foreign students, 1000-2000.

Language of Instruction: Serbo-Croat.

Degrees and Diplomas: First Degree, 2-3 yrs. Second Degree, 4-5 yrs. Third Degree or specialization, up to a further 2 yrs. Also doctorate.

Libraries: Central Library; University Library; Department libraries.

Publication: Bulletin (every two months).

Academic Staff, 19897: 480.

Student Enrolment, 1989-90: 5055 (Also 2566 part-time).

7792 **UNIVERZA 'EDVARDA KARDELJA' V LJUBLJANI**

University of Ljubljana
Trg osvoboditve 11, 61 000 Ljubljana
Telephone: (61) 331-716
Fax: (61) 331-734
Rektor: Boris Sket (1989-)
Glavni tajnik: Slavko Hozvan

F. of Arts and Science (including Sociology, Psychology, Archaeology, Ethnology, Slavic, and Germanic Languages and Literature, Classical Philology, Comparative Literature and Literary Theory, Comparative Linguistics and Orientalistics, Musicology)
Dean: Mirko Pak; *staff* 135 (34)
F. of Law
Dean: Lojze Ude; *staff* 20

F. of Economic Studies
Dean: Lado Rupnik; *staff* 58 (1)
F. of Sociology, Political Sciences and Journalism
Dean: Niko Toš; *staff* 60 (23)
F. of Natural Sciences and Technology (including Pharmacy, Textile Industry, Mining and Mineral Sciences, and Chemical Education and Information)
Dean: Franc Kozjek; *staff* 172 (22)
F.of Architecture, Constructional Engineering and Geodesy
Dean: Jože Koželj; *staff* 88 (9)
F. of Electric and Electronic Engineering
Dean: Baldomir Zajc; *staff* 103 (15)
F. of Mechanical Engineering
Dean: Branko Gašperšićx; *staff* 87 (3)
F. of Medicine (including Dentistry)
Dean: Lidija Andolšek-Jeras; *staff* 226 (3)
F. of Biotechnical Engineering (Agronomy, Biology, Forestry, Wood Engineering, Food Science, and Cattle Breeding)
Dean: Jože Kovać; *staff* 203 (36)
F. of Veterinary Science
Dean: Milan Pogačnik; *staff* 60 (4)
F. of Physical Education
Dean: Janko Strel; *staff* 31 (5)
A. of Music
Dean: Marjan Gabrijelčič; *staff* 29 (17)
A. of Theatre, Radio, Film and Television
Dean: Mile Korun; *staff* 21
A. of Fine Arts
Dean: Dušan Tršar; *staff* 24 (1)
A. of Pedagogy
Dean: Veljko Troha; *staff* 70 (21)
Higher Nautical S. (Piran)
Dean: Zdravko Klasek; *staff* 14 (15)
S. for Health Services Workers
Dean: Čačinović-Vogrinčič; *staff* 33 (28)
S. for Safety Engineers
Dean: Jože Janežič; *staff* 4 (16)
S. for Social Welfare Workers
Dean: Nikolaj Abrahamsberg; *staff* 9 (14)
S. of Internal Affairs
Dean: Boris Žnidaršič; *staff* 13 (12)
I. of Biology
Head: Andrej Čokl
I. of Geography
Head: Rado Genorio
I. of Mathematics, Physics and Geography
Head: Zvonimir Bohte
I. of Sociology
Head: Vojko Antončič
A. of Pedagogy
Head: Darko Štrajn
Computer Ce.
Head: Franc Mandelc

Founded 1595 as Jesuit college, acquired university status 1919. An independent self-governing institution. Governing body: the University Council, with Executive Bodies. Some residential facilities for students.

Arrangements for co-operation with the Universities of: Leipzig; Olomuc; Bratislava; Bratislava (Technical); Prague; Warsaw; Budapest (Technical); Minsk; Oulu; Regensburg; Trieste; Katowice; Klagenfurt; Tbilisi; Udine; Brunel; Trento; Venice; Seattle; Carbondale; Cleveland; Pittsburgh.

Academic Year: October to September (October-January; February-May).

Admission Requirements: Secondary school certificate and entrance examination for Medicine, Architecture, Civil Engineering, and Surveying, Fine Arts, Music, Drama, Cinema, and Television.

Fees (US $): Foreign students, 1500-3000.

Language of Instruction: Slovene.

Degrees and Diplomas: First Degree, 2-3 yrs. Second Degree, 4-5 yrs. Third Degree or specialization, up to a further 2 yrs. Also doctorate by thesis.

Libraries: National and University Library, *c.* 1,140,590 vols; Central Technical Library, *c.* 112,200.

Special Facilities (Museums, etc.): University Museum.

Publication: Objave univerze v Ljubljani.

Academic Staff, 1987:

Rank	Full-time	Part-time
Redni profesorji (Professors)	359	51
Izredni profesorji (Associate Professors)	215	45
Docenti (Assistant Professors)	200	38
Lektorji	23	4
Predavatelji	193	79
Asistenti	352	41
Drugi sodelavci	78	19
Total	1420	277

Student Enrolment, 1989-90:

Of the country	20,068
Of other countries	109
Total	20,177*

*Also 3199 external students.

7793 **UNIVERZA V MARIBORU**
University of Maribor
Krekova ul. 2, 62000 Maribor
Telephone: (62) 212-281
Fax: (62) 212013
Rektor: Aloyz Križman (1989-91)
Glavni tajnik: Josip Sever

F. of Business Economics
Dean: Dusan Radonjič; *staff* 76 (16)
F. of Technical Sciences (Mechanical, Textile, Electrical, Civil, and Chemical Engineering; Computer Science)
Dean: Valter Doleček; *staff* 137 (70)
F. of Organizational Sciences (Organization of Work Processes, Information Sciences)
Dean: Jože Florjancić; *staff* 38 (16)
F. of Pedagogy
Dean: Jože Vauhnik; *staff* 63 (48)
S. of Law
Dean: Mitja Novak; *staff* 14 (5)
C. of Agriculture (including Animal Husbandry)
Dean: Milan Erjavec; *staff* 17 (12)

Founded 1975, incorporating previously existing institutes established 1959-1961. An independent self-governing institution financed by the Republic of Slovenia. Governing bodies: the University Council; the Administrative Board. Residential facilities for *c.* 30 academic staff and *c.* 2000 students.

Arrangements for co-operation with the Universities of: Massachusetts; Bayreuth; Budapest (Technical); Graz (Technical); Łódź; Marburg; Guangxi; Virginia State. Riga Polytechnical Institute; University of Economics, Berlin; College of Agriculture, Kaposvar; Teachers' Training College, Szombathely.

Academic Year: September to August (October-January; February-May).

Admission Requirements: Secondary school certificate or recognized foreign equivalent, or entrance examination.

Fees (US$): Foreign students, 1500-2000 per annum.

Language of Instruction: Slovene.

Degrees and Diplomas: First Degree, 2-3 yrs. Second Degree (Bachelor), 4-5 yrs. Third Degree (Master of Science) or specialization, up to a further 2-3 yrs. Also Ph.D..

Libraries: Central Library, *c.* 500,000 vols; school libraries.

Publications: Naše goapodarstvo (bimonthly); Organizaciji in kadri (bimonthly); Časopis za zgodovino in narodopisje (biannually); Znanstvena revija (biannually).

Academic Staff, 1989-90:

Rank	Full-time	Part-time
Redni profesorji (Professors)	82	38
Izredni profesorji (Associate Professors)	37	24
Docenti (Assistant Professors)	58	18
Predavatelji (Lecturers)	127	51
Asistenti (Assistants)	66	36
Total	370	167

Student Enrolment, 1989-90:

	Men	Women	Total
Of the country	3461	4222	7683
Of other countries	32	2	34
Total	3493	4224	7717*

*Also 5538 external students.

7794 **UNIVERZITET 'DŽEMAL BIJEDIĆ' U MOSTARU**

University of Mostar

Trg 14 februar bb, 88 000 Mostar

Telephone: (088) 39-140/1

Fax: (088) 39-141

Rektor: Berislav Blažević (1986-)

General Secretary: Edin Semić

F. of Economics
Dean: Frano Ljubić; *staff* 45 (15)
F. of Law
Dean: Drago Radulović; *staff* 32 (6)
F. of Mechanical Engineering
Dean: Himzo Djukić; *staff* 55 (15)
F. of Civil Engineering
Dean: Dragan Milašinović; *staff* 25 (20)
A. of Education
Dean: Rudolf Kraljević; *staff* 25 (5)
I. of Work Protection
Director: Sadik Begović; *staff* 12
I. of Agricultural Research and Development
Director: Jakov Pehar; *staff* 40
I. of Hydrology
Director: Kemal Bubalo; *staff* 15
I. of Economic Development
Director: Velija Hadjocvić; *staff* 12 (10)
I. for Caustic Water Exploitation
Head: Milored Milićević; *staff* 10 (4)
I. for Aircraft Technologoey
Head: Šefik Karabeg; *staff* 20 (10)

Founded 1977. An independent self-governing institution. Governing bodies: the University Assembly, comprising 93 members; the Executive Committee, comprising 15 members. Residential facilities for academic staff and 440 students.

Arrangements for co-operation with: University of Stuttgart; Autonomous University of Barcelona; Çukurova University, Adana.

Academic Year: September to June (September-January; February-June).

Admission Requirements: Secondary school certificate.

Fees: None.

Language of Instruction: Serbo-Croat.

Degrees and Diplomas: First degree, 2-3 yrs. Second degree, 4 yrs. Also doctorate.

Library: Central Library, 150,000 vols.

Publication: Bilten.

Academic Staff, 1989-90:

Rank	Full-time	Part-time
Redovni profesori (Professors)	24	10
Vanredni profesori (Associate Professors)	30	5
Docenti (Assistant Professors)	65	24
Predavači (Lecturers)	10	7
Asistenti (Assistants)	60	15
Total	189	61

Student Enrolment, 1989-90:

	Men	Women	Total
Of the country	2650	1300	3950
Of other countries	35	–	35
Total	2685	1300	3985*

7795 **UNIVERZITET U NIŠU**

University of Niš

Trg bratstva i jedinstva 2, 18 000 Niš

Telephone: (018) 25-544

Rektor: Dimitrije Mihajlović (1985-87)

Generalni sekretar: Dragoslav Djokić

F. of Electronic Engineering
Dean: Dragiša Krstić; *staff* 73 (19)
F. of Civil Engineering (including Architecture)
Dean: Slobodan Kobliška; *staff* 64 (20)
F. of Mechanical Engineering
Dean: Života Živković; *staff* 75 (14)
F. of Medicine (including Pharmacy)
Dean: Lazar Vlajin; *staff* 244 (5)
F. of Work Protection
Dean: Miroljub Petrović; *staff* 46 (5)
F. of Technology
Dean: Živan Stojković; *staff* 31 (41)
F. of Philosophy
Dean: Ljubiša Mitrović; *staff* 121 (57)
F. of Economics
Dean: Nikola Javanović; *staff* 62 (6)
F. of Law
Dean: Ljubiša Jovanović; *staff* 45 (3)
Ce. for Lifelong Education

Also 16 institutes of the Faculty of Medicine and 11 institutes and laboratories of the faculties.

Founded 1965, incorporating faculties formerly attached to University of Belgrade. An independent self-governing institution. Governing body: the University Council. Residential facilities for academic staff and 980 students.

Academic Year: October to September (October-January; February-June).

Admission Requirements: Secondary school certificate or equivalent.

Fees: None.

Language of Instruction: Serbo-Croat.

Degrees and Diplomas: First Degree, 2 yrs. Second Degree, 4-5 yrs. Third Degree or specialization, up to a further 2 yrs. Also doctorate, a further 3 yrs and thesis.

Libraries: Central Library, *c.* 7000 vols; Faculty libraries: Medicine, *c.* 7300; Law, *c.* 6500; Economics, *c.* 7000; Philosophy, *c.* 21,000; Technology, *c.* 11,000.

Publications: Pregled predavanja; Bilten; Glasnik Univerziteta.

Academic Staff, 1986-87:

Rank	Full-time	Part-time
Redovni profesori (Professors)	115	40
Vanredni profesori (Associate Professors)	89	35
Docenti (Assistant Professors)	181	46
Predavači (Lecturers)	37	15
Asistenti (Assistants)	339	34
Total	761	170

Student Enrolment, 1986-87:

	Men	Women	Total
Of the country	4680	4619	9299
Of other countries	595	62	657
Total	5275	4681	9956*

*Also 7710 external students.

7796 **UNIVERZITET U NOVA SADU**

University of Novi Sad

Veljka Vlahovića 3, 21 000 Novi Sad

Telephone: (21) 611-422

Fax: (21) 611-725

Rektor: Jevrem Jonjić

Generalni sekretar: Petar Radonjanin

F. of Agriculture (including Veterinary Medicine, Stockbreeding and Horticulture)
Dean: Radomir Jovanović
F. of Natural Sciences and Mathematics
Dean: Ištvan Bikit
F. of Economics (Subotica)
Dean: Jovan Rekecki
F. of Technical Sciences
Dean: Miodrag Zlokolica
F. of Medicine
Dean: Aleksandar Monćilović
F. of Law
Dean: Antun Mulenica
F. of Technology (Food Products)
Dean: Božidar Milić
F. of Philosophy (including Sociology, History, Pedagogy, Literature, South Slavic Languages, Hungarology, Slovak Studies)
Dean: Milan Tripković
F. of Education (Zrenjanin)
F. of Physical Education
Dean: Julijan Malacko
F. of Technical Studies (Zrenjanin)
Dean: Zarko Mitrović

A. of Arts
Dean: Nenad Ostojić
Also 64 integrated institutes and clinics.

Founded 1960 with faculties of arts, agriculture, and law (established 1954/5 as faculties of the University of Belgrade). An independent self-governing body of faculties and institutes financed by the Province of Vojodina. Governing body: the University Assembly, comprising 50 professors, 25 students, and 24 members of the Administration. Residential facilities for academic staff and *c.* 3500 students.

Arrangements for co-operation with: University of Illinois at Chicago; University of Halle; State University of Uzgorod; Technical University, Budapest; Atila Jozsef University, Szeged; Janus Pannonius University, Pecs; Comenius University, Bratislava; University of Plovdiv; University of Regensburg.

Academic Year: October to June (October-January; February-June).

Admission Requirements: Secondary school or secondary vocational school certificate, or entrance examination.

Fees (US $): 1000-2500.

Languages of Instruction: Serbo-Croat and some Hungarian, Slovak, Ruthenian, and Romanian.

Degrees and Diplomas: First Degree, 2 yrs. Second Degree, 4 yrs in all faculties except Medicine, 6 yrs; Techn. Sc., 5 yrs. Third Degree or specialization, up to a further 2 yrs. Doctorates in all faculties.

Libraries: Faculty libraries: Economics, *c.* 37,000 vols; Medicine, *c.* 6500; Agriculture, *c.* 15,000; Law, 62,000; Technology, *c.* 4200; Natural Sciences and Mathematics, *c.* 32,000; Philosophy, *c.* 180,000.

Publication: Glasnik Univerzitet u Novum Sadu (Courrier).

Academic Staff: c. 1750 (370).

Student Enrolment: c. 22,620 (Also 17,460 external students).

7797 **SVEUČILIŠTE JOSIPA JURGA STROSSMAYERA U OSIJEKU**
University of Osijek
Ul. Braće Radića 15, 54 000 Osijek
Telephone: (54) 31822
Fax: (54) 24-750
Rektor: Ivan Mecanović
Generalni sekretar: Antun Ignac

F. of Economics
Dean: Borivoj Matić; *staff* 42 (4)
F. of Law
Dean: Branko Babac; *staff* 30 (8)
F. of Education
Dean: Milan Ratković; *staff* 127 (62)
F. of Agriculture (including Animal Husbandry)
Dean: Marija Ivezić; *staff* 71 (30)
F. of Biotechnology
Dean: Ludvig Purkat; *staff* 26 (18)
F. of Civil Engineering
Dean: Aleksandar Šolc; *staff* 45 (9)
F. of Mechanical Engineering (Slavonski Brod)
Dean: Mijo Cicvarić; *staff* 33 (38)
F. of Electrical Engineering
Dean: Rusmir Mahmitćehajić; *staff* 21 (7)
I. of Agriculture
Dean: Antun Novoselović; *staff* 258
I. of History
Dean: Ante Vukadin; *staff* 12
Social Research Ce. of Slavonija and Baranja Slavonski Brod
Dean: Mile Konjević; *staff* 19

Founded 1975 and incorporating Faculty of Economics formerly attached to University of Zagreb. An independent self-governing institution. Governing body: the University Assembly. Residential facilities for students.

Arrangements for co-operation with the Universities of: Augsburg; Gdańsk; Halle-Wittenberg; Pecs; Juba. Technical College of Business Administration, Pforzheim; College of Technology, Bremen; Keszthely University of Agriculture.

Academic Year: October to September (October-February; March-September).

Admission Requirements: Secondary school certificate.

Fees: None.

Language of Instruction: Croatian or Serbian.

Degrees and Diplomas: Diploma, first level, 2 yrs; second level, 4-5 yrs. Magister, a further 2 yrs. Doctorates by thesis.

Library: Faculty libraries, total, *c.* 250,000 vols.

Publication: Bilten.

Academic Staff, 1989-90:

Rank	Full-time	Part-time
Professors	53	34
Associate Professors	105	39
Assistants	146	63
Total	304	136

Student Enrolment, 1989-90:

	Men	Women	Total
Of the country	2925	2901	5826*

*Also 1194 external students.

7798 ***UNIVERSITETI I PRISHTINËS UNIVERZITET U PRIŠTINI**
University of Prishtina
M. Tito 53, 38 000 Prishtina
Telephone: (38) 24-970
Fax: (38) 27-628
Rektor: Skënder Karahoda (1989-91)
Generalni sekretar: Destan Halimi

F. of Law
Dean: Mirko Perunović
F. of Economics
Dean: Radisav Andjelković
F. of Medicine
Dean: Alush Gashi
F. of Philology
Dean: Shefqet Pllana
F. of Philosophy
Dean: Radivoje Kulić
F. of Electrotechnics
Dean: Jusuf Krasniqi
F. of Machinery
Dean: Khevat Perjuci
F. of Civil Engineering and Architecture
Dean: Vukomir Savić
F. of Natural Science and Mathematics
Dean: Muharrem Berisha
F. of Arts
Dean: Bashkim Shehu
F. of Physical Culture
Dean: Mustafë Aliu
F. of Agriculture
Dean: Božidar Lazić
F. of Mining and Metallurgy (Kosovska Mitrovica)
Dean: Reshat Abrashi
High Economical S. (Pejë-Peć)
Director: Ivović Slobodan
High Technical S. (Mitrovicë të Titos-Titova Mitrovica)
Director: Ismail Krashiqi
High Pedagogical S. (Prishtinë-Prishtina)
Director: Milan Filipović
High Pedagogical S. (Gjilan-Gjilane)
Director: Vasilije Bojović
High Pedagogical S. (Prizren)
Director: Ruzhdi Tutunxhiu
High Pedagogical S. (Gjakovë-Djakovica)
Director: Hilmi Hasimja
High Technical S. (Ferizaj-Uroševac)
Director: Isak Jashari

Founded 1970 incorporating faculties formerly attached to University of Belgrade and intended particularly to meet the needs of the population of the Autonomous Region of Kosovo. An independent self-governing institution. Governing bodies: the University Council; the Faculty Councils and Boards.

Arrangements for co-operation with: University of Jena; Polytechnical Institute of Iaši; University of Sofia; University of Rome 'La Sapienza'; University of Dagestan; University of Kuansy, Nanning; Marmara University;University of Valladolid; University of Budapest.

Academic Year: October to June (October-January; February-June).

Admission Requirements: Secondary school certificate or equivalent, or 4 yrs practical work and entrance examination.

Fees: None.

Languages of Instruction: Albanian and Serbo-Croat.

Degrees and Diplomas: First Degree, 2-3 yrs. Second Degree, 4 yrs in all faculties except Medicine, 5 yrs. Doctorates in all faculties.
Academic Staff, 1986-87: 2000.
Student Enrolment, 1986-87:

Of the country	26,000	7000	33,000*

*Also 688 foreign students.

7799 **SVEUČILIŠTE 'VLADIMIR BAKARIĆ U RIJECI**
University of Rijeka
Ulica Aldo Negri 1, 51 000 Rijeka
Rektor: Predrag Stanković

F. of Medicine (including Dentistry)
F. of Engineering (Construction, Marine, Civil)
F. of Economics
F. of Industrial Education
Naval S.
S. of Economics (Pula)
A. of Education
A. of Education (Pula)
A. of Education (Gospić)

Founded 1973 and incorporating faculties formerly attached to University of Zagreb. An independent self-governing institution financed by the State. Governing bodies: the Skupština (Assembly); the Savjet Sveučilišta (University Council).
Academic Year: September to July.
Languages of Instruction: Serbo-Croat and Albanian.
Degrees and Diplomas: Diploma, first level, 2 yrs; second level, 4 yrs, except Medicine; Dentistry, 5 yrs; Engineering, 4 ½ yrs. Magister, a further 2 yrs. Doctorates by thesis.
Library: c. 305,030 vols.
Academic Staff: c. 370 (300).
Student Enrolment: c. 8750 (Also *c.* 3900 external students).

7800 **UNIVERZITET U SARAJEVU**
University of Sarajevo
Obala Vojvode Stepe 7-11, 71 000 Sarajevo
Telephone: (071) 214-320
Rektor: Božidar Matić

F. of Architecture and Town Planning
F. of Economics
F. of Electrical Engineering
F. of Political Science
F. of Physical Education
F. of Pharmacy
F. of Philosophy
F. of Civil Engineering
F. of Mechanical Engineering
F. of Mechanical Engineering (Zenica)
F. of Medicine
F. of Metallurgy (Zenica)
F. of Agriculture
F. of Law
F. of Science
F. of Transport Engineering
F. of Dentistry
F. of Forestry
F. of Veterinary Medicine
A. of Fine Arts
A. of Drama
A. of Music
S. of Education
S. of Nursing
S. of Economics and Commerce
S. of Management
S. of Social Work
I. of Biology
I. of Architecture
I. of Computer Sciences
I. of Economics
I. of Organization and Economics I. of Oriental Research
I. of Thermo-and Nuclear Techniques
I. of Welding
Electroenergetic I.
I. of Work Protection
I. of Ergonomics

Founded 1949 with the faculty of medicine. An independent self-governing institution financed by the Republic. Governing body: the University Council, composed of 130 members from the university and other cultural and political institutions including two student representatives. Residential facilities for students in six hostels.
Arrangements for co-operation with the Universities of: Greifswald; Budapest; Kharkov; Mannheim; Khartoum; Algiers; Tripoli; Benghazi; Tehran; Brussels; Baghdad; Iaşi; Wrocław; Lahore; Cracow; Grenoble III; Innsbruck; California; Bursa; Tianjin; Las Villas; Murray, Kentucky; New York, Utica.
Academic Year: October to September (October-January; February-June).
Admission Requirements: Secondary school certificate or recognized equivalent, and entrance examination.
Fees: None.
Language of Instruction: Serbo-Croat.
Degrees and Diplomas: First Degree, 2 yrs. Second Degree, 4-5 yrs. Third Degree or specialization, up to a further 2 yrs. Doctoratesin all faculties.
Libraries: Central Library; faculty libraries.
Publications: Bilten (Bulletin); Pregled predavanja (calendar); Doktorske disertacije-Rezimei.
Academic Staff: c. 1230.
Student Enrolment: c. 24,030 (Also *c.* 9330 part-time students).

7801 ***UNIVERZITET 'KIRIL I METÓDIJ' U SKOPJU**
University of Skopje
Bulevar 'Krste Misirkov' bb, 91 000 Skopje
Telephone: (38-91) 237712
Rektor: Todor Džunov (1986-88)

F. of Law
Dean: Nikola Matovski
F. of Economics
Dean: Nikola Klusev
F. of Philology
Dean: Nadežda Momiroska
F. of Philosophy
Dean: Tome Nikolovski
F. of Architecture
Dean: Georgi Konstantinovski
F. of Civil Engineering
Dean: Alexander Angelov
F. of Mechanical Engineering
Dean: Gabrilo Gavriloski
F. of Electrical Studies
F. of Technology and Metallurgy
F. of Mining and Geology
F. of Natural Sciences and Mathematics
F. of Civil Defence and Security
F. of Medicine and Pharmacy
F. of Dentistry
F. of Physical Education
F. of Agriculture
F. of Forestry
F. of Music
F. of Art
F. of Drama
A. of Education
A. of Education (Štip)
S. of Agriculture (Strumica)
I. of Economics
I. of Social and Political Sciences
I. of Folklore
I. of Seismology
I. of Yugoslav History
I. of Veterinary Medicine
I. of Rice Studies (Kočani)

Founded 1949 incorporating faculties of letters 1946, and agriculture and medicine 1947. The university is an independent self-governing institution. Residential facilities for students.
Arrangements for co-operation with the Universities of: Halle; Bradford; Cracow; Cracow (Technical); Warsaw; Katowice; Craiova; Aachen (Technical); Erlangen; Clausthal (Technical); Sofia; Voronezh; Tashkent; Prague (Charles); Bratislava (Comenius); Nankai; Roorke, India; Boğaziçi; Grenoble I; California State; Arizona State;Bloomington; Wayne, Detroit; Texas A&M.
Academic Year: October to June (October-January; February-June).

Admission Requirements: Secondary school certificate. Entrance examination for Faculty of Medicine.
Fees: None.
Language of Instruction: Macedonian.
Degrees and Diplomas: First Degree, 2-3 yrs. Second Degree, 4-5 yrs. Third Degree or specialization, up to a further 2 yrs. Also doctorate.
Library: Central Library.
Publication: Bulletin (monthly).
Academic Staff, 1986-87: 1766
Student Enrolment, 1986-87: 34,429 (Including 780 foreign students).

7802 **SVEUČILIŠTE U SPLITU**
University of Split
Livanjska 5, 58 000 Split
Telephone: 49-966

F. of Law
F. of Electrical, Mechanical and Marine Engineering
F. of Economics
F. of Philosophy (Zadar)
F. of Chemical Engineering
F. of Civil Engineering
F. of Tourism and Foreign Trade (Dubrovnik)
I. for Oceanography and Fisheries
I. of Adriatic Agricultural Research
Founded 1974 and incorporating faculties formerly attached to University of Zagreb. An independent self-governing institution financed by the Republic. Governing bodies: the University Assembly, comprising 113 members; the University Council, comprising 25 members; the UniversitySenate. Someresidential facilities for students.
Academic Year: September to August (September-January; January-August).
Admission Requirements: Secondary school certificate or recognized equivalent, and entrance examination.
Fees: None.
Language of Instruction: Croatian.
Degrees and Diplomas: First Degree, 2-3 yrs. Second Degree, 4-5 yrs. Third Degree or specialization, up to a further 2 yrs. Also doctorate.
Library: Faculty libraries.
Academic Staff: c. 380 (280).
Student Enrolment: c. 11,650.

7803 **UNIVERZITET 'VELJKO VLAHOVIĆ' U TITOGRADU**
University of Titograd
Cetinski put 6b, 81000 Titograd
Telephone: (81) 52-981
Rektor: Miloš Radulović (1987-)
Generalni sekretar: Dragiša Ivanović

F. of Economics
Dean: Janko Gogić
F. of Law
Dean: Blagota Mitrić
F. of Electrical Engineering
Dean: Dušan Petranović
F. of Mechanical Engineering
Dean: Božidar Nikolić
F. of Metallurgy
Dean: Boško Perović
F. of Philosophy (Nikšić)
Dean: Blagoje Cerović
Maritime F. (Kotor)
Dean: Stevan Nikić
F. of Civil Engineering
Dean: Dušan Dragović
A. of Music
Dean: Branko Opačić
F. of Fine Arts (Cetinje)
Dean: Nikola Gvozdenović
F. of Natural Science
Dean: Slobodan Backović
I. of History
Director: Jovan Bojović
I. of Agriculture
Director: Žarko Kalezić
I. of Biomedicine
Director: Nikola Kovačević
I. of Foreign Languages
Director: Milisav Filipović
I. for Technical Research
Director: Bactrić Vulićević
Founded 1974 and incorporating facilities formerly attached to University of Belgrade. An independent self-governing institution financed by the State. Governing bodies: the Executive Council; the University Assembly, comprising 64 members. Residential facilities for academic staff and students.
Arrangements for co-operation with the universities of: Florida State; Moscow State; Bari; Karlsruhe; Rostov on Don.
Academic Year: October to July (October-January; February-July).
Admission Requirements: Secondary school certificate or recognized equivalent.
Language of Instruction: Serbo-Croat.
Degrees and Diplomas: First Degree, 2-3 yrs. Second Degree, at least 4 yrs. Third Degree or specialization, up to a further 2 yrs. Doctorates by thesis.
Publication: Bilten (quarterly).
Press or Publishing House: Publishing Centre.
Academic Staff: c. 835.
Student Enrolment: c. 8000.

7804 **UNIVERZITET U TUZLI**
University of Tuzla
Rudarska 71, 75 000 Tuzla
Telephone: (075) 34-650
Rektor: Ibro Pašić

F. of Chemical Technology
F. of Mining and Geology
F. of Medicine
F. of Electrical Engineering
F. of Economics
C. of Education
I. of Chemical Engineering
I. of Coal Research and Carbochemistry
Mining Research I.
Work and Environmental Protection Research I.
I. of Economics
Data Processing Ce.
Founded 1976, incorporating faculties formerly forming part of the University of Sarajevo. The University is avoluntary self-governing association of faculties and institutes. Governing body: the University Assembly. Residential facilities for students.
Academic Year: September to June (September-February; February-June).
Admission Requirements: Secondary school certificate.
Fees: None.
Language of Instruction: Serbo-Croat.
Degrees and Diplomas: First Degree, 2-3 yrs. Second Degree, 4-5 yrs. Also doctorate.
Publications: Bilten; Lecture Review.
Academic Staff: c. 450.
Student Enrolment: c. 15,000.

7805 ***UNIVERZITET UMETNOSTI U BEOGRADU**
University of the Arts
Vuka Karadžića 12/1, 11 000 Beograd
Telephone: 185-144
Electronic mail: epmfsol@8ayubgss21.EARN
Rektor: Darinka Matić-Marović (1989-91)
Generalni Sekretar: Dobrila Šoškić-Petrović

F. of Music
Dean: Srdjan Hofman; *staff* 137 (10)
F. of Fine Arts
Dean: Momčilo Antonović; *staff* 67
F. of Applied Arts and Design
Dean: Rajko Nikolić; *staff* 72 (6)
F. of Dramatic Arts
Dean: Svetozar Rapajić; *staff* 95 (16)
I. for Theatre, Film, Radio, and Television
Director: Dejan Kosanović; *staff* 17
Founded 1957 as Academy of Arts, acquired present title and status 1973. An artistic, scientific, and educational institution, whose activity

helps development and strengthening of creativity. Financed by the Fund for Univrsity Education (Governemnt of the Republic of Serbia). Governing body: the Assembly. Residential facilities for academic staff and students.

Arrangements for co-operation with the State University of New York at Albany.

Academic Year: October to September (October-January; February-May).

Admission Requirements: Secondary school certificate or recognized equivalent, and entrance examination.

Fees: None. Foreign students, 1000-2000 US$ per annum.

Language of Instruction: Serbo-Croat.

Degrees and Diplomas: Diploma, 4-5 yrs. Magistar nauka o umetnosti, Master of Sciences in Arts. Doktor nauka o umetnosti, Doctor.

Library: Faculty libraries, total *c.* 129,000 vols. Also *c.* 10,000 records.

Publication: Bilten.

Press or Publishing House: Department for Publishing.

Academic Staff, 1989-90:

Rank	Full-time	Part-time
Redovni profesori (Professors)	118	12
Vanredni profesori (Associate Professors)	71	10
Docenti (Assistant Professors)	56	10
Predavači (Lecturers)	8	–
Saradnici u nastavi (Associates in Teaching)	33	–
Asistenti (Assistants)	85	–
Total	371	32

Student Enrolment, 1989-90:

	Men	Women	Total
Of the country	619	9852	1604
Of other countries	13	5	18
Total	632	990	1622

7806 ***SVEUČILIŠTE U ZAGREBU**

University of Zagreb

Trg Maršala Tita 14, 41 000 Zagreb

Telephone: 272-411

Fax: 41-420-388

Rektor: Zvonomir Šeparović (1989-90)

Tajnik Skupštine (Assembly Secretary): Tajnik Skupštine

F. of Law
Dean: Smiljko Sokol; *staff* 151 (5)
F. of Economics
Dean: Josip Pavlović; *staff* 269
F. of Philosophy (Psychology, Sociology, History, History of Art, Archaeology, Ethnology, Yugoslav Languages and Literature, Slavonic Languages and Literature, Romanistics, Italian Language and Literature, German Language and Literature, English Language and Literature, Phonetics, General Linguistics, and Oriental Studies)
Dean: Branimir Sverko; *staff* 609 (5)
F. of Natural Sciences and Mathematics
Dean: Ante Deljac; *staff* 476 (17)
F. of Medicine
Dean: Želimir Jakšić; *staff* 806 (197)
F. of Dentistry
Dean: Goran Knežević; *staff* 196 (32)
F. of Veterinary Medicine
Dean: Tomo Martinčić; *staff* 336
F. of Pharmacy and Biochemistry
Dean: Ivan Jalšenjak; *staff* 149 (1)
F. of Architecture
Dean: Ante Vulin; *staff* 154 (4)
F. of Civil Engineering
Dean: M. Andjelić; *staff* 617 (55)
F. of Surveying Dean: Miljenko Solarić; *staff* 100 (3)
F. of Mechanical and Marine Engineering
Dean: Andrija Mulo; *staff* 963 (21)
F. of Electrical Engineering
Dean: Vladimir Naglić; *staff* 323 (69)
F. of Technology
Dean: Ivan Eškinja; *staff* 317 (5)
F. of Food and Biotechnology
Dean: Egon Bauman; *staff* 168 (2)
F. of Mining, Geology, and Petroleum Engineering
Dean: Josip Tišljar; *staff* 184 (36)
F. of Agriculture
Dean: Željko Vidaček; *staff* 753 (20)
F. of Forestry
Dean: Zdenko Pavlin; *staff* 193 (12)
F. of Political Sciences
Dean: Ante Pažanin; *staff* 78 (10)
F. for the Study of the Handicapped
Dean: Milko Mejovšek; *staff* 59 (20)
F. of Physical Education
Dean: Boris Volčanšek; *staff* 100 (26)
F. of Management and Computer Sciences
Dean: Miroslav Žugaj; *staff* 80 (1)
F. of Metallurgy
Dean: Darko Maljković; *staff* 119 (11)
A. of Fine Arts
Dean: Eugen Kokot; *staff* 50
A. for Drama, Film and Television
Dean: Nenad Puhovski; *staff* 50
A. of Music
Dean: Igor Gjadrov; *staff* 79
I. of Agriculture
Director: Branimir Gjurasin; *staff* 40 (23)
S. of Printing Technology
Dean: Ante Cicvarić; *staff* 51 (2)
Also 5 associated institutes.

Founded 1669 by edict of Emperor Leopold I giving university status to the existing Jesuit Academy. Reorganized 1874 and 1940. In 1973 the faculties established in Rijeka were detached and became the University of Rijeka; in 1974 the faculties established in Split and Zadar were detached and became the University of Split; in 1975 the Faculty of Economics in Osijek was detached to become part of the University of Osijek. An independent self-governing institution. Governing bodies: the University Assembly, composed of 101 members; the Scientific Teaching Council, composed of 58 members. Residential facilities for students.

Arrangements for co-operation with: Kiev State University; Leningrad State University; University of Rostock; Technical University of Dresden; Eötvös Loránd University; Jagiellonian University, Cracow; Technical University of Cracow; University of Warsaw; Babeş-Bolyai University; Johannes Gutenberg University of Mainz; University of Hamburg; University of Munich; University of Trieste; University of Padua; The Johns Hopkins University; New York State University; University of Pittsburgh; Florida State University; Indiana University; University of California at Los Angeles; Beijing University; East China Normal University, Shanghai; Technical University of Košice; Ain Shams University; Freiberg Mining Academy; University of Basrah; University of Ankara; University of Graz.

Academic Year: October to June (October-January; February-June).

Admission Requirements: Secondary school certificate or recognized equivalent, and entrance examination.

Fees: None.

Language of Instruction: Croatian or Serbian.

Degrees and Diplomas: First Degree, 2-3 yrs. Second Degree, 4-5 yrs. Third Degree or specialization, up to a further 2 yrs. Also doctorate.

Libraries: National and University Library, *c.* 1,200,000 vols; faculty and institute libraries.

Special Facilities (Museums, etc.): Museums: Mineralogy and Petrography; Geology and Palaeontology.

Publication: University Messenger.

Academic Staff, 1989-90:

Rank	Full-time	Part-time
Asistenti	1382	158
Docenti	637	103
Izvanredni Profesori	335	53
Redovni Profesori	945	238
Total	3299	452

Student Enrolment, 1989-90:

Men	Women	Total
20,803	18,367	39,170*

*Also *c.* 5566 external students.

ZAIRE

7807 **UNIVERSITÉ DE KINSHASA**
University of Kinshasa
B.P. 127, Kinshasa XI
Telex: 982 23 068
Telephone: 30-123
Recteur: Mpeye Nyango

F. of Medicine (including Dentistry)
F. of Pharmacy
F. of Law
F. of Engineering
F. of Science
F. of Economics
Also 6 Research Centres and Institutes.

Founded 1949 as Université Lovanium, became a campus of the Université nationale du Zaïre 1971, and acquired present status and title 1981. A State institution. Governing body: the Conseil d'administration d'Universités.

Academic Year: October to June (October-February; February-June).

Admission Requirements: Secondary school certificate and entrance examination.

Language of Instruction: French.

Degrees and Diplomas: Gradué. Licence in–Economics, 4 yrs; Law; Civil Engineering; Science, 5 yrs. Doctor of–Medicine, 6 yrs. Doctorat de spécialité (3e cycle). Doctorate. Also diploma of specialization in Medicine.

Library: c. 300,000 vols.

Publications: Bulletin d'Information (monthly); Cahiers: économiques et sociaux (quarterly); des Religions Africaines (weekly).

Academic Staff: c. 700.

Student Enrolment: c. 7000.

7808 **UNIVERSITÉ DE KISANGANI**
University of Kisangani
B.P. 2012, Kisangani, Haut Zaïre
Telex: 19
Telephone: 2152
Recteur: Mwabila Malela
Secrétaire général (Administration): Makwanza Batumanisa

F. of Sciences
DEan: Hugo Gevaerts; *staff* 54 (16)
F. of Education and Psychology
Dean: Lokombe Kitete; *staff* 72 (10)
F. of Medicine
DEan: Labama Lokwa; *staff* 54 (16)
F. of Social, Administrative, and Political Sciences
Dean: Rutazibwa Iyeze; *staff* 32 (13)
Ce. for Development Research (C.R.I.D.E.)
Head: Mulyum wa Mamba I.
I. of Applied Social Sciences
Also 2 Research Institutes.

Founded 1963 as Université libre du Congo, became a campus of the Université nationale du Zaïre 1971, and acquired present status and title 1981. A State institution. Governing body: the Conseil d'administration. Residential facilities for academic staff and students.

Arrangements for co-operation with: Free University of Brussels; Universities of Rwanda and Burundi.

Academic Year: October to July (October-February; February-July).

Admission Requirements: Secondary school certificate and entrance examination.

Fees (Zaires): 5000 per annum.

Language of Instruction: French.

Degrees and Diplomas: Gradué. Licence in–Education, 4 yrs; Science; Psychology, 5 yrs. Doctor of–Medicine, 6 yrs. Doctorat de Spécialité (3e cycle). Doctorate. Also diploma of specialization in Medicine.

Library: c. 46,000 vols.

Publications: Bulletin d'Information (monthly); Revue Zaïroise de Pédagogie et Psychologie. Kisangani Médical; Annalesde la Faculté des Sciences.

Press or Publishing House: Presses universitaires de Kisangani.

Academic Staff, 1989-90:

Rank	Full-time	Part-time
Professeurs ordinaires	10	7
Professeurs	13	25
Professeurs associés	30	4
Chefs de Travaux	100	–
Assistants	65	–
Total	218	36

Student Enrolment, 1989-90:

	Men	Women	Total
Of the country	3542	650	4192

7809 **UNIVERSITÉ DE LUBUMBASHI**
University of Lubumbashi
B.P. 1825, Lubumbashi (Shaba)
Telephone: 5403/7

F. of Letters
F. of Veterinary Medicine
F. of Social, Political, and Administrative Sciences
Polytechnic F. (Mining, Chemical and Metallurgical Engineering)
F. of Science
Also 4 Research Centres.

Founded 1955 as Université officielle du Congo, became a campus of the Université nationale du Zaïre 1971, and acquired present status and title 1981. A State institution. Governing body: the Conseil d'administration d'Universités.

Academic Year: October to June (October-February; February-June).

Admission Requirements: Secondary school certificate and entrance examination.

Language of Instruction: French.

Degrees and Diplomas: Gradué. Licence in–Letters; Sociology, 4 yrs; Engineering; Sciences, 5 yrs. Doctor of Veterinary Medicine, 6 yrs. Doctorat en spécialité (3e cycle). Doctorate.

Library: c. 92,230 vols.

Academic Staff: c. 400.

Student Enrolment: c. 4370.

Other Institutions

Technical Education

7810 **ACADÉMIE DES BEAUX-ARTS**
B.P. 9349, Kinshasa

Fine Arts

7811 **INSTITUT SUPÉRIEUR D'ÉTUDES AGRONOMIQUES DE BENGAMISA**
B.P. 202, Kisangani

Agriculture
Forestry

Founded 1968 as Institut supérieur d'Enseignement agricole. Attached to the Université nationale du Zaïre 1971 and acquired present title 1974. Became an autonomous institution 1981. Governing body: the Conseil d'administration. Residential facilities for academic staff and for c. 200 students.

Academic Year: October to July (October-February; February-June).

Admission Requirements: Secondary school certificate.

Language of Instruction: French.

Degrees and Diplomas: Gradué en Techniques agronomiques, 3 yrs.

Library: c. 2260 vols.

Publication: Information (monthly).
Academic Staff: c. 30 (20).
Student Enrolment: c. 340.

7812 **INSTITUT SUPÉRIEUR D'ÉTUDES AGRONOMIQUES DE MONDONGO**
B.P. 60, Lisala

Agriculture

Founded 1972 and attached to the Université nationale du Zaïre. Became an autonomous institution 1981. Governing body: the Conseil d'administration.

Academic Year: October to July (October-February; March-July).
Admission Requirements: Secondary school certificate.
Language of Instruction: French.
Degrees and Diplomas: Gradué en Techniques agronomiques, 3 yrs.
Library: c. 1350 vols.
Academic Staff: c. 15 (10).
Student Enrolment: c. 110.

7813 **INSTITUT SUPÉRIEUR D'ARTS ET MÉTIERS**
B.P. 15.198, Kinshasa/Gombe
Telephone: 69494; 69027

Dressmaking

Founded 1968 as Ecole normale, became Institut supérieur d'Enseignement technique féminin 1971, acquired present title and status 1975 and attached to the Université nationale du Zaïre. Became an autonomous institution 1981. Governing body: the Conseil d'administration. Residential facilities for students.

Academic Year: October to July (October-December; January-March; April-July).
Admission Requirements: Secondary school certificate.
Language of Instruction: French.
Degrees and Diplomas: Gradué, 3 yrs.
Library: c. 450 vols.
Publication: Méthode de coupe (annually).
Academic Staff: c. 25.
Student Enrolment: c. 120 (Women).

7814 **INSTITUT NATIONAL DES ARTS**
B.P. 8332, Kinshasa

Dramatic Arts
Music

Attached to the Université nationale du Zaïre 1971. Became an autonomous institution 1981. Governing body: the Conseil d'administration.

7815 **INSTITUT DU BÂTIMENT ET DES TRAVAUX PUBLICS**
Avenue Momobutu, B.P. 4731, Kinshasa-Ngaliema
Telephone: 59-3925

Construction Engineering
Public Works Engineering

Founded 1961. Attached to the Université nationale du Zaïre 1971. Became an autonomous institution 1981. Governing body: the Conseil d'administration. Residential facilities for academic staff and students.

Academic Year: October to July (October-February; February-July).
Admission Requirements: Secondary school certificate or recognized equivalent.
Language of Instruction: French.
Degrees and Diplomas: Gradué en–Architecture; en Travaux publics; Géomètre-Topographe, 3 yrs. Licence in–Architecture; Geometry-Topography, 5 yrs.
Library: Total, c. 10,800 vols.
Academic Staff: c. 90 (20).
Student Enrolment: c. 810.

7816 **INSTITUT SUPÉRIEUR DE COMMERCE**
B.P. 16596, Kinshasa
Telephone: 31797; 31789; 31931

Commerce and Business Administration

Founded 1964 as Ecole supérieure by the Congrégation des Missionaires de Scheut. Attached to the Université nationale du Zaïre 1971. Became an autonomous institution 1981. Governing body: the Conseil d'administration.

Academic Year: October to July (October-February; February-July).
Admission Requirements: Secondary school certificate or equivalent, and entrance examination.
Language of Instruction: French.
Degrees and Diplomas: Gradué en–Sciences commerciales et financières; Sciences commerciales et administratives, 3 yrs.
Academic Staff: c. 50.
Student Enrolment: c. 450.

7817 **INSTITUT SUPÉRIEUR DE COMMERCE**
B.P. 2012, Kinsangani

Commerce

Attached to the Université nationale du Zaïre 1971. Became an autonomous institution 1981. Governing body: the Conseil d'administration.

7818 **INSTITUT SUPÉRIEUR DES TECHNIQUES MÉDICALES**
B.P. 774, Kinshasa

Medicine (including Nursing)

Attached to the Université nationale du Zaïre 1971. Became an autonomous institution 1981. Governing body: the Conseil d'administration.

Degrees and Diplomas: Gradué en Techniques médicales, 3 yrs.

7819 **INSTITUT SUPÉRIEUR D'ÉTUDES SOCIALES**
B.P. 2849, Bukairi

Social Sciences

Attached to the Université nationale du Zaïre 1971. Became an autonomous institution 1981. Governing body: the Conseil d'administration.

Degrees and Diplomas: Gradué en Sciences sociales, 3 yrs.

7820 **INSTITUT SUPÉRIEUR D'ÉTUDES SOCIALES**
B.P. 1575, Lubumbashi

Social Sciences

Attached to the Université nationale du Zaïre 1971. Became an autonomous institution 1981. Governing body: the Conseil d'administration.

7821 **INSTITUT SUPÉRIEUR DE STATISTIQUE**
B.P. 2471, Lubumbashi
Telephone: (22) 3905
Directeur général: Mbaya Kazadi
Secrétaire général: Anyenyola Welo

Sec. of Statistics
Dean: Kabwe Bukasa; *staff* 21 (14)
D. of Applied Mathematics
Chairman: Bope Bushebu; *staff* 21 (14)
D. of Applied Economics
Chairman: Monga Ilunga; *staff* 21 (14)

Founded 1967. Attached to the Université nationale du Zaïre 1971. Became an autonomous institution 1975. Governing body: the Comité de Gestion. Residential facilities for academic staff.

Academic Year: October to July.
Admission Requirements: Secondary school certificate or equivalent, and entrance examination.
Fees (Zaires): 5000.
Language of Instruction: French.
Degrees and Diplomas: Gradué en–Statistique; Technicien en Travaux statistiques, 3 yrs. Licence, 5 yrs.
Library: Central Library, c. 3000 vols.
Publication: Annales de l'Institut supérieur de Statistique.
Academic Staff, 1990: 20 (15).
Student Enrolment, 1990:

	Men	Women	Total
Of the country	920	43	963
Of other countries	2	–	2
Total	922	43	965

7822 **INSTITUT SUPÉRIEUR DE TECHNIQUES APPLIQUUÉES**
B.P. 7999, Kinshasa 1
Telephone: 24813; 23592
Directeur: Bayombo Mbokoliabwe (1986-91)
Secrétaire général: Ntiama Kabama

D. of Civil Aviation
Head: Marian Rabenda; *staff* 12 (2)

D. of Electrical Engineering
Head: Andrzej Frydryszak; *staff* 16 (3)
D. of Electronics
Head: Andrzej Fitzke; *staff* 31 (10)
D. of Meteorology
Head: Kazimiers Stefaniski; *staff* 11 (2)
D. of Mechanical Engineering
Head: Jerzy Langer; *staff* 31 (3)

Founded 1971 incorporating Institut d'Aviation civile (1964), Centre de Formation Météorologique (1964) and Ecole nationale des Postes et Télécommunications (1965). Attached to the Université nationale du Zaïre. Became an autonomous institution 1981. Governing body: the Conseil d'administration. Residential facilities for students.

Academic Year: October to July (October-February; February-July).

Admission Requirements: Secondary school certificate or equivalent and entrance examination.

Fees (Zaires): 1000 per annum; foreign students, 5000.

Languages of Instruction: French and English.

Degrees and Diplomas: Gradué en Techniques appliquées, 4 yrs.

Library: Central Library, 8000 vols.

Academic Staff, 1986-87:

Rank	Full-time	Part-time
Professeurs ordinaires	4	1
Professeurs	2	1
Professeurs associés	7	1
Chefs de travaux	24	2
Assistants	37	21
Assistants de Pratique professionnelle	37	1
Chargés de Pratique professionnelle	37	3
Total	142	30

Student Enrolment, 1986-87:

	Men	Women	Total
Of the country	3397	62	3459
Of other countries	10	2	12
Total	3407	64	3471

7823 **INSTITUT SUPÉRIEUR DES SCIENCES ET TECHNIQUES DE L' INFORMATION**
B.P. 14,998, Kinshasa

Journalism
Public Relations

Attached to the Université nationale du Zaïre 1971. Became an autonomous institution 1981. Governing body: the Conseil d'administration.

Degrees and Diplomas: Gradué en Sciences et Techniques de l'Information, 3 yrs.

Teacher Training

7824 **INSTITUT DE FORMATION DES CADRES DE L'ENSEIGNEMENT PRIMAIRE**
B.P. 711, Kisangani

Teacher Training (primary level)

Attached to the Université nationale du Zaïre 1971. Became an autonomous institution 1981. Governing body: the Conseil d'administration.

7825 **INSTITUT SUPÉRIEUR PÉDAGOGIQUE NATIONAL**
B.P. 8815, Kinshasa Binza

Teacher Training

Founded 1961. Attached to the Université nationale du Zaïre 1971. Became an autonomous institution 1981. Governing body: the Conseil d'administration.

Degrees and Diplomas: Gradué en Pédagogie appliquée, 3 yrs. Licence, a further 2 yrs.

7826 **INSTITUT SUPÉRIEUR PÉDAGOGIQUE**
B.P. 854, Bukavu
Telephone: 3187

Teacher Training

Founded 1964 by the Dominican Order as Ecole normale moyenne. Recognized by the State 1966. Attached to the Université nationale du Zaïre with present title 1971. Became an autonomous institution 1981. Governing body: the Conseil d'administration. Residential facilities for academic staff and students.

Academic Year: October to July (October-March; March-October).

Admission Requirements: Secondary school certificate.

Fees (Zaires): 1000 per annum.

Language of Instruction: French.

Degrees and Diplomas: Gradué en Pédagogie appliquée, 3 yrs. Licence, a further 2 yrs.

Library: *c.* 21,000 vols.

Academic Staff: *c.* 100 (30).

Student Enrolment: *c.* 850.

7827 **INSTITUT SUPÉRIEUR PÉDAGOGIQUE**
B.P. 340, Bunia
Directeur: Bura Pulunyo (1986-91)
Secrétaire administratif: Sanza Mulangu

Teacher Training

Founded 1968 as Ecole normale moyenne. Attached to the Université nationale du Zaïre with present title 1971. Became an autonomous institution 1981. Governing body: the Conseil d'administration. Residential facilities for academic staff and students. Residential facilities for academic staff and students.

Academic Year: October to June (October-February; February-June).

Admission Requirements: Secondary school certificate.

Fees (Zaires): 1000 per annum.

Language of Instruction: French.

Degrees and Diplomas: Gradué en Pédagogie appliquée, 3 yrs.

Library: Central Library.

Publication: Bulletin.

Academic Staff, 1986-87:

Rank	Full-time	Part-time
Professeur	–	1
Professeurs associés	4	1
Chefs de travaux	19	–
Assistants	22	7
Total	44	9

Student Enrolment, 1986-87:

	Men	Women	Total
Of the country	370	34	404

7828 **INSTITUT SUPÉRIEUR PÉDAGOGIQUE**
B.P. 282, Kananga
Telephone: 2330

Teacher Training

Founded as Teacher Training College by the Presbyterian and Methodist Churches 1966. Attached to the Université nationale du Zaïre 1971 and acquired present title 1973. Became an autonomous institution 1981. Governing body: the Conseil d'administration. Residential facilities for academic staf and students.

Academic Year: October to July (October-December; January-July).

Admission Requirements: Secondary school certificate or recognized equivalent, and entrance examination.

Languages of Instruction: French and English.

Degrees and Diplomas: Gradué en Pédagogie appliquée, 3 yrs. Licence, 5 yrs.

Library: *c.* 10,580 vols.

Academic Staff: *c.* 90.

Student Enrolment: *c.* 850.

7829 **INSTITUT SUPÉRIEUR PÉDAGOGIQUE**
B.P. 258, Kikwit (Bandundu)

Teacher Training

Founded 1966 as a school of the Diocese of Kikwit and recognized by the State. Attached to the Université nationale du Zaïre with present title 1971. Became an autonomous institution 1981. Governing body: the Conseil d'administration. Residential facilities for academic staff.

Academic Year: October to July (October-February; February-July).

Admission Requirements: Secondary school certificate or equivalent.

Language of Instruction: French.

Degrees and Diplomas: Gradué en Pédagogie appliquée, 3 yrs.

Library: *c.* 6000 vols.

Academic Staff: *c.* 60.

Student Enrolment: *c.* 510.

7830 **INSTITUT SUPÉRIEUR PÉDAGOGIQUE**
B.P. 3580, Kinshasa-Gombe
Telephone: 31-408
Directeur: Musa Mundedi (1986-90)
Secrétaire administratif: Longo Tshueté

Teacher Training (for Women)

Founded as school by the Association des Religieuses du Sacré-Coeur 1961. Attached to the Université nationale du Zaïre with present title 1971. Became an autonomous institution 1981. Governing body: the Conseil d'administration. Residential facilities for academic staff and students.

Academic Year: October to July (October-February; February-July).

Admission Requirements: Secondary school certificate and entrance examination.

Fees (Zaires): 1000 per annum.

Language of Instruction: French.

Degrees and Diplomas: Gradué en Pédagogie appliquée, 3 yrs.

Library: c. 15,000 vols.

Academic Staff, 1986-87:

Rank	Full-time	Part-time
Professeur ordinaire	–	1
Professeurs	3	–
Professeurs associés	11	1
Chefs de travaux	34	1
Assistants	24	–
Assistants de Pratique professionnelle	5	–
Total	76	3

Student Enrolment, 1986-87:

	Women
Of the country	885
Of other countries	1
Total	886

7831 **INSTITUT SUPÉRIEUR PÉDAGOGIQUE**
B.P. 1514, Kisangani
Directeur: Lokomba Baruti Wa Yakutu (1984-89)
Secrétaire administratif: Kamandji Luhembwe

Teacher Training

Founded as Ecole normale moyenne 1967. Attached to the Université nationale du Zaïre with present title 1971. Became an autonomous institution 1981. Governing body: the Conseil d'administration. Residential facilities for academic staff.

Academic Year: October to July (October-December; January-March; April-July).

Admission Requirements: Secondary school certificate and entrance examination.

Fees (Zaires): 1000 per annum.

Language of Instruction: French.

Degrees and Diplomas: Gradué en Pédagogie appliquée, 3 yrs.

Library: c. 12,300 vols.

Academic Staff: c. 70.

Student Enrolment: c. 680.

7832 **INSTITUT SUPÉRIEUR PÉDAGOGIQUE**
Teacher Training College
B.P. 1796, Lubumbashi
Telephone: 22-4585
Directeur général: Ngoy-Fiama Bitambile
Secrétaire général: Kamba Muzenga

D. of Teacher Training and Psycho-Pedagogy
Head: Mutamba Samby; *staff* 7
D. of English and African Studies
Head: Kamwema Shamwana; *staff* 7
D. of French
Head: Kashombo Ntompa; *staff* 14 (6)
D. of History and Social Sciences
Head: Mulowayi Katshimwena; *staff* 10 (6)
D. of Biology and Chemistry
Head: Mme. Thomas; *staff* 10 (5)
D. of Mathematics and Physics
Head: Marc Hoffenboon; *staff* 14 (3)
D. of Chemistry and Physics
Head: Mwipate Yatchennda; *staff* 14
D. of Geography and Natural Sciences
Head: Dibanga Baloji; *staff* 11
D. of Gymnastics and Natural Sciences
Head: Camille Fontaine
Research Ce.
Head: Muya Bia Lushiku

Also Language Laboratories, Biology and Chemistry Laboratories.

Founded 1959 as school. Became an autonomous institution 1981, with the status of Teacher Training College, awarding University levely degrees acknowledged by central Government. Governing body: the Conseil d'administration. Residential facilities for academic staff and some students.

Academic Year: October to June (October-March; April-June).

Admission Requirements: Secondary school certificate.

Fees (Zaires): 5000 per annum; foreign students, 10,000.

Language of Instruction: French.

Degrees and Diplomas: Gradué en Pédagogie appliquée (G3), 3 yrs. Licence en Pédagogie appliquée, a further 2 yrs.

Libraries: Central Library, 26,420 vols; libraries of the departments, c. 3000.

Special Facilities (Museums, etc.): Computer Network (7 P.C.s).

Publication: MBEGU (biannually).

Academic Staff, 1989-90:

Rank	Full-time	Part-time
Professeurs ordinaires	1	3
Professeurs	1	7
Professeurs associés	4	5
Chefs des Travaux	16	3
Assistants	40	–
Assistants de Pratique professionnelle	18	–
Total	80	19

Student Enrolment, 1989-90:

	Men	Women	Total
Of the country	523	168	693
Of other countries	2	–	2
Total	525	168	695

7833 **INSTITUT SUPÉRIEUR PÉDAGOGIQUE**
B.P. 116, Mbandaka

Teacher Training

Founded as school. Attached to the Université nationale du Zaïre with present title 1971. Became an autonomous institution 1981. Governing body: the Conseil d'administration.

7834 **INSTITUT SUPÉRIEUR PÉDAGOGIQUE**
B.P. 127, Mbanza-Ngungu

Teacher Training

Founded as school. Attached to the Université nationale du Zaïre with present title 1971. Became an autonomous institution 1981. Governing body: the Conseil d'administration.

7835 **INSTITUT SUPÉRIEUR PÉDAGOGIQUE**
B.P. 682, Mbujimayi

Teacher Training

Founded as Ecole normale moyenne 1968. Attached to the Université nationale du Zaïre with present title 1971. Became an autonomous institution 1981. Governing body: the Conseil d'administration. Residential facilities for academic staff and 40 students.

Academic Year: October to July (October-December; January-March; April-July).

Admission Requirements: Secondary school certificate or recognized equivalent, and entrance examination.

Fees (Zaires): 1000 per annum.

Language of Instruction: French.

Degrees and Diplomas: Gradué en Pédagogie appliquée, 3 yrs.

Library: c. 10,000 vols.

Academic Staff: c. 50 (10).

Student Enrolment: c. 440.

7836 **INSTITUT SUPÉRIEUR PÉDAGOGIQUE TECHNIQUE**
B.P. 3287, Kinshasa-Gombe

Teacher Training (Technical)

Founded 1976. Attached to the Université nationale du Zaïre. Became an autonomous institution 1981. Governing body: the Conseil d'administration. Residential facilities for students.

Academic Year: October to July (October-February; March-June).

Admission Requirements: Secondary school certificate.

Language of Instruction: French.

Degrees and Diplomas: Gradué en Pédagogie appliquée, 3 yrs.

Academic Staff: c. 20.

Student Enrolment: c. 100 (Men).

7837 **INSTITUT SUPÉRIEUR PÉDAGOGIQUE TECHNIQUE**

B.P. 75, Likasi

Teacher Training (Technical)

Attached to the Université nationale du Zaïre 1971. Became an autonomous institution 1981. Governing body: the Conseil d'administration.

UNITED NATIONS UNIVERSITY

UNITED NATIONS UNIVERSITY
Toho Seimei Building, 15-1 Shibuya 2-chome, Shibuya-ku,
Tokyo 150
Cables : unatuniv tokyo Telex : J25442 unatuniv
Telephone : (3) 499-2811
Fax : (3) 499-2828
Rector : Heitor Gurgulino de Souza
Vice-Rector : Roland J. Fuchs

The Charter of the University, adopted by the General Assembly of the United Nations on 6 December 1973, specifies that it 'shall enjoy autonomy within the framework of the United Nations' and that it shall enjoy 'the academic freedom required for the achievement of its objectives, with particular reference to the choice of subjects and methods of research and training, and selection of persons and institutions to share in its tasks, and freedom of expression.'

Purposes

The University, which effectively came into being in 1975, is conceived as a worldwide network of research and training centres and programmes devoted to 'pressing global problems of human survival, development and welfare.' It is concerned with advanced research and training and dissemination of knowledge but does not provide courses of study leading to the award of degrees. Its purpose is to give impetus, universality, and permanence to the search for practical knowledge needed to assure civilized survival. It seeks to bring together from East and West, North and South, the most knowledgeable experts, the most perceptive minds, and the most promising younger scholars for joint studies of maximum mutual value and worldwide applicability.

A central objective of the University is the continuing growth of vigorous academic and scientific communities everywhere and particularly in the developing countries. According to its charter, the University 'shall endeavour to alleviate the intellectual isolation of persons in such communities in the developing countries which might otherwise become a reason for them moving to developed countries.' Because so many of the world's most serious problems are concentrated in developing regions, the University, while serving the whole world, is strongly oriented toward the needs of developing countries.

A formal agreement, approved by their respective governing bodies, provides for active co-operation between the United Nations University (UNU) and the International Association of Universities (IAU) wherever feasible and mutually desirable.

At present, the University carries out research, training and knowledge dissemination in the five main categories that address major contemporary issues : Peace, Culture and Governance ; the Global Economy ; Global Life Support Systems ; Science and Technology ; and Population, Health and Human Welfare.

Organization

The governing body of the University, the Council, is made up of twenty-four distinguished educators and leading citizens, each from a different country, serving as individuals rather than governmental representatives. Council members serve for six-year terms and are appointed jointly by the Secretary-General of the United Nations and the Director-General of Unesco. The Rector of the University is also a member of the Council, and the Secretary-General of the United Nations, the Director-General of Unesco and the Director of Unitar (United Nations Institute for Training and Research) are members ex officio. The Chief Executive Officer is the Rector ; he is appointed by the Secretary-General of the United Nations, with the concurrence of the Director-General of Unesco, from among a list of candidates submitted to him by the Council of the University.

The University, which has a small academic and administrative staff at its Headquarters in Tokyo, is working through its own research and training centres and programmes and networks of institutions, and individual scholars and scientists in different parts of the world. In 1984, the UNU established its first research and training centre in Helsinki, Finland, the UNU World Institute for Development Economics (UNU/WIDER). In 1989, the second research and training centre, the UNU Institute for New Technologies (UNU/INTECH) was set up in Maastricht, Netherlands. Several others are in various stages of development, including the UNU Institute for Natural Resources in Africa (UNU/INRA), the UNU International Institute for Software Technology (UNUIIST), and the UNU Institute of Advanced Studies in Japan. Between 1976 and November 1990, 1024 Fellows have been trained by UNU, and almost 300 books were published based on the University's research.

Finance

The University relies on two types of financial support : endowment income (together with other contributions to the annual operating budget) ; and project support.

The establishment of a substantial endowment fund and operating contributions is necessary to provide reliable support for the basic operations of the University. This is the surest guarantee of the University's viability, autonomy, quality and academic freedom. In November 1990, pledges to the University's fund totalled US $190.0 million from twenty- six countries, of which US $176.9 million had been received.

THE EUROPEAN UNIVERSITY INSTITUTE

THE EUROPEAN UNIVERSITY INSTITUTE
Badia Fiesolana, 50016
S. Domenico di Fiesole, Florence
Cables : univeur
Telex : 571528 IUE
Telephone : (55) 50921
Fax : (56) 599887
Principal : Emile Noël
Secretary : Marcello Buzzonetti

The European University Institute is an international organization set up by the Member States of the European Communities. The idea was first launched in June 1955. The ensuing negotiations led to the signature by representatives of the six original Member States of the European Communities (Belgium, France, Germany, Italy, Luxembourg, Netherlands), on 19 April 1972, of the Convention setting up a European University Institute. Britain, Denmark, Ireland, as well as Greece and Spain, acceded later.

The Institute officially opened in autumn 1976 in the Badia Fiesolana. This famous building was made available by the Italian government.

The mission of the Institute is to contribute through its activities and through its influence to the development of Europe's cultural and academic heritage in its unity and in its diversity. It carries out this mission through teaching and research at the highest university level in the social and human sciences.

Structure

The Institute comprises three authorities :

- The High Council composed of two representatives of each Member State is responsible for the main guidance of the Institute, directs its activities and supervises its development. It is assisted by a Budget and Finance Committee which does the groundwork for its deliberations on budgetary and financial matters.
- The Principal of the Institute directs the Institute. He carries out or supervises the carrying out of acts and decisions pursuant to the Convention. He is responsible for the administration of the Institute and is assisted in his work by the Secretary.
- The Academic Council has general powers with regard to research and teaching, and among other things draws up the study and research programme. It is composed of the Principal, the Secretary, the full-time professors, one representative of the research and administrative staff, a representative of the research students and the Librarian.

Aims and Methods

Article 2 of the Convention lays down that « the aim of the Institute shall be to contribute, by its activities in the fields of higher education and research, to the development of the cultural and scientific heritage of Europe, as a whole and in its constituent parts. Its work shall also be concerned with the great movements and institutions which characterize the history and development of Europe. It shall take into account relations with cultures outside Europe. This aim shall be pursued through teaching and research at the highest university level. » Research work is carried on through seminars. Some seminars are designed to offer the research students opportunities to present their problems and findings for discussion and criticism by other students and members of the academic staff. Other seminars in the Institute's research programme should help the research students to widen their range of interests both within their chosen discipline and within other related disciplines. Each department concentrates on a few major themes.

Article 2 of the Convention also states that « the Institute should also be a forum for the exchange and discussion of ideas and experience in subjects falling within the area of study and research with which it is concerned. » With this in mind, colloquia are organized at the Institute, bringing together small groups of people from the academic and scientific world and the members of the departments most directly concerned.

Research Student Admission and Length of Stay

The Institute takes in research students, in general nationals of the European Community Member States, intending to do a doctoral thesis at the Institute or who wish to obtain some additional training in the framework of their doctoral studies at another university. Students may also enrol for the on-year M.A. Programme in comparative European and international law and the M.A. course in Economics.

Teaching and Research Programme

This programme is pursued in the four Departments, with a European, comparative and interdisciplinary approach : History and Civilization, Economics, Law, Political and Social Sciences :

History and Civilization
Contemporary History :
History of the European Community ;
Economic History of Europe in the 19th and 20th centuries ;
Political History of Europe in the 19th and 20th centuries ;
Socio-cultural History.
Modern History :
Socio-economic History of Europe, from the 16th to the 19th century ;
Political-social History, Ancient Régime ;
Cultural-social History, History of ideas and mentalities, from the 15th to the 18th century.

Economics
European Economics :
European Economic Policy ;
European Monetary Policy.
International Economics :
International Economic Relations ;
International Monetary and Financial Relations.
Comparative Economics :
Comparative Economic Systems ;
Centralized Economies and East/West Economic Relations.
Economic Theory :
Microeconomic Theory ;
Macroeconomic Theory.

Law
European Law :
European Community Law ;
Economic Law ;
Administrative Law (Cultural Law) ;
Company Law.
International and Comparative Law :
Public International Law ;
Labour and Social Law ;
Comparative Law.
Legal Theory.

Political and Social Sciences
European Integration ; Mediterranean Studies ; Comparative Government and Political Institutions ; Sociology ; Social and Political Philosophy ; Public Policy Analysis ; Economic and Social Policies.

Library

The Library is fully computerized. It has some 310,000 documents, including microfilms. Some 3000 periodicals are received.

Computing for Quantitative Research

The Institute has a prime 995511 computer for researchers wishing to do quantitative research.

OFFICERS OF THE INTERNATIONAL ASSOCIATION OF UNIVERSITIES - IAU

Administrative Board
1990-1995

PRESIDENT
WALTER J. KAMBA
Vice-Chancellor, University of Zimbabwe

HONORARY PRESIDENTS

ROGER GAUDRY
Ancien Recteur,
Université de Montréal, Canada

MARTIN MEYERSON
President Emeritus,
University of Pennsylvania, USA

BLAGOVEST SENDOV
President,
Academy of Sciences, Bulgaria

GUILLERMO SOBRERÓN
Former Rector,
National Autonomous University of Mexico

JUSTIN THORENS
Ancien Recteur,
Université de Genève, Switzerland

CONSTANTINE K. ZURAYK
Professor Emeritus,
American University of Beirut, Lebanon

VICE-PRESIDENTS

OLLI LEHTO
Chancellor, University of Helsinki, Finland

WATARU MORI
Former President, University of Tokyy, Japan

MEMBERS OF THE ADMINISTRATIVE BOARD

Theodor Berchem	*President, University of Würzburg, Federal Republic of Germany*
L. Michael Birt	*Vice-Chancellor, University of New South Wales, Australia*
Michel Falise	*Président, Fédération universitaire et polytechnique de Lille, France*
Fernando Hinestrosa	*Rector, Universidad Externado de Colombia*
David L. Johnston	*Principal, McGill University, Canada*
Alexander Konovalov	*Rector, Kazan State University, USSR*
José Martins Romêo	*Rector, Universidade Federal Fluminense, Brazil*
Bolesław Mazurkiewicz	*Rector, Technical University of Gdansk, Poland*
Guoguang Mu	*President, Nankai University, People's Republic of China*
Colm Ó hEocha	*President, University College, Galway, Ireland*
Avelino José Porto	*Rector, Universidad de Belgrano, Argentina*
Maamoun Salama	*President, Cairo University, Egypt*
Akilagpa Sawyerr	*Vice-Chancellor, University of Ghana*
Abdul Majid Sheikh Hussein	*President, Al-Baath University, Syria*
Partap N. Srivastava	*Former Vice-Chancellor, Jawaharlal Nehru University, India*
Michael P. Stathopoulos	*Rector, University of Athens, Greece*
Charas Suwanwela	*President, Chulalongkorn University, Thailand*
Charles E. Young	*Chancellor, University of California, Los Angeles, USA*

DEPUTY MEMBERS

Mostafa H.B. Abdel Motaal, *Former President, Menoufia University, Egypt ;* Abdullah Juma Al-Kobaisi, *President, University of Qatar ;* Clark Lannerdahl Brundin, *Vice-Chancellor, University of Warwick, United Kingdom ;* Geoffrey Caston, *Vice-Chancellor, University of the South Pacific, Fiji ;* John Di Biaggio, *President, Michigan State University, USA ;* Jorge dos Santos Veiga, *Vice-Rector, Universidade de Coimbra, Portugal ;* Luis González-Cosio, *Rector, Instituto Tecnológico y de Estudios Superiores de Occidente, Guadalajara, Mexico ;* Abiy Kifle, *President, Addis Ababa University, Ethiopia ;* Yung-Chan Kwon, *Former President, Kon-Kuk University, Seoul, Republic of Korea ;* Manickam Lakshmanan, *Vice-Chancellor, Madurai-Kamaraj University, India ;* Magne Lerheim, *Former Director, University of Bergen, Norway ;* Hassan Mekouar, *Recteur, Université Mohammed I, Morocco ;* Hanna Nasir, *President, Birzeit University, Palestine ;* Maurice Ntahobari, *Recteur, Université nationale du Rwanda ;* Radim Palouš, *Rector, Charles University, Prague, Czechoslovakia ;* Julio Terán Dutari, *Rector, Pontificia Universidad Católica del Ecuador ;* Thomas Tlou, *Vice-Chancellor, University of Botswana ;* Ergün Togrol, *Rector, Bogaziçi University, Turkey ;* Slobodan Unković, *Rector, University of Belgrade, Yougoslavia ;* Hans van Ginkel, *Rector, University of Utrecht, Netherlands*

Secretary-General
FRANZ EBERHARD
Director, International Universities Bureau

IAU–INTERNATIONAL ASSOCIATION OF UNIVERSITIES LIST OF PUBLICATIONS

PERIODICALS

+ *Higher Education Policy*
Quarterly Journal
ISSN 0279-4631

+ *IAU bulletin*
Bimonthly
ISSN 0020-6032

REFERENCE WORKS

* *International Handbook of Universities*
Twelfth Edition, 1991. xi + 1389 pages + index.
ISBN 92-9002-154-3

* *World List of Universities, Other Institutions of Higher Education and University Organizations*
Eighteenth Edition, 1990, xxii + 706 pages
ISBN 92-9002-048-2

Collection of Agreements Concerning the Equivalence of University Qualifications
1954-1961
Reprinted 1966. vii + 655 pages
ISBN 92-9002-013-X
Reissued 1977 (7 microfiches)

First Supplement to Collection of Agreements
1977. iv + 279 pages (3 microfiches)
ISBN 92-9002-031-8

Second Supplement to Collection of Agreements
1983. iv + 527 pages (6 microfiches)
ISBN 92-9002-039-3

Documents Concerning the Equivalence of University Qualifications
1957. 280 loose leaves (microfilm)

PAPERS OF THE INTERNATIONAL ASSOCIATION OF UNIVERSITIES

1. *Three Aspects of University Development Today*
1953. 46 pages.

2. *Health at the University*
1954. 76 pages.

3. *Student Mental Health*
1958. 76 pages.

4. *University Education and Public Service*
1959. 151 pages.
ISBN 92-9002-102-0

5. *The Interplay of Scientific and Cultural Values in Higher Education Today*
1960. 81 pages.
ISBN 92-9002-103-9

6. *The Expansion of Higher Education*
1960. 117 pages.
ISBN 92-9002-104-7

7. *University Autonomy - Its Meaning Today*
1965. 139 pages.
ISBN 92-9002-110-1

8. *The Administration of Universities*
1967. xiii + 99 pages.
ISBN 92-9002-114-4

9. *International University Co-operation*
1969. xvi + 161 pages.
ISBN 92-9002-115-2

10. *The University and the Needs of Contemporary Society*
1970. xv + 81 pages.
ISBN 92-9002-116-0

11. *Problems of Integrated Higher Education - An International Case Study of the Gesamthochschule*
1972. 85 pages.
ISBN 92-9002-120-9

12. *The Social Responsibility of the University in Asian Countries - Obligations and Opportunities*
1973. 124 pages.
ISBN 92-9002-122-5

13. *A Critical Approach to Inter-University Co-operation*
1974. 138 pages.
ISBN 92-9002-124-1

14. *Differing Types of Higher Education*
1977. 86 pages.
ISBN 92-9002-130-6

15. *The Right to Education and Access to Higher Education*
1978. 107 pages.
ISBN 92-9002-132-2

16. *The Role of the University in Developing Countries : Its Responsibility Toward the Natural and Cultural Environment*
1979. 95 pages.
ISBN 92-9002-133-0

17. *Contemporary Scientific and Technical Changes : Their Impact on the Humanities in University Education*
1983. 80 pages.
ISBN 92-9002-140-3

18. *The Future of University Education*
1983. 86 pages.
ISBN 92-9002-242-6

19. *Universities and Regional Development*
1985. 47 pages.
ISBN 92-9002-144-6

20. *International University Co-operation, a Critical Analysis : Failures, Successes and Perspectives*
1989. 103 pages.
ISBN 92-9002-150-0

+ May be ordered from : Kogan Page, 120 Pentonville Road, London, United Kingdom N1 9JN. Tel : (71) 278-0433. Telefax : (71) 837- 6348.
* May be ordered from : Globe Book Services Ltd., Stockton House, 1 Melbourne Place, London, United Kingdom WC2B 4LF. Tel : (71) 379-4687. Telefax : (71) 379-4980, or Stockton Press, 15 East 26 Street, New York, NY 10010. Tel : (1-800) 221-2123. Telefax : (1- 212) 779-9479 (Orders from USA and Canada).

PUBLICATIONS

REPORTS

Report of the International Conference of Universities, Nice, December 1950
1951. 162 pages.

Report of Proceedings. Second General Conference of the International Association of Universities, Istanbul, September 1955
1956. 232 pages.
ISBN 92-9002-101-2

Report of Proceedings. Third General Conference of the International Association of Universities, Mexico. September 1960
1961. 224 Pages.
ISBN 92-9002-107-1

Report of the Fourth General Conference of the International Association of Universities, Tokyo, 31 August - 6 September1965
1966. 264 pages.
ISBN 92-9002-112-8

Report of the Fifth General Conference of the International Association of Universities, Montreal, 30 August - 5 September, 1970
1971. 291 pages.
ISBN 92-9002-118-7

Report of the Sixth General Conference of the International Association of Universities, Moscow, 19-25 August 1975
1977. 309 pages.
ISBN 92-9002-127-6

Report of the Seventh General Conference of the International Association of Universities, Manila, 25-30 August 1980
1981. 322 pages.
ISBN 92-9002-137-3

Report of the Eighth General Conference of the International Association of Universities, Los Angeles, 12-17 August 1985
1986. 203 pages.
ISBN 92-9002-146-2

Report of the Ninth General Conference of the International Association of Universities, Helsinki, 5-11 August 1990
1991.
ISBN 92-9002-1551

Administrative Reports of the International Association of Universities
(issued on the occasion of each General Conference)
1951-1954
1955. 40 pages.
ISBN 92-9002-100-4

1955-1959
1960. 58 pages.
ISBN 92-9002-105-5

1960-1964
1965. 129 pages.
ISBN 92-9002-111-X

1965-1969
1970. 117 pages.
ISBN 92-9002-117-9

1970-1974
1975. 113 pages.
ISBN 92-9002-125-X

1975-1979
1980. 104 pages.
ISBN 92-9002-136-5

1980-1984
1985. 78 pages.
ISBN 92-9002-145-4

1985-1989
1990. 83 pages.
ISBN 92-9002-152-7

OTHER STUDIES AND REPORTS

The Staffing of Higher Education
1960. 169 pages.
ISBN 92-9002-106-3

Some Economic Aspects of Educational Development in Europe
1961. 144 pages.
ISBN 92-9002-108-X

Formal Programmes of International Co-operation between University Institutions.
1960. 39 pages in 4° (published by Unesco).

Report of a Meeting of Heads of African Institutions of Higher Education, Khartoum, 16-19 September 1963.
1964. 107 pages.
ISBN 92-9002-109-8

JOINT UNESCO-IAU RESEARCH PROGRAMME IN HIGHER EDUCATION

(published jointly by Unesco and IAU)

The International Study of University Admissions :
Vol. I : *Access to Higher Education,* by Frank Bowles.
1963. 212 pages.
Bound : ISBN 92-3-100574-X
Paper : ISBN 92-3-100575-8

Vol. II : *National Studies*
1965. 648 pages.
ISBN 92-3-100608-8

Higher Education and Development in South-East Asia : Summary Report
1965. 94 pages.
ISBN 92-3-100543-X

Higher Education and Development in South-East Asia :
Vol. I : *Director's Report,* by Howard Hayden
1967. 508 pages.
ISBN 92-3-100651-7
Vol. II : *Country Profiles*
1967. 615 pages.
ISBN 92-3-100650-9
Vol. III : Part 1. *High-level manpower for development,*
by Guy Hunter
1967. 184 pages.
ISBN 92-3-100649-5
Part 2. *Language policy and higher education,*
by Richard Noss
1967. 216 pages.
ISBN 92-3-100648-7

Teaching and Learning : An Introduction to New Methods and Resources in Higher Education,
by N. MacKenzie, M. Eraut, H.C. Jones
1970. 209 pages.
ISBN 92-3-100798-X
Second edition, revised. 1976. 224 pages.
ISBN 92-3-100798-X

Lifelong Education and University Resources (eight case studies)
1978. 193 pages.
ISBN 92-3-101397-1

New Trends and New Responsibilities for Universities in Latin America
1980. 96 pages.
ISBN 92-3-101830-2

Universities and Environmental Education
1986. 127 pages.
ISBN 92-3-102364-0

INDEX

The names of institutions included in this volume are in many cases accompanied by translation into English. These institutions thus appear twice in the index, the English version of the names being printed in italics, e.g. Helsingin Yliopisto is also indexed as *University of Helsinki.* In a number of cases, where universities are widely known by shorter names than their full ones, these have also been included. The *University of Göttingen,* for example, is indexed under this name as well as under its official title and its formal English version.